AN ATLAS OF FIGURE DRAWINGS

AN ATLAS OF FIGURE DRAWINGS

Studies on the Psychological
Characteristics of Medical Students—III

by
Caroline Bedell Thomas

The Johns Hopkins Press
Baltimore, 1966

To my husband,

DR. HENRY M. THOMAS, JR.,

who for twenty years has contributed invaluable support to the Study of the Precursors of Hypertension and Coronary Disease through his wisdom, understanding, and encouragement.

FOREWORD

The use of projective test techniques to assess personality is now so common that few practitioners are fully aware of the tenuous nature of the supporting research. The very simplicity of the figure drawing technique and the ease with which the task is accepted by subjects has given the method a disarming advantage over others. Yet almost from its introduction, figure drawing, no less than other projective devices, has been plagued by contradictory findings relative to its validity as an index of personality functioning.

This volume is unique in that it makes no special plea for the validity of figure drawings. Rather Dr. Thomas quite simply presents us with all the raw data, describes in careful detail how she made use of it, and by implication challenges the research-minded reader to test out his own speculations and hypotheses. It is indeed a mode of presentation to be emulated.

Nonetheless, Dr. Thomas does have some definite notions of how these data may be most profitably viewed. It is her conviction that genetic factors are of basic significance in the determination of all psychobiological systems. She imposes an order on the data which allows the reader to comprehend the relevance of figure drawings to the thesis. Final conclusions, of course, cannot yet be drawn from this impressive long-term study. The important point, however, is that others are free to reorganize the data to suit their own special predilections because these data are fully presented.

There are several additional features that recommend this publication to researcher and clinician alike. Certainly the precision of the scoring system is commendable, including its application to the sample of well over 800 illustrations. Moreover, this painstaking effort very likely represents the largest single published collection of normative data on young nonpathological adults.

Even a cursory survey of the material reveals the wide variety and richness of the productions among a group of young people generally considered to be homogeneous in most respects. And Dr. Thomas shows some intriguing associations between biological and psychological attributes.

This compendium is a fitting companion to the preceding two volumes in the series of studies on the *Psychological Characteristics of Medical Students.* Together with those volumes, which explore Rorschach responses in a population of more than 1,000 medical students, this *Atlas* provides a wealth of projective material which should stimulate much comparative research.

STANLEY D. IMBER, PH.D.
The Johns Hopkins University
School of Medicine

March 2, 1966   *Baltimore, Maryland*

PREFACE

Although psychologists have long been interested in the concept that the spontaneous drawings of ordinary folk reflect their personality characteristics, the use of human figure drawings as a recognized testing procedure for personality assessment was introduced less than twenty years ago. In 1948 Buck described the House-Tree-Person Test, and in 1949 Machover published her book, *Personality Projection in the Drawing of the Human Figure* (1, 2). Since that time, the human Figure-drawing Test has been widely used by clinical psychologists as a projective technique, usually in conjunction with other projective tests such as the Rorschach Test or the Thematic Apperception Test (3).

Because it is relatively brief and simple to administer, the Figure-drawing Test appears to have much in its favor as a psychological screening test. Its use as a research tool, however, has been limited by the lack of a systematic, reproducible scoring classification and by the absence of any large body of normative data. For the most part, each investigator has devised his own scale, with little reference to the work of others. Moreover, these scales are often limited to one or two aspects of the figure drawing without regard to the many other variables in constant use by clinical psychologists. Although the need for a practical classification has been frequently cited, there is no established scoring system today which is at all comparable to the methods of Beck and of Klopfer for scoring Rorschach protocols. Despite the fact that figure drawings, which can only be fully comprehended by inspection, are the basic data of the Figure-drawing Test, illustrations in the best-known books on the subject are limited in number and scope, while those accompanying scientific articles on the test are so infrequent as to be of negligible importance. Notwithstanding the wealth and variety of material available, published collections of drawings by mental patients are meager, and those by normal subjects are, to all intents and purposes, nonexistent (4). Finally, biological correlates of the figure-drawing attributes of normal adults have never before been sought in a systematic way—as is done here and in a companion study (5).

The *raison d'etre* of *An Atlas of Figure Drawings*, therefore, is to fill a fourfold need: to supply a broad spectrum of normative data in the form of drawings by healthy young adults of superior intelligence; to describe a reliable method of classification; to demonstrate the application of the method to each drawing; and to set forth in detail the psychobiological characteristics of each subject so that they may be studied in conjunction with the pair of figures drawn by that subject. Thus, this *Atlas* provides a definitive denominator for figure-drawing studies involving healthy young adults of superior intelligence.

The figures in this volume were all drawn by 870 Johns Hopkins medical students who were participants in the long-term Study of the Precursors of Hypertension and Coronary Disease. Genetic, physiological, psychological, and metabolic characteristics of successive classes of medical students have been recorded, and the subjects are being followed over the years to determine which characteristics are associated with the early onset of the disorders in question. It is our thesis that the genetic background of the individual is of paramount importance in determining whether or not a given individual will develop hypertension or coronary disease at a relatively early age, and that the range of phenotypic expression of physiological, metabolic, and psychological characteristics found in healthy young adults reflects genetic differences which affect the entire psychobiological make-up of the individual, rather than single systems. Accordingly, within each sophistication-of-body-concept level, the *Atlas* brings together for ready visual comparison the figure drawings of subjects with different parental histories in regard to coronary disease and hypertension, as well as stroke, diabetes, and obesity.

The Precursors Study, which has been in progress since 1946, was the first prospective study of hypertension and coronary disease in which systematic observations were made of the subject's psychological make-up. Descriptive studies have been made of the personality of *patients* with hypertension or with coronary disease, but the psychological traits of the *prehypertensive* or the *precoronary* individual were at best conjectural, and based on fragmentary or uncontrolled retrospective information. Accordingly, it was decided to make major use of projective techniques in the Precursors Study in order to record over-all individual psychodynamic patterns rather than rely on non-projective tests which might not include items that would clearly reflect the prehypertensive or precoronary personality. Volumes I and II of this series of *Studies on the Psychological Characteristics of Medical Students* presented the responses of 1,154 medical students to the Rorschach Test, a test which has been employed since the beginning of the Study (6, 7). Volume III is devoted to the figure drawings of 870 of the same students. The Figure-drawing Test was introduced into the Study protocol in 1951, just two years after it was first described by Machover (2).

A word needs to be said here in regard to the applicability of studies made on medical students to the population at large. In the first place, physicians are subject to the same spectrum of mental and physical disorders as other people. Also, despite the special nature of the population, medical students represent a substantial segment of the young adults of superior intelligence in this country, and it seems likely that their figure drawings in many ways resemble those of college students and college graduates in general. It is important to emphasize that the subjects whose drawings are presented in this *Atlas* all appeared to embody a relatively high level of "normality" in terms of total human performance at the time the test was taken, although some of them, then or later, suffered from emotional disturbances of varying degrees of severity.

In thanking the many individuals whose contributions have made this work possible, the Johns Hopkins medical students, whose generous co-operation was essential to its success, deserve first mention. It goes without saying that the steadfast backing of The Johns Hopkins University School of Medicine has been indispensable. Particular gratitude goes to the late Perrin H. Long, who, as Professor of Preventive Medicine, sponsored this research project in its initial stages, and to A. McGehee Harvey, Professor of Medicine, who has continued to support it. We should also like to voice our special appreciation to Philip Bard and Thomas B. Turner, successive Deans of the Medical School, for their patience and understanding in coping with the Study's administrative problems.

We should like to express our grateful thanks to the psychologists who administered the Figure-drawing Test, first to Shirley A. Mark, at whose suggestion the test was included in the Precursors Study protocol, and then to Henry J. Mark, William A. Zielonka, and Edward W. Slockbower. Particular credit goes to Leona Wise Jones, a psychologist who took the major responsibility in devising the scoring system for the structural and graphic characteristics of the figure drawings, and who carried out the scoring of all the figure drawings in this volume. Dr. Jones carefully appraised the reliability of the method with Margaret H. Sanderson, another psychologist who acted as the second judge. Our sincere appreciation also goes to the members of our staff who have collaborated in the preparation of Volume III: Selina Maxcy Wolf, Evelyn G. Severn, Marie V. Bowman, and June D. Himmighoefer.

We gratefully acknowledge the financial support of the figure-drawing research program within the Study of the Precursors of Hypertension and Coronary Disease from the following sources: the Veterans Administration (1951–54), the National Heart Institute through Grant HE-01891 (1954–66), and, especially, the Tobacco Industry Research Committee, now The Council for Tobacco Research—U.S.A. Since 1955 they have provided supplemental funds and other assistance, which have been most helpful in broadening our approach to the psychological aspects of the Precursors Study and in making possible the publication of Volumes II and III of this series. We also wish to acknowledge the co-operation of the Computing Center of the Johns Hopkins Medical Institutions in the machine processing used in the preparation of this volume.

CONTENTS

LIST OF TABLES

INTRODUCTION

So that the reader may clearly comprehend the various kinds of information provided by the *Atlas of Figure Drawings*, the nature and arrangement of the material presented are described in detail in the following sections.

POPULATION

All of the figure drawings were obtained from Johns Hopkins medical students in the classes of 1952 through 1964 who were participants in the Study of the Precursors of Hypertension and Coronary Disease (8, 9). Of the 1,030 students registered in the designated classes, 977 were Precursors Study participants, and 870, or 89.0 per cent of the participants, co-operated in taking the Figure-drawing Test. Outright refusal to be tested was extremely rare; most of those untested either dropped out of medical school before the test was scheduled or were unavailable because of academic or other commitments.

Sex and Race

As may be seen in Table 1, the great majority of subjects tested were white males. White females formed a much smaller group, and only a scattering of subjects of non-European ancestry was represented. Accordingly, the main body of the *Atlas* is devoted to drawings by the male and female subjects of European ancestry, while the drawings by the twenty-five subjects of non-European ancestry are gathered together in the final section.

Age

Ninety-eight per cent of the 870 subjects were between the ages of 20 and 29 inclusive at the time the Figure-drawing Test was administered. The mean age of the subjects was 23.8 years, and their median age was 23 years.

Intelligence

In view of the rigorous standards of academic achievement required for a student to gain admission to medical school, it may be assumed that all of the subjects were of superior intelligence. The scores of individual Wechsler-Bellevue tests administered to an unselected sample of forty-seven subjects in the class of 1948 support this view (10).

Health

The subjects were all in a state of good health, both physical and emotional, compatible with regular attendance at medical school. None had clinical hypertension or coronary disease.

AIMS OF THE PRECURSORS STUDY

It is the hypothesis of the Precursors Study that hypertension and coronary artery disease are closely related disorders in which multiple factors play a determining role (11, 12). The exact form of the disease and age at onset depend on the nature and number of genetic factors present as well as on the stresses encountered during life (13–18). It was our threefold purpose: (1) to study, in young adults, the occurrence of certain genetic, physiologic, metabolic, and psychological traits which are thought to precede the development of hypertension and/or coronary disease, (2) to relate the characteristics of the subjects to the presence or absence of hypertension and/or coronary disease in their parents, and (3) to determine, by follow-up studies, which traits are associated with the early onset of disease. This *Atlas* is intended to further these general goals by indicating the scope of a projective psychological test, the Figure-drawing Test, and relating it to other factors under investigation.

FIGURE-DRAWING TEST PROCEDURE

The Figure-drawing Test was added to the protocol of the Precursors Study in 1951 (19). It was administered by a psychologist on the same occasion that the Rorschach test was given (6, 7, 10, 20). In but a few instances, subjects in the classes of 1952 through 1957

2

were tested individually, while those in the classes of 1958 through 1964 were tested in the group situation. Unlike the Rorschach test, no attempt is made here to distinguish the individual from the group Figure-drawing Tests. In the group situation subjects were seated in alternate seats, with few exceptions.

The psychologist's instructions were simple: first, to draw a human figure—not a stick figure—in pencil on a sheet of paper of standard size (8½ by 11 inches). After one figure was completed, there were further instructions to draw a figure of the opposite sex on another sheet of paper. Among the 870 subjects tested, a few completed only one figure, a few drew stick figures, a few drew two figures on one page, and a few drew in ink; in general, however, the instructions were well carried out (19). The subjects were asked to label their drawings in order of completion, 1 and 2, but again, some failed to do so. The drawings were interpreted and filed. A few of the drawings were smudged or otherwise soiled *after* they were completed, but in 1962–64 they were all protected by a laminated plastic process.

ARRANGEMENT OF DRAWINGS

For the *Atlas*, the figure drawings were photographed and reduced by approximately 54 per cent, so that the original 8½ by 11 inch piece of paper on which each figure was drawn is represented here by the outline boxing in each drawing. The identifying material, remarks, and systematic labels written on the face of the original sheet have been removed to preserve confidentiality and to focus attention on the drawings themselves. The placement of the drawings on the page has been scrupulously maintained, however.

Each pair of drawings is so arranged that the figure drawn first is placed on the left-hand side of the page. Where the drawings were unnumbered by the subject, the male figure is placed to the left and the female figure to the right. Two figures on the same page or a single figure only are shown on the left-hand side. Where figures were drawn with the axis of the body at right angles to the long axis of the page they have been so placed.

Sophistication-of-Body-Concept

In order to facilitate comparison, the figure drawings have first been grouped according to their global impression in regard to sophistication-of-body-concept. In general, the five-point scale rating of sophistication-of-body-concept devised by Witkin, Dyk, Faterson, Goodenough and Karp has been used, ranging from most sophisticated to most primitive (21). We have modified slightly the Witkin definitions of the five sophistication-of-body-concept categories. To their five categories we have added a small group of anomalous drawings.

In presenting these groups in the *Atlas* we have placed the group of anomalous drawings first and then have reversed Witkin's order so that the spectrum begins with the childish, primitive pictures and proceeds to the mature and sophisticated ones as follows:

Anomalous drawings (coded 0):

> stick figures and heads only. These drawings do not fulfill the requirements of the Figure-drawing Test, since the subjects were instructed to draw human figures and not stick figures. Therefore, the criteria for sophistication-of-body-concept have not been applied. Although, by and large, the stick figures are closely related to the primitive group, the anomalous drawings vary in degree of elaboration.

Most primitive drawings (coded 5):

> considered to be most primitive and infantile in respect to sophistication-of-body-concept. These drawings show a very low level of form, with almost no evidence of role or sex identity and little or no detailing.

Moderately primitive drawings (coded 4):

> features of differentiation through form, identity, or detailing are still largely lacking, but these drawings show slightly more complexity in some respects.

Drawings at an intermediate level of sophistication (coded 3):

> identification of sex is evident, there are attempts at shaping and a fair level of integration of parts is manifest. A minimum of detailing is present.

Moderately sophisticated drawings (coded 2):

> show a definite attempt at role assignment with regard to age, activity, occupation, and so on, through adequate detailing, shaping, and clothing. Continuity of outline (i.e., integration of parts) is attempted. The end product is, however, less deliberate, the outline less decisive and/or skillful and the head and/or hand treatment is less sophisticated than in drawings by the most sophisticated group.

Most sophisticated drawings (coded 1):

> manifest high form level. Appendages and details are represented in proper relation to body outline, with some expressiveness or individuality in mode of presentation and appropriate, even imaginative, detailing. In general, great emphasis is given to detail of head, facial expression, clothing, body features and shape, and/or sex attributes. There is rational integration of body parts and of clothing accessories, all decisively and purposefully drawn.

Pairs of drawings in which one figure drawing is anomalous and the other is not have been included in the group of anomalous drawings. Otherwise, pairs of drawings in which the two figures differ in degree of sophistication are called "mixed" and are introduced between the appropriate categories. At the very end, figure drawings by the subjects of non-European ancestry are presented.

4

Within each sophistication-of-body-concept category the figure drawings have been arranged according to a spectrum of parental disorders, so that drawings by subjects with similar parental histories are grouped together. The spectrum of parental disorders adopted is as follows:

1. *Coronary artery disease*
2. *Hypertension* in the absence of coronary disease
3. *Stroke* without coronary disease or hypertension
4. *Diabetes* without coronary disease, hypertension, or stroke
5. *Obesity* without coronary disease, hypertension, stroke, or diabetes
6. *Both parents unaffected* by coronary disease, hypertension, stroke, diabetes, or obesity
7. *Unknown parental history*

It should be noted that only instances of hypertension, stroke, diabetes, or obesity occurring in the *absence* of disorders with higher priorities in this spectrum are grouped together. Additional instances of parental diabetes, for example, may be found scattered through the coronary disease, hypertension and stroke portions of the spectrum.

Within each parental disorder grouping, precedence is given to the degree of positivity of the parental history as follows:

1. Drawings by subjects with positive parental history precede those by subjects with questionable parental history (where the history of a parent is partially known, an unknown history for a specific disorder is ranked after "questionable.")
2. Drawings by subjects with two affected parents precede those by subjects with one affected parent.
3. Drawings by subjects whose parents were affected under the age of sixty-five precede those by subjects whose parents were affected at age sixty-five or after.
4. Drawings by subjects with affected fathers precede those by subjects with affected mothers.

The health status of the parents of each individual subject is summarized under the figure drawings by that subject in the section entitled "General Characteristics of Subject."

FIGURE-DRAWING CHARACTERISTICS

Directly under each pair of figure drawings, their characteristics have been coded according to specifically defined categories. These categories embrace structural, graphic, and global characteristics as well as the concepts of height of figure in relationship to total length of page, and body proportions in relationship to height. The coding of the structural and graphic characteristics (including height and body proportions) was carried out as described in detail elsewhere and as summarized below (19, 22). The coding of the global characteristics concerned with sophistication-of-body-concept closely followed the criteria of Witkin, *et al.* (21).

The over-all reliability of the coding of structural and graphic characteristics, as evidenced by agreement between two judges, was high (19). Agreement was above the 90 per cent level for structural characteristics, body measurements, and proportion, but somewhat lower (73.9 per cent agreement) for categories involving graphic characteristics. The coding of sophistication-of-body-concept, based as it is on a synthesis of criteria involving form, detailing, identity, and sex differentiation, would appear to be susceptible to a variety of interpretations. Actual disagreement between two judges, however, occurred in less than 10 per cent of the total number of drawings.

Codes and Distributions

Each characteristic is described in a series of subordinate, discrete categories to which code numbers have been assigned. The code numbers are shown in Tables 2–36, together with the definitions of the categories to which they refer.* In the Plates, the code numbers appear in the boxes under the heading "Figure-drawing Characteristics." They have been selected by two independent judges as designating the category which most closely defines or describes a particular figure drawing in regard to a given characteristic. In some cases, categories have no descriptive statement. They have been reserved for use as intermediate points for a compromise judgment between two judges (see Tables 6, 7, 8, 11, 12, 13, 18, 19, 20, 21, 23, 24, 31, 33, and 34). Tables 2–36 are presented in the same order as the figure-drawing characteristics listed in the Plates.

The codes for levels of form, detailing, identity and sex differentiation, and for sophistication-of-body-concept have been slightly modified from those of Witkin, *et al.*, principally by introducing an intermediate category for form, detailing, and identity and sex differentiation, and also by adding "anomalous drawings" to the sophistication-of-body-concept categories (21).

The measurement of figure height and the proportionate length or width of the various body parts were coded according to a method described in detail elsewhere (22). It may be summarized here by saying that the scale value for height is directly related to the over-all length of the standard (8½ by 11 inches) sheet of paper on which the figure was drawn. A scale value coded 05 indicates that the height

*The published "Manual of Instructions" explains the coding of structural and graphic characteristics in detail (22). However, the codes provided in Tables 2-36 should be used for interpreting the code numbers in the Plates of the *Atlas*. The coding in the *Atlas* differs from that in the "Manual of Instructions" in two minor respects: first, the order of presentation of figure-drawing characteristics has been slightly altered; and second, the category code numbers for the following characteristics have been rearranged: vertical midline, horizontal midline, long axis of figure in relation to axis of page, relative size of male and female figures, body shading, hair shading, nudity, and transparency.

6

of the figure was 50–59 per cent of the total length of the page, while a scale value coded 02 indicates that the figure height was 20–29 per cent of the total length of the page. According to this method, the height and the body parts of a perfectly proportioned figure should all have the same scale value. Body parts which are coded with higher scale values than those assigned to height are relatively larger, and those with lower scale values than height are relatively smaller than would be expected in a perfectly proportioned figure. In badly proportioned figures, such as ones with an enormous head or a very long neck, the scale values may exceed 09, or 90–99.

The percentage distributions for the categories of each characteristic are also shown in Tables 2–36. They are based on figure drawings by 787 white male subjects and by 56 white female subjects, referred to in these tables as "men" and "women." Thus, by turning to the appropriate table, the meaning of each coded figure-drawing characteristic can be determined, both in descriptive terms and in respect to its relative frequency. The actual base numbers vary somewhat from table to table, as a few men drew but a single figure, and measurements could not be made in every instance (19, 22).

GENERAL CHARACTERISTICS OF THE SUBJECT

Identification

For purposes of identification, each subject has been assigned the same confidential code number that was used in Volumes I and II of this series (6, 7). These numbers appear in the identification section of each Plate.

The other identifying information is given as follows:
Sex: M = male, F = female
Marital status: S = single, M = married, U = unknown
The age at psychological tests (Figure-drawing Test, Strong Vocational Interest Test) is often different from the subject's age at the time of physiological and metabolic data which were obtained on a different occasion.

Parental History

Coding and Definitions. The ratings for parental disorders are based on physician's diagnoses as reported by the subject. Inquiry about each parent's health status was made on repeated occasions both during the subject's sojourn in medical school and after graduation (14, 17, 18). The ratings presented in the Parental History section of each plate summarize the most recent information about each parent.

Each disorder is represented by a single letter as follows:

C = coronary disease, including myocardial infarction, coronary insufficiency, angina pectoris, arteriosclerotic heart disease, and sudden death otherwise unexplained

H = hypertension, primary or secondary, treated or untreated, corroborated by blood pressure readings when available

S = stroke, including cerebral hemorrhage and cerebral thrombosis

D = diabetes mellitus

O = obesity

The ratings for each disorder are as follows:

+ = positive, where diagnosis is definite

? = questionable, where diagnosis is doubtful or evidence is conflicting

— = negative, where parent is unaffected

U = unknown, where parental history is unknown

( ) = parent 65 or over at onset of disorder

In the case of obesity, a + indicates that, at some time in his adult life, the parent was 20 per cent or more above average body weight, while a ? indicates that he was 10–19 per cent above average body weight. "Average body weight" is here defined as the average weight for a given height at age twenty-five for each sex as set forth in actuarial tables (23). It is thought that the average weight at age twenty-five is a good baseline with which to compare a parent's maximum weight later in life. Since the 1912 tables have heretofore been the yardstick for subjects in the Precursors Study, it seems appropriate to use the same tables as the basis for estimating parental obesity. The reasons for using the 1912 tables rather than those provided by the more recent Build and Blood Pressure Study have been discussed elsewhere (24–27).

Distributions. The distribution of parental disorders by sophistication-of-body-concept level of the figure drawings and by sex of the subject is set forth in detail in Table 37. For each disorder, the sum of the positive (+), indeterminate (?/U) and negative (—) instances equals the total number of subjects in that particular sophistication level group *after* subtracting those whose parental history is entirely unknown (last column). Such unknown history occurs when a subject was adopted as an infant, or when one parent died young or was otherwise lost sight of and the other parent is completely negative. The majority of parents in this study were between the ages of fifty and sixty-five years. In this table no distinction has been made between those whose disorders occurred at sixty-five years of age or over, and the others.* The distributions for the five parental disorders are independent of each other. A subject's parents (one or both) may be positive for one or more disorders and negative for others. In a

*In the Plates, age of sixty-five or over at onset is indicated by parentheses.

8

relatively small proportion of subjects, both parents are free from all five disorders (next to last column).

Examination of Table 37 shows that a high proportion of the subjects drawing anomalous figures reported one or more parental disorders, and that none of the twenty-two men and women with known parental history who drew anomalous figures reported that both parents were unaffected by all five disorders. It is also apparent that female subjects were more likely to draw sophisticated figures than male subjects and less likely to draw primitive or intermediate level figures. When the sophistication level groups are pooled in Table 38, this difference between the sexes was found to be highly significant $(x^2_{(2)} = 17.75, p < .0002)$.

Differences in regard to parental disorders are less striking. Apparently, male subjects reporting parental coronary disease, hypertension, or obesity are *more* likely to draw either primitive *or* sophisticated figures and *less* likely to draw figures of intermediate levels of sophistication than are male subjects with two parents unaffected by all five disorders (Table 38). This difference reaches significance in respect to coronary disease $(x^2_{(2)} = 6.28, p < .05)$, but does not attain significance for the other parental disorders. The small number of female subjects in each parental history cell, particularly for female subjects with anomalous or primitive drawings, makes it impossible to determine whether such a trend would be present among a larger number of female subjects. For the total male and female groups the distribution of positive parental disorders is quite similar.

At this juncture, before all parents have developed the disorders they may eventually have, and before the subjects themselves have been affected in sufficient numbers to make more direct correlations, one can only speculate as to the possibility that individual subjects may reveal a pre-coronary type of personality through a figure drawing. The finding of a higher proportion of parental coronary disease at *both* ends of the sophistication scale brings to mind the work of Bahnson and Wardwell; in studying male patients who had suffered a myocardial infarction, they found *two* subgroups whose psychological characteristics were almost diametrically opposite to each other (28).

Physiological and Metabolic Data

Blood Pressure and Heart Rate. While the subjects were in medical school repeated systolic and diastolic pressure and heart rate determinations were recorded in the recumbent position on several occasions. The circumstances under which the values listed in the *Atlas* were obtained were as follows (11, 29–32):

> Admission = values recorded by the Personnel Health Service at the physical examination performed on the subject's entrance into The Johns Hopkins University School of Medicine.

9

Initial = values obtained as soon as the subject lay down at the beginning of a series of physiological tests carried out in the Precursors Study laboratory.

Control = resting values obtained approximately fifteen minutes after the initial values, when blood pressure and heart rate had stabilized.

Cold pressor change = the maximum change from the above control values during the cold pressor test. The maximum changes did not necessarily occur simultaneously.

Exercise change = the maximum change from the control values preceding the exercise test recorded immediately after the double Master two-step exercise test. On the average, the exercise control values, obtained approximately fifteen minutes after the cold pressor control values, were almost identical and are not given here (11).

Smoking change = the change recorded after smoking a single cigarette during a ballistocardiographic smoking test. This test was carried out on a different day from that on which the cold pressor and exercise tests were given. The control values for the smoking test, which were in general similar to those for the cold pressor test, are not given here.

Age. The age in years given in this section represents the age of the subject at the time of the series of physiological tests, when most of the physiological and metabolic data were obtained. As a rule, admission data were recorded when subjects were from two months to a year younger; change on smoking was recorded when subjects were a year older, on the average.

Height. Height in inches was recorded with shoes, to meet the requirements of the exercise test.

Weight. Weight was recorded in pounds. Subjects were weighed in trousers and shoes (men), or in light clothing and low-heeled shoes (women).

Percentage Overweight. Percentage overweight was calculated by comparing the weight of the subject with the average weight for the appropriate sex, height, and age given in actuarial tables (see discussion under section on Parental History: Coding and Definitions) (23–27).

Ponderal Index. The ponderal index was calculated by dividing height by the cube root of weight (33).

Cholesterol. The total serum cholesterol was determined by a modification of the Bloor method (34).

Vital Capacity. The forced vital capacity recorded was the best of three attempts to exhale maximally into a standard water spirometer.

Age. The "age at psychological test" shown in the *Atlas* always refers to age at Figure-drawing Test and Rorschach Test. In most cases it was also the age at Strong Vocational Interest Test. As indicated below, it does not refer to age at habit survey, which almost always was the same as age at physiological and metabolic tests.

Habit Survey. At the same time that the physiological and metabolic data were collected, the Precursors Study subjects were asked to answer a questionnaire concerning many of their daily habits, including smoking habits and "habits of nervous tension." For the most part, subjects were in the first or second year of medical school when the habit survey was completed.

The smoking habits recorded in the *Atlas* follow the classification shown on page 12, which is used in the Precursors Study (11, 24). The "habits of nervous tension" portion of the questionnaire has been analyzed in detail elsewhere (35). Its exact wording and the twenty-five possible responses are shown on page 12. In the *Atlas*, all of the habits of nervous tension to which the subject responded positively are listed by numbers corresponding to those on page 12. Thus, for example, when the habits of nervous tension are recorded as 3, 7, and 8 it indicates that when that particular subject found himself in situations of stress, he reacted with *depression, decreased activity,* and an *increased urge to sleep;* whereas, a subject whose habits of nervous tension are recorded as 5, 6, and 19 reacted with *general tension, increased activity,* and *gripe sessions.*

Strong Vocational Interest Test. The Strong Vocational Interest Test was administered to the classes of 1958 through 1964, usually at the same time that the Figure-drawing Test was given; the classes of 1952 through 1957 did not take the Strong Test. The Vocational Interest Blank for Men (Revised), Form M, by Edward K. Strong, Jr., was used to test both male and female subjects. The completed tests were scored by Testscor of Minneapolis, Minn., on an improved scoring machine in July, 1962, and thereafter. The standard scores given in the *Atlas* for each occupation and for interest maturity, occupational level, and masculinity-femininity were obtained in this way from the Hankes report form.

These standard scores are expressed in two-digit numbers ranging from 74 to −10. A high score (45 or above) means that the subject has the interests of persons successfully engaged in that particular occupation. An intermediate score (30 to 44) means that the person probably has those interests. A low score (29 or below) means that a person does not have the interests of persons successfully engaged in that occupation.

The Strong Tests of twenty-eight subjects were scored in single-digit numbers by Dr. Helen Hofer Gee, who tested them for another purpose; the original forms for these subjects were not available for rescoring. These scores are on a ten-point scale in which 0 is the lowest score and 9 is the highest.

Nonsmoker
Occasional smoker
Regular smoker
    Cigarettes
        Light = one to ten a day
        Moderate = eleven to nineteen a day
        Heavy = twenty or more a day
    Pipes
    Cigars
    Pipes and cigars
    Mixed = cigarettes combined with pipes and/or cigars
Former smoker

HABITS OF NERVOUS TENSION

Whenever you find yourself in situations of undue pressure or stress, how do you usually react? (Underline all reactions which are characteristic of you.)

1. Exhaustion or excessive fatigue
2. Exhilaration
3. Depressed feelings
4. Uneasy or anxious feelings (sighing, tight feelings in throat or chest, dry mouth, clammy hands, etc.)
5. General tension ("keyed up" feelings—difficulty in becoming relaxed)
6. Increased activity
7. Decreased activity
8. An increased urge to sleep
9. Increased difficulty in sleeping
10. Increased urge to eat
11. Loss of appetite
12. Nausea
13. Vomiting
14. Diarrhoea
15. Constipation
16. Urinary frequency
17. Tremulousness or shakiness
18. Anger { expressed / concealed
19. Gripe sessions
20. Concern about your physical health
21. A tendency to check and recheck your work to assure yourself of accuracy
22. An urge to confide and seek advice or reassurance
23. An urge to be by yourself and get away from it all
24. Irritability with concern as to who is to blame
25. Philosophic effort with no reactions out of the ordinary

Briefly describe your chief reactions to pressure or stress and the situations in which they most commonly occur (competitions, examinations, family situations, etc.) .

REFERENCES

1. Buck, J. N.: The H-T-P technique, a qualitative and quantitative scoring manual. J. Clin. Psychol. Monogr. Suppl., **5**:1948.

2. Machover, K.: Personality projection in the drawing of the human figure. Charles C Thomas, Springfield, Ill., 1949.

3. Jones, L. W. and Thomas, C. B.: Studies on figure drawings: A review of the literature (1949–1959). Psychiat. Quart. Suppl., **35**:212, Part 2, 1961.

4. Vernier, C. M.: Projective test productions. I. Projective drawings. Grune & Stratton, New York, N.Y., 1952.

5. Thomas, C. B., Jones, L. W., and Ross, D. C.: Studies on figure drawings: Biological implications of structural and graphic characteristics. Psychiat. Quart. In press.

6. Thomas, C. B., Ross, D. C. and Freed, E. S.: An index of Rorschach responses: Studies on the psychological characteristics of medical students—I. The Johns Hopkins Press, Baltimore, Md., 1964.

7. Thomas, C. B., Ross, D. C., and Freed, E. S.: An index of responses to the group Rorschach test: Studies on the psychological characteristics of medical students—II. The Johns Hopkins Press, Baltimore, Md., 1965.

8. Thomas, C. B.: Observations on some possible precursors of essential hypertension and coronary artery disease. Bull. Johns Hopkins Hosp., **89**:419, 1951.

9. Thomas, C. B.: Characteristics of the individual as guideposts to the prevention of heart disease. Ann. Intern. Med., **47**:389, 1957.

10. Molish, H. B., Molish, E. E., and Thomas, C. B.: A Rorschach study of a group of medical students. Psychiat. Quart., **24**:744, 1950.

11. Thomas, C. B.: Characteristics of smokers compared with nonsmokers in a population of healthy young adults, including observations on family history, blood pressure, heart rate, body weight, cholesterol, and certain psychologic traits. Ann. Intern. Med., **53**:697, 1960.

12. Thomas, C. B.: Pathogenetic interrelations in hypertension and coronary artery disease. Dis. Nerv. Syst., Monogr. Suppl., **22**:39, 1961.

13. Thomas, C. B.: The heritage of hypertension. Amer. J. Med. Sci., **224**:367, 1952.

14. Thomas, C. B. and Cohen, B. H.: The familial occurrence of hypertension and coronary artery disease, with observations concerning obesity and diabetes. Ann. Intern. Med., **42**:90, 1955.

15. Thomas, C. B.: Observations on some possible precursors of essential hypertension and coronary artery disease. V. Hypercholesteremia in healthy young adults. Amer. J. Med. Sci., **232**:389, 1956.

16. Thomas, C. B.: Familial patterns in hypertension and coronary heart disease. Circulation, **20**:25, 1959.

17. Thomas, C. B., Ross, D. C., and Higinbothom, C. Q.: Precursors of hypertension and coronary disease among healthy medical students: Discriminant function analysis. II. Using parental history as the criterion. Bull. Johns Hopkins Hosp., **115**:245, 1964.

18. Thomas, C. B. and Ross, D. C.: The heritage of hypertension and coronary disease: Discriminant function analysis of the characteristics of healthy young adults. Amer. J. Med. Sci., **248**:505, 1964.

19. Jones, L. W. and Thomas, C. B.: Studies on figure drawings: Structural and graphic characteristics. Psychiat. Quart. Suppl., **38**:76, Part 1, 1964.

20. Bruce, J. M., Jr., and Thomas, C. B.: A method of rating certain personality factors as determined by the Rorschach test for use in a study of the precursors of hypertension and coronary artery disease. Psychiat. Quart. Suppl., **27**:207, 1953.

21. Witkin, H. A., Dyk, R. B., Faterson, H. F., Goodenough, D. R., and Karp, S. A.: Psychological differentiation: Studies of development. John Wiley & Sons, Inc., New York and London, 1962.

22. Jones, L. W. and Thomas, C. B.: Studies on figure drawings: Manual of instructions for coding structural and graphic characteristics. Psychiat. Quart. Suppl., **39**:241, Part 2, 1965.

23. Association of Life Insurance Directors and Actuarial Society of America, New York, N.Y., 1912, p. 38. Published by a committee.

24. Thomas, C. B., Ross, D. C., and Higinbothom, C. Q.: Precursors of hypertension and coronary disease among healthy medical students: Discriminant function analysis. I. Using smoking habits as the criterion. Bull. Johns Hopkins Hosp., **115**:174, 1964.

25. Build and blood pressure study. Vol. I, Society of Actuaries, Chicago, Ill., 1959.

26. Hutchinson, J. J.: Clinical implications of an extensive actuarial study of build and blood pressure. Ann. Intern. Med., **54**:90, 1961.

27. Seltzer, C. C. and Mayer, J.: A simple criterion of obesity. Clin. Nutrition, **38**:A-101, 1965.

28. Bahnson, C. B. and Wardwell, W. I.: Parent constellation and psychosexual identification in male patients with myocardial infarction. Psychol. Reports, **10**:831 (Monograph Supplement 3-V10), 1962.

29. Thomas, C. B., Stanley, J. A., and Kendrick, M. A.: Observations on some possible precursors of essential hypertension and coronary artery disease. VII. The subjective reaction to the cold pressor test as expressed in the verbal response. J. Chron. Dis., **14**:355, 1961.

30. Thomas, C. B.: The cardiovascular response of normal young adults to exercise as determined by the double Master two-step test. Bull. Johns Hopkins Hosp., **89**:181, 1951.

31. Thomas, C. B., Bateman, J. L., and Lindberg, E. F. with the statistical assistance of Bornhold, H. J.: Observations on the individual effects of smoking on the blood pressure, heart rate, stroke volume and cardiac output of healthy young adults. Ann. Intern. Med., **44**:874, 1956.

32. Thomas, C. B. and Murphy, E. A.: Observations on some possible precursors of essential hypertension and coronary artery disease. VI. Comparison of the circulatory reactivity to the cold pressor test and to the smoking test. Ann. Intern. Med., **50**:970, 1959.

33. Sheldon, W. H., with the collaboration of Dupertuis, C. W. and McDermott, E.: Atlas of men. A guide for somatotyping the adult male at all ages. Harper & Brothers, New York, N.Y., 1954.

34. Thomas, C. B. and Eisenberg, F. F.: Observations on the variability of total serum cholesterol in Johns Hopkins medical students. J. Chron. Dis., **6**:1, 1957.

35. Thomas, C. B. and Ross, D. C.: Observations on some possible precursors of essential hypertension and coronary artery disease. VIII. Relationship of cholesterol level to certain habit patterns under stress. Bull. Johns Hopkins Hosp., **113**:225, 1963.

14

Table 1. Distribution of Subjects by Sex and Race

	European Ancestry	Oriental Ancestry	Near and Middle Eastern Ancestry	Total
Males	788	15	7	810
Females	57	3	0	60
Total	845	18	7	870

Table 2. Type of Figure—Stick Drawing

	Percentage Distribution	
Code	Figures drawn by	
	Men N = 788	Women N = 57
0 = neither figure a stick drawing	97.8	98.2
1 = male only a stick drawing	0.8	0.0
2 = female only a stick drawing	0.0	0.0
3 = both stick drawings, sex indeterminate	0.0	0.0
4 = both stick drawings, sex identifiable	1.1	1.8
5 = one figure a stick drawing, sex indeterminate	0.3	0.0
9 = other	0.0	0.0

Table 3. Sex Sequence

	Percentage Distribution	
Code	Figures drawn by	
	Men N = 788	Women N = 57
0 = man first, woman second	65.2	35.1
1 = woman first, man second	19.9	47.4
2 = man and woman, order undetermined or both on one page	13.6	17.5
3 = man only or with other figure of indeterminate sex	0.9	0.0
4 = woman only or with other figure of indeterminate sex	0.3	0.0
5 = two figures, indeterminate sex	0.0	0.0
6 = one figure, indeterminate sex	0.1	0.0
9 = other	0.1	0.0

Table 4. Posture

Code	Percentage Distribution			
	Male Figure drawn by		Female Figure drawn by	
	Men N = 786*	Women N = 57	Men N = 780*	Women N = 57
0 = uncertain—feet missing or hidden	5.4	7.0	7.6	7.0
1 = standing	77.3	84.2	78.6	78.9
2 = walking	10.1	3.5	6.4	3.5
3 = sitting	2.3	1.8	2.8	5.3
4 = leaning	0.6	0.0	0.3	1.8
5 = running	1.4	0.0	0.3	0.0
6 = activity, other	1.3	1.8	1.5	1.8
7 = reclining	0.0	0.0	0.5	0.0
8 = crouching or kneeling	0.1	0.0	1.0	0.0
9 = other	1.5	1.8	1.0	1.8

* Ten men drew single figures; seven of these were male figures, two were female figures, and one was a figure of indeterminate sex which has been coded with the male figures in Tables 4 through 36.

Table 5. Perspective

Code	Percentage Distribution			
	Male Figure drawn by		Female Figure drawn by	
	Men N = 786	Women N = 57	Men N = 780	Women N = 57
A. Head and Body Concordant				
0 = front, full view	58.4	86.0	53.1	77.2
1 = front, three-quarter view	4.8	0.0	7.3	7.0
2 = side view	21.4	5.3	27.8	5.3
3 = back, full view	0.5	0.0	0.5	0.0
4 = back, three-quarter view	0.1	0.0	0.3	0.0
B. Head and Body Discordant				
5 = profile head, body front, full view	7.0	3.5	4.5	1.8
6 = profile head, body front, three-quarter view	3.3	3.5	3.1	1.8
7 = profile head, body back, full view	0.0	0.0	0.3	0.0
8 = profile head, body back, three-quarter view	0.5	0.0	0.5	1.8
A. or B.				
9 = other, including combinations and uncertain	3.9	1.8	2.7	5.3

Table 6. Vertical Midline

Code	Percentage Distribution			
	Male Figure drawn by		Female Figure drawn by	
	Men N = 786	Women N = 57	Men N = 780	Women N = 57
0 = front, midline lacking	31.3	40.3	47.6	57.9
1 = front, midline doubtful, including structural line	1.1	1.8	1.0	0.0
*2 =	0.3	0.0	0.1	0.0
3 = front, midline apparent	34.0	45.6	10.3	21.1
4 = side or three-quarters, midline lacking	18.6	1.8	36.8	15.8
5 = side or three-quarters, midline doubtful, including structural line	1.3	1.8	0.0	0.0
6 =	0.0	0.0	0.0	0.0
7 = side or three-quarters, midline apparent	10.3	7.0	2.3	1.8
8 = back, vertical midline apparent	0.5	0.0	0.4	0.0
9 = other	2.7	1.8	1.5	3.5

* The undefined categories in this table and in subsequent ones have been reserved for a compromise judgment when two judges disagreed (see text under "Codes and Distributions").

Table 7. Bilateral Symmetry (not including forearms)

Code	Percentage Distribution			
	Male Figure drawn by		Female Figure drawn by	
	Men N = 786	Women N = 57	Men N = 780	Women N = 57
0 = none—side or three-quarters position	31.0	8.8	40.3	19.3
1 = little symmetry—figure halves lopsided	3.8	1.8	2.3	0.0
2 =	9.2	8.8	5.8	5.3
3 = figure halves similar	39.9	61.4	41.2	52.6
4 =	7.6	7.0	4.9	5.3
5 = figure halves almost identical	5.6	10.5	4.2	14.0
9 = other, including figure distortion or incompleteness	2.8	1.8	1.4	3.5

Table 8. Horizontal Midline

Code	Percentage Distribution			
	Male Figure drawn by		Female Figure drawn by	
	Men N = 786	Women N = 57	Men N = 780	Women N = 57
0 = none	21.5	17.5	41.7	29.8
1 =	0.0	0.0	0.0	0.0
2 = doubtful—at normal waistline	1.4	3.5	2.2	1.8
3 =	0.0	0.0	0.1	0.0
4 = present—at normal waistline	62.1	56.1	54.1	63.2
5 =	0.1	0.0	0.0	0.0
6 = line at other than normal waistline—e.g., bottom edge of jacket	12.7	21.1	0.9	1.8
9 = other	2.2	1.8	1.0	3.5

Table 9. Omission of Appendages (hidden or missing)

Code	Percentage Distribution			
	Male Figure drawn by		Female Figure drawn by	
	Men N = 786	Women N = 57	Men N = 780	Women N = 57
0 = no omissions	78.9	68.4	74.7	59.6
1 = arm(s) and leg(s)—all or part, but more than hands or feet	0.9	1.8	2.2	0.0
2 = arm(s) only—all or part but more than hand(s)	1.8	3.5	3.2	8.8
3 = leg(s) only—all or part but more than feet	3.3	3.5	3.1	3.5
4 = hand(s) and leg(s) as in 3	0.8	0.0	1.2	3.5
5 = foot or feet and arm(s) as in 2	0.0	0.0	0.9	0.0
6 = foot or feet and hand(s)	0.9	1.8	1.5	3.5
7 = hand(s) only	10.1	19.3	10.0	14.0
8 = foot or feet only (if on second sheet regarded as missing)	1.5	1.8	2.1	1.8
9 = other, including uncertain	1.9	0.0	1.2	5.3

Table 10. Position of Both Arms (exclusive of hands)

Code	Percentage Distribution			
	Male Figure drawn by		Female Figure drawn by	
	Men N = 786	Women N = 57	Men N = 780	Women N = 57
0 = both arms completely visible, in similar positions	51.1	68.4	46.5	63.2
1 = both arms completely visible and in different positions	21.5	21.1	16.9	12.3
2 = right arm visible, left arm hidden, all or part	6.4	0.0	9.5	5.3
3 = right arm visible, left arm missing, all or part	0.1	0.0	0.4	0.0
4 = left arm visible, right arm hidden all or part	17.9	5.3	20.6	12.3
5 = left arm visible, right arm missing, all or part	0.1	0.0	0.0	0.0
6 = both arms either incomplete or not visible, all or part	1.8	5.3	5.6	5.3
7 = both arms visible but misplaced	0.4	0.0	0.0	0.0
9 = other	0.6	0.0	0.4	1.8

18

Table 11. Position of Right Arm (exclusive of hand)

Code	Percentage Distribution			
	Male Figure drawn by		Female Figure drawn by	
	Men N = 786	Women N = 57	Men N = 780	Women N = 57
0 = parallel to body axis, figure in upright position	27.0	29.8	20.3	28.1
1 =	1.7	1.8	2.7	0.0
2 = extended away from body from shoulder	20.5	15.8	19.9	17.5
3 =	1.8	0.0	2.1	0.0
4 = extended away from body only from elbow	8.1	3.5	7.3	5.3
5 = wrist near or against body, arms akimbo or bent	18.1	33.3	20.5	29.8
6 = activity position: diving, dancing, swinging in walking, etc.	1.9	5.3	1.0	1.8
7 = side or three-quarter view— arm not visible, missing or hidden, all or part	17.9	5.3	22.7	10.5
8 = front or back view—arm not visible, missing or hidden, all or part	1.8	5.3	3.1	5.3
9 = other	1.3	0.0	0.5	1.8

Table 12. Position of Left Arm (exclusive of hand)

Code	Percentage Distribution			
	Male Figure drawn by		Female Figure drawn by	
	Men N = 786	Women N = 57	Men N = 780	Women N = 57
0 = parallel to body axis, figure in upright position	31.9	29.8	23.8	22.8
1 =	2.2	1.8	2.2	0.0
2 = extended away from body from shoulder	15.9	14.0	18.3	15.8
3 =	1.8	0.0	1.2	0.0
4 = extended away from body only from elbow	13.2	7.0	13.7	7.0
5 = wrist near or against body, arms akimbo or bent	23.2	36.8	24.1	40.3
6 = activity position: diving, dancing, swinging in walking, etc.	2.2	5.3	1.0	1.8
7 = side or three-quarter view— arm not visible, missing or hidden, all or part	6.5	0.0	11.4	5.3
8 = front or back view—arm not visible, missing or hidden, all or part	1.7	5.3	3.6	5.3
9 = other	1.5	0.0	0.6	1.8

Table 13. Position of Legs (exclusive of feet)

Code	Percentage Distribution			
	Male Figure drawn by		Female Figure drawn by	
	Men N = 786	Women N = 57	Men N = 780	Women N = 57
0 = misplaced, missing or hidden —wholly or partially	2.5	1.8	4.2	7.0
1 = no evidence of relative position (e.g., side view, long skirt, etc.)	15.3	1.8	21.0	7.0
2 = parallel or closed	6.1	10.5	5.4	3.5
3 =	1.9	5.3	2.1	0.0
4 = slightly apart	25.7	43.9	33.2	54.4
5 =	8.4	7.0	7.7	3.5
6 = widely apart	25.4	21.1	16.8	12.3
7 = crossed	1.1	0.0	0.9	1.8
8 = activity position	12.7	5.3	7.8	5.3
9 = other	0.8	3.5	0.9	5.3

Table 14. Long Axis of Figure in Relation to Axis of Page

Code	Percentage Distribution			
	Male Figure drawn by		Female Figure drawn by	
	Men N = 786	Women N = 57	Men N = 780	Women N = 57
0 = incongruent figure axis (e.g., seated, bending)	3.8	1.8	5.9	3.5
1 = parallel to long axis of page	91.3	91.2	89.9	89.5
2 = parallel to short axis of page	2.4	3.5	2.1	3.5
3 = full length of figure at or between 20° and 70° angles from the long or short axis of page	1.8	3.5	1.8	1.8
9 = other	0.6	0.0	0.4	1.8

Table 15. Location of Figure in Regard to Right and Left Halves of Page (exclusive of forearm, toes, nose, or edge of garment)

Code	Percentage Distribution			
	Male Figure drawn by		Female Figure drawn by	
	Men N = 786	Women N = 57	Men N = 780	Women N = 57
0 = approximately centered — long or short axis of page bisects figure vertically	5.4	7.0	6.8	5.3
1 = more than half within left half	61.5	75.4	52.2	64.9
2 = totally within left half	23.4	8.8	29.9	21.1
3 = more than half within right half	6.8	1.8	7.3	0.0
4 = totally within right half	0.6	3.5	1.4	3.5
5 = 1 and cut off at left edge	0.0	0.0	0.0	0.0
6 = 2 and cut off at left edge	0.0	0.0	0.1	0.0
7 = 3 and cut off at right edge	0.1	0.0	0.1	0.0
8 = 4 and cut off at right edge	0.0	0.0	0.0	0.0
9 = other (e.g., two figures on same page)	2.2	3.5	2.2	5.3

Table 16. Location of Figure in Regard to Upper and Lower Halves of Page (exclusive of forearm, toes, nose, or edge of garment)

Code	Percentage Distribution			
	Male Figure drawn by		Female Figure drawn by	
	Men N = 786	Women N = 57	Men N = 780	Women N = 57
0 = approximately centered—less than ½ inch marginal difference above and below figure	19.2	31.6	15.6	22.8
1 = more than half in upper half	46.6	38.6	49.2	38.6
2 = totally in upper half	7.4	1.8	6.5	1.8
3 = more than half in lower half	21.4	19.3	22.9	26.3
4 = totally in lower half	0.1	0.0	0.3	0.0
5 = 1 and cut off at top edge	0.1	0.0	0.1	0.0
6 = 2 and cut off at top edge	0.0	0.0	0.0	0.0
7 = 3 and cut off at lower edge or continued on another page	4.3	7.0	4.4	7.0
8 = 4 and cut off at lower edge or continued on another page	0.0	0.0	0.0	0.0
9 = other (e.g., two figures on same page, one above and one below, also 0 and cut off)	0.9	1.8	0.9	3.5

Table 17. Location of Figure in Regard to Four Quadrants of Page (exclusive of forearm, toes, nose, or edge of garment)

Code	Percentage Distribution			
	Male Figure drawn by		Female Figure drawn by	
	Men N = 786	Women N = 57	Men N = 780	Women N = 57
0 = totally in upper left quadrant	4.8	1.8	4.6	0.0
1 = totally in upper right quadrant	0.3	0.0	0.3	1.8
2 = totally in lower left quadrant	0.0	0.0	0.0	0.0
3 = totally in lower right quadrant	0.1	0.0	0.1	0.0
4 = figure within two or more quadrants	94.0	98.2	94.2	96.4
9 = other	0.8	0.0	0.8	1.8

Table 18. Relative Size of Male and Female Figures

Code	Percentage Distribution	
	Figures drawn by	
	Men N = 788	Women N = 57
0 = man larger than woman	43.6	43.9
1 =	2.8	5.3
2 = approximately equivalent in size	14.7	14.0
3 =	2.2	3.5
4 = man smaller than woman	26.8	21.1
5 = figures incompatible for comparison	8.4	12.3
7 = only one figure drawn	1.3	0.0
9 = other	0.3	0.0

Table 19. Line Pressure of Figure Boundary Chiefly Constant

Code	Percentage Distribution			
	Male Figure drawn by		Female Figure drawn by	
	Men N = 786	Women N = 57	Men N = 780	Women N = 57
0 = varying from one of the following categories to another	56.1	68.4	63.5	66.7
1 = light or vague, constant	17.8	15.8	16.9	17.5
2 =	2.0	1.8	2.2	1.8
3 = medium, constant	7.5	1.8	6.0	7.0
4 =	1.7	7.0	1.3	1.8
5 = firm or heavy, constant	14.8	5.3	10.0	3.5
9 = other	0.1	0.0	0.1	1.8

Table 20. Line Pressure of Figure Boundary Chiefly Variable

Code	Percentage Distribution			
	Male Figure drawn by		Female Figure drawn by	
	Men N = 786	Women N = 57	Men N = 780	Women N = 57
0 = chiefly constant	43.6	31.2	36.4	31.2
1 = light and medium, variable	18.7	22.8	19.2	28.1
2 =	5.3	10.5	5.8	10.5
3 = light and firm or heavy, variable	10.2	15.8	13.8	3.5
4 =	6.4	8.8	7.1	8.8
5 = medium and firm or heavy, variable	15.6	10.5	17.6	15.8
9 = other	0.1	0.0	0.1	1.8

Table 21. Line Continuity of Figure Boundary

Code	Percentage Distribution			
	Male Figure drawn by		Female Figure drawn by	
	Men N = 786	Women N = 57	Men N = 780	Women N = 57
0 = chiefly noncontinuous	58.7	64.9	62.1	64.9
1 =	8.3	10.5	8.1	5.3
2 = partly continuous, partly noncontinuous	12.6	12.3	12.9	10.5
3 =	6.2	1.8	5.9	5.3
4 = chiefly continuous	14.1	10.5	10.9	12.3
9 = other	0.1	0.0	0.1	1.8

Table 22. Body Shading

Code	Percentage Distribution			
	Male Figure drawn by		Female Figure drawn by	
	Men N = 786	Women N = 57	Men N = 780	Women N = 57
0 = no shading	37.5	24.6	27.4	21.1
1 = above waistline, exclusive of clothing accessories	4.7	5.3	15.9	10.5
2 = below waistline, exclusive of clothing accessories	7.4	5.3	6.4	10.5
3 = above and below waistline (1 and 2)	17.2	14.0	25.3	12.3
4 = clothing accessories only— tie, belt, jewelry, collar, socks, shoes, etc.	12.3	17.5	3.7	5.3
5 = 1 and accessories	2.5	5.3	6.8	10.5
6 = 2 and accessories	5.5	12.3	3.1	8.8
7 = 3 and accessories	10.9	14.0	10.4	17.5
9 = other	1.9	1.8	1.0	3.5

Table 23. Hair Shading

Code	Percentage Distribution			
	Male Figure drawn by		Female Figure drawn by	
	Men N = 786	Women N = 57	Men N = 780	Women N = 57
0 = hair missing or almost completely hidden	13.5	14.0	2.2	3.5
1 = coiffure shaded and confined within distinct, definite outline	17.0	21.1	12.1	24.6
2 =	6.9	5.3	9.0	10.5
3 = coiffure shaded, but not confined within outline	43.4	43.9	57.4	43.9
4 =	0.0	0.0	0.0	0.0
5 = coiffure not shaded, but distinctly outlined	8.5	3.5	14.6	14.0
6 =	0.3	0.0	0.0	0.0
7 = only lines, few or scattered, denoting hair	9.9	12.3	4.4	3.5
9 = other	0.5	0.0	0.4	0.0

Table 24. Nudity and Clothing Transparency

Code	Percentage Distribution			
	Male Figure drawn by		Female Figure drawn by	
	Men N = 786	Women N = 57	Men N = 780	Women N = 57
0 = completely nude	16.8	10.5	22.9	12.3
1 =	0.0	0.0	0.0	0.0
2 = minimal clothing, no transparency	2.0	3.5	5.6	1.8
3 = nude only above waistline, no transparency	9.2	0.0	3.1	0.0
4 = nude only below waistline, no transparency	0.1	0.0	0.0	0.0
5 = transparency in partially clothed figure (2, 3, or 4)	1.0	0.0	0.4	1.8
6 = transparency in fully clothed figure	3.1	3.5	6.3	1.8
7 = fully clothed figure, no transparency	62.1	80.7	57.8	78.9
9 = other, including stick drawing	5.7	1.8	3.8	3.5

Table 25. Form Level

Code	Percentage Distribution			
	Male Figure drawn by		Female Figure drawn by	
	Men N = 786	Women N = 57	Men N = 780	Women N = 57
0 = anomalous (stick figure or head only)	2.4	1.8	1.7	3.5
1 = sophisticated	34.4	50.9	34.1	56.1
3 = intermediate	48.1	45.6	49.4	38.6
5 = primitive	15.1	1.8	14.9	1.8

Table 26. Level of Detailing

Code	Percentage Distribution			
	Male Figure drawn by		Female Figure drawn by	
	Men N = 786	Women N = 57	Men N = 780	Women N = 57
0 = anomalous (stick figure or head only)	2.4	1.8	1.7	3.5
1 = sophisticated	25.3	35.1	23.3	26.3
3 = intermediate	52.7	52.6	55.6	64.9
5 = primitive	19.6	10.5	19.4	5.3

Table 27. Identity and Sex Differentiation

Code	Percentage Distribution			
	Male Figure drawn by		Female Figure drawn by	
	Men N = 786	Women N = 57	Men N = 780	Women N = 57
0 = anomalous (stick figure or head only)	2.4	1.8	1.7	3.5
1 = sophisticated	76.2	82.5	78.6	89.5
3 = intermediate	15.6	15.8	16.0	7.0
5 = primitive	5.7	0.0	3.7	0.0

Table 28. Over-all Sophistication-of-Body-Concept Level

Code	Percentage Distribution			
	Male Figure drawn by		Female Figure drawn by	
	Men N = 786	Women N = 57	Men N = 780	Women N = 57
0 = anomalous (stick figure or head only)	2.4	1.8	1.7	3.5
1 = most sophisticated	9.2	24.6	9.0	22.8
2 = moderately sophisticated	29.9	40.3	30.3	43.9
3 = intermediate	40.7	28.1	40.5	26.3
4 = moderately primitive	13.7	5.3	15.0	3.5
5 = most primitive	4.1	0.0	3.6	0.0

Table 29. Height of Upright Figure in Relation to Long Axis of Page

Code of Scale Values	Percentage Distribution			
	Male Figure drawn by		Female Figure drawn by	
	Men N = 708*	Women N = 52*	Men N = 682*	Women N = 48*
00 = 0–9	0.1	0.0	0.1	0.0
01 = 10–19	0.7	0.0	0.6	0.0
02 = 20–29	3.0	3.8	4.0	2.1
03 = 30–39	8.6	5.8	9.5	4.2
04 = 40–49	15.0	13.5	17.3	8.3
05 = 50–59	20.9	17.3	19.9	31.2
06 = 60–69	19.2	25.0	21.6	18.7
07 = 70–79	17.9	25.0	14.4	29.2
08 = 80–89	10.9	9.6	9.4	4.2
09 = 90–99	3.7	0.0	2.9	0.0
10 = 100 or over	0.0	0.0	0.3	2.1

* The numbers are smaller than those in the preceding tables, since not all figures are measurable for height.

Table 30. Proportion of Head in Relation to Total Height of Figure

Code of Scale Values	Percentage Distribution			
	Male Figure drawn by		Female Figure drawn by	
	Men N = 688*	Women N = 50*	Men N = 670*	Women N = 47*
00 = 0– 9	0.0	0.0	0.0	0.0
01 = 10– 19	0.1	0.0	0.3	0.0
02 = 20– 29	1.0	0.0	0.9	0.0
03 = 30– 39	3.2	4.0	5.7	6.4
04 = 40– 49	10.3	14.0	10.6	2.1
05 = 50– 59	18.2	4.0	15.7	17.0
06 = 60– 69	16.1	20.0	16.7	19.1
07 = 70– 79	15.4	16.0	19.6	27.7
08 = 80– 89	10.2	16.0	6.7	12.8
09 = 90– 99	14.5	16.0	14.3	2.1
10 = 100–109	2.5	4.0	1.8	8.5
11 = 110–119	2.8	4.0	2.2	0.0
12 = 120 or over	5.7	2.0	5.5	4.3

* In this table and those following, the numbers indicate all the subjects drawing figures in which both height and the body part under consideration are measurable.

Table 31. Proportionate Length of Neck in Relation to Total Height of Figure

Code of Scale Values	Percentage Distribution			
	Male Figure drawn by		Female Figure drawn by	
	Men N = 663	Women N = 49	Men N = 655	Women N = 47
00 = 0– 19	2.4	0.0	1.7	0.0
01 =	1.5	2.0	1.2	2.1
02 = 20– 39	6.5	12.2	6.1	2.1
03 =	5.9	6.1	5.6	8.5
04 = 40– 59	14.8	10.2	15.9	8.5
05 =	9.2	6.1	8.7	14.9
06 = 60– 79	19.0	22.4	19.8	25.5
07 =	9.4	12.2	8.2	6.4
08 = 80– 99	15.5	6.1	15.9	14.9
09 =	0.0	2.0	0.0	2.1
10 = 100–119	6.6	14.3	6.9	10.6
11 =	0.0	0.0	0.0	0.0
12 = 120–139	4.5	4.1	5.6	4.3
13 =	0.0	0.0	0.0	0.0
14 = 140 or over	4.7	2.0	4.3	0.0

Table 32. Proportionate Width of Shoulders in Relation to Total Height of Figure

Code of Scale Values	Percentage Distribution			
	Male Figure drawn by		Female Figure drawn by	
	Men N = 482	Women N = 48	Men N = 420	Women N = 38
00 = 0– 9	0.2	0.0	0.2	0.0
01 = 10– 19	0.2	0.0	0.2	0.0
02 = 20– 29	2.3	4.2	4.0	2.6
03 = 30– 39	3.7	4.2	6.9	10.5
04 = 40– 49	6.4	14.6	16.2	15.8
05 = 50– 59	14.1	10.4	20.0	21.1
06 = 60– 69	16.4	12.5	21.2	26.3
07 = 70– 79	17.6	22.9	14.8	15.8
08 = 80– 89	12.2	20.8	9.0	2.6
09 = 90– 99	13.5	10.4	5.2	2.6
10 = 100–109	6.0	0.0	1.0	0.0
11 = 110–119	4.1	0.0	0.5	2.6
12 = 120 or over	3.1	0.0	1.0	0.0

Table 33. Proportionate Length of Right Arm in Relation to Total Height of Figure

Code of Scale Values	Percentage Distribution			
	Male Figure drawn by		Female Figure drawn by	
	Men N = 509	Women N = 39	Men N = 467	Women N = 32
00 = 0–19	0.8	2.6	0.6	3.1
01 =	0.2	0.0	0.4	0.0
02 = 20–39	13.0	7.7	24.6	9.4
03 =	2.6	2.6	1.7	6.2
04 = 40–59	37.5	35.9	39.8	34.4
05 =	3.1	2.6	4.1	6.2
06 = 60–79	32.0	33.3	23.3	31.2
07 =	2.2	2.6	0.6	0.0
08 = 80–99	7.9	12.8	4.3	9.4
09 =	0.0	0.0	0.0	0.0
10 = 100 or over	0.8	0.0	0.4	0.0

Table 34. Proportionate Length of Left Arm in Relation to Total Height of Figure

Code of Scale Values	Percentage Distribution			
	Male Figure drawn by		Female Figure drawn by	
	Men N = 587	Women N = 43	Men N = 534	Women N = 34
00 = 0–19	0.9	2.3	1.1	2.9
01 =	0.0	0.0	0.4	0.0
02 = 20–39	13.3	11.6	24.9	11.8
03 =	1.9	0.0	3.2	0.0
04 = 40–59	37.1	32.6	38.0	35.3
05 =	3.2	2.3	3.9	8.8
06 = 60–79	31.0	37.2	22.3	32.4
07 =	2.7	0.0	1.9	0.0
08 = 80–99	8.2	14.0	4.3	8.8
09 =	0.0	0.0	0.0	0.0
10 = 100 or over	1.7	0.0	0.0	0.0

Table 35. Proportionate Chest Width in Relation to Total Height of Figure

| | Percentage Distribution | | | |
| | Male Figure drawn by | | Female Figure drawn by | |
Code of Scale Values	Men N = 633	Women N = 50	Men N = 607	Women N = 40
00 = 0– 9	0.3	0.0	0.3	0.0
01 = 10– 19	0.5	0.0	0.5	0.0
02 = 20– 29	3.6	4.0	6.6	5.0
03 = 30– 39	9.6	14.0	12.2	15.0
04 = 40– 49	15.6	14.0	18.3	27.5
05 = 50– 59	17.1	22.0	23.1	17.5
06 = 60– 69	19.6	32.0	15.6	27.5
07 = 70– 79	16.0	10.0	10.7	5.0
08 = 80– 89	6.9	2.0	6.9	0.0
09 = 90– 99	5.2	2.0	3.1	0.0
10 = 100–109	2.7	0.0	1.3	0.0
11 = 110–119	1.3	0.0	0.8	2.5
12 = 120 or over	1.6	0.0	0.5	0.0

Table 36. Proportionate Girth Width in Relation to Total Height of Figure

| | Percentage Distribution | | | |
| | Male Figure drawn by | | Female Figure drawn by | |
Code of Scale Values	Men N = 635	Women N = 49	Men N = 606	Women N = 41
00 = 0– 9	0.2	0.0	0.3	0.0
01 = 10– 19	0.8	0.0	0.5	2.4
02 = 20– 29	2.2	4.1	5.6	7.3
03 = 30– 39	8.7	6.1	14.0	17.1
04 = 40– 49	12.0	20.4	14.5	17.1
05 = 50– 59	18.0	6.1	18.8	17.1
06 = 60– 69	16.5	18.4	15.7	26.8
07 = 70– 79	12.9	26.5	12.7	4.9
08 = 80– 89	7.9	12.2	6.1	2.4
09 = 90– 99	10.9	4.1	5.4	0.0
10 = 100–109	3.8	2.0	2.0	0.0
11 = 110–119	2.8	0.0	1.6	4.9
12 = 120 or over	3.5	0.0	2.6	0.0

Table 37. Distribution of Parental Disorders by Sophistication-of-Body-Concept Level of Figure Drawings and by Sex of Subject

Group	Sophistication-of-body-concept level and code numbers*	Total Subjects Sex	N	Coronary disease +	?/U	−	Hypertension +	?/U	−	Stroke +	?/U	−	Diabetes +	?/U	−	Obesity +	?/U	−	Both parents unaffected by all five disorders	Parental history unknown
I.	Anomalous (0,0 or 0,X or X,0)**	M	21	8	1	11	10	3	7	2	0	18	2	2	16	8	8	4	0	1
		F	2	2	0	0	2	0	0	1	0	1	1	0	1	0	1	1	0	0
II.	Most primitive (5,5)	M	24	5	3	15	8	1	14	1	1	21	4	1	18	10	6	7	5	1
		F	0	0	0	0	0	0	0	0	0	0	0	0	0	0	0	0	0	0
III.	Mixed primitive (5,4 or 4,5)	M	8	1	1	6	4	0	4	0	0	8	0	0	8	2	3	3	1	0
		F	0	0	0	0	0	0	0	0	0	0	0	0	0	0	0	0	0	0
IV.	Moderately primitive (4,4)	M	92	25	13	54	27	14	51	11	3	78	7	1	84	42	22	28	13	0
		F	2	1	0	1	1	0	1	1	0	1	0	0	2	0	1	1	1	0
V.	Mixed moderately primitive and intermediate (4,3 or 3,4)	M	28	7	7	14	8	3	17	1	2	25	2	1	25	13	8	7	3	0
		F	0	0	0	0	0	0	0	0	0	0	0	0	0	0	0	0	0	0
VI.	Mixed moderately primitive and moderately sophisticated (4,2 or 2,4)	M	3	1	0	2	2	1	0	0	0	3	0	0	3	1	1	1	0	0
		F	0	0	0	0	0	0	0	0	0	0	0	0	0	0	0	0	0	0
VII.	Intermediate (3,3)	M	292	52	47	191	87	28	175	26	13	251	21	12	257	102	79	109	55	2
		F	15	5	2	8	3	3	9	4	2	9	2	9	4	7	4	4	2	0
VIII.	Mixed intermediate and moderately sophisticated (3,2 or 2,3)	M	26	9	1	16	7	2	17	2	0	24	2	1	23	12	7	7	3	0
		F	2	0	0	2	0	0	2	0	0	2	0	0	2	1	0	1	1	0
IX.	Mixed intermediate and most sophisticated (3,1 or 1,3)	M	3	1	0	2	2	0	1	1	0	2	0	0	3	1	1	1	0	0
		F	0	0	0	0	0	0	0	0	0	0	0	0	0	0	0	0	0	0
X.	Moderately sophisticated (2,2)	M	216	59	29	125	74	21	118	18	1	194	19	5	189	92	58	63	30	3
		F	22	4	6	11	7	3	11	2	0	19	2	0	19	10	4	7	4	1
XI.	Mixed sophisticated (2,1 or 1,2)	M	10	3	1	6	4	0	6	1	0	9	1	0	9	1	2	7	0	0
		F	1	0	1	0	1	0	0	0	0	1	0	0	1	0	0	1	0	0
XII.	Most sophisticated (1,1)	M	65	12	13	39	21	7	36	4	3	57	5	2	57	24	17	23	11	1
		F	13	2	1	10	4	0	9	1	0	12	0	2	11	6	3	4	3	0
	TOTAL	M	788	183	116	481	254	80	446	67	23	690	63	25	692	308	212	260	121	8
		F	57	14	10	32	18	6	32	9	2	45	5	11	40	24	13	19	11	1

* These pairs of code numbers appear in each plate opposite "sophistication" in the section on Figure Drawing Characteristics. Also see Table 28.
** X = any other code number.
+ = one or both parents positive for that disorder.

?/U = questionable or unknown for that particular disorder: indeterminate (for obesity, ? indicates overweight by 10–19 per cent).
− = both parents negative for that disorder.

Table 38. Percentage Distribution of Positive Parental Disorders by Sophistication-of-Body-Concept Level and by Sex of Subject

Pooled groups*	Sophistication-of-body-concept level	Total subjects** Sex	N	Coronary disease	Hypertension	Stroke	Diabetes	Obesity	Both parents unaffected by all five disorders
I–VI	Anomalous and Primitive	M	174	27.0	33.9	8.6	8.6	43.7	12.6
		F	4	(75.0)	(75.0)	(50.0)	(25.0)	(0.0)	(25.0)
VII–IX	Intermediate	M	319	19.4	30.1	9.1	7.2	36.1	18.2
		F	17	29.4	17.6	23.5	11.8	47.1	17.6
X–XII	Sophisticated	M	287	25.8	34.5	8.0	8.7	40.8	14.3
		F	35	17.1	34.3	8.6	5.7	45.7	20.0
I–XII	TOTAL	M	780	23.5	32.6	8.6	8.1	39.5	15.5
		F	56	25.0	32.1	16.1	8.9	42.9	19.6

* See Table 37.
** Total subjects with known parental history.
*** Since each subject has two parents, either of whom may be affected, the percentages shown are nearly twice the prevalence rates in the parental generation. (In a few instances both parents are affected by the same disorder; those subjects are only counted once.)
( ) = total number too small for percentages to be meaningful.

AN ATLAS OF
FIGURE DRAWINGS

The figure drawings have been cropped in order to eliminate identifying material and writing. Their exact placement on the original 8½ by 11 inch sheet of paper is indicated by the location of the drawing within the outlined frame.

I. ANOMALOUS DRAWINGS

A small group of anomalous drawings, which falls outside the defined categories of sophistication-of-body-concept, is first presented. Even where one drawing is anomalous and its mate is not, both drawings are included in this section.

Although instructed to draw human figures and not stick figures, twenty-three subjects drew either stick figures or heads only. Since these drawings do not meet the requirements of the Figure-drawing Test, the criteria for sophistication-of-body-concept have not been applied. Although, by and large, the stick figures are closely related to the primitive group, the anomalous drawings vary in degree of elaboration. Where possible, they have been classified for structural and graphic characteristics.

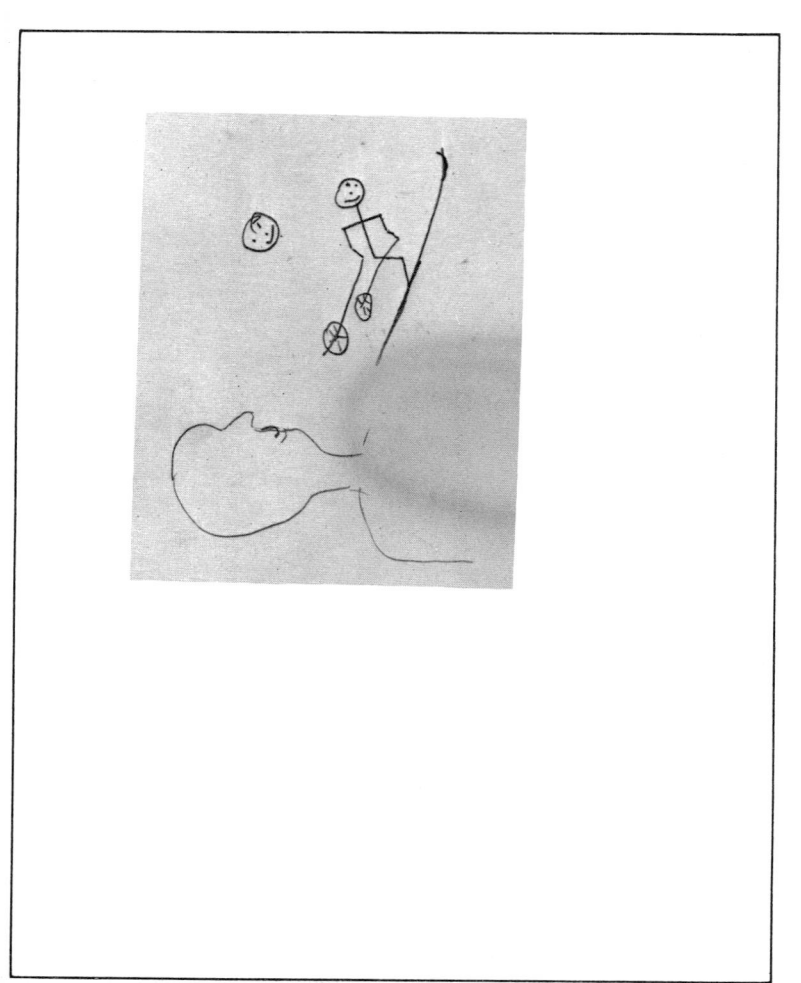

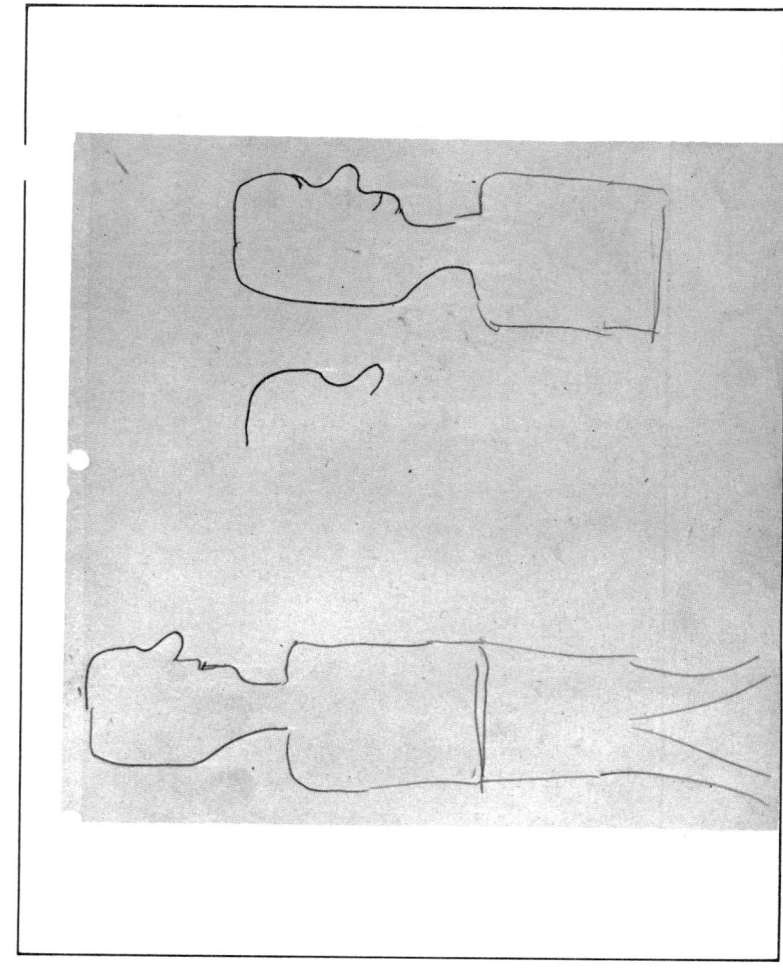

FIGURE-DRAWING CHARACTERISTICS*

Structural	Male Female Both		Structural	Male	Female	Structural and Graphic	Male Female Both		Graphic, Global and Height	Male	Female	Body Proportions	Male	Female
Type	9		Omission of Appendages	1	9	Upper and Lower Halves	7	9	Hair Shading	0	9	Head	12	
Sex Sequence	3		Position of Both Arms	6	9	Four Quarters	4	9	Nudity and Transparency	9	9	Neck	12	
Posture	0	9	Position of Right Arm	8	9	Relative Size	5		Form	5	0	Shoulders		
Perspective	5	9	Position of Left Arm	8	9	Constant Line Pressure	0	9	Detailing	5	0	Right Arm		
Vertical Midline	0	9	Position of Legs	0	9	Variable Line Pressure	5	9	Identity and Sex	5	0	Left Arm		
Bilateral Symmetry	9	9	Relation of Long Axes	2	9	Line Continuity	4	9	Sophistication	5	0	Chest		
Horizontal Midline	4	9	Right and Left Halves	2	9	Body Shading	0	9	Height			Girth	11	

GENERAL CHARACTERISTICS OF SUBJECT

IDENTIFICATION
No. 342
Sex M
Marital status M
Age 26 yrs. at
psychological tests

PARENTAL HISTORY				
Father				
C	H	S	D	O
+	-	-	-	+
Mother				
C	H	S	D	O
+	+	-	-	+

PHYSIOLOGICAL AND METABOLIC DATA

	Admission	Initial	Control	Cold pressor change	Exercise change	Smoking change
Systolic pressure	132	108	108	+06	+26	+08
Diastolic pressure	70	70	70	+12	00	-06
Heart rate	76	78	64	+06	+22	-01

	Height 72 in.	Ponderal index 12.95
Age 24 yrs.	Weight 171 lbs.	Cholesterol 258 mg. per 100 ml.
	Overweight +04 %	Vital capacity 5.3 liters

HABIT SURVEY

Smoking habits: pipe smoker

Age begun 21 yrs.   Inhalation: no

Habits of nervous tension: 2, 5, 6, 14, 16, 21

*These multiple crude attempts to draw a human figure reveal a close relationship between the two types of anomalous drawings, stick figures and heads, and between anomalous drawings (drawn first) and most primitive drawings (drawn second). The figure with belt and legs has been coded as a most primitive male figure. The skiing stick figure has been treated as an anomalous drawing of indeterminate sex. It is worthy of note that both parents had coronary disease under the age of 65 and were obese; the mother also had hypertension.

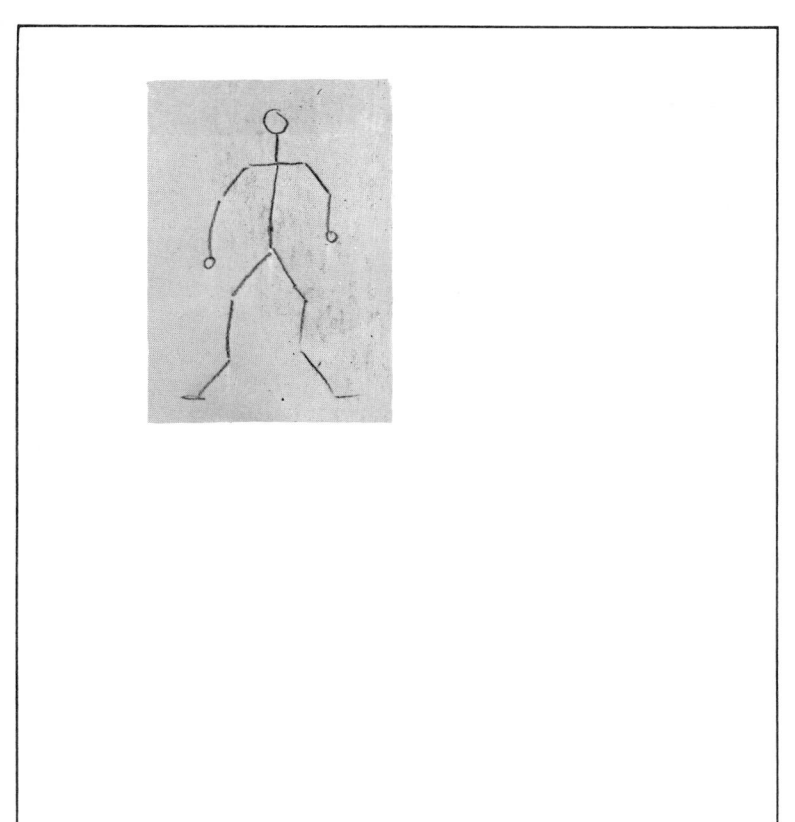

FIGURE-DRAWING CHARACTERISTICS

Structural	Male	Female	Structural	Male	Female	Structural and Graphic	Male	Female	Graphic, Global and Height	Male	Female	Body Proportions	Male	Female
	Both						Both							
Type	1		Omission of Appendages	0	2	Upper and Lower Halves	2	0	Hair Shading	0	5	Head	02	11
Sex Sequence	0		Position of Both Arms	0	6	Four Quarters	0	4	Nudity and Transparency	9	0	Neck		12
Posture	1	1	Position of Right Arm	2	7	Relative Size	5		Form	0	3	Shoulders		
Perspective	9	2	Position of Left Arm	2	7	Constant Line Pressure	3	0	Detailing	0	5	Right Arm	02	
Vertical Midline	9	4	Position of Legs	6	1	Variable Line Pressure	0	3	Identity and Sex	0	3	Left Arm	02	
Bilateral Symmetry	9	0	Relation of Long Axes	1	1	Line Continuity	2	0	Sophistication	0	4	Chest		10
Horizontal Midline	9	0	Right and Left Halves	2	4	Body Shading	9	0	Height	03	08	Girth		13

GENERAL CHARACTERISTICS OF SUBJECT

IDENTIFICATION
No. 236
Sex M
Marital status M
Age 24 yrs. at
psychological tests

PARENTAL HISTORY				
Father				
C	H	S	D	O
+	+	-	+	+
Mother				
C	H	S	D	O
-	-	-	-	+

PHYSIOLOGICAL AND METABOLIC DATA

	Admission	Initial	Control	Cold pressor change	Exercise change	Smoking change
Systolic pressure	112	138	118	+24	+26	
Diastolic pressure	74	68	66	+42	00	
Heart rate	72	80	71	+18	+08	

Age 22 yrs.	Height 74 in.	Ponderal index 12.37
	Weight 214 lbs.	Cholesterol 230 mg. per 100 ml.
	Overweight +24 %	Vital capacity 5.4 liters

HABIT SURVEY

Smoking habits: heavy cigarette smoker

Age begun 17 yrs.   Inhalation: yes

Habits of nervous tension: 3, 5, 6, 9, 10, 18, 19, 22

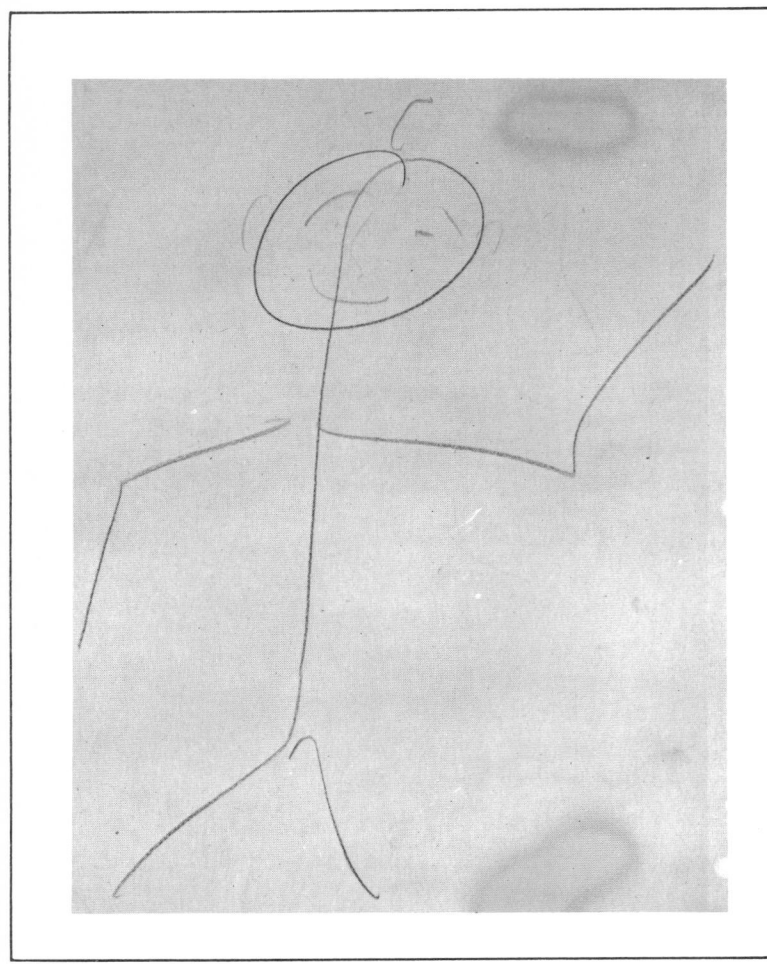

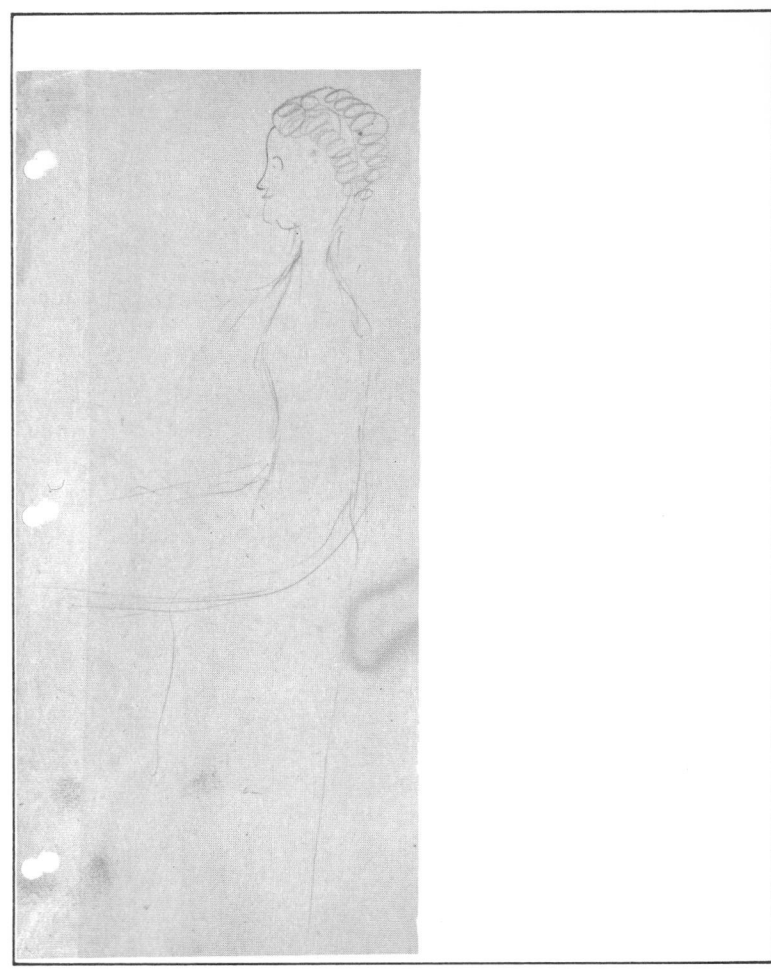

FIGURE-DRAWING CHARACTERISTICS

Structural	Male Female Both	Structural	Male	Female	Structural and Graphic	Male Female Both		Graphic, Global and Height	Male	Female	Body Proportions	Male	Female
Type	1	Omission of Appendages	9	1	Upper and Lower Halves	0	7	Hair Shading	7	3	Head	14	10
Sex Sequence	0	Position of Both Arms	0	6	Four Quarters	4	4	Nudity and Transparency	9	9	Neck		10
Posture	1 0	Position of Right Arm	2	7	Relative Size	5		Form	0	5	Shoulders		
Perspective	0 2	Position of Left Arm	2	7	Constant Line Pressure	5	1	Detailing	0	5	Right Arm		
Vertical Midline	9 4	Position of Legs	6	0	Variable Line Pressure	0	0	Identity and Sex	0	5	Left Arm		
Bilateral Symmetry	9 0	Relation of Long Axes	1	1	Line Continuity	4	0	Sophistication	0	5	Chest		07
Horizontal Midline	9 0	Right and Left Halves	1	6	Body Shading	9	0	Height	08		Girth		09

GENERAL CHARACTERISTICS OF SUBJECT

IDENTIFICATION
No. 249
Sex M
Marital status S
Age 23 yrs. at
psychological tests

PARENTAL HISTORY				
Father				
C	H	S	D	O
+	-	-	-	-
Mother				
C	H	S	D	O
-	+	-	-	-

PHYSIOLOGICAL AND METABOLIC DATA

	Admission	Initial	Control	Cold pressor change	Exercise change	Smoking change
Systolic pressure	102	114	112	+16	+23	
Diastolic pressure	70	68	68	+10	-10	
Heart rate	66	84	77	+04	+20	

Age 21 yrs.	Height 69 in.	Ponderal index 13.04
	Weight 148 lbs.	Cholesterol 190 mg. per 100 ml.
	Overweight -01 %	Vital capacity 4.1 liters

HABIT SURVEY

Smoking habits: pipe smoker

Age begun 17 yrs.   Inhalation:

Habits of nervous tension: 3, 4, 5, 9, 11, 19

FIGURE-DRAWING CHARACTERISTICS*

Structural	Male Female Both	Structural	Male	Female	Structural and Graphic	Male Female Both	Graphic, Global and Height	Male	Female	Body Proportions	Male	Female
Type	1	Omission of Appendages	0	0	Upper and Lower Halves	2 0	Hair Shading	0	7	Head	03	07
Sex Sequence	0	Position of Both Arms	0	0	Four Quarters	0 4	Nudity and Transparency	9	7	Neck		00
Posture	1 1	Position of Right Arm	2	2	Relative Size	5	Form	0	3	Shoulders		06
Perspective	0 0	Position of Left Arm	2	2	Constant Line Pressure	3 0	Detailing	0	3	Right Arm		02
Vertical Midline	9 0	Position of Legs	6	4	Variable Line Pressure	0 1	Identity and Sex	0	3	Left Arm		02
Bilateral Symmetry	9 3	Relation of Long Axes	1	1	Line Continuity	4 4	Sophistication	0	3	Chest		
Horizontal Midline	9 0	Right and Left Halves	2	1	Body Shading	9 0	Height	01	04	Girth		

GENERAL CHARACTERISTICS OF SUBJECT

IDENTIFICATION
No. 301
Sex M
Marital status S
Age 26 yrs. at psychological tests

PARENTAL HISTORY
Father
C   H   S   D   O
+   -   +   -   +
Mother
C   H   S   D   O
-   -   -   -   +

PHYSIOLOGICAL AND METABOLIC DATA

	Admission	Initial	Control	Cold pressor change	Exercise change	Smoking change
Systolic pressure	140	133	124	+10	+50	
Diastolic pressure	80	72	68	+10	-04	
Heart rate	92	96	86	00	+29	

Age 24 yrs.	Height	71 in.	Ponderal index 11.18	
	Weight	256 lbs.	Cholesterol	350 mg. per 100 ml.
	Overweight +60 %		Vital capacity	4.3 liters

HABIT SURVEY
Smoking habits: light cigarette smoker
Age begun 18 yrs.   Inhalation: no
Habits of nervous tension: 5, 6, 10, 16

*After the stick figure was drawn, the psychologist asked the subject "to draw a little more elaborately".

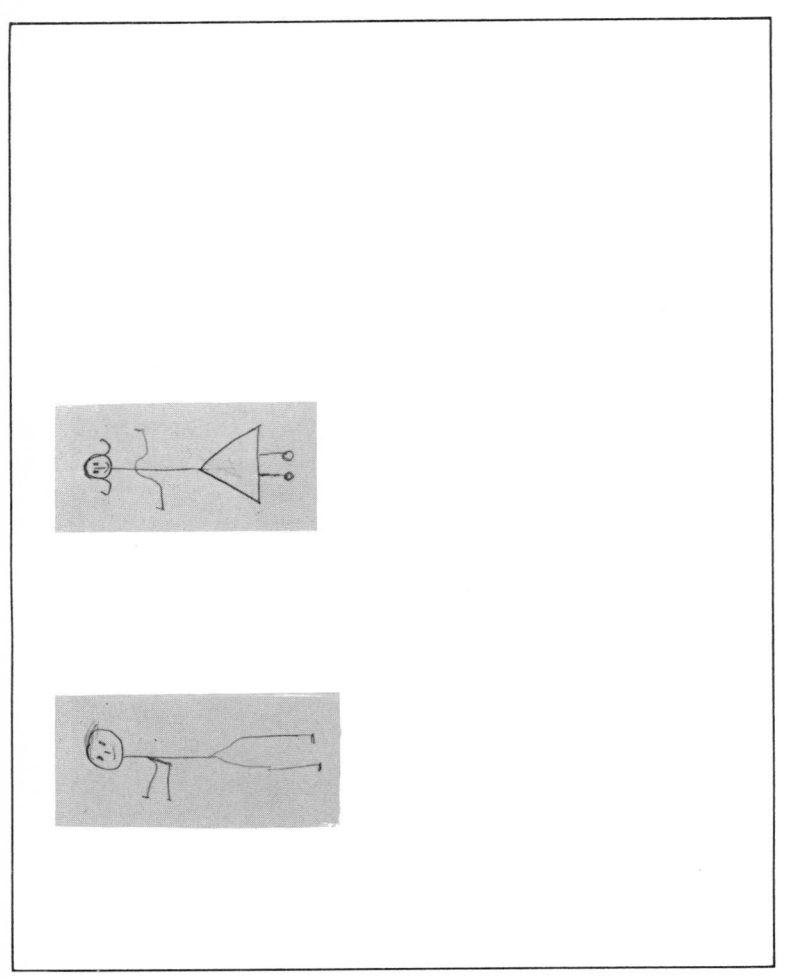

FIGURE-DRAWING CHARACTERISTICS

Structural	Male Female Both		Structural	Male	Female	Structural and Graphic	Male Female Both		Graphic, Global and Height	Male	Female	Body Proportions	Male	Female
Type	4		Omission of Appendages	0	0	Upper and Lower Halves	2	2	Hair Shading	7	7	Head	03	02
Sex Sequence	2		Position of Both Arms	9	0	Four Quarters	0	1	Nudity and Transparency	9	9	Neck		
Posture	1	1	Position of Right Arm	9	2	Relative Size	0		Form	0	0	Shoulders		
Perspective	9	0	Position of Left Arm	9	2	Constant Line Pressure	3	0	Detailing	0	0	Right Arm		
Vertical Midline	9	9	Position of Legs	5	5	Variable Line Pressure	0	5	Identity and Sex	0	0	Left Arm		
Bilateral Symmetry	9	9	Relation of Long Axes	2	2	Line Continuity	4	4	Sophistication	0	0	Chest		
Horizontal Midline	9	9	Right and Left Halves	9	9	Body Shading	9	9	Height	02	02	Girth		

GENERAL CHARACTERISTICS OF SUBJECT

IDENTIFICATION
No. 371
Sex M
Marital status M
Age 25 yrs. at psychological tests

PARENTAL HISTORY
Father
C H S D O
+ + - - +
Mother
C H S D O
- - - - -

PHYSIOLOGICAL AND METABOLIC DATA

	Admission	Initial	Control	Cold pressor change	Exercise change	Smoking change
Systolic pressure	128	128	116	+12	+44	00
Diastolic pressure	70	82	70	+12	-02	00
Heart rate	84	96	83	+06	+20	+09

Age 23 yrs.	Height 69 in.	Ponderal index 12.50
	Weight 168 lbs.	Cholesterol mg. per 100 ml.
	Overweight +11 %	Vital capacity 4.5 liters

HABIT SURVEY

Smoking habits: light cigarette smoker

Age begun 18 yrs.   Inhalation: sometimes

Habits of nervous tension: 4, 5, 6, 8, 14, 20, 21

FIGURE-DRAWING CHARACTERISTICS

Structural	Male Female Both	Structural	Male	Female	Structural and Graphic	Male Female Both		Graphic, Global and Height	Male	Female	Body Proportions	Male	Female
Type	1	Omission of Appendages	0	0	Upper and Lower Halves	1	1	Hair Shading	0	7	Head	09	09
Sex Sequence	2	Position of Both Arms	0	1	Four Quarters	4	4	Nudity and Transparency	9	6	Neck		
Posture	1 1	Position of Right Arm	2	2	Relative Size	0		Form	0	0	Shoulders		
Perspective	0 0	Position of Left Arm	2	0	Constant Line Pressure	5	5	Detailing	0	0	Right Arm		
Vertical Midline	9 3	Position of Legs	6	6	Variable Line Pressure	0	0	Identity and Sex	0	0	Left Arm		
Bilateral Symmetry	9 3	Relation of Long Axes	1	1	Line Continuity	4	4	Sophistication	0	0	Chest		01
Horizontal Midline	9 0	Right and Left Halves	1	1	Body Shading	9	0	Height	04	04	Girth		00

GENERAL CHARACTERISTICS OF SUBJECT

IDENTIFICATION
No. 379
Sex M
Marital status S
Age 22 yrs. at
psychological tests

PARENTAL HISTORY				
Father				
C	H	S	D	O
+	-	-	-	-
Mother				
C	H	S	D	O
-	+	-	-	-

PHYSIOLOGICAL AND METABOLIC DATA

	Admission	Initial	Control	Cold pressor change	Exercise change	Smoking change
Systolic pressure	130	110	112	00	+30	
Diastolic pressure	84	72	72	+16	00	
Heart rate	96	80	71	-04	+36	

Age 22 yrs.	Height	68 in.	Ponderal index 12.37
	Weight	166 lbs.	Cholesterol 254 mg. per 100 ml.
	Overweight +14 %		Vital capacity 4.5 liters

HABIT SURVEY

Smoking habits: nonsmoker

Age begun   yrs.   Inhalation:

Habits of nervous tension: 5, 6, 9, 11, 14, 16,

23

FIGURE-DRAWING CHARACTERISTICS

Structural	Male Female Both	Structural	Male	Female	Structural and Graphic	Male Female Both		Graphic, Global and Height	Male	Female	Body Proportions	Male	Female
Type	1	Omission of Appendages	9	0	Upper and Lower Halves	2	1	Hair Shading	7	5	Head	05	09
Sex Sequence	2	Position of Both Arms	0	0	Four Quarters	0	4	Nudity and Transparency	9	7	Neck		08
Posture	1 1	Position of Right Arm	2	2	Relative Size	5		Form	0	5	Shoulders		05
Perspective	0 5	Position of Left Arm	2	2	Constant Line Pressure	5	0	Detailing	0	5	Right Arm		02
Vertical Midline	9 0	Position of Legs	6	6	Variable Line Pressure	0	5	Identity and Sex	0	5	Left Arm		02
Bilateral Symmetry	9 1	Relation of Long Axes	1	1	Line Continuity	4	2	Sophistication	0	4	Chest		05
Horizontal Midline	9 0	Right and Left Halves	2	2	Body Shading	9	0	Height	01	04	Girth		06

GENERAL CHARACTERISTICS OF SUBJECT

IDENTIFICATION
No. 469
Sex M
Marital status M
Age 24 yrs. at
psychological tests

PARENTAL HISTORY
Father
C   H   S   D   O
+   +   -   +   ?
Mother
C   H   S   D   O
-   -   -   -   -

PHYSIOLOGICAL AND METABOLIC DATA

	Admission	Initial	Control	Cold pressor change	Exercise change	Smoking change
Systolic pressure	150	130	100	+20	00	
Diastolic pressure	76	68	62	+06	-12	
Heart rate	114	80	83	+10	+53	

Age 21 yrs.	Height 70 in.	Ponderal index 12.61
	Weight 171 lbs.	Cholesterol 237 mg. per 100 ml.
	Overweight +12 %	Vital capacity 4.0 liters

HABIT SURVEY

Smoking habits: moderate cigarette smoker

Age begun 16 yrs.   Inhalation: yes

Habits of nervous tension: 3, 5, 9, 18

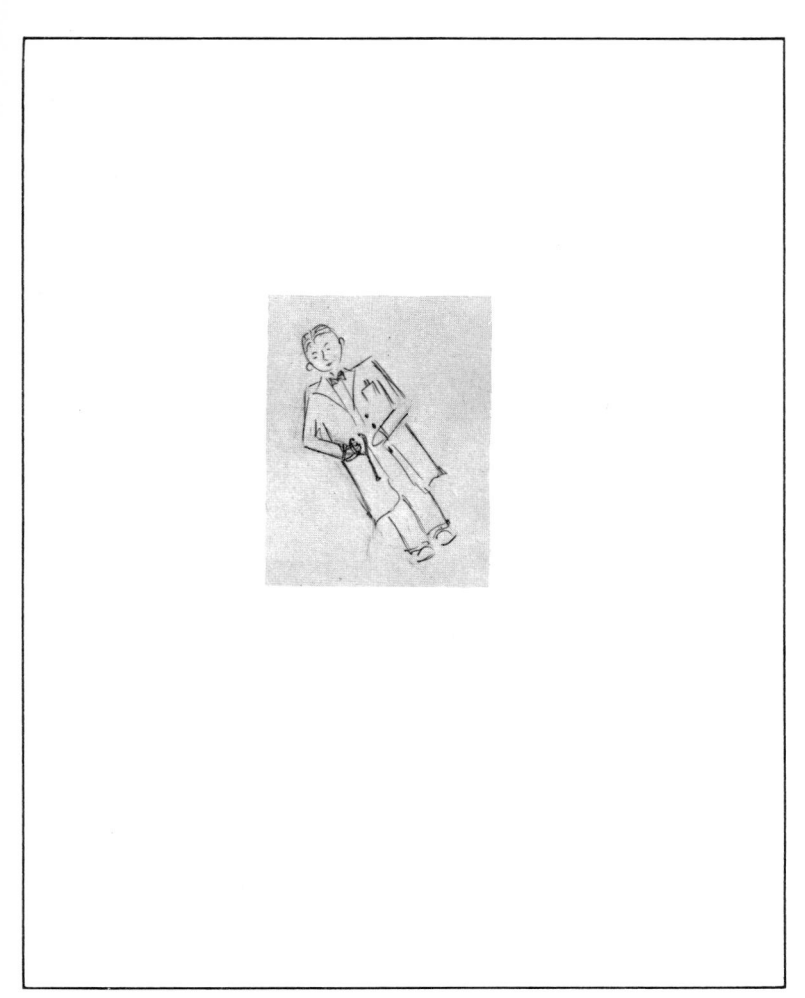

FIGURE-DRAWING CHARACTERISTICS

Structural	Male Female Both		Structural	Male	Female	Structural and Graphic	Male Female Both		Graphic, Global and Height	Male	Female	Body Proportions	Male	Female
Type	0		Omission of Appendages	0	9	Upper and Lower Halves	1	9	Hair Shading	1	5	Head	03	
Sex Sequence	0		Position of Both Arms	0	9	Four Quarters	4	9	Nudity and Transparency	7	9	Neck	02	
Posture	1	9	Position of Right Arm	5	9	Relative Size	5		Form	3	0	Shoulders	03	
Perspective	0	9	Position of Left Arm	5	9	Constant Line Pressure	0	9	Detailing	1	0	Right Arm	02	
Vertical Midline	3	9	Position of Legs	2	9	Variable Line Pressure	1	9	Identity and Sex	1	0	Left Arm	02	
Bilateral Symmetry	3	9	Relation of Long Axes	3	9	Line Continuity	0	9	Sophistication	2	0	Chest	03	
Horizontal Midline	0	9	Right and Left Halves	1	9	Body Shading	4	9	Height	02		Girth	04	

GENERAL CHARACTERISTICS OF SUBJECT

IDENTIFICATION
No. 360
Sex F
Marital status S
Age 23 yrs. at psychological tests

PARENTAL HISTORY				
Father				
C	H	S	D	O
-	+	-	-	?
Mother				
C	H	S	D	O
+	-	-	-	-

PHYSIOLOGICAL AND METABOLIC DATA

	Admission	Initial	Control	Cold pressor change	Exercise change	Smoking change
Systolic pressure	120	112	110	+07	+44	+10
Diastolic pressure	70	64	66	+14	00	+02
Heart rate	84	78	83	00	+08	+05

Age 22 yrs.	Height	66	in.	Ponderal index	12.48	
	Weight	148	lbs.	Cholesterol	185	mg. per 100 ml.
	Overweight +11 %			Vital capacity	4.8	liters

HABIT SURVEY
Smoking habits: light cigarette smoker
Age begun   yrs.   Inhalation:
Habits of nervous tension:

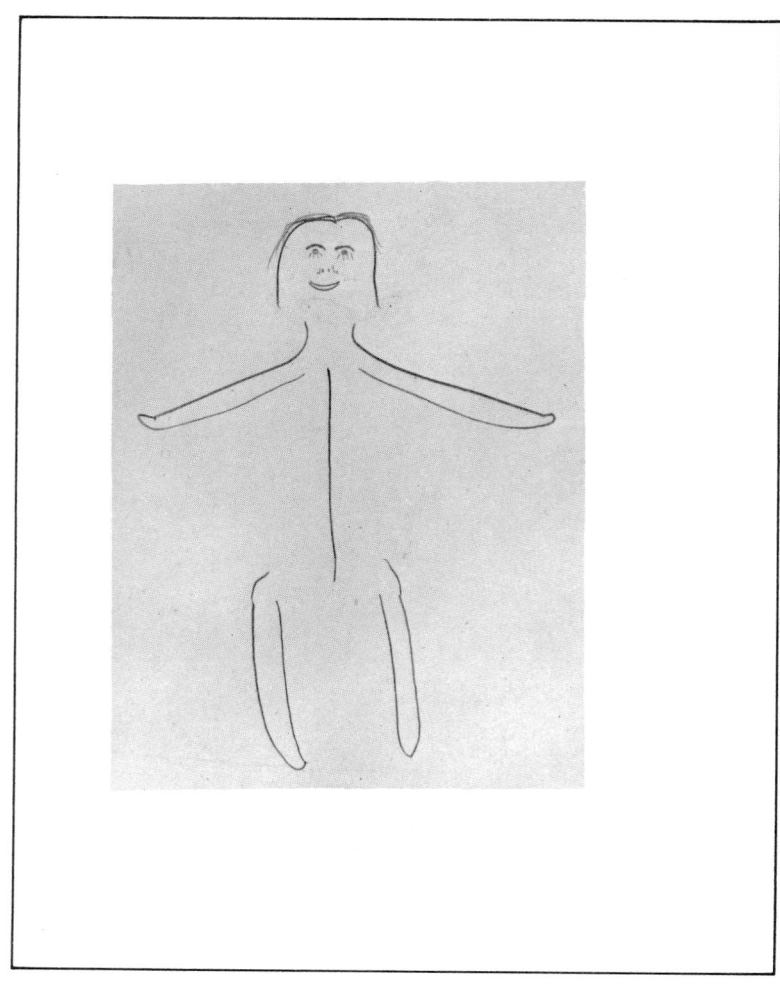

FIGURE-DRAWING CHARACTERISTICS

Structural	Male Female Both	Structural	Male	Female	Structural and Graphic	Male Female Both		Graphic, Global and Height	Male	Female	Body Proportions	Male	Female
Type	4	Omission of Appendages	0	9	Upper and Lower Halves	1	1	Hair Shading	0	3	Head	09	
Sex Sequence	2	Position of Both Arms	0	0	Four Quarters	4	4	Nudity and Transparency	9	9	Neck		
Posture	1 1	Position of Right Arm	2	2	Relative Size	2		Form	0	0	Shoulders		
Perspective	0 0	Position of Left Arm	2	2	Constant Line Pressure	5	0	Detailing	0	0	Right Arm		
Vertical Midline	9 9	Position of Legs	6	6	Variable Line Pressure	0	5	Identity and Sex	0	0	Left Arm		
Bilateral Symmetry	9 9	Relation of Long Axes	1	1	Line Continuity	4	4	Sophistication	0	0	Chest		
Horizontal Midline	9 9	Right and Left Halves	1	1	Body Shading	9	9	Height	05	05	Girth		

GENERAL CHARACTERISTICS OF SUBJECT

IDENTIFICATION
No. 404
Sex F
Marital status S
Age 31 yrs. at
psychological tests

PARENTAL HISTORY					
Father					
C	H	S	D	O	
-	+	+	(+)	-	
Mother					
C	H	S	D	O	
+	+	?	-	-	

PHYSIOLOGICAL AND METABOLIC DATA

	Admission	Initial	Control	Cold pressor change	Exercise change	Smoking change
Systolic pressure	120	96	98	+12	+32	+02
Diastolic pressure	80	72	72	+20	-12	-02
Heart rate	72	84	81	-10	+26	-02

Age 30 yrs.	Height 66 in.	Ponderal index 12.21
	Weight 158 lbs.	Cholesterol 280 mg. per 100 ml.
	Overweight +15 %	Vital capacity 3.8 liters

HABIT SURVEY
Smoking habits: heavy cigarette smoker
Age begun 28 yrs.   Inhalation: yes
Habits of nervous tension: 5, 19, 25

FIGURE-DRAWING CHARACTERISTICS

Structural	Male Female Both	Structural	Male	Female	Structural and Graphic	Male Female Both		Graphic, Global and Height	Male	Female	Body Proportions	Male	Female
Type	4	Omission of Appendages	9	9	Upper and Lower Halves	2	2	Hair Shading	0	7	Head	03	04
Sex Sequence	2	Position of Both Arms	0	0	Four Quarters	0	0	Nudity and Transparency	9	9	Neck		
Posture	1 1	Position of Right Arm	2	2	Relative Size	4		Form	0	0	Shoulders		
Perspective	9 0	Position of Left Arm	2	2	Constant Line Pressure	3	3	Detailing	0	0	Right Arm		
Vertical Midline	9 9	Position of Legs	6	6	Variable Line Pressure	0	0	Identity and Sex	0	0	Left Arm		
Bilateral Symmetry	9 9	Relation of Long Axes	1	1	Line Continuity	4	4	Sophistication	0	0	Chest		
Horizontal Midline	9 9	Right and Left Halves	2	2	Body Shading	9	9	Height	01	01	Girth		

GENERAL CHARACTERISTICS OF SUBJECT

IDENTIFICATION
No. 302
Sex M
Marital status S
Age 28 yrs. at
psychological tests

PARENTAL HISTORY
Father
C   H   S   D   O
(+)   -   -   -   -
Mother
C   H   S   D   O
-   (+)   -   -   -

PHYSIOLOGICAL AND METABOLIC DATA

	Admission	Initial	Control	Cold pressor change	Exercise change	Smoking change
Systolic pressure	140	130	112	+22	+54	+04
Diastolic pressure	76	80	76	+26	00	+08
Heart rate	84	96	81	00	+44	+21

Age 26 yrs.	Height	70 in.	Ponderal index 12.49
	Weight	176 lbs.	Cholesterol 335 mg. per 100 ml.
	Overweight +11 %		Vital capacity 5.6 liters

HABIT SURVEY

Smoking habits: occasional smoker

Age begun 22 yrs.   Inhalation: no

Habits of nervous tension: 4, 5, 6, 9, 11, 16, 17, 18, 22

FIGURE-DRAWING CHARACTERISTICS

Structural	Male	Female	Structural	Male	Female	Structural and Graphic	Male	Female	Graphic, Global and Height	Male	Female	Body Proportions	Male	Female
	Both						Both							
Type	4		Omission of Appendages	0	0	Upper and Lower Halves	2	1	Hair Shading	7	7	Head	03	03
Sex Sequence	0		Position of Both Arms	0	1	Four Quarters	0	4	Nudity and Transparency	6	6	Neck	03	07
Posture	1	1	Position of Right Arm	4	4	Relative Size	4		Form	0	0	Shoulders	02	02
Perspective	0	0	Position of Left Arm	4	5	Constant Line Pressure	0	0	Detailing	0	0	Right Arm	02	02
Vertical Midline	3	3	Position of Legs	6	6	Variable Line Pressure	5	4	Identity and Sex	0	0	Left Arm	00	02
Bilateral Symmetry	3	2	Relation of Long Axes	1	1	Line Continuity	2	2	Sophistication	0	0	Chest	02	03
Horizontal Midline	4	4	Right and Left Halves	2	2	Body Shading	4	5	Height	02	03	Girth	02	03

GENERAL CHARACTERISTICS OF SUBJECT

IDENTIFICATION

No. G21
Sex M
Marital status S
Age 23 yrs. at
psychological tests

PARENTAL HISTORY

Father

C	H	S	D	O
-	U	+	-	+

Mother

C	H	S	D	O
(?)	U	-	-	+

PHYSIOLOGICAL AND METABOLIC DATA

	Admission	Initial	Control	Cold pressor change	Exercise change	Smoking change
Systolic pressure	138	130	118	+22	+32	+12
Diastolic pressure	78	60	60	+32	-12	+15
Heart rate	76	80	71	+02	+16	+18

Age 23 yrs.

Height 72 in.
Weight 161 lbs.
Overweight -02 %

Ponderal index 13.24
Cholesterol 172 mg. per 100 ml.
Vital capacity liters

HABIT SURVEY

Smoking habits: heavy cigarette smoker
Age begun 19 yrs. Inhalation: yes
Habits of nervous tension: 3, 4, 5, 6, 10, 11, 21, 22, 23

STRONG VOCATIONAL INTEREST TEST

Occupation	Artist	Psychologist	Architect	Physician	Osteopath	Dentist	Veterinarian	Mathematician	Physicist	Engineer	Chemist	Production Manager
Standard Score	41	55	52	54	37	38	05	44	44	45	54	28

Occupation	Farmer	Aviator	Carpenter	Printer	Math.-Sci. Teacher	Ind. Arts Teacher	Voc. Agric. Teacher	Policeman	Forest Serv. Man	Y.M.C.A. Phys. Dir.	Personnel Director	Public Administrator
Standard Score	31	35	25	35	39	25	25	20	22	15	36	41

Occupation	Y.M.C.A. Secretary	Soc. Sci. H.S. Teacher	City Sch. Sup't.	Social Worker	Minister	Musician Performer	C.P.A.	Senior C.P.A.	Accountant	Office Man	Purchasing Agent	Banker
Standard Score	21	29	28	38	59	47	34	36	19	21	14	12

Occupation	Mortician	Pharmacist	Sales Manager	Real Est. Manager	Life Ins. Salesman	Advertising Man	Lawyer	Author-Journalist	President Mfg. Co.	Interest Maturity	Occupational Level	Masculinity-Femininity
Standard Score	11	15	16	22	15	33	38	38	29	56	58	43

FIGURE-DRAWING CHARACTERISTICS

Structural	Male Female Both	Structural	Male	Female	Structural and Graphic	Male Female Both		Graphic, Global and Height	Male	Female	Body Proportions	Male	Female
Type	4	Omission of Appendages	0	0	Upper and Lower Halves	0	3	Hair Shading	6	3	Head	05	04
Sex Sequence	0	Position of Both Arms	0	0	Four Quarters	4	4	Nudity and Transparency	9	9	Neck		
Posture	1 1	Position of Right Arm	2	2	Relative Size	1		Form	0	0	Shoulders		
Perspective	0 0	Position of Left Arm	2	2	Constant Line Pressure	5	5	Detailing	0	0	Right Arm		
Vertical Midline	9 9	Position of Legs	6	6	Variable Line Pressure	0	0	Identity and Sex	0	0	Left Arm		
Bilateral Symmetry	9 9	Relation of Long Axes	1	1	Line Continuity	4	4	Sophistication	0	0	Chest		
Horizontal Midline	9 9	Right and Left Halves	1	1	Body Shading	9	9	Height	05	05	Girth		

GENERAL CHARACTERISTICS OF SUBJECT

IDENTIFICATION
No. 515
Sex M
Marital status M
Age 24 yrs. at
psychological tests

PARENTAL HISTORY
Father
C   H   S   D   O
-   +   -   ?   ?
Mother
C   H   S   D   O
-   -   -   -   -

PHYSIOLOGICAL AND METABOLIC DATA

	Admission	Initial	Control	Cold pressor change	Exercise change	Smoking change
Systolic pressure	125	124	118	+16	+34	+06
Diastolic pressure	68	70	80	+21	-08	+22
Heart rate	72	76	83	-12	+02	+13

	Height 69 in.	Ponderal index 12.96
Age 22 yrs.	Weight 151 lbs.	Cholesterol 265 mg. per 100 ml.
	Overweight +01 %	Vital capacity 4.1 liters

HABIT SURVEY
Smoking habits: former smoker
Age begun 15 yrs.   Inhalation:
Habits of nervous tension: 4, 5, 6, 8, 12,
16, 17

FIGURE-DRAWING CHARACTERISTICS

Structural	Male Female Both		Structural	Male	Female	Structural and Graphic	Male Female Both		Graphic, Global and Height	Male	Female	Body Proportions	Male	Female
Type	4		Omission of Appendages	0	0	Upper and Lower Halves	1	0	Hair Shading	3	3	Head	12	12
Sex Sequence	0		Position of Both Arms	0	4	Four Quarters	4	4	Nudity and Transparency	9	9	Neck	18	22
Posture	1	1	Position of Right Arm	5	4	Relative Size	4		Form	0	0	Shoulders	10	
Perspective	0	2	Position of Left Arm	5	4	Constant Line Pressure	3	0	Detailing	0	0	Right Arm	08	10
Vertical Midline	0	4	Position of Legs	6	2	Variable Line Pressure	0	3	Identity and Sex	0	0	Left Arm	06	
Bilateral Symmetry	3	0	Relation of Long Axes	1	1	Line Continuity	0	0	Sophistication	0	0	Chest	12	12
Horizontal Midline	0	4	Right and Left Halves	1	1	Body Shading	0	0	Height	07	08	Girth		10

GENERAL CHARACTERISTICS OF SUBJECT

IDENTIFICATION
No. 052
Sex M
Marital status M
Age 24 yrs. at
psychological tests

PARENTAL HISTORY
Father
C   H   S   D   O
–   +   –   –   ?
Mother
C   H   S   D   O
–   –   –   –   –

PHYSIOLOGICAL AND METABOLIC DATA

	Admission	Initial	Control	Cold pressor change	Exercise change	Smoking change
Systolic pressure		118	112	+08	+06	+06
Diastolic pressure		68	70	+20	–12	–02
Heart rate		68	68	+08	+24	–01

Age 22 yrs.	Height	68	in.	Ponderal index	13.36	
	Weight	132	lbs.	Cholesterol	176	mg. per 100 ml.
	Overweight	–10	%	Vital capacity	4.3	liters

HABIT SURVEY

Smoking habits: mixed smoker

   Age begun 17 yrs.   Inhalation: sometimes

Habits of nervous tension: 2, 3, 4, 5, 6, 9,

11, 19, 24

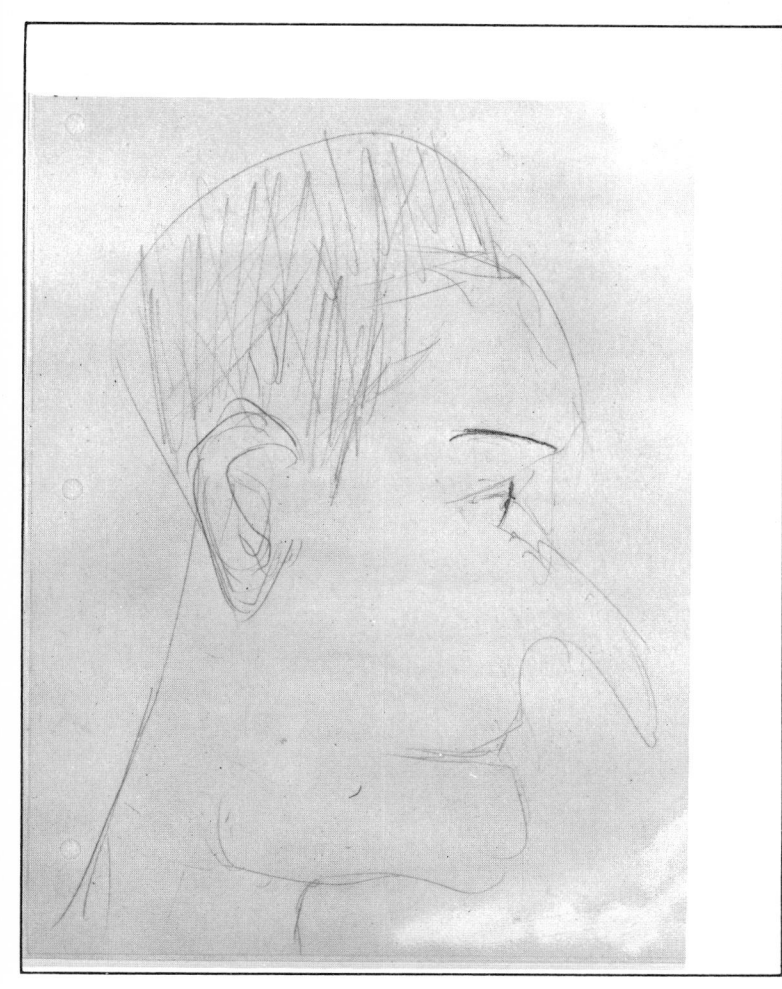

FIGURE-DRAWING CHARACTERISTICS

Structural	Male	Female	Structural	Male	Female	Structural and Graphic	Male	Female	Graphic, Global and Height	Male	Female	Body Proportions	Male	Female
	Both						Both							
Type	0		Omission of Appendages	9	9	Upper and Lower Halves	9	9	Hair Shading	1	3	Head		
Sex Sequence	0		Position of Both Arms	9	9	Four Quarters	9	9	Nudity and Transparency	9	9	Neck		
Posture	9	9	Position of Right Arm	9	9	Relative Size	9		Form	0	0	Shoulders		
Perspective	9	9	Position of Left Arm	9	9	Constant Line Pressure	1	1	Detailing	0	0	Right Arm		
Vertical Midline	9	9	Position of Legs	9	9	Variable Line Pressure	0	0	Identity and Sex	0	0	Left Arm		
Bilateral Symmetry	9	9	Relation of Long Axes	9	9	Line Continuity	0	0	Sophistication	0	0	Chest		
Horizontal Midline	9	9	Right and Left Halves	9	9	Body Shading	9	9	Height			Girth		

GENERAL CHARACTERISTICS OF SUBJECT

IDENTIFICATION	PARENTAL HISTORY
No. 074	Father
Sex M	C H S D O
Marital status M	− + − − +
Age 23 yrs. at	Mother
psychological tests	C H S D O
	− − − − −

PHYSIOLOGICAL AND METABOLIC DATA

	Admission	Initial	Control	Cold pressor change	Exercise change	Smoking change
Systolic pressure	120	117	112	+21	+35	+11
Diastolic pressure	80	75	77	+23	−06	+10
Heart rate	70	66	64	+08	+13	+24

Age 23 yrs.   Height   70   in.   Ponderal index 13.26

Weight   147   lbs.   Cholesterol   192   mg. per 100 ml.

Overweight −05 %   Vital capacity   5.2   liters

HABIT SURVEY

Smoking habits: pipe smoker

Age begun 16 yrs.   Inhalation: no

Habits of nervous tension: 2, 5, 6, 8, 11, 22

STRONG VOCATIONAL INTEREST TEST

Occupation	Artist	Psychologist	Architect	Physician	Osteopath	Dentist	Veterinarian	Mathematician	Physicist	Engineer	Chemist	Production Manager
Standard Score	27	53	33	59	52	35	15	27	29	43	52	41

Occupation	Farmer	Aviator	Carpenter	Printer	Math.-Sci. Teacher	Ind. Arts Teacher	Voc. Agric. Teacher	Policeman	Forest Serv. Man	Y.M.C.A. Phys. Dir.	Personnel Director	Public Administrator
Standard Score	27	52	26	43	46	31	25	32	25	33	53	53

Occupation	Y.M.C.A. Secretary	Soc. Sci. H.S. Teacher	City Sch. Sup't.	Social Worker	Minister	Musician Performer	C.P.A.	Senior C.P.A.	Accountant	Office Man	Purchasing Agent	Banker
Standard Score	23	30	23	45	64	49	30	50	32	34	30	12

Occupation	Mortician	Pharmacist	Sales Manager	Real Est. Manager	Life Ins. Salesman	Advertising Man	Lawyer	Author-Journalist	President Mfg. Co.	Interest Maturity	Occupational Level	Masculinity-Femininity
Standard Score	30	42	32	28	25	38	29	32	40	58	53	52

FIGURE-DRAWING CHARACTERISTICS

Structural	Male Female Both		Structural	Male	Female	Structural and Graphic	Male Female Both		Graphic, Global and Height	Male	Female	Body Proportions	Male	Female
Type	4		Omission of Appendages	0	0	Upper and Lower Halves	2	2	Hair Shading	0	3	Head	04	04
Sex Sequence	2		Position of Both Arms	0	0	Four Quarters	4	4	Nudity and Transparency	6	6	Neck	08	06
Posture	1	1	Position of Right Arm	2	2	Relative Size	3		Form	0	0	Shoulders		
Perspective	0	0	Position of Left Arm	2	2	Constant Line Pressure	0	0	Detailing	0	0	Right Arm		
Vertical Midline	3	3	Position of Legs	6	6	Variable Line Pressure	3	5	Identity and Sex	0	0	Left Arm		
Bilateral Symmetry	4	4	Relation of Long Axes	1	1	Line Continuity	0	0	Sophistication	0	0	Chest	00	00
Horizontal Midline	4	4	Right and Left Halves	0	1	Body Shading	4	1	Height	02	02	Girth	01	02

GENERAL CHARACTERISTICS OF SUBJECT

IDENTIFICATION
No. 476
Sex M
Marital status M
Age 28 yrs. at
psychological tests

PARENTAL HISTORY
Father
C H S D O
- (?) - - +
Mother
C H S D O
- (?) - - -

PHYSIOLOGICAL AND METABOLIC DATA

	Admission	Initial	Control	Cold pressor change	Exercise change	Smoking change
Systolic pressure	120	130	124	+06	+26	
Diastolic pressure	80	76	72	+06	00	
Heart rate	76	92	88	+13	+12	

	Height 71 in.	Ponderal index 12.67
Age 28 yrs.	Weight 176 lbs.	Cholesterol 276 mg. per 100 ml.
	Overweight +07 %	Vital capacity liters

HABIT SURVEY

Smoking habits: light cigarette smoker

Age begun 14 yrs.　　Inhalation: yes

Habits of nervous tension: 3, 5, 18

FIGURE-DRAWING CHARACTERISTICS

Structural	Male Female Both	Structural	Male	Female	Structural and Graphic	Male Female Both		Graphic, Global and Height	Male	Female	Body Proportions	Male	Female
Type	4	Omission of Appendages	0	0	Upper and Lower Halves	1	1	Hair Shading	0	0	Head	03	02
Sex Sequence	0	Position of Both Arms	0	0	Four Quarters	4	4	Nudity and Transparency	9	9	Neck		
Posture	6	1	Position of Right Arm	2	2	Relative Size	2		Form	0	0	Shoulders		
Perspective	9	9	Position of Left Arm	2	2	Constant Line Pressure	5	5	Detailing	0	0	Right Arm		
Vertical Midline	9	9	Position of Legs	8	6	Variable Line Pressure	0	0	Identity and Sex	0	0	Left Arm		
Bilateral Symmetry	9	9	Relation of Long Axes	1	1	Line Continuity	4	4	Sophistication	0	0	Chest		
Horizontal Midline	9	9	Right and Left Halves	2	2	Body Shading	9	9	Height	03	03	Girth		

GENERAL CHARACTERISTICS OF SUBJECT

IDENTIFICATION
No. 221
Sex M
Marital status   M
Age 26 yrs. at
psychological tests

PARENTAL HISTORY
Father
C   H   S   D   O
–   –   –   –   ?
Mother
C   H   S   D   O
– (?) –   –   –

PHYSIOLOGICAL AND METABOLIC DATA

	Admission	Initial	Control	Cold pressor change	Exercise change	Smoking change
Systolic pressure	130	114	112	+08	+20	
Diastolic pressure	82	72	66	+20	-02	
Heart rate	80	72	67	+08	+21	

Age 24 yrs.	Height 72 in. Ponderal index 12.39
	Weight 196 lbs. Cholesterol 215 mg. per 100 ml.
	Overweight +19 % Vital capacity 5.4 liters

HABIT SURVEY
Smoking habits: heavy cigarette smoker
Age begun 18 yrs.   Inhalation: yes
Habits of nervous tension: 4, 5, 6, 9,
10, 25

FIGURE-DRAWING CHARACTERISTICS

Structural	Male Female Both	Structural	Male	Female	Structural and Graphic	Male Female Both		Graphic, Global and Height	Male	Female	Body Proportions	Male	Female
Type	1	Omission of Appendages	0	0	Upper and Lower Halves	2	1	Hair Shading	7	3	Head	06	05
Sex Sequence	0	Position of Both Arms	0	4	Four Quarters	0	4	Nudity and Transparency	6	0	Neck		06
Posture	1 1	Position of Right Arm	2	7	Relative Size	5		Form	0	5	Shoulders		
Perspective	0 2	Position of Left Arm	2	3	Constant Line Pressure	0	0	Detailing	0	5	Right Arm		
Vertical Midline	3 4	Position of Legs	6	1	Variable Line Pressure	5	3	Identity and Sex	0	5	Left Arm		02
Bilateral Symmetry	2 0	Relation of Long Axes	1	1	Line Continuity	4	3	Sophistication	0	4	Chest	02	06
Horizontal Midline	4 0	Right and Left Halves	2	2	Body Shading	0	2	Height	02	04	Girth	04	06

GENERAL CHARACTERISTICS OF SUBJECT

IDENTIFICATION
No. G51
Sex M
Marital status S
Age 23 yrs. at
psychological tests

PARENTAL HISTORY
Father
C   H   S   D   O
-   -   -   ?   -
Mother
C   H   S   D   O
-   -   -   -   -

PHYSIOLOGICAL AND METABOLIC DATA

	Admission	Initial	Control	Cold pressor change	Exercise change	Smoking change
Systolic pressure	130	124	124	+06	+30	+04
Diastolic pressure	80	68	68	+18	-12	+04
Heart rate	80	68	64	+16	+09	00

Age 22 yrs.	Height	71	in.	Ponderal index 13.47	
	Weight	146	lbs.	Cholesterol	217	mg. per 100 ml.
	Overweight -08 %			Vital capacity	liters

HABIT SURVEY
Smoking habits: nonsmoker
Age begun   yrs.   Inhalation:
Habits of nervous tension: 3, 4, 5, 6, 9, 10,
19, 22

STRONG VOCATIONAL INTEREST TEST

Occupation	Artist	Psychologist	Architect	Physician	Osteopath	Dentist	Veterinarian	Mathematician	Physicist	Engineer	Chemist	Production Manager
Standard Score	29	24	20	28	31	26	12	09	-08	07	05	27

Occupation	Farmer	Aviator	Carpenter	Printer	Math.-Sci. Teacher	Ind. Arts Teacher	Voc. Agric. Teacher	Policeman	Forest Serv. Man	Y.M.C.A. Phys. Dir.	Personnel Director	Public Administrator
Standard Score	22	17	-02	20	18	-02	13	19	14	30	39	32

Occupation	Y.M.C.A. Secretary	Soc. Sci. H.S. Teacher	City Sch. Sup't.	Social Worker	Minister	Musician Performer	C.P.A.	Senior C.P.A.	Accountant	Office Man	Purchasing Agent	Banker
Standard Score	34	37	32	33	59	31	23	15	14	18	23	22

Occupation	Mortician	Pharmacist	Sales Manager	Real Est. Manager	Life Ins. Salesman	Advertising Man	Lawyer	Author-Journalist	President Mfg. Co.	Interest Maturity	Occupational Level	Masculinity-Femininity
Standard Score	27	19	41	43	49	48	47	42	32	52	67	35

Plate 18   **ANOMALOUS DRAWINGS**   51

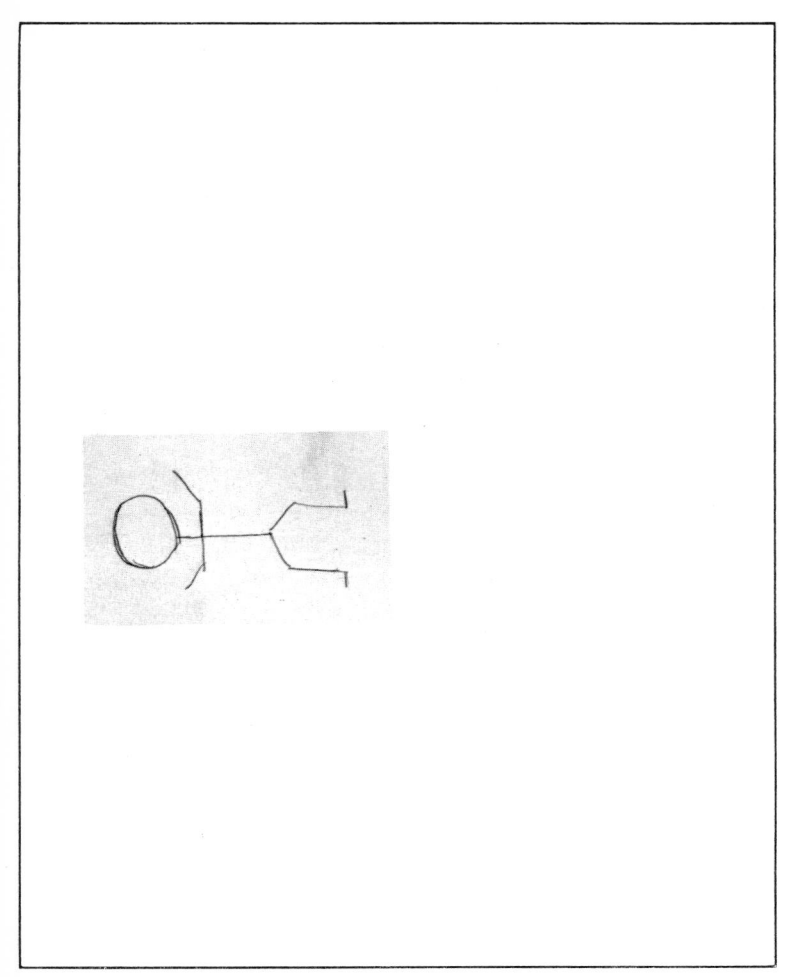

FIGURE-DRAWING CHARACTERISTICS

Structural	Male Female Both	Structural	Male	Female	Structural and Graphic	Male Female Both	Graphic, Global and Height	Male	Female	Body Proportions	Male	Female
Type	5	Omission of Appendages	9		Upper and Lower Halves	9	Hair Shading	9		Head		
Sex Sequence	6	Position of Both Arms	9		Four Quarters	9	Nudity and Transparency	9		Neck		
Posture	9	Position of Right Arm	9		Relative Size	7	Form	0		Shoulders		
Perspective	9	Position of Left Arm	9		Constant Line Pressure	9	Detailing	0		Right Arm		
Vertical Midline	9	Position of Legs	9		Variable Line Pressure	9	Identity and Sex	0		Left Arm		
Bilateral Symmetry	9	Relation of Long Axes	9		Line Continuity	9	Sophistication	0		Chest		
Horizontal Midline	9	Right and Left Halves	9		Body Shading	9	Height	0		Girth		

GENERAL CHARACTERISTICS OF SUBJECT

IDENTIFICATION
No. 532
Sex M
Marital status   S
Age 28 yrs. at
psychological tests

PARENTAL HISTORY
Father
C   H   S   D   O
-    -   -   -   +
Mother
C   H   S   D   O
-    -   -   -   -

PHYSIOLOGICAL AND METABOLIC DATA

	Admission	Initial	Control	Cold pressor change	Exercise change	Smoking change
Systolic pressure	116	120	114	+04	+22	
Diastolic pressure	60	80	80	+26	+10	
Heart rate	60	88	70	+10	+33	

Age 26 yrs.

Height   68   in.
Weight   166 lbs.
Overweight +11 %

Ponderal index 12.37
Cholesterol   230   mg. per 100 ml.
Vital capacity 4.8   liters

HABIT SURVEY
Smoking habits: mixed smoker
Age begun 18   yrs.   Inhalation: yes
Habits of nervous tension: 23

FIGURE-DRAWING CHARACTERISTICS

Structural	Male Female Both		Structural	Male	Female	Structural and Graphic	Male Female Both		Graphic, Global and Height	Male	Female	Body Proportions	Male	Female
Type	0		Omission of Appendages	9	9	Upper and Lower Halves	9	9	Hair Shading	3	7	Head	19	09
Sex Sequence	0		Position of Both Arms	6	6	Four Quarters	9	9	Nudity and Transparency	9	9	Neck	12	05
Posture	9	9	Position of Right Arm	9	9	Relative Size	9		Form	0	0	Shoulders		
Perspective	9	9	Position of Left Arm	9	9	Constant Line Pressure	0	1	Detailing	0	0	Right Arm		
Vertical Midline	9	9	Position of Legs	0	0	Variable Line Pressure	1	0	Identity and Sex	0	0	Left Arm		
Bilateral Symmetry	9	9	Relation of Long Axes	9	9	Line Continuity	0	0	Sophistication	0	0	Chest		
Horizontal Midline	9	9	Right and Left Halves	9	9	Body Shading	9	9	Height			Girth		

GENERAL CHARACTERISTICS OF SUBJECT

IDENTIFICATION
No. C49
Sex M
Marital status M
Age 30 yrs. at
psychological tests

PARENTAL HISTORY
Father
C   H   S   D   O
−   −   −   −   ?
Mother
C   H   S   D   O
−   −   −   −

PHYSIOLOGICAL AND METABOLIC DATA

	Admission	Initial	Control	Cold pressor change	Exercise change	Smoking change
Systolic pressure	134	108	110	+20	+28	+08
Diastolic pressure	80	80	80	+20	−15	+11
Heart rate	72	60	53	+08	+38	+32

Age 30 yrs.	Height	73	in.	Ponderal index	12.83	
	Weight	184	lbs.	Cholesterol	270	mg. per 100 ml.
	Overweight +03 %			Vital capacity	6.1	liters

HABIT SURVEY
Smoking habits: occasional smoker
Age begun 20 yrs.   Inhalation: yes
Habits of nervous tension: 5, 6, 9, 14, 16

STRONG VOCATIONAL INTEREST TEST

Occupation	Artist	Psychologist	Architect	Physician	Osteopath	Dentist	Veterinarian	Mathematician	Physicist	Engineer	Chemist	Production Manager
Standard Score	31	52	36	53	46	32	20	28	24	31	34	27

Occupation	Farmer	Aviator	Carpenter	Printer	Math.-Sci. Teacher	Ind. Arts Teacher	Voc. Agric. Teacher	Policeman	Forest Serv. Man	Y.M.C.A. Phys. Dir.	Personnel Director	Public Administrator
Standard Score	28	35	16	33	40	20	25	35	38	49	53	59

Occupation	Y.M.C.A. Secretary	Soc. Sci. H.S. Teacher	City Sch. Sup't.	Social Worker	Minister	Musician Performer	C.P.A.	Senior C.P.A.	Accountant	Office Man	Purchasing Agent	Banker
Standard Score	45	42	49	54	62	45	33	39	20	24	12	15

Occupation	Mortician	Pharmacist	Sales Manager	Real Est. Manager	Life Ins. Salesman	Advertising Man	Lawyer	Author-Journalist	President Mfg. Co.	Interest Maturity	Occupational Level	Masculinity-Femininity
Standard Score	22	21	28	32	33	34	42	37	26	59	57	39

FIGURE-DRAWING CHARACTERISTICS

Structural	Male Female Both	Structural	Male	Female	Structural and Graphic	Male Female Both		Graphic, Global and Height	Male	Female	Body Proportions	Male	Female
Type	0	Omission of Appendages	9	4	Upper and Lower Halves	7	9	Hair Shading	3	3	Head	47	12
Sex Sequence	1	Position of Both Arms	9	1	Four Quarters	9	4	Nudity and Transparency	9	0	Neck		20
Posture	9 3	Position of Right Arm	9	3	Relative Size	5		Form	0	1	Shoulders		
Perspective	9 6	Position of Left Arm	9	5	Constant Line Pressure	3	0	Detailing	0	3	Right Arm		
Vertical Midline	9 4	Position of Legs	9	1	Variable Line Pressure	0	3	Identity and Sex	0	1	Left Arm		
Bilateral Symmetry	9 0	Relation of Long Axes	9	0	Line Continuity	0	2	Sophistication	0	2	Chest		
Horizontal Midline	9 0	Right and Left Halves	9	3	Body Shading	9	1	Height			Girth		

GENERAL CHARACTERISTICS OF SUBJECT

IDENTIFICATION

No. E05

Sex M

Marital status S

Age 21 yrs. at psychological tests

PARENTAL HISTORY

Father

C H S D O

– – – – ?

Mother

C H S D O

– – – – –

PHYSIOLOGICAL AND METABOLIC DATA

	Admission	Initial	Control	Cold pressor change	Exercise change	Smoking change
Systolic pressure	140	118	110	+11	+28	+09
Diastolic pressure	70	62	70	+19	-21	+08
Heart rate	80	60	66	00	+20	+17

Age 20 yrs.	Height 69 in.	Ponderal index 13.17
	Weight 144 lbs.	Cholesterol 286 mg. per 100 ml.
	Overweight -03 %	Vital capacity 5.1 liters

HABIT SURVEY

Smoking habits: occasional smoker

  Age begun 18 yrs.   Inhalation: sometimes

Habits of nervous tension: 2, 3, 4, 5, 6, 9,

11, 16, 17, 25

STRONG VOCATIONAL INTEREST TEST

Occupation	Artist	Psychologist	Architect	Physician	Osteopath	Dentist	Veterinarian	Mathematician	Physicist	Engineer	Chemist	Production Manager
Standard Score	33	46	40	53	38	32	11	32	29	38	46	33

Occupation	Farmer	Aviator	Carpenter	Printer	Math.-Sci. Teacher	Ind. Arts Teacher	Voc. Agric. Teacher	Policeman	Forest Serv. Man	Y.M.C.A. Phys. Dir.	Personnel Director	Public Administrator
Standard Score	26	43	05	31	36	13	14	19	27	31	48	48

Occupation	Y.M.C.A. Secretary	Soc. Sci. H.S. Teacher	City Sch. Sup't.	Social Worker	Minister	Musician Performer	C.P.A.	Senior C.P.A.	Accountant	Office Man	Purchasing Agent	Banker
Standard Score	25	28	34	40	64	45	36	41	27	27	20	12

Occupation	Mortician	Pharmacist	Sales Manager	Real Est. Manager	Life Ins. Salesman	Advertising Man	Lawyer	Author-Journalist	President Mfg. Co.	Interest Maturity	Occupational Level	Masculinity-Femininity
Standard Score	11	22	29	29	27	44	43	39	37	57	63	45

FIGURE-DRAWING CHARACTERISTICS

Structural	Male Female Both	Structural	Male	Female	Structural and Graphic	Male Female Both		Graphic, Global and Height	Male	Female	Body Proportions	Male	Female
Type	0	Omission of Appendages	1	0	Upper and Lower Halves	1	3	Hair Shading	7	5	Head	25	07
Sex Sequence	0	Position of Both Arms	6	0	Four Quarters	4	4	Nudity and Transparency	9	6	Neck		08
Posture	9 1	Position of Right Arm	9	0	Relative Size	5		Form	0	5	Shoulders		06
Perspective	9 0	Position of Left Arm	9	0	Constant Line Pressure	1	1	Detailing	0	5	Right Arm		04
Vertical Midline	9 0	Position of Legs	9	6	Variable Line Pressure	0	0	Identity and Sex	0	5	Left Arm		04
Bilateral Symmetry	9 1	Relation of Long Axes	9	1	Line Continuity	0	0	Sophistication	0	5	Chest		05
Horizontal Midline	9 0	Right and Left Halves	3	1	Body Shading	9	1	Height		05	Girth		07

GENERAL CHARACTERISTICS OF SUBJECT

IDENTIFICATION
No. 033
Sex M
Marital status S
Age 23 yrs. at
psychological tests

PARENTAL HISTORY
Father
C H S D O
-   -   -   -   ?
Mother
C H S D O
-   -   -   -   -

PHYSIOLOGICAL AND METABOLIC DATA

	Admission	Initial	Control	Cold pressor change	Exercise change	Smoking change
Systolic pressure		108	104	+26	+54	+06
Diastolic pressure		75	82	+16	-22	+01
Heart rate		56	54	+04	+17	+06

Age 22 yrs.	Height 71 in.	Ponderal index 13.10
	Weight 159 lbs.	Cholesterol 240 mg. per 100 ml.
	Overweight +01 %	Vital capacity 5.6 liters

HABIT SURVEY
Smoking habits: nonsmoker
Age begun   yrs.   Inhalation:
Habits of nervous tension: 5, 6, 11

STRONG VOCATIONAL INTEREST TEST

Occupation	Artist	Psychologist	Architect	Physician	Osteopath	Dentist	Veterinarian	Mathematician	Physicist	Engineer	Chemist	Production Manager
Standard Score	49	52	40	44	27	21	01	42	36	31	34	18

Occupation	Farmer	Aviator	Carpenter	Printer	Math.-Sci. Teacher	Ind. Arts Teacher	Voc. Agric. Teacher	Policeman	Forest Serv. Man	Y.M.C.A. Phys. Dir.	Personnel Director	Public Administrator
Standard Score	18	18	-09	12	23	-10	08	05	10	22	32	39

Occupation	Y.M.C.A. Secretary	Soc. Sci. H.S. Teacher	City Sch. Sup't.	Social Worker	Minister	Musician Performer	C.P.A.	Senior C.P.A.	Accountant	Office Man	Purchasing Agent	Banker
Standard Score	20	29	43	39	64	46	37	14	05	06	09	13

Occupation	Mortician	Pharmacist	Sales Manager	Real Est. Manager	Life Ins. Salesman	Advertising Man	Lawyer	Author-Journalist	President Mfg. Co.	Interest Maturity	Occupational Level	Masculinity-Femininity
Standard Score	14	27	42	39	40	52	59	54	47	46	71	33

FIGURE-DRAWING CHARACTERISTICS

Structural	Male	Female	Structural	Male	Female	Structural and Graphic	Male	Female	Graphic, Global and Height	Male	Female	Body Proportions	Male	Female
	Both						Both							
Type	4		Omission of Appendages	9	9	Upper and Lower Halves	1	1	Hair Shading	0	1	Head	06	06
Sex Sequence	0		Position of Both Arms	0	0	Four Quarters	4	4	Nudity and Transparency	9	9	Neck		
Posture	1	1	Position of Right Arm	2	2	Relative Size	5		Form	0	0	Shoulders		
Perspective	0	0	Position of Left Arm	2	2	Constant Line Pressure	3	0	Detailing	0	0	Right Arm		
Vertical Midline	9	9	Position of Legs	6	6	Variable Line Pressure	0	3	Identity and Sex	0	0	Left Arm		
Bilateral Symmetry	9	9	Relation of Long Axes	1	1	Line Continuity	4	4	Sophistication	0	0	Chest		
Horizontal Midline	9	9	Right and Left Halves	2	2	Body Shading	9	9	Height	03	04	Girth		

GENERAL CHARACTERISTICS OF SUBJECT

IDENTIFICATION

No. G59

Sex M

Marital status S

Age 22 yrs. at

psychological tests

PARENTAL HISTORY

Father

C   H   S   D   O

–   –   –   –   –

Mother

C   H   S   D   O

–   –   –   –   ?

PHYSIOLOGICAL AND METABOLIC DATA

	Admission	Initial	Control	Cold pressor change	Exercise change	Smoking change
Systolic pressure	170	150	136	+18	+38	+12
Diastolic pressure	70	56	60	+22	–12	+03
Heart rate	110	76	72	00	+10	00

Age 22 yrs.

Height   70   in.   Ponderal index 12.39

Weight   180   lbs.   Cholesterol   160   mg. per 100 ml.

Overweight +17 %   Vital capacity   liters

HABIT SURVEY

Smoking habits: nonsmoker

Age begun   yrs.   Inhalation:

Habits of nervous tension: 4, 5, 11

STRONG VOCATIONAL INTEREST TEST

Occupation	Artist	Psychologist	Architect	Physician	Osteopath	Dentist	Veterinarian	Mathematician	Physicist	Engineer	Chemist	Production Manager
Standard Score	30	59	36	54	32	27	12	42	27	30	48	17

Occupation	Farmer	Aviator	Carpenter	Printer	Math.-Sci. Teacher	Ind. Arts Teacher	Voc. Agric. Teacher	Policeman	Forest Serv. Man	Y.M.C.A. Phys. Dir.	Personnel Director	Public Administrator
Standard Score	31	27	07	42	44	09	19	19	20	26	44	53

Occupation	Y.M.C.A. Secretary	Soc. Sci. H.S. Teacher	City Sch. Sup't.	Social Worker	Minister	Musician Performer	C.P.A.	Senior C.P.A.	Accountant	Office Man	Purchasing Agent	Banker
Standard Score	32	49	43	51	59	45	45	50	27	35	14	17

Occupation	Mortician	Pharmacist	Sales Manager	Real Est. Manager	Life Ins. Salesman	Advertising Man	Lawyer	Author-Journalist	President Mfg. Co.	Interest Maturity	Occupational Level	Masculinity-Femininity
Standard Score	17	28	18	27	27	35	45	38	18	59	57	40

FIGURE-DRAWING CHARACTERISTICS

Structural	Male Female Both		Structural	Male	Female	Structural and Graphic	Male Female Both		Graphic, Global and Height	Male	Female	Body Proportions	Male	Female
Type	4		Omission of Appendages	0	0	Upper and Lower Halves	2	2	Hair Shading	3	3	Head	04	03
Sex Sequence	0		Position of Both Arms	0	0	Four Quarters	0	0	Nudity and Transparency	9	9	Neck	04	02
Posture	1	1	Position of Right Arm	5	5	Relative Size	0		Form	0	0	Shoulders	03	01
Perspective	0	0	Position of Left Arm	5	5	Constant Line Pressure	3	0	Detailing	0	0	Right Arm	02	00
Vertical Midline	3	3	Position of Legs	6	6	Variable Line Pressure	0	5	Identity and Sex	0	0	Left Arm	02	00
Bilateral Symmetry	3	0	Relation of Long Axes	1	1	Line Continuity	3	3	Sophistication	0	0	Chest	02	
Horizontal Midline	4	4	Right and Left Halves	2	2	Body Shading	0	1	Height	03	01	Girth	01	

GENERAL CHARACTERISTICS OF SUBJECT

IDENTIFICATION
No. 657
Sex M
Marital status M
Age 24 yrs. at
psychological tests

PARENTAL HISTORY
Father
C   H   S   D   0
U   U   -   -   -
Mother
C   H   S   D   0
-   -   -   -   -

PHYSIOLOGICAL AND METABOLIC DATA

	Admission	Initial	Control	Cold pressor change	Exercise change	Smoking change
Systolic pressure	120	128	116	+20	+42	00
Diastolic pressure	80	68	66	+38	+04	00
Heart rate	72	84	71	−08	+17	+19

Age 22 yrs.	Height 74 in.	Ponderal index 13.10
	Weight 180 lbs.	Cholesterol 210 mg. per 100 ml.
	Overweight +04 %	Vital capacity 5.8 liters

HABIT SURVEY
Smoking habits: nonsmoker
Age begun   yrs.   Inhalation:
Habits of nervous tension: 1, 2, 4, 5, 6, 9,
15, 16, 24, 25

II. MOST PRIMITIVE DRAWINGS

The drawings by twenty-four subjects in this section represent those considered to be most primitive and infantile in respect to sophistication-of-body-concept. These drawings show a very low level of form, with almost no evidence of role or sex identity and little or no detailing.

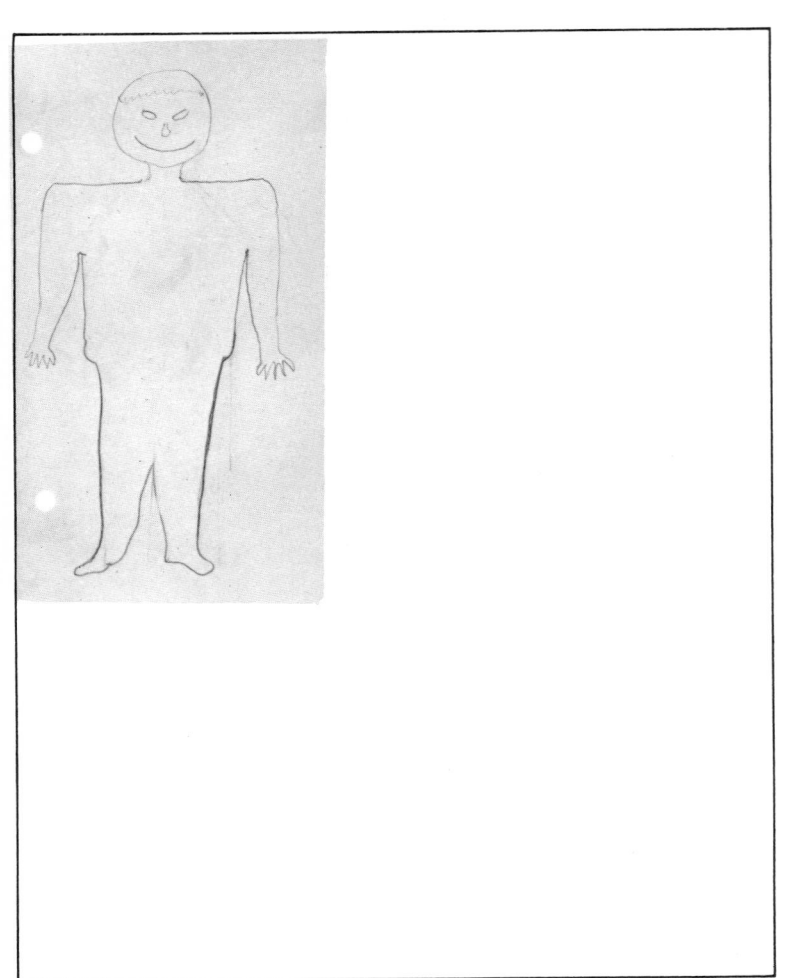

FIGURE-DRAWING CHARACTERISTICS

Structural	Male Female Both	Structural	Male	Female	Structural and Graphic	Male	Female Both	Graphic, Global and Height	Male	Female	Body Proportions	Male	Female
Type	0	Omission of Appendages	0	0	Upper and Lower Halves	1	1	Hair Shading	5	7	Head	07	09
Sex Sequence	0	Position of Both Arms	0	0	Four Quarters	4	4	Nudity and Transparency	9	7	Neck	05	05
Posture	1	1	Position of Right Arm	0	0	Relative Size	0		Form	5	5	Shoulders	09	08
Perspective	0	0	Position of Left Arm	0	0	Constant Line Pressure	0	0	Detailing	5	5	Right Arm	04	02
Vertical Midline	0	0	Position of Legs	4	4	Variable Line Pressure	3	1	Identity and Sex	5	3	Left Arm	04	03
Bilateral Symmetry	4	4	Relation of Long Axes	1	1	Line Continuity	3	3	Sophistication	5	5	Chest	07	06
Horizontal Midline	0	0	Right and Left Halves	2	2	Body Shading	0	0	Height	05	05	Girth	09	09

GENERAL CHARACTERISTICS OF SUBJECT

IDENTIFICATION
No. G23
Sex M
Marital status S
Age 23 yrs. at
psychological tests

PARENTAL HISTORY				
Father				
C	H	S	D	O
+	−	−	−	+
Mother				
C	H	S	D	O
−	−	−	−	−

PHYSIOLOGICAL AND METABOLIC DATA

	Admission	Initial	Control	Cold pressor change	Exercise change	Smoking change
Systolic pressure	122	126	122	+30	+48	−01
Diastolic pressure	70	76	80	+22	−02	+09
Heart rate	72	68	59	+30	+63	+03

Age 22 yrs.	Height	65	in.	Ponderal index	12.77	
	Weight	132	lbs.	Cholesterol	177	mg. per 100 ml.
	Overweight	−02 %		Vital capacity		liters

HABIT SURVEY

Smoking habits: nonsmoker

Age begun   yrs.   Inhalation:

Habits of nervous tension: 4, 5, 11, 12, 13,
17

Plate 25   **MOST PRIMITIVE DRAWINGS**   59

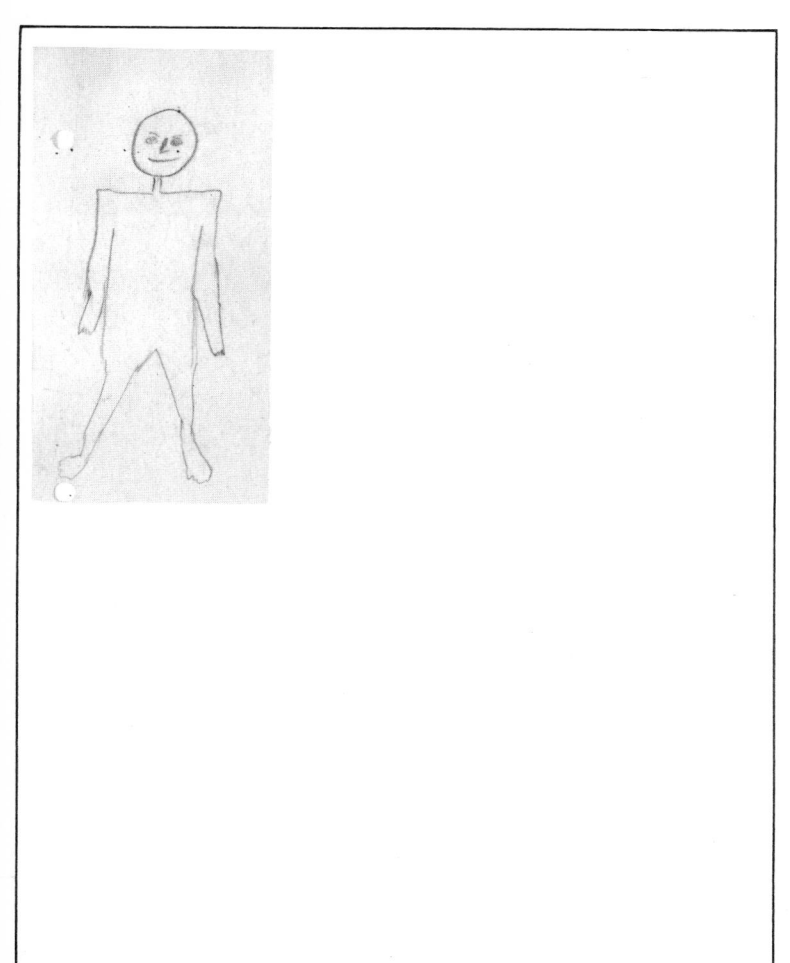

FIGURE-DRAWING CHARACTERISTICS

Structural	Male Female Both	Structural	Male	Female	Structural and Graphic	Male Female Both		Graphic, Global and Height	Male	Female	Body Proportions	Male	Female
Type	0	Omission of Appendages	0	0	Upper and Lower Halves	2	2	Hair Shading	0	3	Head	05	04
Sex Sequence	2	Position of Both Arms	0	0	Four Quarters	0	0	Nudity and Transparency	0	0	Neck	06	06
Posture	1 1	Position of Right Arm	0	0	Relative Size	0		Form	5	5	Shoulders	05	04
Perspective	0 0	Position of Left Arm	0	0	Constant Line Pressure	0	0	Detailing	5	5	Right Arm	02	02
Vertical Midline	0 0	Position of Legs	6	6	Variable Line Pressure	1	1	Identity and Sex	5	5	Left Arm	04	02
Bilateral Symmetry	2 1	Relation of Long Axes	1	1	Line Continuity	1	3	Sophistication	5	5	Chest	04	04
Horizontal Midline	0 0	Right and Left Halves	2	2	Body Shading	0	0	Height	04	03	Girth	05	05

GENERAL CHARACTERISTICS OF SUBJECT

IDENTIFICATION
No. 708
Sex M
Marital status   M
Age 25 yrs. at
psychological tests

PARENTAL HISTORY
Father
C   H   S   D   O
+   ?   -   -   +
Mother
C   H   S   D   O
-    -   -   +   ?

PHYSIOLOGICAL AND METABOLIC DATA

	Admission	Initial	Control	Cold pressor change	Exercise change	Smoking change
Systolic pressure	120	128	122	+08	+52	00
Diastolic pressure	80	70	72	+08	-08	+10
Heart rate	78	64	63	+20	+34	+03

Age 24 yrs.	Height 71 in.	Ponderal index 12.43
	Weight 186 lbs.	Cholesterol 265 mg. per 100 ml.
	Overweight +16 %	Vital capacity 4.1 liters

HABIT SURVEY

Smoking habits: heavy cigarette smoker

Age begun 17 yrs.   Inhalation: yes

Habits of nervous tension: 3, 4, 5, 6, 9, 10, 16, 18, 21, 22

FIGURE-DRAWING CHARACTERISTICS

Structural	Male Female Both	Structural	Male	Female	Structural and Graphic	Male Female Both		Graphic, Global and Height	Male	Female	Body Proportions	Male	Female
Type	0	Omission of Appendages	8	8	Upper and Lower Halves	1	1	Hair Shading	3	3	Head	11	09
Sex Sequence	0	Position of Both Arms	0	0	Four Quarters	4	4	Nudity and Transparency	9	9	Neck	10	08
Posture	0 0	Position of Right Arm	2	2	Relative Size	0		Form	5	5	Shoulders	09	05
Perspective	0 0	Position of Left Arm	2	2	Constant Line Pressure	0	0	Detailing	5	5	Right Arm	02	02
Vertical Midline	3 3	Position of Legs	6	6	Variable Line Pressure	1	1	Identity and Sex	5	5	Left Arm	02	02
Bilateral Symmetry	2 2	Relation of Long Axes	1	1	Line Continuity	2	3	Sophistication	5	5	Chest	11	07
Horizontal Midline	0 0	Right and Left Halves	1	1	Body Shading	0	0	Height	07	05	Girth	14	09

GENERAL CHARACTERISTICS OF SUBJECT

IDENTIFICATION
No. 468
Sex M
Marital status M
Age 25 yrs. at
psychological tests

PARENTAL HISTORY				
Father				
C	H	S	D	O
+	+	-	-	?
Mother				
C	H	S	D	O
-	-	-	-	-

PHYSIOLOGICAL AND METABOLIC DATA

	Admission	Initial	Control	Cold pressor change	Exercise change	Smoking change
Systolic pressure	120	106	100	+24	+32	00
Diastolic pressure	70	62	66	+16	-06	+02
Heart rate	72	90	97	-04	+03	+03
Age 23 yrs.	Height 66 in.	Weight 147 lbs.	Overweight +05 %	Ponderal index 12.50	Cholesterol 203 mg. per 100 ml.	Vital capacity liters

HABIT SURVEY
Smoking habits: nonsmoker
Age begun yrs.   Inhalation:
Habits of nervous tension: 5, 6, 14, 16, 25

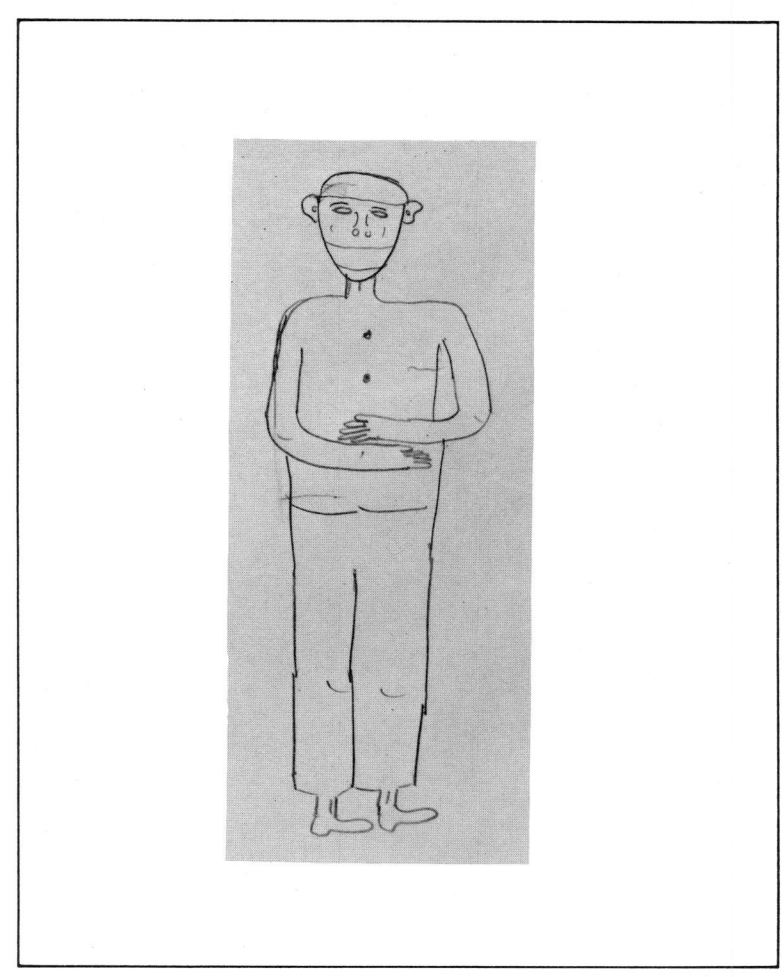

FIGURE-DRAWING CHARACTERISTICS

Structural	Male	Female	Structural	Male	Female	Structural and Graphic	Male	Female	Graphic, Global and Height	Male	Female	Body Proportions	Male	Female
	Both						Both							
Type	0		Omission of Appendages	0	0	Upper and Lower Halves	0	1	Hair Shading	0	3	Head	09	07
Sex Sequence	1		Position of Both Arms	0	0	Four Quarters	4	4	Nudity and Transparency	7	7	Neck	06	08
Posture	1	1	Position of Right Arm	5	2	Relative Size	0		Form	5	5	Shoulders	07	
Perspective	0	0	Position of Left Arm	5	2	Constant Line Pressure	5	0	Detailing	5	5	Right Arm	06	08
Vertical Midline	3	3	Position of Legs	2	6	Variable Line Pressure	0	5	Identity and Sex	3	3	Left Arm	06	07
Bilateral Symmetry	2	3	Relation of Long Axes	1	1	Line Continuity	3	3	Sophistication	5	5	Chest	06	08
Horizontal Midline	6	0	Right and Left Halves	1	1	Body Shading	6	3	Height	07	06	Girth	09	10

GENERAL CHARACTERISTICS OF SUBJECT

IDENTIFICATION
No. 625
Sex M
Marital status M
Age 28 yrs. at
psychological tests

PARENTAL HISTORY				
Father				
C	H	S	D	O
+	-	-	+	+
Mother				
C	H	S	D	O
-	-	-	-	+

PHYSIOLOGICAL AND METABOLIC DATA

	Admission	Initial	Control	Cold pressor change	Exercise change	Smoking change
Systolic pressure	110	116	112	+18	+40	+05
Diastolic pressure	65	78	72	+18	-02	+03
Heart rate	74	88	70	-04	+37	+08

Age 25 yrs.	Height	71 in.	Ponderal index 13.10
	Weight	159 lbs.	Cholesterol 335 mg. per 100 ml.
	Overweight -02 %		Vital capacity 4.6 liters

HABIT SURVEY
Smoking habits: nonsmoker
Age begun   yrs.   Inhalation:
Habits of nervous tension: 5, 9, 11, 16, 19, 21

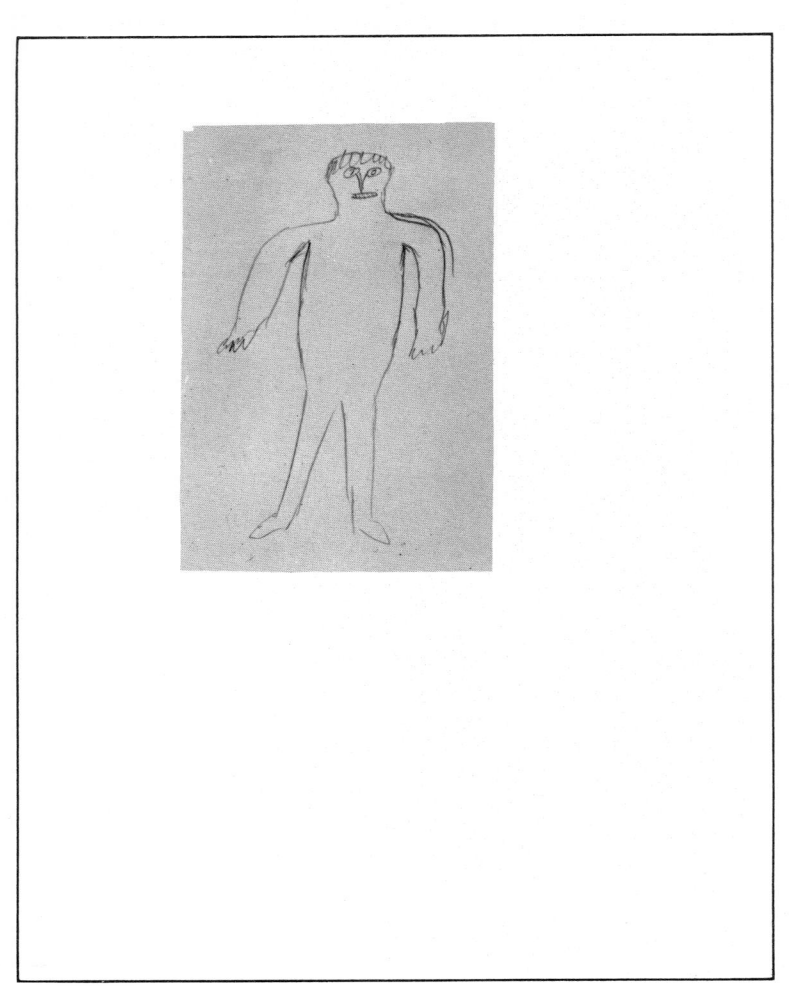

FIGURE-DRAWING CHARACTERISTICS

Structural	Male Female Both	Structural	Male	Female	Structural and Graphic	Male Female Both		Graphic, Global and Height	Male	Female	Body Proportions	Male	Female
Type	0	Omission of Appendages	0	7	Upper and Lower Halves	2	1	Hair Shading	7	7	Head		
Sex Sequence	2	Position of Both Arms	1	3	Four Quarters	4	4	Nudity and Transparency	0	0	Neck		
Posture	1 1	Position of Right Arm	2	2	Relative Size	2		Form	5	5	Shoulders	06	05
Perspective	0 0	Position of Left Arm	0	8	Constant Line Pressure	0	0	Detailing	5	5	Right Arm	02	02
Vertical Midline	0 0	Position of Legs	6	6	Variable Line Pressure	1	1	Identity and Sex	3	3	Left Arm	02	
Bilateral Symmetry	1 1	Relation of Long Axes	1	1	Line Continuity	2	0	Sophistication	5	5	Chest	04	04
Horizontal Midline	0 0	Right and Left Halves	1	1	Body Shading	0	0	Height	04	04	Girth	06	05

GENERAL CHARACTERISTICS OF SUBJECT

IDENTIFICATION
No. 345
Sex M
Marital status S
Age 24 yrs. at
psychological tests

PARENTAL HISTORY
Father
C   H   S   D   O
(+)   -   -   -   -
Mother
C   H   S   D   O
-   -   -   -   -

PHYSIOLOGICAL AND METABOLIC DATA

	Admission	Initial	Control	Cold pressor change	Exercise change	Smoking change
Systolic pressure	110	118	116	-06	+22	-06
Diastolic pressure	60	60	58	+04	+02	+06
Heart rate	88	80	65	-06	+26	+01

	Height	72 in.	Ponderal index 13.38
Age 22 yrs.	Weight	156 lbs.	Cholesterol 163 mg. per 100 ml.
	Overweight -04 %		Vital capacity 4.7 liters

HABIT SURVEY

Smoking habits: moderate cigarette smoker

Age begun 17 yrs.   Inhalation: yes

Habits of nervous tension: 5, 6, 9, 11

FIGURE-DRAWING CHARACTERISTICS

Structural	Male Female Both		Structural	Male	Female	Structural and Graphic	Male Female Both		Graphic, Global and Height	Male	Female	Body Proportions	Male	Female
Type	0		Omission of Appendages	6	8	Upper and Lower Halves	2	2	Hair Shading	0	3	Head	04	03
Sex Sequence	0		Position of Both Arms	1	0	Four Quarters	0	0	Nudity and Transparency	3	3	Neck	06	02
Posture	1	1	Position of Right Arm	5	5	Relative Size	0		Form	5	5	Shoulders	03	03
Perspective	5	0	Position of Left Arm	2	5	Constant Line Pressure	3	5	Detailing	5	5	Right Arm	02	01
Vertical Midline	0	0	Position of Legs	6	6	Variable Line Pressure	0	0	Identity and Sex	5	5	Left Arm		01
Bilateral Symmetry	1	2	Relation of Long Axes	1	1	Line Continuity	4	4	Sophistication	5	5	Chest	03	03
Horizontal Midline	4	4	Right and Left Halves	9	2	Body Shading	0	0	Height	02	02	Girth	03	03

GENERAL CHARACTERISTICS OF SUBJECT

IDENTIFICATION
No. B78
Sex M
Marital status S
Age 23 yrs. at
psychological tests

PARENTAL HISTORY				
Father				
C	H	S	D	O
(?)	–	(+)	(?)	+
Mother				
C	H	S	D	O
?	–	–	–	–

PHYSIOLOGICAL AND METABOLIC DATA

	Admission	Initial	Control	Cold pressor change	Exercise change	Smoking change
Systolic pressure	102	100	108	+17	+30	+10
Diastolic pressure	68	62	72	+23	-08	-01
Heart rate	72	54	55	+12	+13	+08

Age 22 yrs.	Height 72 in.	Ponderal index 13.46
	Weight 153 lbs.	Cholesterol 217 mg. per 100 ml.
	Overweight -06 %	Vital capacity 4.7 liters

HABIT SURVEY

Smoking habits: nonsmoker

Age begun   yrs.   Inhalation:

Habits of nervous tension: 3, 4, 5, 9, 22

STRONG VOCATIONAL INTEREST TEST

Occupation	Artist	Psychologist	Architect	Physician	Osteopath	Dentist	Veterinarian	Mathematician	Physicist	Engineer	Chemist	Production Manager
Standard Score	4	6	5	7	7	4	3	2	3	4	5	6

Occupation	Farmer	Aviator	Carpenter	Printer	Math.-Sci. Teacher	Ind. Arts Teacher	Voc. Agric. Teacher	Policeman	Forest Serv. Man	Y.M.C.A. Phys. Dir.	Personnel Director	Public Administrator
Standard Score	5	5	3	5	6	2	3	4	7	6	6	7

Occupation	Y.M.C.A. Secretary	Soc. Sci. H.S. Teacher	City Sch. Sup't.	Social Worker	Minister	Musician Performer	C.P.A.	Senior C.P.A.	Accountant	Office Man	Purchasing Agent	Banker
Standard Score	5	6	4	7	6	7	2	5	2	3	2	1

Occupation	Mortician	Pharmacist	Sales Manager	Real Est. Manager	Life Ins. Salesman	Advertising Man	Lawyer	Author-Journalist	President Mfg. Co.	Interest Maturity	Occupational Level	Masculinity-Femininity
Standard Score	4	4	3	4	4	4	3	4	5	7	4	3

FIGURE-DRAWING CHARACTERISTICS

Structural	Male Female Both	Structural	Male	Female	Structural and Graphic	Male Female Both		Graphic, Global and Height	Male	Female	Body Proportions	Male	Female
Type	0	Omission of Appendages	0	0	Upper and Lower Halves	2	1	Hair Shading	7	5	Head	03	04
Sex Sequence	2	Position of Both Arms	0	0	Four Quarters	9	9	Nudity and Transparency	0	0	Neck	04	06
Posture	1	1	Position of Right Arm	2	0	Relative Size	4		Form	5	5	Shoulders	02	05
Perspective	0	0	Position of Left Arm	2	0	Constant Line Pressure	0	0	Detailing	5	5	Right Arm	04	04
Vertical Midline	0	0	Position of Legs	6	6	Variable Line Pressure	1	1	Identity and Sex	3	3	Left Arm	02	04
Bilateral Symmetry	1	1	Relation of Long Axes	1	1	Line Continuity	2	2	Sophistication	5	5	Chest	03	05
Horizontal Midline	0	0	Right and Left Halves	9	9	Body Shading	0	1	Height	04	05	Girth	04	06

GENERAL CHARACTERISTICS OF SUBJECT

IDENTIFICATION
No. 339
Sex M
Marital status M
Age 25 yrs. at
psychological tests

PARENTAL HISTORY
Father
C H S D O
? + - - +
Mother
C H S D O
- (+) - - -

PHYSIOLOGICAL AND METABOLIC DATA

	Admission	Initial	Control	Cold pressor change	Exercise change	Smoking change
Systolic pressure	130	118	110	+20	+36	+06
Diastolic pressure	84	76	66	+20	-06	00
Heart rate	80	84	70	00	+26	-02

Age 23 yrs.

Height	70 in.	Ponderal index 12.37
Weight	181 lbs.	Cholesterol 236 mg. per 100 ml.
Overweight +17 %		Vital capacity 4.8 liters

HABIT SURVEY

Smoking habits: nonsmoker

Age begun   yrs.   Inhalation:

Habits of nervous tension: 4, 5, 6, 22

Plate 31   MOST PRIMITIVE DRAWINGS   65

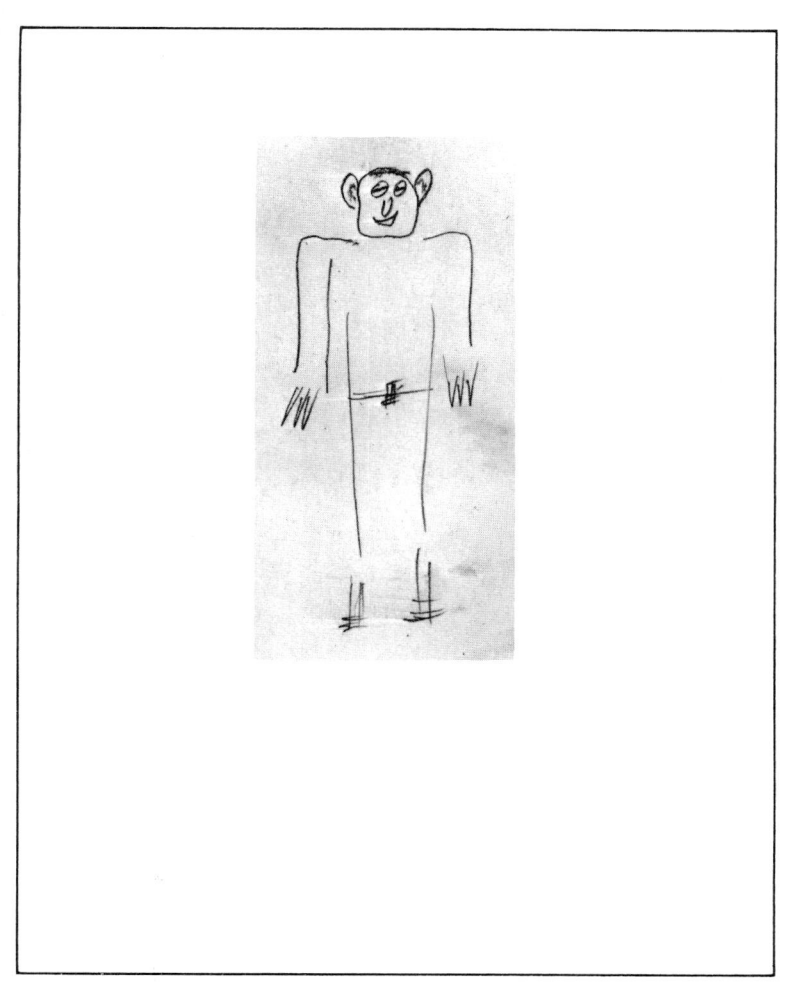

FIGURE-DRAWING CHARACTERISTICS

Structural	Male Female Both		Structural	Male	Female	Structural and Graphic	Male Female Both		Graphic, Global and Height	Male	Female	Body Proportions	Male	Female
Type	0		Omission of Appendages	0	9	Upper and Lower Halves	1	2	Hair Shading	3	7	Head	05	05
Sex Sequence	0		Position of Both Arms	0	0	Four Quarters	4	0	Nudity and Transparency	9	9	Neck	00	10
Posture	1	9	Position of Right Arm	0	2	Relative Size	0		Form	5	5	Shoulders	07	
Perspective	0	0	Position of Left Arm	0	2	Constant Line Pressure	0	5	Detailing	5	5	Right Arm	04	
Vertical Midline	0	0	Position of Legs	4	4	Variable Line Pressure	3	0	Identity and Sex	5	5	Left Arm	04	
Bilateral Symmetry	5	9	Relation of Long Axes	1	3	Line Continuity	3	3	Sophistication	5	5	Chest		04
Horizontal Midline	4	0	Right and Left Halves	1	2	Body Shading	4	0	Height	04	03	Girth	05	07

GENERAL CHARACTERISTICS OF SUBJECT

IDENTIFICATION
No. 313
Sex M
Marital status   S
Age 26 yrs. at
psychological tests

PARENTAL HISTORY				
Father				
C	H	S	D	O
(?)	-	-	-	-
Mother				
C	H	S	D	O
-	+	-	-	+

PHYSIOLOGICAL AND METABOLIC DATA

	Admission	Initial	Control	Cold pressor change	Exercise change	Smoking change
Systolic pressure	130	126	102	+12	+42	+04
Diastolic pressure	80	64	62	+02	+01	+02
Heart rate	80	84	71	00	+17	+07

Age 23 yrs.	Height	72	in.	Ponderal index 12.80	
	Weight	178	lbs.	Cholesterol	272	mg. per 100 ml.
	Overweight +09 %			Vital capacity	5.0	liters

HABIT SURVEY
Smoking habits: heavy cigarette smoker
Age begun 16 yrs.   Inhalation: yes
Habits of nervous tension: 5, 6, 9, 25

FIGURE-DRAWING CHARACTERISTICS

Structural	Male	Female	Structural	Male	Female	Structural and Graphic	Male	Female	Graphic, Global and Height	Male	Female	Body Proportions	Male	Female
	Both						Both							
Type	0		Omission of Appendages	0	0	Upper and Lower Halves	3	0	Hair Shading	1	3	Head	16	16
Sex Sequence	0		Position of Both Arms	4	4	Four Quarters	4	4	Nudity and Transparency	7	7	Neck	14	10
Posture	1	1	Position of Right Arm	7	7	Relative Size	2		Form	5	5	Shoulders		
Perspective	9	2	Position of Left Arm	3	0	Constant Line Pressure	0	2	Detailing	5	5	Right Arm		
Vertical Midline	4	4	Position of Legs	5	6	Variable Line Pressure	3	0	Identity and Sex	3	3	Left Arm	08	04
Bilateral Symmetry	0	0	Relation of Long Axes	1	1	Line Continuity	3	1	Sophistication	5	5	Chest	23	12
Horizontal Midline	4	0	Right and Left Halves	1	2	Body Shading	3	7	Height	08	08	Girth	22	23

GENERAL CHARACTERISTICS OF SUBJECT

IDENTIFICATION
No. A57
Sex M
Marital status S
Age 23 yrs. at
psychological tests

PARENTAL HISTORY				
Father				
C	H	S	D	O
–	+	–	–	?
Mother				
C	H	S	D	O
–	–	–	–	?

PHYSIOLOGICAL AND METABOLIC DATA

	Admission	Initial	Control	Cold pressor change	Exercise change	Smoking change
Systolic pressure	125	133	128	+13	+26	+02
Diastolic pressure	75	74	69	+13	–04	+02
Heart rate	76	80	66	+14	+09	–09

Age 22 yrs.	Height	76	in.	Ponderal index 13.22
	Weight	190	lbs.	Cholesterol 250 mg. per 100 ml.
	Overweight +04 %			Vital capacity liters

HABIT SURVEY

Smoking habits: nonsmoker

Age begun   yrs.   Inhalation:

Habits of nervous tension: 3, 4, 5, 6, 9, 19, 22

STRONG VOCATIONAL INTEREST TEST

Occupation	Artist	Psychologist	Architect	Physician	Osteopath	Dentist	Veterinarian	Mathematician	Physicist	Engineer	Chemist	Production Manager
Standard Score	23	17	13	16	25	14	15	10	00	08	06	15

Occupation	Farmer	Aviator	Carpenter	Printer	Math.-Sci. Teacher	Ind. Arts Teacher	Voc. Agric. Teacher	Policeman	Forest Serv. Man	Y.M.C.A. Phys. Dir.	Personnel Director	Public Administrator
Standard Score	21	17	–03	21	18	–10	08	15	–09	21	24	18

Occupation	Y.M.C.A. Secretary	Soc. Sci. H.S. Teacher	City Sch. Sup't.	Social Worker	Minister	Musician Performer	C.P.A.	Senior C.P.A.	Accountant	Office Man	Purchasing Agent	Banker
Standard Score	24	28	20	26	60	27	45	27	27	35	25	36

Occupation	Mortician	Pharmacist	Sales Manager	Real Est. Manager	Life Ins. Salesman	Advertising Man	Lawyer	Author- Journalist	President Mfg. Co.	Interest Maturity	Occupational Level	Masculinity- Femininity
Standard Score	36	37	44	58	55	48	47	41	39	47	62	31

Plate 33   MOST PRIMITIVE DRAWINGS   67

FIGURE-DRAWING CHARACTERISTICS

Structural	Male Female Both		Structural	Male	Female	Structural and Graphic	Male Female Both		Graphic, Global and Height	Male	Female	Body Proportions	Male	Female
Type	0		Omission of Appendages	0	2	Upper and Lower Halves	1	1	Hair Shading	7	7	Head	14	12
Sex Sequence	0		Position of Both Arms	1	6	Four Quarters	4	4	Nudity and Transparency	3	9	Neck	26	20
Posture	2	1	Position of Right Arm	0	7	Relative Size	2		Form	5	5	Shoulders		
Perspective	6	2	Position of Left Arm	5	7	Constant Line Pressure	0	0	Detailing	5	5	Right Arm	04	
Vertical Midline	4	4	Position of Legs	8	1	Variable Line Pressure	5	5	Identity and Sex	5	1	Left Arm	03	
Bilateral Symmetry	0	0	Relation of Long Axes	1	1	Line Continuity	4	4	Sophistication	5	5	Chest		07
Horizontal Midline	4	0	Right and Left Halves	1	0	Body Shading	0	0	Height	07	07	Girth		05

GENERAL CHARACTERISTICS OF SUBJECT

IDENTIFICATION
No. B18
Sex M
Marital status M
Age 22 yrs. at
psychological tests

PARENTAL HISTORY				
Father				
C	H	S	D	O
−	+	−	+	−
Mother				
C	H	S	D	O
−	−	−	−	−

PHYSIOLOGICAL AND METABOLIC DATA

	Admission	Initial	Control	Cold pressor change	Exercise change	Smoking change
Systolic pressure	120	114	104	+16	+28	+14
Diastolic pressure	64	44	64	+12	−24	+11
Heart rate	64	48	59	+06	+11	+12

Age 22 yrs.	Height	72 in.	Ponderal index	12.93	
	Weight	173 lbs.	Cholesterol	270	mg. per 100 ml.
	Overweight +06 %		Vital capacity	4.7	liters

HABIT SURVEY

Smoking habits: pipe smoker

Age begun 17 yrs.   Inhalation: yes

Habits of nervous tension: 25

STRONG VOCATIONAL INTEREST TEST

Occupation	Artist	Psychologist	Architect	Physician	Osteopath	Dentist	Veterinarian	Mathematician	Physicist	Engineer	Chemist	Production Manager
Standard Score	32	36	28	58	41	38	34	42	40	46	52	34

Occupation	Farmer	Aviator	Carpenter	Printer	Math.-Sci. Teacher	Ind. Arts Teacher	Voc. Agric. Teacher	Policeman	Forest Serv. Man	Y.M.C.A. Phys. Dir.	Personnel Director	Public Administrator
Standard Score	40	48	07	24	33	06	20	25	17	18	06	24

Occupation	Y.M.C.A. Secretary	Soc. Sci. H.S. Teacher	City Sch. Sup't.	Social Worker	Minister	Musician Performer	C.P.A.	Senior C.P.A.	Accountant	Office Man	Purchasing Agent	Banker
Standard Score	01	10	10	13	61	26	27	35	18	21	24	18

Occupation	Mortician	Pharmacist	Sales Manager	Real Est. Manager	Life Ins. Salesman	Advertising Man	Lawyer	Author-Journalist	President Mfg. Co.	Interest Maturity	Occupational Level	Masculinity-Femininity
Standard Score	14	31	25	32	25	27	41	40	36	43	64	59

FIGURE-DRAWING CHARACTERISTICS

Structural	Male Female Both		Structural	Male	Female	Structural and Graphic	Male Female Both		Graphic, Global and Height	Male	Female	Body Proportions	Male	Female
Type	0		Omission of Appendages	0	7	Upper and Lower Halves	1	0	Hair Shading	3	3	Head	08	13
Sex Sequence	0		Position of Both Arms	1	4	Four Quarters	4	4	Nudity and Transparency	7	9	Neck	10	10
Posture	1	2	Position of Right Arm	0	7	Relative Size	4		Form	5	5	Shoulders	08	
Perspective	0	2	Position of Left Arm	2	4	Constant Line Pressure	3	0	Detailing	5	5	Right Arm	04	
Vertical Midline	3	4	Position of Legs	4	8	Variable Line Pressure	0	1	Identity and Sex	5	3	Left Arm	04	
Bilateral Symmetry	3	0	Relation of Long Axes	1	1	Line Continuity	3	3	Sophistication	5	5	Chest	06	11
Horizontal Midline	0	0	Right and Left Halves	1	1	Body Shading	3	0	Height	06	08	Girth	07	12

GENERAL CHARACTERISTICS OF SUBJECT

IDENTIFICATION
No. E66
Sex M
Marital status S
Age 21 yrs. at
psychological tests

PARENTAL HISTORY				
Father				
C	H	S	D	O
-	+	-	-	?
Mother				
C	H	S	D	O
-	-	-	-	-

PHYSIOLOGICAL AND METABOLIC DATA

	Admission	Initial	Control	Cold pressor change	Exercise change	Smoking change
Systolic pressure	120	131	95	+09	+20	+03
Diastolic pressure	50	65	54	+19	-05	+06
Heart rate	84	72	72	+12	+07	+23

Age 22 yrs.	Height	72	in.	Ponderal index	11.77	
	Weight	226	lbs.	Cholesterol	210	mg. per 100 ml.
	Overweight +39 %			Vital capacity	5.4	liters

HABIT SURVEY

Smoking habits: moderate cigarette smoker

Age begun 14 yrs.   Inhalation: yes

Habits of nervous tension: 3, 4, 5, 9, 10, 16, 18, 22, 24

STRONG VOCATIONAL INTEREST TEST

Occupation	Artist	Psychologist	Architect	Physician	Osteopath	Dentist	Veterinarian	Mathematician	Physicist	Engineer	Chemist	Production Manager
Standard Score	33	39	34	47	35	37	23	34	23	23	29	19

Occupation	Farmer	Aviator	Carpenter	Printer	Math.-Sci. Teacher	Ind. Arts Teacher	Voc. Agric. Teacher	Policeman	Forest Serv. Man	Y.M.C.A. Phys. Dir.	Personnel Director	Public Administrator
Standard Score	23	20	02	17	31	-08	13	17	03	29	28	36

Occupation	Y.M.C.A. Secretary	Soc. Sci. H.S. Teacher	City Sch. Sup't.	Social Worker	Minister	Musician Performer	C.P.A.	Senior C.P.A.	Accountant	Office Man	Purchasing Agent	Banker
Standard Score	21	29	35	32	64	43	44	30	23	23	26	31

Occupation	Mortician	Pharmacist	Sales Manager	Real Est. Manager	Life Ins. Salesman	Advertising Man	Lawyer	Author-Journalist	President Mfg. Co.	Interest Maturity	Occupational Level	Masculinity-Femininity
Standard Score	28	32	32	38	40	38	50	41	29	49	65	37

FIGURE-DRAWING CHARACTERISTICS

Structural	Male Female Both		Structural	Male	Female	Structural and Graphic	Male Female Both		Graphic, Global and Height	Male	Female	Body Proportions	Male	Female
Type	0		Omission of Appendages	0	0	Upper and Lower Halves	1	1	Hair Shading	3	7	Head	07	08
Sex Sequence	0		Position of Both Arms	2	0	Four Quarters	4	4	Nudity and Transparency	0	7	Neck	10	04
Posture	3	1	Position of Right Arm	2	2	Relative Size	0		Form	5	5	Shoulders		03
Perspective	2	0	Position of Left Arm	7	2	Constant Line Pressure	0	5	Detailing	5	5	Right Arm	02	02
Vertical Midline	4	0	Position of Legs	1	6	Variable Line Pressure	5	0	Identity and Sex	5	3	Left Arm		02
Bilateral Symmetry	0	4	Relation of Long Axes	0	1	Line Continuity	0	0	Sophistication	5	5	Chest	05	03
Horizontal Midline	0	4	Right and Left Halves	1	1	Body Shading	0	1	Height		03	Girth	05	05

GENERAL CHARACTERISTICS OF SUBJECT

IDENTIFICATION
No. 510
Sex M
Marital status S
Age 24 yrs. at
psychological tests

PARENTAL HISTORY				
Father				
C	H	S	D	O
-	-	-	-	?
Mother				
C	H	S	D	O
-	+	-	-	+

PHYSIOLOGICAL AND METABOLIC DATA

	Admission	Initial	Control	Cold pressor change	Exercise change	Smoking change
Systolic pressure	138	114	102	+10	+24	
Diastolic pressure	70	64	66	+22	-02	
Heart rate	82	84	80	+08	+14	

Age 22 yrs.	Height	70	in.	Ponderal index	13.20	
	Weight	149	lbs.	Cholesterol	222	mg. per 100 ml.
	Overweight	-03	%	Vital capacity	4.4	liters

HABIT SURVEY
Smoking habits: unknown
Age begun yrs. Inhalation:
Habits of nervous tension:

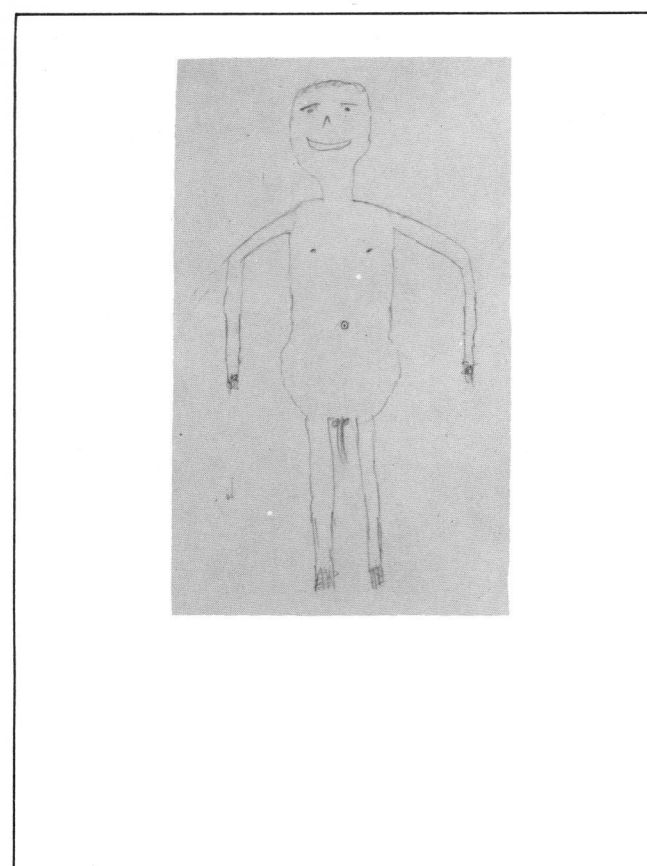

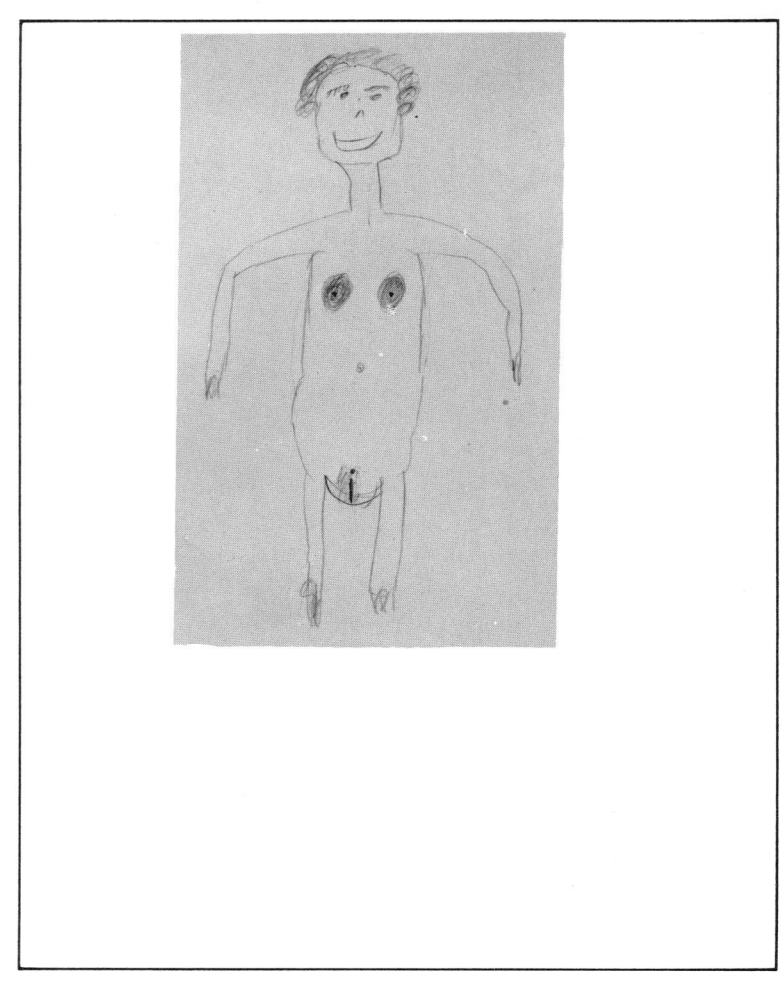

FIGURE-DRAWING CHARACTERISTICS

Structural	Male Female Both		Structural	Male	Female	Structural and Graphic	Male Female Both		Graphic, Global and Height	Male	Female	Body Proportions	Male	Female
Type	0		Omission of Appendages	0	0	Upper and Lower Halves	1	1	Hair Shading	3	3	Head	08	08
Sex Sequence	0		Position of Both Arms	0	0	Four Quarters	4	4	Nudity and Transparency	0	0	Neck		12
Posture	1	1	Position of Right Arm	2	2	Relative Size	4		Form	5	5	Shoulders	05	05
Perspective	0	0	Position of Left Arm	2	2	Constant Line Pressure	1	0	Detailing	3	3	Right Arm	04	04
Vertical Midline	0	0	Position of Legs	5	6	Variable Line Pressure	0	1	Identity and Sex	3	3	Left Arm	04	04
Bilateral Symmetry	3	3	Relation of Long Axes	1	1	Line Continuity	0	0	Sophistication	5	5	Chest	05	05
Horizontal Midline	0	0	Right and Left Halves	1	1	Body Shading	2	3	Height	05	06	Girth	06	08

GENERAL CHARACTERISTICS OF SUBJECT

IDENTIFICATION
No. A54
Sex M
Marital status S
Age 22 yrs. at
psychological tests

PARENTAL HISTORY				
Father				
C	H	S	D	O
–	–	–	–	–
Mother				
C	H	S	D	O
–	+	–	–	?

PHYSIOLOGICAL AND METABOLIC DATA

	Admission	Initial	Control	Cold pressor change	Exercise change	Smoking change
Systolic pressure	136	124	122	+03	+32	00
Diastolic pressure	80	68	65	+08	–10	+01
Heart rate	84	69	72	+14	+11	00

Age 21 yrs.	Height 71 in.	Ponderal index 12.48
	Weight 184 lbs.	Cholesterol 210 mg. per 100 ml.
	Overweight +17 %	Vital capacity liters

HABIT SURVEY
Smoking habits: nonsmoker
Age begun yrs.　Inhalation:
Habits of nervous tension: 4, 5, 9, 11, 16, 21, 22

STRONG VOCATIONAL INTEREST TEST

Occupation	Artist	Psychologist	Architect	Physician	Osteopath	Dentist	Veterinarian	Mathematician	Physicist	Engineer	Chemist	Production Manager
Standard Score	2	7	1	6	5	2	3	2	2	3	3	4

Occupation	Farmer	Aviator	Carpenter	Printer	Math.-Sci. Teacher	Ind. Arts Teacher	Voc. Agric. Teacher	Policeman	Forest Serv. Man	Y.M.C.A. Phys. Dir.	Personnel Director	Public Administrator
Standard Score	4	4	1	3	5	1	2	2	2	2	5	6

Occupation	Y.M.C.A. Secretary	Soc. Sci. H.S. Teacher	City Sch. Sup't.	Social Worker	Minister	Musician Performer	C.P.A.	Senior C.P.A.	Accountant	Office Man	Purchasing Agent	Banker
Standard Score	2	5	4	5	6	4	6	5	2	4	2	3

Occupation	Mortician	Pharmacist	Sales Manager	Real Est. Manager	Life Ins. Salesman	Advertising Man	Lawyer	Author-Journalist	President Mfg. Co.	Interest Maturity	Occupational Level	Masculinity-Femininity
Standard Score	4	6	4	6	5	4	6	4	4	5	6	4

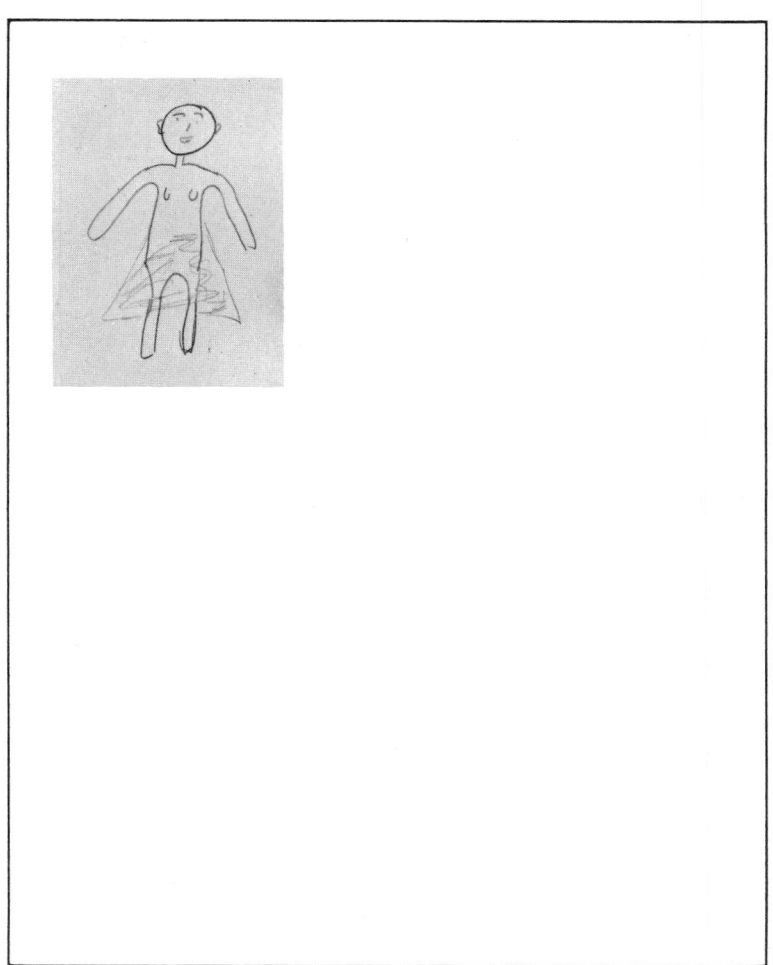

FIGURE-DRAWING CHARACTERISTICS

Structural	Male Female Both		Structural	Male	Female	Structural and Graphic	Male Female Both		Graphic, Global and Height	Male	Female	Body Proportions	Male	Female
Type	0		Omission of Appendages	9	9	Upper and Lower Halves	2	2	Hair Shading	0	0	Head	03	04
Sex Sequence	0		Position of Both Arms	0	0	Four Quarters	0	0	Nudity and Transparency	9	5	Neck	04	04
Posture	1	1	Position of Right Arm	2	2	Relative Size	0		Form	5	5	Shoulders	02	02
Perspective	0	0	Position of Left Arm	2	2	Constant Line Pressure	4	4	Detailing	5	5	Right Arm	01	02
Vertical Midline	0	0	Position of Legs	6	6	Variable Line Pressure	0	0	Identity and Sex	5	3	Left Arm	02	02
Bilateral Symmetry	1	2	Relation of Long Axes	1	1	Line Continuity	4	4	Sophistication	5	5	Chest	02	02
Horizontal Midline	0	0	Right and Left Halves	2	2	Body Shading	0	2	Height	03	02	Girth	03	03

GENERAL CHARACTERISTICS OF SUBJECT

IDENTIFICATION
No. 547
Sex M
Marital status S
Age 24 yrs. at
psychological tests

PARENTAL HISTORY
Father
C   H   S   D   O
-    -   ?   +   +
Mother
C   H   S   D   O
-    -   -   -   +

PHYSIOLOGICAL AND METABOLIC DATA

	Admission	Initial	Control	Cold pressor change	Exercise change	Smoking change
Systolic pressure	130	130	120	+10	+70	+09
Diastolic pressure	80	60	60	+20	00	+14
Heart rate	72	80	76	-08	+35	+04

Age 22 yrs.

Height 71 in.
Weight 148 lbs.
Overweight -06 %

Ponderal index 13.42
Cholesterol 210 mg. per 100 ml.
Vital capacity 5.5 liters

HABIT SURVEY
Smoking habits: nonsmoker
Age begun   yrs.   Inhalation:
Habits of nervous tension: 2, 5, 6, 9, 11, 18

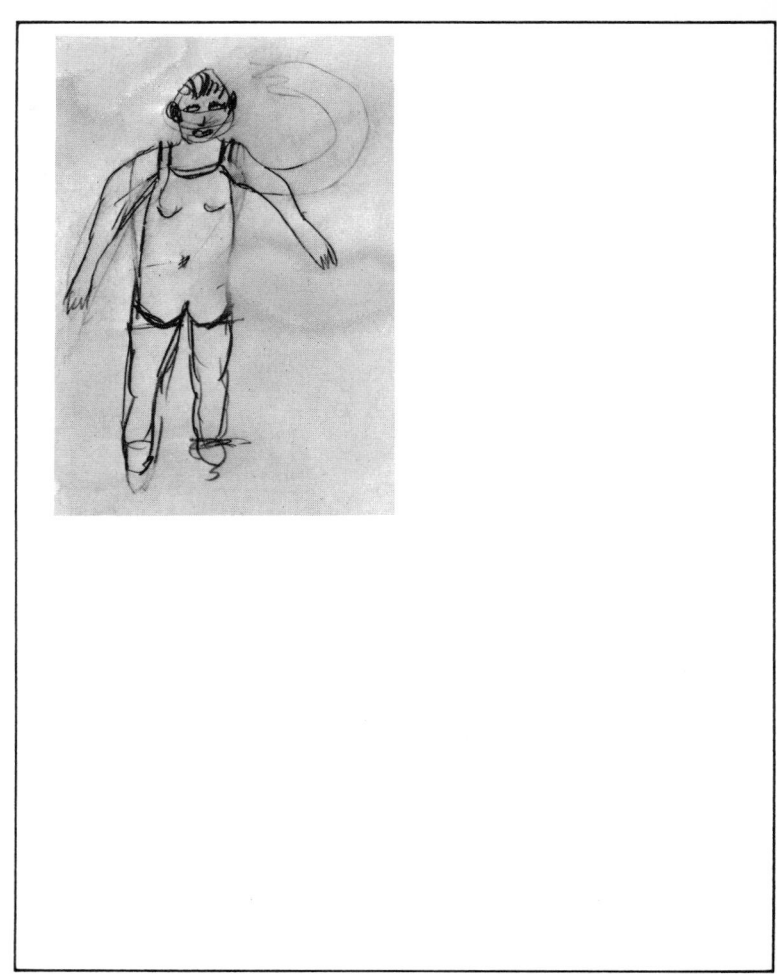

FIGURE-DRAWING CHARACTERISTICS

Structural	Male Female Both	Structural	Male	Female	Structural and Graphic	Male Female Both		Graphic, Global and Height	Male	Female	Body Proportions	Male	Female
Type	0	Omission of Appendages	0	0	Upper and Lower Halves	2	2	Hair Shading	3	3	Head	05	05
Sex Sequence	0	Position of Both Arms	2	0	Four Quarters	0	0	Nudity and Transparency	7	2	Neck	01	00
Posture	2	1	Position of Right Arm	2	2	Relative Size	4		Form	5	5	Shoulders		04
Perspective	2	0	Position of Left Arm	7	2	Constant Line Pressure	0	5	Detailing	5	3	Right Arm	02	04
Vertical Midline	4	0	Position of Legs	8	6	Variable Line Pressure	5	0	Identity and Sex	3	3	Left Arm		02
Bilateral Symmetry	0	2	Relation of Long Axes	1	1	Line Continuity	2	0	Sophistication	5	5	Chest	06	04
Horizontal Midline	4	0	Right and Left Halves	2	2	Body Shading	0	1	Height	03	04	Girth	05	06

GENERAL CHARACTERISTICS OF SUBJECT

IDENTIFICATION

No. G43
Sex M
Marital status S
Age 22 yrs. at
psychological tests

PARENTAL HISTORY

Father
C	H	S	D	O
-	-	-	-	+

Mother
C	H	S	D	O
-	-	-	-	?

PHYSIOLOGICAL AND METABOLIC DATA

	Admission	Initial	Control	Cold pressor change	Exercise change	Smoking change
Systolic pressure	120	140	122	+16	+48	+06
Diastolic pressure	75	78	68	+18	-08	00
Heart rate	76	68	63	-04	+18	+05

Age 21 yrs.
Height 72 in.   Ponderal index 13.21
Weight 162 lbs.   Cholesterol 150 mg. per 100 ml.
Overweight 00 %   Vital capacity liters

HABIT SURVEY

Smoking habits: nonsmoker
Age begun yrs.   Inhalation:
Habits of nervous tension: 4, 5, 6, 9, 10, 11, 16, 21, 22, 23, 24

STRONG VOCATIONAL INTEREST TEST

Occupation	Artist	Psychologist	Architect	Physician	Osteopath	Dentist	Veterinarian	Mathematician	Physicist	Engineer	Chemist	Production Manager
Standard Score	34	40	35	53	46	41	39	26	23	31	40	26

Occupation	Farmer	Aviator	Carpenter	Printer	Math.-Sci. Teacher	Ind. Arts Teacher	Voc. Agric. Teacher	Policeman	Forest Serv. Man	Y.M.C.A. Phys. Dir.	Personnel Director	Public Administrator
Standard Score	44	38	20	32	39	28	42	25	35	38	25	42

Occupation	Y.M.C.A. Secretary	Soc. Sci. H.S. Teacher	City Sch. Sup't.	Social Worker	Minister	Musician Performer	C.P.A.	Senior C.P.A.	Accountant	Office Man	Purchasing Agent	Banker
Standard Score	20	34	23	33	59	37	25	39	23	24	19	18

Occupation	Mortician	Pharmacist	Sales Manager	Real Est. Manager	Life Ins. Salesman	Advertising Man	Lawyer	Author-Journalist	President Mfg. Co.	Interest Maturity	Occupational Level	Masculinity-Femininity
Standard Score	28	33	26	30	27	33	30	35	25	51	61	47

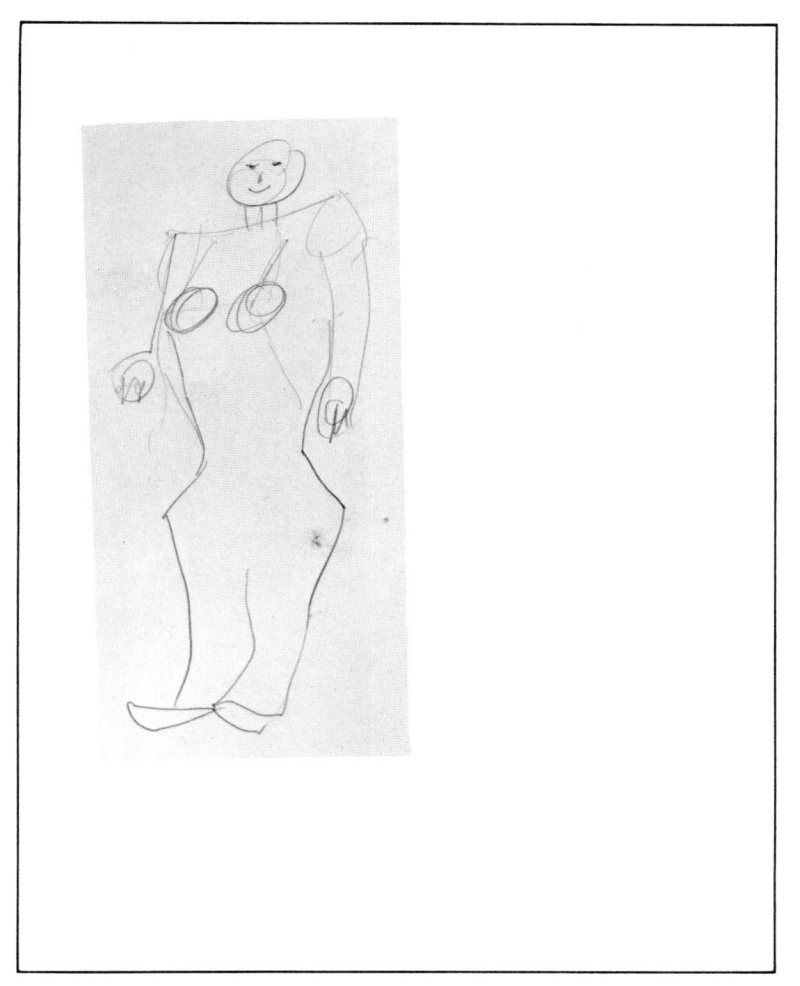
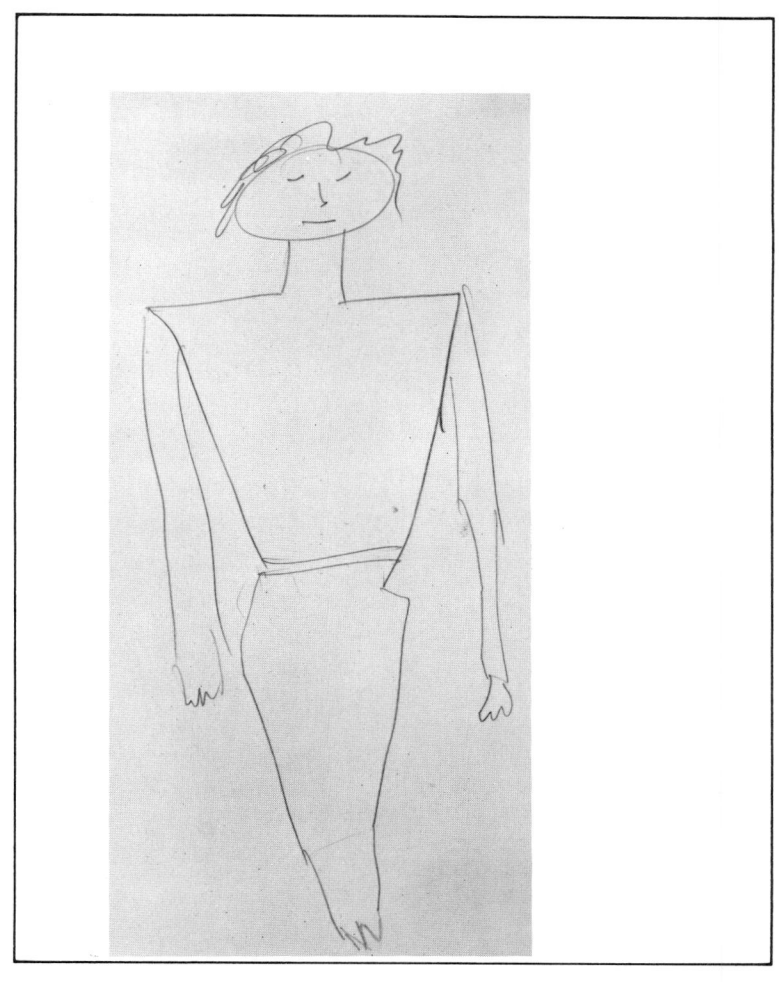

FIGURE-DRAWING CHARACTERISTICS

Structural	Male	Female	Structural	Male	Female	Structural and Graphic	Male	Female	Graphic, Global and Height	Male	Female	Body Proportions	Male	Female
	Both						Both							
Type	0		Omission of Appendages	8	0	Upper and Lower Halves	3	1	Hair Shading	7	0	Head	07	05
Sex Sequence	1		Position of Both Arms	0	4	Four Quarters	4	4	Nudity and Transparency	9	9	Neck	20	06
Posture	0	1	Position of Right Arm	0	7	Relative Size	0		Form	5	5	Shoulders	12	
Perspective	0	1	Position of Left Arm	0	0	Constant Line Pressure	3	0	Detailing	5	5	Right Arm	10	
Vertical Midline	0	4	Position of Legs	0	1	Variable Line Pressure	0	2	Identity and Sex	5	5	Left Arm	10	06
Bilateral Symmetry	3	0	Relation of Long Axes	1	1	Line Continuity	3	2	Sophistication	5	5	Chest	11	
Horizontal Midline	4	0	Right and Left Halves	1	2	Body Shading	0	0	Height		06	Girth	08	

GENERAL CHARACTERISTICS OF SUBJECT

IDENTIFICATION

No. E72
Sex M
Marital status S
Age 23 yrs. at
psychological tests

PARENTAL HISTORY

Father
C   H   S   D   O
–   –   –   –   +

Mother
C   H   S   D   O
–   –   –   –   ?

PHYSIOLOGICAL AND METABOLIC DATA

	Admission	Initial	Control	Cold pressor change	Exercise change	Smoking change
Systolic pressure	130	132	120	+14	+30	
Diastolic pressure	80	60	60	+10	00	
Heart rate	72	68	60	–04	+23	

Age 23 yrs.
Height 74 in.   Ponderal index 12.82
Weight 192 lbs.   Cholesterol 192 mg. per 100 ml.
Overweight +10 %   Vital capacity 6.2 liters

HABIT SURVEY

Smoking habits: pipe and cigar smoker
Age begun 21 yrs.   Inhalation: no
Habits of nervous tension: 4, 5, 6. 8, 9, 10, 17

STRONG VOCATIONAL INTEREST TEST

Occupation	Artist	Psychologist	Architect	Physician	Osteopath	Dentist	Veterinarian	Mathematician	Physicist	Engineer	Chemist	Production Manager
Standard Score	51	59	53	66	53	45	14	43	47	52	53	36

Occupation	Farmer	Aviator	Carpenter	Printer	Math.-Sci. Teacher	Ind. Arts Teacher	Voc. Agric. Teacher	Policeman	Forest Serv. Man	Y.M.C.A. Phys. Dir.	Personnel Director	Public Administrator
Standard Score	26	45	27	37	38	23	16	27	35	36	44	48

Occupation	Y.M.C.A. Secretary	Soc. Sci. H.S. Teacher	City Sch. Sup't.	Social Worker	Minister	Musician Performer	C.P.A.	Senior C.P.A.	Accountant	Office Man	Purchasing Agent	Banker
Standard Score	23	19	28	44	64	60	26	26	13	12	14	05

Occupation	Mortician	Pharmacist	Sales Manager	Real Est. Manager	Life Ins. Salesman	Advertising Man	Lawyer	Author-Journalist	President Mfg. Co.	Interest Maturity	Occupational Level	Masculinity-Femininity
Standard Score	18	28	32	31	29	43	45	47	38	48	o0	43

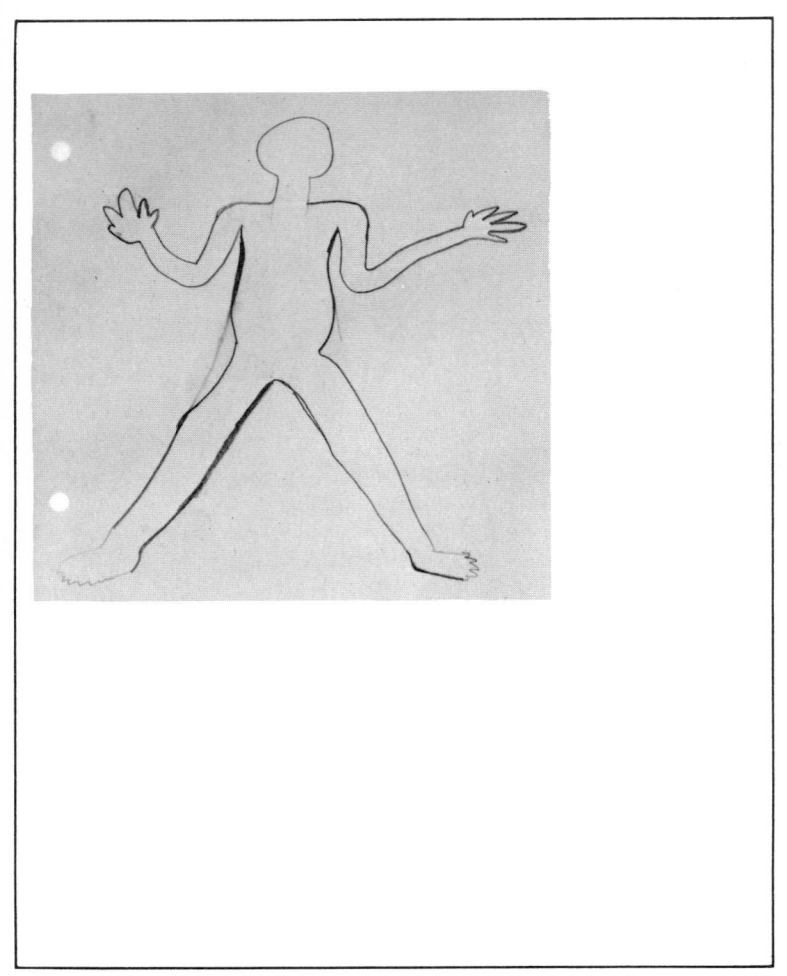

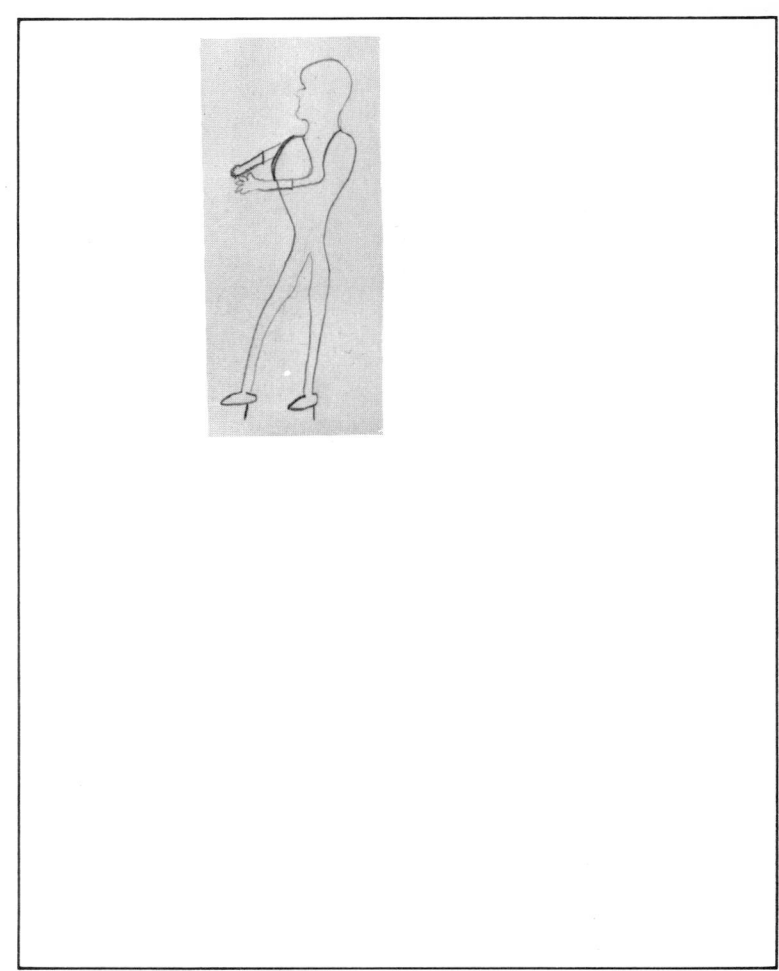

FIGURE-DRAWING CHARACTERISTICS

Structural	Male Female Both	Structural	Male	Female	Structural and Graphic	Male Female Both		Graphic, Global and Height	Male	Female	Body Proportions	Male	Female
Type	0	Omission of Appendages	0	0	Upper and Lower Halves	1	2	Hair Shading	0	0	Head		05
Sex Sequence	0	Position of Both Arms	0	4	Four Quarters	4	0	Nudity and Transparency	0	9	Neck		04
Posture	1 1	Position of Right Arm	4	7	Relative Size	0		Form	5	5	Shoulders	06	
Perspective	0 2	Position of Left Arm	4	4	Constant Line Pressure	0	0	Detailing	5	5	Right Arm	04	
Vertical Midline	0 4	Position of Legs	6	6	Variable Line Pressure	3	3	Identity and Sex	5	5	Left Arm	06	02
Bilateral Symmetry	3 0	Relation of Long Axes	1	1	Line Continuity	4	4	Sophistication	5	5	Chest	04	05
Horizontal Midline	0 0	Right and Left Halves	1	2	Body Shading	0	0	Height	05	03	Girth	05	03

GENERAL CHARACTERISTICS OF SUBJECT

IDENTIFICATION
No. 766
Sex M
Marital status S
Age 24 yrs. at
psychological tests

PARENTAL HISTORY
Father
C   H   S   D   0
-    -   -   -   ?
Mother
C   H   S   D   0
-    -   -   -   -

PHYSIOLOGICAL AND METABOLIC DATA

	Admission	Initial	Control	Cold pressor change	Exercise change	Smoking change
Systolic pressure	120	110	110	+10	+20	+07
Diastolic pressure	80	62	64	+10	+10	+04
Heart rate	80	76	79	00	+04	-09

Age 24 yrs.	Height	70	in.	Ponderal index 13.18
	Weight	150	lbs.	Cholesterol 203 mg. per 100 ml.
	Overweight -04 %			Vital capacity 5.3 liters

HABIT SURVEY
Smoking habits: light cigarette smoker
Age begun 22 yrs.   Inhalation: no
Habits of nervous tension: 3, 4, 5, 6, 10, 19,
21, 22, 23, 25

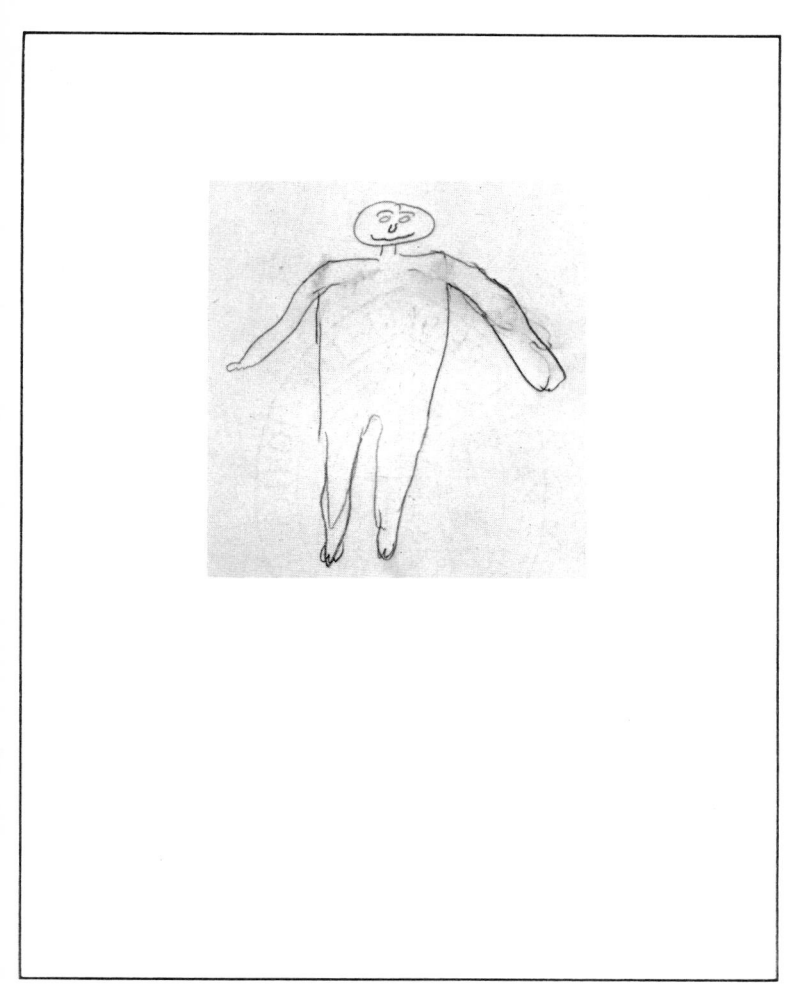

FIGURE-DRAWING CHARACTERISTICS

Structural	Male Female Both	Structural	Male	Female	Structural and Graphic	Male Female Both		Graphic, Global and Height	Male	Female	Body Proportions	Male	Female
Type	0	Omission of Appendages	9	0	Upper and Lower Halves	1	0	Hair Shading	0	3	Head	03	05
Sex Sequence	0	Position of Both Arms	0	0	Four Quarters	4	4	Nudity and Transparency	0	7	Neck	04	06
Posture	1 1	Position of Right Arm	2	2	Relative Size	4		Form	5	5	Shoulders	05	05
Perspective	0 0	Position of Left Arm	2	2	Constant Line Pressure	0	0	Detailing	5	5	Right Arm	03	04
Vertical Midline	0 0	Position of Legs	4	5	Variable Line Pressure	5	3	Identity and Sex	5	5	Left Arm		03
Bilateral Symmetry	2 3	Relation of Long Axes	1	1	Line Continuity	1	2	Sophistication	5	5	Chest	06	06
Horizontal Midline	0 0	Right and Left Halves	1	0	Body Shading	0	1	Height	03	04	Girth	07	09

GENERAL CHARACTERISTICS OF SUBJECT

IDENTIFICATION
No. E08
Sex M
Marital status S
Age 23 yrs. at
psychological tests

PARENTAL HISTORY

Father

C H S D O

− − − − ?

Mother

C H S D O

− − − − −

PHYSIOLOGICAL AND METABOLIC DATA

	Admission	Initial	Control	Cold pressor change	Exercise change	Smoking change
Systolic pressure	110	110	110	+12	+40	+01
Diastolic pressure	70	60	66	+26	−36	−03
Heart rate	65	56	50	−04	+08	−05

Age 22 yrs.	Height 74 in.	Ponderal index 12.89
	Weight 189 lbs.	Cholesterol 215 mg. per 100 ml.
	Overweight +09 %	Vital capacity 5.3 liters

HABIT SURVEY

Smoking habits: nonsmoker

Age begun   yrs.   Inhalation:

Habits of nervous tension: 5, 6, 8, 10, 16, 22

STRONG VOCATIONAL INTEREST TEST

Occupation	Artist	Psychologist	Architect	Physician	Osteopath	Dentist	Veterinarian	Mathematician	Physicist	Engineer	Chemist	Production Manager
Standard Score	28	38	29	38	20	21	12	41	29	36	38	27

Occupation	Farmer	Aviator	Carpenter	Printer	Math.-Sci. Teacher	Ind. Arts Teacher	Voc. Agric. Teacher	Policeman	Forest Serv. Man	Y.M.C.A. Phys. Dir.	Personnel Director	Public Administrator
Standard Score	18	19	−07	19	26	−06	07	16	01	24	28	33

Occupation	Y.M.C.A. Secretary	Soc. Sci. H.S. Teacher	City Sch. Sup't.	Social Worker	Minister	Musician Performer	C.P.A.	Senior C.P.A.	Accountant	Office Man	Purchasing Agent	Banker
Standard Score	17	24	39	26	64	31	45	35	29	31	33	23

Occupation	Mortician	Pharmacist	Sales Manager	Real Est. Manager	Life Ins. Salesman	Advertising Man	Lawyer	Author-Journalist	President Mfg. Co.	Interest Maturity	Occupational Level	Masculinity-Femininity
Standard Score	24	35	44	33	38	44	46	43	43	47	68	41

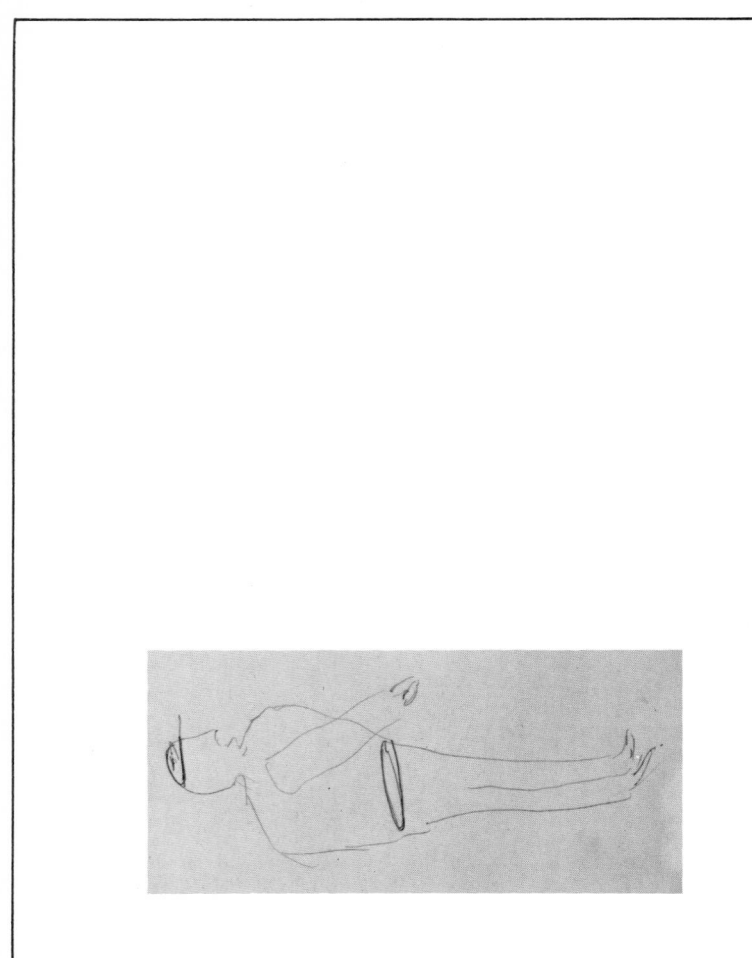

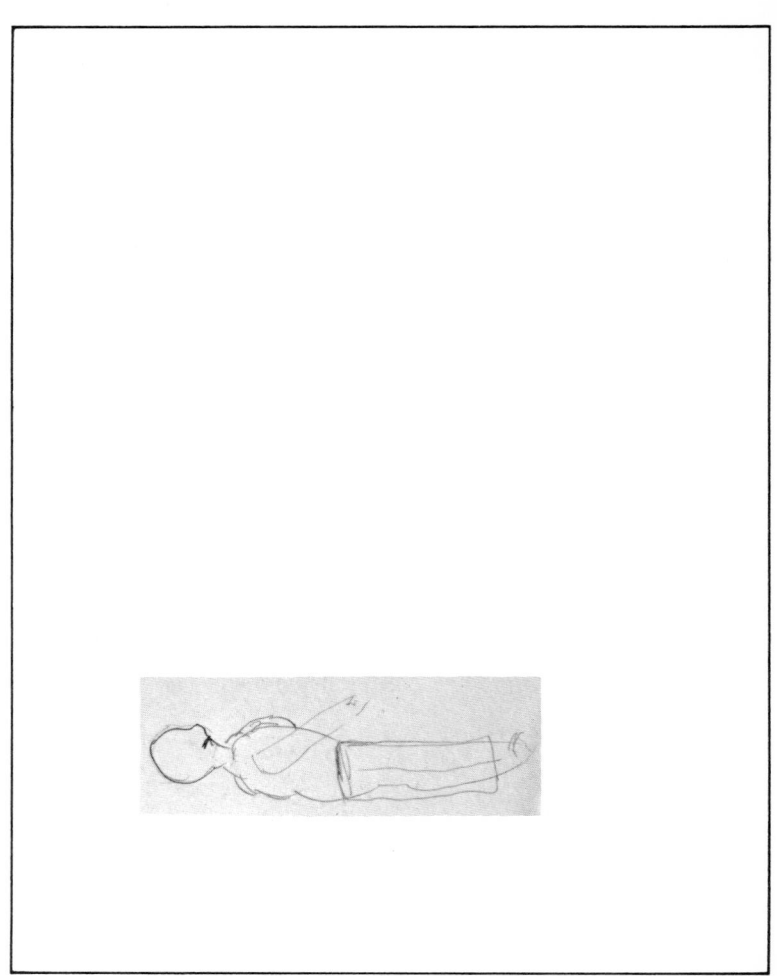

FIGURE-DRAWING CHARACTERISTICS

Structural	Male Female Both		Structural	Male	Female	Structural and Graphic	Male Female Both		Graphic, Global and Height	Male	Female	Body Proportions	Male	Female
Type	0		Omission of Appendages	0	6	Upper and Lower Halves	0	1	Hair Shading	0	0	Head	05	05
Sex Sequence	0		Position of Both Arms	2	2	Four Quarters	4	4	Nudity and Transparency	9	6	Neck	00	04
Posture	1	0	Position of Right Arm	2	2	Relative Size	0		Form	5	5	Shoulders		
Perspective	2	2	Position of Left Arm	7	7	Constant Line Pressure	1	0	Detailing	5	5	Right Arm	04	02
Vertical Midline	4	4	Position of Legs	1	1	Variable Line Pressure	0	1	Identity and Sex	3	3	Left Arm		
Bilateral Symmetry	0	0	Relation of Long Axes	2	2	Line Continuity	2	2	Sophistication	5	5	Chest	11	05
Horizontal Midline	4	4	Right and Left Halves	2	2	Body Shading	0	0	Height	05	03	Girth	08	06

GENERAL CHARACTERISTICS OF SUBJECT

IDENTIFICATION
No. 401
Sex M
Marital status   S
Age 24 yrs. at
psychological tests

PARENTAL HISTORY				
Father				
C	H	S	D	O
–	–	–	–	–
Mother				
C	H	S	D	O
–	–	–	–	–

PHYSIOLOGICAL AND METABOLIC DATA

	Admission	Initial	Control	Cold pressor change	Exercise change	Smoking change
Systolic pressure	122	124	110	00	+24	+04
Diastolic pressure	70	64	62	+04	–08	+06
Heart rate	74	90	75	–04	+27	+09

	Height 76 in.	Ponderal index 13.24	
Age 22 yrs.	Weight 189 lbs.	Cholesterol 250 mg. per 100 ml.	
	Overweight +03 %	Vital capacity 5.8 liters	

HABIT SURVEY

Smoking habits: heavy cigarette smoker

Age begun   yrs.   Inhalation:

Habits of nervous tension:

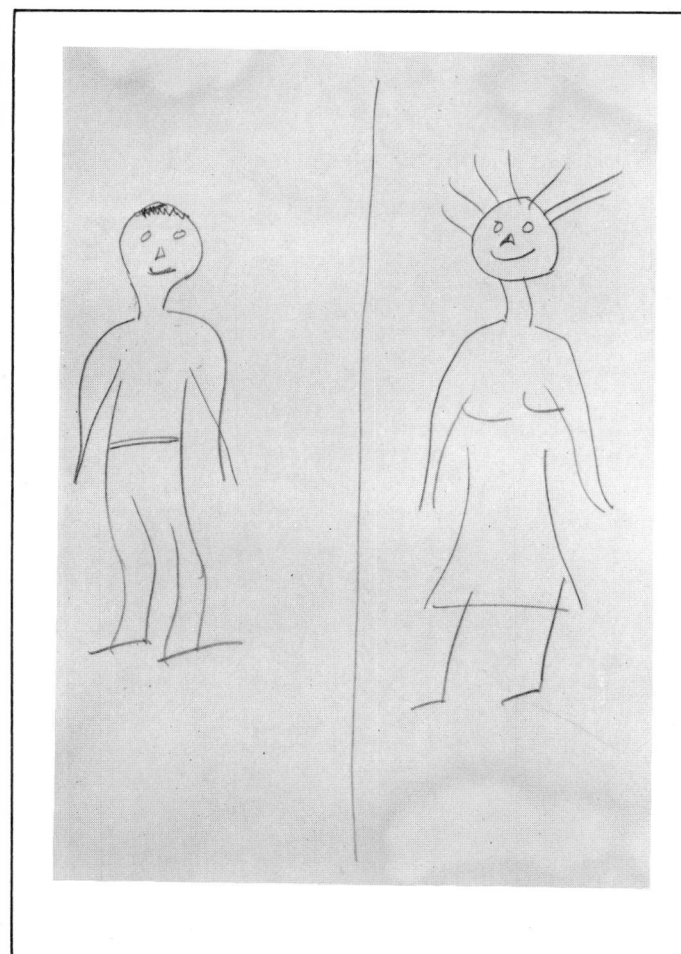

FIGURE-DRAWING CHARACTERISTICS

Structural	Male Female Both	Structural	Male	Female	Structural and Graphic	Male Female Both		Graphic, Global and Height	Male	Female	Body Proportions	Male	Female
Type	0	Omission of Appendages	7	7	Upper and Lower Halves	1	1	Hair Shading	7	7	Head		07
Sex Sequence	2	Position of Both Arms	0	0	Four Quarters	4	4	Nudity and Transparency	3	3	Neck		14
Posture	1 1	Position of Right Arm	2	2	Relative Size	4		Form	5	5	Shoulders	04	04
Perspective	0 0	Position of Left Arm	2	2	Constant Line Pressure	0	5	Detailing	5	5	Right Arm		
Vertical Midline	0 0	Position of Legs	4	6	Variable Line Pressure	5	0	Identity and Sex	5	5	Left Arm		
Bilateral Symmetry	1 1	Relation of Long Axes	1	1	Line Continuity	3	3	Sophistication	5	5	Chest	03	05
Horizontal Midline	4 0	Right and Left Halves	9	9	Body Shading	0	1	Height	04	05	Girth	04	05

GENERAL CHARACTERISTICS OF SUBJECT

IDENTIFICATION
No. 647
Sex M
Marital status M
Age 28 yrs. at
psychological tests

PARENTAL HISTORY
Father
C   H   S   D   O
-    -   -   -   -
Mother
C   H   S   D   O
-    -   -   -   -

PHYSIOLOGICAL AND METABOLIC DATA

	Admission	Initial	Control	Cold pressor change	Exercise change	Smoking change
Systolic pressure	125	116	104	+16	+42	+06
Diastolic pressure	78	64	60	+22	+10	+10
Heart rate	72	64	67		+44	+10

Age 25 yrs.	Height 70 in.	Ponderal index 12.66
	Weight 169 lbs.	Cholesterol 217 mg. per 100 ml.
	Overweight +08 %	Vital capacity 4.6 liters

HABIT SURVEY
Smoking habits: occasional smoker
Age begun   yrs.   Inhalation:
Habits of nervous tension: 1, 3, 4, 5, 6, 9,
11, 16, 18, 22, 24, 25

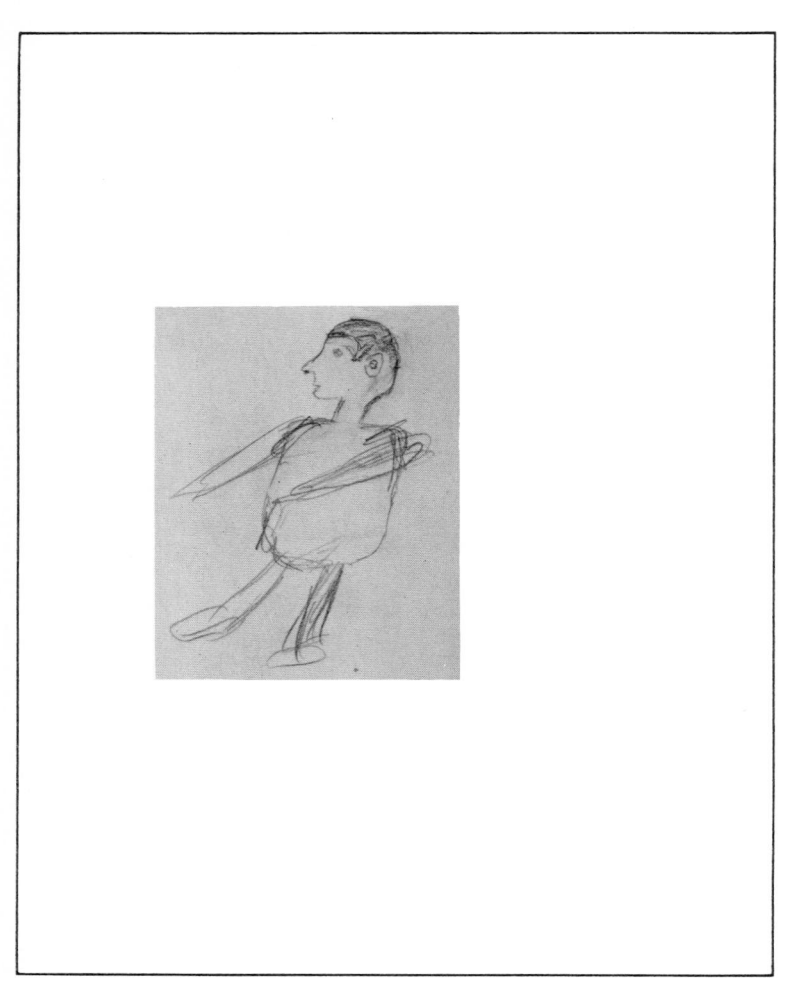

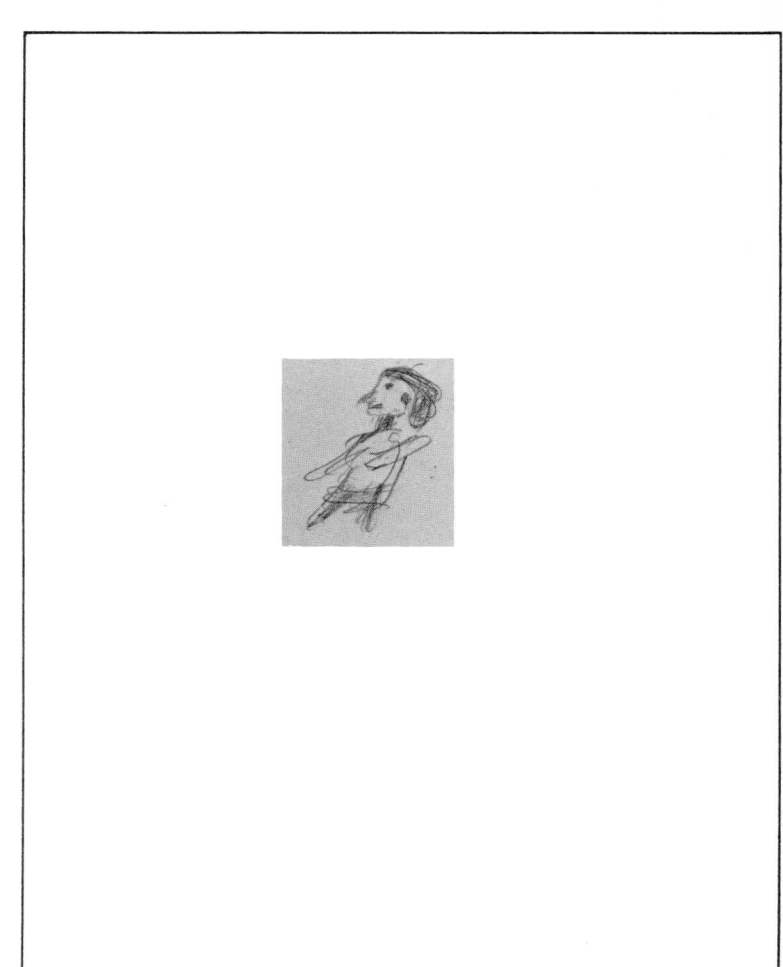

FIGURE-DRAWING CHARACTERISTICS

Structural	Male Female Both		Structural	Male	Female	Structural and Graphic	Male Female Both		Graphic, Global and Height	Male	Female	Body Proportions	Male	Female
Type	0		Omission of Appendages	7	6	Upper and Lower Halves	0	1	Hair Shading	2	3	Head	06	04
Sex Sequence	0		Position of Both Arms	0	0	Four Quarters	4	4	Nudity and Transparency	0	0	Neck	07	04
Posture	2	2	Position of Right Arm	2	2	Relative Size	0		Form	5	5	Shoulders		
Perspective	6	6	Position of Left Arm	2	2	Constant Line Pressure	2	2	Detailing	5	5	Right Arm		
Vertical Midline	4	4	Position of Legs	8	8	Variable Line Pressure	0	0	Identity and Sex	5	5	Left Arm		
Bilateral Symmetry	0	0	Relation of Long Axes	3	3	Line Continuity	0	0	Sophistication	5	5	Chest		
Horizontal Midline	0	0	Right and Left Halves	1	1	Body Shading	0	0	Height	03	01	Girth		

GENERAL CHARACTERISTICS OF SUBJECT

IDENTIFICATION
No. F31
Sex M
Marital status S
Age 24 yrs. at
psychological tests

PARENTAL HISTORY
Father
C   H   S   D   O
-   -   -   -   -
Mother
C   H   S   D   O
-   -   -   -   -

PHYSIOLOGICAL AND METABOLIC DATA

	Admission	Initial	Control	Cold pressor change	Exercise change	Smoking change
Systolic pressure	120	112	108	+02	+24	
Diastolic pressure	80	72	70	+14	+10	
Heart rate	80	64	70	+04	+25	

Age 22 yrs.	Height 69 in.	Ponderal index 13.23
	Weight 142 lbs.	Cholesterol 234 mg. per 100 ml.
	Overweight -03 %	Vital capacity liters

HABIT SURVEY
Smoking habits: occasional smoker
Age begun 19 yrs.   Inhalation: no
Habits of nervous tension: 2, 4, 5

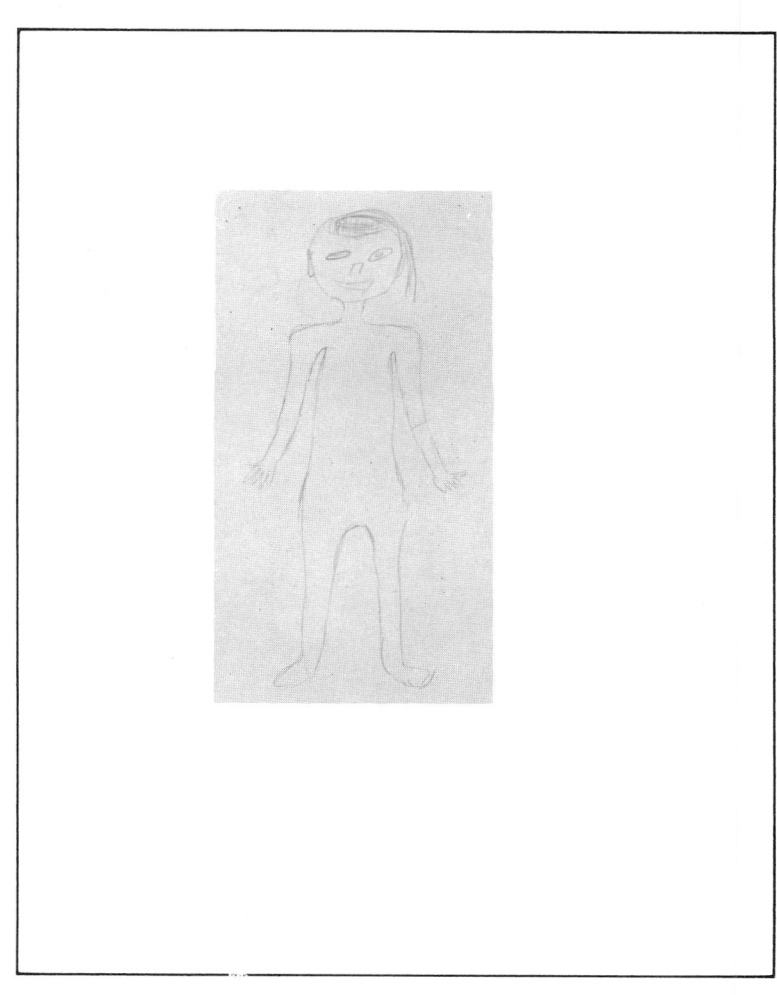

FIGURE-DRAWING CHARACTERISTICS

Structural	Male Female Both	Structural	Male	Female	Structural and Graphic	Male Female Both	Graphic, Global and Height	Male	Female	Body Proportions	Male	Female
Type	0	Omission of Appendages	0	0	Upper and Lower Halves	1 1	Hair Shading	3	3	Head	07	07
Sex Sequence	0	Position of Both Arms	0	0	Four Quarters	4 4	Nudity and Transparency	0	0	Neck	04	06
Posture	1 1	Position of Right Arm	3	1	Relative Size	2	Form	5	5	Shoulders	05	05
Perspective	0 0	Position of Left Arm	3	1	Constant Line Pressure	1 1	Detailing	5	5	Right Arm	04	04
Vertical Midline	0 0	Position of Legs	6	6	Variable Line Pressure	0 0	Identity and Sex	5	5	Left Arm	04	04
Bilateral Symmetry	1 3	Relation of Long Axes	1	1	Line Continuity	0 0	Sophistication	5	5	Chest	04	03
Horizontal Midline	0 0	Right and Left Halves	2	1	Body Shading	0 0	Height	05	05	Girth	05	05

GENERAL CHARACTERISTICS OF SUBJECT

IDENTIFICATION	PARENTAL HISTORY
No. G67	Father
Sex M	C H S D O
Marital status S	· - - - -
Age 23 yrs. at	Mother
psychological tests	C H S D O
	- - - - -

PHYSIOLOGICAL AND METABOLIC DATA

	Admission	Initial	Control	Cold pressor change	Exercise change	Smoking change
Systolic pressure	100	116	108	-06	+12	-03
Diastolic pressure	80	74	76	+08	-12	-04
Heart rate	84	64	58	-08	+17	-03

Age 22 yrs.	Height 72 in.	Ponderal index 12.37
	Weight 197 lbs.	Cholesterol 203 mg. per 100 ml.
	Overweight +21 %	Vital capacity liters

HABIT SURVEY

Smoking habits: nonsmoker

Age begun   yrs.   Inhalation:

Habits of nervous tension: 4, 7, 25

STRONG VOCATIONAL INTEREST TEST

Occupation	Artist	Psychologist	Architect	Physician	Osteopath	Dentist	Veterinarian	Mathematician	Physicist	Engineer	Chemist	Production Manager
Standard Score	45	53	43	52	34	36	11	51	52	50	60	27

Occupation	Farmer	Aviator	Carpenter	Printer	Math.-Sci. Teacher	Ind. Arts Teacher	Voc. Agric. Teacher	Policeman	Forest Serv. Man	Y.M.C.A. Phys. Dir.	Personnel Director	Public Administrator
Standard Score	37	45	19	29	35	13	15	20	23	11	26	42

Occupation	Y.M.C.A. Secretary	Soc. Sci. H.S. Teacher	City Sch. Sup't.	Social Worker	Minister	Musician Performer	C.P.A.	Senior C.P.A.	Accountant	Office Man	Purchasing Agent	Banker
Standard Score	08	14	22	30	59	40	45	40	21	21	11	13

Occupation	Mortician	Pharmacist	Sales Manager	Real Est. Manager	Life Ins. Salesman	Advertising Man	Lawyer	Author-Journalist	President Mfg. Co.	Interest Maturity	Occupational Level	Masculinity-Femininity
Standard Score	06	22	19	28	14	34	38	45	35	44	58	51

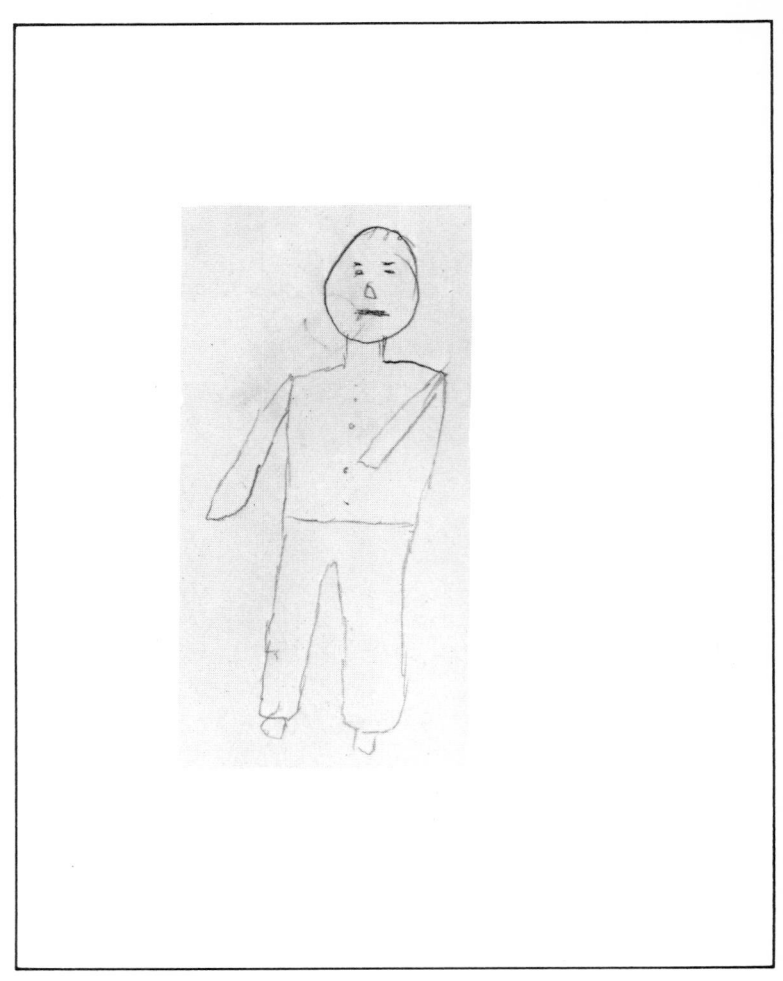

FIGURE-DRAWING CHARACTERISTICS

Structural	Male Female Both	Structural	Male	Female	Structural and Graphic	Male Female Both		Graphic, Global and Height	Male	Female	Body Proportions	Male	Female
Type	0	Omission of Appendages	7	0	Upper and Lower Halves	0	0	Hair Shading	7	7	Head	09	09
Sex Sequence	1	Position of Both Arms	1	0	Four Quarters	4	4	Nudity and Transparency	7	7	Neck	08	10
Posture	1 1	Position of Right Arm	2	2	Relative Size	4		Form	5	5	Shoulders	06	06
Perspective	0 0	Position of Left Arm	5	2	Constant Line Pressure	0	1	Detailing	5	5	Right Arm	04	02
Vertical Midline	3 0	Position of Legs	3	3	Variable Line Pressure	3	0	Identity and Sex	5	5	Left Arm		02
Bilateral Symmetry	3 2	Relation of Long Axes	1	1	Line Continuity	0	0	Sophistication	5	5	Chest	07	07
Horizontal Midline	4 4	Right and Left Halves	1	1	Body Shading	0	0	Height	05	07	Girth	08	07

GENERAL CHARACTERISTICS OF SUBJECT

IDENTIFICATION	PARENTAL HISTORY
No. E55	Father
Sex M	C H S D O
Marital status S	– – – – –
Age 21 yrs. at	Mother
psychological tests	C H S D O
	– – – – –

PHYSIOLOGICAL AND METABOLIC DATA

	Admission	Initial	Control	Cold pressor change	Exercise change	Smoking change
Systolic pressure	120	118	112	+15	+40	
Diastolic pressure	80	70	70	+10	–20	
Heart rate	100	84	76	–08	+24	

Age 20 yrs.	Height	72	in.	Ponderal index	12.90	
	Weight	174	lbs.	Cholesterol	200	mg. per 100 ml.
	Overweight +08 %			Vital capacity	5.0	liters

HABIT SURVEY

Smoking habits: nonsmoker

Age begun   yrs.   Inhalation:

Habits of nervous tension: 4, 5, 18

STRONG VOCATIONAL INTEREST TEST

Occupation	Artist	Psychologist	Architect	Physician	Osteopath	Dentist	Veterinarian	Mathematician	Physicist	Engineer	Chemist	Production Manager
Standard Score	31	63	37	68	46	37	20	35	28	31	46	22

Occupation	Farmer	Aviator	Carpenter	Printer	Math.-Sci. Teacher	Ind. Arts Teacher	Voc. Agric. Teacher	Policeman	Forest Serv. Man	Y.M.C.A. Phys. Dir.	Personnel Director	Public Administrator
Standard Score	27	37	14	43	54	22	28	27	19	41	45	49

Occupation	Y.M.C.A. Secretary	Soc. Sci. H.S. Teacher	City Sch. Sup't.	Social Worker	Minister	Musician Performer	C.P.A.	Senior C.P.A.	Accountant	Office Man	Purchasing Agent	Banker
Standard Score	36	46	44	55	64	63	34	46	22	29	12	11

Occupation	Mortician	Pharmacist	Sales Manager	Real Est. Manager	Life Ins. Salesman	Advertising Man	Lawyer	Author-Journalist	President Mfg. Co.	Interest Maturity	Occupational Level	Masculinity-Femininity
Standard Score	18	32	22	26	25	34	39	36	16	61	54	46

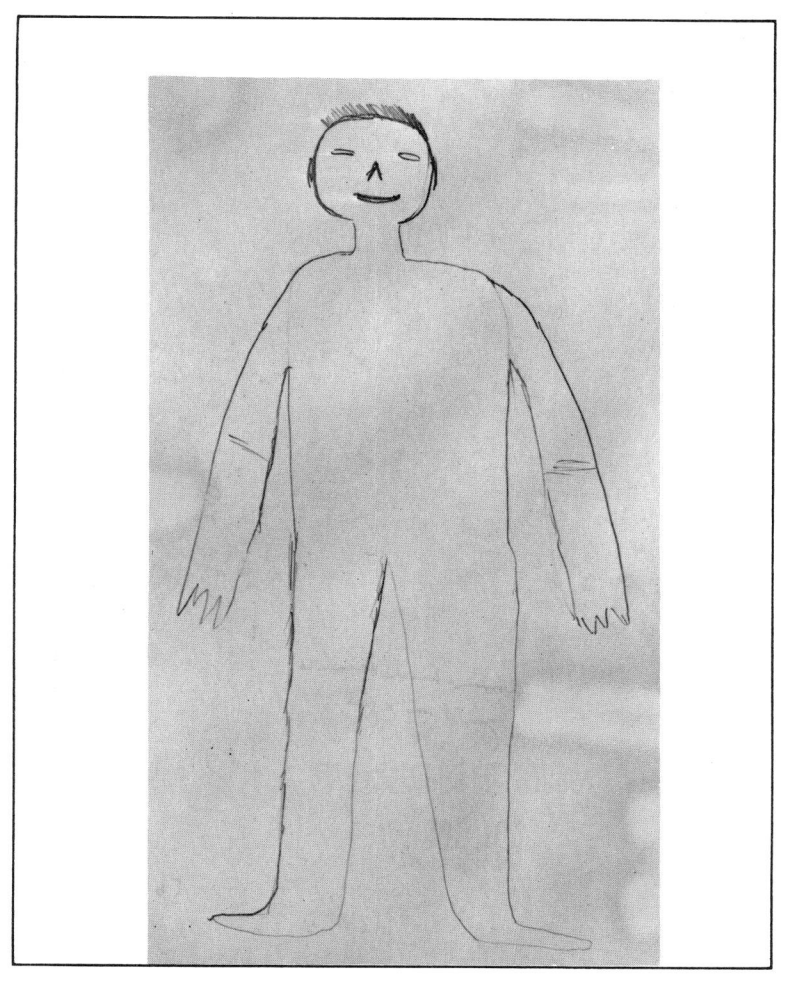

FIGURE-DRAWING CHARACTERISTICS

Structural	Male Female Both		Structural	Male	Female	Structural and Graphic	Male Female Both		Graphic, Global and Height	Male	Female	Body Proportions	Male	Female
Type	0		Omission of Appendages	0	1	Upper and Lower Halves	3	1	Hair Shading	3	3	Head		07
Sex Sequence	0		Position of Both Arms	0	6	Four Quarters	4	4	Nudity and Transparency	0	9	Neck		12
Posture	1	0	Position of Right Arm	2	7	Relative Size	5		Form	5	5	Shoulders	09	
Perspective	0	2	Position of Left Arm	2	7	Constant Line Pressure	0	4	Detailing	5	5	Right Arm	08	
Vertical Midline	0	4	Position of Legs	6	0	Variable Line Pressure	5	0	Identity and Sex	3	3	Left Arm	08	
Bilateral Symmetry	1	0	Relation of Long Axes	1	1	Line Continuity	0	1	Sophistication	5	5	Chest	10	06
Horizontal Midline	0	0	Right and Left Halves	3	1	Body Shading	1	0	Height	09		Girth	13	09

GENERAL CHARACTERISTICS OF SUBJECT

IDENTIFICATION
No. 669
Sex M
Marital status S
Age 26 yrs. at
psychological tests

PARENTAL HISTORY				
Father				
C	H	S	D	O
-	-	-	-	-
Mother				
C	H	S	D	O
U	U	U	U	U

PHYSIOLOGICAL AND METABOLIC DATA

	Admission	Initial	Control	Cold pressor change	Exercise change	Smoking change
Systolic pressure	110	112	100	+20	+22	+10
Diastolic pressure	70	78	70	+18	+12	+02
Heart rate	64	72	65	+16	+10	-04

Age 25 yrs.	Height 72 in.	Ponderal index 12.93	
	Weight 173 lbs.	Cholesterol 203 mg. per 100 ml.
	Overweight +04 %	Vital capacity 5.0 liters

HABIT SURVEY
Smoking habits: nonsmoker
Age begun yrs. Inhalation:
Habits of nervous tension: 5

III. MIXED PRIMITIVE DRAWINGS

In this section, represented by eight subjects, one drawing is most primitive and the other is moderately primitive.

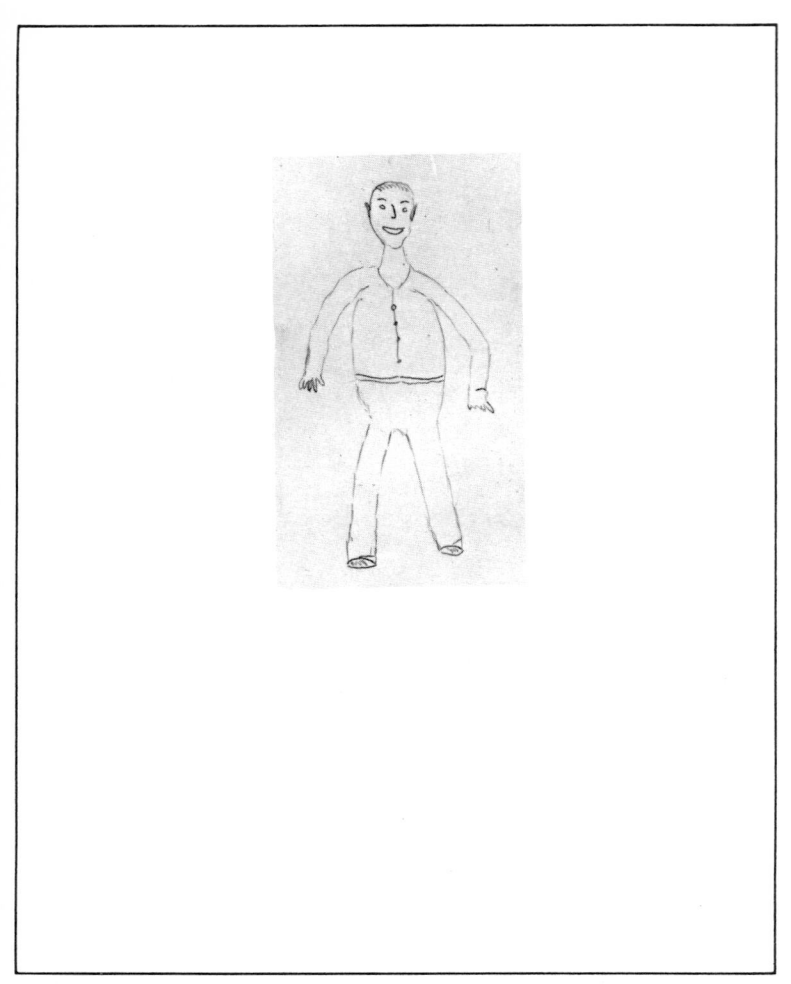

FIGURE-DRAWING CHARACTERISTICS

Structural	Male Female Both		Structural	Male	Female	Structural and Graphic	Male Female Both		Graphic, Global and Height	Male	Female	Body Proportions	Male	Female
Type	0		Omission of Appendages	0	1	Upper and Lower Halves	1	1	Hair Shading	3	3	Head	05	07
Sex Sequence	0		Position of Both Arms	0	6	Four Quarters	4	4	Nudity and Transparency	7	9	Neck	06	02
Posture	1	0	Position of Right Arm	2	8	Relative Size	5		Form	5	5	Shoulders	04	
Perspective	0	0	Position of Left Arm	2	8	Constant Line Pressure	0	0	Detailing	3	5	Right Arm	02	
Vertical Midline	3	3	Position of Legs	6	0	Variable Line Pressure	3	1	Identity and Sex	3	5	Left Arm	04	
Bilateral Symmetry	3	9	Relation of Long Axes	1	1	Line Continuity	0	0	Sophistication	4	5	Chest	03	05
Horizontal Midline	4	0	Right and Left Halves	3	1	Body Shading	0	1	Height	04		Girth	05	

GENERAL CHARACTERISTICS OF SUBJECT

IDENTIFICATION
No. G11
Sex M
Marital status M
Age 23 yrs. at
psychological tests

PARENTAL HISTORY				
Father				
C	H	S	D	O
+	+	–	–	–
Mother				
C	H	S	D	O
–	–	–	–	?

PHYSIOLOGICAL AND METABOLIC DATA

	Admission	Initial	Control	Cold pressor change	Exercise change	Smoking change
Systolic pressure	120	138	122	+28	+36	+05
Diastolic pressure	76	72	70	+26	–02	+06
Heart rate	80	80	70	+32	+16	–01

Age 22 yrs.	Height 75 in.	Ponderal index 13.79
	Weight 161 lbs.	Cholesterol 177 mg. per 100 ml.
	Overweight –10 %	Vital capacity liters

HABIT SURVEY

Smoking habits: nonsmoker

Age begun   yrs.   Inhalation:

Habits of nervous tension: 5, 11, 21

Plate 49   **MIXED PRIMITIVE DRAWINGS**   85

FIGURE-DRAWING CHARACTERISTICS

Structural	Male Female Both	Structural	Male	Female	Structural and Graphic	Male Female Both		Graphic, Global and Height	Male	Female	Body Proportions	Male	Female
Type	0	Omission of Appendages	7	0	Upper and Lower Halves	1	1	Hair Shading	0	3	Head	08	08
Sex Sequence	0	Position of Both Arms	1	2	Four Quarters	4	4	Nudity and Transparency	7	6	Neck	00	04
Posture	1 1	Position of Right Arm	2	4	Relative Size	0		Form	5	5	Shoulders		
Perspective	0 2	Position of Left Arm	5	7	Constant Line Pressure	0	0	Detailing	5	5	Right Arm		04
Vertical Midline	3 4	Position of Legs	6	4	Variable Line Pressure	5	5	Identity and Sex	5	3	Left Arm		
Bilateral Symmetry	3 0	Relation of Long Axes	1	1	Line Continuity	0	0	Sophistication	5	4	Chest	07	07
Horizontal Midline	4 4	Right and Left Halves	1	2	Body Shading	4	2	Height	06	05	Girth	10	09

GENERAL CHARACTERISTICS OF SUBJECT

IDENTIFICATION
No. 343
Sex M
Marital status S
Age 26 yrs. at psychological tests

PARENTAL HISTORY
Father
C H S D O
(?) – – – ?
Mother
C H S D O
– – – – –

PHYSIOLOGICAL AND METABOLIC DATA

	Admission	Initial	Control	Cold pressor change	Exercise change	Smoking change
Systolic pressure	120	142	122	+14	+44	
Diastolic pressure	74	70	72	+12	+04	
Heart rate	72	84	75	+10	+52	

	Height 66 in.	Ponderal index 12.83
Age 24 yrs.	Weight 136 lbs.	Cholesterol 215 mg. per 100 ml.
	Overweight –04 %	Vital capacity 4.4 liters

HABIT SURVEY
Smoking habits: occasional smoker
Age begun 20 yrs.   Inhalation: yes
Habits of nervous tension: 4

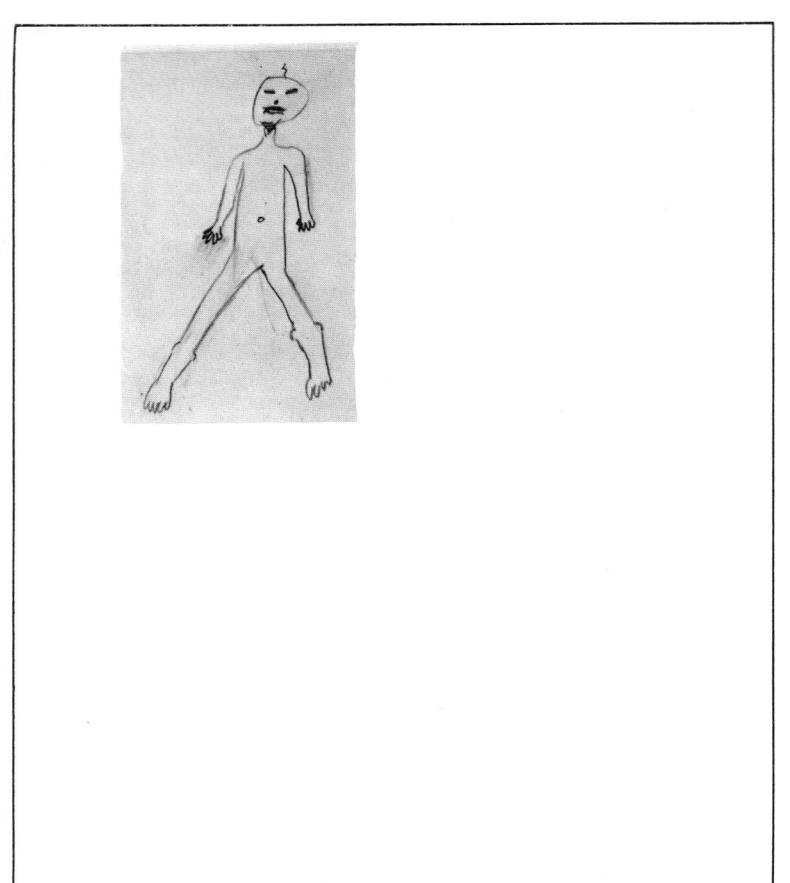

FIGURE-DRAWING CHARACTERISTICS

Structural	Male Female Both	Structural	Male	Female	Structural and Graphic	Male Female Both		Graphic, Global and Height	Male	Female	Body Proportions	Male	Female
Type	0	Omission of Appendages	0	5	Upper and Lower Halves	2	2	Hair Shading	7	7	Head	04	04
Sex Sequence	0	Position of Both Arms	1	6	Four Quarters	0	0	Nudity and Transparency	0	7	Neck	07	08
Posture	1 0	Position of Right Arm	4	7	Relative Size	4		Form	5	5	Shoulders	03	
Perspective	0 2	Position of Left Arm	1	7	Constant Line Pressure	0	3	Detailing	5	5	Right Arm	02	
Vertical Midline	0 4	Position of Legs	6	0	Variable Line Pressure	5	0	Identity and Sex	5	3	Left Arm	02	
Bilateral Symmetry	1 0	Relation of Long Axes	1	1	Line Continuity	3	0	Sophistication	5	4	Chest	02	04
Horizontal Midline	0 0	Right and Left Halves	2	2	Body Shading	0	0	Height	03	04	Girth	03	06

GENERAL CHARACTERISTICS OF SUBJECT

IDENTIFICATION
No. 712
Sex M
Marital status S
Age 22 yrs. at
psychological tests

PARENTAL HISTORY				
Father				
C	H	S	D	O
–	+	–	–	–
Mother				
C	H	S	D	O
–	–	–	–	–

PHYSIOLOGICAL AND METABOLIC DATA

	Admission	Initial	Control	Cold pressor change	Exercise change	Smoking change
Systolic pressure	120	116	114	+16	+48	+05
Diastolic pressure	80	78	74	+16	–10	+10
Heart rate	80	88	82	+04	+21	00

Age 22 yrs.	Height 70 in.	Ponderal index 13.11
	Weight 152 lbs.	Cholesterol 222 mg. per 100 ml.
	Overweight –01 %	Vital capacity 4.1 liters

HABIT SURVEY

Smoking habits: nonsmoker

Age begun   yrs.   Inhalation:

Habits of nervous tension: 4, 5, 6, 22, 25

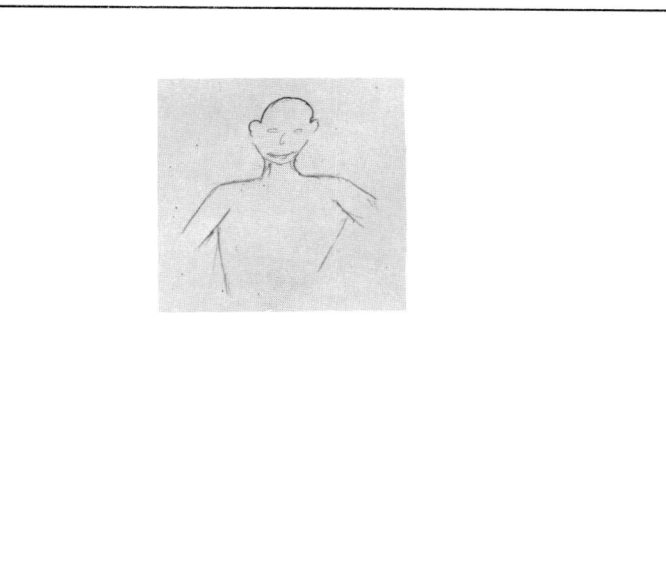

FIGURE-DRAWING CHARACTERISTICS

Structural	Male Female Both	Structural	Male	Female	Structural and Graphic	Male Female Both		Graphic, Global and Height	Male	Female	Body Proportions	Male	Female
Type	0	Omission of Appendages	1	1	Upper and Lower Halves	2	1	Hair Shading	0	3	Head	05	06
Sex Sequence	0	Position of Both Arms	6	6	Four Quarters	4	4	Nudity and Transparency	9	7	Neck	04	05
Posture	0 0	Position of Right Arm	8	8	Relative Size	5		Form	5	3	Shoulders	06	06
Perspective	0 0	Position of Left Arm	8	8	Constant Line Pressure	0	0	Detailing	5	3	Right Arm		
Vertical Midline	0 0	Position of Legs	0	0	Variable Line Pressure	2	1	Identity and Sex	5	3	Left Arm		
Bilateral Symmetry	9 3	Relation of Long Axes	1	1	Line Continuity	0	0	Sophistication	5	4	Chest	06	05
Horizontal Midline	0 4	Right and Left Halves	1	2	Body Shading	0	1	Height		05	Girth		04

GENERAL CHARACTERISTICS OF SUBJECT

IDENTIFICATION
No. G42
Sex M
Marital status M
Age 23 yrs. at
psychological tests

PARENTAL HISTORY				
Father				
C	H	S	D	O
–	+	–	–	–
Mother				
C	H	S	D	O
–	–	–	–	–

PHYSIOLOGICAL AND METABOLIC DATA

	Admission	Initial	Control	Cold pressor change	Exercise change	Smoking change
Systolic pressure	140	118	114	+22	+36	-01
Diastolic pressure	88	68	68	+30	00	+04
Heart rate	102	92	83	+08	+28	+06

Age 23 yrs.	Height	70 in.	Ponderal index 13.01
	Weight	156 lbs.	Cholesterol 224 mg. per 100 ml.
	Overweight +01 %		Vital capacity liters

HABIT SURVEY
Smoking habits: moderate cigarette smoker
Age begun 16 yrs.   Inhalation: yes
Habits of nervous tension: 4, 5, 9, 11

STRONG VOCATIONAL INTEREST TEST

Occupation	Artist	Psychologist	Architect	Physician	Osteopath	Dentist	Veterinarian	Mathematician	Physicist	Engineer	Chemist	Production Manager
Standard Score	38	32	41	57	46	48	38	41	43	44	48	26

Occupation	Farmer	Aviator	Carpenter	Printer	Math.-Sci. Teacher	Ind. Arts Teacher	Voc. Agric. Teacher	Policeman	Forest Serv. Man	Y.M.C.A. Phys. Dir.	Personnel Director	Public Administrator
Standard Score	36	40	23	29	31	10	17	29	27	16	09	26

Occupation	Y.M.C.A. Secretary	Soc. Sci. H.S. Teacher	City Sch. Sup't.	Social Worker	Minister	Musician Performer	C.P.A.	Senior C.P.A.	Accountant	Office Man	Purchasing Agent	Banker
Standard Score	05	12	11	16	59	35	30	34	18	22	21	22

Occupation	Mortician	Pharmacist	Sales Manager	Real Est. Manager	Life Ins. Salesman	Advertising Man	Lawyer	Author-Journalist	President Mfg. Co.	Interest Maturity	Occupational Level	Masculinity-Femininity
Standard Score	24	32	27	36	30	29	38	39	42	45	60	48

FIGURE-DRAWING CHARACTERISTICS

Structural	Male Female Both		Structural	Male	Female	Structural and Graphic	Male Female Both		Graphic, Global and Height	Male	Female	Body Proportions	Male	Female
Type	0		Omission of Appendages	0	0	Upper and Lower Halves	1	0	Hair Shading	3	3	Head	06	08
Sex Sequence	0		Position of Both Arms	0	1	Four Quarters	4	4	Nudity and Transparency	0	0	Neck	08	14
Posture	1	1	Position of Right Arm	2	1	Relative Size	4		Form	5	5	Shoulders	03	09
Perspective	0	0	Position of Left Arm	2	5	Constant Line Pressure	3	3	Detailing	5	5	Right Arm	02	06
Vertical Midline	0	0	Position of Legs	4	6	Variable Line Pressure	0	0	Identity and Sex	5	3	Left Arm		06
Bilateral Symmetry	2	2	Relation of Long Axes	1	1	Line Continuity	0	0	Sophistication	5	4	Chest	04	10
Horizontal Midline	4	0	Right and Left Halves	1	1	Body Shading	0	0	Height	04	07	Girth	05	07

GENERAL CHARACTERISTICS OF SUBJECT

IDENTIFICATION
No. E50
Sex M
Marital status S
Age 22 yrs. at
psychological tests

PARENTAL HISTORY				
Father				
C	H	S	D	O
-	+	-	-	+
Mother				
C	H	S	D	O
-	-	-	-	-

PHYSIOLOGICAL AND METABOLIC DATA

	Admission	Initial	Control	Cold pressor change	Exercise change	Smoking change
Systolic pressure	98	128	118	+12	+12	+02
Diastolic pressure	60	80	72	+14	-22	+03
Heart rate	76	72	62	+04	+09	+06

Age 22 yrs.	Height	72 in.	Ponderal index	12.33	
	Weight	199 lbs.	Cholesterol	240	mg. per 100 ml.
	Overweight +22 %		Vital capacity	5.6	liters

HABIT SURVEY

Smoking habits: nonsmoker

Age begun   yrs.   Inhalation:

Habits of nervous tension: 1, 2, 3, 4, 5, 6, 9, 10, 15, 16, 18, 19, 22, 24

STRONG VOCATIONAL INTEREST TEST

Occupation	Artist	Psychologist	Architect	Physician	Osteopath	Dentist	Veterinarian	Mathematician	Physicist	Engineer	Chemist	Production Manager
Standard Score	22	41	20	47	37	21	18	17	05	11	22	18

Occupation	Farmer	Aviator	Carpenter	Printer	Math.-Sci. Teacher	Ind. Arts Teacher	Voc. Agric. Teacher	Policeman	Forest Serv. Man	Y.M.C.A. Phys. Dir.	Personnel Director	Public Administrator
Standard Score	18	12	-10	24	38	-08	13	20	15	44	44	53

Occupation	Y.M.C.A. Secretary	Soc. Sci. H.S. Teacher	City Sch. Sup't.	Social Worker	Minister	Musician Performer	C.P.A.	Senior C.P.A.	Accountant	Office Man	Purchasing Agent	Banker
Standard Score	47	51	49	52	64	42	40	37	23	32	14	25

Occupation	Mortician	Pharmacist	Sales Manager	Real Est. Manager	Life Ins. Salesman	Advertising Man	Lawyer	Author-Journalist	President Mfg. Co.	Interest Maturity	Occupational Level	Masculinity-Femininity
Standard Score	23	31	33	32	43	39	45	36	29	64	63	36

FIGURE-DRAWING CHARACTERISTICS

Structural	Male	Female	Structural	Male	Female	Structural and Graphic	Male	Female	Graphic, Global and Height	Male	Female	Body Proportions	Male	Female
	Both						Both							
Type	0		Omission of Appendages	7	3	Upper and Lower Halves	1	1	Hair Shading	2	3	Head	05	04
Sex Sequence	0		Position of Both Arms	0	0	Four Quarters	4	4	Nudity and Transparency	7	0	Neck	06	10
Posture	1	0	Position of Right Arm	0	1	Relative Size	5		Form	5	5	Shoulders	06	04
Perspective	5	5	Position of Left Arm	0	1	Constant Line Pressure	0	0	Detailing	3	5	Right Arm		02
Vertical Midline	3	0	Position of Legs	6	6	Variable Line Pressure	2	2	Identity and Sex	1	5	Left Arm		02
Bilateral Symmetry	2	2	Relation of Long Axes	1	1	Line Continuity	1	1	Sophistication	4	5	Chest	06	04
Horizontal Midline	6	0	Right and Left Halves	1	1	Body Shading	0	0	Height	04		Girth	05	03

GENERAL CHARACTERISTICS OF SUBJECT

IDENTIFICATION

No. A35

Sex M

Marital status S

Age 23 yrs. at psychological tests

PARENTAL HISTORY

Father

C   H   S   D   O

–   –   –   –   +

Mother

C   H   S   D   O

–   –   –   –   –

PHYSIOLOGICAL AND METABOLIC DATA

	Admission	Initial	Control	Cold pressor change	Exercise change	Smoking change
Systolic pressure	120	120	105	+05	+33	+15
Diastolic pressure	60	50	56	+14	-16	+18
Heart rate	68	72	64	+10	+13	+09

Age 22 yrs.

Height 70 in.   Ponderal index 13.23

Weight 148 lbs.   Cholesterol 203 mg. per 100 ml.

Overweight -04 %   Vital capacity   liters

HABIT SURVEY

Smoking habits: former smoker

Age begun 18 yrs.   Inhalation: yes

Habits of nervous tension: 5, 8, 11, 16, 22

STRONG VOCATIONAL INTEREST TEST

Occupation	Artist	Psychologist	Architect	Physician	Osteopath	Dentist	Veterinarian	Mathematician	Physicist	Engineer	Chemist	Production Manager
Standard Score	3	6	3	7	6	2	2	2	2	3	4	3

Occupation	Farmer	Aviator	Carpenter	Printer	Math.-Sci. Teacher	Ind. Arts Teacher	Voc. Agric. Teacher	Policeman	Forest Serv. Man	Y.M.C.A. Phys. Dir.	Personnel Director	Public Administrator
Standard Score	6	4	3	5	6	1	3	5	5	6	5	7

Occupation	Y.M.C.A. Secretary	Soc. Sci. H.S. Teacher	City Sch. Sup't.	Social Worker	Minister	Musician Performer	C.P.A.	Senior C.P.A.	Accountant	Office Man	Purchasing Agent	Banker
Standard Score	5	7	5	7	6	6	3	6	2	4	1	2

Occupation	Mortician	Pharmacist	Sales Manager	Real Est. Manager	Life Ins. Salesman	Advertising Man	Lawyer	Author-Journalist	President Mfg. Co.	Interest Maturity	Occupational Level	Masculinity-Femininity
Standard Score	2	3	2	4	3	3	4	4	2	7	4	4

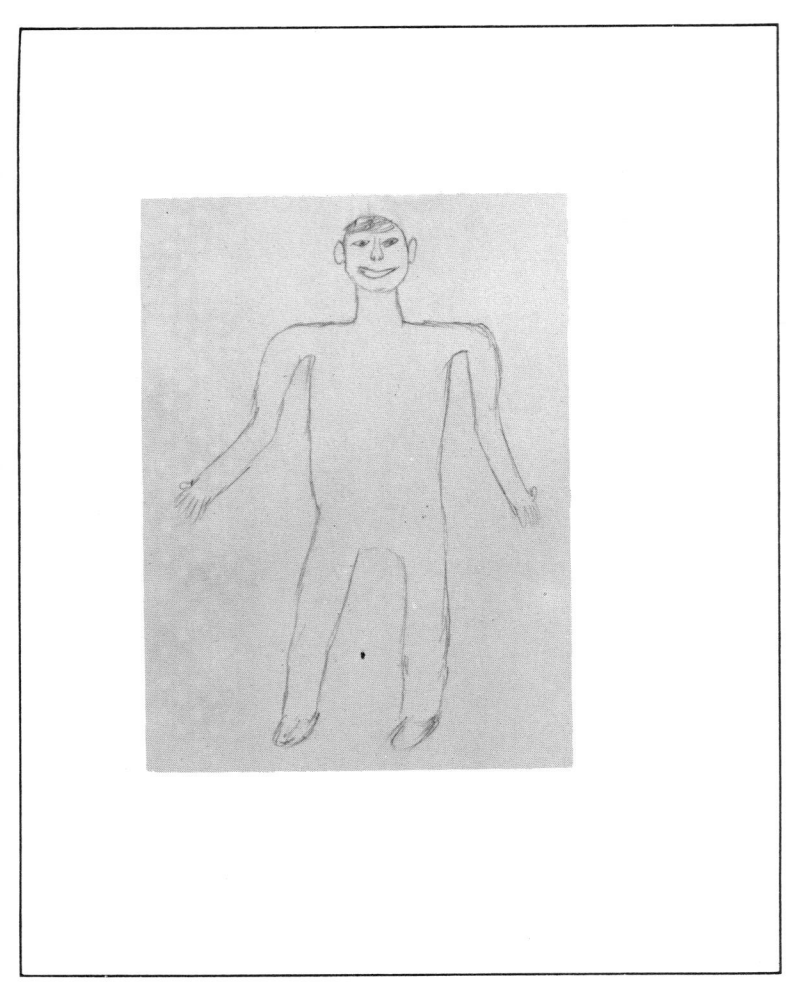

FIGURE-DRAWING CHARACTERISTICS

Structural	Male Female Both	Structural	Male	Female	Structural and Graphic	Male Female Both		Graphic, Global and Height	Male	Female	Body Proportions	Male	Female
Type	0	Omission of Appendages	0	8	Upper and Lower Halves	1	3	Hair Shading	3	3	Head	06	07
Sex Sequence	0	Position of Both Arms	0	0	Four Quarters	4	4	Nudity and Transparency	0	6	Neck	10	14
Posture	1 1	Position of Right Arm	2	2	Relative Size	4		Form	5	5	Shoulders	09	08
Perspective	0 0	Position of Left Arm	2	2	Constant Line Pressure	2	2	Detailing	5	5	Right Arm	04	04
Vertical Midline	0 0	Position of Legs	6	6	Variable Line Pressure	0	0	Identity and Sex	5	3	Left Arm	04	04
Bilateral Symmetry	3 3	Relation of Long Axes	1	1	Line Continuity	0	0	Sophistication	5	4	Chest	07	08
Horizontal Midline	0 0	Right and Left Halves	0	0	Body Shading	0	0	Height	05	07	Girth	08	07

GENERAL CHARACTERISTICS OF SUBJECT

IDENTIFICATION
No. F12
Sex M
Marital status S
Age 21 yrs. at
psychological tests

PARENTAL HISTORY
Father
C   H   S   D   O
–   –   –   –   ?
Mother
C   H   S   D   O
–   –   –   –   –

PHYSIOLOGICAL AND METABOLIC DATA

	Admission	Initial	Control	Cold pressor change	Exercise change	Smoking change
Systolic pressure	100	126	114	+10	+26	+10
Diastolic pressure	60	70	72	+18	+06	00
Heart rate	72	68	87	–08	+01	00

Age 19 yrs.   Height 74 in.   Ponderal index 13.78
Weight 155 lbs.   Cholesterol 254 mg. per 100 ml.
Overweight –09 %   Vital capacity   liters

HABIT SURVEY

Smoking habits: nonsmoker

Age begun   yrs.   Inhalation:

Habits of nervous tension: 1, 4, 6, 25

STRONG VOCATIONAL INTEREST TEST

Occupation	Artist	Psychologist	Architect	Physician	Osteopath	Dentist	Veterinarian	Mathematician	Physicist	Engineer	Chemist	Production Manager
Standard Score	32	36	29	49	41	39	26	32	41	49	44	43

Occupation	Farmer	Aviator	Carpenter	Printer	Math.-Sci. Teacher	Ind. Arts Teacher	Voc. Agric. Teacher	Policeman	Forest Serv. Man	Y.M.C.A. Phys. Dir.	Personnel Director	Public Administrator
Standard Score	35	40	17	23	27	19	24	19	22	14	25	38

Occupation	Y.M.C.A. Secretary	Soc. Sci. H.S. Teacher	City Sch. Sup't.	Social Worker	Minister	Musician Performer	C.P.A.	Senior C.P.A.	Accountant	Office Man	Purchasing Agent	Banker
Standard Score	08	16	14	19	58	24	28	28	12	15	27	16

Occupation	Mortician	Pharmacist	Sales Manager	Real Est. Manager	Life Ins. Salesman	Advertising Man	Lawyer	Author-Journalist	President Mfg. Co.	Interest Maturity	Occupational Level	Masculinity-Femininity
Standard Score	24	21	26	34	22	30	36	35	47	49	65	53

FIGURE-DRAWING CHARACTERISTICS

Structural	Male Female Both	Structural	Male	Female	Structural and Graphic	Male Female Both		Graphic, Global and Height	Male	Female	Body Proportions	Male	Female
Type	0	Omission of Appendages	6	4	Upper and Lower Halves	3	7	Hair Shading	0	3	Head	12	15
Sex Sequence	2	Position of Both Arms	6	0	Four Quarters	4	4	Nudity and Transparency	9	7	Neck		12
Posture	2 0	Position of Right Arm	7	0	Relative Size	4		Form	5	5	Shoulders		09
Perspective	1 0	Position of Left Arm	7	0	Constant Line Pressure	1	1	Detailing	5	5	Right Arm		
Vertical Midline	5 0	Position of Legs	8	0	Variable Line Pressure	0	0	Identity and Sex	5	3	Left Arm		06
Bilateral Symmetry	0 3	Relation of Long Axes	1	1	Line Continuity	0	0	Sophistication	5	4	Chest		08
Horizontal Midline	0 4	Right and Left Halves	1	1	Body Shading	3	3	Height	08		Girth		09

GENERAL CHARACTERISTICS OF SUBJECT

IDENTIFICATION
No. F40
Sex M
Marital status S
Age 24 yrs. at
psychological tests

PARENTAL HISTORY
Father
C H S D O
- - - - -
Mother
C H S D O
- - - - -

PHYSIOLOGICAL AND METABOLIC DATA

	Admission	Initial	Control	Cold pressor change	Exercise change	Smoking change
Systolic pressure	130	102	98	+22	+32	+10
Diastolic pressure	80	72	72	+28	+14	+16
Heart rate	72	76	72	+24	+17	+09

Age 22 yrs.	Height 71 in.	Ponderal index 13.08
	Weight 160 lbs.	Cholesterol 266 mg. per 100 ml.
	Overweight +01 %	Vital capacity liters

HABIT SURVEY

Smoking habits: nonsmoker

Age begun   yrs.   Inhalation:

Habits of nervous tension: 1, 2, 3, 4, 5, 6, 8, 9, 10, 18, 19, 21, 22, 24

STRONG VOCATIONAL INTEREST TEST

Occupation	Artist	Psychologist	Architect	Physician	Osteopath	Dentist	Veterinarian	Mathematician	Physicist	Engineer	Chemist	Production Manager
Standard Score	34	43	44	63	50	44	26	32	36	49	51	36

Occupation	Farmer	Aviator	Carpenter	Printer	Math.-Sci. Teacher	Ind. Arts Teacher	Voc. Agric. Teacher	Policeman	Forest Serv. Man	Y.M.C.A. Phys. Dir.	Personnel Director	Public Administrator
Standard Score	38	52	23	42	44	26	26	30	30	39	35	38

Occupation	Y.M.C.A. Secretary	Soc. Sci. H.S. Teacher	City Sch. Sup't.	Social Worker	Minister	Musician Performer	C.P.A.	Senior C.P.A.	Accountant	Office Man	Purchasing Agent	Banker
Standard Score	23	22	23	33	58	49	39	46	28	26	25	13

Occupation	Mortician	Pharmacist	Sales Manager	Real Est. Manager	Life Ins. Salesman	Advertising Man	Lawyer	Author-Journalist	President Mfg. Co.	Interest Maturity	Occupational Level	Masculinity-Femininity
Standard Score	17	32	28	31	25	33	37	34	38	56	57	54

IV. MODERATELY PRIMITIVE DRAWINGS

In this section, the drawings by ninety-four subjects are a little less primitive. Although features of differentiation through form, identity, or detailing are still largely lacking, these drawings show slightly more complexity in some respect.

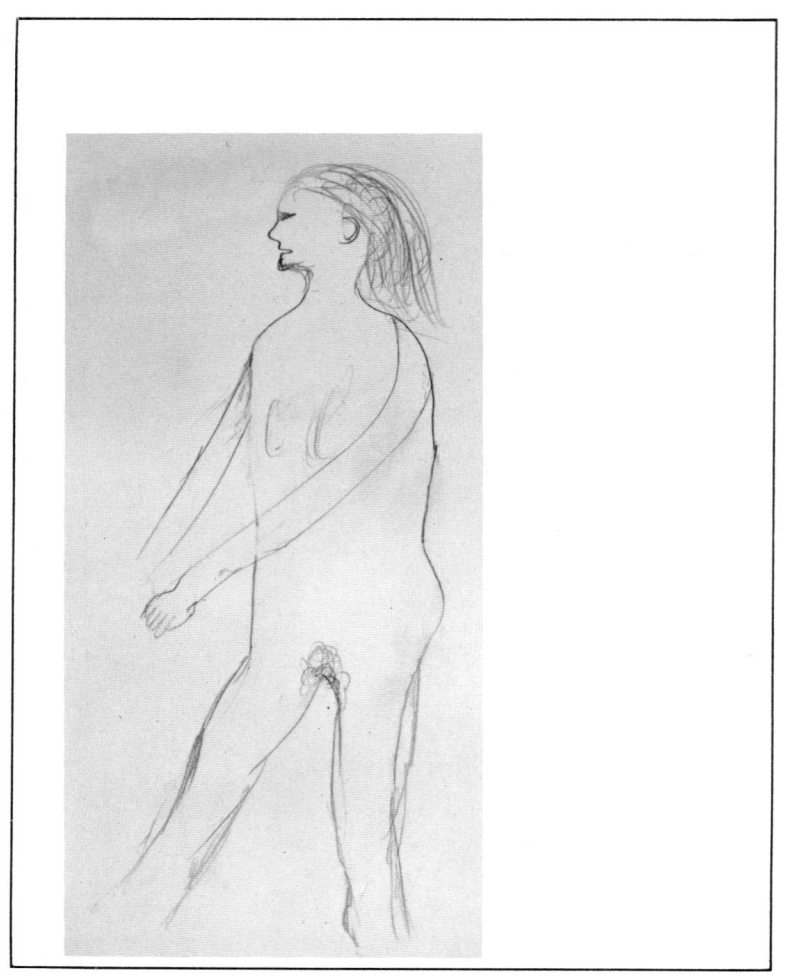
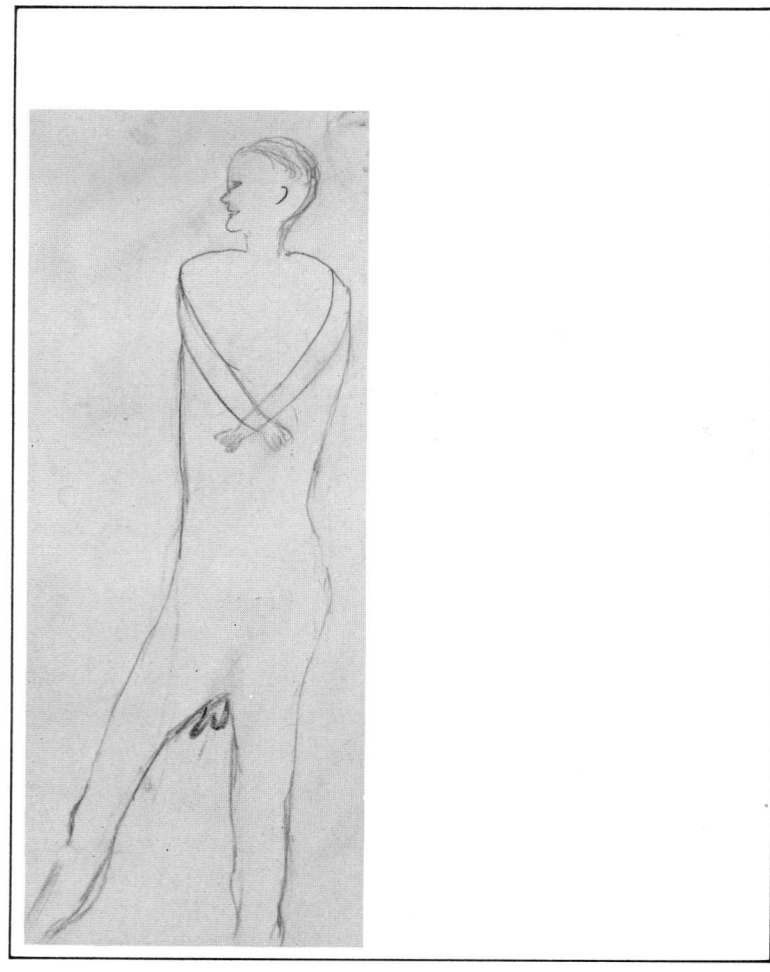

FIGURE-DRAWING CHARACTERISTICS

Structural	Male	Female	Structural	Male	Female	Structural and Graphic	Male	Female	Graphic, Global and Height	Male	Female	Body Proportions	Male	Female
	Both						Both							
Type	0		Omission of Appendages	3	4	Upper and Lower Halves	7	7	Hair Shading	3	3	Head	07	08
Sex Sequence	1		Position of Both Arms	0	0	Four Quarters	4	4	Nudity and Transparency	0	0	Neck	06	10
Posture	0	0	Position of Right Arm	5	2	Relative Size	5		Form	5	5	Shoulders	07	
Perspective	5	6	Position of Left Arm	5	2	Constant Line Pressure	0	0	Detailing	3	3	Right Arm	04	
Vertical Midline	0	4	Position of Legs	6	6	Variable Line Pressure	3	3	Identity and Sex	3	3	Left Arm	04	10
Bilateral Symmetry	1	0	Relation of Long Axes	1	1	Line Continuity	1	1	Sophistication	4	4	Chest	08	
Horizontal Midline	0	0	Right and Left Halves	2	1	Body Shading	2	3	Height			Girth	08	

GENERAL CHARACTERISTICS OF SUBJECT

IDENTIFICATION		PARENTAL HISTORY	
No. D48		Father	
Sex M		C H S D 0	
Marital status S		+ - - - -	
Age 21 yrs. at		Mother	
psychological tests		C H S D 0	
		+ - - - -	

PHYSIOLOGICAL AND METABOLIC DATA

	Admission	Initial	Control	Cold pressor change	Exercise change	Smoking change
Systolic pressure	145	148	118	+12	+76	+05
Diastolic pressure	90	78	78	+14	-10	00
Heart rate	100	72	65	+04	+02	00

Age 21 yrs.	Height	71	in.	Ponderal index	12.66	
	Weight	177	lbs.	Cholesterol	252	mg. per 100 ml.
	Overweight +09 %			Vital capacity	5.9	liters

HABIT SURVEY

Smoking habits: nonsmoker

Age begun   yrs.   Inhalation:

Habits of nervous tension: 6, 9

STRONG VOCATIONAL INTEREST TEST

Occupation	Artist	Psychologist	Architect	Physician	Osteopath	Dentist	Veterinarian	Mathematician	Physicist	Engineer	Chemist	Production Manager
Standard Score	43	39	47	58	52	48	41	36	42	42	48	25

Occupation	Farmer	Aviator	Carpenter	Printer	Math.-Sci. Teacher	Ind. Arts Teacher	Voc. Agric. Teacher	Policeman	Forest Serv. Man	Y.M.C.A. Phys. Dir.	Personnel Director	Public Administrator
Standard Score	42	37	28	29	40	24	28	29	38	35	18	30

Occupation	Y.M.C.A. Secretary	Soc. Sci. H.S. Teacher	City Sch. Sup't.	Social Worker	Minister	Musician Performer	C.P.A.	Senior C.P.A.	Accountant	Office Man	Purchasing Agent	Banker
Standard Score	17	17	19	27	63	50	18	27	08	18	09	13

Occupation	Mortician	Pharmacist	Sales Manager	Real Est. Manager	Life Ins. Salesman	Advertising Man	Lawyer	Author-Journalist	President Mfg. Co.	Interest Maturity	Occupational Level	Masculinity-Femininity
Standard Score	18	29	20	31	21	32	27	38	33	50	56	41

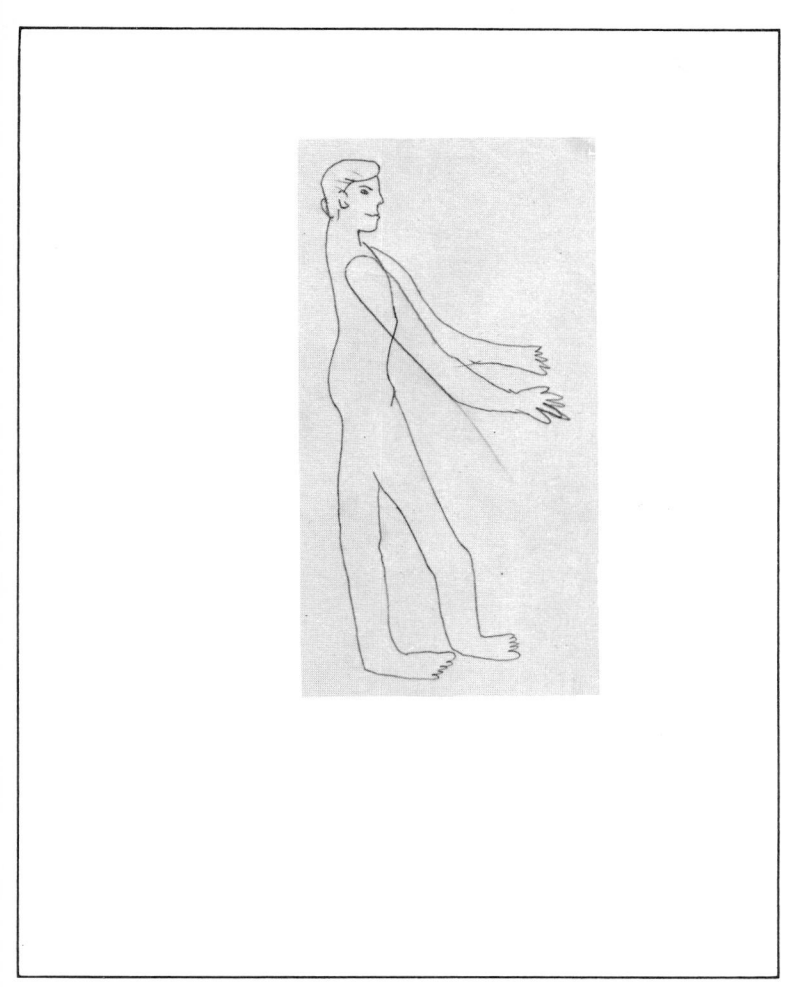

FIGURE-DRAWING CHARACTERISTICS

Structural	Male Female Both		Structural	Male	Female	Structural and Graphic	Male Female Both		Graphic, Global and Height	Male	Female	Body Proportions	Male	Female
Type	0		Omission of Appendages	0	3	Upper and Lower Halves	1	7	Hair Shading	5	3	Head	05	14
Sex Sequence	0		Position of Both Arms	2	2	Four Quarters	4	4	Nudity and Transparency	0	0	Neck	04	10
Posture	1	0	Position of Right Arm	2	4	Relative Size	4		Form	5	5	Shoulders		
Perspective	2	2	Position of Left Arm	7	7	Constant Line Pressure	0	5	Detailing	5	5	Right Arm	06	07
Vertical Midline	4	4	Position of Legs	5	6	Variable Line Pressure	5	0	Identity and Sex	3	1	Left Arm		
Bilateral Symmetry	0	0	Relation of Long Axes	1	1	Line Continuity	3	2	Sophistication	4	4	Chest	04	08
Horizontal Midline	0	0	Right and Left Halves	1	1	Body Shading	0	0	Height	05		Girth	04	10

GENERAL CHARACTERISTICS OF SUBJECT

IDENTIFICATION
No. 624
Sex M
Marital status S
Age 22 yrs. at
psychological tests

PARENTAL HISTORY

Father

C	H	S	D	O
?	-	-	-	+

Mother

C	H	S	D	O
+	?	-	+	+

PHYSIOLOGICAL AND METABOLIC DATA

	Admission	Initial	Control	Cold pressor change	Exercise change	Smoking change
Systolic pressure	140	116	100	+30	00	-03
Diastolic pressure	92	82	74	+34	-02	+02
Heart rate	80	56	48	+20	+38	+01

Age 21 yrs.	Height 74 in.	Ponderal index 12.61
	Weight 202 lbs.	Cholesterol 250 mg. per 100 ml.
	Overweight +17 %	Vital capacity 6.2 liters

HABIT SURVEY

Smoking habits: mixed smoker

Age begun 13 yrs.   Inhalation: sometimes

Habits of nervous tension: 4, 5, 6, 9, 16, 22, 25

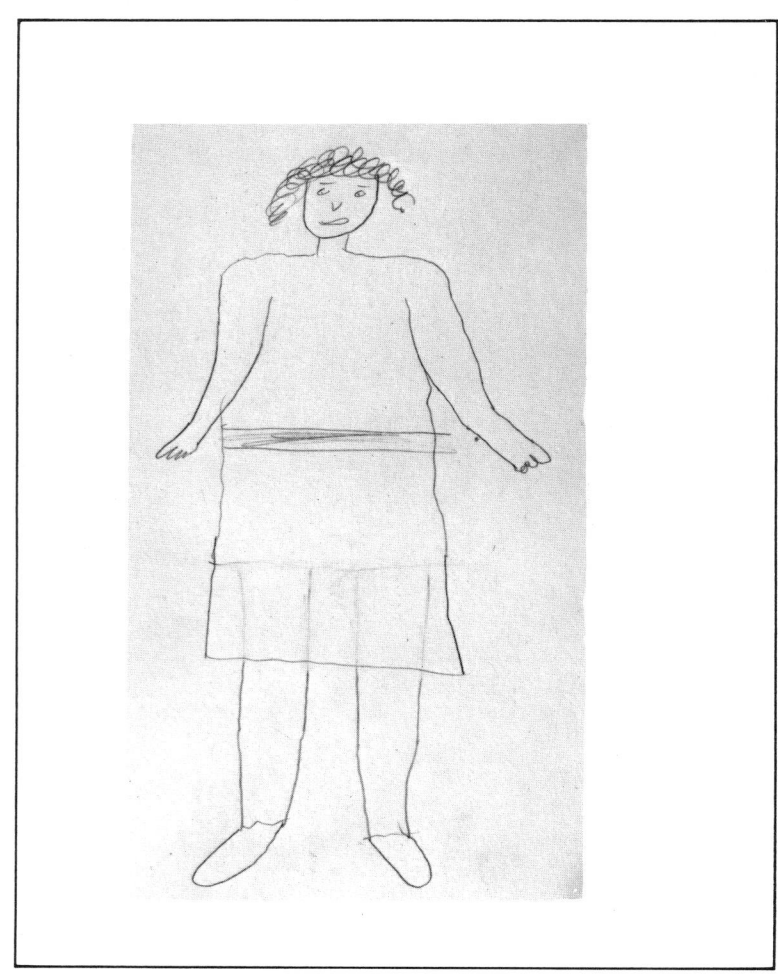

FIGURE-DRAWING CHARACTERISTICS

Structural	Male Female Both	Structural	Male	Female	Structural and Graphic	Male	Female Both	Graphic, Global and Height	Male	Female	Body Proportions	Male	Female
Type	0	Omission of Appendages	3	0	Upper and Lower Halves	7	0	Hair Shading	0	3	Head	07	06
Sex Sequence	0	Position of Both Arms	1	0	Four Quarters	4	4	Nudity and Transparency	7	3	Neck	06	06
Posture	0 1	Position of Right Arm	0	4	Relative Size	0		Form	5	5	Shoulders	14	09
Perspective	0 0	Position of Left Arm	2	4	Constant Line Pressure	3	0	Detailing	5	5	Right Arm	10	04
Vertical Midline	3 0	Position of Legs	6	6	Variable Line Pressure	0	1	Identity and Sex	5	5	Left Arm	10	06
Bilateral Symmetry	1 2	Relation of Long Axes	1	1	Line Continuity	3	2	Sophistication	4	4	Chest	17	08
Horizontal Midline	4 4	Right and Left Halves	1	1	Body Shading	0	4	Height		07	Girth	20	14

GENERAL CHARACTERISTICS OF SUBJECT

IDENTIFICATION
No. 455
Sex M
Marital status M
Age 27 yrs. at
psychological tests

PARENTAL HISTORY
Father
C   H   S   D   O
(+)   −   −   −   ?
Mother
C   H   S   D   O
?   +   −   −   −

PHYSIOLOGICAL AND METABOLIC DATA

	Admission	Initial	Control	Cold pressor change	Exercise change	Smoking change
Systolic pressure	128	126	122	+32	+30	
Diastolic pressure	80	76	76	+20	−04	
Heart rate	84	90	77	+08	+30	

Age 24 yrs.	Height	71 in.	Ponderal index 12.87
	Weight	168 lbs.	Cholesterol 250 mg. per 100 ml.
	Overweight +05 %		Vital capacity 4.3 liters

HABIT SURVEY
Smoking habits: heavy cigarette smoker
Age begun 17 yrs.   Inhalation: yes
Habits of nervous tension: 3, 4, 5, 6, 11,
16, 18, 21

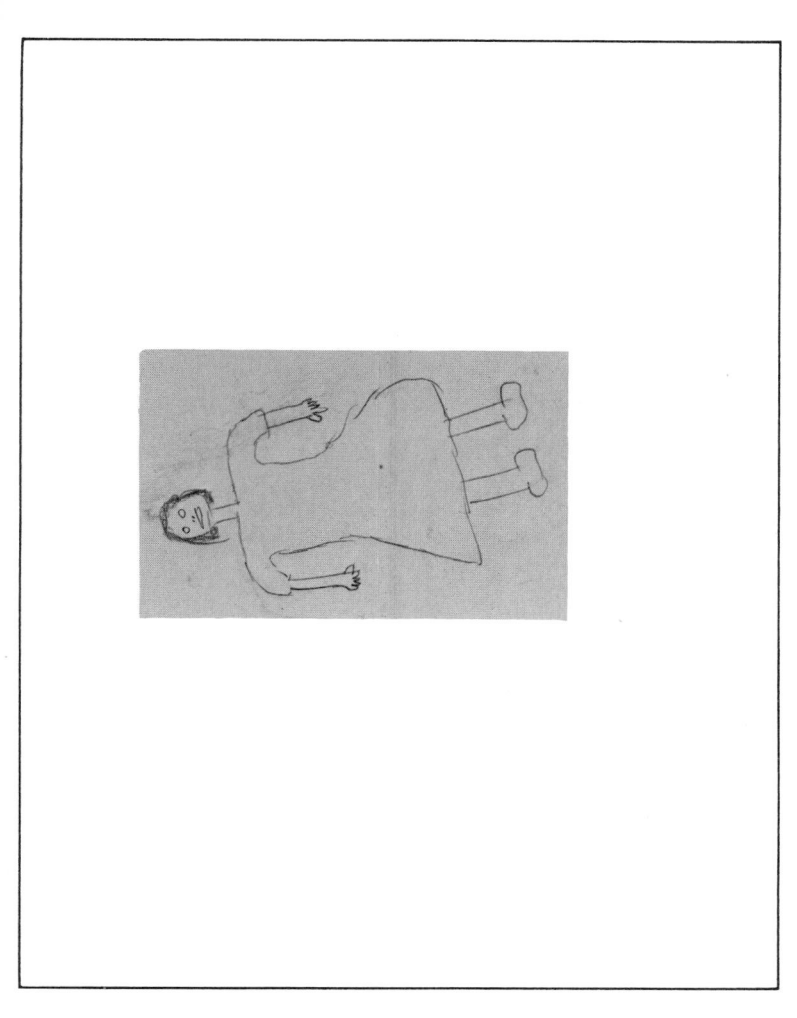

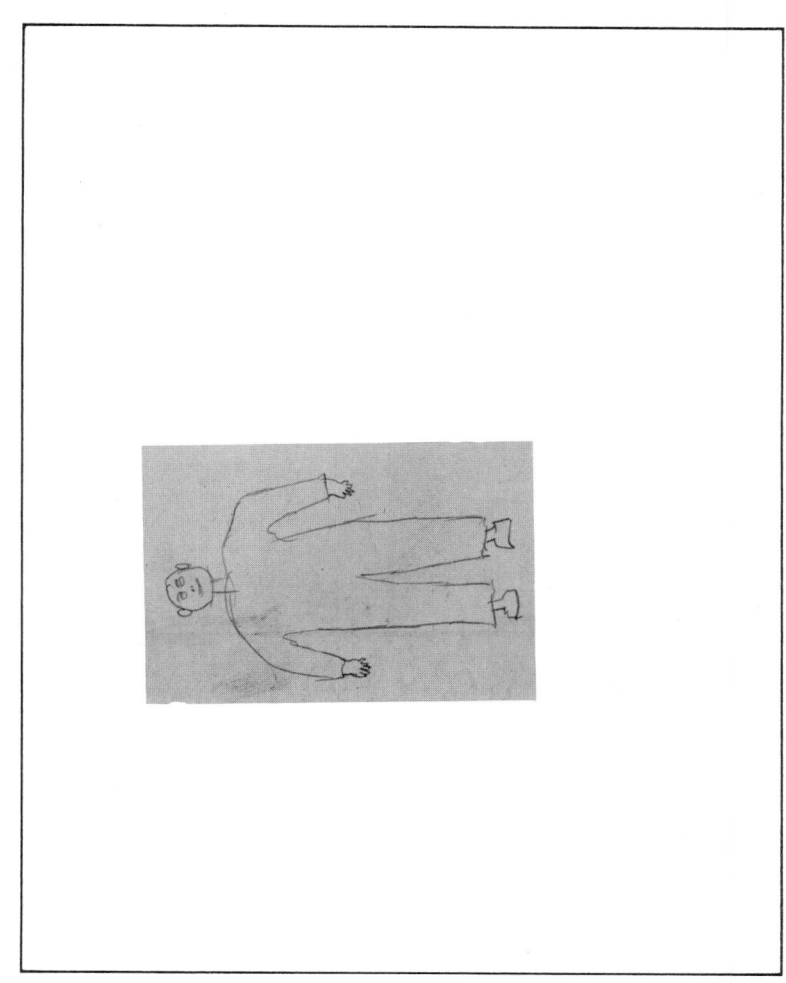

FIGURE-DRAWING CHARACTERISTICS

Structural	Male Female Both		Structural	Male	Female	Structural and Graphic	Male Female Both		Graphic, Global and Height	Male	Female	Body Proportions	Male	Female
Type	0		Omission of Appendages	0	0	Upper and Lower Halves	1	1	Hair Shading	0	3	Head	04	04
Sex Sequence	1		Position of Both Arms	0	0	Four Quarters	4	4	Nudity and Transparency	7	7	Neck	06	08
Posture	1	1	Position of Right Arm	2	1	Relative Size	4		Form	5	5	Shoulders	05	
Perspective	0	0	Position of Left Arm	2	1	Constant Line Pressure	3	3	Detailing	5	5	Right Arm	02	02
Vertical Midline	0	0	Position of Legs	6	5	Variable Line Pressure	0	0	Identity and Sex	5	5	Left Arm	02	02
Bilateral Symmetry	3	3	Relation of Long Axes	2	3	Line Continuity	0	0	Sophistication	4	4	Chest	05	05
Horizontal Midline	0	0	Right and Left Halves	2	3	Body Shading	0	0	Height	03	04	Girth	07	06

GENERAL CHARACTERISTICS OF SUBJECT

IDENTIFICATION
No. 208
Sex M
Marital status S
Age 25 yrs. at psychological tests

PARENTAL HISTORY				
Father				
C	H	S	D	O
+	-	-	-	-
Mother				
C	H	S	D	O
-	+	-	-	+

PHYSIOLOGICAL AND METABOLIC DATA

	Admission	Initial	Control	Cold pressor change	Exercise change	Smoking change
Systolic pressure	158	126	128	+14	+30	
Diastolic pressure	74	72	72	+10	+01	
Heart rate	92	96	83	+02	+11	

Age 23 yrs.	Height 77 in.	Ponderal index 13.74
	Weight 176 lbs.	Cholesterol 267 mg. per 100 ml.
	Overweight −07 %	Vital capacity 5.3 liters

HABIT SURVEY

Smoking habits: heavy cigarette smoker

Age begun 16 yrs.   Inhalation: yes

Habits of nervous tension: 5, 6, 9

FIGURE-DRAWING CHARACTERISTICS

Structural	Male Female Both	Structural	Male	Female	Structural and Graphic	Male Female Both		Graphic, Global and Height	Male	Female	Body Proportions	Male	Female
Type	0	Omission of Appendages	3	3	Upper and Lower Halves	7	7	Hair Shading	1	1	Head	13	13
Sex Sequence	2	Position of Both Arms	0	0	Four Quarters	4	4	Nudity and Transparency	7	7	Neck	18	18
Posture	0 0	Position of Right Arm	0	0	Relative Size	5		Form	3	3	Shoulders	10	11
Perspective	0 0	Position of Left Arm	0	0	Constant Line Pressure	1	1	Detailing	3	3	Right Arm	10	08
Vertical Midline	0 0	Position of Legs	0	0	Variable Line Pressure	0	0	Identity and Sex	3	3	Left Arm	10	06
Bilateral Symmetry	3 3	Relation of Long Axes	1	1	Line Continuity	0	0	Sophistication	4	4	Chest	06	07
Horizontal Midline	4 0	Right and Left Halves	1	1	Body Shading	0	0	Height			Girth	08	08

GENERAL CHARACTERISTICS OF SUBJECT

IDENTIFICATION
No. 246
Sex F
Marital status S
Age 25 yrs. at
psychological tests

PARENTAL HISTORY				
Father				
C	H	S	D	O
+	+	+	−	?
Mother				
C	H	S	D	O
−	−	−	−	−

PHYSIOLOGICAL AND METABOLIC DATA

	Admission	Initial	Control	Cold pressor change	Exercise change	Smoking change
Systolic pressure	94	108	96	+12	+42	
Diastolic pressure	64	66	60	+22	+04	
Heart rate	76	88	88	+20	+27	

	Height	63 in.	Ponderal index	12.28
Age 27 yrs.	Weight	135 lbs.	Cholesterol	223 mg. per 100 ml.
	Overweight +08 %		Vital capacity	3.2 liters

HABIT SURVEY

Smoking habits: heavy cigarette smoker

    Age begun 19 yrs.   Inhalation: yes

Habits of nervous tension: 1, 3, 4, 5, 9, 10, 14, 16, 18, 23

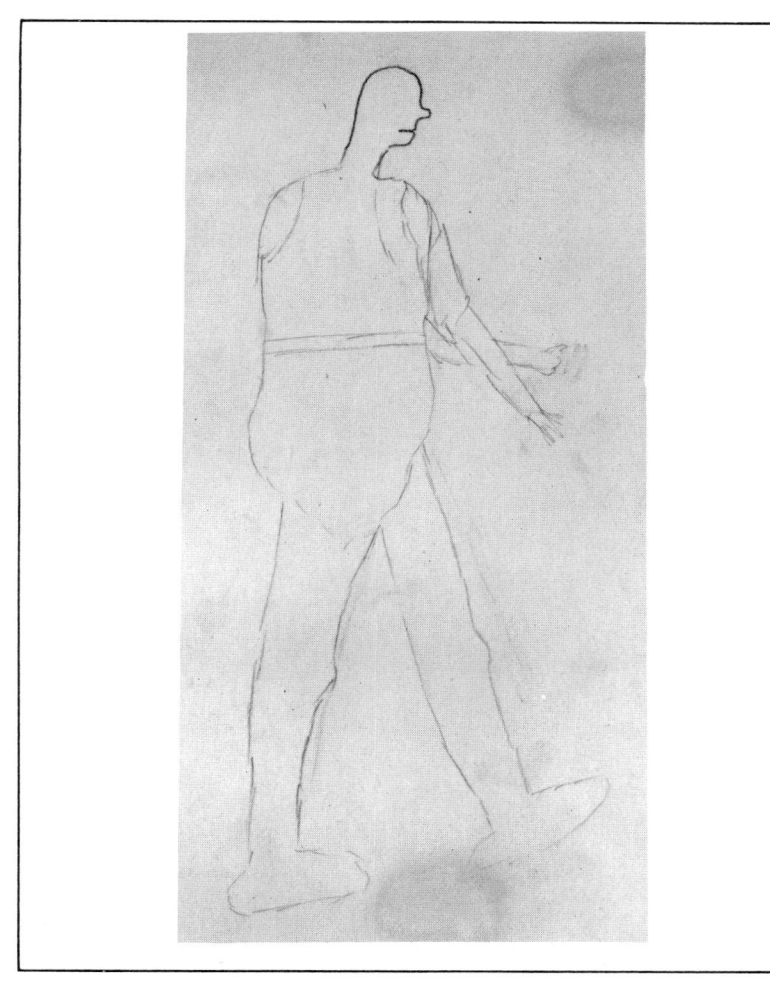

FIGURE-DRAWING CHARACTERISTICS

Structural	Male Female Both	Structural	Male	Female	Structural and Graphic	Male Female Both		Graphic, Global and Height	Male	Female	Body Proportions	Male	Female
Type	0	Omission of Appendages	0	3	Upper and Lower Halves	0	7	Hair Shading	0	3	Head	06	09
Sex Sequence	2	Position of Both Arms	9	0	Four Quarters	4	4	Nudity and Transparency	9	7	Neck	10	18
Posture	2 0	Position of Right Arm	9	5	Relative Size	5		Form	5	3	Shoulders		07
Perspective	9 0	Position of Left Arm	9	5	Constant Line Pressure	1	1	Detailing	5	3	Right Arm		10
Vertical Midline	9 3	Position of Legs	8	0	Variable Line Pressure	0	0	Identity and Sex	3	3	Left Arm		10
Bilateral Symmetry	9 3	Relation of Long Axes	1	3	Line Continuity	0	0	Sophistication	4	4	Chest		09
Horizontal Midline	4 4	Right and Left Halves	1	3	Body Shading	0	3	Height	09		Girth		10

GENERAL CHARACTERISTICS OF SUBJECT

IDENTIFICATION
No.   269
Sex   M
Marital status   S
Age   23 yrs. at psychological tests

PARENTAL HISTORY				
Father				
C	H	S	D	O
+	-	-	-	+
Mother				
C	H	S	D	O
-	-	-	-	-

PHYSIOLOGICAL AND METABOLIC DATA

	Admission	Initial	Control	Cold pressor change	Exercise change	Smoking change
Systolic pressure	112	124	95	+18	+25	
Diastolic pressure	60	72	65	+16	-05	
Heart rate	80	94	71	+08	+23	

Age 21 yrs.	Height	70 in.		Ponderal index	12.54	
	Weight	174 lbs.		Cholesterol	250 mg. per 100 ml.
	Overweight +14 %			Vital capacity	liters

HABIT SURVEY
Smoking habits: nonsmoker
Age begun   yrs.   Inhalation:
Habits of nervous tension: 5, 7, 11, 18, 21

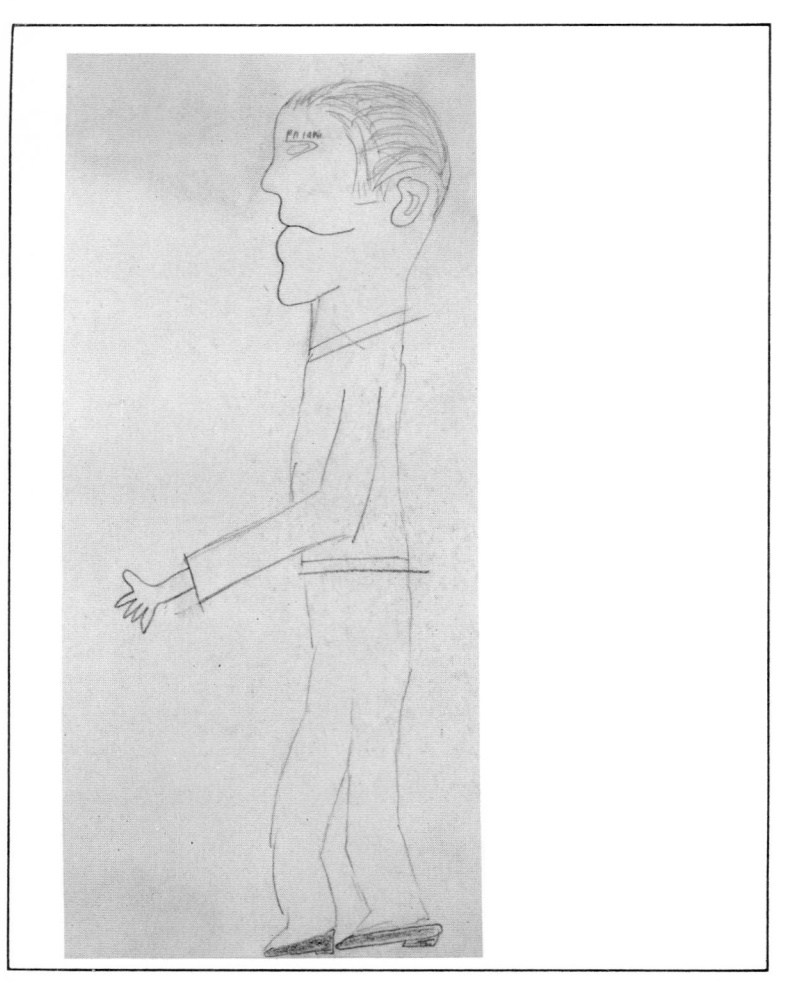

FIGURE-DRAWING CHARACTERISTICS

Structural	Male Female Both	Structural	Male	Female	Structural and Graphic	Male Female Both		Graphic, Global and Height	Male	Female	Body Proportions	Male	Female
Type	0	Omission of Appendages	0	1	Upper and Lower Halves	3	7	Hair Shading	1	3	Head	17	19
Sex Sequence	2	Position of Both Arms	4	6	Four Quarters	4	4	Nudity and Transparency	7	6	Neck	12	18
Posture	2 0	Position of Right Arm	7	7	Relative Size	4		Form	5	5	Shoulders		
Perspective	2 2	Position of Left Arm	4	7	Constant Line Pressure	0	0	Detailing	5	5	Right Arm		
Vertical Midline	4 4	Position of Legs	8	0	Variable Line Pressure	3	3	Identity and Sex	1	1	Left Arm	10	
Bilateral Symmetry	0 0	Relation of Long Axes	1	1	Line Continuity	0	0	Sophistication	4	4	Chest	07	11
Horizontal Midline	4 0	Right and Left Halves	1	3	Body Shading	4	3	Height	09		Girth	08	10

GENERAL CHARACTERISTICS OF SUBJECT

IDENTIFICATION
No. 331
Sex M
Marital status S
Age 22 yrs. at
psychological tests

PARENTAL HISTORY				
Father				
C	H	S	D	O
+	?	+	+	?
Mother				
C	H	S	D	O
−	−	−	−	−

PHYSIOLOGICAL AND METABOLIC DATA

	Admission	Initial	Control	Cold pressor change	Exercise change	Smoking change
Systolic pressure	150	126	118	+10	+38	
Diastolic pressure	90	72	74	+16	−02	
Heart rate	76	66	58	+02	+11	

Age 20 yrs.	Height 73 in.	Ponderal index 13.00
	Weight 177 lbs.	Cholesterol 235 mg. per 100 ml.
	Overweight +07 %	Vital capacity 5.0 liters

Plate 63   **MODERATELY PRIMITIVE DRAWINGS**   101

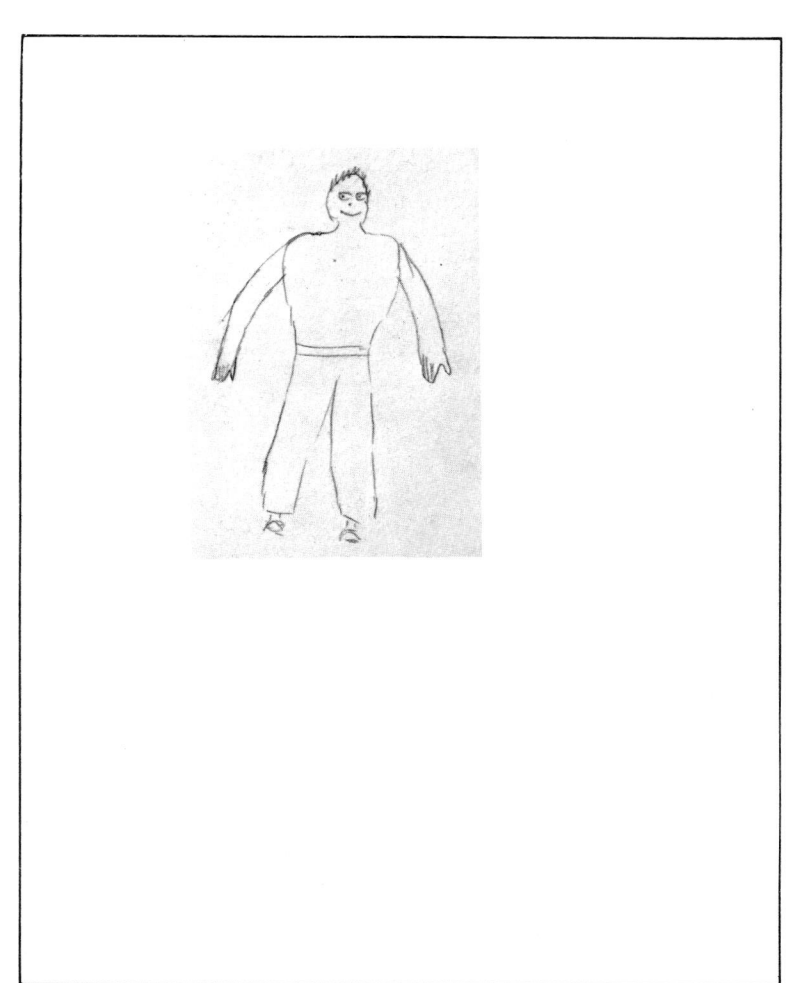

FIGURE-DRAWING CHARACTERISTICS

Structural	Male Female Both		Structural	Male	Female	Structural and Graphic	Male Female Both		Graphic, Global and Height	Male	Female	Body Proportions	Male	Female
Type	0		Omission of Appendages	0	0	Upper and Lower Halves	1	1	Hair Shading	7	5	Head		
Sex Sequence	0		Position of Both Arms	0	0	Four Quarters	4	4	Nudity and Transparency	3	7	Neck		
Posture	1	1	Position of Right Arm	2	2	Relative Size	0		Form	5	5	Shoulders	04	03
Perspective	0	0	Position of Left Arm	2	2	Constant Line Pressure	0	0	Detailing	5	5	Right Arm	04	02
Vertical Midline	0	0	Position of Legs	6	6	Variable Line Pressure	1	1	Identity and Sex	3	5	Left Arm	02	02
Bilateral Symmetry	3	3	Relation of Long Axes	1	1	Line Continuity	0	2	Sophistication	4	4	Chest	05	04
Horizontal Midline	4	0	Right and Left Halves	1	2	Body Shading	0	0	Height	03	03	Girth	04	05

GENERAL CHARACTERISTICS OF SUBJECT

IDENTIFICATION
No. 358
Sex M
Marital status M
Age 25 yrs. at
psychological tests

PARENTAL HISTORY				
Father				
C	H	S	D	O
+	-	-	-	+
Mother				
C	H	S	D	O
-	-	-	-	-

PHYSIOLOGICAL AND METABOLIC DATA

	Admission	Initial	Control	Cold pressor change	Exercise change	Smoking change
Systolic pressure	130	126	108	+18	+46	
Diastolic pressure	80	74	74	+04	+02	
Heart rate	80	90	86	-08	+19	

Age 23 yrs.	Height	67	in.	Ponderal index 12.17
	Weight	167	lbs.	Cholesterol 250 mg. per 100 ml.
	Overweight +17 %			Vital capacity 4.0 liters

HABIT SURVEY
Smoking habits: nonsmoker
Age begun   yrs.   Inhalation:
Habits of nervous tension: 4, 5, 18, 21

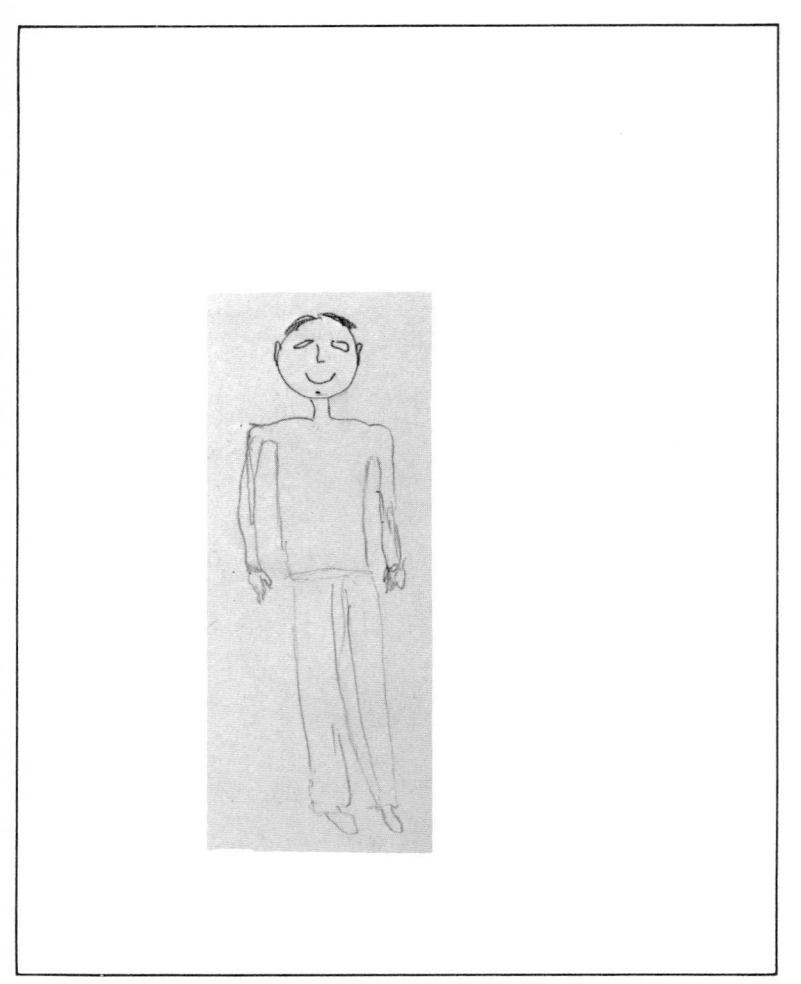

FIGURE-DRAWING CHARACTERISTICS

Structural	Male Female Both	Structural	Male	Female	Structural and Graphic	Male Female Both		Graphic, Global and Height	Male	Female	Body Proportions	Male	Female
Type	0	Omission of Appendages	0	0	Upper and Lower Halves	3	3	Hair Shading	3	3	Head	07	06
Sex Sequence	0	Position of Both Arms	0	0	Four Quarters	4	4	Nudity and Transparency	9	9	Neck	06	08
Posture	1 1	Position of Right Arm	0	0	Relative Size	0		Form	5	5	Shoulders	05	05
Perspective	0 0	Position of Left Arm	0	0	Constant Line Pressure	0	0	Detailing	5	5	Right Arm	04	02
Vertical Midline	0 0	Position of Legs	4	4	Variable Line Pressure	1	1	Identity and Sex	5	5	Left Arm	04	02
Bilateral Symmetry	3 3	Relation of Long Axes	1	1	Line Continuity	0	2	Sophistication	4	4	Chest	04	05
Horizontal Midline	4 4	Right and Left Halves	2	2	Body Shading	0	0	Height	05	05	Girth	05	06

GENERAL CHARACTERISTICS OF SUBJECT

IDENTIFICATION
No. 454
Sex M
Marital status S
Age 27 yrs. at
psychological tests

PARENTAL HISTORY				
Father				
C	H	S	D	O
+	-	-	-	-
Mother				
C	H	S	D	O
-	-	-	-	-

PHYSIOLOGICAL AND METABOLIC DATA

	Admission	Initial	Control	Cold pressor change	Exercise change	Smoking change
Systolic pressure	130	122	108	+20	+32	
Diastolic pressure	70	64	62	+16	+18	
Heart rate	84	72	71	+04	+15	

Age 25 yrs.	Height	77 in.	Ponderal index	13.30	
	Weight	194 lbs.	Cholesterol	210	mg. per 100 ml.
	Overweight	00 %	Vital capacity	5.2	liters

HABIT SURVEY
Smoking habits: unknown
Age begun   yrs.   Inhalation:
Habits of nervous tension:

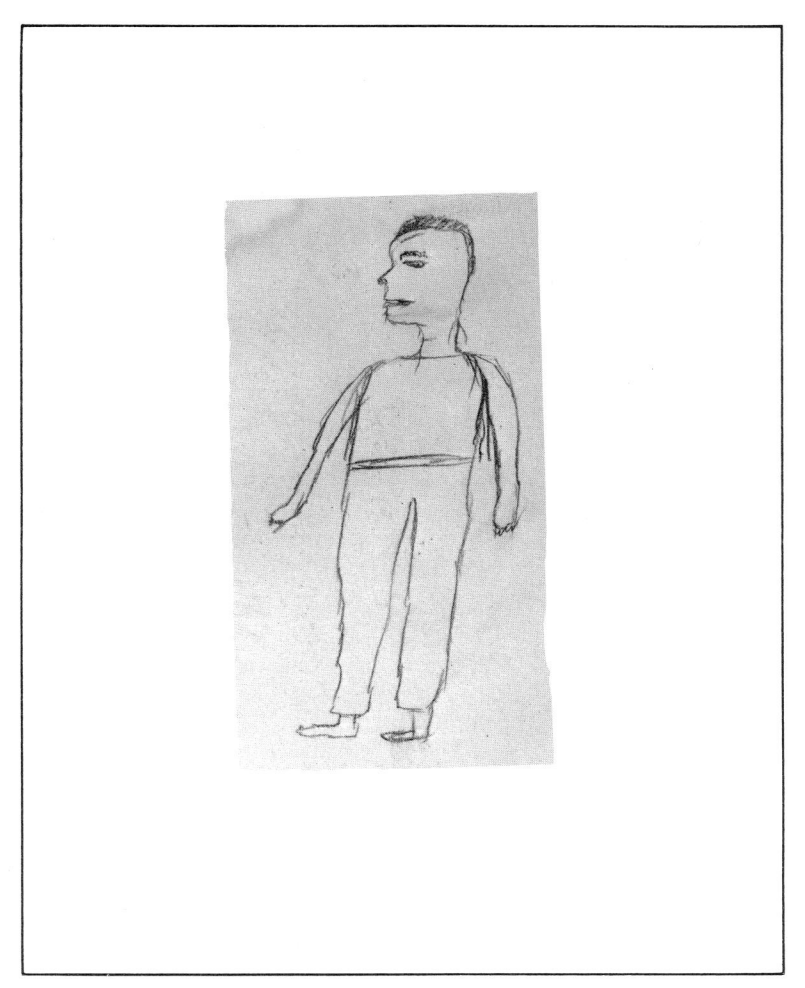

FIGURE-DRAWING CHARACTERISTICS

Structural	Male Female Both	Structural	Male	Female	Structural and Graphic	Male Female Both		Graphic, Global and Height	Male	Female	Body Proportions	Male	Female
Type	0	Omission of Appendages	0	0	Upper and Lower Halves	1	1	Hair Shading	3	3	Head	09	07
Sex Sequence	0	Position of Both Arms	1	4	Four Quarters	4	4	Nudity and Transparency	7	7	Neck	10	08
Posture	1	1	Position of Right Arm	2	7	Relative Size	0		Form	5	5	Shoulders	06	
Perspective	5	6	Position of Left Arm	0	0	Constant Line Pressure	3	3	Detailing	5	5	Right Arm	05	
Vertical Midline	0	4	Position of Legs	4	5	Variable Line Pressure	0	0	Identity and Sex	3	3	Left Arm	04	03
Bilateral Symmetry	1	0	Relation of Long Axes	1	1	Line Continuity	0	0	Sophistication	4	4	Chest	06	
Horizontal Midline	4	0	Right and Left Halves	3	4	Body Shading	0	0	Height	05	04	Girth	08	

GENERAL CHARACTERISTICS OF SUBJECT

IDENTIFICATION
No. 542
Sex M
Marital status S
Age 21 yrs. at psychological tests

PARENTAL HISTORY				
Father				
C	H	S	D	O
+	−	−	−	+
Mother				
C	H	S	D	O
−	−	−	−	−

PHYSIOLOGICAL AND METABOLIC DATA

	Admission	Initial	Control	Cold pressor change	Exercise change	Smoking change
Systolic pressure	120	120	98	+10	+38	
Diastolic pressure	70	72	68	+06	−06	
Heart rate	72	72	71	00	+23	

Age 20 yrs.

Height 70 in. Ponderal index 13.00
Weight 156 lbs. Cholesterol 217 mg. per 100 ml.
Overweight +03 % Vital capacity 5.4 liters

HABIT SURVEY

Smoking habits: unknown

Age begun yrs. Inhalation:

Habits of nervous tension:

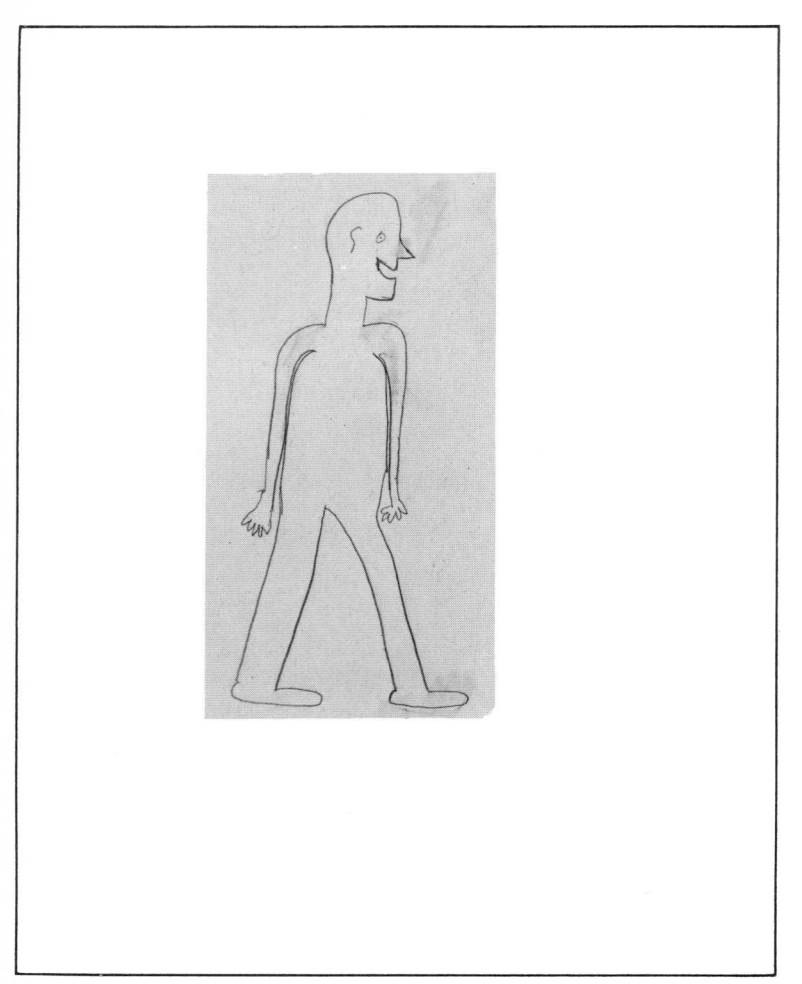

FIGURE-DRAWING CHARACTERISTICS

Structural	Male	Female	Structural	Male	Female	Structural and Graphic	Male	Female	Graphic, Global and Height	Male	Female	Body Proportions	Male	Female
	Both						Both							
Type	0		Omission of Appendages	0	3	Upper and Lower Halves	1	1	Hair Shading	0	3	Head	09	11
Sex Sequence	0		Position of Both Arms	0	2	Four Quarters	4	4	Nudity and Transparency	0	7	Neck	08	04
Posture	2	0	Position of Right Arm	0	0	Relative Size	4		Form	5	5	Shoulders	05	
Perspective	5	2	Position of Left Arm	0	7	Constant Line Pressure	5	0	Detailing	5	5	Right Arm	04	04
Vertical Midline	0	4	Position of Legs	8	0	Variable Line Pressure	0	5	Identity and Sex	5	3	Left Arm	04	
Bilateral Symmetry	2	0	Relation of Long Axes	1	1	Line Continuity	4	4	Sophistication	4	4	Chest	04	08
Horizontal Midline	0	0	Right and Left Halves	2	1	Body Shading	0	0	Height	05	06	Girth	06	07

GENERAL CHARACTERISTICS OF SUBJECT

IDENTIFICATION
No. 717
Sex M
Marital status S
Age 22 yrs. at psychological tests

PARENTAL HISTORY
Father
C   H   S   D   O
+   -   -   -   -
Mother
C   H   S   D   O
-   -   -   -   ?

PHYSIOLOGICAL AND METABOLIC DATA

	Admission	Initial	Control	Cold pressor change	Exercise change	Smoking change
Systolic pressure	140	126	118	+20	+40	+13
Diastolic pressure	80	72	64	+30	-04	+05
Heart rate	72	88	84	-12	+10	+19

Age 21 yrs.	Height 74 in.	Ponderal index 12.91	
	Weight 188 lbs.	Cholesterol 237 mg. per 100 ml.	
	Overweight +09 %	Vital capacity 5.2 liters	

HABIT SURVEY
Smoking habits: occasional smoker
Age begun 19 yrs.   Inhalation: yes
Habits of nervous tension: 5, 6, 22

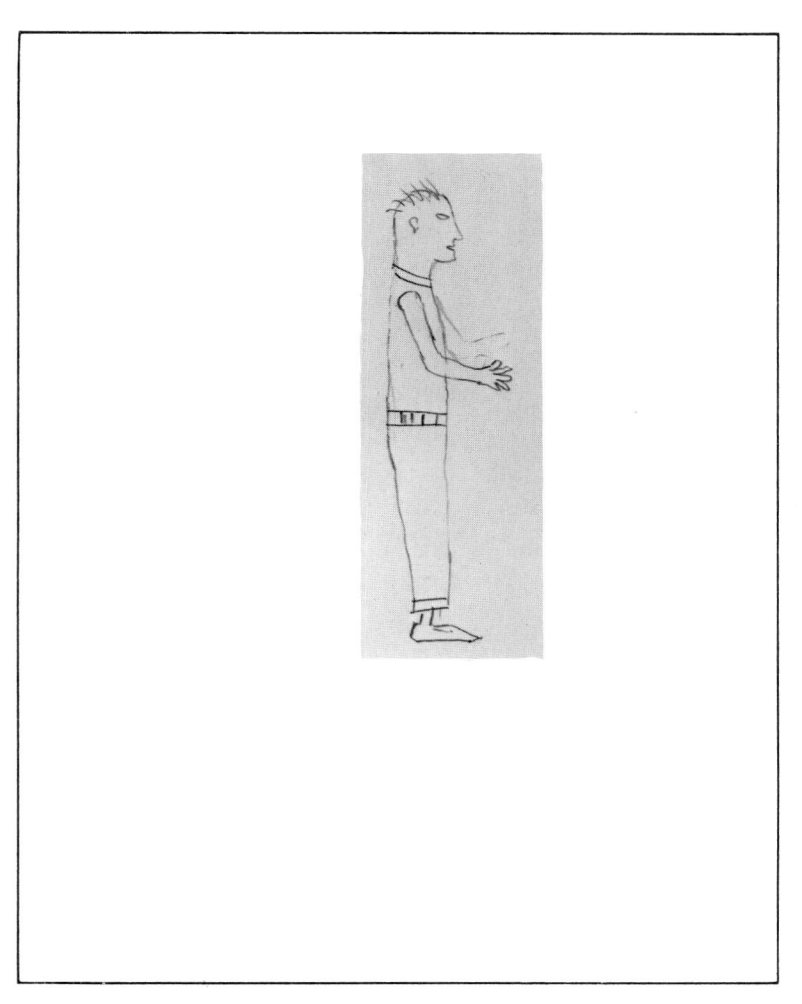

FIGURE-DRAWING CHARACTERISTICS

Structural	Male Female Both	Structural	Male	Female	Structural and Graphic	Male Female Both		Graphic, Global and Height	Male	Female	Body Proportions	Male	Female
Type	0	Omission of Appendages	0	0	Upper and Lower Halves	1	1	Hair Shading	7	3	Head	05	09
Sex Sequence	0	Position of Both Arms	2	0	Four Quarters	4	4	Nudity and Transparency	7	7	Neck	06	05
Posture	1 1	Position of Right Arm	4	0	Relative Size	4		Form	3	3	Shoulders		04
Perspective	2 0	Position of Left Arm	7	0	Constant Line Pressure	0	0	Detailing	5	5	Right Arm	03	04
Vertical Midline	4 0	Position of Legs	1	6	Variable Line Pressure	3	3	Identity and Sex	1	1	Left Arm		04
Bilateral Symmetry	0 3	Relation of Long Axes	1	1	Line Continuity	0	0	Sophistication	4	4	Chest	04	05
Horizontal Midline	4 4	Right and Left Halves	3	3	Body Shading	0	1	Height	04	05	Girth	04	07

GENERAL CHARACTERISTICS OF SUBJECT

IDENTIFICATION
No. F02
Sex M
Marital status M
Age 24 yrs. at
psychological tests

PARENTAL HISTORY					
Father					
C	H	S	D	O	
+	-	-	-	+	
Mother					
C	H	S	D	O	
-	-	-	-	-	

PHYSIOLOGICAL AND METABOLIC DATA

	Admission	Initial	Control	Cold pressor change	Exercise change	Smoking change
Systolic pressure	160	146	138	+08	+18	00
Diastolic pressure	84	62	64	+12	+04	00
Heart rate	88	96	74	+08	+12	+14

Age 22 yrs.	Height	74 in.	Ponderal index 12.78
	Weight	194 lbs.	Cholesterol 224 mg. per 100 ml.
	Overweight +12 %		Vital capacity liters

HABIT SURVEY

Smoking habits: light cigarette smoker

Age begun 18 yrs.   Inhalation: no

Habits of nervous tension: 4, 5, 16

STRONG VOCATIONAL INTEREST TEST

Occupation	Artist	Psychologist	Architect	Physician	Osteopath	Dentist	Veterinarian	Mathematician	Physicist	Engineer	Chemist	Production Manager
Standard Score	32	59	34	49	27	25	08	32	23	25	37	19

Occupation	Farmer	Aviator	Carpenter	Printer	Math.-Sci. Teacher	Ind. Arts Teacher	Voc. Agric. Teacher	Policeman	Forest Serv. Man	Y.M.C.A. Phys. Dir.	Personnel Director	Public Administrator
Standard Score	15	18	-09	25	32	-04	07	09	10	26	47	51

Occupation	Y.M.C.A. Secretary	Soc. Sci. H.S. Teacher	City Sch. Sup't.	Social Worker	Minister	Musician Performer	C.P.A.	Senior C.P.A.	Accountant	Office Man	Purchasing Agent	Banker
Standard Score	32	42	41	58	58	53	50	37	23	24	18	22

Occupation	Mortician	Pharmacist	Sales Manager	Real Est. Manager	Life Ins. Salesman	Advertising Man	Lawyer	Author-Journalist	President Mfg. Co.	Interest Maturity	Occupational Level	Masculinity-Femininity
Standard Score	14	29	37	34	37	47	53	42	40	61	67	38

FIGURE-DRAWING CHARACTERISTICS

Structural	Male Female Both	Structural	Male	Female	Structural and Graphic	Male Female Both	Graphic, Global and Height	Male	Female	Body Proportions	Male	Female
Type	0	Omission of Appendages	0	0	Upper and Lower Halves	2 2	Hair Shading	1	3	Head	05	06
Sex Sequence	0	Position of Both Arms	2	0	Four Quarters	0 0	Nudity and Transparency	7	7	Neck	02	04
Posture	1 1	Position of Right Arm	0	2	Relative Size	0	Form	5	5	Shoulders		02
Perspective	2 0	Position of Left Arm	7	2	Constant Line Pressure	0 2	Detailing	3	3	Right Arm	02	02
Vertical Midline	4 0	Position of Legs	1	6	Variable Line Pressure	1 0	Identity and Sex	1	1	Left Arm		02
Bilateral Symmetry	0 3	Relation of Long Axes	1	1	Line Continuity	0 0	Sophistication	4	4	Chest	05	02
Horizontal Midline	4 4	Right and Left Halves	2	2	Body Shading	0 5	Height	03	02	Girth	05	03

GENERAL CHARACTERISTICS OF SUBJECT

IDENTIFICATION
No.   F03
Sex   M
Marital status   S
Age   24   yrs. at
psychological tests

PARENTAL HISTORY				
Father				
C	H	S	D	O
+	-	+	-	-
Mother				
C	H	S	D	O
-	-	-	-	-

PHYSIOLOGICAL AND METABOLIC DATA

	Admission	Initial	Control	Cold pressor change	Exercise change	Smoking change
Systolic pressure	140	104	96	+06	+22	-10
Diastolic pressure	80	50	50	+20	00	-02
Heart rate	72	68	62	+12	+09	+08

Age 22 yrs.	Height 71 in.	Ponderal index 12.52
	Weight 182 lbs.	Cholesterol 188 mg. per 100 ml.
	Overweight +15 %	Vital capacity liters

HABIT SURVEY
Smoking habits: pipe smoker
Age begun 18 yrs.   Inhalation: sometimes
Habits of nervous tension: 2, 4, 5, 6, 11, 16,
18, 19, 22

STRONG VOCATIONAL INTEREST TEST

Occupation	Artist	Psychologist	Architect	Physician	Osteopath	Dentist	Veterinarian	Mathematician	Physicist	Engineer	Chemist	Production Manager
Standard Score	35	44	34	49	37	26	18	17	02	11	14	20

Occupation	Farmer	Aviator	Carpenter	Printer	Math.-Sci. Teacher	Ind. Arts Teacher	Voc. Agric. Teacher	Policeman	Forest Serv. Man	Y.M.C.A. Phys. Dir.	Personnel Director	Public Administrator
Standard Score	15	19	05	33	28	09	14	26	12	38	43	41

Occupation	Y.M.C.A. Secretary	Soc. Sci. H.S. Teacher	City Sch. Sup't.	Social Worker	Minister	Musician Performer	C.P.A.	Senior C.P.A.	Accountant	Office Man	Purchasing Agent	Banker
Standard Score	38	49	40	54	58	59	29	29	18	30	20	22

Occupation	Mortician	Pharmacist	Sales Manager	Real Est. Manager	Life Ins. Salesman	Advertising Man	Lawyer	Author-Journalist	President Mfg. Co.	Interest Maturity	Occupational Level	Masculinity-Femininity
Standard Score	33	37	35	43	44	51	45	41	23	59	56	25

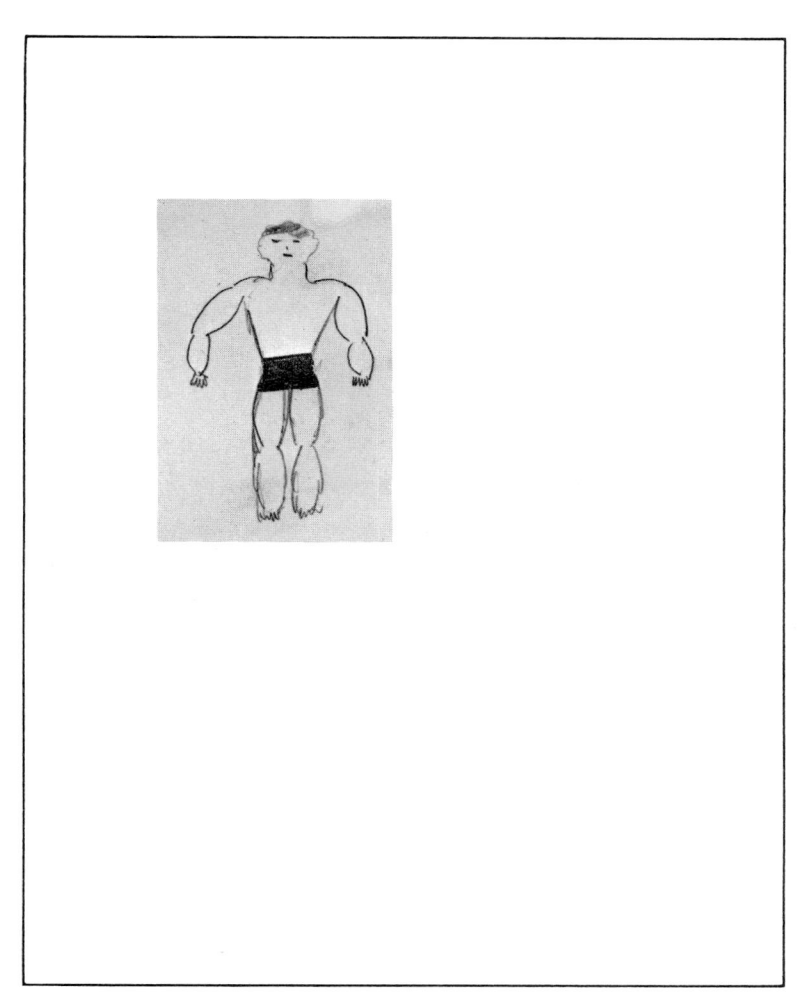

FIGURE-DRAWING CHARACTERISTICS

Structural	Male Female Both		Structural	Male	Female	Structural and Graphic	Male Female Both		Graphic, Global and Height	Male	Female	Body Proportions	Male	Female
Type	0		Omission of Appendages	0	0	Upper and Lower Halves	2	1	Hair Shading	3	3	Head		06
Sex Sequence	0		Position of Both Arms	1	0	Four Quarters	0	4	Nudity and Transparency	3	2	Neck		06
Posture	1	1	Position of Right Arm	2	2	Relative Size	4		Form	3	3	Shoulders	04	03
Perspective	0	0	Position of Left Arm	0	2	Constant Line Pressure	0	0	Detailing	3	3	Right Arm	02	02
Vertical Midline	0	0	Position of Legs	4	4	Variable Line Pressure	5	5	Identity and Sex	1	3	Left Arm	02	02
Bilateral Symmetry	3	3	Relation of Long Axes	1	1	Line Continuity	2	2	Sophistication	4	4	Chest	04	02
Horizontal Midline	4	4	Right and Left Halves	2	1	Body Shading	2	3	Height	03	04	Girth	03	05

GENERAL CHARACTERISTICS OF SUBJECT

IDENTIFICATION
No. F13
Sex M
Marital status S
Age 24 yrs. at
psychological tests

PARENTAL HISTORY				
Father				
C	H	S	D	O
+	-	+	-	+
Mother				
C	H	S	D	O
-	-	-	-	-

PHYSIOLOGICAL AND METABOLIC DATA

	Admission	Initial	Control	Cold pressor change	Exercise change	Smoking change
Systolic pressure	140	122	108	+12	+22	+11
Diastolic pressure	70	70	72	+24	+14	+06
Heart rate	68	64	67	+20	+33	+17

Age 22 yrs.
Height 74 in.
Weight 190 lbs.
Overweight +10 %
Ponderal index 12.87
Cholesterol 190 mg. per 100 ml.
Vital capacity liters

HABIT SURVEY

Smoking habits: light cigarette smoker

Age begun 21 yrs.   Inhalation: yes

Habits of nervous tension: 2, 4, 5, 6, 9, 11

STRONG VOCATIONAL INTEREST TEST

Occupation	Artist	Psychologist	Architect	Physician	Osteopath	Dentist	Veterinarian	Mathematician	Physicist	Engineer	Chemist	Production Manager
Standard Score	17	28	24	33	27	15	12	16	05	27	23	33

Occupation	Farmer	Aviator	Carpenter	Printer	Math.-Sci. Teacher	Ind. Arts Teacher	Voc. Agric. Teacher	Policeman	Forest Serv. Man	Y.M.C.A. Phys. Dir.	Personnel Director	Public Administrator
Standard Score	29	38	09	31	34	06	18	32	30	40	44	40

Occupation	Y.M.C.A. Secretary	Soc. Sci. H.S. Teacher	City Sch. Sup't.	Social Worker	Minister	Musician Performer	C.P.A.	Senior C.P.A.	Accountant	Office Man	Purchasing Agent	Banker
Standard Score	29	40	34	35	58	33	34	43	31	38	34	25

Occupation	Mortician	Pharmacist	Sales Manager	Real Est. Manager	Life Ins. Salesman	Advertising Man	Lawyer	Author-Journalist	President Mfg. Co.	Interest Maturity	Occupational Level	Masculinity-Femininity
Standard Score	20	33	38	40	32	39	38	30	18	58	56	50

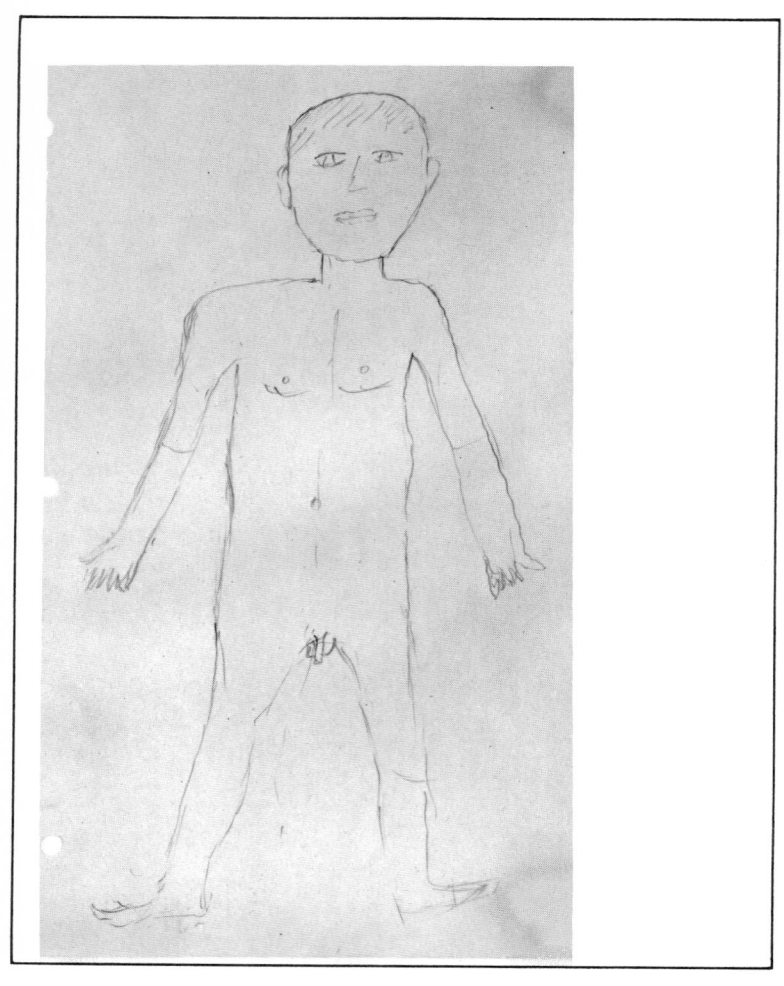

FIGURE-DRAWING CHARACTERISTICS

Structural	Male Female Both		Structural	Male	Female	Structural and Graphic	Male Female Both		Graphic, Global and Height	Male	Female	Body Proportions	Male	Female
Type	0		Omission of Appendages	0	7	Upper and Lower Halves	0	0	Hair Shading	7	1	Head	14	09
Sex Sequence	0		Position of Both Arms	0	0	Four Quarters	4	4	Nudity and Transparency	0	0	Neck	07	08
Posture	1	1	Position of Right Arm	1	0	Relative Size	0		Form	5	5	Shoulders	10	08
Perspective	0	0	Position of Left Arm	1	0	Constant Line Pressure	0	1	Detailing	3	3	Right Arm	08	06
Vertical Midline	0	0	Position of Legs	6	6	Variable Line Pressure	1	0	Identity and Sex	4	4	Left Arm	08	
Bilateral Symmetry	2	2	Relation of Long Axes	1	1	Line Continuity	0	0	Sophistication	4	4	Chest	08	06
Horizontal Midline	0	0	Right and Left Halves	1	1	Body Shading	3	2	Height	09	08	Girth	11	09

GENERAL CHARACTERISTICS OF SUBJECT

IDENTIFICATION
No. G41
Sex M
Marital status S
Age 23 yrs. at
psychological tests

PARENTAL HISTORY					
Father					
C	H	S	D	O	
+	-	-	+	?	
Mother					
C	H	S	D	O	
-	(+)	-	-	-	

PHYSIOLOGICAL AND METABOLIC DATA

	Admission	Initial	Control	Cold pressor change	Exercise change	Smoking change
Systolic pressure	145	134	140	+22	+30	+09
Diastolic pressure	85	76	80	+20	-02	+05
Heart rate	80	68	68	+10	+26	+01

Height	70 in.	Ponderal index	12.59	
Age 22 yrs.	Weight	172 lbs.	Cholesterol	185 mg. per 100 ml.
	Overweight +12 %	Vital capacity		liters

HABIT SURVEY

Smoking habits: nonsmoker

Age begun   yrs.   Inhalation:

Habits of nervous tension: 4, 5, 6, 11, 21, 23

STRONG VOCATIONAL INTEREST TEST

Occupation	Artist	Psychologist	Architect	Physician	Osteopath	Dentist	Veterinarian	Mathematician	Physicist	Engineer	Chemist	Production Manager
Standard Score	31	35	38	52	54	45	39	26	21	34	35	38

Occupation	Farmer	Aviator	Carpenter	Printer	Math.-Sci. Teacher	Ind. Arts Teacher	Voc. Agric. Teacher	Policeman	Forest Serv. Man	Y.M.C.A. Phys. Dir.	Personnel Director	Public Administrator
Standard Score	40	44	33	45	40	36	39	35	36	46	36	46

Occupation	Y.M.C.A. Secretary	Soc. Sci. H.S. Teacher	City Sch. Sup't.	Social Worker	Minister	Musician Performer	C.P.A.	Senior C.P.A.	Accountant	Office Man	Purchasing Agent	Banker
Standard Score	35	39	28	41	59	53	17	42	20	33	25	21

Occupation	Mortician	Pharmacist	Sales Manager	Real Est. Manager	Life Ins. Salesman	Advertising Man	Lawyer	Author-Journalist	President Mfg. Co.	Interest Maturity	Occupational Level	Masculinity-Femininity
Standard Score	33	34	26	30	29	35	26	33	24	56	54	41

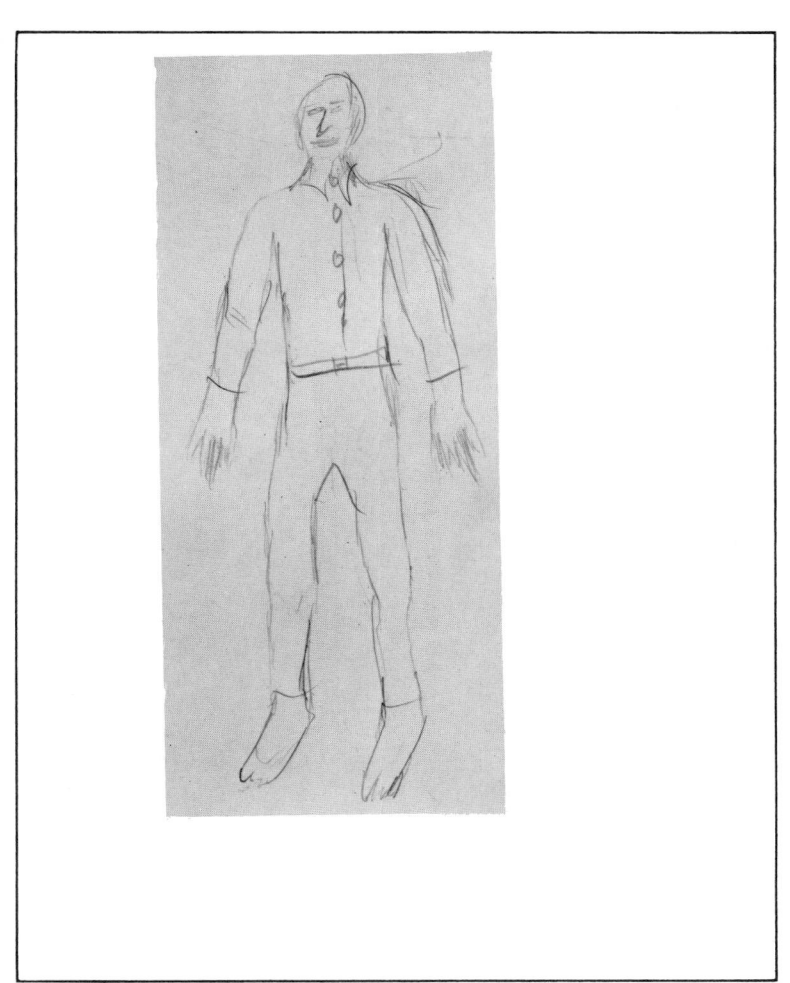
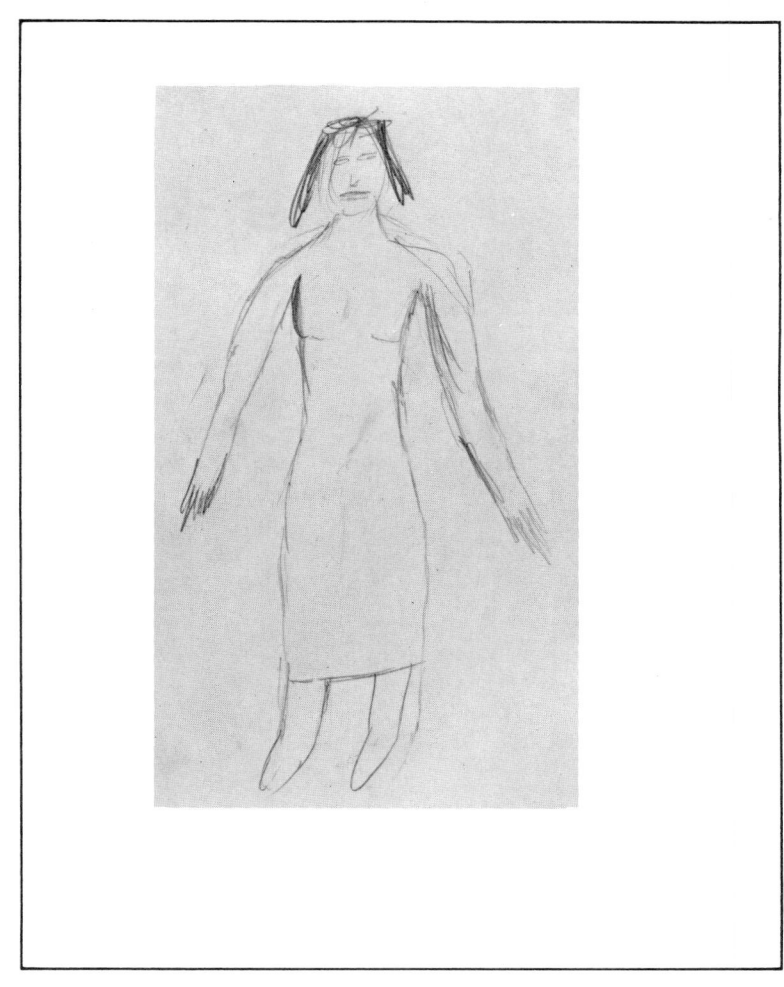

FIGURE-DRAWING CHARACTERISTICS

Structural	Male Female Both	Structural	Male	Female	Structural and Graphic	Male Female Both		Graphic, Global and Height	Male	Female	Body Proportions	Male	Female
Type	0	Omission of Appendages	0	0	Upper and Lower Halves	1	1	Hair Shading	7	3	Head	07	07
Sex Sequence	0	Position of Both Arms	0	0	Four Quarters	4	4	Nudity and Transparency	7	7	Neck	08	08
Posture	1 1	Position of Right Arm	1	1	Relative Size	1		Form	3	3	Shoulders	07	07
Perspective	0 0	Position of Left Arm	1	1	Constant Line Pressure	0	0	Detailing	5	5	Right Arm	06	06
Vertical Midline	3 0	Position of Legs	6	4	Variable Line Pressure	1	2	Identity and Sex	3	3	Left Arm	06	06
Bilateral Symmetry	3 3	Relation of Long Axes	1	1	Line Continuity	0	0	Sophistication	4	4	Chest	05	06
Horizontal Midline	4 0	Right and Left Halves	1	1	Body Shading	1	1	Height	07	07	Girth	06	06

GENERAL CHARACTERISTICS OF SUBJECT

IDENTIFICATION

No. A01

Sex M

Marital status S

Age 21 yrs. at
psychological tests

PARENTAL HISTORY

Father

C	H	S	D	O
+	?	+	-	+

Mother

C	H	S	D	O
-	-	-	-	?

PHYSIOLOGICAL AND METABOLIC DATA

	Admission	Initial	Control	Cold pressor change	Exercise change	Smoking change
Systolic pressure	130	154	112	+18	+30	-02
Diastolic pressure	80	85	66	+08	-08	00
Heart rate	72	80	61	+11	+07	+01

Age 21 yrs.	Height 72 in.	Ponderal index 12.46
	Weight 193 lbs.	Cholesterol 258 mg. per 100 ml.
	Overweight +19 %	Vital capacity liters

HABIT SURVEY

Smoking habits: nonsmoker

Age begun   yrs.   Inhalation:

Habits of nervous tension: 2, 3, 4, 5, 6, 9,

10, 16, 18, 21, 23, 24

STRONG VOCATIONAL INTEREST TEST

Occupation	Artist	Psychologist	Architect	Physician	Osteopath	Dentist	Veterinarian	Mathematician	Physicist	Engineer	Chemist	Production Manager
Standard Score	46	48	42	49	40	36	05	28	19	21	29	21

Occupation	Farmer	Aviator	Carpenter	Printer	Math.-Sci. Teacher	Ind. Arts Teacher	Voc. Agric. Teacher	Policeman	Forest Serv. Man	Y.M.C.A. Phys. Dir.	Personnel Director	Public Administrator
Standard Score	15	14	-08	28	25	-10	05	20	09	29	36	45

Occupation	Y.M.C.A. Secretary	Soc. Sci. H.S. Teacher	City Sch. Sup't.	Social Worker	Minister	Musician Performer	C.P.A.	Senior C.P.A.	Accountant	Office Man	Purchasing Agent	Banker
Standard Score	32	39	44	47	60	55	50	27	19	25	10	18

Occupation	Mortician	Pharmacist	Sales Manager	Real Est. Manager	Life Ins. Salesman	Advertising Man	Lawyer	Author-Journalist	President Mfg. Co.	Interest Maturity	Occupational Level	Masculinity-Femininity
Standard Score	14	22	26	31	35	48	57	52	31	58	64	24

FIGURE-DRAWING CHARACTERISTICS

Structural	Male	Female	Structural	Male	Female	Structural and Graphic	Male	Female	Graphic, Global and Height	Male	Female	Body Proportions	Male	Female
		Both						Both						
Type		0	Omission of Appendages	0	0	Upper and Lower Halves	1	1	Hair Shading	0	3	Head	05	04
Sex Sequence		0	Position of Both Arms	4	4	Four Quarters	4	4	Nudity and Transparency	3	3	Neck	04	05
Posture	2	1	Position of Right Arm	7	7	Relative Size		2	Form	5	5	Shoulders		
Perspective	2	2	Position of Left Arm	4	4	Constant Line Pressure	0	0	Detailing	5	5	Right Arm		
Vertical Midline	4	4	Position of Legs	8	1	Variable Line Pressure	2	2	Identity and Sex	1	1	Left Arm	02	02
Bilateral Symmetry	0	0	Relation of Long Axes	1	1	Line Continuity	2	1	Sophistication	4	4	Chest	03	03
Horizontal Midline	4	4	Right and Left Halves	1	1	Body Shading	0	4	Height	03	03	Girth	03	03

GENERAL CHARACTERISTICS OF SUBJECT

IDENTIFICATION
No. B47
Sex M
Marital status S
Age 22 yrs. at
psychological tests

PARENTAL HISTORY				
Father				
C	H	S	D	O
+	+	-	+	?
Mother				
C	H	S	D	O
-	U	-	-	-

PHYSIOLOGICAL AND METABOLIC DATA

	Admission	Initial	Control	Cold pressor change	Exercise change	Smoking change
Systolic pressure	110	124	116	+04	+14	
Diastolic pressure	65	82	74	+06	-10	
Heart rate	52	68	55	+06	+16	

Age 21 yrs.	Height	72 in.	Ponderal index 13.09
	Weight	166 lbs.	Cholesterol 212 mg. per 100 ml.
	Overweight +02 %		Vital capacity liters

HABIT SURVEY

Smoking habits: nonsmoker

Age begun　yrs.　　Inhalation:

Habits of nervous tension: 2, 4, 5, 6, 9, 11,

17, 18, 24, 25

STRONG VOCATIONAL INTEREST TEST

Occupation	Artist	Psychologist	Architect	Physician	Osteopath	Dentist	Veterinarian	Mathematician	Physicist	Engineer	Chemist	Production Manager
Standard Score	28	46	34	49	42	34	31	29	25	37	42	32

Occupation	Farmer	Aviator	Carpenter	Printer	Math.-Sci. Teacher	Ind. Arts Teacher	Voc. Agric. Teacher	Policeman	Forest Serv. Man	Y.M.C.A. Phys. Dir.	Personnel Director	Public Administrator
Standard Score	47	46	27	51	49	26	40	41	39	36	36	44

Occupation	Y.M.C.A. Secretary	Soc. Sci. H.S. Teacher	City Sch. Sup't.	Social Worker	Minister	Musician Performer	C.P.A.	Senior C.P.A.	Accountant	Office Man	Purchasing Agent	Banker
Standard Score	27	39	24	39	61	49	24	47	32	36	22	22

Occupation	Mortician	Pharmacist	Sales Manager	Real Est. Manager	Life Ins. Salesman	Advertising Man	Lawyer	Author-Journalist	President Mfg. Co.	Interest Maturity	Occupational Level	Masculinity-Femininity
Standard Score	20	30	25	31	25	35	27	30	21	58	47	52

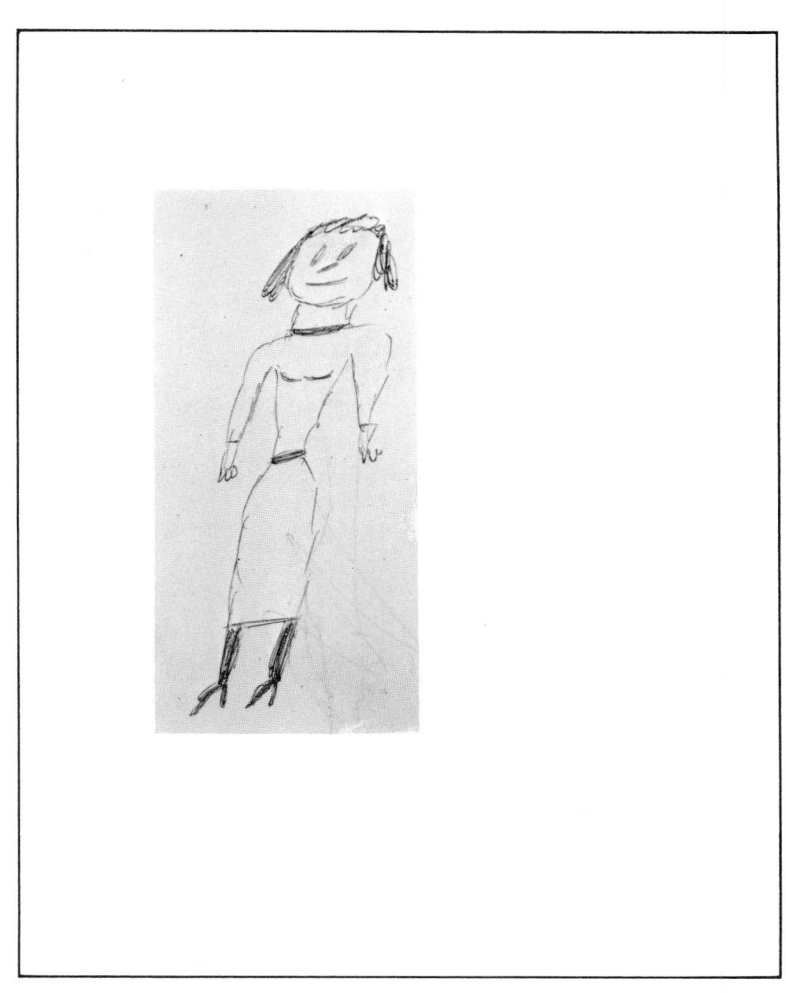

FIGURE-DRAWING CHARACTERISTICS

Structural	Male Female Both		Structural	Male	Female	Structural and Graphic	Male Female Both		Graphic, Global and Height	Male	Female	Body Proportions	Male	Female
Type	0		Omission of Appendages	0	0	Upper and Lower Halves	0	1	Hair Shading	3	3	Head	06	07
Sex Sequence	2		Position of Both Arms	0	0	Four Quarters	4	4	Nudity and Transparency	7	7	Neck	08	08
Posture	1	1	Position of Right Arm	1	1	Relative Size	2		Form	3	3	Shoulders	05	05
Perspective	0	0	Position of Left Arm	1	1	Constant Line Pressure	1	1	Detailing	3	3	Right Arm	02	02
Vertical Midline	3	0	Position of Legs	6	6	Variable Line Pressure	0	0	Identity and Sex	1	1	Left Arm	02	02
Bilateral Symmetry	1	1	Relation of Long Axes	1	1	Line Continuity	0	0	Sophistication	4	4	Chest	03	03
Horizontal Midline	4	4	Right and Left Halves	2	2	Body Shading	4	5	Height	05	05	Girth	03	02

GENERAL CHARACTERISTICS OF SUBJECT

IDENTIFICATION
No. E45
Sex M
Marital status S
Age 21 yrs. at
psychological tests

PARENTAL HISTORY				
Father				
C	H	S	D	O
+	-	-	-	?
Mother				
C	H	S	D	O
-	+	-	-	+

PHYSIOLOGICAL AND METABOLIC DATA

	Admission	Initial	Control	Cold pressor change	Exercise change	Smoking change
Systolic pressure	120	112	108	+01	+21	
Diastolic pressure	90	68	70	+20	-08	
Heart rate	78	56	54	00	+14	

Age 21 yrs.	Height 71 in.	Ponderal index 12.82
	Weight 170 lbs.	Cholesterol 308 mg. per 100 ml.
	Overweight +08 %	Vital capacity 4.5 liters

HABIT SURVEY

Smoking habits: nonsmoker

Age begun   yrs.   Inhalation:

Habits of nervous tension: 5, 9

STRONG VOCATIONAL INTEREST TEST

Occupation	Artist	Psychologist	Architect	Physician	Osteopath	Dentist	Veterinarian	Mathematician	Physicist	Engineer	Chemist	Production Manager
Standard Score	34	32	31	43	28	30	13	35	39	52	45	40

Occupation	Farmer	Aviator	Carpenter	Printer	Math.-Sci. Teacher	Ind. Arts Teacher	Voc. Agric. Teacher	Policeman	Forest Serv. Man	Y.M.C.A. Phys. Dir.	Personnel Director	Public Administrator
Standard Score	32	45	17	24	21	07	09	20	12	12	22	30

Occupation	Y.M.C.A. Secretary	Soc. Sci. H.S. Teacher	City Sch. Sup't.	Social Worker	Minister	Musician Performer	C.P.A.	Senior C.P.A.	Accountant	Office Man	Purchasing Agent	Banker
Standard Score	07	06	09	15	64	24	32	26	16	14	29	21

Occupation	Mortician	Pharmacist	Sales Manager	Real Est. Manager	Life Ins. Salesman	Advertising Man	Lawyer	Author-Journalist	President Mfg. Co.	Interest Maturity	Occupational Level	Masculinity-Femininity
Standard Score	20	28	27	33	23	32	39	40	48	40	65	54

FIGURE-DRAWING CHARACTERISTICS

Structural	Male Female Both	Structural	Male	Female	Structural and Graphic	Male Female Both		Graphic, Global and Height	Male	Female	Body Proportions	Male	Female
Type	0	Omission of Appendages	0	0	Upper and Lower Halves	1	1	Hair Shading	3	3	Head	19	19
Sex Sequence	0	Position of Both Arms	2	2	Four Quarters	4	4	Nudity and Transparency	7	7	Neck	14	26
Posture	1	1	Position of Right Arm	0	0	Relative Size	2		Form	3	3	Shoulders		
Perspective	2	2	Position of Left Arm	7	7	Constant Line Pressure	3	3	Detailing	3	3	Right Arm	06	02
Vertical Midline	7	4	Position of Legs	1	1	Variable Line Pressure	0	0	Identity and Sex	1	1	Left Arm		
Bilateral Symmetry	0	0	Relation of Long Axes	1	1	Line Continuity	4	4	Sophistication	3	3	Chest		08
Horizontal Midline	6	0	Right and Left Halves	1	1	Body Shading	0	0	Height	06	07	Girth		03

GENERAL CHARACTERISTICS OF SUBJECT

IDENTIFICATION
No. E78
Sex M
Marital status S
Age 23 yrs. at
psychological tests

PARENTAL HISTORY
Father
C H S D O
-   -   -   -   -
Mother
C H S D O
+   -   -   -   -

PHYSIOLOGICAL AND METABOLIC DATA

	Admission	Initial	Control	Cold pressor change	Exercise change	Smoking change
Systolic pressure	90	105	105	+15	+24	
Diastolic pressure	60	65	65	+13	-15	
Heart rate	72	72	68	00	+20	

Age 23 yrs.	Height 75 in.	Ponderal index 13.20
	Weight 183 lbs.	Cholesterol 210 mg. per 100 ml.
	Overweight +02 %	Vital capacity 6.1 liters

HABIT SURVEY

Smoking habits: occasional smoker

Age begun 16 yrs.　　Inhalation: no

Habits of nervous tension: 5, 6, 21, 22, 25

STRONG VOCATIONAL INTEREST TEST

Occupation	Artist	Psychologist	Architect	Physician	Osteopath	Dentist	Veterinarian	Mathematician	Physicist	Engineer	Chemist	Production Manager
Standard Score	46	59	41	61	44	42	18	39	35	31	39	21

Occupation	Farmer	Aviator	Carpenter	Printer	Math.-Sci. Teacher	Ind. Arts Teacher	Voc. Agric. Teacher	Policeman	Forest Serv. Man	Y.M.C.A. Phys. Dir.	Personnel Director	Public Administrator
Standard Score	14	22	08	27	37	06	18	20	07	32	31	40

Occupation	Y.M.C.A. Secretary	Soc. Sci. H.S. Teacher	City Sch. Sup't.	Social Worker	Minister	Musician Performer	C.P.A.	Senior C.P.A.	Accountant	Office Man	Purchasing Agent	Banker
Standard Score	26	34	42	48	64	69	41	25	12	18	11	19

Occupation	Mortician	Pharmacist	Sales Manager	Real Est. Manager	Life Ins. Salesman	Advertising Man	Lawyer	Author-Journalist	President Mfg. Co.	Interest Maturity	Occupational Level	Masculinity-Femininity
Standard Score	25	48	29	28	32	46	44	50	37	51	62	26

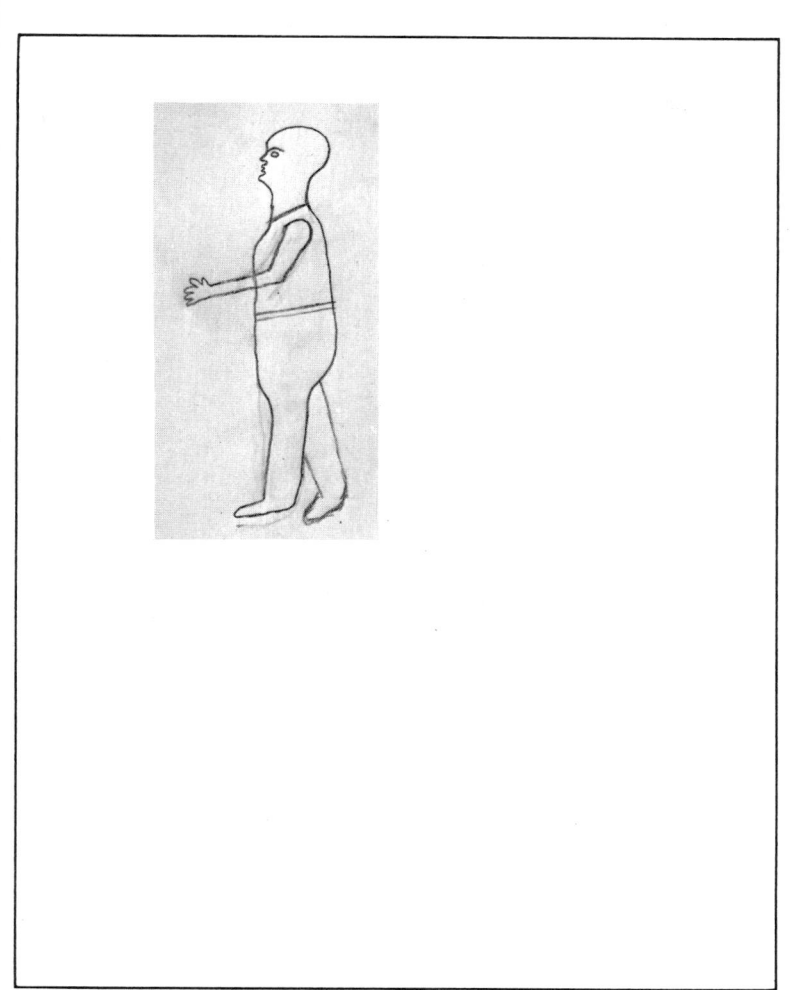

FIGURE-DRAWING CHARACTERISTICS

Structural	Male Female Both		Structural	Male	Female	Structural and Graphic	Male Female Both		Graphic, Global and Height	Male	Female	Body Proportions	Male	Female
Type	0		Omission of Appendages	0	2	Upper and Lower Halves	2	2	Hair Shading	0	3	Head	04	05
Sex Sequence	2		Position of Both Arms	4	6	Four Quarters	0	0	Nudity and Transparency	7	6	Neck	10	08
Posture	2	1	Position of Right Arm	7	7	Relative Size	0		Form	3	3	Shoulders		
Perspective	2	2	Position of Left Arm	4	7	Constant Line Pressure	5	0	Detailing	3	3	Right Arm		
Vertical Midline	4	4	Position of Legs	8	4	Variable Line Pressure	0	5	Identity and Sex	3	1	Left Arm	04	
Bilateral Symmetry	0	0	Relation of Long Axes	1	1	Line Continuity	4	4	Sophistication	4	4	Chest	05	04
Horizontal Midline	4	4	Right and Left Halves	2	2	Body Shading	0	6	Height	04	03	Girth	06	05

GENERAL CHARACTERISTICS OF SUBJECT

IDENTIFICATION
No. 262
Sex M
Marital status M
Age 27 yrs. at psychological tests

PARENTAL HISTORY
Father
C H S D O
- - (+) - -
Mother
C H S D O
+ + (+) + +

PHYSIOLOGICAL AND METABOLIC DATA

	Admission	Initial	Control	Cold pressor change	Exercise change	Smoking change
Systolic pressure	138	122	110	+16	+40	
Diastolic pressure	78	82	76	+08	-12	
Heart rate	88	72	81	+10	+22	

Age 25 yrs.	Height 72 in.	Ponderal index 12.82
	Weight 177 lbs.	Cholesterol 237 mg. per 100 ml.
	Overweight +06 %	Vital capacity 5.1 liters

HABIT SURVEY
Smoking habits: heavy cigarette smoker
Age begun 15 yrs.   Inhalation: yes
Habits of nervous tension: 5, 16, 19, 22

FIGURE-DRAWING CHARACTERISTICS

Structural	Male Female Both		Structural	Male	Female	Structural and Graphic	Male Female Both		Graphic, Global and Height	Male	Female	Body Proportions	Male	Female
Type	0		Omission of Appendages	0	0	Upper and Lower Halves	1	3	Hair Shading	3	3	Head		08
Sex Sequence	0		Position of Both Arms	0	2	Four Quarters	4	4	Nudity and Transparency	6	6	Neck		16
Posture	1	2	Position of Right Arm	2	0	Relative Size	4		Form	3	3	Shoulders	06	
Perspective	0	2	Position of Left Arm	2	7	Constant Line Pressure	0	1	Detailing	3	3	Right Arm	04	04
Vertical Midline	3	4	Position of Legs	4	7	Variable Line Pressure	3	0	Identity and Sex	1	1	Left Arm	04	
Bilateral Symmetry	3	0	Relation of Long Axes	1	1	Line Continuity	0	0	Sophistication	4	4	Chest	06	10
Horizontal Midline	4	4	Right and Left Halves	1	2	Body Shading	3	3	Height	06	07	Girth	07	13

GENERAL CHARACTERISTICS OF SUBJECT

IDENTIFICATION
No. 329
Sex M
Marital status S
Age 24 yrs. at
psychological tests

PARENTAL HISTORY
Father
C   H   S   D   O
(+) (+)   -   -   -
Mother
C   H   S   D   O
-   -   -   -   -

PHYSIOLOGICAL AND METABOLIC DATA

	Admission	Initial	Control	Cold pressor change	Exercise change	Smoking change
Systolic pressure	116	116	106	+25	+27	
Diastolic pressure	60	64	66	+26	00	
Heart rate	96	76	66	+06	+19	

Age 22 yrs.	Height 73 in.	Ponderal index 13.77
	Weight 149 lbs.	Cholesterol 203 mg. per 100 ml.
	Overweight −11 %	Vital capacity 5.6 liters

HABIT SURVEY

Smoking habits: nonsmoker

Age begun   yrs.   Inhalation:

Habits of nervous tension: 5

Plate 77   **MODERATELY PRIMITIVE DRAWINGS**   115

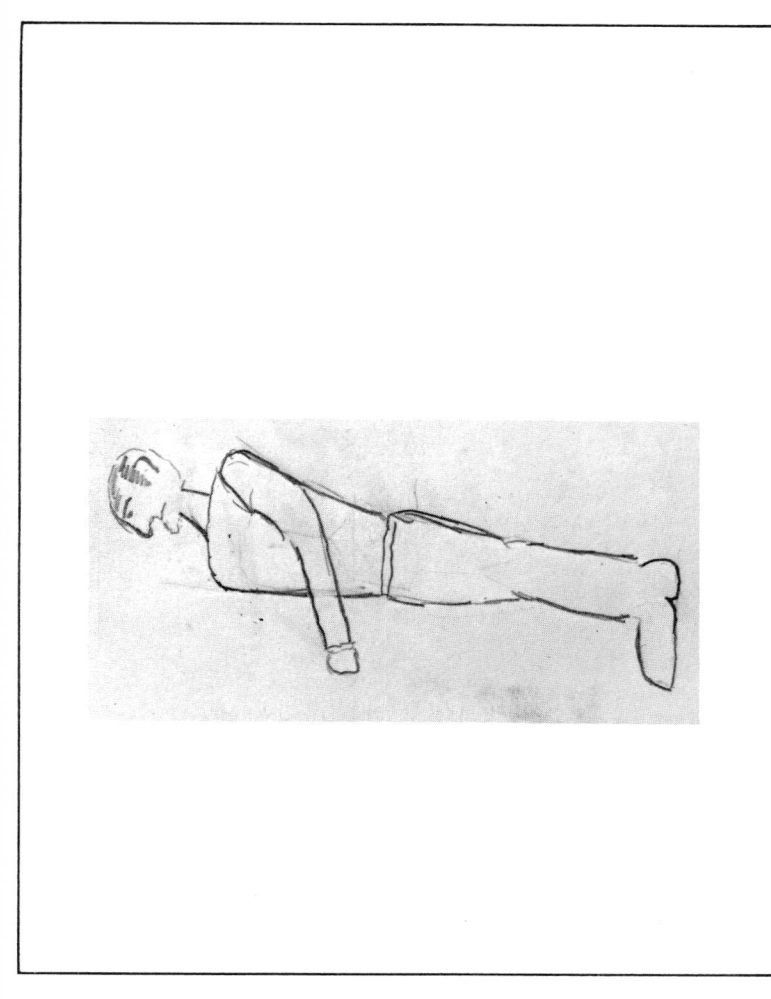

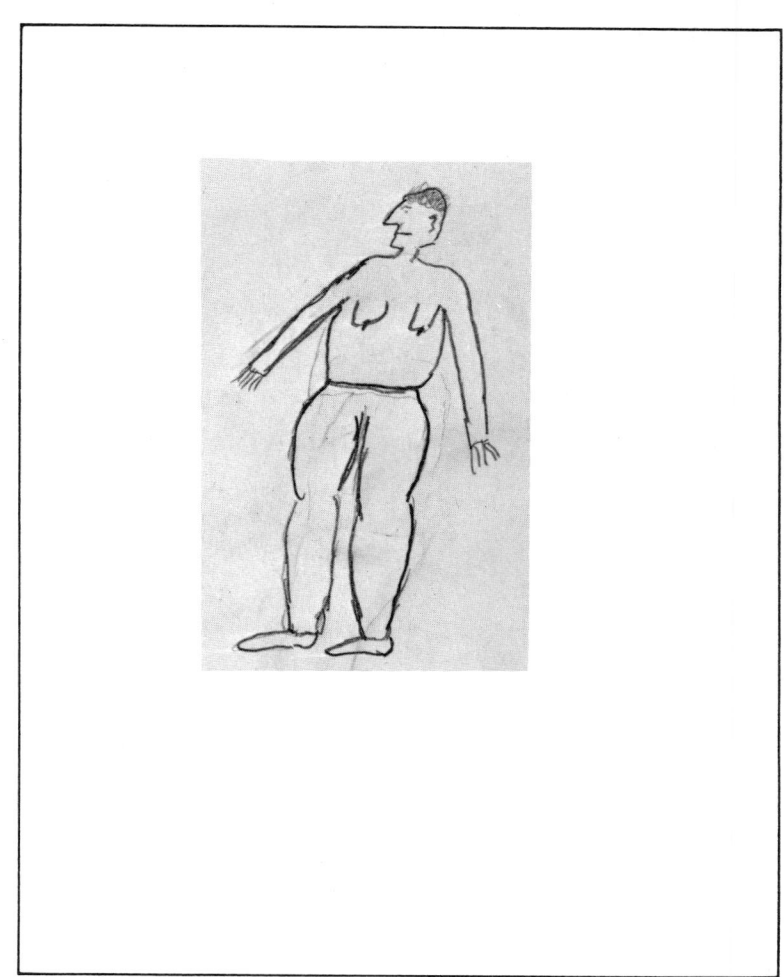

FIGURE-DRAWING CHARACTERISTICS

Structural	Male Female Both	Structural	Male	Female	Structural and Graphic	Male Female Both		Graphic, Global and Height	Male	Female	Body Proportions	Male	Female
Type	0	Omission of Appendages	0	0	Upper and Lower Halves	1	1	Hair Shading	1	3	Head	06	04
Sex Sequence	0	Position of Both Arms	4	0	Four Quarters	4	4	Nudity and Transparency	7	3	Neck	08	02
Posture	1 1	Position of Right Arm	7	2	Relative Size	0		Form	3	3	Shoulders		04
Perspective	2 5	Position of Left Arm	4	2	Constant Line Pressure	5	5	Detailing	5	5	Right Arm		04
Vertical Midline	4 0	Position of Legs	1	4	Variable Line Pressure	0	0	Identity and Sex	3	3	Left Arm	06	04
Bilateral Symmetry	0 3	Relation of Long Axes	2	0	Line Continuity	0	2	Sophistication	4	4	Chest	10	05
Horizontal Midline	4 4	Right and Left Halves	1	1	Body Shading	0	0	Height	06	05	Girth	06	06

GENERAL CHARACTERISTICS OF SUBJECT

IDENTIFICATION
No. 430
Sex M
Marital status S
Age 26 yrs. at
psychological tests

PARENTAL HISTORY
Father
C   H   S   D   O
(+) (+) +   −   −
Mother
C   H   S   D   O
−   −   −   −   −

PHYSIOLOGICAL AND METABOLIC DATA

	Admission	Initial	Control	Cold pressor change	Exercise change	Smoking change
Systolic pressure	112	125	120	+22	+20	
Diastolic pressure	74	80	75	+19	−07	
Heart rate	80	64	61	+18	+33	

Age 23 yrs.	Height 72 in.	Ponderal index 12.95
	Weight 172 lbs.	Cholesterol 280 mg. per 100 ml.
	Overweight +05 %	Vital capacity 4.8 liters

HABIT SURVEY
Smoking habits: pipe smoker
Age begun 16 yrs.   Inhalation: no
Habits of nervous tension: 5, 6, 9, 11, 12
21, 22

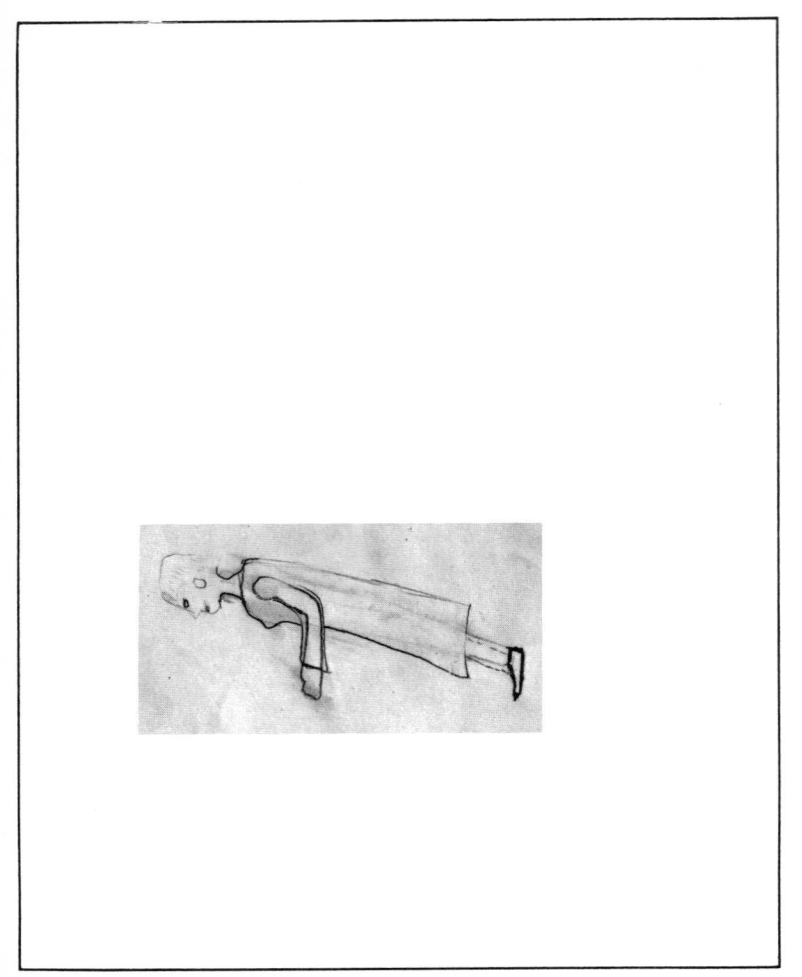

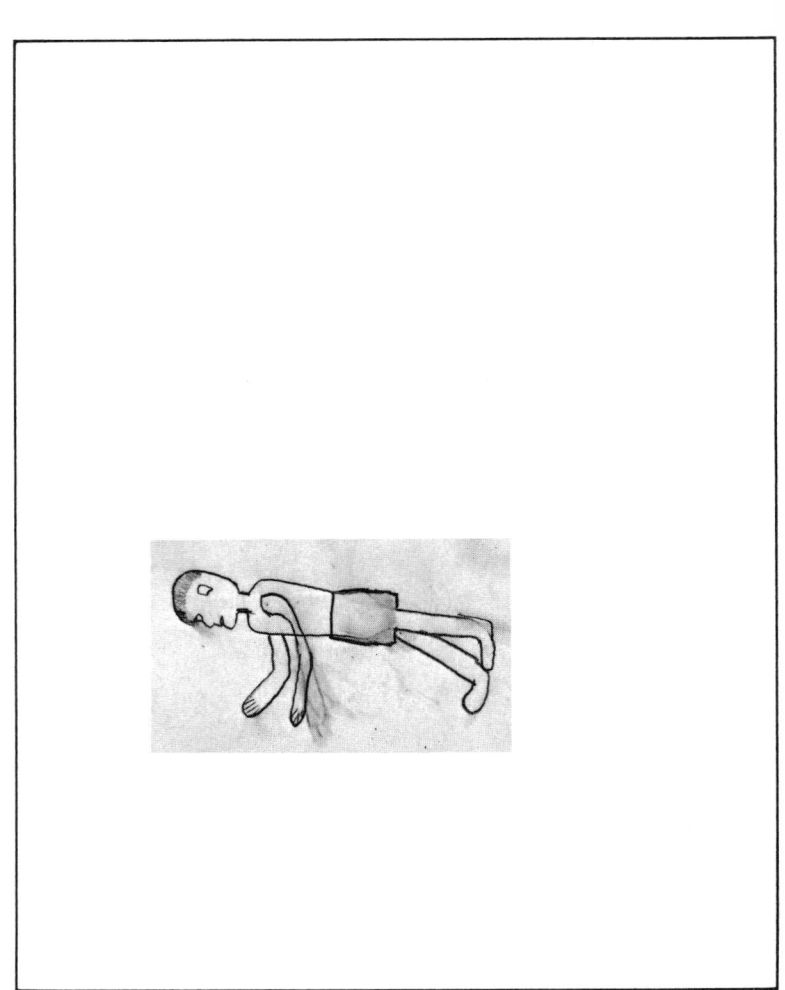

FIGURE-DRAWING CHARACTERISTICS

Structural	Male Female Both	Structural	Male	Female	Structural and Graphic	Male Female Both	Graphic, Global and Height	Male	Female	Body Proportions	Male	Female
Type	0	Omission of Appendages	0	0	Upper and Lower Halves	1　　1	Hair Shading	1	1	Head	05	05
Sex Sequence	1	Position of Both Arms	4	4	Four Quarters	4　　4	Nudity and Transparency	3	6	Neck	03	06
Posture	2　　1	Position of Right Arm	7	7	Relative Size	4	Form	5	5	Shoulders		
Perspective	2　　2	Position of Left Arm	4	4	Constant Line Pressure	5　　0	Detailing	5	5	Right Arm		
Vertical Midline	4　　4	Position of Legs	8	1	Variable Line Pressure	0　　3	Identity and Sex	3	3	Left Arm	02	04
Bilateral Symmetry	0　　0	Relation of Long Axes	2	3	Line Continuity	4　　2	Sophistication	4	4	Chest	04	04
Horizontal Midline	4　　0	Right and Left Halves	2	2	Body Shading	0　　0	Height	03	03	Girth	03	05

GENERAL CHARACTERISTICS OF SUBJECT

IDENTIFICATION
No. 581
Sex M
Marital status S
Age 24 yrs. at
psychological tests

PARENTAL HISTORY				
Father				
C	H	S	D	O
(+)	-	(+)	-	+
Mother				
C	H	S	D	O
-	-	-	-	?

PHYSIOLOGICAL AND METABOLIC DATA

	Admission	Initial	Control	Cold pressor change	Exercise change	Smoking change
Systolic pressure	110					
Diastolic pressure	70					
Heart rate	74					

Age 24 yrs.	Height 66 in.	Ponderal index 12.03
	Weight 165 lbs.	Cholesterol mg. per 100 ml.
	Overweight +17 %	Vital capacity liters

HABIT SURVEY
Smoking habits: nonsmoker
Age begun yrs. Inhalation:
Habits of nervous tension:

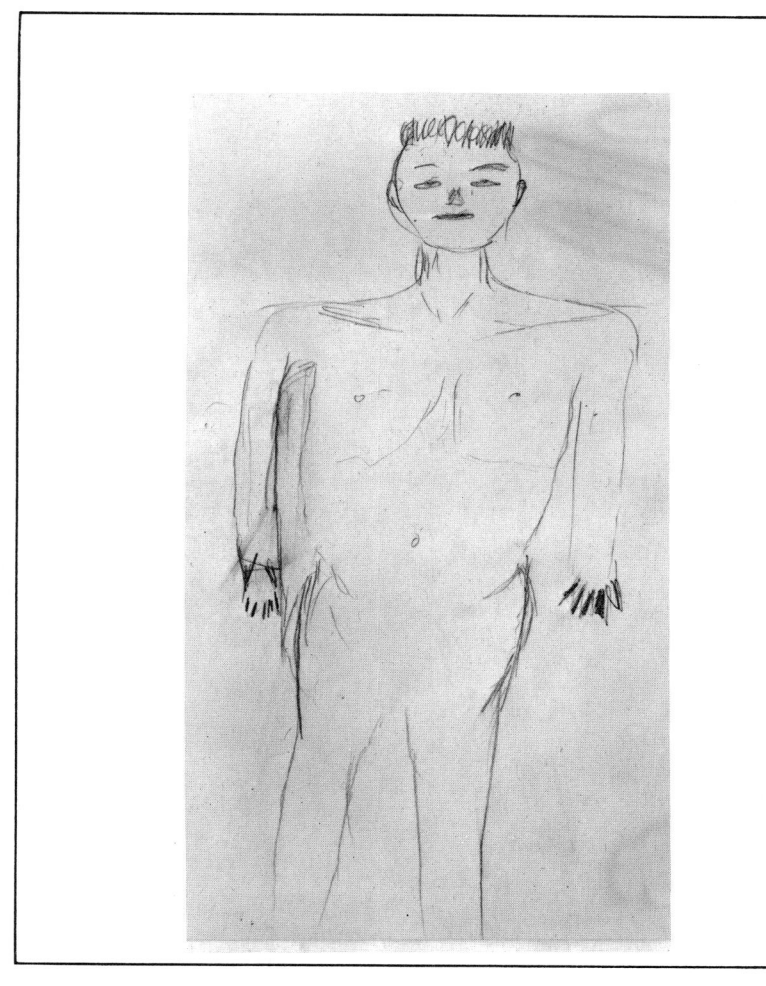

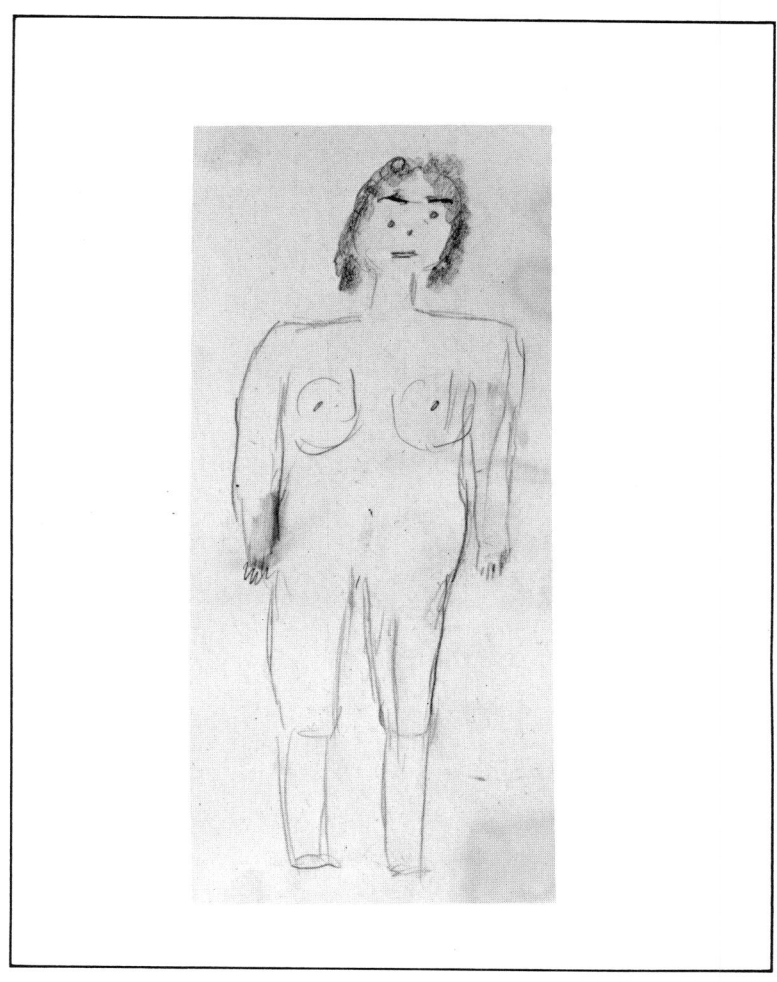

FIGURE-DRAWING CHARACTERISTICS

Structural	Male Female Both	Structural	Male	Female	Structural and Graphic	Male Female Both		Graphic, Global and Height	Male	Female	Body Proportions	Male	Female
Type	0	Omission of Appendages	3	8	Upper and Lower Halves	7	0	Hair Shading	3	3	Head	09	
Sex Sequence	0	Position of Both Arms	0	0	Four Quarters	4	4	Nudity and Transparency	0	0	Neck	16	12
Posture	0 0	Position of Right Arm	0	0	Relative Size	0		Form	3	5	Shoulders	15	10
Perspective	0 0	Position of Left Arm	0	0	Constant Line Pressure	0	0	Detailing	3	5	Right Arm	08	06
Vertical Midline	0 0	Position of Legs	6	6	Variable Line Pressure	2	1	Identity and Sex	1	1	Left Arm	08	06
Bilateral Symmetry	2 3	Relation of Long Axes	1	1	Line Continuity	0	0	Sophistication	4	4	Chest	12	09
Horizontal Midline	0 0	Right and Left Halves	3	1	Body Shading	1	3	Height			Girth	13	13

GENERAL CHARACTERISTICS OF SUBJECT

IDENTIFICATION
No. 765
Sex M
Marital status M
Age 25 yrs. at
psychological tests

PARENTAL HISTORY
Father
C   H   S   D   O
(+)   -   -   -   +
Mother
C   H   S   D   O
-   ?   -   -   +

PHYSIOLOGICAL AND METABOLIC DATA

	Admission	Initial	Control	Cold pressor change	Exercise change	Smoking change
Systolic pressure	130	108	104	+18	+42	
Diastolic pressure	92	68	70	+20	00	
Heart rate	80	76	71	-24	+17	

Age 24 yrs.   Height 67 in.   Ponderal index 12.02

Weight 173 lbs.   Cholesterol 230 mg. per 100 ml.

Overweight +20 %   Vital capacity 5.4 liters

HABIT SURVEY

Smoking habits: former smoker

Age begun 15 yrs.   Inhalation:

Habits of nervous tension: 5, 6, 10, 16, 22

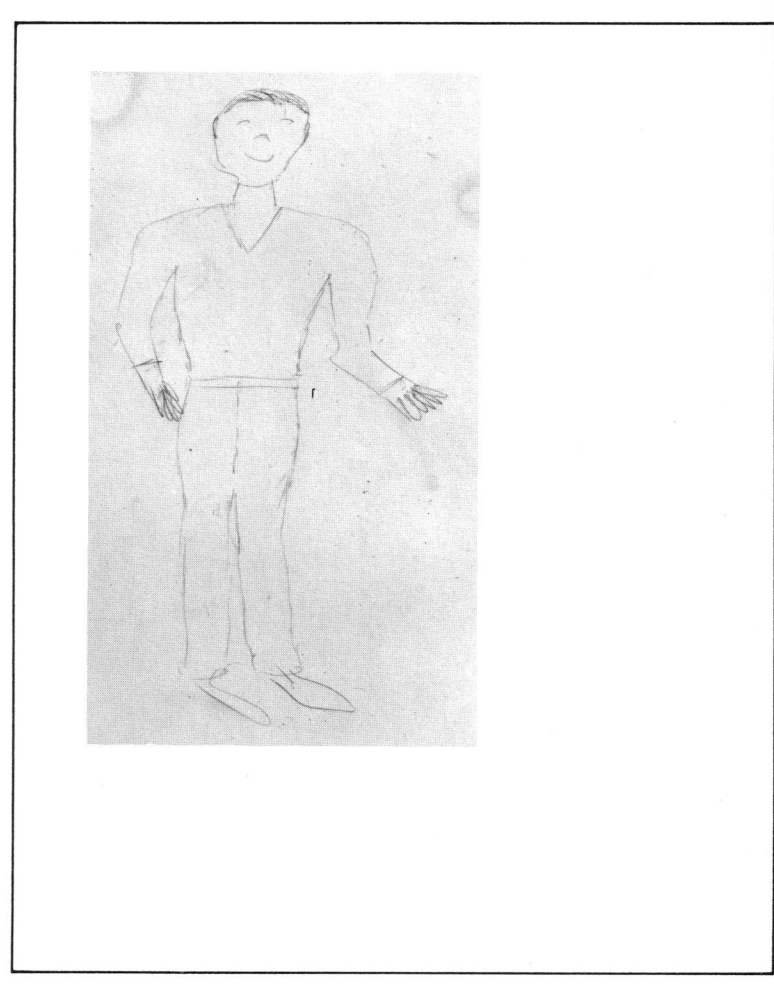

FIGURE-DRAWING CHARACTERISTICS

Structural	Male Female Both		Structural	Male	Female	Structural and Graphic	Male Female Both		Graphic, Global and Height	Male	Female	Body Proportions	Male	Female
Type	0		Omission of Appendages	0	0	Upper and Lower Halves	1	1	Hair Shading	2	3	Head	08	07
Sex Sequence	1		Position of Both Arms	1	1	Four Quarters	4	4	Nudity and Transparency	7	7	Neck	06	04
Posture	1	1	Position of Right Arm	5	5	Relative Size	0		Form	3	3	Shoulders	09	06
Perspective	0	0	Position of Left Arm	3	3	Constant Line Pressure	1	1	Detailing	5	5	Right Arm	04	04
Vertical Midline	3	0	Position of Legs	4	4	Variable Line Pressure	0	0	Identity and Sex	1	1	Left Arm	04	04
Bilateral Symmetry	2	2	Relation of Long Axes	1	1	Line Continuity	0	0	Sophistication	4	4	Chest	07	06
Horizontal Midline	4	4	Right and Left Halves	2	2	Body Shading	0	3	Height	06	06	Girth	07	06

GENERAL CHARACTERISTICS OF SUBJECT

IDENTIFICATION
No. F45
Sex M
Marital status S
Age 29 yrs. at
psychological tests

PARENTAL HISTORY				
Father				
C	H	S	D	O
(+)	+	-	-	-
Mother				
C	H	S	D	O
-	+	+	-	-

PHYSIOLOGICAL AND METABOLIC DATA

	Admission	Initial	Control	Cold pressor change	Exercise change	Smoking change
Systolic pressure	124	120	114	+14	+46	+04
Diastolic pressure	88	88	80	+18	+20	+04
Heart rate	72	68	64	+12	+32	+08

Age 27 yrs.	Height 68 in.		Ponderal index 13.57	
	Weight 126 lbs.		Cholesterol 224 mg. per 100 ml.	
	Overweight -16 %		Vital capacity liters	

HABIT SURVEY
Smoking habits: nonsmoker
Age begun   yrs.   Inhalation:
Habits of nervous tension: 5, 6, 22

Plate 81   **MODERATELY PRIMITIVE DRAWINGS**   119

FIGURE-DRAWING CHARACTERISTICS

Structural	Male Female Both	Structural	Male	Female	Structural and Graphic	Male Female Both		Graphic, Global and Height	Male	Female	Body Proportions	Male	Female
Type	0	Omission of Appendages	0		Upper and Lower Halves	1		Hair Shading	0		Head	11	
Sex Sequence	3	Position of Both Arms	0		Four Quarters	4		Nudity and Transparency	0		Neck	10	
Posture	1		Position of Right Arm	2		Relative Size	7		Form	5		Shoulders		
Perspective	6		Position of Left Arm	2		Constant Line Pressure	5		Detailing	5		Right Arm		
Vertical Midline	4		Position of Legs	4		Variable Line Pressure	0		Identity and Sex	5		Left Arm	04	
Bilateral Symmetry	0		Relation of Long Axes	1		Line Continuity	4		Sophistication	4		Chest		
Horizontal Midline	0		Right and Left Halves	1		Body Shading	0		Height	06		Girth		

GENERAL CHARACTERISTICS OF SUBJECT

IDENTIFICATION
No. 353
Sex M
Marital status M
Age 29 yrs. at
psychological tests

PARENTAL HISTORY
Father
C   H   S   D   O
-   -   (+) -   -
Mother
C   H   S   D   O
(+) +   ?   -   ?

PHYSIOLOGICAL AND METABOLIC DATA

	Admission	Initial	Control	Cold pressor change	Exercise change	Smoking change
Systolic pressure	126	134	122	+02	+32	-08
Diastolic pressure	76	66	62	+20	00	+04
Heart rate	72	90	81	00	+10	+02

Age 28 yrs.	Height 74 in.	Ponderal index 12.87
	Weight 190 lbs.	Cholesterol 243 mg. per 100 ml.
	Overweight +04 %	Vital capacity 5.8 liters

HABIT SURVEY
Smoking habits: former smoker
Age begun   yrs.   Inhalation:
Habits of nervous tension: 4, 5, 11, 20,
21, 22

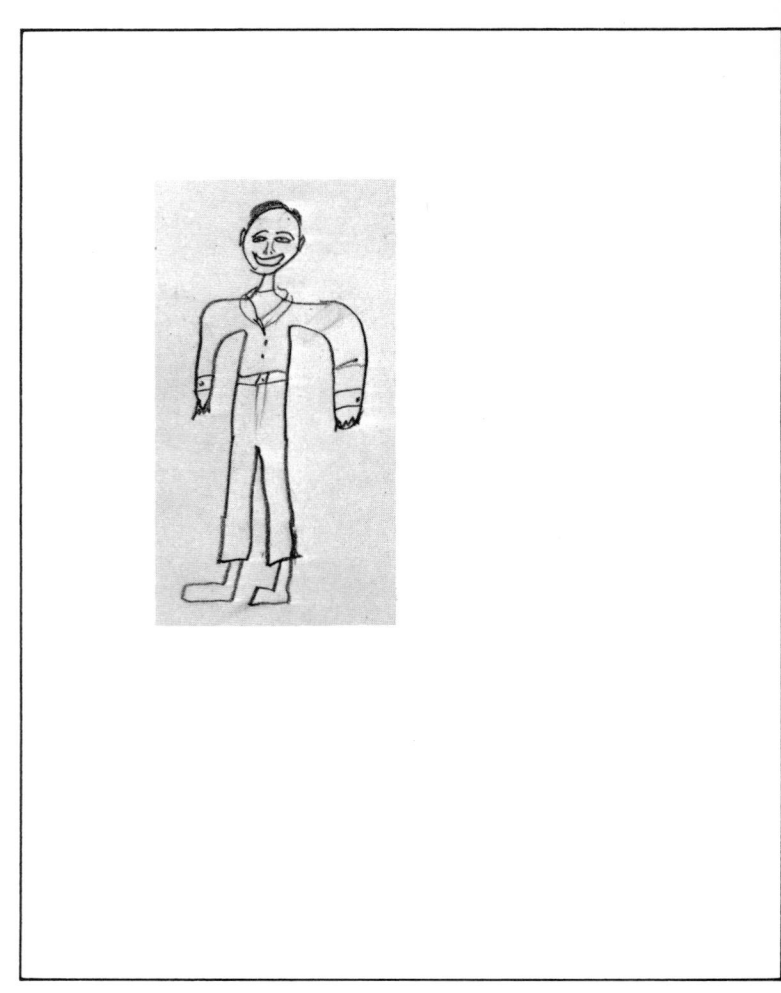

FIGURE-DRAWING CHARACTERISTICS

Structural	Male Female	Structural	Male	Female	Structural and Graphic	Male Female		Graphic, Global and Height	Male	Female	Body Proportions	Male	Female
	Both					Both							
Type	0	Omission of Appendages	0	0	Upper and Lower Halves	1	1	Hair Shading	3	3	Head	05	06
Sex Sequence	1	Position of Both Arms	0	0	Four Quarters	4	4	Nudity and Transparency	7	7	Neck	06	08
Posture	1	1	Position of Right Arm	2	2	Relative Size	2		Form	3	3	Shoulders		
Perspective	0	0	Position of Left Arm	2	2	Constant Line Pressure	5	0	Detailing	3	3	Right Arm	02	02
Vertical Midline	3	3	Position of Legs	4	4	Variable Line Pressure	0	3	Identity and Sex	3	3	Left Arm	02	02
Bilateral Symmetry	1	1	Relation of Long Axes	1	1	Line Continuity	4	4	Sophistication	4	4	Chest	02	02
Horizontal Midline	4	4	Right and Left Halves	2	2	Body Shading	0	0	Height	04	04	Girth	03	03

GENERAL CHARACTERISTICS OF SUBJECT

IDENTIFICATION
No. 350
Sex M
Marital status S
Age 25 yrs. at
psychological tests

PARENTAL HISTORY				
Father				
C	H	S	D	O
?	+	-	-	+
Mother				
C	H	S	D	O
(?)	+	-	-	-

PHYSIOLOGICAL AND METABOLIC DATA

	Admission	Initial	Control	Cold pressor change	Exercise change	Smoking change
Systolic pressure	120	130	108	+02	+46	
Diastolic pressure	70	64	66	+04	+04	
Heart rate	84	96	83	00	+28	

Age 24 yrs.	Height	70	in.	Ponderal index 12.31
	Weight	184	lbs.	Cholesterol 340 mg. per 100 ml.
	Overweight +19 %			Vital capacity liters

HABIT SURVEY
Smoking habits: nonsmoker
Age begun yrs. Inhalation:
Habits of nervous tension: 5, 6, 18, 22

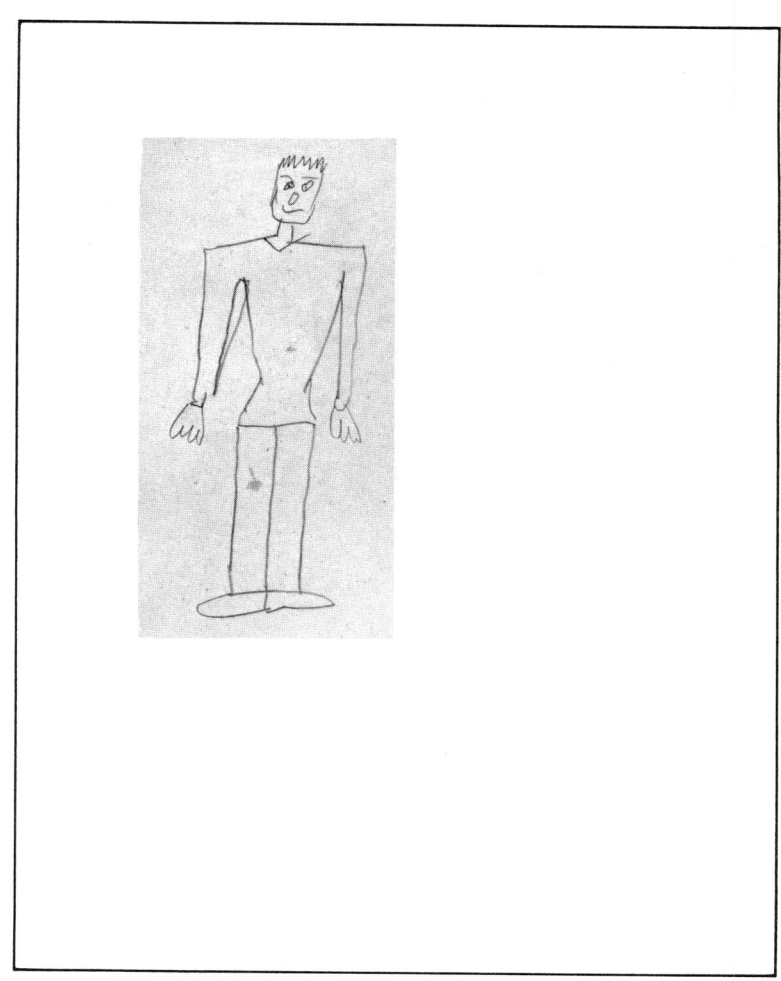

FIGURE-DRAWING CHARACTERISTICS

Structural	Male Female Both	Structural	Male	Female	Structural and Graphic	Male Female Both		Graphic, Global and Height	Male	Female	Body Proportions	Male	Female
Type	0	Omission of Appendages	0	0	Upper and Lower Halves	1	2	Hair Shading	7	3	Head	05	03
Sex Sequence	1	Position of Both Arms	1	0	Four Quarters	4	0	Nudity and Transparency	7	7	Neck	06	06
Posture	1 1	Position of Right Arm	2	0	Relative Size	0		Form	5	5	Shoulders	06	04
Perspective	0 0	Position of Left Arm	0	0	Constant Line Pressure	0	0	Detailing	5	5	Right Arm	04	04
Vertical Midline	0 0	Position of Legs	2	4	Variable Line Pressure	5	1	Identity and Sex	1	1	Left Arm	04	04
Bilateral Symmetry	1 3	Relation of Long Axes	1	1	Line Continuity	4	4	Sophistication	4	4	Chest	04	03
Horizontal Midline	6 4	Right and Left Halves	2	2	Body Shading	0	0	Height	04	04	Girth	03	04

GENERAL CHARACTERISTICS OF SUBJECT

IDENTIFICATION
No. 325
Sex M
Marital status S
Age 25 yrs. at
psychological tests

PARENTAL HISTORY				
Father				
C	H	S	D	O
?	U	U	U	U
Mother				
C	H	S	D	O
–	–	–	–	–

PHYSIOLOGICAL AND METABOLIC DATA

	Admission	Initial	Control	Cold pressor change	Exercise change	Smoking change
Systolic pressure	120	102	92	+06	+38	-02
Diastolic pressure	70	58	62	+08	-01	+04
Heart rate	72	78	77	+10	+09	+06

Age 22 yrs.	Height	72 in.	Ponderal index 13.26
	Weight	160 lbs.	Cholesterol 250 mg. per 100 ml.
	Overweight -02 %		Vital capacity 5.1 liters

HABIT SURVEY

Smoking habits: mixed smoker

Age begun 16 yrs.   Inhalation: yes

Habits of nervous tension: 2, 3, 4, 5, 6, 9, 10, 19

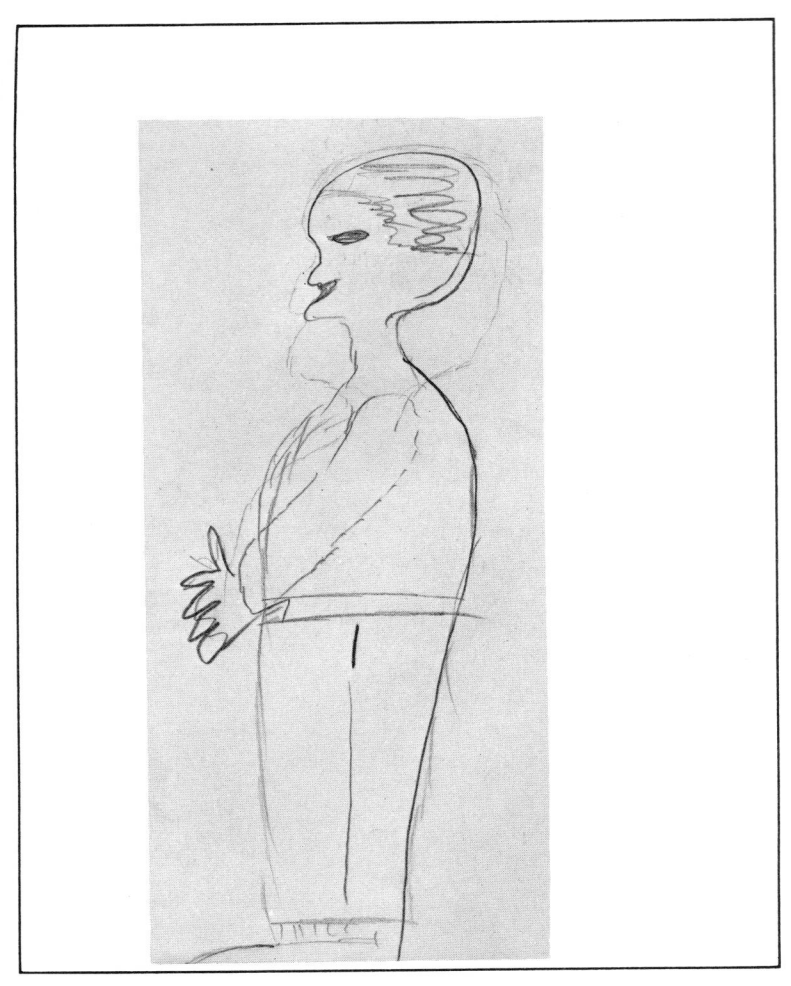

FIGURE-DRAWING CHARACTERISTICS

Structural	Male Female Both		Structural	Male	Female	Structural and Graphic	Male Female Both		Graphic, Global and Height	Male	Female	Body Proportions	Male	Female
Type	0		Omission of Appendages	0	0	Upper and Lower Halves	3	3	Hair Shading	7	3	Head	13	13
Sex Sequence	0		Position of Both Arms	4	0	Four Quarters	4	4	Nudity and Transparency	7	7	Neck	14	18
Posture	1	1	Position of Right Arm	7	2	Relative Size	4		Form	5	5	Shoulders		14
Perspective	2	0	Position of Left Arm	3	2	Constant Line Pressure	0	0	Detailing	5	5	Right Arm		08
Vertical Midline	5	0	Position of Legs	1	4	Variable Line Pressure	4	5	Identity and Sex	3	3	Left Arm	06	06
Bilateral Symmetry	0	2	Relation of Long Axes	1	1	Line Continuity	1	2	Sophistication	4	4	Chest	14	16
Horizontal Midline	4	4	Right and Left Halves	1	1	Body Shading	0	0	Height	08	09	Girth	15	22

GENERAL CHARACTERISTICS OF SUBJECT

IDENTIFICATION
No. 526
Sex M
Marital status M
Age 24 yrs. at
psychological tests

PARENTAL HISTORY
Father
C   H   S   D   O
?   ?   –   –   ?
Mother
C   H   S   D   O
–   –   –   –   –

PHYSIOLOGICAL AND METABOLIC DATA

	Admission	Initial	Control	Cold pressor change	Exercise change	Smoking change
Systolic pressure	120	108	94	+16	+32	+06
Diastolic pressure	80	68	64	+16	–04	+12
Heart rate	72	72	71	00	+17	00

Age 22 yrs.	Height 73 in.	Ponderal index 12.74
	Weight 188 lbs.	Cholesterol 237 mg. per 100 ml.
	Overweight +12 %	Vital capacity 5.0 liters

HABIT SURVEY
Smoking habits: nonsmoker
Age begun   yrs.   Inhalation:
Habits of nervous tension: 5, 6, 9

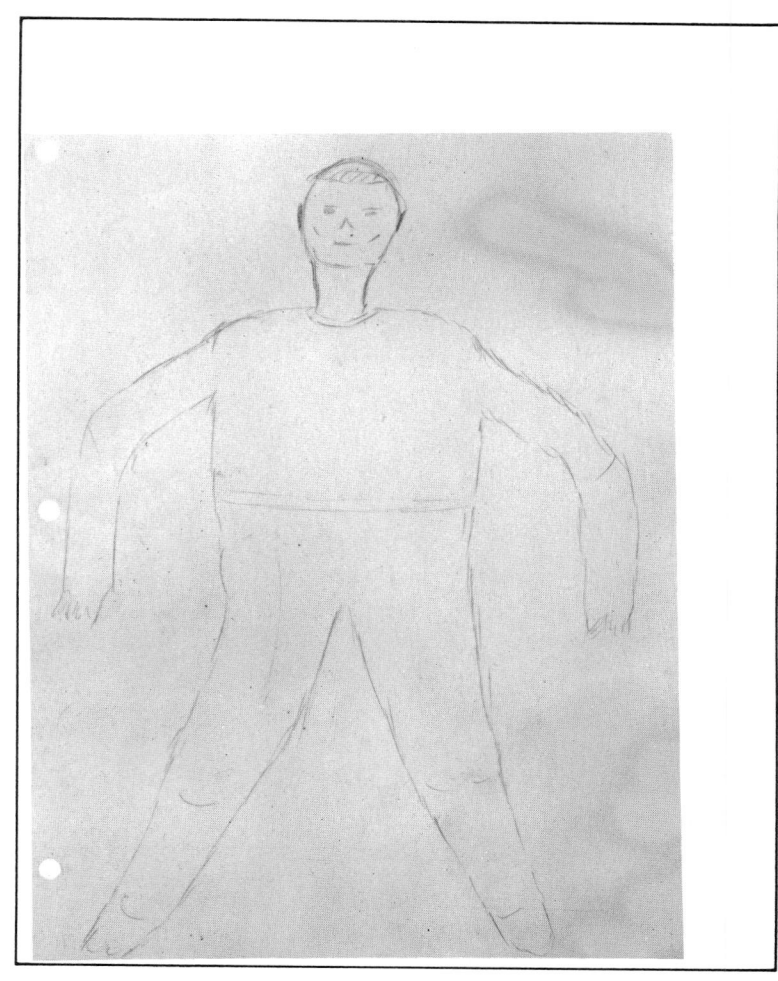

FIGURE-DRAWING CHARACTERISTICS

Structural	Male Female Both	Structural	Male	Female	Structural and Graphic	Male Female Both		Graphic, Global and Height	Male	Female	Body Proportions	Male	Female
Type	0	Omission of Appendages	0	8	Upper and Lower Halves	3	0	Hair Shading	3	3	Head	08	08
Sex Sequence	1	Position of Both Arms	0	0	Four Quarters	4	4	Nudity and Transparency	7	9	Neck	16	12
Posture	1 0	Position of Right Arm	2	2	Relative Size	4		Form	5	5	Shoulders	10	09
Perspective	0 0	Position of Left Arm	2	2	Constant Line Pressure	1	1	Detailing	3	3	Right Arm	08	08
Vertical Midline	0 0	Position of Legs	6	6	Variable Line Pressure	0	0	Identity and Sex	3	3	Left Arm	08	07
Bilateral Symmetry	3 3	Relation of Long Axes	1	1	Line Continuity	0	0	Sophistication	4	4	Chest	13	09
Horizontal Midline	4 4	Right and Left Halves	1	1	Body Shading	2	3	Height	08		Girth	17	12

GENERAL CHARACTERISTICS OF SUBJECT

IDENTIFICATION
No. 764
Sex M
Marital status M
Age 25 yrs. at
psychological tests

PARENTAL HISTORY				
Father				
C	H	S	D	O
?	-	-	-	-
Mother				
C	H	S	D	O
-	-	-	-	-

PHYSIOLOGICAL AND METABOLIC DATA

	Admission	Initial	Control	Cold pressor change	Exercise change	Smoking change
Systolic pressure	130	126	110	+08	+46	+20
Diastolic pressure	78	72	58	+16	-04	+20
Heart rate	76	80	77	+12		+06

Age 23 yrs.	Height 70 in.	Ponderal index 12.39
	Weight 180 lbs.	Cholesterol 214 mg. per 100 ml.
	Overweight +16 %	Vital capacity 5.8 liters

HABIT SURVEY
Smoking habits: occasional smoker
Age begun 17 yrs.   Inhalation: yes
Habits of nervous tension: 2, 5, 6

FIGURE-DRAWING CHARACTERISTICS

Structural	Male Female Both	Structural	Male	Female	Structural and Graphic	Male Female Both	Graphic, Global and Height	Male	Female	Body Proportions	Male	Female
Type	0	Omission of Appendages	0	0	Upper and Lower Halves	1	3	Hair Shading	1	1	Head	09	11
Sex Sequence	0	Position of Both Arms	1	0	Four Quarters	4	4	Nudity and Transparency	7	7	Neck	05	08
Posture	1	1	Position of Right Arm	5	1	Relative Size	4		Form	5	5	Shoulders		09
Perspective	6	0	Position of Left Arm	2	1	Constant Line Pressure	0	0	Detailing	5	5	Right Arm	06	04
Vertical Midline	7	3	Position of Legs	4	6	Variable Line Pressure	1	1	Identity and Sex	3	3	Left Arm	06	04
Bilateral Symmetry	0	2	Relation of Long Axes	1	1	Line Continuity	1	2	Sophistication	4	4	Chest		07
Horizontal Midline	4	4	Right and Left Halves	1	1	Body Shading	0	0	Height	07	08	Girth		11

GENERAL CHARACTERISTICS OF SUBJECT

IDENTIFICATION
No. G28
Sex M
Marital status S
Age 22 yrs. at
psychological tests

PARENTAL HISTORY				
Father				
C	H	S	D	O
?	-	-	-	-
Mother				
C	H	S	D	O
-	-	-	-	+

PHYSIOLOGICAL AND METABOLIC DATA

	Admission	Initial	Control	Cold pressor change	Exercise change	Smoking change
Systolic pressure	128	118	112	+10	+26	+06
Diastolic pressure	74	58	58	+14	+02	+06
Heart rate	68	52	60	+04	+12	+01

Age 21 yrs.	Height	72	in.	Ponderal index	13.00	
	Weight	170	lbs.	Cholesterol	217	mg. per 100 ml.
	Overweight	+05	%	Vital capacity		liters

HABIT SURVEY

Smoking habits: cigar smoker

Age begun 20 yrs.   Inhalation: no

Habits of nervous tension: 5

STRONG VOCATIONAL INTEREST TEST

Occupation	Artist	Psychologist	Architect	Physician	Osteopath	Dentist	Veterinarian	Mathematician	Physicist	Engineer	Chemist	Production Manager
Standard Score	28	64	34	63	50	41	19	31	30	36	52	32

Occupation	Farmer	Aviator	Carpenter	Printer	Math.-Sci. Teacher	Ind. Arts Teacher	Voc. Agric. Teacher	Policeman	Forest Serv. Man	Y.M.C.A. Phys. Dir.	Personnel Director	Public Administrator
Standard Score	23	44	18	45	51	20	30	37	35	47	59	63

Occupation	Y.M.C.A. Secretary	Soc. Sci. H.S. Teacher	City Sch. Sup't.	Social Worker	Minister	Musician Performer	C.P.A.	Senior C.P.A.	Accountant	Office Man	Purchasing Agent	Banker
Standard Score	34	49	49	63	59	56	42	53	26	31	14	14

Occupation	Mortician	Pharmacist	Sales Manager	Real Est. Manager	Life Ins. Salesman	Advertising Man	Lawyer	Author- Journalist	President Mfg. Co.	Interest Maturity	Occupational Level	Masculinity- Femininity
Standard Score	19	31	22	26	25	36	44	34	18	64	51	48

Plate 87 **MODERATELY PRIMITIVE DRAWINGS** 125

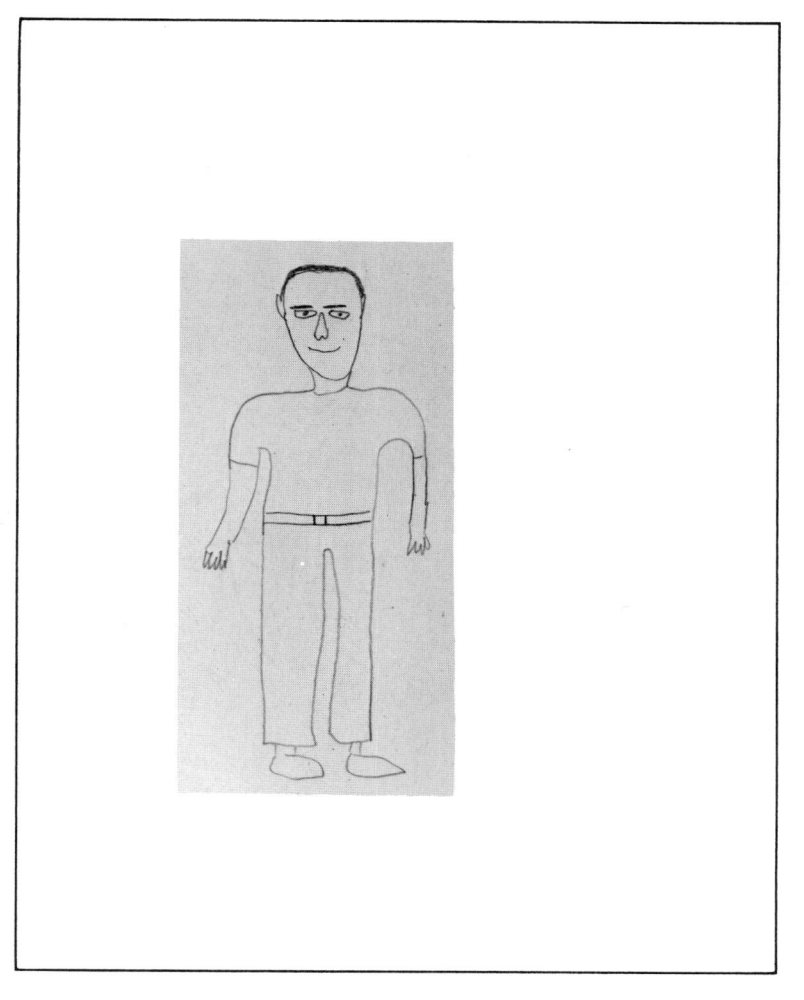

FIGURE-DRAWING CHARACTERISTICS

Structural	Male Female Both	Structural	Male	Female	Structural and Graphic	Male Female Both		Graphic, Global and Height	Male	Female	Body Proportions	Male	Female
Type	0	Omission of Appendages	0	0	Upper and Lower Halves	3	3	Hair Shading	3	3	Head	09	09
Sex Sequence	0	Position of Both Arms	1	0	Four Quarters	4	4	Nudity and Transparency	7	7	Neck	05	04
Posture	1 1	Position of Right Arm	1	0	Relative Size	0		Form	5	5	Shoulders	07	05
Perspective	0 0	Position of Left Arm	0	0	Constant Line Pressure	0	0	Detailing	3	3	Right Arm	04	02
Vertical Midline	0 0	Position of Legs	5	6	Variable Line Pressure	1	5	Identity and Sex	3	3	Left Arm	04	02
Bilateral Symmetry	2 2	Relation of Long Axes	1	1	Line Continuity	4	4	Sophistication	4	4	Chest	05	04
Horizontal Midline	4 4	Right and Left Halves	1	2	Body Shading	0	0	Height	05	04	Girth	07	06

GENERAL CHARACTERISTICS OF SUBJECT

IDENTIFICATION
No. B16
Sex M
Marital status S
Age 22 yrs. at
psychological tests

PARENTAL HISTORY				
Father				
C	H	S	D	O
?	+	-	-	?
Mother				
C	H	S	D	O
-	-	-	-	-

PHYSIOLOGICAL AND METABOLIC DATA

	Admission	Initial	Control	Cold pressor change	Exercise change	Smoking change
Systolic pressure	145	124	116	+26	+46	-03
Diastolic pressure	80	62	60	+22	-20	+02
Heart rate	80	74	68	+26	+39	+04

Age 22 yrs.	Height 67 in.	Ponderal index 13.19
	Weight 131 lbs.	Cholesterol 255 mg. per 100 ml.
	Overweight -08 %	Vital capacity 5.0 liters

HABIT SURVEY
Smoking habits: nonsmoker
Age begun   yrs.   Inhalation:
Habits of nervous tension: 2, 3, 6, 9

STRONG VOCATIONAL INTEREST TEST

Occupation	Artist	Psychologist	Architect	Physician	Osteopath	Dentist	Veterinarian	Mathematician	Physicist	Engineer	Chemist	Production Manager
Standard Score	28	43	20	43	42	33	22	21	18	24	26	29

Occupation	Farmer	Aviator	Carpenter	Printer	Math.-Sci. Teacher	Ind. Arts Teacher	Voc. Agric. Teacher	Policeman	Forest Serv. Man	Y.M.C.A. Phys. Dir.	Personnel Director	Public Administrator
Standard Score	27	34	09	30	31	11	24	27	13	31	39	41

Occupation	Y.M.C.A. Secretary	Soc. Sci. H.S. Teacher	City Sch. Sup't.	Social Worker	Minister	Musician Performer	C.P.A.	Senior C.P.A.	Accountant	Office Man	Purchasing Agent	Banker
Standard Score	25	35	32	42	61	34	29	27	16	29	25	21

Occupation	Mortician	Pharmacist	Sales Manager	Real Est. Manager	Life Ins. Salesman	Advertising Man	Lawyer	Author-Journalist	President Mfg. Co.	Interest Maturity	Occupational Level	Masculinity-Femininity
Standard Score	32	34	41	49	43	38	48	37	36	51	60	52

FIGURE-DRAWING CHARACTERISTICS

Structural	Male Female Both	Structural	Male	Female	Structural and Graphic	Male Female Both		Graphic, Global and Height	Male	Female	Body Proportions	Male	Female
Type	0	Omission of Appendages	0	0	Upper and Lower Halves	0	1	Hair Shading	0	3	Head	06	06
Sex Sequence	1	Position of Both Arms	0	0	Four Quarters	4	4	Nudity and Transparency	7	7	Neck	10	06
Posture	1 1	Position of Right Arm	0	0	Relative Size	0		Form	5	5	Shoulders	10	07
Perspective	0 0	Position of Left Arm	0	0	Constant Line Pressure	3	0	Detailing	5	5	Right Arm	06	04
Vertical Midline	3 3	Position of Legs	6	6	Variable Line Pressure	0	3	Identity and Sex	1	1	Left Arm	06	04
Bilateral Symmetry	3 3	Relation of Long Axes	1	1	Line Continuity	4	0	Sophistication	4	4	Chest	07	09
Horizontal Midline	4 4	Right and Left Halves	1	1	Body Shading	0	0	Height	06	05	Girth	09	06

GENERAL CHARACTERISTICS OF SUBJECT

IDENTIFICATION
No. B27
Sex M
Marital status S
Age 23 yrs. at
psychological tests

PARENTAL HISTORY				
Father				
C	H	S	D	O
?	?	-	-	+
Mother				
C	H	S	D	O
-	-	-	-	-

PHYSIOLOGICAL AND METABOLIC DATA

	Admission	Initial	Control	Cold pressor change	Exercise change	Smoking change
Systolic pressure	150	124	122	+12	+26	+03
Diastolic pressure	100	50	62	+22	-10	-01
Heart rate	84	68	68	+08	+13	+01

Age 21 yrs.	Height 74 in.	Ponderal index 12.46
	Weight 210 lbs.	Cholesterol 265 mg. per 100 ml.
	Overweight +22 %	Vital capacity 5.6 liters

HABIT SURVEY
Smoking habits: nonsmoker
Age begun yrs. Inhalation:
Habits of nervous tension: 1, 3, 4, 5, 6, 8,
9, 10, 16, 23, 25

STRONG VOCATIONAL INTEREST TEST

Occupation	Artist	Psychologist	Architect	Physician	Osteopath	Dentist	Veterinarian	Mathematician	Physicist	Engineer	Chemist	Production Manager
Standard Score	28	35	29	39	39	33	07	30	29	40	48	36

Occupation	Farmer	Aviator	Carpenter	Printer	Math.-Sci. Teacher	Ind. Arts Teacher	Voc. Agric. Teacher	Policeman	Forest Serv. Man	Y.M.C.A. Phys. Dir.	Personnel Director	Public Administrator
Standard Score	31	44	16	37	40	08	14	27	27	18	36	45

Occupation	Y.M.C.A. Secretary	Soc. Sci. H.S. Teacher	City Sch. Sup't.	Social Worker	Minister	Musician Performer	C.P.A.	Senior C.P.A.	Accountant	Office Man	Purchasing Agent	Banker
Standard Score	17	26	15	23	61	36	38	48	41	36	38	24

Occupation	Mortician	Pharmacist	Sales Manager	Real Est. Manager	Life Ins. Salesman	Advertising Man	Lawyer	Author-Journalist	President Mfg. Co.	Interest Maturity	Occupational Level	Masculinity-Femininity
Standard Score	30	34	24	29	18	33	36	35	30	51	57	47

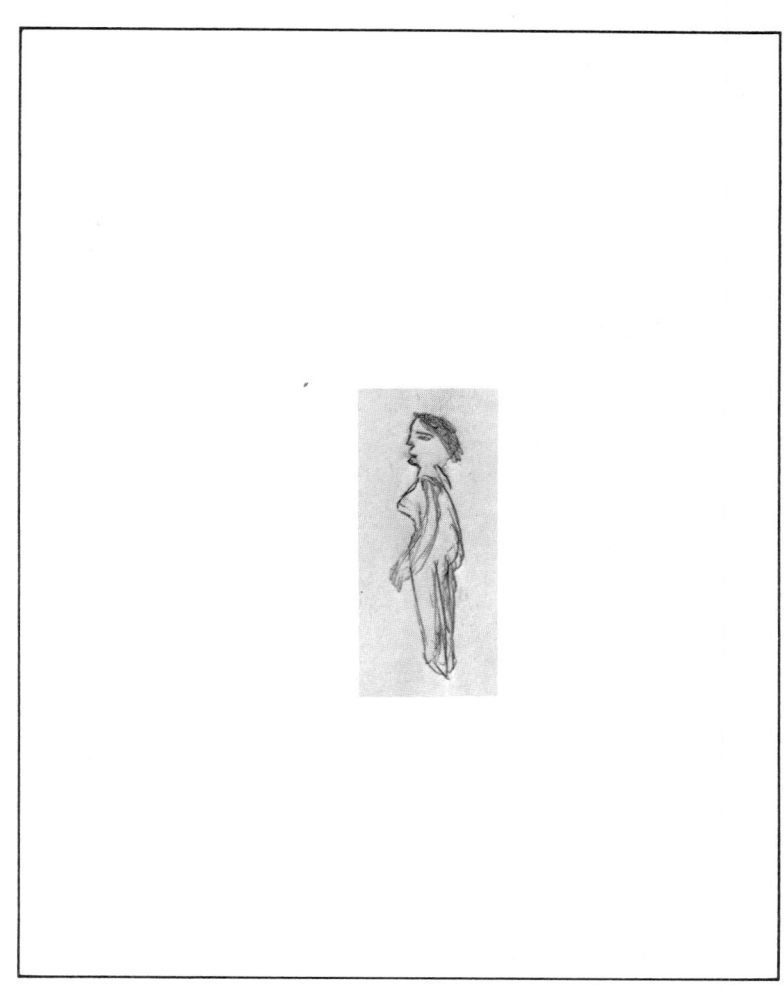

FIGURE-DRAWING CHARACTERISTICS

Structural	Male Female Both	Structural	Male	Female	Structural and Graphic	Male Female Both		Graphic, Global and Height	Male	Female	Body Proportions	Male	Female
Type	0	Omission of Appendages	7	8	Upper and Lower Halves	1	3	Hair Shading	3	3	Head	06	04
Sex Sequence	0	Position of Both Arms	1	4	Four Quarters	4	4	Nudity and Transparency	3	9	Neck	05	02
Posture	1 0	Position of Right Arm	5	7	Relative Size	0		Form	5	5	Shoulders	05	
Perspective	0 2	Position of Left Arm	1	4	Constant Line Pressure	2	0	Detailing	5	5	Right Arm		
Vertical Midline	0 4	Position of Legs	6	1	Variable Line Pressure	0	1	Identity and Sex	3	3	Left Arm	04	02
Bilateral Symmetry	2 0	Relation of Long Axes	1	1	Line Continuity	0	0	Sophistication	4	4	Chest	04	03
Horizontal Midline	4 0	Right and Left Halves	1	4	Body Shading	3	0	Height	05		Girth	06	04

GENERAL CHARACTERISTICS OF SUBJECT

IDENTIFICATION
No. C76
Sex M
Marital status S
Age 27 yrs. at psychological tests

PARENTAL HISTORY
Father
C   H   S   D   O
?   -   -   +   -
Mother
C   H   S   D   O
-   -   -   -   -

PHYSIOLOGICAL AND METABOLIC DATA

	Admission	Initial	Control	Cold pressor change	Exercise change	Smoking change
Systolic pressure	125	128	121	+04	+39	+04
Diastolic pressure	70	56	55	+20	+07	-01
Heart rate	88	72	73	+04	+10	-02

Age 26 yrs.   Height 76 in.   Weight 186 lbs.   Overweight -03 %

Ponderal index 13.31   Cholesterol 200 mg. per 100 ml.   Vital capacity 6.4 liters

HABIT SURVEY
Smoking habits: nonsmoker
Age begun   yrs.   Inhalation:
Habits of nervous tension: 5, 6, 9

STRONG VOCATIONAL INTEREST TEST

Occupation	Artist	Psychologist	Architect	Physician	Osteopath	Dentist	Veterinarian	Mathematician	Physicist	Engineer	Chemist	Production Manager
Standard Score	21	29	18	45	49	41	40	18	05	12	18	28

Occupation	Farmer	Aviator	Carpenter	Printer	Math.-Sci. Teacher	Ind. Arts Teacher	Voc. Agric. Teacher	Policeman	Forest Serv. Man	Y.M.C.A. Phys. Dir.	Personnel Director	Public Administrator
Standard Score	45	29	25	41	51	29	48	40	36	55	37	45

Occupation	Y.M.C.A. Secretary	Soc. Sci. H.S. Teacher	City Sch. Sup't.	Social Worker	Minister	Musician Performer	C.P.A.	Senior C.P.A.	Accountant	Office Man	Purchasing Agent	Banker
Standard Score	54	59	45	48	62	49	07	39	22	42	14	32

Occupation	Mortician	Pharmacist	Sales Manager	Real Est. Manager	Life Ins. Salesman	Advertising Man	Lawyer	Author- Journalist	President Mfg. Co.	Interest Maturity	Occupational Level	Masculinity- Femininity
Standard Score	31	23	18	29	31	22	28	24	08	63	44	44

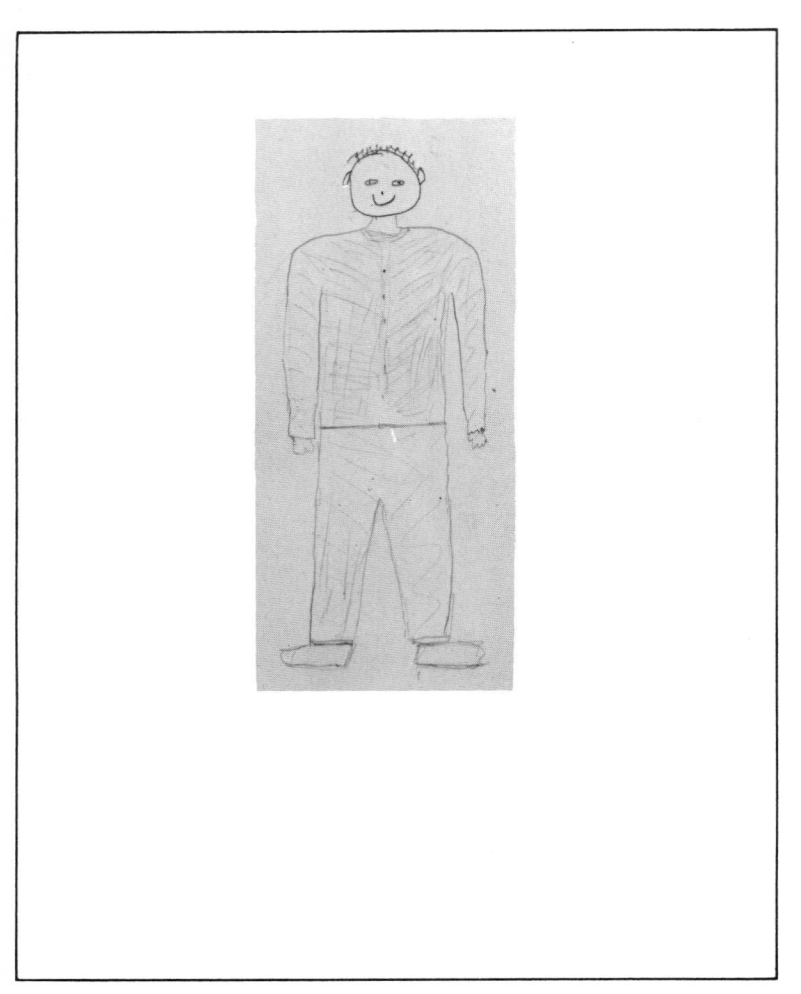

FIGURE-DRAWING CHARACTERISTICS

Structural	Male Female Both	Structural	Male	Female	Structural and Graphic	Male Female Both		Graphic, Global and Height	Male	Female	Body Proportions	Male	Female
Type	0	Omission of Appendages	0	0	Upper and Lower Halves	1	1	Hair Shading	7	3	Head	05	05
Sex Sequence	0	Position of Both Arms	0	0	Four Quarters	4	4	Nudity and Transparency	7	7	Neck	05	06
Posture	1 1	Position of Right Arm	0	0	Relative Size	0		Form	5	5	Shoulders	07	06
Perspective	0 0	Position of Left Arm	0	0	Constant Line Pressure	1	1	Detailing	3	3	Right Arm	05	04
Vertical Midline	3 0	Position of Legs	6	6	Variable Line Pressure	0	0	Identity and Sex	3	3	Left Arm	05	04
Bilateral Symmetry	4 4	Relation of Long Axes	1	1	Line Continuity	1	0	Sophistication	4	4	Chest	06	05
Horizontal Midline	4 4	Right and Left Halves	1	1	Body Shading	7	7	Height	05	04	Girth	08	06

GENERAL CHARACTERISTICS OF SUBJECT

IDENTIFICATION
No. D23
Sex M
Marital status S
Age 23 yrs. at
psychological tests

PARENTAL HISTORY
Father
C H S D O
? + - - -
Mother
C H S D O
- - - - -

PHYSIOLOGICAL AND METABOLIC DATA

	Admission	Initial	Control	Cold pressor change	Exercise change	Smoking change
Systolic pressure	134	130	118	+22	+44	+02
Diastolic pressure	70	71	70	+12	-01	+06
Heart rate	78	88	81	+08	+15	+04

Age 23 yrs.	Height 75 in.	Ponderal index 13.18
	Weight 184 lbs.	Cholesterol 248 mg. per 100 ml.
	Overweight +02 %	Vital capacity liters

HABIT SURVEY

Smoking habits: nonsmoker

Age begun yrs.   Inhalation:

Habits of nervous tension: 3, 5, 19, 21, 22

STRONG VOCATIONAL INTEREST TEST

Occupation	Artist	Psychologist	Architect	Physician	Osteopath	Dentist	Veterinarian	Mathematician	Physicist	Engineer	Chemist	Production Manager
Standard Score	29	53	34	49	56	33	26	17	18	31	31	39

Occupation	Farmer	Aviator	Carpenter	Printer	Math.-Sci. Teacher	Ind. Arts Teacher	Voc. Agric. Teacher	Policeman	Forest Serv. Man	Y.M.C.A. Phys. Dir.	Personnel Director	Public Administrator
Standard Score	32	44	29	40	42	30	35	39	43	49	66	67

Occupation	Y.M.C.A. Secretary	Soc. Sci. H.S. Teacher	City Sch. Sup't.	Social Worker	Minister	Musician Performer	C.P.A.	Senior C.P.A.	Accountant	Office Man	Purchasing Agent	Banker
Standard Score	37	48	37	61	63	47	37	48	33	36	21	13

Occupation	Mortician	Pharmacist	Sales Manager	Real Est. Manager	Life Ins. Salesman	Advertising Man	Lawyer	Author-Journalist	President Mfg. Co.	Interest Maturity	Occupational Level	Masculinity-Femininity
Standard Score	33	39	32	35	37	37	41	36	34	62	53	37

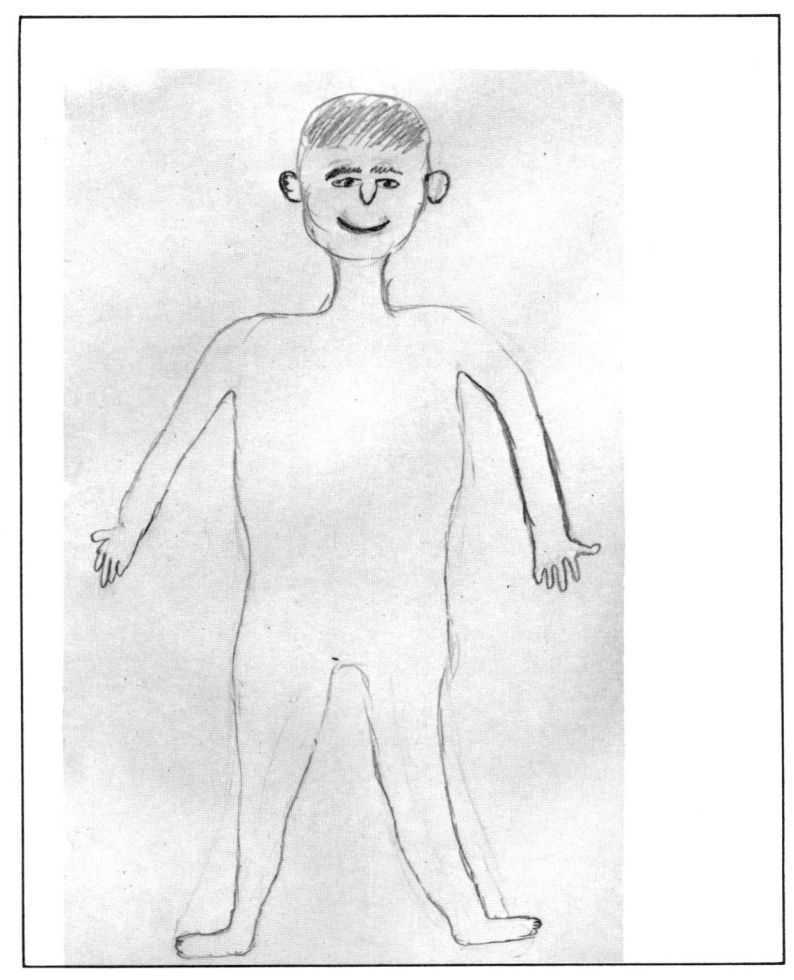
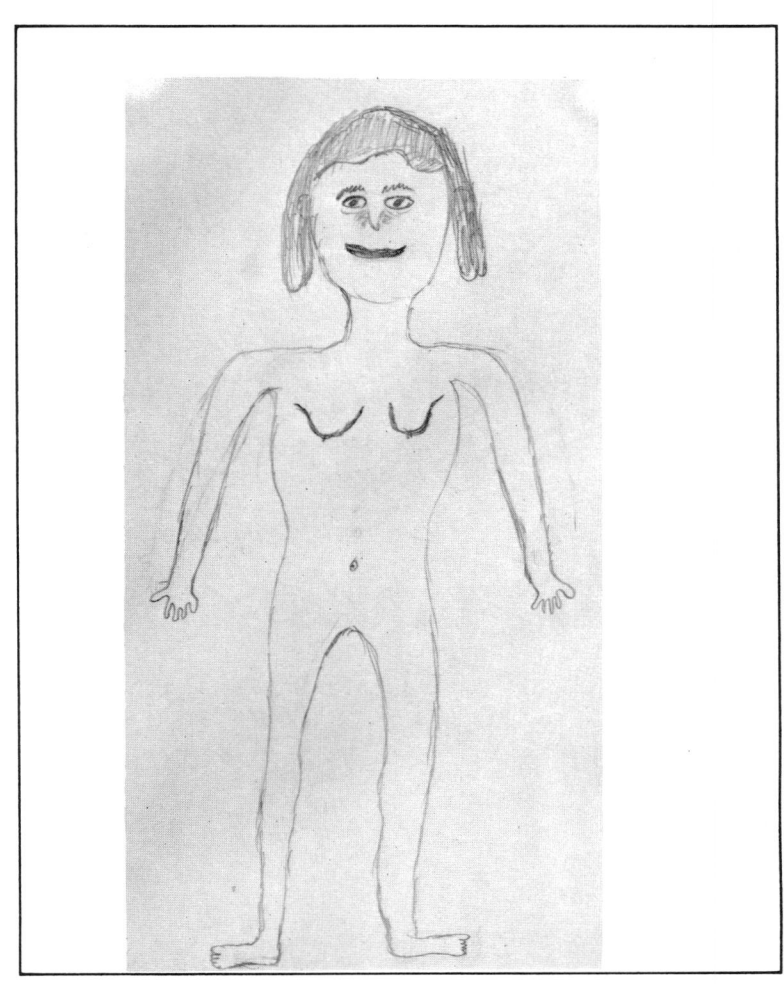

FIGURE-DRAWING CHARACTERISTICS

Structural	Male Female Both	Structural	Male	Female	Structural and Graphic	Male Female Both		Graphic, Global and Height	Male	Female	Body Proportions	Male	Female
Type	0	Omission of Appendages	0	0	Upper and Lower Halves	3	3	Hair Shading	1	3	Head	14	16
Sex Sequence	0	Position of Both Arms	0	0	Four Quarters	4	4	Nudity and Transparency	0	0	Neck	08	16
Posture	1	1	Position of Right Arm	2	2	Relative Size	1		Form	5	5	Shoulders	11	09
Perspective	0	0	Position of Left Arm	2	2	Constant Line Pressure	0	0	Detailing	3	3	Right Arm	06	06
Vertical Midline	0	0	Position of Legs	6	6	Variable Line Pressure	4	2	Identity and Sex	3	1	Left Arm	06	06
Bilateral Symmetry	3	3	Relation of Long Axes	1	1	Line Continuity	0	0	Sophistication	4	4	Chest	10	09
Horizontal Midline	0	0	Right and Left Halves	1	1	Body Shading	0	1	Height	09	09	Girth	13	09

GENERAL CHARACTERISTICS OF SUBJECT

IDENTIFICATION
No. 649
Sex M
Marital status M
Age 25 yrs. at
psychological tests

PARENTAL HISTORY
Father
C H S D O
- - - - -
Mother
C H S D O
? + - - +

PHYSIOLOGICAL AND METABOLIC DATA

	Admission	Initial	Control	Cold pressor change	Exercise change	Smoking change
Systolic pressure	120	124	114	+06	+38	+02
Diastolic pressure	70	62	68	+24	+02	+01
Heart rate	80	88	80	+16	+06	+11

Age 22 yrs.	Height	76 in.	Ponderal index 13.62
	Weight	174 lbs.	Cholesterol 197 mg. per 100 ml.
	Overweight -05 %		Vital capacity liters

HABIT SURVEY

Smoking habits: mixed smoker

Age begun 19 yrs.   Inhalation: yes

Habits of nervous tension: 2, 5, 6, 9, 16, 21, 23

FIGURE-DRAWING CHARACTERISTICS

Structural	Male Female Both		Structural	Male	Female	Structural and Graphic	Male	Female Both		Graphic, Global and Height	Male	Female	Body Proportions	Male	Female
Type	0		Omission of Appendages	0	0	Upper and Lower Halves	2	2		Hair Shading	7	3	Head	01	01
Sex Sequence	0		Position of Both Arms	0	0	Four Quarters	0	4		Nudity and Transparency	0	0	Neck	00	02
Posture	1	1	Position of Right Arm	2	2	Relative Size	4			Form	5	5	Shoulders	00	00
Perspective	0	0	Position of Left Arm	2	2	Constant Line Pressure	4	0		Detailing	5	5	Right Arm	00	00
Vertical Midline	0	0	Position of Legs	6	6	Variable Line Pressure	0	2		Identity and Sex	5	5	Left Arm	00	00
Bilateral Symmetry	2	2	Relation of Long Axes	1	1	Line Continuity	4	0		Sophistication	4	4	Chest	00	00
Horizontal Midline	0	0	Right and Left Halves	2	1	Body Shading	0	0		Height	00	00	Girth	00	00

GENERAL CHARACTERISTICS OF SUBJECT

IDENTIFICATION
No. C59
Sex M
Marital status S
Age 22 yrs. at
psychological tests

PARENTAL HISTORY				
Father				
C	H	S	D	O
-	-	-	-	-
Mother				
C	H	S	D	O
?	-	-	-	-

PHYSIOLOGICAL AND METABOLIC DATA

	Admission	Initial	Control	Cold pressor change	Exercise change	Smoking change
Systolic pressure	120	130	120	-02	+55	+14
Diastolic pressure	80	65	64	+17	-04	+16
Heart rate	68	60	56	+12	+30	+09

Age 23 yrs.   Height 72 in.   Ponderal index 13.04
Weight 168 lbs.   Cholesterol 252 mg. per 100 ml.
Overweight +02 %   Vital capacity 5.7 liters

HABIT SURVEY

Smoking habits: heavy cigarette smoker
Age begun 20 yrs.   Inhalation: yes
Habits of nervous tension: 5, 10, 23, 25

STRONG VOCATIONAL INTEREST TEST

Occupation	Artist	Psychologist	Architect	Physician	Osteopath	Dentist	Veterinarian	Mathematician	Physicist	Engineer	Chemist	Production Manager
Standard Score	12	39	13	40	35	12	26	18	08	23	23	29

Occupation	Farmer	Aviator	Carpenter	Printer	Math.-Sci. Teacher	Ind. Arts Teacher	Voc. Agric. Teacher	Policeman	Forest Serv. Man	Y.M.C.A. Phys. Dir.	Personnel Director	Public Administrator
Standard Score	30	40	04	25	37	04	29	34	34	40	50	57

Occupation	Y.M.C.A. Secretary	Soc. Sci. H.S. Teacher	City Sch. Sup't.	Social Worker	Minister	Musician Performer	C.P.A.	Senior C.P.A.	Accountant	Office Man	Purchasing Agent	Banker
Standard Score	32	44	39	49	62	25	35	47	29	36	14	28

Occupation	Mortician	Pharmacist	Sales Manager	Real Est. Manager	Life Ins. Salesman	Advertising Man	Lawyer	Author-Journalist	President Mfg. Co.	Interest Maturity	Occupational Level	Masculinity-Femininity
Standard Score	24	23	36	35	35	33	40	27	22	58	54	52

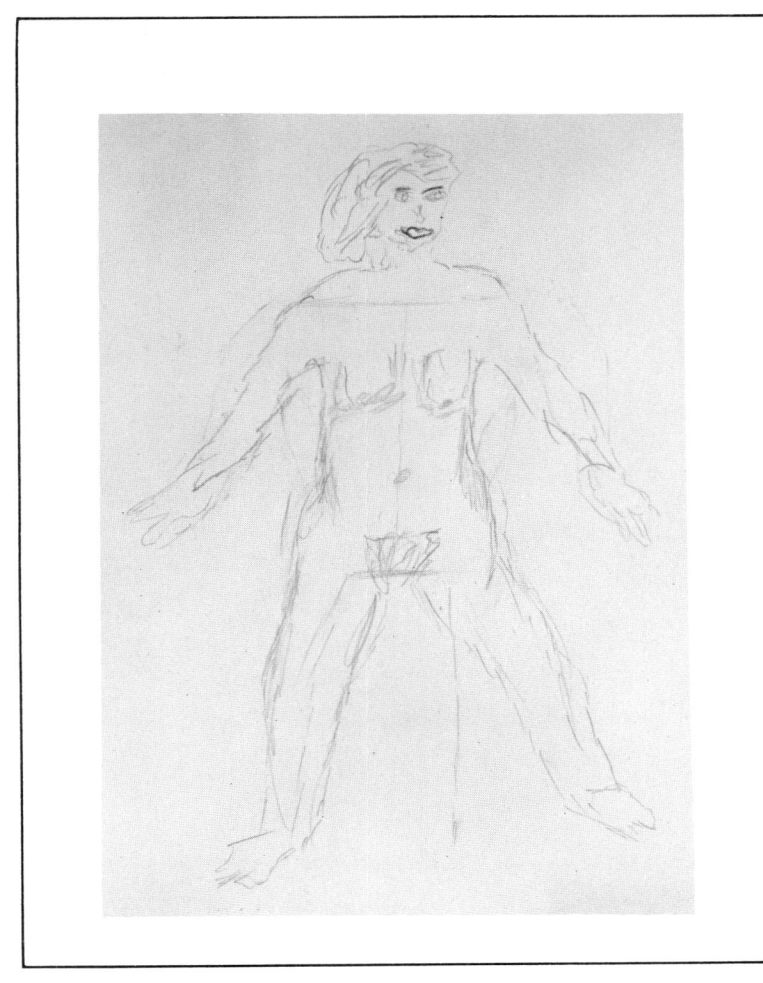

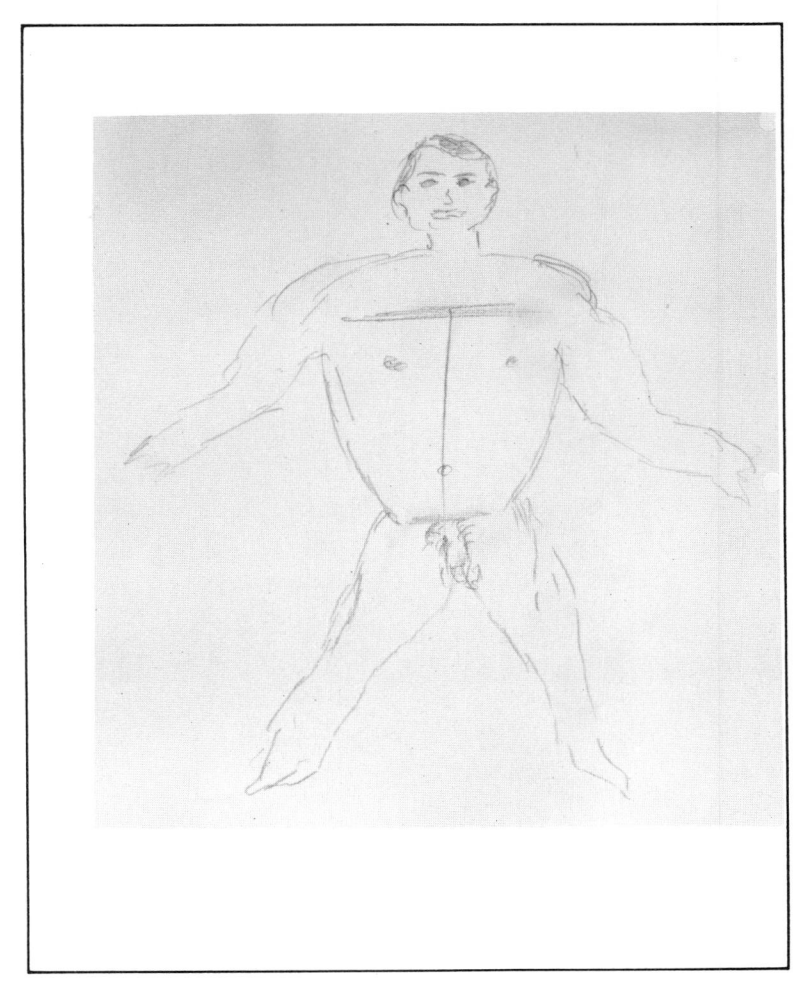

FIGURE-DRAWING CHARACTERISTICS

Structural	Male Female Both	Structural	Male	Female	Structural and Graphic	Male Female Both		Graphic, Global and Height	Male	Female	Body Proportions	Male	Female
Type	0	Omission of Appendages	0	0	Upper and Lower Halves	1	3	Hair Shading	3	3	Head	08	08
Sex Sequence	1	Position of Both Arms	0	0	Four Quarters	4	4	Nudity and Transparency	0	0	Neck	08	06
Posture	1 1	Position of Right Arm	2	2	Relative Size	4		Form	3	3	Shoulders	10	08
Perspective	0 0	Position of Left Arm	2	2	Constant Line Pressure	1	1	Detailing	3	3	Right Arm	06	08
Vertical Midline	0 0	Position of Legs	6	6	Variable Line Pressure	0	0	Identity and Sex	1	1	Left Arm	07	08
Bilateral Symmetry	3 3	Relation of Long Axes	1	1	Line Continuity	0	0	Sophistication	4	4	Chest	11	08
Horizontal Midline	0 0	Right and Left Halves	3	3	Body Shading	3	3	Height	07	07	Girth	08	10

GENERAL CHARACTERISTICS OF SUBJECT

IDENTIFICATION
No. E64
Sex M
Marital status S
Age 22 yrs. at
psychological tests

PARENTAL HISTORY				
Father				
C	H	S	D	O
-	+	?	-	+
Mother				
C	H	S	D	O
?	-	-	-	-

PHYSIOLOGICAL AND METABOLIC DATA

	Admission	Initial	Control	Cold pressor change	Exercise change	Smoking change
Systolic pressure	125	125	122	+28	+26	+01
Diastolic pressure	60	77	73	+28	-11	+04
Heart rate	70	60	54	-18	+01	+02

Age 23 yrs.	Height 72 in.	Ponderal index 12.79
	Weight 178 lbs.	Cholesterol 180 mg. per 100 ml.
	Overweight +09 %	Vital capacity 5.1 liters

HABIT SURVEY

Smoking habits: pipe smoker

Age begun 18 yrs.   Inhalation: no

Habits of nervous tension: 2, 5, 6, 16, 22

STRONG VOCATIONAL INTEREST TEST

Occupation	Artist	Psychologist	Architect	Physician	Osteopath	Dentist	Veterinarian	Mathematician	Physicist	Engineer	Chemist	Production Manager
Standard Score	32	35	30	56	44	43	29	28	27	38	43	26

Occupation	Farmer	Aviator	Carpenter	Printer	Math.-Sci. Teacher	Ind. Arts Teacher	Voc. Agric. Teacher	Policeman	Forest Serv. Man	Y.M.C.A. Phys. Dir.	Personnel Director	Public Administrator
Standard Score	32	44	17	25	39	13	14	35	26	37	26	36

Occupation	Y.M.C.A. Secretary	Soc. Sci. H.S. Teacher	City Sch. Sup't.	Social Worker	Minister	Musician Performer	C.P.A.	Senior C.P.A.	Accountant	Office Man	Purchasing Agent	Banker
Standard Score	17	28	20	29	64	39	37	33	24	22	19	18

Occupation	Mortician	Pharmacist	Sales Manager	Real Est. Manager	Life Ins. Salesman	Advertising Man	Lawyer	Author-Journalist	President Mfg. Co.	Interest Maturity	Occupational Level	Masculinity-Femininity
Standard Score	16	28	24	28	29	31	38	36	27	52	57	45

FIGURE-DRAWING CHARACTERISTICS

Structural	Male Female Both		Structural	Male	Female	Structural and Graphic	Male Female Both		Graphic, Global and Height	Male	Female	Body Proportions	Male	Female
Type	0		Omission of Appendages	0	7	Upper and Lower Halves	2	1	Hair Shading	0	2	Head	04	03
Sex Sequence	0		Position of Both Arms	1	2	Four Quarters	4	4	Nudity and Transparency	7	7	Neck	04	04
Posture	1	1	Position of Right Arm	2	5	Relative Size	2		Form	5	5	Shoulders	02	
Perspective	0	6	Position of Left Arm	0	7	Constant Line Pressure	5	0	Detailing	3	3	Right Arm	02	
Vertical Midline	0	4	Position of Legs	6	4	Variable Line Pressure	0	4	Identity and Sex	5	3	Left Arm	02	
Bilateral Symmetry	2	0	Relation of Long Axes	1	1	Line Continuity	4	4	Sophistication	4	4	Chest	02	
Horizontal Midline	4	0	Right and Left Halves	1	0	Body Shading	7	3	Height	03	03	Girth	04	

GENERAL CHARACTERISTICS OF SUBJECT

IDENTIFICATION
No. C53
Sex M
Marital status S
Age 22 yrs. at
psychological tests

PARENTAL HISTORY				
Father				
C	H	S	D	O
(?)	–	–	–	?
Mother				
C	H	S	D	O
–	+	–	–	–

PHYSIOLOGICAL AND METABOLIC DATA

	Admission	Initial	Control	Cold pressor change	Exercise change	Smoking change
Systolic pressure	135	130	104	+22	+26	+02
Diastolic pressure	90	60	64	+10	–06	+06
Heart rate	88	80	86	+20	+11	+16

Age 23 yrs.	Height 72 in.	Ponderal index 13.77
	Weight 143 lbs.	Cholesterol 233 mg. per 100 ml.
	Overweight –13 %	Vital capacity liters

HABIT SURVEY

Smoking habits: nonsmoker

Age begun yrs. Inhalation:

Habits of nervous tension: 4, 5, 6, 14, 21, 24

STRONG VOCATIONAL INTEREST TEST

Occupation	Artist	Psychologist	Architect	Physician	Osteopath	Dentist	Veterinarian	Mathematician	Physicist	Engineer	Chemist	Production Manager
Standard Score	47	55	46	59	39	41	11	46	46	44	54	22

Occupation	Farmer	Aviator	Carpenter	Printer	Math.-Sci. Teacher	Ind. Arts Teacher	Voc. Agric. Teacher	Policeman	Forest Serv. Man	Y.M.C.A. Phys. Dir.	Personnel Director	Public Administrator
Standard Score	27	33	14	33	32	14	15	17	22	22	29	42

Occupation	Y.M.C.A. Secretary	Soc. Sci. H.S. Teacher	City Sch. Sup't.	Social Worker	Minister	Musician Performer	C.P.A.	Senior C.P.A.	Accountant	Office Man	Purchasing Agent	Banker
Standard Score	17	22	28	35	62	48	32	30	12	10	07	09

Occupation	Mortician	Pharmacist	Sales Manager	Real Est. Manager	Life Ins. Salesman	Advertising Man	Lawyer	Author-Journalist	President Mfg. Co.	Interest Maturity	Occupational Level	Masculinity-Femininity
Standard Score	09	22	19	26	25	41	44	49	34	50	62	38

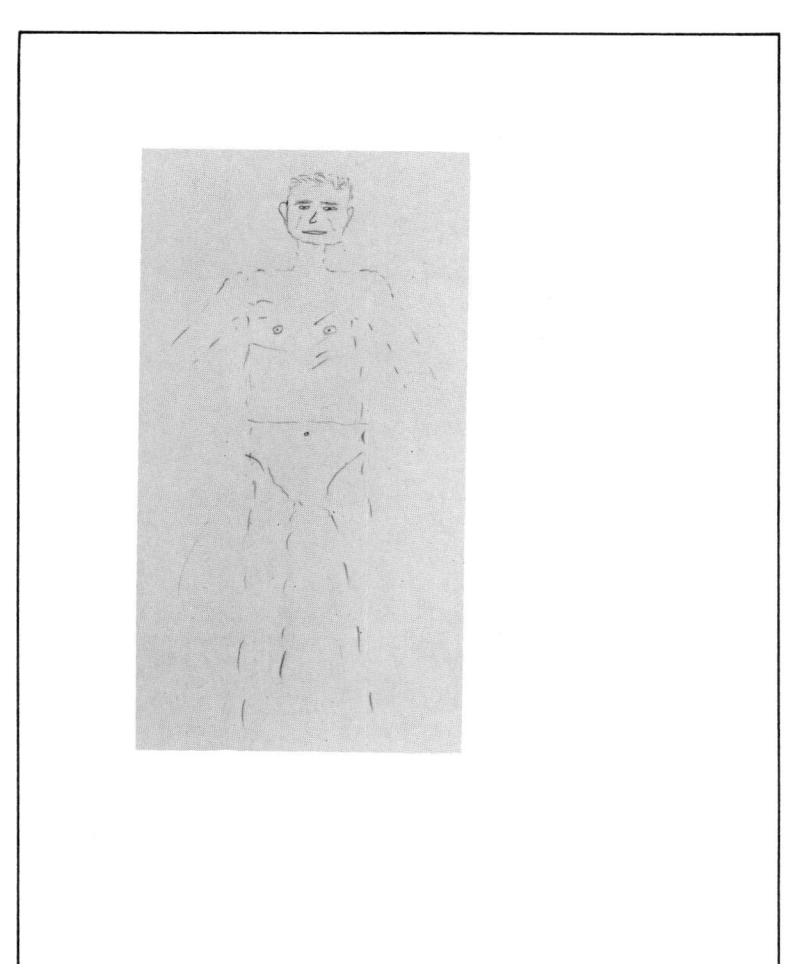

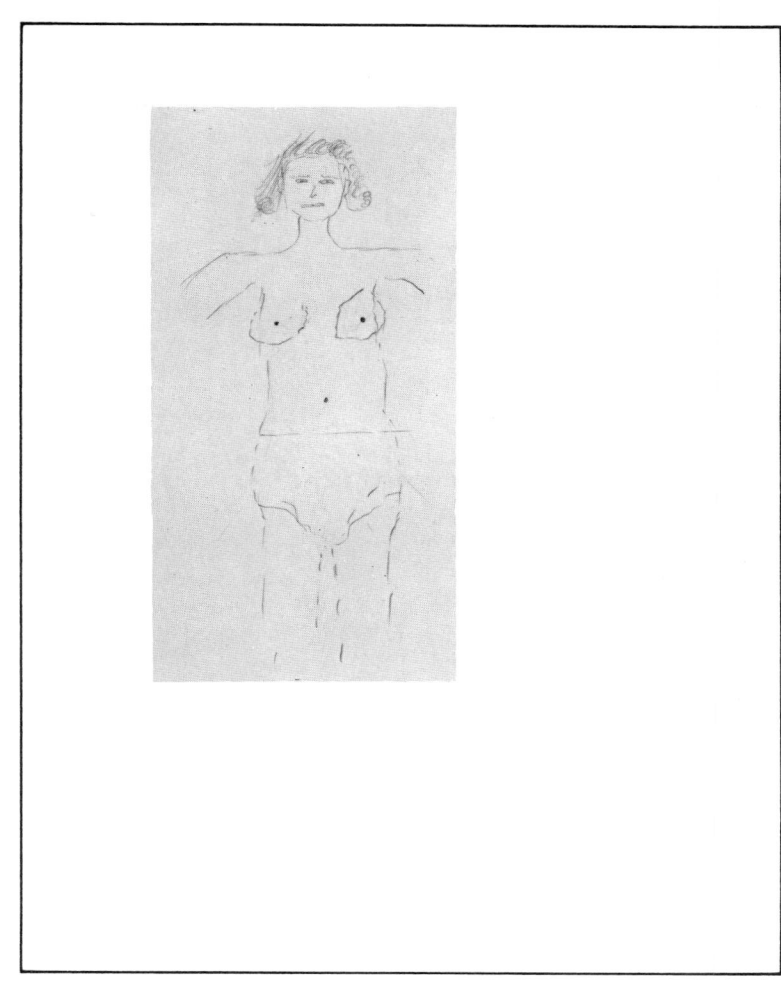

FIGURE-DRAWING CHARACTERISTICS

Structural	Male	Female	Structural	Male	Female	Structural and Graphic	Male	Female	Graphic, Global and Height	Male	Female	Body Proportions	Male	Female
	Both						Both							
Type	0		Omission of Appendages	1	1	Upper and Lower Halves	1	1	Hair Shading	3	3	Head	05	06
Sex Sequence	0		Position of Both Arms	6	6	Four Quarters	4	4	Nudity and Transparency	5	3	Neck	08	08
Posture	0	0	Position of Right Arm	8	8	Relative Size	5		Form	3	3	Shoulders	07	
Perspective	0	0	Position of Left Arm	8	8	Constant Line Pressure	0	2	Detailing	3	3	Right Arm		
Vertical Midline	0	0	Position of Legs	6	4	Variable Line Pressure	1	0	Identity and Sex	1	1	Left Arm		
Bilateral Symmetry	3	3	Relation of Long Axes	1	1	Line Continuity	0	0	Sophistication	4	4	Chest	05	06
Horizontal Midline	4	4	Right and Left Halves	2	2	Body Shading	1	0	Height			Girth	07	08

GENERAL CHARACTERISTICS OF SUBJECT

IDENTIFICATION

No. A14

Sex M

Marital status M

Age 24 yrs. at

psychological tests

PARENTAL HISTORY

Father

C	H	S	D	O
-	?	-	-	+

Mother

C	H	S	D	O
-	+	+	+	+

PHYSIOLOGICAL AND METABOLIC DATA

	Admission	Initial	Control	Cold pressor change	Exercise change	Smoking change
Systolic pressure	130	138	130	+08	+20	00
Diastolic pressure	70	72	69	+18	-09	+02
Heart rate	84	92	70	+15	+29	+03

Age 23 yrs.

Height 71 in.   Ponderal index 12.89

Weight 167 lbs.   Cholesterol 190 mg. per 100 ml.

Overweight +05 %   Vital capacity   liters

HABIT SURVEY

Smoking habits: heavy cigarette smoker

Age begun 16 yrs.   Inhalation: yes

Habits of nervous tension: 1, 5, 6, 16, 17, 21

STRONG VOCATIONAL INTEREST TEST

Occupation	Artist	Psychologist	Architect	Physician	Osteopath	Dentist	Veterinarian	Mathematician	Physicist	Engineer	Chemist	Production Manager
Standard Score	2	6	2	5	7	3	3	1	2	3	4	7

Occupation	Farmer	Aviator	Carpenter	Printer	Math.-Sci. Teacher	Ind. Arts Teacher	Voc. Agric. Teacher	Policeman	Forest Serv. Man	Y.M.C.A. Phys. Dir.	Personnel Director	Public Administrator
Standard Score	4	4	4	6	6	4	3	5	6	6	7	7

Occupation	Y.M.C.A. Secretary	Soc. Sci. H.S. Teacher	City Sch. Sup't.	Social Worker	Minister	Musician Performer	C.P.A.	Senior C.P.A.	Accountant	Office Man	Purchasing Agent	Banker
Standard Score	5	6	4	7	6	4	3	6	4	6	3	2

Occupation	Mortician	Pharmacist	Sales Manager	Real Est. Manager	Life Ins. Salesman	Advertising Man	Lawyer	Author-Journalist	President Mfg. Co.	Interest Maturity	Occupational Level	Masculinity-Femininity
Standard Score	5	7	4	5	4	4	3	2	4	7	4	5

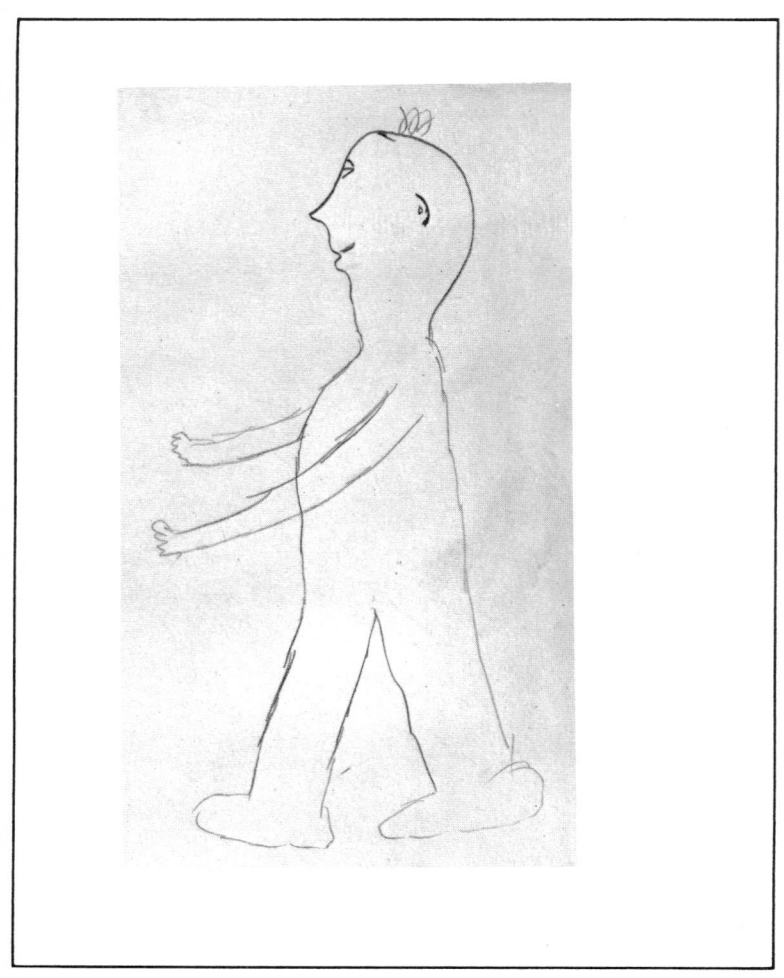

FIGURE-DRAWING CHARACTERISTICS

Structural	Male Female Both	Structural	Male	Female	Structural and Graphic	Male Female Both		Graphic, Global and Height	Male	Female	Body Proportions	Male	Female
Type	0	Omission of Appendages	0	7	Upper and Lower Halves	1	0	Hair Shading	7	3	Head	11	15
Sex Sequence	2	Position of Both Arms	4	4	Four Quarters	4	4	Nudity and Transparency	0	7	Neck	20	14
Posture	2 3	Position of Right Arm	7	7	Relative Size	4		Form	5	5	Shoulders		
Perspective	2 2	Position of Left Arm	4	5	Constant Line Pressure	0	0	Detailing	5	5	Right Arm		
Vertical Midline	4 4	Position of Legs	8	1	Variable Line Pressure	2	2	Identity and Sex	3	1	Left Arm	08	06
Bilateral Symmetry	0 0	Relation of Long Axes	1	0	Line Continuity	0	0	Sophistication	4	4	Chest	10	10
Horizontal Midline	0 0	Right and Left Halves	1	2	Body Shading	0	0	Height	07		Girth	11	12

GENERAL CHARACTERISTICS OF SUBJECT

IDENTIFICATION
No. 556
Sex M
Marital status S
Age 24 yrs. at
psychological tests

PARENTAL HISTORY
Father
C H S D O
– + – – ?
Mother
C H S D O
– – – –

PHYSIOLOGICAL AND METABOLIC DATA

	Admission	Initial	Control	Cold pressor change	Exercise change	Smoking change
Systolic pressure	120	120	120	+10	+40	
Diastolic pressure	80	80	80	+10	+10	
Heart rate	72	60	83	00	–03	

Age 22 yrs.   Height 68 in.   Ponderal index 12.97

Weight 144 lbs.   Cholesterol 167 mg. per 100 ml.

Overweight –01 %   Vital capacity 5.0 liters

HABIT SURVEY
Smoking habits: occasional smoker
Age begun 19 yrs.   Inhalation: yes
Habits of nervous tension: 4, 5, 6, 17, 22

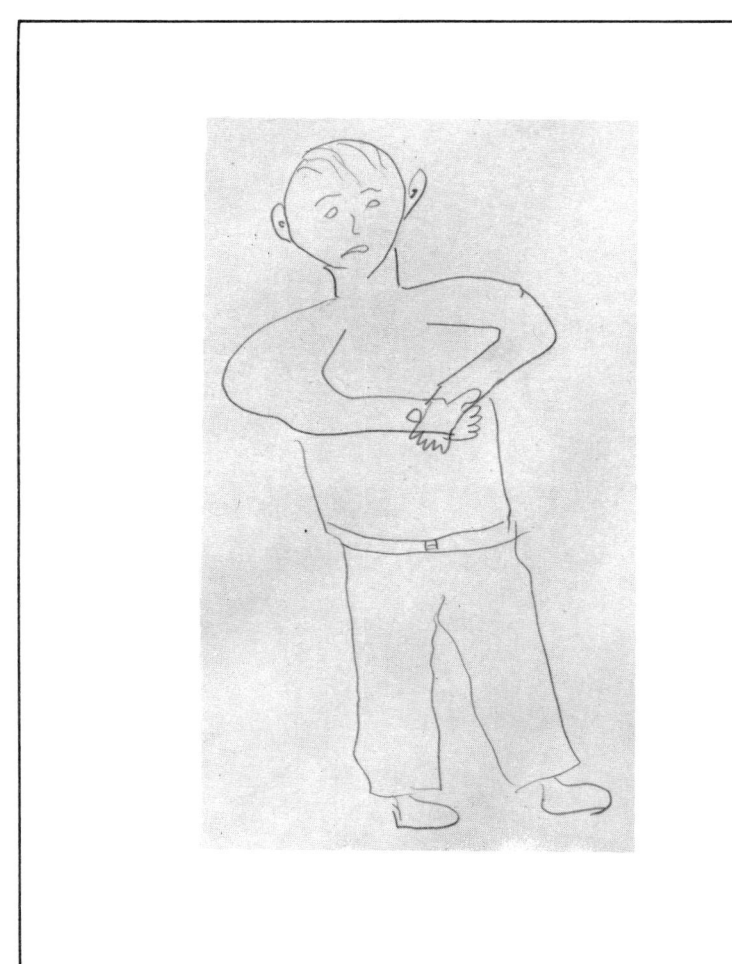

FIGURE-DRAWING CHARACTERISTICS

Structural	Male Female Both	Structural	Male	Female	Structural and Graphic	Male Female Both		Graphic, Global and Height	Male	Female	Body Proportions	Male	Female
Type	0	Omission of Appendages	0	0	Upper and Lower Halves	1	1	Hair Shading	7	7	Head	12	09
Sex Sequence	0	Position of Both Arms	0	2	Four Quarters	4	4	Nudity and Transparency	3	0	Neck	10	12
Posture	1 1	Position of Right Arm	5	3	Relative Size	0		Form	5	5	Shoulders		
Perspective	0 2	Position of Left Arm	5	7	Constant Line Pressure	0	4	Detailing	5	5	Right Arm	06	05
Vertical Midline	0 4	Position of Legs	6	5	Variable Line Pressure	5	0	Identity and Sex	1	1	Left Arm	05	
Bilateral Symmetry	1 0	Relation of Long Axes	3	1	Line Continuity	3	3	Sophistication	4	4	Chest		07
Horizontal Midline	4 0	Right and Left Halves	0	1	Body Shading	0	0	Height	07	06	Girth	11	09

GENERAL CHARACTERISTICS OF SUBJECT

IDENTIFICATION
No. 653
Sex M
Marital status S
Age 24 yrs. at
psychological tests

PARENTAL HISTORY
Father
C   H   S   D   0
–   +   –   –   –
Mother
C   H   S   D   0
–   –   –   –   –

PHYSIOLOGICAL AND METABOLIC DATA

	Admission	Initial	Control	Cold pressor change	Exercise change	Smoking change
Systolic pressure	130	124	122	+16	+16	+10
Diastolic pressure	80	68	72	+16	-02	+06
Heart rate	80	84	74	+06	+09	+10

Age 22 yrs.	Height 74 in.	Ponderal index 12.63
	Weight 201 lbs.	Cholesterol 243 mg. per 100 ml.
	Overweight +16 %	Vital capacity liters

HABIT SURVEY
Smoking habits: heavy cigarette smoker
Age begun 18 yrs.   Inhalation: yes
Habits of nervous tension: 3, 6, 10, 19, 22

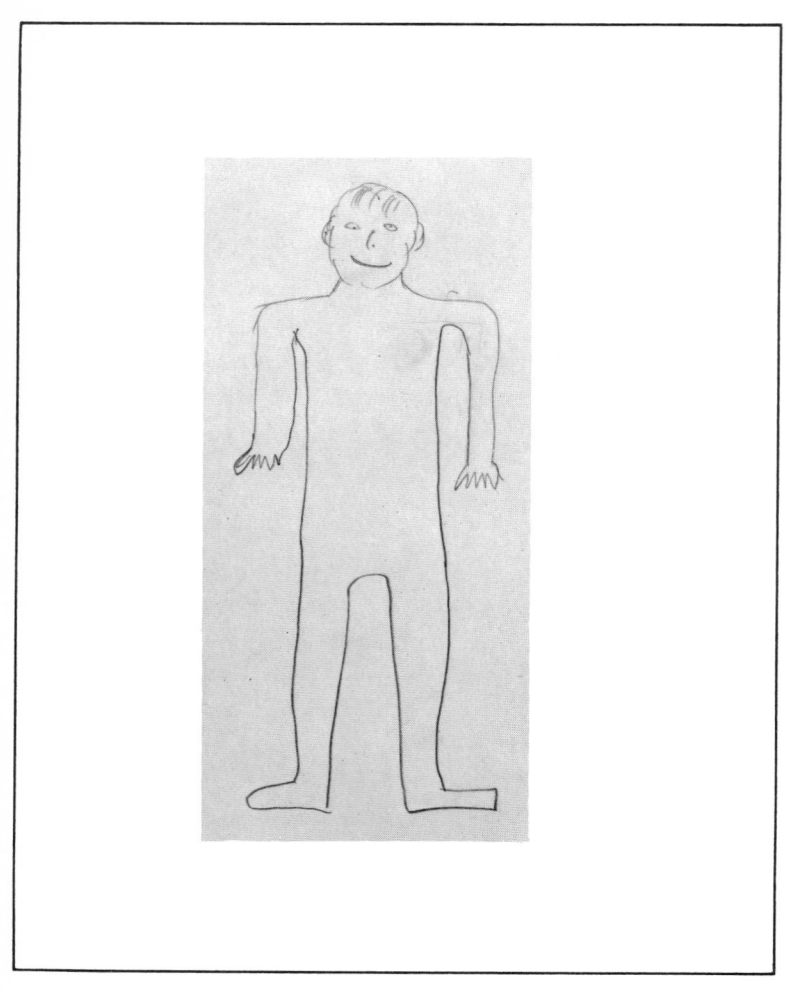

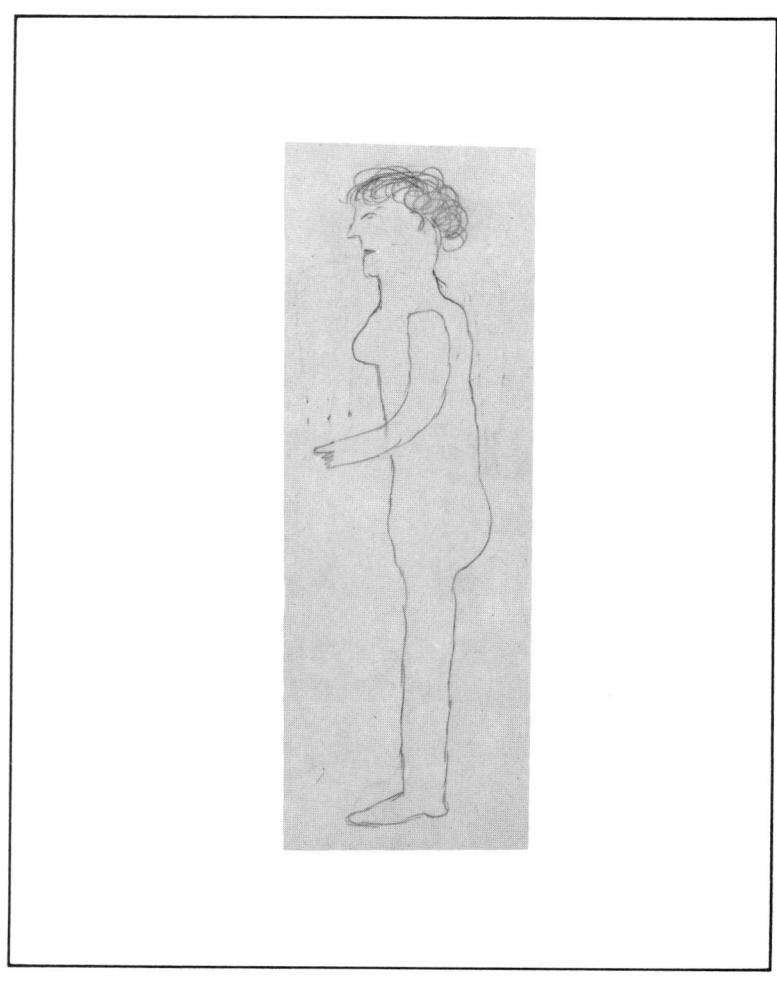

FIGURE-DRAWING CHARACTERISTICS

Structural	Male Female Both	Structural	Male	Female	Structural and Graphic	Male Female Both		Graphic, Global and Height	Male	Female	Body Proportions	Male	Female
Type	0	Omission of Appendages	0	0	Upper and Lower Halves	0	0	Hair Shading	3	3	Head	09	07
Sex Sequence	0	Position of Both Arms	0	4	Four Quarters	4	4	Nudity and Transparency	0	0	Neck	04	08
Posture	1	1	Position of Right Arm	0	7	Relative Size	4		Form	5	5	Shoulders	09	
Perspective	0	2	Position of Left Arm	0	4	Constant Line Pressure	0	2	Detailing	5	5	Right Arm	04	
Vertical Midline	0	4	Position of Legs	6	1	Variable Line Pressure	4	0	Identity and Sex	5	1	Left Arm	04	04
Bilateral Symmetry	3	0	Relation of Long Axes	1	1	Line Continuity	3	0	Sophistication	4	4	Chest	06	07
Horizontal Midline	0	0	Right and Left Halves	1	3	Body Shading	0	0	Height	06	07	Girth	08	09

GENERAL CHARACTERISTICS OF SUBJECT

IDENTIFICATION
No. A53
Sex M
Marital status S
Age 23 yrs. at
psychological tests

PARENTAL HISTORY				
Father				
C	H	S	D	O
-	+	-	-	+
Mother				
C	H	S	D	O
-	-	-	-	?

PHYSIOLOGICAL AND METABOLIC DATA

	Admission	Initial	Control	Cold pressor change	Exercise change	Smoking change
Systolic pressure	145	130	128	+15	+44	+09
Diastolic pressure	85	68	69	+19	-25	-04
Heart rate	82	68	59	+12	+39	+01

Age 22 yrs.

Height	71 in.	Ponderal index 12.86
Weight	168 lbs.	Cholesterol 210 mg. per 100 ml.
Overweight +08 %		Vital capacity liters

HABIT SURVEY

Smoking habits: nonsmoker

Age begun yrs.   Inhalation:

Habits of nervous tension: 3, 4, 5, 6, 9, 11, 18, 20, 23

STRONG VOCATIONAL INTEREST TEST

Occupation	Artist	Psychologist	Architect	Physician	Osteopath	Dentist	Veterinarian	Mathematician	Physicist	Engineer	Chemist	Production Manager
Standard Score	4	7	5	7	5	4	2	5	4	3	4	2

Occupation	Farmer	Aviator	Carpenter	Printer	Math.-Sci. Teacher	Ind. Arts Teacher	Voc. Agric. Teacher	Policeman	Forest Serv. Man	Y.M.C.A. Phys. Dir.	Personnel Director	Public Administrator
Standard Score	4	2	2	4	6	1	2	3	2	6	6	6

Occupation	Y.M.C.A. Secretary	Soc. Sci. H.S. Teacher	City Sch. Sup't.	Social Worker	Minister	Musician Performer	C.P.A.	Senior C.P.A.	Accountant	Office Man	Purchasing Agent	Banker
Standard Score	5	6	5	6	6	6	4	5	2	4	1	1

Occupation	Mortician	Pharmacist	Sales Manager	Real Est. Manager	Life Ins. Salesman	Advertising Man	Lawyer	Author-Journalist	President Mfg. Co.	Interest Maturity	Occupational Level	Masculinity-Femininity
Standard Score	2	2	2	4	3	4	6	5	3	6	5	2

FIGURE-DRAWING CHARACTERISTICS

Structural	Male Female Both	Structural	Male	Female	Structural and Graphic	Male Female Both	Graphic, Global and Height	Male	Female	Body Proportions	Male	Female
Type	0	Omission of Appendages	0	0	Upper and Lower Halves	1 1	Hair Shading	5	3	Head	05	07
Sex Sequence	0	Position of Both Arms	1	1	Four Quarters	4 4	Nudity and Transparency	7	7	Neck	04	03
Posture	2 1	Position of Right Arm	0	1	Relative Size	4	Form	3	3	Shoulders	05	04
Perspective	0 0	Position of Left Arm	5	0	Constant Line Pressure	0 0	Detailing	3	3	Right Arm	04	04
Vertical Midline	0 0	Position of Legs	8	4	Variable Line Pressure	5 5	Identity and Sex	1	1	Left Arm	04	02
Bilateral Symmetry	2 3	Relation of Long Axes	1	1	Line Continuity	3 3	Sophistication	4	4	Chest	04	04
Horizontal Midline	4 4	Right and Left Halves	2	1	Body Shading	4 5	Height	04	04	Girth	04	03

GENERAL CHARACTERISTICS OF SUBJECT

IDENTIFICATION

No. C05

Sex M

Marital status S

Age 22 yrs. at psychological tests

PARENTAL HISTORY

Father

C	H	S	D	O
-	+	-	-	-

Mother

C	H	S	D	O
-	-	-	-	-

PHYSIOLOGICAL AND METABOLIC DATA

	Admission	Initial	Control	Cold pressor change	Exercise change	Smoking change
Systolic pressure	120	140	118	+10	+32	+14
Diastolic pressure	75	80	70	+08	-10	+06
Heart rate	84	84	75	+16	+04	+03

Age 23 yrs.

Height 70 in.
Weight 159 lbs.
Overweight +03 %

Ponderal index 12.93
Cholesterol 215 mg. per 100 ml.
Vital capacity 5.3 liters

HABIT SURVEY

Smoking habits: former smoker

  Age begun 15 yrs.   Inhalation:

Habits of nervous tension: 5, 6, 11, 22

STRONG VOCATIONAL INTEREST TEST

Occupation	Artist	Psychologist	Architect	Physician	Osteopath	Dentist	Veterinarian	Mathematician	Physicist	Engineer	Chemist	Production Manager
Standard Score	25	30	24	41	44	30	23	19	17	26	28	31

Occupation	Farmer	Aviator	Carpenter	Printer	Math.-Sci. Teacher	Ind. Arts Teacher	Voc. Agric. Teacher	Policeman	Forest Serv. Man	Y.M.C.A. Phys. Dir.	Personnel Director	Public Administrator
Standard Score	36	38	19	36	41	22	29	32	41	52	49	50

Occupation	Y.M.C.A. Secretary	Soc. Sci. H.S. Teacher	City Sch. Sup't.	Social Worker	Minister	Musician Performer	C.P.A.	Senior C.P.A.	Accountant	Office Man	Purchasing Agent	Banker
Standard Score	48	44	36	43	62	43	18	43	23	31	18	22

Occupation	Mortician	Pharmacist	Sales Manager	Real Est. Manager	Life Ins. Salesman	Advertising Man	Lawyer	Author- Journalist	President Mfg. Co.	Interest Maturity	Occupational Level	Masculinity- Femininity
Standard Score	29	32	29	28	32	31	28	29	28	62	56	44

FIGURE-DRAWING CHARACTERISTICS

Structural	Male	Female	Structural	Male	Female	Structural and Graphic	Male	Female	Graphic, Global and Height	Male	Female	Body Proportions	Male	Female
	Both						Both							
Type	0		Omission of Appendages	0	0	Upper and Lower Halves	3	1	Hair Shading	3	3	Head	10	09
Sex Sequence	1		Position of Both Arms	2	2	Four Quarters	4	4	Nudity and Transparency	3	7	Neck	16	12
Posture	1	1	Position of Right Arm	2	4	Relative Size	0		Form	3	3	Shoulders		
Perspective	2	2	Position of Left Arm	7	7	Constant Line Pressure	1	1	Detailing	3	3	Right Arm	03	02
Vertical Midline	4	4	Position of Legs	1	1	Variable Line Pressure	0	0	Identity and Sex	3	3	Left Arm		
Bilateral Symmetry	0	0	Relation of Long Axes	1	1	Line Continuity	0	0	Sophistication	4	4	Chest	04	04
Horizontal Midline	4	4	Right and Left Halves	1	2	Body Shading	0	0	Height	07	06	Girth	05	05

GENERAL CHARACTERISTICS OF SUBJECT

IDENTIFICATION

No. E11

Sex M

Marital status S

Age 21 yrs. at psychological tests

PARENTAL HISTORY

Father

C	H	S	D	O
-	+	-	-	?

Mother

C	H	S	D	O
-	-	-	-	-

PHYSIOLOGICAL AND METABOLIC DATA

	Admission	Initial	Control	Cold pressor change	Exercise change	Smoking change
Systolic pressure	120	118	110	+10	+29	
Diastolic pressure	75	70	70	+16	-06	
Heart rate	70	72	65	+04	+10	

Age 21 yrs.	Height	75 in.	Ponderal index 13.59
	Weight	168 lbs.	Cholesterol 200 mg. per 100 ml.
	Overweight -05 %		Vital capacity 4.7 liters

HABIT SURVEY

Smoking habits: heavy cigarette smoker

Age begun 18 yrs.   Inhalation: yes

Habits of nervous tension: 4, 5, 6

STRONG VOCATIONAL INTEREST TEST

Occupation	Artist	Psychologist	Architect	Physician	Osteopath	Dentist	Veterinarian	Mathematician	Physicist	Engineer	Chemist	Production Manager
Standard Score	38	52	38	58	48	38	31	25	19	31	35	28

Occupation	Farmer	Aviator	Carpenter	Printer	Math.-Sci. Teacher	Ind. Arts Teacher	Voc. Agric. Teacher	Policeman	Forest Serv. Man	Y.M.C.A. Phys. Dir.	Personnel Director	Public Administrator
Standard Score	38	43	17	35	40	23	42	29	46	49	49	54

Occupation	Y.M.C.A. Secretary	Soc. Sci. H.S. Teacher	City Sch. Sup't.	Social Worker	Minister	Musician Performer	C.P.A.	Senior C.P.A.	Accountant	Office Man	Purchasing Agent	Banker
Standard Score	43	45	39	55	64	56	19	38	16	24	10	13

Occupation	Mortician	Pharmacist	Sales Manager	Real Est. Manager	Life Ins. Salesman	Advertising Man	Lawyer	Author- Journalist	President Mfg. Co.	Interest Maturity	Occupational Level	Masculinity- Femininity
Standard Score	23	26	29	33	32	38	37	37	27	58	53	39

FIGURE-DRAWING CHARACTERISTICS

Structural	Male Female Both	Structural	Male	Female	Structural and Graphic	Male Female Both		Graphic, Global and Height	Male	Female	Body Proportions	Male	Female
Type	0	Omission of Appendages	0	0	Upper and Lower Halves	1	0	Hair Shading	3	3	Head	10	09
Sex Sequence	1	Position of Both Arms	0	0	Four Quarters	4	4	Nudity and Transparency	7	7	Neck	08	08
Posture	1 1	Position of Right Arm	2	2	Relative Size	4		Form	5	5	Shoulders	06	05
Perspective	0 0	Position of Left Arm	2	2	Constant Line Pressure	5	0	Detailing	5	5	Right Arm	03	04
Vertical Midline	3 3	Position of Legs	6	6	Variable Line Pressure	0	3	Identity and Sex	1	1	Left Arm	02	04
Bilateral Symmetry	2 2	Relation of Long Axes	1	1	Line Continuity	3	3	Sophistication	4	4	Chest	06	07
Horizontal Midline	2 4	Right and Left Halves	1	2	Body Shading	0	7	Height	06	06	Girth	06	09

GENERAL CHARACTERISTICS OF SUBJECT

IDENTIFICATION
No. M62
Sex M
Marital status M
Age 26 yrs. at
psychological tests

PARENTAL HISTORY
Father
C   H   S   D   O
-   -   -   -   +
Mother
C   H   S   D   O
-   +   -   -   +

PHYSIOLOGICAL AND METABOLIC DATA

	Admission	Initial	Control	Cold pressor change	Exercise change	Smoking change
Systolic pressure	120	108	98	+18	+22	00
Diastolic pressure	80	54	54	+28	-02	-01
Heart rate	80	64	59	-16	+06	+16

Age 24 yrs.	Height 71 in.	Ponderal index 12.72
	Weight 174 lbs.	Cholesterol 217 mg. per 100 ml.
	Overweight +09 %	Vital capacity 4.6 liters

HABIT SURVEY
Smoking habits: former smoker
Age begun   yrs.   Inhalation:
Habits of nervous tension: 1, 5, 8, 16, 19

FIGURE-DRAWING CHARACTERISTICS

Structural	Male Female Both	Structural	Male	Female	Structural and Graphic	Male Female Both		Graphic, Global and Height	Male	Female	Body Proportions	Male	Female
Type	0	Omission of Appendages	7	1	Upper and Lower Halves	0	0	Hair Shading	3	3	Head	09	09
Sex Sequence	0	Position of Both Arms	0	6	Four Quarters	4	4	Nudity and Transparency	7	7	Neck	05	01
Posture	1 0	Position of Right Arm	2	8	Relative Size	5		Form	3	3	Shoulders	07	09
Perspective	0 0	Position of Left Arm	2	8	Constant Line Pressure	0	0	Detailing	5	5	Right Arm		
Vertical Midline	3 0	Position of Legs	6	6	Variable Line Pressure	5	5	Identity and Sex	3	3	Left Arm		
Bilateral Symmetry	3 3	Relation of Long Axes	1	1	Line Continuity	0	0	Sophistication	4	4	Chest	06	07
Horizontal Midline	6 4	Right and Left Halves	1	1	Body Shading	7	7	Height	07		Girth	09	09

GENERAL CHARACTERISTICS OF SUBJECT

IDENTIFICATION
No. F74
Sex M
Marital status
Age 24 yrs. at
psychological tests

PARENTAL HISTORY				
Father				
C	H	S	D	O
-	-	-	-	+
Mother				
C	H	S	D	O
-	+	-	-	?

PHYSIOLOGICAL AND METABOLIC DATA

	Admission	Initial	Control	Cold pressor change	Exercise change	Smoking change
Systolic pressure	130	170	124	+04	+16	+02
Diastolic pressure	80	58	54	+20	-14	+06
Heart rate	80	84	74	+08	+41	-03

Age 22 yrs.	Height	72 in.	Ponderal index 11.84
	Weight	225 lbs.	Cholesterol 265 mg. per 100 ml.
	Overweight +38 %		Vital capacity 5.6 liters

HABIT SURVEY
Smoking habits: heavy cigarette smoker
Age begun 17 yrs.   Inhalation: no
Habits of nervous tension: 6, 25

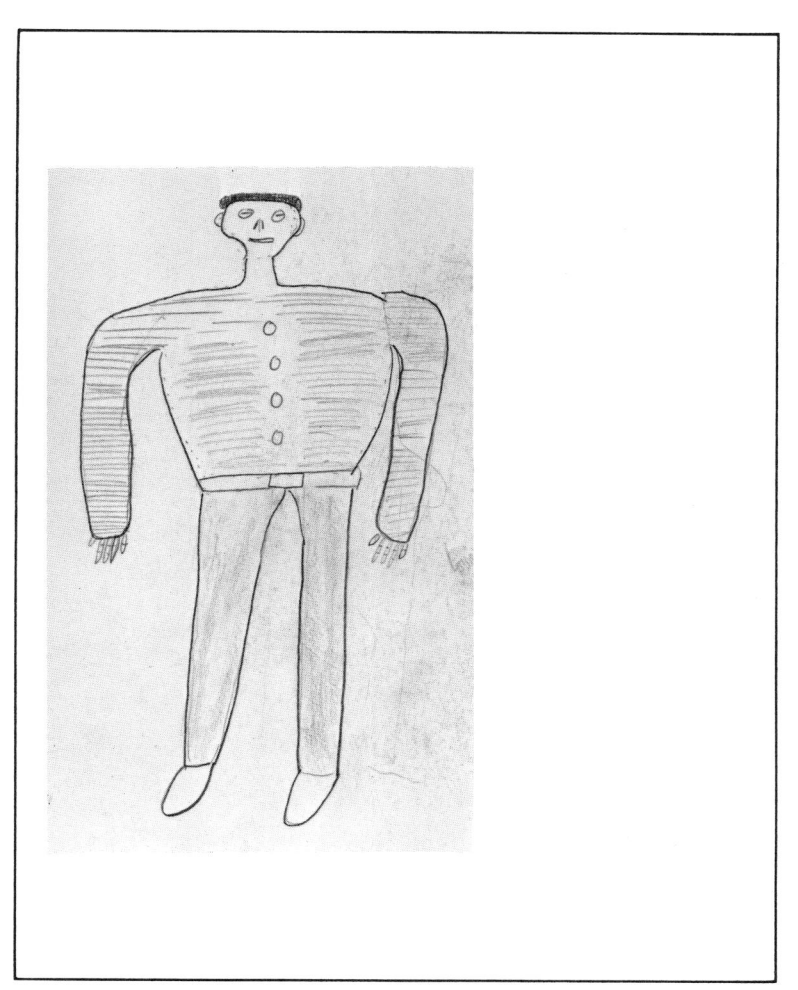

FIGURE-DRAWING CHARACTERISTICS

Structural	Male Female Both	Structural	Male	Female	Structural and Graphic	Male Female Both		Graphic, Global and Height	Male	Female	Body Proportions	Male	Female
Type	0	Omission of Appendages	0	0	Upper and Lower Halves	0	0	Hair Shading	1	1	Head	05	04
Sex Sequence	0	Position of Both Arms	1	2	Four Quarters	4	4	Nudity and Transparency	7	0	Neck	08	08
Posture	1 1	Position of Right Arm	1	4	Relative Size	0		Form	5	5	Shoulders	14	
Perspective	0 2	Position of Left Arm	0	7	Constant Line Pressure	5	5	Detailing	5	5	Right Arm	06	04
Vertical Midline	3 4	Position of Legs	6	1	Variable Line Pressure	0	0	Identity and Sex	3	3	Left Arm	06	
Bilateral Symmetry	1 0	Relation of Long Axes	1	1	Line Continuity	4	2	Sophistication	4	4	Chest	11	05
Horizontal Midline	4 0	Right and Left Halves	1	2	Body Shading	3	2	Height	06	05	Girth	10	05

GENERAL CHARACTERISTICS OF SUBJECT

IDENTIFICATION
No. C35
Sex M
Marital status S
Age 22 yrs. at
psychological tests

PARENTAL HISTORY				
Father				
C	H	S	D	O
-	-	-	-	-
Mother				
C	H	S	D	O
-	+	-	-	-

PHYSIOLOGICAL AND METABOLIC DATA

	Admission	Initial	Control	Cold pressor change	Exercise change	Smoking change
Systolic pressure	130	110	108	+22	+42	+08
Diastolic pressure	80	70	70	+20	-10	+08
Heart rate	74	64	59	+16	+41	+17

Age 23 yrs.	Height 70 in.	Ponderal index 12.82
	Weight 163 lbs.	Cholesterol 190 mg. per 100 ml.
	Overweight +05 %	Vital capacity 4.9 liters

HABIT SURVEY

Smoking habits: nonsmoker

Age begun   yrs.   Inhalation:

Habits of nervous tension: 1, 3, 4, 5, 6, 8, 9, 10, 16, 18, 19, 20, 22

STRONG VOCATIONAL INTEREST TEST

Occupation	Artist	Psychologist	Architect	Physician	Osteopath	Dentist	Veterinarian	Mathematician	Physicist	Engineer	Chemist	Production Manager
Standard Score	25	32	20	35	28	18	20	23	13	22	31	32

Occupation	Farmer	Aviator	Carpenter	Printer	Math.-Sci. Teacher	Ind. Arts Teacher	Voc. Agric. Teacher	Policeman	Forest Serv. Man	Y.M.C.A. Phys. Dir.	Personnel Director	Public Administrator
Standard Score	37	36	10	31	33	03	22	28	27	21	29	39

Occupation	Y.M.C.A. Secretary	Soc. Sci. H.S. Teacher	City Sch. Sup't.	Social Worker	Minister	Musician Performer	C.P.A.	Senior C.P.A.	Accountant	Office Man	Purchasing Agent	Banker
Standard Score	23	38	24	33	62	37	34	42	24	29	21	31

Occupation	Mortician	Pharmacist	Sales Manager	Real Est. Manager	Life Ins. Salesman	Advertising Man	Lawyer	Author-Journalist	President Mfg. Co.	Interest Maturity	Occupational Level	Masculinity-Femininity
Standard Score	17	35	25	37	30	35	40	36	25	53	53	50

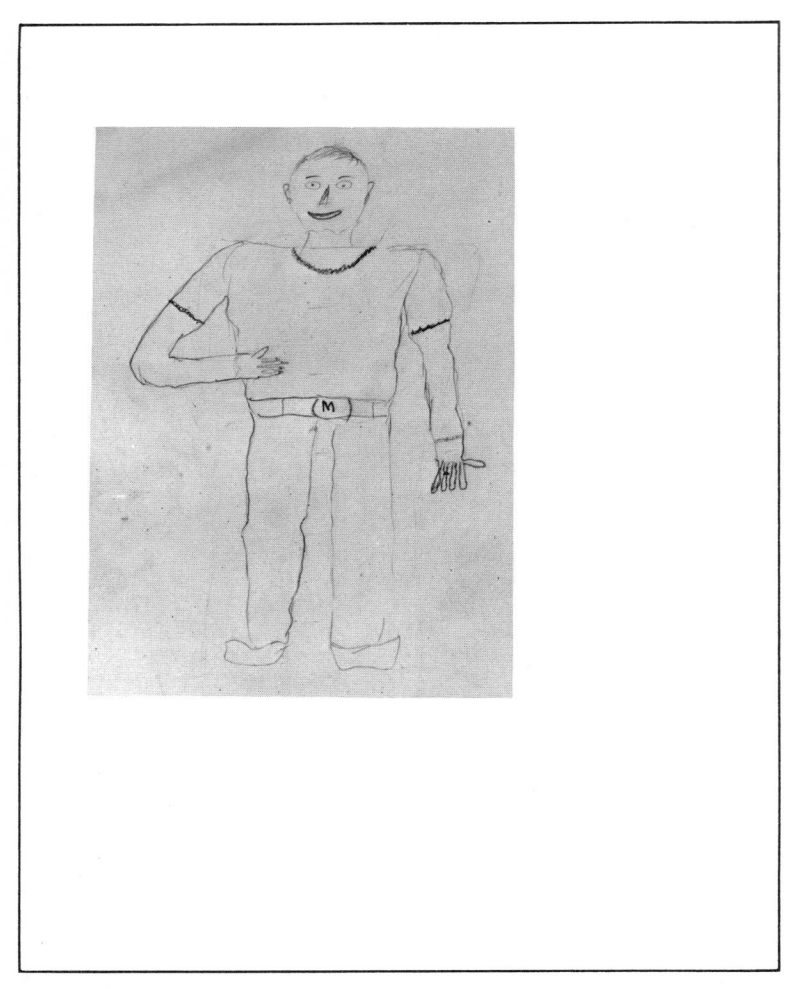

FIGURE-DRAWING CHARACTERISTICS

Structural	Male Female Both	Structural	Male	Female	Structural and Graphic	Male Female Both		Graphic, Global and Height	Male	Female	Body Proportions	Male	Female
Type	0	Omission of Appendages	0	0	Upper and Lower Halves	1	0	Hair Shading	3	3	Head	06	07
Sex Sequence	0	Position of Both Arms	1	1	Four Quarters	4	4	Nudity and Transparency	7	7	Neck	06	04
Posture	1	1	Position of Right Arm	5	5	Relative Size	2		Form	5	5	Shoulders	09	07
Perspective	0	0	Position of Left Arm	0	0	Constant Line Pressure	1	1	Detailing	3	3	Right Arm	06	06
Vertical Midline	0	0	Position of Legs	4	4	Variable Line Pressure	0	0	Identity and Sex	3	3	Left Arm	06	04
Bilateral Symmetry	3	3	Relation of Long Axes	1	1	Line Continuity	0	1	Sophistication	4	4	Chest	08	09
Horizontal Midline	4	4	Right and Left Halves	1	1	Body Shading	0	0	Height	05	05	Girth	09	12

GENERAL CHARACTERISTICS OF SUBJECT

IDENTIFICATION
No. D78
Sex M
Marital status S
Age 22 yrs. at psychological tests

PARENTAL HISTORY				
Father				
C	H	S	D	O
-	-	-	-	?
Mother				
C	H	S	D	O
-	+	-	-	?

PHYSIOLOGICAL AND METABOLIC DATA

	Admission	Initial	Control	Cold pressor change	Exercise change	Smoking change
Systolic pressure	150	139	120	+30	+52	00
Diastolic pressure	80	72	80	-02	-10	+04
Heart rate	70	88	79	+20	+24	-05

Age 22 yrs.	Height 76 in.	Ponderal index 13.97
	Weight 161 lbs.	Cholesterol 193 mg. per 100 ml.
	Overweight -12 %	Vital capacity liters

HABIT SURVEY

Smoking habits: former smoker

Age begun 8 yrs.   Inhalation:

Habits of nervous tension: 4, 5, 6, 18, 22

STRONG VOCATIONAL INTEREST TEST

Occupation	Artist	Psychologist	Architect	Physician	Osteopath	Dentist	Veterinarian	Mathematician	Physicist	Engineer	Chemist	Production Manager
Standard Score	33	54	37	59	36	35	20	52	42	36	54	22

Occupation	Farmer	Aviator	Carpenter	Printer	Math.-Sci. Teacher	Ind. Arts Teacher	Voc. Agric. Teacher	Policeman	Forest Serv. Man	Y.M.C.A. Phys. Dir.	Personnel Director	Public Administrator
Standard Score	41	31	27	47	53	23	31	29	23	31	32	41

Occupation	Y.M.C.A. Secretary	Soc. Sci. H.S. Teacher	City Sch. Sup't.	Social Worker	Minister	Musician Performer	C.P.A.	Senior C.P.A.	Accountant	Office Man	Purchasing Agent	Banker
Standard Score	37	42	35	44	63	60	29	47	27	34	10	24

Occupation	Mortician	Pharmacist	Sales Manager	Real Est. Manager	Life Ins. Salesman	Advertising Man	Lawyer	Author-Journalist	President Mfg. Co.	Interest Maturity	Occupational Level	Masculinity-Femininity
Standard Score	10	23	13	15	11	26	28	33	13	56	50	41

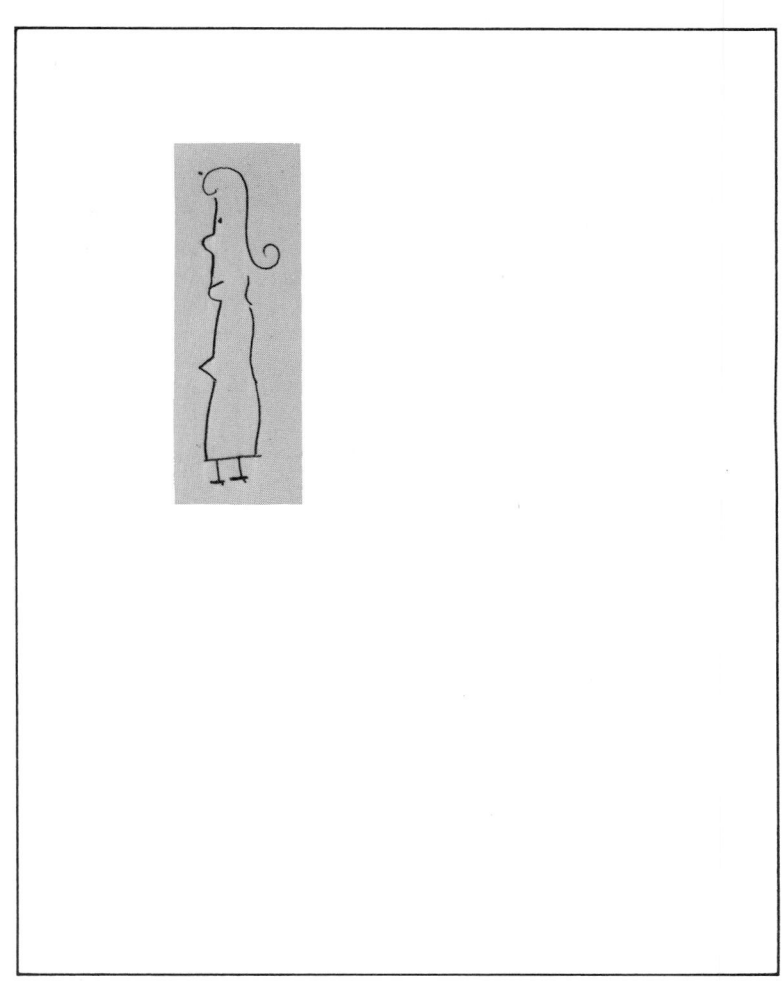

FIGURE-DRAWING CHARACTERISTICS

Structural	Male Female Both	Structural	Male	Female	Structural and Graphic	Male Female Both		Graphic, Global and Height	Male	Female	Body Proportions	Male	Female
Type	0	Omission of Appendages	9	2	Upper and Lower Halves	1	2	Hair Shading	5	5	Head	05	09
Sex Sequence	0	Position of Both Arms	7	6	Four Quarters	4	0	Nudity and Transparency	9	9	Neck	02	
Posture	9 1	Position of Right Arm	9	7	Relative Size	0		Form	5	3	Shoulders		
Perspective	9 2	Position of Left Arm	9	7	Constant Line Pressure	5	5	Detailing	3	5	Right Arm		
Vertical Midline	9 4	Position of Legs	9	5	Variable Line Pressure	0	0	Identity and Sex	3	3	Left Arm		
Bilateral Symmetry	9 0	Relation of Long Axes	1	1	Line Continuity	4	4	Sophistication	4	4	Chest		02
Horizontal Midline	4 0	Right and Left Halves	2	2	Body Shading	0	0	Height	03	03	Girth		03

GENERAL CHARACTERISTICS OF SUBJECT

IDENTIFICATION
No. 742
Sex M
Marital status S
Age 22 yrs. at
psychological tests

PARENTAL HISTORY				
Father				
C	H	S	D	O
-	(+)	-	-	-
Mother				
C	H	S	D	O
-	-	-	-	+

PHYSIOLOGICAL AND METABOLIC DATA

	Admission	Initial	Control	Cold pressor change	Exercise change	Smoking change
Systolic pressure	105	120	108	+20	+46	+05
Diastolic pressure	58	64	58	+26	+02	+15
Heart rate	72	68	60	-04	+31	00

Age 22 yrs.	Height 70 in.	Ponderal index 12.82	
	Weight 163 lbs.	Cholesterol 197 mg. per 100 ml.	
	Overweight +06 %	Vital capacity 5.1 liters	

HABIT SURVEY
Smoking habits: nonsmoker
Age begun   yrs.   Inhalation:
Habits of nervous tension: 5, 6, 25

 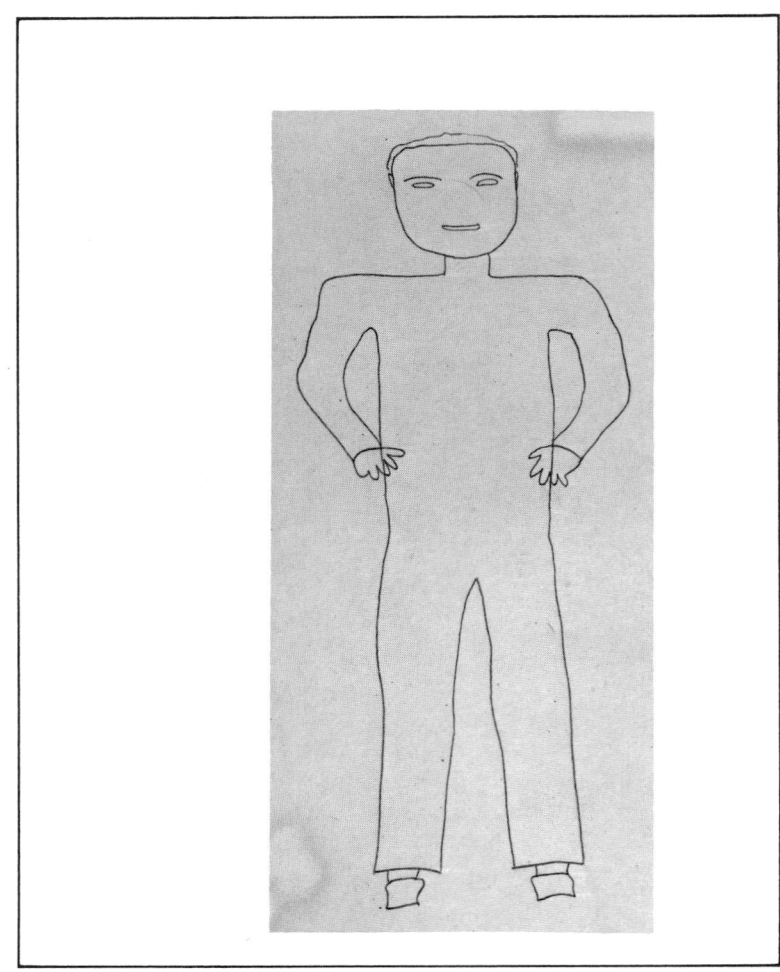

FIGURE-DRAWING CHARACTERISTICS

Structural	Male Female Both	Structural	Male	Female	Structural and Graphic	Male Female Both		Graphic, Global and Height	Male	Female	Body Proportions	Male	Female
Type	0	Omission of Appendages	0	0	Upper and Lower Halves	3	3	Hair Shading	5	5	Head	09	15
Sex Sequence	1	Position of Both Arms	0	0	Four Quarters	4	4	Nudity and Transparency	7	7	Neck	06	08
Posture	1 1	Position of Right Arm	5	5	Relative Size	4		Form	5	5	Shoulders	11	13
Perspective	0 0	Position of Left Arm	5	5	Constant Line Pressure	3	3	Detailing	5	5	Right Arm	06	06
Vertical Midline	0 0	Position of Legs	6	6	Variable Line Pressure	0	0	Identity and Sex	3	3	Left Arm	04	06
Bilateral Symmetry	3 3	Relation of Long Axes	1	1	Line Continuity	4	4	Sophistication	4	4	Chest	08	09
Horizontal Midline	0 0	Right and Left Halves	3	0	Body Shading	0	0	Height	08	08	Girth	13	16

GENERAL CHARACTERISTICS OF SUBJECT

IDENTIFICATION
No. 347
Sex M
Marital status S
Age 25 yrs. at psychological tests

PARENTAL HISTORY
Father
C   H   S   D   O
-   ?   (+)   -   -
Mother
C   H   S   D   O
-   -   -   -   -

PHYSIOLOGICAL AND METABOLIC DATA

	Admission	Initial	Control	Cold pressor change	Exercise change	Smoking change
Systolic pressure	126	126	124	+08	+58	-02
Diastolic pressure	66	74	70	+04	-02	+08
Heart rate	96	90	95	00	+35	+30

Age 23 yrs.	Height 72 in.	Ponderal index 13.11
	Weight 166 lbs.	Cholesterol 200 mg. per 100 ml.
	Overweight +01 %	Vital capacity 4.3 liters

HABIT SURVEY
Smoking habits: nonsmoker
Age begun yrs. Inhalation:
Habits of nervous tension: 1, 3, 4, 5, 6, 9, 11, 17, 21, 22

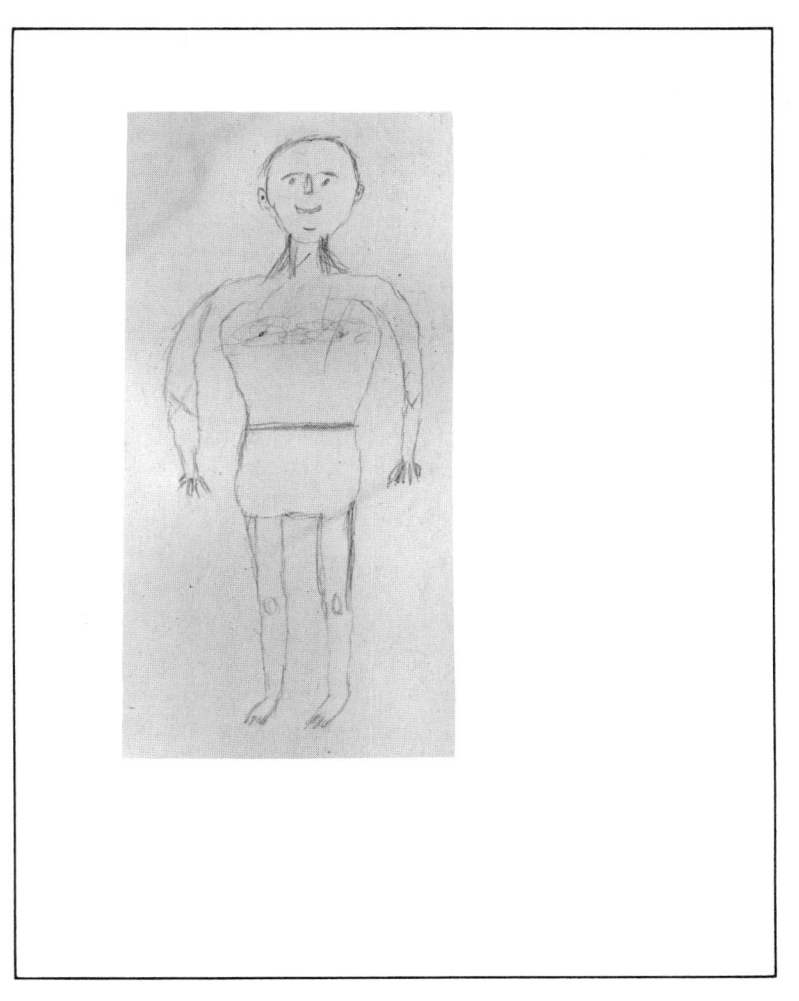

FIGURE-DRAWING CHARACTERISTICS

Structural	Male Female Both	Structural	Male	Female	Structural and Graphic	Male Female Both	Graphic, Global and Height	Male	Female	Body Proportions	Male	Female
Type	0	Omission of Appendages	0	0	Upper and Lower Halves	1 1	Hair Shading	3	3	Head	08	09
Sex Sequence	0	Position of Both Arms	0	0	Four Quarters	4 4	Nudity and Transparency	3	6	Neck	10	07
Posture	1 1	Position of Right Arm	0	5	Relative Size	0	Form	5	5	Shoulders	07	07
Perspective	0 0	Position of Left Arm	0	5	Constant Line Pressure	1 1	Detailing	5	5	Right Arm	05	04
Vertical Midline	0 0	Position of Legs	4	4	Variable Line Pressure	0 0	Identity and Sex	3	3	Left Arm	04	04
Bilateral Symmetry	3 3	Relation of Long Axes	1	1	Line Continuity	0 0	Sophistication	4	4	Chest	07	06
Horizontal Midline	4 4	Right and Left Halves	1	1	Body Shading	7 3	Height	06	05	Girth	07	06

GENERAL CHARACTERISTICS OF SUBJECT

IDENTIFICATION
No. F51
Sex M
Marital status S
Age 25 yrs. at
psychological tests

PARENTAL HISTORY					
Father					
C	H	S	D	O	
–	?	–	–	–	
Mother					
C	H	S	D	O	
–	–	–	–	+	

PHYSIOLOGICAL AND METABOLIC DATA

	Admission	Initial	Control	Cold pressor change	Exercise change	Smoking change
Systolic pressure	130	130	120	+06	+48	+04
Diastolic pressure	70	92	90	+10	+10	+10
Heart rate	66	64	64	+12	+14	+22

Age 23 yrs.	Height 73 in.	Ponderal index 12.70
	Weight 190 lbs.	Cholesterol 222 mg. per 100 ml.
	Overweight +12 %	Vital capacity liters

HABIT SURVEY
Smoking habits: occasional smoker
Age begun 20 yrs.   Inhalation: yes
Habits of nervous tension: 6, 11, 22

STRONG VOCATIONAL INTEREST TEST

Occupation	Artist	Psychologist	Architect	Physician	Osteopath	Dentist	Veterinarian	Mathematician	Physicist	Engineer	Chemist	Production Manager
Standard Score	17	18	26	33	33	28	29	16	08	22	25	34

Occupation	Farmer	Aviator	Carpenter	Printer	Math.-Sci. Teacher	Ind. Arts Teacher	Voc. Agric. Teacher	Policeman	Forest Serv. Man	Y.M.C.A. Phys. Dir.	Personnel Director	Public Administrator
Standard Score	37	33	25	35	42	22	34	30	36	35	39	42

Occupation	Y.M.C.A. Secretary	Soc. Sci. H.S. Teacher	City Sch. Sup't.	Social Worker	Minister	Musician Performer	C.P.A.	Senior C.P.A.	Accountant	Office Man	Purchasing Agent	Banker
Standard Score	34	39	23	32	58	34	35	57	49	50	41	36

Occupation	Mortician	Pharmacist	Sales Manager	Real Est. Manager	Life Ins. Salesman	Advertising Man	Lawyer	Author-Journalist	President Mfg. Co.	Interest Maturity	Occupational Level	Masculinity-Femininity
Standard Score	38	31	33	32	29	24	20	19	26	61	54	41

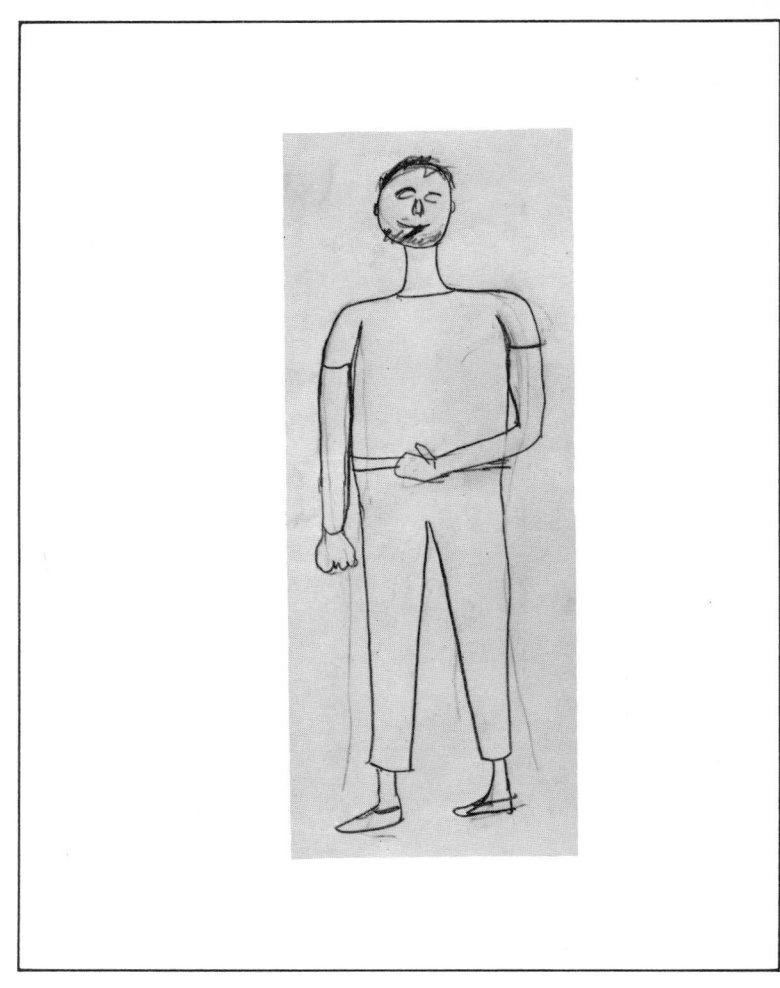

FIGURE-DRAWING CHARACTERISTICS

Structural	Male Female Both	Structural	Male	Female	Structural and Graphic	Male Female Both		Graphic, Global and Height	Male	Female	Body Proportions	Male	Female
Type	0	Omission of Appendages	0	0	Upper and Lower Halves	0	1	Hair Shading	3	3	Head	07	06
Sex Sequence	1	Position of Both Arms	1	1	Four Quarters	4	4	Nudity and Transparency	7	7	Neck	14	07
Posture	1 1	Position of Right Arm	0	2	Relative Size	0		Form	3	3	Shoulders	08	05
Perspective	0 0	Position of Left Arm	5	5	Constant Line Pressure	5	4	Detailing	3	3	Right Arm	06	04
Vertical Midline	0 0	Position of Legs	6	5	Variable Line Pressure	0	0	Identity and Sex	1	1	Left Arm	06	04
Bilateral Symmetry	3 3	Relation of Long Axes	1	1	Line Continuity	4	4	Sophistication	4	4	Chest	07	05
Horizontal Midline	4 4	Right and Left Halves	3	1	Body Shading	0	1	Height	07	05	Girth	10	05

GENERAL CHARACTERISTICS OF SUBJECT

IDENTIFICATION
No. A11
Sex M
Marital status S
Age 23 yrs. at
psychological tests

PARENTAL HISTORY					
Father					
C	H	S	D	O	
-	?	-	-	?	
Mother					
C	H	S	D	O	
-	-	-	-	-	

PHYSIOLOGICAL AND METABOLIC DATA

	Admission	Initial	Control	Cold pressor change	Exercise change	Smoking change
Systolic pressure	160	136	122	+08	+43	+05
Diastolic pressure	110	78	68	+12	+02	+06
Heart rate	88	80	77	+10	+11	+15

Age 23 yrs.

Height 70 in.   Ponderal index 12.54
Weight 174 lbs.   Cholesterol 230 mg. per 100 ml.
Overweight +12 %   Vital capacity liters

HABIT SURVEY

Smoking habits: moderate cigarette smoker
Age begun 18 yrs.   Inhalation: yes
Habits of nervous tension: 5, 6, 8, 11, 19, 23, 24

STRONG VOCATIONAL INTEREST TEST

Occupation	Artist	Psychologist	Architect	Physician	Osteopath	Dentist	Veterinarian	Mathematician	Physicist	Engineer	Chemist	Production Manager
Standard Score	20	37	25	46	46	30	25	21	27	49	42	48

Occupation	Farmer	Aviator	Carpenter	Printer	Math.-Sci. Teacher	Ind. Arts Teacher	Voc. Agric. Teacher	Policeman	Forest Serv. Man	Y.M.C.A. Phys. Dir.	Personnel Director	Public Administrator
Standard Score	36	58	24	36	34	25	21	43	32	33	49	54

Occupation	Y.M.C.A. Secretary	Soc. Sci. H.S. Teacher	City Sch. Sup't.	Social Worker	Minister	Musician Performer	C.P.A.	Senior C.P.A.	Accountant	Office Man	Purchasing Agent	Banker
Standard Score	14	27	26	33	60	20	32	47	36	34	39	28

Occupation	Mortician	Pharmacist	Sales Manager	Real Est. Manager	Life Ins. Salesman	Advertising Man	Lawyer	Author-Journalist	President Mfg. Co.	Interest Maturity	Occupational Level	Masculinity-Femininity
Standard Score	30	35	35	40	27	30	41	29	34	52	56	65

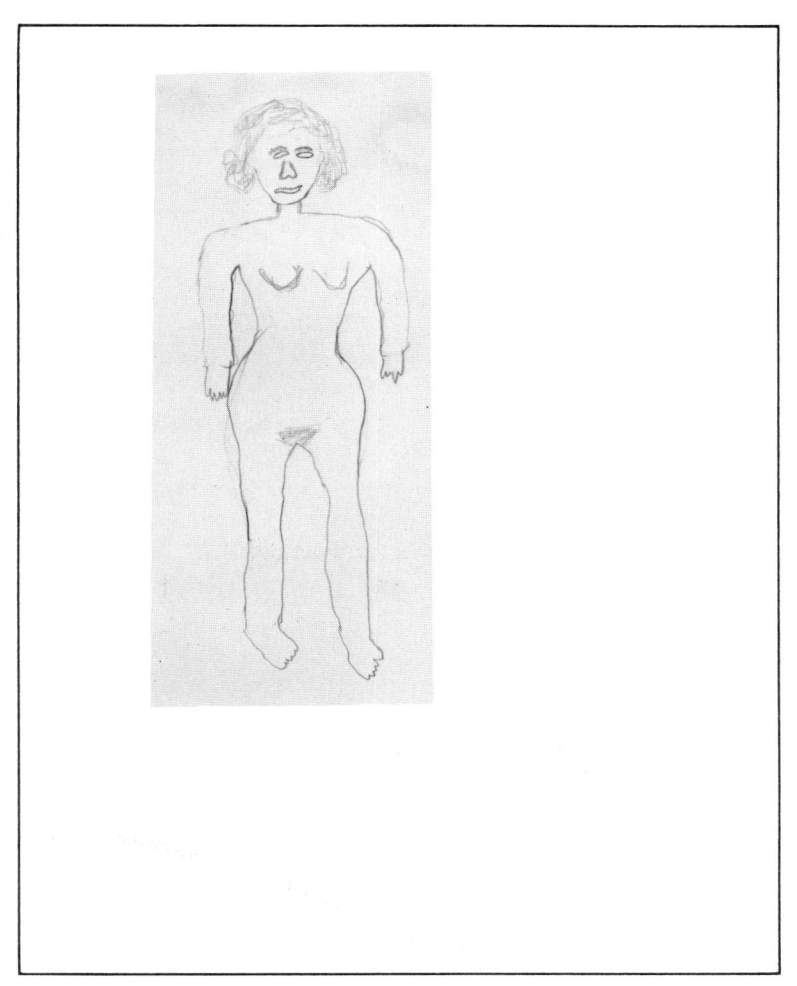

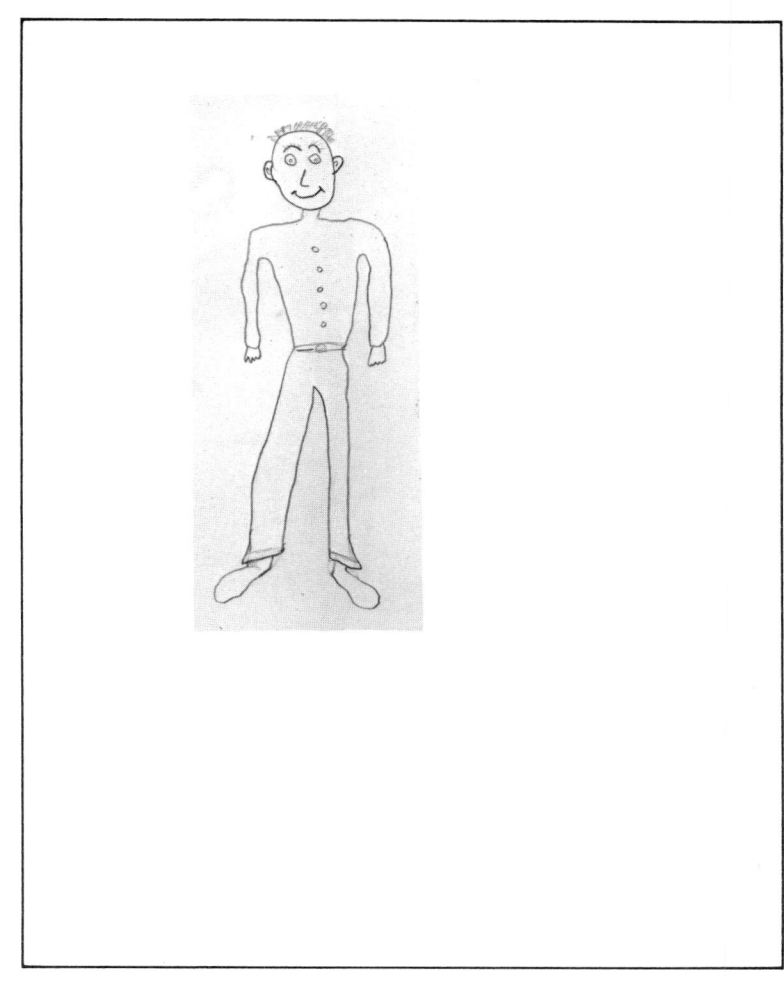

FIGURE-DRAWING CHARACTERISTICS

Structural	Male Female Both	Structural	Male	Female	Structural and Graphic	Male Female Both	Graphic, Global and Height	Male	Female	Body Proportions	Male	Female
Type	0	Omission of Appendages	0	0	Upper and Lower Halves	1 1	Hair Shading	3	3	Head	06	08
Sex Sequence	1	Position of Both Arms	0	0	Four Quarters	4 4	Nudity and Transparency	7	0	Neck	04	04
Posture	1 1	Position of Right Arm	0	0	Relative Size	2	Form	5	5	Shoulders	05	07
Perspective	0 0	Position of Left Arm	0	0	Constant Line Pressure	0 0	Detailing	3	3	Right Arm	02	04
Vertical Midline	3 0	Position of Legs	6	6	Variable Line Pressure	5 4	Identity and Sex	1	1	Left Arm	02	04
Bilateral Symmetry	2 2	Relation of Long Axes	1	1	Line Continuity	4 1	Sophistication	4	4	Chest	04	05
Horizontal Midline	4 0	Right and Left Halves	2	1	Body Shading	0 3	Height	05	06	Girth	03	05

GENERAL CHARACTERISTICS OF SUBJECT

IDENTIFICATION
No. D32
Sex M
Marital status S
Age 21 yrs. at
psychological tests

PARENTAL HISTORY					
Father					
C	H	S	D	O	
-	?	-	-	+	
Mother					
C	H	S	D	O	
-	-	-	-	-	

PHYSIOLOGICAL AND METABOLIC DATA

	Admission	Initial	Control	Cold pressor change	Exercise change	Smoking change
Systolic pressure	120	118	112	+02	+18	+04
Diastolic pressure	82	70	72	00	-12	+04
Heart rate	80	80	83	00	+32	-04

Age 21 yrs.	Height 70 in.	Ponderal index 12.39
	Weight 180 lbs.	Cholesterol 208 mg. per 100 ml.
	Overweight +18 %	Vital capacity 4.5 liters

HABIT SURVEY

Smoking habits: nonsmoker

Age begun   yrs.   Inhalation:

Habits of nervous tension: 2, 3, 4, 6, 18, 19, 22

STRONG VOCATIONAL INTEREST TEST

Occupation	Artist	Psychologist	Architect	Physician	Osteopath	Dentist	Veterinarian	Mathematician	Physicist	Engineer	Chemist	Production Manager
Standard Score	56	65	57	62	37	38	00	48	45	40	51	24

Occupation	Farmer	Aviator	Carpenter	Printer	Math.-Sci. Teacher	Ind. Arts Teacher	Voc. Agric. Teacher	Policeman	Forest Serv. Man	Y.M.C.A. Phys. Dir.	Personnel Director	Public Administrator
Standard Score	17	29	-01	30	26	-05	04	02	06	17	31	36

Occupation	Y.M.C.A. Secretary	Soc. Sci. H.S. Teacher	City Sch. Sup't.	Social Worker	Minister	Musician Performer	C.P.A.	Senior C.P.A.	Accountant	Office Man	Purchasing Agent	Banker
Standard Score	12	22	30	41	63	63	42	23	10	07	08	00

Occupation	Mortician	Pharmacist	Sales Manager	Real Est. Manager	Life Ins. Salesman	Advertising Man	Lawyer	Author-Journalist	President Mfg. Co.	Interest Maturity	Occupational Level	Masculinity-Femininity
Standard Score	11	22	23	32	28	50	56	55	35	45	69	31

FIGURE-DRAWING CHARACTERISTICS

Structural	Male Female Both	Structural	Male	Female	Structural and Graphic	Male Female Both	Graphic, Global and Height	Male	Female	Body Proportions	Male	Female
Type	0	Omission of Appendages	0	0	Upper and Lower Halves	1	1	Hair Shading	1	3	Head	05	04
Sex Sequence	0	Position of Both Arms	0	0	Four Quarters	4	4	Nudity and Transparency	7	7	Neck	05	06
Posture	1	1	Position of Right Arm	2	2	Relative Size	4		Form	3	5	Shoulders	04	05
Perspective	0	0	Position of Left Arm	2	2	Constant Line Pressure	0	0	Detailing	5	5	Right Arm	04	02
Vertical Midline	0	0	Position of Legs	6	6	Variable Line Pressure	1	1	Identity and Sex	3	3	Left Arm	03	03
Bilateral Symmetry	3	3	Relation of Long Axes	1	1	Line Continuity	1	0	Sophistication	4	4	Chest	03	04
Horizontal Midline	4	4	Right and Left Halves	1	1	Body Shading	0	3	Height	03	03	Girth	04	05

GENERAL CHARACTERISTICS OF SUBJECT

IDENTIFICATION
No. 514
Sex M
Marital status S
Age 24 yrs. at
psychological tests

PARENTAL HISTORY
Father
C   H   S   D   O
–   –   –   –   –
Mother
C   H   S   D   O
–   ?   –   –   ?

PHYSIOLOGICAL AND METABOLIC DATA

	Admission	Initial	Control	Cold pressor change	Exercise change	Smoking change
Systolic pressure	100	120	100	+08	+32	
Diastolic pressure	60	64	66	+04	00	
Heart rate	68	76	69	+04	+08	

Age 22 yrs.	Height 72 in.	Ponderal index 13.00
	Weight 170 lbs.	Cholesterol 177 mg. per 100 ml.
	Overweight +04 %	Vital capacity 5.8 liters

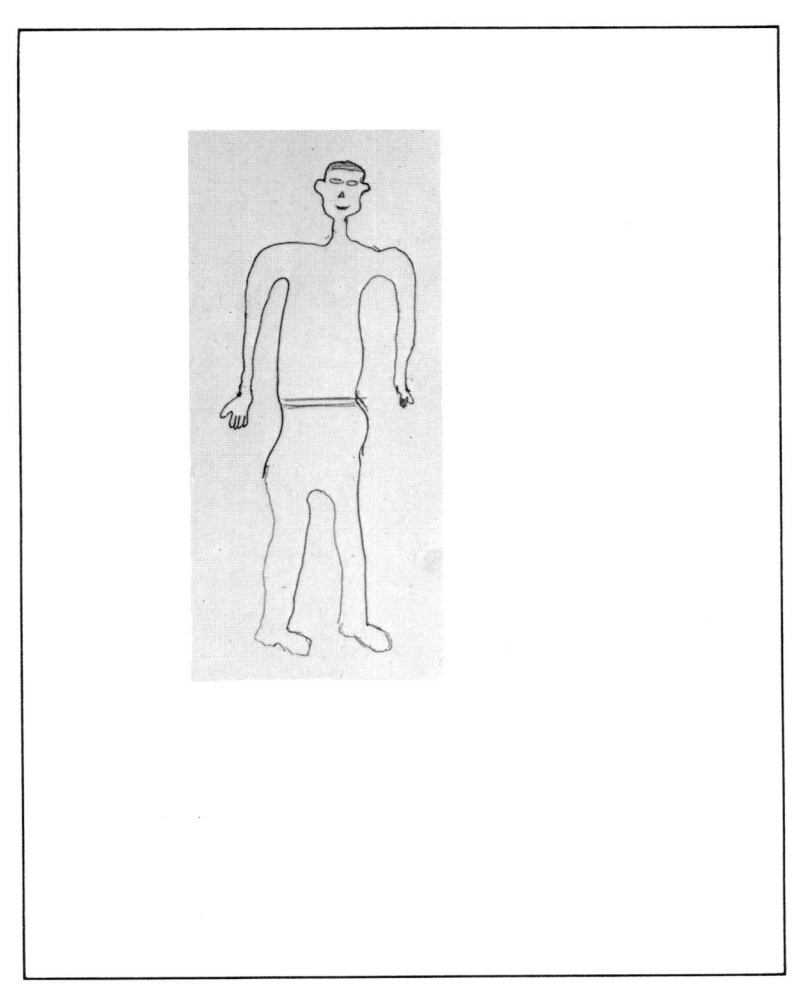

FIGURE-DRAWING CHARACTERISTICS

Structural	Male	Female	Structural	Male	Female	Structural and Graphic	Male	Female	Graphic, Global and Height	Male	Female	Body Proportions	Male	Female
	Both						Both							
Type	0		Omission of Appendages	0	0	Upper and Lower Halves	1	1	Hair Shading	1	3	Head	04	07
Sex Sequence	0		Position of Both Arms	0	4	Four Quarters	4	4	Nudity and Transparency	9	0	Neck	08	10
Posture	1	1	Position of Right Arm	0	7	Relative Size	4		Form	5	3	Shoulders	06	
Perspective	0	2	Position of Left Arm	0	5	Constant Line Pressure	0	0	Detailing	5	5	Right Arm	04	
Vertical Midline	0	4	Position of Legs	5	1	Variable Line Pressure	1	1	Identity and Sex	5	3	Left Arm	04	04
Bilateral Symmetry	1	0	Relation of Long Axes	1	1	Line Continuity	3	0	Sophistication	4	4	Chest	03	05
Horizontal Midline	4	0	Right and Left Halves	1	2	Body Shading	0	0	Height	05	06	Girth	05	06

GENERAL CHARACTERISTICS OF SUBJECT

IDENTIFICATION
No. E01
Sex M
Marital status M
Age 23 yrs. at
psychological tests

PARENTAL HISTORY				
Father				
C	H	S	D	O
–	–	–	–	–
Mother				
C	H	S	D	O
–	?	–	–	–

PHYSIOLOGICAL AND METABOLIC DATA

	Admission	Initial	Control	Cold pressor change	Exercise change	Smoking change
Systolic pressure	120	118	114	+02	+44	+04
Diastolic pressure	75	68	68	+10	–08	+08
Heart rate	80	60	75	00	+19	+23

Age 23 yrs.	Height	72 in.	Ponderal index	12.70
	Weight	182 lbs.	Cholesterol	250 mg. per 100 ml.
	Overweight +11 %		Vital capacity	5.4 liters

HABIT SURVEY

Smoking habits: nonsmoker

Age begun   yrs.   Inhalation:

Habits of nervous tension: 1, 3, 4, 5, 6, 9, 10

STRONG VOCATIONAL INTEREST TEST

Occupation	Artist	Psychologist	Architect	Physician	Osteopath	Dentist	Veterinarian	Mathematician	Physicist	Engineer	Chemist	Production Manager
Standard Score	15	23	19	43	50	44	42	31	25	35	36	27

Occupation	Farmer	Aviator	Carpenter	Printer	Math.-Sci. Teacher	Ind. Arts Teacher	Voc. Agric. Teacher	Policeman	Forest Serv. Man	Y.M.C.A. Phys. Dir.	Personnel Director	Public Administrator
Standard Score	51	40	29	43	57	40	51	36	31	43	20	31

Occupation	Y.M.C.A. Secretary	Soc. Sci. H.S. Teacher	City Sch. Sup't.	Social Worker	Minister	Musician Performer	C.P.A.	Senior C.P.A.	Accountant	Office Man	Purchasing Agent	Banker
Standard Score	32	42	31	22	64	31	19	44	36	39	30	31

Occupation	Mortician	Pharmacist	Sales Manager	Real Est. Manager	Life Ins. Salesman	Advertising Man	Lawyer	Author-Journalist	President Mfg. Co.	Interest Maturity	Occupational Level	Masculinity-Femininity
Standard Score	33	43	15	26	24	13	21	20	17	54	50	59

FIGURE-DRAWING CHARACTERISTICS

Structural	Male Female Both	Structural	Male	Female	Structural and Graphic	Male Female Both		Graphic, Global and Height	Male	Female	Body Proportions	Male	Female
Type	0	Omission of Appendages	0	0	Upper and Lower Halves	1	0	Hair Shading	3	3	Head	05	09
Sex Sequence	0	Position of Both Arms	0	4	Four Quarters	4	4	Nudity and Transparency	7	7	Neck	06	08
Posture	1	2	Position of Right Arm	0	7	Relative Size	4		Form	5	5	Shoulders	07	
Perspective	0	2	Position of Left Arm	0	5	Constant Line Pressure	1	1	Detailing	5	5	Right Arm	04	
Vertical Midline	3	4	Position of Legs	5	8	Variable Line Pressure	0	0	Identity and Sex	3	1	Left Arm	04	05
Bilateral Symmetry	3	0	Relation of Long Axes	1	1	Line Continuity	0	0	Sophistication	4	4	Chest	04	08
Horizontal Midline	4	4	Right and Left Halves	1	0	Body Shading	2	0	Height	05	07	Girth	07	10

GENERAL CHARACTERISTICS OF SUBJECT

IDENTIFICATION
No. B42
Sex M
Marital status S
Age 23 yrs. at psychological tests

PARENTAL HISTORY
Father
C   H   S   D   O
−   −   −   −   +
Mother
C   H   S   D   O
−   −   ?   −   −

PHYSIOLOGICAL AND METABOLIC DATA

	Admission	Initial	Control	Cold pressor change	Exercise change	Smoking change
Systolic pressure	120	114	108	+16	+16	+07
Diastolic pressure	80	58	64	+14	−02	+06
Heart rate	90	74	61	+02	+27	00

Age 23 yrs.	Height	70 in.	Ponderal index 12.68
	Weight	168 lbs.	Cholesterol 200 mg. per 100 ml.
	Overweight +08 %		Vital capacity 4.8 liters

HABIT SURVEY
Smoking habits: nonsmoker
Age begun   yrs.   Inhalation:
Habits of nervous tension: 5, 6, 9, 12, 14, 16, 21

STRONG VOCATIONAL INTEREST TEST

Occupation	Artist	Psychologist	Architect	Physician	Osteopath	Dentist	Veterinarian	Mathematician	Physicist	Engineer	Chemist	Production Manager
Standard Score	14	22	10	30	27	21	33	07	−02	10	08	33

Occupation	Farmer	Aviator	Carpenter	Printer	Math.-Sci. Teacher	Ind. Arts Teacher	Voc. Agric. Teacher	Policeman	Forest Serv. Man	Y.M.C.A. Phys. Dir.	Personnel Director	Public Administrator
Standard Score	36	29	10	30	34	11	35	40	27	43	48	49

Occupation	Y.M.C.A. Secretary	Soc. Sci. H.S. Teacher	City Sch. Sup't.	Social Worker	Minister	Musician Performer	C.P.A.	Senior C.P.A.	Accountant	Office Man	Purchasing Agent	Banker
Standard Score	39	52	35	42	61	30	22	43	31	42	37	42

Occupation	Mortician	Pharmacist	Sales Manager	Real Est. Manager	Life Ins. Salesman	Advertising Man	Lawyer	Author-Journalist	President Mfg. Co.	Interest Maturity	Occupational Level	Masculinity-Femininity
Standard Score	41	37	42	42	42	32	38	26	24	58	52	48

FIGURE-DRAWING CHARACTERISTICS

Structural	Male	Female	Structural	Male	Female	Structural and Graphic	Male	Female	Graphic, Global and Height	Male	Female	Body Proportions	Male	Female
	Both						Both							
Type	0		Omission of Appendages	7	0	Upper and Lower Halves	1	1	Hair Shading	7	7	Head	09	07
Sex Sequence	0		Position of Both Arms	0	4	Four Quarters	4	4	Nudity and Transparency	7	7	Neck	08	06
Posture	2	2	Position of Right Arm	0	7	Relative Size	0		Form	3	5	Shoulders		
Perspective	6	2	Position of Left Arm	0	0	Constant Line Pressure	0	1	Detailing	3	5	Right Arm	04	
Vertical Midline	4	4	Position of Legs	8	8	Variable Line Pressure	1	0	Identity and Sex	3	3	Left Arm		02
Bilateral Symmetry	0	0	Relation of Long Axes	1	1	Line Continuity	0	0	Sophistication	4	4	Chest		04
Horizontal Midline	6	0	Right and Left Halves	2	1	Body Shading	3	0	Height	06	04	Girth		11

GENERAL CHARACTERISTICS OF SUBJECT

IDENTIFICATION
No. 349
Sex M
Marital status M
Age 24 yrs. at psychological tests

PARENTAL HISTORY				
Father				
C	H	S	D	O
–	–	–	–	+
Mother				
C	H	S	D	O
–	–	–	–	+

PHYSIOLOGICAL AND METABOLIC DATA

	Admission	Initial	Control	Cold pressor change	Exercise change	Smoking change
Systolic pressure	122	120	116	+06	+26	
Diastolic pressure	66	72	74	+12	00	
Heart rate	76	78	71	00	+16	

Age 23 yrs.	Height 72 in.	Ponderal index 12.80
	Weight 178 lbs.	Cholesterol 250 mg. per 100 ml.
	Overweight +09 %	Vital capacity 4.5 liters

HABIT SURVEY

Smoking habits: moderate **cigarette** smoker

   Age begun * yrs.   Inhalation: yes

Habits of nervous tension: 4, 6, 9, 11, 16, 21

* very young

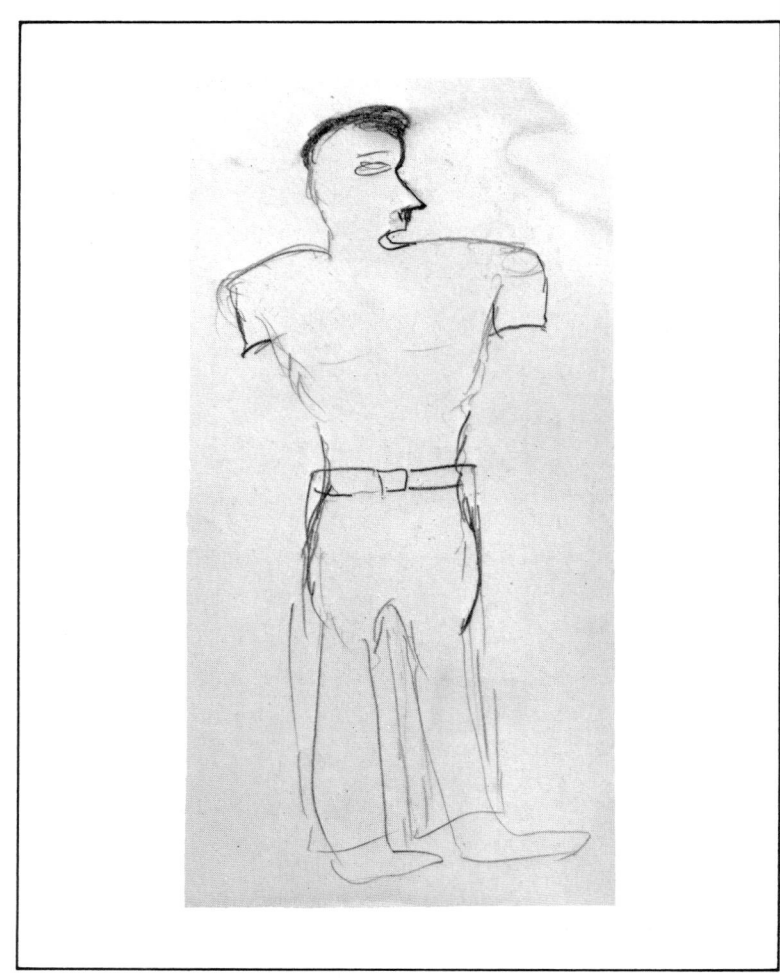

FIGURE-DRAWING CHARACTERISTICS

Structural	Male	Female	Structural	Male	Female	Structural and Graphic	Male	Female	Graphic, Global and Height	Male	Female	Body Proportions	Male	Female
	Both						Both							
Type	0		Omission of Appendages	2	2	Upper and Lower Halves	0	0	Hair Shading	3	3	Head	09	09
Sex Sequence	1		Position of Both Arms	6	6	Four Quarters	4	4	Nudity and Transparency	5	7	Neck	04	12
Posture	1	1	Position of Right Arm	8	7	Relative Size	2		Form	5	5	Shoulders	13	
Perspective	5	6	Position of Left Arm	8	7	Constant Line Pressure	0	0	Detailing	5	5	Right Arm		
Vertical Midline	0	4	Position of Legs	4	4	Variable Line Pressure	3	4	Identity and Sex	1	3	Left Arm		
Bilateral Symmetry	2	0	Relation of Long Axes	1	1	Line Continuity	0	0	Sophistication	4	4	Chest	10	
Horizontal Midline	4	0	Right and Left Halves	0	2	Body Shading	0	3	Height	08	08	Girth	09	

GENERAL CHARACTERISTICS OF SUBJECT

IDENTIFICATION
No. F65
Sex M
Marital status S
Age 25 yrs. at
psychological tests

PARENTAL HISTORY				
Father				
C	H	S	D	O
-	-	-	-	?
Mother				
C	H	S	D	O
-	-	-	-	+

PHYSIOLOGICAL AND METABOLIC DATA

	Admission	Initial	Control	Cold pressor change	Exercise change	Smoking change
Systolic pressure	132	114	112	+08	+38	00
Diastolic pressure	82	82	82	+16	+18	+01
Heart rate	98	80	79	+16	00	-01

Age 23 yrs.	Height	68 in.	Ponderal index	12.83
	Weight	149 lbs.	Cholesterol	234 mg. per 100 ml.
	Overweight +01 %		Vital capacity	liters

HABIT SURVEY
Smoking habits: light cigarette smoker
Age begun   yrs.   Inhalation:
Habits of nervous tension:

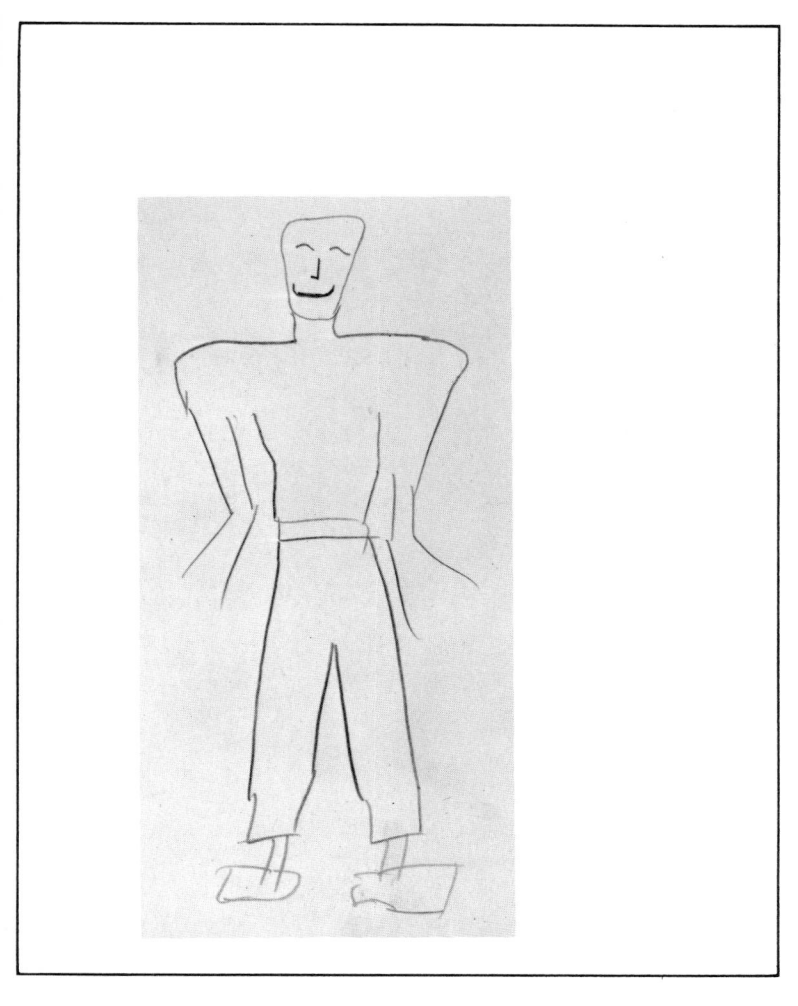

FIGURE-DRAWING CHARACTERISTICS

Structural	Male Female Both	Structural	Male	Female	Structural and Graphic	Male Female Both		Graphic, Global and Height	Male	Female	Body Proportions	Male	Female
Type	0	Omission of Appendages	7	2	Upper and Lower Halves	3	3	Hair Shading	0	3	Head	08	12
Sex Sequence	0	Position of Both Arms	0	0	Four Quarters	4	4	Nudity and Transparency	3	3	Neck	07	10
Posture	1 1	Position of Right Arm	4	2	Relative Size	0		Form	5	5	Shoulders	12	05
Perspective	0 0	Position of Left Arm	4	2	Constant Line Pressure	0	2	Detailing	5	5	Right Arm		
Vertical Midline	0 0	Position of Legs	5	5	Variable Line Pressure	5	0	Identity and Sex	3	3	Left Arm		
Bilateral Symmetry	2 2	Relation of Long Axes	1	1	Line Continuity	4	1	Sophistication	4	4	Chest	05	06
Horizontal Midline	4 4	Right and Left Halves	1	1	Body Shading	0	1	Height	07	07	Girth	05	08

GENERAL CHARACTERISTICS OF SUBJECT

IDENTIFICATION	PARENTAL HISTORY
No. B60	Father
Sex M	C H S D O
Marital status S	– – – – ?
Age 22 yrs. at	Mother
psychological tests	C H S D O
	– – – – +

PHYSIOLOGICAL AND METABOLIC DATA

	Admission	Initial	Control	Cold pressor change	Exercise change	Smoking change
Systolic pressure	136	148	132	+10	+48	+08
Diastolic pressure	90	86	88	+06	00	+08
Heart rate	116	112	88	+08	+23	+04

Age 22 yrs.	Height 73 in.	Ponderal index 11.50
	Weight 256 lbs.	Cholesterol 278 mg. per 100 ml.
	Overweight +40 %	Vital capacity 5.2 liters

HABIT SURVEY

Smoking habits: occasional smoker

  Age begun 18 yrs.   Inhalation: no

Habits of nervous tension: 8, 10, 16, 25

STRONG VOCATIONAL INTEREST TEST

Occupation	Artist	Psychologist	Architect	Physician	Osteopath	Dentist	Veterinarian	Mathematician	Physicist	Engineer	Chemist	Production Manager
Standard Score	38	51	38	53	40	26	13	28	18	24	34	22

Occupation	Farmer	Aviator	Carpenter	Printer	Math.-Sci. Teacher	Ind. Arts Teacher	Voc. Agric. Teacher	Policeman	Forest Serv. Man	Y.M.C.A. Phys. Dir.	Personnel Director	Public Administrator
Standard Score	19	30	06	29	28	01	17	28	27	51	55	55

Occupation	Y.M.C.A. Secretary	Soc. Sci. H.S. Teacher	City Sch. Sup't.	Social Worker	Minister	Musician Performer	C.P.A.	Senior C.P.A.	Accountant	Office Man	Purchasing Agent	Banker
Standard Score	40	43	46	59	61	52	35	36	18	29	19	11

Occupation	Mortician	Pharmacist	Sales Manager	Real Est. Manager	Life Ins. Salesman	Advertising Man	Lawyer	Author- Journalist	President Mfg. Co.	Interest Maturity	Occupational Level	Masculinity- Femininity
Standard Score	25	29	39	36	41	47	49	45	29	58	61	32

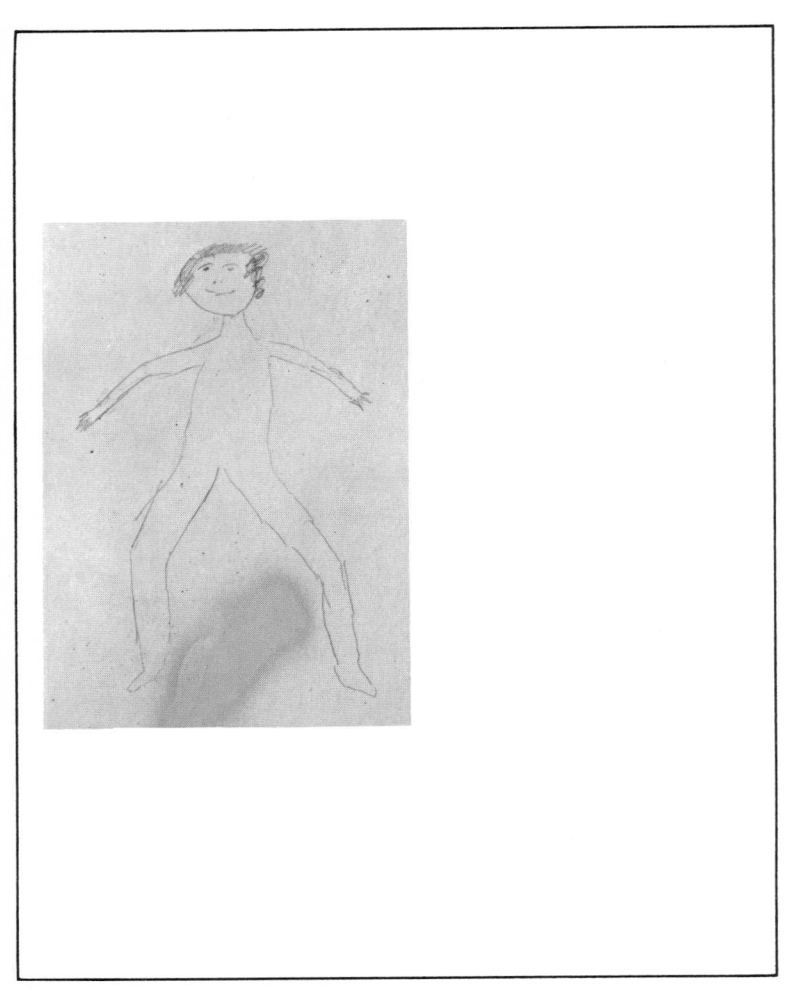

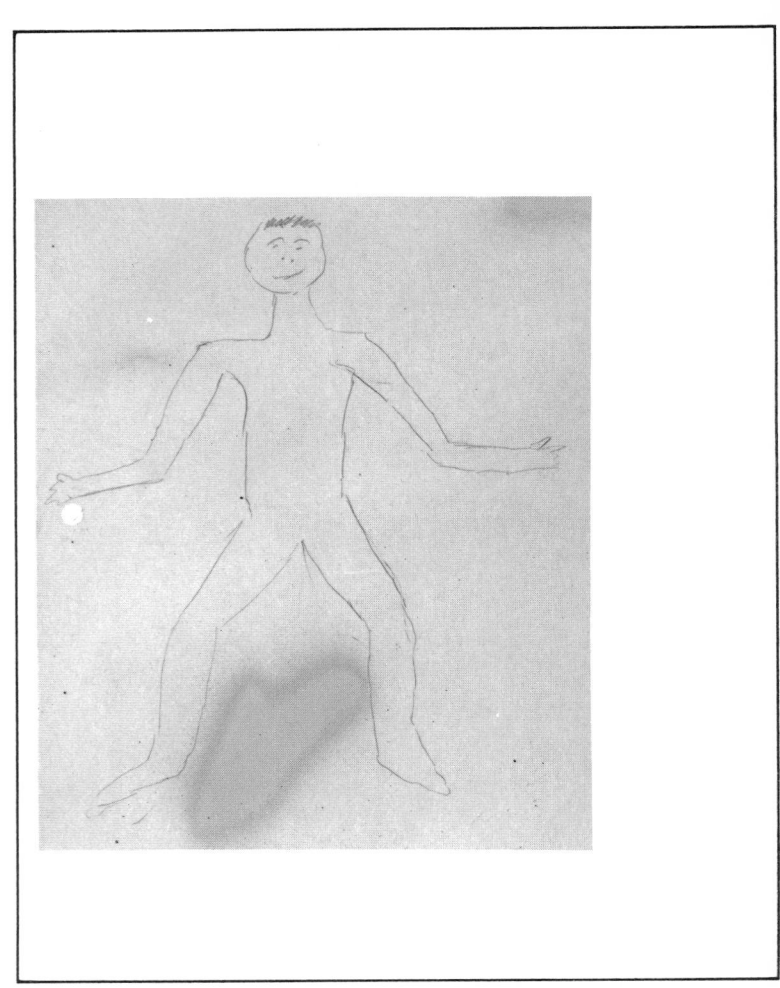

FIGURE-DRAWING CHARACTERISTICS

Structural	Male Female Both	Structural	Male	Female	Structural and Graphic	Male Female Both		Graphic, Global and Height	Male	Female	Body Proportions	Male	Female
Type	0	Omission of Appendages	0	0	Upper and Lower Halves	0	1	Hair Shading	3	3	Head	06	06
Sex Sequence	1	Position of Both Arms	0	0	Four Quarters	4	4	Nudity and Transparency	0	0	Neck	10	08
Posture	9 9	Position of Right Arm	2	2	Relative Size	0		Form	5	5	Shoulders	07	03
Perspective	0 0	Position of Left Arm	2	2	Constant Line Pressure	1	1	Detailing	5	5	Right Arm	06	04
Vertical Midline	0 0	Position of Legs	6	6	Variable Line Pressure	0	0	Identity and Sex	5	5	Left Arm	06	02
Bilateral Symmetry	3 3	Relation of Long Axes	1	1	Line Continuity	0	0	Sophistication	4	4	Chest	05	03
Horizontal Midline	0 0	Right and Left Halves	1	2	Body Shading	0	0	Height	06	04	Girth	06	05

GENERAL CHARACTERISTICS OF SUBJECT

IDENTIFICATION
No. 308
Sex M
Marital status   S
Age 25 yrs. at
psychological tests

PARENTAL HISTORY
Father
C   H   S   D   O
-     -   -   -   +
Mother
C   H   S   D   O
-     -   -   -   -

PHYSIOLOGICAL AND METABOLIC DATA

	Admission	Initial	Control	Cold pressor change	Exercise change	Smoking change
Systolic pressure	140	154	138	+21	+36	00
Diastolic pressure	90	78	78	+18	00	+02
Heart rate	80	108	98	+14	+07	00

	Height	73 in.	Ponderal index 11.11	
Age 23 yrs.	Weight	284 lbs.	Cholesterol 243 mg. per 100 ml.	
	Overweight +59 %		Vital capacity 5.5 liters	

HABIT SURVEY
Smoking habits: pipe smoker
Age begun 19 yrs.   Inhalation: no
Habits of nervous tension: 5, 10, 22

Plate 117   **MODERATELY PRIMITIVE DRAWINGS**   155

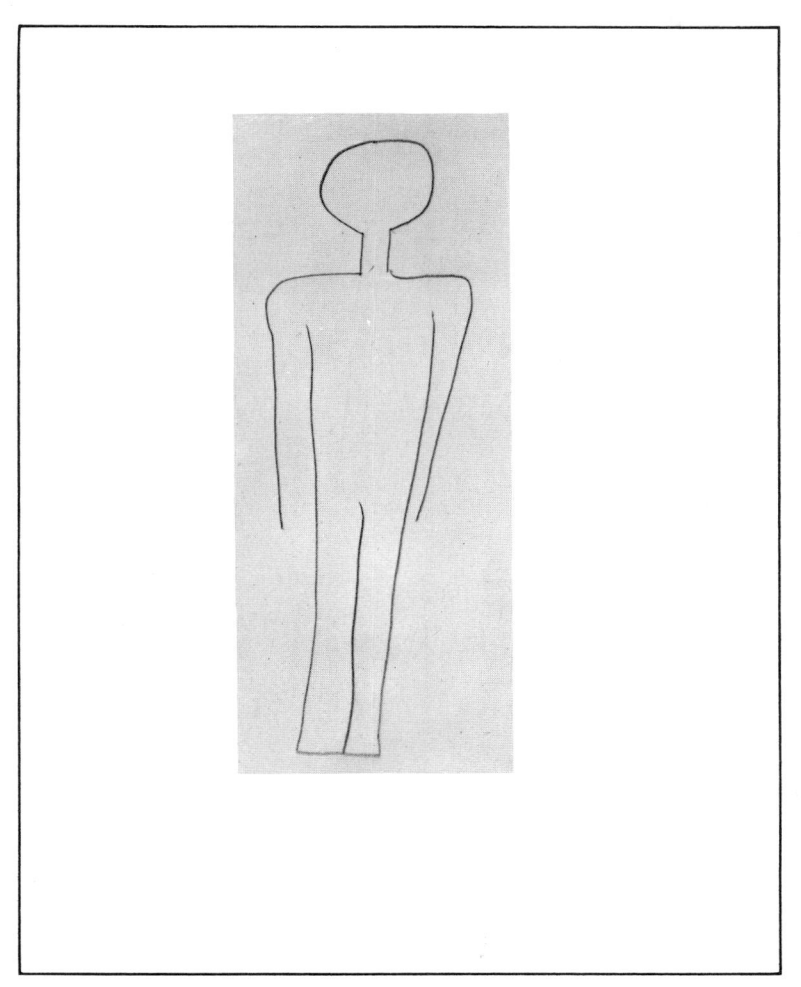
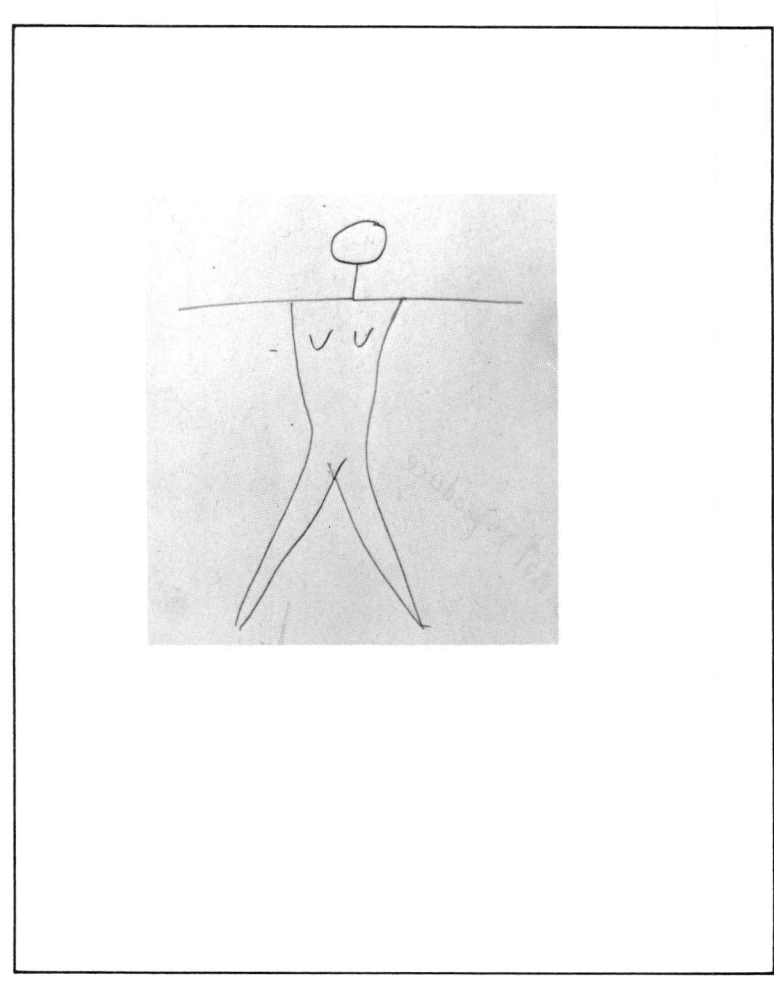

FIGURE-DRAWING CHARACTERISTICS

Structural	Male Female Both		Structural	Male	Female	Structural and Graphic Both		Male Female	Graphic, Global and Height	Male	Female	Body Proportions	Male	Female
Type	0		Omission of Appendages	6	6	Upper and Lower Halves	1	1	Hair Shading	0	0	Head		03
Sex Sequence	0		Position of Both Arms	0	0	Four Quarters	4	4	Nudity and Transparency	9	0	Neck		10
Posture	1	9	Position of Right Arm	0	2	Relative Size	0		Form	5	5	Shoulders	08	04
Perspective	9	0	Position of Left Arm	0	2	Constant Line Pressure	5	0	Detailing	5	5	Right Arm		
Vertical Midline	0	0	Position of Legs	2	6	Variable Line Pressure	0	5	Identity and Sex	5	3	Left Arm		
Bilateral Symmetry	3	3	Relation of Long Axes	1	1	Line Continuity	4	4	Sophistication	4	4	Chest	06	05
Horizontal Midline	0	0	Right and Left Halves	1	1	Body Shading	0	0	Height	06	04	Girth	06	03

GENERAL CHARACTERISTICS OF SUBJECT

IDENTIFICATION

No. 752
Sex M
Marital status S
Age 25 yrs. at
psychological tests

PARENTAL HISTORY

Father

C	H	S	D	O
-	-	-	-	+

Mother

C	H	S	D	O
-	-	-	-	-

PHYSIOLOGICAL AND METABOLIC DATA

	Admission	Initial	Control	Cold pressor change	Exercise change	Smoking change
Systolic pressure	110	120	116	+08	+26	+07
Diastolic pressure	80	72	67	+15	-17	+02
Heart rate	88	76	67	+12	+36	+03

Age 25 yrs.	Height 73 in.	Ponderal index 12.35
	Weight 206 lbs.	Cholesterol 222 mg. per 100 ml.
	Overweight +19 %	Vital capacity liters

HABIT SURVEY

Smoking habits: heavy cigarette smoker
Age begun 20 yrs.   Inhalation: yes
Habits of nervous tension: 5, 22

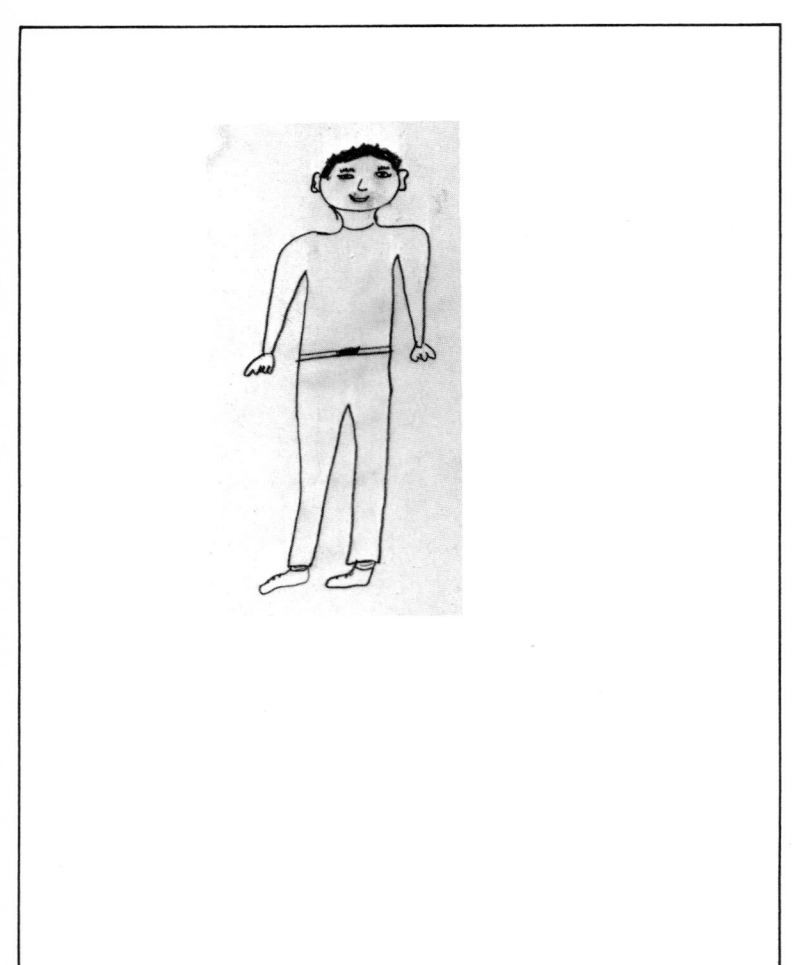

FIGURE-DRAWING CHARACTERISTICS

Structural	Male Female Both	Structural	Male	Female	Structural and Graphic	Male Female Both	Graphic, Global and Height	Male	Female	Body Proportions	Male	Female
Type	0	Omission of Appendages	0	0	Upper and Lower Halves	1 1	Hair Shading	3	3	Head	05	07
Sex Sequence	0	Position of Both Arms	0	0	Four Quarters	4 4	Nudity and Transparency	7	7	Neck	06	06
Posture	1 1	Position of Right Arm	0	0	Relative Size	4	Form	3	3	Shoulders	06	06
Perspective	0 0	Position of Left Arm	0	0	Constant Line Pressure	5 5	Detailing	5	5	Right Arm	02	02
Vertical Midline	0 0	Position of Legs	5	6	Variable Line Pressure	0 0	Identity and Sex	3	3	Left Arm	02	02
Bilateral Symmetry	3 3	Relation of Long Axes	1	1	Line Continuity	4 4	Sophistication	4	4	Chest	04	05
Horizontal Midline	4 4	Right and Left Halves	1	1	Body Shading	4 5	Height	04	05	Girth	06	04

GENERAL CHARACTERISTICS OF SUBJECT

IDENTIFICATION
No. F49
Sex M
Marital status S
Age 23 yrs. at psychological tests

PARENTAL HISTORY					
Father					
C	H	S	D	O	
-	-	-	-	+	
Mother					
C	H	S	D	O	
-	-	-	-	-	

PHYSIOLOGICAL AND METABOLIC DATA

	Admission	Initial	Control	Cold pressor change	Exercise change	Smoking change
Systolic pressure	140	118	110	+08	+34	+06
Diastolic pressure	58	70	68	+14	+12	+06
Heart rate	88	76	86	+12	+26	+17

Age 21 yrs.
Height 69 in. Ponderal index 12.37
Weight 174 lbs. Cholesterol 244 mg. per 100 ml.
Overweight +17 % Vital capacity liters

HABIT SURVEY

Smoking habits: cigar smoker

Age begun 21 yrs.   Inhalation: no

Habits of nervous tension: 5, 6, 9, 10, 19, 23, 24, 25

STRONG VOCATIONAL INTEREST TEST

Occupation	Artist	Psychologist	Architect	Physician	Osteopath	Dentist	Veterinarian	Mathematician	Physicist	Engineer	Chemist	Production Manager
Standard Score	29	47	27	42	28	28	13	29	20	25	37	26

Occupation	Farmer	Aviator	Carpenter	Printer	Math.-Sci. Teacher	Ind. Arts Teacher	Voc. Agric. Teacher	Policeman	Forest Serv. Man	Y.M.C.A. Phys. Dir.	Personnel Director	Public Administrator
Standard Score	26	29	08	36	35	03	18	13	12	16	29	38

Occupation	Y.M.C.A. Secretary	Soc. Sci. H.S. Teacher	City Sch. Sup't.	Social Worker	Minister	Musician Performer	C.P.A.	Senior C.P.A.	Accountant	Office Man	Purchasing Agent	Banker
Standard Score	17	35	27	36	58	39	59	50	36	34	25	28

Occupation	Mortician	Pharmacist	Sales Manager	Real Est. Manager	Life Ins. Salesman	Advertising Man	Lawyer	Author- Journalist	President Mfg. Co.	Interest Maturity	Occupational Level	Masculinity- Femininity
Standard Score	24	34	36	40	33	38	45	38	35	55	61	45

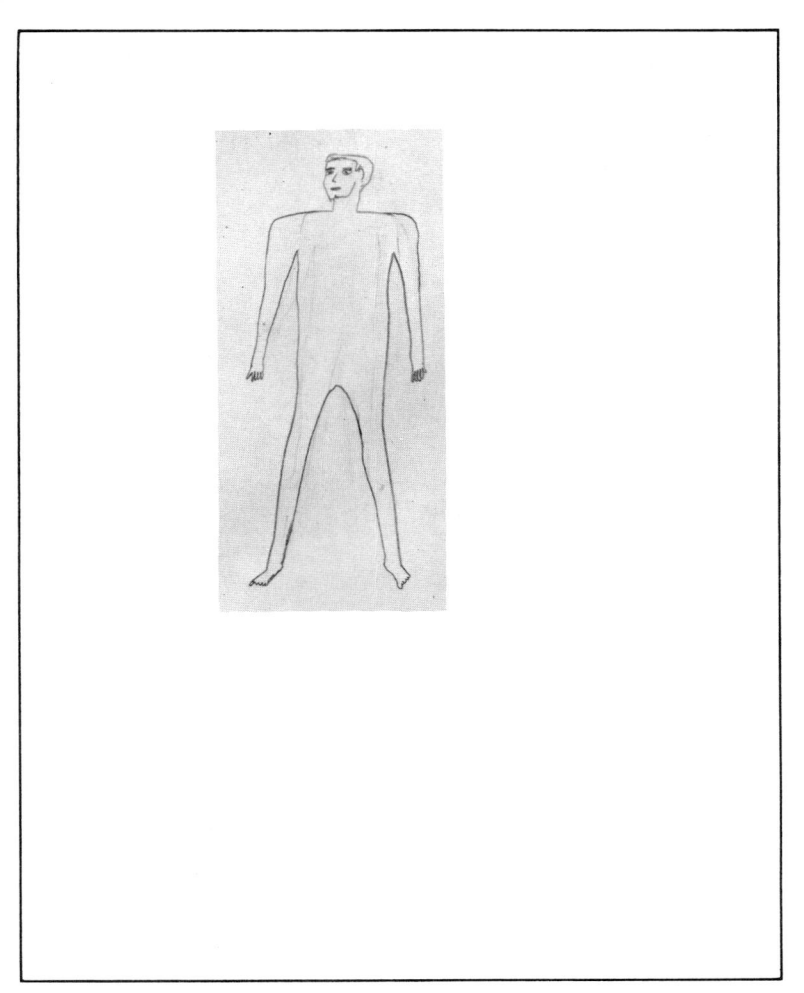

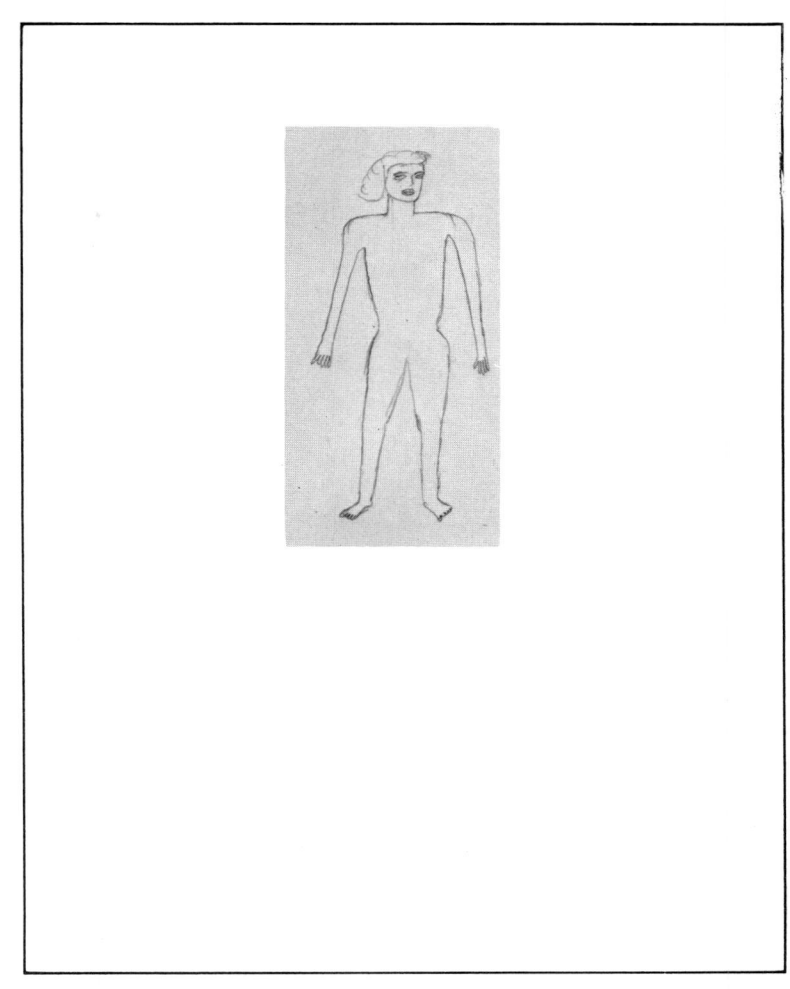

FIGURE-DRAWING CHARACTERISTICS

Structural	Male	Female	Structural	Male	Female	Structural and Graphic	Male	Female	Graphic, Global and Height	Male	Female	Body Proportions	Male	Female
	Both						Both							
Type	0		Omission of Appendages	0	0	Upper and Lower Halves	1	1	Hair Shading	5	5	Head	03	03
Sex Sequence	0		Position of Both Arms	0	0	Four Quarters	4	4	Nudity and Transparency	0	0	Neck	04	04
Posture	1	1	Position of Right Arm	1	0	Relative Size	0		Form	3	3	Shoulders	06	05
Perspective	0	0	Position of Left Arm	1	0	Constant Line Pressure	3	0	Detailing	5	5	Right Arm	04	02
Vertical Midline	0	0	Position of Legs	6	6	Variable Line Pressure	0	5	Identity and Sex	3	3	Left Arm	04	04
Bilateral Symmetry	3	3	Relation of Long Axes	1	1	Line Continuity	4	2	Sophistication	4	4	Chest	04	04
Horizontal Midline	0	0	Right and Left Halves	1	1	Body Shading	0	0	Height	04	03	Girth	05	04

GENERAL CHARACTERISTICS OF SUBJECT

IDENTIFICATION
No. G40
Sex M
Marital status M
Age 23 yrs. at
psychological tests

PARENTAL HISTORY					
Father					
C	H	S	D	O
-	-	-	-	+
Mother					
C	H	S	D	O
-	-	-	-	-

PHYSIOLOGICAL AND METABOLIC DATA

	Admission	Initial	Control	Cold pressor change	Exercise change	Smoking change
Systolic pressure	110	116	108	+14	+22	+06
Diastolic pressure	60	54	66	+20	-02	+05
Heart rate	70	64	60	+04	+12	+04

Age 22 yrs.	Height 72 in.	Ponderal index 13.31
	Weight 158 lbs.	Cholesterol 140 mg. per 100 ml.
	Overweight -03 %	Vital capacity liters

HABIT SURVEY

Smoking habits: nonsmoker

Age begun   yrs.   Inhalation:

Habits of nervous tension: 1, 3, 4, 5, 6, 8, 9, 11, 17, 18, 20, 23

STRONG VOCATIONAL INTEREST TEST

Occupation	Artist	Psychologist	Architect	Physician	Osteopath	Dentist	Veterinarian	Mathematician	Physicist	Engineer	Chemist	Production Manager
Standard Score	22	23	27	33	34	27	21	28	26	34	34	32

Occupation	Farmer	Aviator	Carpenter	Printer	Math.-Sci. Teacher	Ind. Arts Teacher	Voc. Agric. Teacher	Policeman	Forest Serv. Man	Y.M.C.A. Phys. Dir.	Personnel Director	Public Administrator
Standard Score	45	39	30	41	42	21	35	35	41	31	35	41

Occupation	Y.M.C.A. Secretary	Soc. Sci. H.S. Teacher	City Sch. Sup't.	Social Worker	Minister	Musician Performer	C.P.A.	Senior C.P.A.	Accountant	Office Man	Purchasing Agent	Banker
Standard Score	32	34	29	29	59	34	23	43	34	35	23	31

Occupation	Mortician	Pharmacist	Sales Manager	Real Est. Manager	Life Ins. Salesman	Advertising Man	Lawyer	Author-Journalist	President Mfg. Co.	Interest Maturity	Occupational Level	Masculinity-Femininity
Standard Score	23	17	20	26	27	24	28	25	21	55	53	51

FIGURE-DRAWING CHARACTERISTICS

Structural	Male Female		Structural	Male	Female	Structural and Graphic	Male Female		Graphic, Global and Height	Male	Female	Body Proportions	Male	Female
	Both						Both							
Type	0		Omission of Appendages	0	0	Upper and Lower Halves	1	1	Hair Shading	3	3	Head	05	04
Sex Sequence	0		Position of Both Arms	0	0	Four Quarters	4	4	Nudity and Transparency	7	7	Neck	04	05
Posture	1	1	Position of Right Arm	0	0	Relative Size	2		Form	5	5	Shoulders	07	05
Perspective	0	0	Position of Left Arm	0	0	Constant Line Pressure	3	3	Detailing	5	5	Right Arm	04	02
Vertical Midline	3	3	Position of Legs	6	4	Variable Line Pressure	0	0	Identity and Sex	3	3	Left Arm	04	02
Bilateral Symmetry	3	2	Relation of Long Axes	1	1	Line Continuity	0	0	Sophistication	4	4	Chest	04	05
Horizontal Midline	4	0	Right and Left Halves	2	2	Body Shading	4	1	Height	04	04	Girth	04	05

GENERAL CHARACTERISTICS OF SUBJECT

IDENTIFICATION
No. A44
Sex M
Marital status M
Age 22 yrs. at
psychological tests

PARENTAL HISTORY				
Father				
C	H	S	D	O
-	-	-	-	+
Mother				
C	H	S	D	O
-	-	-	-	-

PHYSIOLOGICAL AND METABOLIC DATA

	Admission	Initial	Control	Cold pressor change	Exercise change	Smoking change
Systolic pressure	110	129	114	+24	+47	+07
Diastolic pressure	80	63	65	+08	-43	+11
Heart rate	72	86	87	+15	+20	+11

Age 21 yrs.	Height	70 in.	Ponderal index 12.30
	Weight	184 lbs.	Cholesterol 258 mg. per 100 ml.
	Overweight +17 %		Vital capacity liters

HABIT SURVEY

Smoking habits: heavy cigarette smoker

Age begun 17 yrs.   Inhalation: yes

Habits of nervous tension: 3, 4, 5, 6, 9, 11, 16, 17, 22

STRONG VOCATIONAL INTEREST TEST

Occupation	Artist	Psychologist	Architect	Physician	Osteopath	Dentist	Veterinarian	Mathematician	Physicist	Engineer	Chemist	Production Manager
Standard Score	51	46	44	44	24	27	07	45	36	33	48	15

Occupation	Farmer	Aviator	Carpenter	Printer	Math.-Sci. Teacher	Ind. Arts Teacher	Voc. Agric. Teacher	Policeman	Forest Serv. Man	Y.M.C.A. Phys. Dir.	Personnel Director	Public Administrator
Standard Score	32	31	09	37	27	-10	08	16	19	13	18	31

Occupation	Y.M.C.A. Secretary	Soc. Sci. H.S. Teacher	City Sch. Sup't.	Social Worker	Minister	Musician Performer	C.P.A.	Senior C.P.A.	Accountant	Office Man	Purchasing Agent	Banker
Standard Score	12	23	19	26	60	47	34	28	15	20	10	17

Occupation	Mortician	Pharmacist	Sales Manager	Real Est. Manager	Life Ins. Salesman	Advertising Man	Lawyer	Author-Journalist	President Mfg. Co.	Interest Maturity	Occupational Level	Masculinity-Femininity
Standard Score	04	15	19	30	22	49	49	56	24	44	59	36

Plate 121   **MODERATELY PRIMITIVE DRAWINGS**   159

FIGURE-DRAWING CHARACTERISTICS

Structural	Male Female Both	Structural	Male	Female	Structural and Graphic	Male Female Both		Graphic, Global and Height	Male	Female	Body Proportions	Male	Female
Type	0	Omission of Appendages	7	4	Upper and Lower Halves	3	3	Hair Shading	7	3	Head	09	09
Sex Sequence	1	Position of Both Arms	0	1	Four Quarters	4	4	Nudity and Transparency	7	7	Neck	12	08
Posture	1 0	Position of Right Arm	0	0	Relative Size	5		Form	3	5	Shoulders	09	
Perspective	9 1	Position of Left Arm	0	5	Constant Line Pressure	1	1	Detailing	3	3	Right Arm	05	
Vertical Midline	3 7	Position of Legs	3	0	Variable Line Pressure	0	0	Identity and Sex	1	1	Left Arm	06	
Bilateral Symmetry	3 0	Relation of Long Axes	3	3	Line Continuity	0	0	Sophistication	4	4	Chest	09	
Horizontal Midline	6 6	Right and Left Halves	1	1	Body Shading	0	5	Height	07		Girth	10	

GENERAL CHARACTERISTICS OF SUBJECT

IDENTIFICATION
No. A81
Sex M
Marital status M
Age 22 yrs. at psychological tests

PARENTAL HISTORY				
Father				
C	H	S	D	O
–	–	–	–	+
Mother				
C	H	S	D	O
–	–	–	–	–

PHYSIOLOGICAL AND METABOLIC DATA

	Admission	Initial	Control	Cold pressor change	Exercise change	Smoking change
Systolic pressure	150	118	120	+04	+38	+07
Diastolic pressure	100	70	78	+08	–06	+01
Heart rate	76	60	59	–04	+19	+09

Age 22 yrs.	Height 72 in.	Ponderal index 13.74
	Weight 144 lbs.	Cholesterol 214 mg. per 100 ml.
	Overweight –12 %	Vital capacity liters

HABIT SURVEY
Smoking habits: heavy cigarette smoker
Age begun 17 yrs.   Inhalation: yes
Habits of nervous tension: 1, 2, 3, 4, 5, 6, 7, 8, 9, 10, 11, 18, 20, 21, 23, 24, 25

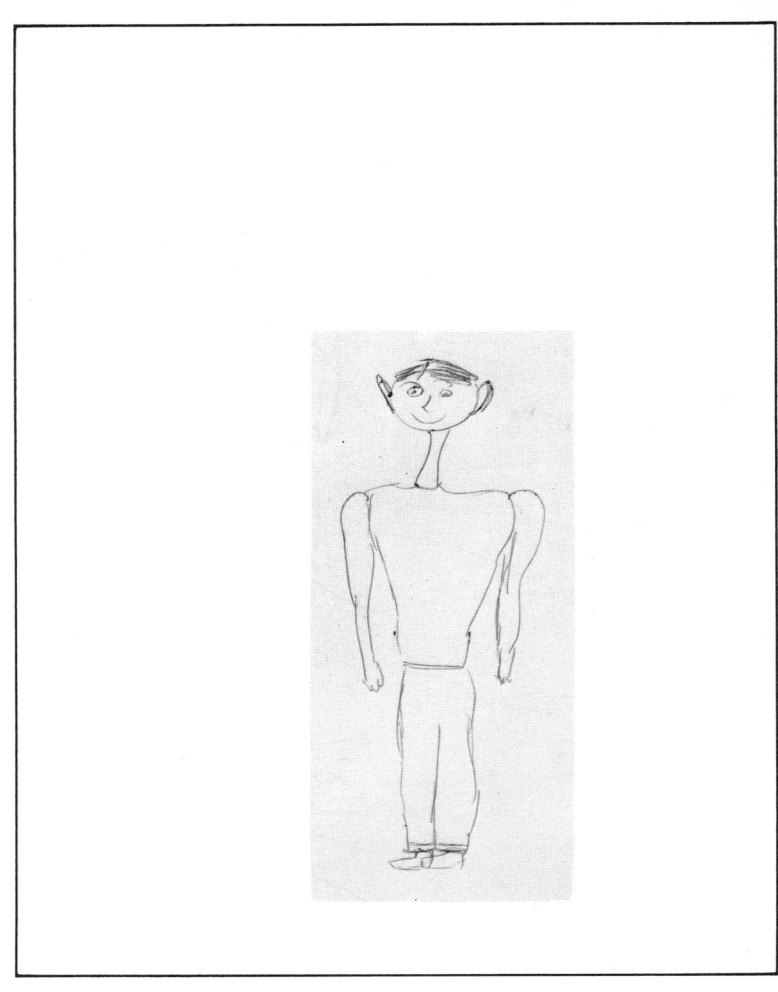

FIGURE-DRAWING CHARACTERISTICS

Structural	Male Female Both		Structural	Male	Female	Structural and Graphic	Male Female Both		Graphic, Global and Height	Male	Female	Body Proportions	Male	Female
Type	0		Omission of Appendages	0	0	Upper and Lower Halves	3	0	Hair Shading	3	3	Head	05	05
Sex Sequence	1		Position of Both Arms	0	0	Four Quarters	4	4	Nudity and Transparency	7	7	Neck	16	12
Posture	1	1	Position of Right Arm	0	5	Relative Size	0		Form	5	5	Shoulders	08	03
Perspective	0	0	Position of Left Arm	0	5	Constant Line Pressure	3	0	Detailing	5	5	Right Arm	04	02
Vertical Midline	0	0	Position of Legs	2	2	Variable Line Pressure	0	1	Identity and Sex	3	3	Left Arm	04	02
Bilateral Symmetry	2	3	Relation of Long Axes	1	1	Line Continuity	1	2	Sophistication	4	4	Chest	06	03
Horizontal Midline	4	4	Right and Left Halves	1	1	Body Shading	0	0	Height	05	04	Girth	03	03

GENERAL CHARACTERISTICS OF SUBJECT

IDENTIFICATION
No. B51
Sex M
Marital status S
Age 22 yrs. at
psychological tests

PARENTAL HISTORY				
Father				
C	H	S	D	O
–	–	–	–	+
Mother				
C	H	S	D	O
–	–	–	–	–

PHYSIOLOGICAL AND METABOLIC DATA

	Admission	Initial	Control	Cold pressor change	Exercise change	Smoking change
Systolic pressure	120	120	114	+24	+28	+10
Diastolic pressure	60	60	58	+22	–18	+16
Heart rate	100	64	63	+04	+24	+05

Age 21 yrs.   Height 71 in.   Ponderal index 13.08
Weight 160 lbs.   Cholesterol 200 mg. per 100 ml.
Overweight +02 %   Vital capacity liters

HABIT SURVEY

Smoking habits: nonsmoker

Age begun yrs.   Inhalation:

Habits of nervous tension: 1, 4, 5

STRONG VOCATIONAL INTEREST TEST

Occupation	Artist	Psychologist	Architect	Physician	Osteopath	Dentist	Veterinarian	Mathematician	Physicist	Engineer	Chemist	Production Manager
Standard Score	21	30	14	36	38	24	31	15	06	10	13	22

Occupation	Farmer	Aviator	Carpenter	Printer	Math.-Sci. Teacher	Ind. Arts Teacher	Voc. Agric. Teacher	Policeman	Forest Serv. Man	Y.M.C.A. Phys. Dir.	Personnel Director	Public Administrator
Standard Score	30	22	06	20	34	12	36	27	23	45	38	34

Occupation	Y.M.C.A. Secretary	Soc. Sci. H.S. Teacher	City Sch. Sup't.	Social Worker	Minister	Musician Performer	C.P.A.	Senior C.P.A.	Accountant	Office Man	Purchasing Agent	Banker
Standard Score	42	45	42	39	61	28	26	29	23	27	22	32

Occupation	Mortician	Pharmacist	Sales Manager	Real Est. Manager	Life Ins. Salesman	Advertising Man	Lawyer	Author-Journalist	President Mfg. Co.	Interest Maturity	Occupational Level	Masculinity-Femininity
Standard Score	31	35	40	42	47	37	38	31	28	55	64	43

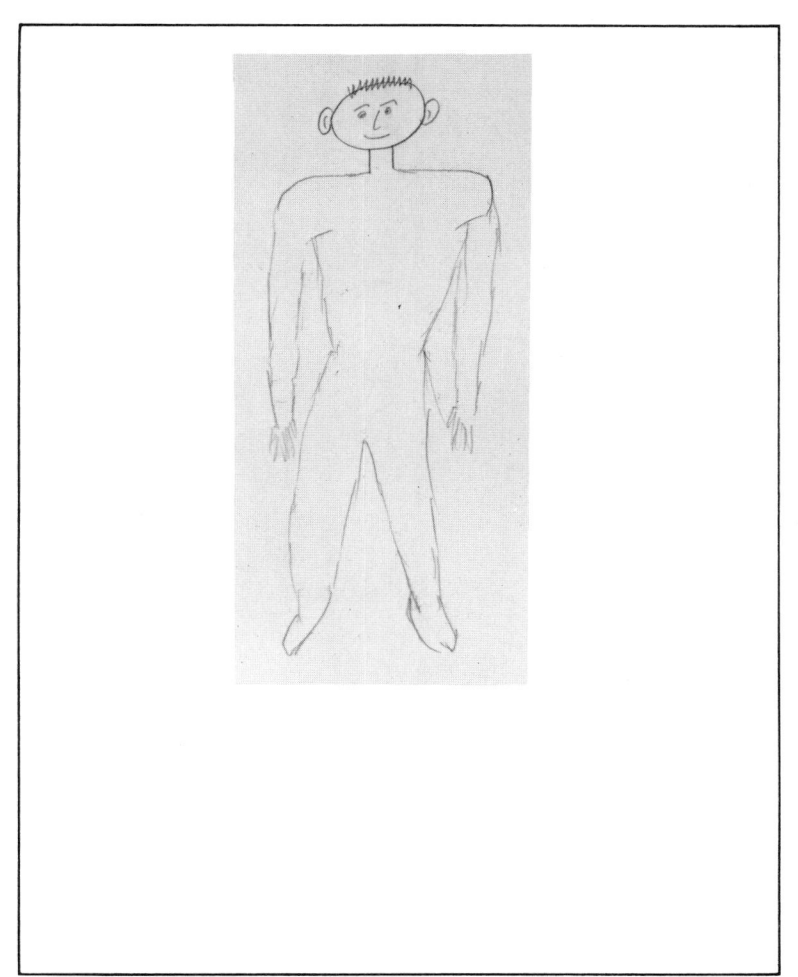

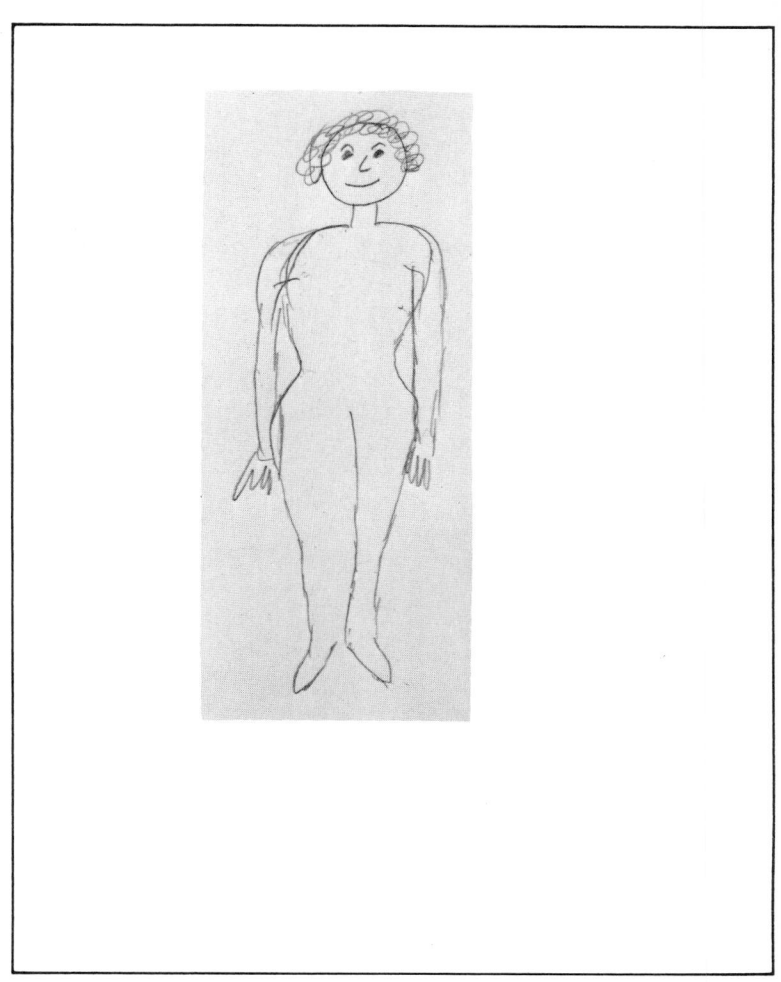

FIGURE-DRAWING CHARACTERISTICS

Structural	Male Female Both	Structural	Male	Female	Structural and Graphic	Male Female Both		Graphic, Global and Height	Male	Female	Body Proportions	Male	Female
Type	0	Omission of Appendages	0	0	Upper and Lower Halves	1	1	Hair Shading	3	3	Head	05	07
Sex Sequence	0	Position of Both Arms	0	0	Four Quarters	4	4	Nudity and Transparency	0	0	Neck	07	06
Posture	1 1	Position of Right Arm	0	0	Relative Size	2		Form	5	5	Shoulders	08	07
Perspective	0 0	Position of Left Arm	0	0	Constant Line Pressure	0	0	Detailing	5	5	Right Arm	06	06
Vertical Midline	0 0	Position of Legs	6	2	Variable Line Pressure	1	1	Identity and Sex	3	3	Left Arm	06	06
Bilateral Symmetry	2 2	Relation of Long Axes	1	1	Line Continuity	0	0	Sophistication	4	4	Chest	07	07
Horizontal Midline	0 0	Right and Left Halves	1	1	Body Shading	0	0	Height	06	06	Girth	05	06

GENERAL CHARACTERISTICS OF SUBJECT

IDENTIFICATION
No. B64
Sex M
Marital status M
Age 22 yrs. at
psychological tests

PARENTAL HISTORY
Father
C   H   S   D   O
–   –   –   –   +
Mother
C   H   S   D   O
–   –   –   –   –

PHYSIOLOGICAL AND METABOLIC DATA

	Admission	Initial	Control	Cold pressor change	Exercise change	Smoking change
Systolic pressure	136	126	120	+18	+22	+08
Diastolic pressure	74	74	85	+16	–25	+08
Heart rate	80	72	61	–12	+18	+25

Age 22 yrs.   Height 72 in.   Ponderal index 12.90
Weight 174 lbs.   Cholesterol 240 mg. per 100 ml.
Overweight +07 %   Vital capacity 5.2 liters

HABIT SURVEY

Smoking habits: nonsmoker

Age begun   yrs.   Inhalation:

Habits of nervous tension: 4, 5, 11, 17, 23

FIGURE-DRAWING CHARACTERISTICS

Structural	Male Female Both		Structural	Male	Female	Structural and Graphic	Male Female Both		Graphic, Global and Height	Male	Female	Body Proportions	Male	Female
Type	0		Omission of Appendages	0	0	Upper and Lower Halves	0	1	Hair Shading	3	3	Head	08	09
Sex Sequence	0		Position of Both Arms	0	0	Four Quarters	4	4	Nudity and Transparency	7	6	Neck	10	10
Posture	1	1	Position of Right Arm	2	2	Relative Size	4		Form	5	5	Shoulders	07	08
Perspective	5	0	Position of Left Arm	2	2	Constant Line Pressure	1	1	Detailing	5	5	Right Arm	04	04
Vertical Midline	0	0	Position of Legs	5	5	Variable Line Pressure	0	0	Identity and Sex	3	3	Left Arm	05	04
Bilateral Symmetry	2	2	Relation of Long Axes	1	1	Line Continuity	0	0	Sophistication	4	4	Chest	07	09
Horizontal Midline	6	0	Right and Left Halves	2	1	Body Shading	3	3	Height	05	06	Girth	11	12

GENERAL CHARACTERISTICS OF SUBJECT

IDENTIFICATION
No. D54
Sex M
Marital status S
Age 21 yrs. at
psychological tests

PARENTAL HISTORY
Father
C H S D O
− − − − +
Mother
C H S D O
− − − − −

PHYSIOLOGICAL AND METABOLIC DATA

	Admission	Initial	Control	Cold pressor change	Exercise change	Smoking change
Systolic pressure	145	122	112	+20	+38	+18
Diastolic pressure	80	65	72	+38	−27	+22
Heart rate	74	72	77	+16	+20	+23

Age 21 yrs.	Height 66 in.	Ponderal index 12.07
	Weight 164 lbs.	Cholesterol 252 mg. per 100 ml.
	Overweight +19 %	Vital capacity liters

HABIT SURVEY
Smoking habits: pipe smoker
Age begun 18 yrs.   Inhalation: no
Habits of nervous tension: 1, 2, 3, 4, 5, 6, 16, 18, 19, 21, 22, 23, 24, 25

STRONG VOCATIONAL INTEREST TEST

Occupation	Artist	Psychologist	Architect	Physician	Osteopath	Dentist	Veterinarian	Mathematician	Physicist	Engineer	Chemist	Production Manager
Standard Score	40	50	34	50	44	27	29	18	10	14	20	22

Occupation	Farmer	Aviator	Carpenter	Printer	Math.-Sci. Teacher	Ind. Arts Teacher	Voc. Agric. Teacher	Policeman	Forest Serv. Man	Y.M.C.A. Phys. Dir.	Personnel Director	Public Administrator
Standard Score	31	36	13	39	33	15	31	35	35	51	45	51

Occupation	Y.M.C.A. Secretary	Soc. Sci. H.S. Teacher	City Sch. Sup't.	Social Worker	Minister	Musician Performer	C.P.A.	Senior C.P.A.	Accountant	Office Man	Purchasing Agent	Banker
Standard Score	42	50	43	61	63	63	24	35	13	25	09	19

Occupation	Mortician	Pharmacist	Sales Manager	Real Est. Manager	Life Ins. Salesman	Advertising Man	Lawyer	Author-Journalist	President Mfg. Co.	Interest Maturity	Occupational Level	Masculinity-Femininity
Standard Score	33	30	32	35	38	45	47	45	26	56	54	32

Plate 125　　　　　　　　**MODERATELY PRIMITIVE DRAWINGS**　　　　　　　　163

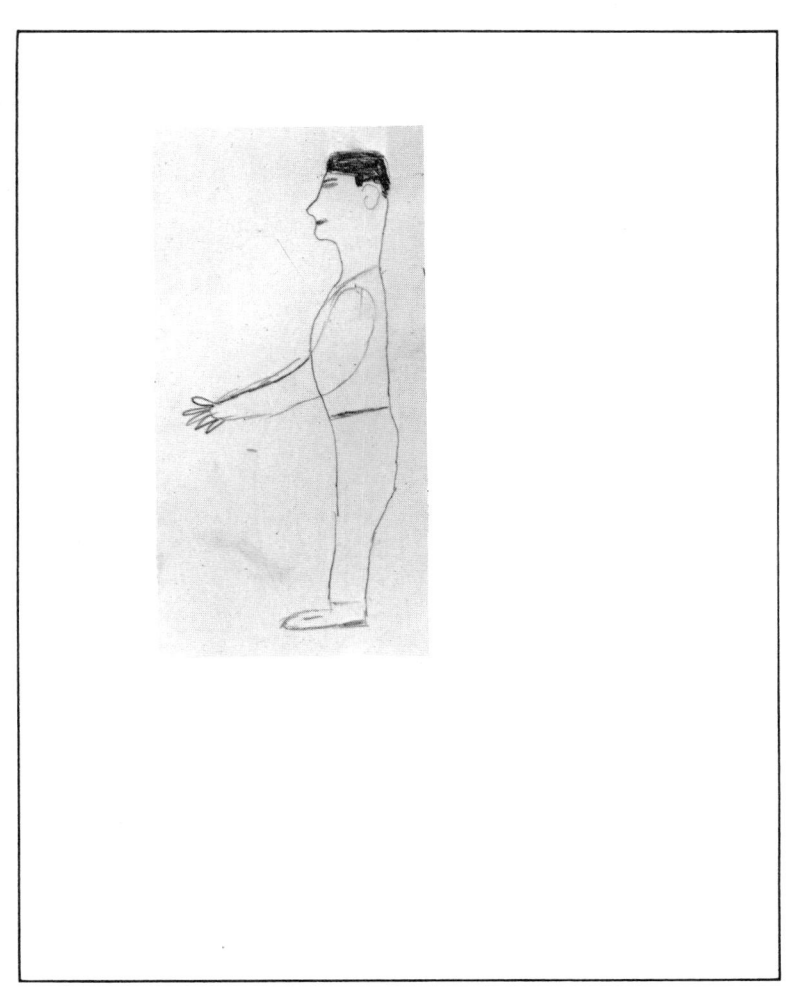

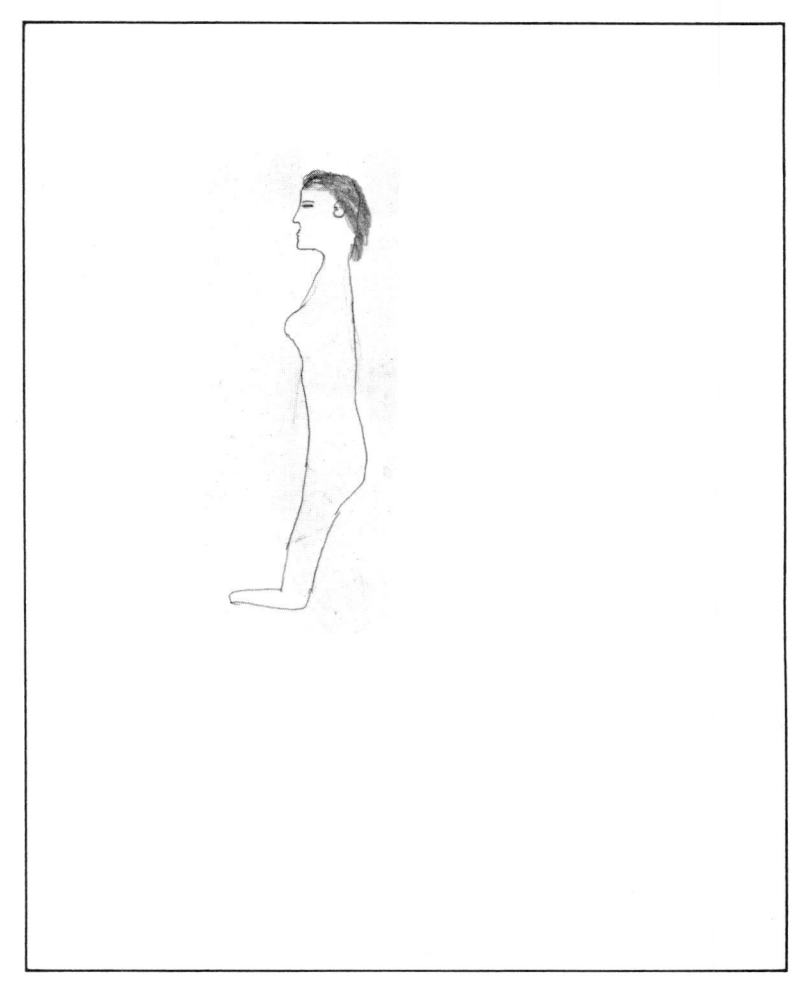

FIGURE-DRAWING CHARACTERISTICS

Structural	Male Female Both		Structural	Male	Female	Structural and Graphic	Male Female Both		Graphic, Global and Height	Male	Female	Body Proportions	Male	Female
Type	0		Omission of Appendages	0	2	Upper and Lower Halves	1	1	Hair Shading	1	3	Head	07	06
Sex Sequence	0		Position of Both Arms	4	6	Four Quarters	4	4	Nudity and Transparency	7	0	Neck	10	
Posture	1	1	Position of Right Arm	7	7	Relative Size	0		Form	3	5	Shoulders		
Perspective	2	2	Position of Left Arm	4	7	Constant Line Pressure	0	3	Detailing	3	5	Right Arm		
Vertical Midline	4	4	Position of Legs	1	1	Variable Line Pressure	1	0	Identity and Sex	1	3	Left Arm	05	
Bilateral Symmetry	0	0	Relation of Long Axes	1	1	Line Continuity	0	1	Sophistication	4	4	Chest	05	04
Horizontal Midline	4	0	Right and Left Halves	2	2	Body Shading	4	0	Height	05	04	Girth	05	05

GENERAL CHARACTERISTICS OF SUBJECT

IDENTIFICATION
No. E14
Sex M
Marital status S
Age 22 yrs. at
psychological tests

PARENTAL HISTORY
Father
C H S D O
-　-　-　-　+
Mother
C H S D O
-　-　-　-　-

PHYSIOLOGICAL AND METABOLIC DATA

	Admission	Initial	Control	Cold pressor change	Exercise change	Smoking change
Systolic pressure		126	118	+04	+31	
Diastolic pressure		58	69	-02	-09	
Heart rate		80	68	00	+29	

Age 22 yrs.	Height	71	in.	Ponderal index 13.17
	Weight	157	lbs.	Cholesterol 210 mg. per 100 ml.
	Overweight -01 %			Vital capacity 5.3 liters

HABIT SURVEY
Smoking habits: heavy cigarette smoker
Age begun 18 yrs.　Inhalation: yes
Habits of nervous tension: 3, 4, 5, 6, 8, 11,
20, 21, 24

STRONG VOCATIONAL INTEREST TEST

Occupation	Artist	Psychologist	Architect	Physician	Osteopath	Dentist	Veterinarian	Mathematician	Physicist	Engineer	Chemist	Production Manager
Standard Score	33	12	27	30	29	31	25	18	14	22	15	24

Occupation	Farmer	Aviator	Carpenter	Printer	Math.-Sci. Teacher	Ind. Arts Teacher	Voc. Agric. Teacher	Policeman	Forest Serv. Man	Y.M.C.A. Phys. Dir.	Personnel Director	Public Administrator
Standard Score	30	19	01	07	09	-10	07	13	00	11	03	14

Occupation	Y.M.C.A. Secretary	Soc. Sci. H.S. Teacher	City Sch. Sup't.	Social Worker	Minister	Musician Performer	C.P.A.	Senior C.P.A.	Accountant	Office Man	Purchasing Agent	Banker
Standard Score	05	07	07	06	-04	24	34	17	15	22	35	35

Occupation	Mortician	Pharmacist	Sales Manager	Real Est. Manager	Life Ins. Salesman	Advertising Man	Lawyer	Author- Journalist	President Mfg. Co.	Interest Maturity	Occupational Level	Masculinity- Femininity
Standard Score	36	39	41	52	43	45	45	44	47	41	69	36

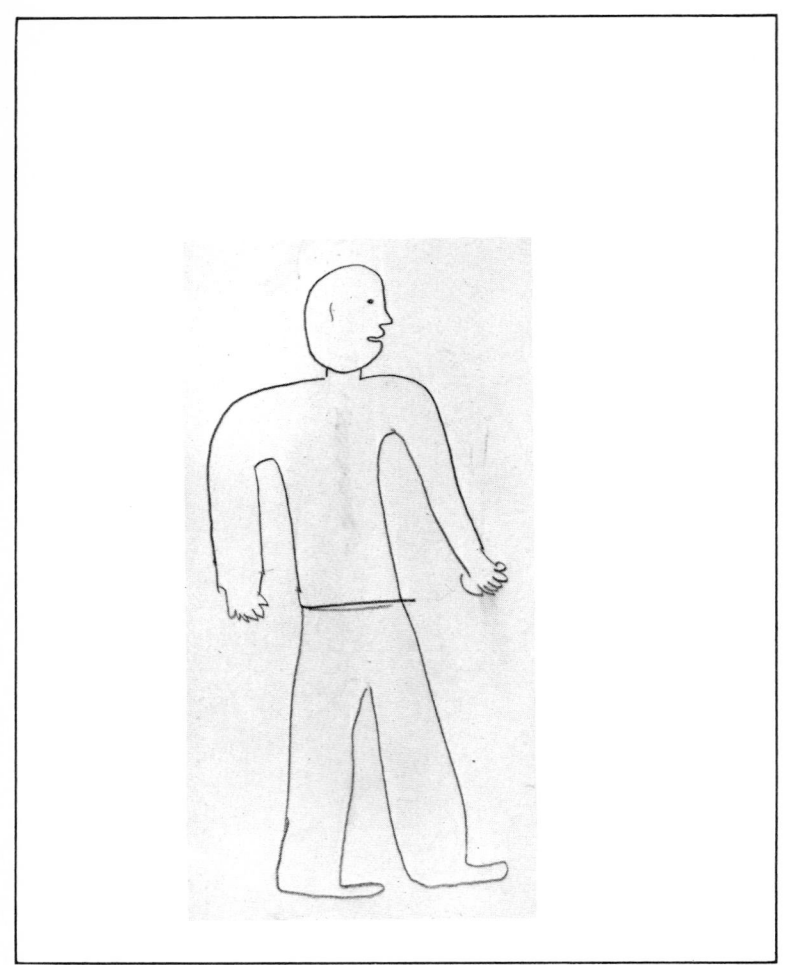

FIGURE-DRAWING CHARACTERISTICS

Structural	Male Female Both		Structural	Male	Female	Structural and Graphic	Male Female Both		Graphic, Global and Height	Male	Female	Body Proportions	Male	Female
Type	0		Omission of Appendages	0	0	Upper and Lower Halves	3	0	Hair Shading	0	1	Head	08	08
Sex Sequence	0		Position of Both Arms	1	0	Four Quarters	4	4	Nudity and Transparency	9	3	Neck	04	04
Posture	1	1	Position of Right Arm	0	0	Relative Size	0		Form	5	5	Shoulders	07	05
Perspective	5	0	Position of Left Arm	1	0	Constant Line Pressure	0	0	Detailing	5	5	Right Arm	06	02
Vertical Midline	0	0	Position of Legs	5	6	Variable Line Pressure	5	5	Identity and Sex	5	3	Left Arm	06	04
Bilateral Symmetry	1	2	Relation of Long Axes	1	1	Line Continuity	4	4	Sophistication	4	4	Chest	04	02
Horizontal Midline	4	4	Right and Left Halves	1	1	Body Shading	0	0	Height	06	05	Girth	06	03

GENERAL CHARACTERISTICS OF SUBJECT

IDENTIFICATION
No. E41
Sex M
Marital status S
Age 22 yrs. at psychological tests

PARENTAL HISTORY					
Father					
C	H	S	D	O	
–	–	–	–	+	
Mother					
C	H	S	D	O	
–	–	–	–	–	

PHYSIOLOGICAL AND METABOLIC DATA

	Admission	Initial	Control	Cold pressor change	Exercise change	Smoking change
Systolic pressure	120	120	120	+12	+20	
Diastolic pressure	70	68	70	+18	-20	
Heart rate	72	80	73	+10	+13	

Age 21 yrs.	Height 72 in.	Ponderal index 13.79
	Weight 142 lbs.	Cholesterol 199 mg. per 100 ml.
	Overweight -12 %	Vital capacity 4.5 liters

HABIT SURVEY
Smoking habits: nonsmoker
Age begun yrs. Inhalation:
Habits of nervous tension: 4, 5, 11, 14

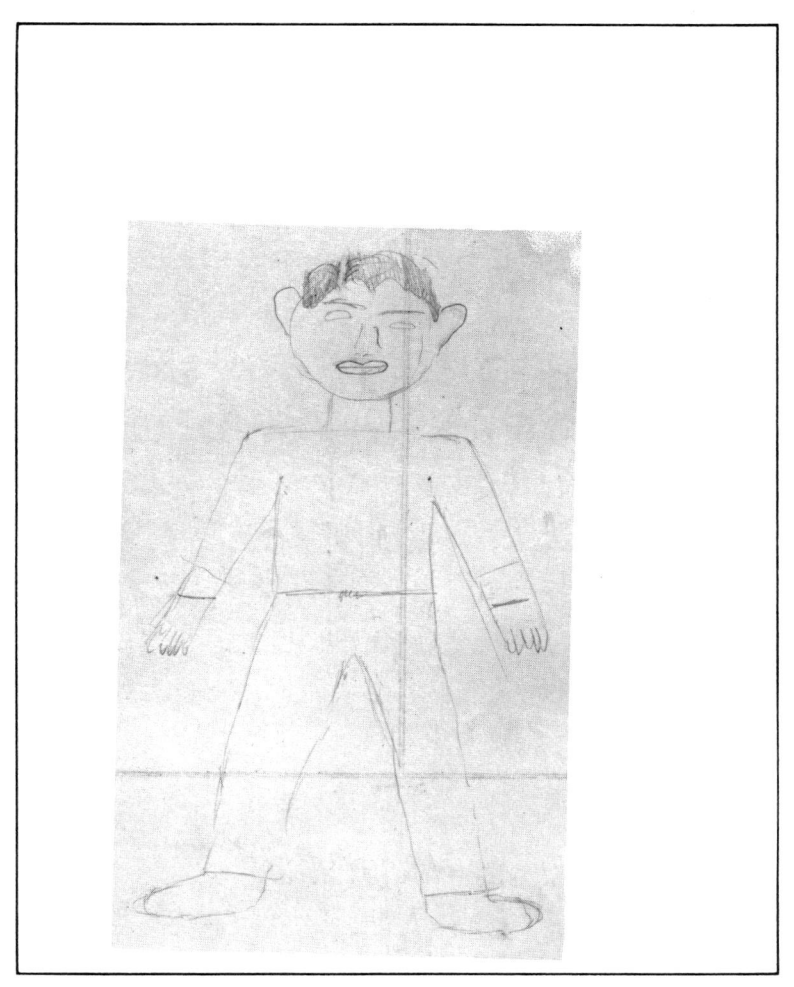

FIGURE-DRAWING CHARACTERISTICS

Structural	Male Female Both	Structural	Male	Female	Structural and Graphic	Male Female Both	Graphic, Global and Height	Male	Female	Body Proportions	Male	Female
Type	0	Omission of Appendages	0	0	Upper and Lower Halves	3 3	Hair Shading	3	3	Head	12	13
Sex Sequence	2	Position of Both Arms	0	0	Four Quarters	4 4	Nudity and Transparency	7	9	Neck	12	08
Posture	1 1	Position of Right Arm	2	2	Relative Size	3	Form	5	5	Shoulders	09	09
Perspective	0 0	Position of Left Arm	2	2	Constant Line Pressure	1 0	Detailing	5	5	Right Arm	06	08
Vertical Midline	0 0	Position of Legs	6	5	Variable Line Pressure	0 1	Identity and Sex	3	3	Left Arm	04	08
Bilateral Symmetry	5 4	Relation of Long Axes	1	1	Line Continuity	0 0	Sophistication	4	4	Chest	07	11
Horizontal Midline	4 4	Right and Left Halves	1	1	Body Shading	0 3	Height	07	08	Girth	10	11

GENERAL CHARACTERISTICS OF SUBJECT

IDENTIFICATION
No. 474
Sex M
Marital status M
Age 25 yrs. at psychological tests

PARENTAL HISTORY
Father
C   H   S   D   O
-   -   -   -   -
Mother
C   H   S   D   O
-   -   -   -   +

PHYSIOLOGICAL AND METABOLIC DATA

	Admission	Initial	Control	Cold pressor change	Exercise change	Smoking change
Systolic pressure	120	114	96	+04	+19	
Diastolic pressure	78	72	64	+02	+02	
Heart rate	72	78	73	+02	+08	

Age 22 yrs.	Height 72 in.	Ponderal index 12.90
	Weight 174 lbs.	Cholesterol 210 mg. per 100 ml.
	Overweight +07 %	Vital capacity 5.5 liters

HABIT SURVEY
Smoking habits: occasional smoker
Age begun 18 yrs.   Inhalation: yes
Habits of nervous tension: 6, 10, 16

FIGURE-DRAWING CHARACTERISTICS

Structural	Male Female		Structural	Male	Female	Structural and Graphic	Male	Female	Graphic, Global and Height	Male	Female	Body Proportions	Male	Female
	Both						Both							
Type	0		Omission of Appendages	0	0	Upper and Lower Halves	2	2	Hair Shading	3	3	Head	03	04
Sex Sequence	0		Position of Both Arms	1	1	Four Quarters	0	0	Nudity and Transparency	3	7	Neck	02	03
Posture	1	1	Position of Right Arm	0	1	Relative Size	4		Form	5	5	Shoulders	02	03
Perspective	0	0	Position of Left Arm	1	5	Constant Line Pressure	0	2	Detailing	5	3	Right Arm	00	02
Vertical Midline	0	0	Position of Legs	5	4	Variable Line Pressure	4	0	Identity and Sex	3	3	Left Arm	00	00
Bilateral Symmetry	2	3	Relation of Long Axes	1	1	Line Continuity	1	0	Sophistication	4	4	Chest	01	02
Horizontal Midline	4	4	Right and Left Halves	2	2	Body Shading	4	3	Height	01	02	Girth	01	03

GENERAL CHARACTERISTICS OF SUBJECT

IDENTIFICATION
No. G30
Sex M
Marital status S
Age 22 yrs. at
psychological tests

PARENTAL HISTORY				
Father				
C	H	S	D	O
–	–	–	–	–
Mother				
C	H	S	D	O
–	–	–	–	+

PHYSIOLOGICAL AND METABOLIC DATA

	Admission	Initial	Control	Cold pressor change	Exercise change	Smoking change
Systolic pressure	130	132	122	+08	+16	+19
Diastolic pressure	70	60	60	+10	-08	+16
Heart rate	70	56	54	+08	+09	+08

Age 21 yrs.	Height 71 in.	Ponderal index 12.84
	Weight 169 lbs.	Cholesterol 197 mg. per 100 ml.
	Overweight +08 %	Vital capacity liters

HABIT SURVEY

Smoking habits: moderate cigarette smoker

Age begun 15 yrs. Inhalation: yes

Habits of nervous tension: 2, 6, 9, 10, 16, 21

STRONG VOCATIONAL INTEREST TEST

Occupation	Artist	Psychologist	Architect	Physician	Osteopath	Dentist	Veterinarian	Mathematician	Physicist	Engineer	Chemist	Production Manager
Standard Score	42	35	39	47	46	36	38	32	33	38	35	26

Occupation	Farmer	Aviator	Carpenter	Printer	Math.-Sci. Teacher	Ind. Arts Teacher	Voc. Agric. Teacher	Policeman	Forest Serv. Man	Y.M.C.A. Phys. Dir.	Personnel Director	Public Administrator
Standard Score	46	44	28	34	28	28	36	27	33	17	10	28

Occupation	Y.M.C.A. Secretary	Soc. Sci. H.S. Teacher	City Sch. Sup't.	Social Worker	Minister	Musician Performer	C.P.A.	Senior C.P.A.	Accountant	Office Man	Purchasing Agent	Banker
Standard Score	14	16	12	25	59	39	16	28	07	10	10	22

Occupation	Mortician	Pharmacist	Sales Manager	Real Est. Manager	Life Ins. Salesman	Advertising Man	Lawyer	Author-Journalist	President Mfg. Co.	Interest Maturity	Occupational Level	Masculinity-Femininity
Standard Score	17	25	19	35	21	31	31	42	33	44	54	50

FIGURE-DRAWING CHARACTERISTICS

Structural	Male Female Both		Structural	Male	Female	Structural and Graphic	Male Female Both		Graphic, Global and Height	Male	Female	Body Proportions	Male	Female
Type	0		Omission of Appendages	0	0	Upper and Lower Halves	1	1	Hair Shading	3	3	Head	09	10
Sex Sequence	0		Position of Both Arms	1	1	Four Quarters	4	4	Nudity and Transparency	7	7	Neck	06	07
Posture	1	1	Position of Right Arm	0	2	Relative Size	2		Form	5	5	Shoulders	06	06
Perspective	0	0	Position of Left Arm	5	0	Constant Line Pressure	5	5	Detailing	3	3	Right Arm	05	05
Vertical Midline	0	0	Position of Legs	6	4	Variable Line Pressure	0	0	Identity and Sex	3	3	Left Arm	04	02
Bilateral Symmetry	2	3	Relation of Long Axes	1	1	Line Continuity	2	2	Sophistication	4	4	Chest	06	07
Horizontal Midline	4	4	Right and Left Halves	1	1	Body Shading	0	0	Height	05	05	Girth	05	07

GENERAL CHARACTERISTICS OF SUBJECT

IDENTIFICATION

No. G47

Sex M

Marital status S

Age 23 yrs. at

psychological tests

PARENTAL HISTORY

Father

C   H   S   D   O

-   -   -   -   -

Mother

C   H   S   D   O

-   -   -   -   +

PHYSIOLOGICAL AND METABOLIC DATA

	Admission	Initial	Control	Cold pressor change	Exercise change	Smoking change
Systolic pressure	140	138	120	+06	+32	+10
Diastolic pressure	80	74	72	+08	-02	+14
Heart rate	82	80	71	+02	+10	+14

Age 22 yrs.

Height 76 in.   Ponderal index 13.38

Weight 183 lbs.   Cholesterol 196 mg. per 100 ml.

Overweight 00 %   Vital capacity liters

HABIT SURVEY

Smoking habits: mixed smoker

Age begun 22 yrs.   Inhalation: sometimes

Habits of nervous tension: 4, 5, 11, 16, 25

STRONG VOCATIONAL INTEREST TEST

Occupation	Artist	Psychologist	Architect	Physician	Osteopath	Dentist	Veterinarian	Mathematician	Physicist	Engineer	Chemist	Production Manager
Standard Score	47	46	48	62	46	48	26	48	51	51	58	30

Occupation	Farmer	Aviator	Carpenter	Printer	Math.-Sci. Teacher	Ind. Arts Teacher	Voc. Agric. Teacher	Policeman	Forest Serv. Man	Y.M.C.A. Phys. Dir.	Personnel Director	Public Administrator
Standard Score	49	57	33	43	39	26	29	25	32	19	22	30

Occupation	Y.M.C.A. Secretary	Soc. Sci. H.S. Teacher	City Sch. Sup't.	Social Worker	Minister	Musician Performer	C.P.A.	Senior C.P.A.	Accountant	Office Man	Purchasing Agent	Banker
Standard Score	05	11	13	20	59	45	32	39	18	19	21	10

Occupation	Mortician	Pharmacist	Sales Manager	Real Est. Manager	Life Ins. Salesman	Advertising Man	Lawyer	Author- Journalist	President Mfg. Co.	Interest Maturity	Occupational Level	Masculinity- Femininity
Standard Score	10	22	14	28	13	33	36	44	33	44	53	57

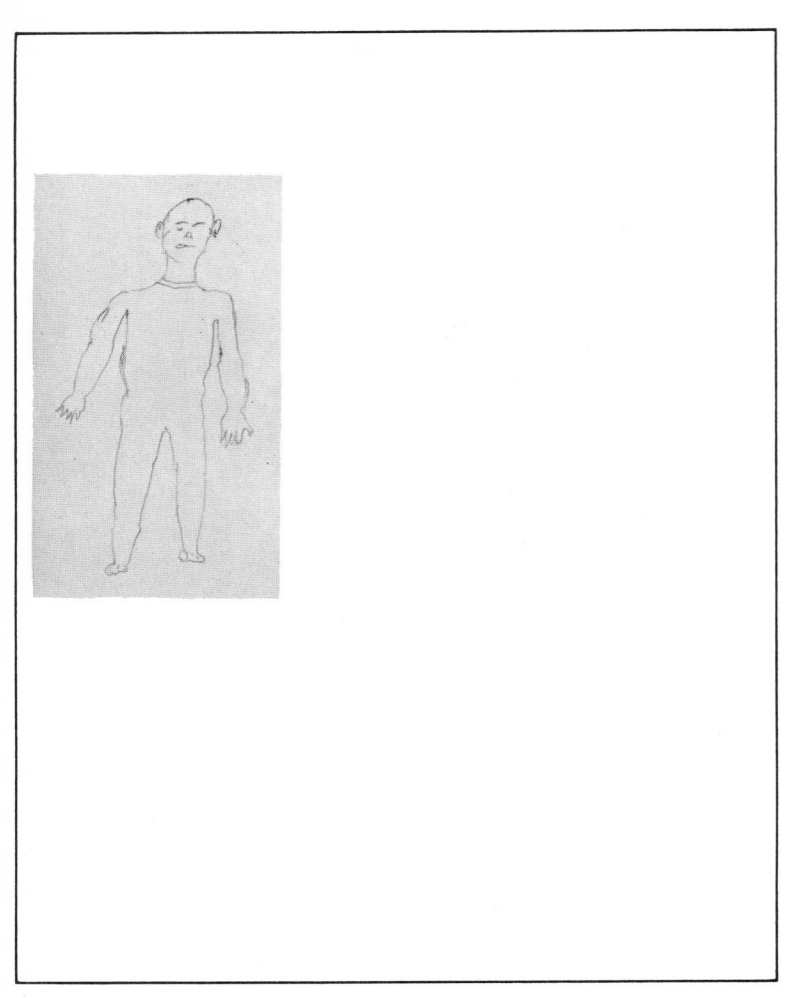

FIGURE-DRAWING CHARACTERISTICS

Structural	Male Female Both		Structural	Male	Female	Structural and Graphic	Male Female Both		Graphic, Global and Height	Male	Female	Body Proportions	Male	Female
Type	0		Omission of Appendages	0	7	Upper and Lower Halves	1	2	Hair Shading	0	2	Head	05	
Sex Sequence	0		Position of Both Arms	1	1	Four Quarters	4	0	Nudity and Transparency	9	7	Neck	08	
Posture	1	1	Position of Right Arm	2	2	Relative Size	0		Form	5	3	Shoulders	05	04
Perspective	0	0	Position of Left Arm	0	0	Constant Line Pressure	1	0	Detailing	5	5	Right Arm	02	01
Vertical Midline	0	0	Position of Legs	5	4	Variable Line Pressure	0	1	Identity and Sex	3	3	Left Arm	02	
Bilateral Symmetry	3	3	Relation of Long Axes	1	1	Line Continuity	0	1	Sophistication	4	4	Chest	04	03
Horizontal Midline	0	4	Right and Left Halves	2	2	Body Shading	0	0	Height	04	02	Girth	05	03

GENERAL CHARACTERISTICS OF SUBJECT

IDENTIFICATION
No. A33
Sex M
Marital status S
Age 22 yrs. at psychological tests

PARENTAL HISTORY
Father
C   H   S   D   O
–   –   –   –   ?
Mother
C   H   S   D   O
–   –   –   –   –

PHYSIOLOGICAL AND METABOLIC DATA

	Admission	Initial	Control	Cold pressor change	Exercise change	Smoking change
Systolic pressure	134	138	128	+26	+42	+05
Diastolic pressure	70	64	68	+29	-22	+03
Heart rate	78	69	63	+19	+23	+08

Age 21 yrs.	Height 74 in.	Ponderal index 13.38
	Weight 169 lbs.	Cholesterol 185 mg. per 100 ml.
	Overweight -02 %	Vital capacity liters

HABIT SURVEY

Smoking habits: heavy cigarette smoker

Age begun 17 yrs.   Inhalation: yes

Habits of nervous tension: 4, 5, 9

STRONG VOCATIONAL INTEREST TEST

Occupation	Artist	Psychologist	Architect	Physician	Osteopath	Dentist	Veterinarian	Mathematician	Physicist	Engineer	Chemist	Production Manager
Standard Score	27	42	33	56	45	41	22	35	28	38	43	32

Occupation	Farmer	Aviator	Carpenter	Printer	Math.-Sci. Teacher	Ind. Arts Teacher	Voc. Agric. Teacher	Policeman	Forest Serv. Man	Y.M.C.A. Phys. Dir.	Personnel Director	Public Administrator
Standard Score	35	40	16	35	42	08	16	35	28	26	33	46

Occupation	Y.M.C.A. Secretary	Soc. Sci. H.S. Teacher	City Sch. Sup't.	Social Worker	Minister	Musician Performer	C.P.A.	Senior C.P.A.	Accountant	Office Man	Purchasing Agent	Banker
Standard Score	22	34	31	33	60	41	36	44	31	35	22	31

Occupation	Mortician	Pharmacist	Sales Manager	Real Est. Manager	Life Ins. Salesman	Advertising Man	Lawyer	Author-Journalist	President Mfg. Co.	Interest Maturity	Occupational Level	Masculinity-Femininity
Standard Score	19	27	17	24	21	25	41	33	17	54	54	52

Plate 131   **MODERATELY PRIMITIVE DRAWINGS**   169

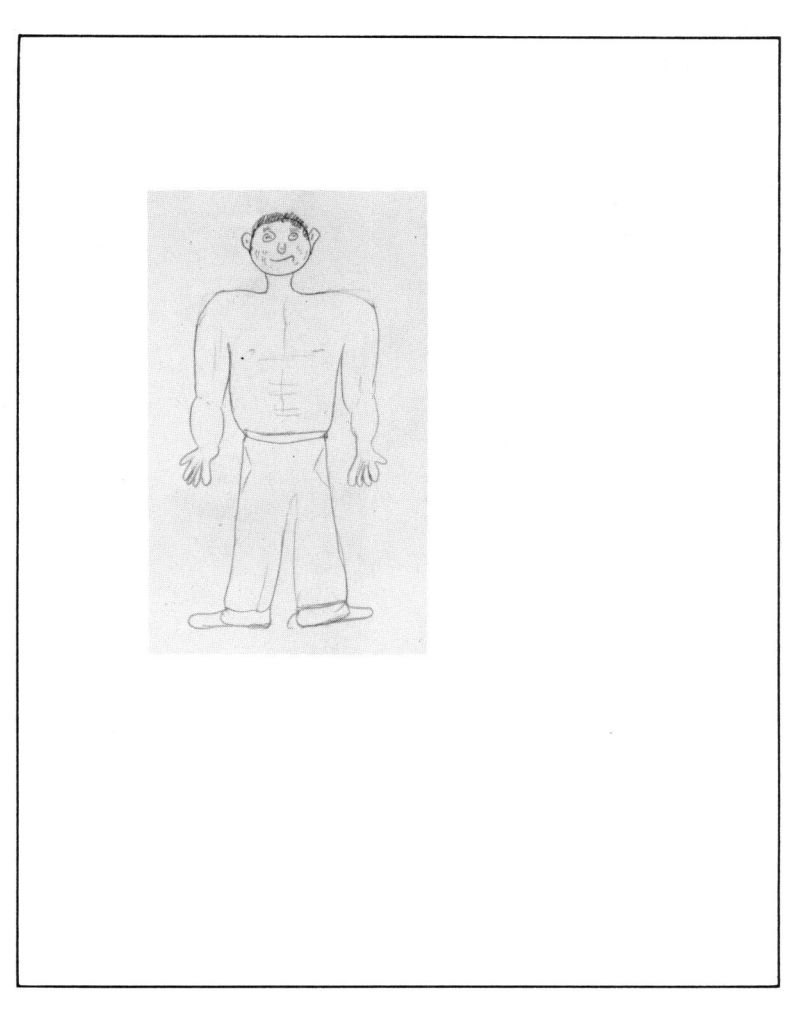

FIGURE-DRAWING CHARACTERISTICS

Structural	Male	Female	Structural	Male	Female	Structural and Graphic	Male	Female	Graphic, Global and Height	Male	Female	Body Proportions	Male	Female
	Both						Both							
Type	0		Omission of Appendages	0	0	Upper and Lower Halves	1	3	Hair Shading	3	3	Head	04	08
Sex Sequence	0		Position of Both Arms	0	4	Four Quarters	4	4	Nudity and Transparency	5	6	Neck	06	12
Posture	1	1	Position of Right Arm	0	7	Relative Size	4		Form	3	3	Shoulders	07	
Perspective	0	2	Position of Left Arm	0	5	Constant Line Pressure	0	0	Detailing	3	3	Right Arm	04	
Vertical Midline	0	7	Position of Legs	4	1	Variable Line Pressure	1	3	Identity and Sex	1	1	Left Arm	04	06
Bilateral Symmetry	2	0	Relation of Long Axes	1	1	Line Continuity	2	0	Sophistication	4	4	Chest	05	05
Horizontal Midline	4	4	Right and Left Halves	1	2	Body Shading	1	6	Height	04	07	Girth	05	06

GENERAL CHARACTERISTICS OF SUBJECT

IDENTIFICATION
No. B53
Sex M
Marital status S
Age 22 yrs. at psychological tests

PARENTAL HISTORY
Father
C H S D O
- - - - ?
Mother
C H S D O
- - - - -

PHYSIOLOGICAL AND METABOLIC DATA

	Admission	Initial	Control	Cold pressor change	Exercise change	Smoking change
Systolic pressure	130	128	118	+06	+28	
Diastolic pressure	70	64	68	+30	-22	
Heart rate	72	73	63	+12	+27	

Age 22 yrs.	Height	73	in.	Ponderal index 13.18
	Weight	170	lbs.	Cholesterol 233 mg. per 100 ml.
	Overweight +01 %			Vital capacity liters

HABIT SURVEY

Smoking habits: mixed smoker

  Age begun 20 yrs.   Inhalation: yes

Habits of nervous tension: 2, 4, 5, 6, 10, 16,

18, 20, 25

STRONG VOCATIONAL INTEREST TEST

Occupation	Artist	Psychologist	Architect	Physician	Osteopath	Dentist	Veterinarian	Mathematician	Physicist	Engineer	Chemist	Production Manager
Standard Score	25	33	23	49	58	34	41	15	18	29	29	34

Occupation	Farmer	Aviator	Carpenter	Printer	Math.-Sci. Teacher	Ind. Arts Teacher	Voc. Agric. Teacher	Policeman	Forest Serv. Man	Y.M.C.A. Phys. Dir.	Personnel Director	Public Administrator
Standard Score	34	45	19	38	40	23	32	40	33	47	44	48

Occupation	Y.M.C.A. Secretary	Soc. Sci. H.S. Teacher	City Sch. Sup't.	Social Worker	Minister	Musician Performer	C.P.A.	Senior C.P.A.	Accountant	Office Man	Purchasing Agent	Banker
Standard Score	37	43	28	46	61	42	22	41	21	38	19	24

Occupation	Mortician	Pharmacist	Sales Manager	Real Est. Manager	Life Ins. Salesman	Advertising Man	Lawyer	Author-Journalist	President Mfg. Co.	Interest Maturity	Occupational Level	Masculinity-Femininity
Standard Score	29	34	27	39	36	33	31	32	26	63	52	50

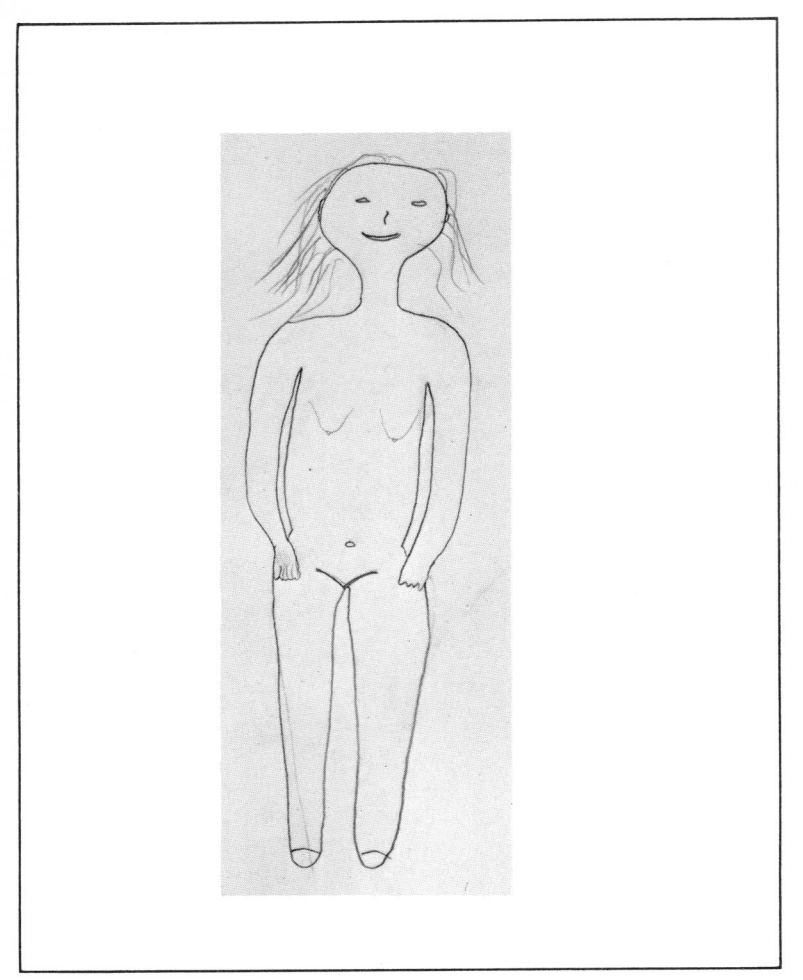

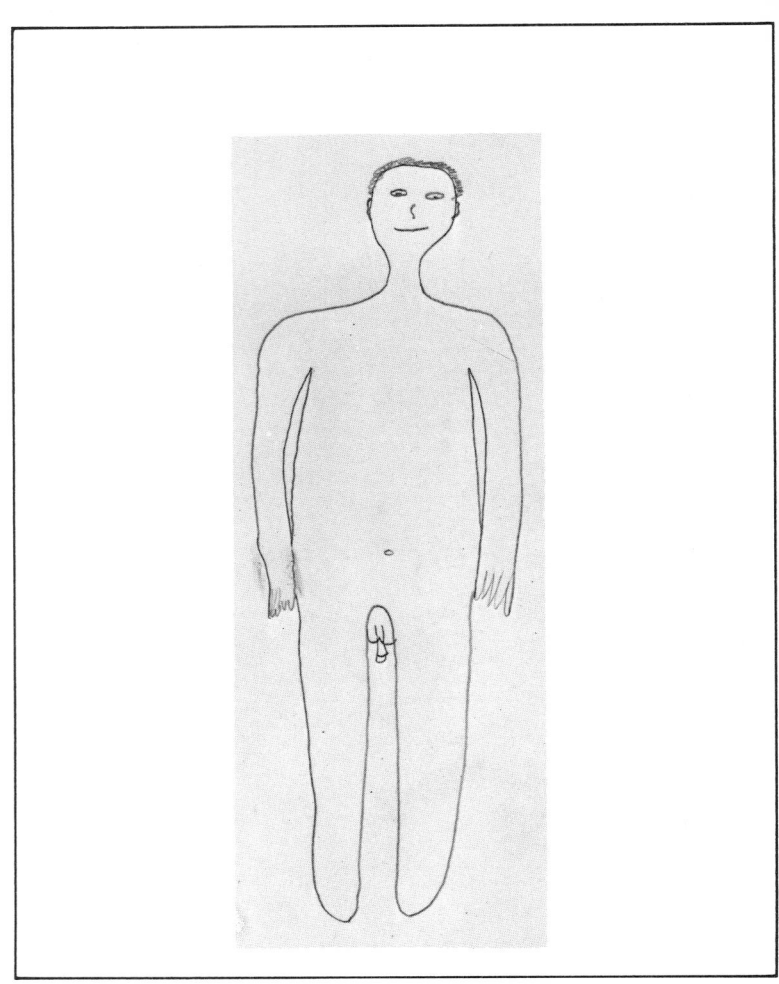

FIGURE-DRAWING CHARACTERISTICS

Structural	Male Female Both	Structural	Male	Female	Structural and Graphic	Male Female Both		Graphic, Global and Height	Male	Female	Body Proportions	Male	Female
Type	0	Omission of Appendages	0	0	Upper and Lower Halves	3	3	Hair Shading	3	7	Head		
Sex Sequence	1	Position of Both Arms	0	0	Four Quarters	4	4	Nudity and Transparency	0	0	Neck		
Posture	1 1	Position of Right Arm	0	0	Relative Size	0		Form	5	3	Shoulders	09	08
Perspective	0 0	Position of Left Arm	0	0	Constant Line Pressure	0	5	Detailing	5	5	Right Arm	06	06
Vertical Midline	0 0	Position of Legs	4	4	Variable Line Pressure	5	0	Identity and Sex	1	1	Left Arm	06	06
Bilateral Symmetry	5 4	Relation of Long Axes	1	1	Line Continuity	4	4	Sophistication	4	4	Chest	08	06
Horizontal Midline	0 0	Right and Left Halves	1	1	Body Shading	0	0	Height	08	07	Girth	09	07

GENERAL CHARACTERISTICS OF SUBJECT

IDENTIFICATION
No. B68
Sex M
Marital status S
Age 23 yrs. at
psychological tests

PARENTAL HISTORY
Father
C   H   S   D   O
–   –   –   –   ?
Mother
C   H   S   D   O
–   –   –   –   –

PHYSIOLOGICAL AND METABOLIC DATA

	Admission	Initial	Control	Cold pressor change	Exercise change	Smoking change
Systolic pressure	136	140	144	+14	+24	00
Diastolic pressure	68	80	84	+08	–28	+02
Heart rate	72	84	70	+32	+29	+07

Age 23 yrs.	Height	70 in.	Ponderal index	13.49	
	Weight	140 lbs.	Cholesterol	218	mg. per 100 ml.
	Overweight –10 %		Vital capacity		liters

HABIT SURVEY

Smoking habits: mixed smoker

Age begun 17 yrs.   Inhalation: no

Habits of nervous tension: 2, 5, 6, 9, 19

STRONG VOCATIONAL INTEREST TEST

Occupation	Artist	Psychologist	Architect	Physician	Osteopath	Dentist	Veterinarian	Mathematician	Physicist	Engineer	Chemist	Production Manager
Standard Score	33	47	35	56	39	35	22	28	18	21	30	20

Occupation	Farmer	Aviator	Carpenter	Printer	Math.-Sci. Teacher	Ind. Arts Teacher	Voc. Agric. Teacher	Policeman	Forest Serv. Man	Y.M.C.A. Phys. Dir.	Personnel Director	Public Administrator
Standard Score	32	26	11	36	42	18	40	24	31	36	40	41

Occupation	Y.M.C.A. Secretary	Soc. Sci. H.S. Teacher	City Sch. Sup't.	Social Worker	Minister	Musician Performer	C.P.A.	Senior C.P.A.	Accountant	Office Man	Purchasing Agent	Banker
Standard Score	38	44	47	48	61	52	29	36	15	26	13	21

Occupation	Mortician	Pharmacist	Sales Manager	Real Est. Manager	Life Ins. Salesman	Advertising Man	Lawyer	Author- Journalist	President Mfg. Co.	Interest Maturity	Occupational Level	Masculinity- Femininity
Standard Score	17	31	24	29	24	38	32	39	16	57	54	39

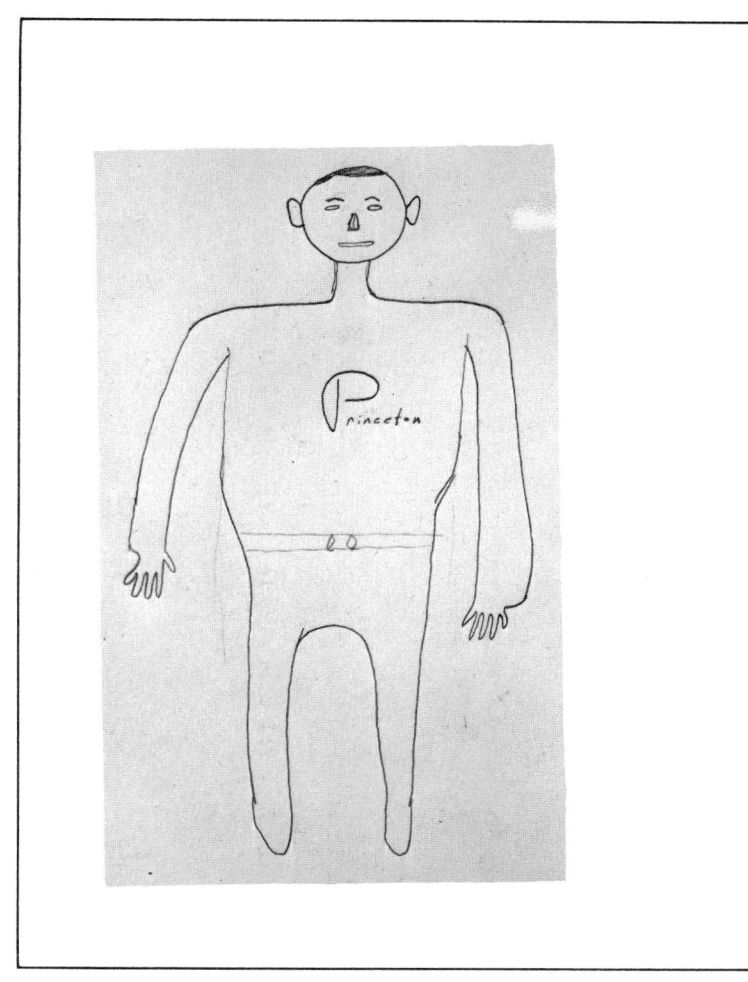

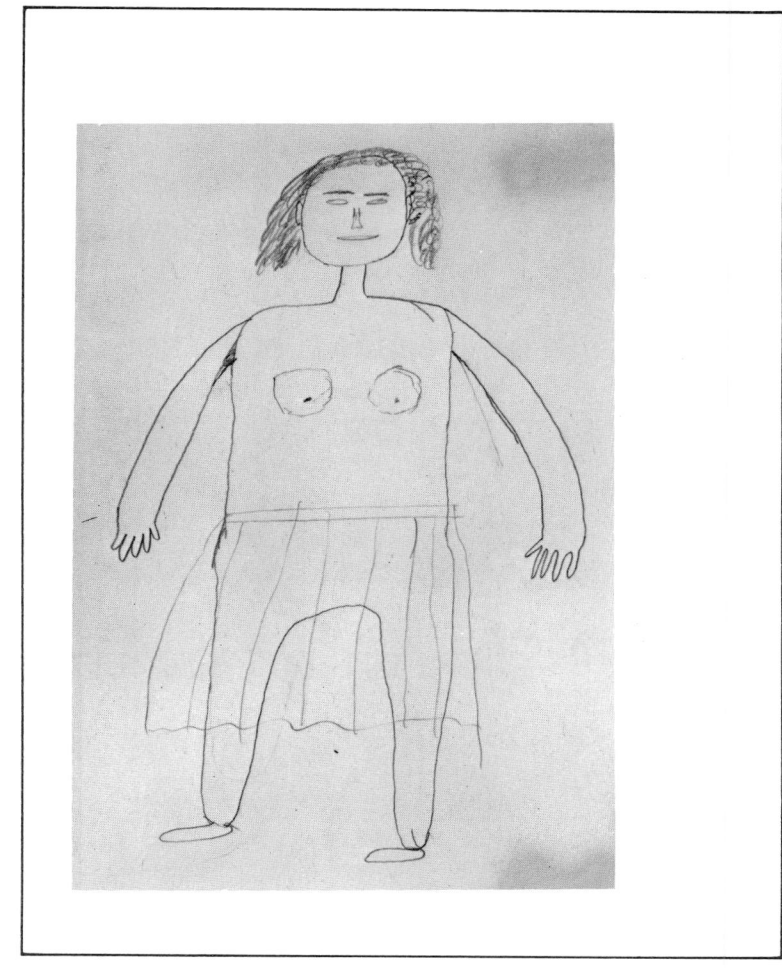

FIGURE-DRAWING CHARACTERISTICS

Structural	Male Female Both	Structural	Male	Female	Structural and Graphic	Male	Female Both	Graphic, Global and Height	Male	Female	Body Proportions	Male	Female
Type	0	Omission of Appendages	0	0	Upper and Lower Halves	0	3	Hair Shading	1	3	Head	08	09
Sex Sequence	0	Position of Both Arms	1	0	Four Quarters	4	4	Nudity and Transparency	9	5	Neck	10	10
Posture	1 1	Position of Right Arm	2	2	Relative Size	4		Form	5	5	Shoulders	13	08
Perspective	0 0	Position of Left Arm	0	2	Constant Line Pressure	0	0	Detailing	5	5	Right Arm	06	06
Vertical Midline	0 0	Position of Legs	6	6	Variable Line Pressure	5	4	Identity and Sex	3	3	Left Arm	08	06
Bilateral Symmetry	4 3	Relation of Long Axes	1	1	Line Continuity	4	3	Sophistication	4	4	Chest	11	11
Horizontal Midline	4 4	Right and Left Halves	1	1	Body Shading	0	3	Height	07	07	Girth	12	15

GENERAL CHARACTERISTICS OF SUBJECT

IDENTIFICATION
No. C52
Sex M
Marital status S
Age 26 yrs. at
psychological tests

PARENTAL HISTORY
Father
C   H   S   D   O
–   –   –   ?
Mother
C   H   S   D   O
–   –   –   –

PHYSIOLOGICAL AND METABOLIC DATA

	Admission	Initial	Control	Cold pressor change	Exercise change	Smoking change
Systolic pressure	120	120	112	+14	+26	-02
Diastolic pressure	80	70	70	+12	00	00
Heart rate	80	64	71	-08	-06	+01

Age 27 yrs.   Height 73 in.   Ponderal index 13.62
Weight 154 lbs.   Cholesterol 151 mg. per 100 ml.
Overweight -12 %   Vital capacity 6.2 liters

HABIT SURVEY
Smoking habits: nonsmoker
Age begun 12 yrs.   Inhalation:
Habits of nervous tension: 4, 5, 6, 17, 25

STRONG VOCATIONAL INTEREST TEST

Occupation	Artist	Psychologist	Architect	Physician	Osteopath	Dentist	Veterinarian	Mathematician	Physicist	Engineer	Chemist	Production Manager
Standard Score	31	41	36	55	41	35	29	31	22	31	39	23

Occupation	Farmer	Aviator	Carpenter	Printer	Math.-Sci. Teacher	Ind. Arts Teacher	Voc. Agric. Teacher	Policeman	Forest Serv. Man	Y.M.C.A. Phys. Dir.	Personnel Director	Public Administrator
Standard Score	32	40	08	29	36	03	14	28	27	37	34	47

Occupation	Y.M.C.A. Secretary	Soc. Sci. H.S. Teacher	City Sch. Sup't.	Social Worker	Minister	Musician Performer	C.P.A.	Senior C.P.A.	Accountant	Office Man	Purchasing Agent	Banker
Standard Score	26	33	28	39	62	43	36	45	26	31	17	22

Occupation	Mortician	Pharmacist	Sales Manager	Real Est. Manager	Life Ins. Salesman	Advertising Man	Lawyer	Author-Journalist	President Mfg. Co.	Interest Maturity	Occupational Level	Masculinity-Femininity
Standard Score	23	23	27	32	35	35	48	37	33	54	58	45

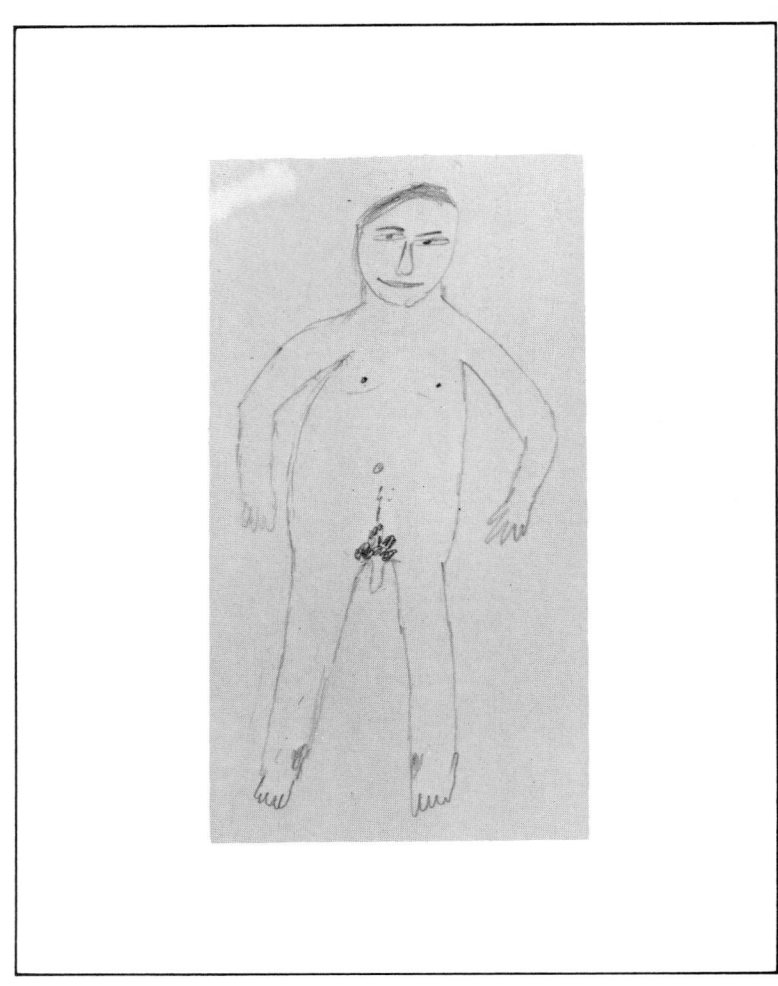

FIGURE-DRAWING CHARACTERISTICS

Structural	Male Female Both	Structural	Male	Female	Structural and Graphic	Male Female Both		Graphic, Global and Height	Male	Female	Body Proportions	Male	Female
Type	0	Omission of Appendages	0	0	Upper and Lower Halves	0	3	Hair Shading	3	3	Head	09	09
Sex Sequence	1	Position of Both Arms	0	1	Four Quarters	4	4	Nudity and Transparency	0	0	Neck	05	04
Posture	1 1	Position of Right Arm	5	0	Relative Size	4		Form	5	5	Shoulders	06	06
Perspective	0 0	Position of Left Arm	5	5	Constant Line Pressure	0	1	Detailing	3	3	Right Arm	06	04
Vertical Midline	0 0	Position of Legs	6	6	Variable Line Pressure	1	0	Identity and Sex	1	1	Left Arm	05	06
Bilateral Symmetry	1 2	Relation of Long Axes	1	1	Line Continuity	0	0	Sophistication	4	4	Chest	06	06
Horizontal Midline	0 2	Right and Left Halves	1	1	Body Shading	2	2	Height	06	07	Girth	11	09

GENERAL CHARACTERISTICS OF SUBJECT

IDENTIFICATION
No. D34
Sex M
Marital status S
Age 28 yrs. at
psychological tests

PARENTAL HISTORY				
Father				
C	H	S	D	0
–	–	–	–	?
Mother				
C	H	S	D	0
–	–	–	–	

PHYSIOLOGICAL AND METABOLIC DATA

	Admission	Initial	Control	Cold pressor change	Exercise change	Smoking change
Systolic pressure	130	122	120	+30	+30	+02
Diastolic pressure	70	60	60	+38	00	+03
Heart rate	70	72	64	+12	+33	+04

Age 27 yrs.	Height	68 in.	Ponderal index	12.85	
	Weight	148 lbs.	Cholesterol	248	mg. per 100 ml.
	Overweight	–01 %	Vital capacity		liters

HABIT SURVEY

Smoking habits: heavy cigarette smoker

Age begun 17 yrs.   Inhalation: yes

Habits of nervous tension:

STRONG VOCATIONAL INTEREST TEST

Occupation	Artist	Psychologist	Architect	Physician	Osteopath	Dentist	Veterinarian	Mathematician	Physicist	Engineer	Chemist	Production Manager
Standard Score	30	31	33	39	13	21	22	35	28	43	34	42

Occupation	Farmer	Aviator	Carpenter	Printer	Math.-Sci. Teacher	Ind. Arts Teacher	Voc. Agric. Teacher	Policeman	Forest Serv. Man	Y.M.C.A. Phys. Dir.	Personnel Director	Public Administrator
Standard Score	29	28	14	20	19	–07	14	16	14	06	21	30

Occupation	Y.M.C.A. Secretary	Soc. Sci. H.S. Teacher	City Sch. Sup't.	Social Worker	Minister	Musician Performer	C.P.A.	Senior C.P.A.	Accountant	Office Man	Purchasing Agent	Banker
Standard Score	03	10	18	17	–04	26	40	35	33	24	38	35

Occupation	Mortician	Pharmacist	Sales Manager	Real Est. Manager	Life Ins. Salesman	Advertising Man	Lawyer	Author-Journalist	President Mfg. Co.	Interest Maturity	Occupational Level	Masculinity-Femininity
Standard Score	21	34	45	43	27	42	43	39	60	45	66	52

FIGURE-DRAWING CHARACTERISTICS

Structural	Male Female Both		Structural	Male	Female	Structural and Graphic	Male Female Both		Graphic, Global and Height	Male	Female	Body Proportions	Male	Female
Type	0		Omission of Appendages	0	0	Upper and Lower Halves	0	0	Hair Shading	3	3	Head	18	18
Sex Sequence	0		Position of Both Arms	4	4	Four Quarters	4	4	Nudity and Transparency	9	3	Neck	06	12
Posture	1	1	Position of Right Arm	7	7	Relative Size	2		Form	5	5	Shoulders		
Perspective	2	2	Position of Left Arm	0	0	Constant Line Pressure	0	0	Detailing	3	5	Right Arm		
Vertical Midline	4	4	Position of Legs	4	4	Variable Line Pressure	3	1	Identity and Sex	1	1	Left Arm	04	04
Bilateral Symmetry	0	0	Relation of Long Axes	1	1	Line Continuity	4	4	Sophistication	4	4	Chest	05	08
Horizontal Midline	4	4	Right and Left Halves	1	1	Body Shading	0	0	Height	07	07	Girth	07	09

GENERAL CHARACTERISTICS OF SUBJECT

IDENTIFICATION
No. B74
Sex M
Marital status M
Age 22 yrs. at
psychological tests

PARENTAL HISTORY
Father
C   H   S   D   0
–   –   –   –   –
Mother
C   H   S   D   0
–   –   –   –   ?

PHYSIOLOGICAL AND METABOLIC DATA

	Admission	Initial	Control	Cold pressor change	Exercise change	Smoking change
Systolic pressure	115	122	122	+18	+28	+06
Diastolic pressure	70	72	64	+10	-16	+10
Heart rate	72	88	76	+04	+24	+06
Age 22 yrs.	Height 69 in.		Ponderal index 12.92			
	Weight 152 lbs.		Cholesterol 212 mg. per 100 ml.			
	Overweight +01 %		Vital capacity 5.6 liters			

HABIT SURVEY
Smoking habits: occasional smoker
Age begun 18 yrs.   Inhalation: no
Habits of nervous tension: 4, 6, 25

STRONG VOCATIONAL INTEREST TEST

Occupation	Artist	Psychologist	Architect	Physician	Osteopath	Dentist	Veterinarian	Mathematician	Physicist	Engineer	Chemist	Production Manager
Standard Score	20	47	22	49	43	34	27	29	30	42	48	35

Occupation	Farmer	Aviator	Carpenter	Printer	Math.-Sci. Teacher	Ind. Arts Teacher	Voc. Agric. Teacher	Policeman	Forest Serv. Man	Y.M.C.A. Phys. Dir.	Personnel Director	Public Administrator
Standard Score	36	40	26	42	55	35	36	31	34	36	49	52

Occupation	Y.M.C.A. Secretary	Soc. Sci. H.S. Teacher	City Sch. Sup't.	Social Worker	Minister	Musician Performer	C.P.A.	Senior C.P.A.	Accountant	Office Man	Purchasing Agent	Banker
Standard Score	37	35	36	44	61	41	36	51	42	37	24	21

Occupation	Mortician	Pharmacist	Sales Manager	Real Est. Manager	Life Ins. Salesman	Advertising Man	Lawyer	Author-Journalist	President Mfg. Co.	Interest Maturity	Occupational Level	Masculinity-Femininity
Standard Score	17	28	23	22	22	25	25	24	32	63	53	53

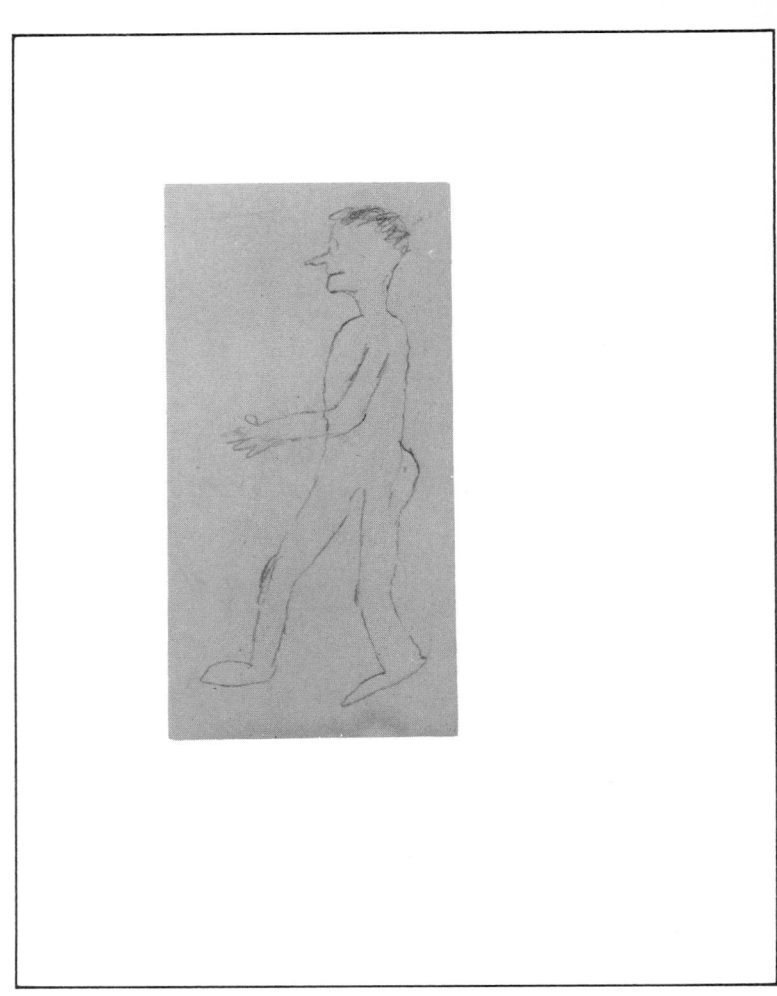

FIGURE-DRAWING CHARACTERISTICS

Structural	Male Female Both	Structural	Male	Female	Structural and Graphic	Male Female Both	Graphic, Global and Height	Male	Female	Body Proportions	Male	Female
Type	0	Omission of Appendages	0	0	Upper and Lower Halves	1 1	Hair Shading	3	3	Head	07	06
Sex Sequence	1	Position of Both Arms	4	4	Four Quarters	4 4	Nudity and Transparency	0	0	Neck	08	08
Posture	2 2	Position of Right Arm	7	7	Relative Size	2	Form	5	5	Shoulders		
Perspective	2 2	Position of Left Arm	4	4	Constant Line Pressure	1 1	Detailing	5	5	Right Arm		
Vertical Midline	4 4	Position of Legs	8	8	Variable Line Pressure	0 0	Identity and Sex	3	3	Left Arm	04	06
Bilateral Symmetry	0 0	Relation of Long Axes	1	1	Line Continuity	0 0	Sophistication	4	4	Chest	06	05
Horizontal Midline	0 0	Right and Left Halves	2	1	Body Shading	0 0	Height	05	05	Girth	06	07

GENERAL CHARACTERISTICS OF SUBJECT

IDENTIFICATION
No.   226
Sex   M
Marital status   S
Age 24 yrs. at
psychological tests

PARENTAL HISTORY
Father
C   H   S   D   0
-    -   -   -   -
Mother
C   H   S   D   0
-    -   -   -   -

PHYSIOLOGICAL AND METABOLIC DATA

	Admission	Initial	Control	Cold pressor change	Exercise change	Smoking change
Systolic pressure	126	128	110	+06	+10	
Diastolic pressure	80	70	72	+12	−08	
Heart rate	72	96	67	+04	+48	

	Height	70 in.	Ponderal index 12.52
Age 23 yrs.	Weight	175 lbs.	Cholesterol 200 mg. per 100 ml.
	Overweight +13 %		Vital capacity 5.5 liters

HABIT SURVEY
Smoking habits: unknown
Age begun   yrs.   Inhalation:
Habits of nervous tension:

FIGURE-DRAWING CHARACTERISTICS

Structural	Male	Female	Structural	Male	Female	Structural and Graphic	Male	Female	Graphic, Global and Height	Male	Female	Body Proportions	Male	Female
	Both						Both							
Type	0		Omission of Appendages	0	0	Upper and Lower Halves	2	2	Hair Shading	1	1	Head	04	04
Sex Sequence	2		Position of Both Arms	0	1	Four Quarters	0	0	Nudity and Transparency	7	7	Neck	04	04
Posture	6	1	Position of Right Arm	2	0	Relative Size	2		Form	3	3	Shoulders	04	04
Perspective	5	5	Position of Left Arm	2	2	Constant Line Pressure	0	0	Detailing	3	3	Right Arm	02	02
Vertical Midline	3	0	Position of Legs	8	5	Variable Line Pressure	5	5	Identity and Sex	1	3	Left Arm	02	02
Bilateral Symmetry	3	3	Relation of Long Axes	1	1	Line Continuity	4	4	Sophistication	4	4	Chest	03	02
Horizontal Midline	4	4	Right and Left Halves	2	2	Body Shading	0	0	Height	03	03	Girth	03	02

GENERAL CHARACTERISTICS OF SUBJECT

IDENTIFICATION
No. 257
Sex M
Marital status S
Age 25 yrs. at
psychological tests

PARENTAL HISTORY
Father
C H S D O
– – – – –
Mother
C H S D O
– – – – –

PHYSIOLOGICAL AND METABOLIC DATA

	Admission	Initial	Control	Cold pressor change	Exercise change	Smoking change
Systolic pressure	112	122	114	+24	+28	
Diastolic pressure	72	72	64	+39	–02	
Heart rate	54	78	64	+02	+30	

	Height 70 in.	Ponderal index 13.06
Age 22 yrs.	Weight 154 lbs.	Cholesterol 195 mg. per 100 ml.
	Overweight 00 %	Vital capacity 5.6 liters

HABIT SURVEY
Smoking habits: unknown
Age begun yrs. Inhalation:
Habits of nervous tension:

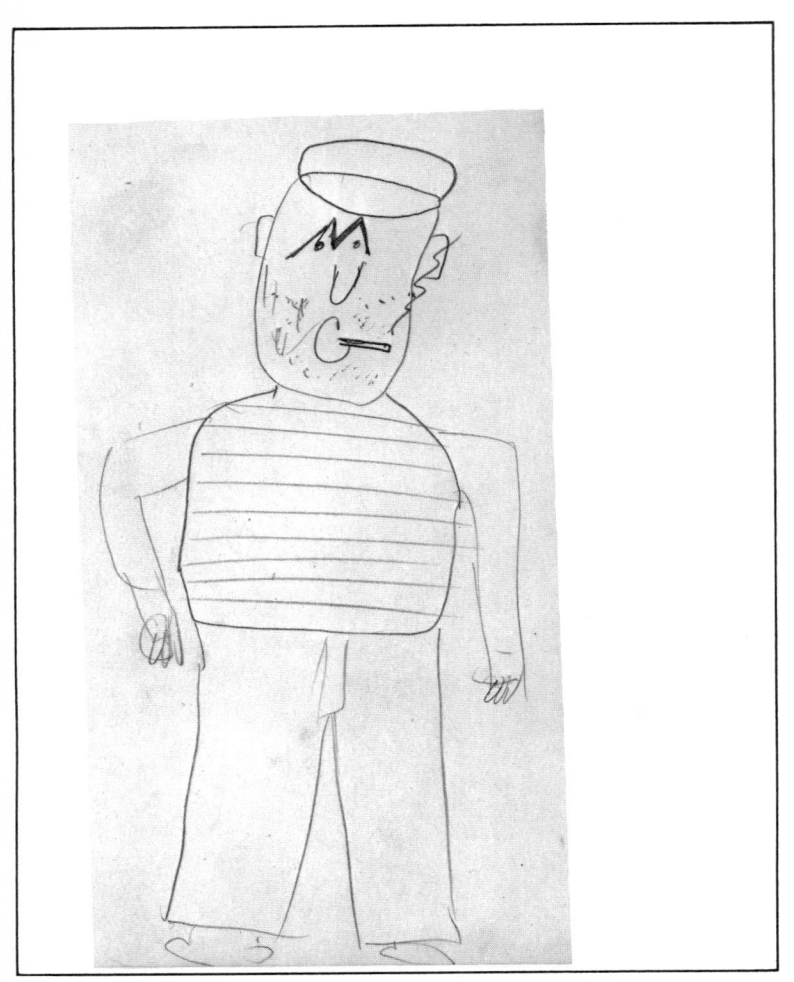

FIGURE-DRAWING CHARACTERISTICS

Structural	Male Female Both	Structural	Male	Female	Structural and Graphic	Male Female Both		Graphic, Global and Height	Male	Female	Body Proportions	Male	Female
Type	0	Omission of Appendages	0	0	Upper and Lower Halves	3	0	Hair Shading	0	3	Head	20	09
Sex Sequence	0	Position of Both Arms	1	0	Four Quarters	4	4	Nudity and Transparency	7	7	Neck	00	06
Posture	1 1	Position of Right Arm	5	5	Relative Size	0		Form	5	5	Shoulders	09	06
Perspective	0 0	Position of Left Arm	0	5	Constant Line Pressure	0	1	Detailing	3	5	Right Arm	08	04
Vertical Midline	3 3	Position of Legs	6	5	Variable Line Pressure	5	0	Identity and Sex	3	3	Left Arm	07	04
Bilateral Symmetry	3 3	Relation of Long Axes	1	1	Line Continuity	3	0	Sophistication	4	4	Chest	12	08
Horizontal Midline	4 4	Right and Left Halves	1	1	Body Shading	0	0	Height	09	06	Girth	15	11

GENERAL CHARACTERISTICS OF SUBJECT

IDENTIFICATION
No. 261
Sex M
Marital status   M
Age 27 yrs. at
psychological tests

PARENTAL HISTORY
Father
C   H   S   D   O
–   –   –   –   –
Mother
C   H   S   D   O
–   –   –   –   –

PHYSIOLOGICAL AND METABOLIC DATA

	Admission	Initial	Control	Cold pressor change	Exercise change	Smoking change
Systolic pressure	120	120	110	+31	+48	
Diastolic pressure	78	62	66	+34	+06	
Heart rate	84	66	75	+16	+21	

Age 25 yrs.

Height	72 in.	Ponderal index 13.05
Weight	168 lbs.	Cholesterol 230 mg. per 100 ml.
Overweight +01 %		Vital capacity 5.5 liters

HABIT SURVEY
Smoking habits: heavy cigarette smoker
Age begun 18 yrs.   Inhalation: yes
Habits of nervous tension: 1, 3, 5, 11, 16, 17,
21, 22

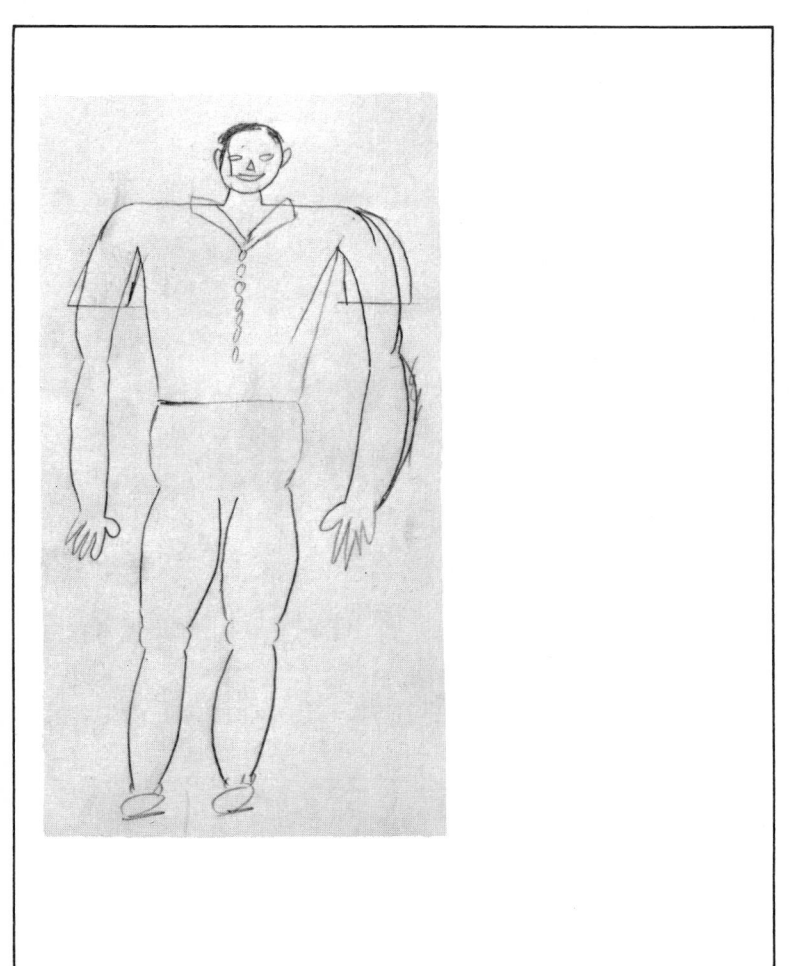

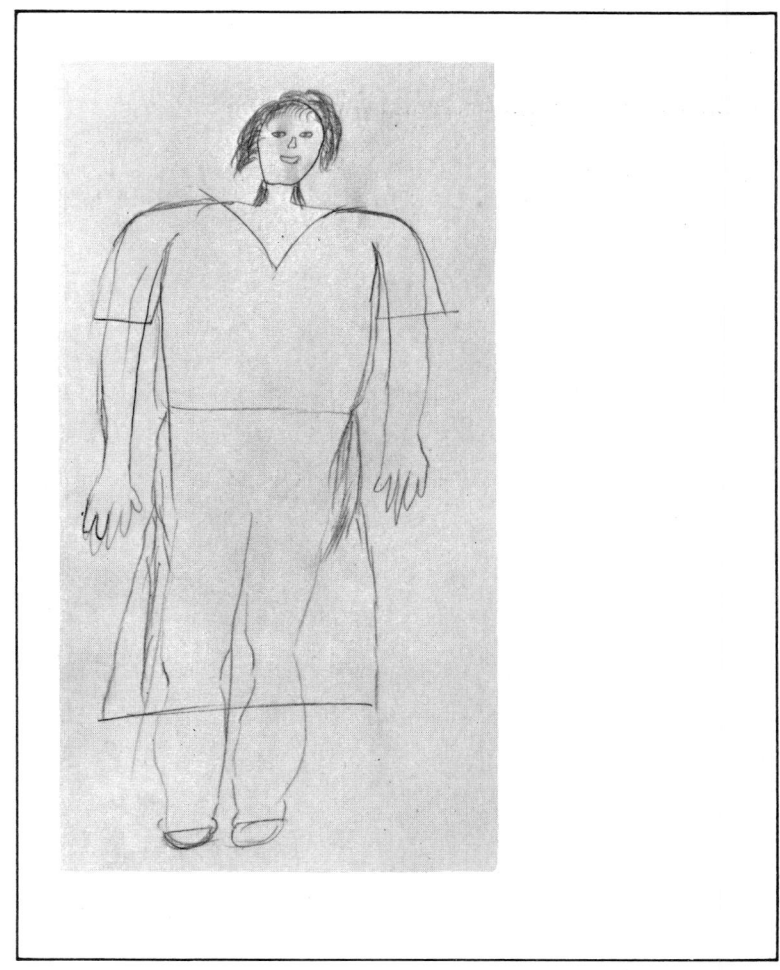

FIGURE-DRAWING CHARACTERISTICS

Structural	Male Female Both		Structural	Male	Female	Structural and Graphic	Male Female Both		Graphic, Global and Height	Male	Female	Body Proportions	Male	Female
Type	0		Omission of Appendages	0	0	Upper and Lower Halves	1	0	Hair Shading	3	3	Head	05	07
Sex Sequence	2		Position of Both Arms	0	0	Four Quarters	4	4	Nudity and Transparency	7	6	Neck	06	08
Posture	1	1	Position of Right Arm	0	0	Relative Size	4		Form	5	5	Shoulders	11	12
Perspective	0	0	Position of Left Arm	0	0	Constant Line Pressure	0	0	Detailing	5	5	Right Arm	08	08
Vertical Midline	3	0	Position of Legs	4	4	Variable Line Pressure	3	3	Identity and Sex	5	5	Left Arm	08	06
Bilateral Symmetry	3	3	Relation of Long Axes	1	1	Line Continuity	2	0	Sophistication	4	4	Chest	09	11
Horizontal Midline	4	4	Right and Left Halves	1	1	Body Shading	0	2	Height	07	08	Girth	09	12

GENERAL CHARACTERISTICS OF SUBJECT

IDENTIFICATION
No. 467
Sex M
Marital status M
Age 28 yrs. at psychological tests

PARENTAL HISTORY
Father
C   H   S   D   O
-   -   -   -   -
Mother
C   H   S   D   O
-   -   -   -   -

PHYSIOLOGICAL AND METABOLIC DATA

	Admission	Initial	Control	Cold pressor change	Exercise change	Smoking change
Systolic pressure	110	130	116	+11	+28	
Diastolic pressure	60	70	74	+14	-14	
Heart rate	64	90	88	00	+15	

Age 25 yrs.	Height 70 in.	Ponderal index 12.79
	Weight 164 lbs.	Cholesterol 230 mg. per 100 ml.
	Overweight +04 %	Vital capacity 4.9 liters

HABIT SURVEY
Smoking habits: light cigarette smoker
Age begun 22 yrs.   Inhalation: yes
Habits of nervous tension: 5, 6, 16, 22

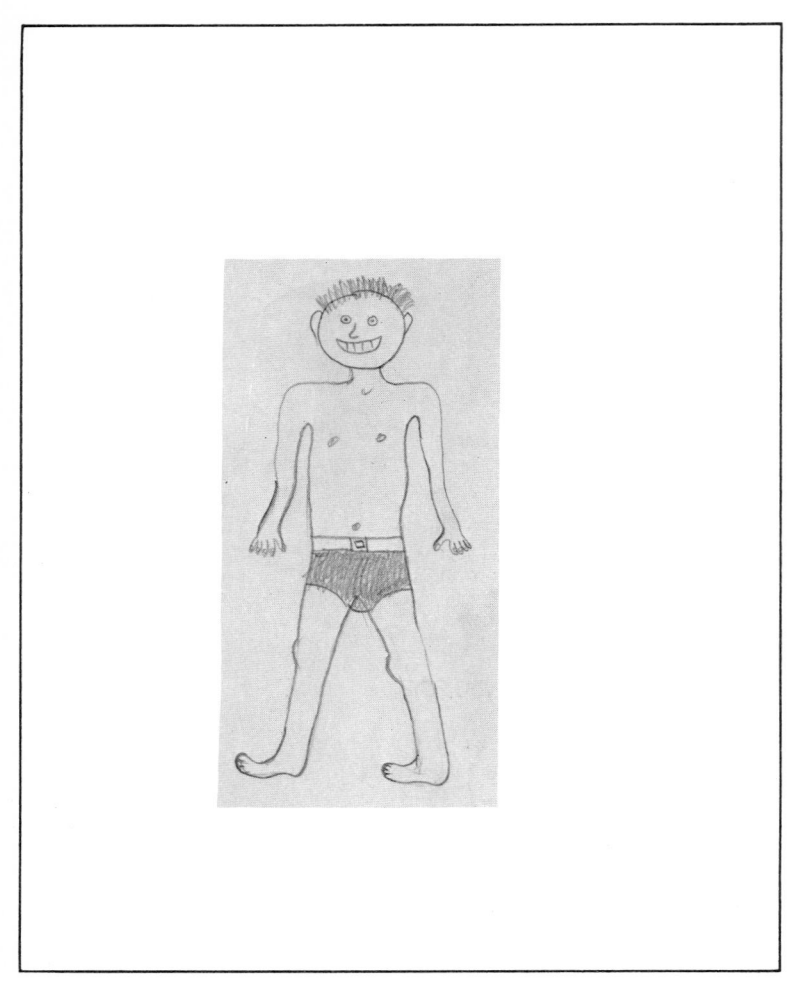

FIGURE-DRAWING CHARACTERISTICS

Structural	Male Female Both	Structural	Male	Female	Structural and Graphic	Male Female Both		Graphic, Global and Height	Male	Female	Body Proportions	Male	Female
Type	0	Omission of Appendages	0	0	Upper and Lower Halves	3	3	Hair Shading	3	1	Head	06	06
Sex Sequence	2	Position of Both Arms	0	0	Four Quarters	4	4	Nudity and Transparency	3	2	Neck	06	06
Posture	1 1	Position of Right Arm	0	2	Relative Size	0		Form	5	5	Shoulders	06	04
Perspective	0 0	Position of Left Arm	0	2	Constant Line Pressure	0	0	Detailing	3	3	Right Arm	04	02
Vertical Midline	0 0	Position of Legs	6	6	Variable Line Pressure	3	3	Identity and Sex	1	1	Left Arm	04	02
Bilateral Symmetry	3 3	Relation of Long Axes	1	1	Line Continuity	4	2	Sophistication	4	4	Chest	04	04
Horizontal Midline	4 4	Right and Left Halves	1	1	Body Shading	3	3	Height	05	04	Girth	05	04

GENERAL CHARACTERISTICS OF SUBJECT

IDENTIFICATION
No. 544
Sex M
Marital status S
Age 24 yrs. at
psychological tests

PARENTAL HISTORY				
Father				
C	H	S	D	O
-	-	-	-	-
Mother				
C	H	S	D	O
-	-	-	-	-

PHYSIOLOGICAL AND METABOLIC DATA

	Admission	Initial	Control	Cold pressor change	Exercise change	Smoking change
Systolic pressure	134	120	105	+05	+45	
Diastolic pressure	68	60	50	+10	+10	
Heart rate	90	84	87	+10	-06	

Age 22 yrs.	Height 73 in.	Ponderal index 13.08
	Weight 174 lbs.	Cholesterol 167 mg. per 100 ml.
	Overweight +04 %	Vital capacity 5.5 liters

HABIT SURVEY

Smoking habits: heavy cigarette smoker

Age begun 18 yrs.   Inhalation: yes

Habits of nervous tension: 4, 5, 6, 22

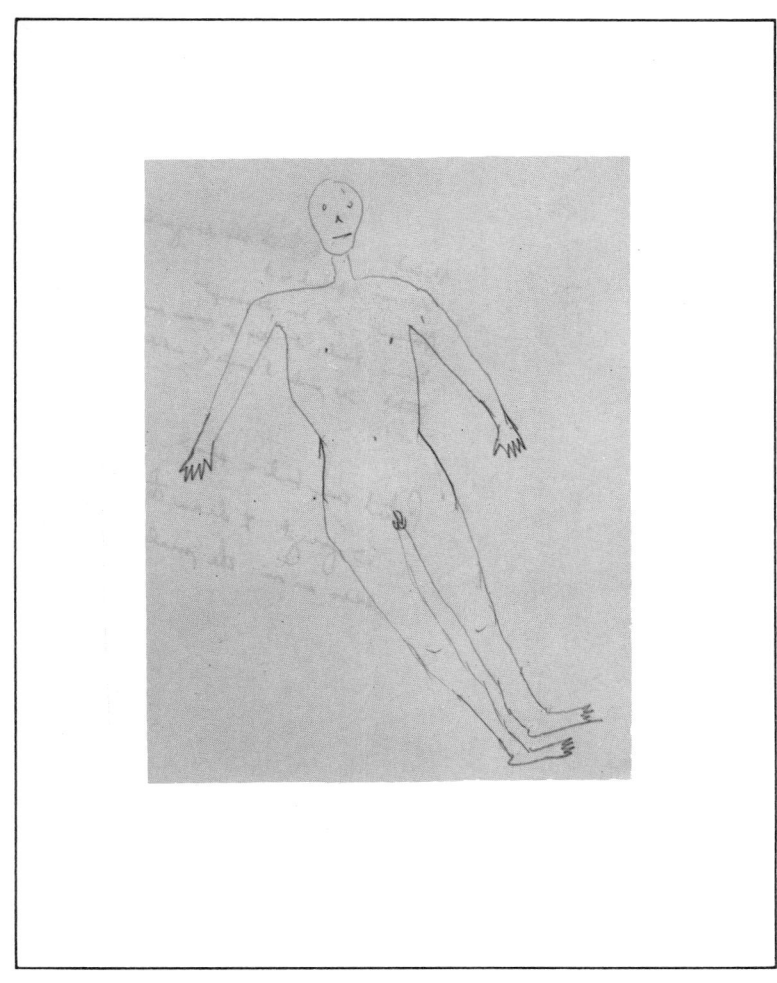
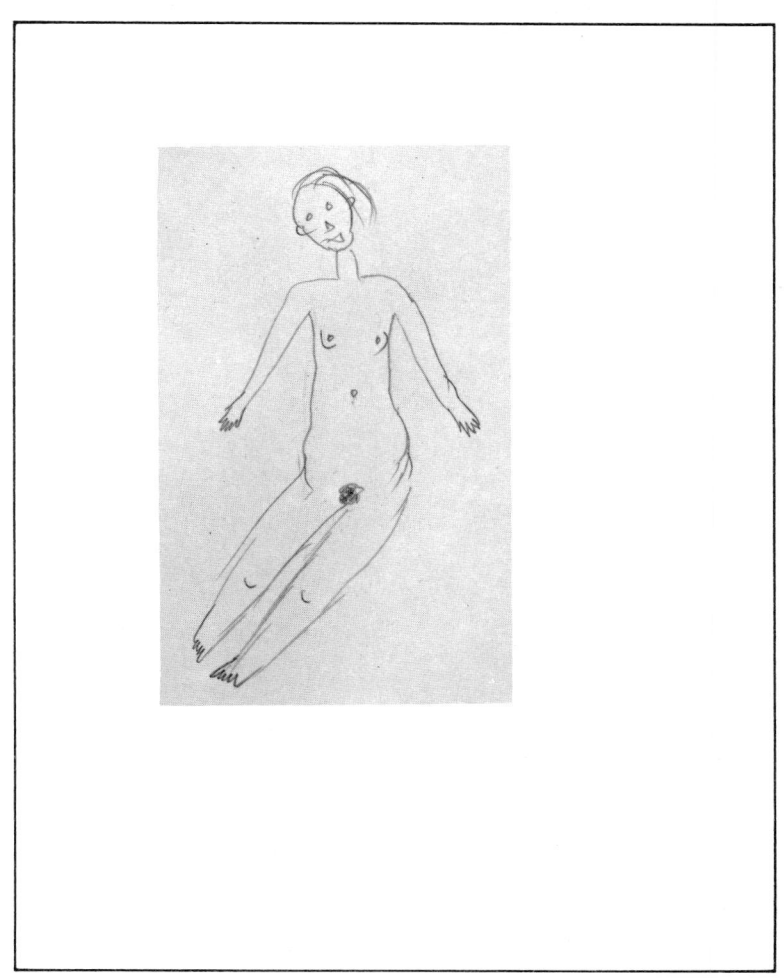

FIGURE-DRAWING CHARACTERISTICS

Structural	Male Female Both		Structural	Male	Female	Structural and Graphic	Male Female Both		Graphic, Global and Height	Male	Female	Body Proportions	Male	Female
Type	0		Omission of Appendages	0	0	Upper and Lower Halves	1	1	Hair Shading	0	7	Head	06	06
Sex Sequence	0		Position of Both Arms	0	0	Four Quarters	4	4	Nudity and Transparency	0	0	Neck	08	08
Posture	9	9	Position of Right Arm	2	2	Relative Size	0		Form	5	5	Shoulders	06	04
Perspective	0	0	Position of Left Arm	2	2	Constant Line Pressure	0	0	Detailing	5	5	Right Arm	04	04
Vertical Midline	0	0	Position of Legs	4	4	Variable Line Pressure	3	5	Identity and Sex	1	1	Left Arm	04	04
Bilateral Symmetry	1	2	Relation of Long Axes	3	0	Line Continuity	1	1	Sophistication	4	4	Chest	06	04
Horizontal Midline	0	0	Right and Left Halves	1	1	Body Shading	2	2	Height			Girth	06	05

GENERAL CHARACTERISTICS OF SUBJECT

IDENTIFICATION
No. 645
Sex M
Marital status M
Age 29 yrs. at
psychological tests

PARENTAL HISTORY
Father
C H S D O
- - - - -
Mother
C H S D O
- - - - -

PHYSIOLOGICAL AND METABOLIC DATA

	Admission	Initial	Control	Cold pressor change	Exercise change	Smoking change
Systolic pressure	130	118	110	+12	+20	
Diastolic pressure	70	70	72	+12	00	
Heart rate	78	84	84	+16	+16	

Age 29 yrs.	Height 72 in.	Ponderal index 12.85
	Weight 176 lbs.	Cholesterol 230 mg. per 100 ml.
	Overweight +03 %	Vital capacity liters

HABIT SURVEY
Smoking habits: former smoker
Age begun 16 yrs.   Inhalation:
Habits of nervous tension: 3, 4, 5, 9, 11,
12, 14, 18

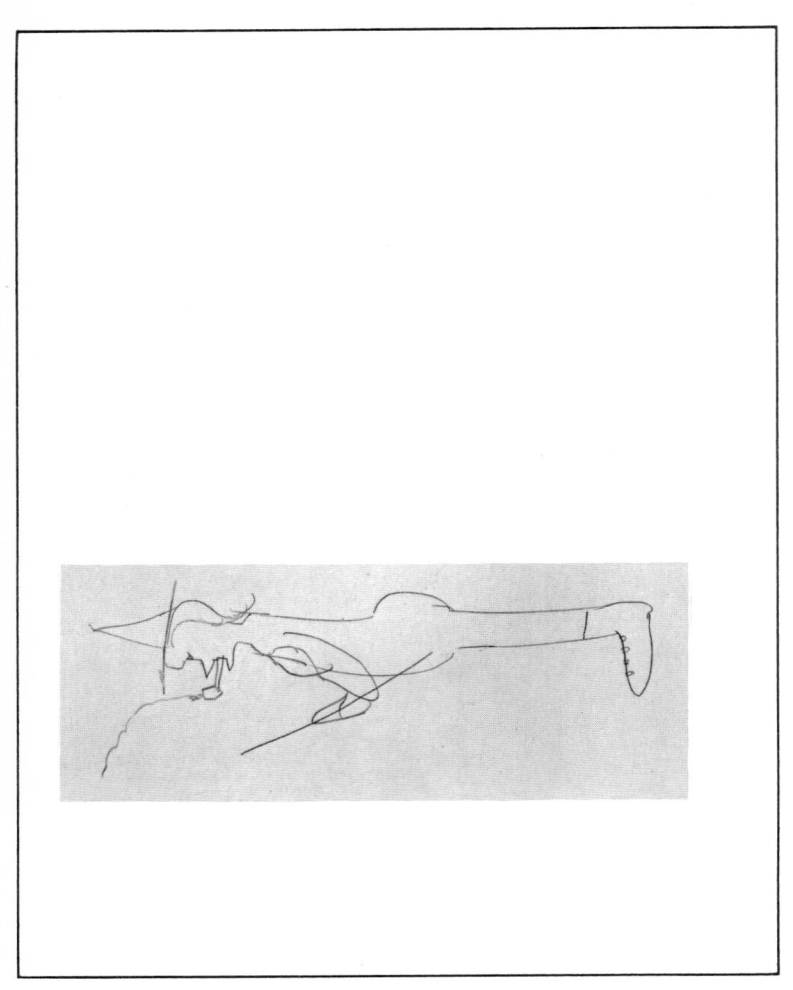

FIGURE-DRAWING CHARACTERISTICS

Structural	Male Female Both	Structural	Male	Female	Structural and Graphic	Male Female Both		Graphic, Global and Height	Male	Female	Body Proportions	Male	Female
Type	0	Omission of Appendages	0	7	Upper and Lower Halves	1	1	Hair Shading	3	5	Head	09	05
Sex Sequence	1	Position of Both Arms	0	4	Four Quarters	4	4	Nudity and Transparency	7	9	Neck	12	04
Posture	2 1	Position of Right Arm	4	7	Relative Size	0		Form	5	5	Shoulders	04	
Perspective	0 2	Position of Left Arm	4	4	Constant Line Pressure	1	3	Detailing	5	3	Right Arm	04	
Vertical Midline	3 4	Position of Legs	8	1	Variable Line Pressure	0	0	Identity and Sex	3	5	Left Arm	04	
Bilateral Symmetry	3 0	Relation of Long Axes	1	2	Line Continuity	0	2	Sophistication	4	4	Chest	03	03
Horizontal Midline	4 0	Right and Left Halves	2	2	Body Shading	0	0	Height	05	05	Girth	05	05

GENERAL CHARACTERISTICS OF SUBJECT

IDENTIFICATION
No. G03
Sex M
Marital status S
Age 23 yrs. at
psychological tests

PARENTAL HISTORY
Father
C H S D O
- - - - -
Mother
C H S D O
- - - - -

PHYSIOLOGICAL AND METABOLIC DATA

	Admission	Initial	Control	Cold pressor change	Exercise change	Smoking change
Systolic pressure	120	132	122	+08	+18	+03
Diastolic pressure	70	70	60	+20	-02	+03
Heart rate	76	68	64	+07	+27	+06

Age 22 yrs. Height 70 in. Weight 158 lbs. Overweight +03 %
Ponderal index 12.94 Cholesterol 197 mg. per 100 ml. Vital capacity liters

HABIT SURVEY

Smoking habits: light cigarette smoker
Age begun 20 yrs.   Inhalation: yes
Habits of nervous tension: 25

STRONG VOCATIONAL INTEREST TEST

Occupation	Artist	Psychologist	Architect	Physician	Osteopath	Dentist	Veterinarian	Mathematician	Physicist	Engineer	Chemist	Production Manager
Standard Score	47	51	44	56	38	30	06	33	22	23	31	18

Occupation	Farmer	Aviator	Carpenter	Printer	Math.-Sci. Teacher	Ind. Arts Teacher	Voc. Agric. Teacher	Policeman	Forest Serv. Man	Y.M.C.A. Phys. Dir.	Personnel Director	Public Administrator
Standard Score	16	27	-05	24	22	-10	01	13	12	28	34	44

Occupation	Y.M.C.A. Secretary	Soc. Sci. H.S. Teacher	City Sch. Sup't.	Social Worker	Minister	Musician Performer	C.P.A.	Senior C.P.A.	Accountant	Office Man	Purchasing Agent	Banker
Standard Score	21	35	37	48	59	56	43	23	15	20	10	14

Occupation	Mortician	Pharmacist	Sales Manager	Real Est. Manager	Life Ins. Salesman	Advertising Man	Lawyer	Author-Journalist	President Mfg. Co.	Interest Maturity	Occupational Level	Masculinity-Femininity
Standard Score	19	25	32	41	41	57	60	54	29	55	68	23

Plate 143   **MODERATELY PRIMITIVE DRAWINGS**   181

FIGURE-DRAWING CHARACTERISTICS

Structural	Male Female Both	Structural	Male	Female	Structural and Graphic	Male Female Both		Graphic, Global and Height	Male	Female	Body Proportions	Male	Female
Type	0	Omission of Appendages	0	0	Upper and Lower Halves	1	1	Hair Shading	2	3	Head	12	12
Sex Sequence	1	Position of Both Arms	0	0	Four Quarters	4	4	Nudity and Transparency	7	7	Neck	06	06
Posture	1 1	Position of Right Arm	0	0	Relative Size	0		Form	5	5	Shoulders	09	07
Perspective	0 0	Position of Left Arm	0	0	Constant Line Pressure	3	3	Detailing	5	5	Right Arm	04	03
Vertical Midline	0 0	Position of Legs	4	4	Variable Line Pressure	0	0	Identity and Sex	3	3	Left Arm	04	04
Bilateral Symmetry	2 2	Relation of Long Axes	1	1	Line Continuity	4	4	Sophistication	4	4	Chest	05	03
Horizontal Midline	0 0	Right and Left Halves	1	1	Body Shading	0	0	Height	05	05	Girth	07	05

GENERAL CHARACTERISTICS OF SUBJECT

IDENTIFICATION	PARENTAL HISTORY
No. A68	**Father**
Sex F	C H S D O
Marital status S	– – – – –
Age 22 yrs. at	**Mother**
psychological tests	C H S D O
	– – – – –

PHYSIOLOGICAL AND METABOLIC DATA

	Admission	Initial	Control	Cold pressor change	Exercise change	Smoking change
Systolic pressure	120	110	100	+13	+38	+03
Diastolic pressure	70	61	56	+25	–14	+04
Heart rate	76	81	76	+09	+44	–04

Age 21 yrs.	Height	70 in.	Ponderal index	14.20	
	Weight	120 lbs.	Cholesterol	217	mg. per 100 ml.
	Overweight	–19 %	Vital capacity		liters

HABIT SURVEY

Smoking habits: nonsmoker

Age begun   yrs.   Inhalation:

Habits of nervous tension: 3, 4, 8, 10, 11,

16, 21

STRONG VOCATIONAL INTEREST TEST

Occupation	Artist	Psychologist	Architect	Physician	Osteopath	Dentist	Veterinarian	Mathematician	Physicist	Engineer	Chemist	Production Manager
Standard Score	24	24	32	47	52	43	42	29	26	37	32	32

Occupation	Farmer	Aviator	Carpenter	Printer	Math.-Sci. Teacher	Ind. Arts Teacher	Voc. Agric. Teacher	Policeman	Forest Serv. Man	Y.M.C.A. Phys. Dir.	Personnel Director	Public Administrator
Standard Score	42	34	34	29	37	22	34	34	18	20	19	31

Occupation	Y.M.C.A. Secretary	Soc. Sci. H.S. Teacher	City Sch. Sup't.	Social Worker	Minister	Musician Performer	C.P.A.	Senior C.P.A.	Accountant	Office Man	Purchasing Agent	Banker
Standard Score	14	24	15	19	60	29	30	41	32	44	29	46

Occupation	Mortician	Pharmacist	Sales Manager	Real Est. Manager	Life Ins. Salesman	Advertising Man	Lawyer	Author-Journalist	President Mfg. Co.	Interest Maturity	Occupational Level	Masculinity-Femininity
Standard Score	41	35	21	30	22	20	29	29	36	47	53	45

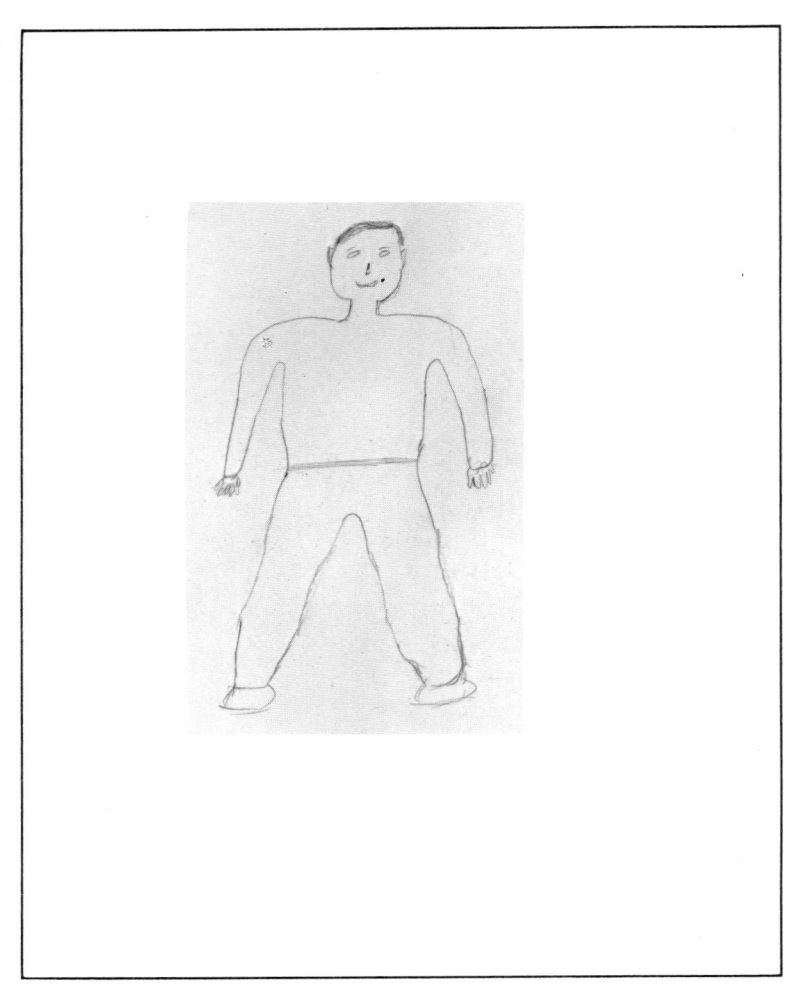

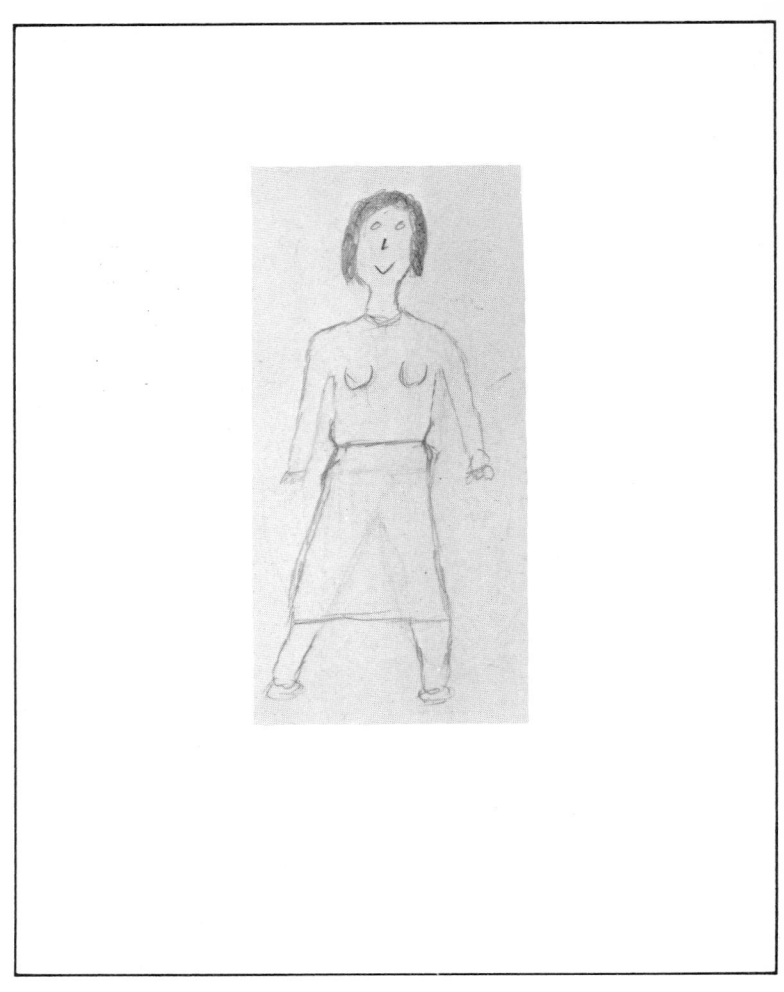

FIGURE-DRAWING CHARACTERISTICS

Structural	Male Female Both	Structural	Male	Female	Structural and Graphic	Male Female Both		Graphic, Global and Height	Male	Female	Body Proportions	Male	Female
Type	0	Omission of Appendages	0	0	Upper and Lower Halves	1	1	Hair Shading	3	3	Head	06	07
Sex Sequence	0	Position of Both Arms	0	0	Four Quarters	4	4	Nudity and Transparency	7	6	Neck	06	08
Posture	1 1	Position of Right Arm	1	1	Relative Size	1		Form	5	5	Shoulders	08	06
Perspective	0 0	Position of Left Arm	1	1	Constant Line Pressure	1	1	Detailing	5	5	Right Arm	04	04
Vertical Midline	0 0	Position of Legs	6	6	Variable Line Pressure	0	0	Identity and Sex	3	1	Left Arm	04	04
Bilateral Symmetry	3 3	Relation of Long Axes	1	1	Line Continuity	0	0	Sophistication	4	4	Chest	07	05
Horizontal Midline	4 4	Right and Left Halves	1	1	Body Shading	4	1	Height	05	05	Girth	08	06

GENERAL CHARACTERISTICS OF SUBJECT

IDENTIFICATION
No. C23
Sex M
Marital status S
Age 22 yrs. at
psychological tests

PARENTAL HISTORY
Father
C   H   S   D   0
-   -   -   -   -
Mother
C   H   S   D   0
-   -   -   -   -

PHYSIOLOGICAL AND METABOLIC DATA

	Admission	Initial	Control	Cold pressor change	Exercise change	Smoking change
Systolic pressure	110	118	108	+06	+20	+02
Diastolic pressure	80	60	64	+16	+04	+13
Heart rate	80	72	63	00	+20	+08

Age 22 yrs.

Height	68 in.	Ponderal index 13.23	
Weight	136 lbs.	Cholesterol	222 mg. per 100 ml.
Overweight	-07 %	Vital capacity	4.3 liters

HABIT SURVEY

Smoking habits: light cigarette smoker

Age begun 18 yrs.   Inhalation: no

Habits of nervous tension: 4, 5, 6, 10, 14, 23

STRONG VOCATIONAL INTEREST TEST

Occupation	Artist	Psychologist	Architect	Physician	Osteopath	Dentist	Veterinarian	Mathematician	Physicist	Engineer	Chemist	Production Manager
Standard Score	41	48	44	56	39	41	09	44	40	37	47	28

Occupation	Farmer	Aviator	Carpenter	Printer	Math.-Sci. Teacher	Ind. Arts Teacher	Voc. Agric. Teacher	Policeman	Forest Serv. Man	Y.M.C.A. Phys. Dir.	Personnel Director	Public Administrator
Standard Score	21	31	15	35	36	03	05	22	08	24	29	33

Occupation	Y.M.C.A. Secretary	Soc. Sci. H.S. Teacher	City Sch. Sup't.	Social Worker	Minister	Musician Performer	C.P.A.	Senior C.P.A.	Accountant	Office Man	Purchasing Agent	Banker
Standard Score	17	26	29	33	62	51	46	38	24	25	21	18

Occupation	Mortician	Pharmacist	Sales Manager	Real Est. Manager	Life Ins. Salesman	Advertising Man	Lawyer	Author-Journalist	President Mfg. Co.	Interest Maturity	Occupational Level	Masculinity-Femininity
Standard Score	17	38	26	29	31	40	49	44	36	50	61	40

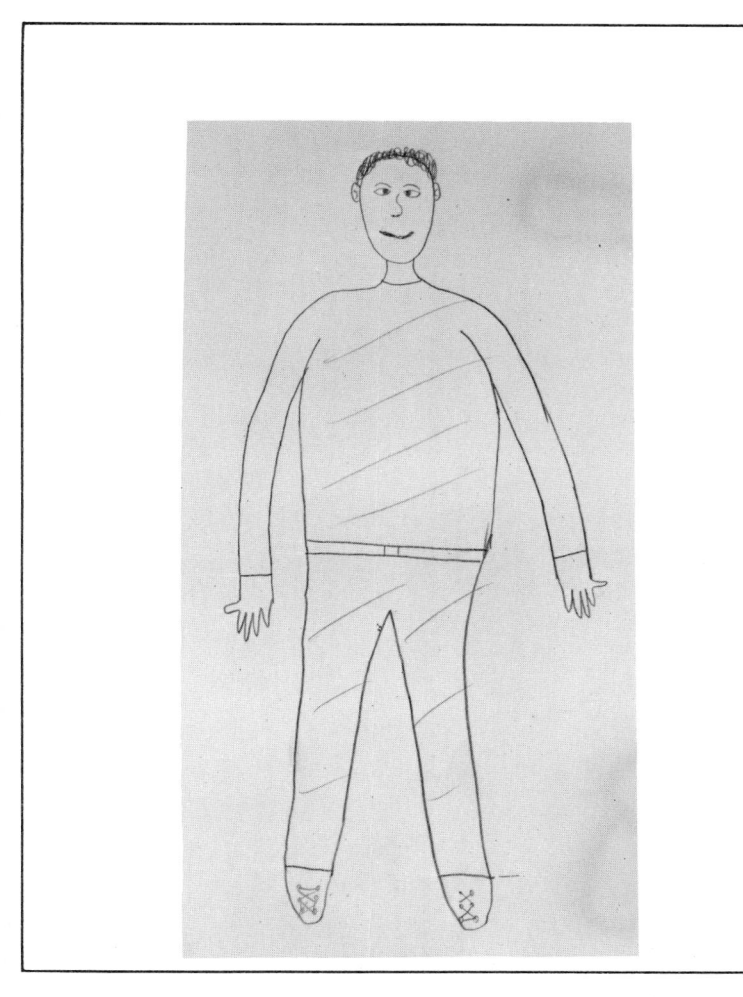

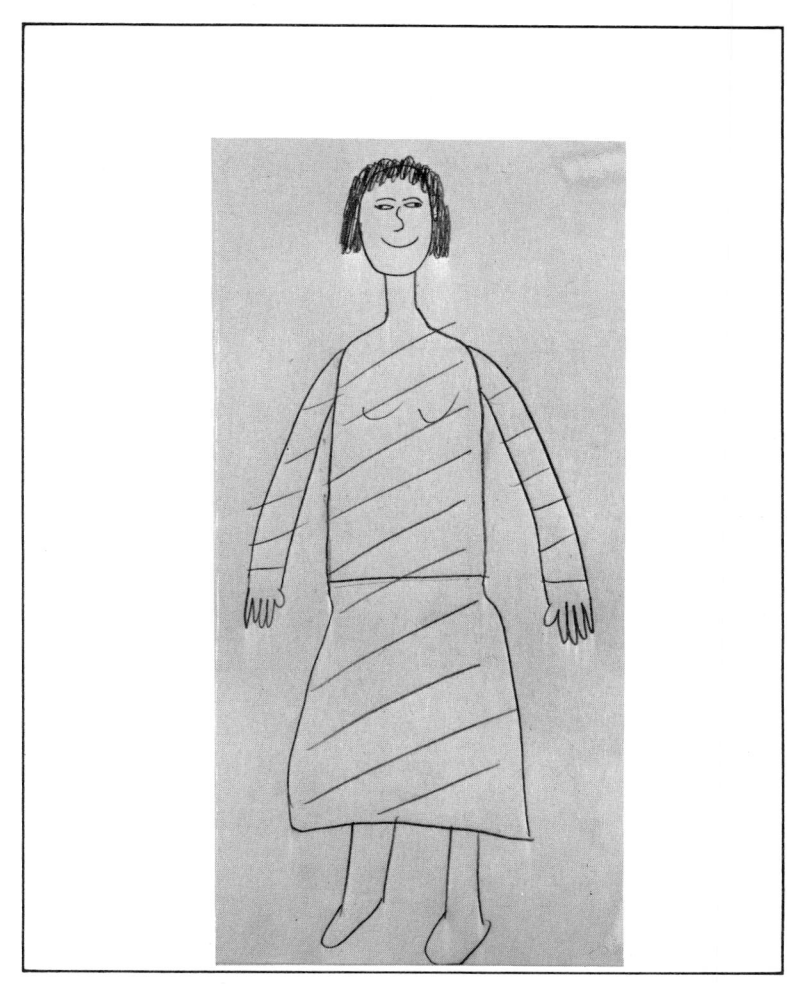

FIGURE-DRAWING CHARACTERISTICS

Structural	Male Female Both	Structural	Male	Female	Structural and Graphic	Male Female Both		Graphic, Global and Height	Male	Female	Body Proportions	Male	Female
Type	0	Omission of Appendages	0	0	Upper and Lower Halves	3	3	Hair Shading	3	3	Head	09	09
Sex Sequence	0	Position of Both Arms	1	0	Four Quarters	4	4	Nudity and Transparency	7	7	Neck	07	14
Posture	1 1	Position of Right Arm	0	2	Relative Size	2		Form	5	5	Shoulders	08	06
Perspective	0 0	Position of Left Arm	2	2	Constant Line Pressure	5	5	Detailing	3	3	Right Arm	08	06
Vertical Midline	0 0	Position of Legs	6	6	Variable Line Pressure	0	0	Identity and Sex	3	3	Left Arm	08	06
Bilateral Symmetry	3 3	Relation of Long Axes	1	1	Line Continuity	4	4	Sophistication	4	4	Chest	08	07
Horizontal Midline	4 4	Right and Left Halves	1	1	Body Shading	0	1	Height	08	08	Girth	09	09

GENERAL CHARACTERISTICS OF SUBJECT

IDENTIFICATION

No. C64

Sex M

Marital status S

Age 20 yrs. at psychological tests

PARENTAL HISTORY

Father

C   H   S   D   O

-   -   -   -   -

Mother

C   H   S   D   O

-   -   -   -   -

PHYSIOLOGICAL AND METABOLIC DATA

	Admission	Initial	Control	Cold pressor change	Exercise change	Smoking change
Systolic pressure	160	130	110	+06	+75	
Diastolic pressure	70	80	70	+25	-10	
Heart rate	84	68	68	+08	+29	

Age 21 yrs.

Height 69 in.   Ponderal index 12.68

Weight 161 lbs.   Cholesterol 208 mg. per 100 ml.

Overweight +08 %   Vital capacity 4.2 liters

HABIT SURVEY

Smoking habits: former smoker

Age begun 16 yrs.   Inhalation:

Habits of nervous tension: 5, 6, 18

STRONG VOCATIONAL INTEREST TEST

Occupation	Artist	Psychologist	Architect	Physician	Osteopath	Dentist	Veterinarian	Mathematician	Physicist	Engineer	Chemist	Production Manager
Standard Score	47	61	43	57	38	29	13	36	23	23	37	17

Occupation	Farmer	Aviator	Carpenter	Printer	Math.-Sci. Teacher	Ind. Arts Teacher	Voc. Agric. Teacher	Policeman	Forest Serv. Man	Y.M.C.A. Phys. Dir.	Personnel Director	Public Administrator
Standard Score	22	25	02	35	31	00	17	14	10	30	36	46

Occupation	Y.M.C.A. Secretary	Soc. Sci. H.S. Teacher	City Sch. Sup't.	Social Worker	Minister	Musician Performer	C.P.A.	Senior C.P.A.	Accountant	Office Man	Purchasing Agent	Banker
Standard Score	26	38	34	48	62	60	34	28	12	16	08	10

Occupation	Mortician	Pharmacist	Sales Manager	Real Est. Manager	Life Ins. Salesman	Advertising Man	Lawyer	Author-Journalist	President Mfg. Co.	Interest Maturity	Occupational Level	Masculinity-Femininity
Standard Score	18	32	32	35	34	59	49	56	33	52	61	27

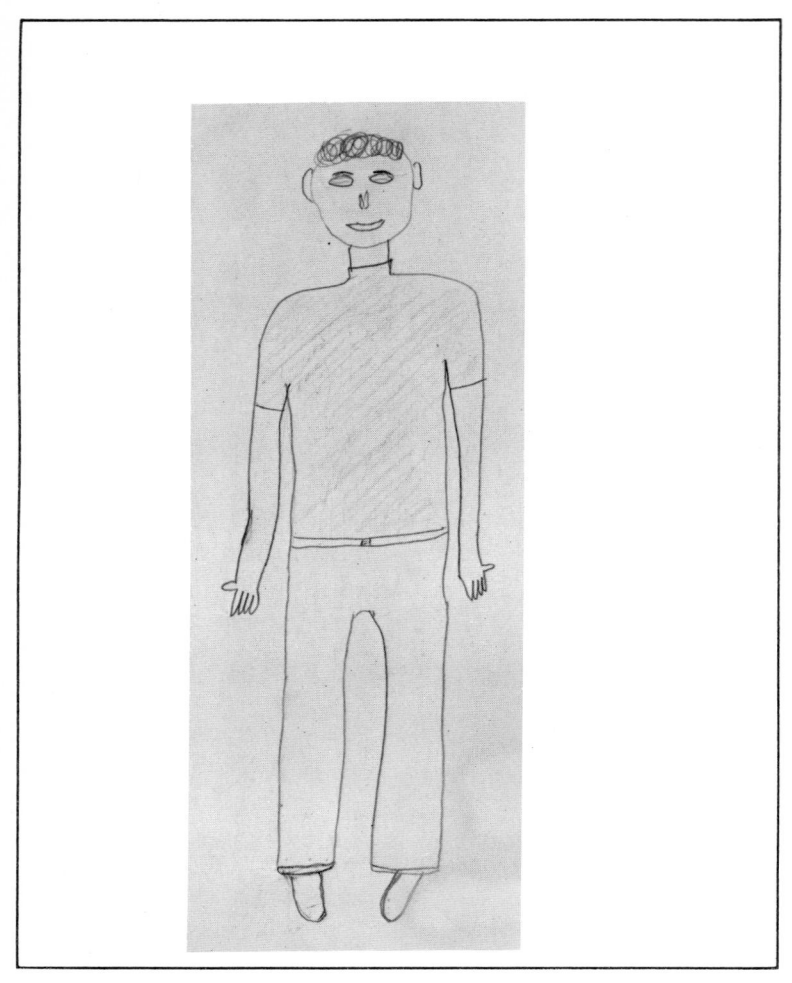

FIGURE-DRAWING CHARACTERISTICS

Structural	Male Female Both	Structural	Male	Female	Structural and Graphic	Male Female Both	Graphic, Global and Height	Male	Female	Body Proportions	Male	Female
Type	0	Omission of Appendages	0	0	Upper and Lower Halves	3 3	Hair Shading	3	1	Head	09	12
Sex Sequence	0	Position of Both Arms	0	0	Four Quarters	4 4	Nudity and Transparency	7	7	Neck	12	10
Posture	1 1	Position of Right Arm	0	0	Relative Size	3	Form	5	5	Shoulders	08	08
Perspective	0 0	Position of Left Arm	0	0	Constant Line Pressure	0 0	Detailing	3	3	Right Arm	08	08
Vertical Midline	0 0	Position of Legs	4	4	Variable Line Pressure	4 5	Identity and Sex	3	3	Left Arm	08	06
Bilateral Symmetry	3 3	Relation of Long Axes	1	1	Line Continuity	4 4	Sophistication	4	4	Chest	07	07
Horizontal Midline	4 0	Right and Left Halves	1	1	Body Shading	1 1	Height	08	08	Girth	10	06

GENERAL CHARACTERISTICS OF SUBJECT

IDENTIFICATION
No. D27
Sex M
Marital status S
Age 22 yrs. at
psychological tests

PARENTAL HISTORY
Father
C   H   S   D   0
-   -   -   -   -
Mother
C   H   S   D   0
-   -   -   -   -

PHYSIOLOGICAL AND METABOLIC DATA

	Admission	Initial	Control	Cold pressor change	Exercise change	Smoking change
Systolic pressure	140	144	132	+12	+26	
Diastolic pressure	75	79	72	+25	-02	
Heart rate	80	64	67	+13	+14	

	Height 70 in.	Ponderal index 12.99
Age 24 yrs.	Weight 157 lbs.	Cholesterol 222 mg. per 100 ml.
	Overweight +01 %	Vital capacity liters

HABIT SURVEY
Smoking habits: nonsmoker
Age begun   yrs.   Inhalation:
Habits of nervous tension: 5, 6, 8, 16

FIGURE-DRAWING CHARACTERISTICS

Structural	Male Female Both		Structural	Male	Female	Structural and Graphic	Male Female Both		Graphic, Global and Height	Male	Female	Body Proportions	Male	Female
Type	0		Omission of Appendages	2	0	Upper and Lower Halves	2	2	Hair Shading	0	5	Head	02	03
Sex Sequence	0		Position of Both Arms	0	0	Four Quarters	4	4	Nudity and Transparency	3	3	Neck	02	04
Posture	1	1	Position of Right Arm	8	2	Relative Size	4		Form	5	5	Shoulders	02	03
Perspective	0	0	Position of Left Arm	8	2	Constant Line Pressure	5	5	Detailing	5	3	Right Arm		02
Vertical Midline	0	0	Position of Legs	5	5	Variable Line Pressure	0	0	Identity and Sex	5	1	Left Arm		02
Bilateral Symmetry	2	1	Relation of Long Axes	1	1	Line Continuity	2	3	Sophistication	4	4	Chest	02	02
Horizontal Midline	4	4	Right and Left Halves	1	3	Body Shading	0	1	Height	02	03	Girth	02	02

GENERAL CHARACTERISTICS OF SUBJECT

IDENTIFICATION
No. E12
Sex M
Marital status S
Age 21 yrs. at psychological tests

PARENTAL HISTORY				
Father				
C	H	S	D	O
-	-	-	-	-
Mother				
C	H	S	D	O
-	-	-	-	-

PHYSIOLOGICAL AND METABOLIC DATA

	Admission	Initial	Control	Cold pressor change	Exercise change	Smoking change
Systolic pressure	100	118	110	+20	+27	
Diastolic pressure	70	80	78	+10	-18	
Heart rate	86	68	59	00	+41	

Age 21 yrs.	Height	66 in.	Ponderal index	14.16	
	Weight	101 lbs.	Cholesterol	225	mg. per 100 ml.
	Overweight	-27 %	Vital capacity		liters

HABIT SURVEY
Smoking habits: nonsmoker
Age begun yrs.   Inhalation:
Habits of nervous tension:

STRONG VOCATIONAL INTEREST TEST

Occupation	Artist	Psychologist	Architect	Physician	Osteopath	Dentist	Veterinarian	Mathematician	Physicist	Engineer	Chemist	Production Manager
Standard Score	36	49	25	48	43	26	19	30	17	15	27	13

Occupation	Farmer	Aviator	Carpenter	Printer	Math.-Sci. Teacher	Ind. Arts Teacher	Voc. Agric. Teacher	Policeman	Forest Serv. Man	Y.M.C.A. Phys. Dir.	Personnel Director	Public Administrator
Standard Score	16	21	-09	31	30	-10	13	15	04	32	31	45

Occupation	Y.M.C.A. Secretary	Soc. Sci. H.S. Teacher	City Sch. Sup't.	Social Worker	Minister	Musician Performer	C.P.A.	Senior C.P.A.	Accountant	Office Man	Purchasing Agent	Banker
Standard Score	29	40	35	50	64	47	47	30	21	25	17	22

Occupation	Mortician	Pharmacist	Sales Manager	Real Est. Manager	Life Ins. Salesman	Advertising Man	Lawyer	Author-Journalist	President Mfg. Co.	Interest Maturity	Occupational Level	Masculinity-Femininity
Standard Score	22	36	38	43	48	46	56	48	30	54	64	32

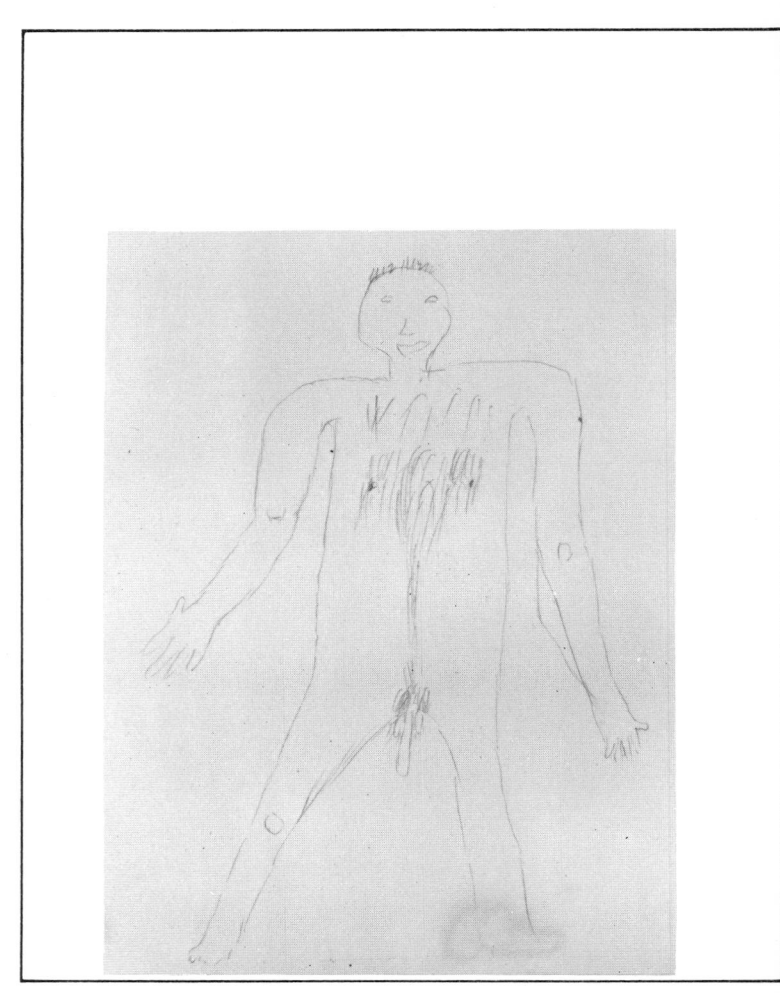

FIGURE-DRAWING CHARACTERISTICS

Structural	Male Female Both	Structural	Male	Female	Structural and Graphic	Male Female Both		Graphic, Global and Height	Male	Female	Body Proportions	Male	Female
Type	0	Omission of Appendages	8	2	Upper and Lower Halves	3	2	Hair Shading	7	3	Head	08	06
Sex Sequence	1	Position of Both Arms	0	6	Four Quarters	4	4	Nudity and Transparency	0	0	Neck	06	05
Posture	1	7	Position of Right Arm	3	8	Relative Size	0		Form	5	5	Shoulders	12	05
Perspective	0	0	Position of Left Arm	3	8	Constant Line Pressure	1	1	Detailing	3	3	Right Arm	08	
Vertical Midline	0	0	Position of Legs	6	2	Variable Line Pressure	0	0	Identity and Sex	1	1	Left Arm	10	
Bilateral Symmetry	1	1	Relation of Long Axes	1	0	Line Continuity	0	0	Sophistication	4	4	Chest	08	04
Horizontal Midline	0	0	Right and Left Halves	3	7	Body Shading	3	3	Height	07		Girth	12	06

GENERAL CHARACTERISTICS OF SUBJECT

IDENTIFICATION
No. E15
Sex M
Marital status S
Age 23 yrs. at
psychological tests

PARENTAL HISTORY				
Father				
C	H	S	D	0
-	-	-	-	-
Mother				
C	H	S	D	0
-	-	-	-	-

PHYSIOLOGICAL AND METABOLIC DATA

	Admission	Initial	Control	Cold pressor change	Exercise change	Smoking change
Systolic pressure		100	100	+10	+20	
Diastolic pressure		58	60	+12	-20	
Heart rate		60	59	+04	+18	

Age 23 yrs.

Height 70 in.   Ponderal index 12.99
Weight 157 lbs.   Cholesterol 260 mg. per 100 ml.
Overweight +01 %   Vital capacity 4.9 liters

HABIT SURVEY

Smoking habits: heavy cigarette smoker
Age begun 20 yrs.   Inhalation: yes
Habits of nervous tension: 3, 4, 5, 6, 9, 11, 16, 18, 22, 23, 25

STRONG VOCATIONAL INTEREST TEST

Occupation	Artist	Psychologist	Architect	Physician	Osteopath	Dentist	Veterinarian	Mathematician	Physicist	Engineer	Chemist	Production Manager
Standard Score	24	39	15	34	41	32	09	23	25	38	42	45

Occupation	Farmer	Aviator	Carpenter	Printer	Math.-Sci. Teacher	Ind. Arts Teacher	Voc. Agric. Teacher	Policeman	Forest Serv. Man	Y.M.C.A. Phys. Dir.	Personnel Director	Public Administrator
Standard Score	22	35	05	20	27	-09	-06	28	25	24	50	49

Occupation	Y.M.C.A. Secretary	Soc. Sci. H.S. Teacher	City Sch. Sup't.	Social Worker	Minister	Musician Performer	C.P.A.	Senior C.P.A.	Accountant	Office Man	Purchasing Agent	Banker
Standard Score	23	23	26	30	64	23	37	31	29	29	28	18

Occupation	Mortician	Pharmacist	Sales Manager	Real Est. Manager	Life Ins. Salesman	Advertising Man	Lawyer	Author-Journalist	President Mfg. Co.	Interest Maturity	Occupational Level	Masculinity-Femininity
Standard Score	21	23	32	31	33	34	46	38	33	54	66	49

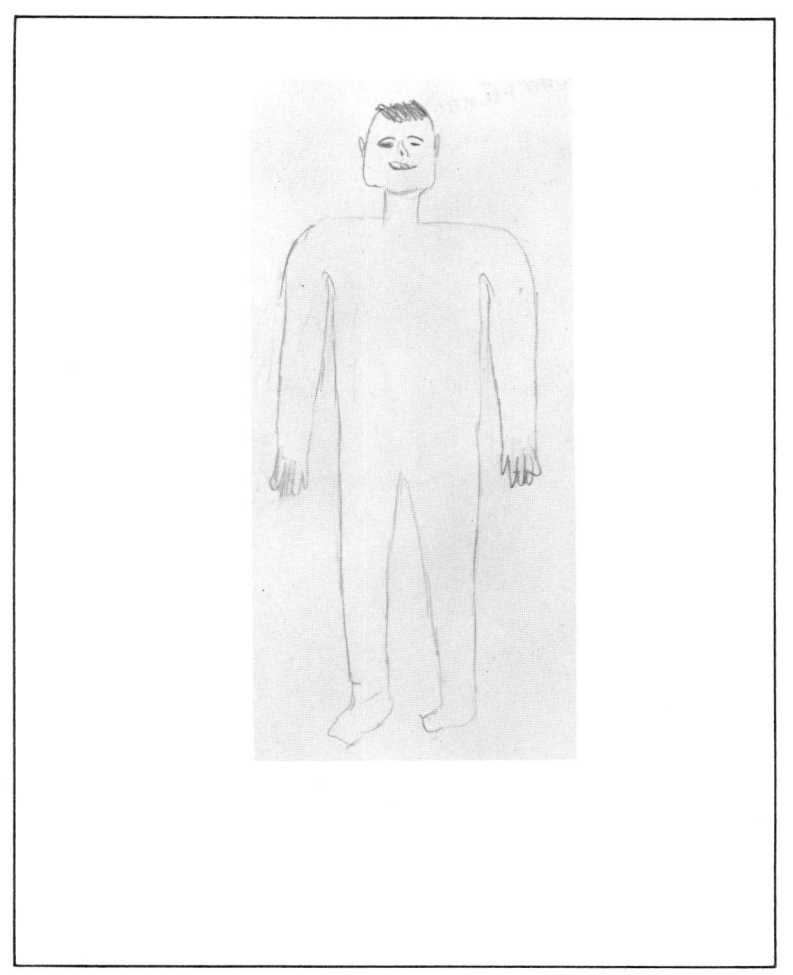

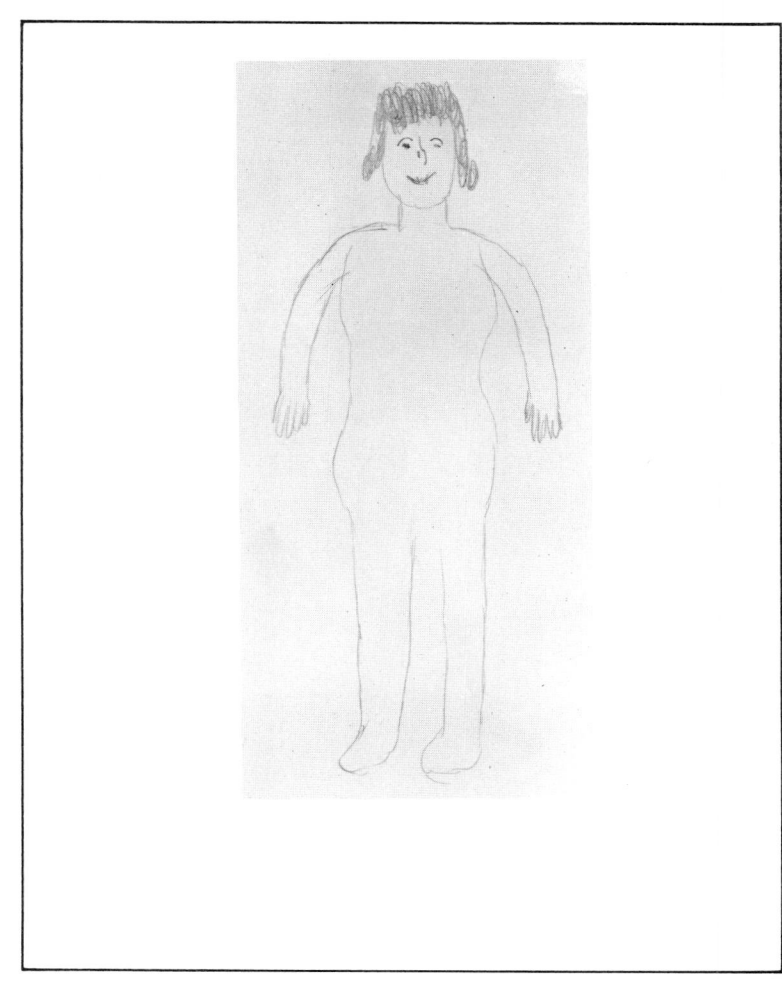

FIGURE-DRAWING CHARACTERISTICS

Structural	Male Female Both	Structural	Male	Female	Structural and Graphic	Male Female Both	Graphic, Global and Height	Male	Female	Body Proportions	Male	Female
Type	0	Omission of Appendages	0	0	Upper and Lower Halves	1 1	Hair Shading	3	3	Head	07	08
Sex Sequence	0	Position of Both Arms	0	0	Four Quarters	4 4	Nudity and Transparency	0	0	Neck	10	07
Posture	1 1	Position of Right Arm	0	2	Relative Size	4	Form	5	5	Shoulders	09	06
Perspective	0 0	Position of Left Arm	0	2	Constant Line Pressure	1 1	Detailing	5	5	Right Arm	06	04
Vertical Midline	0 0	Position of Legs	4	4	Variable Line Pressure	0 0	Identity and Sex	5	5	Left Arm	06	04
Bilateral Symmetry	3 3	Relation of Long Axes	1	1	Line Continuity	0 0	Sophistication	4	4	Chest	07	08
Horizontal Midline	0 0	Right and Left Halves	3	3	Body Shading	0 0	Height	06	07	Girth	09	09

GENERAL CHARACTERISTICS OF SUBJECT

IDENTIFICATION
No. E75
Sex M
Marital status S
Age 21 yrs. at psychological tests

PARENTAL HISTORY					
Father					
C	H	S	D	O	
–	–	–	–	–	
Mother					
C	H	S	D	O	
–	–	–	–	–	

PHYSIOLOGICAL AND METABOLIC DATA

	Admission	Initial	Control	Cold pressor change	Exercise change	Smoking change
Systolic pressure	110	120	118	+21	+32	+07
Diastolic pressure	70	70	72	+20	–13	–03
Heart rate	100	72	65	+08	+32	+14

Age 21 yrs.	Height 67 in.	Ponderal index 13.08
	Weight 134 lbs.	Cholesterol 176 mg. per 100 ml.
	Overweight –05 %	Vital capacity 4.5 liters

HABIT SURVEY

Smoking habits: light cigarette smoker

Age begun 14 yrs.   Inhalation: yes

Habits of nervous tension: 5

STRONG VOCATIONAL INTEREST TEST

Occupation	Artist	Psychologist	Architect	Physician	Osteopath	Dentist	Veterinarian	Mathematician	Physicist	Engineer	Chemist	Production Manager
Standard Score	41	28	30	41	44	40	29	22	19	23	24	27

Occupation	Farmer	Aviator	Carpenter	Printer	Math.-Sci. Teacher	Ind. Arts Teacher	Voc. Agric. Teacher	Policeman	Forest Serv. Man	Y.M.C.A. Phys. Dir.	Personnel Director	Public Administrator
Standard Score	27	28	06	17	11	–09	17	24	20	24	19	34

Occupation	Y.M.C.A. Secretary	Soc. Sci. H.S. Teacher	City Sch. Sup't.	Social Worker	Minister	Musician Performer	C.P.A.	Senior C.P.A.	Accountant	Office Man	Purchasing Agent	Banker
Standard Score	16	26	23	28	64	29	25	17	01	12	14	18

Occupation	Mortician	Pharmacist	Sales Manager	Real Est. Manager	Life Ins. Salesman	Advertising Man	Lawyer	Author-Journalist	President Mfg. Co.	Interest Maturity	Occupational Level	Masculinity-Femininity
Standard Score	33	21	29	45	43	39	52	49	39	41	64	40

V. MIXED PRIMITIVE AND INTERMEDIATE DRAWINGS

In this section, represented by twenty-eight subjects, one drawing of each pair is moderately primitive and the other is intermediate in level of sophistication.

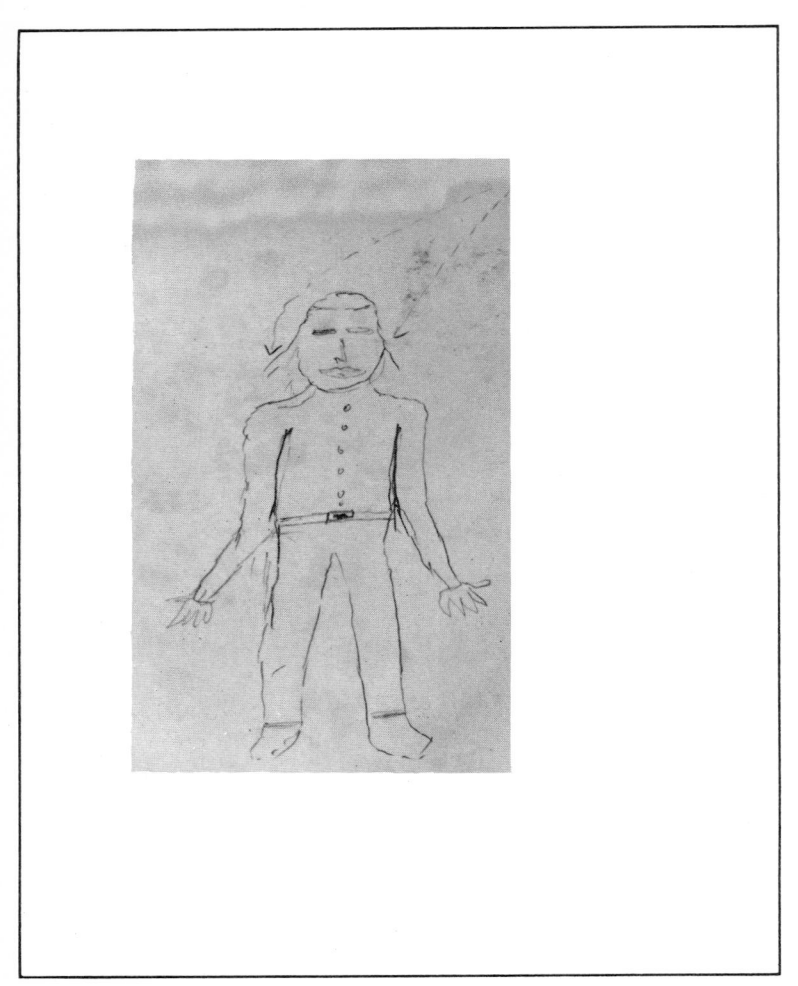

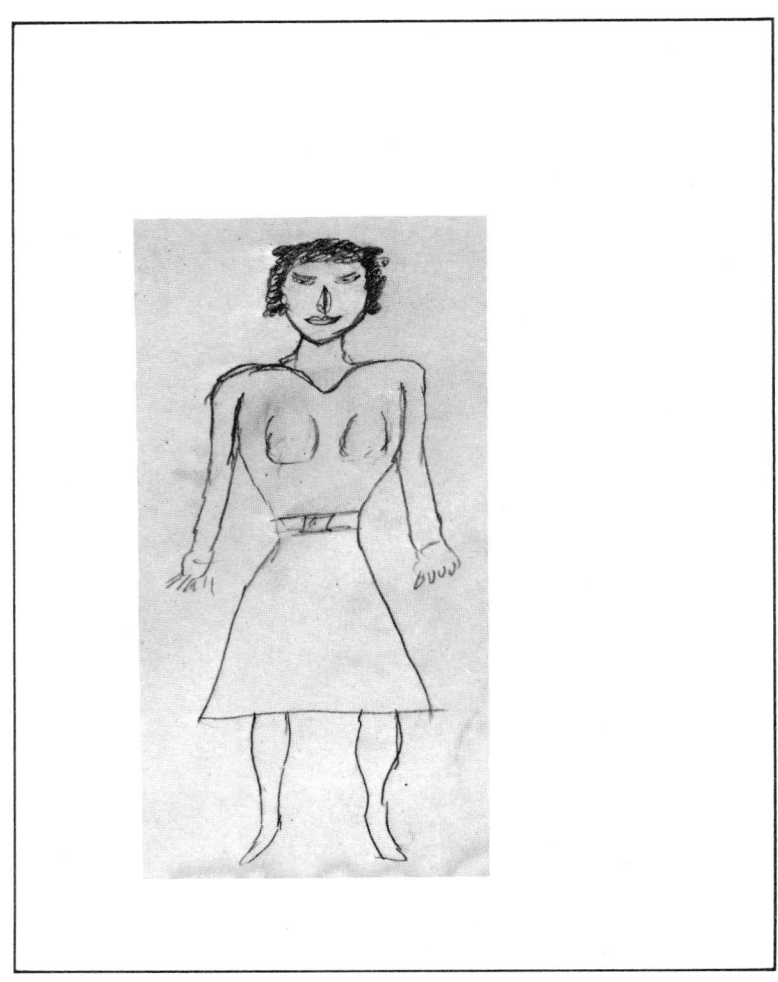

FIGURE-DRAWING CHARACTERISTICS

Structural	Male Female Both	Structural	Male	Female	Structural and Graphic	Male Female Both		Graphic, Global and Height	Male	Female	Body Proportions	Male	Female
Type	0	Omission of Appendages	0	0	Upper and Lower Halves	3	3	Hair Shading	7	3	Head	08	08
Sex Sequence	0	Position of Both Arms	0	0	Four Quarters	4	4	Nudity and Transparency	7	7	Neck	02	08
Posture	1 1	Position of Right Arm	4	0	Relative Size	4		Form	5	3	Shoulders	07	08
Perspective	0 0	Position of Left Arm	4	0	Constant Line Pressure	0	0	Detailing	5	3	Right Arm	06	04
Vertical Midline	3 0	Position of Legs	6	6	Variable Line Pressure	1	5	Identity and Sex	1	1	Left Arm	04	04
Bilateral Symmetry	3 3	Relation of Long Axes	1	1	Line Continuity	0	2	Sophistication	4	3	Chest	05	08
Horizontal Midline	4 4	Right and Left Halves	1	1	Body Shading	0	1	Height	05	06	Girth	07	05

GENERAL CHARACTERISTICS OF SUBJECT

IDENTIFICATION
No. 341
Sex M
Marital status M
Age 26 yrs. at
psychological tests

PARENTAL HISTORY				
Father				
C	H	S	D	O
(+)	−	−	(+)	?
Mother				
C	H	S	D	O
(+)	−	−	−	−

PHYSIOLOGICAL AND METABOLIC DATA

	Admission	Initial	Control	Cold pressor change	Exercise change	Smoking change
Systolic pressure	130	125	110	+06	+32	
Diastolic pressure	88	60	68	+02	−02	
Heart rate	72	68	68	+04	+15	

	Height	76 in.	Ponderal index 13.22	
Age 22 yrs.	Weight	190 lbs.	Cholesterol	280 mg. per 100 ml.
	Overweight +04 %		Vital capacity	5.6 liters

HABIT SURVEY
Smoking habits: unknown
Age begun   yrs.   Inhalation:
Habits of nervous tension:

FIGURE-DRAWING CHARACTERISTICS

Structural	Male Female Both		Structural	Male	Female	Structural and Graphic	Male Female Both		Graphic, Global and Height	Male	Female	Body Proportions	Male	Female
Type	0		Omission of Appendages	0	0	Upper and Lower Halves	3	3	Hair Shading	7	3	Head	07	09
Sex Sequence	2		Position of Both Arms	4	0	Four Quarters	4	4	Nudity and Transparency	7	7	Neck	18	06
Posture	1	1	Position of Right Arm	7	2	Relative Size	2		Form	5	3	Shoulders		05
Perspective	2	0	Position of Left Arm	4	2	Constant Line Pressure	0	3	Detailing	5	3	Right Arm		04
Vertical Midline	4	3	Position of Legs	4	6	Variable Line Pressure	1	0	Identity and Sex	3	1	Left Arm	05	02
Bilateral Symmetry	0	3	Relation of Long Axes	1	1	Line Continuity	4	2	Sophistication	4	3	Chest	07	06
Horizontal Midline	4	4	Right and Left Halves	1	2	Body Shading	0	6	Height	07	07	Girth	11	06

GENERAL CHARACTERISTICS OF SUBJECT

IDENTIFICATION
No. 250
Sex M
Marital status S
Age 22 yrs. at psychological tests

PARENTAL HISTORY				
Father				
C	H	S	D	O
+	?	-	-	+
Mother				
C	H	S	D	O
-	-	-	-	-

PHYSIOLOGICAL AND METABOLIC DATA

	Admission	Initial	Control	Cold pressor change	Exercise change	Smoking change
Systolic pressure	118	112	100		+24	
Diastolic pressure	70	72	76		-21	
Heart rate	64	56	52		+35	

Age 23 yrs.	Height 68 in.	Ponderal index 12.77
	Weight 151 lbs.	Cholesterol 223 mg. per 100 ml.
	Overweight +03 %	Vital capacity 4.2 liters

HABIT SURVEY
Smoking habits: nonsmoker
Age begun   yrs.   Inhalation:
Habits of nervous tension: 4, 5, 6, 9, 11, 14, 18, 22

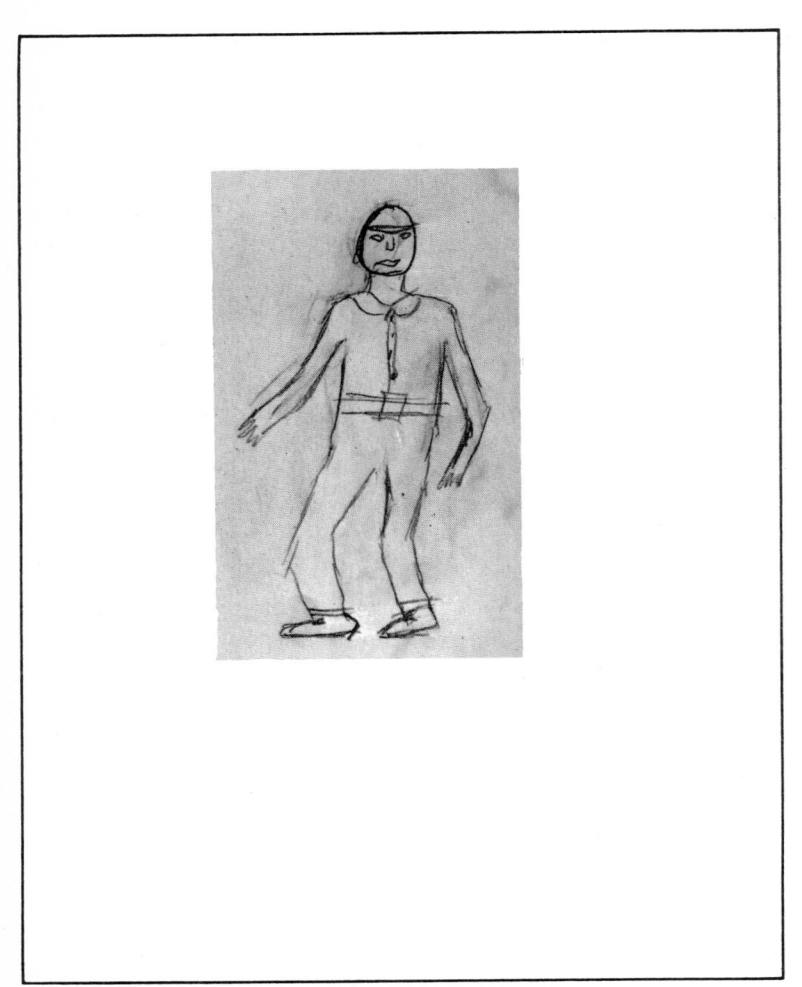

FIGURE-DRAWING CHARACTERISTICS

Structural	Male Female Both	Structural	Male	Female	Structural and Graphic	Male Female Both		Graphic, Global and Height	Male	Female	Body Proportions	Male	Female
Type	0	Omission of Appendages	0	0	Upper and Lower Halves	1	1	Hair Shading	0	3	Head	06	05
Sex Sequence	0	Position of Both Arms	1	1	Four Quarters	4	4	Nudity and Transparency	7	7	Neck	06	10
Posture	9 1	Position of Right Arm	2	2	Relative Size	2		Form	3	3	Shoulders	05	05
Perspective	0 0	Position of Left Arm	5	5	Constant Line Pressure	0	0	Detailing	3	5	Right Arm	04	04
Vertical Midline	3 0	Position of Legs	5	5	Variable Line Pressure	4	3	Identity and Sex	1	3	Left Arm	04	04
Bilateral Symmetry	3 3	Relation of Long Axes	1	1	Line Continuity	0	0	Sophistication	3	4	Chest	04	05
Horizontal Midline	4 0	Right and Left Halves	1	1	Body Shading	0	0	Height	04	05	Girth	06	06

GENERAL CHARACTERISTICS OF SUBJECT

IDENTIFICATION
No. 348
Sex M
Marital status M
Age 32 yrs. at
psychological tests

PARENTAL HISTORY
Father
C   H   S   D   O.
+   -   -   -   -
Mother
C   H   S   D   O
-   -   -   -   -

PHYSIOLOGICAL AND METABOLIC DATA

	Admission	Initial	Control	Cold pressor change	Exercise change	Smoking change
Systolic pressure	135	116	106	+20	+22	
Diastolic pressure	90	84	80	+10	-06	
Heart rate	80	72	68	+10	+05	

Age 30 yrs.	Height 74 in.	Ponderal index 12.85
	Weight 191 lbs.	Cholesterol 172 mg. per 100 ml.
	Overweight +04 %	Vital capacity 4.3 liters

HABIT SURVEY
Smoking habits: nonsmoker
Age begun   yrs.   Inhalation:
Habits of nervous tension: 6, 25

Plate 153   MIXED PRIMITIVE AND INTERMEDIATE DRAWINGS   193

FIGURE-DRAWING CHARACTERISTICS

Structural	Male Female Both	Structural	Male	Female	Structural and Graphic	Male Female Both	Graphic, Global and Height	Male	Female	Body Proportions	Male	Female
Type	0	Omission of Appendages	0	0	Upper and Lower Halves	1 3	Hair Shading	3	3	Head	04	
Sex Sequence	1	Position of Both Arms	2	1	Four Quarters	4 4	Nudity and Transparency	0	0	Neck	04	
Posture	3 7	Position of Right Arm	3	4	Relative Size	5	Form	5	3	Shoulders		
Perspective	2 9	Position of Left Arm	7	5	Constant Line Pressure	0 0	Detailing	3	3	Right Arm	02	
Vertical Midline	0 4	Position of Legs	1	9	Variable Line Pressure	5 5	Identity and Sex	5	1	Left Arm		
Bilateral Symmetry	0 0	Relation of Long Axes	0	0	Line Continuity	0 0	Sophistication	4	3	Chest		
Horizontal Midline	0 0	Right and Left Halves	1	9	Body Shading	3 3	Height			Girth		

GENERAL CHARACTERISTICS OF SUBJECT

IDENTIFICATION

No. G63

Sex M

Marital status M

Age 23 yrs. at

psychological tests

PARENTAL HISTORY

Father

C   H   S   D   O

+   -   -   -   ?

Mother

C   H   S   D   O

-    -   -   -   -

PHYSIOLOGICAL AND METABOLIC DATA

	Admission	Initial	Control	Cold pressor change	Exercise change	Smoking change
Systolic pressure	135	130	124	+10	+24	-01
Diastolic pressure	80	72	74	+16	-02	-14
Heart rate	72	68	67	+14	+21	-07

Age 22 yrs.

Height 74 in.

Weight 182 lbs.

Overweight +05 %

Ponderal index 13.05

Cholesterol 243 mg. per 100 ml.

Vital capacity liters

HABIT SURVEY

Smoking habits: occasional smoker

Age begun 16 yrs.   Inhalation: no

Habits of nervous tension: 2, 5, 6, 9, 24, 25

STRONG VOCATIONAL INTEREST TEST

Occupation	Artist	Psychologist	Architect	Physician	Osteopath	Dentist	Veterinarian	Mathematician	Physicist	Engineer	Chemist	Production Manager
Standard Score	37	43	36	41	29	29	-06	35	34	49	52	35

Occupation	Farmer	Aviator	Carpenter	Printer	Math.-Sci. Teacher	Ind. Arts Teacher	Voc. Agric. Teacher	Policeman	Forest Serv. Man	Y.M.C.A. Phys. Dir.	Personnel Director	Public Administrator
Standard Score	18	35	07	29	20	-05	-05	20	18	16	44	45

Occupation	Y.M.C.A. Secretary	Soc. Sci. H.S. Teacher	City Sch. Sup't.	Social Worker	Minister	Musician Performer	C.P.A.	Senior C.P.A.	Accountant	Office Man	Purchasing Agent	Banker
Standard Score	13	17	16	29	59	35	49	41	34	25	24	14

Occupation	Mortician	Pharmacist	Sales Manager	Real Est. Manager	Life Ins. Salesman	Advertising Man	Lawyer	Author-Journalist	President Mfg. Co.	Interest Maturity	Occupational Level	Masculinity-Femininity
Standard Score	07	14	29	28	23	39	43	44	45	54	65	45

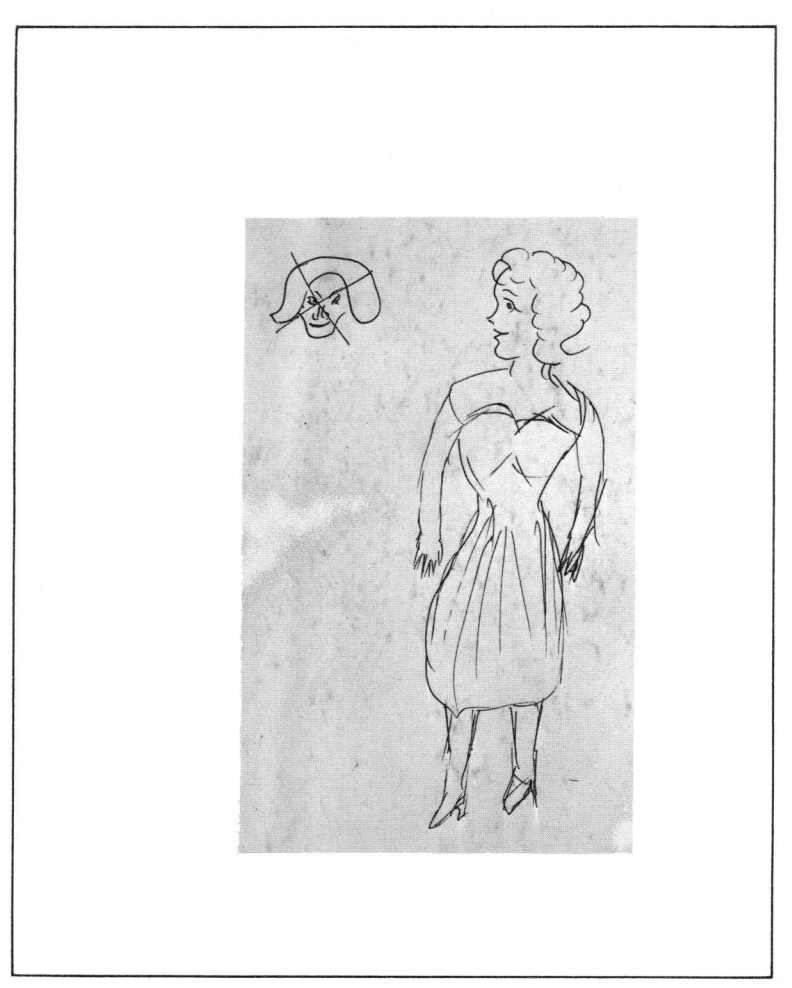

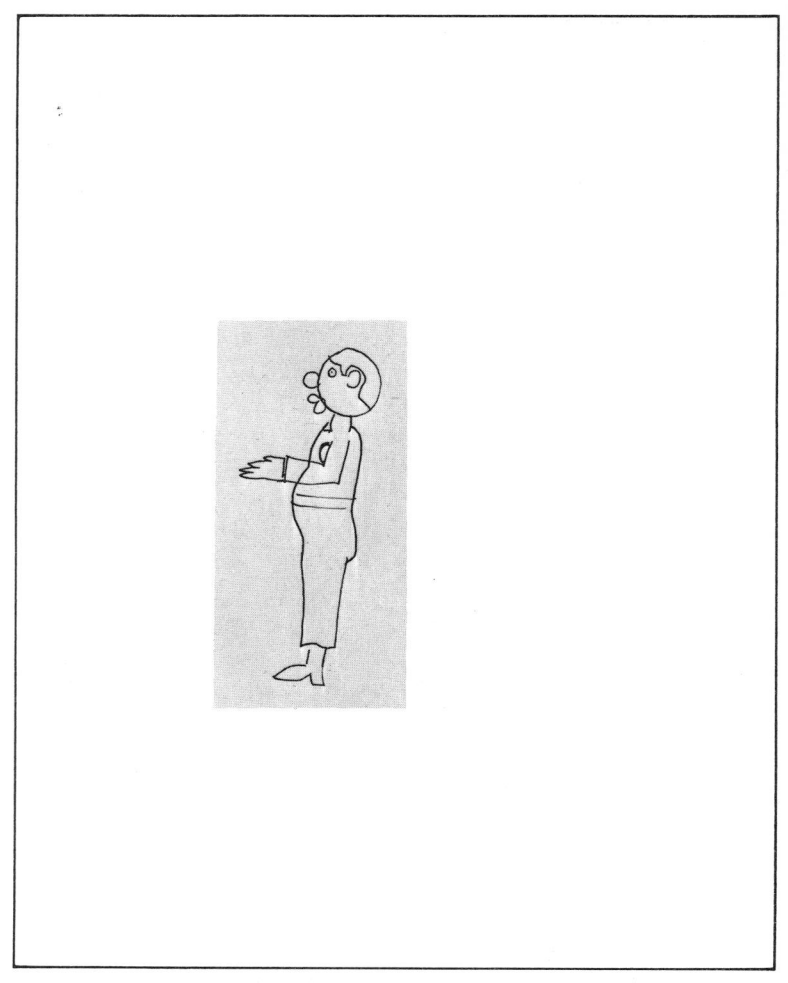

FIGURE-DRAWING CHARACTERISTICS

Structural	Male Female Both	Structural	Male	Female	Structural and Graphic	Male Female Both		Graphic, Global and Height	Male	Female	Body Proportions	Male	Female
Type	0	Omission of Appendages	0	0	Upper and Lower Halves	3	3	Hair Shading	5	5	Head	05	07
Sex Sequence	1	Position of Both Arms	4	0	Four Quarters	4	4	Nudity and Transparency	7	7	Neck	04	03
Posture	1 1	Position of Right Arm	7	0	Relative Size	4		Form	5	1	Shoulders		06
Perspective	2 5	Position of Left Arm	4	0	Constant Line Pressure	5	3	Detailing	5	3	Right Arm		04
Vertical Midline	4 0	Position of Legs	1	4	Variable Line Pressure	0	0	Identity and Sex	3	1	Left Arm	02	04
Bilateral Symmetry	0 3	Relation of Long Axes	1	1	Line Continuity	4	0	Sophistication	4	3	Chest	03	06
Horizontal Midline	4 0	Right and Left Halves	2	4	Body Shading	0	3	Height	03	06	Girth	05	04

GENERAL CHARACTERISTICS OF SUBJECT

IDENTIFICATION
No. C45
Sex M
Marital status S
Age 23 yrs. at psychological tests

PARENTAL HISTORY
Father
C H S D O
+ + - - +
Mother
C H S D O
- + - - +

PHYSIOLOGICAL AND METABOLIC DATA

	Admission	Initial	Control	Cold pressor change	Exercise change	Smoking change
Systolic pressure	110	130	128	+02	+32	+07
Diastolic pressure	70	60	58	+20	-10	+13
Heart rate	84	64	65	+04	+23	+01

Age 23 yrs.	Height	73 in.	Ponderal index	12.39	
	Weight	204 lbs.	Cholesterol	205	mg. per 100 ml.
	Overweight +21 %		Vital capacity		liters

HABIT SURVEY

Smoking habits: heavy cigarette smoker

Age begun 20 yrs.   Inhalation: yes

Habits of nervous tension: 1, 2, 5, 9, 25

STRONG VOCATIONAL INTEREST TEST

Occupation	Artist	Psychologist	Architect	Physician	Osteopath	Dentist	Veterinarian	Mathematician	Physicist	Engineer	Chemist	Production Manager
Standard Score	24	25	22	37	38	14	16	09	-07	12	13	38

Occupation	Farmer	Aviator	Carpenter	Printer	Math.-Sci. Teacher	Ind. Arts Teacher	Voc. Agric. Teacher	Policeman	Forest Serv. Man	Y.M.C.A. Phys. Dir.	Personnel Director	Public Administrator
Standard Score	11	16	05	19	20	-05	06	29	09	35	42	42

Occupation	Y.M.C.A. Secretary	Soc. Sci. H.S. Teacher	City Sch. Sup't.	Social Worker	Minister	Musician Performer	C.P.A.	Senior C.P.A.	Accountant	Office Man	Purchasing Agent	Banker
Standard Score	32	37	28	42	62	38	36	33	29	36	39	30

Occupation	Mortician	Pharmacist	Sales Manager	Real Est. Manager	Life Ins. Salesman	Advertising Man	Lawyer	Author-Journalist	President Mfg. Co.	Interest Maturity	Occupational Level	Masculinity-Femininity
Standard Score	41	38	46	46	49	44	44	36	38	61	63	32

Plate 155　　　MIXED PRIMITIVE AND INTERMEDIATE DRAWINGS　　　195

FIGURE-DRAWING CHARACTERISTICS

Structural	Male Female Both		Structural	Male	Female	Structural and Graphic	Male Female Both		Graphic, Global and Height	Male	Female	Body Proportions	Male	Female
Type	0		Omission of Appendages	0	0	Upper and Lower Halves	3	0	Hair Shading	5	3	Head	10	04
Sex Sequence	1		Position of Both Arms	7	0	Four Quarters	4	4	Nudity and Transparency	7	7	Neck	05	03
Posture	1	1	Position of Right Arm	2	2	Relative Size	0		Form	5	3	Shoulders		04
Perspective	2	0	Position of Left Arm	4	2	Constant Line Pressure	0	0	Detailing	5	3	Right Arm		02
Vertical Midline	4	0	Position of Legs	1	6	Variable Line Pressure	1	1	Identity and Sex	3	3	Left Arm	04	02
Bilateral Symmetry	0	3	Relation of Long Axes	1	1	Line Continuity	4	4	Sophistication	4	3	Chest	08	04
Horizontal Midline	4	4	Right and Left Halves	1	1	Body Shading	0	0	Height	05	03	Girth	03	03

GENERAL CHARACTERISTICS OF SUBJECT

IDENTIFICATION
No. E22
Sex M
Marital status S
Age 20 yrs. at
psychological tests

PARENTAL HISTORY				
Father				
C	H	S	D	O
+	+	-	-	?
Mother				
C	H	S	D	O
-	?	-	-	-

PHYSIOLOGICAL AND METABOLIC DATA

	Admission	Initial	Control	Cold pressor change	Exercise change	Smoking change
Systolic pressure	110	108	100	+12	+37	00
Diastolic pressure	70	68	74	+17	-36	-01
Heart rate	60	64	60	00	+10	-06

Age 19 yrs.	Height	74 in.	Ponderal index	13.24	
	Weight	175 lbs.	Cholesterol	255	mg. per 100 ml.
	Overweight +03 %		Vital capacity	4.7	liters

HABIT SURVEY
Smoking habits: nonsmoker
Age begun　yrs.　Inhalation:
Habits of nervous tension: 6, 9, 11

STRONG VOCATIONAL INTEREST TEST

Occupation	Artist	Psychologist	Architect	Physician	Osteopath	Dentist	Veterinarian	Mathematician	Physicist	Engineer	Chemist	Production Manager
Standard Score	20	29	17	35	38	26	34	16	04	14	15	28

Occupation	Farmer	Aviator	Carpenter	Printer	Math.-Sci. Teacher	Ind. Arts Teacher	Voc. Agric. Teacher	Policeman	Forest Serv. Man	Y.M.C.A. Phys. Dir.	Personnel Director	Public Administrator
Standard Score	31	24	03	21	28	02	24	34	24	46	40	48

Occupation	Y.M.C.A. Secretary	Soc. Sci. H.S. Teacher	City Sch. Sup't.	Social Worker	Minister	Musician Performer	C.P.A.	Senior C.P.A.	Accountant	Office Man	Purchasing Agent	Banker
Standard Score	38	45	42	42	64	33	40	38	29	35	25	38

Occupation	Mortician	Pharmacist	Sales Manager	Real Est. Manager	Life Ins. Salesman	Advertising Man	Lawyer	Author-Journalist	President Mfg. Co.	Interest Maturity	Occupational Level	Masculinity-Femininity
Standard Score	29	32	37	41	42	33	46	32	28	56	61	44

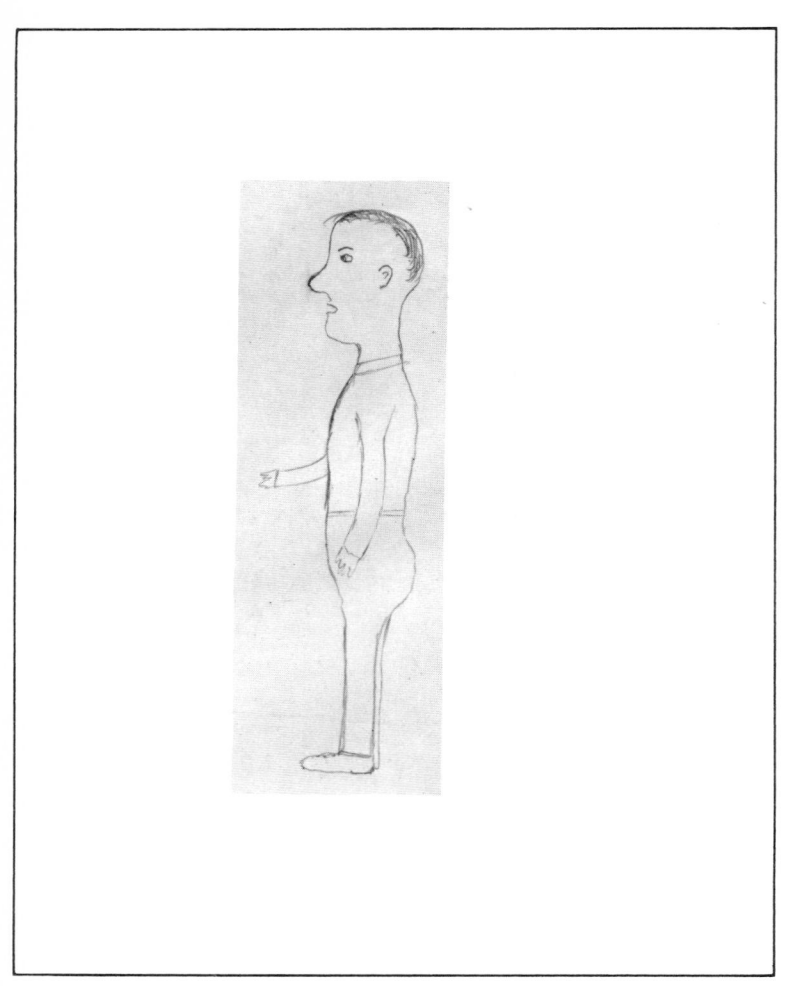

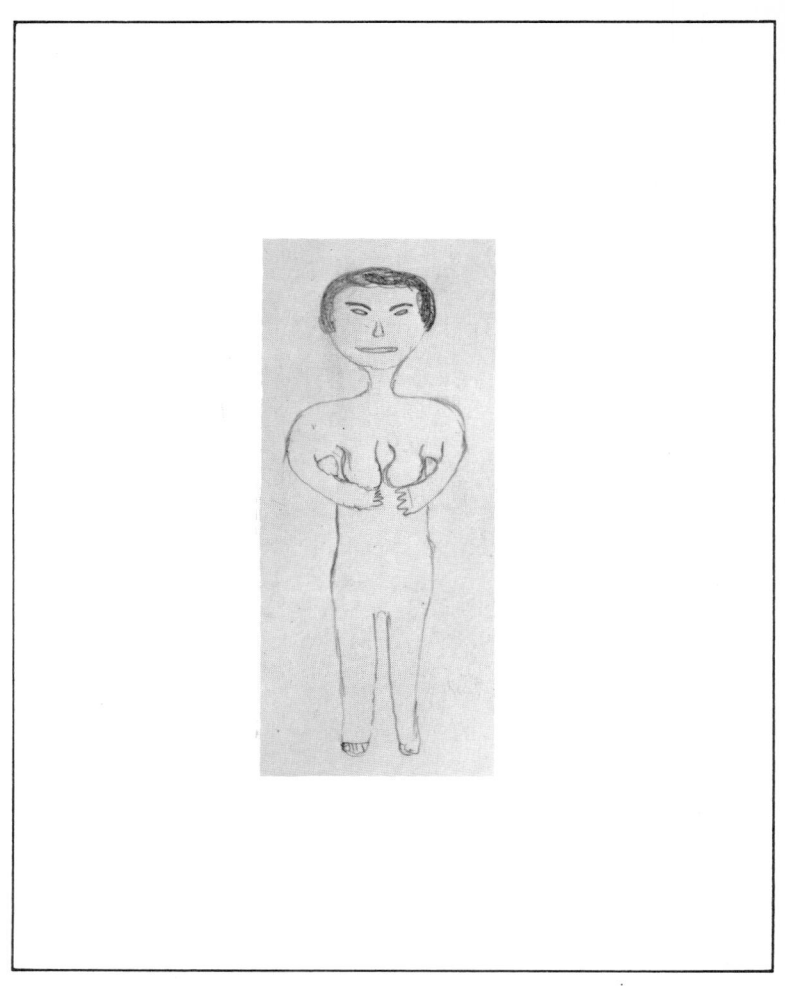

FIGURE-DRAWING CHARACTERISTICS

Structural	Male Female Both	Structural	Male	Female	Structural and Graphic	Male Female Both	Graphic, Global and Height	Male	Female	Body Proportions	Male	Female
Type	0	Omission of Appendages	0	0	Upper and Lower Halves	0 3	Hair Shading	2	2	Head	11	07
Sex Sequence	0	Position of Both Arms	4	0	Four Quarters	4 4	Nudity and Transparency	7	0	Neck	08	08
Posture	1 1	Position of Right Arm	7	5	Relative Size	0	Form	3	3	Shoulders		06
Perspective	2 0	Position of Left Arm	0	5	Constant Line Pressure	0 0	Detailing	3	3	Right Arm		02
Vertical Midline	4 0	Position of Legs	1	4	Variable Line Pressure	4 1	Identity and Sex	1	1	Left Arm	04	02
Bilateral Symmetry	0 3	Relation of Long Axes	1	1	Line Continuity	0 0	Sophistication	3	4	Chest	06	04
Horizontal Midline	4 0	Right and Left Halves	2	1	Body Shading	0 0	Height	06	05	Girth	06	06

GENERAL CHARACTERISTICS OF SUBJECT

IDENTIFICATION

No. G17
Sex M
Marital status M
Age 22 yrs. at
psychological tests

PARENTAL HISTORY

Father					
	C	H	S	D	O
	(+)	+	+	−	+
Mother					
	C	H	S	D	O
	−	?	−	−	+

PHYSIOLOGICAL AND METABOLIC DATA

	Admission	Initial	Control	Cold pressor change	Exercise change	Smoking change
Systolic pressure	115	150	130	+42	+40	+05
Diastolic pressure	65	74	70	+28	00	00
Heart rate	76	56	53	+06	+08	00

Age 21 yrs.

Height 72 in.
Weight 188 lbs.
Overweight +16 %

Ponderal index 12.57
Cholesterol 250 mg. per 100 ml.
Vital capacity 4.0 liters

HABIT SURVEY

Smoking habits: nonsmoker

Age begun   yrs.   Inhalation:

Habits of nervous tension: 3, 5, 8, 11, 14, 23

STRONG VOCATIONAL INTEREST TEST

Occupation	Artist	Psychologist	Architect	Physician	Osteopath	Dentist	Veterinarian	Mathematician	Physicist	Engineer	Chemist	Production Manager
Standard Score	38	34	39	43	30	38	18	46	36	42	47	30

Occupation	Farmer	Aviator	Carpenter	Printer	Math.-Sci. Teacher	Ind. Arts Teacher	Voc. Agric. Teacher	Policeman	Forest Serv. Man	Y.M.C.A. Phys. Dir.	Personnel Director	Public Administrator
Standard Score	40	40	24	40	34	12	19	25	28	16	19	28

Occupation	Y.M.C.A. Secretary	Soc. Sci. H.S. Teacher	City Sch. Sup't.	Social Worker	Minister	Musician Performer	C.P.A.	Senior C.P.A.	Accountant	Office Man	Purchasing Agent	Banker
Standard Score	07	23	19	20	59	38	34	38	33	26	35	31

Occupation	Mortician	Pharmacist	Sales Manager	Real Est. Manager	Life Ins. Salesman	Advertising Man	Lawyer	Author-Journalist	President Mfg. Co.	Interest Maturity	Occupational Level	Masculinity-Femininity
Standard Score	15	27	24	32	21	33	40	39	30	45	59	52

FIGURE-DRAWING CHARACTERISTICS

Structural	Male Female Both	Structural	Male	Female	Structural and Graphic	Male Female Both		Graphic, Global and Height	Male	Female	Body Proportions	Male	Female
Type	0	Omission of Appendages	0	1	Upper and Lower Halves	3	7	Hair Shading	7	5	Head	11	12
Sex Sequence	0	Position of Both Arms	1	6	Four Quarters	4	4	Nudity and Transparency	7	0	Neck	10	12
Posture	2 3	Position of Right Arm	4	8	Relative Size	5		Form	3	5	Shoulders	10	12
Perspective	5 0	Position of Left Arm	5	8	Constant Line Pressure	1	1	Detailing	3	3	Right Arm	06	
Vertical Midline	3 0	Position of Legs	8	7	Variable Line Pressure	0	0	Identity and Sex	1	1	Left Arm	08	
Bilateral Symmetry	3 9	Relation of Long Axes	1	0	Line Continuity	4	0	Sophistication	3	4	Chest	09	11
Horizontal Midline	4 0	Right and Left Halves	1	1	Body Shading	0	1	Height	08		Girth	10	11

GENERAL CHARACTERISTICS OF SUBJECT

IDENTIFICATION
No. 318
Sex M
Marital status M
Age 24 yrs. at psychological tests

PARENTAL HISTORY					
Father					
C	H	S	D	O	
?	U	–	–	–	
Mother					
C	H	S	D	O	
?	–	?	–	+	

PHYSIOLOGICAL AND METABOLIC DATA

	Admission	Initial	Control	Cold pressor change	Exercise change	Smoking change
Systolic pressure	116	118	102	+08	+46	00
Diastolic pressure	58	62	62	+20	00	–02
Heart rate	72	90	73	+24	+24	+07

Age 20 yrs.	Height 68 in.	Ponderal index 12.25
	Weight 171 lbs.	Cholesterol 215 mg. per 100 ml.
	Overweight +19 %	Vital capacity 4.0 liters

HABIT SURVEY
Smoking habits: occasional smoker
Age begun 16 yrs. Inhalation: no
Habits of nervous tension: 3, 4, 17, 18,
22, 24, 25

Lower legs and feet were
drawn on second page

FIGURE-DRAWING CHARACTERISTICS

Structural	Male Female Both		Structural	Male	Female	Structural and Graphic	Male Female Both		Graphic, Global and Height	Male	Female	Body Proportions	Male	Female
Type	0		Omission of Appendages	0	0	Upper and Lower Halves	2	7	Hair Shading	1	3	Head	09	15
Sex Sequence	0		Position of Both Arms	7	2	Four Quarters	4	4	Nudity and Transparency	9	7	Neck	04	20
Posture	1	1	Position of Right Arm	9	4	Relative Size	4		Form	5	3	Shoulders		
Perspective	9	2	Position of Left Arm	9	7	Constant Line Pressure	5	0	Detailing	5	3	Right Arm		04
Vertical Midline	9	4	Position of Legs	4	4	Variable Line Pressure	0	5	Identity and Sex	3	3	Left Arm		
Bilateral Symmetry	0	0	Relation of Long Axes	1	1	Line Continuity	0	0	Sophistication	4	3	Chest		09
Horizontal Midline	4	4	Right and Left Halves	1	2	Body Shading	4	6	Height	04	10	Girth		12

GENERAL CHARACTERISTICS OF SUBJECT

IDENTIFICATION
No. 426
Sex M
Marital status S
Age 23 yrs. at
psychological tests

PARENTAL HISTORY				
Father				
C	H	S	D	O
?	-	-	?	+
Mother				
C	H	S	D	O
-	+	-	-	-

PHYSIOLOGICAL AND METABOLIC DATA

	Admission	Initial	Control	Cold pressor change	Exercise change	Smoking change
Systolic pressure	140	136	130	+04	+34	
Diastolic pressure	90	84	84	+22	00	
Heart rate	88	90	100	+06	+11	

	Height	70	in.	Ponderal index	12.66
Age 21 yrs.	Weight	169	lbs.	Cholesterol	197 mg. per 100 ml.
	Overweight +10 %			Vital capacity	4.7 liters

HABIT SURVEY
Smoking habits: nonsmoker
Age begun   yrs.   Inhalation:
Habits of nervous tension: 6, 9, 16, 19

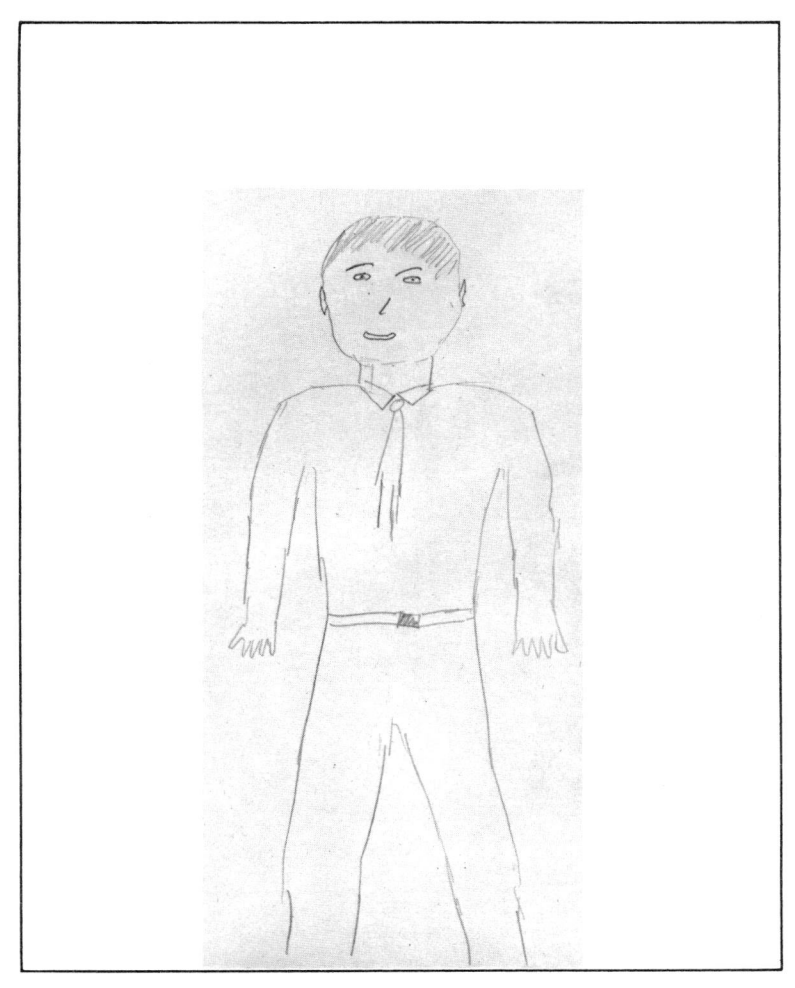

FIGURE-DRAWING CHARACTERISTICS

Structural	Male	Female	Structural	Male	Female	Structural and Graphic	Male	Female	Graphic, Global and Height	Male	Female	Body Proportions	Male	Female
	Both						Both							
Type	0		Omission of Appendages	3	3	Upper and Lower Halves	7	7	Hair Shading	1	7	Head	12	16
Sex Sequence	0		Position of Both Arms	0	4	Four Quarters	4	4	Nudity and Transparency	7	3	Neck	10	20
Posture	0	0	Position of Right Arm	0	7	Relative Size	5		Form	3	5	Shoulders	11	
Perspective	0	2	Position of Left Arm	0	0	Constant Line Pressure	0	0	Detailing	3	5	Right Arm	06	
Vertical Midline	3	4	Position of Legs	0	0	Variable Line Pressure	1	1	Identity and Sex	3	3	Left Arm	06	06
Bilateral Symmetry	3	0	Relation of Long Axes	1	1	Line Continuity	1	0	Sophistication	3	4	Chest	08	13
Horizontal Midline	4	4	Right and Left Halves	3	3	Body Shading	4	2	Height			Girth	12	18

GENERAL CHARACTERISTICS OF SUBJECT

IDENTIFICATION
No. 452
Sex M
Marital status S
Age 24 yrs. at
psychological tests

PARENTAL HISTORY				
Father				
C	H	S	D	O
?	-	-	-	-
Mother				
C	H	S	D	O
-	-	-	-	-

PHYSIOLOGICAL AND METABOLIC DATA

	Admission	Initial	Control	Cold pressor change	Exercise change	Smoking change
Systolic pressure	130	130	104	+12	+41	+08
Diastolic pressure	70	70	68	+12	+02	+10
Heart rate	72	80	75	+04	+12	+23

Age 22 yrs.	Height	75 in.	Ponderal index 13.28
	Weight	180 lbs.	Cholesterol 190 mg. per 100 ml.
	Overweight +01 %		Vital capacity 5.2 liters

HABIT SURVEY

Smoking habits: heavy cigarette smoker

Age begun 16 yrs.   Inhalation: yes

Habits of nervous tension: 4, 5, 6, 7, 9, 11, 14, 16, 17, 19, 21, 22, 23, 24

FIGURE-DRAWING CHARACTERISTICS

Structural	Male Female Both		Structural	Male	Female	Structural and Graphic	Male	Female Both		Graphic, Global and Height	Male	Female	Body Proportions	Male	Female
Type	0		Omission of Appendages	7	0	Upper and Lower Halves	3	1		Hair Shading	3	3	Head	12	09
Sex Sequence	0		Position of Both Arms	4	4	Four Quarters	4	4		Nudity and Transparency	7	7	Neck	12	12
Posture	5	1	Position of Right Arm	7	7	Relative Size	0			Form	3	5	Shoulders		
Perspective	2	2	Position of Left Arm	5	5	Constant Line Pressure	0	0		Detailing	3	5	Right Arm		
Vertical Midline	4	4	Position of Legs	8	1	Variable Line Pressure	2	2		Identity and Sex	1	3	Left Arm	08	06
Bilateral Symmetry	0	0	Relation of Long Axes	0	1	Line Continuity	0	2		Sophistication	3	4	Chest	09	07
Horizontal Midline	4	0	Right and Left Halves	1	0	Body Shading	7	0		Height		06	Girth	09	07

GENERAL CHARACTERISTICS OF SUBJECT

IDENTIFICATION
No. F76
Sex M
Marital status S
Age 22 yrs. at
psychological tests

PARENTAL HISTORY
Father
C H S D O
? - - - ?
Mother
C H S D O
- - - - ?

PHYSIOLOGICAL AND METABOLIC DATA

	Admission	Initial	Control	Cold pressor change	Exercise change	Smoking change
Systolic pressure	135	110	104	+26	+26	+04
Diastolic pressure	80	80	72	+18	+08	+06
Heart rate	72	68	64	+12	+12	+02

Age 20 yrs.	Height	70	in.	Ponderal index 13.23	
	Weight	148	lbs.	Cholesterol 250	mg. per 100 ml.
	Overweight -03 %			Vital capacity	liters

HABIT SURVEY
Smoking habits: nonsmoker
Age begun yrs. Inhalation:
Habits of nervous tension: 3, 11, 14, 16, 17, 22

STRONG VOCATIONAL INTEREST TEST

Occupation	Artist	Psychologist	Architect	Physician	Osteopath	Dentist	Veterinarian	Mathematician	Physicist	Engineer	Chemist	Production Manager
Standard Score	38	48	44	60	38	35	19	39	37	41	49	22

Occupation	Farmer	Aviator	Carpenter	Printer	Math.-Sci. Teacher	Ind. Arts Teacher	Voc. Agric. Teacher	Policeman	Forest Serv. Man	Y.M.C.A. Phys. Dir.	Personnel Director	Public Administrator
Standard Score	32	47	12	35	39	11	20	25	33	40	39	40

Occupation	Y.M.C.A. Secretary	Soc. Sci. H.S. Teacher	City Sch. Sup't.	Social Worker	Minister	Musician Performer	C.P.A.	Senior C.P.A.	Accountant	Office Man	Purchasing Agent	Banker
Standard Score	21	19	23	34	58	53	32	46	22	22	16	11

Occupation	Mortician	Pharmacist	Sales Manager	Real Est. Manager	Life Ins. Salesman	Advertising Man	Lawyer	Author-Journalist	President Mfg. Co.	Interest Maturity	Occupational Level	Masculinity-Femininity
Standard Score	15	26	29	28	25	42	40	40	22	51	56	48

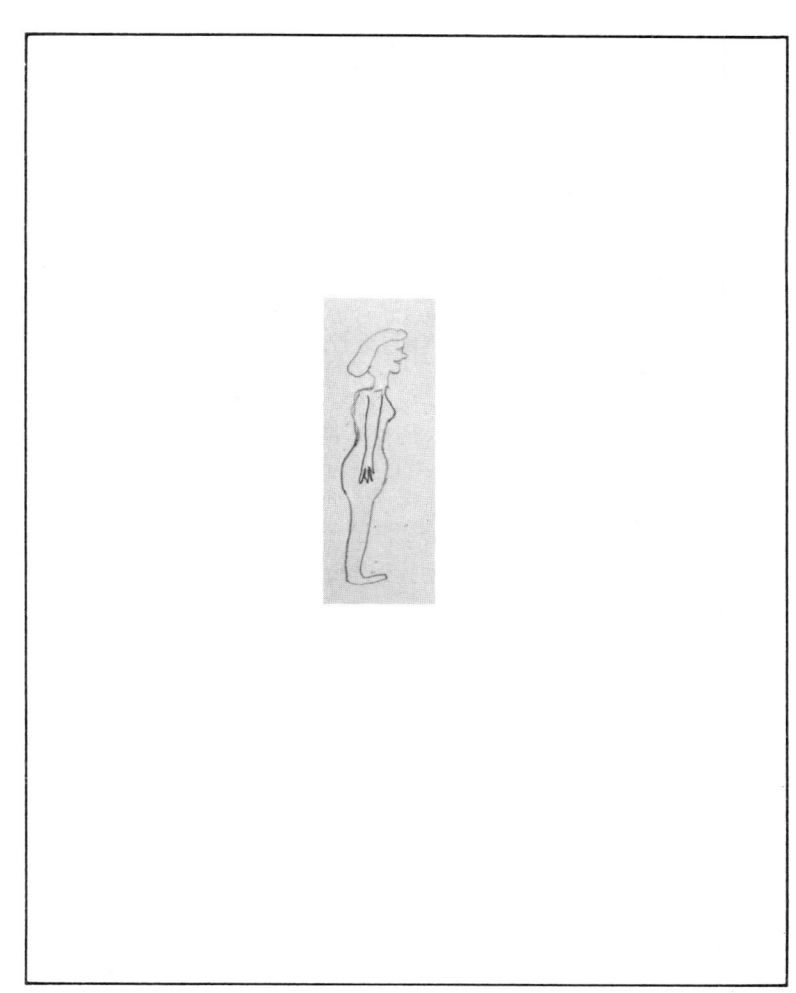

FIGURE-DRAWING CHARACTERISTICS

Structural	Male	Female	Structural	Male	Female	Structural and Graphic	Male	Female	Graphic, Global and Height	Male	Female	Body Proportions	Male	Female
	Both						Both							
Type	0		Omission of Appendages	0	0	Upper and Lower Halves	1	1	Hair Shading	7	5	Head	04	03
Sex Sequence	0		Position of Both Arms	2	2	Four Quarters	4	4	Nudity and Transparency	0	0	Neck	04	05
Posture	1	1	Position of Right Arm	0	0	Relative Size	0		Form	5	3	Shoulders		
Perspective	2	2	Position of Left Arm	7	7	Constant Line Pressure	0	0	Detailing	5	5	Right Arm	02	02
Vertical Midline	4	4	Position of Legs	1	1	Variable Line Pressure	5	4	Identity and Sex	3	3	Left Arm		
Bilateral Symmetry	0	0	Relation of Long Axes	1	1	Line Continuity	4	2	Sophistication	4	3	Chest	04	02
Horizontal Midline	0	0	Right and Left Halves	0	2	Body Shading	0	0	Height	03	02	Girth	05	02

GENERAL CHARACTERISTICS OF SUBJECT

IDENTIFICATION
No. E49
Sex M
Marital status S
Age 21 yrs. at psychological tests

PARENTAL HISTORY
Father
C H S D O
? - ? - +
Mother
C H S D O
- - - - ?

PHYSIOLOGICAL AND METABOLIC DATA

	Admission	Initial	Control	Cold pressor change	Exercise change	Smoking change
Systolic pressure	94	98	100	+13	+45	
Diastolic pressure	60	50	54	+18	-04	
Heart rate	60	80	66	00	+34	

Age 20 yrs.	Height 74 in.	Ponderal index 13.33
	Weight 171 lbs.	Cholesterol 200 mg. per 100 ml.
	Overweight 00 %	Vital capacity 5.4 liters

HABIT SURVEY

Smoking habits: occasional smoker

Age begun   yrs.   Inhalation: no

Habits of nervous tension: 3, 9, 16, 23, 24, 25

STRONG VOCATIONAL INTEREST TEST

Occupation	Artist	Psychologist	Architect	Physician	Osteopath	Dentist	Veterinarian	Mathematician	Physicist	Engineer	Chemist	Production Manager
Standard Score	21	41	23	52	39	35	30	35	29	31	46	27

Occupation	Farmer	Aviator	Carpenter	Printer	Math.-Sci. Teacher	Ind. Arts Teacher	Voc. Agric. Teacher	Policeman	Forest Serv. Man	Y.M.C.A. Phys. Dir.	Personnel Director	Public Administrator
Standard Score	37	34	21	36	50	24	35	26	15	26	25	36

Occupation	Y.M.C.A. Secretary	Soc. Sci. H.S. Teacher	City Sch. Sup't.	Social Worker	Minister	Musician Performer	C.P.A.	Senior C.P.A.	Accountant	Office Man	Purchasing Agent	Banker
Standard Score	26	32	28	34	64	40	32	46	29	35	25	25

Occupation	Mortician	Pharmacist	Sales Manager	Real Est. Manager	Life Ins. Salesman	Advertising Man	Lawyer	Author-Journalist	President Mfg. Co.	Interest Maturity	Occupational Level	Masculinity-Femininity
Standard Score	21	39	26	30	22	27	26	25	27	56	53	51

FIGURE-DRAWING CHARACTERISTICS

Structural	Male	Female	Structural	Male	Female	Structural and Graphic	Male	Female	Graphic, Global and Height	Male	Female	Body Proportions	Male	Female
	Both						Both							
Type	0		Omission of Appendages	0	9	Upper and Lower Halves	1	3	Hair Shading	7	5	Head	07	08
Sex Sequence	0		Position of Both Arms	1	0	Four Quarters	4	4	Nudity and Transparency	7	7	Neck	10	10
Posture	1	1	Position of Right Arm	0	0	Relative Size	4		Form	3	5	Shoulders		07
Perspective	6	0	Position of Left Arm	7	0	Constant Line Pressure	0	0	Detailing	3	5	Right Arm	04	05
Vertical Midline	7	3	Position of Legs	4	6	Variable Line Pressure	3	4	Identity and Sex	3	5	Left Arm	05	06
Bilateral Symmetry	0	3	Relation of Long Axes	1	1	Line Continuity	3	4	Sophistication	3	4	Chest		05
Horizontal Midline	4	0	Right and Left Halves	1	3	Body Shading	0	0	Height	05	05	Girth		07

GENERAL CHARACTERISTICS OF SUBJECT

IDENTIFICATION
No. E30
Sex M
Marital status S
Age 23 yrs. at
psychological tests

PARENTAL HISTORY
Father
C   H   S   D   O
-   (+)   -   -   +
Mother
C   H   S   D   O
?   +   -   -   -

PHYSIOLOGICAL AND METABOLIC DATA

	Admission	Initial	Control	Cold pressor change	Exercise change	Smoking change
Systolic pressure	120	120	110	+13	+28	
Diastolic pressure	70	76	80	+08	-18	
Heart rate	72	72	49	00	+10	

Age 22 yrs.	Height	78 in.	Ponderal index	13.93	
	Weight	176 lbs.	Cholesterol	230	mg. per 100 ml.
	Overweight	-09 %	Vital capacity	5.8	liters

HABIT SURVEY
Smoking habits: nonsmoker
Age begun ___ yrs.   Inhalation:
Habits of nervous tension: 3, 5, 6, 8, 22

STRONG VOCATIONAL INTEREST TEST

Occupation	Artist	Psychologist	Architect	Physician	Osteopath	Dentist	Veterinarian	Mathematician	Physicist	Engineer	Chemist	Production Manager
Standard Score	22	46	27	47	31	29	22	40	26	29	45	25

Occupation	Farmer	Aviator	Carpenter	Printer	Math.-Sci. Teacher	Ind. Arts Teacher	Voc. Agric. Teacher	Policeman	Forest Serv. Man	Y.M.C.A. Phys. Dir.	Personnel Director	Public Administrator
Standard Score	37	35	22	51	55	19	40	36	25	39	33	42

Occupation	Y.M.C.A. Secretary	Soc. Sci. H.S. Teacher	City Sch. Sup't.	Social Worker	Minister	Musician Performer	C.P.A.	Senior C.P.A.	Accountant	Office Man	Purchasing Agent	Banker
Standard Score	32	44	40	39	64	50	37	54	36	42	23	30

Occupation	Mortician	Pharmacist	Sales Manager	Real Est. Manager	Life Ins. Salesman	Advertising Man	Lawyer	Author-Journalist	President Mfg. Co.	Interest Maturity	Occupational Level	Masculinity-Femininity
Standard Score	14	40	20	24	19	28	32	30	11	56	45	49

Plate 163   MIXED PRIMITIVE AND INTERMEDIATE DRAWINGS   203

FIGURE-DRAWING CHARACTERISTICS

Structural	Male Female Both		Structural	Male	Female	Structural and Graphic	Male Female Both		Graphic, Global and Height	Male	Female	Body Proportions	Male	Female
Type	0		Omission of Appendages	1	4	Upper and Lower Halves	3	7	Hair Shading	3	3	Head	08	07
Sex Sequence	0		Position of Both Arms	5	1	Four Quarters	4	4	Nudity and Transparency	7	7	Neck	07	07
Posture	0	6	Position of Right Arm	8	5	Relative Size	0		Form	3	5	Shoulders	07	
Perspective	0	1	Position of Left Arm	2	3	Constant Line Pressure	1	1	Detailing	3	3	Right Arm		
Vertical Midline	3	4	Position of Legs	6	8	Variable Line Pressure	0	0	Identity and Sex	1	3	Left Arm	07	
Bilateral Symmetry	3	0	Relation of Long Axes	1	0	Line Continuity	0	0	Sophistication	3	4	Chest	07	
Horizontal Midline	4	0	Right and Left Halves	1	1	Body Shading	3	5	Height			Girth	09	

GENERAL CHARACTERISTICS OF SUBJECT

IDENTIFICATION
No. C39
Sex M
Marital status S
Age 22 yrs. at
psychological tests

PARENTAL HISTORY				
Father				
C	H	S	D	O
U	+	–	–	–
Mother				
C	H	S	D	O
–	–	–	–	–

PHYSIOLOGICAL AND METABOLIC DATA

	Admission	Initial	Control	Cold pressor change	Exercise change	Smoking change
Systolic pressure	125	134	129	+11	+17	+10
Diastolic pressure	60	112	105	+12	+19	+04
Heart rate	80	72	60	+08	+15	+15

	Height 71 in.	Ponderal index 13.68
Age 22 yrs.	Weight 140 lbs.	Cholesterol 202 mg. per 100 ml.
	Overweight –11 %	Vital capacity 5.3 liters

HABIT SURVEY
Smoking habits: moderate cigarette smoker
Age begun 19 yrs.   Inhalation: yes
Habits of nervous tension: 2, 5, 6, 8, 22

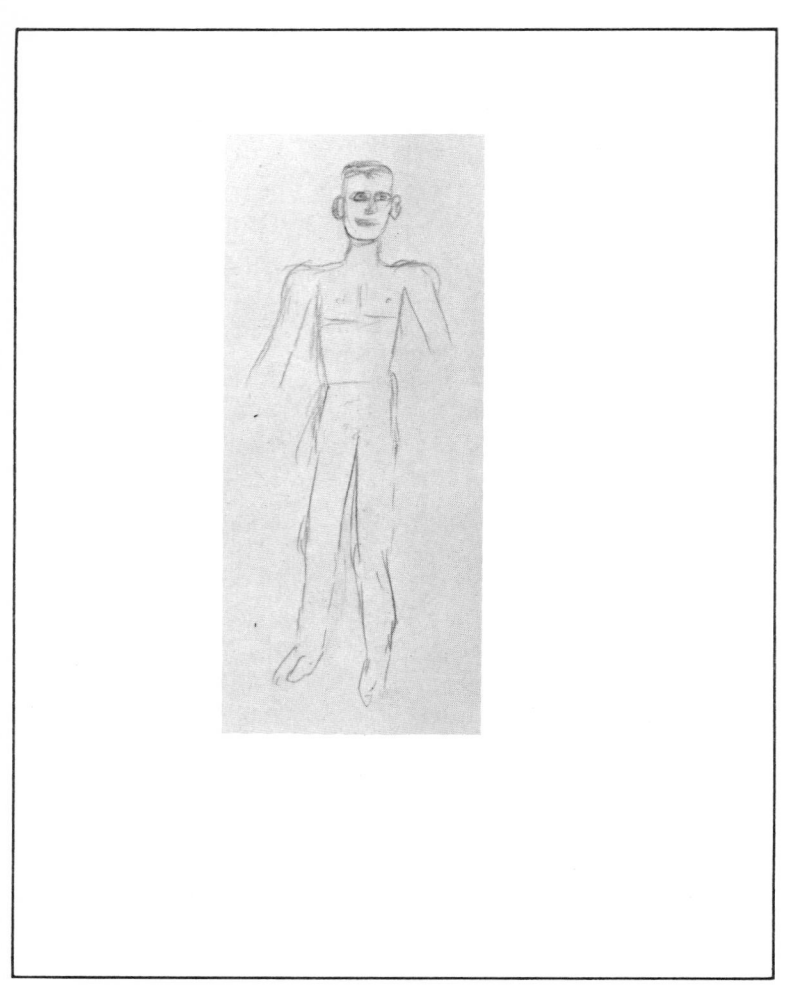

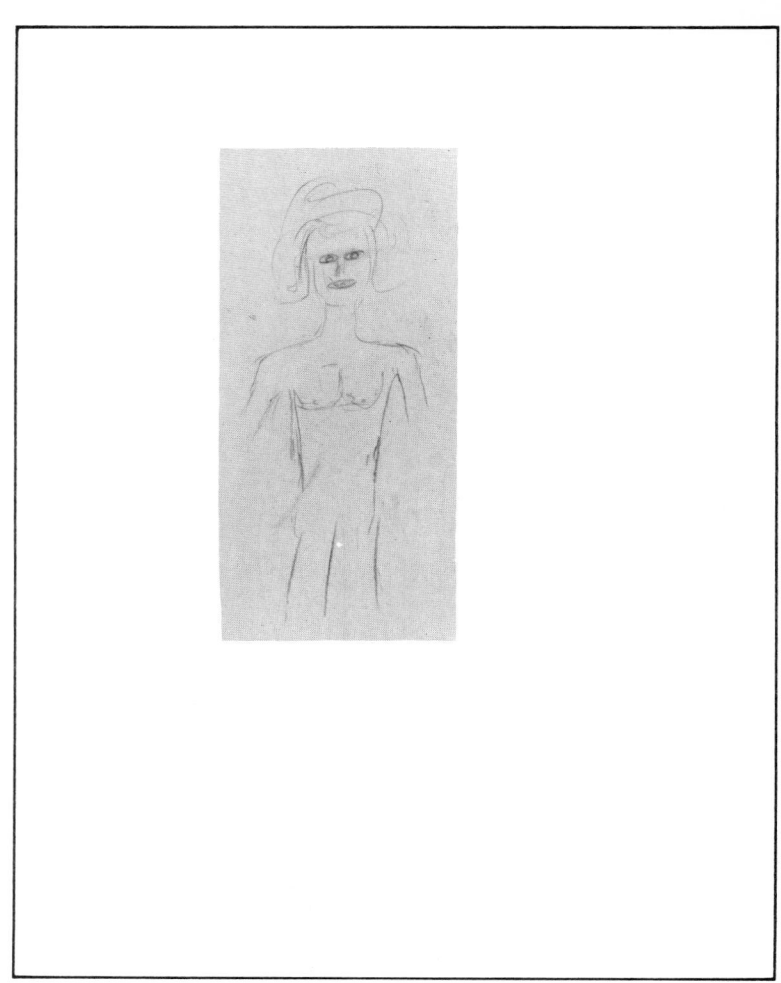

FIGURE-DRAWING CHARACTERISTICS

Structural	Male Female Both		Structural	Male	Female	Structural and Graphic	Male Female Both		Graphic, Global and Height	Male	Female	Body Proportions	Male	Female
Type	0		Omission of Appendages	2	1	Upper and Lower Halves	1	1	Hair Shading	3	7	Head	06	08
Sex Sequence	0		Position of Both Arms	6	6	Four Quarters	4	4	Nudity and Transparency	0	0	Neck	08	08
Posture	1	0	Position of Right Arm	8	8	Relative Size	5		Form	3	3	Shoulders	06	06
Perspective	0	0	Position of Left Arm	8	8	Constant Line Pressure	1	1	Detailing	3	3	Right Arm		
Vertical Midline	0	0	Position of Legs	4	0	Variable Line Pressure	0	0	Identity and Sex	1	3	Left Arm		
Bilateral Symmetry	2	2	Relation of Long Axes	1	1	Line Continuity	0	0	Sophistication	3	4	Chest	04	04
Horizontal Midline	2	0	Right and Left Halves	1	1	Body Shading	3	1	Height	05		Girth	04	05

GENERAL CHARACTERISTICS OF SUBJECT

IDENTIFICATION
No. E42
Sex M
Marital status S
Age 23 yrs. at
psychological tests

PARENTAL HISTORY				
Father				
C	H	S	D	O
–	+	–	–	?
Mother				
C	H	S	D	O
–	–	–	–	–

PHYSIOLOGICAL AND METABOLIC DATA

	Admission	Initial	Control	Cold pressor change	Exercise change	Smoking change
Systolic pressure	100	110	110	-02	+10	-01
Diastolic pressure	60	70	70	+20	-20	00
Heart rate	70	72	74	+08	+05	+10

	Height 70 in.	Ponderal index 12.82
Age 23 yrs.	Weight 163 lbs.	Cholesterol 372 mg. per 100 ml.
	Overweight +05 %	Vital capacity liters

HABIT SURVEY
Smoking habits: nonsmoker
Age begun   yrs.   Inhalation:
Habits of nervous tension: 5, 6, 9. 14

FIGURE-DRAWING CHARACTERISTICS

Structural	Male Female Both		Structural	Male	Female	Structural and Graphic	Male Female Both		Graphic, Global and Height	Male	Female	Body Proportions	Male	Female
Type	0		Omission of Appendages	3	0	Upper and Lower Halves	7	1	Hair Shading	3	3	Head	11	06
Sex Sequence	0		Position of Both Arms	0	2	Four Quarters	4	4	Nudity and Transparency	7	7	Neck	12	14
Posture	0	1	Position of Right Arm	2	2	Relative Size	0		Form	3	5	Shoulders	10	
Perspective	0	6	Position of Left Arm	2	7	Constant Line Pressure	1	0	Detailing	3	3	Right Arm	08	05
Vertical Midline	3	4	Position of Legs	4	4	Variable Line Pressure	0	1	Identity and Sex	1	1	Left Arm	08	04
Bilateral Symmetry	3	0	Relation of Long Axes	1	1	Line Continuity	3	0	Sophistication	3	4	Chest	11	
Horizontal Midline	4	4	Right and Left Halves	1	2	Body Shading	0	1	Height		08	Girth	12	

GENERAL CHARACTERISTICS OF SUBJECT

IDENTIFICATION

No. G45
Sex M
Marital status S
Age 24 yrs. at
psychological tests

PARENTAL HISTORY

Father

C	H	S	D	O
-	-	-	-	+

Mother

C	H	S	D	O
-	+	-	-	+

PHYSIOLOGICAL AND METABOLIC DATA

	Admission	Initial	Control	Cold pressor change	Exercise change	Smoking change
Systolic pressure	120	134	116	+14	+44	
Diastolic pressure	85	84	80	+12	+08	
Heart rate	84	100	76	+06	+29	

Age 23 yrs.   Height 71 in.   Ponderal index 13.52

Weight 145 lbs.   Cholesterol 217 mg. per 100 ml.

Overweight -09 %   Vital capacity liters

HABIT SURVEY

Smoking habits: nonsmoker

Age begun yrs.   Inhalation:

Habits of nervous tension: 3, 5, 18, 23

STRONG VOCATIONAL INTEREST TEST

Occupation	Artist	Psychologist	Architect	Physician	Osteopath	Dentist	Veterinarian	Mathematician	Physicist	Engineer	Chemist	Production Manager
Standard Score	38	46	44	66	50	48	16	46	48	52	58	35

Occupation	Farmer	Aviator	Carpenter	Printer	Math.-Sci. Teacher	Ind. Arts Teacher	Voc. Agric. Teacher	Policeman	Forest Serv. Man	Y.M.C.A. Phys. Dir.	Personnel Director	Public Administrator
Standard Score	36	47	26	36	45	24	26	33	30	32	37	44

Occupation	Y.M.C.A. Secretary	Soc. Sci. H.S. Teacher	City Sch. Sup't.	Social Worker	Minister	Musician Performer	C.P.A.	Senior C.P.A.	Accountant	Office Man	Purchasing Agent	Banker
Standard Score	22	18	24	26	59	44	30	41	23	26	18	14

Occupation	Mortician	Pharmacist	Sales Manager	Real Est. Manager	Life Ins. Salesman	Advertising Man	Lawyer	Author-Journalist	President Mfg. Co.	Interest Maturity	Occupational Level	Masculinity-Femininity
Standard Score	14	21	14	17	12	29	29	37	24	50	59	52

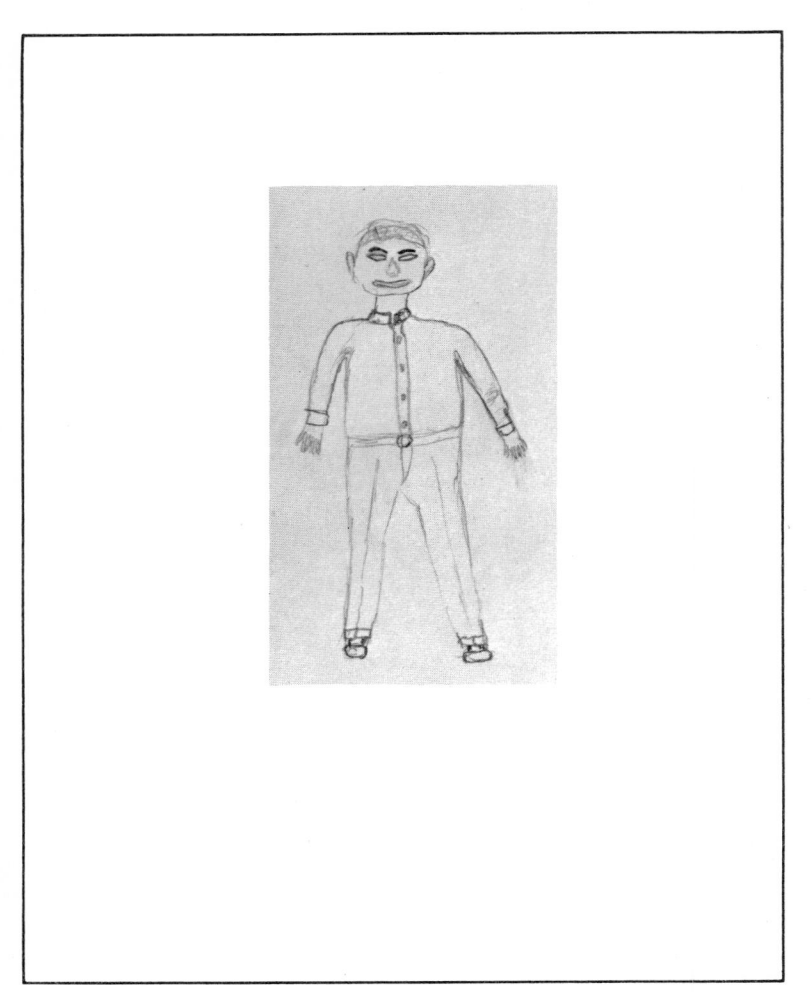

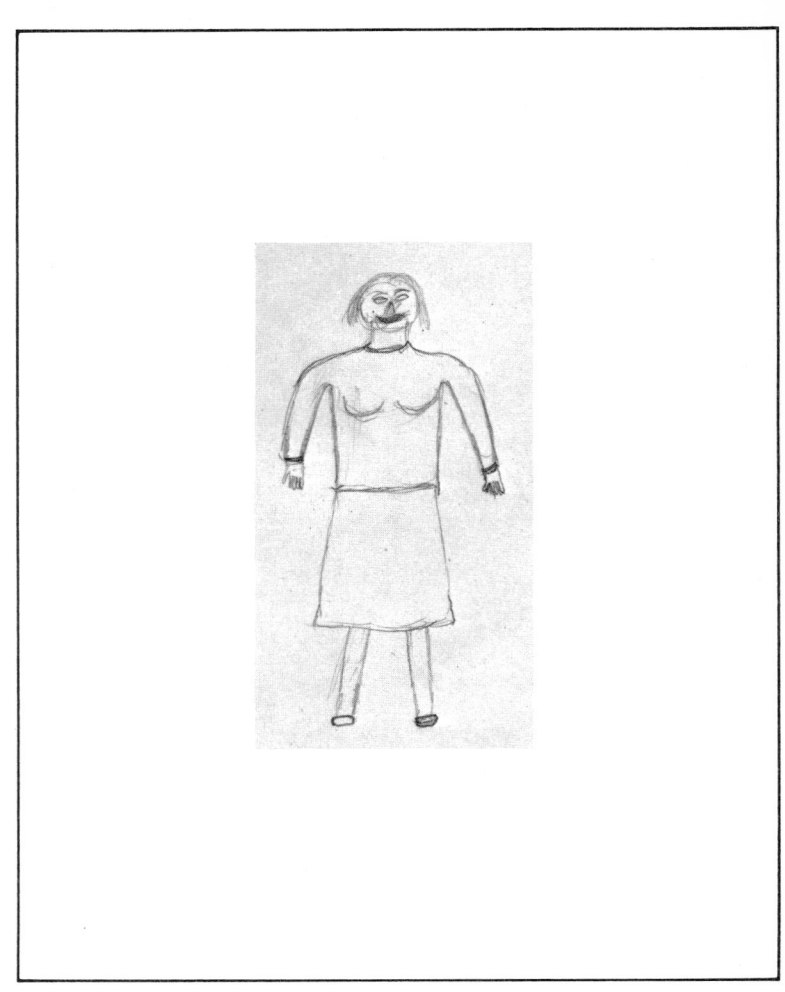

FIGURE-DRAWING CHARACTERISTICS

Structural	Male Female Both	Structural	Male	Female	Structural and Graphic	Male Female Both		Graphic, Global and Height	Male	Female	Body Proportions	Male	Female
Type	0	Omission of Appendages	0	0	Upper and Lower Halves	1	1	Hair Shading	3	3	Head	05	04
Sex Sequence	0	Position of Both Arms	0	0	Four Quarters	4	4	Nudity and Transparency	7	7	Neck	08	06
Posture	1　　1	Position of Right Arm	2	2	Relative Size	2		Form	3	3	Shoulders	05	06
Perspective	0　　0	Position of Left Arm	2	2	Constant Line Pressure	0	0	Detailing	3	5	Right Arm	02	02
Vertical Midline	3　　0	Position of Legs	6	6	Variable Line Pressure	1	1	Identity and Sex	1	1	Left Arm	02	02
Bilateral Symmetry	1　　3	Relation of Long Axes	1	1	Line Continuity	0	0	Sophistication	3	4	Chest	05	05
Horizontal Midline	4　　4	Right and Left Halves	1	1	Body Shading	3	5	Height	04	04	Girth	07	06

GENERAL CHARACTERISTICS OF SUBJECT

IDENTIFICATION
No. 536
Sex M
Marital status S
Age 23 yrs. at
psychological tests

PARENTAL HISTORY
Father
C H S D O
– ? – – –
Mother
C H S D O
– – – – –

PHYSIOLOGICAL AND METABOLIC DATA

	Admission	Initial	Control	Cold pressor change	Exercise change	Smoking change
Systolic pressure	120	120	110	+10	+40	+05
Diastolic pressure	60	60	70	+10	–10	+02
Heart rate	72	72	67	+02	+15	+05

Age 21 yrs.	Height 74 in.	Ponderal index 13.20
	Weight 176 lbs.	Cholesterol 197 mg. per 100 ml.
	Overweight +02 %	Vital capacity 5.0 liters

HABIT SURVEY
Smoking habits: heavy cigarette smoker
Age begun 17 yrs.　　Inhalation: yes
Habits of nervous tension: 5, 6, 8, 9, 10

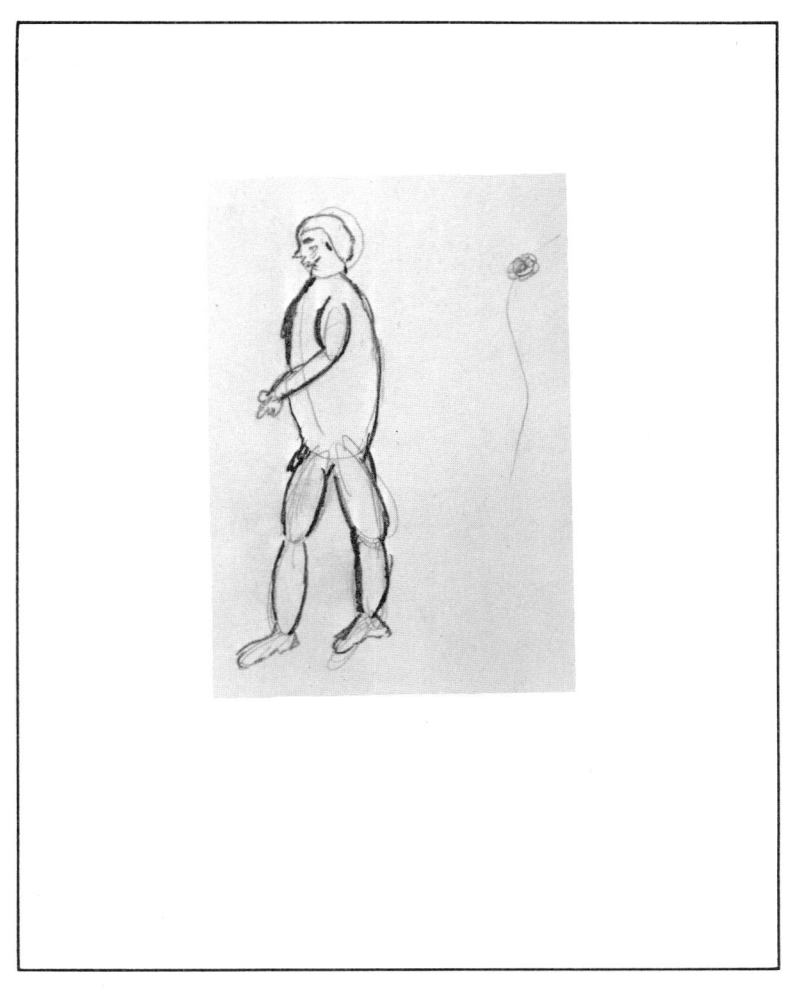

FIGURE-DRAWING CHARACTERISTICS

Structural	Male Female Both		Structural	Male	Female	Structural and Graphic	Male Female Both		Graphic, Global and Height	Male	Female	Body Proportions	Male	Female
Type	0		Omission of Appendages	0	0	Upper and Lower Halves	1	0	Hair Shading	5	3	Head	04	05
Sex Sequence	0		Position of Both Arms	4	1	Four Quarters	4	4	Nudity and Transparency	0	0	Neck	00	
Posture	2	1	Position of Right Arm	7	5	Relative Size	4		Form	5	3	Shoulders		
Perspective	2	5	Position of Left Arm	4	2	Constant Line Pressure	0	0	Detailing	5	3	Right Arm		04
Vertical Midline	4	0	Position of Legs	8	4	Variable Line Pressure	4	4	Identity and Sex	3	1	Left Arm	02	04
Bilateral Symmetry	0	0	Relation of Long Axes	1	1	Line Continuity	1	1	Sophistication	4	3	Chest	06	06
Horizontal Midline	0	0	Right and Left Halves	2	1	Body Shading	2	3	Height	04	05	Girth	06	06

GENERAL CHARACTERISTICS OF SUBJECT

IDENTIFICATION				
No. D51				
Sex M				
Marital status M				
Age 22 yrs. at				
psychological tests				

PARENTAL HISTORY				
Father				
C	H	S	D	O
–	–	–	–	+
Mother				
C	H	S	D	O
–	–	–	+	+

PHYSIOLOGICAL AND METABOLIC DATA

	Admission	Initial	Control	Cold pressor change	Exercise change	Smoking change
Systolic pressure	140	154		+10		+02
Diastolic pressure	80	110		+12		+02
Heart rate	75	93		–03		+14

Age 22 yrs.	Height 72 in.	Ponderal index 11.54
	Weight 243 lbs.	Cholesterol 296 mg. per 100 ml.
	Overweight +49 %	Vital capacity 5.6 liters

HABIT SURVEY

Smoking habits: heavy cigarette smoker

Age begun 20 yrs.   Inhalation: yes

Habits of nervous tension: 6, 12, 14, 16

STRONG VOCATIONAL INTEREST TEST

Occupation	Artist	Psychologist	Architect	Physician	Osteopath	Dentist	Veterinarian	Mathematician	Physicist	Engineer	Chemist	Production Manager
Standard Score	26	41	21	47	55	30	33	19	12	23	30	32

Occupation	Farmer	Aviator	Carpenter	Printer	Math.-Sci. Teacher	Ind. Arts Teacher	Voc. Agric. Teacher	Policeman	Forest Serv. Man	Y.M.C.A. Phys. Dir.	Personnel Director	Public Administrator
Standard Score	27	37	09	31	38	07	27	37	25	47	48	51

Occupation	Y.M.C.A. Secretary	Soc. Sci. H.S. Teacher	City Sch. Sup't.	Social Worker	Minister	Musician Performer	C.P.A.	Senior C.P.A.	Accountant	Office Man	Purchasing Agent	Banker
Standard Score	36	47	35	50	63	40	24	36	25	37	22	23

Occupation	Mortician	Pharmacist	Sales Manager	Real Est. Manager	Life Ins. Salesman	Advertising Man	Lawyer	Author-Journalist	President Mfg. Co.	Interest Maturity	Occupational Level	Masculinity-Femininity
Standard Score	34	41	34	38	44	36	41	34	32	58	58	42

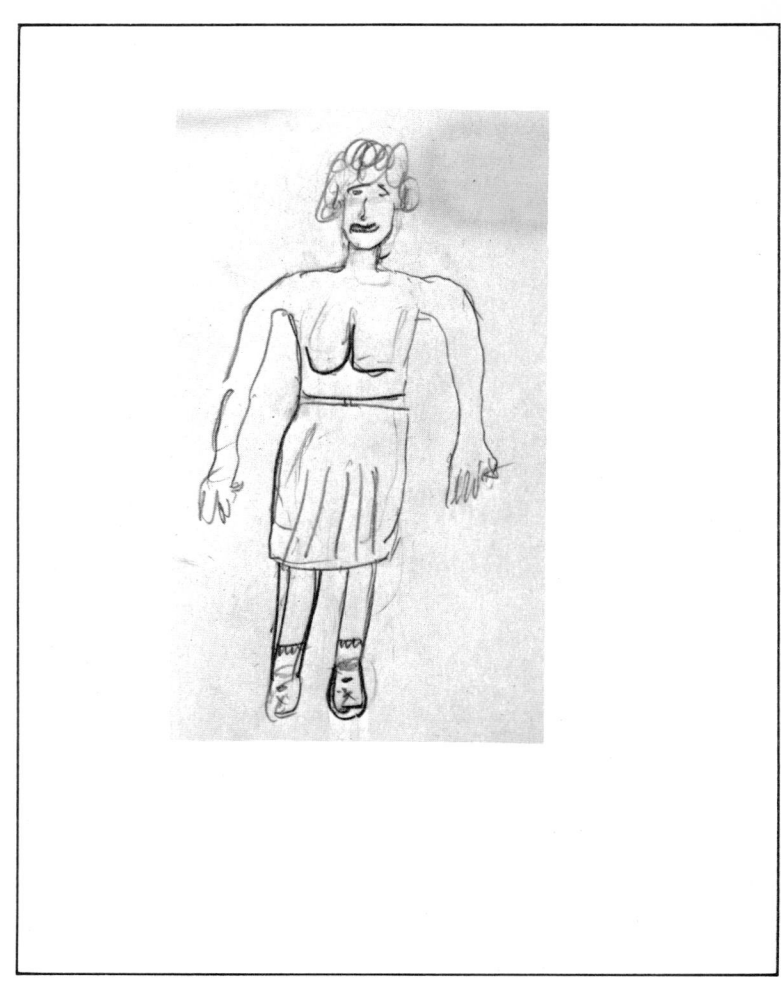

FIGURE-DRAWING CHARACTERISTICS

Structural	Male Female Both	Structural	Male	Female	Structural and Graphic	Male Female Both		Graphic, Global and Height	Male	Female	Body Proportions	Male	Female
Type	0	Omission of Appendages	0	0	Upper and Lower Halves	1	1	Hair Shading	3	3	Head	05	07
Sex Sequence	0	Position of Both Arms	1	1	Four Quarters	4	4	Nudity and Transparency	6	3	Neck	05	06
Posture	2	1	Position of Right Arm	2	0	Relative Size	4		Form	3	5	Shoulders	06	08
Perspective	0	0	Position of Left Arm	0	2	Constant Line Pressure	0	0	Detailing	3	3	Right Arm	04	06
Vertical Midline	0	0	Position of Legs	8	4	Variable Line Pressure	3	5	Identity and Sex	1	3	Left Arm	04	05
Bilateral Symmetry	3	2	Relation of Long Axes	1	1	Line Continuity	0	2	Sophistication	3	4	Chest	05	06
Horizontal Midline	4	4	Right and Left Halves	1	1	Body Shading	4	7	Height	05	06	Girth	06	07

GENERAL CHARACTERISTICS OF SUBJECT

IDENTIFICATION
No. F52
Sex M
Marital status S
Age 25 yrs. at
psychological tests

PARENTAL HISTORY
Father
C   H   S   D   O
−   −   −   −   +
Mother
C   H   S   D   O
−   −   −   −   ?

PHYSIOLOGICAL AND METABOLIC DATA

	Admission	Initial	Control	Cold pressor change	Exercise change	Smoking change
Systolic pressure	134	110	104	+08	+24	+02
Diastolic pressure	84	72	70	+16	+18	+05
Heart rate	80	84	80	+12	+20	+08

Age 23 yrs.	Height	67	in.	Ponderal index 11.96
	Weight	176	lbs.	Cholesterol 224 mg. per 100 ml.
	Overweight +23 %			Vital capacity liters

HABIT SURVEY

Smoking habits: heavy cigarette smoker

Age begun 20 yrs.   Inhalation: yes

Habits of nervous tension: 2, 5, 6, 10

STRONG VOCATIONAL INTEREST TEST

Occupation	Artist	Psychologist	Architect	Physician	Osteopath	Dentist	Veterinarian	Mathematician	Physicist	Engineer	Chemist	Production Manager
Standard Score	26	42	24	52	49	35	26	07	02	12	25	26

Occupation	Farmer	Aviator	Carpenter	Printer	Math.-Sci. Teacher	Ind. Arts Teacher	Voc. Agric. Teacher	Policeman	Forest Serv. Man	Y.M.C.A. Phys. Dir.	Personnel Director	Public Administrator
Standard Score	21	26	05	36	33	06	17	27	07	44	49	43

Occupation	Y.M.C.A. Secretary	Soc. Sci. H.S. Teacher	City Sch. Sup't.	Social Worker	Minister	Musician Performer	C.P.A.	Senior C.P.A.	Accountant	Office Man	Purchasing Agent	Banker
Standard Score	37	47	34	51	58	49	41	39	27	41	27	23

Occupation	Mortician	Pharmacist	Sales Manager	Real Est. Manager	Life Ins. Salesman	Advertising Man	Lawyer	Author-Journalist	President Mfg. Co.	Interest Maturity	Occupational Level	Masculinity-Femininity
Standard Score	38	44	46	46	49	49	46	37	29	62	60	41

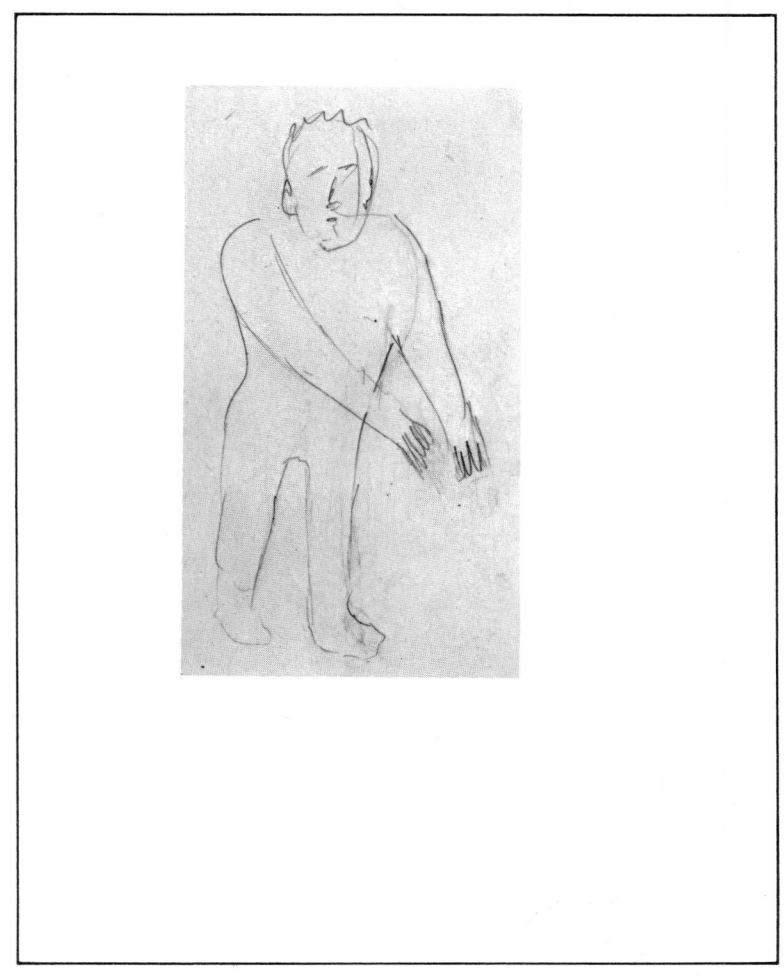

FIGURE-DRAWING CHARACTERISTICS

Structural	Male Female Both	Structural	Male	Female	Structural and Graphic	Male Female Both		Graphic, Global and Height	Male	Female	Body Proportions	Male	Female
Type	0	Omission of Appendages	0	0	Upper and Lower Halves	1	3	Hair Shading	5	5	Head	10	12
Sex Sequence	2	Position of Both Arms	0	0	Four Quarters	4	4	Nudity and Transparency	0	7	Neck		10
Posture	1 1	Position of Right Arm	2	5	Relative Size	4		Form	5	5	Shoulders		08
Perspective	9 0	Position of Left Arm	2	5	Constant Line Pressure	0	0	Detailing	5	3	Right Arm	07	06
Vertical Midline	0 0	Position of Legs	4	4	Variable Line Pressure	1	1	Identity and Sex	3	3	Left Arm	06	07
Bilateral Symmetry	3 1	Relation of Long Axes	1	1	Line Continuity	0	0	Sophistication	4	3	Chest		06
Horizontal Midline	0 0	Right and Left Halves	1	2	Body Shading	0	1	Height	05	08	Girth		

GENERAL CHARACTERISTICS OF SUBJECT

IDENTIFICATION
No. E38
Sex M
Marital status M
Age 21 yrs. at
psychological tests

PARENTAL HISTORY
Father
C H S D O
- - - - ?
Mother
C H S D O
- - - - +

PHYSIOLOGICAL AND METABOLIC DATA

	Admission	Initial	Control	Cold pressor change	Exercise change	Smoking change
Systolic pressure		140	120	+18	+40	+12
Diastolic pressure		80	76	+18	-06	+18
Heart rate		88	75	+08	-12	+15

Age 21 yrs.   Height 69 in.   Ponderal index 12.92
Weight 152 lbs.   Cholesterol 284 mg. per 100 ml.
Overweight +02 %   Vital capacity 5.1 liters

HABIT SURVEY

Smoking habits: occasional smoker
Age begun   yrs.   Inhalation: no
Habits of nervous tension: 6

STRONG VOCATIONAL INTEREST TEST

Occupation	Artist	Psychologist	Architect	Physician	Osteopath	Dentist	Veterinarian	Mathematician	Physicist	Engineer	Chemist	Production Manager
Standard Score	30	50	30	59	57	37	22	27	31	44	46	43

Occupation	Farmer	Aviator	Carpenter	Printer	Math.-Sci. Teacher	Ind. Arts Teacher	Voc. Agric. Teacher	Policeman	Forest Serv. Man	Y.M.C.A. Phys. Dir.	Personnel Director	Public Administrator
Standard Score	36	42	31	46	47	32	29	42	42	48	52	65

Occupation	Y.M.C.A. Secretary	Soc. Sci. H.S. Teacher	City Sch. Sup't.	Social Worker	Minister	Musician Performer	C.P.A.	Senior C.P.A.	Accountant	Office Man	Purchasing Agent	Banker
Standard Score	44	43	40	56	64	47	26	39	20	26	17	12

Occupation	Mortician	Pharmacist	Sales Manager	Real Est. Manager	Life Ins. Salesman	Advertising Man	Lawyer	Author-Journalist	President Mfg. Co.	Interest Maturity	Occupational Level	Masculinity-Femininity
Standard Score	19	22	20	24	26	28	38	34	27	64	54	44

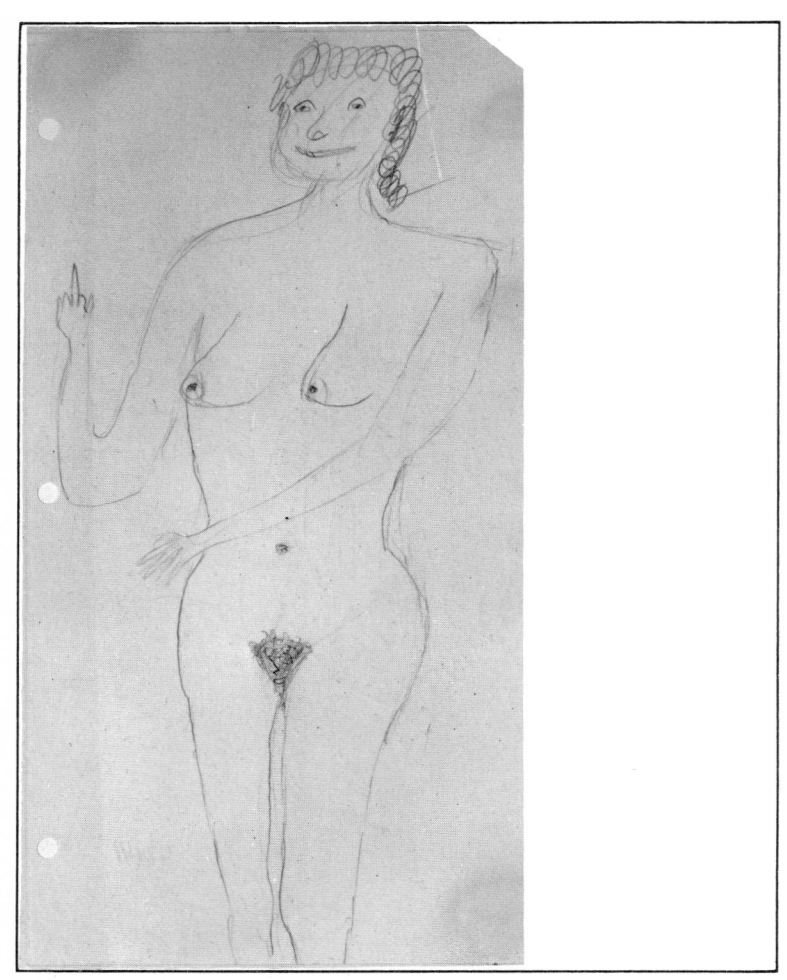 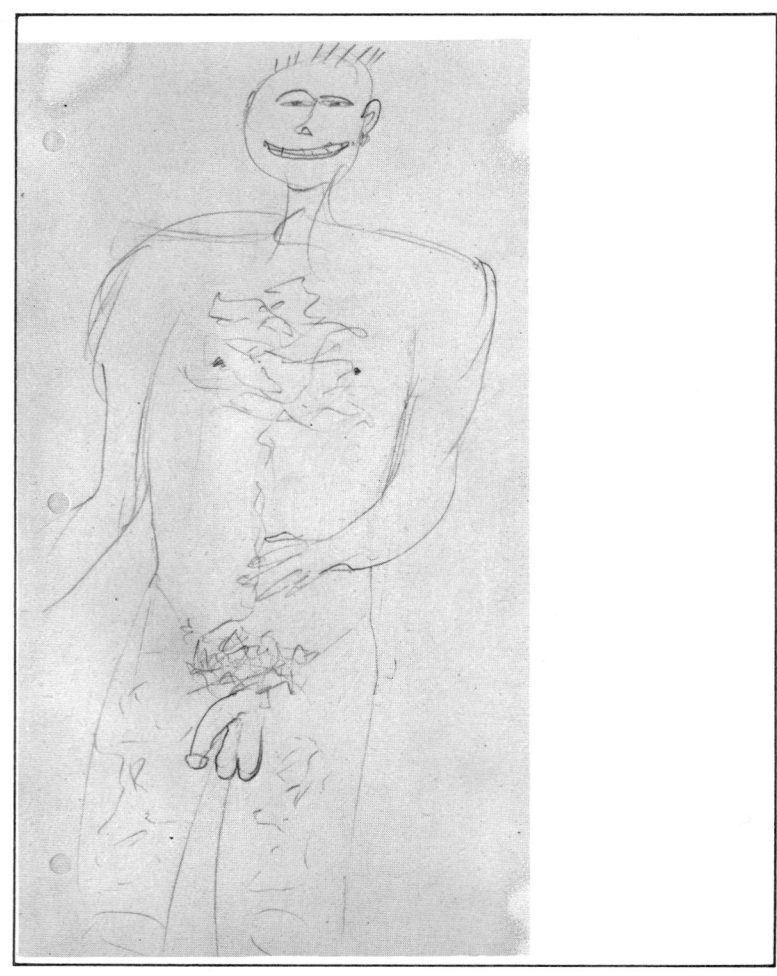

FIGURE-DRAWING CHARACTERISTICS

Structural	Male	Female	Structural	Male	Female	Structural and Graphic	Male	Female	Graphic, Global and Height	Male	Female	Body Proportions	Male	Female
	Both						Both							
Type		0	Omission of Appendages	1	3	Upper and Lower Halves	7	7	Hair Shading	7	3	Head	11	09
Sex Sequence		1	Position of Both Arms	1	1	Four Quarters	4	4	Nudity and Transparency	0	0	Neck	12	10
Posture	0	0	Position of Right Arm	4	2	Relative Size		5	Form	3	3	Shoulders	15	
Perspective	1	1	Position of Left Arm	5	5	Constant Line Pressure	1	1	Detailing	3	3	Right Arm		10
Vertical Midline	4	4	Position of Legs	4	4	Variable Line Pressure	0	0	Identity and Sex	1	1	Left Arm	10	12
Bilateral Symmetry	0	0	Relation of Long Axes	1	1	Line Continuity	0	0	Sophistication	4	3	Chest	11	
Horizontal Midline	0	0	Right and Left Halves	1	1	Body Shading	3	3	Height			Girth	13	12

GENERAL CHARACTERISTICS OF SUBJECT

IDENTIFICATION
No. C41
Sex M
Marital status S
Age 20 yrs. at
psychological tests

PARENTAL HISTORY
Father
C H S D O
-   -   -   -   +
Mother
C H S D O
-   -   -   -   -

PHYSIOLOGICAL AND METABOLIC DATA

	Admission	Initial	Control	Cold pressor change	Exercise change	Smoking change
Systolic pressure	125	110	105	-03	+29	+12
Diastolic pressure	55	72	74	+10	+31	+18
Heart rate	84	78	64	-08	+19	+15

Age 20 yrs.	Height	74	in.	Ponderal index	13.17	
	Weight	178	lbs.	Cholesterol	255	mg. per 100 ml.
	Overweight +04 %			Vital capacity	5.6	liters

HABIT SURVEY

Smoking habits: heavy cigarette smoker

Age begun 14 yrs.   Inhalation: yes

Habits of nervous tension: 2, 5, 6, 9, 16

STRONG VOCATIONAL INTEREST TEST

Occupation	Artist	Psychologist	Architect	Physician	Osteopath	Dentist	Veterinarian	Mathematician	Physicist	Engineer	Chemist	Production Manager
Standard Score	16	48	17	55	55	31	29	15	14	28	36	32

Occupation	Farmer	Aviator	Carpenter	Printer	Math.-Sci. Teacher	Ind. Arts Teacher	Voc. Agric. Teacher	Policeman	Forest Serv. Man	Y.M.C.A. Phys. Dir.	Personnel Director	Public Administrator
Standard Score	28	42	10	33	48	21	35	31	19	41	54	57

Occupation	Y.M.C.A. Secretary	Soc. Sci. H.S. Teacher	City Sch. Sup't.	Social Worker	Minister	Musician Performer	C.P.A.	Senior C.P.A.	Accountant	Office Man	Purchasing Agent	Banker
Standard Score	37	45	40	53	62	40	33	45	26	32	21	15

Occupation	Mortician	Pharmacist	Sales Manager	Real Est. Manager	Life Ins. Salesman	Advertising Man	Lawyer	Author- Journalist	President Mfg. Co.	Interest Maturity	Occupational Level	Masculinity- Femininity
Standard Score	25	39	33	34	33	33	39	26	24	63	57	55

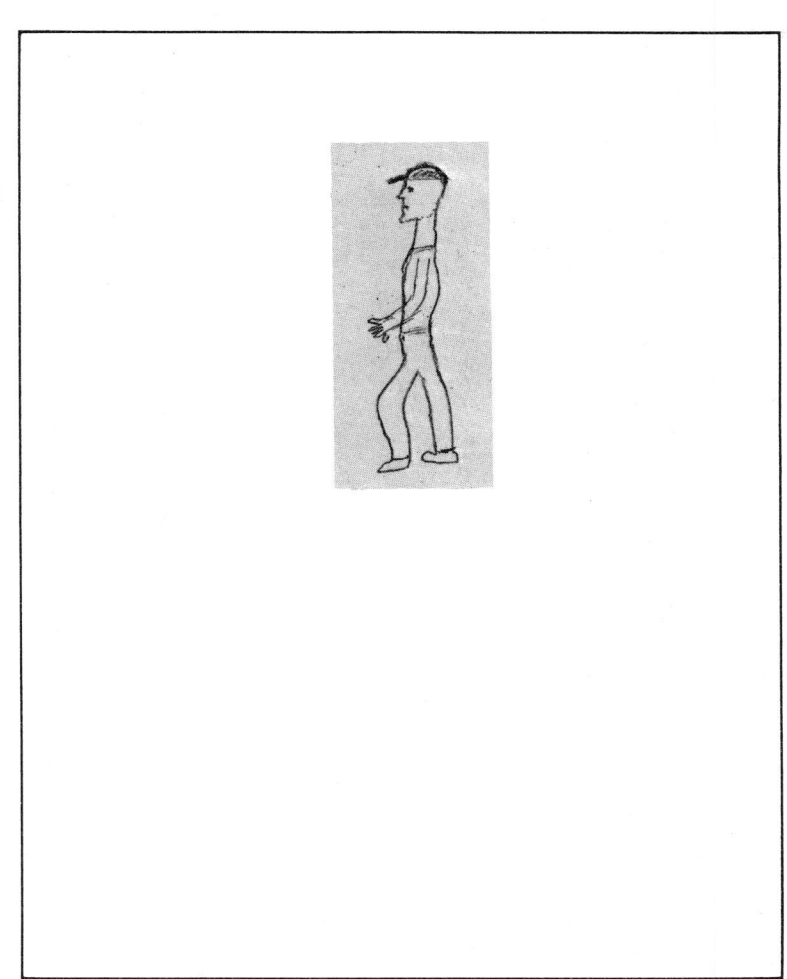

FIGURE-DRAWING CHARACTERISTICS

Structural	Male Female Both		Structural	Male	Female	Structural and Graphic	Male Female Both		Graphic, Global and Height	Male	Female	Body Proportions	Male	Female
Type	0		Omission of Appendages	0	0	Upper and Lower Halves	2	2	Hair Shading	0	3	Head	04	03
Sex Sequence	1		Position of Both Arms	4	0	Four Quarters	4	4	Nudity and Transparency	7	7	Neck	08	04
Posture	2	1	Position of Right Arm	7	2	Relative Size	0		Form	5	5	Shoulders		02
Perspective	2	0	Position of Left Arm	4	2	Constant Line Pressure	5	0	Detailing	3	5	Right Arm		02
Vertical Midline	5	0	Position of Legs	8	6	Variable Line Pressure	0	5	Identity and Sex	1	3	Left Arm	02	00
Bilateral Symmetry	0	3	Relation of Long Axes	1	1	Line Continuity	2	2	Sophistication	3	4	Chest	02	02
Horizontal Midline	4	0	Right and Left Halves	3	1	Body Shading	0	1	Height	03	02	Girth	02	02

GENERAL CHARACTERISTICS OF SUBJECT

IDENTIFICATION
No. 333
Sex M
Marital status M
Age 29 yrs. at
psychological tests

PARENTAL HISTORY				
Father				
C	H	S	D	0
–	–	–	–	–
Mother				
C	H	S	D	0
–	–	–	–	+

PHYSIOLOGICAL AND METABOLIC DATA

	Admission	Initial	Control	Cold pressor change	Exercise change	Smoking change
Systolic pressure	130	140	120	00	+28	
Diastolic pressure	90	80	76	–02	–02	
Heart rate	84	98	91	00	+23	

Age 26 yrs.	Height	70 in.	Ponderal index 13.29
	Weight	146 lbs.	Cholesterol 243 mg. per 100 ml.
	Overweight –08 %		Vital capacity 4.3 liters

HABIT SURVEY
Smoking habits: nonsmoker
Age begun   yrs.   Inhalation:
Habits of nervous tension: 1, 5, 6, 9, 11, 22

FIGURE-DRAWING CHARACTERISTICS

Structural	Male Female Both	Structural	Male	Female	Structural and Graphic	Male Female Both	Graphic, Global and Height	Male	Female	Body Proportions	Male	Female
Type	0	Omission of Appendages	0	0	Upper and Lower Halves	1 1	Hair Shading	7	3	Head	09	03
Sex Sequence	0	Position of Both Arms	0	0	Four Quarters	4 4	Nudity and Transparency	7	7	Neck		06
Posture	1 1	Position of Right Arm	5	0	Relative Size	0	Form	5	3	Shoulders	08	03
Perspective	0 0	Position of Left Arm	5	0	Constant Line Pressure	5 0	Detailing	3	3	Right Arm	04	02
Vertical Midline	0 0	Position of Legs	4	4	Variable Line Pressure	0 5	Identity and Sex	1	1	Left Arm	02	02
Bilateral Symmetry	4 3	Relation of Long Axes	1	1	Line Continuity	3 2	Sophistication	4	3	Chest	07	02
Horizontal Midline	4 4	Right and Left Halves	1	3	Body Shading	4 5	Height	04	02	Girth	03	02

GENERAL CHARACTERISTICS OF SUBJECT

IDENTIFICATION
No. A51
Sex M
Marital status S
Age 20 yrs. at
psychological tests

PARENTAL HISTORY
Father
C   H   S   D   O
–   –   –   –   ?
Mother
C   H   S   D   O
–   –   –   –   ?

PHYSIOLOGICAL AND METABOLIC DATA

	Admission	Initial	Control	Cold pressor change	Exercise change	Smoking change
Systolic pressure	120	121	120	+13	+48	+01
Diastolic pressure	80	60	61	+12	-11	+14
Heart rate	90	80	78	+16	+19	+04

Age 20 yrs.	Height	73 in.	Ponderal index 13.49
	Weight	158 lbs.	Cholesterol 203 mg. per 100 ml.
	Overweight -05 %		Vital capacity liters

HABIT SURVEY

Smoking habits: former smoker

Age begun   yrs.   Inhalation:

Habits of nervous tension: 2, 5, 8, 11, 16

STRONG VOCATIONAL INTEREST TEST

Occupation	Artist	Psychologist	Architect	Physician	Osteopath	Dentist	Veterinarian	Mathematician	Physicist	Engineer	Chemist	Production Manager
Standard Score	38	41	40	60	49	47	29	35	42	48	57	29

Occupation	Farmer	Aviator	Carpenter	Printer	Math.-Sci. Teacher	Ind. Arts Teacher	Voc. Agric. Teacher	Policeman	Forest Serv. Man	Y.M.C.A. Phys. Dir.	Personnel Director	Public Administrator
Standard Score	42	48	19	32	41	21	28	27	38	24	23	38

Occupation	Y.M.C.A. Secretary	Soc. Sci. H.S. Teacher	City Sch. Sup't.	Social Worker	Minister	Musician Performer	C.P.A.	Senior C.P.A.	Accountant	Office Man	Purchasing Agent	Banker
Standard Score	15	20	16	26	60	37	17	35	11	12	14	07

Occupation	Mortician	Pharmacist	Sales Manager	Real Est. Manager	Life Ins. Salesman	Advertising Man	Lawyer	Author- Journalist	President Mfg. Co.	Interest Maturity	Occupational Level	Masculinity- Femininity
Standard Score	07	17	14	25	17	26	35	37	29	50	59	53

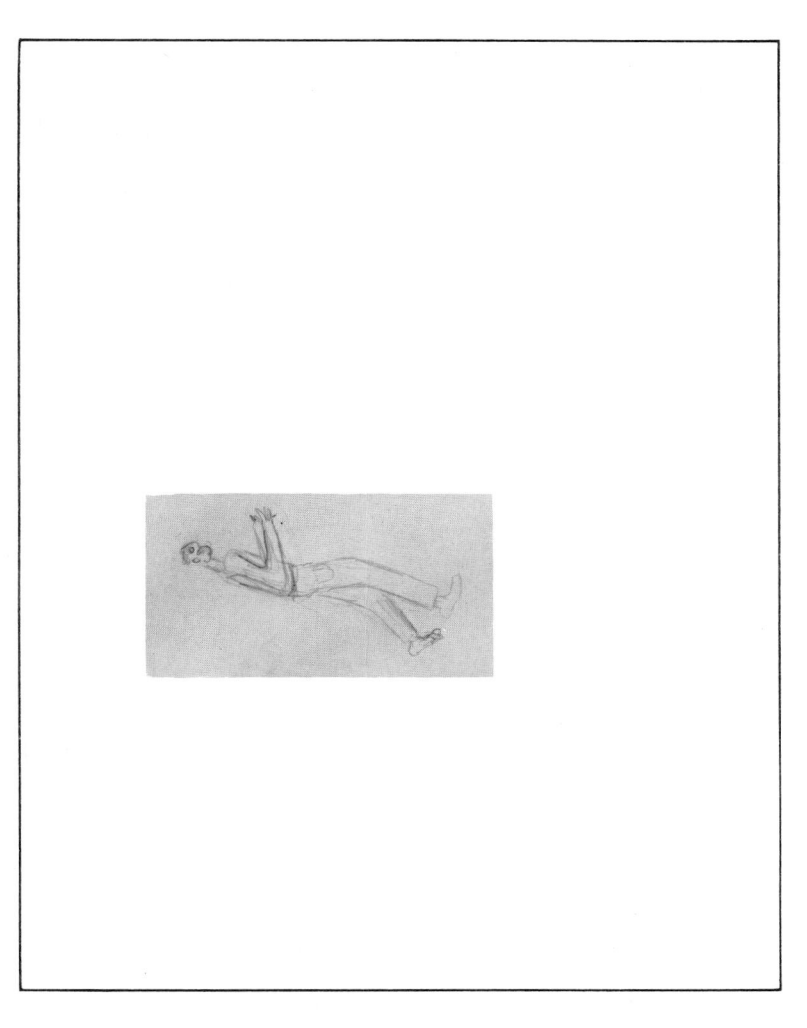

FIGURE-DRAWING CHARACTERISTICS

Structural	Male Female Both		Structural	Male	Female	Structural and Graphic	Male Female Both		Graphic, Global and Height	Male	Female	Body Proportions	Male	Female
Type	0		Omission of Appendages	0	1	Upper and Lower Halves	1	1	Hair Shading	3	3	Head	02	03
Sex Sequence	0		Position of Both Arms	2	6	Four Quarters	4	4	Nudity and Transparency	7	0	Neck	04	12
Posture	5	6	Position of Right Arm	4	2	Relative Size	4		Form	3	3	Shoulders		
Perspective	2	0	Position of Left Arm	7	2	Constant Line Pressure	1	1	Detailing	5	5	Right Arm	02	
Vertical Midline	4	0	Position of Legs	8	6	Variable Line Pressure	0	0	Identity and Sex	3	1	Left Arm		
Bilateral Symmetry	0	2	Relation of Long Axes	2	1	Line Continuity	0	0	Sophistication	3	4	Chest	02	05
Horizontal Midline	4	0	Right and Left Halves	2	1	Body Shading	3	3	Height	02		Girth	02	05

GENERAL CHARACTERISTICS OF SUBJECT

IDENTIFICATION
No. G15
Sex M
Marital status M
Age 23 yrs. at psychological tests

PARENTAL HISTORY					
Father					
C	H	S	D	O	
-	-	-	-	?	
Mother					
C	H	S	D	O	
-	-	-	-	-	

PHYSIOLOGICAL AND METABOLIC DATA

	Admission	Initial	Control	Cold pressor change	Exercise change	Smoking change
Systolic pressure	125	100	100	+12	+30	+05
Diastolic pressure	70	64	76	+22	-24	+11
Heart rate	84	76	72	+02	+28	00
Age 22 yrs.	Height 66 in. Weight 126 lbs. Overweight -09 %			Ponderal index 13.17 Cholesterol 197 mg. per 100 ml. Vital capacity liters		

HABIT SURVEY

Smoking habits: occasional smoker

Age begun 16 yrs.   Inhalation: no

Habits of nervous tension: 1, 3, 5, 7, 8, 11, 14, 23, 25

STRONG VOCATIONAL INTEREST TEST

Occupation	Artist	Psychologist	Architect	Physician	Osteopath	Dentist	Veterinarian	Mathematician	Physicist	Engineer	Chemist	Production Manager
Standard Score	39	29	43	43	40	47	26	29	33	43	49	36

Occupation	Farmer	Aviator	Carpenter	Printer	Math.-Sci. Teacher	Ind. Arts Teacher	Voc. Agric. Teacher	Policeman	Forest Serv. Man	Y.M.C.A. Phys. Dir.	Personnel Director	Public Administrator
Standard Score	47	48	38	42	29	25	25	27	20	15	15	21

Occupation	Y.M.C.A. Secretary	Soc. Sci. H.S. Teacher	City Sch. Sup't.	Social Worker	Minister	Musician Performer	C.P.A.	Senior C.P.A.	Accountant	Office Man	Purchasing Agent	Banker
Standard Score	05	09	-09	14	59	39	20	33	23	32	35	24

Occupation	Mortician	Pharmacist	Sales Manager	Real Est. Manager	Life Ins. Salesman	Advertising Man	Lawyer	Author-Journalist	President Mfg. Co.	Interest Maturity	Occupational Level	Masculinity-Femininity
Standard Score	26	31	25	35	18	32	27	37	36	41	51	60

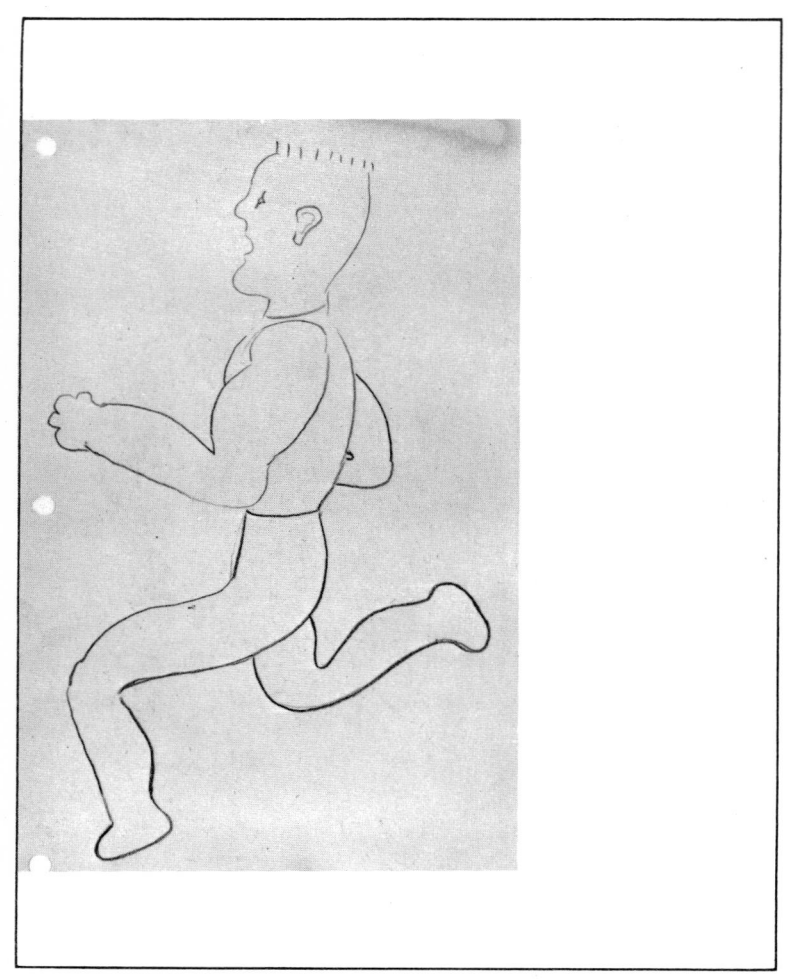

FIGURE-DRAWING CHARACTERISTICS

Structural	Male Female Both		Structural	Male	Female	Structural and Graphic	Male Female Both		Graphic, Global and Height	Male	Female	Body Proportions	Male	Female
Type	0		Omission of Appendages	0	0	Upper and Lower Halves	0	1	Hair Shading	7	5	Head	12	09
Sex Sequence	0		Position of Both Arms	4	0	Four Quarters	4	4	Nudity and Transparency	2	7	Neck	08	10
Posture	5	1	Position of Right Arm	7	2	Relative Size	0		Form	3	3	Shoulders		06
Perspective	2	0	Position of Left Arm	6	2	Constant Line Pressure	0	0	Detailing	5	3	Right Arm		06
Vertical Midline	4	0	Position of Legs	8	6	Variable Line Pressure	3	1	Identity and Sex	1	1	Left Arm	08	06
Bilateral Symmetry	0	3	Relation of Long Axes	1	1	Line Continuity	4	4	Sophistication	3	4	Chest	09	05
Horizontal Midline	4	4	Right and Left Halves	2	1	Body Shading	0	2	Height		04	Girth	06	04

GENERAL CHARACTERISTICS OF SUBJECT

IDENTIFICATION
No. 357
Sex M
Marital status M
Age 24 yrs. at psychological tests

PARENTAL HISTORY
Father
C   H   S   D   O
-   -   -   -   -
Mother
C   H   S   D   O
-   -   -   -   ?

PHYSIOLOGICAL AND METABOLIC DATA

	Admission	Initial	Control	Cold pressor change	Exercise change	Smoking change
Systolic pressure	118	112	98	+10	+22	
Diastolic pressure	60	68	66	+06	-16	
Heart rate	76	96	73	+08	+17	

Age 21 yrs.	Height 74 in.	Ponderal index 13.99
	Weight 148 lbs.	Cholesterol 188 mg. per 100 ml.
	Overweight -14 %	Vital capacity liters

HABIT SURVEY
Smoking habits: nonsmoker
Age begun   yrs.   Inhalation:
Habits of nervous tension: 2, 6, 9, 11

Plate 175　　　　　MIXED PRIMITIVE AND INTERMEDIATE DRAWINGS　　　　　215

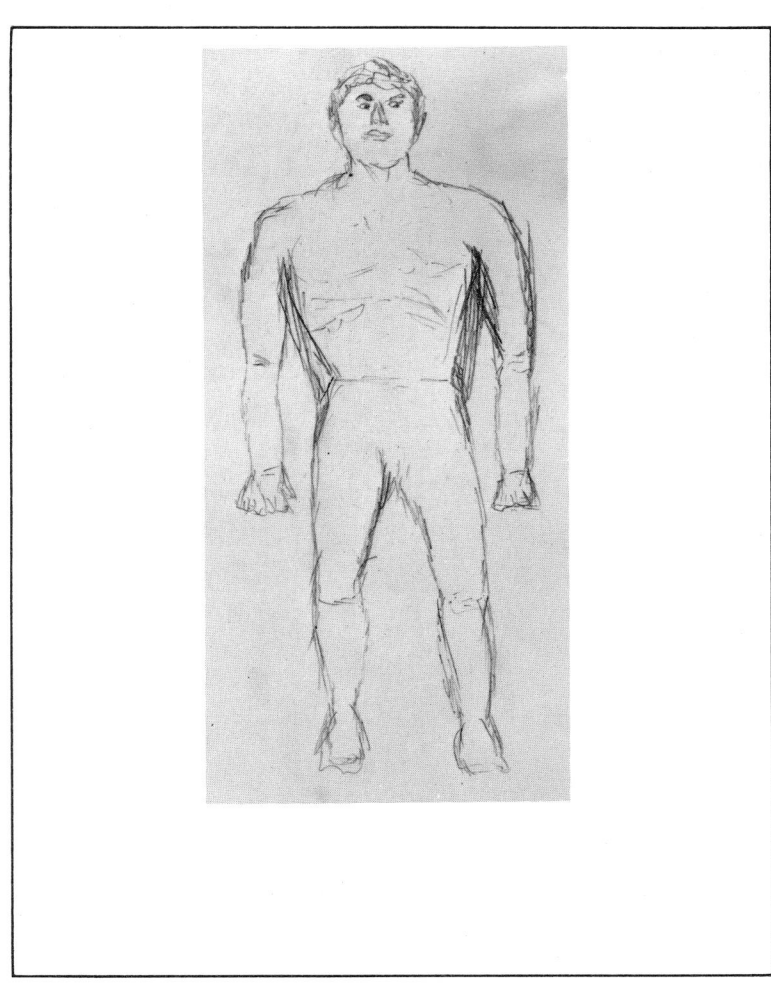

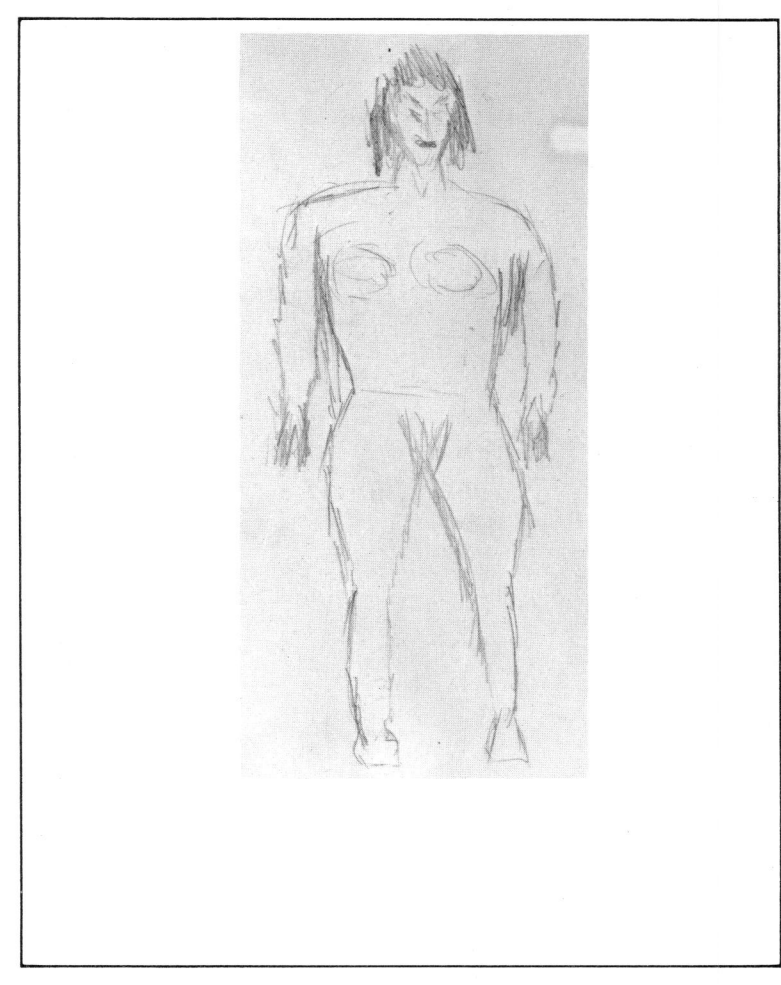

FIGURE-DRAWING CHARACTERISTICS

Structural	Male Female Both		Structural	Male	Female	Structural and Graphic	Male Female Both		Graphic, Global and Height	Male	Female	Body Proportions	Male	Female
Type	0		Omission of Appendages	0	0	Upper and Lower Halves	1	1	Hair Shading	3	3	Head	09	09
Sex Sequence	0		Position of Both Arms	0	0	Four Quarters	4	4	Nudity and Transparency	0	0	Neck	05	10
Posture	1	1	Position of Right Arm	0	0	Relative Size	2		Form	1	3	Shoulders	10	10
Perspective	0	0	Position of Left Arm	0	0	Constant Line Pressure	0	1	Detailing	3	5	Right Arm	08	06
Vertical Midline	0	0	Position of Legs	6	6	Variable Line Pressure	1	0	Identity and Sex	1	1	Left Arm	08	06
Bilateral Symmetry	3	3	Relation of Long Axes	1	1	Line Continuity	0	0	Sophistication	3	4	Chest	09	09
Horizontal Midline	4	2	Right and Left Halves	1	0	Body Shading	3	3	Height	07	07	Girth	09	09

GENERAL CHARACTERISTICS OF SUBJECT

IDENTIFICATION
No. F77
Sex M
Marital status M
Age 23 yrs. at
psychological tests

PARENTAL HISTORY					
Father					
C	H	S	D	O	
-	-	-	-	-	
Mother					
C	H	S	D	O	
-	-	-	-	-	

PHYSIOLOGICAL AND METABOLIC DATA

	Admission	Initial	Control	Cold pressor change	Exercise change	Smoking change
Systolic pressure	120	130	116	+32	+40	+03
Diastolic pressure	80	70	80	+24	+20	+01
Heart rate	76	72	79	+36	+32	-02

Age 22 yrs.	Height 75 in.	Ponderal index 13.13
	Weight 186 lbs.	Cholesterol 234 mg. per 100 ml.
	Overweight +04 %	Vital capacity liters

HABIT SURVEY

Smoking habits: occasional smoker

Age begun 18 yrs.　　Inhalation: no

Habits of nervous tension: 1, 4, 6, 16, 20, 25

STRONG VOCATIONAL INTEREST TEST

Occupation	Artist	Psychologist	Architect	Physician	Osteopath	Dentist	Veterinarian	Mathematician	Physicist	Engineer	Chemist	Production Manager
Standard Score	44	36	49	57	46	51	20	39	45	49	50	30

Occupation	Farmer	Aviator	Carpenter	Printer	Math.-Sci. Teacher	Ind. Arts Teacher	Voc. Agric. Teacher	Policeman	Forest Serv. Man	Y.M.C.A. Phys. Dir.	Personnel Director	Public Administrator
Standard Score	48	56	38	38	35	30	21	29	27	20	19	23

Occupation	Y.M.C.A. Secretary	Soc. Sci. H.S. Teacher	City Sch. Sup't.	Social Worker	Minister	Musician Performer	C.P.A.	Senior C.P.A.	Accountant	Office Man	Purchasing Agent	Banker
Standard Score	09	11	08	16	58	47	18	25	12	13	18	12

Occupation	Mortician	Pharmacist	Sales Manager	Real Est. Manager	Life Ins. Salesman	Advertising Man	Lawyer	Author-Journalist	President Mfg. Co.	Interest Maturity	Occupational Level	Masculinity-Femininity
Standard Score	20	28	14	28	12	33	31	39	25	43	53	47

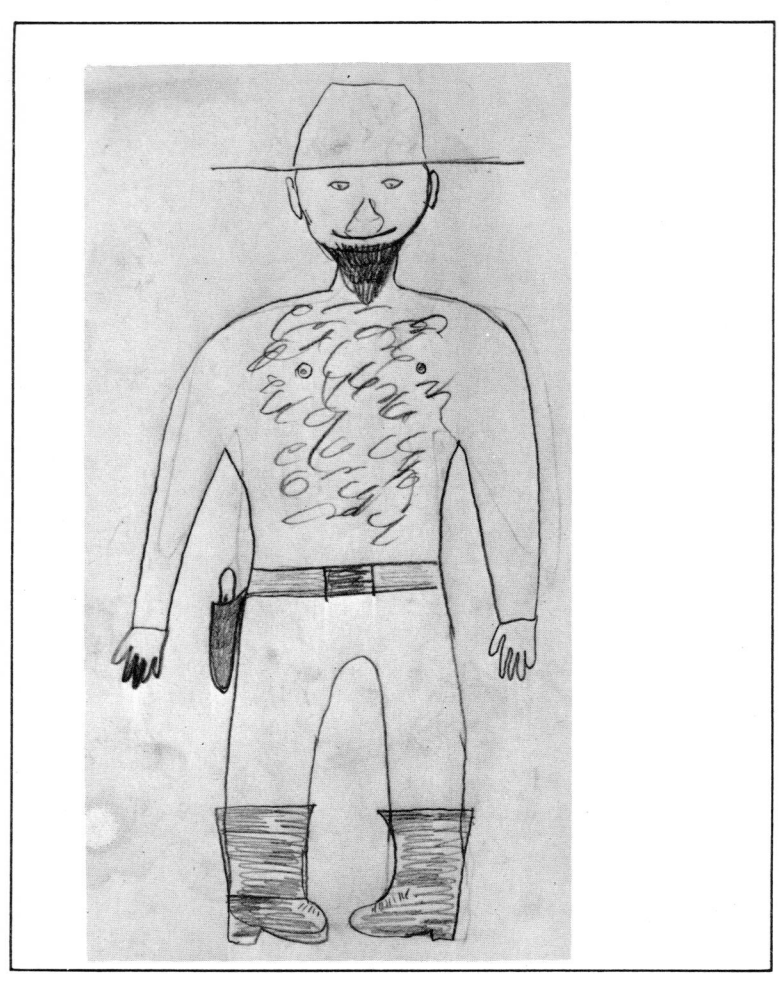

FIGURE-DRAWING CHARACTERISTICS

Structural	Male Female Both	Structural	Male	Female	Structural and Graphic	Male Female Both	Graphic, Global and Height	Male	Female	Body Proportions	Male	Female
Type	0	Omission of Appendages	0	0	Upper and Lower Halves	0 1	Hair Shading	0	3	Head	09	15
Sex Sequence	0	Position of Both Arms	0	4	Four Quarters	4 4	Nudity and Transparency	3	0	Neck	12	08
Posture	1 6	Position of Right Arm	0	7	Relative Size	0	Form	3	5	Shoulders	13	
Perspective	0 2	Position of Left Arm	0	2	Constant Line Pressure	0 5	Detailing	1	5	Right Arm	08	
Vertical Midline	0 4	Position of Legs	6	8	Variable Line Pressure	5 0	Identity and Sex	1	3	Left Arm	08	07
Bilateral Symmetry	4 0	Relation of Long Axes	1	1	Line Continuity	4 4	Sophistication	3	4	Chest	10	10
Horizontal Midline	4 0	Right and Left Halves	1	1	Body Shading	5 0	Height	09	08	Girth	12	10

GENERAL CHARACTERISTICS OF SUBJECT

IDENTIFICATION
No. B66
Sex M
Marital status S
Age 21 yrs. at
psychological tests

PARENTAL HISTORY
Father
C   H   S   D   O
-   -   -   -   -
Mother
C   H   S   D   O
-   -   -   -   -

PHYSIOLOGICAL AND METABOLIC DATA

	Admission	Initial	Control	Cold pressor change	Exercise change	Smoking change
Systolic pressure	120	112	108	+08	+36	+03
Diastolic pressure	80	50	70	+08	-22	-01
Heart rate	80	80	70	+04	+30	-03

Age 21 yrs.	Height 70 in.	Ponderal index 12.80
	Weight 164 lbs.	Cholesterol 233 mg. per 100 ml.
	Overweight +07 %	Vital capacity 4.8 liters

HABIT SURVEY
Smoking habits: occasional smoker
Age begun 21 yrs.   Inhalation: no
Habits of nervous tension: 5, 6, 9, 11, 21, 22

STRONG VOCATIONAL INTEREST TEST

Occupation	Artist	Psychologist	Architect	Physician	Osteopath	Dentist	Veterinarian	Mathematician	Physicist	Engineer	Chemist	Production Manager
Standard Score	24	29	22	37	33	29	29	09	02	10	20	28

Occupation	Farmer	Aviator	Carpenter	Printer	Math.-Sci. Teacher	Ind. Arts Teacher	Voc. Agric. Teacher	Policeman	Forest Serv. Man	Y.M.C.A. Phys. Dir.	Personnel Director	Public Administrator
Standard Score	36	35	16	39	41	15	34	40	32	48	36	38

Occupation	Y.M.C.A. Secretary	Soc. Sci. H.S. Teacher	City Sch. Sup't.	Social Worker	Minister	Musician Performer	C.P.A.	Senior C.P.A.	Accountant	Office Man	Purchasing Agent	Banker
Standard Score	40	52	36	46	61	52	20	42	19	36	23	21

Occupation	Mortician	Pharmacist	Sales Manager	Real Est. Manager	Life Ins. Salesman	Advertising Man	Lawyer	Author-Journalist	President Mfg. Co.	Interest Maturity	Occupational Level	Masculinity-Femininity
Standard Score	33	35	36	39	42	38	37	30	17	58	49	41

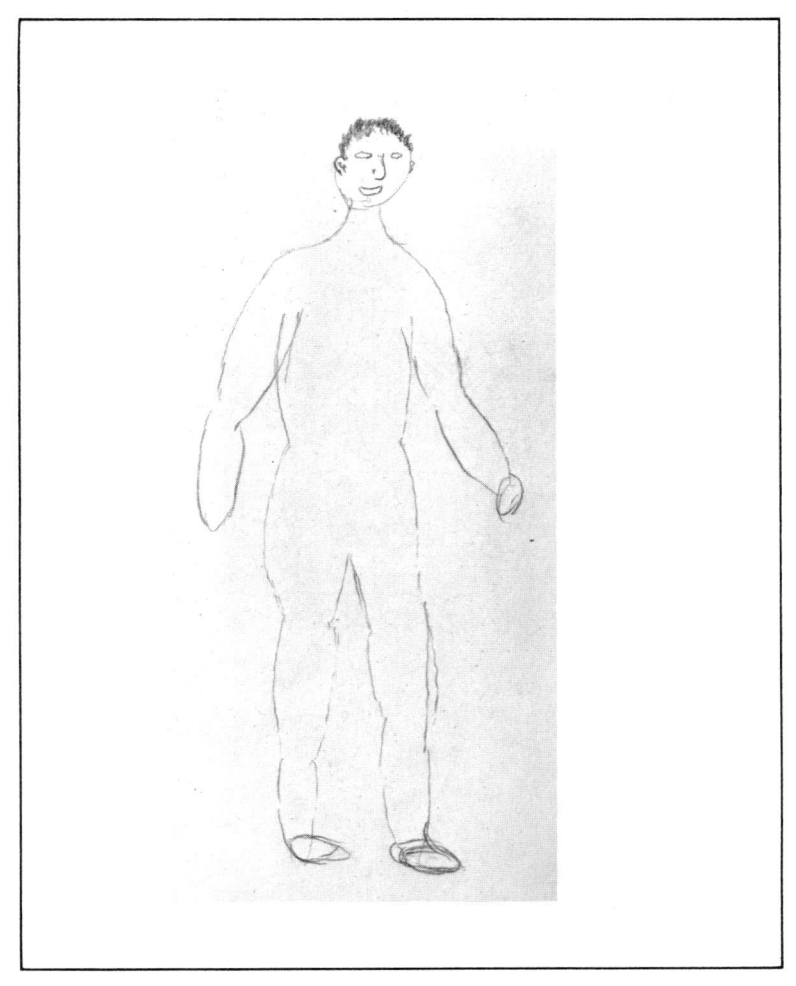

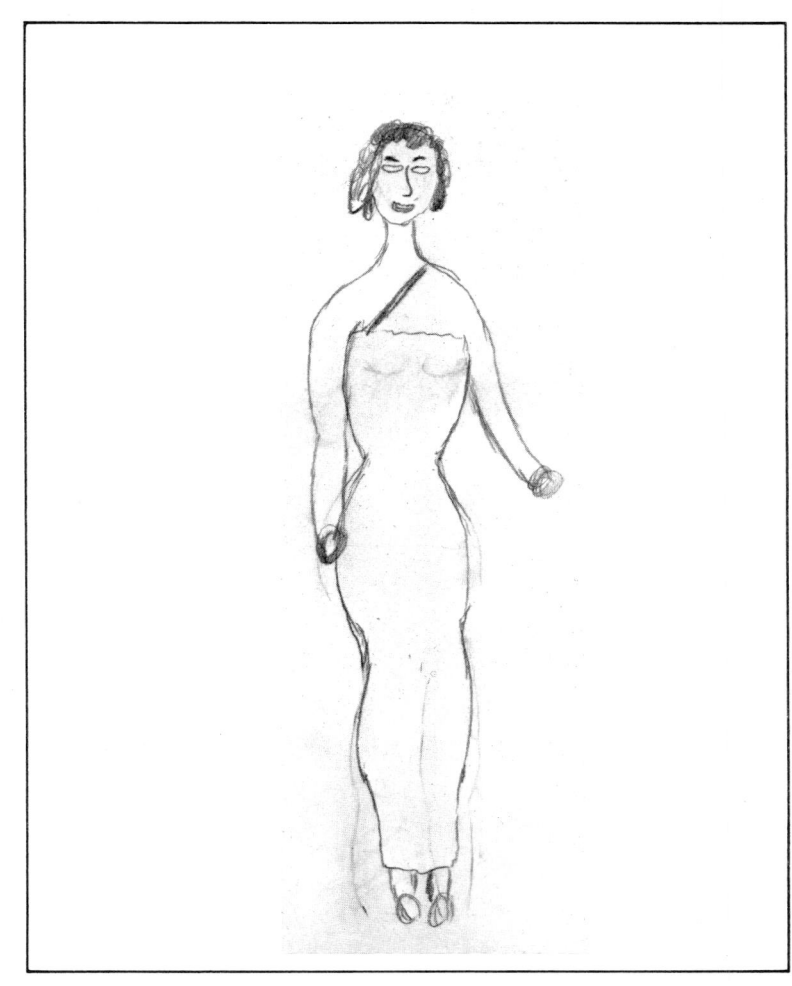

FIGURE-DRAWING CHARACTERISTICS

Structural	Male Female Both	Structural	Male	Female	Structural and Graphic	Male Female Both		Graphic, Global and Height	Male	Female	Body Proportions	Male	Female
Type	0	Omission of Appendages	0	0	Upper and Lower Halves	0	3	Hair Shading	3	3	Head	07	08
Sex Sequence	0	Position of Both Arms	0	1	Four Quarters	4	4	Nudity and Transparency	0	7	Neck	10	10
Posture	1 1	Position of Right Arm	2	0	Relative Size	3		Form	3	3	Shoulders	06	06
Perspective	0 0	Position of Left Arm	2	2	Constant Line Pressure	1	3	Detailing	5	3	Right Arm		06
Vertical Midline	0 0	Position of Legs	5	1	Variable Line Pressure	0	0	Identity and Sex	3	3	Left Arm	06	06
Bilateral Symmetry	3 3	Relation of Long Axes	1	1	Line Continuity	0	0	Sophistication	4	3	Chest	06	06
Horizontal Midline	0 0	Right and Left Halves	1	1	Body Shading	0	5	Height	08	08	Girth	07	05

GENERAL CHARACTERISTICS OF SUBJECT

IDENTIFICATION

No. E23
Sex M
Marital status S
Age 22 yrs. at
psychological tests

PARENTAL HISTORY

Father
C   H   S   D   O
-   -   -   -   -
Mother
C   H   S   D   O
-   -   -   -   -

PHYSIOLOGICAL AND METABOLIC DATA

	Admission	Initial	Control	Cold pressor change	Exercise change	Smoking change
Systolic pressure	120	120	116	+06	+23	
Diastolic pressure	70	70	68	+14	-18	
Heart rate	80	60	54	00	+34	

Age 22 yrs.   Height   74   in.   Ponderal index 13.55
Weight   163   lbs.   Cholesterol   230   mg. per 100 ml.
Overweight -06 %   Vital capacity   5.1   liters

HABIT SURVEY

Smoking habits: light cigarette smoker
Age begun 17 yrs.   Inhalation: yes
Habits of nervous tension: 1, 5, 8, 9, 11, 19

STRONG VOCATIONAL INTEREST TEST

Occupation	Artist	Psychologist	Architect	Physician	Osteopath	Dentist	Veterinarian	Mathematician	Physicist	Engineer	Chemist	Production Manager
Standard Score	39	41	43	51	42	48	19	38	39	50	49	42

Occupation	Farmer	Aviator	Carpenter	Printer	Math.-Sci. Teacher	Ind. Arts Teacher	Voc. Agric. Teacher	Policeman	Forest Serv. Man	Y.M.C.A. Phys. Dir.	Personnel Director	Public Administrator
Standard Score	42	56	31	48	35	27	20	37	23	29	24	38

Occupation	Y.M.C.A. Secretary	Soc. Sci. H.S. Teacher	City Sch. Sup't.	Social Worker	Minister	Musician Performer	C.P.A.	Senior C.P.A.	Accountant	Office Man	Purchasing Agent	Banker
Standard Score	15	20	11	26	64	47	13	33	19	24	23	15

Occupation	Mortician	Pharmacist	Sales Manager	Real Est. Manager	Life Ins. Salesman	Advertising Man	Lawyer	Author-Journalist	President Mfg. Co.	Interest Maturity	Occupational Level	Masculinity-Femininity
Standard Score	17	22	19	27	19	33	32	41	24	45	51	50

VI. MIXED PRIMITIVE AND SOPHISTICATED DRAWINGS

In this section, represented by three subjects, one drawing of each pair is moderately primitive and one is moderately sophisticated.

FIGURE-DRAWING CHARACTERISTICS

Structural	Male Female Both	Structural	Male	Female	Structural and Graphic	Male Female Both	Graphic, Global and Height	Male	Female	Body Proportions	Male	Female
Type	0	Omission of Appendages	0	0	Upper and Lower Halves	0 3	Hair Shading	3	5	Head	07	07
Sex Sequence	0	Position of Both Arms	0	4	Four Quarters	4 4	Nudity and Transparency	7	7	Neck	03	01
Posture	4 1	Position of Right Arm	2	7	Relative Size	4	Form	1	3	Shoulders	05	
Perspective	0 2	Position of Left Arm	2	4	Constant Line Pressure	0 0	Detailing	3	5	Right Arm	04	
Vertical Midline	3 0	Position of Legs	7	1	Variable Line Pressure	1 4	Identity and Sex	1	1	Left Arm	04	06
Bilateral Symmetry	3 0	Relation of Long Axes	1	1	Line Continuity	0 0	Sophistication	2	4	Chest	05	08
Horizontal Midline	4 4	Right and Left Halves	1	1	Body Shading	4 0	Height	06	07	Girth	07	08

GENERAL CHARACTERISTICS OF SUBJECT

IDENTIFICATION
No. A52
Sex M
Marital status S
Age 23 yrs. at
psychological tests

PARENTAL HISTORY					
Father					
C	H	S	D	O	
+	+	–	–	–	
Mother					
C	H	S	D	O	
–	–	–	–	–	

PHYSIOLOGICAL AND METABOLIC DATA

	Admission	Initial	Control	Cold pressor change	Exercise change	Smoking change
Systolic pressure	120	134	122	+12	+38	+02
Diastolic pressure	75	65	67	+15	–07	+10
Heart rate	72	72	66	+17	+30	+09

Age 22 yrs.	Height	72 in.		Ponderal index 13.56	
	Weight	150 lbs.		Cholesterol	217 mg. per 100 ml.
	Overweight –08 %			Vital capacity	liters

HABIT SURVEY

Smoking habits: former smoker

Age begun 16 yrs.   Inhalation:

Habits of nervous tension: 1, 2, 4, 5, 6, 8, 9, 12, 14, 19, 21, 22

STRONG VOCATIONAL INTEREST TEST

Occupation	Artist	Psychologist	Architect	Physician	Osteopath	Dentist	Veterinarian	Mathematician	Physicist	Engineer	Chemist	Production Manager
Standard Score	29	21	31	44	46	46	33	34	30	42	36	29

Occupation	Farmer	Aviator	Carpenter	Printer	Math.-Sci. Teacher	Ind. Arts Teacher	Voc. Agric. Teacher	Policeman	Forest Serv. Man	Y.M.C.A. Phys. Dir.	Personnel Director	Public Administrator
Standard Score	42	34	27	36	41	25	35	36	28	35	18	23

Occupation	Y.M.C.A. Secretary	Soc. Sci. H.S. Teacher	City Sch. Sup't.	Social Worker	Minister	Musician Performer	C.P.A.	Senior C.P.A.	Accountant	Office Man	Purchasing Agent	Banker
Standard Score	22	24	18	21	60	38	14	28	25	34	28	30

Occupation	Mortician	Pharmacist	Sales Manager	Real Est. Manager	Life Ins. Salesman	Advertising Man	Lawyer	Author-Journalist	President Mfg. Co.	Interest Maturity	Occupational Level	Masculinity-Femininity
Standard Score	28	33	28	31	27	26	22	28	30	50	57	47

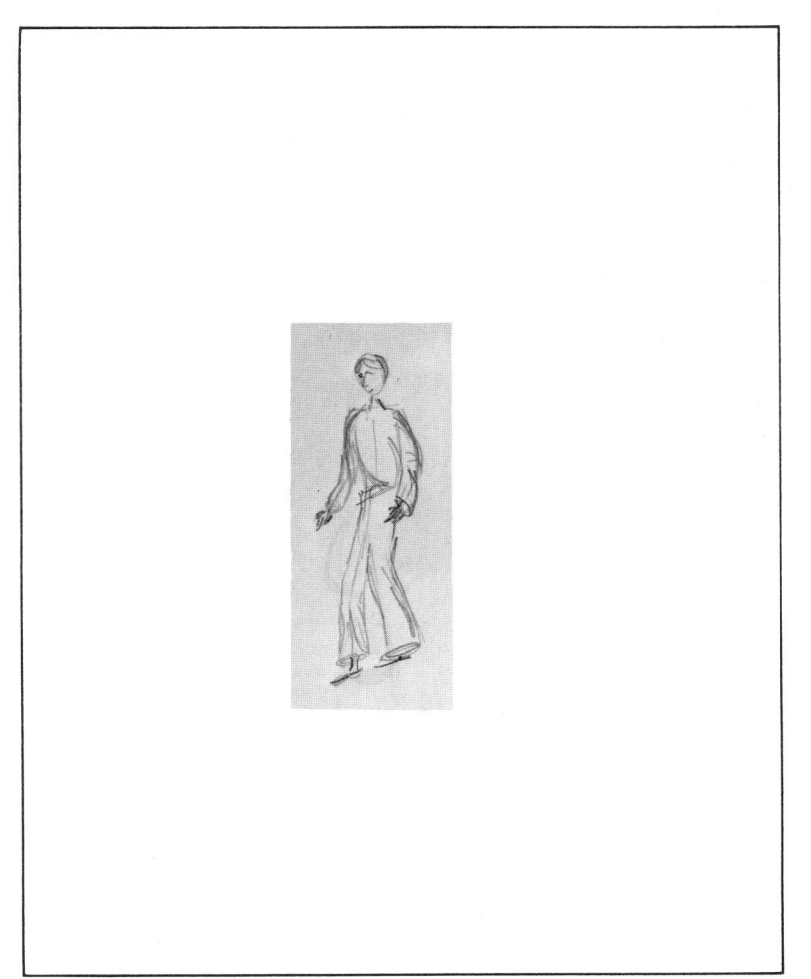

FIGURE-DRAWING CHARACTERISTICS

Structural	Male Female Both	Structural	Male	Female	Structural and Graphic	Male Female Both		Graphic, Global and Height	Male	Female	Body Proportions	Male	Female
Type	0	Omission of Appendages	0	0	Upper and Lower Halves	0	3	Hair Shading	3	3	Head	03	03
Sex Sequence	0	Position of Both Arms	0	0	Four Quarters	4	4	Nudity and Transparency	7	2	Neck	04	04
Posture	2 1	Position of Right Arm	4	2	Relative Size	4		Form	3	1	Shoulders		02
Perspective	1 0	Position of Left Arm	4	2	Constant Line Pressure	0	0	Detailing	5	3	Right Arm	02	02
Vertical Midline	5 0	Position of Legs	8	7	Variable Line Pressure	1	1	Identity and Sex	5	1	Left Arm	02	02
Bilateral Symmetry	0 3	Relation of Long Axes	1	1	Line Continuity	0	0	Sophistication	4	2	Chest		02
Horizontal Midline	4 0	Right and Left Halves	2	2	Body Shading	3	3	Height	03	04	Girth		02

GENERAL CHARACTERISTICS OF SUBJECT

IDENTIFICATION
No. 457
Sex M
Marital status S
Age 26 yrs. at
psychological tests

PARENTAL HISTORY
Father
C   H   S   D   O
−   (+)   −   −   ?
Mother
C   H   S   D   O
−   −   −   −   −

PHYSIOLOGICAL AND METABOLIC DATA

	Admission	Initial	Control	Cold pressor change	Exercise change	Smoking change
Systolic pressure	130	118	113	+02	+29	+04
Diastolic pressure	70	74	68	+04	−02	00
Heart rate	80	90	79	00	+04	+04

Age 24 yrs.

Height	72 in.	Ponderal index	13.46	
Weight	153 lbs.	Cholesterol	230	mg. per 100 ml.
Overweight	−07 %	Vital capacity	5.3	liters

HABIT SURVEY

Smoking habits: heavy cigarette smoker

Age begun 17 yrs.   Inhalation: yes

Habits of nervous tension: 18, 19, 22, 25

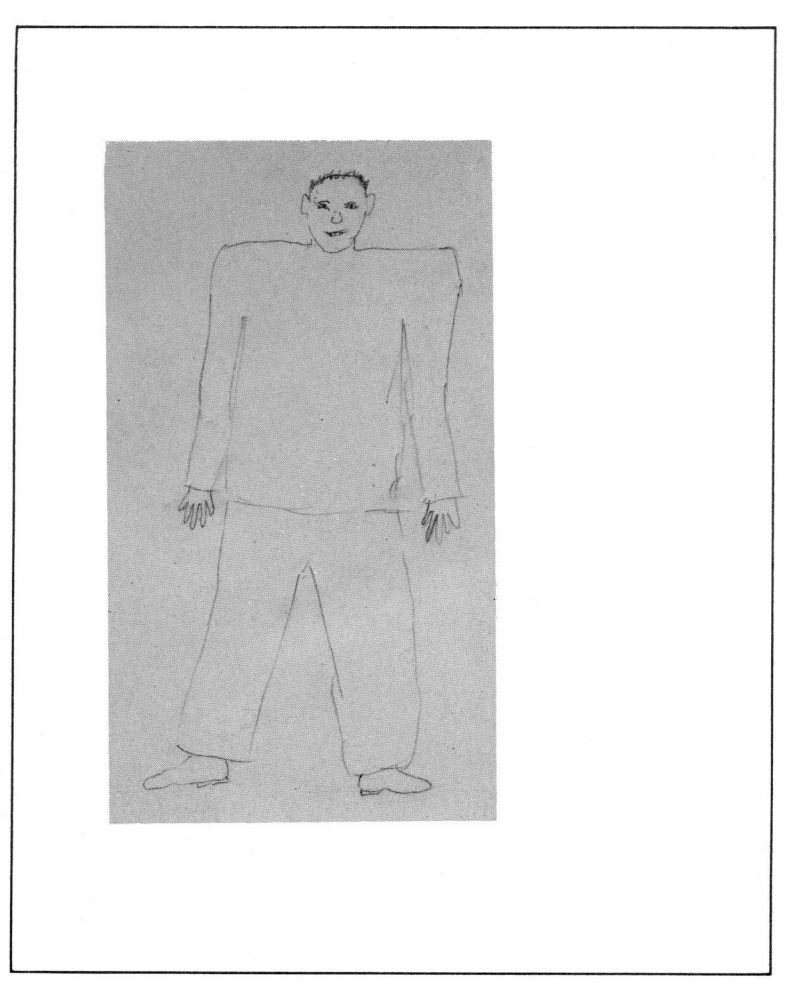

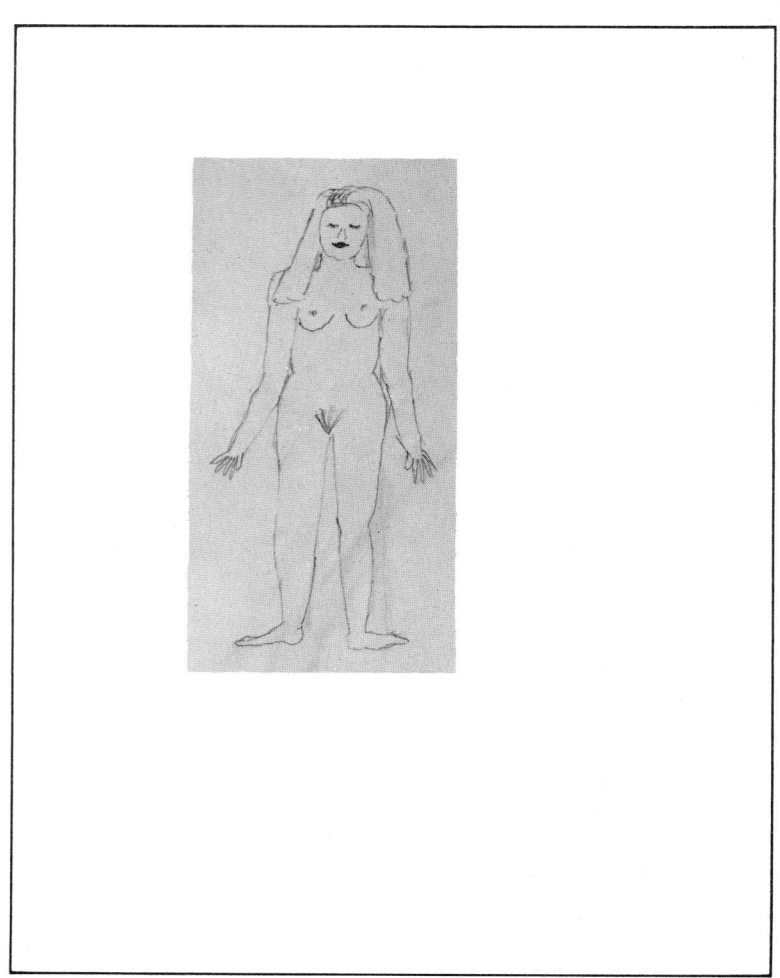

FIGURE-DRAWING CHARACTERISTICS

Structural	Male Female Both	Structural	Male	Female	Structural and Graphic	Male Female Both	Graphic, Global and Height	Male	Female	Body Proportions	Male	Female
Type	0	Omission of Appendages	0	0	Upper and Lower Halves	0 1	Hair Shading	3	1	Head	06	05
Sex Sequence	2	Position of Both Arms	0	0	Four Quarters	4 4	Nudity and Transparency	7	0	Neck	02	04
Posture	1 1	Position of Right Arm	0	4	Relative Size	0	Form	3	3	Shoulders	10	05
Perspective	0 0	Position of Left Arm	0	4	Constant Line Pressure	1 1	Detailing	3	1	Right Arm	06	04
Vertical Midline	0 0	Position of Legs	6	5	Variable Line Pressure	0 0	Identity and Sex	3	1	Left Arm	06	04
Bilateral Symmetry	3 3	Relation of Long Axes	1	1	Line Continuity	2 0	Sophistication	4	2	Chest	08	04
Horizontal Midline	6 0	Right and Left Halves	1	1	Body Shading	0 2	Height	06	05	Girth	11	05

GENERAL CHARACTERISTICS OF SUBJECT

IDENTIFICATION
No. 233
Sex M
Marital status M
Age 24 yrs. at psychological tests

PARENTAL HISTORY
Father
C H S D O
- - - - +
Mother
C H S D O
- ? - - -

PHYSIOLOGICAL AND METABOLIC DATA

	Admission	Initial	Control	Cold pressor change	Exercise change	Smoking change
Systolic pressure	118	110	110	-06	+50	
Diastolic pressure	76	72	76	-06	+04	
Heart rate	72	94	86	00	+19	

Age 24 yrs.	Height 76 in.	Ponderal index 14.03
	Weight 159 lbs.	Cholesterol 172 mg. per 100 ml.
	Overweight -15 %	Vital capacity 5.1 liters

HABIT SURVEY
Smoking habits: occasional smoker
Age begun 16 yrs.   Inhalation: yes
Habits of nervous tension: 3, 4, 5, 11, 14

VII. DRAWINGS AT AN INTERMEDIATE LEVEL OF SOPHISTICATION

These drawings by 307 subjects are intermediate—between the primitive and sophisticated groups. Identification of sex is evident, there are attempts at shaping and a fair level of integration of parts is manifest. A minimum of detailing is present.

FIGURE-DRAWING CHARACTERISTICS

Structural	Male Female Both	Structural	Male	Female	Structural and Graphic	Male Female Both	Graphic, Global and Height	Male	Female	Body Proportions	Male	Female
Type	0	Omission of Appendages	3		Upper and Lower Halves	3	Hair Shading	3		Head	09	
Sex Sequence	3	Position of Both Arms	1		Four Quarters	4	Nudity and Transparency	7		Neck	08	
Posture	0	Position of Right Arm	2		Relative Size	7	Form	3		Shoulders	09	
Perspective	5	Position of Left Arm	0		Constant Line Pressure	1	Detailing	3		Right Arm	08	
Vertical Midline	0	Position of Legs	0		Variable Line Pressure	0	Identity and Sex	1		Left Arm	08	
Bilateral Symmetry	2	Relation of Long Axes	1		Line Continuity	0	Sophistication	3		Chest	08	
Horizontal Midline	4	Right and Left Halves	1		Body Shading	7	Height			Girth	10	

GENERAL CHARACTERISTICS OF SUBJECT

IDENTIFICATION

No. 654
Sex M
Marital status M
Age 25 yrs. at
psychological tests

PARENTAL HISTORY

Father

C	H	S	D	O
(+)	+	(+)	-	-

Mother

C	H	S	D	O
+	+	-	+	+

PHYSIOLOGICAL AND METABOLIC DATA

	Admission	Initial	Control	Cold pressor change	Exercise change	Smoking change
Systolic pressure	132	120	120	+18	+46	-02
Diastolic pressure	80	64	74	+30	-04	+06
Heart rate	82	88	83	-18	+24	+07

Age 23 yrs.

Height   74   in.
Weight   184   lbs.
Overweight +05 %

Ponderal index 13.01
Cholesterol   217   mg. per 100 ml.
Vital capacity   5.7   liters

HABIT SURVEY

Smoking habits: pipe smoker
Age begun 17 yrs.   Inhalation: yes
Habits of nervous tension: 1, 3, 4, 5, 6, 8, 9, 11, 12, 16, 18, 20, 22, 23, 24

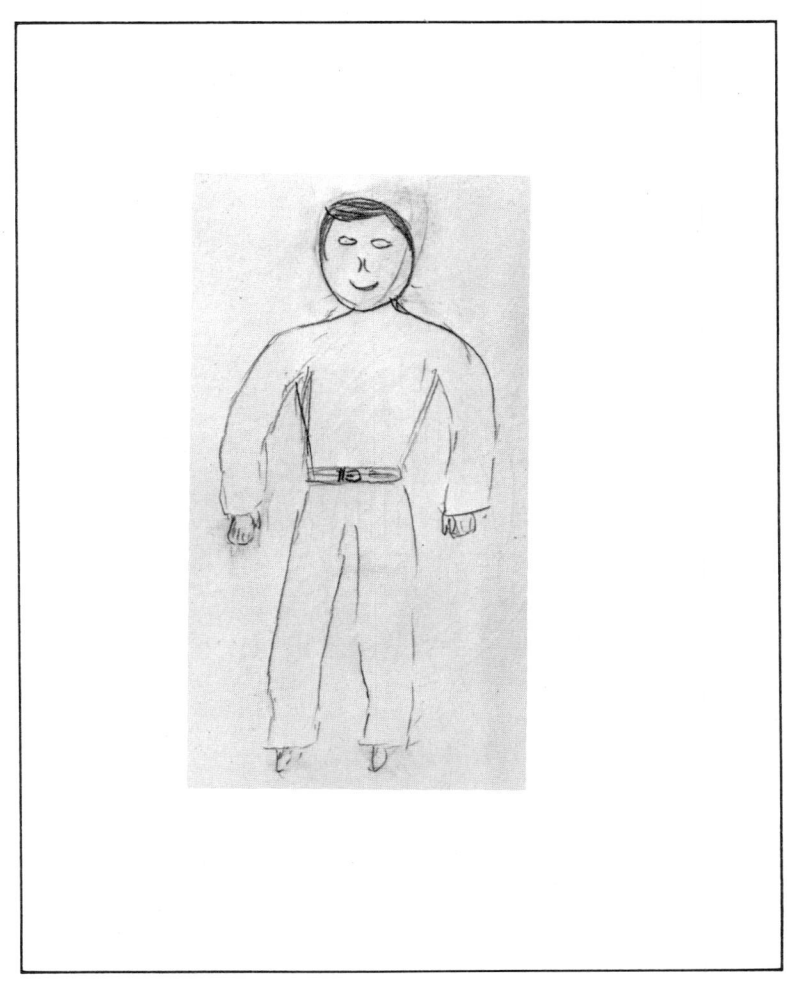

FIGURE-DRAWING CHARACTERISTICS

Structural	Male Female Both	Structural	Male	Female	Structural and Graphic	Male Female Both		Graphic, Global and Height	Male	Female	Body Proportions	Male	Female
Type	0	Omission of Appendages	0	0	Upper and Lower Halves	0	0	Hair Shading	1	1	Head	09	10
Sex Sequence	1	Position of Both Arms	0	1	Four Quarters	4	4	Nudity and Transparency	7	7	Neck	02	02
Posture	1 1	Position of Right Arm	0	0	Relative Size	4		Form	3	3	Shoulders	09	06
Perspective	0 0	Position of Left Arm	0	5	Constant Line Pressure	0	0	Detailing	3	3	Right Arm	04	06
Vertical Midline	0 0	Position of Legs	5	5	Variable Line Pressure	3	5	Identity and Sex	1	1	Left Arm	04	06
Bilateral Symmetry	3 3	Relation of Long Axes	1	1	Line Continuity	0	0	Sophistication	3	3	Chest	06	06
Horizontal Midline	4 4	Right and Left Halves	1	1	Body Shading	4	5	Height	06	06	Girth	06	06

GENERAL CHARACTERISTICS OF SUBJECT

IDENTIFICATION
No. E39
Sex F
Marital status S
Age 21 yrs. at
psychological tests

PARENTAL HISTORY
Father
C   H   S   D   O
+   -   +   +   ?
Mother
C   H   S   D   O
?   -   -   -   -

PHYSIOLOGICAL AND METABOLIC DATA

	Admission	Initial	Control	Cold pressor change	Exercise change	Smoking change
Systolic pressure	120	122	118	+02	+32	+02
Diastolic pressure	70	68	70	+08	-20	+04
Heart rate	80	88	84	+08	+86	-06

Age 21 yrs.	Height 64 in.	Ponderal index 12.83
	Weight 124 lbs.	Cholesterol 320 mg. per 100 ml.
	Overweight -02 %	Vital capacity 3.2 liters

HABIT SURVEY
Smoking habits: occasional smoker
Age begun 17 yrs.   Inhalation: no
Habits of nervous tension: 3, 4, 5, 9, 15, 16, 23

STRONG VOCATIONAL INTEREST TEST

Occupation	Artist	Psychologist	Architect	Physician	Osteopath	Dentist	Veterinarian	Mathematician	Physicist	Engineer	Chemist	Production Manager
Standard Score	51	53	53	63	44	39	16	40	42	41	48	16

Occupation	Farmer	Aviator	Carpenter	Printer	Math.-Sci. Teacher	Ind. Arts Teacher	Voc. Agric. Teacher	Policeman	Forest Serv. Man	Y.M.C.A. Phys. Dir.	Personnel Director	Public Administrator
Standard Score	39	46	26	39	35	17	17	22	22	30	23	36

Occupation	Y.M.C.A. Secretary	Soc. Sci. H.S. Teacher	City Sch. Sup't.	Social Worker	Minister	Musician Performer	C.P.A.	Senior C.P.A.	Accountant	Office Man	Purchasing Agent	Banker
Standard Score	16	20	14	36	64	63	27	33	08	17	07	05

Occupation	Mortician	Pharmacist	Sales Manager	Real Est. Manager	Life Ins. Salesman	Advertising Man	Lawyer	Author-Journalist	President Mfg. Co.	Interest Maturity	Occupational Level	Masculinity-Femininity
Standard Score	14	29	18	28	21	41	39	48	28	48	53	40

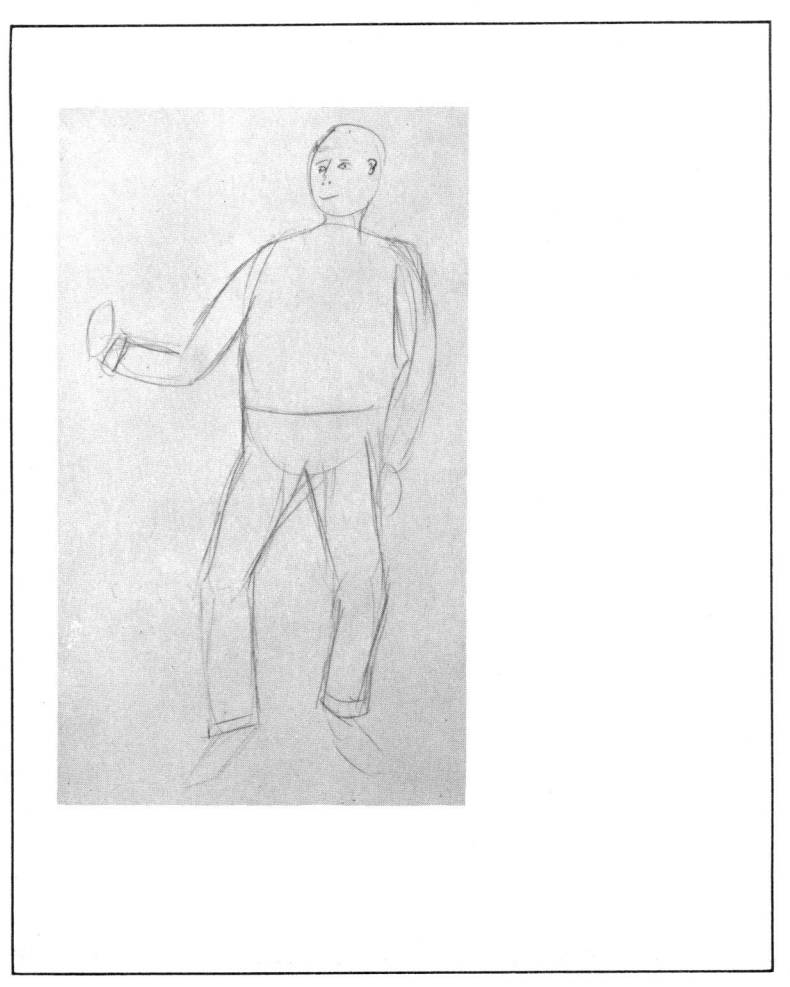

FIGURE-DRAWING CHARACTERISTICS

Structural	Male Female Both	Structural	Male	Female	Structural and Graphic	Male Female Both		Graphic, Global and Height	Male	Female	Body Proportions	Male	Female
Type	0	Omission of Appendages	0	0	Upper and Lower Halves	1	1	Hair Shading	0	5	Head	07	07
Sex Sequence	0	Position of Both Arms	1	0	Four Quarters	4	4	Nudity and Transparency	7	6	Neck	04	03
Posture	1 1	Position of Right Arm	2	5	Relative Size	2		Form	5	3	Shoulders	06	07
Perspective	0 0	Position of Left Arm	0	5	Constant Line Pressure	2	0	Detailing	3	3	Right Arm	06	06
Vertical Midline	0 0	Position of Legs	6	6	Variable Line Pressure	0	1	Identity and Sex	1	1	Left Arm	06	06
Bilateral Symmetry	3 3	Relation of Long Axes	1	1	Line Continuity	0	0	Sophistication	3	3	Chest	07	08
Horizontal Midline	4 4	Right and Left Halves	1	1	Body Shading	2	3	Height	07	07	Girth	09	07

GENERAL CHARACTERISTICS OF SUBJECT

IDENTIFICATION
No. A60
Sex M
Marital status M
Age 23 yrs. at
psychological tests

PARENTAL HISTORY				
Father				
C	H	S	D	O
?	+	+	–	–
Mother				
C	H	S	D	O
+	+	–	–	+

PHYSIOLOGICAL AND METABOLIC DATA

	Admission	Initial	Control	Cold pressor change	Exercise change	Smoking change
Systolic pressure	120	142	127	+34	+49	+02
Diastolic pressure	70	62	60	+43	–10	+04
Heart rate	72	88	80	+06	+31	+02

Age 22 yrs.	Height 68 in.	Ponderal index 13.08
	Weight 141 lbs.	Cholesterol 217 mg. per 100 ml.
	Overweight –03 %	Vital capacity liters

HABIT SURVEY
Smoking habits: nonsmoker
Age begun yrs. Inhalation:
Habits of nervous tension: 3, 4, 5, 6, 11

STRONG VOCATIONAL INTEREST TEST

Occupation	Artist	Psychologist	Architect	Physician	Osteopath	Dentist	Veterinarian	Mathematician	Physicist	Engineer	Chemist	Production Manager
Standard Score	26	40	32	49	39	38	15	43	37	42	46	29

Occupation	Farmer	Aviator	Carpenter	Printer	Math.-Sci. Teacher	Ind. Arts Teacher	Voc. Agric. Teacher	Policeman	Forest Serv. Man	Y.M.C.A. Phys. Dir.	Personnel Director	Public Administrator
Standard Score	36	34	23	39	53	28	34	31	29	39	39	40

Occupation	Y.M.C.A. Secretary	Soc. Sci. H.S. Teacher	City Sch. Sup't.	Social Worker	Minister	Musician Performer	C.P.A.	Senior C.P.A.	Accountant	Office Man	Purchasing Agent	Banker
Standard Score	32	38	44	33	60	36	33	44	30	29	24	26

Occupation	Mortician	Pharmacist	Sales Manager	Real Est. Manager	Life Ins. Salesman	Advertising Man	Lawyer	Author-Journalist	President Mfg. Co.	Interest Maturity	Occupational Level	Masculinity-Femininity
Standard Score	10	24	19	21	17	25	38	30	22	55	58	52

Plate 184   DRAWINGS AT AN INTERMEDIATE LEVEL OF SOPHISTICATION   227

FIGURE-DRAWING CHARACTERISTICS

Structural	Male	Female	Structural	Male	Female	Structural and Graphic	Male	Female	Graphic, Global and Height	Male	Female	Body Proportions	Male	Female
	Both						Both							
Type	0		Omission of Appendages	0	0	Upper and Lower Halves	3	3	Hair Shading	1	3	Head	09	07
Sex Sequence	0		Position of Both Arms	0	0	Four Quarters	4	4	Nudity and Transparency	7	7	Neck	07	06
Posture	1	1	Position of Right Arm	2	2	Relative Size	0		Form	3	3	Shoulders	08	07
Perspective	5	0	Position of Left Arm	2	2	Constant Line Pressure	0	0	Detailing	3	3	Right Arm	06	05
Vertical Midline	3	0	Position of Legs	4	6	Variable Line Pressure	3	1	Identity and Sex	1	1	Left Arm	06	06
Bilateral Symmetry	3	4	Relation of Long Axes	1	1	Line Continuity	0	0	Sophistication	3	3	Chest	06	06
Horizontal Midline	6	4	Right and Left Halves	0	1	Body Shading	6	0	Height	08	07	Girth	06	05

GENERAL CHARACTERISTICS OF SUBJECT

IDENTIFICATION
No. 504
Sex F
Marital status M
Age 28 yrs. at
psychological tests

PARENTAL HISTORY					
Father					
C	H	S	D	O	
+	-	-	-	?	
Mother					
C	H	S	D	O	
(?)	+	-	-	-	

PHYSIOLOGICAL AND METABOLIC DATA

	Admission	Initial	Control	Cold pressor change	Exercise change	Smoking change
Systolic pressure	130	120	100	+20	+40	+18
Diastolic pressure	88	80	70	00	00	+16
Heart rate	64	84	61	-12	+54	+30

Age 26 yrs.	Height 68 in.	Ponderal index 12.37	
	Weight 166 lbs.	Cholesterol 160 mg. per 100 ml.	
	Overweight +16 %	Vital capacity 3.7 liters	

HABIT SURVEY

Smoking habits: light cigarette smoker

Age begun 20 yrs.   Inhalation: yes

Habits of nervous tension: 1, 4, 5, 8, 10, 12, 13, 23

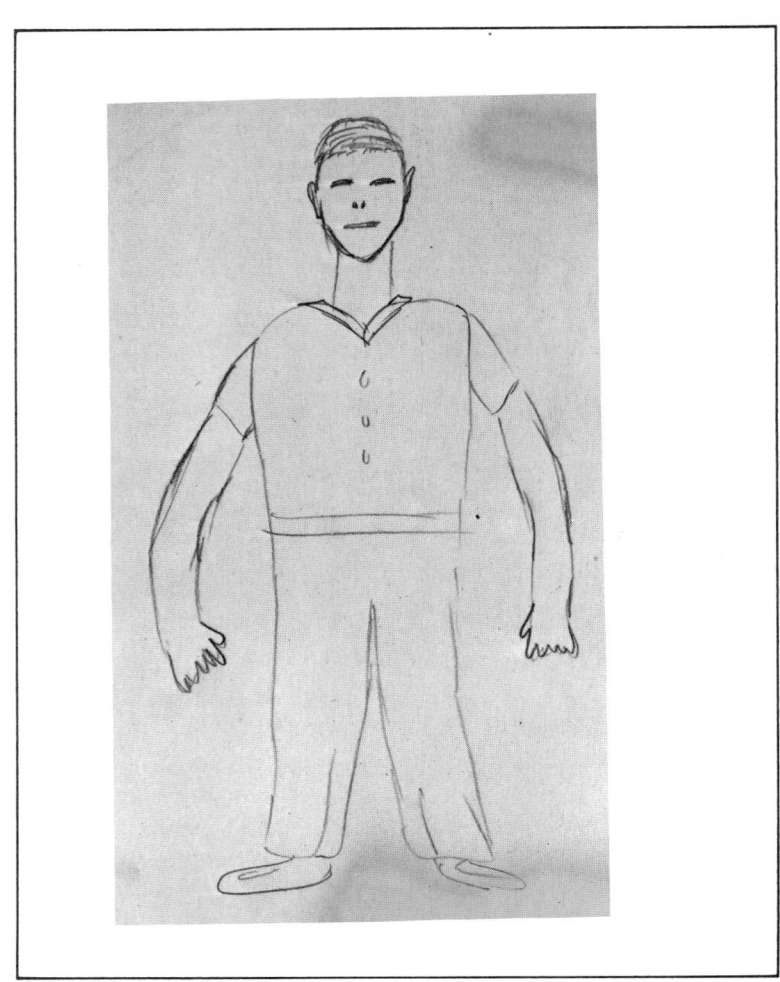

FIGURE-DRAWING CHARACTERISTICS

Structural	Male Female Both	Structural	Male	Female	Structural and Graphic	Male Female Both		Graphic, Global and Height	Male	Female	Body Proportions	Male	Female
Type	0	Omission of Appendages	0	0	Upper and Lower Halves	0	1	Hair Shading	3	3	Head	12	12
Sex Sequence	1	Position of Both Arms	0	0	Four Quarters	4	4	Nudity and Transparency	7	7	Neck	18	08
Posture	1 1	Position of Right Arm	2	5	Relative Size	0		Form	3	3	Shoulders	08	06
Perspective	0 0	Position of Left Arm	2	5	Constant Line Pressure	0	3	Detailing	3	3	Right Arm	10	06
Vertical Midline	3 3	Position of Legs	6	4	Variable Line Pressure	5	0	Identity and Sex	1	1	Left Arm	10	06
Bilateral Symmetry	3 3	Relation of Long Axes	1	1	Line Continuity	0	4	Sophistication	3	3	Chest	10	09
Horizontal Midline	4 4	Right and Left Halves	1	0	Body Shading	0	0	Height	08	08	Girth	12	06

GENERAL CHARACTERISTICS OF SUBJECT

IDENTIFICATION
No. 324
Sex M
Marital status S
Age 26 yrs. at
psychological tests

PARENTAL HISTORY				
Father				
C	H	S	D	O
(+)	-	-	-	?
Mother				
C	H	S	D	O
(?)	+	-	-	-

PHYSIOLOGICAL AND METABOLIC DATA

	Admission	Initial	Control	Cold pressor change	Exercise change	Smoking change
Systolic pressure	144	142	132	+22	+18	
Diastolic pressure	96	86	84	+24	00	
Heart rate	80	84	79	+18	+21	

Age 25 yrs.	Height 74 in.	Ponderal index 11.86
	Weight 243 lbs.	Cholesterol 280 mg. per 100 ml.
	Overweight +36 %	Vital capacity 4.4 liters

HABIT SURVEY

Smoking habits: light cigarette smoker

Age begun 22 yrs.   Inhalation: no

Habits of nervous tension: 10, 18, 19, 23, 25

FIGURE-DRAWING CHARACTERISTICS

Structural	Male Female Both	Structural	Male	Female	Structural and Graphic	Male Female Both		Graphic, Global and Height	Male	Female	Body Proportions	Male	Female
Type	0	Omission of Appendages	3	2	Upper and Lower Halves	7	3	Hair Shading	9	5	Head	16	12
Sex Sequence	0	Position of Both Arms	2	6	Four Quarters	4	4	Nudity and Transparency	7	7	Neck	14	08
Posture	3 1	Position of Right Arm	4	8	Relative Size	0		Form	3	3	Shoulders		06
Perspective	2 0	Position of Left Arm	7	8	Constant Line Pressure	0	0	Detailing	3	3	Right Arm	08	
Vertical Midline	7 0	Position of Legs	0	4	Variable Line Pressure	5	5	Identity and Sex	3	3	Left Arm		
Bilateral Symmetry	0 3	Relation of Long Axes	0	1	Line Continuity	4	2	Sophistication	3	3	Chest	09	07
Horizontal Midline	0 4	Right and Left Halves	1	1	Body Shading	0	0	Height		07	Girth	09	09

GENERAL CHARACTERISTICS OF SUBJECT

IDENTIFICATION
No. 352
Sex M
Marital status S
Age 25 yrs. at
psychological tests

PARENTAL HISTORY
Father
C   H   S   D   O
+   -   -   -   -
Mother
C   H   S   D   O
-   -   -   -   -

PHYSIOLOGICAL AND METABOLIC DATA

	Admission	Initial	Control	Cold pressor change	Exercise change	Smoking change
Systolic pressure	120	112	106	+12	+22	
Diastolic pressure	80	72	70	+20	00	
Heart rate	72	78	68	+04	+20	

	Height 68 in.	Ponderal index 12.47
Age 24 yrs.	Weight 162 lbs.	Cholesterol 222 mg. per 100 ml.
	Overweight +09 %	Vital capacity 4.3 liters

HABIT SURVEY
Smoking habits: light cigarette smoker
Age begun 18 yrs.   Inhalation: yes
Habits of nervous tension: 1, 5, 9

FIGURE-DRAWING CHARACTERISTICS

Structural	Male Female Both		Structural	Male	Female	Structural and Graphic	Male Female Both		Graphic, Global and Height	Male	Female	Body Proportions	Male	Female
Type	0		Omission of Appendages		8	Upper and Lower Halves		3	Hair Shading		5	Head		10
Sex Sequence	4		Position of Both Arms		2	Four Quarters		4	Nudity and Transparency		7	Neck		06
Posture	0		Position of Right Arm		4	Relative Size	7		Form		3	Shoulders		
Perspective	2		Position of Left Arm		7	Constant Line Pressure		1	Detailing		5	Right Arm		06
Vertical Midline	4		Position of Legs		5	Variable Line Pressure		0	Identity and Sex		3	Left Arm		
Bilateral Symmetry	0		Relation of Long Axes		1	Line Continuity		0	Sophistication		3	Chest		08
Horizontal Midline	4		Right and Left Halves		1	Body Shading		0	Height	07		Girth		10

GENERAL CHARACTERISTICS OF SUBJECT

IDENTIFICATION

No. 361

Sex M

Marital status S

Age 23 yrs. at

psychological tests

PARENTAL HISTORY

Father

C H S D O

+ + ? - -

Mother

C H S D O

- - - - -

PHYSIOLOGICAL AND METABOLIC DATA

	Admission	Initial	Control	Cold pressor change	Exercise change	Smoking change
Systolic pressure	120	124	110	+20	+26	
Diastolic pressure	80	86	86	+20	+02	
Heart rate	80	78	77	-04	+08	

Age 21 yrs.

Height   70 in.

Weight   184 lbs.

Overweight +20 %

Ponderal index 12.31

Cholesterol   285 mg. per 100 ml.

Vital capacity 4.7 liters

HABIT SURVEY

Smoking habits: occasional smoker

   Age begun 21 yrs.   Inhalation: yes

Habits of nervous tension: 6, 11, 16, 25

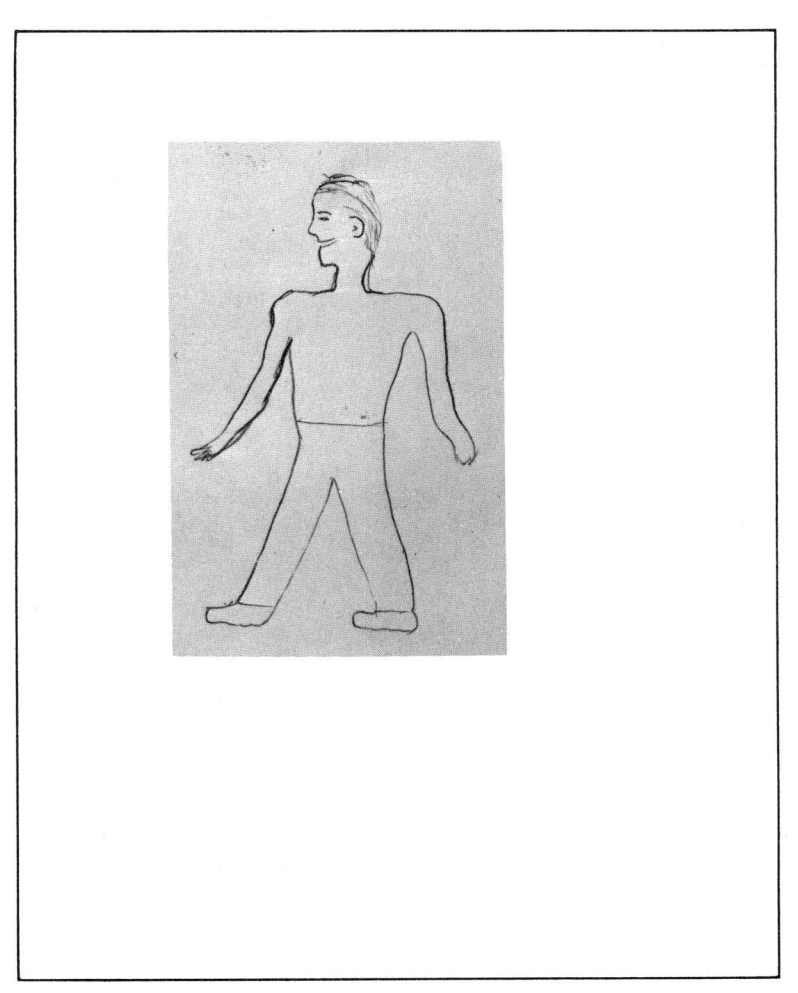

FIGURE-DRAWING CHARACTERISTICS

Structural	Male	Female	Structural	Male	Female	Structural and Graphic	Male	Female	Graphic, Global and Height	Male	Female	Body Proportions	Male	Female
	Both						Both							
Type	0		Omission of Appendages	0	0	Upper and Lower Halves	1	1	Hair Shading	3	3	Head	07	06
Sex Sequence	0		Position of Both Arms	0	0	Four Quarters	4	4	Nudity and Transparency	3	7	Neck	08	06
Posture	1	1	Position of Right Arm	2	0	Relative Size	0		Form	3	3	Shoulders	07	04
Perspective	5	0	Position of Left Arm	2	0	Constant Line Pressure	0	0	Detailing	3	3	Right Arm	04	02
Vertical Midline	0	0	Position of Legs	6	4	Variable Line Pressure	3	3	Identity and Sex	3	3	Left Arm	04	02
Bilateral Symmetry	3	3	Relation of Long Axes	1	1	Line Continuity	4	2	Sophistication	3	3	Chest	05	03
Horizontal Midline	4	4	Right and Left Halves	1	1	Body Shading	0	1	Height	04	04	Girth	05	04

GENERAL CHARACTERISTICS OF SUBJECT

<table>
<tr><td colspan="2">IDENTIFICATION</td><td colspan="2">PARENTAL HISTORY</td><td colspan="7" style="text-align:center">PHYSIOLOGICAL AND METABOLIC DATA</td><td colspan="2">HABIT SURVEY</td></tr>
</table>

IDENTIFICATION	PARENTAL HISTORY
No. 355	**Father**
Sex M	C H S D O
Marital status S	+ + - (+) +
Age 27 yrs. at	**Mother**
psychological tests	C H S D O
	- - - - -

PHYSIOLOGICAL AND METABOLIC DATA

	Admission	Initial	Control	Cold pressor change	Exercise change	Smoking change
Systolic pressure	140	146	150	+06	+34	+08
Diastolic pressure	76	86	86	+14	00	-02
Heart rate	68	72	61	+06	+20	-03

Age 25 yrs.	Height 74 in.	Ponderal index 12.74
	Weight 196 lbs.	Cholesterol 228 mg. per 100 ml.
	Overweight +09 %	Vital capacity 6.2 liters

HABIT SURVEY

Smoking habits: nonsmoker

Age begun   yrs.   Inhalation:

Habits of nervous tension: 3, 4, 5, 14, 22

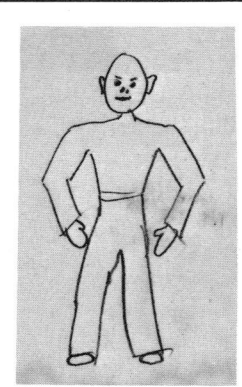

FIGURE-DRAWING CHARACTERISTICS

Structural	Male Female Both	Structural	Male	Female	Structural and Graphic	Male Female Both		Graphic, Global and Height	Male	Female	Body Proportions	Male	Female
Type	0	Omission of Appendages	0	0	Upper and Lower Halves	2	2	Hair Shading	0	5	Head	05	03
Sex Sequence	0	Position of Both Arms	0	0	Four Quarters	0	0	Nudity and Transparency	7	7	Neck	02	06
Posture	1 1	Position of Right Arm	5	5	Relative Size	0		Form	3	3	Shoulders	04	03
Perspective	0 0	Position of Left Arm	5	5	Constant Line Pressure	5	0	Detailing	5	5	Right Arm	02	02
Vertical Midline	0 0	Position of Legs	6	5	Variable Line Pressure	0	5	Identity and Sex	3	3	Left Arm	02	02
Bilateral Symmetry	5 3	Relation of Long Axes	1	1	Line Continuity	4	4	Sophistication	3	3	Chest	03	03
Horizontal Midline	4 4	Right and Left Halves	2	2	Body Shading	0	1	Height	03	02	Girth	02	02

GENERAL CHARACTERISTICS OF SUBJECT

IDENTIFICATION
No. 376
Sex M
Marital status S
Age 26 yrs. at
psychological tests

PARENTAL HISTORY
Father
C   H   S   D   O
+   -   -   -   +
Mother
C   H   S   D   O
-   -   -   -   -

PHYSIOLOGICAL AND METABOLIC DATA

	Admission	Initial	Control	Cold pressor change	Exercise change	Smoking change
Systolic pressure	136	92	92	+02	+20	-08
Diastolic pressure	78	72	72	00	+02	+02
Heart rate	92	78	87	+06	+04	00

Age 24 yrs.	Height	74	in.	Ponderal index 13.58
	Weight	162	lbs.	Cholesterol 288 mg. per 100 ml.
	Overweight -08 %			Vital capacity 5.3 liters

HABIT SURVEY
Smoking habits: heavy cigarette smoker
Age begun 18 yrs.   Inhalation: yes
Habits of nervous tension: 4, 5, 11, 17, 18,
22, 24

FIGURE-DRAWING CHARACTERISTICS

Structural	Male Female Both	Structural	Male	Female	Structural and Graphic	Male Female Both		Graphic, Global and Height	Male	Female	Body Proportions	Male	Female
Type	0	Omission of Appendages	0	0	Upper and Lower Halves	1	1	Hair Shading	1	5	Head	11	08
Sex Sequence	2	Position of Both Arms	0	2	Four Quarters	4	4	Nudity and Transparency	7	7	Neck	12	12
Posture	1 1	Position of Right Arm	0	0	Relative Size	0		Form	3	3	Shoulders	09	
Perspective	5 2	Position of Left Arm	0	7	Constant Line Pressure	0	0	Detailing	3	3	Right Arm	06	04
Vertical Midline	3 4	Position of Legs	6	1	Variable Line Pressure	2	2	Identity and Sex	3	3	Left Arm	06	
Bilateral Symmetry	3 0	Relation of Long Axes	1	1	Line Continuity	0	2	Sophistication	3	3	Chest	10	08
Horizontal Midline	4 4	Right and Left Halves	1	2	Body Shading	2	0	Height	08	06	Girth	13	10

GENERAL CHARACTERISTICS OF SUBJECT

IDENTIFICATION
No. 417
Sex M
Marital status   M
Age 27 yrs. at
psychological tests

PARENTAL HISTORY				
Father				
C	H	S	D	O
+	-	-	-	-
Mother				
C	H	S	D	O
-	+	-	-	-

PHYSIOLOGICAL AND METABOLIC DATA

	Admission	Initial	Control	Cold pressor change	Exercise change	Smoking change
Systolic pressure	164	130	125	+02	+59	
Diastolic pressure	70	76	72	+08	+06	
Heart rate	96	84	79	-15	+21	

Age 25 yrs.	Height 72 in.	Ponderal index 13.32
	Weight 158 lbs.	Cholesterol 222 mg. per 100 ml.
	Overweight -05 %	Vital capacity 4.6 liters

HABIT SURVEY
Smoking habits: nonsmoker
Age begun   yrs.   Inhalation:
Habits of nervous tension: 4, 5, 6, 9, 11, 21, 23

FIGURE-DRAWING CHARACTERISTICS

Structural	Male Female Both	Structural	Male	Female	Structural and Graphic	Male Female Both		Graphic, Global and Height	Male	Female	Body Proportions	Male	Female
Type	0	Omission of Appendages	0	0	Upper and Lower Halves	1	0	Hair Shading	3	7	Head	09	08
Sex Sequence	0	Position of Both Arms	4	4	Four Quarters	4	4	Nudity and Transparency	7	7	Neck	02	08
Posture	2	2	Position of Right Arm	7	7	Relative Size	2		Form	3	3	Shoulders		
Perspective	2	2	Position of Left Arm	6	6	Constant Line Pressure	5	0	Detailing	3	3	Right Arm		
Vertical Midline	7	7	Position of Legs	8	8	Variable Line Pressure	0	1	Identity and Sex	1	1	Left Arm	04	06
Bilateral Symmetry	0	0	Relation of Long Axes	1	1	Line Continuity	1	0	Sophistication	3	3	Chest	08	08
Horizontal Midline	6	0	Right and Left Halves	2	2	Body Shading	6	3	Height	06	06	Girth	08	08

GENERAL CHARACTERISTICS OF SUBJECT

IDENTIFICATION
No. 449
Sex M
Marital status S
Age 26 yrs. at
psychological tests

PARENTAL HISTORY				
Father				
C	H	S	D	O
+	+	-	-	+
Mother				
C	H	S	D	O
-	-	-	-	-

PHYSIOLOGICAL AND METABOLIC DATA

	Admission	Initial	Control	Cold pressor change	Exercise change	Smoking change
Systolic pressure	126	126	114	+14	+26	+10
Diastolic pressure	78	68	68	+04	+06	+06
Heart rate	74	78	86	-04	-03	+24

Age 24 yrs.	Height	74 in.	Ponderal index	13.06	
	Weight	182 lbs.	Cholesterol	210	mg. per 100 ml.
	Overweight +03 %		Vital capacity	6.2	liters

HABIT SURVEY

Smoking habits: occasional smoker

Age begun 16 yrs.   Inhalation: yes

Habits of nervous tension: 4, 5, 6, 9, 16

23, 25

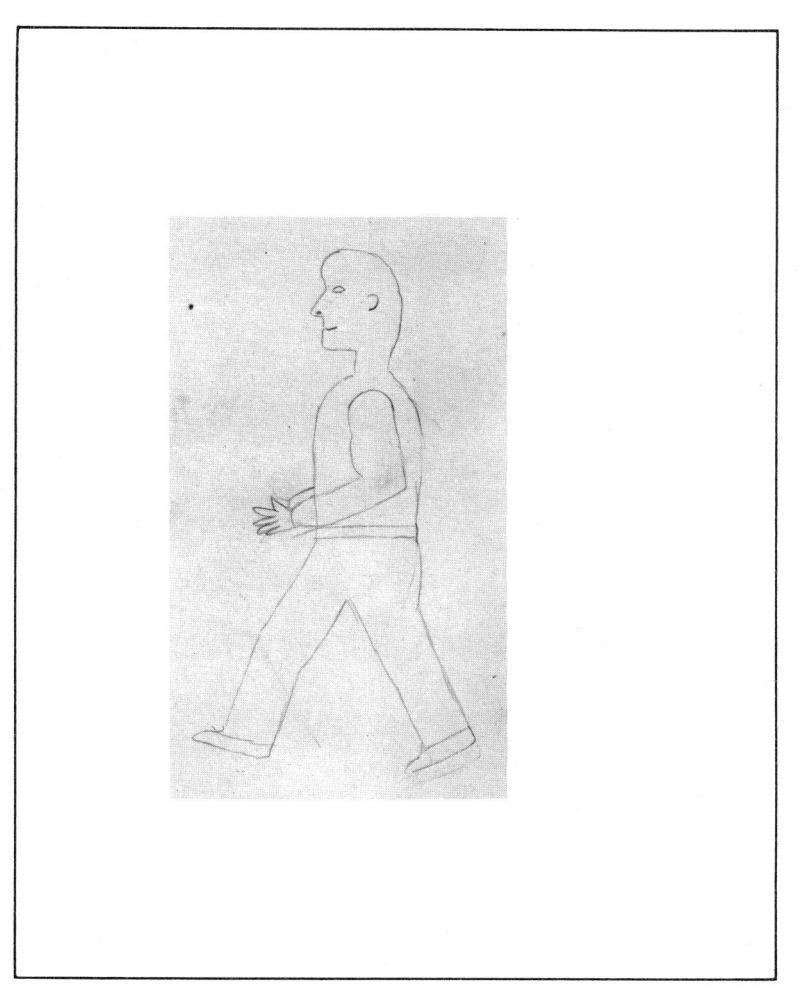

FIGURE-DRAWING CHARACTERISTICS

Structural	Male Female Both	Structural	Male	Female	Structural and Graphic	Male Female Both		Graphic, Global and Height	Male	Female	Body Proportions	Male	Female
Type	0	Omission of Appendages	0	0	Upper and Lower Halves	0	1	Hair Shading	0	1	Head	08	06
Sex Sequence	0	Position of Both Arms	4	4	Four Quarters	4	4	Nudity and Transparency	7	7	Neck	07	05
Posture	2 1	Position of Right Arm	7	7	Relative Size	0		Form	3	3	Shoulders		
Perspective	2 2	Position of Left Arm	4	4	Constant Line Pressure	1	0	Detailing	5	5	Right Arm		
Vertical Midline	4 4	Position of Legs	8	1	Variable Line Pressure	0	1	Identity and Sex	1	1	Left Arm	05	02
Bilateral Symmetry	0 0	Relation of Long Axes	1	1	Line Continuity	3	3	Sophistication	3	3	Chest	07	05
Horizontal Midline	4 4	Right and Left Halves	1	1	Body Shading	0	0	Height	05	04	Girth	08	07

GENERAL CHARACTERISTICS OF SUBJECT

IDENTIFICATION
No. 567
Sex M
Marital status M
Age 22 yrs. at
psychological tests

PARENTAL HISTORY				
Father				
C	H	S	D	O
+	-	-	-	?
Mother				
C	H	S	D	O
-	?	?	-	?

PHYSIOLOGICAL AND METABOLIC DATA

	Admission	Initial	Control	Cold pressor change	Exercise change	Smoking change
Systolic pressure	130	160	138	00	+22	+02
Diastolic pressure	70	100	88	+10	-28	+06
Heart rate	78	88	83	-12	+11	+03

Age 21 yrs.	Height 73 in.	Ponderal index 12.88
	Weight 182 lbs.	Cholesterol 237 mg. per 100 ml.
	Overweight +09 %	Vital capacity liters

HABIT SURVEY

Smoking habits: heavy cigarette smoker

Age begun 17 yrs.   Inhalation: yes

Habits of nervous tension: 4, 5, 9, 10, 11,

16, 17, 25

FIGURE-DRAWING CHARACTERISTICS

Structural	Male Female Both	Structural	Male	Female	Structural and Graphic	Male Female Both	Graphic, Global and Height	Male	Female	Body Proportions	Male	Female
Type	0	Omission of Appendages	0	0	Upper and Lower Halves	0 3	Hair Shading	3	3	Head	08	09
Sex Sequence	0	Position of Both Arms	0	1	Four Quarters	4 4	Nudity and Transparency	7	7	Neck	07	07
Posture	1 1	Position of Right Arm	2	2	Relative Size	4	Form	3	3	Shoulders	07	08
Perspective	5 5	Position of Left Arm	2	5	Constant Line Pressure	1 1	Detailing	3	3	Right Arm	04	04
Vertical Midline	0 0	Position of Legs	4	4	Variable Line Pressure	0 0	Identity and Sex	1	1	Left Arm	04	06
Bilateral Symmetry	3 3	Relation of Long Axes	1	1	Line Continuity	0 0	Sophistication	3	3	Chest	07	07
Horizontal Midline	4 4	Right and Left Halves	1	1	Body Shading	3 3	Height	06	07	Girth	09	07

GENERAL CHARACTERISTICS OF SUBJECT

IDENTIFICATION
No. 578
Sex M
Marital status M
Age 23 yrs. at
psychological tests

PARENTAL HISTORY
Father
C H S D O
+ - - - -
Mother
C H S D O
- - - - -

PHYSIOLOGICAL AND METABOLIC DATA

	Admission	Initial	Control	Cold pressor change	Exercise change	Smoking change
Systolic pressure	90	112	94	+10	+56	
Diastolic pressure	60	58	48	+14	00	
Heart rate	80	72	65	+20	+21	

Age 23 yrs.	Height	72 in.	Ponderal index 13.43
	Weight	154 lbs.	Cholesterol mg. per 100 ml.
	Overweight -06 %		Vital capacity 5.0 liters

HABIT SURVEY
Smoking habits: heavy cigarette smoker
Age begun 20 yrs.   Inhalation: yes
Habits of nervous tension: 6, 14

Plate 194   DRAWINGS AT AN INTERMEDIATE LEVEL OF SOPHISTICATION   237

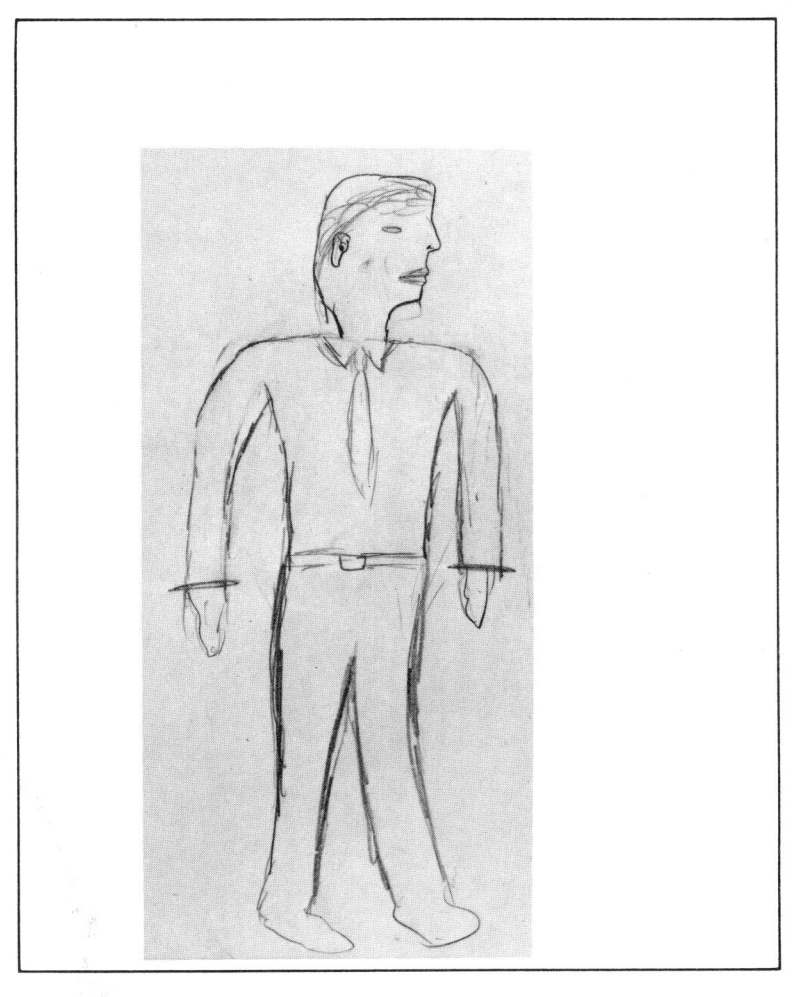

FIGURE-DRAWING CHARACTERISTICS

Structural	Male Female Both		Structural	Male	Female	Structural and Graphic	Male Female Both		Graphic, Global and Height	Male	Female	Body Proportions	Male	Female
Type	0		Omission of Appendages	0	0	Upper and Lower Halves	3	3	Hair Shading	1	3	Head	09	14
Sex Sequence	0		Position of Both Arms	0	0	Four Quarters	4	4	Nudity and Transparency	7	6	Neck	12	12
Posture	1	1	Position of Right Arm	0	0	Relative Size	0		Form	3	3	Shoulders	09	08
Perspective	5	5	Position of Left Arm	0	0	Constant Line Pressure	0	0	Detailing	3	3	Right Arm	08	06
Vertical Midline	3	3	Position of Legs	5	4	Variable Line Pressure	5	5	Identity and Sex	1	1	Left Arm	06	04
Bilateral Symmetry	3	3	Relation of Long Axes	1	1	Line Continuity	0	0	Sophistication	3	3	Chest	08	08
Horizontal Midline	4	4	Right and Left Halves	1	1	Body Shading	0	5	Height	08	07	Girth	09	08

GENERAL CHARACTERISTICS OF SUBJECT

IDENTIFICATION
No. 617
Sex M
Marital status S
Age 25 yrs. at
psychological tests

PARENTAL HISTORY				
Father				
C	H	S	D	O
+	-	+	-	-
Mother				
C	H	S	D	O
-	-	-	-	-

PHYSIOLOGICAL AND METABOLIC DATA

	Admission	Initial	Control	Cold pressor change	Exercise change	Smoking change
Systolic pressure	150	122	118	+32	+28	+02
Diastolic pressure	80	78	72	+34	-02	-01
Heart rate	76	68	72	00	+28	+05

Age 22 yrs.	Height 68 in.	Ponderal index 13.10
	Weight 140 lbs.	Cholesterol 197 mg. per 100 ml.
	Overweight -04 %	Vital capacity 4.6 liters

HABIT SURVEY
Smoking habits: nonsmoker
Age begun   yrs.   Inhalation:
Habits of nervous tension: 3, 4, 5, 7, 9, 10,
18

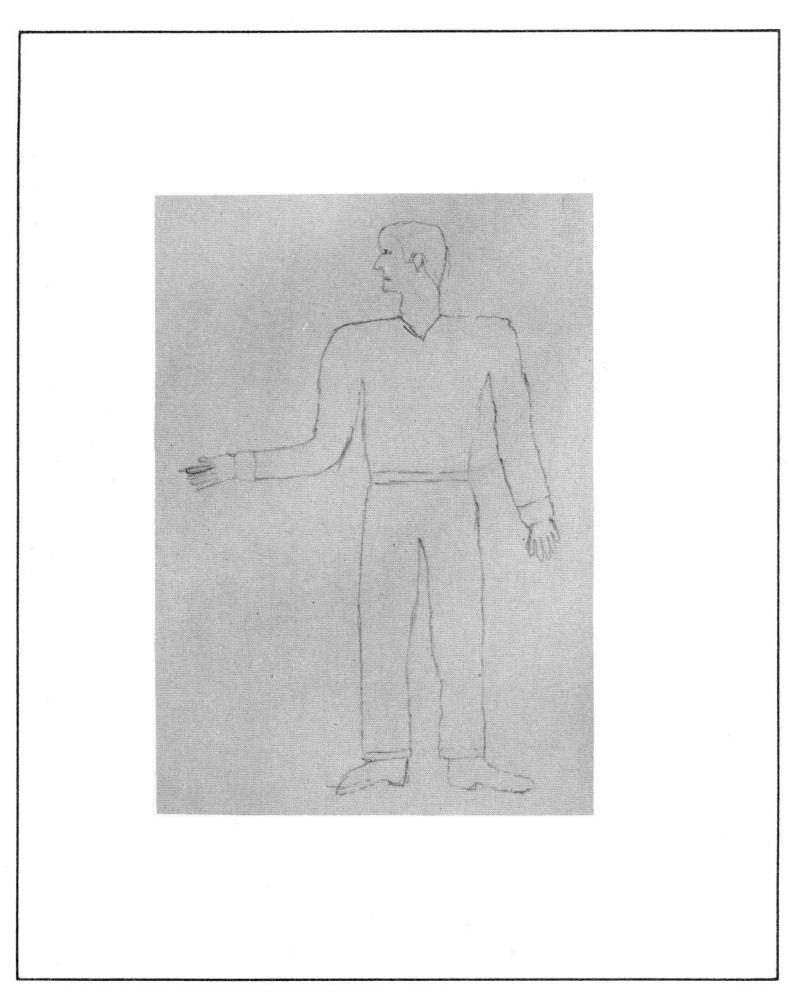

FIGURE-DRAWING CHARACTERISTICS

Structural	Male Female Both	Structural	Male	Female	Structural and Graphic	Male Female Both	Graphic, Global and Height	Male	Female	Body Proportions	Male	Female
Type	0	Omission of Appendages	0	0	Upper and Lower Halves	0 0	Hair Shading	5	5	Head	05	05
Sex Sequence	0	Position of Both Arms	1	0	Four Quarters	4 4	Nudity and Transparency	7	7	Neck	08	07
Posture	1 1	Position of Right Arm	4	2	Relative Size	0	Form	3	3	Shoulders	07	06
Perspective	5 5	Position of Left Arm	2	2	Constant Line Pressure	0 0	Detailing	3	3	Right Arm	06	04
Vertical Midline	0 0	Position of Legs	4	6	Variable Line Pressure	1 1	Identity and Sex	1	1	Left Arm	06	04
Bilateral Symmetry	3 3	Relation of Long Axes	1	1	Line Continuity	0 0	Sophistication	3	3	Chest	06	05
Horizontal Midline	4 0	Right and Left Halves	3	1	Body Shading	0 1	Height	06	05	Girth	06	06

GENERAL CHARACTERISTICS OF SUBJECT

IDENTIFICATION
No. 633
Sex M
Marital status M
Age 25 yrs. at
psychological tests

PARENTAL HISTORY
Father
C H S D O
+ ? - - -
Mother
C H S D O
- - - - -

PHYSIOLOGICAL AND METABOLIC DATA

	Admission	Initial	Control	Cold pressor change	Exercise change	Smoking change
Systolic pressure	120	124	116	+10	+26	+08
Diastolic pressure	80	70	66	+28	+06	+10
Heart rate	80	84	76	-08	+12	+16

Age 22 yrs. Height 70 in. Ponderal index 12.84
Weight 162 lbs. Cholesterol 197 mg. per 100 ml.
Overweight +05 % Vital capacity 5.0 liters

HABIT SURVEY
Smoking habits: light cigarette smoker
Age begun 16 yrs.   Inhalation: yes
Habits of nervous tension: 4, 5, 9

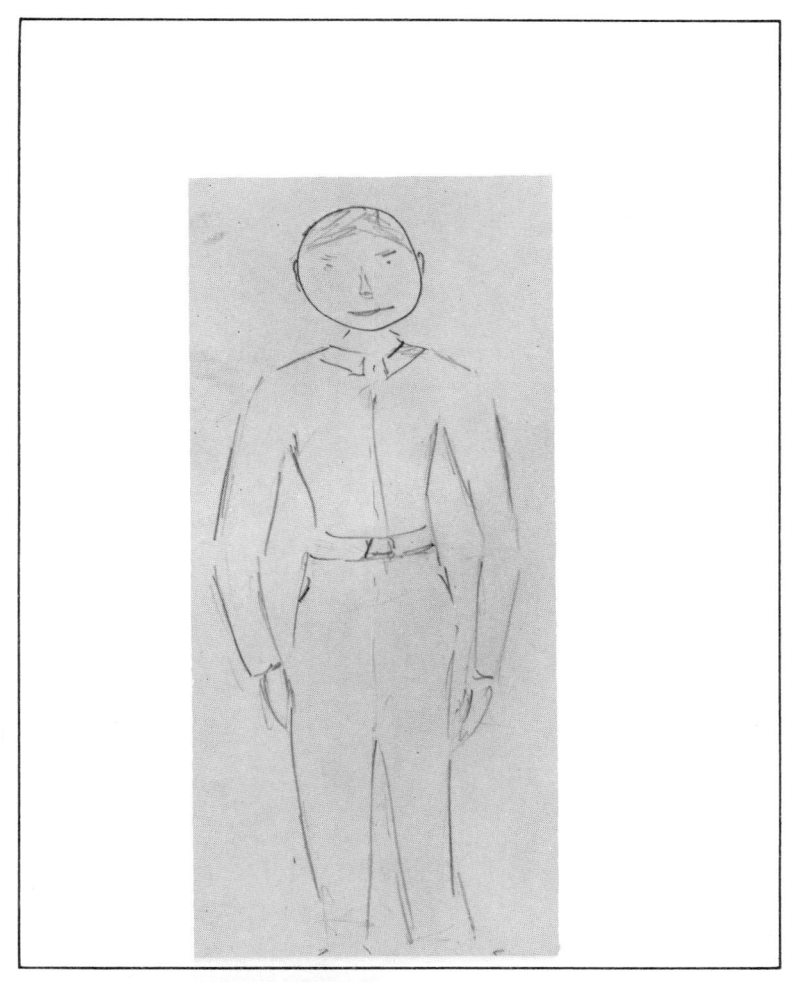

FIGURE-DRAWING CHARACTERISTICS

Structural	Male Female Both	Structural	Male	Female	Structural and Graphic	Male Female Both		Graphic, Global and Height	Male	Female	Body Proportions	Male	Female
Type	0	Omission of Appendages	8	0	Upper and Lower Halves	7	3	Hair Shading	1	1	Head	09	08
Sex Sequence	0	Position of Both Arms	0	0	Four Quarters	4	4	Nudity and Transparency	7	7	Neck	05	08
Posture	0 1	Position of Right Arm	5	5	Relative Size	2		Form	3	3	Shoulders	09	09
Perspective	0 0	Position of Left Arm	5	5	Constant Line Pressure	0	0	Detailing	3	3	Right Arm	10	08
Vertical Midline	3 3	Position of Legs	4	4	Variable Line Pressure	3	3	Identity and Sex	3	1	Left Arm	08	08
Bilateral Symmetry	3 3	Relation of Long Axes	1	1	Line Continuity	0	0	Sophistication	3	3	Chest	06	07
Horizontal Midline	4 4	Right and Left Halves	1	1	Body Shading	0	0	Height		08	Girth	07	07

GENERAL CHARACTERISTICS OF SUBJECT

IDENTIFICATION
No. 636
Sex F
Marital status M
Age 25 yrs. at psychological tests

PARENTAL HISTORY
Father
C   H   S   D   O
+   U   -   -   -
Mother
C   H   S   D   O
-   U   -   -   -

PHYSIOLOGICAL AND METABOLIC DATA

	Admission	Initial	Control	Cold pressor change	Exercise change	Smoking change
Systolic pressure	110	112	102	+02	+18	+02
Diastolic pressure	70	62	52	+10	-10	00
Heart rate	72	80	75	+04	+16	-01

Age 23 yrs.	Height 64 in.	Ponderal index 13.11
	Weight 116 lbs.	Cholesterol 217 mg. per 100 ml.
	Overweight -09 %	Vital capacity 2.8 liters

HABIT SURVEY
Smoking habits: nonsmoker
Age begun   yrs.   Inhalation:
Habits of nervous tension: 1, 2, 5, 6, 9,
15, 25

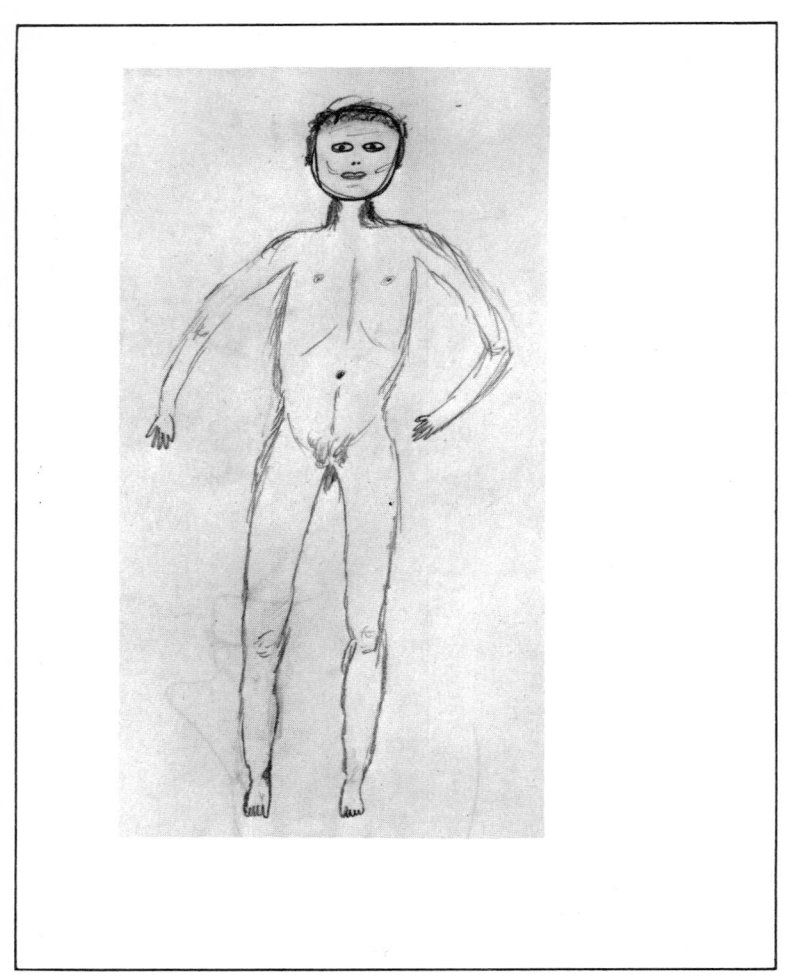

FIGURE-DRAWING CHARACTERISTICS

Structural	Male Female Both		Structural	Male	Female	Structural and Graphic	Male Female Both		Graphic, Global and Height	Male	Female	Body Proportions	Male	Female
Type	0		Omission of Appendages	0	0	Upper and Lower Halves	1	1	Hair Shading	3	3	Head	08	11
Sex Sequence	2		Position of Both Arms	1	4	Four Quarters	4	4	Nudity and Transparency	0	0	Neck	08	10
Posture	1	1	Position of Right Arm	2	7	Relative Size	4		Form	3	3	Shoulders	06	
Perspective	0	2	Position of Left Arm	5	2	Constant Line Pressure	0	0	Detailing	3	3	Right Arm	06	
Vertical Midline	0	4	Position of Legs	5	1	Variable Line Pressure	4	4	Identity and Sex	1	1	Left Arm	06	08
Bilateral Symmetry	2	0	Relation of Long Axes	1	1	Line Continuity	0	0	Sophistication	3	3	Chest	06	07
Horizontal Midline	0	0	Right and Left Halves	1	1	Body Shading	3	1	Height	07	08	Girth	06	08

GENERAL CHARACTERISTICS OF SUBJECT

IDENTIFICATION
No. 676
Sex M
Marital status M
Age 30 yrs. at
psychological tests

PARENTAL HISTORY
Father
C   H   S   D   O
+   -   -   -   -
Mother
C   H   S   D   O
-   -   -   -   -

PHYSIOLOGICAL AND METABOLIC DATA

	Admission	Initial	Control	Cold pressor change	Exercise change	Smoking change
Systolic pressure	120	118	110	+04	+30	+03
Diastolic pressure	80	64	62	+08	-04	+03
Heart rate	80	60	54	+06	+21	+10

Age 29 yrs.	Height	72	in.	Ponderal index	13.38	
	Weight	156	lbs.	Cholesterol	217	mg. per 100 ml.
	Overweight	-09	%	Vital capacity	5.5	liters

HABIT SURVEY

Smoking habits: occasional smoker

Age begun 19 yrs.   Inhalation: yes

Habits of nervous tension: 5, 6, 9, 11, 14, 16, 18, 21, 24

FIGURE-DRAWING CHARACTERISTICS

Structural	Male	Female	Structural	Male	Female	Structural and Graphic	Male	Female	Graphic, Global and Height	Male	Female	Body Proportions	Male	Female
	Both						Both							
Type	0		Omission of Appendages	0	0	Upper and Lower Halves	1	3	Hair Shading	1	3	Head	06	09
Sex Sequence	2		Position of Both Arms	4	4	Four Quarters	4	4	Nudity and Transparency	7	7	Neck	06	08
Posture	1	1	Position of Right Arm	7	7	Relative Size	0		Form	3	3	Shoulders		
Perspective	2	2	Position of Left Arm	4	4	Constant Line Pressure	1	1	Detailing	3	3	Right Arm		
Vertical Midline	7	4	Position of Legs	1	1	Variable Line Pressure	0	0	Identity and Sex	1	1	Left Arm	06	05
Bilateral Symmetry	0	0	Relation of Long Axes	1	1	Line Continuity	0	0	Sophistication	3	3	Chest	09	08
Horizontal Midline	4	4	Right and Left Halves	3	1	Body Shading	4	2	Height	07	06	Girth	09	10

GENERAL CHARACTERISTICS OF SUBJECT

IDENTIFICATION
No. 740
Sex M
Marital status S
Age 27 yrs. at psychological tests

PARENTAL HISTORY

Father					
C	H	S	D	O	
+	+	−	−	−	
Mother					
C	H	S	D	O	
−	+	−	−	+	

PHYSIOLOGICAL AND METABOLIC DATA

	Admission	Initial	Control	Cold pressor change	Exercise change	Smoking change
Systolic pressure	140	142	130	+12	+52	−07
Diastolic pressure	90	84	82	+12	+04	−01
Heart rate	76	84	83	+16	+20	−07

Age 27 yrs.	Height 77 in.	Ponderal index 11.68
	Weight 286 lbs.	Cholesterol 222 mg. per 100 ml.
	Overweight +45 %	Vital capacity 4.6 liters

HABIT SURVEY

Smoking habits: mixed smoker

  Age begun 19 yrs.   Inhalation: no

Habits of nervous tension: 1, 3, 4, 5, 6, 9, 11, 17, 18, 19, 21, 22, 24, 25

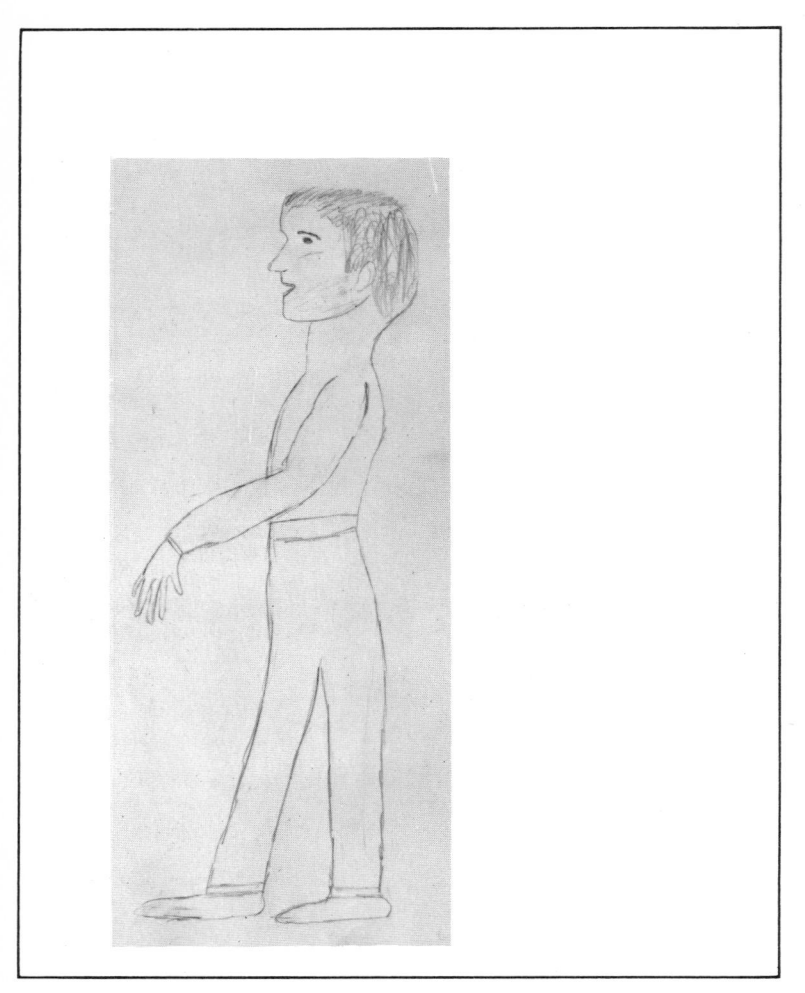

FIGURE-DRAWING CHARACTERISTICS

Structural	Male Female Both	Structural	Male	Female	Structural and Graphic	Male Female Both		Graphic, Global and Height	Male	Female	Body Proportions	Male	Female
Type	0	Omission of Appendages	0	3	Upper and Lower Halves	3	7	Hair Shading	3	2	Head	11	13
Sex Sequence	2	Position of Both Arms	4	4	Four Quarters	4	4	Nudity and Transparency	7	7	Neck	16	18
Posture	1 0	Position of Right Arm	7	7	Relative Size	4		Form	3	3	Shoulders		
Perspective	2 2	Position of Left Arm	4	4	Constant Line Pressure	0	0	Detailing	3	3	Right Arm		
Vertical Midline	4 4	Position of Legs	6	1	Variable Line Pressure	1	1	Identity and Sex	1	1	Left Arm	07	08
Bilateral Symmetry	0 0	Relation of Long Axes	1	1	Line Continuity	0	0	Sophistication	3	3	Chest	07	10
Horizontal Midline	4 4	Right and Left Halves	2	1	Body Shading	0	0	Height	08		Girth	07	09

GENERAL CHARACTERISTICS OF SUBJECT

IDENTIFICATION
No. 748
Sex M
Marital status S
Age 24 yrs. at
psychological tests

PARENTAL HISTORY
Father
C   H   S   D   O
+   +   +   -   +
Mother
C   H   S   D   O
-   -   -   -   ?

PHYSIOLOGICAL AND METABOLIC DATA

	Admission	Initial	Control	Cold pressor change	Exercise change	Smoking change
Systolic pressure	120	114	108	+12	+34	
Diastolic pressure	75	80	74	+16	-10	
Heart rate	72	66	65	+20	+42	

Age 21 yrs.	Height	70 in.	Ponderal index 12.76
	Weight	165 lbs.	Cholesterol 250 mg. per 100 ml.
	Overweight +08 %		Vital capacity 4.9 liters

HABIT SURVEY
Smoking habits: nonsmoker
Age begun   yrs.   Inhalation:
Habits of nervous tension: 4, 5, 6, 9, 16,
21, 25

FIGURE-DRAWING CHARACTERISTICS

Structural	Male Female Both		Structural	Male	Female	Structural and Graphic	Male Female Both		Graphic, Global and Height	Male	Female	Body Proportions	Male	Female
Type	0		Omission of Appendages	0	0	Upper and Lower Halves	1	1	Hair Shading	2	3	Head	05	04
Sex Sequence	0		Position of Both Arms	1	1	Four Quarters	4	4	Nudity and Transparency	7	7	Neck	04	04
Posture	1	1	Position of Right Arm	4	2	Relative Size	0		Form	3	3	Shoulders	05	03
Perspective	0	0	Position of Left Arm	5	0	Constant Line Pressure	1	1	Detailing	3	3	Right Arm	02	02
Vertical Midline	3	0	Position of Legs	6	1	Variable Line Pressure	0	0	Identity and Sex	1	1	Left Arm	03	02
Bilateral Symmetry	3	3	Relation of Long Axes	1	1	Line Continuity	0	0	Sophistication	3	3	Chest	03	03
Horizontal Midline	4	4	Right and Left Halves	0	1	Body Shading	6	5	Height	04	03	Girth	05	04

GENERAL CHARACTERISTICS OF SUBJECT

IDENTIFICATION
No. 769
Sex M
Marital status M
Age 26 yrs. at
psychological tests

PARENTAL HISTORY				
Father				
C	H	S	D	O
+	-	+	-	-
Mother				
C	H	S	D	O
-	-	-	-	+

PHYSIOLOGICAL AND METABOLIC DATA

	Admission	Initial	Control	Cold pressor change	Exercise change	Smoking change
Systolic pressure	120	112	104	+12	+32	+13
Diastolic pressure	70	68	62	+14	-04	+19
Heart rate	84	72	68	-04	+32	+11

Age 26 yrs.	Height	74	in.	Ponderal index	13.05	
	Weight	182	lbs.	Cholesterol	308	mg. per 100 ml.
	Overweight	+01	%	Vital capacity	5.9	liters

HABIT SURVEY

Smoking habits: nonsmoker

  Age begun   yrs.   Inhalation:

Habits of nervous tension: 5, 6, 21

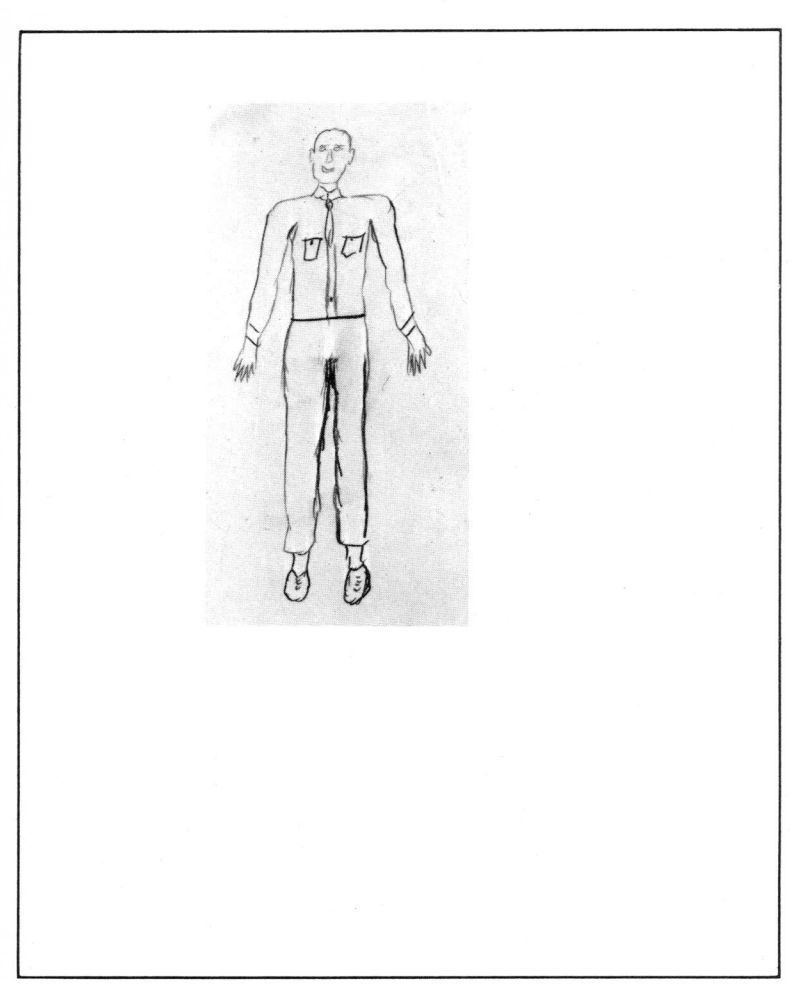

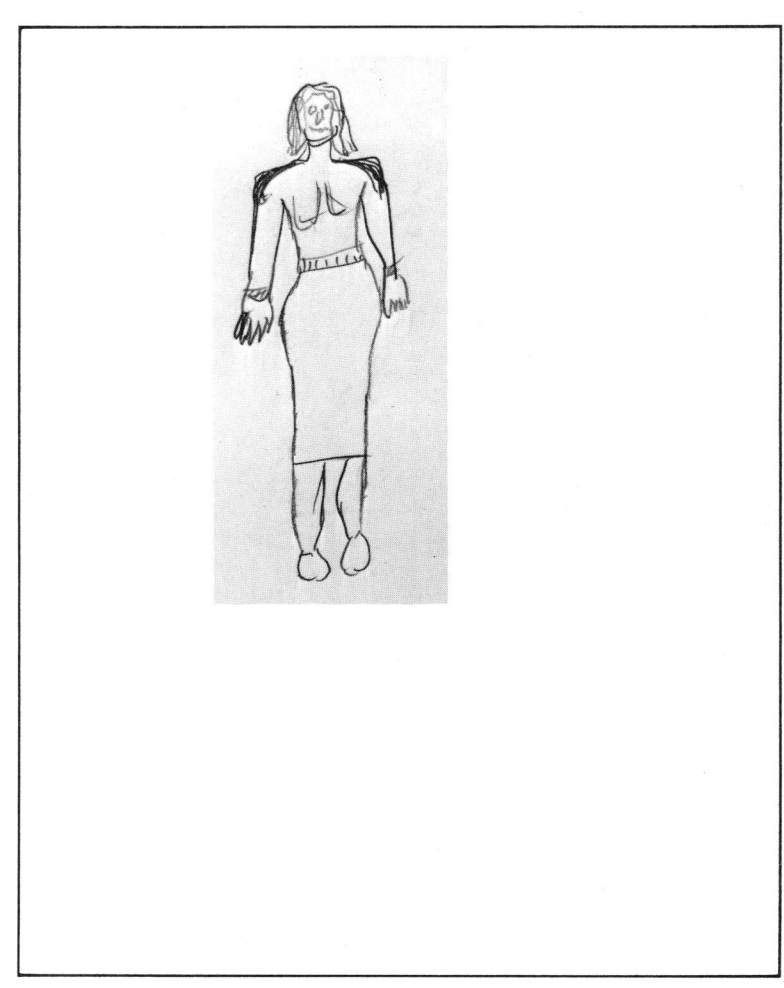

FIGURE-DRAWING CHARACTERISTICS

Structural	Male Female Both		Structural	Male	Female	Structural and Graphic	Male Female Both		Graphic, Global and Height	Male	Female	Body Proportions	Male	Female
Type	0		Omission of Appendages	0	0	Upper and Lower Halves	1	1	Hair Shading	0	3	Head	04	04
Sex Sequence	0		Position of Both Arms	0	0	Four Quarters	4	4	Nudity and Transparency	7	7	Neck	04	04
Posture	1	1	Position of Right Arm	1	0	Relative Size	4		Form	3	3	Shoulders	05	05
Perspective	0	0	Position of Left Arm	1	0	Constant Line Pressure	0	0	Detailing	3	3	Right Arm	04	04
Vertical Midline	3	0	Position of Legs	4	4	Variable Line Pressure	3	5	Identity and Sex	1	1	Left Arm	04	03
Bilateral Symmetry	3	3	Relation of Long Axes	1	1	Line Continuity	0	1	Sophistication	3	3	Chest	03	03
Horizontal Midline	4	4	Right and Left Halves	2	2	Body Shading	0	1	Height	05	05	Girth	04	04

GENERAL CHARACTERISTICS OF SUBJECT

IDENTIFICATION
No. F63
Sex M
Marital status S
Age 24 yrs. at psychological tests

PARENTAL HISTORY				
Father				
C	H	S	D	O
+	-	-	-	-
Mother				
C	H	S	D	O
-	-	-	-	+

PHYSIOLOGICAL AND METABOLIC DATA

	Admission	Initial	Control	Cold pressor change	Exercise change	Smoking change
Systolic pressure	110	104	104	-10	+12	-10
Diastolic pressure	56	78	78	-08	+04	-01
Heart rate	70	64	64	+08	+12	+24

Age 21 yrs.	Height 70 in.	Ponderal index 13.62
	Weight 136 lbs.	Cholesterol 222 mg. per 100 ml.
	Overweight -11 %	Vital capacity liters

HABIT SURVEY

Smoking habits: light cigarette smoker

Age begun 20 yrs.   Inhalation: yes

Habits of nervous tension: 3, 4, 5, 6, 9, 11, 16, 22

STRONG VOCATIONAL INTEREST TEST

Occupation	Artist	Psychologist	Architect	Physician	Osteopath	Dentist	Veterinarian	Mathematician	Physicist	Engineer	Chemist	Production Manager
Standard Score	31	42	36	61	56	42	37	32	33	45	49	41

Occupation	Farmer	Aviator	Carpenter	Printer	Math.-Sci. Teacher	Ind. Arts Teacher	Voc. Agric. Teacher	Policeman	Forest Serv. Man	Y.M.C.A. Phys. Dir.	Personnel Director	Public Administrator
Standard Score	37	46	20	32	42	17	30	37	31	33	37	45

Occupation	Y.M.C.A. Secretary	Soc. Sci. H.S. Teacher	City Sch. Sup't.	Social Worker	Minister	Musician Performer	C.P.A.	Senior C.P.A.	Accountant	Office Man	Purchasing Agent	Banker
Standard Score	17	26	27	37	58	42	34	39	22	27	24	18

Occupation	Mortician	Pharmacist	Sales Manager	Real Est. Manager	Life Ins. Salesman	Advertising Man	Lawyer	Author-Journalist	President Mfg. Co.	Interest Maturity	Occupational Level	Masculinity-Femininity
Standard Score	26	36	32	32	31	33	38	35	36	51	61	50

FIGURE-DRAWING CHARACTERISTICS

Structural	Male	Female	Structural	Male	Female	Structural and Graphic	Male	Female	Graphic, Global and Height	Male	Female	Body Proportions	Male	Female
	Both						Both							
Type	0		Omission of Appendages	2	0	Upper and Lower Halves	0	3	Hair Shading	1	3	Head	09	09
Sex Sequence	0		Position of Both Arms	6	0	Four Quarters	4	4	Nudity and Transparency	7	7	Neck	02	12
Posture	1	1	Position of Right Arm	8	0	Relative Size	4		Form	3	3	Shoulders	09	09
Perspective	0	0	Position of Left Arm	8	0	Constant Line Pressure	0	0	Detailing	3	3	Right Arm		06
Vertical Midline	0	0	Position of Legs	6	4	Variable Line Pressure	1	4	Identity and Sex	1	1	Left Arm		06
Bilateral Symmetry	2	2	Relation of Long Axes	1	1	Line Continuity	0	0	Sophistication	3	3	Chest	07	07
Horizontal Midline	4	4	Right and Left Halves	1	1	Body Shading	5	5	Height	06	07	Girth	08	06

GENERAL CHARACTERISTICS OF SUBJECT

IDENTIFICATION
No. F64
Sex M
Marital status S
Age 24 yrs. at
psychological tests

PARENTAL HISTORY				
Father				
C	H	S	D	O
+	–	–	+	–
Mother				
C	H	S	D	O
–	–	–	–	+

PHYSIOLOGICAL AND METABOLIC DATA

	Admission	Initial	Control	Cold pressor change	Exercise change	Smoking change
Systolic pressure	122	90	86	–06	+30	+02
Diastolic pressure	72	68	62	–04	+26	+02
Heart rate	68	72	75	+08	+07	–02

Age 23 yrs.	Height 66 in.	Ponderal index 11.83
	Weight 174 lbs.	Cholesterol 320 mg. per 100 ml.
	Overweight +24 %	Vital capacity liters

HABIT SURVEY

Smoking habits: nonsmoker

    Age begun   yrs.   Inhalation:

Habits of nervous tension:

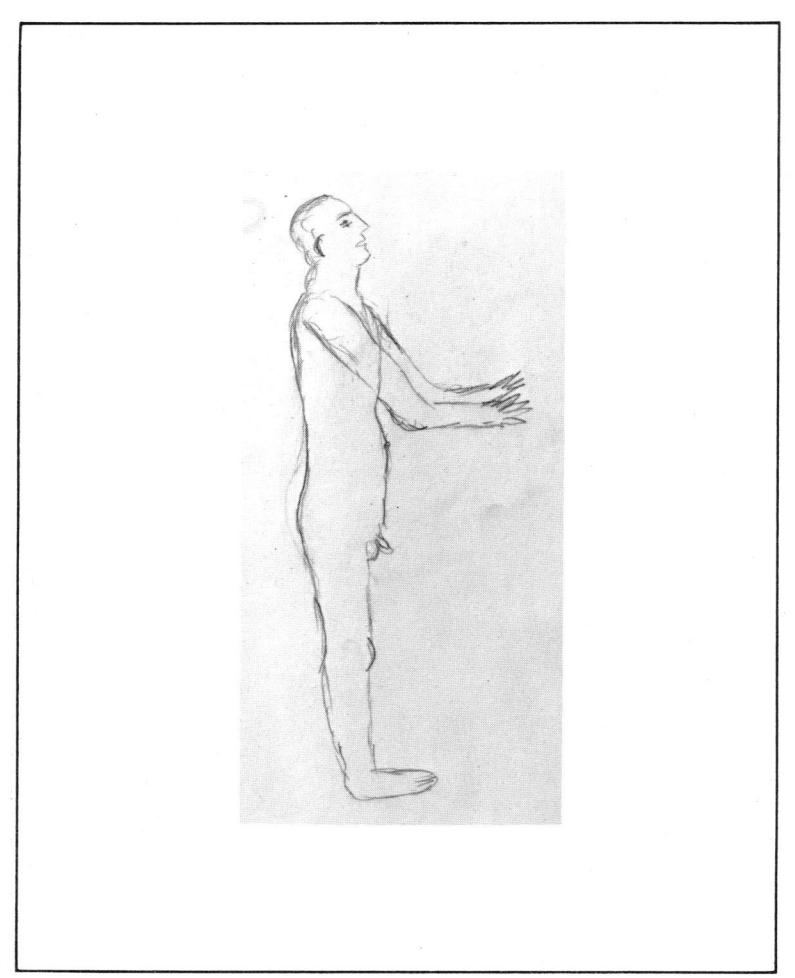

FIGURE-DRAWING CHARACTERISTICS

Structural	Male Female / Both	Structural	Male	Female	Structural and Graphic	Male Female / Both		Graphic, Global and Height	Male	Female	Body Proportions	Male	Female
Type	0	Omission of Appendages	0	0	Upper and Lower Halves	0	1	Hair Shading	2	3	Head	06	04
Sex Sequence	2	Position of Both Arms	2	0	Four Quarters	4	4	Nudity and Transparency	0	7	Neck	08	04
Posture	1	1	Position of Right Arm	2	0	Relative Size	0		Form	3	3	Shoulders		05
Perspective	2	0	Position of Left Arm	7	5	Constant Line Pressure	0	0	Detailing	3	3	Right Arm	06	04
Vertical Midline	4	0	Position of Legs	1	4	Variable Line Pressure	2	1	Identity and Sex	1	1	Left Arm		04
Bilateral Symmetry	0	3	Relation of Long Axes	1	1	Line Continuity	0	0	Sophistication	3	3	Chest	06	05
Horizontal Midline	0	4	Right and Left Halves	1	2	Body Shading	0	7	Height	06	05	Girth	05	05

GENERAL CHARACTERISTICS OF SUBJECT

IDENTIFICATION

No. F71
Sex M
Marital status S
Age 23 yrs. at
psychological tests

PARENTAL HISTORY

Father

C	H	S	D	O
+	-	-	-	-

Mother

C	H	S	D	O
-	-	-	-	-

PHYSIOLOGICAL AND METABOLIC DATA

	Admission	Initial	Control	Cold pressor change	Exercise change	Smoking change
Systolic pressure	122	128	112	-02	+08	00
Diastolic pressure	60	84	80	+12	+16	+01
Heart rate	80	84	77	-04	+21	-07

Age 21 yrs.
Height 70 in.
Weight 168 lbs.
Overweight +10 %

Ponderal index 12.68
Cholesterol 217 mg. per 100 ml.
Vital capacity liters

HABIT SURVEY

Smoking habits: nonsmoker
Age begun yrs. Inhalation:
Habits of nervous tension: 6, 11, 25

FIGURE-DRAWING CHARACTERISTICS

Structural	Male Female Both	Structural	Male	Female	Structural and Graphic	Male Female Both		Graphic, Global and Height	Male	Female	Body Proportions	Male	Female
Type	0	Omission of Appendages	0	0	Upper and Lower Halves	3	3	Hair Shading	1	2	Head	06	07
Sex Sequence	0	Position of Both Arms	4	4	Four Quarters	4	4	Nudity and Transparency	6	6	Neck	06	07
Posture	2 1	Position of Right Arm	7	7	Relative Size	3		Form	3	3	Shoulders		
Perspective	2 2	Position of Left Arm	4	4	Constant Line Pressure	0	0	Detailing	3	3	Right Arm		
Vertical Midline	7 4	Position of Legs	8	1	Variable Line Pressure	2	5	Identity and Sex	1	1	Left Arm	07	08
Bilateral Symmetry	0 0	Relation of Long Axes	1	1	Line Continuity	0	0	Sophistication	3	3	Chest	06	06
Horizontal Midline	4 4	Right and Left Halves	2	2	Body Shading	0	6	Height	08	08	Girth	04	07

GENERAL CHARACTERISTICS OF SUBJECT

IDENTIFICATION
No. G22
Sex M
Marital status M
Age 27 yrs. at
psychological tests

PARENTAL HISTORY				
Father				
C	H	S	D	O
+	+	-	-	+
Mother				
C	H	S	D	O
-	-	-	-	-

PHYSIOLOGICAL AND METABOLIC DATA

	Admission	Initial	Control	Cold pressor change	Exercise change	Smoking change
Systolic pressure	120	118	118	+14	+40	+03
Diastolic pressure	80	78	70	+18	+04	-06
Heart rate	80	84	70	+16	+37	+14

	Height	66 in.	Ponderal index 13.33
Age 26 yrs.	Weight	121 lbs.	Cholesterol 203 mg. per 100 ml.
	Overweight -15 %		Vital capacity liters

HABIT SURVEY
Smoking habits: mixed smoker
Age begun 19 yrs.   Inhalation: sometimes
Habits of nervous tension: 5, 6, 9, 11

STRONG VOCATIONAL INTEREST TEST

Occupation	Artist	Psychologist	Architect	Physician	Osteopath	Dentist	Veterinarian	Mathematician	Physicist	Engineer	Chemist	Production Manager
Standard Score	27	55	43	59	35	35	13	43	39	45	51	29

Occupation	Farmer	Aviator	Carpenter	Printer	Math.-Sci. Teacher	Ind. Arts Teacher	Voc. Agric. Teacher	Policeman	Forest Serv. Man	Y.M.C.A. Phys. Dir.	Personnel Director	Public Administrator
Standard Score	37	39	25	39	54	27	37	27	38	25	43	51

Occupation	Y.M.C.A. Secretary	Soc. Sci. H.S. Teacher	City Sch. Sup't.	Social Worker	Minister	Musician Performer	C.P.A.	Senior C.P.A.	Accountant	Office Man	Purchasing Agent	Banker
Standard Score	30	35	39	42	59	46	35	52	29	32	17	18

Occupation	Mortician	Pharmacist	Sales Manager	Real Est. Manager	Life Ins. Salesman	Advertising Man	Lawyer	Author-Journalist	President Mfg. Co.	Interest Maturity	Occupational Level	Masculinity-Femininity
Standard Score	14	25	19	22	12	27	28	29	16	58	54	56

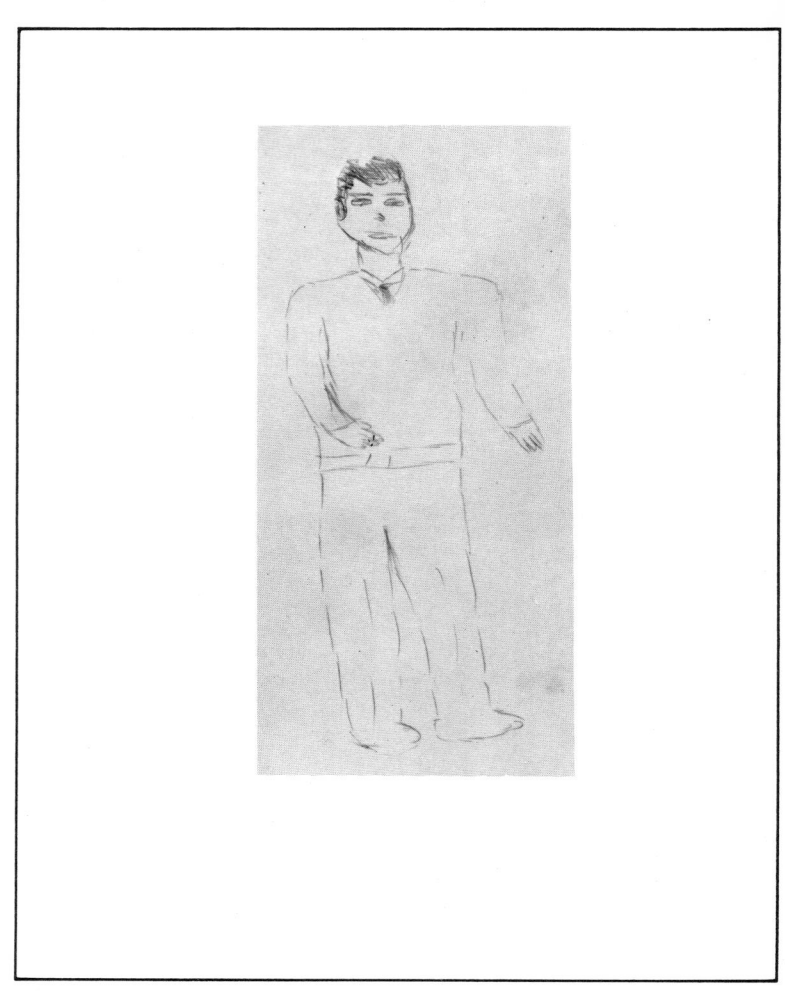

FIGURE-DRAWING CHARACTERISTICS

Structural	Male Female Both	Structural	Male	Female	Structural and Graphic	Male Female Both	Graphic, Global and Height	Male	Female	Body Proportions	Male	Female
Type	0	Omission of Appendages	0	0	Upper and Lower Halves	1 3	Hair Shading	3	3	Head	07	09
Sex Sequence	1	Position of Both Arms	1	1	Four Quarters	4 4	Nudity and Transparency	7	7	Neck	07	07
Posture	1 1	Position of Right Arm	5	5	Relative Size	2	Form	3	3	Shoulders	08	
Perspective	0 9	Position of Left Arm	2	2	Constant Line Pressure	1 0	Detailing	3	3	Right Arm	04	04
Vertical Midline	3 4	Position of Legs	4	5	Variable Line Pressure	0 1	Identity and Sex	1	1	Left Arm	04	04
Bilateral Symmetry	3 0	Relation of Long Axes	1	1	Line Continuity	0 0	Sophistication	3	3	Chest	06	
Horizontal Midline	4 4	Right and Left Halves	1	1	Body Shading	6 0	Height	06	06	Girth	09	

GENERAL CHARACTERISTICS OF SUBJECT

IDENTIFICATION
No. A15
Sex M
Marital status S
Age 22 yrs. at
psychological tests

PARENTAL HISTORY
Father
C   H   S   D   O
+   -   -   -   +
Mother
C   H   S   D   O
-   +   -   -   -

PHYSIOLOGICAL AND METABOLIC DATA

	Admission	Initial	Control	Cold pressor change	Exercise change	Smoking change
Systolic pressure	130	130	120	+20	+70	+14
Diastolic pressure	74	58	66	+14	-22	+08
Heart rate	72	68	62	+25	+26	+22

Age 21 yrs.

Height	73 in.	Ponderal index 13.39
Weight	162 lbs.	Cholesterol 217 mg. per 100 ml.
Overweight -03 %		Vital capacity liters

HABIT SURVEY

Smoking habits: light cigarette smoker

Age begun 17 yrs.   Inhalation: yes

Habits of nervous tension: 4, 5, 6, 9, 21

STRONG VOCATIONAL INTEREST TEST

Occupation	Artist	Psychologist	Architect	Physician	Osteopath	Dentist	Veterinarian	Mathematician	Physicist	Engineer	Chemist	Production Manager
Standard Score	32	50	35	51	27	28	18	41	30	36	40	27

Occupation	Farmer	Aviator	Carpenter	Printer	Math.-Sci. Teacher	Ind. Arts Teacher	Voc. Agric. Teacher	Policeman	Forest Serv. Man	Y.M.C.A. Phys. Dir.	Personnel Director	Public Administrator
Standard Score	26	35	04	26	28	02	20	19	20	24	39	50

Occupation	Y.M.C.A. Secretary	Soc. Sci. H.S. Teacher	City Sch. Sup't.	Social Worker	Minister	Musician Performer	C.P.A.	Senior C.P.A.	Accountant	Office Man	Purchasing Agent	Banker
Standard Score	22	28	34	42	60	39	42	40	19	21	20	27

Occupation	Mortician	Pharmacist	Sales Manager	Real Est. Manager	Life Ins. Salesman	Advertising Man	Lawyer	Author- Journalist	President Mfg. Co.	Interest Maturity	Occupational Level	Masculinity- Femininity
Standard Score	20	26	40	39	34	42	50	41	39	51	62	45

Plate 206   DRAWINGS AT AN INTERMEDIATE LEVEL OF SOPHISTICATION   249

FIGURE-DRAWING CHARACTERISTICS

Structural	Male Female Both		Structural	Male	Female	Structural and Graphic	Male Female Both		Graphic, Global and Height	Male	Female	Body Proportions	Male	Female
Type	0		Omission of Appendages	0	0	Upper and Lower Halves	1	1	Hair Shading	0	3	Head	02	04
Sex Sequence	0		Position of Both Arms	0	0	Four Quarters	4	4	Nudity and Transparency	7	7	Neck	02	02
Posture	1	1	Position of Right Arm	0	5	Relative Size	4		Form	3	3	Shoulders	05	06
Perspective	0	0	Position of Left Arm	0	5	Constant Line Pressure	4	0	Detailing	3	3	Right Arm	02	02
Vertical Midline	3	0	Position of Legs	4	4	Variable Line Pressure	0	5	Identity and Sex	1	1	Left Arm	02	02
Bilateral Symmetry	5	5	Relation of Long Axes	1	1	Line Continuity	2	0	Sophistication	3	3	Chest	04	04
Horizontal Midline	6	0	Right and Left Halves	2	1	Body Shading	5	5	Height	03	03	Girth	05	05

GENERAL CHARACTERISTICS OF SUBJECT

IDENTIFICATION
No. A47
Sex M
Marital status S
Age 27 yrs. at
psychological tests

PARENTAL HISTORY				
Father				
C	H	S	D	O
+	+	-	+	?
Mother				
C	H	S	D	O
-	-	-	-	?

PHYSIOLOGICAL AND METABOLIC DATA

	Admission	Initial	Control	Cold pressor change	Exercise change	Smoking change
Systolic pressure	130	148	136	+20	+38	+07
Diastolic pressure	82	80	78	+18	-12	+16
Heart rate	74	58	55	+30	+05	+12

Age 27 yrs.	Height 77 in.	Ponderal index 14.08
	Weight 164 lbs.	Cholesterol 230 mg. per 100 ml.
	Overweight -17 %	Vital capacity liters

HABIT SURVEY

Smoking habits: heavy cigarette smoker

Age begun 16 yrs.   Inhalation: yes

Habits of nervous tension: 2, 4, 5, 6, 9, 11, 16, 17, 22, 24

STRONG VOCATIONAL INTEREST TEST

Occupation	Artist	Psychologist	Architect	Physician	Osteopath	Dentist	Veterinarian	Mathematician	Physicist	Engineer	Chemist	Production Manager
Standard Score	38	41	47	46	41	36	08	30	29	45	40	29

Occupation	Farmer	Aviator	Carpenter	Printer	Math.-Sci. Teacher	Ind. Arts Teacher	Voc. Agric. Teacher	Policeman	Forest Serv. Man	Y.M.C.A. Phys. Dir.	Personnel Director	Public Administrator
Standard Score	30	50	16	30	33	19	18	28	31	28	39	37

Occupation	Y.M.C.A. Secretary	Soc. Sci. H.S. Teacher	City Sch. Sup't.	Social Worker	Minister	Musician Performer	C.P.A.	Senior C.P.A.	Accountant	Office Man	Purchasing Agent	Banker
Standard Score	20	21	20	29	60	41	26	27	22	24	22	11

Occupation	Mortician	Pharmacist	Sales Manager	Real Est. Manager	Life Ins. Salesman	Advertising Man	Lawyer	Author-Journalist	President Mfg. Co.	Interest Maturity	Occupational Level	Masculinity-Femininity
Standard Score	19	19	30	37	27	45	38	45	29	50	61	48

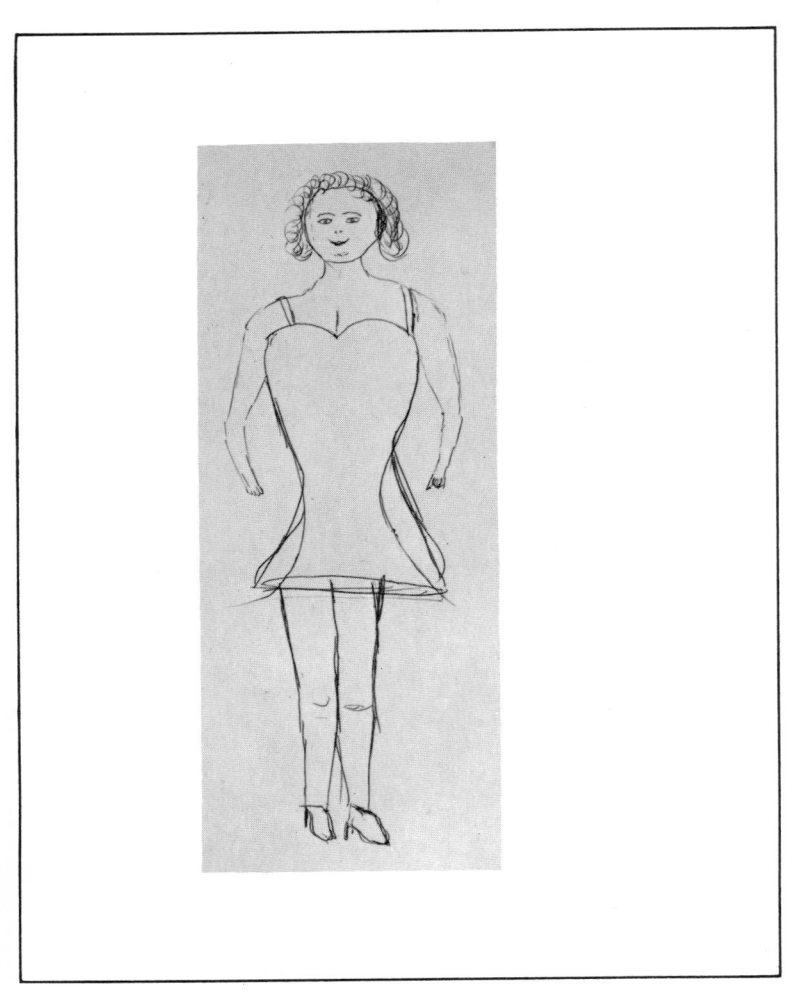

FIGURE-DRAWING CHARACTERISTICS

Structural	Male Female Both	Structural	Male	Female	Structural and Graphic	Male Female Both		Graphic, Global and Height	Male	Female	Body Proportions	Male	Female
Type	0	Omission of Appendages	0	0	Upper and Lower Halves	1	0	Hair Shading	2	3	Head	06	06
Sex Sequence	1	Position of Both Arms	1	0	Four Quarters	4	4	Nudity and Transparency	7	2	Neck	05	06
Posture	1 1	Position of Right Arm	3	5	Relative Size	4		Form	3	3	Shoulders	06	08
Perspective	0 0	Position of Left Arm	0	5	Constant Line Pressure	3	0	Detailing	3	3	Right Arm	04	04
Vertical Midline	0 0	Position of Legs	3	2	Variable Line Pressure	0	2	Identity and Sex	1	1	Left Arm	04	04
Bilateral Symmetry	3 2	Relation of Long Axes	1	1	Line Continuity	2	0	Sophistication	3	3	Chest	05	07
Horizontal Midline	4 0	Right and Left Halves	1	1	Body Shading	1	3	Height	05	07	Girth	07	05

GENERAL CHARACTERISTICS OF SUBJECT

IDENTIFICATION
No. A63
Sex M
Marital status S
Age 22 yrs. at
psychological tests

PARENTAL HISTORY					
Father					
C	H	S	D	O	
+	-	-	-	+	
Mother					
C	H	S	D	O	
-	+	-	-	?	

PHYSIOLOGICAL AND METABOLIC DATA

	Admission	Initial	Control	Cold pressor change	Exercise change	Smoking change
Systolic pressure	134	128	116	+25	+40	
Diastolic pressure	82	54	62	+28	-42	
Heart rate	70	88	86	+02	+14	

Age 22 yrs.	Height 67 in.	Ponderal index 13.21
	Weight 130 lbs.	Cholesterol 250 mg. per 100 ml.
	Overweight -08 %	Vital capacity liters

HABIT SURVEY
Smoking habits: light cigarette smoker
Age begun 19 yrs.   Inhalation: yes
Habits of nervous tension: 3, 5, 9, 11, 23

STRONG VOCATIONAL INTEREST TEST

Occupation	Artist	Psychologist	Architect	Physician	Osteopath	Dentist	Veterinarian	Mathematician	Physicist	Engineer	Chemist	Production Manager
Standard Score	29	38	30	46	39	36	13	26	19	26	29	22

Occupation	Farmer	Aviator	Carpenter	Printer	Math.-Sci. Teacher	Ind. Arts Teacher	Voc. Agric. Teacher	Policeman	Forest Serv. Man	Y.M.C.A. Phys. Dir.	Personnel Director	Public Administrator
Standard Score	21	20	-08	26	31	04	14	21	11	27	39	35

Occupation	Y.M.C.A. Secretary	Soc. Sci. H.S. Teacher	City Sch. Sup't.	Social Worker	Minister	Musician Performer	C.P.A.	Senior C.P.A.	Accountant	Office Man	Purchasing Agent	Banker
Standard Score	27	39	40	36	60	40	41	30	22	34	22	28

Occupation	Mortician	Pharmacist	Sales Manager	Real Est. Manager	Life Ins. Salesman	Advertising Man	Lawyer	Author-Journalist	President Mfg. Co.	Interest Maturity	Occupational Level	Masculinity-Femininity
Standard Score	25	34	36	37	39	40	48	38	36	56	65	38

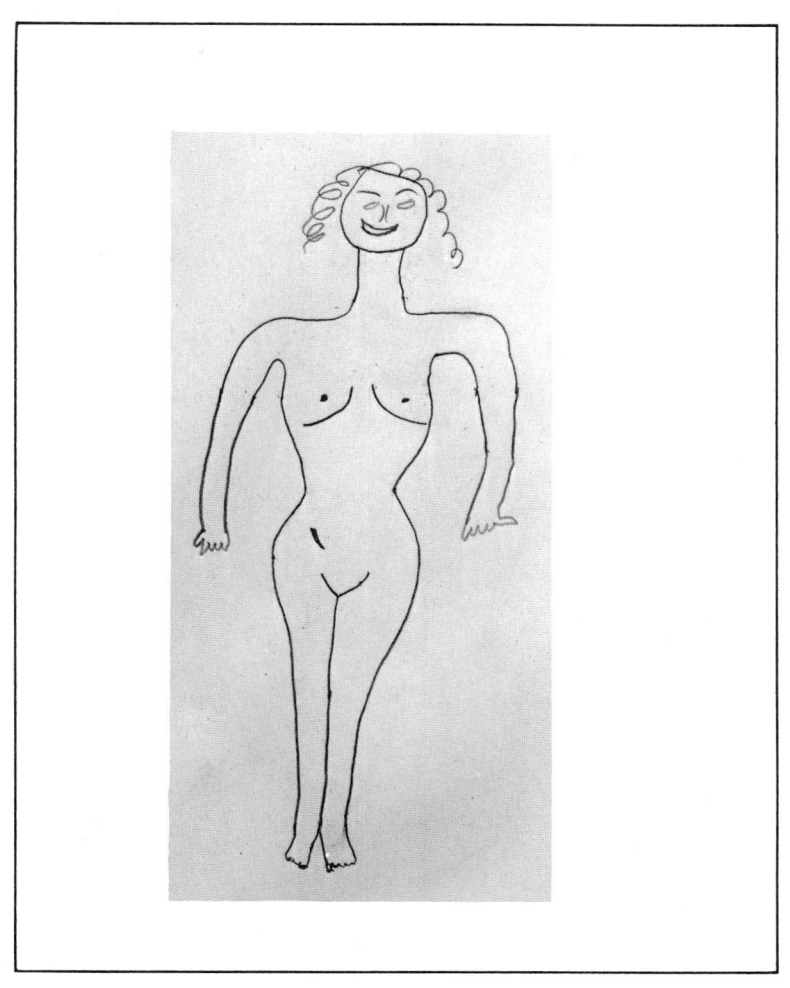

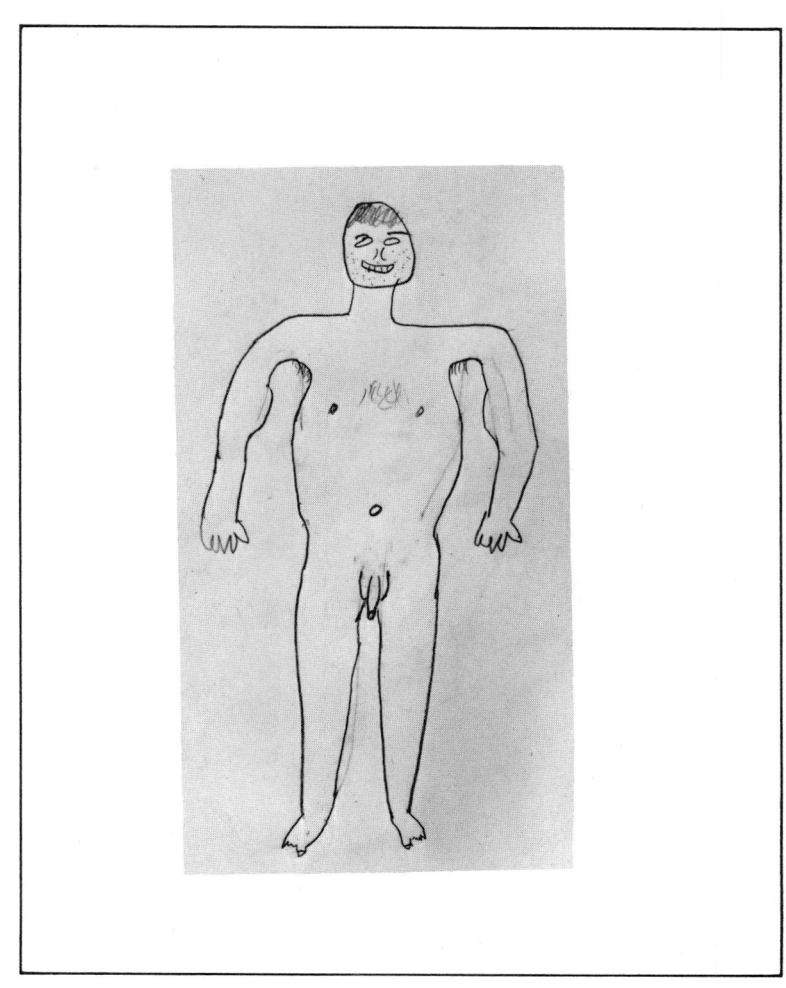

FIGURE-DRAWING CHARACTERISTICS

Structural	Male Female Both	Structural	Male	Female	Structural and Graphic	Male Female Both		Graphic, Global and Height	Male	Female	Body Proportions	Male	Female
Type	0	Omission of Appendages	0	0	Upper and Lower Halves	0	0	Hair Shading	2	7	Head	07	06
Sex Sequence	1	Position of Both Arms	0	0	Four Quarters	4	4	Nudity and Transparency	0	0	Neck	08	20
Posture	1 1	Position of Right Arm	0	0	Relative Size	4		Form	3	3	Shoulders	09	09
Perspective	0 0	Position of Left Arm	0	0	Constant Line Pressure	5	5	Detailing	3	3	Right Arm	06	06
Vertical Midline	0 0	Position of Legs	4	2	Variable Line Pressure	0	0	Identity and Sex	1	1	Left Arm	06	06
Bilateral Symmetry	2 3	Relation of Long Axes	1	1	Line Continuity	3	4	Sophistication	3	3	Chest	07	07
Horizontal Midline	0 0	Right and Left Halves	1	1	Body Shading	1	2	Height	07	07	Girth	09	06

GENERAL CHARACTERISTICS OF SUBJECT

IDENTIFICATION
No. B01
Sex M
Marital status S
Age 23 yrs. at
psychological tests

PARENTAL HISTORY

Father				
C	H	S	D	O
+	-	-	-	-
Mother				
C	H	S	D	O
-	-	-	-	-

PHYSIOLOGICAL AND METABOLIC DATA

	Admission	Initial	Control	Cold pressor change	Exercise change	Smoking change
Systolic pressure	140	130	118	+23	+60	+06
Diastolic pressure	70	66	64	+04	-22	+02
Heart rate	78	86	74	+04	+33	+08

Age 22 yrs.	Height 74 in.	Ponderal index 12.94
	Weight 187 lbs.	Cholesterol 212 mg. per 100 ml.
	Overweight +08 %	Vital capacity 5.9 liters

HABIT SURVEY

Smoking habits: heavy cigarette smoker

    Age begun 18 yrs.   Inhalation: yes

Habits of nervous tension: 4, 5, 6, 8, 9, 11, 12, 14, 17, 19, 25

FIGURE-DRAWING CHARACTERISTICS

Structural	Male Female Both	Structural	Male	Female	Structural and Graphic	Male Female Both	Graphic, Global and Height	Male	Female	Body Proportions	Male	Female
Type	0	Omission of Appendages	0	3	Upper and Lower Halves	7 7	Hair Shading	2	3	Head	11	
Sex Sequence	0	Position of Both Arms	0	0	Four Quarters	4 4	Nudity and Transparency	7	7	Neck	07	
Posture	1 0	Position of Right Arm	0	0	Relative Size	4	Form	3	3	Shoulders	10	08
Perspective	0 0	Position of Left Arm	0	0	Constant Line Pressure	1 1	Detailing	3	3	Right Arm	07	05
Vertical Midline	3 0	Position of Legs	6	6	Variable Line Pressure	0 0	Identity and Sex	1	1	Left Arm	07	06
Bilateral Symmetry	3 3	Relation of Long Axes	1	1	Line Continuity	0 0	Sophistication	3	3	Chest	07	07
Horizontal Midline	4 4	Right and Left Halves	1	1	Body Shading	7 5	Height	08		Girth	10	08

GENERAL CHARACTERISTICS OF SUBJECT

IDENTIFICATION
No. B17
Sex M
Marital status S
Age 22 yrs. at
psychological tests

PARENTAL HISTORY				
Father				
C	H	S	D	O
+	-	-	-	-
Mother				
C	H	S	D	O
-	-	-	-	-

PHYSIOLOGICAL AND METABOLIC DATA

	Admission	Initial	Control	Cold pressor change	Exercise change	Smoking change
Systolic pressure	90	126	122	+12	+44	+13
Diastolic pressure	60	58	58	+16	00	+12
Heart rate	84	85	77	+11	+23	+03

Age 22 yrs.	Height	70 in.	Ponderal index	12.94	
	Weight	158 lbs.	Cholesterol	180	mg. per 100 ml.
	Overweight +03 %		Vital capacity	5.0	liters

HABIT SURVEY
Smoking habits: nonsmoker
Age begun   yrs.   Inhalation:
Habits of nervous tension: 4, 5, 18

STRONG VOCATIONAL INTEREST TEST

Occupation	Artist	Psychologist	Architect	Physician	Osteopath	Dentist	Veterinarian	Mathematician	Physicist	Engineer	Chemist	Production Manager
Standard Score	17	34	22	44	42	37	34	18	19	36	34	40

Occupation	Farmer	Aviator	Carpenter	Printer	Math.-Sci. Teacher	Ind. Arts Teacher	Voc. Agric. Teacher	Policeman	Forest Serv. Man	Y.M.C.A. Phys. Dir.	Personnel Director	Public Administrator
Standard Score	30	42	20	25	39	17	33	37	29	36	45	45

Occupation	Y.M.C.A. Secretary	Soc. Sci. H.S. Teacher	City Sch. Sup't.	Social Worker	Minister	Musician Performer	C.P.A.	Senior C.P.A.	Accountant	Office Man	Purchasing Agent	Banker
Standard Score	27	25	24	34	61	28	29	48	31	34	33	30

Occupation	Mortician	Pharmacist	Sales Manager	Real Est. Manager	Life Ins. Salesman	Advertising Man	Lawyer	Author-Journalist	President Mfg. Co.	Interest Maturity	Occupational Level	Masculinity-Femininity
Standard Score	38	35	37	38	34	29	32	24	33	56	57	56

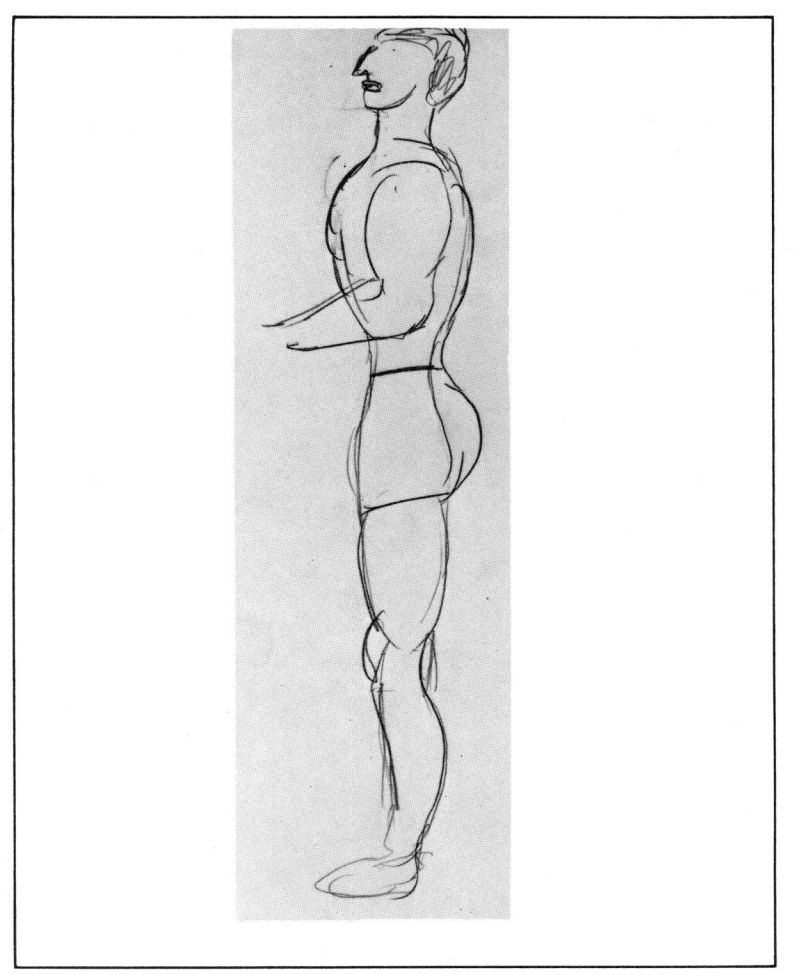

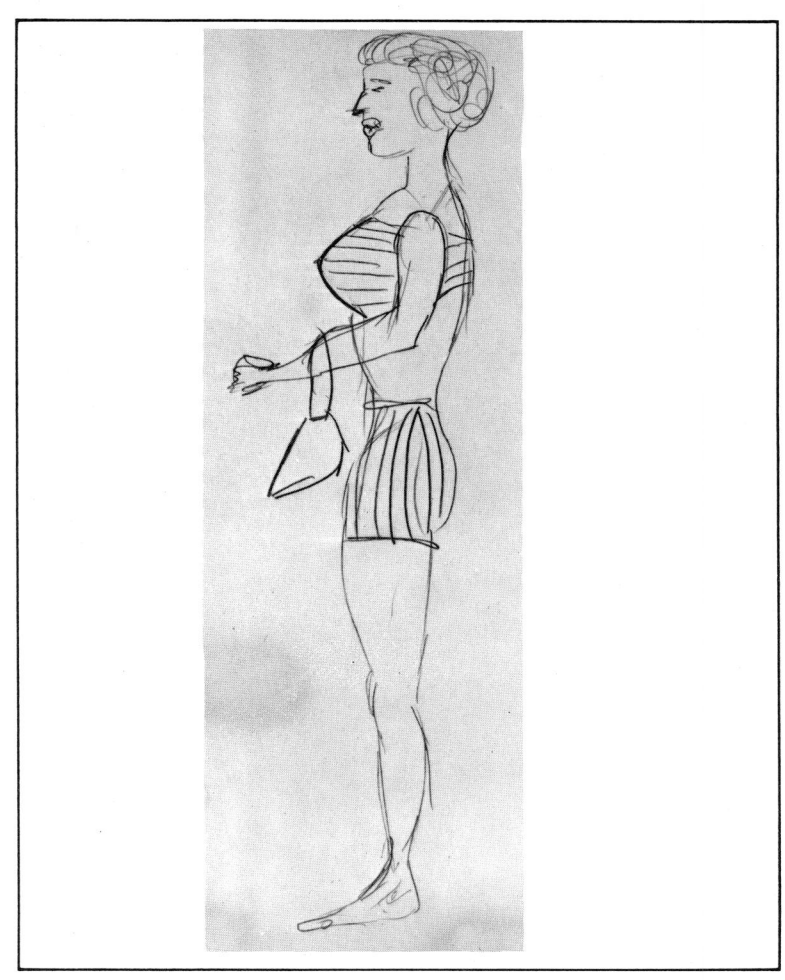

FIGURE-DRAWING CHARACTERISTICS

Structural	Male	Female	Structural	Male	Female	Structural and Graphic	Male	Female	Graphic, Global and Height	Male	Female	Body Proportions	Male	Female
	Both						Both							
Type	0		Omission of Appendages	7	0	Upper and Lower Halves	5	0	Hair Shading	3	3	Head		09
Sex Sequence	2		Position of Both Arms	4	4	Four Quarters	4	4	Nudity and Transparency	3	2	Neck	12	10
Posture	1	1	Position of Right Arm	7	7	Relative Size	2		Form	1	3	Shoulders		
Perspective	2	2	Position of Left Arm	4	4	Constant Line Pressure	0	0	Detailing	5	3	Right Arm		
Vertical Midline	4	4	Position of Legs	1	1	Variable Line Pressure	4	4	Identity and Sex	1	1	Left Arm		08
Bilateral Symmetry	0	0	Relation of Long Axes	1	1	Line Continuity	1	1	Sophistication	3	3	Chest	10	09
Horizontal Midline	4	4	Right and Left Halves	3	1	Body Shading	0	2	Height		09	Girth	06	06

GENERAL CHARACTERISTICS OF SUBJECT

IDENTIFICATION
No. B62
Sex M
Marital status S
Age 22 yrs. at
psychological tests

PARENTAL HISTORY				
Father				
C	H	S	D	O
+	+	(+)	+	+
Mother				
C	H	S	D	O
–	–	–	–	–

PHYSIOLOGICAL AND METABOLIC DATA

	Admission	Initial	Control	Cold pressor change	Exercise change	Smoking change
Systolic pressure	140	130	122	+18	+34	+12
Diastolic pressure	80	70	74	+24	-14	+12
Heart rate	80	68	64	+22	+29	+20

Height 71 in.   Ponderal index 12.35
Weight 190 lbs.   Cholesterol 200 mg. per 100 ml.
Age 22 yrs.   Overweight +20 %   Vital capacity 5.0 liters

HABIT SURVEY

Smoking habits: light cigarette smoker
Age begun 18 yrs.   Inhalation: yes
Habits of nervous tension: 3, 5, 8, 16, 20, 21, 25

STRONG VOCATIONAL INTEREST TEST

Occupation	Artist	Psychologist	Architect	Physician	Osteopath	Dentist	Veterinarian	Mathematician	Physicist	Engineer	Chemist	Production Manager
Standard Score	16	42	21	49	56	38	25	23	21	34	42	37

Occupation	Farmer	Aviator	Carpenter	Printer	Math.-Sci. Teacher	Ind. Arts Teacher	Voc. Agric. Teacher	Policeman	Forest Serv. Man	Y.M.C.A. Phys. Dir.	Personnel Director	Public Administrator
Standard Score	30	41	36	45	54	35	26	49	36	53	57	60

Occupation	Y.M.C.A. Secretary	Soc. Sci. H.S. Teacher	City Sch. Sup't.	Social Worker	Minister	Musician Performer	C.P.A.	Senior C.P.A.	Accountant	Office Man	Purchasing Agent	Banker
Standard Score	45	47	36	52	61	41	20	48	32	42	21	18

Occupation	Mortician	Pharmacist	Sales Manager	Real Est. Manager	Life Ins. Salesman	Advertising Man	Lawyer	Author-Journalist	President Mfg. Co.	Interest Maturity	Occupational Level	Masculinity-Femininity
Standard Score	26	29	23	23	28	23	26	23	22	66	47	46

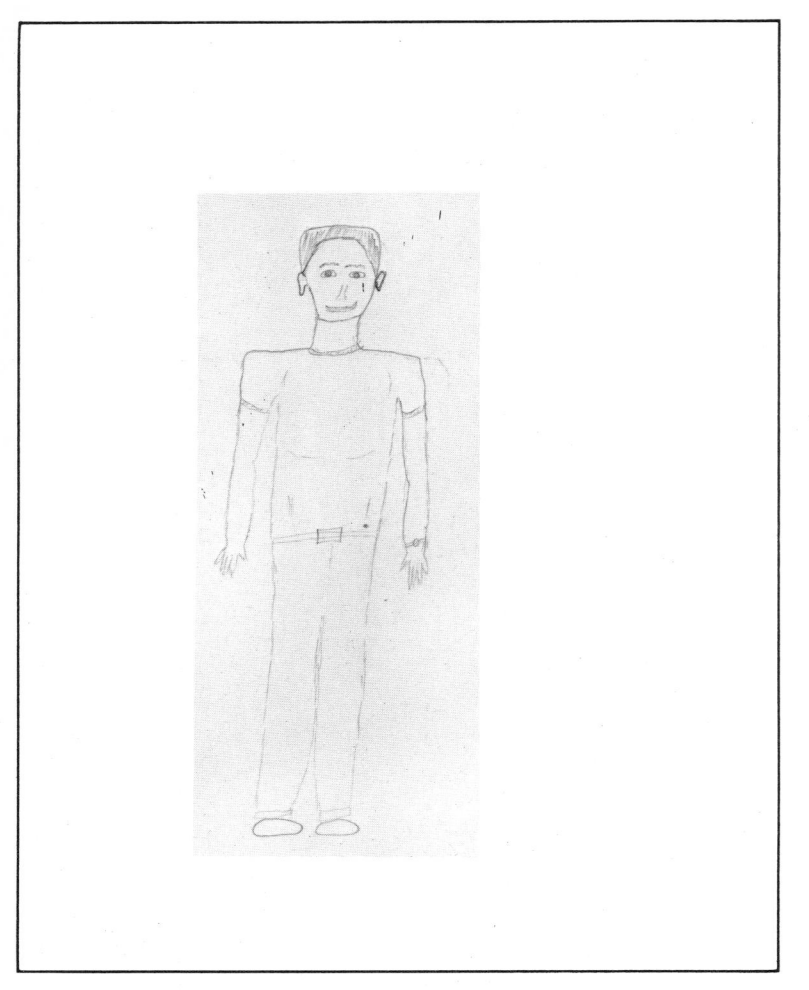

FIGURE-DRAWING CHARACTERISTICS

Structural	Male Female Both	Structural	Male	Female	Structural and Graphic	Male Female Both		Graphic, Global and Height	Male	Female	Body Proportions	Male	Female
Type	0	Omission of Appendages	0	0	Upper and Lower Halves	3	3	Hair Shading	1	3	Head	07	07
Sex Sequence	0	Position of Both Arms	0	4	Four Quarters	4	4	Nudity and Transparency	7	7	Neck	08	07
Posture	1 4	Position of Right Arm	0	7	Relative Size	5		Form	3	3	Shoulders	07	
Perspective	0 9	Position of Left Arm	0	4	Constant Line Pressure	1	0	Detailing	3	3	Right Arm	04	
Vertical Midline	0 4	Position of Legs	3	1	Variable Line Pressure	0	1	Identity and Sex	3	1	Left Arm	04	04
Bilateral Symmetry	3 0	Relation of Long Axes	1	0	Line Continuity	0	2	Sophistication	3	3	Chest	05	05
Horizontal Midline	4 4	Right and Left Halves	1	3	Body Shading	1	0	Height	06		Girth	06	03

GENERAL CHARACTERISTICS OF SUBJECT

IDENTIFICATION
No. C26
Sex M
Marital status S
Age 22 yrs. at psychological tests

PARENTAL HISTORY					
Father					
C	H	S	D	O	
+	+	-	-	?	
Mother					
C	H	S	D	O	
-	-	-	-	-	

PHYSIOLOGICAL AND METABOLIC DATA

	Admission	Initial	Control	Cold pressor change	Exercise change	Smoking change
Systolic pressure	150	150	128	+08	+47	
Diastolic pressure	74	80	70	+10	00	
Heart rate	98	88	81	00	+19	

Age 22 yrs.	Height 70 in.	Ponderal index 12.05
	Weight 196 lbs.	Cholesterol 175 mg. per 100 ml.
	Overweight +27 %	Vital capacity 5.0 liters

HABIT SURVEY
Smoking habits: heavy cigarette smoker
Age begun 15 yrs.   Inhalation: yes
Habits of nervous tension: 4, 5, 6, 22

STRONG VOCATIONAL INTEREST TEST

Occupation	Artist	Psychologist	Architect	Physician	Osteopath	Dentist	Veterinarian	Mathematician	Physicist	Engineer	Chemist	Production Manager
Standard Score	20	43	12	52	47	28	33	15	02	10	22	32

Occupation	Farmer	Aviator	Carpenter	Printer	Math.-Sci. Teacher	Ind. Arts Teacher	Voc. Agric. Teacher	Policeman	Forest Serv. Man	Y.M.C.A. Phys. Dir.	Personnel Director	Public Administrator
Standard Score	31	30	02	35	46	11	36	37	25	50	49	56

Occupation	Y.M.C.A. Secretary	Soc. Sci. H.S. Teacher	City Sch. Sup't.	Social Worker	Minister	Musician Performer	C.P.A.	Senior C.P.A.	Accountant	Office Man	Purchasing Agent	Banker
Standard Score	41	57	47	55	62	47	26	42	26	39	19	29

Occupation	Mortician	Pharmacist	Sales Manager	Real Est. Manager	Life Ins. Salesman	Advertising Man	Lawyer	Author-Journalist	President Mfg. Co.	Interest Maturity	Occupational Level	Masculinity-Femininity
Standard Score	25	38	33	33	35	36	44	33	15	62	51	47

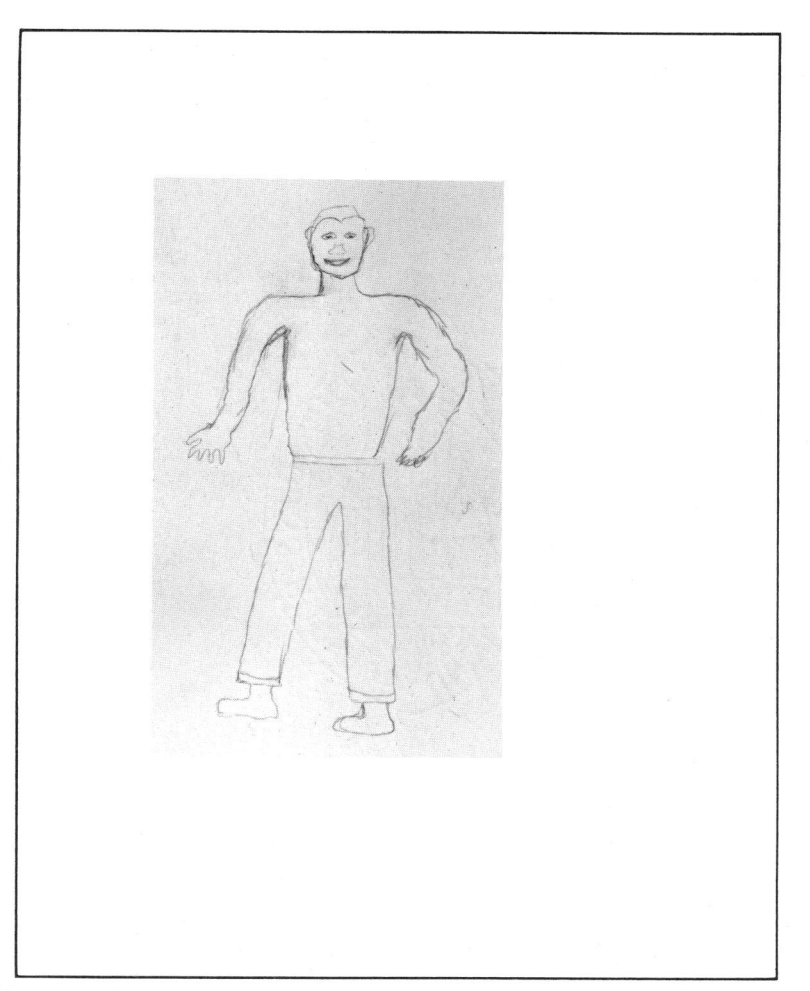

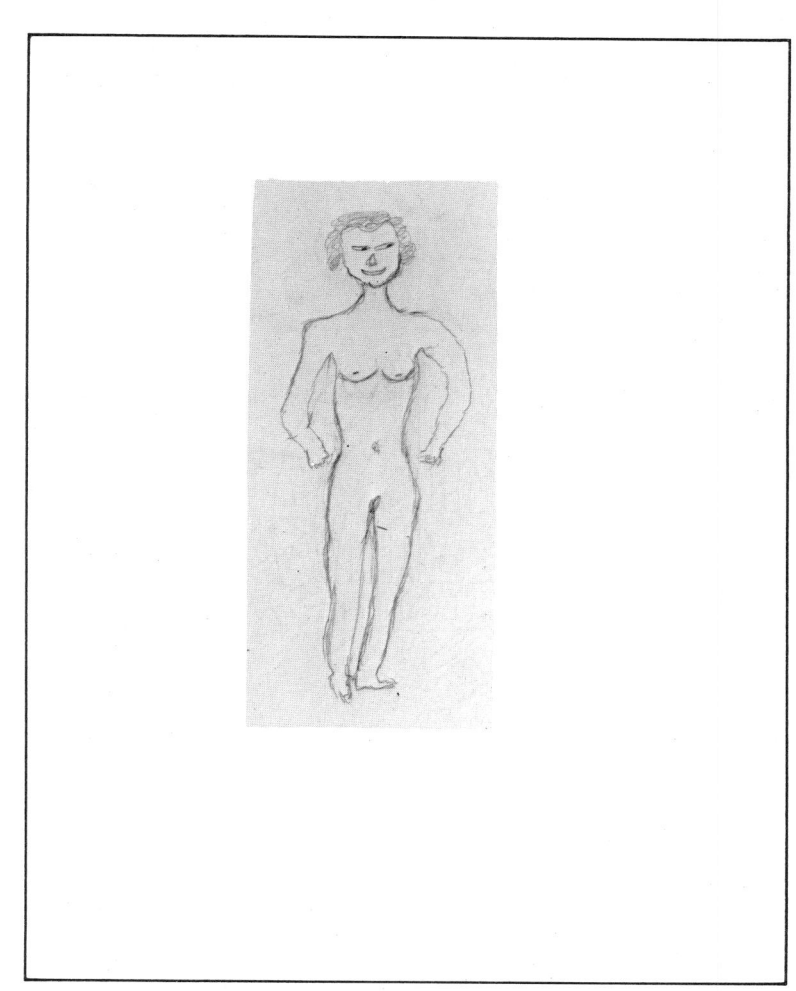

FIGURE-DRAWING CHARACTERISTICS

Structural	Male Female Both		Structural	Male	Female	Structural and Graphic	Male Female Both		Graphic, Global and Height	Male	Female	Body Proportions	Male	Female
Type	0		Omission of Appendages	0	0	Upper and Lower Halves	1	1	Hair Shading	5	3	Head	05	05
Sex Sequence	0		Position of Both Arms	1	0	Four Quarters	4	4	Nudity and Transparency	3	0	Neck	06	07
Posture	1	1	Position of Right Arm	2	5	Relative Size	0		Form	3	3	Shoulders	07	06
Perspective	0	0	Position of Left Arm	5	5	Constant Line Pressure	1	1	Detailing	3	3	Right Arm	04	04
Vertical Midline	0	0	Position of Legs	6	4	Variable Line Pressure	0	0	Identity and Sex	1	1	Left Arm	04	04
Bilateral Symmetry	3	3	Relation of Long Axes	1	1	Line Continuity	0	0	Sophistication	3	3	Chest	05	04
Horizontal Midline	4	0	Right and Left Halves	1	1	Body Shading	0	3	Height	05	05	Girth	05	04

GENERAL CHARACTERISTICS OF SUBJECT

IDENTIFICATION

No. C68

Sex M

Marital status S

Age 22 yrs. at psychological tests

PARENTAL HISTORY

Father

C	H	S	D	O
+	+	-	-	+

Mother

C	H	S	D	O
-	-	-	-	?

PHYSIOLOGICAL AND METABOLIC DATA

	Admission	Initial	Control	Cold pressor change	Exercise change	Smoking change
Systolic pressure	120	108	96	+12	+22	+05
Diastolic pressure	80	70	64	+22	-14	+04
Heart rate	62	52	45	-04	+15	-02

Age 22 yrs.

Height 73 in.

Weight 190 lbs.

Overweight +13 %

Ponderal index 12.70

Cholesterol 240 mg. per 100 ml.

Vital capacity 6.5 liters

HABIT SURVEY

Smoking habits: heavy cigarette smoker

Age begun 19 yrs.   Inhalation: yes

Habits of nervous tension: 4, 5, 6, 9, 10, 16, 18, 19, 23, 24

STRONG VOCATIONAL INTEREST TEST

Occupation	Artist	Psychologist	Architect	Physician	Osteopath	Dentist	Veterinarian	Mathematician	Physicist	Engineer	Chemist	Production Manager
Standard Score	40	41	36	52	41	37	25	38	35	36	55	22

Occupation	Farmer	Aviator	Carpenter	Printer	Math.-Sci. Teacher	Ind. Arts Teacher	Voc. Agric. Teacher	Policeman	Forest Serv. Man	Y.M.C.A. Phys. Dir.	Personnel Director	Public Administrator
Standard Score	36	39	02	25	29	-06	05	15	20	22	16	28

Occupation	Y.M.C.A. Secretary	Soc. Sci. H.S. Teacher	City Sch. Sup't.	Social Worker	Minister	Musician Performer	C.P.A.	Senior C.P.A.	Accountant	Office Man	Purchasing Agent	Banker
Standard Score	10	20	13	22	62	41	37	33	20	22	20	13

Occupation	Mortician	Pharmacist	Sales Manager	Real Est. Manager	Life Ins. Salesman	Advertising Man	Lawyer	Author-Journalist	President Mfg. Co.	Interest Maturity	Occupational Level	Masculinity-Femininity
Standard Score	22	30	29	36	29	41	45	47	31	44	64	40

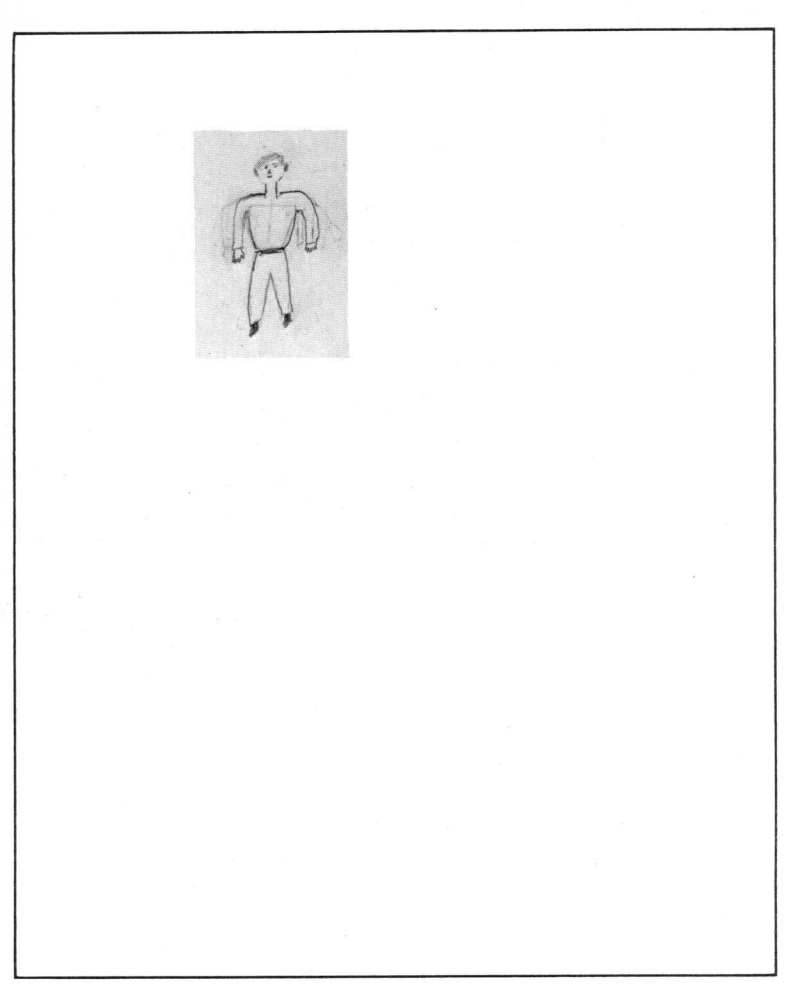

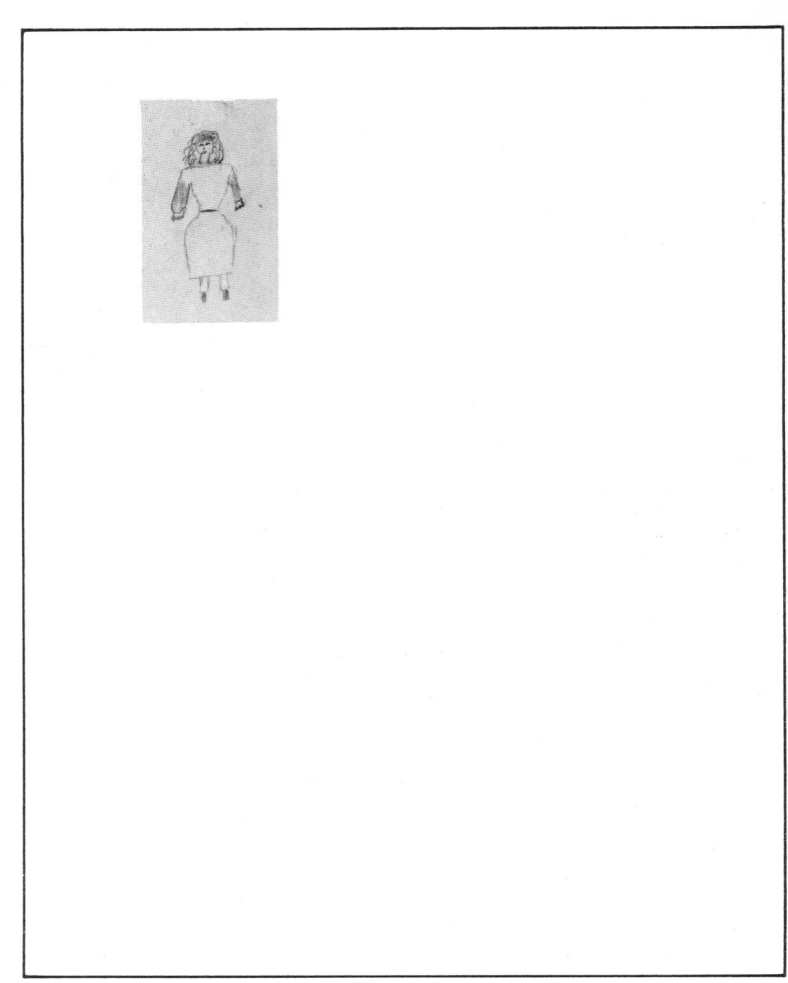

FIGURE-DRAWING CHARACTERISTICS

Structural	Male	Female	Structural	Male	Female	Structural and Graphic	Male	Female	Graphic, Global and Height	Male	Female	Body Proportions	Male	Female
	Both						Both							
Type	0		Omission of Appendages	0	0	Upper and Lower Halves	2	2	Hair Shading	3	3	Head	02	01
Sex Sequence	0		Position of Both Arms	0	0	Four Quarters	0	0	Nudity and Transparency	7	7	Neck	01	01
Posture	2	1	Position of Right Arm	0	1	Relative Size	0		Form	3	3	Shoulders	03	02
Perspective	0	0	Position of Left Arm	0	1	Constant Line Pressure	0	1	Detailing	5	5	Right Arm	00	00
Vertical Midline	0	0	Position of Legs	8	4	Variable Line Pressure	3	0	Identity and Sex	1	1	Left Arm	00	00
Bilateral Symmetry	3	4	Relation of Long Axes	1	1	Line Continuity	4	0	Sophistication	3	3	Chest	02	01
Horizontal Midline	4	4	Right and Left Halves	2	2	Body Shading	4	5	Height	01	01	Girth	01	01

GENERAL CHARACTERISTICS OF SUBJECT

IDENTIFICATION
No. C73
Sex M
Marital status S
Age 22 yrs. at
psychological tests

PARENTAL HISTORY					
Father					
C	H	S	D	O	
+	+	–	–	+	
Mother					
C	H	S	D	O	
–	–	–	–	–	

PHYSIOLOGICAL AND METABOLIC DATA

	Admission	Initial	Control	Cold pressor change	Exercise change	Smoking change
Systolic pressure	134	130	120	+14	+20	+01
Diastolic pressure	68	75	78	+25	-13	+01
Heart rate	74	88	74	+12	+20	00

Age 22 yrs.	Height	73	in.	Ponderal index 13.04
	Weight	176	lbs.	Cholesterol 215 mg. per 100 ml.
	Overweight +05 %			Vital capacity 5.6 liters

HABIT SURVEY

Smoking habits: light cigarette smoker

Age begun 20 yrs.   Inhalation: yes

Habits of nervous tension: 4, 5, 6, 9, 11, 13, 16, 21, 22

STRONG VOCATIONAL INTEREST TEST

Occupation	Artist	Psychologist	Architect	Physician	Osteopath	Dentist	Veterinarian	Mathematician	Physicist	Engineer	Chemist	Production Manager
Standard Score	22	18	09	27	39	20	33	09	-06	06	08	21

Occupation	Farmer	Aviator	Carpenter	Printer	Math.-Sci. Teacher	Ind. Arts Teacher	Voc. Agric. Teacher	Policeman	Forest Serv. Man	Y.M.C.A. Phys. Dir.	Personnel Director	Public Administrator
Standard Score	28	17	02	18	22	-10	13	32	20	34	27	36

Occupation	Y.M.C.A. Secretary	Soc. Sci. H.S. Teacher	City Sch. Sup't.	Social Worker	Minister	Musician Performer	C.P.A.	Senior C.P.A.	Accountant	Office Man	Purchasing Agent	Banker
Standard Score	34	44	34	36	62	26	23	18	19	33	21	35

Occupation	Mortician	Pharmacist	Sales Manager	Real Est. Manager	Life Ins. Salesman	Advertising Man	Lawyer	Author-Journalist	President Mfg. Co.	Interest Maturity	Occupational Level	Masculinity-Femininity
Standard Score	38	35	38	45	50	38	47	38	29	53	59	37

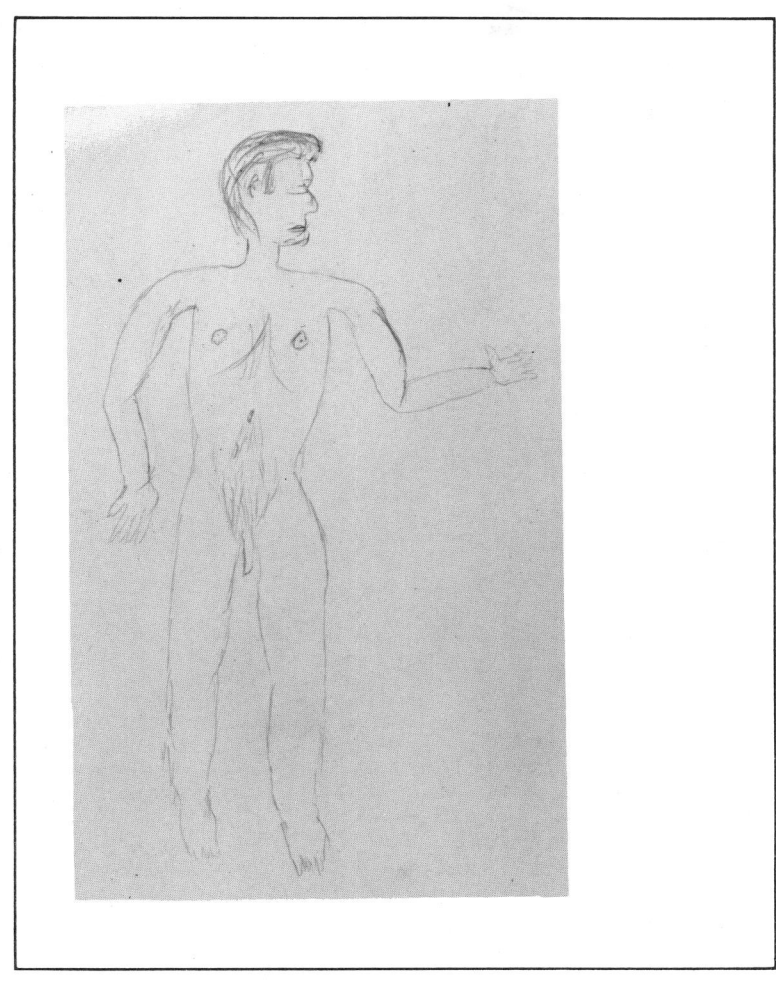

FIGURE-DRAWING CHARACTERISTICS

Structural	Male / Female (Both)		Structural	Male	Female	Structural and Graphic	Male / Female (Both)		Graphic, Global and Height	Male	Female	Body Proportions	Male	Female
Type	0		Omission of Appendages	0	0	Upper and Lower Halves	0	0	Hair Shading	3	3	Head	09	09
Sex Sequence	0		Position of Both Arms	1	2	Four Quarters	4	4	Nudity and Transparency	0	0	Neck	08	12
Posture	1	1	Position of Right Arm	5	2	Relative Size	2		Form	3	3	Shoulders	09	
Perspective	5	2	Position of Left Arm	2	7	Constant Line Pressure	1	1	Detailing	3	3	Right Arm	06	08
Vertical Midline	0	4	Position of Legs	5	1	Variable Line Pressure	0	0	Identity and Sex	1	1	Left Arm	06	
Bilateral Symmetry	3	0	Relation of Long Axes	1	1	Line Continuity	0	0	Sophistication	3	3	Chest	06	07
Horizontal Midline	0	0	Right and Left Halves	1	1	Body Shading	3	2	Height	08	08	Girth	06	08

GENERAL CHARACTERISTICS OF SUBJECT

IDENTIFICATION
No. D28
Sex M
Marital status M
Age 22 yrs. at
psychological tests

PARENTAL HISTORY
Father
C H S D O
+ - - - -
Mother
C H S D O
- - - - -

PHYSIOLOGICAL AND METABOLIC DATA

	Admission	Initial	Control	Cold pressor change	Exercise change	Smoking change
Systolic pressure	134	140	130	+08	+40	+05
Diastolic pressure	62	80	70	+20	-02	+06
Heart rate	88	80	79	00	+30	+19

Age 22 yrs.	Height 69 in.	Ponderal index 11.79
	Weight 200 lbs.	Cholesterol 205 mg. per 100 ml.
	Overweight +33 %	Vital capacity 4.1 liters

HABIT SURVEY

Smoking habits: heavy cigarette smoker

Age begun 17 yrs.   Inhalation: yes

Habits of nervous tension: 4, 5, 6

STRONG VOCATIONAL INTEREST TEST

Occupation	Artist	Psychologist	Architect	Physician	Osteopath	Dentist	Veterinarian	Mathematician	Physicist	Engineer	Chemist	Production Manager
Standard Score	23	47	19	55	41	18	16	25	16	23	35	30

Occupation	Farmer	Aviator	Carpenter	Printer	Math.-Sci. Teacher	Ind. Arts Teacher	Voc. Agric. Teacher	Policeman	Forest Serv. Man	Y.M.C.A. Phys. Dir.	Personnel Director	Public Administrator
Standard Score	21	28	-05	27	42	00	22	21	20	45	54	52

Occupation	Y.M.C.A. Secretary	Soc. Sci. H.S. Teacher	City Sch. Sup't.	Social Worker	Minister	Musician Performer	C.P.A.	Senior C.P.A.	Accountant	Office Man	Purchasing Agent	Banker
Standard Score	44	47	47	54	63	44	44	44	31	32	14	22

Occupation	Mortician	Pharmacist	Sales Manager	Real Est. Manager	Life Ins. Salesman	Advertising Man	Lawyer	Author-Journalist	President Mfg. Co.	Interest Maturity	Occupational Level	Masculinity-Femininity
Standard Score	21	30	37	34	39	34	50	35	27	62	62	44

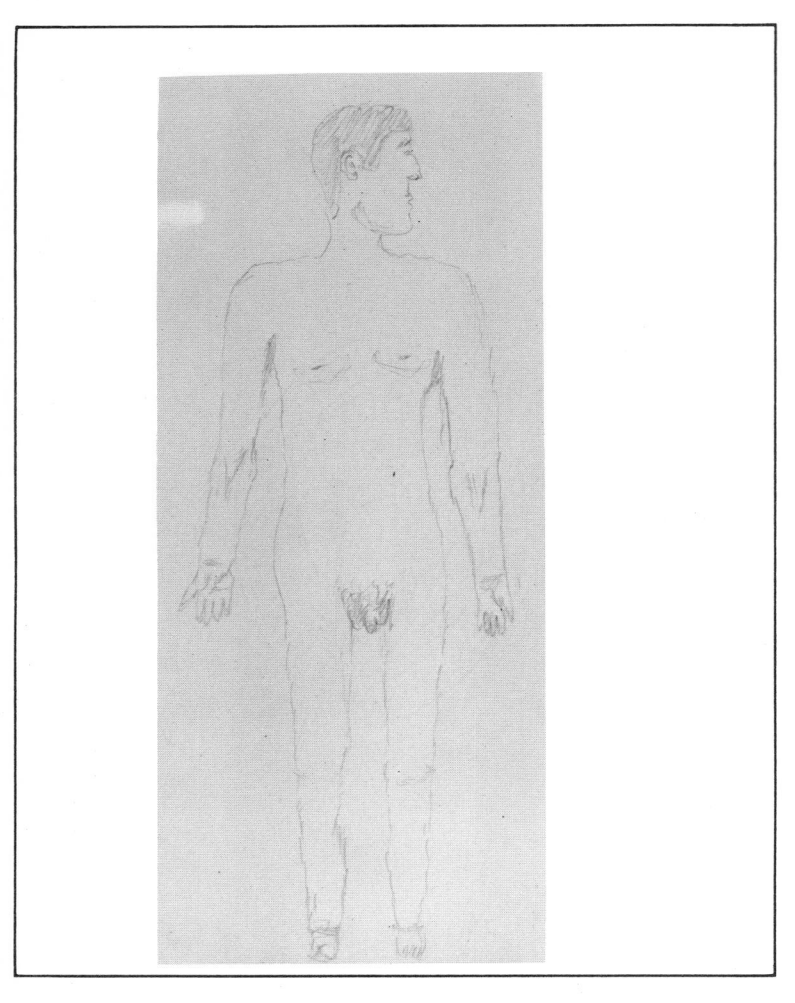

FIGURE-DRAWING CHARACTERISTICS

Structural	Male Female Both		Structural	Male	Female	Structural and Graphic	Male Female Both		Graphic, Global and Height	Male	Female	Body Proportions	Male	Female
Type	0		Omission of Appendages	0	3	Upper and Lower Halves	3	7	Hair Shading	1	3	Head	11	11
Sex Sequence	0		Position of Both Arms	0	2	Four Quarters	4	4	Nudity and Transparency	0	0	Neck	08	08
Posture	1	0	Position of Right Arm	0	5	Relative Size	3		Form	1	1	Shoulders	10	
Perspective	5	2	Position of Left Arm	0	7	Constant Line Pressure	1	1	Detailing	3	3	Right Arm	08	
Vertical Midline	0	4	Position of Legs	4	1	Variable Line Pressure	0	0	Identity and Sex	1	1	Left Arm	08	
Bilateral Symmetry	3	0	Relation of Long Axes	1	1	Line Continuity	0	0	Sophistication	3	3	Chest	08	08
Horizontal Midline	0	0	Right and Left Halves	1	0	Body Shading	3	1	Height	09		Girth	09	12

GENERAL CHARACTERISTICS OF SUBJECT

IDENTIFICATION

No. D47
Sex M
Marital status S
Age 23 yrs. at psychological tests

PARENTAL HISTORY

Father

C	H	S	D	O
+	-	-	-	+

Mother

C	H	S	D	O
-	-	-	-	-

PHYSIOLOGICAL AND METABOLIC DATA

	Admission	Initial	Control	Cold pressor change	Exercise change	Smoking change
Systolic pressure	120	122	116	+20	+54	+07
Diastolic pressure	80	60	68	+18	00	+06
Heart rate	82	100	94	+12	+36	+01

Age 23 yrs.
Height 72 in.
Weight 172 lbs.
Overweight +05 %
Ponderal index 12.95
Cholesterol 232 mg. per 100 ml.
Vital capacity 5.1 liters

HABIT SURVEY

Smoking habits: former smoker
Age begun   yrs.   Inhalation:
Habits of nervous tension: 4, 5, 8, 16, 19

STRONG VOCATIONAL INTEREST TEST

Occupation	Artist	Psychologist	Architect	Physician	Osteopath	Dentist	Veterinarian	Mathematician	Physicist	Engineer	Chemist	Production Manager
Standard Score	49	57	47	65	49	49	25	46	48	39	52	23

Occupation	Farmer	Aviator	Carpenter	Printer	Math.-Sci. Teacher	Ind. Arts Teacher	Voc. Agric. Teacher	Policeman	Forest Serv. Man	Y.M.C.A. Phys. Dir.	Personnel Director	Public Administrator
Standard Score	41	37	31	44	49	27	38	27	33	27	20	38

Occupation	Y.M.C.A. Secretary	Soc. Sci. H.S. Teacher	City Sch. Sup't.	Social Worker	Minister	Musician Performer	C.P.A.	Senior C.P.A.	Accountant	Office Man	Purchasing Agent	Banker
Standard Score	26	38	25	40	63	60	24	30	10	15	04	14

Occupation	Mortician	Pharmacist	Sales Manager	Real Est. Manager	Life Ins. Salesman	Advertising Man	Lawyer	Author- Journalist	President Mfg. Co.	Interest Maturity	Occupational Level	Masculinity- Femininity
Standard Score	12	26	09	22	16	29	34	44	21	47	49	44

Plate 216   DRAWINGS AT AN INTERMEDIATE LEVEL OF SOPHISTICATION   259

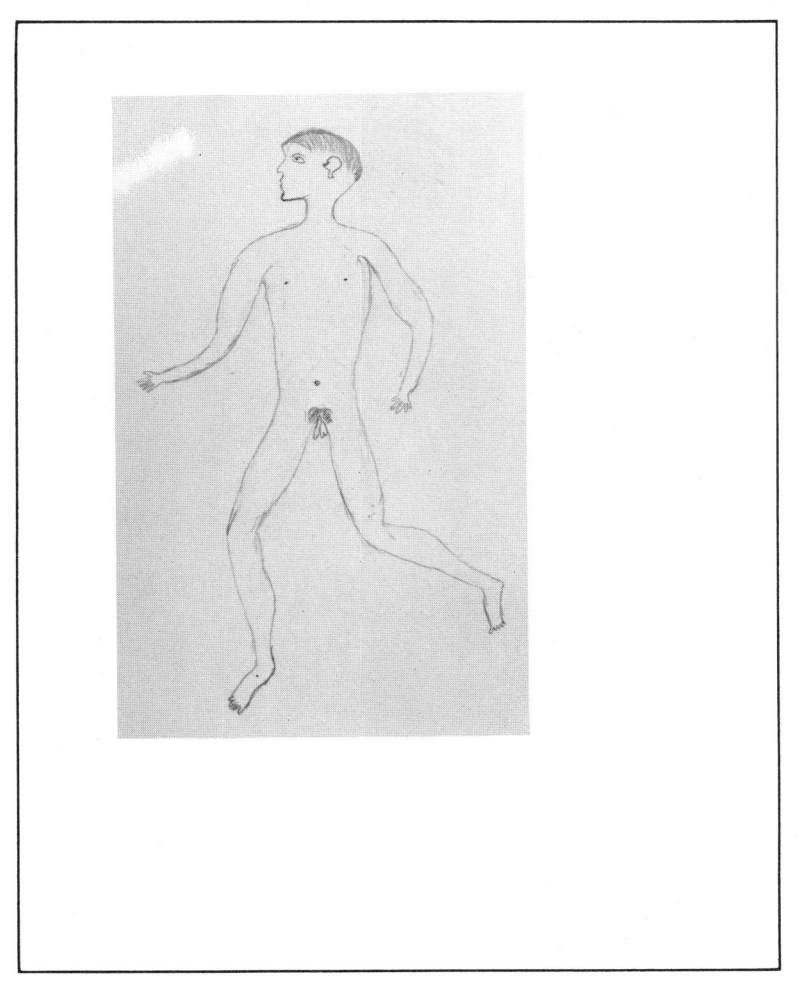

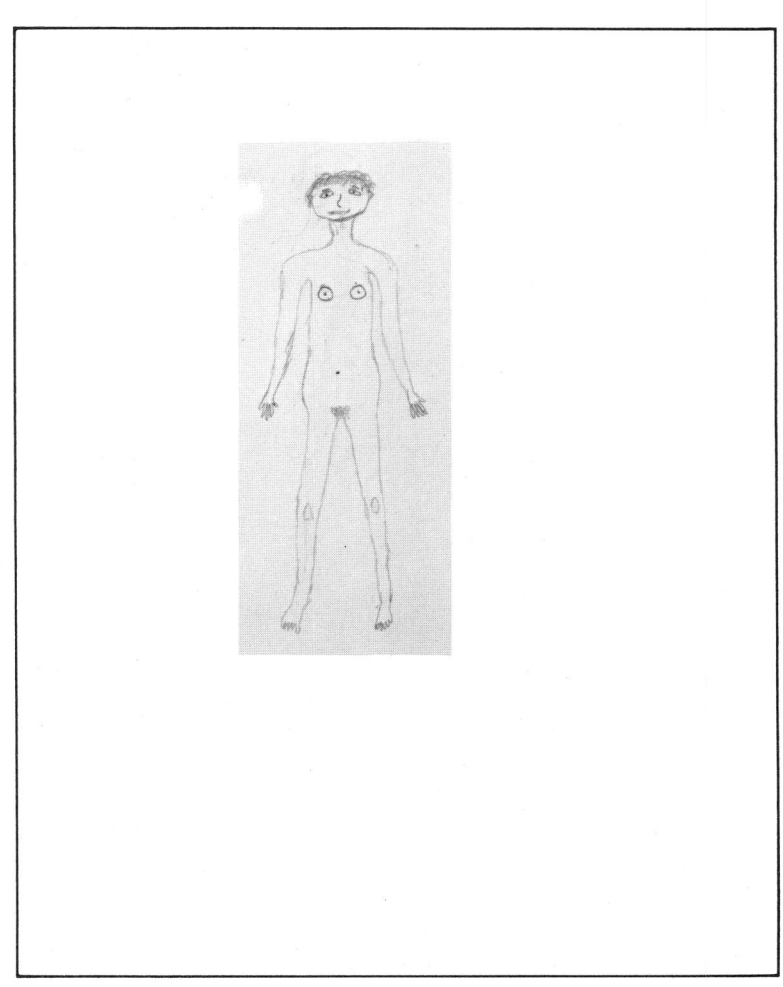

FIGURE-DRAWING CHARACTERISTICS

Structural	Male Female Both		Structural	Male	Female	Structural and Graphic	Male	Female Both		Graphic, Global and Height	Male	Female	Body Proportions	Male	Female
Type	0		Omission of Appendages	0	0	Upper and Lower Halves	1	1		Hair Shading	3	3	Head	05	04
Sex Sequence	0		Position of Both Arms	0	0	Four Quarters	4	4		Nudity and Transparency	0	0	Neck	06	07
Posture	5	1	Position of Right Arm	6	0	Relative Size	0			Form	3	3	Shoulders	05	04
Perspective	5	0	Position of Left Arm	6	0	Constant Line Pressure	1	1		Detailing	3	3	Right Arm	04	03
Vertical Midline	0	0	Position of Legs	8	6	Variable Line Pressure	0	0		Identity and Sex	1	1	Left Arm	04	04
Bilateral Symmetry	3	3	Relation of Long Axes	1	1	Line Continuity	0	0		Sophistication	3	3	Chest	05	03
Horizontal Midline	0	0	Right and Left Halves	1	2	Body Shading	2	2		Height	06	05	Girth	04	04

GENERAL CHARACTERISTICS OF SUBJECT

IDENTIFICATION
No. D57
Sex M
Marital status S
Age 24 yrs. at
psychological tests

PARENTAL HISTORY
Father
C   H   S   D   O
+   -   -   -   ?
Mother
C   H   S   D   O
-   -   -   -   -

PHYSIOLOGICAL AND METABOLIC DATA

	Admission	Initial	Control	Cold pressor change	Exercise change	Smoking change
Systolic pressure	145	122	118	+04	+37	+08
Diastolic pressure	90	78	76	+22	-08	+02
Heart rate	80	92	88	+04	+48	+27

Age 24 yrs.	Height	68	in.	Ponderal index	12.81	
	Weight	150	lbs.	Cholesterol	236	mg. per 100 ml.
	Overweight	+01	%	Vital capacity	4.1	liters

HABIT SURVEY
Smoking habits: moderate cigarette smoker
Age begun 18 yrs.   Inhalation: yes
Habits of nervous tension: 4, 5, 6, 9, 11, 16, 21, 22

STRONG VOCATIONAL INTEREST TEST

Occupation	Artist	Psychologist	Architect	Physician	Osteopath	Dentist	Veterinarian	Mathematician	Physicist	Engineer	Chemist	Production Manager
Standard Score	40	35	37	55	50	42	32	22	16	23	32	18

Occupation	Farmer	Aviator	Carpenter	Printer	Math.-Sci. Teacher	Ind. Arts Teacher	Voc. Agric. Teacher	Policeman	Forest Serv. Man	Y.M.C.A. Phys. Dir.	Personnel Director	Public Administrator
Standard Score	39	38	11	43	37	08	22	28	32	38	31	36

Occupation	Y.M.C.A. Secretary	Soc. Sci. H.S. Teacher	City Sch. Sup't.	Social Worker	Minister	Musician Performer	C.P.A.	Senior C.P.A.	Accountant	Office Man	Purchasing Agent	Banker
Standard Score	28	42	31	39	63	56	24	34	16	27	21	23

Occupation	Mortician	Pharmacist	Sales Manager	Real Est. Manager	Life Ins. Salesman	Advertising Man	Lawyer	Author-Journalist	President Mfg. Co.	Interest Maturity	Occupational Level	Masculinity-Femininity
Standard Score	30	45	31	39	35	45	44	44	21	53	55	39

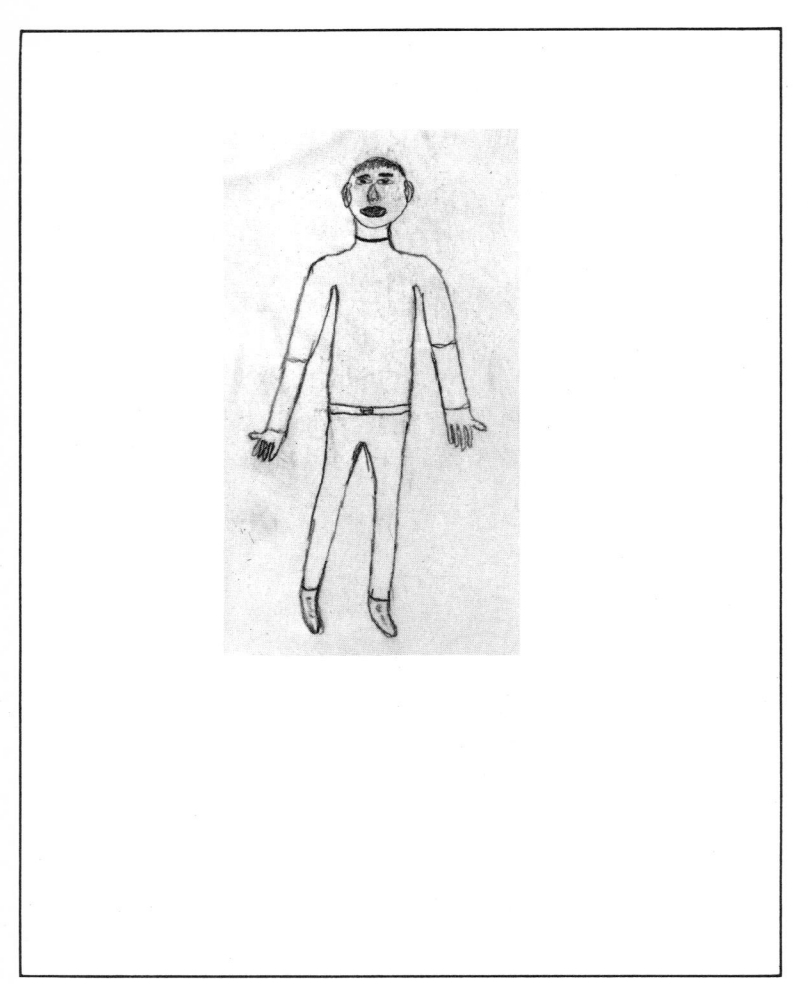

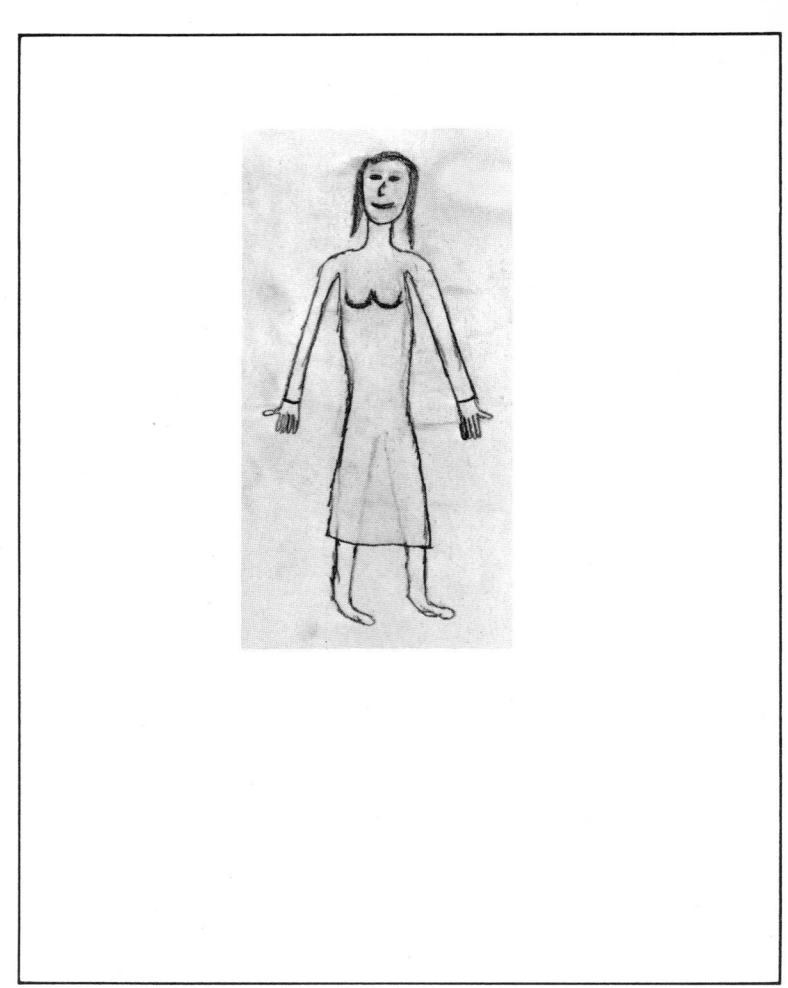

FIGURE-DRAWING CHARACTERISTICS

Structural	Male	Female	Structural	Male	Female	Structural and Graphic	Male	Female	Graphic, Global and Height	Male	Female	Body Proportions	Male	Female
	Both						Both							
Type	0		Omission of Appendages	0	0	Upper and Lower Halves	1	1	Hair Shading	3	3	Head	06	05
Sex Sequence	0		Position of Both Arms	0	0	Four Quarters	4	4	Nudity and Transparency	7	6	Neck	08	08
Posture	1	1	Position of Right Arm	2	2	Relative Size	2		Form	1	3	Shoulders	05	04
Perspective	0	0	Position of Left Arm	2	2	Constant Line Pressure	3	0	Detailing	3	3	Right Arm	04	04
Vertical Midline	0	0	Position of Legs	6	6	Variable Line Pressure	0	5	Identity and Sex	3	3	Left Arm	04	04
Bilateral Symmetry	3	3	Relation of Long Axes	1	1	Line Continuity	0	0	Sophistication	3	3	Chest	03	03
Horizontal Midline	4	0	Right and Left Halves	1	1	Body Shading	0	1	Height	05	05	Girth	05	04

GENERAL CHARACTERISTICS OF SUBJECT

IDENTIFICATION
No. D79
Sex M
Marital status S
Age 21 yrs. at
psychological tests

PARENTAL HISTORY				
Father				
C	H	S	D	O
+	+	+	-	?
Mother				
C	H	S	D	O
-	-	-	-	-

PHYSIOLOGICAL AND METABOLIC DATA

	Admission	Initial	Control	Cold pressor change	Exercise change	Smoking change
Systolic pressure	120	118	110	+12	+23	+02
Diastolic pressure	80	70	68	+20	-18	00
Heart rate	82	76	68	+04	+35	+03

Age 21 yrs.	Height 73 in.	Ponderal index 13.49
	Weight 158 lbs.	Cholesterol 256 mg. per 100 ml.
	Overweight -05 %	Vital capacity 5.5 liters

HABIT SURVEY
Smoking habits: pipe smoker
Age begun 17 yrs.   Inhalation: no
Habits of nervous tension: 6, 8, 19, 24

STRONG VOCATIONAL INTEREST TEST

Occupation	Artist	Psychologist	Architect	Physician	Osteopath	Dentist	Veterinarian	Mathematician	Physicist	Engineer	Chemist	Production Manager
Standard Score	40	48	45	66	49	50	29	52	51	51	59	23

Occupation	Farmer	Aviator	Carpenter	Printer	Math.-Sci. Teacher	Ind. Arts Teacher	Voc. Agric. Teacher	Policeman	Forest Serv. Man	Y.M.C.A. Phys. Dir.	Personnel Director	Public Administrator
Standard Score	47	42	35	49	52	32	31	26	24	28	22	28

Occupation	Y.M.C.A. Secretary	Soc. Sci. H.S. Teacher	City Sch. Sup't.	Social Worker	Minister	Musician Performer	C.P.A.	Senior C.P.A.	Accountant	Office Man	Purchasing Agent	Banker
Standard Score	15	22	26	26	63	50	26	39	20	21	12	10

Occupation	Mortician	Pharmacist	Sales Manager	Real Est. Manager	Life Ins. Salesman	Advertising Man	Lawyer	Author-Journalist	President Mfg. Co.	Interest Maturity	Occupational Level	Masculinity-Femininity
Standard Score	13	34	12	22	15	24	30	35	31	50	54	51

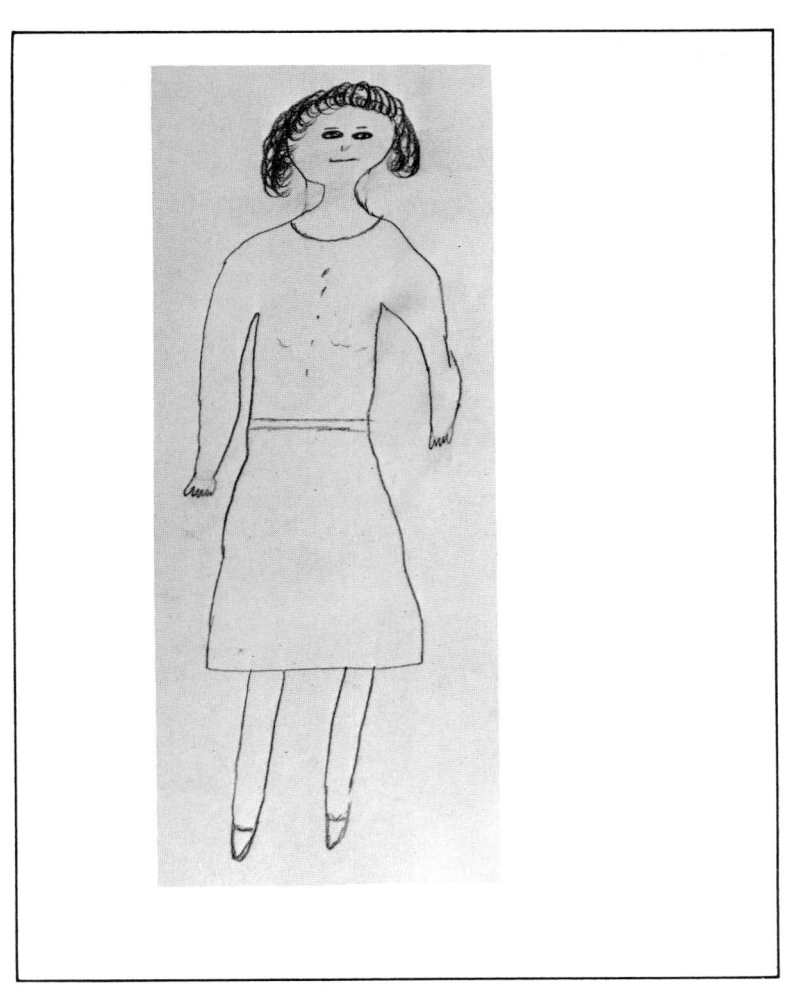

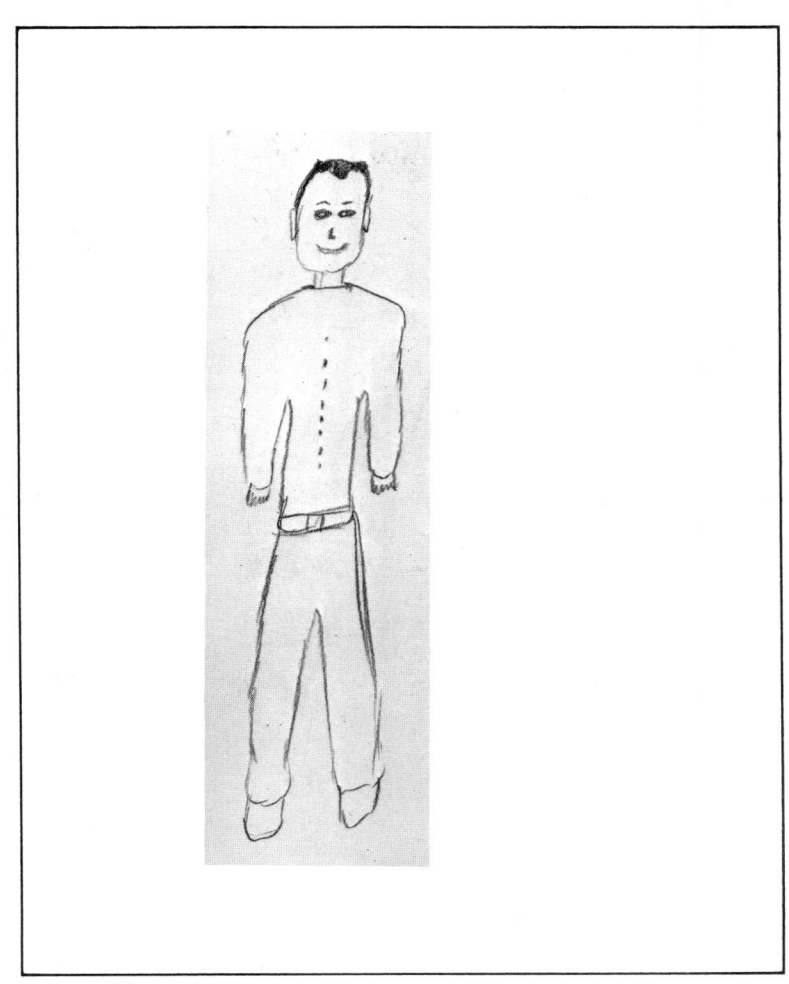

FIGURE-DRAWING CHARACTERISTICS

Structural	Male Female Both		Structural	Male	Female	Structural and Graphic	Male Female Both		Graphic, Global and Height	Male	Female	Body Proportions	Male	Female
Type	0		Omission of Appendages	0	0	Upper and Lower Halves	0	1	Hair Shading	2	3	Head	09	08
Sex Sequence	1		Position of Both Arms	0	1	Four Quarters	4	4	Nudity and Transparency	7	7	Neck	05	08
Posture	1	1	Position of Right Arm	0	0	Relative Size	4		Form	3	3	Shoulders	06	07
Perspective	0	0	Position of Left Arm	0	2	Constant Line Pressure	0	0	Detailing	3	3	Right Arm	04	06
Vertical Midline	3	3	Position of Legs	4	6	Variable Line Pressure	3	5	Identity and Sex	3	3	Left Arm	04	05
Bilateral Symmetry	2	2	Relation of Long Axes	1	1	Line Continuity	0	2	Sophistication	3	3	Chest	03	06
Horizontal Midline	4	4	Right and Left Halves	1	1	Body Shading	0	1	Height	07	08	Girth	04	08

GENERAL CHARACTERISTICS OF SUBJECT

IDENTIFICATION
No. E32
Sex M
Marital status S
Age 22 yrs. at
psychological tests

PARENTAL HISTORY				
Father				
C	H	S	D	O
+	-	-	-	-
Mother				
C	H	S	D	O
-	+	-	-	?

PHYSIOLOGICAL AND METABOLIC DATA

	Admission	Initial	Control	Cold pressor change	Exercise change	Smoking change
Systolic pressure	114	118	110	+08	+28	+08
Diastolic pressure	70	62	68	-08	-16	+11
Heart rate		56	50	00	+36	+03

Age 21 yrs.	Height 72 in.	Ponderal index 12.90
	Weight 174 lbs.	Cholesterol 220 mg. per 100 ml.
	Overweight +07 %	Vital capacity 5.2 liters

HABIT SURVEY

Smoking habits: nonsmoker

Age begun   yrs.   Inhalation:

Habits of nervous tension: 1, 3, 4, 8, 9, 20

STRONG VOCATIONAL INTEREST TEST

Occupation	Artist	Psychologist	Architect	Physician	Osteopath	Dentist	Veterinarian	Mathematician	Physicist	Engineer	Chemist	Production Manager
Standard Score	38	61	39	62	42	30	14	32	23	24	39	29

Occupation	Farmer	Aviator	Carpenter	Printer	Math.-Sci. Teacher	Ind. Arts Teacher	Voc. Agric. Teacher	Policeman	Forest Serv. Man	Y.M.C.A. Phys. Dir.	Personnel Director	Public Administrator
Standard Score	26	35	05	37	42	08	19	28	23	44	48	55

Occupation	Y.M.C.A. Secretary	Soc. Sci. H.S. Teacher	City Sch. Sup't.	Social Worker	Minister	Musician Performer	C.P.A.	Senior C.P.A.	Accountant	Office Man	Purchasing Agent	Banker
Standard Score	38	51	47	56	64	64	38	39	18	32	17	17

Occupation	Mortician	Pharmacist	Sales Manager	Real Est. Manager	Life Ins. Salesman	Advertising Man	Lawyer	Author- Journalist	President Mfg. Co.	Interest Maturity	Occupational Level	Masculinity- Femininity
Standard Score	15	26	23	28	27	43	49	43	20	57	56	40

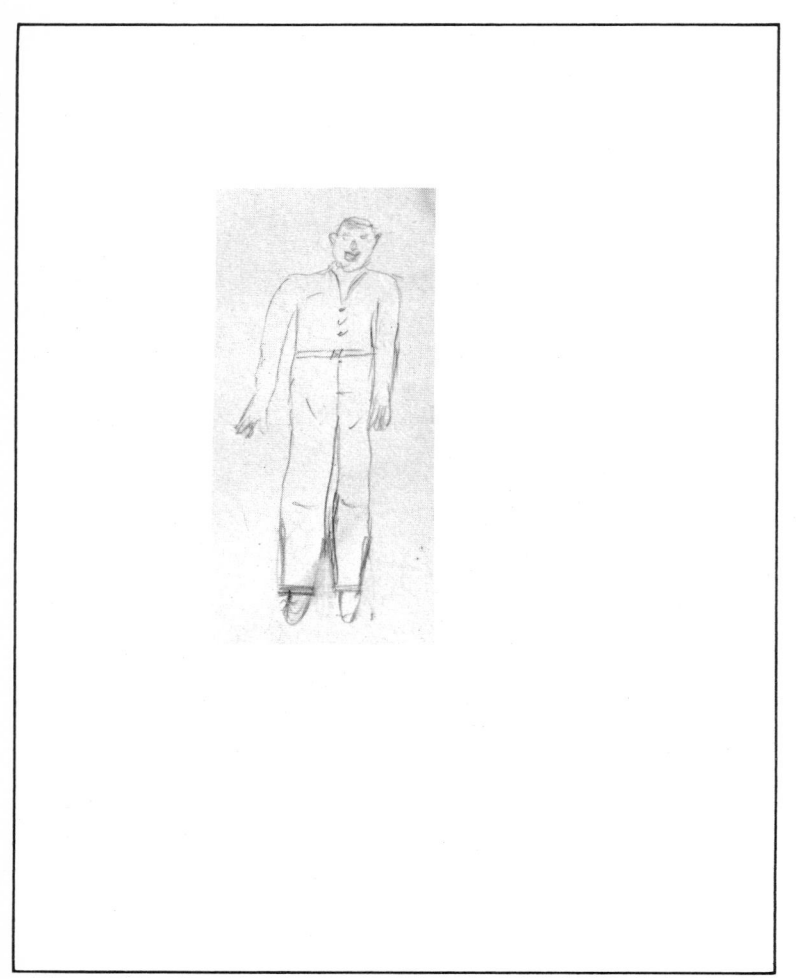

FIGURE-DRAWING CHARACTERISTICS

Structural	Male Female Both		Structural	Male	Female	Structural and Graphic	Male Female Both		Graphic, Global and Height	Male	Female	Body Proportions	Male	Female
Type	0		Omission of Appendages	0	0	Upper and Lower Halves	1	3	Hair Shading	1	2	Head	04	06
Sex Sequence	0		Position of Both Arms	1	4	Four Quarters	4	4	Nudity and Transparency	7	7	Neck	02	10
Posture	1	1	Position of Right Arm	2	7	Relative Size	4		Form	3	3	Shoulders	04	
Perspective	0	2	Position of Left Arm	0	0	Constant Line Pressure	0	0	Detailing	3	3	Right Arm	04	
Vertical Midline	3	4	Position of Legs	4	1	Variable Line Pressure	1	1	Identity and Sex	1	1	Left Arm	02	04
Bilateral Symmetry	3	0	Relation of Long Axes	1	1	Line Continuity	0	0	Sophistication	3	3	Chest	03	05
Horizontal Midline	4	4	Right and Left Halves	2	2	Body Shading	2	0	Height	04	06	Girth	05	05

GENERAL CHARACTERISTICS OF SUBJECT

IDENTIFICATION
No. 565
Sex M
Marital status M
Age 25 yrs. at
psychological tests

PARENTAL HISTORY				
Father				
C	H	S	D	O
-	-	-	-	-
Mother				
C	H	S	D	O
+	-	-	-	-

PHYSIOLOGICAL AND METABOLIC DATA

	Admission	Initial	Control	Cold pressor change	Exercise change	Smoking change
Systolic pressure	120	110	90	+10	+30	
Diastolic pressure	75	60	60	+20	00	
Heart rate	78	64	68	00	+18	

Age 21 yrs.	Height 74 in.	Ponderal index 13.49
	Weight 165 lbs.	Cholesterol 237 mg. per 100 ml.
	Overweight −04 %	Vital capacity 5.7 liters

HABIT SURVEY

Smoking habits: nonsmoker

  Age begun   yrs.   Inhalation:

Habits of nervous tension: 3, 5, 6, 8, 16,

21, 23

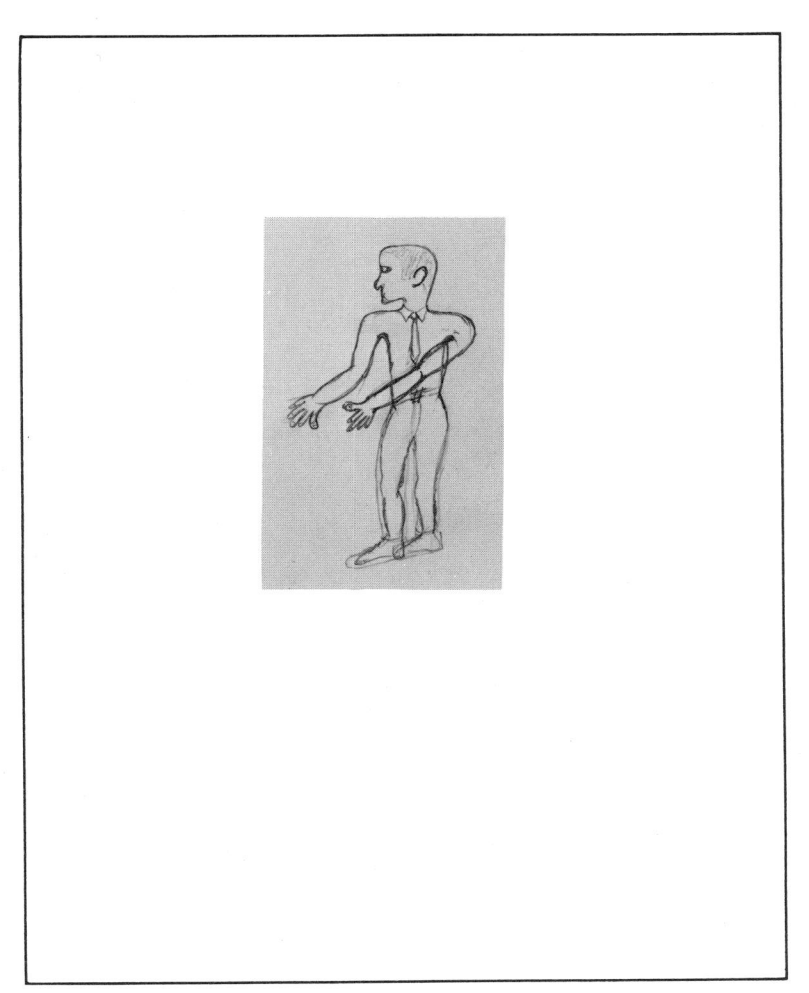

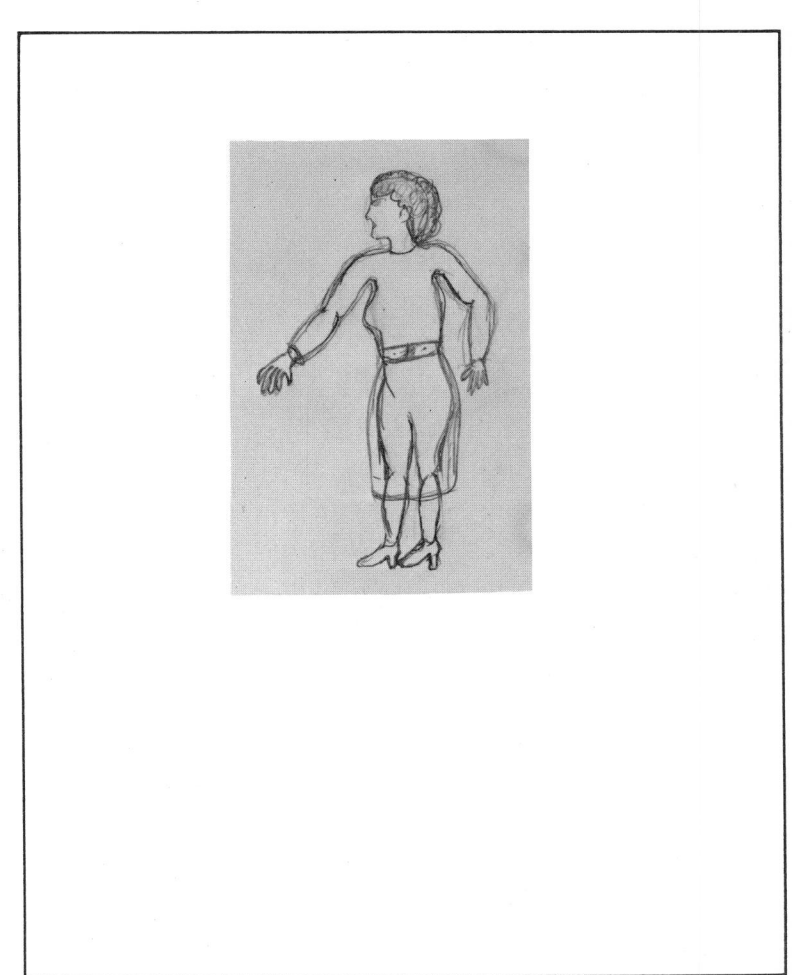

FIGURE-DRAWING CHARACTERISTICS

Structural	Male Female Both		Structural	Male	Female	Structural and Graphic	Male Female Both		Graphic, Global and Height	Male	Female	Body Proportions	Male	Female
Type	0		Omission of Appendages	0	0	Upper and Lower Halves	1	1	Hair Shading	2	3	Head	05	05
Sex Sequence	0		Position of Both Arms	0	1	Four Quarters	4	4	Nudity and Transparency	6	6	Neck	03	04
Posture	1	1	Position of Right Arm	2	2	Relative Size	4		Form	3	3	Shoulders	04	
Perspective	5	6	Position of Left Arm	2	5	Constant Line Pressure	0	0	Detailing	3	3	Right Arm	02	04
Vertical Midline	3	4	Position of Legs	4	4	Variable Line Pressure	3	4	Identity and Sex	1	1	Left Arm	03	04
Bilateral Symmetry	3	0	Relation of Long Axes	1	1	Line Continuity	1	0	Sophistication	3	3	Chest	03	
Horizontal Midline	4	4	Right and Left Halves	3	3	Body Shading	4	4	Height	03	04	Girth	03	

GENERAL CHARACTERISTICS OF SUBJECT

IDENTIFICATION
No. 730
Sex M
Marital status S
Age 23 yrs. at
psychological tests

PARENTAL HISTORY
Father
C H S D O
- ? - - -
Mother
C H S D O
+ + - - +

PHYSIOLOGICAL AND METABOLIC DATA

	Admission	Initial	Control	Cold pressor change	Exercise change	Smoking change
Systolic pressure	120	108	100	+24	+28	+01
Diastolic pressure	74	70	70	+24	+10	+08
Heart rate	74	80	72	+12	+37	+01

Age 23 yrs.	Height 72 in.	Ponderal index 13.04
	Weight 168 lbs.	Cholesterol 276 mg. per 100 ml.
	Overweight +02 %	Vital capacity 5.2 liters

HABIT SURVEY
Smoking habits: nonsmoker
Age begun yrs. Inhalation:
Habits of nervous tension: 5, 6, 9, 19

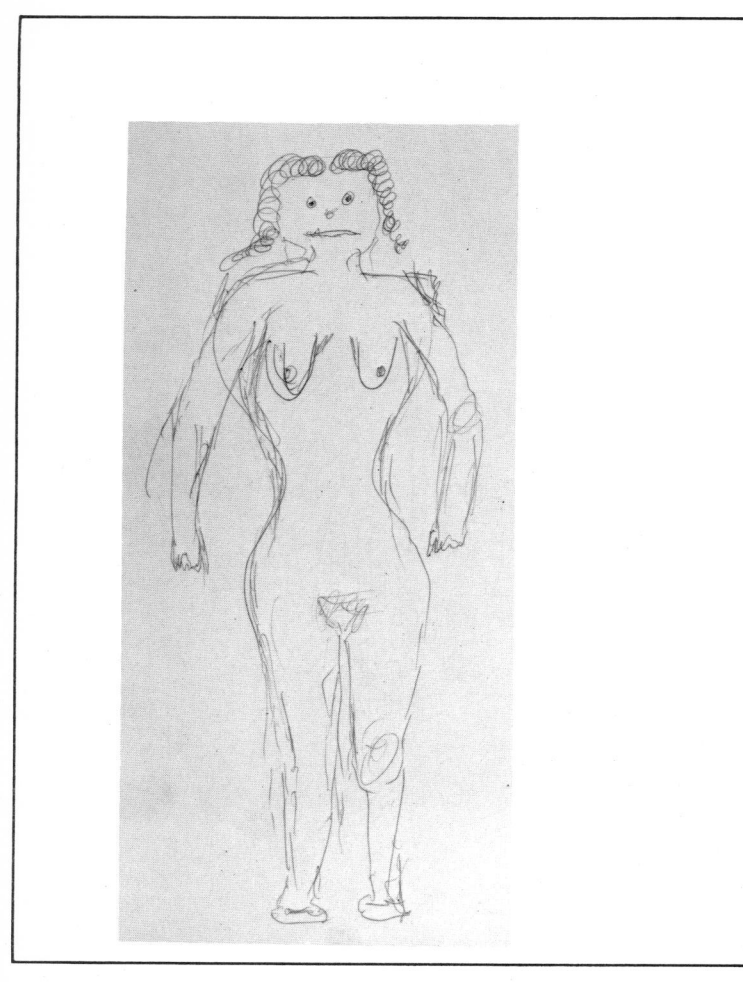
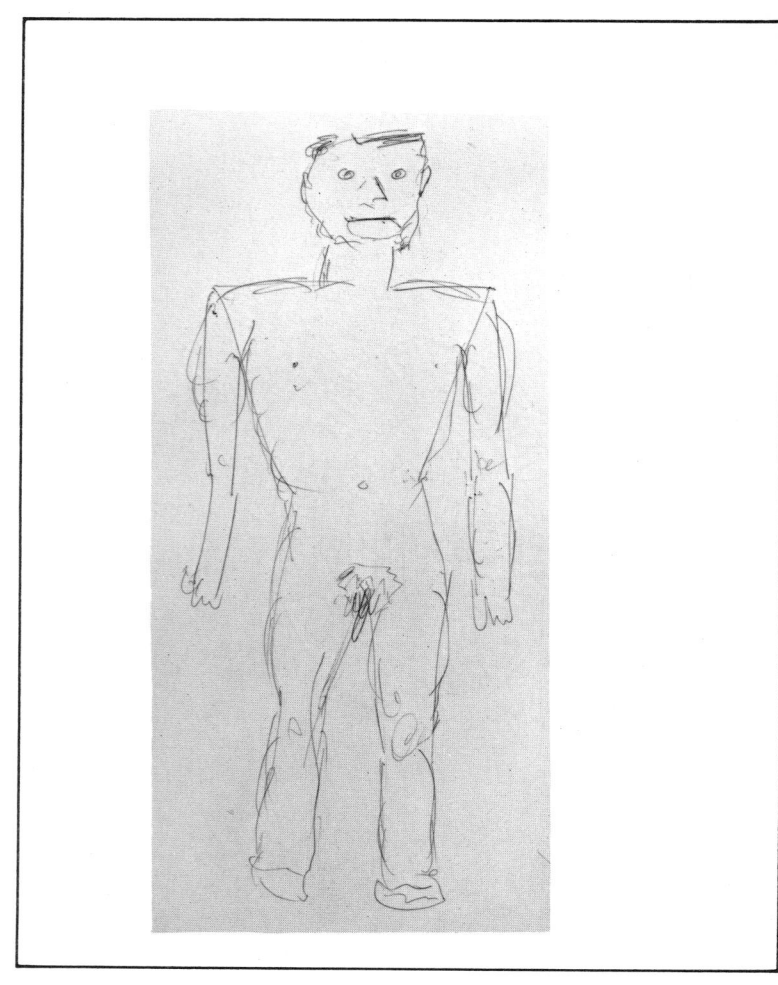

FIGURE-DRAWING CHARACTERISTICS

Structural	Male Female Both	Structural	Male	Female	Structural and Graphic	Male Female Both	Graphic, Global and Height	Male	Female	Body Proportions	Male	Female
Type	0	Omission of Appendages	0	0	Upper and Lower Halves	0 3	Hair Shading	3	3	Head	08	07
Sex Sequence	1	Position of Both Arms	0	0	Four Quarters	4 4	Nudity and Transparency	0	0	Neck	16	06
Posture	1 1	Position of Right Arm	0	5	Relative Size	2	Form	3	3	Shoulders	12	09
Perspective	0 0	Position of Left Arm	0	5	Constant Line Pressure	2 1	Detailing	3	3	Right Arm	08	08
Vertical Midline	0 0	Position of Legs	5	4	Variable Line Pressure	0 0	Identity and Sex	1	1	Left Arm	08	07
Bilateral Symmetry	3 3	Relation of Long Axes	1	1	Line Continuity	0 0	Sophistication	3	3	Chest	10	09
Horizontal Midline	0 0	Right and Left Halves	1	1	Body Shading	2 3	Height	08	08	Girth	08	06

GENERAL CHARACTERISTICS OF SUBJECT

IDENTIFICATION
No. E24
Sex M
Marital status M
Age 22 yrs. at
psychological tests

PARENTAL HISTORY
Father
C   H   S   D   O
–   –   –   –   –
Mother
C   H   S   D   O
+   –   –   –   –

PHYSIOLOGICAL AND METABOLIC DATA

	Admission	Initial	Control	Cold pressor change	Exercise change	Smoking change
Systolic pressure		130	118	+06	+34	+07
Diastolic pressure		68	78	+02	–20	+15
Heart rate		72	72	+08	+19	+02

Age 22 yrs.			
Height	71 in.	Ponderal index	13.00
Weight	163 lbs.	Cholesterol	296 mg. per 100 ml.
Overweight +03 %		Vital capacity	5.4 liters

HABIT SURVEY
Smoking habits: nonsmoker
Age begun   yrs.   Inhalation:
Habits of nervous tension: 2, 5, 6, 24

STRONG VOCATIONAL INTEREST TEST

Occupation	Artist	Psychologist	Architect	Physician	Osteopath	Dentist	Veterinarian	Mathematician	Physicist	Engineer	Chemist	Production Manager
Standard Score	23	50	20	44	41	29	20	18	12	16	25	26

Occupation	Farmer	Aviator	Carpenter	Printer	Math.-Sci. Teacher	Ind. Arts Teacher	Voc. Agric. Teacher	Policeman	Forest Serv. Man	Y.M.C.A. Phys. Dir.	Personnel Director	Public Administrator
Standard Score	28	39	07	34	39	15	30	27	19	43	46	49

Occupation	Y.M.C.A. Secretary	Soc. Sci. H.S. Teacher	City Sch. Sup't.	Social Worker	Minister	Musician Performer	C.P.A.	Senior C.P.A.	Accountant	Office Man	Purchasing Agent	Banker
Standard Score	41	46	36	52	64	41	33	42	24	31	17	21

Occupation	Mortician	Pharmacist	Sales Manager	Real Est. Manager	Life Ins. Salesman	Advertising Man	Lawyer	Author-Journalist	President Mfg. Co.	Interest Maturity	Occupational Level	Masculinity-Femininity
Standard Score	24	28	40	35	44	41	41	35	27	58	56	52

Plate 222   DRAWINGS AT AN INTERMEDIATE LEVEL OF SOPHISTICATION   265

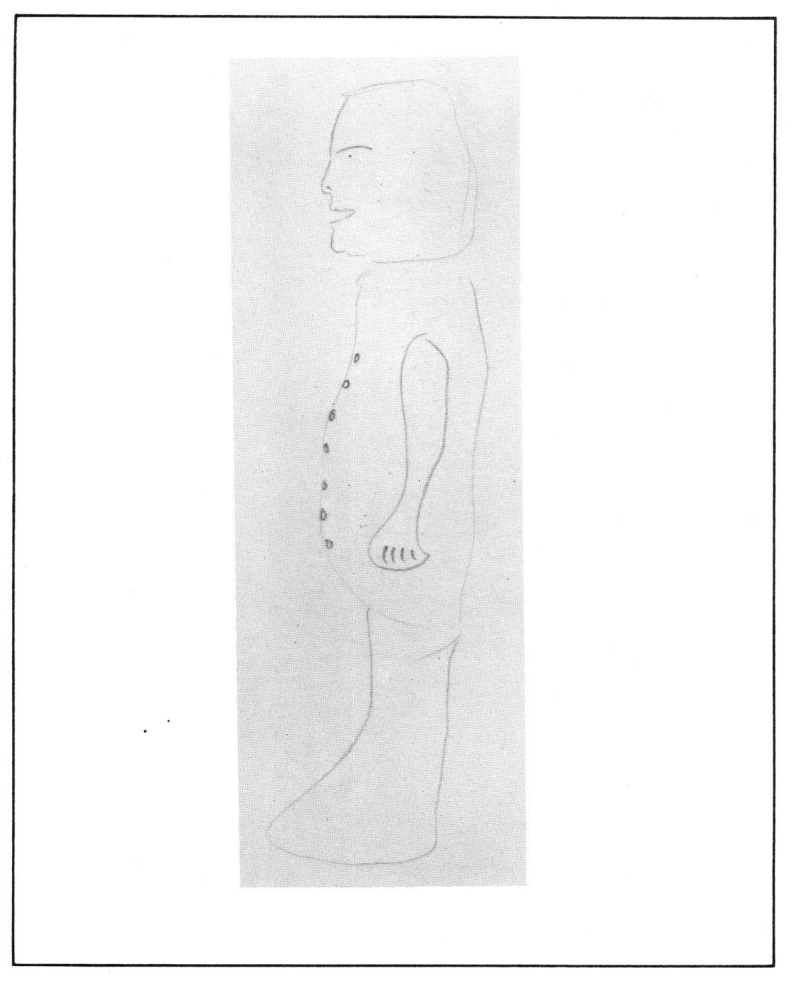

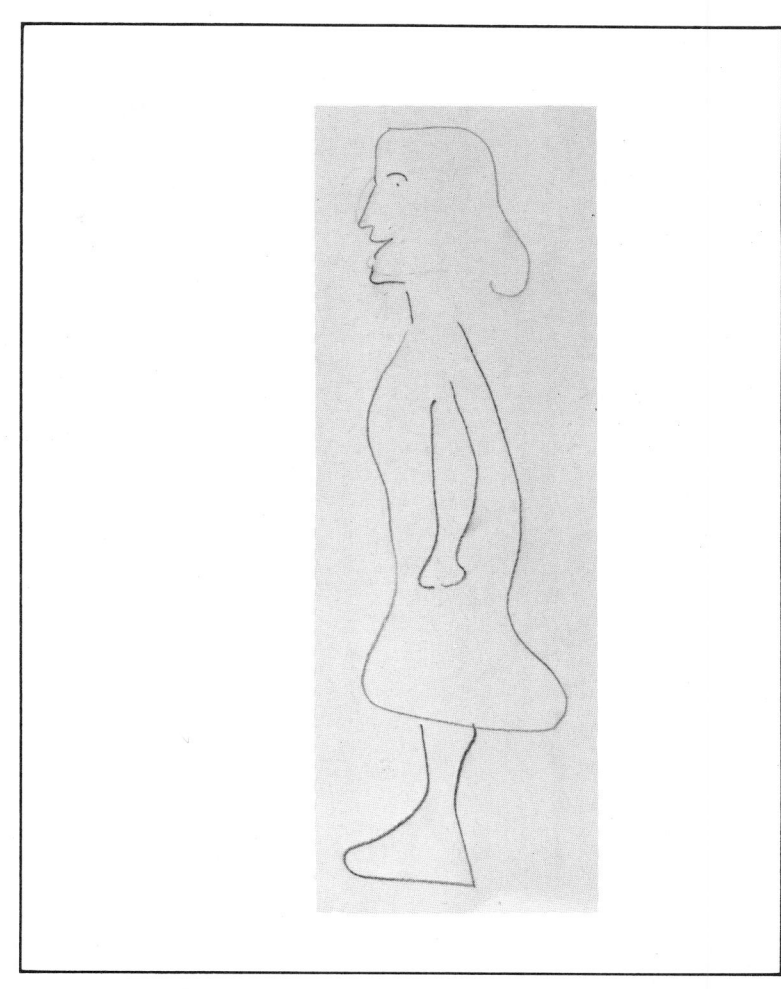

FIGURE-DRAWING CHARACTERISTICS

Structural	Male Female Both	Structural	Male	Female	Structural and Graphic	Male Female Both	Graphic, Global and Height	Male	Female	Body Proportions	Male	Female
Type	0	Omission of Appendages	0	0	Upper and Lower Halves	0 0	Hair Shading	5	5	Head	13	12
Sex Sequence	0	Position of Both Arms	4	4	Four Quarters	4 4	Nudity and Transparency	7	7	Neck		12
Posture	1 1	Position of Right Arm	7	7	Relative Size	0	Form	3	3	Shoulders		
Perspective	2 2	Position of Left Arm	0	0	Constant Line Pressure	1 0	Detailing	5	5	Right Arm		
Vertical Midline	7 4	Position of Legs	1	1	Variable Line Pressure	0 5	Identity and Sex	3	3	Left Arm	06	04
Bilateral Symmetry	0 0	Relation of Long Axes	1	1	Line Continuity	4 4	Sophistication	4	4	Chest	10	07
Horizontal Midline	2 0	Right and Left Halves	0	3	Body Shading	0 0	Height	08	08	Girth	10	12

GENERAL CHARACTERISTICS OF SUBJECT

IDENTIFICATION

No. E77

Sex M

Marital status S

Age 21 yrs. at
psychological tests

PARENTAL HISTORY

Father

C H S D O

+ ? - - ?

Mother

C H S D O

- - - - ?

PHYSIOLOGICAL AND METABOLIC DATA

	Admission	Initial	Control	Cold pressor change	Exercise change	Smoking change
Systolic pressure	100	135	118	+12	+32	
Diastolic pressure	70	75	74	+26	-12	
Heart rate	70	80	73	00	+15	

Age 20 yrs.

Height 71 in.   Ponderal index 12.88

Weight 167 lbs.   Cholesterol 180 mg. per 100 ml.

Overweight +07 %   Vital capacity 4.9 liters

HABIT SURVEY

Smoking habits: nonsmoker

Age begun   yrs.   Inhalation:

Habits of nervous tension: 3, 10, 14

STRONG VOCATIONAL INTEREST TEST

Occupation	Artist	Psychologist	Architect	Physician	Osteopath	Dentist	Veterinarian	Mathematician	Physicist	Engineer	Chemist	Production Manager
Standard Score	38	62	38	62	49	34	11	30	30	34	42	29

Occupation	Farmer	Aviator	Carpenter	Printer	Math.-Sci. Teacher	Ind. Arts Teacher	Voc. Agric. Teacher	Policeman	Forest Serv. Man	Y.M.C.A. Phys. Dir.	Personnel Director	Public Administrator
Standard Score	18	40	09	37	39	18	17	29	19	39	47	48

Occupation	Y.M.C.A. Secretary	Soc. Sci. H.S. Teacher	City Sch. Sup't.	Social Worker	Minister	Musician Performer	C.P.A.	Senior C.P.A.	Accountant	Office Man	Purchasing Agent	Banker
Standard Score	32	40	47	58	64	60	33	35	16	25	09	09

Occupation	Mortician	Pharmacist	Sales Manager	Real Est. Manager	Life Ins. Salesman	Advertising Man	Lawyer	Author-Journalist	President Mfg. Co.	Interest Maturity	Occupational Level	Masculinity-Femininity
Standard Score	13	32	30	30	32	43	46	41	29	59	58	41

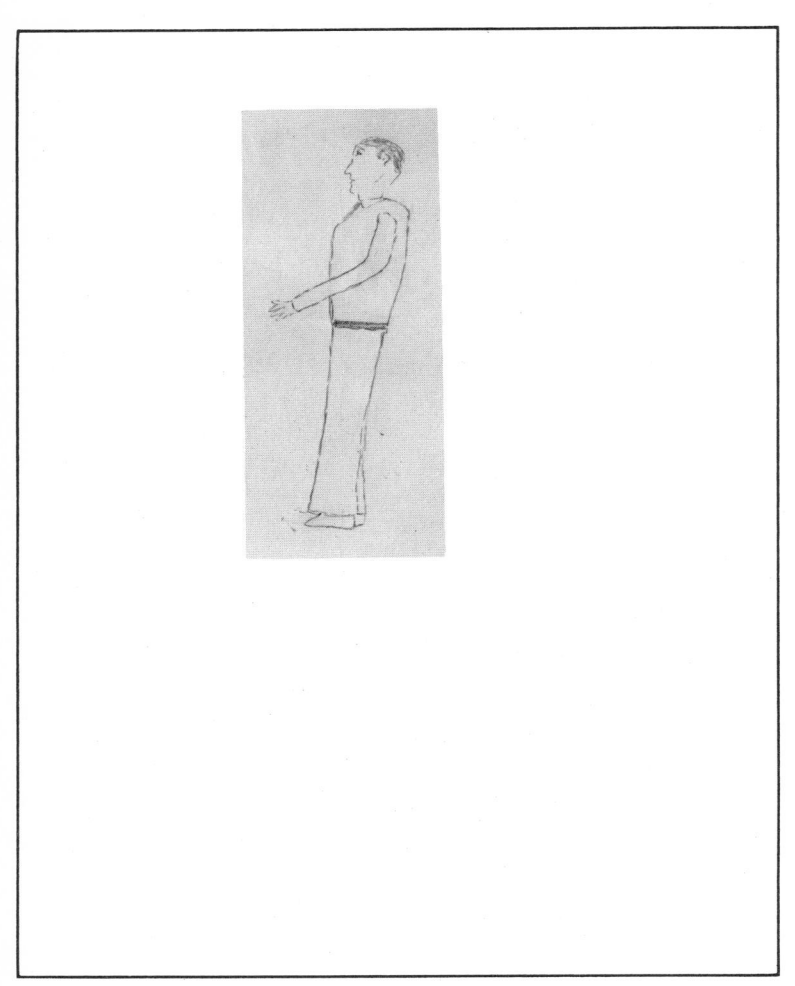

FIGURE-DRAWING CHARACTERISTICS

Structural	Male Female / Both		Structural	Male	Female	Structural and Graphic	Male Female / Both		Graphic, Global and Height	Male	Female	Body Proportions	Male	Female
Type	0		Omission of Appendages	0	0	Upper and Lower Halves	1	1	Hair Shading	3	3	Head	05	03
Sex Sequence	0		Position of Both Arms	4	4	Four Quarters	4	4	Nudity and Transparency	7	7	Neck	02	00
Posture	1	1	Position of Right Arm	7	7	Relative Size	0		Form	3	1	Shoulders		
Perspective	2	2	Position of Left Arm	4	4	Constant Line Pressure	0	0	Detailing	3	3	Right Arm		
Vertical Midline	5	4	Position of Legs	1	1	Variable Line Pressure	1	1	Identity and Sex	1	1	Left Arm	04	02
Bilateral Symmetry	0	0	Relation of Long Axes	1	1	Line Continuity	0	0	Sophistication	3	3	Chest	05	03
Horizontal Midline	4	4	Right and Left Halves	2	2	Body Shading	4	0	Height	04	03	Girth	04	03

GENERAL CHARACTERISTICS OF SUBJECT

IDENTIFICATION
No. 204
Sex M
Marital status S
Age 26 yrs. at
psychological tests

PARENTAL HISTORY				
Father				
C	H	S	D	O
(+)	–	–	+	?
Mother				
C	H	S	D	O
–	?	–	–	–

PHYSIOLOGICAL AND METABOLIC DATA

	Admission	Initial	Control	Cold pressor change	Exercise change	Smoking change
Systolic pressure	156	156	134	+08	+32	
Diastolic pressure	78	72	78	+24	–06	
Heart rate	84	84	68	+02	+13	

Age 23 yrs.	Height	72	in.	Ponderal index	12.39
	Weight	196	lbs.	Cholesterol	208 mg. per 100 ml.
	Overweight +20 %			Vital capacity	4.9 liters

HABIT SURVEY
Smoking habits: unknown
Age begun   yrs.   Inhalation:
Habits of nervous tension:

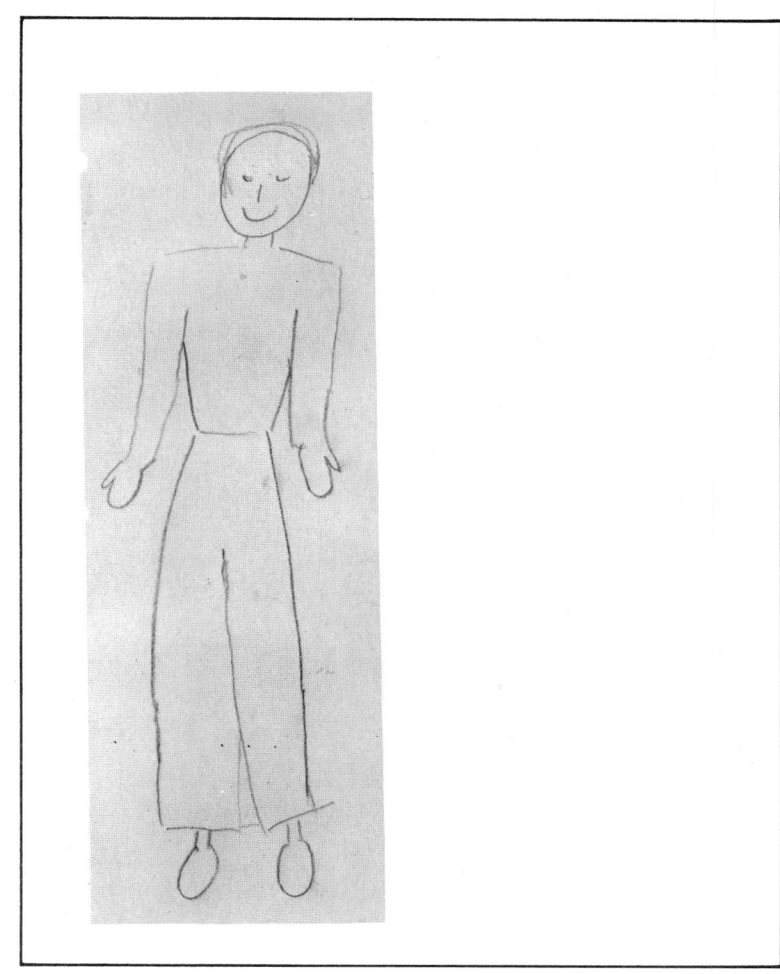

FIGURE-DRAWING CHARACTERISTICS

Structural	Male Female Both		Structural	Male	Female	Structural and Graphic	Male Female Both		Graphic, Global and Height	Male	Female	Body Proportions	Male	Female
Type	0		Omission of Appendages	0	2	Upper and Lower Halves	0	0	Hair Shading	0	3	Head	08	08
Sex Sequence	1		Position of Both Arms	0	0	Four Quarters	4	4	Nudity and Transparency	7	7	Neck	04	08
Posture	1	4	Position of Right Arm	0	5	Relative Size	0		Form	3	3	Shoulders	08	07
Perspective	0	5	Position of Left Arm	0	5	Constant Line Pressure	0	1	Detailing	5	3	Right Arm	06	
Vertical Midline	0	0	Position of Legs	4	9	Variable Line Pressure	3	0	Identity and Sex	3	1	Left Arm	06	
Bilateral Symmetry	3	3	Relation of Long Axes	1	3	Line Continuity	2	3	Sophistication	3	3	Chest	05	06
Horizontal Midline	4	4	Right and Left Halves	2	2	Body Shading	0	0	Height	08	07	Girth	04	05

GENERAL CHARACTERISTICS OF SUBJECT

IDENTIFICATION
No. 206
Sex F
Marital status S
Age 24 yrs. at psychological tests

PARENTAL HISTORY
Father
C H S D O
(+) - - - +
Mother
C H S D O
- + (?) - -

PHYSIOLOGICAL AND METABOLIC DATA

	Admission	Initial	Control	Cold pressor change	Exercise change	Smoking change
Systolic pressure	120	120	104	+12	+28	
Diastolic pressure	80	72	72	+15	00	
Heart rate	88	104	79	+12	+28	

Age 21 yrs.   Height 65 in.   Ponderal index 12.93
Weight 127 lbs.   Cholesterol 190 mg. per 100 ml.
Overweight -02 %   Vital capacity 3.6 liters

HABIT SURVEY

Smoking habits: light cigarette smoker
Age begun 19 yrs.   Inhalation: sometimes
Habits of nervous tension: 2, 4, 5, 6, 9, 11, 14, 16, 17, 21

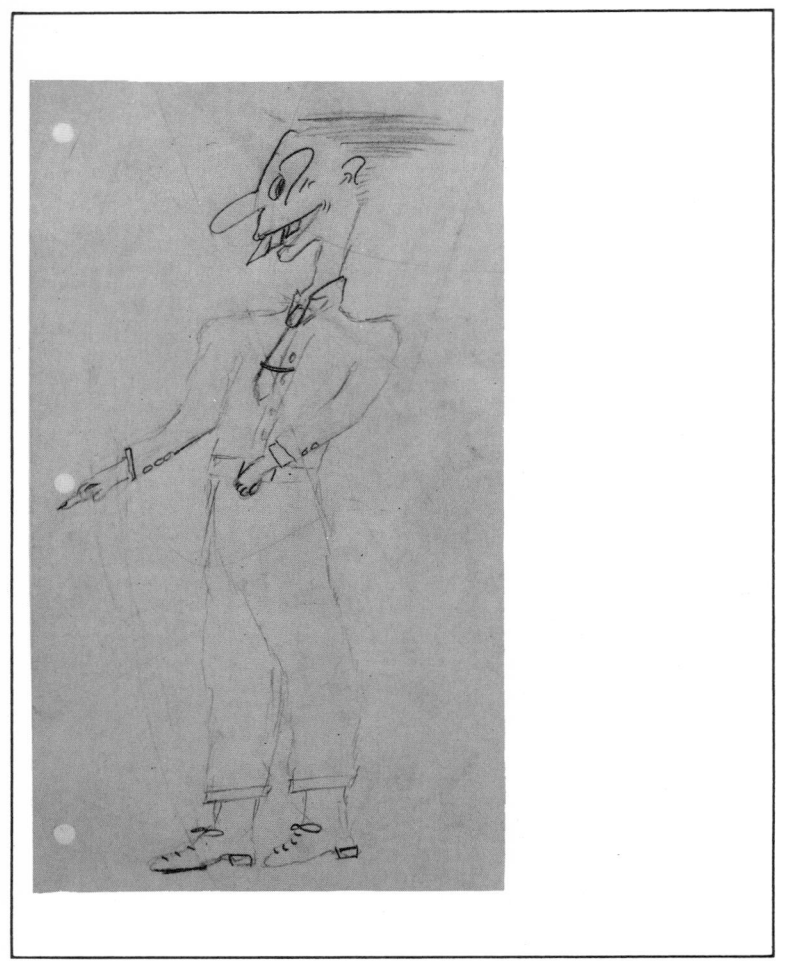

FIGURE-DRAWING CHARACTERISTICS

Structural	Male Female Both	Structural	Male	Female	Structural and Graphic	Male Female Both	Graphic, Global and Height	Male	Female	Body Proportions	Male	Female
Type	0	Omission of Appendages	0	0	Upper and Lower Halves	0 3	Hair Shading	3	1	Head	11	08
Sex Sequence	2	Position of Both Arms	1	4	Four Quarters	4 4	Nudity and Transparency	7	7	Neck	18	10
Posture	1 1	Position of Right Arm	4	7	Relative Size	0	Form	3	3	Shoulders		
Perspective	6 6	Position of Left Arm	5	4	Constant Line Pressure	0 0	Detailing	3	3	Right Arm	05	
Vertical Midline	7 7	Position of Legs	4	4	Variable Line Pressure	3 3	Identity and Sex	1	1	Left Arm	04	06
Bilateral Symmetry	0 0	Relation of Long Axes	1	1	Line Continuity	0 0	Sophistication	3	3	Chest		
Horizontal Midline	4 2	Right and Left Halves	2	1	Body Shading	0 3	Height	08	08	Girth		

GENERAL CHARACTERISTICS OF SUBJECT

IDENTIFICATION
No. 212
Sex M
Marital status M
Age 26 yrs. at
psychological tests

PARENTAL HISTORY
Father
C   H   S   D   O
(+) (+)   -   -   +
Mother
C   H   S   D   O
-    -   -   -   -

PHYSIOLOGICAL AND METABOLIC DATA

	Admission	Initial	Control	Cold pressor change	Exercise change	Smoking change
Systolic pressure	110	126	114	+10	+20	
Diastolic pressure	60	68	62	+24	-04	
Heart rate	79	84	83	+04	+17	

Age 23 yrs.	Height 68 in.	Ponderal index 13.42
	Weight 130 lbs.	Cholesterol 223 mg. per 100 ml.
	Overweight -12 %	Vital capacity 4.2 liters

HABIT SURVEY
Smoking habits: heavy cigarette smoker
Age begun 17 yrs.   Inhalation: yes
Habits of nervous tension: 5, 6, 9

Plate 226   DRAWINGS AT AN INTERMEDIATE LEVEL OF SOPHISTICATION   269

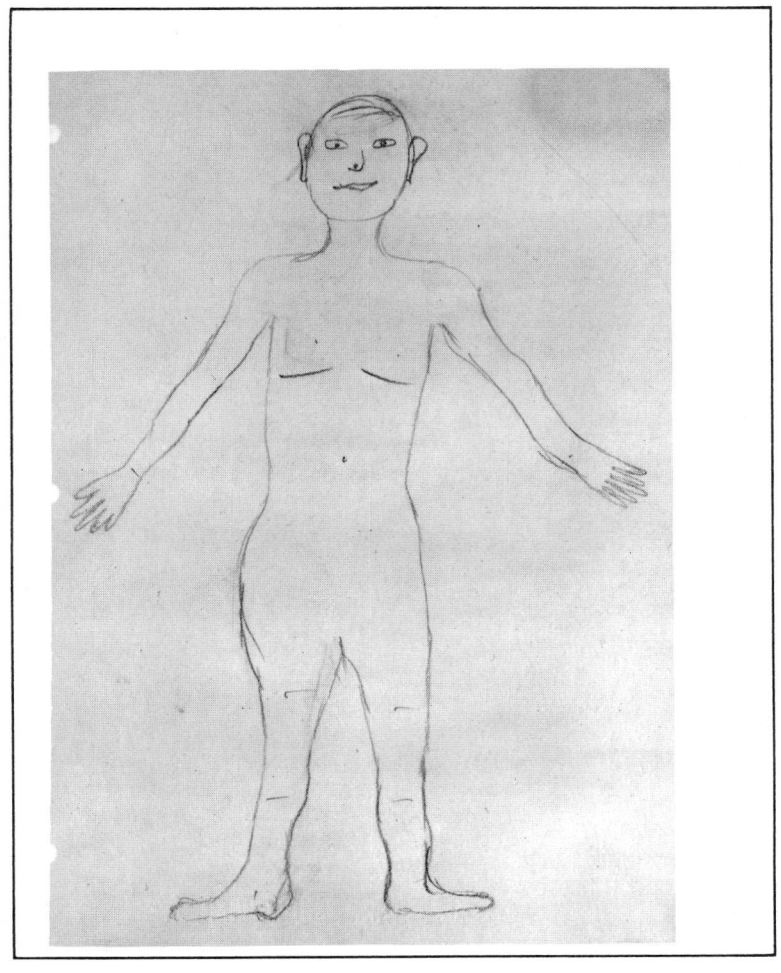

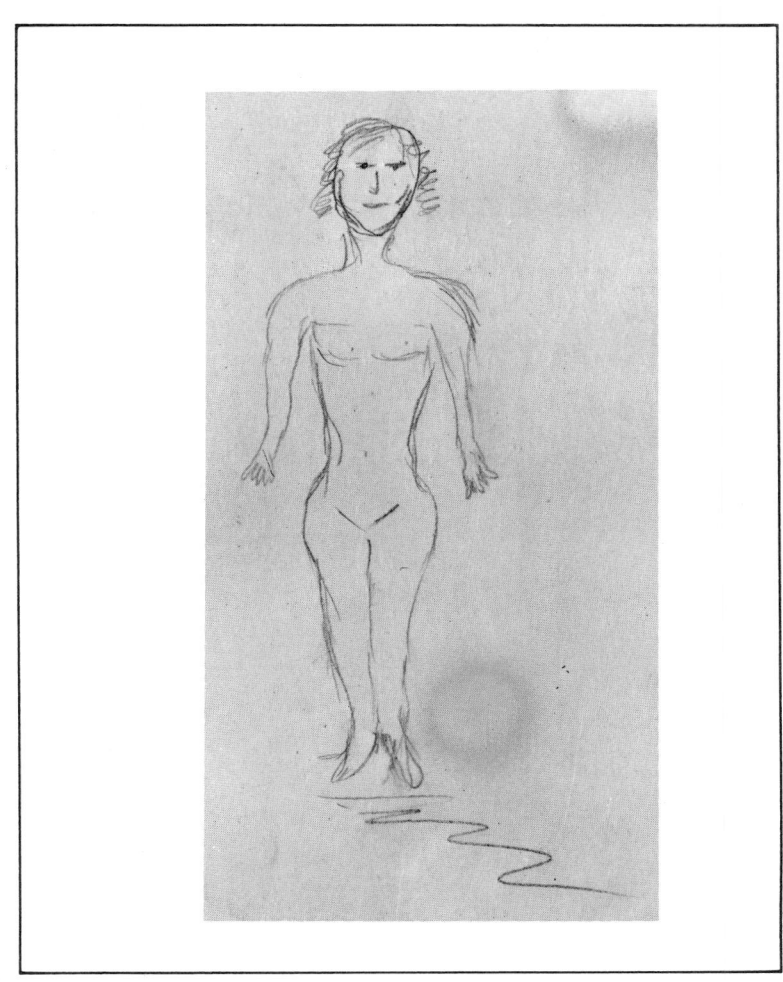

FIGURE-DRAWING CHARACTERISTICS

Structural	Male Female Both	Structural	Male	Female	Structural and Graphic	Male Female Both		Graphic, Global and Height	Male	Female	Body Proportions	Male	Female
Type	0	Omission of Appendages	0	0	Upper and Lower Halves	3	1	Hair Shading	7	3	Head	10	10
Sex Sequence	0	Position of Both Arms	0	0	Four Quarters	4	4	Nudity and Transparency	0	0	Neck	10	10
Posture	1 1	Position of Right Arm	2	2	Relative Size	0		Form	3	3	Shoulders	09	08
Perspective	0 0	Position of Left Arm	2	2	Constant Line Pressure	0	0	Detailing	3	3	Right Arm	06	04
Vertical Midline	0 0	Position of Legs	6	2	Variable Line Pressure	1	1	Identity and Sex	3	1	Left Arm	06	04
Bilateral Symmetry	3 3	Relation of Long Axes	1	1	Line Continuity	0	0	Sophistication	3	3	Chest	07	06
Horizontal Midline	0 0	Right and Left Halves	1	1	Body Shading	3	1	Height	08	07	Girth	09	05

GENERAL CHARACTERISTICS OF SUBJECT

<table>
<tr><td rowspan="2">

IDENTIFICATION

No.   241

Sex M

Marital status   M

Age 28 yrs. at

psychological tests

</td><td rowspan="2">

PARENTAL HISTORY

Father

C   H   S   D   O

(+)   -   -   -   -

Mother

C   H   S   D   O

-    -   -   -   -

</td><td colspan="7">

PHYSIOLOGICAL AND METABOLIC DATA

</td></tr>
<tr><td></td><td>Admission</td><td>Initial</td><td>Control</td><td>Cold pressor change</td><td>Exercise change</td><td>Smoking change</td></tr>
</table>

PHYSIOLOGICAL AND METABOLIC DATA	Admission	Initial	Control	Cold pressor change	Exercise change	Smoking change
Systolic pressure	102	130	110	+12	+28	
Diastolic pressure	65	78	68	+20	-08	
Heart rate	60	72	61	+06	+12	

Age 26 yrs.   Height   72 in.   Ponderal index 13.70

Weight   145 lbs.   Cholesterol   200   mg. per 100 ml.

Overweight -14 %   Vital capacity   4.1   liters

HABIT SURVEY

Smoking habits: unknown

Age begun   yrs.   Inhalation:

Habits of nervous tension:

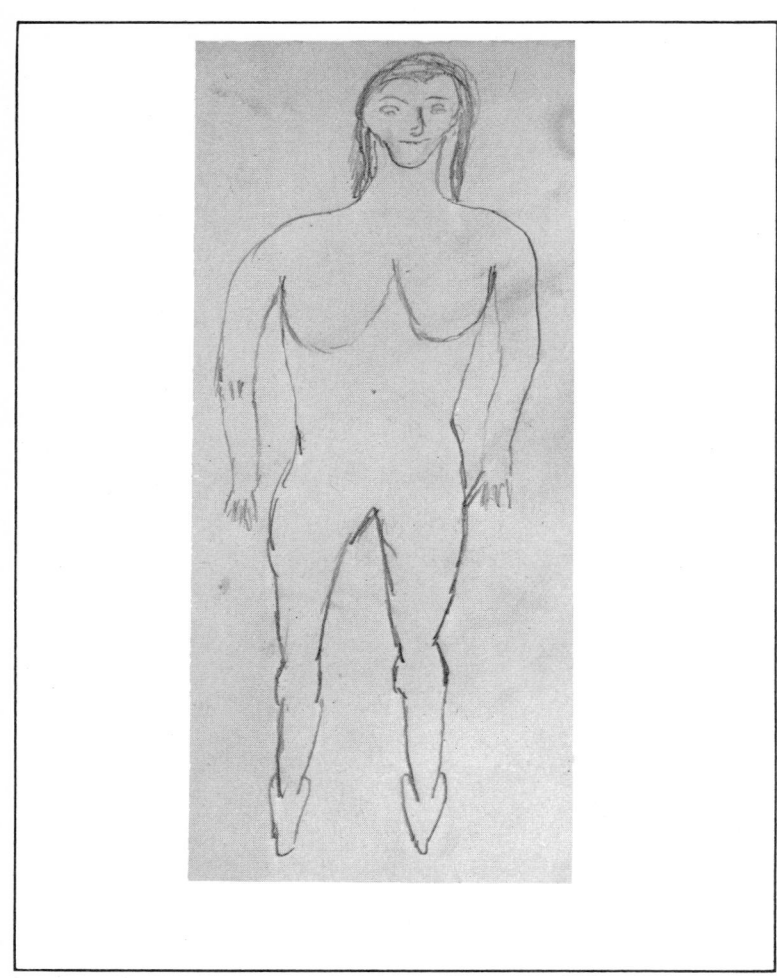

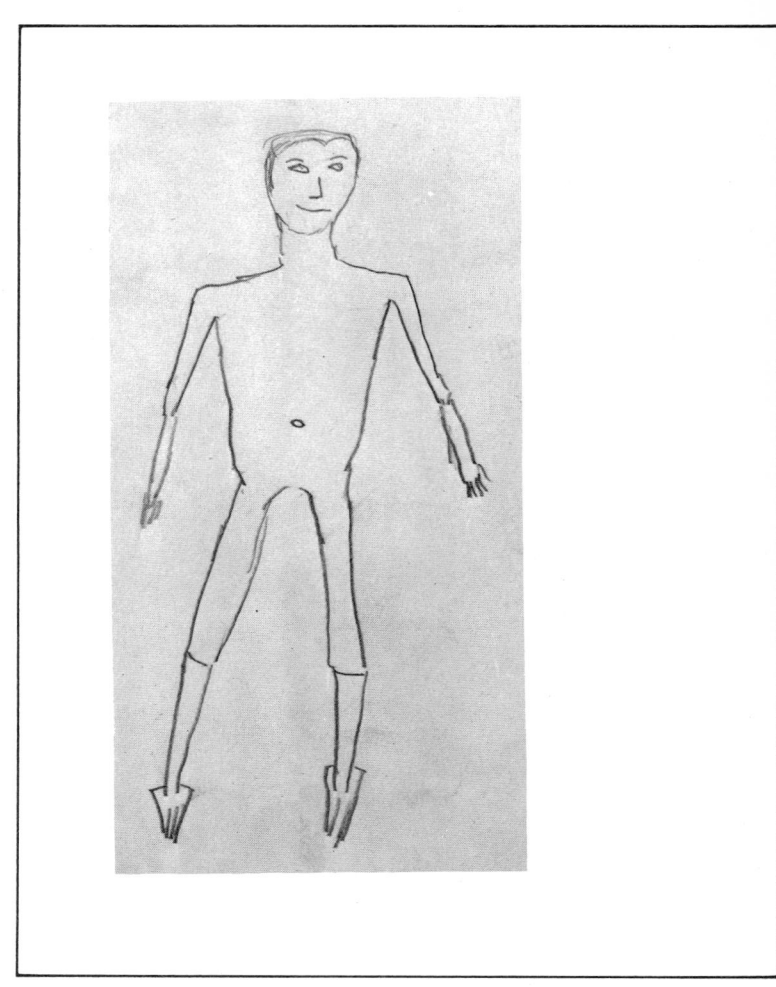

FIGURE-DRAWING CHARACTERISTICS

Structural	Male　Female Both	Structural	Male	Female	Structural and Graphic	Male　Female Both		Graphic, Global and Height	Male	Female	Body Proportions	Male	Female
Type	0	Omission of Appendages	0	0	Upper and Lower Halves	0	1	Hair Shading	3	3	Head	08	09
Sex Sequence	1	Position of Both Arms	0	0	Four Quarters	4	4	Nudity and Transparency	0	0	Neck	10	10
Posture	1　1	Position of Right Arm	2	0	Relative Size	4		Form	5	3	Shoulders	09	10
Perspective	0　0	Position of Left Arm	2	0	Constant Line Pressure	0	0	Detailing	5	5	Right Arm	06	08
Vertical Midline	0　0	Position of Legs	6	6	Variable Line Pressure	5	3	Identity and Sex	3	1	Left Arm	06	06
Bilateral Symmetry	3　3	Relation of Long Axes	1	1	Line Continuity	2	0	Sophistication	3	3	Chest	08	11
Horizontal Midline	0　0	Right and Left Halves	1	0	Body Shading	2	1	Height	07	08	Girth	07	11

GENERAL CHARACTERISTICS OF SUBJECT

IDENTIFICATION
No.　242
Sex　M
Marital status　M
Age　25　yrs. at
psychological tests

PARENTAL HISTORY				
Father				
C	H	S	D	O
(+)	+	-	-	-
Mother				
C	H	S	D	O
-	?	-	-	-

PHYSIOLOGICAL AND METABOLIC DATA

	Admission	Initial	Control	Cold pressor change	Exercise change	Smoking change
Systolic pressure	138	128	116	+16	+28	
Diastolic pressure	84	68	66	+30	00	
Heart rate	84	96	77	+04	+34	

Age 23 yrs.

Height　72　in.　　　Ponderal index 12.55
Weight　189　lbs.　　Cholesterol　210　mg. per 100 ml.
Overweight +15 %　　Vital capacity　4.6　liters

HABIT SURVEY
Smoking habits:　light cigarette smoker
Age begun　18　yrs.　　Inhalation:　yes
Habits of nervous tension:　5, 6, 10

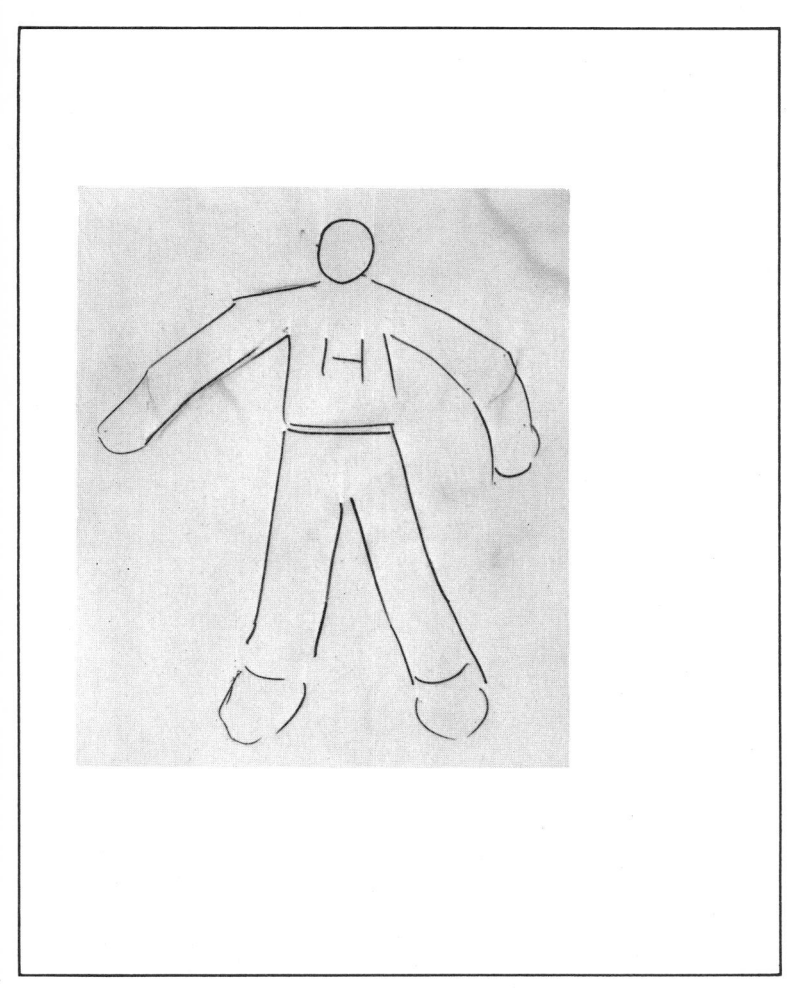

FIGURE-DRAWING CHARACTERISTICS

Structural	Male Female Both	Structural	Male	Female	Structural and Graphic	Male Female Both		Graphic, Global and Height	Male	Female	Body Proportions	Male	Female
Type	0	Omission of Appendages	0	0	Upper and Lower Halves	1	1	Hair Shading	0	0	Head	05	
Sex Sequence	0	Position of Both Arms	0	0	Four Quarters	4	4	Nudity and Transparency	7	9	Neck	00	
Posture	1	1	Position of Right Arm	2	2	Relative Size	4		Form	3	3	Shoulders		07
Perspective	0	0	Position of Left Arm	2	2	Constant Line Pressure	5	0	Detailing	5	5	Right Arm	06	06
Vertical Midline	0	0	Position of Legs	6	6	Variable Line Pressure	0	5	Identity and Sex	1	1	Left Arm	06	06
Bilateral Symmetry	3	3	Relation of Long Axes	1	1	Line Continuity	3	3	Sophistication	3	3	Chest	05	06
Horizontal Midline	4	4	Right and Left Halves	1	1	Body Shading	0	0	Height	05	06	Girth	07	08

GENERAL CHARACTERISTICS OF SUBJECT

IDENTIFICATION
No. 268
Sex M
Marital status S
Age 24 yrs. at
psychological tests

PARENTAL HISTORY				
Father				
C	H	S	D	O
(+)	-	(+)	-	-
Mother				
C	H	S	D	O
-	-	-	-	?

PHYSIOLOGICAL AND METABOLIC DATA

	Admission	Initial	Control	Cold pressor change	Exercise change	Smoking change
Systolic pressure	130	110	110	+20	+30	
Diastolic pressure	72	70	60	+10	-10	
Heart rate	76	64	61	-04	+27	

Age 24 yrs.	Height	71 in.	Ponderal index	13.08
	Weight	160 lbs.	Cholesterol	223 mg. per 100 ml.
	Overweight	00 %	Vital capacity	5.9 liters

HABIT SURVEY
Smoking habits: nonsmoker
Age begun   yrs.   Inhalation:
Habits of nervous tension: 4, 5, 8, 10, 14, 17,
21, 24

FIGURE-DRAWING CHARACTERISTICS

Structural	Male Female Both	Structural	Male	Female	Structural and Graphic	Male Female Both		Graphic, Global and Height	Male	Female	Body Proportions	Male	Female
Type	0	Omission of Appendages	0	0	Upper and Lower Halves	2	2	Hair Shading	7	5	Head	04	04
Sex Sequence	0	Position of Both Arms	4	4	Four Quarters	0	0	Nudity and Transparency	7	7	Neck	06	04
Posture	2 2	Position of Right Arm	7	7	Relative Size	0		Form	3	3	Shoulders		
Perspective	2 2	Position of Left Arm	4	4	Constant Line Pressure	5	5	Detailing	3	3	Right Arm		
Vertical Midline	7 4	Position of Legs	8	8	Variable Line Pressure	0	0	Identity and Sex	1	1	Left Arm	04	02
Bilateral Symmetry	0 0	Relation of Long Axes	1	1	Line Continuity	3	4	Sophistication	3	3	Chest	06	04
Horizontal Midline	6 0	Right and Left Halves	2	2	Body Shading	0	0	Height	04	03	Girth	06	04

GENERAL CHARACTERISTICS OF SUBJECT

IDENTIFICATION
No. 447
Sex M
Marital status S
Age 26 yrs. at
psychological tests

PARENTAL HISTORY				
Father				
C	H	S	D	O
(+)	+	–	–	–
Mother				
C	H	S	D	O
–	–	–	–	–

PHYSIOLOGICAL AND METABOLIC DATA

	Admission	Initial	Control	Cold pressor change	Exercise change	Smoking change
Systolic pressure	110	132	106	+18	+19	
Diastolic pressure	70	70	68	+14	–04	
Heart rate	60	78	88	–04	–02	

Age 24 yrs.	Height	73	in.	Ponderal index	13.36	
	Weight	163	lbs.	Cholesterol	203	mg. per 100 ml.
	Overweight	–05	%	Vital capacity	6.0	liters

HABIT SURVEY
Smoking habits: former smoker
Age begun 15 yrs. Inhalation:
Habits of nervous tension: 2, 4, 5, 11, 17, 22

Plate 230   **DRAWINGS AT AN INTERMEDIATE LEVEL OF SOPHISTICATION**   273

FIGURE-DRAWING CHARACTERISTICS

Structural	Male Female Both		Structural	Male	Female	Structural and Graphic	Male Female Both		Graphic, Global and Height	Male	Female	Body Proportions	Male	Female
Type	0		Omission of Appendages	0	0	Upper and Lower Halves	1	1	Hair Shading	2	3	Head	05	04
Sex Sequence	1		Position of Both Arms	0	0	Four Quarters	4	4	Nudity and Transparency	7	7	Neck		
Posture	1	1	Position of Right Arm	5	5	Relative Size	0		Form	3	3	Shoulders	08	05
Perspective	0	0	Position of Left Arm	5	5	Constant Line Pressure	5	5	Detailing	3	3	Right Arm	04	02
Vertical Midline	0	0	Position of Legs	6	6	Variable Line Pressure	0	0	Identity and Sex	1	1	Left Arm	04	02
Bilateral Symmetry	3	3	Relation of Long Axes	1	1	Line Continuity	3	3	Sophistication	3	3	Chest	06	04
Horizontal Midline	4	4	Right and Left Halves	1	2	Body Shading	0	1	Height	03	03	Girth	06	04

GENERAL CHARACTERISTICS OF SUBJECT

IDENTIFICATION
No. 635
Sex M
Marital status S
Age 25 yrs. at
psychological tests

PARENTAL HISTORY				
Father				
C	H	S	D	O
(+)	+	-	-	-
Mother				
C	H	S	D	O
-	-	-	-	-

PHYSIOLOGICAL AND METABOLIC DATA

	Admission	Initial	Control	Cold pressor change	Exercise change	Smoking change
Systolic pressure	120	138	128	+02	+40	+04
Diastolic pressure	80	76	78	+04	-06	+06
Heart rate	68	68	60	+16	+19	+09

Age 22 yrs.	Height 70 in.	Ponderal index 12.89
	Weight 160 lbs.	Cholesterol 237 mg. per 100 ml.
	Overweight +04 %	Vital capacity 4.8 liters

HABIT SURVEY
Smoking habits: former smoker
Age begun 19 yrs.   Inhalation:
Habits of nervous tension: 4, 5, 9, 11, 16,
17, 21

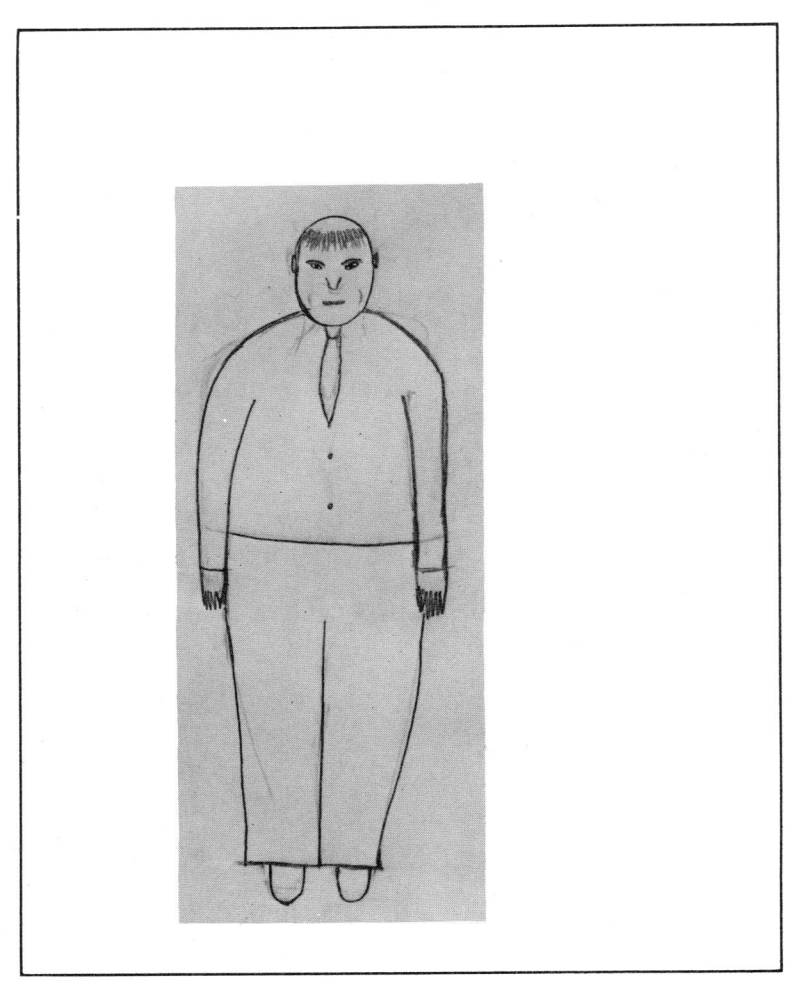

FIGURE-DRAWING CHARACTERISTICS

Structural	Male Female Both	Structural	Male	Female	Structural and Graphic	Male Female Both		Graphic, Global and Height	Male	Female	Body Proportions	Male	Female
Type	0	Omission of Appendages	0	0	Upper and Lower Halves	3	1	Hair Shading	3	3	Head	09	06
Sex Sequence	0	Position of Both Arms	0	2	Four Quarters	4	4	Nudity and Transparency	7	7	Neck	00	07
Posture	1 1	Position of Right Arm	0	0	Relative Size	0		Form	3	3	Shoulders	08	
Perspective	0 2	Position of Left Arm	0	7	Constant Line Pressure	5	5	Detailing	3	3	Right Arm	06	02
Vertical Midline	3 4	Position of Legs	2	1	Variable Line Pressure	0	0	Identity and Sex	3	3	Left Arm	06	
Bilateral Symmetry	4 0	Relation of Long Axes	1	1	Line Continuity	4	1	Sophistication	3	3	Chest	07	05
Horizontal Midline	4 0	Right and Left Halves	1	2	Body Shading	0	0	Height	07	04	Girth	12	07

GENERAL CHARACTERISTICS OF SUBJECT

IDENTIFICATION
No. 658
Sex M
Marital status S
Age 29 yrs. at
psychological tests

PARENTAL HISTORY
Father
C   H   S   D   O
(+) (+) (+)   −   −
Mother
C   H   S   D   O
−   −   −   −   ?

PHYSIOLOGICAL AND METABOLIC DATA

	Admission	Initial	Control	Cold pressor change	Exercise change	Smoking change
Systolic pressure	120	122	118	+18	+40	+05
Diastolic pressure	80	76	84	+10	−06	+02
Heart rate	80	92	87	−06	+43	+03

Age 26 yrs.	Height 72 in.	Ponderal index 12.35
	Weight 198 lbs.	Cholesterol 258 mg. per 100 ml.
	Overweight +18 %	Vital capacity 5.6 liters

HABIT SURVEY

Smoking habits: light cigarette smoker

Age begun 20 yrs.   Inhalation: sometimes

Habits of nervous tension: 4, 5, 6, 7, 8, 9, 10, 14, 15, 18, 21, 22

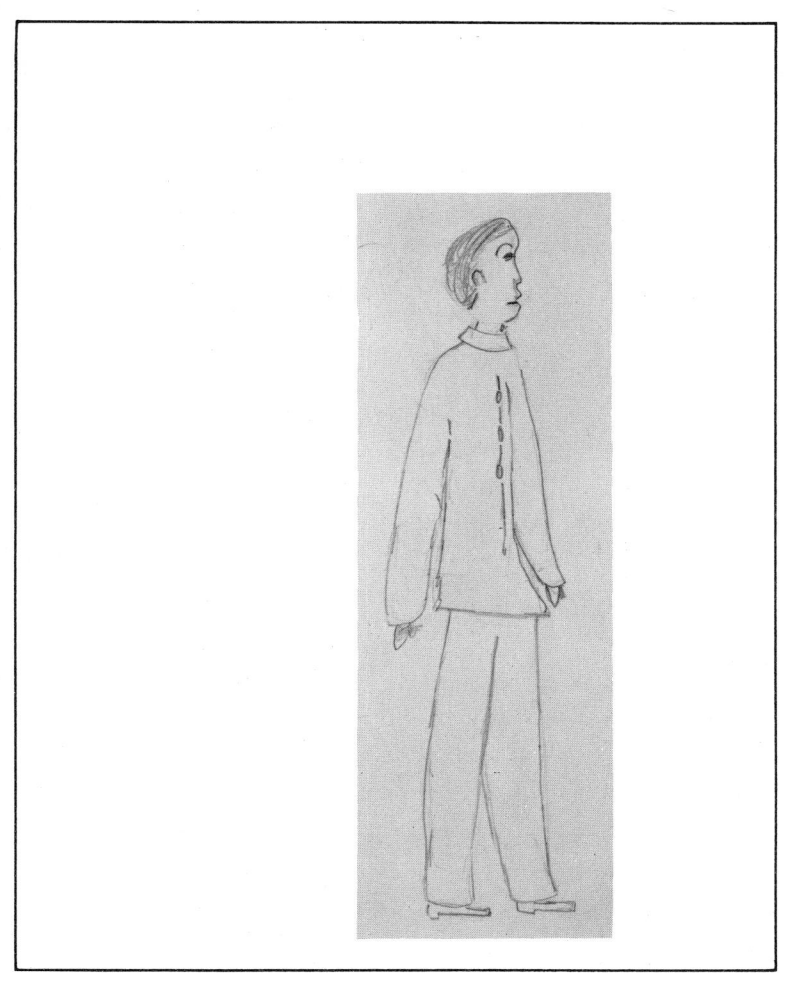
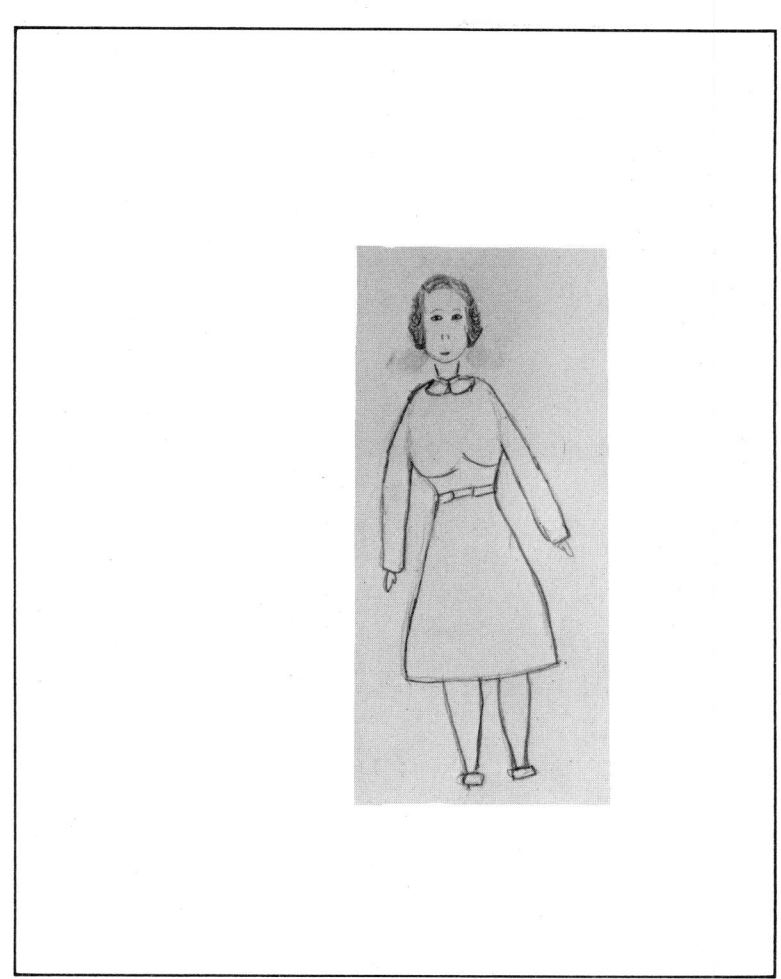

FIGURE-DRAWING CHARACTERISTICS

Structural	Male Female Both		Structural	Male	Female	Structural and Graphic	Male Female Both		Graphic, Global and Height	Male	Female	Body Proportions	Male	Female
Type	0		Omission of Appendages	0	0	Upper and Lower Halves	3	3	Hair Shading	3	2	Head	08	07
Sex Sequence	0		Position of Both Arms	0	0	Four Quarters	4	4	Nudity and Transparency	7	7	Neck	05	05
Posture	1	1	Position of Right Arm	0	2	Relative Size	0		Form	3	1	Shoulders		03
Perspective	6	0	Position of Left Arm	0	2	Constant Line Pressure	0	0	Detailing	3	3	Right Arm	08	04
Vertical Midline	7	0	Position of Legs	4	4	Variable Line Pressure	3	5	Identity and Sex	1	1	Left Arm	06	04
Bilateral Symmetry	0	3	Relation of Long Axes	1	1	Line Continuity	0	2	Sophistication	3	3	Chest		04
Horizontal Midline	6	4	Right and Left Halves	4	4	Body Shading	0	1	Height	07	05	Girth		04

GENERAL CHARACTERISTICS OF SUBJECT

IDENTIFICATION
No. 711
Sex F
Marital status S
Age 25 yrs. at
psychological tests

PARENTAL HISTORY				
Father				
C	H	S	D	O
(+)	?	+	-	-
Mother				
C	H	S	D	O
-	-	-	-	-

PHYSIOLOGICAL AND METABOLIC DATA

	Admission	Initial	Control	Cold pressor change	Exercise change	Smoking change
Systolic pressure	120	108	100	+04	+36	+04
Diastolic pressure	80	56	62	+04	+02	+01
Heart rate	80	78	64	+02	+30	-06

Age 22 yrs.   Height 66 in.   Ponderal index 13.69
Weight 112 lbs.   Cholesterol 273 mg. per 100 ml.
Overweight -16 %   Vital capacity 3.1 liters

HABIT SURVEY

Smoking habits: nonsmoker
Age begun   yrs.   Inhalation:
Habits of nervous tension: 4, 5, 6, 9, 11, 12, 14, 16, 17, 19, 22, 24

FIGURE-DRAWING CHARACTERISTICS

Structural	Male Female Both	Structural	Male	Female	Structural and Graphic	Male Female Both	Graphic, Global and Height	Male	Female	Body Proportions	Male	Female
Type	0	Omission of Appendages	7	0	Upper and Lower Halves	1 1	Hair Shading	3	3	Head	07	07
Sex Sequence	1	Position of Both Arms	0	1	Four Quarters	4 4	Nudity and Transparency	7	7	Neck	02	07
Posture	1 1	Position of Right Arm	5	4	Relative Size	2	Form	1	1	Shoulders	09	07
Perspective	0 0	Position of Left Arm	5	5	Constant Line Pressure	1 1	Detailing	3	3	Right Arm		06
Vertical Midline	0 0	Position of Legs	6	4	Variable Line Pressure	0 0	Identity and Sex	1	1	Left Arm		04
Bilateral Symmetry	3 3	Relation of Long Axes	1	1	Line Continuity	0 0	Sophistication	3	3	Chest	07	06
Horizontal Midline	4 4	Right and Left Halves	1	1	Body Shading	6 1	Height	07	07	Girth	08	06

GENERAL CHARACTERISTICS OF SUBJECT

IDENTIFICATION
No. A69
Sex M
Marital status M
Age 27 yrs. at
psychological tests

PARENTAL HISTORY					
Father					
C	H	S	D	O	
(+)	-	-	-	-	
Mother					
C	H	S	D	O	
-	-	-	-	+	

PHYSIOLOGICAL AND METABOLIC DATA

	Admission	Initial	Control	Cold pressor change	Exercise change	Smoking change
Systolic pressure	138	118	116	+12	+46	+02
Diastolic pressure	70	70	67	+15	-11	+06
Heart rate	78	88	77	+09	+22	+07

Age 26 yrs.   Height 72 in.   Ponderal index 13.09
Weight 166 lbs.   Cholesterol 273 mg. per 100 ml.
Overweight -01 %   Vital capacity   liters

HABIT SURVEY

Smoking habits: heavy cigarette smoker
Age begun 16 yrs.   Inhalation: yes
Habits of nervous tension: 5, 6, 11, 14

STRONG VOCATIONAL INTEREST TEST

Occupation	Artist	Psychologist	Architect	Physician	Osteopath	Dentist	Veterinarian	Mathematician	Physicist	Engineer	Chemist	Production Manager
Standard Score	3	7	3	7	7	4	3	3	4	4	5	5

Occupation	Farmer	Aviator	Carpenter	Printer	Math.-Sci. Teacher	Ind. Arts Teacher	Voc. Agric. Teacher	Policeman	Forest Serv. Man	Y.M.C.A. Phys. Dir.	Personnel Director	Public Administrator
Standard Score	5	5	2	5	7	2	4	4	5	6	6	6

Occupation	Y.M.C.A. Secretary	Soc. Sci. H.S. Teacher	City Sch. Sup't.	Social Worker	Minister	Musician Performer	C.P.A.	Senior C.P.A.	Accountant	Office Man	Purchasing Agent	Banker
Standard Score	4	5	4	6	6	6	5	6	2	2	2	2

Occupation	Mortician	Pharmacist	Sales Manager	Real Est. Manager	Life Ins. Salesman	Advertising Man	Lawyer	Author-Journalist	President Mfg. Co.	Interest Maturity	Occupational Level	Masculinity-Femininity
Standard Score	2	4	3	4	3	4	5	4	3	6	5	5

Plate 234   DRAWINGS AT AN INTERMEDIATE LEVEL OF SOPHISTICATION   277

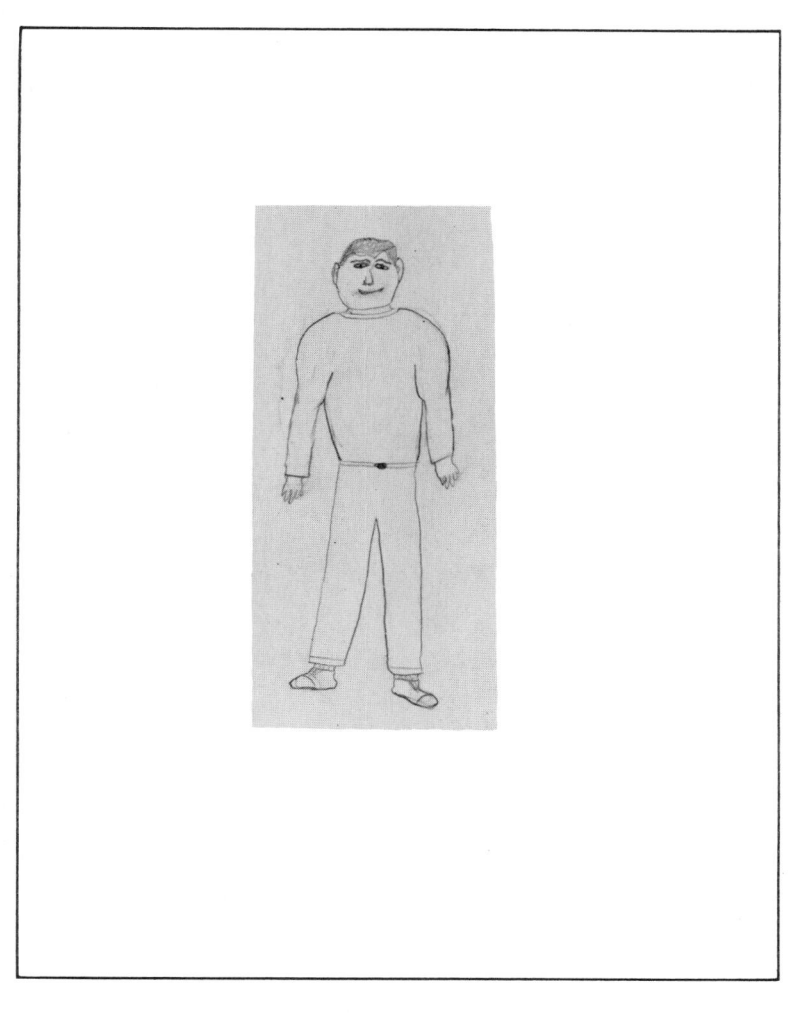

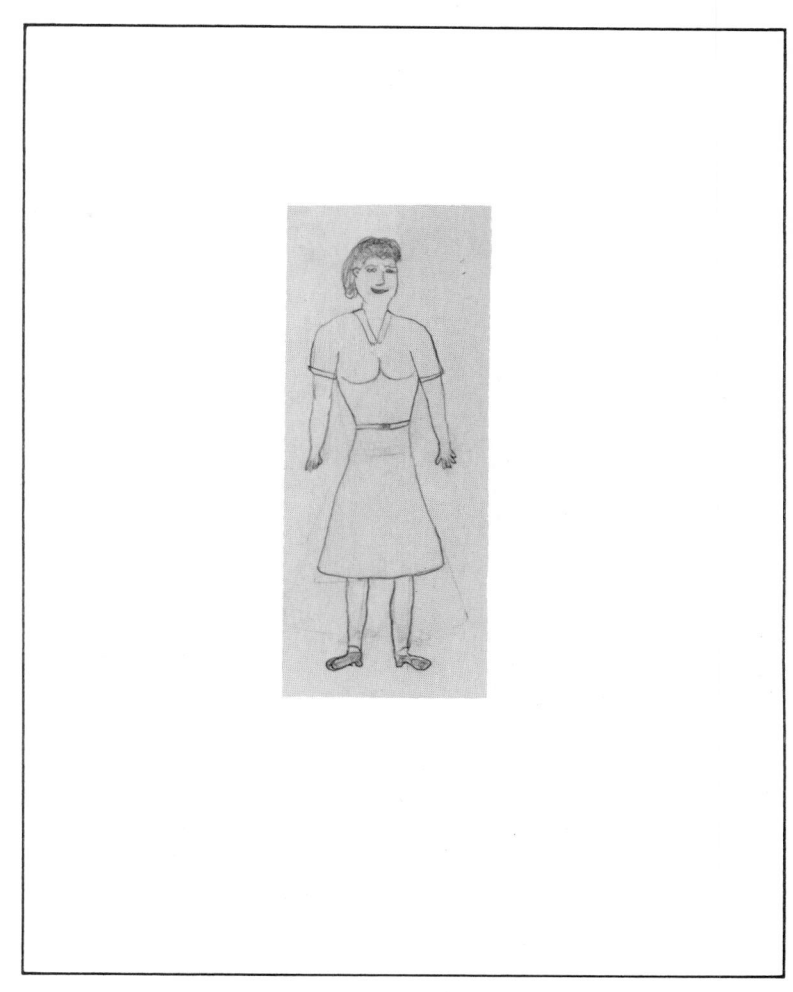

FIGURE-DRAWING CHARACTERISTICS

Structural	Male Female Both		Structural	Male	Female	Structural and Graphic	Male Female Both		Graphic, Global and Height	Male	Female	Body Proportions	Male	Female
Type	0		Omission of Appendages	0	0	Upper and Lower Halves	1	1	Hair Shading	1	1	Head	05	05
Sex Sequence	0		Position of Both Arms	0	0	Four Quarters	4	4	Nudity and Transparency	7	7	Neck	01	03
Posture	1	1	Position of Right Arm	0	1	Relative Size	0		Form	3	3	Shoulders	05	04
Perspective	0	0	Position of Left Arm	0	1	Constant Line Pressure	0	0	Detailing	3	3	Right Arm	04	03
Vertical Midline	0	0	Position of Legs	6	6	Variable Line Pressure	5	4	Identity and Sex	1	1	Left Arm	04	02
Bilateral Symmetry	3	3	Relation of Long Axes	1	1	Line Continuity	4	2	Sophistication	3	3	Chest	04	04
Horizontal Midline	4	4	Right and Left Halves	1	1	Body Shading	4	5	Height	05	04	Girth	05	03

GENERAL CHARACTERISTICS OF SUBJECT

IDENTIFICATION
No. C38
Sex M
Marital status S
Age 20 yrs. at
psychological tests

PARENTAL HISTORY				
Father				
C	H	S	D	O
(+)	(+)	–	–	–
Mother				
C	H	S	D	O
–	–	–	–	+

PHYSIOLOGICAL AND METABOLIC DATA

	Admission	Initial	Control	Cold pressor change	Exercise change	Smoking change
Systolic pressure	124	90	100	+18	+50	+07
Diastolic pressure	60	50	62	+30	–07	+10
Heart rate	100	68	65	+08	+71	–06

Age 21 yrs.
Height 74 in.
Weight 188 lbs.
Overweight +09 %
Ponderal index 12.91
Cholesterol 183 mg. per 100 ml.
Vital capacity 4.8 liters

HABIT SURVEY
Smoking habits: nonsmoker
Age begun   yrs.   Inhalation:
Habits of nervous tension: 2, 5, 6, 11, 16, 22

STRONG VOCATIONAL INTEREST TEST

Occupation	Artist	Psychologist	Architect	Physician	Osteopath	Dentist	Veterinarian	Mathematician	Physicist	Engineer	Chemist	Production Manager
Standard Score	29	40	26	56	51	36	16	28	31	44	46	41

Occupation	Farmer	Aviator	Carpenter	Printer	Math.-Sci. Teacher	Ind. Arts Teacher	Voc. Agric. Teacher	Policeman	Forest Serv. Man	Y.M.C.A. Phys. Dir.	Personnel Director	Public Administrator
Standard Score	21	41	14	35	32	09	02	34	19	30	46	52

Occupation	Y.M.C.A. Secretary	Soc. Sci. H.S. Teacher	City Sch. Sup't.	Social Worker	Minister	Musician Performer	C.P.A.	Senior C.P.A.	Accountant	Office Man	Purchasing Agent	Banker
Standard Score	22	27	25	36	62	33	39	39	29	34	21	17

Occupation	Mortician	Pharmacist	Sales Manager	Real Est. Manager	Life Ins. Salesman	Advertising Man	Lawyer	Author- Journalist	President Mfg. Co.	Interest Maturity	Occupational Level	Masculinity- Femininity
Standard Score	22	33	26	29	28	33	45	39	39	56	63	46

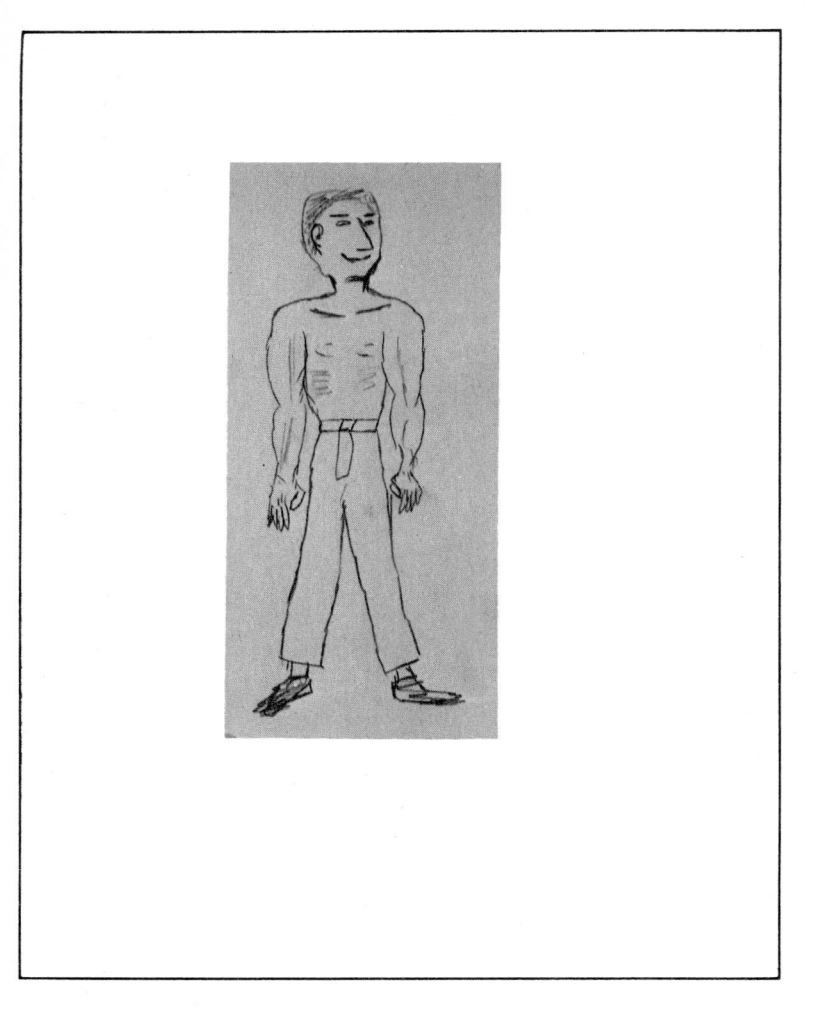

FIGURE-DRAWING CHARACTERISTICS

Structural	Male Female Both	Structural	Male	Female	Structural and Graphic	Male Female Both		Graphic, Global and Height	Male	Female	Body Proportions	Male	Female
Type	0	Omission of Appendages	0	0	Upper and Lower Halves	1	1	Hair Shading	1	2	Head	07	06
Sex Sequence	0	Position of Both Arms	0	0	Four Quarters	4	4	Nudity and Transparency	3	7	Neck	05	12
Posture	1	1	Position of Right Arm	0	0	Relative Size	0		Form	3	3	Shoulders	06	04
Perspective	0	0	Position of Left Arm	0	0	Constant Line Pressure	0	0	Detailing	3	3	Right Arm	04	04
Vertical Midline	3	0	Position of Legs	6	6	Variable Line Pressure	5	4	Identity and Sex	1	1	Left Arm	04	04
Bilateral Symmetry	3	3	Relation of Long Axes	1	1	Line Continuity	0	2	Sophistication	3	3	Chest	03	03
Horizontal Midline	4	4	Right and Left Halves	1	1	Body Shading	5	7	Height	05	05	Girth	03	02

GENERAL CHARACTERISTICS OF SUBJECT

IDENTIFICATION
No. C56
Sex M
Marital status S
Age 22 yrs. at
psychological tests

PARENTAL HISTORY				
Father				
C	H	S	D	O
(+)	-	-	-	-
Mother				
C	H	S	D	O
-	-	-	-	?

PHYSIOLOGICAL AND METABOLIC DATA

	Admission	Initial	Control	Cold pressor change	Exercise change	Smoking change
Systolic pressure	130	138	120	+10	+30	
Diastolic pressure	80	65	68	+12	-18	
Heart rate	68	68	55	+08	+12	

Age 23 yrs. Height 67 in. Weight 167 lbs. Overweight +17 %
Ponderal index 12.16 Cholesterol 212 mg. per 100 ml. Vital capacity 3.9 liters

HABIT SURVEY

Smoking habits: nonsmoker
Age begun   yrs.   Inhalation:
Habits of nervous tension: 4, 5, 6, 9, 10, 14, 16, 18, 19, 22

STRONG VOCATIONAL INTEREST TEST

Occupation	Artist	Psychologist	Architect	Physician	Osteopath	Dentist	Veterinarian	Mathematician	Physicist	Engineer	Chemist	Production Manager
Standard Score	29	43	30	67	67	48	50	24	25	32	42	32

Occupation	Farmer	Aviator	Carpenter	Printer	Math.-Sci. Teacher	Ind. Arts Teacher	Voc. Agric. Teacher	Policeman	Forest Serv. Man	Y.M.C.A. Phys. Dir.	Personnel Director	Public Administrator
Standard Score	37	50	27	49	48	30	40	39	36	49	36	45

Occupation	Y.M.C.A. Secretary	Soc. Sci. H.S. Teacher	City Sch. Sup't.	Social Worker	Minister	Musician Performer	C.P.A.	Senior C.P.A.	Accountant	Office Man	Purchasing Agent	Banker
Standard Score	29	36	25	41	62	48	28	52	26	34	21	19

Occupation	Mortician	Pharmacist	Sales Manager	Real Est. Manager	Life Ins. Salesman	Advertising Man	Lawyer	Author-Journalist	President Mfg. Co.	Interest Maturity	Occupational Level	Masculinity-Femininity
Standard Score	37	45	25	34	30	30	30	29	24	55	50	51

Plate 236   **DRAWINGS AT AN INTERMEDIATE LEVEL OF SOPHISTICATION**   279

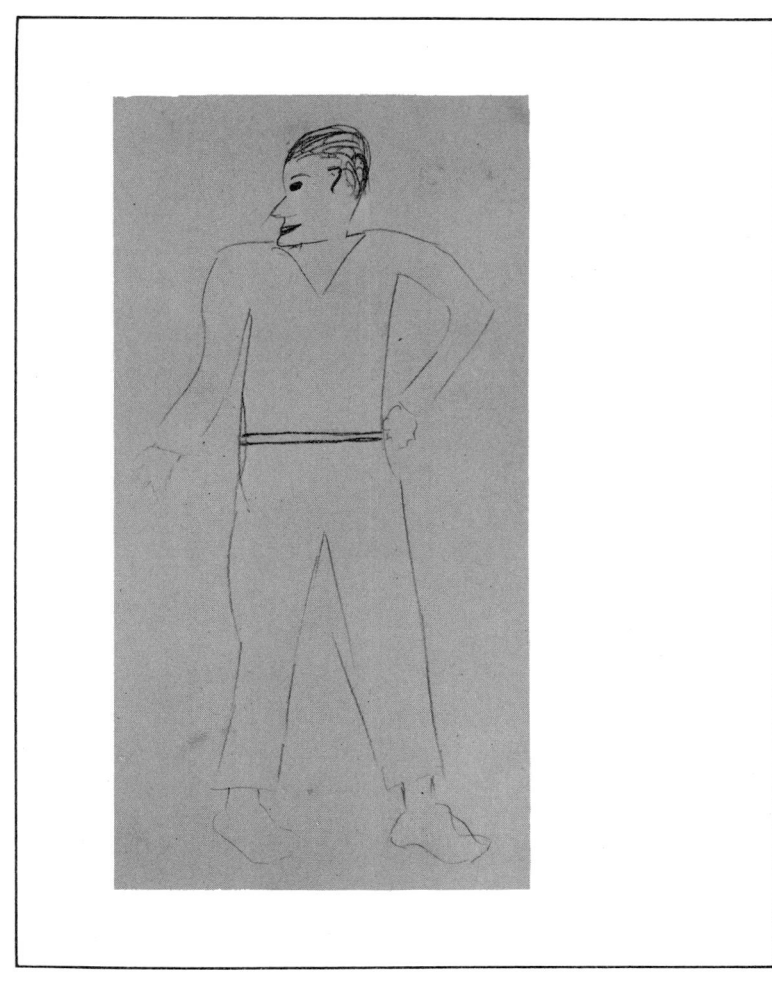

FIGURE-DRAWING CHARACTERISTICS

Structural	Male Female Both	Structural	Male	Female	Structural and Graphic	Male Female Both		Graphic, Global and Height	Male	Female	Body Proportions	Male	Female
Type	0	Omission of Appendages	0	0	Upper and Lower Halves	0	0	Hair Shading	1	3	Head	10	07
Sex Sequence	2	Position of Both Arms	1	1	Four Quarters	4	4	Nudity and Transparency	7	7	Neck	00	02
Posture	1	1	Position of Right Arm	4	2	Relative Size	0		Form	3	3	Shoulders	09	08
Perspective	5	0	Position of Left Arm	5	0	Constant Line Pressure	1	0	Detailing	3	3	Right Arm	06	04
Vertical Midline	0	0	Position of Legs	6	4	Variable Line Pressure	0	3	Identity and Sex	1	3	Left Arm	06	04
Bilateral Symmetry	3	3	Relation of Long Axes	1	3	Line Continuity	2	3	Sophistication	3	3	Chest	07	08
Horizontal Midline	4	0	Right and Left Halves	1	1	Body Shading	0	0	Height	08	07	Girth	09	08

GENERAL CHARACTERISTICS OF SUBJECT

IDENTIFICATION
No. 223
Sex M
Marital status M
Age 29 yrs. at
psychological tests

PARENTAL HISTORY
Father
C H S D O
- + + - -
Mother
C H S D O
(+) (?) - - +

PHYSIOLOGICAL AND METABOLIC DATA

	Admission	Initial	Control	Cold pressor change	Exercise change	Smoking change
Systolic pressure	100					
Diastolic pressure	62					
Heart rate	76					

Age 26 yrs.	Height 70 in.	Ponderal index 12.59
	Weight 172 lbs.	Cholesterol 215 mg. per 100 ml.
	Overweight +09 %	Vital capacity liters

HABIT SURVEY
Smoking habits: unknown
Age begun   yrs.   Inhalation:
Habits of nervous tension:

FIGURE-DRAWING CHARACTERISTICS

Structural	Male Female Both	Structural	Male	Female	Structural and Graphic	Male Female Both	Graphic, Global and Height	Male	Female	Body Proportions	Male	Female
Type	0	Omission of Appendages	3	3	Upper and Lower Halves	7 9	Hair Shading	1	3	Head	19	03
Sex Sequence	0	Position of Both Arms	2	9	Four Quarters	4 9	Nudity and Transparency	7	7	Neck	04	04
Posture	3 3	Position of Right Arm	2	9	Relative Size	5	Form	3	3	Shoulders		
Perspective	2 2	Position of Left Arm	7	9	Constant Line Pressure	0 3	Detailing	3	3	Right Arm	12	
Vertical Midline	4 4	Position of Legs	0	0	Variable Line Pressure	1 0	Identity and Sex	1	1	Left Arm		
Bilateral Symmetry	0 0	Relation of Long Axes	0	0	Line Continuity	2 0	Sophistication	3	3	Chest	13	
Horizontal Midline	0 0	Right and Left Halves	3	3	Body Shading	4 1	Height			Girth	18	

GENERAL CHARACTERISTICS OF SUBJECT

IDENTIFICATION
No. 323
Sex M
Marital status M
Age 35 yrs. at
psychological tests

PARENTAL HISTORY
Father
C   H   S   D   O
-   -   -   -   +
Mother
C   H   S   D   O
(+)   +   -   -   -

PHYSIOLOGICAL AND METABOLIC DATA

	Admission	Initial	Control	Cold pressor change	Exercise change	Smoking change
Systolic pressure	140	142	130	+24	+60	00
Diastolic pressure	92	76	74	00	+04	00
Heart rate	88	84	84	+14	+29	+09

Age 29 yrs.	Height	73	in.	Ponderal index	11.91	
	Weight	230	lbs.	Cholesterol	185	mg. per 100 ml.
	Overweight +30 %			Vital capacity	5.2	liters

HABIT SURVEY
Smoking habits: former smoker
Age begun   yrs.   Inhalation:
Habits of nervous tension: 21

FIGURE-DRAWING CHARACTERISTICS

Structural	Male Female Both	Structural	Male	Female	Structural and Graphic	Male Female Both		Graphic, Global and Height	Male	Female	Body Proportions	Male	Female
Type	0	Omission of Appendages	7	6	Upper and Lower Halves	0	1	Hair Shading	3	5	Head	12	12
Sex Sequence	0	Position of Both Arms	0	0	Four Quarters	4	4	Nudity and Transparency	7	7	Neck	14	10
Posture	1 1	Position of Right Arm	5	5	Relative Size	0		Form	3	3	Shoulders	08	06
Perspective	0 0	Position of Left Arm	5	5	Constant Line Pressure	0	0	Detailing	3	3	Right Arm		
Vertical Midline	3 0	Position of Legs	6	4	Variable Line Pressure	5	1	Identity and Sex	1	1	Left Arm		
Bilateral Symmetry	3 3	Relation of Long Axes	1	1	Line Continuity	1	2	Sophistication	3	3	Chest	06	05
Horizontal Midline	6 4	Right and Left Halves	1	2	Body Shading	6	1	Height	08	06	Girth	07	02

GENERAL CHARACTERISTICS OF SUBJECT

IDENTIFICATION
No. 561
Sex M
Marital status S
Age 23 yrs. at
psychological tests

PARENTAL HISTORY
Father
C   H   S   D   O
?   -   -   -   ?
Mother
C   H   S   D   O
?   ?   -   -   -

PHYSIOLOGICAL AND METABOLIC DATA

	Admission	Initial	Control	Cold pressor change	Exercise change	Smoking change
Systolic pressure	130	130	130	00	+20	+02
Diastolic pressure	80	70	70	+10	-10	+04
Heart rate	76	72	83	-06	+28	+03

Age 22 yrs.

Height	71 in.	Ponderal index 12.97
Weight	164 lbs.	Cholesterol 222 mg. per 100 ml.
Overweight +04 %		Vital capacity 5.5 liters

HABIT SURVEY
Smoking habits: light cigarette smoker
Age begun   yrs.   Inhalation:
Habits of nervous tension:

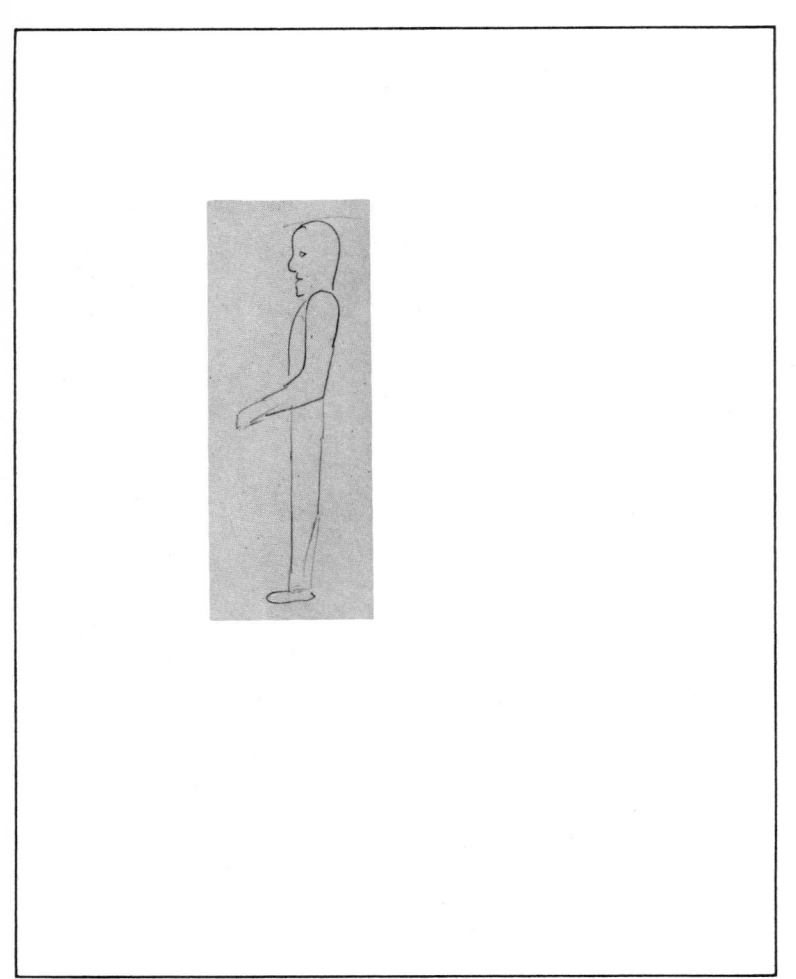

FIGURE-DRAWING CHARACTERISTICS

Structural	Male Female Both	Structural	Male	Female	Structural and Graphic	Male Female Both		Graphic, Global and Height	Male	Female	Body Proportions	Male	Female
Type	0	Omission of Appendages	0	2	Upper and Lower Halves	1	1	Hair Shading	0	3	Head	06	05
Sex Sequence	0	Position of Both Arms	4	6	Four Quarters	4	4	Nudity and Transparency	9	3	Neck	00	10
Posture	1 1	Position of Right Arm	7	7	Relative Size	4		Form	3	3	Shoulders		
Perspective	2 6	Position of Left Arm	4	7	Constant Line Pressure	0	0	Detailing	5	3	Right Arm		
Vertical Midline	4 4	Position of Legs	1	4	Variable Line Pressure	1	1	Identity and Sex	1	1	Left Arm	04	
Bilateral Symmetry	0 0	Relation of Long Axes	1	1	Line Continuity	4	0	Sophistication	3	3	Chest	03	
Horizontal Midline	0 4	Right and Left Halves	2	2	Body Shading	0	0	Height	04	05	Girth	03	

GENERAL CHARACTERISTICS OF SUBJECT

IDENTIFICATION
No. 322
Sex M
Marital status   M
Age 29 yrs. at
psychological tests

PARENTAL HISTORY				
Father				
C	H	S	D	0
?	+	-	-	-
Mother				
C	H	S	D	0
-	+	-	-	-

PHYSIOLOGICAL AND METABOLIC DATA

	Admission	Initial	Control	Cold pressor change	Exercise change	Smoking change
Systolic pressure	122	126	114	+06	+26	
Diastolic pressure	64	68	64	+12	00	
Heart rate	60	64	53	+06	+17	

Age 27 yrs.	Height 71 in.	Ponderal index 12.74
	Weight 173 lbs.	Cholesterol mg. per 100 ml.
	Overweight +06 %	Vital capacity 4.1 liters

HABIT SURVEY

Smoking habits: unknown

    Age begun   yrs.   Inhalation:

Habits of nervous tension:

Plate 240   DRAWINGS AT AN INTERMEDIATE LEVEL OF SOPHISTICATION   283

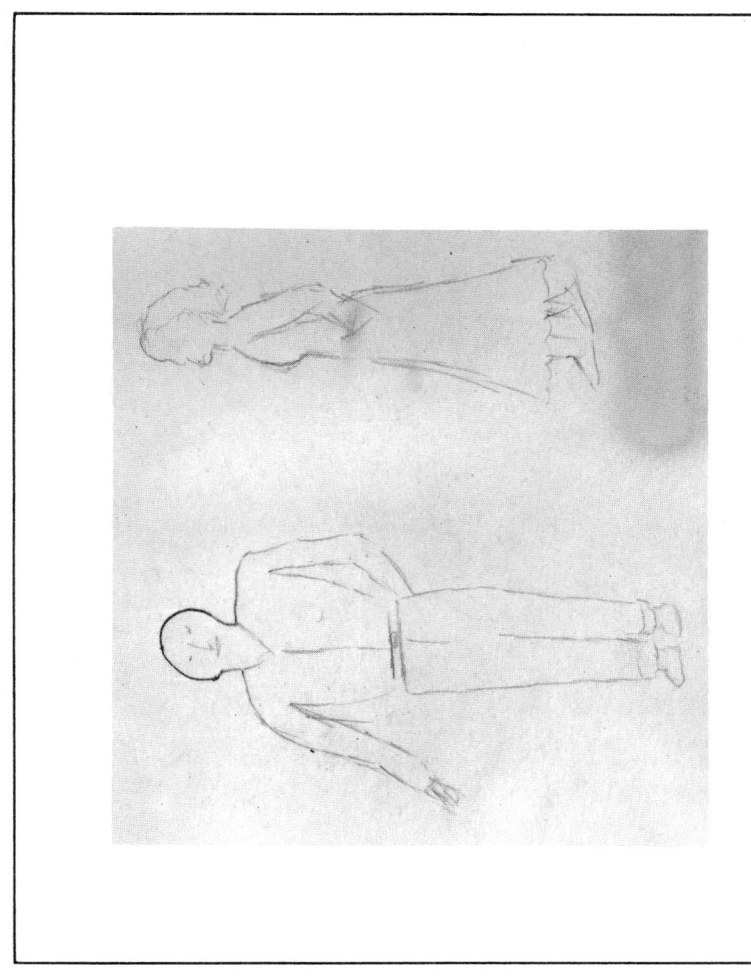

FIGURE-DRAWING CHARACTERISTICS

Structural	Male Female Both		Structural	Male	Female	Structural and Graphic	Male Female Both		Graphic, Global and Height	Male	Female	Body Proportions	Male	Female
Type	0		Omission of Appendages	7	7	Upper and Lower Halves	3	1	Hair Shading	0	5	Head		05
Sex Sequence	2		Position of Both Arms	1	4	Four Quarters	4	4	Nudity and Transparency	7	7	Neck		04
Posture	1	2	Position of Right Arm	2	7	Relative Size	0		Form	3	3	Shoulders	07	
Perspective	0	2	Position of Left Arm	5	5	Constant Line Pressure	0	1	Detailing	5	5	Right Arm	04	
Vertical Midline	3	4	Position of Legs	2	8	Variable Line Pressure	3	0	Identity and Sex	3	1	Left Arm		
Bilateral Symmetry	3	0	Relation of Long Axes	2	2	Line Continuity	0	0	Sophistication	3	3	Chest	06	04
Horizontal Midline	4	0	Right and Left Halves	9	9	Body Shading	0	0	Height	05	04	Girth	06	04

GENERAL CHARACTERISTICS OF SUBJECT

IDENTIFICATION
No. 363
Sex M
Marital status   S
Age 26 yrs. at
psychological tests

PARENTAL HISTORY
Father
C   H   S   D   O
?   -   -   +   -
Mother
C   H   S   D   O
-    -   -   -   -

PHYSIOLOGICAL AND METABOLIC DATA

	Admission	Initial	Control	Cold pressor change	Exercise change	Smoking change
Systolic pressure	110	104	98	+02	+27	-08
Diastolic pressure	74	70	76	+08	-14	+02
Heart rate	80	64	64	00	+14	+03

Age 24 yrs.	Height 75 in.	Ponderal index 13.36
	Weight 177 lbs.	Cholesterol 235 mg. per 100 ml.
	Overweight -03%	Vital capacity 6.0 liters

HABIT SURVEY
Smoking habits: mixed smoker
Age begun 18 yrs.   Inhalation: yes
Habits of nervous tension: 2, 4, 6, 8, 9, 11,
16, 18

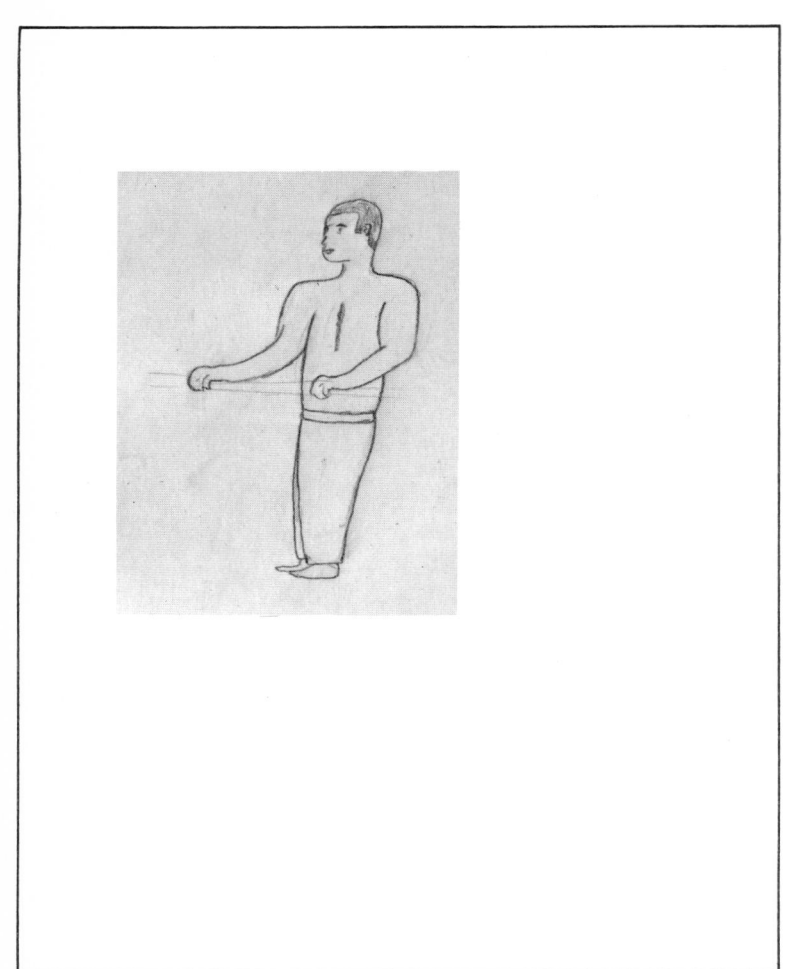

FIGURE-DRAWING CHARACTERISTICS

Structural	Male Female Both		Structural	Male	Female	Structural and Graphic	Male	Female		Graphic, Global and Height	Male	Female	Body Proportions	Male	Female
Type	0		Omission of Appendages	0	0	Upper and Lower Halves	1	1		Hair Shading	1	1	Head	05	06
Sex Sequence	2		Position of Both Arms	0	0	Four Quarters	4	4		Nudity and Transparency	3	7	Neck	04	04
Posture	1	1	Position of Right Arm	4	2	Relative Size	4			Form	1	3	Shoulders		06
Perspective	1	0	Position of Left Arm	4	2	Constant Line Pressure	5	0		Detailing	3	3	Right Arm	04	02
Vertical Midline	4	0	Position of Legs	1	5	Variable Line Pressure	0	1		Identity and Sex	3	3	Left Arm	04	02
Bilateral Symmetry	0	3	Relation of Long Axes	1	1	Line Continuity	4	4		Sophistication	3	3	Chest		04
Horizontal Midline	4	4	Right and Left Halves	2	2	Body Shading	1	3		Height	04	04	Girth		05

GENERAL CHARACTERISTICS OF SUBJECT

IDENTIFICATION
No. 405
Sex M
Marital status S
Age 25 yrs. at
psychological tests

PARENTAL HISTORY				
Father				
C	H	S	D	O
?	+	–	–	?
Mother				
C	H	S	D	O
–	–	–	–	+

PHYSIOLOGICAL AND METABOLIC DATA

	Admission	Initial	Control	Cold pressor change	Exercise change	Smoking change
Systolic pressure	130	120	105	+08	+35	
Diastolic pressure	80	78	68	+04	+02	
Heart rate	84	84	81	+04	+07	

	Height	69 in.	Ponderal index 13.17	
Age 23 yrs.	Weight	144 lbs.	Cholesterol 265 mg. per 100 ml.	
	Overweight –05 %		Vital capacity 4.7 liters	

HABIT SURVEY
Smoking habits: unknown
Age begun yrs. Inhalation:
Habits of nervous tension:

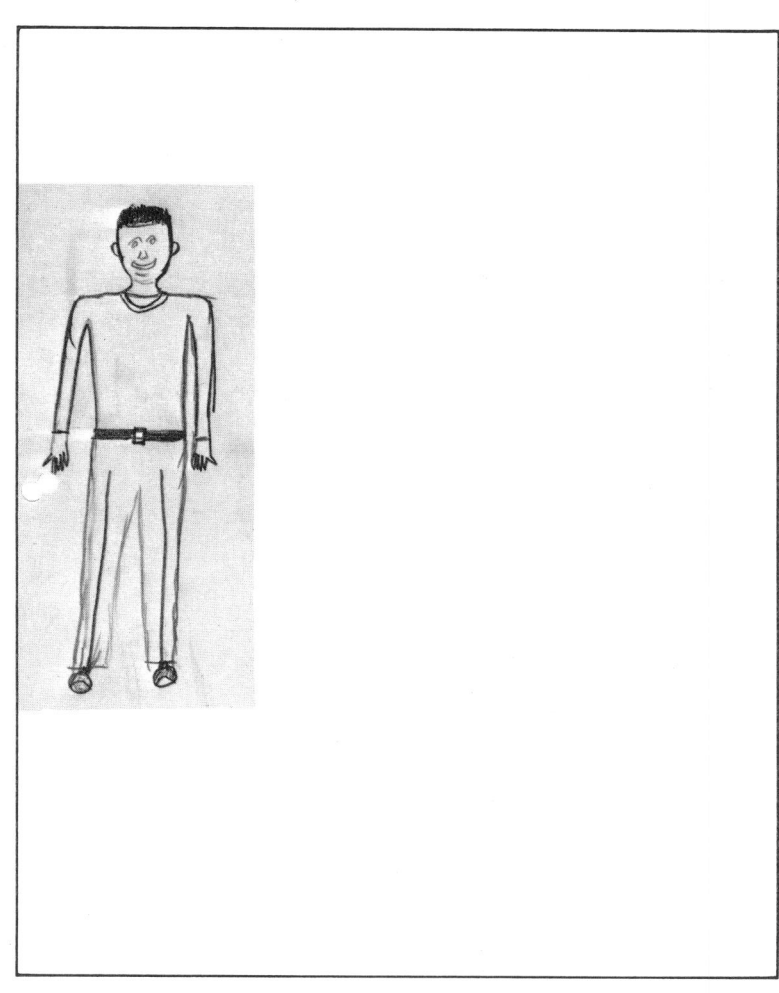

FIGURE-DRAWING CHARACTERISTICS

Structural	Male Female Both		Structural	Male	Female	Structural and Graphic	Male Female Both		Graphic, Global and Height	Male	Female	Body Proportions	Male	Female
Type	0		Omission of Appendages	0	0	Upper and Lower Halves	1	1	Hair Shading	3	3	Head	06	06
Sex Sequence	1		Position of Both Arms	1	0	Four Quarters	4	4	Nudity and Transparency	7	7	Neck	05	06
Posture	1	1	Position of Right Arm	1	0	Relative Size	1		Form	3	3	Shoulders	05	04
Perspective	0	0	Position of Left Arm	0	0	Constant Line Pressure	5	0	Detailing	3	3	Right Arm	04	03
Vertical Midline	0	0	Position of Legs	6	6	Variable Line Pressure	0	3	Identity and Sex	1	1	Left Arm	04	02
Bilateral Symmetry	4	4	Relation of Long Axes	1	1	Line Continuity	1	1	Sophistication	3	3	Chest	04	03
Horizontal Midline	4	4	Right and Left Halves	2	2	Body Shading	6	7	Height	05	05	Girth	05	04

GENERAL CHARACTERISTICS OF SUBJECT

IDENTIFICATION
No. 580
Sex M
Marital status S
Age 24 yrs. at
psychological tests

PARENTAL HISTORY
Father
C H S D O
? – – – –
Mother
C H S D O
– – – – –

PHYSIOLOGICAL AND METABOLIC DATA

	Admission	Initial	Control	Cold pressor change	Exercise change	Smoking change
Systolic pressure	124	122	118	+04	+54	
Diastolic pressure	70	64	68	00	00	
Heart rate	78	84	84	+12	+27	

Age 24 yrs.	Height 73 in.	Ponderal index 12.74
	Weight 188 lbs.	Cholesterol 217 mg. per 100 ml.
	Overweight +10 %	Vital capacity 6.0 liters

HABIT SURVEY
Smoking habits: nonsmoker
Age begun yrs. Inhalation:
Habits of nervous tension: 5, 9, 18, 19, 22

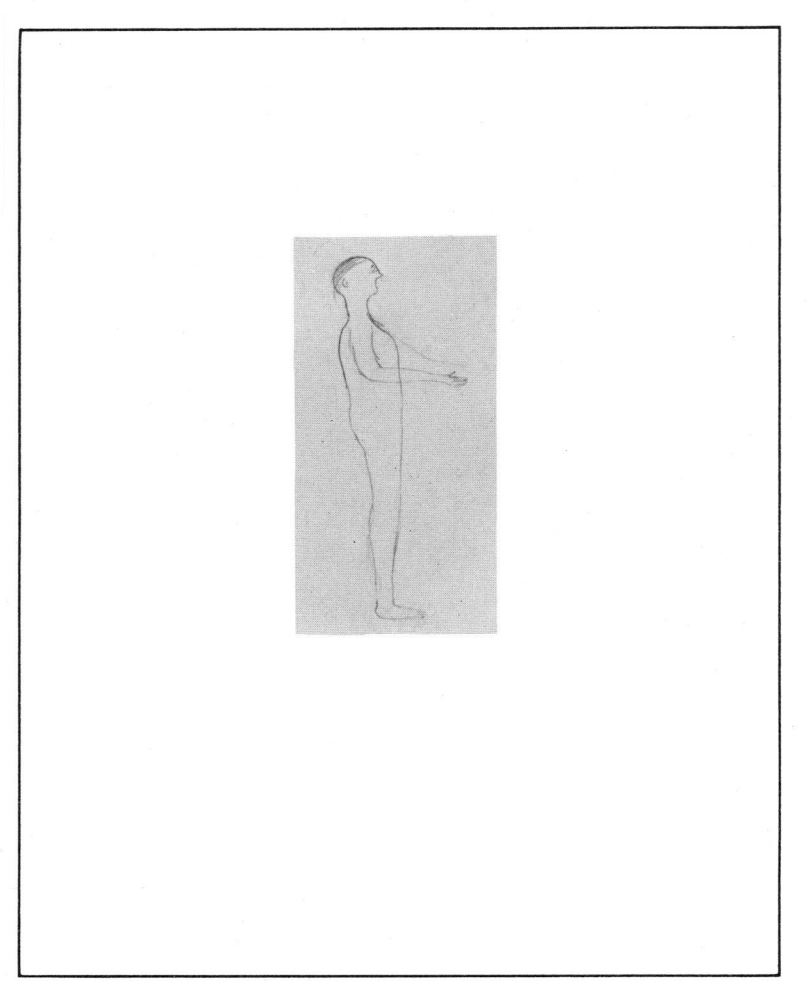

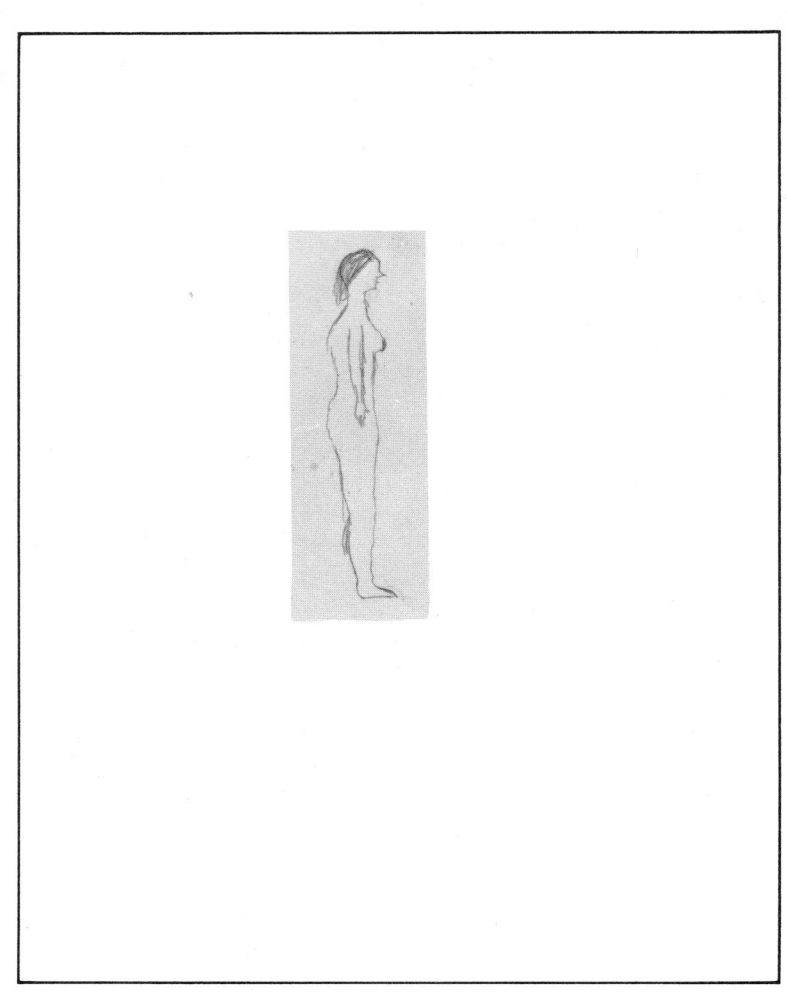

FIGURE-DRAWING CHARACTERISTICS

Structural	Male Female Both		Structural	Male	Female	Structural and Graphic	Male Female Both		Graphic, Global and Height	Male	Female	Body Proportions	Male	Female
Type	0		Omission of Appendages	0	0	Upper and Lower Halves	1	1	Hair Shading	3	3	Head	03	03
Sex Sequence	0		Position of Both Arms	2	2	Four Quarters	4	4	Nudity and Transparency	0	0	Neck	07	06
Posture	1	1	Position of Right Arm	4	0	Relative Size	0		Form	3	3	Shoulders		
Perspective	2	2	Position of Left Arm	7	7	Constant Line Pressure	0	0	Detailing	5	5	Right Arm	02	02
Vertical Midline	4	4	Position of Legs	1	1	Variable Line Pressure	1	1	Identity and Sex	1	1	Left Arm		
Bilateral Symmetry	0	0	Relation of Long Axes	1	1	Line Continuity	0	0	Sophistication	3	3	Chest	04	03
Horizontal Midline	0	0	Right and Left Halves	2	2	Body Shading	0	0	Height	03	03	Girth	04	03

GENERAL CHARACTERISTICS OF SUBJECT

IDENTIFICATION
No. 601
Sex M
Marital status M
Age 29 yrs. at
psychological tests

PARENTAL HISTORY				
Father				
C	H	S	D	O
?	-	-	-	-
Mother				
C	H	S	D	O
-	-	-	-	-

PHYSIOLOGICAL AND METABOLIC DATA

	Admission	Initial	Control	Cold pressor change	Exercise change	Smoking change
Systolic pressure	124	110	108	+04	+22	00
Diastolic pressure	80	76	72	+08	-12	-02
Heart rate	80	60	70	00	+18	+02

Age 26 yrs.	Height 72 in.	Ponderal index 12.92
	Weight 173 lbs.	Cholesterol 237 mg. per 100 ml.
	Overweight +03 %	Vital capacity 5.2 liters

HABIT SURVEY

Smoking habits: pipe smoker

Age begun 18 yrs.   Inhalation: no

Habits of nervous tension: 2, 4, 5, 16

Plate 244   DRAWINGS AT AN INTERMEDIATE LEVEL OF SOPHISTICATION   287

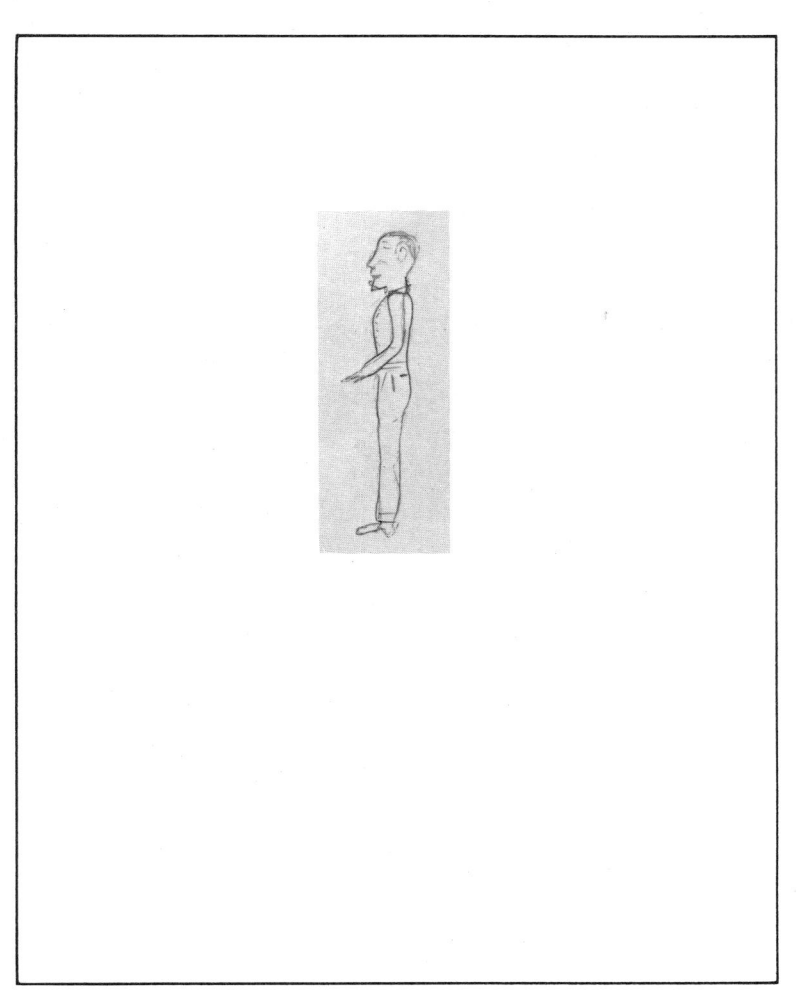

FIGURE-DRAWING CHARACTERISTICS

Structural	Male Female Both	Structural	Male	Female	Structural and Graphic	Male Female Both		Graphic, Global and Height	Male	Female	Body Proportions	Male	Female
Type	0	Omission of Appendages	0	0	Upper and Lower Halves	2	1	Hair Shading	3	3	Head	04	04
Sex Sequence	0	Position of Both Arms	4	4	Four Quarters	0	4	Nudity and Transparency	6	7	Neck	02	03
Posture	1 1	Position of Right Arm	7	7	Relative Size	2		Form	1	1	Shoulders		
Perspective	2 2	Position of Left Arm	4	5	Constant Line Pressure	0	0	Detailing	3	3	Right Arm		
Vertical Midline	7 4	Position of Legs	1	1	Variable Line Pressure	5	5	Identity and Sex	1	1	Left Arm	02	03
Bilateral Symmetry	0 0	Relation of Long Axes	1	1	Line Continuity	1	1	Sophistication	3	3	Chest	02	02
Horizontal Midline	4 4	Right and Left Halves	2	2	Body Shading	2	0	Height	03	03	Girth	02	03

GENERAL CHARACTERISTICS OF SUBJECT

IDENTIFICATION
No. 659
Sex M
Marital status S
Age 25 yrs. at
psychological tests

PARENTAL HISTORY				
Father				
C	H	S	D	O
?	-	-	-	-
Mother				
C	H	S	D	O
-	-	-	-	-

PHYSIOLOGICAL AND METABOLIC DATA

	Admission	Initial	Control	Cold pressor change	Exercise change	Smoking change
Systolic pressure	120	126	116	+02	+22	+08
Diastolic pressure	78	72	74	+16	-12	+10
Heart rate	74	88	86	-26	+25	+12

Age 23 yrs.	Height 72 in.	Ponderal index 13.04
	Weight 168 lbs.	Cholesterol 273 mg. per 100 ml.
	Overweight +02 %	Vital capacity 6.0 liters

HABIT SURVEY
Smoking habits: heavy cigarette smoker
Age begun 17 yrs.   Inhalation: yes
Habits of nervous tension: 5, 6, 9, 11, 17,
21, 23

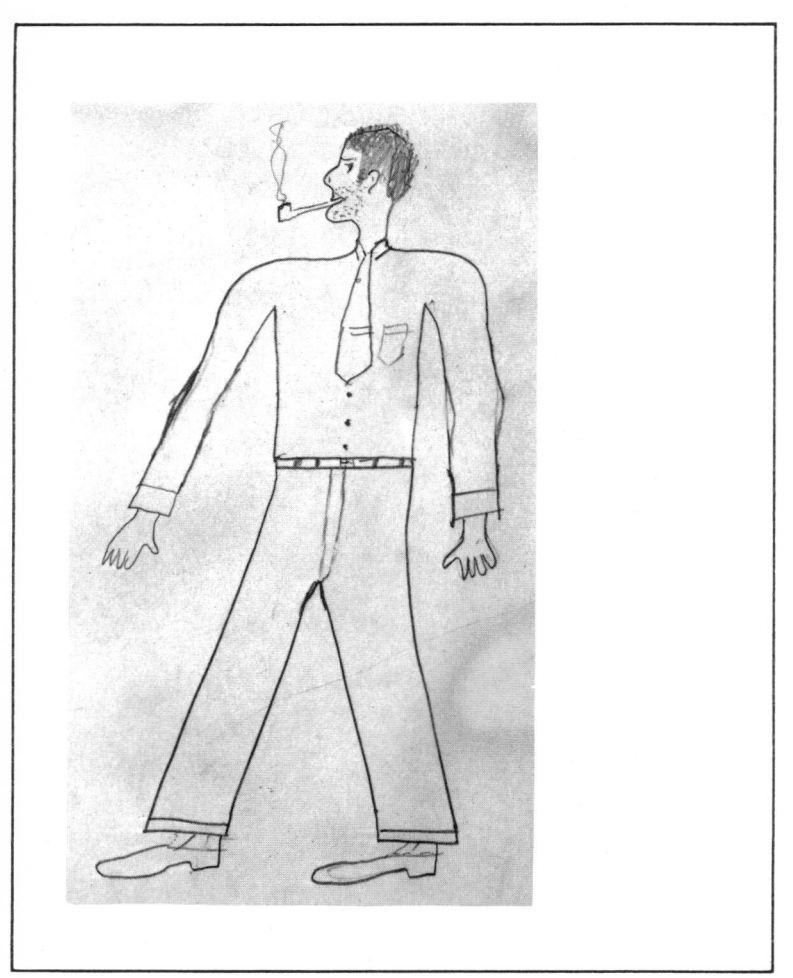

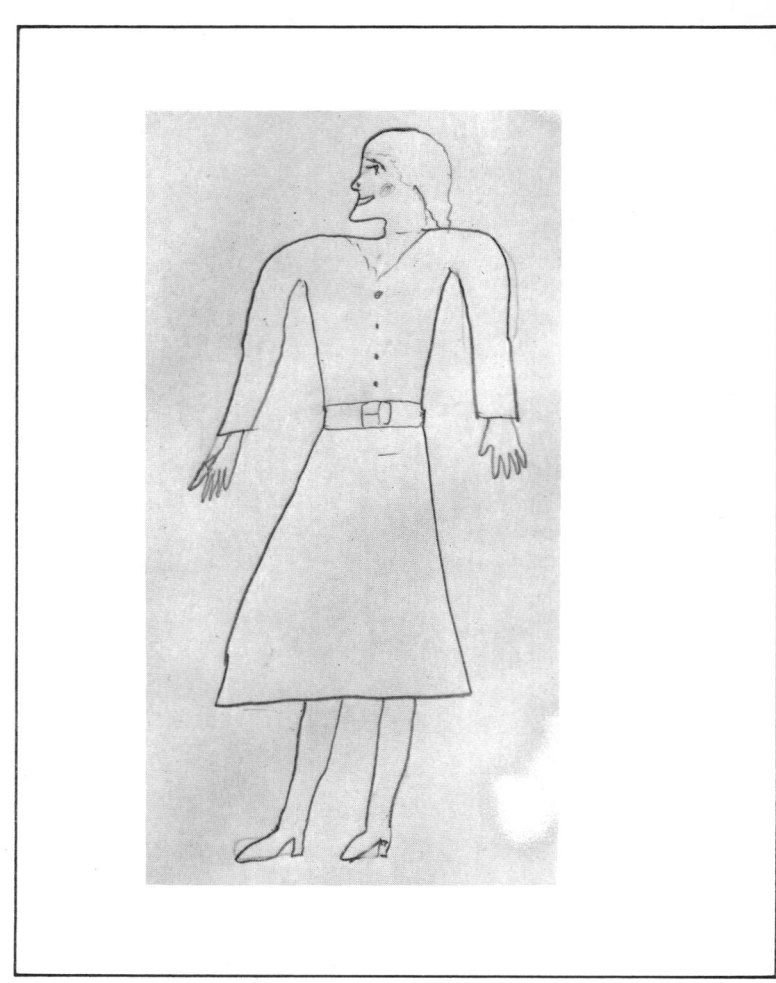

FIGURE-DRAWING CHARACTERISTICS

Structural	Male	Female	Structural	Male	Female	Structural and Graphic	Male	Female	Graphic, Global and Height	Male	Female	Body Proportions	Male	Female
	Both						Both							
Type	0		Omission of Appendages	0	0	Upper and Lower Halves	0	0	Hair Shading	3	5	Head	07	07
Sex Sequence	0		Position of Both Arms	1	1	Four Quarters	4	4	Nudity and Transparency	7	7	Neck	08	06
Posture	1	1	Position of Right Arm	2	2	Relative Size	0		Form	3	3	Shoulders	09	09
Perspective	5	5	Position of Left Arm	0	0	Constant Line Pressure	5	5	Detailing	3	3	Right Arm	08	06
Vertical Midline	3	3	Position of Legs	6	5	Variable Line Pressure	0	0	Identity and Sex	1	1	Left Arm	08	06
Bilateral Symmetry	2	2	Relation of Long Axes	1	1	Line Continuity	4	4	Sophistication	3	3	Chest	07	07
Horizontal Midline	4	4	Right and Left Halves	1	1	Body Shading	0	0	Height	08	07	Girth	09	07

GENERAL CHARACTERISTICS OF SUBJECT

IDENTIFICATION
No.　673
Sex　M
Marital status　S
Age　25　yrs. at psychological tests

PARENTAL HISTORY					
Father					
C	H	S	D	O	
?	+	-	+	+	
Mother					
C	H	S	D	O	
-	+	-	-	-	

PHYSIOLOGICAL AND METABOLIC DATA

	Admission	Initial	Control	Cold pressor change	Exercise change	Smoking change
Systolic pressure	120	110	90	+10	+30	+04
Diastolic pressure	70	60	60	+10	-10	+02
Heart rate	76	72	71	-04	+29	+01

Age 22 yrs.	Height	69	in.	Ponderal index	12.55	
	Weight	166	lbs.	Cholesterol	203	mg. per 100 ml.
	Overweight	+11	%	Vital capacity	4.2	liters

HABIT SURVEY
Smoking habits:　heavy cigarette smoker
Age begun　18　yrs.　　Inhalation:　yes
Habits of nervous tension:　1,　5,　11,　23

Plate 246   **DRAWINGS AT AN INTERMEDIATE LEVEL OF SOPHISTICATION**   289

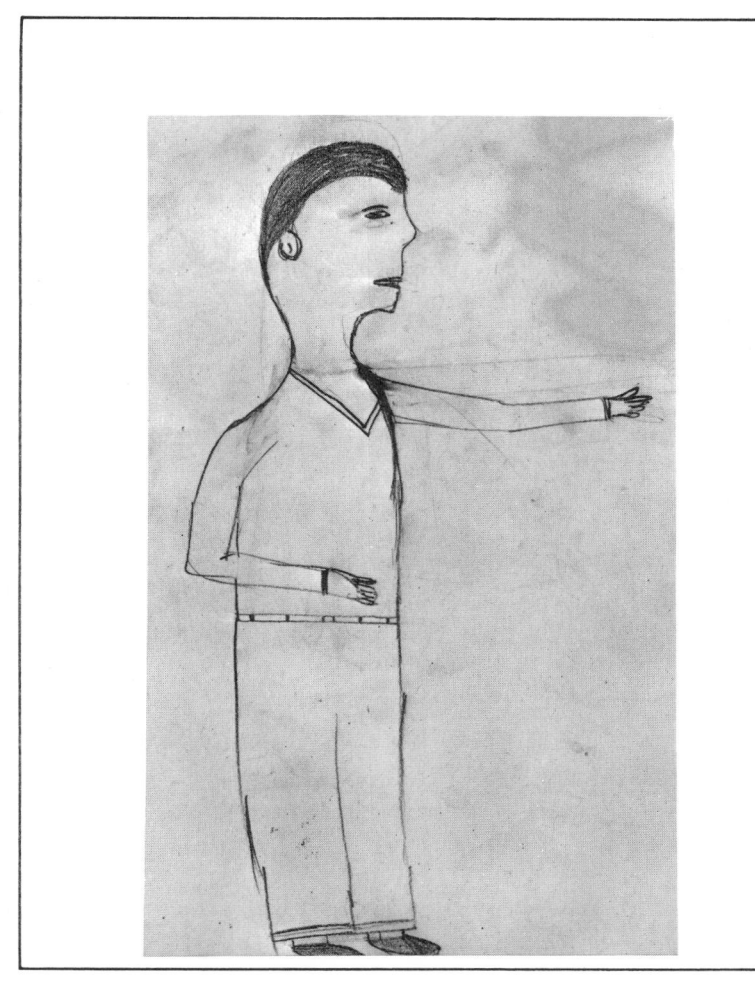

FIGURE-DRAWING CHARACTERISTICS

Structural	Male Female Both		Structural	Male	Female	Structural and Graphic	Male Female Both		Graphic, Global and Height	Male	Female	Body Proportions	Male	Female
Type	0		Omission of Appendages	0	0	Upper and Lower Halves	3	5	Hair Shading	1	1	Head	14	12
Sex Sequence	0		Position of Both Arms	1	2	Four Quarters	4	4	Nudity and Transparency	7	7	Neck	18	16
Posture	1	1	Position of Right Arm	5	2	Relative Size	4		Form	3	3	Shoulders		
Perspective	6	2	Position of Left Arm	2	7	Constant Line Pressure	0	0	Detailing	3	3	Right Arm	07	06
Vertical Midline	4	4	Position of Legs	3	4	Variable Line Pressure	5	5	Identity and Sex	1	1	Left Arm	07	
Bilateral Symmetry	0	0	Relation of Long Axes	1	1	Line Continuity	1	1	Sophistication	3	3	Chest		07
Horizontal Midline	4	0	Right and Left Halves	1	1	Body Shading	4	4	Height	08	09	Girth		10

GENERAL CHARACTERISTICS OF SUBJECT

<table>
<tr><th colspan="2">IDENTIFICATION</th></tr>
<tr><td colspan="2">No. 738</td></tr>
<tr><td colspan="2">Sex M</td></tr>
<tr><td colspan="2">Marital status M</td></tr>
<tr><td colspan="2">Age 23 yrs. at</td></tr>
<tr><td colspan="2">psychological tests</td></tr>
</table>

PARENTAL HISTORY

Father
C	H	S	D	O
?	U	?	–	?

Mother
C	H	S	D	O
–	?	–	+	+

PHYSIOLOGICAL AND METABOLIC DATA

	Admission	Initial	Control	Cold pressor change	Exercise change	Smoking change
Systolic pressure	110	124	108	+20	+26	+08
Diastolic pressure	66	58	62	+28	–02	+06
Heart rate	78	72	64	–12	+06	+03

Age 22 yrs.

Height 70 in.
Weight 182 lbs.
Overweight +18 %

Ponderal index 12.35
Cholesterol 243 mg. per 100 ml.
Vital capacity 5.6 liters

HABIT SURVEY

Smoking habits: nonsmoker
Age begun   yrs.   Inhalation:
Habits of nervous tension: 4, 5, 6, 9, 17

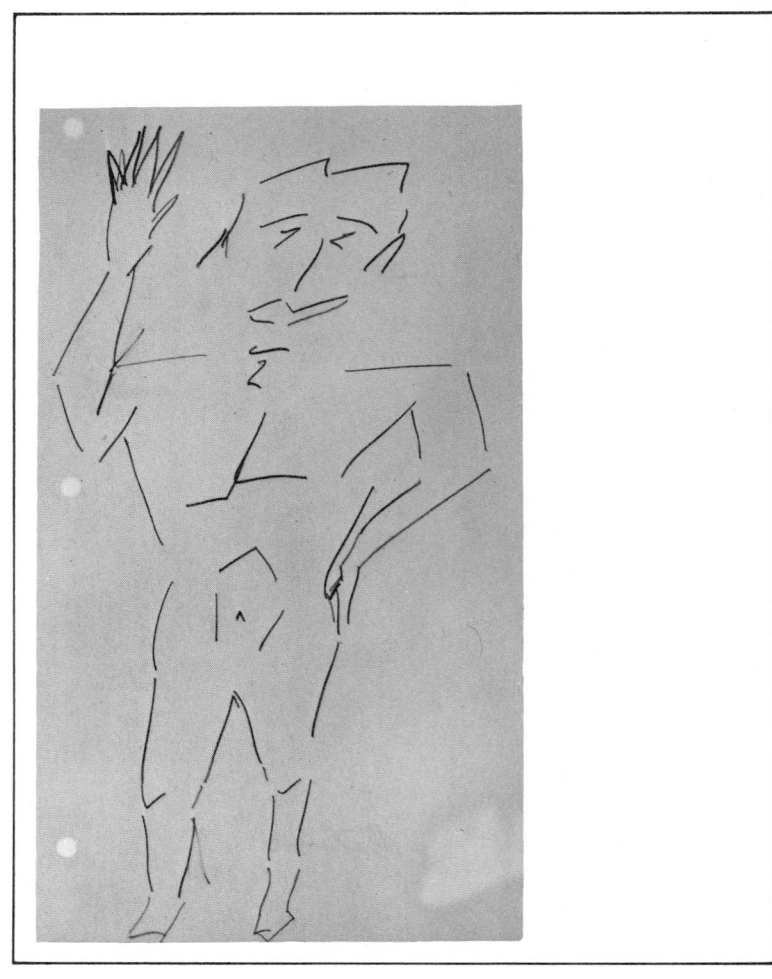

FIGURE-DRAWING CHARACTERISTICS

Structural	Male Female Both	Structural	Male	Female	Structural and Graphic	Male Female Both	Graphic, Global and Height	Male	Female	Body Proportions	Male	Female
Type	0	Omission of Appendages	0	5	Upper and Lower Halves	3 3	Hair Shading	5	5	Head		16
Sex Sequence	1	Position of Both Arms	1	2	Four Quarters	4 4	Nudity and Transparency	0	0	Neck		
Posture	1 3	Position of Right Arm	2	5	Relative Size	4	Form	3	3	Shoulders	14	12
Perspective	0 0	Position of Left Arm	5	8	Constant Line Pressure	5 0	Detailing	3	3	Right Arm		10
Vertical Midline	0 0	Position of Legs	6	9	Variable Line Pressure	0 5	Identity and Sex	1	1	Left Arm	07	
Bilateral Symmetry	1 1	Relation of Long Axes	1	0	Line Continuity	2 2	Sophistication	3	3	Chest	12	11
Horizontal Midline	0 0	Right and Left Halves	1	1	Body Shading	3 0	Height	08		Girth	10	14

GENERAL CHARACTERISTICS OF SUBJECT

IDENTIFICATION
No. 759
Sex M
Marital status S
Age 22 yrs. at
psychological tests

PARENTAL HISTORY				
Father				
C	H	S	D	O
?	+	-	-	+
Mother				
C	H	S	D	O
-	-	-	?	?

PHYSIOLOGICAL AND METABOLIC DATA

	Admission	Initial	Control	Cold pressor change	Exercise change	Smoking change
Systolic pressure	120	123	133	+22	+35	
Diastolic pressure	80	72	81	+13	-17	
Heart rate	68	72	70	-06		

Age 24 yrs.	Height 72 in.	Ponderal index 12.07
	Weight 212 lbs.	Cholesterol 243 mg. per 100 ml.
	Overweight +28 %	Vital capacity liters

HABIT SURVEY

Smoking habits: nonsmoker

   Age begun   yrs.   Inhalation:

Habits of nervous tension: 3, 4, 5, 6, 9, 11, 19, 22, 23

Plate 248   DRAWINGS AT AN INTERMEDIATE LEVEL OF SOPHISTICATION   291

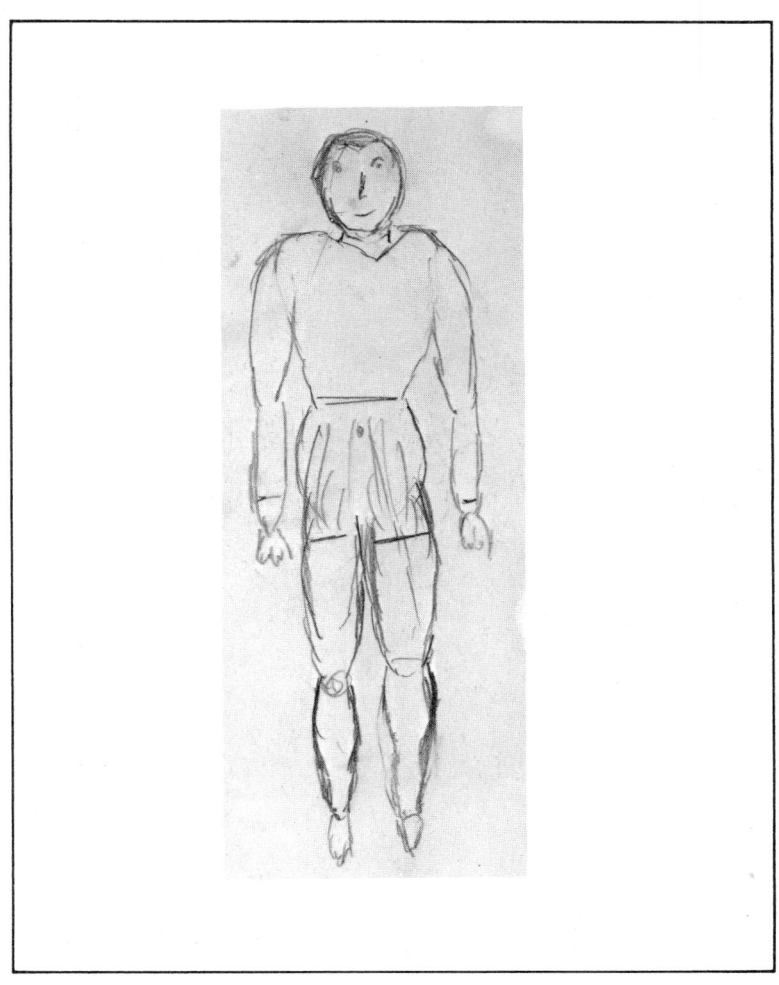

FIGURE-DRAWING CHARACTERISTICS

Structural	Male Female Both	Structural	Male	Female	Structural and Graphic	Male Female Both		Graphic, Global and Height	Male	Female	Body Proportions	Male	Female
Type	0	Omission of Appendages	0	0	Upper and Lower Halves	0	1	Hair Shading	3	3	Head	08	06
Sex Sequence	1	Position of Both Arms	0	2	Four Quarters	4	4	Nudity and Transparency	5	0	Neck	04	05
Posture	1 1	Position of Right Arm	0	0	Relative Size	0		Form	3	3	Shoulders	08	
Perspective	0 2	Position of Left Arm	0	7	Constant Line Pressure	0	3	Detailing	3	3	Right Arm	08	06
Vertical Midline	0 4	Position of Legs	4	1	Variable Line Pressure	5	0	Identity and Sex	3	3	Left Arm	08	
Bilateral Symmetry	2 0	Relation of Long Axes	1	1	Line Continuity	0	0	Sophistication	3	3	Chest	07	06
Horizontal Midline	4 0	Right and Left Halves	1	2	Body Shading	2	0	Height	07	07	Girth	05	07

GENERAL CHARACTERISTICS OF SUBJECT

IDENTIFICATION

No. F27
Sex M
Marital status M
Age 24 yrs. at
psychological tests

PARENTAL HISTORY

Father
C H S D O
?   -   -   -   ?
Mother
C H S D O
-   -   -   -   +

PHYSIOLOGICAL AND METABOLIC DATA

	Admission	Initial	Control	Cold pressor change	Exercise change	Smoking change
Systolic pressure	140	138	112	+10	+30	+18
Diastolic pressure	90	80	76	+22	+08	+16
Heart rate	60	64	72	+12	+27	+32

Age 22 yrs.   Height 76 in.   Ponderal index 12.95
Weight 202 lbs.   Cholesterol 243 mg. per 100 ml.
Overweight +10 %   Vital capacity   liters

HABIT SURVEY

Smoking habits: occasional smoker
Age begun 21 yrs.   Inhalation: no
Habits of nervous tension: 4, 5, 6, 16, 23

STRONG VOCATIONAL INTEREST TEST

Occupation	Artist	Psychologist	Architect	Physician	Osteopath	Dentist	Veterinarian	Mathematician	Physicist	Engineer	Chemist	Production Manager
Standard Score	34	40	43	54	41	39	25	32	29	37	38	32

Occupation	Farmer	Aviator	Carpenter	Printer	Math.-Sci. Teacher	Ind. Arts Teacher	Voc. Agric. Teacher	Policeman	Forest Serv. Man	Y.M.C.A. Phys. Dir.	Personnel Director	Public Administrator
Standard Score	37	38	26	35	38	27	34	27	31	36	33	33

Occupation	Y.M.C.A. Secretary	Soc. Sci. H.S. Teacher	City Sch. Sup't.	Social Worker	Minister	Musician Performer	C.P.A.	Senior C.P.A.	Accountant	Office Man	Purchasing Agent	Banker
Standard Score	22	32	26	31	58	45	31	36	24	25	25	21

Occupation	Mortician	Pharmacist	Sales Manager	Real Est. Manager	Life Ins. Salesman	Advertising Man	Lawyer	Author-Journalist	President Mfg. Co.	Interest Maturity	Occupational Level	Masculinity-Femininity
Standard Score	22	35	28	31	28	33	36	34	38	52	59	46

FIGURE-DRAWING CHARACTERISTICS

Structural	Male Female / Both	Structural	Male	Female	Structural and Graphic	Male Female / Both		Graphic, Global and Height	Male	Female	Body Proportions	Male	Female
Type	0	Omission of Appendages	0	0	Upper and Lower Halves	3	3	Hair Shading	3	3	Head	06	09
Sex Sequence	0	Position of Both Arms	4	1	Four Quarters	4	4	Nudity and Transparency	7	7	Neck	08	07
Posture	1	1	Position of Right Arm	7	4	Relative Size	4		Form	3	3	Shoulders		06
Perspective	2	0	Position of Left Arm	0	0	Constant Line Pressure	0	0	Detailing	3	3	Right Arm		04
Vertical Midline	7	0	Position of Legs	1	5	Variable Line Pressure	1	1	Identity and Sex	1	3	Left Arm	06	05
Bilateral Symmetry	0	3	Relation of Long Axes	1	1	Line Continuity	1	1	Sophistication	3	3	Chest	07	05
Horizontal Midline	6	4	Right and Left Halves	2	1	Body Shading	4	1	Height	05	06	Girth	07	07

GENERAL CHARACTERISTICS OF SUBJECT

IDENTIFICATION
No. F28
Sex M
Marital status S
Age 23 yrs. at
psychological tests

PARENTAL HISTORY				
Father				
C	H	S	D	O
?	?	-	-	-
Mother				
C	H	S	D	O
-	-	-	-	-

PHYSIOLOGICAL AND METABOLIC DATA

	Admission	Initial	Control	Cold pressor change	Exercise change	Smoking change
Systolic pressure	108	116	102	+12	+32	-01
Diastolic pressure	64	72	70	+18	+08	+01
Heart rate	70	84	84	+04	+29	+01
Age 21 yrs.	Height 69 in.		Ponderal index 13.80			
	Weight 125 lbs.		Cholesterol 197 mg. per 100 ml.			
	Overweight -15 %		Vital capacity liters			

HABIT SURVEY
Smoking habits: mixed smoker
Age begun 21 yrs.   Inhalation: no
Habits of nervous tension: 1, 2, 4, 5, 6, 8, 9, 12, 14, 18, 23

STRONG VOCATIONAL INTEREST TEST

Occupation	Artist	Psychologist	Architect	Physician	Osteopath	Dentist	Veterinarian	Mathematician	Physicist	Engineer	Chemist	Production Manager
Standard Score	48	68	49	74	61	50	29	47	51	52	66	30

Occupation	Farmer	Aviator	Carpenter	Printer	Math.-Sci. Teacher	Ind. Arts Teacher	Voc. Agric. Teacher	Policeman	Forest Serv. Man	Y.M.C.A. Phys. Dir.	Personnel Director	Public Administrator
Standard Score	41	62	34	53	50	31	33	31	37	34	38	48

Occupation	Y.M.C.A. Secretary	Soc. Sci. H.S. Teacher	City Sch. Sup't.	Social Worker	Minister	Musician Performer	C.P.A.	Senior C.P.A.	Accountant	Office Man	Purchasing Agent	Banker
Standard Score	20	30	24	48	58	64	31	39	08	13	09	05

Occupation	Mortician	Pharmacist	Sales Manager	Real Est. Manager	Life Ins. Salesman	Advertising Man	Lawyer	Author-Journalist	President Mfg. Co.	Interest Maturity	Occupational Level	Masculinity-Femininity
Standard Score	10	31	14	25	17	36	43	47	27	49	51	52

FIGURE-DRAWING CHARACTERISTICS

Structural	Male Female Both	Structural	Male	Female	Structural and Graphic	Male Female Both		Graphic, Global and Height	Male	Female	Body Proportions	Male	Female
Type	0	Omission of Appendages	0	0	Upper and Lower Halves	1	3	Hair Shading	3	2	Head	07	09
Sex Sequence	2	Position of Both Arms	1	4	Four Quarters	4	4	Nudity and Transparency	7	7	Neck	06	08
Posture	2 2	Position of Right Arm	4	7	Relative Size	4		Form	5	3	Shoulders		
Perspective	9 2	Position of Left Arm	0	4	Constant Line Pressure	4	0	Detailing	3	3	Right Arm	04	
Vertical Midline	4 4	Position of Legs	8	8	Variable Line Pressure	0	1	Identity and Sex	3	1	Left Arm	04	05
Bilateral Symmetry	0 0	Relation of Long Axes	1	1	Line Continuity	4	0	Sophistication	3	3	Chest		07
Horizontal Midline	4 4	Right and Left Halves	1	4	Body Shading	0	2	Height	05	07	Girth		05

GENERAL CHARACTERISTICS OF SUBJECT

IDENTIFICATION
No. A03
Sex M
Marital status S
Age 22 yrs. at
psychological tests

PARENTAL HISTORY				
Father				
C	H	S	D	O
?	+	-	-	?
Mother				
C	H	S	D	O
-	+	-	-	-

PHYSIOLOGICAL AND METABOLIC DATA

	Admission	Initial	Control	Cold pressor change	Exercise change	Smoking change
Systolic pressure	140	160	152	+04	+54	
Diastolic pressure	75	80	86	+16	+22	
Heart rate	88	92	87	+08	+12	

Age 21 yrs.	Height 74 in.	Ponderal index 12.29
	Weight 218 lbs.	Cholesterol 222 mg. per 100 ml.
	Overweight +27 %	Vital capacity liters

HABIT SURVEY
Smoking habits: nonsmoker
Age begun yrs. Inhalation:
Habits of nervous tension: 6, 9

STRONG VOCATIONAL INTEREST TEST

Occupation	Artist	Psychologist	Architect	Physician	Osteopath	Dentist	Veterinarian	Mathematician	Physicist	Engineer	Chemist	Production Manager
Standard Score	34	43	47	63	52	42	22	40	34	40	45	25

Occupation	Farmer	Aviator	Carpenter	Printer	Math.-Sci. Teacher	Ind. Arts Teacher	Voc. Agric. Teacher	Policeman	Forest Serv. Man	Y.M.C.A. Phys. Dir.	Personnel Director	Public Administrator
Standard Score	33	40	25	42	48	32	30	29	25	35	33	36

Occupation	Y.M.C.A. Secretary	Soc. Sci. H.S. Teacher	City Sch. Sup't.	Social Worker	Minister	Musician Performer	C.P.A.	Senior C.P.A.	Accountant	Office Man	Purchasing Agent	Banker
Standard Score	24	35	28	38	60	58	32	43	24	33	16	19

Occupation	Mortician	Pharmacist	Sales Manager	Real Est. Manager	Life Ins. Salesman	Advertising Man	Lawyer	Author- Journalist	President Mfg. Co.	Interest Maturity	Occupational Level	Masculinity- Femininity
Standard Score	21	34	23	29	24	32	34	32	26	59	56	45

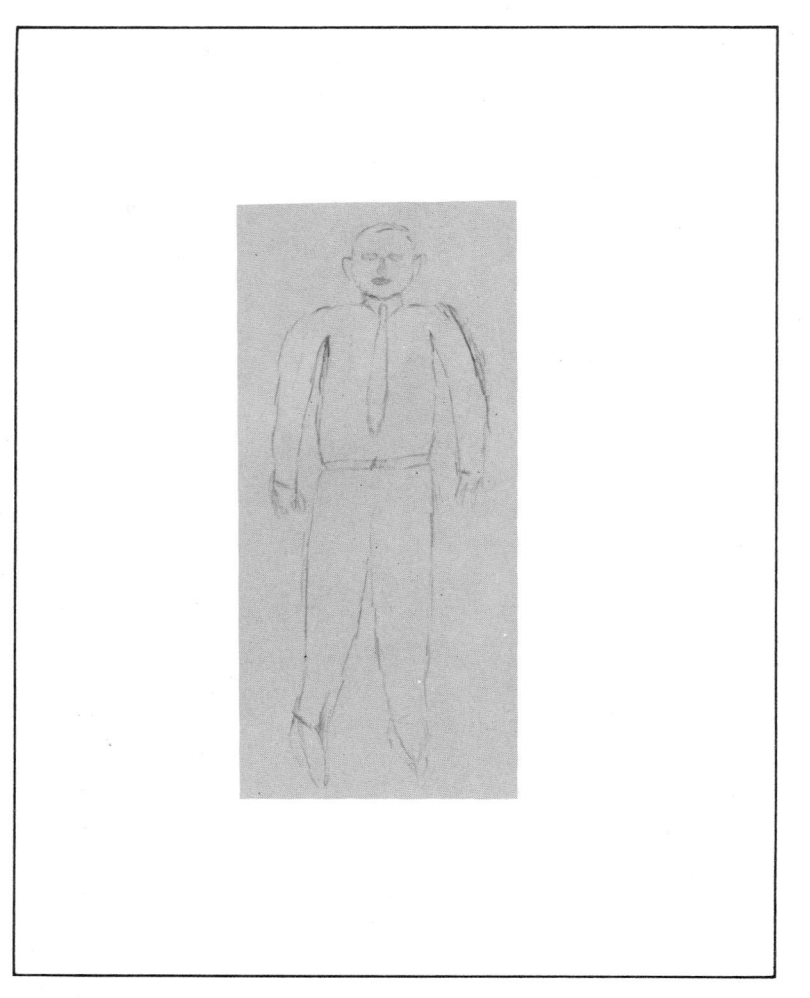

FIGURE-DRAWING CHARACTERISTICS

Structural	Male Female Both		Structural	Male	Female	Structural and Graphic	Male Female Both		Graphic, Global and Height	Male	Female	Body Proportions	Male	Female
Type	0		Omission of Appendages	0	7	Upper and Lower Halves	0	1	Hair Shading	7	7	Head	06	04
Sex Sequence	0		Position of Both Arms	0	4	Four Quarters	4	4	Nudity and Transparency	7	7	Neck	03	05
Posture	1	1	Position of Right Arm	0	7	Relative Size	0		Form	3	3	Shoulders	07	
Perspective	0	2	Position of Left Arm	0	0	Constant Line Pressure	1	1	Detailing	3	5	Right Arm	04	
Vertical Midline	3	4	Position of Legs	4	1	Variable Line Pressure	0	0	Identity and Sex	1	1	Left Arm	04	02
Bilateral Symmetry	3	0	Relation of Long Axes	1	1	Line Continuity	0	0	Sophistication	3	3	Chest	05	04
Horizontal Midline	4	4	Right and Left Halves	1	2	Body Shading	0	0	Height	06	04	Girth	06	05

GENERAL CHARACTERISTICS OF SUBJECT

IDENTIFICATION
No. A16
Sex M
Marital status S
Age 22 yrs. at
psychological tests

PARENTAL HISTORY
Father
C   H   S   D   O
?   -   -   -   ?
Mother
C   H   S   D   O
-    -   -   -   ?

PHYSIOLOGICAL AND METABOLIC DATA

	Admission	Initial	Control	Cold pressor change	Exercise change	Smoking change
Systolic pressure	130	138	130	+14	+44	+03
Diastolic pressure	85	74	80	+14	-16	+08
Heart rate	78	54	59	+05	+22	+11

Age 21 yrs.	Height 71 in.	Ponderal index 12.75
	Weight 173 lbs.	Cholesterol 203 mg. per 100 ml.
	Overweight +10 %	Vital capacity liters

HABIT SURVEY

Smoking habits: moderate cigarette smoker

Age begun 17 yrs.   Inhalation: yes

Habits of nervous tension: 6, 9, 19, 21, 22, 25

STRONG VOCATIONAL INTEREST TEST

Occupation	Artist	Psychologist	Architect	Physician	Osteopath	Dentist	Veterinarian	Mathematician	Physicist	Engineer	Chemist	Production Manager
Standard Score	24	45	28	50	38	30	31	28	14	26	30	34

Occupation	Farmer	Aviator	Carpenter	Printer	Math.-Sci. Teacher	Ind. Arts Teacher	Voc. Agric. Teacher	Policeman	Forest Serv. Man	Y.M.C.A. Phys. Dir.	Personnel Director	Public Administrator
Standard Score	37	43	20	47	42	24	43	40	35	38	47	58

Occupation	Y.M.C.A. Secretary	Soc. Sci. H.S. Teacher	City Sch. Sup't.	Social Worker	Minister	Musician Performer	C.P.A.	Senior C.P.A.	Accountant	Office Man	Purchasing Agent	Banker
Standard Score	37	51	46	50	60	45	35	47	29	36	27	31

Occupation	Mortician	Pharmacist	Sales Manager	Real Est. Manager	Life Ins. Salesman	Advertising Man	Lawyer	Author-Journalist	President Mfg. Co.	Interest Maturity	Occupational Level	Masculinity-Femininity
Standard Score	30	31	36	32	30	39	46	36	22	56	50	50

Plate 252   DRAWINGS AT AN INTERMEDIATE LEVEL OF SOPHISTICATION   295

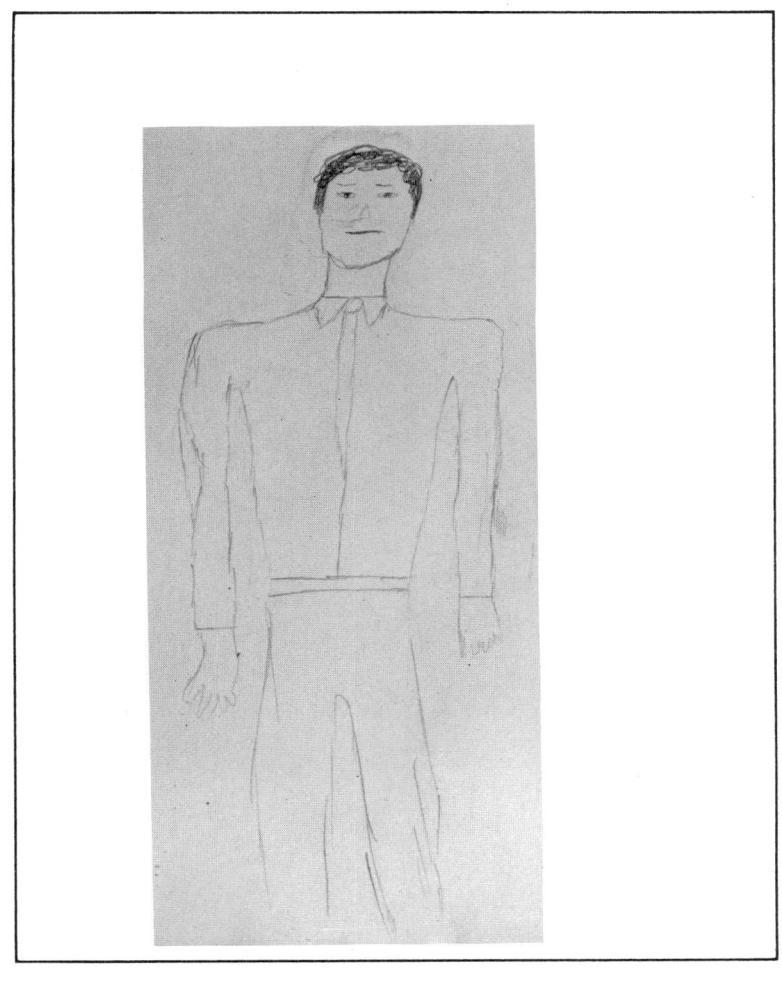

FIGURE-DRAWING CHARACTERISTICS

Structural	Male Female Both		Structural	Male	Female	Structural and Graphic	Male Female Both		Graphic, Global and Height	Male	Female	Body Proportions	Male	Female
Type	0		Omission of Appendages	3	0	Upper and Lower Halves	7	3	Hair Shading	3	5	Head	09	11
Sex Sequence	0		Position of Both Arms	0	0	Four Quarters	4	4	Nudity and Transparency	7	7	Neck	12	08
Posture	0	1	Position of Right Arm	0	0	Relative Size	0		Form	3	3	Shoulders	12	09
Perspective	0	0	Position of Left Arm	0	0	Constant Line Pressure	1	1	Detailing	3	3	Right Arm	08	07
Vertical Midline	3	3	Position of Legs	4	4	Variable Line Pressure	0	0	Identity and Sex	1	1	Left Arm	08	06
Bilateral Symmetry	3	3	Relation of Long Axes	1	1	Line Continuity	0	0	Sophistication	3	3	Chest	09	09
Horizontal Midline	4	4	Right and Left Halves	1	1	Body Shading	0	0	Height		08	Girth	09	09

GENERAL CHARACTERISTICS OF SUBJECT

IDENTIFICATION

No. B12
Sex M
Marital status S
Age 22 yrs. at
psychological tests

PARENTAL HISTORY

Father
C H S D O
?   -   -   -   -
Mother
C H S D O
-   -   -   -   ?

PHYSIOLOGICAL AND METABOLIC DATA

	Admission	Initial	Control	Cold pressor change	Exercise change	Smoking change
Systolic pressure	96	118	112	+03	+28	-01
Diastolic pressure	64	68	70	+03	-14	+18
Heart rate	82	72	60	+09	+40	+18

Age 22 yrs.   Height 71 in.   Ponderal index 12.54
Weight 181 lbs.   Cholesterol 233 mg. per 100 ml.
Overweight +15 %   Vital capacity 6.2 liters

HABIT SURVEY

Smoking habits: light cigarette smoker
Age begun 17 yrs.   Inhalation: no
Habits of nervous tension: 4, 5, 6, 9, 10, 22, 23

STRONG VOCATIONAL INTEREST TEST

Occupation	Artist	Psychologist	Architect	Physician	Osteopath	Dentist	Veterinarian	Mathematician	Physicist	Engineer	Chemist	Production Manager
Standard Score	28	51	35	68	55	44	29	29	39	50	53	44

Occupation	Farmer	Aviator	Carpenter	Printer	Math.-Sci. Teacher	Ind. Arts Teacher	Voc. Agric. Teacher	Policeman	Forest Serv. Man	Y.M.C.A. Phys. Dir.	Personnel Director	Public Administrator
Standard Score	31	50	23	46	51	34	31	37	39	39	44	49

Occupation	Y.M.C.A. Secretary	Soc. Sci. H.S. Teacher	City Sch. Sup't.	Social Worker	Minister	Musician Performer	C.P.A.	Senior C.P.A.	Accountant	Office Man	Purchasing Agent	Banker
Standard Score	25	34	36	39	61	38	31	46	28	26	20	10

Occupation	Mortician	Pharmacist	Sales Manager	Real Est. Manager	Life Ins. Salesman	Advertising Man	Lawyer	Author-Journalist	President Mfg. Co.	Interest Maturity	Occupational Level	Masculinity-Femininity
Standard Score	20	36	28	25	26	32	35	34	33	57	56	57

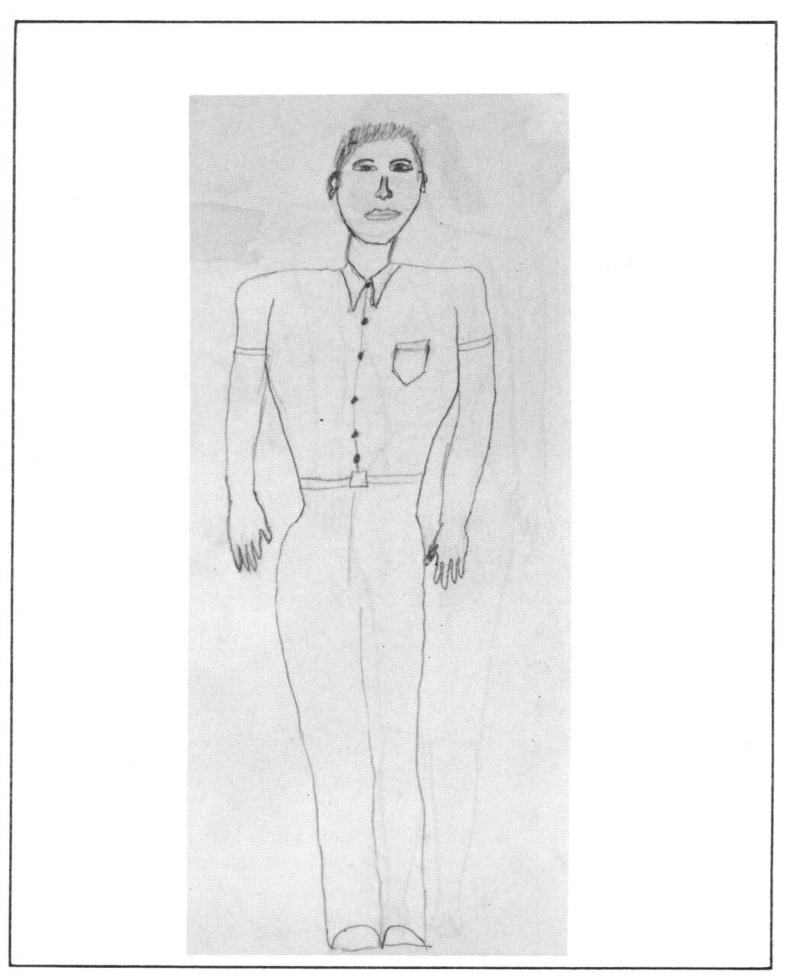

FIGURE-DRAWING CHARACTERISTICS

Structural	Male Female		Structural	Male	Female	Structural and Graphic	Male	Female	Graphic, Global and Height	Male	Female	Body Proportions	Male	Female
	Both						Both							
Type	0		Omission of Appendages	0	0	Upper and Lower Halves	3	3	Hair Shading	3	3	Head	09	08
Sex Sequence	0		Position of Both Arms	0	0	Four Quarters	4	4	Nudity and Transparency	7	7	Neck	08	08
Posture	1	1	Position of Right Arm	0	0	Relative Size	2		Form	3	3	Shoulders	10	09
Perspective	0	0	Position of Left Arm	0	0	Constant Line Pressure	3	0	Detailing	3	3	Right Arm	06	07
Vertical Midline	3	0	Position of Legs	2	4	Variable Line Pressure	0	5	Identity and Sex	1	1	Left Arm	08	07
Bilateral Symmetry	2	3	Relation of Long Axes	1	1	Line Continuity	3	3	Sophistication	3	3	Chest	08	07
Horizontal Midline	4	4	Right and Left Halves	1	0	Body Shading	4	1	Height	08	09	Girth	07	06

GENERAL CHARACTERISTICS OF SUBJECT

IDENTIFICATION
No. B15
Sex M
Marital status S
Age 21 yrs. at
psychological tests

PARENTAL HISTORY
Father
C H S D O
? - - - +
Mother
C H S D O
- - (+) - +

PHYSIOLOGICAL AND METABOLIC DATA

	Admission	Initial	Control	Cold pressor change	Exercise change	Smoking change
Systolic pressure	108	126	114	+12	+24	+06
Diastolic pressure	66	58	52	+44	-02	+04
Heart rate	80	84	81	+08	00	+09

Age 21 yrs.	Height 68 in.	Ponderal index 12.98
	Weight 144 lbs.	Cholesterol 225 mg. per 100 ml.
	Overweight -01 %	Vital capacity 4.7 liters

HABIT SURVEY
Smoking habits: nonsmoker
Age begun yrs. Inhalation:
Habits of nervous tension: 4, 5, 18, 21

STRONG VOCATIONAL INTEREST TEST

Occupation	Artist	Psychologist	Architect	Physician	Osteopath	Dentist	Veterinarian	Mathematician	Physicist	Engineer	Chemist	Production Manager
Standard Score	21	34	17	37	38	18	27	16	09	17	27	26

Occupation	Farmer	Aviator	Carpenter	Printer	Math.-Sci. Teacher	Ind. Arts Teacher	Voc. Agric. Teacher	Policeman	Forest Serv. Man	Y.M.C.A. Phys. Dir.	Personnel Director	Public Administrator
Standard Score	29	33	09	35	37	14	36	27	31	43	49	48

Occupation	Y.M.C.A. Secretary	Soc. Sci. H.S. Teacher	City Sch. Sup't.	Social Worker	Minister	Musician Performer	C.P.A.	Senior C.P.A.	Accountant	Office Man	Purchasing Agent	Banker
Standard Score	42	43	37	48	61	33	18	40	24	33	23	22

Occupation	Mortician	Pharmacist	Sales Manager	Real Est. Manager	Life Ins. Salesman	Advertising Man	Lawyer	Author-Journalist	President Mfg. Co.	Interest Maturity	Occupational Level	Masculinity-Femininity
Standard Score	33	35	44	43	44	36	35	29	39	57	57	44

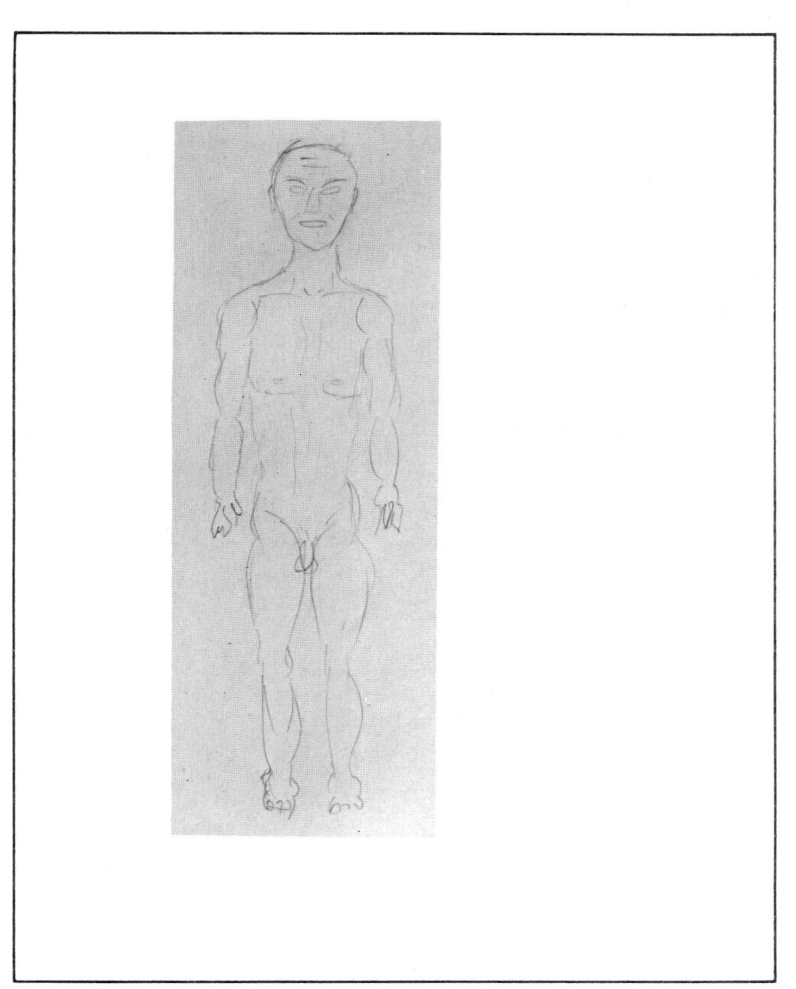

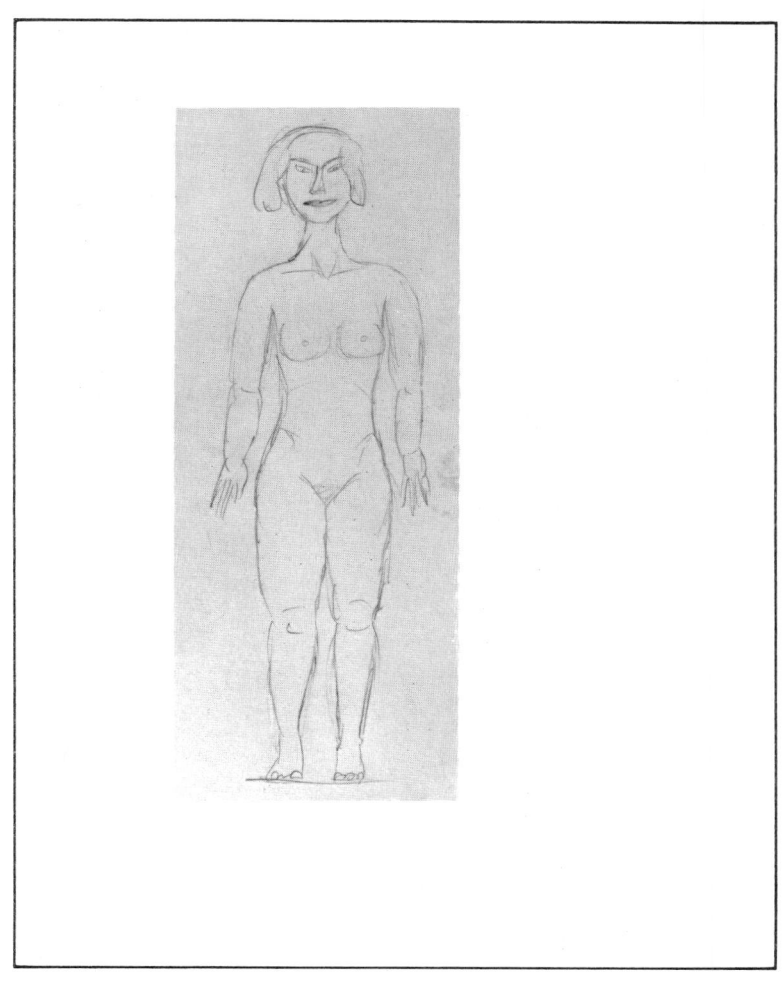

FIGURE-DRAWING CHARACTERISTICS

Structural	Male Female Both	Structural	Male	Female	Structural and Graphic	Male Female Both		Graphic, Global and Height	Male	Female	Body Proportions	Male	Female
Type	0	Omission of Appendages	0	0	Upper and Lower Halves	1	1	Hair Shading	0	5	Head	08	07
Sex Sequence	0	Position of Both Arms	0	0	Four Quarters	4	4	Nudity and Transparency	0	0	Neck	08	14
Posture	1	1	Position of Right Arm	0	0	Relative Size	2		Form	3	1	Shoulders	07	06
Perspective	0	0	Position of Left Arm	0	0	Constant Line Pressure	1	1	Detailing	3	3	Right Arm	06	04
Vertical Midline	0	0	Position of Legs	4	4	Variable Line Pressure	0	0	Identity and Sex	1	1	Left Arm	06	05
Bilateral Symmetry	4	4	Relation of Long Axes	1	1	Line Continuity	0	0	Sophistication	3	3	Chest	05	05
Horizontal Midline	0	0	Right and Left Halves	1	1	Body Shading	3	3	Height	07	07	Girth	05	06

GENERAL CHARACTERISTICS OF SUBJECT

IDENTIFICATION

No. B25
Sex M
Marital status M
Age 26 yrs. at psychological tests

PARENTAL HISTORY

Father
C H S D O
?   -   -   -   +
Mother
C H S D O
-   -   -   -   +

PHYSIOLOGICAL AND METABOLIC DATA

	Admission	Initial	Control	Cold pressor change	Exercise change	Smoking change
Systolic pressure	120	126	118	+22	+44	+10
Diastolic pressure	80	64	64	+24	-22	+13
Heart rate	88	82	78	+12	+19	+15

Age 25 yrs.
Height 76 in.   Ponderal index 12.40
Weight 230 lbs.   Cholesterol 218 mg. per 100 ml.
Overweight +26 %   Vital capacity 6.7 liters

HABIT SURVEY

Smoking habits: heavy cigarette smoker
Age begun 17 yrs.   Inhalation: yes
Habits of nervous tension: 4, 5, 6, 9, 17, 21

STRONG VOCATIONAL INTEREST TEST

Occupation	Artist	Psychologist	Architect	Physician	Osteopath	Dentist	Veterinarian	Mathematician	Physicist	Engineer	Chemist	Production Manager
Standard Score	50	55	56	61	38	42	17	55	51	55	67	24

Occupation	Farmer	Aviator	Carpenter	Printer	Math.-Sci. Teacher	Ind. Arts Teacher	Voc. Agric. Teacher	Policeman	Forest Serv. Man	Y.M.C.A. Phys. Dir.	Personnel Director	Public Administrator
Standard Score	42	40	23	42	42	19	20	17	35	14	21	42

Occupation	Y.M.C.A. Secretary	Soc. Sci. H.S. Teacher	City Sch. Sup't.	Social Worker	Minister	Musician Performer	C.P.A.	Senior C.P.A.	Accountant	Office Man	Purchasing Agent	Banker
Standard Score	06	22	19	28	61	47	32	39	17	15	15	10

Occupation	Mortician	Pharmacist	Sales Manager	Real Est. Manager	Life Ins. Salesman	Advertising Man	Lawyer	Author-Journalist	President Mfg. Co.	Interest Maturity	Occupational Level	Masculinity-Femininity
Standard Score	01	24	11	19	05	31	31	46	25	45	57	49

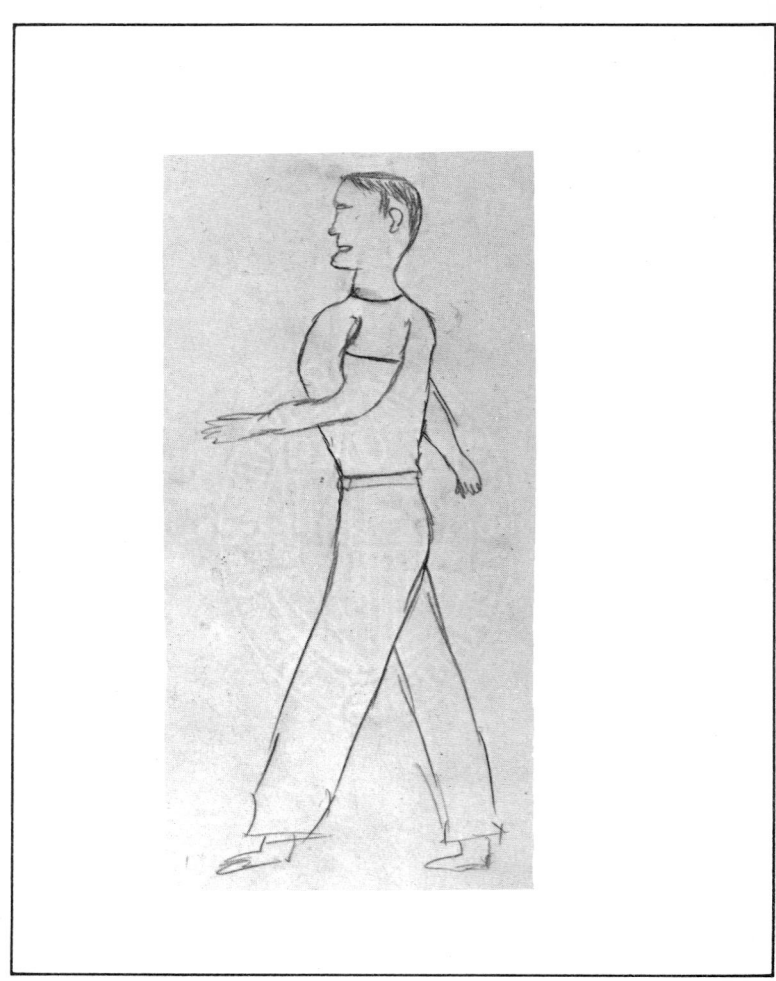

FIGURE-DRAWING CHARACTERISTICS

Structural	Male Female Both	Structural	Male	Female	Structural and Graphic	Male Female Both	Graphic, Global and Height	Male	Female	Body Proportions	Male	Female
Type	0	Omission of Appendages	0	0	Upper and Lower Halves	3 1	Hair Shading	1	3	Head	08	07
Sex Sequence	1	Position of Both Arms	4	4	Four Quarters	4 4	Nudity and Transparency	7	0	Neck	07	06
Posture	2 2	Position of Right Arm	7	7	Relative Size	2	Form	3	3	Shoulders		
Perspective	2 2	Position of Left Arm	4	0	Constant Line Pressure	0 0	Detailing	3	3	Right Arm		
Vertical Midline	4 4	Position of Legs	8	8	Variable Line Pressure	4 5	Identity and Sex	1	1	Left Arm	06	06
Bilateral Symmetry	0 0	Relation of Long Axes	1	1	Line Continuity	0 0	Sophistication	3	3	Chest	09	08
Horizontal Midline	4 0	Right and Left Halves	1	0	Body Shading	0 3	Height	07	07	Girth	06	08

GENERAL CHARACTERISTICS OF SUBJECT

IDENTIFICATION
No. C01
Sex M
Marital status S
Age 22 yrs. at psychological tests

PARENTAL HISTORY
Father
C   H   S   D   O
?   -   -   -   ?
Mother
C   H   S   D   O
-   -   -   -   ?

PHYSIOLOGICAL AND METABOLIC DATA

	Admission	Initial	Control	Cold pressor change	Exercise change	Smoking change
Systolic pressure	120	106	112	+18		-08
Diastolic pressure	80	84	88	+08		+04
Heart rate	84	66	54	+20		+10

Age 22 yrs.	Height	71	in.	Ponderal index	12.89	
	Weight	167	lbs.	Cholesterol	360	mg. per 100 ml.
	Overweight +05 %			Vital capacity	5.1	liters

HABIT SURVEY
Smoking habits: nonsmoker
Age begun   yrs.   Inhalation:
Habits of nervous tension: 4, 5, 6, 9, 16, 18, 22, 25

FIGURE-DRAWING CHARACTERISTICS

Structural	Male Female Both	Structural	Male	Female	Structural and Graphic	Male Female Both		Graphic, Global and Height	Male	Female	Body Proportions	Male	Female
Type	0	Omission of Appendages	0	0	Upper and Lower Halves	0	1	Hair Shading	3	3	Head	05	05
Sex Sequence	0	Position of Both Arms	0	0	Four Quarters	4	4	Nudity and Transparency	7	7	Neck	03	05
Posture	1 1	Position of Right Arm	5	5	Relative Size	0		Form	3	3	Shoulders	06	05
Perspective	0 0	Position of Left Arm	5	5	Constant Line Pressure	0	1	Detailing	3	3	Right Arm	04	02
Vertical Midline	3 0	Position of Legs	4	4	Variable Line Pressure	2	0	Identity and Sex	1	1	Left Arm	04	02
Bilateral Symmetry	3 3	Relation of Long Axes	1	1	Line Continuity	0	0	Sophistication	3	3	Chest	06	04
Horizontal Midline	6 2	Right and Left Halves	1	1	Body Shading	4	3	Height	06	05	Girth	07	05

GENERAL CHARACTERISTICS OF SUBJECT

IDENTIFICATION

No. C11

Sex M

Marital status S

Age 22 yrs. at psychological tests

PARENTAL HISTORY

Father

C	H	S	D	O
?	+	+	(?)	+

Mother

C	H	S	D	O
-	-	-	-	?

PHYSIOLOGICAL AND METABOLIC DATA

	Admission	Initial	Control	Cold pressor change	Exercise change	Smoking change
Systolic pressure	150	130	130	+25	+40	+06
Diastolic pressure	90	70	70	+02	00	00
Heart rate	100	100	90	+12	+17	+11

Age 22 yrs.	Height 71 in.	Ponderal index 12.70
	Weight 175 lbs.	Cholesterol 215 mg. per 100 ml.
	Overweight +09 %	Vital capacity 5.2 liters

HABIT SURVEY

Smoking habits: heavy cigarette smoker

Age begun 14 yrs.   Inhalation: yes

Habits of nervous tension: 1, 3, 4, 5, 6, 9, 11, 16, 23

STRONG VOCATIONAL INTEREST TEST

Occupation	Artist	Psychologist	Architect	Physician	Osteopath	Dentist	Veterinarian	Mathematician	Physicist	Engineer	Chemist	Production Manager
Standard Score	49	43	44	65	52	47	15	43	42	47	52	25

Occupation	Farmer	Aviator	Carpenter	Printer	Math.-Sci. Teacher	Ind. Arts Teacher	Voc. Agric. Teacher	Policeman	Forest Serv. Man	Y.M.C.A. Phys. Dir.	Personnel Director	Public Administrator
Standard Score	26	42	13	30	25	-08	-09	24	20	13	20	33

Occupation	Y.M.C.A. Secretary	Soc. Sci. H.S. Teacher	City Sch. Sup't.	Social Worker	Minister	Musician Performer	C.P.A.	Senior C.P.A.	Accountant	Office Man	Purchasing Agent	Banker
Standard Score	02	11	12	29	62	54	38	28	13	16	14	10

Occupation	Mortician	Pharmacist	Sales Manager	Real Est. Manager	Life Ins. Salesman	Advertising Man	Lawyer	Author-Journalist	President Mfg. Co.	Interest Maturity	Occupational Level	Masculinity-Femininity
Standard Score	14	28	18	36	24	41	53	52	31	47	60	41

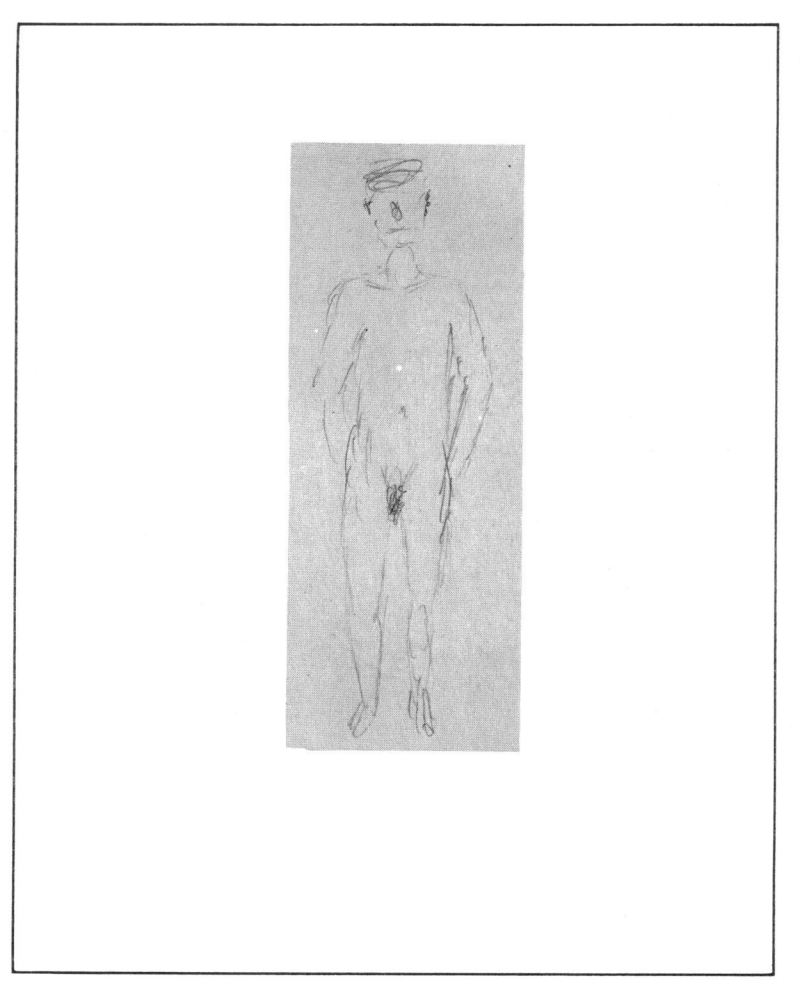

FIGURE-DRAWING CHARACTERISTICS

Structural	Male	Female	Structural	Male	Female	Structural and Graphic	Male	Female	Graphic, Global and Height	Male	Female	Body Proportions	Male	Female
	Both						Both							
Type	0		Omission of Appendages	7	7	Upper and Lower Halves	1	1	Hair Shading	3	3	Head	05	07
Sex Sequence	0		Position of Both Arms	0	1	Four Quarters	4	4	Nudity and Transparency	0	0	Neck	08	08
Posture	1	1	Position of Right Arm	5	4	Relative Size	3		Form	3	3	Shoulders	05	05
Perspective	0	0	Position of Left Arm	5	0	Constant Line Pressure	1	0	Detailing	5	5	Right Arm		05
Vertical Midline	0	0	Position of Legs	4	4	Variable Line Pressure	0	1	Identity and Sex	1	1	Left Arm		04
Bilateral Symmetry	3	3	Relation of Long Axes	1	1	Line Continuity	0	0	Sophistication	3	3	Chest	04	04
Horizontal Midline	0	0	Right and Left Halves	1	1	Body Shading	3	3	Height	06	06	Girth	05	04

GENERAL CHARACTERISTICS OF SUBJECT

IDENTIFICATION

No. C66
Sex M
Marital status S
Age 23 yrs. at
psychological tests

PARENTAL HISTORY

Father
C	H	S	D	O
?	+	-	-	+

Mother
C	H	S	D	O
-	?	-	-	-

PHYSIOLOGICAL AND METABOLIC DATA

	Admission	Initial	Control	Cold pressor change	Exercise change	Smoking change
Systolic pressure	110	128	122	+18	+38	+02
Diastolic pressure	60	65	70	+28	-12	00
Heart rate	84	76	71	-04	+20	-02

Age 24 yrs.
Height 77 in.
Weight 210 lbs.
Overweight +09 %
Ponderal index 12.96
Cholesterol 256 mg. per 100 ml.
Vital capacity 5.7 liters

HABIT SURVEY

Smoking habits: occasional smoker
Age begun 22 yrs.　Inhalation: no
Habits of nervous tension: 6

STRONG VOCATIONAL INTEREST TEST

Occupation	Artist	Psychologist	Architect	Physician	Osteopath	Dentist	Veterinarian	Mathematician	Physicist	Engineer	Chemist	Production Manager
Standard Score	20	42	21	44	42	20	38	15	08	26	29	36

Occupation	Farmer	Aviator	Carpenter	Printer	Math.-Sci. Teacher	Ind. Arts Teacher	Voc. Agric. Teacher	Policeman	Forest Serv. Man	Y.M.C.A. Phys. Dir.	Personnel Director	Public Administrator
Standard Score	32	40	18	40	37	26	43	34	34	38	49	63

Occupation	Y.M.C.A. Secretary	Soc. Sci. H.S. Teacher	City Sch. Sup't.	Social Worker	Minister	Musician Performer	C.P.A.	Senior C.P.A.	Accountant	Office Man	Purchasing Agent	Banker
Standard Score	35	42	33	50	62	36	20	44	23	34	34	24

Occupation	Mortician	Pharmacist	Sales Manager	Real Est. Manager	Life Ins. Salesman	Advertising Man	Lawyer	Author-Journalist	President Mfg. Co.	Interest Maturity	Occupational Level	Masculinity-Femininity
Standard Score	33	42	41	35	31	38	27	31	31	58	55	52

Plate 258   DRAWINGS AT AN INTERMEDIATE LEVEL OF SOPHISTICATION   301

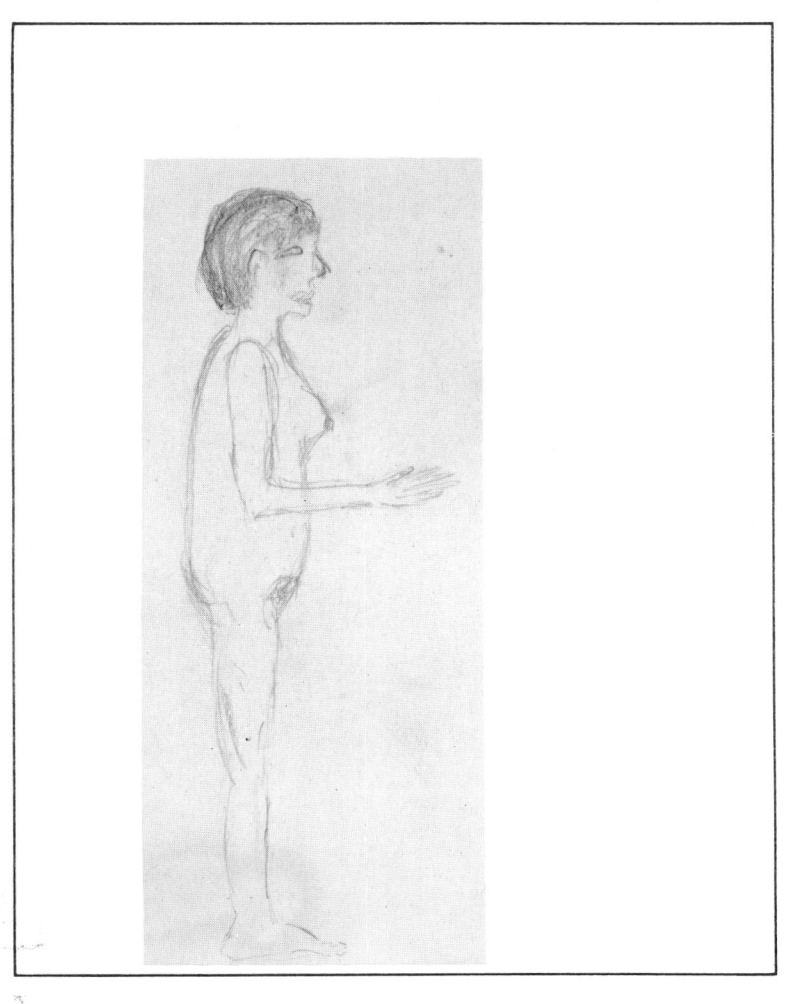
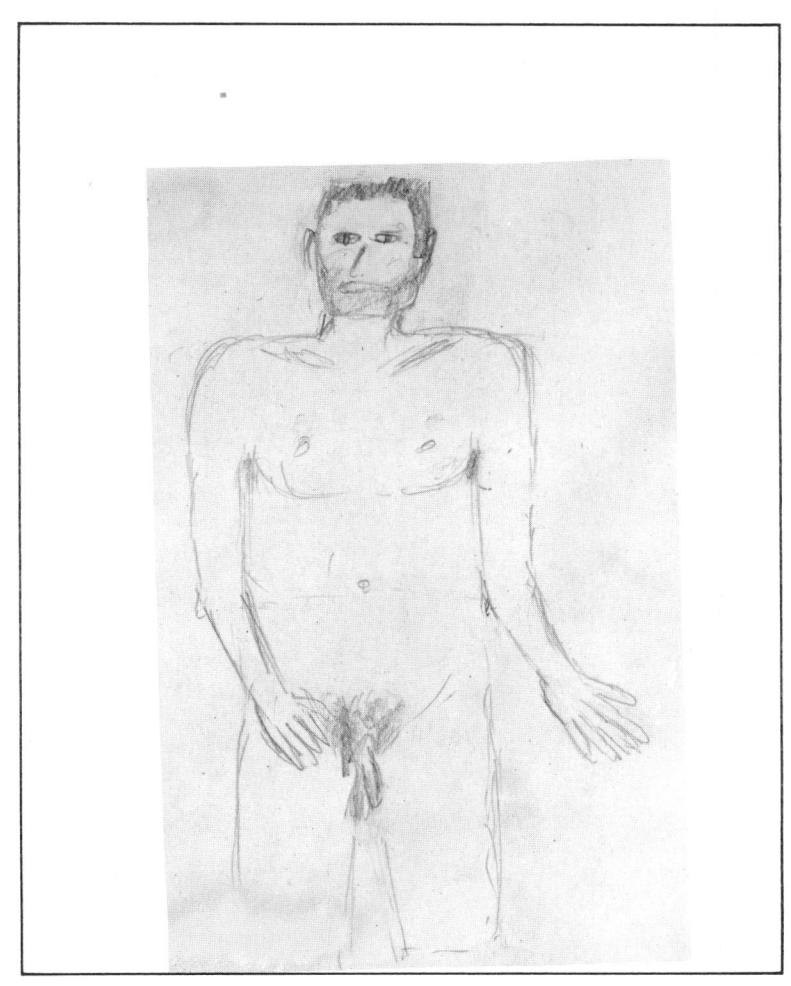

FIGURE-DRAWING CHARACTERISTICS

Structural	Male Female Both		Structural	Male	Female	Structural and Graphic	Male Female Both		Graphic, Global and Height	Male	Female	Body Proportions	Male	Female
Type	0		Omission of Appendages	3	0	Upper and Lower Halves	7	3	Hair Shading	3	3	Head	09	09
Sex Sequence	1		Position of Both Arms	1	2	Four Quarters	4	4	Nudity and Transparency	0	0	Neck	08	08
Posture	0	1	Position of Right Arm	5	4	Relative Size	0		Form	1	3	Shoulders	14	
Perspective	0	2	Position of Left Arm	4	7	Constant Line Pressure	1	1	Detailing	1	3	Right Arm	10	08
Vertical Midline	0	4	Position of Legs	4	1	Variable Line Pressure	0	0	Identity and Sex	1	1	Left Arm	10	
Bilateral Symmetry	3	0	Relation of Long Axes	1	1	Line Continuity	0	0	Sophistication	3	3	Chest	10	07
Horizontal Midline	0	0	Right and Left Halves	1	2	Body Shading	3	3	Height		08	Girth	15	11

GENERAL CHARACTERISTICS OF SUBJECT

IDENTIFICATION
No. D26
Sex M
Marital status S
Age 23 yrs. at
psychological tests

PARENTAL HISTORY				
Father				
C	H	S	D	O
?	-	-	-	?
Mother				
C	H	S	D	O
-	-	-	-	-

PHYSIOLOGICAL AND METABOLIC DATA

	Admission	Initial	Control	Cold pressor change	Exercise change	Smoking change
Systolic pressure	116	120	114	-02	+16	00
Diastolic pressure	70	82	78	+10	-18	+02
Heart rate	84	84	88	+16	+15	+12

Age 23 yrs.	Height 75 in.	Ponderal index 13.71
	Weight 164 lbs.	Cholesterol 420 mg. per 100 ml.
	Overweight -09 %	Vital capacity 5.5 liters

HABIT SURVEY
Smoking habits: occasional smoker
Age begun 17 yrs.   Inhalation: yes
Habits of nervous tension: 5, 6, 9, 10, 16,
19

STRONG VOCATIONAL INTEREST TEST

Occupation	Artist	Psychologist	Architect	Physician	Osteopath	Dentist	Veterinarian	Mathematician	Physicist	Engineer	Chemist	Production Manager
Standard Score	21	32	31	59	59	42	38	17	19	38	34	40

Occupation	Farmer	Aviator	Carpenter	Printer	Math.-Sci. Teacher	Ind. Arts Teacher	Voc. Agric. Teacher	Policeman	Forest Serv. Man	Y.M.C.A. Phys. Dir.	Personnel Director	Public Administrator
Standard Score	40	49	40	43	50	45	46	48	43	51	42	51

Occupation	Y.M.C.A. Secretary	Soc. Sci. H.S. Teacher	City Sch. Sup't.	Social Worker	Minister	Musician Performer	C.P.A.	Senior C.P.A.	Accountant	Office Man	Purchasing Agent	Banker
Standard Score	34	36	25	39	63	43	10	44	29	37	28	25

Occupation	Mortician	Pharmacist	Sales Manager	Real Est. Manager	Life Ins. Salesman	Advertising Man	Lawyer	Author-Journalist	President Mfg. Co.	Interest Maturity	Occupational Level	Masculinity-Femininity
Standard Score	37	34	26	31	29	20	20	19	25	63	49	51

FIGURE-DRAWING CHARACTERISTICS

Structural	Male Female Both	Structural	Male	Female	Structural and Graphic	Male Female Both	Graphic, Global and Height	Male	Female	Body Proportions	Male	Female
Type	0	Omission of Appendages	0	0	Upper and Lower Halves	2	2	Hair Shading	7	3	Head	04	04
Sex Sequence	0	Position of Both Arms	4	4	Four Quarters	0	0	Nudity and Transparency	7	7	Neck	02	01
Posture	1	1	Position of Right Arm	7	7	Relative Size	2		Form	3	3	Shoulders		
Perspective	2	2	Position of Left Arm	0	0	Constant Line Pressure	1	0	Detailing	3	3	Right Arm		
Vertical Midline	4	4	Position of Legs	1	1	Variable Line Pressure	0	3	Identity and Sex	1	3	Left Arm	02	01
Bilateral Symmetry	0	0	Relation of Long Axes	1	1	Line Continuity	1	1	Sophistication	3	3	Chest	04	04
Horizontal Midline	4	4	Right and Left Halves	2	2	Body Shading	2	0	Height	02	02	Girth	04	04

GENERAL CHARACTERISTICS OF SUBJECT

IDENTIFICATION

No. E16
Sex M
Marital status S
Age 23 yrs. at
psychological tests

PARENTAL HISTORY

Father
C H S D O
? - - - -
Mother
C H S D O
- - - - +

PHYSIOLOGICAL AND METABOLIC DATA

	Admission	Initial	Control	Cold pressor change	Exercise change	Smoking change
Systolic pressure	100	117	115	+13	+23	
Diastolic pressure	60	70	72	+18	-11	
Heart rate	70	72	64	00	+30	

Age 22 yrs.
Height 74 in.
Weight 173 lbs.
Overweight 00 %
Ponderal index 13.28
Cholesterol 200 mg. per 100 ml.
Vital capacity 5.4 liters

HABIT SURVEY

Smoking habits: nonsmoker
Age begun   yrs.   Inhalation:
Habits of nervous tension: 3, 4, 5, 6, 9, 14, 19, 21, 22

STRONG VOCATIONAL INTEREST TEST

Occupation	Artist	Psychologist	Architect	Physician	Osteopath	Dentist	Veterinarian	Mathematician	Physicist	Engineer	Chemist	Production Manager
Standard Score	33	40	30	43	35	29	13	28	12	14	26	18

Occupation	Farmer	Aviator	Carpenter	Printer	Math.-Sci. Teacher	Ind. Arts Teacher	Voc. Agric. Teacher	Policeman	Forest Serv. Man	Y.M.C.A. Phys. Dir.	Personnel Director	Public Administrator
Standard Score	18	17	13	43	35	06	13	26	13	36	28	37

Occupation	Y.M.C.A. Secretary	Soc. Sci. H.S. Teacher	City Sch. Sup't.	Social Worker	Minister	Musician Performer	C.P.A.	Senior C.P.A.	Accountant	Office Man	Purchasing Agent	Banker
Standard Score	34	48	32	50	64	53	40	41	30	41	17	30

Occupation	Mortician	Pharmacist	Sales Manager	Real Est. Manager	Life Ins. Salesman	Advertising Man	Lawyer	Author-Journalist	President Mfg. Co.	Interest Maturity	Occupational Level	Masculinity-Femininity
Standard Score	18	29	21	31	30	39	42	42	17	57	54	29

FIGURE-DRAWING CHARACTERISTICS

Structural	Male Female Both	Structural	Male	Female	Structural and Graphic	Male Female Both		Graphic, Global and Height	Male	Female	Body Proportions	Male	Female
Type	0	Omission of Appendages	0	3	Upper and Lower Halves	0	0	Hair Shading	3	3	Head	08	08
Sex Sequence	0	Position of Both Arms	1	2	Four Quarters	4	4	Nudity and Transparency	7	7	Neck	07	12
Posture	1 0	Position of Right Arm	2	4	Relative Size	4		Form	3	3	Shoulders	06	
Perspective	0 2	Position of Left Arm	4	7	Constant Line Pressure	0	0	Detailing	3	3	Right Arm	04	06
Vertical Midline	3 4	Position of Legs	5	0	Variable Line Pressure	4	5	Identity and Sex	1	1	Left Arm	06	
Bilateral Symmetry	2 0	Relation of Long Axes	1	1	Line Continuity	2	4	Sophistication	3	3	Chest	08	06
Horizontal Midline	4 0	Right and Left Halves	1	2	Body Shading	4	3	Height	07		Girth	09	08

GENERAL CHARACTERISTICS OF SUBJECT

IDENTIFICATION
No. E63
Sex M
Marital status S
Age 22 yrs. at
psychological tests

PARENTAL HISTORY				
Father				
C	H	S	D	O
?	-	-	-	-
Mother				
C	H	S	D	O
-	-	-	-	-

PHYSIOLOGICAL AND METABOLIC DATA

	Admission	Initial	Control	Cold pressor change	Exercise change	Smoking change
Systolic pressure	130	118	118	+14	+24	+04
Diastolic pressure	80	70	70	+25	-05	+07
Heart rate	68	72	62	00	+35	+04

Age 22 yrs.   Height 72 in.   Weight 168 lbs.   Overweight +03 %

Ponderal index 13.04   Cholesterol 296 mg. per 100 ml.   Vital capacity 4.6 liters

HABIT SURVEY
Smoking habits: nonsmoker
Age begun   yrs.   Inhalation:
Habits of nervous tension: 5, 9, 10, 22

STRONG VOCATIONAL INTEREST TEST

Occupation	Artist	Psychologist	Architect	Physician	Osteopath	Dentist	Veterinarian	Mathematician	Physicist	Engineer	Chemist	Production Manager
Standard Score	29	53	32	49	35	27	22	28	18	25	29	20

Occupation	Farmer	Aviator	Carpenter	Printer	Math.-Sci. Teacher	Ind. Arts Teacher	Voc. Agric. Teacher	Policeman	Forest Serv. Man	Y.M.C.A. Phys. Dir.	Personnel Director	Public Administrator
Standard Score	24	35	07	36	42	15	29	25	15	37	41	42

Occupation	Y.M.C.A. Secretary	Soc. Sci. H.S. Teacher	City Sch. Sup't.	Social Worker	Minister	Musician Performer	C.P.A.	Senior C.P.A.	Accountant	Office Man	Purchasing Agent	Banker
Standard Score	31	42	37	51	64	53	37	40	19	33	21	21

Occupation	Mortician	Pharmacist	Sales Manager	Real Est. Manager	Life Ins. Salesman	Advertising Man	Lawyer	Author-Journalist	President Mfg. Co.	Interest Maturity	Occupational Level	Masculinity-Femininity
Standard Score	19	41	40	40	36	44	40	36	29	58	58	47

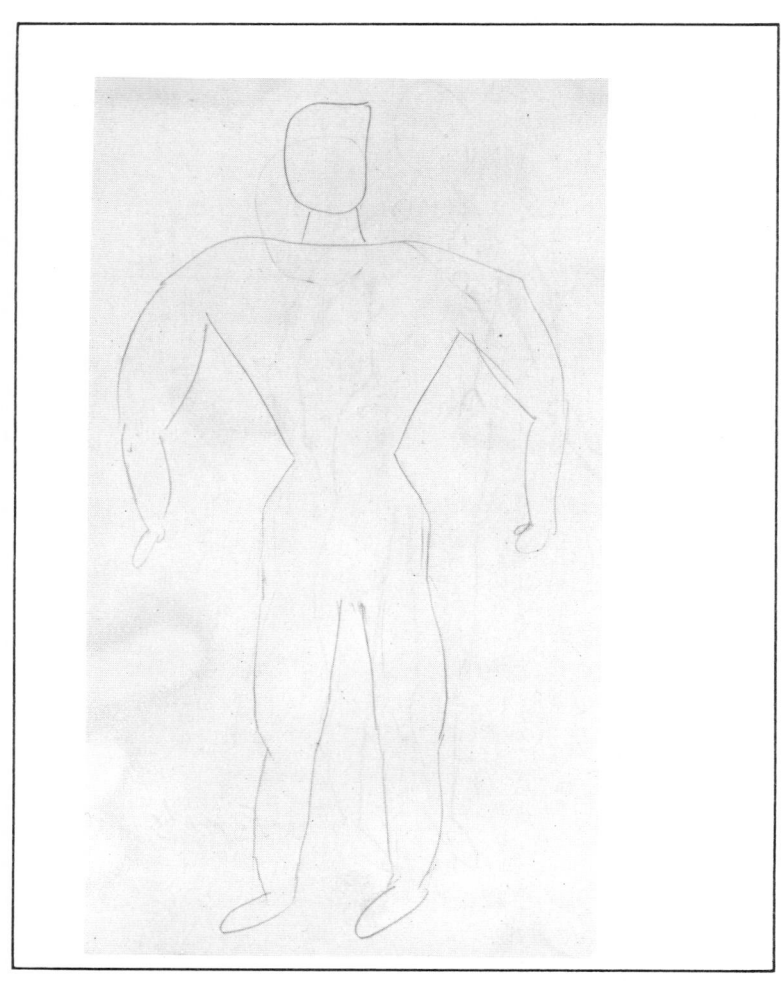

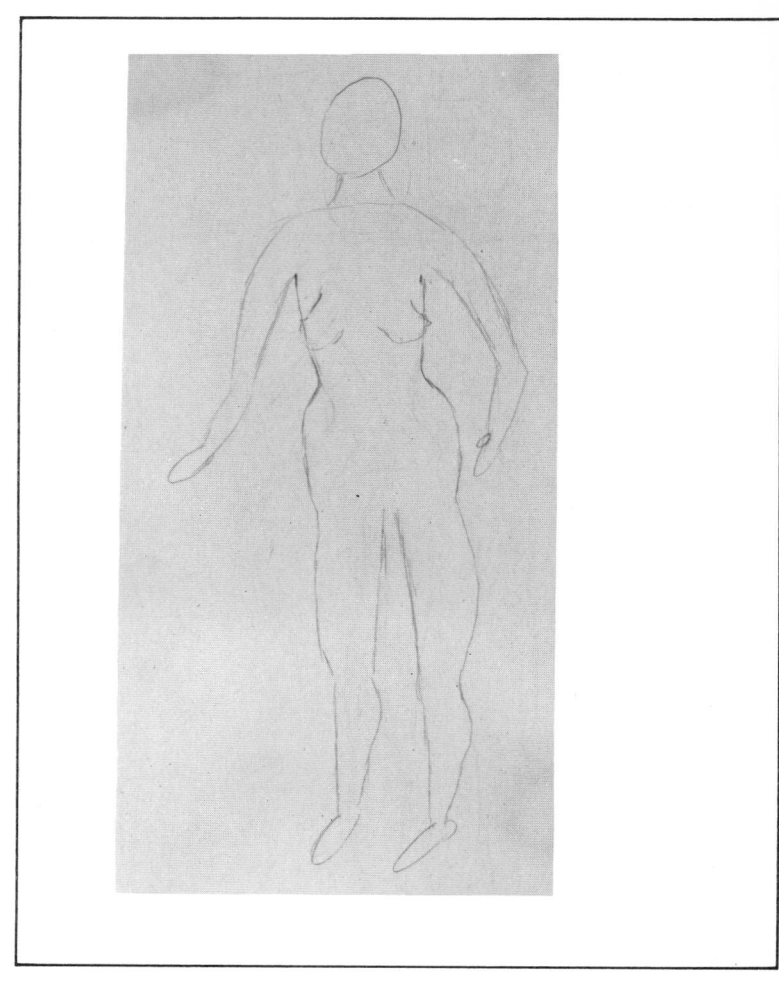

FIGURE-DRAWING CHARACTERISTICS

Structural	Male Female Both		Structural	Male	Female	Structural and Graphic	Male Female Both		Graphic, Global and Height	Male	Female	Body Proportions	Male	Female
Type	0		Omission of Appendages	0	0	Upper and Lower Halves	0	0	Hair Shading	0	0	Head	08	08
Sex Sequence	0		Position of Both Arms	0	1	Four Quarters	4	4	Nudity and Transparency	0	0	Neck	10	10
Posture	1	1	Position of Right Arm	2	2	Relative Size	1		Form	3	3	Shoulders	10	07
Perspective	0	0	Position of Left Arm	2	5	Constant Line Pressure	1	1	Detailing	5	5	Right Arm	08	06
Vertical Midline	0	0	Position of Legs	5	4	Variable Line Pressure	0	0	Identity and Sex	1	1	Left Arm	07	06
Bilateral Symmetry	3	3	Relation of Long Axes	1	1	Line Continuity	3	0	Sophistication	3	3	Chest	10	06
Horizontal Midline	0	0	Right and Left Halves	1	1	Body Shading	0	0	Height	09	08	Girth	06	07

GENERAL CHARACTERISTICS OF SUBJECT

IDENTIFICATION
No. E70
Sex M
Marital status S
Age 22 yrs. at
psychological tests

PARENTAL HISTORY
Father
C H S D O
? - - - -
Mother
C H S D O
- - - - -

PHYSIOLOGICAL AND METABOLIC DATA

	Admission	Initial	Control	Cold pressor change	Exercise change	Smoking change
Systolic pressure	130	115	114	+10	+38	
Diastolic pressure	80	65	66	-04	-08	
Heart rate	72	60	62	+04	+06	

Age 22 yrs.	Height 72 in.	Ponderal index 13.48
	Weight 152 lbs.	Cholesterol 176 mg. per 100 ml.
	Overweight -07 %	Vital capacity 5.1 liters

HABIT SURVEY

Smoking habits: pipe and cigar smoker

Age begun 18 yrs.   Inhalation: no

Habits of nervous tension: 8, 9, 11, 18, 19, 23

STRONG VOCATIONAL INTEREST TEST

Occupation	Artist	Psychologist	Architect	Physician	Osteopath	Dentist	Veterinarian	Mathematician	Physicist	Engineer	Chemist	Production Manager
Standard Score	45	36	42	55	40	50	26	42	42	48	48	35

Occupation	Farmer	Aviator	Carpenter	Printer	Math.-Sci. Teacher	Ind. Arts Teacher	Voc. Agric. Teacher	Policeman	Forest Serv. Man	Y.M.C.A. Phys. Dir.	Personnel Director	Public Administrator
Standard Score	42	42	31	35	37	24	20	30	39	17	14	33

Occupation	Y.M.C.A. Secretary	Soc. Sci. H.S. Teacher	City Sch. Sup't.	Social Worker	Minister	Musician Performer	C.P.A.	Senior C.P.A.	Accountant	Office Man	Purchasing Agent	Banker
Standard Score	12	19	19	20	64	37	21	23	09	16	15	22

Occupation	Mortician	Pharmacist	Sales Manager	Real Est. Manager	Life Ins. Salesman	Advertising Man	Lawyer	Author-Journalist	President Mfg. Co.	Interest Maturity	Occupational Level	Masculinity-Femininity
Standard Score	10	19	18	28	19	32	36	44	36	45	58	53

Plate 262   DRAWINGS AT AN INTERMEDIATE LEVEL OF SOPHISTICATION   305

FIGURE-DRAWING CHARACTERISTICS

Structural	Male	Female	Structural	Male	Female	Structural and Graphic	Male	Female	Graphic, Global and Height	Male	Female	Body Proportions	Male	Female
	Both						Both							
Type	0		Omission of Appendages	0	6	Upper and Lower Halves	2	2	Hair Shading	3	3	Head	04	04
Sex Sequence	2		Position of Both Arms	2	0	Four Quarters	0	0	Nudity and Transparency	7	3	Neck	06	06
Posture	2	1	Position of Right Arm	6	5	Relative Size	2		Form	3	3	Shoulders		
Perspective	1	1	Position of Left Arm	7	5	Constant Line Pressure	5	5	Detailing	3	3	Right Arm	04	
Vertical Midline	4	4	Position of Legs	8	5	Variable Line Pressure	0	0	Identity and Sex	1	1	Left Arm		
Bilateral Symmetry	0	0	Relation of Long Axes	3	1	Line Continuity	2	2	Sophistication	3	3	Chest		
Horizontal Midline	4	4	Right and Left Halves	2	2	Body Shading	0	4	Height	04	04	Girth		

GENERAL CHARACTERISTICS OF SUBJECT

IDENTIFICATION
No. 238
Sex M
Marital status M
Age 24 yrs. at
psychological tests

PARENTAL HISTORY				
Father				
C	H	S	D	O
-	-	-	-	-
Mother				
C	H	S	D	O
?	+	-	-	+

PHYSIOLOGICAL AND METABOLIC DATA

	Admission	Initial	Control	Cold pressor change	Exercise change	Smoking change
Systolic pressure	150	130	100	+40	+50	
Diastolic pressure	82	80	50	+50	+20	
Heart rate	86	72	71	+04	+38	

Age 24 yrs.	Height 71 in.	Ponderal index 13.30
	Weight 152 lbs.	Cholesterol 230 mg. per 100 ml.
	Overweight -05 %	Vital capacity 5.4 liters

HABIT SURVEY

Smoking habits: nonsmoker

Age begun   yrs.   Inhalation:

Habits of nervous tension: 6, 18, 23, 25

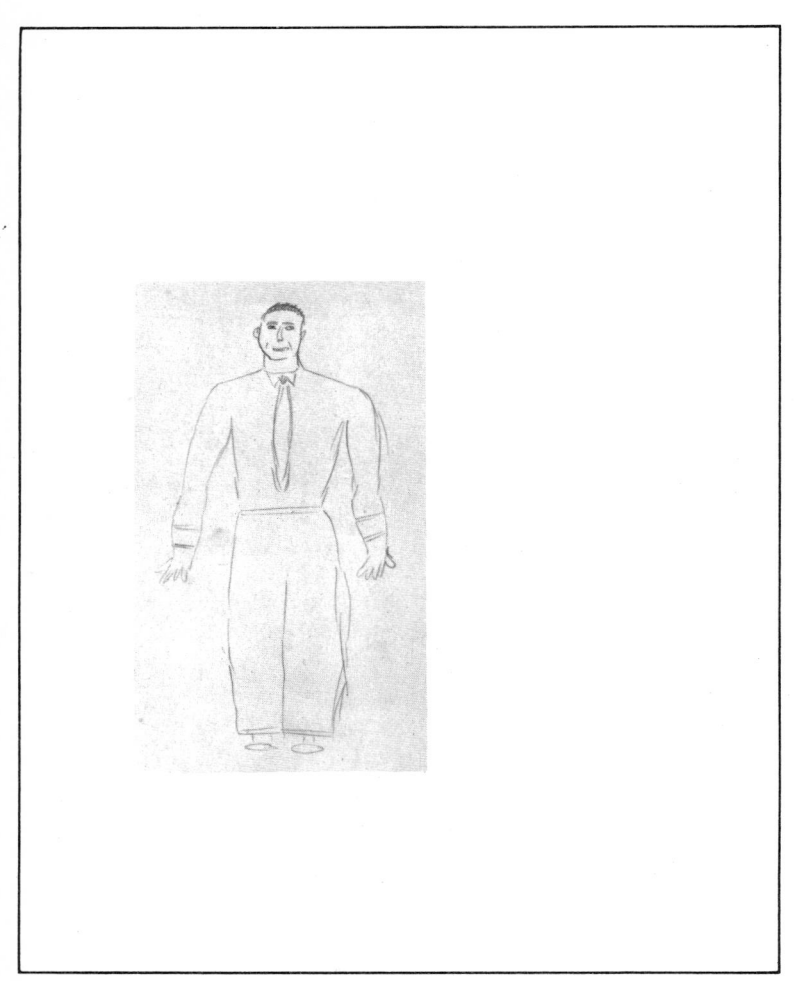

FIGURE-DRAWING CHARACTERISTICS

Structural	Male Female Both	Structural	Male	Female	Structural and Graphic	Male Female Both		Graphic, Global and Height	Male	Female	Body Proportions	Male	Female
Type	0	Omission of Appendages	0	0	Upper and Lower Halves	3	3	Hair Shading	3	5	Head	04	08
Sex Sequence	0	Position of Both Arms	1	2	Four Quarters	4	4	Nudity and Transparency	7	7	Neck	06	12
Posture	1	1	Position of Right Arm	2	4	Relative Size	4		Form	1	3	Shoulders	06	
Perspective	0	2	Position of Left Arm	0	7	Constant Line Pressure	1	0	Detailing	3	3	Right Arm	04	06
Vertical Midline	3	4	Position of Legs	2	4	Variable Line Pressure	0	3	Identity and Sex	1	1	Left Arm	04	
Bilateral Symmetry	2	0	Relation of Long Axes	1	1	Line Continuity	0	3	Sophistication	3	3	Chest	05	06
Horizontal Midline	4	4	Right and Left Halves	2	2	Body Shading	0	0	Height	04	06	Girth	05	04

GENERAL CHARACTERISTICS OF SUBJECT

IDENTIFICATION
No. 533
Sex M
Marital status S
Age 22 yrs. at
psychological tests

PARENTAL HISTORY
Father
C   H   S   D   O
–   –   –   –   –
Mother
C   H   S   D   O
?   –   –   –   +

PHYSIOLOGICAL AND METABOLIC DATA

	Admission	Initial	Control	Cold pressor change	Exercise change	Smoking change
Systolic pressure	106	112	106	+15	+34	+08
Diastolic pressure	60	65	68	+12	-02	+14
Heart rate	72	68	69	+22	+17	+26

Age 20 yrs.	Height	74 in.	Ponderal index	13.28
	Weight	173 lbs.	Cholesterol	167 mg. per 100 ml.
	Overweight +01 %		Vital capacity	6.0 liters

HABIT SURVEY

Smoking habits: light cigarette smoker

Age begun 17 yrs.   Inhalation: yes

Habits of nervous tension: 2, 4, 5, 6, 9, 11, 14, 17, 18, 24

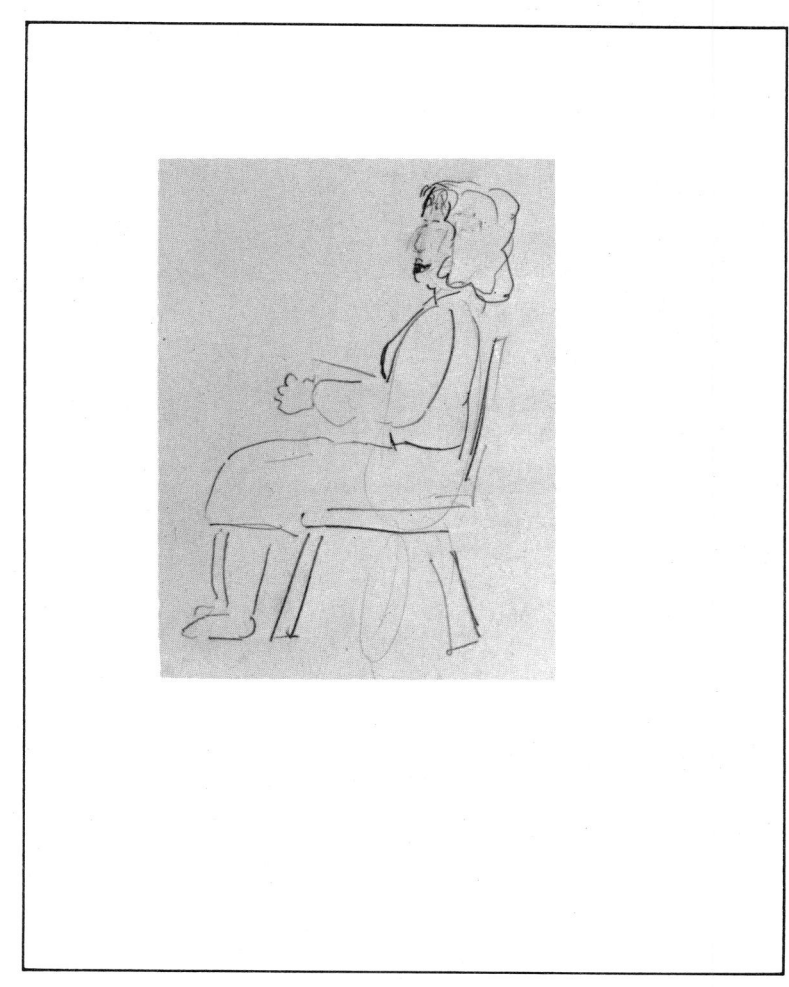

FIGURE-DRAWING CHARACTERISTICS

Structural	Male Female Both		Structural	Male	Female	Structural and Graphic	Male Female Both		Graphic, Global and Height	Male	Female	Body Proportions	Male	Female
Type	0		Omission of Appendages	0	0	Upper and Lower Halves	3	1	Hair Shading	7	5	Head	09	08
Sex Sequence	0		Position of Both Arms	4	4	Four Quarters	4	4	Nudity and Transparency	7	7	Neck	07	05
Posture	1	3	Position of Right Arm	7	7	Relative Size	5		Form	1	3	Shoulders		
Perspective	1	2	Position of Left Arm	0	4	Constant Line Pressure	0	0	Detailing	3	5	Right Arm		
Vertical Midline	7	4	Position of Legs	4	1	Variable Line Pressure	2	2	Identity and Sex	1	1	Left Arm	06	06
Bilateral Symmetry	0	0	Relation of Long Axes	1	0	Line Continuity	1	1	Sophistication	3	3	Chest		06
Horizontal Midline	6	4	Right and Left Halves	3	1	Body Shading	2	0	Height	06		Girth		07

GENERAL CHARACTERISTICS OF SUBJECT

IDENTIFICATION
No. 558
Sex M
Marital status M
Age 27 yrs. at
psychological tests

PARENTAL HISTORY				
Father				
C	H	S	D	O
–	–	–	–	+
Mother				
C	H	S	D	O
?	–	?	–	–

PHYSIOLOGICAL AND METABOLIC DATA

	Admission	Initial	Control	Cold pressor change	Exercise change	Smoking change
Systolic pressure	120	112	110	+10	+20	
Diastolic pressure	65	76	76	+18	+02	
Heart rate	70	60	61	+12	+12	

Age 25 yrs.	Height 69 in.	Ponderal index 12.53		
	Weight 167 lbs.	Cholesterol 217 mg. per 100 ml.		
	Overweight +09 %	Vital capacity 5.5 liters		

HABIT SURVEY
Smoking habits: nonsmoker
Age begun yrs. Inhalation:
Habits of nervous tension: 2, 4, 5, 6, 8, 16,
18, 23, 25

FIGURE-DRAWING CHARACTERISTICS

Structural	Male Female Both		Structural	Male	Female	Structural and Graphic	Male Female Both		Graphic, Global and Height	Male	Female	Body Proportions	Male	Female
Type	0		Omission of Appendages	7	7	Upper and Lower Halves	0	1	Hair Shading	7	3	Head	06	05
Sex Sequence	2		Position of Both Arms	6	0	Four Quarters	4	4	Nudity and Transparency	7	7	Neck	10	06
Posture	1	1	Position of Right Arm	8	5	Relative Size	2		Form	3	3	Shoulders	05	05
Perspective	0	0	Position of Left Arm	8	5	Constant Line Pressure	1	1	Detailing	3	3	Right Arm		
Vertical Midline	3	3	Position of Legs	6	6	Variable Line Pressure	0	0	Identity and Sex	1	1	Left Arm		
Bilateral Symmetry	3	3	Relation of Long Axes	1	1	Line Continuity	0	0	Sophistication	3	3	Chest	05	04
Horizontal Midline	4	4	Right and Left Halves	9	9	Body Shading	6	6	Height	04	04	Girth	04	03

GENERAL CHARACTERISTICS OF SUBJECT

IDENTIFICATION
No. 563
Sex F
Marital status S
Age 25 yrs. at
psychological tests

PARENTAL HISTORY				
Father				
C	H	S	D	O
-	+	+	-	+
Mother				
C	H	S	D	O
?	-	-	-	-

PHYSIOLOGICAL AND METABOLIC DATA

	Admission	Initial	Control	Cold pressor change	Exercise change	Smoking change
Systolic pressure	110	126	110	+10	+45	
Diastolic pressure	72	76	78	+12	-10	
Heart rate	80	96	94	+06	+36	

Age 23 yrs.	Height	70	in.	Ponderal index	12.64	
	Weight	170	lbs.	Cholesterol	177	mg. per 100 ml.
	Overweight +13 %			Vital capacity	4.2	liters

HABIT SURVEY

Smoking habits: heavy cigarette smoker

Age begun 20 yrs.   Inhalation: yes

Habits of nervous tension: 4, 5

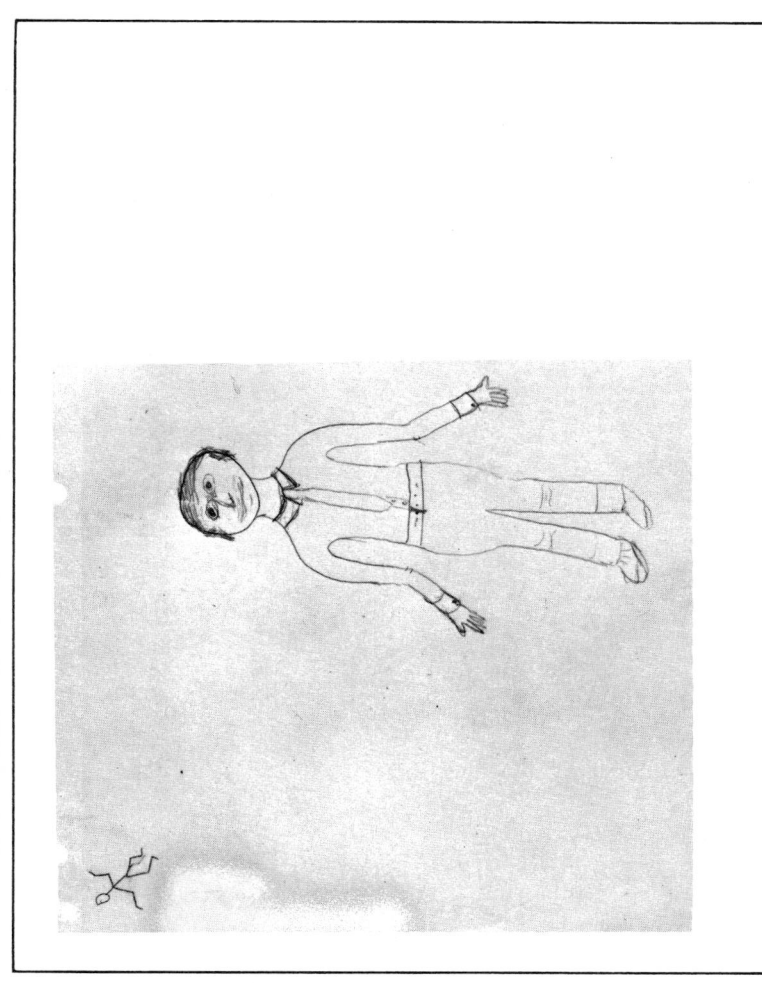

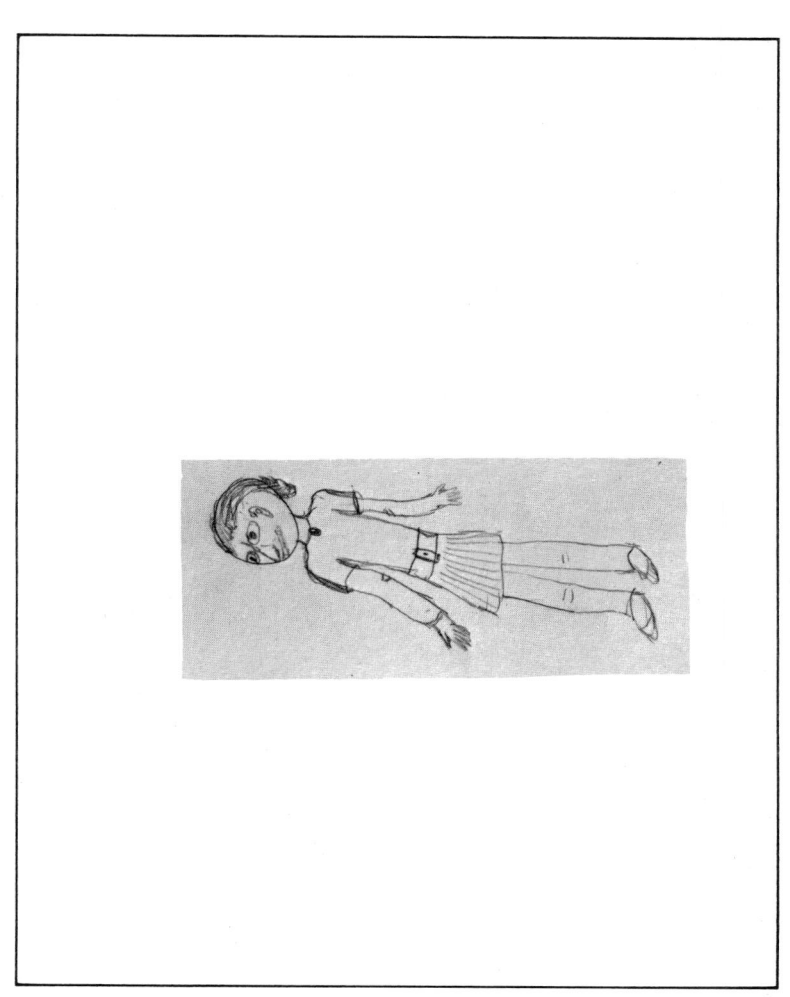

FIGURE-DRAWING CHARACTERISTICS

Structural	Male Female Both	Structural	Male	Female	Structural and Graphic	Male Female Both		Graphic, Global and Height	Male	Female	Body Proportions	Male	Female
Type	0	Omission of Appendages	0	0	Upper and Lower Halves	0	3	Hair Shading	2	2	Head	06	06
Sex Sequence	2	Position of Both Arms	0	0	Four Quarters	4	4	Nudity and Transparency	7	6	Neck	08	03
Posture	1 1	Position of Right Arm	3	4	Relative Size	0		Form	3	3	Shoulders	05	03
Perspective	0 9	Position of Left Arm	3	4	Constant Line Pressure	0	0	Detailing	3	3	Right Arm	04	04
Vertical Midline	3 0	Position of Legs	4	4	Variable Line Pressure	1	1	Identity and Sex	1	1	Left Arm	04	02
Bilateral Symmetry	3 2	Relation of Long Axes	2	2	Line Continuity	2	1	Sophistication	3	3	Chest	03	02
Horizontal Midline	4 4	Right and Left Halves	0	1	Body Shading	2	3	Height	04	04	Girth	05	03

GENERAL CHARACTERISTICS OF SUBJECT

IDENTIFICATION
No. 572
Sex M
Marital status   S
Age 22 yrs. at
psychological tests

PARENTAL HISTORY
Father
C H S D O
- - - - -
Mother
C H S D O
? - - - -

PHYSIOLOGICAL AND METABOLIC DATA

	Admission	Initial	Control	Cold pressor change	Exercise change	Smoking change
Systolic pressure	118	102	104	+15	+36	
Diastolic pressure	60	64	60	+04	+10	
Heart rate	80	76	69	+10	+46	

Age 21 yrs.

Height 70 in.
Weight 150 lbs.
Overweight -02 %

Ponderal index 13.18
Cholesterol 185 mg. per 100 ml.
Vital capacity 4.6 liters

HABIT SURVEY
Smoking habits: nonsmoker
Age begun   yrs.   Inhalation:
Habits of nervous tension: 4, 5, 6, 9, 11, 14, 23

FIGURE-DRAWING CHARACTERISTICS

Structural	Male Female Both	Structural	Male	Female	Structural and Graphic	Male Female Both	Graphic, Global and Height	Male	Female	Body Proportions	Male	Female
Type	0	Omission of Appendages	0	0	Upper and Lower Halves	3 3	Hair Shading	3	3	Head	05	05
Sex Sequence	0	Position of Both Arms	0	0	Four Quarters	4 4	Nudity and Transparency	7	7	Neck	08	06
Posture	1 1	Position of Right Arm	0	0	Relative Size	2	Form	3	3	Shoulders	07	05
Perspective	0 0	Position of Left Arm	0	0	Constant Line Pressure	0 0	Detailing	3	3	Right Arm	06	04
Vertical Midline	3 0	Position of Legs	5	4	Variable Line Pressure	4 5	Identity and Sex	1	1	Left Arm	06	04
Bilateral Symmetry	4 4	Relation of Long Axes	1	1	Line Continuity	2 2	Sophistication	3	3	Chest	05	04
Horizontal Midline	4 4	Right and Left Halves	1	1	Body Shading	2 1	Height	06	06	Girth	06	04

GENERAL CHARACTERISTICS OF SUBJECT

IDENTIFICATION	PARENTAL HISTORY
No. F73	Father
Sex M	C H S D O
Marital status S	- - - - -
Age 24 yrs. at	Mother
psychological tests	C H S D O
	? + - - +

PHYSIOLOGICAL AND METABOLIC DATA

	Admission	Initial	Control	Cold pressor change	Exercise change	Smoking change
Systolic pressure	160	120	108	+18	+42	+08
Diastolic pressure	84	78	78	+26	+22	+13
Heart rate	76	88	94	+04	+24	+20

Age 22 yrs.	Height	74 in.	Ponderal index 13.26
	Weight	174 lbs.	Cholesterol 190 mg. per 100 ml.
	Overweight +01 %		Vital capacity liters

HABIT SURVEY

Smoking habits: heavy cigarette smoker

Age begun 18 yrs.   Inhalation: yes

Habits of nervous tension: 4, 6, 21

STRONG VOCATIONAL INTEREST TEST

Occupation	Artist	Psychologist	Architect	Physician	Osteopath	Dentist	Veterinarian	Mathematician	Physicist	Engineer	Chemist	Production Manager
Standard Score	11	33	13	42	38	21	29	19	09	25	32	38

Occupation	Farmer	Aviator	Carpenter	Printer	Math.-Sci. Teacher	Ind. Arts Teacher	Voc. Agric. Teacher	Policeman	Forest Serv. Man	Y.M.C.A. Phys. Dir.	Personnel Director	Public Administrator
Standard Score	38	35	18	38	48	21	28	37	27	30	43	48

Occupation	Y.M.C.A. Secretary	Soc. Sci. H.S. Teacher	City Sch. Sup't.	Social Worker	Minister	Musician Performer	C.P.A.	Senior C.P.A.	Accountant	Office Man	Purchasing Agent	Banker
Standard Score	33	43	33	38	58	26	30	51	45	47	23	35

Occupation	Mortician	Pharmacist	Sales Manager	Real Est. Manager	Life Ins. Salesman	Advertising Man	Lawyer	Author-Journalist	President Mfg. Co.	Interest Maturity	Occupational Level	Masculinity-Femininity
Standard Score	19	26	19	26	19	20	25	20	18	62	48	51

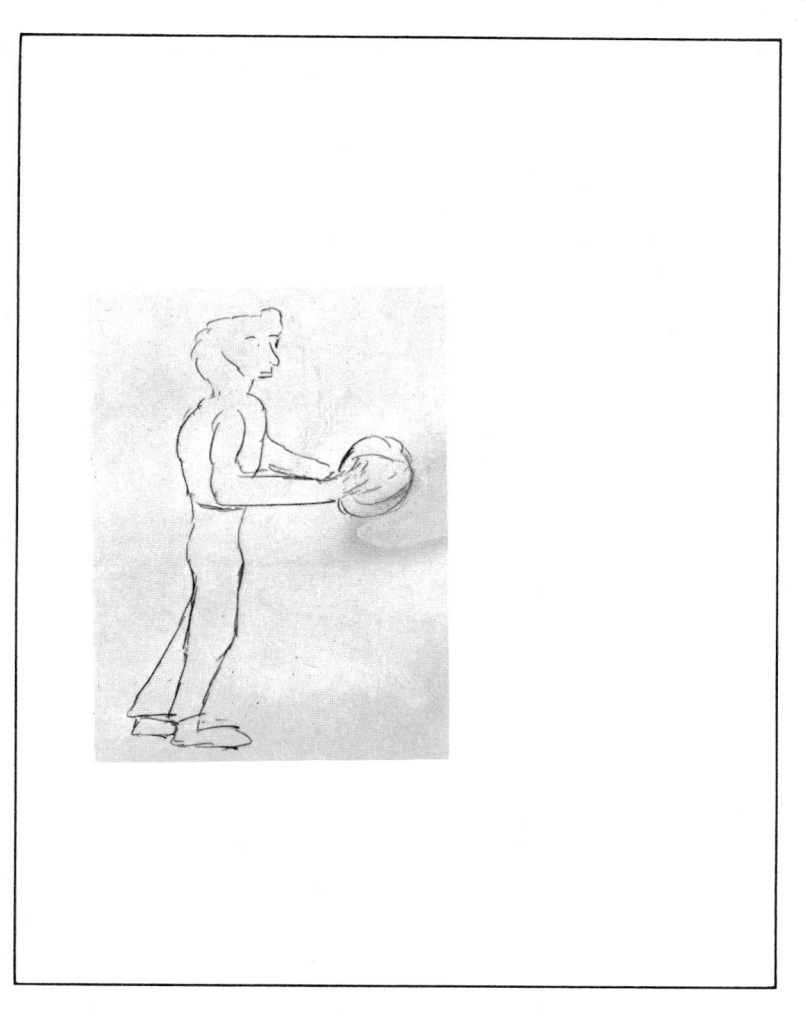

FIGURE-DRAWING CHARACTERISTICS

Structural	Male Female Both	Structural	Male	Female	Structural and Graphic	Male Female Both		Graphic, Global and Height	Male	Female	Body Proportions	Male	Female
Type	0	Omission of Appendages	0	0	Upper and Lower Halves	3	0	Hair Shading	5	5	Head	05	05
Sex Sequence	0	Position of Both Arms	2	2	Four Quarters	4	4	Nudity and Transparency	3	7	Neck	04	04
Posture	1 1	Position of Right Arm	4	4	Relative Size	2		Form	3	3	Shoulders		
Perspective	2 2	Position of Left Arm	7	7	Constant Line Pressure	0	0	Detailing	3	3	Right Arm	05	02
Vertical Midline	4 4	Position of Legs	1	1	Variable Line Pressure	2	5	Identity and Sex	1	1	Left Arm		
Bilateral Symmetry	0 0	Relation of Long Axes	1	1	Line Continuity	0	2	Sophistication	3	3	Chest	06	03
Horizontal Midline	4 4	Right and Left Halves	2	1	Body Shading	0	0	Height	04	04	Girth	04	03

GENERAL CHARACTERISTICS OF SUBJECT

IDENTIFICATION

No. G35
Sex M
Marital status M
Age 23 yrs. at
psychological tests

PARENTAL HISTORY

Father
C H S D O
- - - - -
Mother
C H S D O
? - - - -

PHYSIOLOGICAL AND METABOLIC DATA

	Admission	Initial	Control	Cold pressor change	Exercise change	Smoking change
Systolic pressure	110	120	112	+06	+48	+08
Diastolic pressure	80	68	72	+06	+06	+05
Heart rate	86	60	67	-06	+13	-08

Age 22 yrs.

Height 74 in.
Weight 175 lbs.
Overweight +01 %

Ponderal index 13.24
Cholesterol 230 mg. per 100 ml.
Vital capacity liters

HABIT SURVEY

Smoking habits: occasional smoker
Age begun 21 yrs.   Inhalation: no
Habits of nervous tension: 5, 6, 11, 16, 25

STRONG VOCATIONAL INTEREST TEST

Occupation	Artist	Psychologist	Architect	Physician	Osteopath	Dentist	Veterinarian	Mathematician	Physicist	Engineer	Chemist	Production Manager
Standard Score	35	41	34	52	38	33	21	30	24	27	35	25

Occupation	Farmer	Aviator	Carpenter	Printer	Math.-Sci. Teacher	Ind. Arts Teacher	Voc. Agric. Teacher	Policeman	Forest Serv. Man	Y.M.C.A. Phys. Dir.	Personnel Director	Public Administrator
Standard Score	28	24	02	22	33	-08	18	20	27	36	34	39

Occupation	Y.M.C.A. Secretary	Soc. Sci. H.S. Teacher	City Sch. Sup't.	Social Worker	Minister	Musician Performer	C.P.A.	Senior C.P.A.	Accountant	Office Man	Purchasing Agent	Banker
Standard Score	31	28	37	33	59	40	36	33	13	18	12	15

Occupation	Mortician	Pharmacist	Sales Manager	Real Est. Manager	Life Ins. Salesman	Advertising Man	Lawyer	Author-Journalist	President Mfg. Co.	Interest Maturity	Occupational Level	Masculinity-Femininity
Standard Score	07	16	32	30	32	38	45	41	25	56	66	41

FIGURE-DRAWING CHARACTERISTICS

Structural	Male Female Both	Structural	Male	Female	Structural and Graphic	Male Female Both		Graphic, Global and Height	Male	Female	Body Proportions	Male	Female
Type	0	Omission of Appendages	0	0	Upper and Lower Halves	1	0	Hair Shading	3	3	Head	06	07
Sex Sequence	0	Position of Both Arms	0	2	Four Quarters	4	4	Nudity and Transparency	7	7	Neck	14	14
Posture	1	1	Position of Right Arm	5	4	Relative Size	4		Form	3	3	Shoulders	05	
Perspective	5	2	Position of Left Arm	5	7	Constant Line Pressure	4	3	Detailing	3	3	Right Arm	04	06
Vertical Midline	3	4	Position of Legs	4	1	Variable Line Pressure	0	0	Identity and Sex	1	1	Left Arm	04	
Bilateral Symmetry	3	0	Relation of Long Axes	1	1	Line Continuity	2	0	Sophistication	3	3	Chest	04	06
Horizontal Midline	4	4	Right and Left Halves	1	1	Body Shading	7	0	Height	06	07	Girth	05	09

GENERAL CHARACTERISTICS OF SUBJECT

IDENTIFICATION
No. CO2
Sex M
Marital status S
Age 22 yrs. at
psychological tests

PARENTAL HISTORY				
Father				
C	H	S	D	O
-	-	-	-	-
Mother				
C	H	S	D	O
?	?	-	-	-

PHYSIOLOGICAL AND METABOLIC DATA

	Admission	Initial	Control	Cold pressor change	Exercise change	Smoking change
Systolic pressure	130	115	110	+30	+50	+04
Diastolic pressure	80	50	60	+15	-10	+05
Heart rate	80	68	60	-20	+34	+23

Age 23 yrs.	Height 74 in.	Ponderal index 13.60
	Weight 161 lbs.	Cholesterol 236 mg. per 100 ml.
	Overweight -08 %	Vital capacity 5.4 liters

HABIT SURVEY

Smoking habits: heavy cigarette smoker

Age begun 18 yrs.   Inhalation: yes

Habits of nervous tension: 4, 5, 6, 9, 11, 12, 16, 19, 20, 21

Plate 270   DRAWINGS AT AN INTERMEDIATE LEVEL OF SOPHISTICATION   313

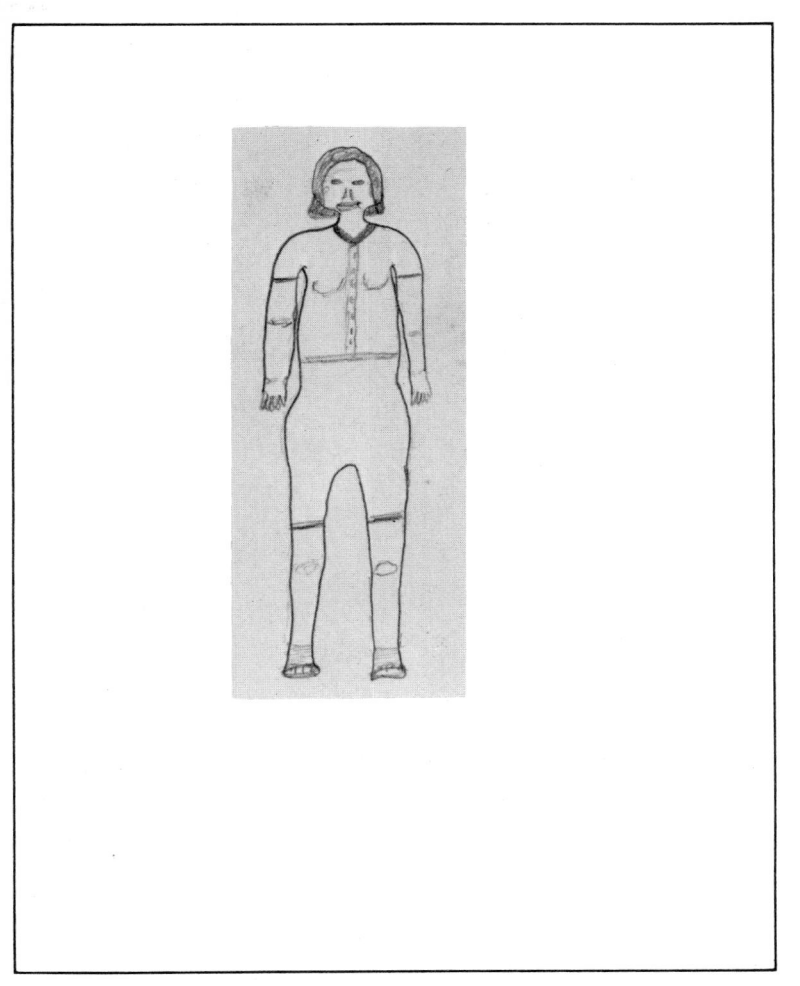

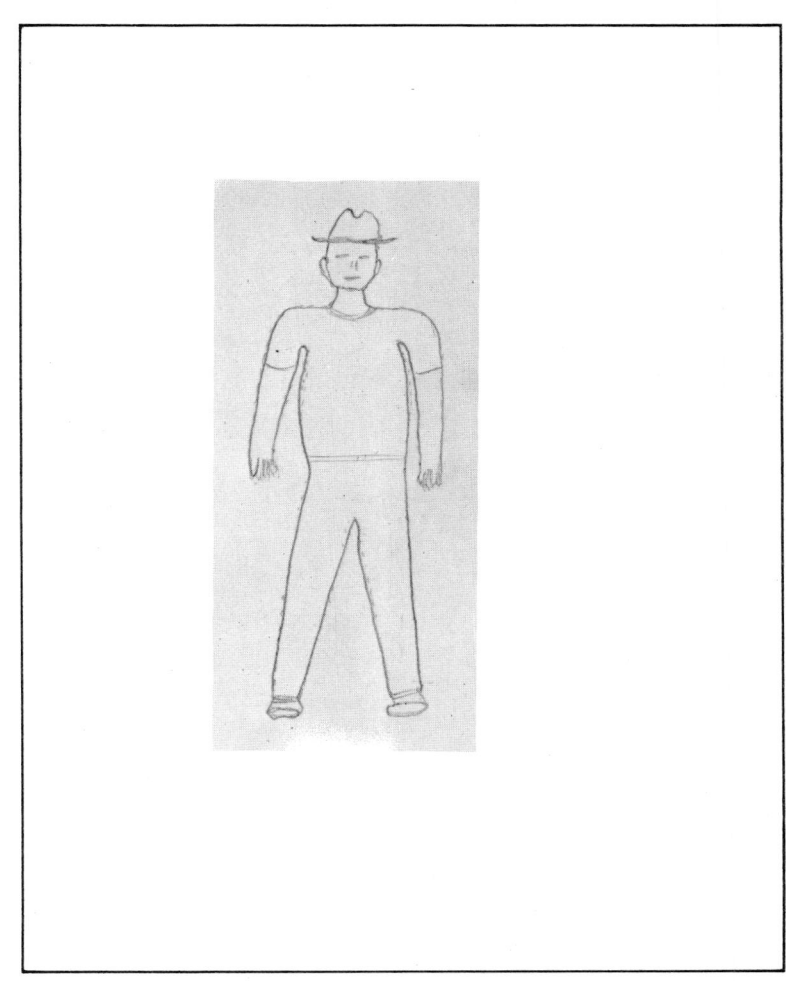

FIGURE-DRAWING CHARACTERISTICS

Structural	Male	Female	Structural	Male	Female	Structural and Graphic	Male	Female	Graphic, Global and Height	Male	Female	Body Proportions	Male	Female
	Both						Both							
Type	0		Omission of Appendages	0	0	Upper and Lower Halves	1	1	Hair Shading	0	1	Head	04	05
Sex Sequence	1		Position of Both Arms	0	0	Four Quarters	4	4	Nudity and Transparency	7	2	Neck	06	02
Posture	1	1	Position of Right Arm	0	0	Relative Size	4		Form	3	3	Shoulders	06	05
Perspective	0	0	Position of Left Arm	0	0	Constant Line Pressure	3	5	Detailing	3	3	Right Arm	04	04
Vertical Midline	0	3	Position of Legs	6	6	Variable Line Pressure	0	0	Identity and Sex	3	3	Left Arm	04	04
Bilateral Symmetry	4	3	Relation of Long Axes	1	1	Line Continuity	4	4	Sophistication	3	3	Chest	04	04
Horizontal Midline	4	4	Right and Left Halves	1	1	Body Shading	0	7	Height	05	05	Girth	06	06

GENERAL CHARACTERISTICS OF SUBJECT

IDENTIFICATION
No. C07
Sex M
Marital status S
Age 22 yrs. at
psychological tests

PARENTAL HISTORY
Father
C   H   S   D   O
–   –   –   –   ?
Mother
C   H   S   D   O
?   –   –   –   ?

PHYSIOLOGICAL AND METABOLIC DATA

	Admission	Initial	Control	Cold pressor change	Exercise change	Smoking change
Systolic pressure	160	125	122	–05	+16	+06
Diastolic pressure	90	70	76	–06	–08	+03
Heart rate	96	92	96	–04	+19	+07

Age 23 yrs.	Height 71 in.	Ponderal index 13.32
	Weight 151 lbs.	Cholesterol 263 mg. per 100 ml.
	Overweight –05 %	Vital capacity 4.6 liters

HABIT SURVEY

Smoking habits: heavy cigarette smoker

Age begun 22 yrs.   Inhalation: yes

Habits of nervous tension: 1, 4, 5, 6, 9, 12, 21

FIGURE-DRAWING CHARACTERISTICS

Structural	Male Female Both	Structural	Male	Female	Structural and Graphic	Male Female Both	Graphic, Global and Height	Male	Female	Body Proportions	Male	Female
Type	0	Omission of Appendages	0	0	Upper and Lower Halves	1	1	Hair Shading	3	2	Head	04	05
Sex Sequence	0	Position of Both Arms	1	4	Four Quarters	4	4	Nudity and Transparency	7	7	Neck	01	04
Posture	1	1	Position of Right Arm	0	7	Relative Size	2		Form	3	3	Shoulders	03	
Perspective	0	2	Position of Left Arm	5	4	Constant Line Pressure	2	2	Detailing	3	3	Right Arm	02	
Vertical Midline	3	4	Position of Legs	4	1	Variable Line Pressure	0	0	Identity and Sex	1	1	Left Arm	03	03
Bilateral Symmetry	2	0	Relation of Long Axes	1	1	Line Continuity	0	0	Sophistication	3	3	Chest	02	03
Horizontal Midline	4	4	Right and Left Halves	2	2	Body Shading	4	0	Height	03	03	Girth	03	03

GENERAL CHARACTERISTICS OF SUBJECT

IDENTIFICATION
No. C10
Sex M
Marital status S
Age 23 yrs. at psychological tests

PARENTAL HISTORY
Father
C H S D O
- - - - -
Mother
C H S D O
? - - - ?

PHYSIOLOGICAL AND METABOLIC DATA

	Admission	Initial	Control	Cold pressor change	Exercise change	Smoking change
Systolic pressure	140					+04
Diastolic pressure	80					+10
Heart rate	70					-02

Age 23 yrs.   Height 70 in.   Ponderal index 13.26
Weight 147 lbs.   Cholesterol 208 mg. per 100 ml.
Overweight -05 %   Vital capacity 4.7 liters

HABIT SURVEY

Smoking habits: pipe smoker
   Age begun 18 yrs.   Inhalation: no
Habits of nervous tension: 1, 4, 5, 8, 10, 23

STRONG VOCATIONAL INTEREST TEST

Occupation	Artist	Psychologist	Architect	Physician	Osteopath	Dentist	Veterinarian	Mathematician	Physicist	Engineer	Chemist	Production Manager
Standard Score	46	59	48	63	39	35	18	45	41	36	55	19

Occupation	Farmer	Aviator	Carpenter	Printer	Math.-Sci. Teacher	Ind. Arts Teacher	Voc. Agric. Teacher	Policeman	Forest Serv. Man	Y.M.C.A. Phys. Dir.	Personnel Director	Public Administrator
Standard Score	30	35	12	36	35	15	29	19	12	22	31	37

Occupation	Y.M.C.A. Secretary	Soc. Sci. H.S. Teacher	City Sch. Sup't.	Social Worker	Minister	Musician Performer	C.P.A.	Senior C.P.A.	Accountant	Office Man	Purchasing Agent	Banker
Standard Score	21	32	27	42	62	58	33	39	14	19	14	12

Occupation	Mortician	Pharmacist	Sales Manager	Real Est. Manager	Life Ins. Salesman	Advertising Man	Lawyer	Author-Journalist	President Mfg. Co.	Interest Maturity	Occupational Level	Masculinity-Femininity
Standard Score	10	26	21	26	21	42	42	46	28	51	58	36

Plate 272   **DRAWINGS AT AN INTERMEDIATE LEVEL OF SOPHISTICATION**   315

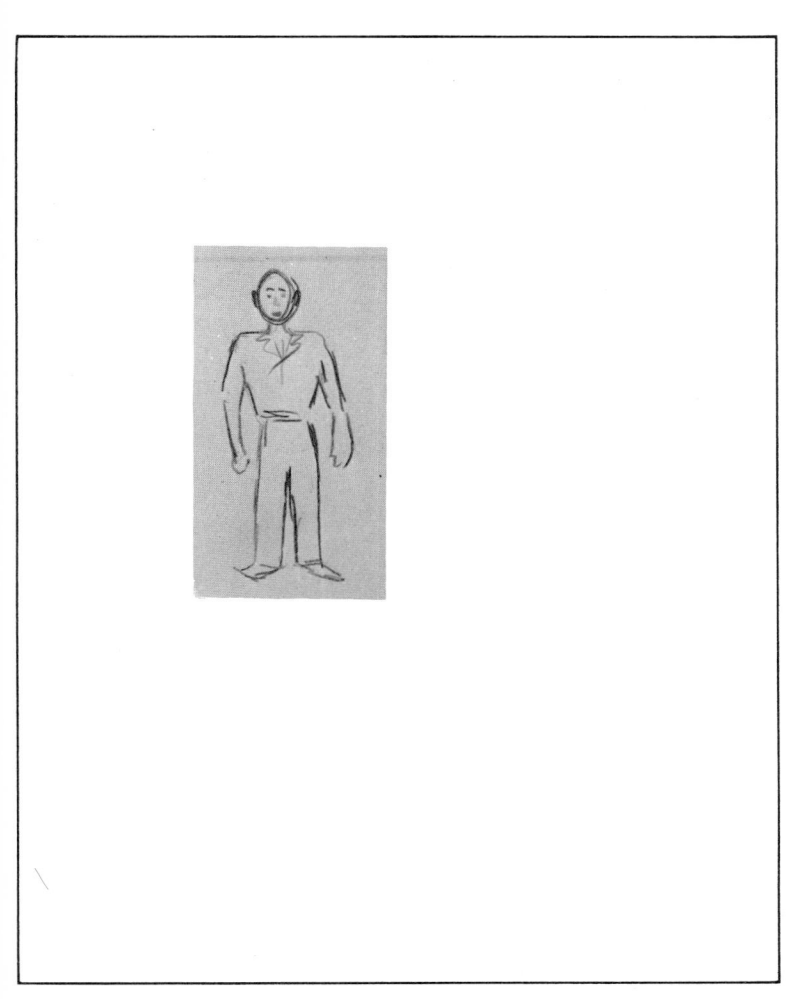

FIGURE-DRAWING CHARACTERISTICS

Structural	Male Female Both	Structural	Male	Female	Structural and Graphic	Male Female Both		Graphic, Global and Height	Male	Female	Body Proportions	Male	Female
Type	0	Omission of Appendages	0	0	Upper and Lower Halves	1	1	Hair Shading	0	3	Head	04	05
Sex Sequence	0	Position of Both Arms	0	0	Four Quarters	4	4	Nudity and Transparency	7	7	Neck	02	04
Posture	1	1	Position of Right Arm	0	5	Relative Size	4		Form	1	3	Shoulders	03	04
Perspective	0	0	Position of Left Arm	0	5	Constant Line Pressure	5	5	Detailing	3	3	Right Arm	02	02
Vertical Midline	3	0	Position of Legs	4	6	Variable Line Pressure	0	0	Identity and Sex	1	1	Left Arm	02	02
Bilateral Symmetry	3	3	Relation of Long Axes	1	1	Line Continuity	2	2	Sophistication	3	3	Chest	03	04
Horizontal Midline	4	4	Right and Left Halves	2	2	Body Shading	0	0	Height	03	03	Girth	03	03

GENERAL CHARACTERISTICS OF SUBJECT

IDENTIFICATION
No. 217
Sex M
Marital status S
Age 24 yrs. at psychological tests

PARENTAL HISTORY				
Father				
C	H	S	D	0
(?)	-	-	-	-
Mother				
C	H	S	D	0
-	-	-	-	-

PHYSIOLOGICAL AND METABOLIC DATA

	Admission	Initial	Control	Cold pressor change	Exercise change	Smoking change
Systolic pressure	118	118	110	+13	+50	
Diastolic pressure	76	66	72	+04	+03	
Heart rate	76	88	81	00	+26	

Age 24 yrs.	Height 72 in.	Ponderal index 13.38
	Weight 156 lbs.	Cholesterol 252 mg. per 100 ml.
	Overweight -05 %	Vital capacity 5.4 liters

HABIT SURVEY
Smoking habits: heavy cigarette smoker
Age begun 17 yrs.   Inhalation: yes
Habits of nervous tension: 1, 8, 11, 23

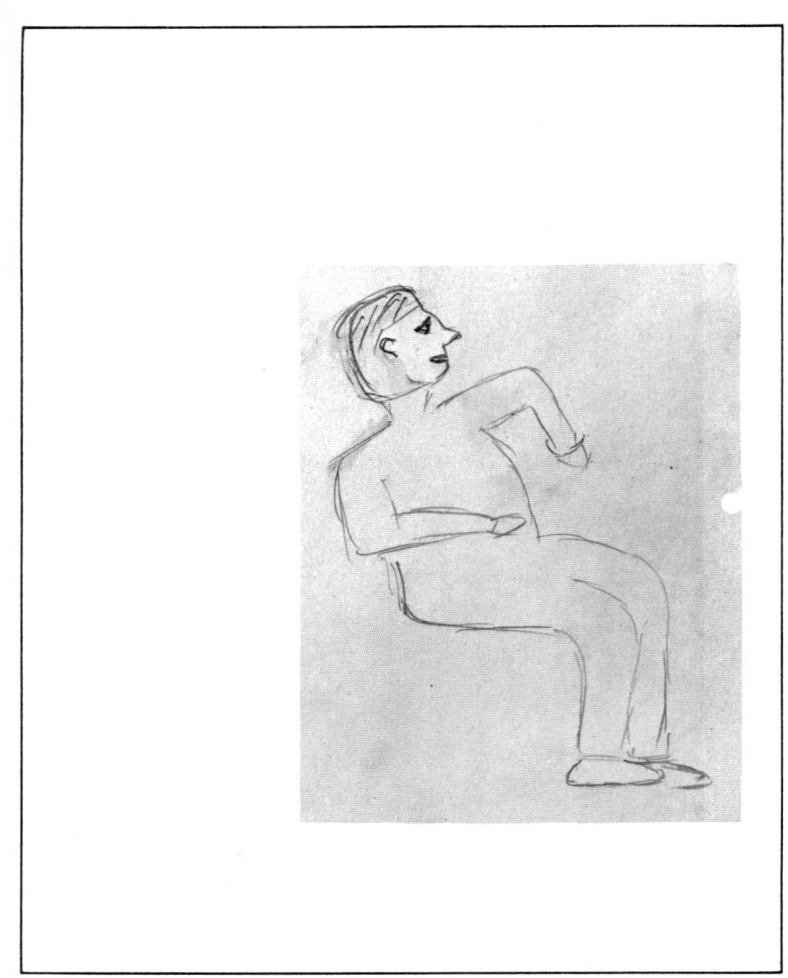

FIGURE-DRAWING CHARACTERISTICS

Structural	Male Female Both	Structural	Male	Female	Structural and Graphic	Male Female Both		Graphic, Global and Height	Male	Female	Body Proportions	Male	Female
Type	0	Omission of Appendages	0	7	Upper and Lower Halves	3	1	Hair Shading	1	3	Head	08	05
Sex Sequence	0	Position of Both Arms	1	0	Four Quarters	4	4	Nudity and Transparency	7	7	Neck	08	06
Posture	3 1	Position of Right Arm	5	5	Relative Size	0		Form	3	1	Shoulders		05
Perspective	6 0	Position of Left Arm	2	5	Constant Line Pressure	0	0	Detailing	5	3	Right Arm	06	
Vertical Midline	4 0	Position of Legs	2	6	Variable Line Pressure	1	5	Identity and Sex	5	3	Left Arm	04	
Bilateral Symmetry	0 3	Relation of Long Axes	0	1	Line Continuity	0	0	Sophistication	3	3	Chest		05
Horizontal Midline	0 4	Right and Left Halves	3	3	Body Shading	0	1	Height		04	Girth		06

GENERAL CHARACTERISTICS OF SUBJECT

IDENTIFICATION
No. 255
Sex M
Marital status M
Age 35 yrs. at
psychological tests

PARENTAL HISTORY
Father
C   H   S   D   O
(?) (?)   -   -   -
Mother
C   H   S   D   O
-   -   -   -   ?

PHYSIOLOGICAL AND METABOLIC DATA

	Admission	Initial	Control	Cold pressor change	Exercise change	Smoking change
Systolic pressure	124	130	110	+24	+42	
Diastolic pressure	84	68	62	+20	-16	
Heart rate	80	88	79	+16	+12	

Age 32 yrs.	Height	73	in.	Ponderal index 13.47	
	Weight	159	lbs.	Cholesterol	300 mg. per 100 ml.
	Overweight -12 %			Vital capacity 4.1	liters

HABIT SURVEY
Smoking habits: mixed smoker
Age begun 16 yrs.   Inhalation: yes
Habits of nervous tension: 2, 5, 6, 9, 10, 16, 21

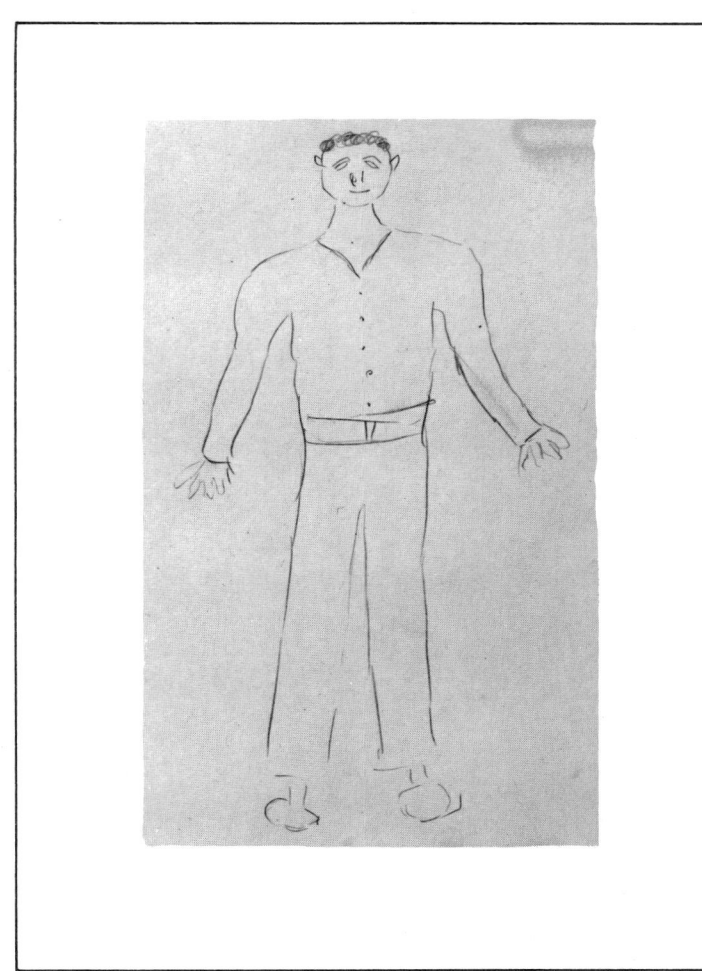

FIGURE-DRAWING CHARACTERISTICS

Structural	Male Female Both	Structural	Male	Female	Structural and Graphic	Male Female Both		Graphic, Global and Height	Male	Female	Body Proportions	Male	Female
Type	0	Omission of Appendages	0	0	Upper and Lower Halves	1	1	Hair Shading	3	3	Head	06	06
Sex Sequence	0	Position of Both Arms	0	0	Four Quarters	4	4	Nudity and Transparency	7	7	Neck	12	12
Posture	1 1	Position of Right Arm	2	2	Relative Size	2		Form	3	3	Shoulders	09	09
Perspective	0 0	Position of Left Arm	2	2	Constant Line Pressure	0	0	Detailing	3	3	Right Arm	06	06
Vertical Midline	3 0	Position of Legs	5	6	Variable Line Pressure	1	1	Identity and Sex	3	3	Left Arm	06	04
Bilateral Symmetry	3 3	Relation of Long Axes	1	1	Line Continuity	0	2	Sophistication	3	3	Chest	06	08
Horizontal Midline	4 4	Right and Left Halves	1	1	Body Shading	0	1	Height	07	07	Girth	07	09

GENERAL CHARACTERISTICS OF SUBJECT

IDENTIFICATION
No. 377
Sex M
Marital status   S
Age   26   yrs. at
psychological tests

PARENTAL HISTORY
Father
C   H   S   D   O
(?)   –   –   –   –
Mother
C   H   S   D   O
–   +   (+)   –   +

PHYSIOLOGICAL AND METABOLIC DATA

	Admission	Initial	Control	Cold pressor change	Exercise change	Smoking change
Systolic pressure	130	136	118	+13	+26	
Diastolic pressure	82	76	70	+36	–02	
Heart rate	76	78	70	+02	+18	

Age 23 yrs.	Height 68 in.	Ponderal index 11.89
	Weight 187 lbs.	Cholesterol 220 mg. per 100 ml.
	Overweight +27 %	Vital capacity 4.2 liters

HABIT SURVEY
Smoking habits: former smoker
Age begun   yrs.   Inhalation:
Habits of nervous tension: 5, 6, 11

FIGURE-DRAWING CHARACTERISTICS

Structural	Male Female Both	Structural	Male	Female	Structural and Graphic	Male Female Both		Graphic, Global and Height	Male	Female	Body Proportions	Male	Female
Type	0	Omission of Appendages	3	3	Upper and Lower Halves	7	7	Hair Shading	7	3	Head	11	12
Sex Sequence	2	Position of Both Arms	4	4	Four Quarters	4	4	Nudity and Transparency	6	7	Neck	06	12
Posture	0 0	Position of Right Arm	7	7	Relative Size	5		Form	3	3	Shoulders		
Perspective	2 2	Position of Left Arm	4	5	Constant Line Pressure	0	0	Detailing	3	3	Right Arm		
Vertical Midline	5 4	Position of Legs	0	0	Variable Line Pressure	2	1	Identity and Sex	1	1	Left Arm	06	06
Bilateral Symmetry	0 0	Relation of Long Axes	1	1	Line Continuity	0	0	Sophistication	3	3	Chest	07	06
Horizontal Midline	5 4	Right and Left Halves	2	2	Body Shading	5	2	Height			Girth	08	06

GENERAL CHARACTERISTICS OF SUBJECT

IDENTIFICATION
No. 473
Sex M
Marital status S
Age 25 yrs. at
psychological tests

PARENTAL HISTORY
Father
C   H   S   D   O
(?) (?)   -   -   -
Mother
C   H   S   D   O
-   -   -   -   -

PHYSIOLOGICAL AND METABOLIC DATA

	Admission	Initial	Control	Cold pressor change	Exercise change	Smoking change
Systolic pressure	120	112	106	+14	+28	
Diastolic pressure	70	70	66	+20	00	
Heart rate	90	74	70	+18	+16	

Age 22 yrs.

Height 71 in.
Weight 162 lbs.
Overweight +03 %

Ponderal index 13.03
Cholesterol 196 mg. per 100 ml.
Vital capacity 5.2 liters

HABIT SURVEY
Smoking habits: occasional smoker
Age begun 17 yrs.   Inhalation: yes
Habits of nervous tension: 4, 5, 6, 8, 11, 22, 24

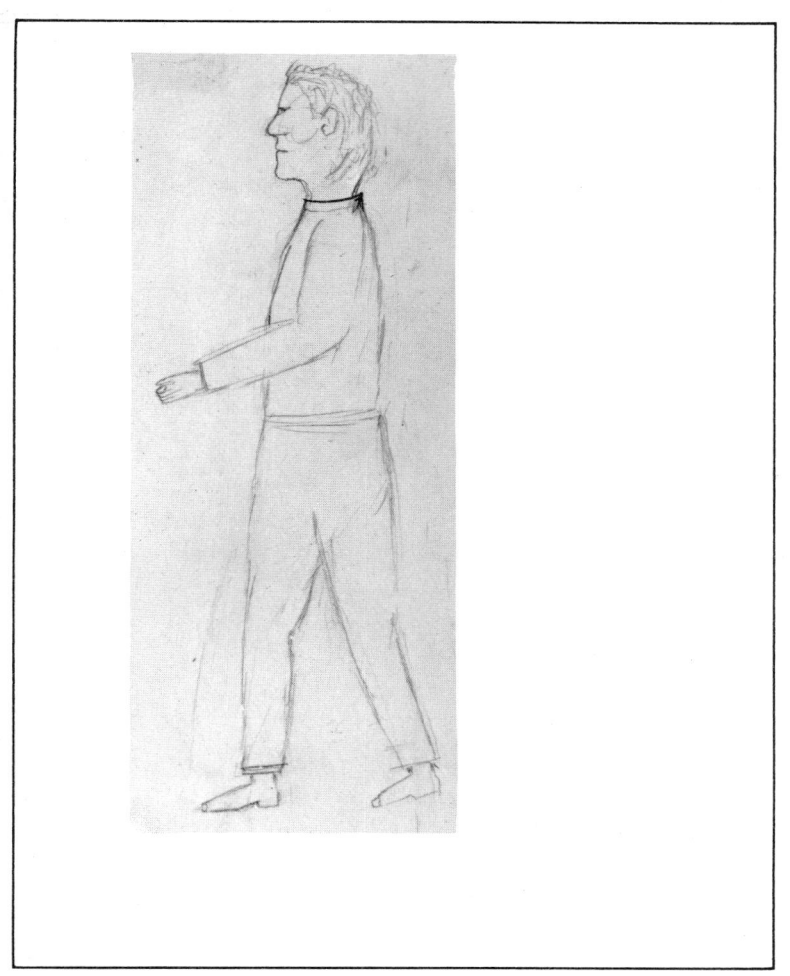

FIGURE-DRAWING CHARACTERISTICS

Structural	Male Female Both		Structural	Male	Female	Structural and Graphic	Male Female Both		Graphic, Global and Height	Male	Female	Body Proportions	Male	Female
Type	0		Omission of Appendages	0	0	Upper and Lower Halves	1	1	Hair Shading	3	3	Head	09	05
Sex Sequence	0		Position of Both Arms	4	4	Four Quarters	4	4	Nudity and Transparency	7	7	Neck	07	05
Posture	2	1	Position of Right Arm	7	7	Relative Size	0		Form	3	3	Shoulders		
Perspective	2	2	Position of Left Arm	4	4	Constant Line Pressure	0	0	Detailing	3	3	Right Arm		
Vertical Midline	4	4	Position of Legs	8	1	Variable Line Pressure	2	2	Identity and Sex	1	1	Left Arm	06	02
Bilateral Symmetry	0	0	Relation of Long Axes	1	1	Line Continuity	0	0	Sophistication	3	3	Chest	07	04
Horizontal Midline	4	4	Right and Left Halves	1	2	Body Shading	0	2	Height	08	04	Girth	09	06

GENERAL CHARACTERISTICS OF SUBJECT

IDENTIFICATION
No. D03
Sex M
Marital status S
Age 22 yrs. at
psychological tests

PARENTAL HISTORY					
Father					
C	H	S	D	O	
(?)	-	-	-	?	
Mother					
C	H	S	D	O	
-	-	-	-	?	

PHYSIOLOGICAL AND METABOLIC DATA

	Admission	Initial	Control	Cold pressor change	Exercise change	Smoking change
Systolic pressure	124	130	115	+20	+55	+08
Diastolic pressure	82	80	72	+08	-12	-04
Heart rate	56	50	53	+12	+26	+14

Age 21 yrs.

Height 72 in.
Weight 154 lbs.
Overweight -05 %

Ponderal index 13.43
Cholesterol 212 mg. per 100 ml.
Vital capacity 5.6 liters

HABIT SURVEY

Smoking habits: nonsmoker

Age begun   yrs.   Inhalation:

Habits of nervous tension: 4, 5, 6, 10, 25

STRONG VOCATIONAL INTEREST TEST

Occupation	Artist	Psychologist	Architect	Physician	Osteopath	Dentist	Veterinarian	Mathematician	Physicist	Engineer	Chemist	Production Manager
Standard Score	37	51	41	58	51	42	29	41	48	52	60	33

Occupation	Farmer	Aviator	Carpenter	Printer	Math.-Sci. Teacher	Ind. Arts Teacher	Voc. Agric. Teacher	Policeman	Forest Serv. Man	Y.M.C.A. Phys. Dir.	Personnel Director	Public Administrator
Standard Score	54	53	39	49	50	36	38	31	46	26	28	48

Occupation	Y.M.C.A. Secretary	Soc. Sci. H.S. Teacher	City Sch. Sup't.	Social Worker	Minister	Musician Performer	C.P.A.	Senior C.P.A.	Accountant	Office Man	Purchasing Agent	Banker
Standard Score	22	27	22	31	63	41	27	40	20	25	15	17

Occupation	Mortician	Pharmacist	Sales Manager	Real Est. Manager	Life Ins. Salesman	Advertising Man	Lawyer	Author-Journalist	President Mfg. Co.	Interest Maturity	Occupational Level	Masculinity-Femininity
Standard Score	13	18	09	22	07	26	27	36	19	51	52	57

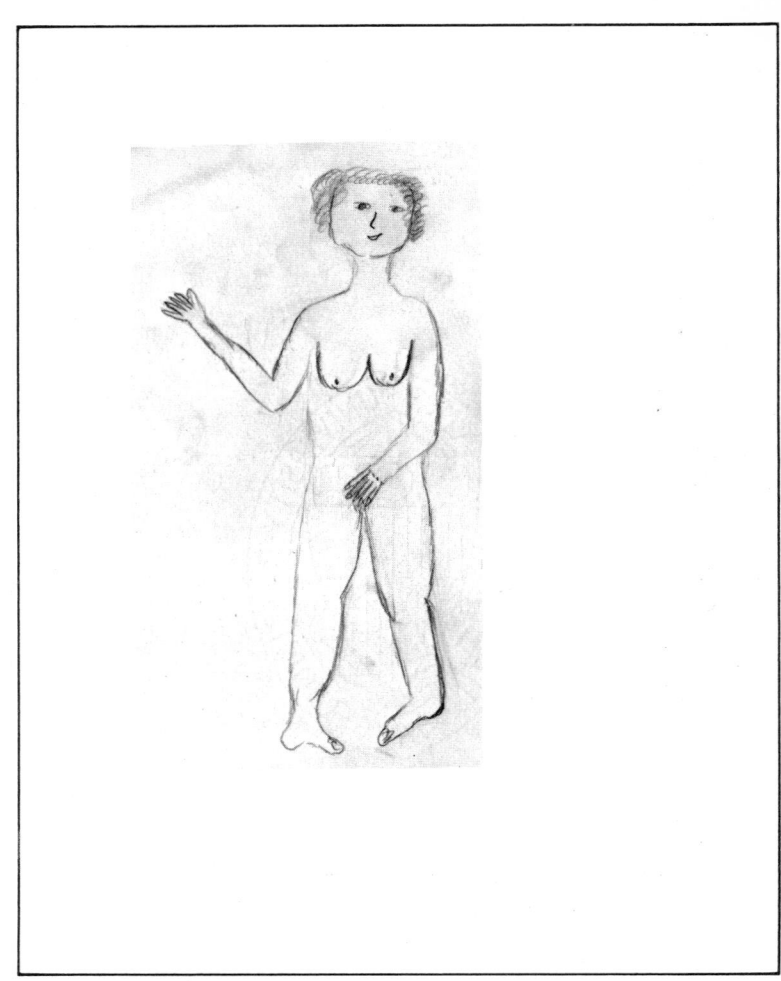

FIGURE-DRAWING CHARACTERISTICS

Structural	Male Female Both	Structural	Male	Female	Structural and Graphic	Male Female Both		Graphic, Global and Height	Male	Female	Body Proportions	Male	Female
Type	0	Omission of Appendages	0	0	Upper and Lower Halves	0	1	Hair Shading	2	3	Head	19	06
Sex Sequence	0	Position of Both Arms	4	1	Four Quarters	4	4	Nudity and Transparency	7	0	Neck	08	12
Posture	2 1	Position of Right Arm	7	2	Relative Size	0		Form	3	3	Shoulders		05
Perspective	2 0	Position of Left Arm	4	5	Constant Line Pressure	0	0	Detailing	3	3	Right Arm		05
Vertical Midline	4 0	Position of Legs	8	6	Variable Line Pressure	3	3	Identity and Sex	1	1	Left Arm	06	04
Bilateral Symmetry	0 3	Relation of Long Axes	0	1	Line Continuity	0	0	Sophistication	3	3	Chest	10	05
Horizontal Midline	4 0	Right and Left Halves	1	1	Body Shading	3	0	Height	07	06	Girth	11	07

GENERAL CHARACTERISTICS OF SUBJECT

IDENTIFICATION
No. D24
Sex M
Marital status S
Age 21 yrs. at
psychological tests

PARENTAL HISTORY				
Father				
C	H	S	D	O
(?)	+	-	(+)	-
Mother				
C	H	S	D	O
-	-	-	-	?

PHYSIOLOGICAL AND METABOLIC DATA						
	Admission	Initial	Control	Cold pressor change	Exercise change	Smoking change
Systolic pressure	125	110	110	+10	+35	+05
Diastolic pressure	70	68	70	+08	-25	+05
Heart rate	70	76	73	+04	+27	+12
Age 21 yrs.	Height 70 in.			Ponderal index 13.18		
	Weight 150 lbs.			Cholesterol 278 mg. per 100 ml.		
	Overweight -02 %			Vital capacity 4.9 liters		

HABIT SURVEY
Smoking habits: occasional smoker
Age begun 19 yrs. Inhalation: sometimes
Habits of nervous tension: 5, 6, 19, 24

FIGURE-DRAWING CHARACTERISTICS

Structural	Male Female Both		Structural	Male	Female	Structural and Graphic	Male Female Both		Graphic, Global and Height	Male	Female	Body Proportions	Male	Female
Type	0		Omission of Appendages	0	0	Upper and Lower Halves	1	1	Hair Shading	1	1	Head	04	03
Sex Sequence	0		Position of Both Arms	0	0	Four Quarters	4	4	Nudity and Transparency	7	7	Neck	02	02
Posture	1	1	Position of Right Arm	0	0	Relative Size	0		Form	3	3	Shoulders	04	02
Perspective	0	0	Position of Left Arm	0	0	Constant Line Pressure	1	1	Detailing	3	3	Right Arm	02	02
Vertical Midline	3	3	Position of Legs	2	4	Variable Line Pressure	0	0	Identity and Sex	1	1	Left Arm	02	02
Bilateral Symmetry	5	5	Relation of Long Axes	1	1	Line Continuity	0	0	Sophistication	3	3	Chest	03	02
Horizontal Midline	4	4	Right and Left Halves	1	2	Body Shading	2	1	Height	03	02	Girth	03	02

GENERAL CHARACTERISTICS OF SUBJECT

IDENTIFICATION
No. 351
Sex M
Marital status S
Age 25 yrs. at
psychological tests

PARENTAL HISTORY
Father
C   H   S   D   O
-    -   -   -   -
Mother
C   H   S   D   O
(?)   +   -   -   -

PHYSIOLOGICAL AND METABOLIC DATA

	Admission	Initial	Control	Cold pressor change	Exercise change	Smoking change
Systolic pressure	124	126	124	+10	+48	
Diastolic pressure	74	84	80	+06	00	
Heart rate	84	84	83	00	-12	

Age 23 yrs.	Height 74 in.	Ponderal index 12.96
	Weight 186 lbs.	Cholesterol 270 mg. per 100 ml.
	Overweight +06 %	Vital capacity 5.4 liters

HABIT SURVEY
Smoking habits: unknown
Age begun   yrs.   Inhalation:
Habits of nervous tension:

FIGURE-DRAWING CHARACTERISTICS

Structural	Male Female Both		Structural	Male	Female	Structural and Graphic	Male Female Both		Graphic, Global and Height	Male	Female	Body Proportions	Male	Female
Type	0		Omission of Appendages	0	0	Upper and Lower Halves	3	3	Hair Shading	3	3	Head	12	15
Sex Sequence	0		Position of Both Arms	4	4	Four Quarters	4	4	Nudity and Transparency	7	7	Neck	10	10
Posture	1	1	Position of Right Arm	7	7	Relative Size	0		Form	3	3	Shoulders		
Perspective	2	2	Position of Left Arm	4	0	Constant Line Pressure	0	0	Detailing	3	3	Right Arm		
Vertical Midline	7	4	Position of Legs	1	5	Variable Line Pressure	5	5	Identity and Sex	1	1	Left Arm	08	06
Bilateral Symmetry	0	0	Relation of Long Axes	1	1	Line Continuity	2	1	Sophistication	3	3	Chest	09	09
Horizontal Midline	4	4	Right and Left Halves	1	1	Body Shading	4	0	Height	09	08	Girth	09	09

GENERAL CHARACTERISTICS OF SUBJECT

IDENTIFICATION
No. 448
Sex M
Marital status S
Age 28 yrs. at psychological tests

PARENTAL HISTORY
Father
C H S D O
- - - - +
Mother
C H S D O
(?) - - - +

PHYSIOLOGICAL AND METABOLIC DATA

	Admission	Initial	Control	Cold pressor change	Exercise change	Smoking change
Systolic pressure	124	125	110	+15	+35	
Diastolic pressure	70	75	65	+12	+15	
Heart rate	60	84	71	+08	+26	

Age 25 yrs.	Height	76	in.	Ponderal index 13.32
	Weight	186	lbs.	Cholesterol 217 mg. per 100 ml.
	Overweight -02 %			Vital capacity 6.7 liters

HABIT SURVEY
Smoking habits: former smoker
Age begun 19 yrs.   Inhalation:
Habits of nervous tension: 5, 6

Plate 280   DRAWINGS AT AN INTERMEDIATE LEVEL OF SOPHISTICATION   323

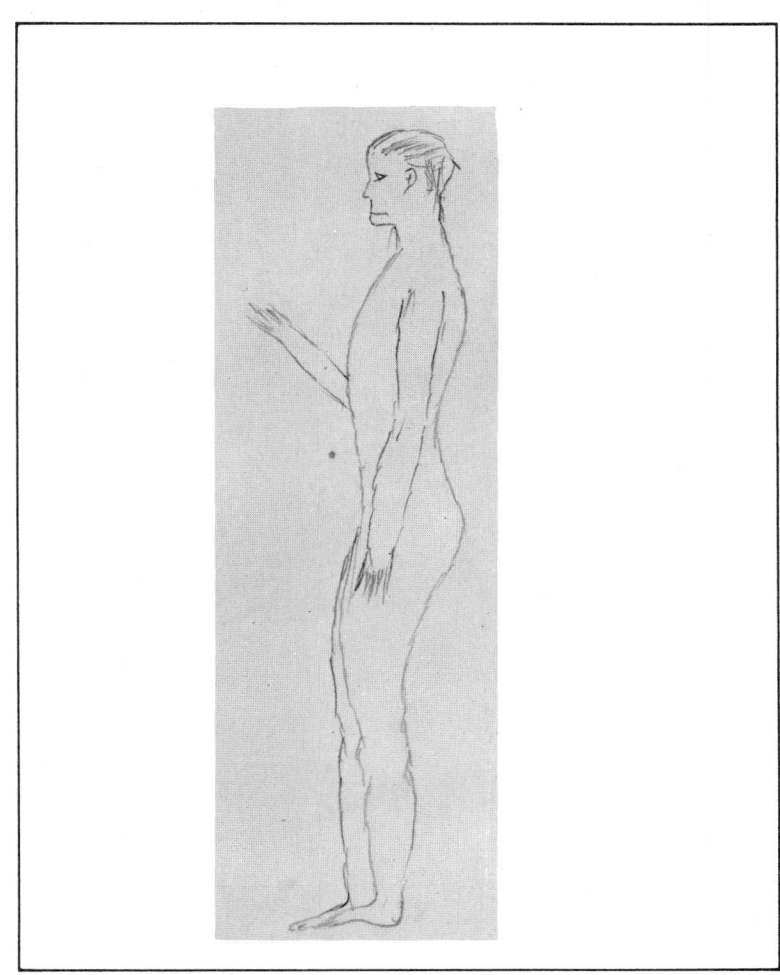

FIGURE-DRAWING CHARACTERISTICS

Structural	Male	Female	Structural	Male	Female	Structural and Graphic	Male	Female	Graphic, Global and Height	Male	Female	Body Proportions	Male	Female
		Both						Both						
Type	0		Omission of Appendages	0	0	Upper and Lower Halves	3	0	Hair Shading	2	7	Head	07	07
Sex Sequence	1		Position of Both Arms	4	4	Four Quarters	4	4	Nudity and Transparency	0	0	Neck	08	06
Posture	1	1	Position of Right Arm	7	7	Relative Size	2		Form	3	3	Shoulders		
Perspective	2	2	Position of Left Arm	0	4	Constant Line Pressure	0	0	Detailing	3	3	Right Arm		
Vertical Midline	4	4	Position of Legs	1	1	Variable Line Pressure	1	3	Identity and Sex	1	1	Left Arm	08	08
Bilateral Symmetry	0	0	Relation of Long Axes	1	1	Line Continuity	0	0	Sophistication	3	3	Chest	07	06
Horizontal Midline	0	0	Right and Left Halves	1	4	Body Shading	0	0	Height	08	08	Girth	06	08

GENERAL CHARACTERISTICS OF SUBJECT

IDENTIFICATION
No. 618
Sex M
Marital status S
Age 26 yrs. at
psychological tests

PARENTAL HISTORY				
Father				
C	H	S	D	O
-	-	(?)	-	-
Mother				
C	H	S	D	O
(?)	-	(+)	-	+

PHYSIOLOGICAL AND METABOLIC DATA

	Admission	Initial	Control	Cold pressor change	Exercise change	Smoking change
Systolic pressure	130	118	114	+14	+28	00
Diastolic pressure	80	68	66	+24	+06	+14
Heart rate	104	88	79	+08	+21	+17

Age 24 yrs.	Height 70 in.	Ponderal index 13.28
	Weight 146 lbs.	Cholesterol 250 mg. per 100 ml.
	Overweight -06 %	Vital capacity 4.3 liters

HABIT SURVEY

Smoking habits: light cigarette smoker

Age begun 19 yrs.   Inhalation: yes

Habits of nervous tension: 1, 4, 5, 17

FIGURE-DRAWING CHARACTERISTICS

Structural	Male Female Both		Structural	Male	Female	Structural and Graphic	Male Female Both		Graphic, Global and Height	Male	Female	Body Proportions	Male	Female
Type	0		Omission of Appendages	0	0	Upper and Lower Halves	1	1	Hair Shading	3	3	Head	07	07
Sex Sequence	0		Position of Both Arms	1	0	Four Quarters	4	4	Nudity and Transparency	7	7	Neck	04	05
Posture	1	1	Position of Right Arm	2	5	Relative Size	4		Form	3	3	Shoulders	04	07
Perspective	0	0	Position of Left Arm	0	5	Constant Line Pressure	5	0	Detailing	3	3	Right Arm	03	04
Vertical Midline	3	0	Position of Legs	4	4	Variable Line Pressure	0	5	Identity and Sex	1	1	Left Arm	03	04
Bilateral Symmetry	3	2	Relation of Long Axes	1	1	Line Continuity	2	2	Sophistication	3	3	Chest	05	06
Horizontal Midline	4	4	Right and Left Halves	2	1	Body Shading	4	4	Height	04	05	Girth	05	06

GENERAL CHARACTERISTICS OF SUBJECT

IDENTIFICATION
No. F78
Sex M
Marital status M
Age 36 yrs. at psychological tests

PARENTAL HISTORY
Father
C H S D O
– – – – –
Mother
C H S D O
(?) + (?) – –

PHYSIOLOGICAL AND METABOLIC DATA

	Admission	Initial	Control	Cold pressor change	Exercise change	Smoking change
Systolic pressure	142	118	106	+22	+30	+02
Diastolic pressure	80	72	72	+28	+18	+04
Heart rate	84	84	76	–12	+21	+01

Age 35 yrs.	Height	68 in.	Ponderal index 12.83
	Weight	149 lbs.	Cholesterol 222 mg. per 100 ml.
	Overweight –04 %		Vital capacity liters

HABIT SURVEY
Smoking habits: nonsmoker
Age begun   yrs.   Inhalation:
Habits of nervous tension: 5, 6, 9, 11, 25

STRONG VOCATIONAL INTEREST TEST

Occupation	Artist	Psychologist	Architect	Physician	Osteopath	Dentist	Veterinarian	Mathematician	Physicist	Engineer	Chemist	Production Manager
Standard Score	26	42	32	59	54	40	39	34	43	45	50	39

Occupation	Farmer	Aviator	Carpenter	Printer	Math.-Sci. Teacher	Ind. Arts Teacher	Voc. Agric. Teacher	Policeman	Forest Serv. Man	Y.M.C.A. Phys. Dir.	Personnel Director	Public Administrator
Standard Score	52	50	39	47	55	41	47	32	41	42	30	41

Occupation	Y.M.C.A. Secretary	Soc. Sci. H.S. Teacher	City Sch. Sup't.	Social Worker	Minister	Musician Performer	C.P.A.	Senior C.P.A.	Accountant	Office Man	Purchasing Agent	Banker
Standard Score	37	33	30	35	58	45	15	39	21	21	09	14

Occupation	Mortician	Pharmacist	Sales Manager	Real Est. Manager	Life Ins. Salesman	Advertising Man	Lawyer	Author- Journalist	President Mfg. Co.	Interest Maturity	Occupational Level	Masculinity- Femininity
Standard Score	24	28	11	22	16	17	23	24	22	58	52	53

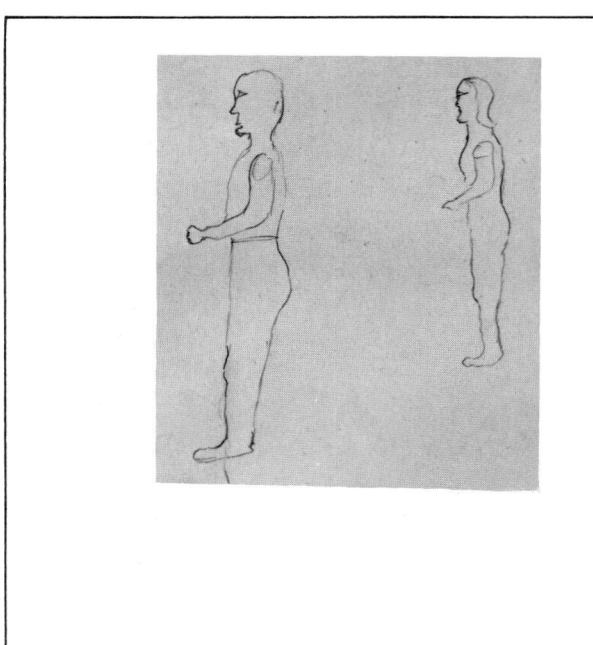

FIGURE-DRAWING CHARACTERISTICS

Structural	Male Female Both		Structural	Male	Female	Structural and Graphic	Male Female Both		Graphic, Global and Height	Male	Female	Body Proportions	Male	Female
Type	0		Omission of Appendages	0	0	Upper and Lower Halves	2	2	Hair Shading	0	5	Head	05	04
Sex Sequence	2		Position of Both Arms	4	4	Four Quarters	0	1	Nudity and Transparency	9	9	Neck	03	05
Posture	1	1	Position of Right Arm	7	7	Relative Size	0		Form	3	3	Shoulders		
Perspective	2	2	Position of Left Arm	4	4	Constant Line Pressure	0	0	Detailing	5	5	Right Arm		
Vertical Midline	4	4	Position of Legs	1	1	Variable Line Pressure	1	1	Identity and Sex	3	3	Left Arm	02	02
Bilateral Symmetry	0	0	Relation of Long Axes	1	1	Line Continuity	0	0	Sophistication	3	3	Chest	04	02
Horizontal Midline	4	0	Right and Left Halves	9	9	Body Shading	0	0	Height	04	03	Girth	03	03

GENERAL CHARACTERISTICS OF SUBJECT

<table>
<tr><td colspan="2">IDENTIFICATION</td></tr>
<tr><td colspan="2">No. 582</td></tr>
<tr><td colspan="2">Sex M</td></tr>
<tr><td colspan="2">Marital status M</td></tr>
<tr><td colspan="2">Age 24 yrs. at</td></tr>
<tr><td colspan="2">psychological tests</td></tr>
</table>

PARENTAL HISTORY					
Father					
C	H	S	D	O	
–	+	–	+	–	
Mother					
C	H	S	D	O	
–	+	–	+	–	

PHYSIOLOGICAL AND METABOLIC DATA

	Admission	Initial	Control	Cold pressor change	Exercise change	Smoking change
Systolic pressure	124	138	126	+14	+60	
Diastolic pressure	80	76	72	+04	00	
Heart rate	84	88	78	+08	+42	

Age 24 yrs.	Height 69 in.	Ponderal index 12.55	
	Weight 166 lbs.	Cholesterol 172 mg. per 100 ml.	
	Overweight +09 %	Vital capacity 4.6 liters	

HABIT SURVEY

Smoking habits: nonsmoker

Age begun   yrs.   Inhalation:

Habits of nervous tension: 5, 6, 17

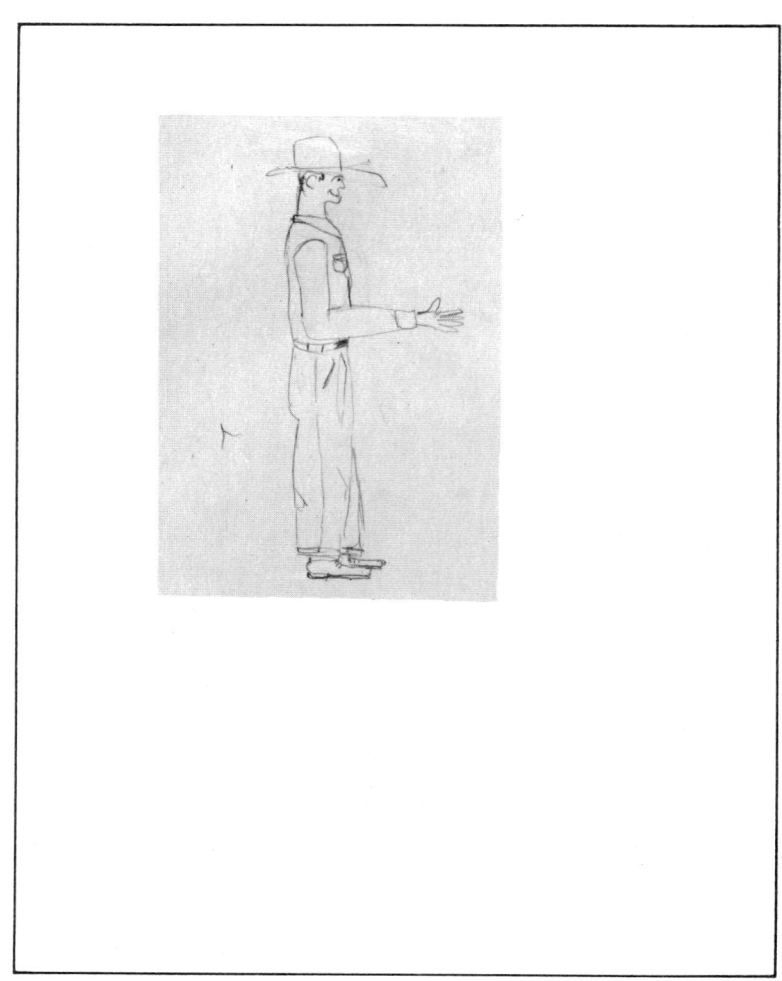

FIGURE-DRAWING CHARACTERISTICS

Structural	Male Female Both		Structural	Male	Female	Structural and Graphic	Male Female Both		Graphic, Global and Height	Male	Female	Body Proportions	Male	Female
Type	0		Omission of Appendages	0	0	Upper and Lower Halves	1	1	Hair Shading	0	3	Head	03	06
Sex Sequence	1		Position of Both Arms	2	1	Four Quarters	4	4	Nudity and Transparency	7	7	Neck	04	06
Posture	1	1	Position of Right Arm	4	4	Relative Size	4		Form	3	3	Shoulders		05
Perspective	2	0	Position of Left Arm	7	5	Constant Line Pressure	1	0	Detailing	1	3	Right Arm	04	06
Vertical Midline	4	3	Position of Legs	1	4	Variable Line Pressure	0	1	Identity and Sex	1	1	Left Arm		06
Bilateral Symmetry	0	3	Relation of Long Axes	1	1	Line Continuity	1	2	Sophistication	3	3	Chest	04	04
Horizontal Midline	4	2	Right and Left Halves	2	2	Body Shading	6	3	Height	04	07	Girth	04	06

GENERAL CHARACTERISTICS OF SUBJECT

IDENTIFICATION
No. B08
Sex M
Marital status M
Age 21 yrs. at
psychological tests

PARENTAL HISTORY				
Father				
C	H	S	D	O
-	+	-	-	?
Mother				
C	H	S	D	O
-	+	-	-	-

PHYSIOLOGICAL AND METABOLIC DATA

	Admission	Initial	Control	Cold pressor change	Exercise change	Smoking change
Systolic pressure	135	118	118	+58	+24	+18
Diastolic pressure	80	68	64	+46	-20	+12
Heart rate	85	84	74	-22	+14	00

Age 20 yrs.	Height 75 in.	Ponderal index 13.49
	Weight 172 lbs.	Cholesterol 212 mg. per 100 ml.
	Overweight -02 %	Vital capacity 5.5 liters

HABIT SURVEY
Smoking habits: nonsmoker
Age begun   yrs.   Inhalation:
Habits of nervous tension: 6, 8

STRONG VOCATIONAL INTEREST TEST

Occupation	Artist	Psychologist	Architect	Physician	Osteopath	Dentist	Veterinarian	Mathematician	Physicist	Engineer	Chemist	Production Manager
Standard Score	29	48	36	59	47	35	26	26	24	37	39	35

Occupation	Farmer	Aviator	Carpenter	Printer	Math.-Sci. Teacher	Ind. Arts Teacher	Voc. Agric. Teacher	Policeman	Forest Serv. Man	Y.M.C.A. Phys. Dir.	Personnel Director	Public Administrator
Standard Score	34	46	25	29	43	27	31	36	32	50	39	45

Occupation	Y.M.C.A. Secretary	Soc. Sci. H.S. Teacher	City Sch. Sup't.	Social Worker	Minister	Musician Performer	C.P.A.	Senior C.P.A.	Accountant	Office Man	Purchasing Agent	Banker
Standard Score	36	34	30	45	61	52	23	38	15	21	14	14

Occupation	Mortician	Pharmacist	Sales Manager	Real Est. Manager	Life Ins. Salesman	Advertising Man	Lawyer	Author-Journalist	President Mfg. Co.	Interest Maturity	Occupational Level	Masculinity-Femininity
Standard Score	19	27	24	27	28	31	31	30	23	59	54	46

Plate 284   DRAWINGS AT AN INTERMEDIATE LEVEL OF SOPHISTICATION   327

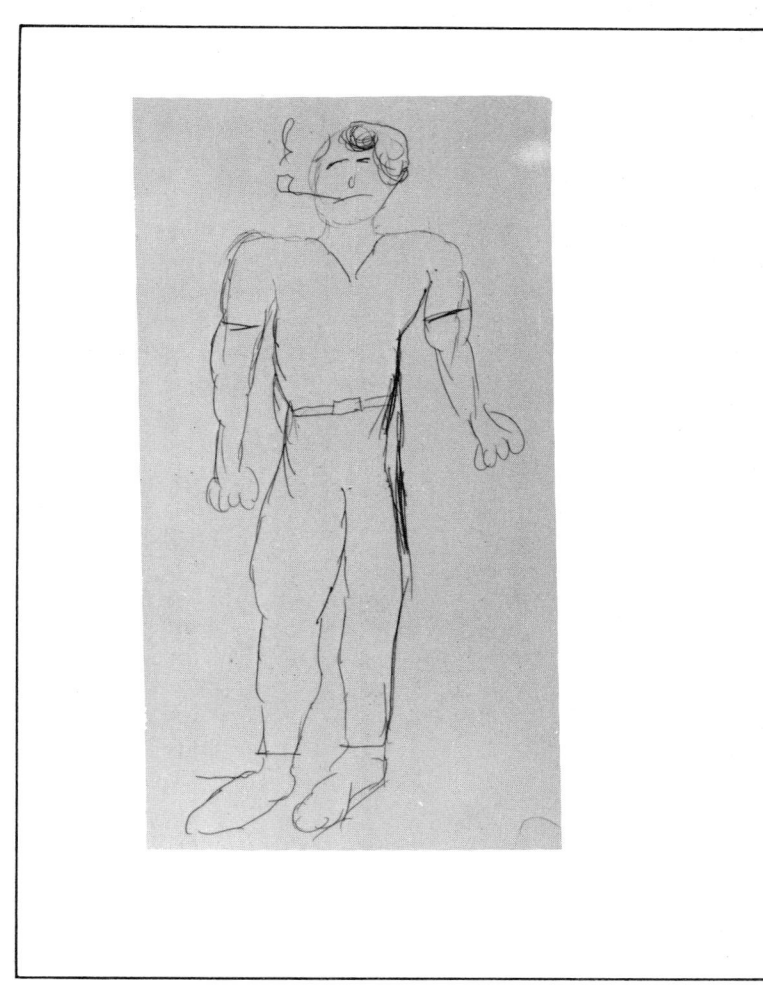

FIGURE-DRAWING CHARACTERISTICS

Structural	Male Female Both		Structural	Male	Female	Structural and Graphic	Male Female Both		Graphic, Global and Height	Male	Female	Body Proportions	Male	Female
Type	0		Omission of Appendages	0	0	Upper and Lower Halves	0	0	Hair Shading	3	2	Head	08	10
Sex Sequence	0		Position of Both Arms	1	4	Four Quarters	4	4	Nudity and Transparency	7	7	Neck	06	06
Posture	1	1	Position of Right Arm	0	7	Relative Size	4		Form	3	3	Shoulders	09	
Perspective	0	2	Position of Left Arm	2	4	Constant Line Pressure	0	0	Detailing	3	3	Right Arm	06	
Vertical Midline	0	4	Position of Legs	4	1	Variable Line Pressure	2	3	Identity and Sex	1	1	Left Arm	06	07
Bilateral Symmetry	2	0	Relation of Long Axes	1	1	Line Continuity	0	0	Sophistication	3	3	Chest	06	09
Horizontal Midline	4	0	Right and Left Halves	1	3	Body Shading	0	1	Height	07	09	Girth	06	08

GENERAL CHARACTERISTICS OF SUBJECT

IDENTIFICATION
No. E18
Sex M
Marital status S
Age 21 yrs. at
psychological tests

PARENTAL HISTORY
Father
C H S D O
- + - - ?
Mother
C H S D O
- + - - +

PHYSIOLOGICAL AND METABOLIC DATA

	Admission	Initial	Control	Cold pressor change	Exercise change	Smoking change
Systolic pressure	120	110	110	+20	+35	
Diastolic pressure	74	70	75	+23	-15	
Heart rate	74	68	60	00	+17	

Age 20 yrs.	Height	72 in.	Ponderal index	13.00
	Weight	170 lbs.	Cholesterol	199 mg. per 100 ml.
	Overweight +06 %		Vital capacity	4.6 liters

HABIT SURVEY

Smoking habits: nonsmoker

Age begun 10 yrs.   Inhalation:

Habits of nervous tension: 5, 6, 9, 11, 16, 21

STRONG VOCATIONAL INTEREST TEST

Occupation	Artist	Psychologist	Architect	Physician	Osteopath	Dentist	Veterinarian	Mathematician	Physicist	Engineer	Chemist	Production Manager
Standard Score	47	37	36	65	61	48	41	28	28	32	46	29

Occupation	Farmer	Aviator	Carpenter	Printer	Math.-Sci. Teacher	Ind. Arts Teacher	Voc. Agric. Teacher	Policeman	Forest Serv. Man	Y.M.C.A. Phys. Dir.	Personnel Director	Public Administrator
Standard Score	37	47	16	34	27	05	19	32	36	36	18	39

Occupation	Y.M.C.A. Secretary	Soc. Sci. H.S. Teacher	City Sch. Sup't.	Social Worker	Minister	Musician Performer	C.P.A.	Senior C.P.A.	Accountant	Office Man	Purchasing Agent	Banker
Standard Score	15	23	18	31	64	49	21	26	10	21	14	14

Occupation	Mortician	Pharmacist	Sales Manager	Real Est. Manager	Life Ins. Salesman	Advertising Man	Lawyer	Author-Journalist	President Mfg. Co.	Interest Maturity	Occupational Level	Masculinity-Femininity
Standard Score	32	40	34	41	38	44	44	49	35	45	58	43

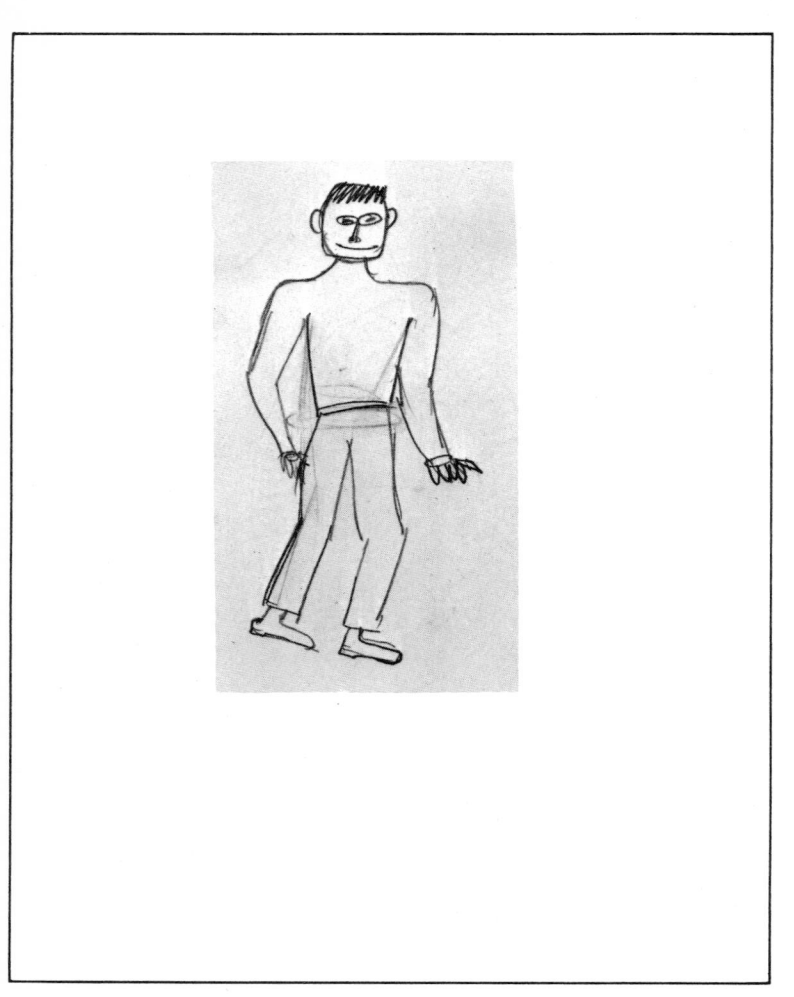

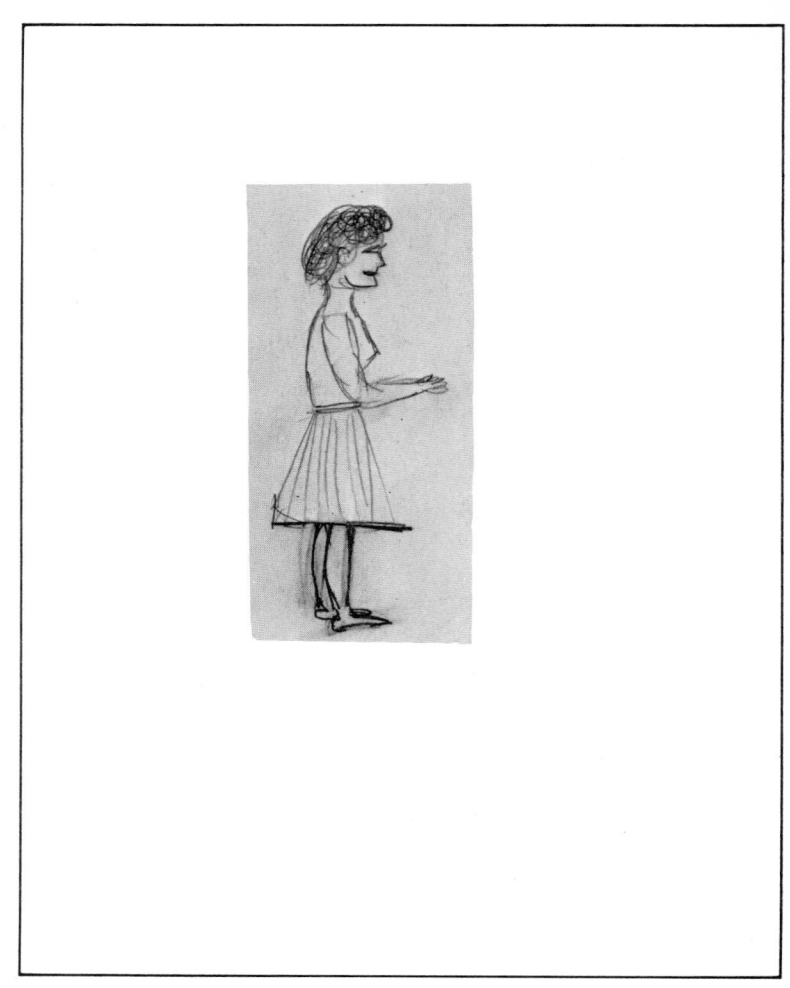

FIGURE-DRAWING CHARACTERISTICS

Structural	Male / Female Both		Structural	Male	Female	Structural and Graphic	Male / Female Both		Graphic, Global and Height	Male	Female	Body Proportions	Male	Female
Type	0		Omission of Appendages	0	0	Upper and Lower Halves	1	1	Hair Shading	7	3	Head	06	06
Sex Sequence	0		Position of Both Arms	1	2	Four Quarters	4	4	Nudity and Transparency	3	9	Neck	07	06
Posture	2	1	Position of Right Arm	5	4	Relative Size	0		Form	3	3	Shoulders	06	
Perspective	0	2	Position of Left Arm	4	7	Constant Line Pressure	0	0	Detailing	5	3	Right Arm	04	04
Vertical Midline	0	4	Position of Legs	8	1	Variable Line Pressure	5	3	Identity and Sex	3	1	Left Arm	04	
Bilateral Symmetry	1	0	Relation of Long Axes	1	1	Line Continuity	1	0	Sophistication	3	3	Chest	04	04
Horizontal Midline	4	4	Right and Left Halves	1	2	Body Shading	0	2	Height	05	04	Girth	04	04

GENERAL CHARACTERISTICS OF SUBJECT

IDENTIFICATION

No. E37
Sex M
Marital status S
Age 24 yrs. at
psychological tests

PARENTAL HISTORY

Father
C	H	S	D	O
–	+	–	–	+

Mother
C	H	S	D	O
–	+	–	–	+

PHYSIOLOGICAL AND METABOLIC DATA

	Admission	Initial	Control	Cold pressor change	Exercise change	Smoking change
Systolic pressure	120	128	108	+22	+36	+17
Diastolic pressure	70	62	70	+20	–12	+12
Heart rate	76	60	57	+04	+22	+21

Age 24 yrs.
Height 75 in.
Weight 188 lbs.
Overweight +03 %
Ponderal index 13.09
Cholesterol 176 mg. per 100 ml.
Vital capacity 5.6 liters

HABIT SURVEY

Smoking habits: nonsmoker
Age begun yrs. Inhalation:
Habits of nervous tension: 2, 6, 25

STRONG VOCATIONAL INTEREST TEST

Occupation	Artist	Psychologist	Architect	Physician	Osteopath	Dentist	Veterinarian	Mathematician	Physicist	Engineer	Chemist	Production Manager
Standard Score	43	45	35	64	59	45	40	39	39	34	41	32

Occupation	Farmer	Aviator	Carpenter	Printer	Math.-Sci. Teacher	Ind. Arts Teacher	Voc. Agric. Teacher	Policeman	Forest Serv. Man	Y.M.C.A. Phys. Dir.	Personnel Director	Public Administrator
Standard Score	37	37	29	29	35	23	45	29	32	34	21	41

Occupation	Y.M.C.A. Secretary	Soc. Sci. H.S. Teacher	City Sch. Sup't.	Social Worker	Minister	Musician Performer	C.P.A.	Senior C.P.A.	Accountant	Office Man	Purchasing Agent	Banker
Standard Score	22	27	29	39	64	48	26	23	09	12	11	27

Occupation	Mortician	Pharmacist	Sales Manager	Real Est. Manager	Life Ins. Salesman	Advertising Man	Lawyer	Author-Journalist	President Mfg. Co.	Interest Maturity	Occupational Level	Masculinity-Femininity
Standard Score	32	41	25	38	30	33	45	41	33	44	58	41

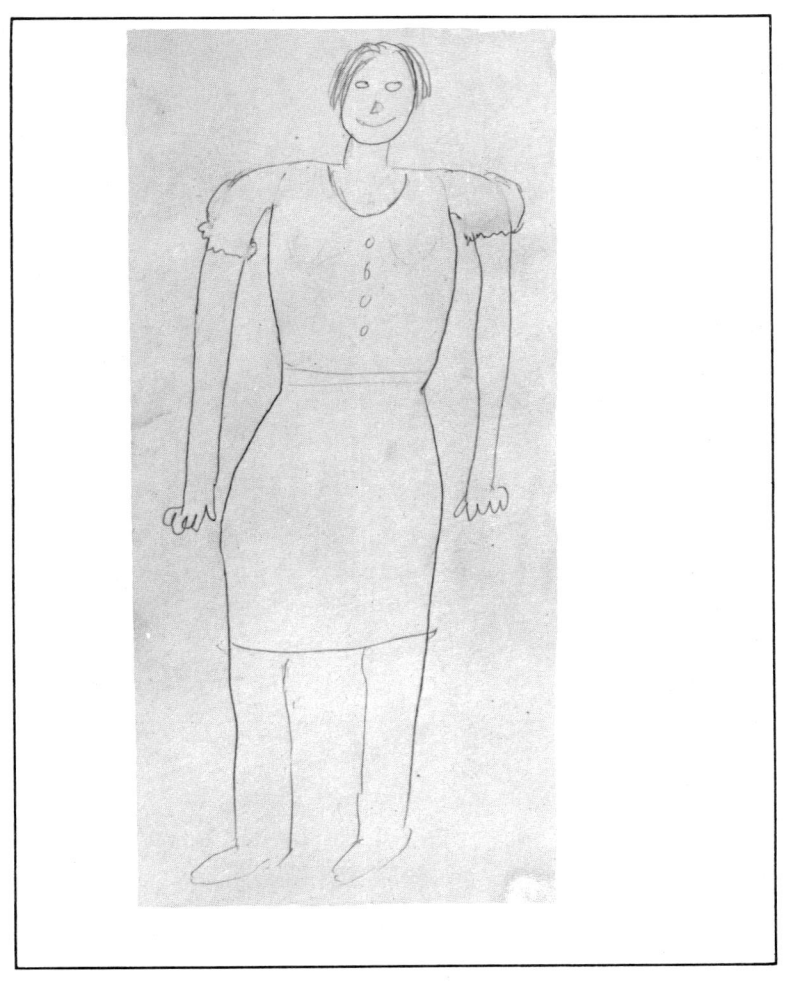
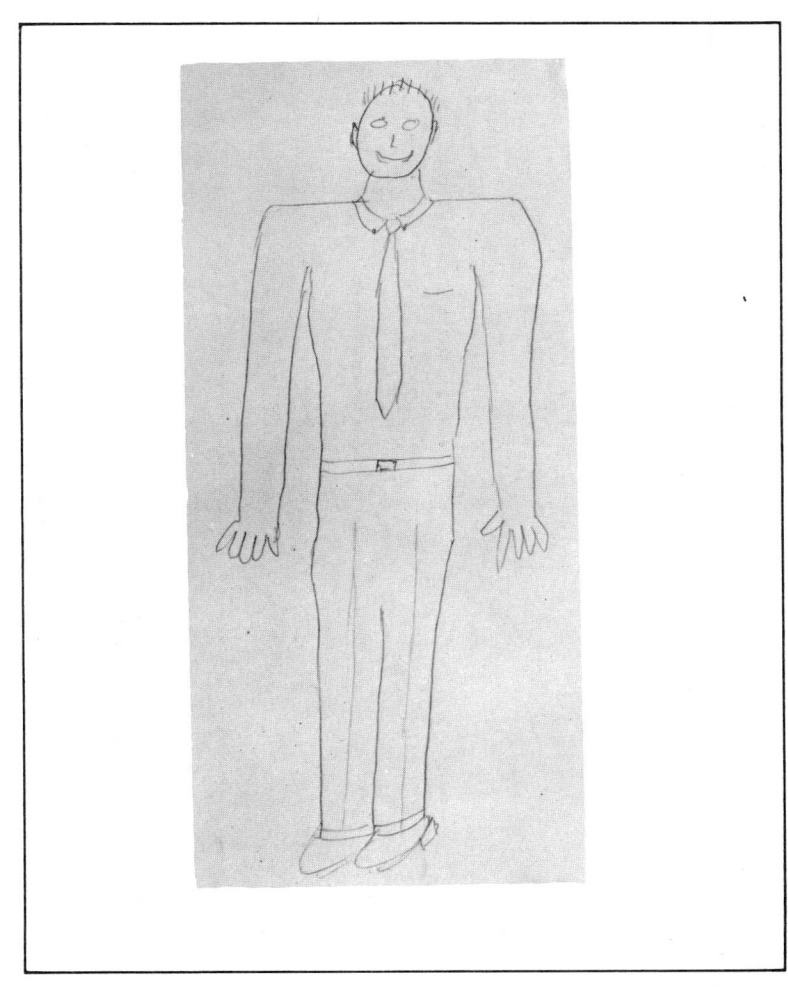

FIGURE-DRAWING CHARACTERISTICS

Structural	Male Female / Both		Structural	Male	Female	Structural and Graphic	Male Female / Both		Graphic, Global and Height	Male	Female	Body Proportions	Male	Female
Type	0		Omission of Appendages	0	0	Upper and Lower Halves	0	1	Hair Shading	7	3	Head	07	08
Sex Sequence	1		Position of Both Arms	0	0	Four Quarters	4	4	Nudity and Transparency	7	7	Neck	08	08
Posture	1	1	Position of Right Arm	0	0	Relative Size	4		Form	3	3	Shoulders	10	10
Perspective	0	0	Position of Left Arm	0	0	Constant Line Pressure	0	0	Detailing	5	5	Right Arm	08	08
Vertical Midline	3	3	Position of Legs	2	5	Variable Line Pressure	1	3	Identity and Sex	1	1	Left Arm	08	08
Bilateral Symmetry	4	3	Relation of Long Axes	1	1	Line Continuity	2	2	Sophistication	3	3	Chest	08	09
Horizontal Midline	4	4	Right and Left Halves	1	1	Body Shading	2	0	Height	08	09	Girth	09	09

GENERAL CHARACTERISTICS OF SUBJECT

IDENTIFICATION

No. G24
Sex M
Marital status S
Age 23 yrs. at
psychological tests

PARENTAL HISTORY

Father
C H S D O
- (+) (+) + +
Mother
C H S D O
- (?) - + +

PHYSIOLOGICAL AND METABOLIC DATA

	Admission	Initial	Control	Cold pressor change	Exercise change	Smoking change
Systolic pressure	120	140	126	-04	+42	+07
Diastolic pressure	70	78	80	+04	-10	+06
Heart rate	60	104	76	-12	+39	+11

Age 22 yrs.
Height 72 in.
Weight 161 lbs.
Overweight -01 %
Ponderal index 13.24
Cholesterol 185 mg. per 100 ml.
Vital capacity liters

HABIT SURVEY

Smoking habits: former smoker
Age begun yrs. Inhalation:
Habits of nervous tension: 4, 5, 9, 16, 21

STRONG VOCATIONAL INTEREST TEST

Occupation	Artist	Psychologist	Architect	Physician	Osteopath	Dentist	Veterinarian	Mathematician	Physicist	Engineer	Chemist	Production Manager
Standard Score	21	39	20	33	41	24	18	26	22	31	40	36

Occupation	Farmer	Aviator	Carpenter	Printer	Math.-Sci. Teacher	Ind. Arts Teacher	Voc. Agric. Teacher	Policeman	Forest Serv. Man	Y.M.C.A. Phys. Dir.	Personnel Director	Public Administrator
Standard Score	32	43	32	45	41	31	30	30	11	28	39	39

Occupation	Y.M.C.A. Secretary	Soc. Sci. H.S. Teacher	City Sch. Sup't.	Social Worker	Minister	Musician Performer	C.P.A.	Senior C.P.A.	Accountant	Office Man	Purchasing Agent	Banker
Standard Score	29	35	19	36	59	39	36	45	36	47	38	29

Occupation	Mortician	Pharmacist	Sales Manager	Real Est. Manager	Life Ins. Salesman	Advertising Man	Lawyer	Author-Journalist	President Mfg. Co.	Interest Maturity	Occupational Level	Masculinity-Femininity
Standard Score	44	47	36	42	29	35	25	29	33	53	50	45

FIGURE-DRAWING CHARACTERISTICS

Structural	Male Female Both		Structural	Male	Female	Structural and Graphic	Male Female Both		Graphic, Global and Height	Male	Female	Body Proportions	Male	Female
Type	0		Omission of Appendages		3	Upper and Lower Halves		7	Hair Shading		3	Head		10
Sex Sequence	4		Position of Both Arms		4	Four Quarters		4	Nudity and Transparency		7	Neck		08
Posture		0	Position of Right Arm		7	Relative Size	7		Form		3	Shoulders		
Perspective		2	Position of Left Arm		4	Constant Line Pressure		3	Detailing		3	Right Arm		
Vertical Midline		4	Position of Legs		0	Variable Line Pressure		0	Identity and Sex		1	Left Arm		06
Bilateral Symmetry		0	Relation of Long Axes		1	Line Continuity		0	Sophistication		3	Chest		09
Horizontal Midline		4	Right and Left Halves		1	Body Shading		0	Height			Girth		13

GENERAL CHARACTERISTICS OF SUBJECT

IDENTIFICATION

No. 273

Sex M

Marital status M

Age 24 yrs. at psychological tests

PARENTAL HISTORY

Father

C	H	S	D	O
-	+	-	-	-

Mother

C	H	S	D	O
-	-	-	-	-

PHYSIOLOGICAL AND METABOLIC DATA

	Admission	Initial	Control	Cold pressor change	Exercise change	Smoking change
Systolic pressure	100	106	100	+04	+36	
Diastolic pressure	64	60	66	+06	-06	
Heart rate	72	74	97	00	+10	

Age 24 yrs.

Height 70 in.   Ponderal index 13.23

Weight 148 lbs.   Cholesterol 252 mg. per 100 ml.

Overweight -05 %   Vital capacity liters

HABIT SURVEY

Smoking habits: occasional smoker

    Age begun 18 yrs.   Inhalation: sometimes

Habits of nervous tension: 5, 6, 17, 22, 25

Plate 288   DRAWINGS AT AN INTERMEDIATE LEVEL OF SOPHISTICATION   331

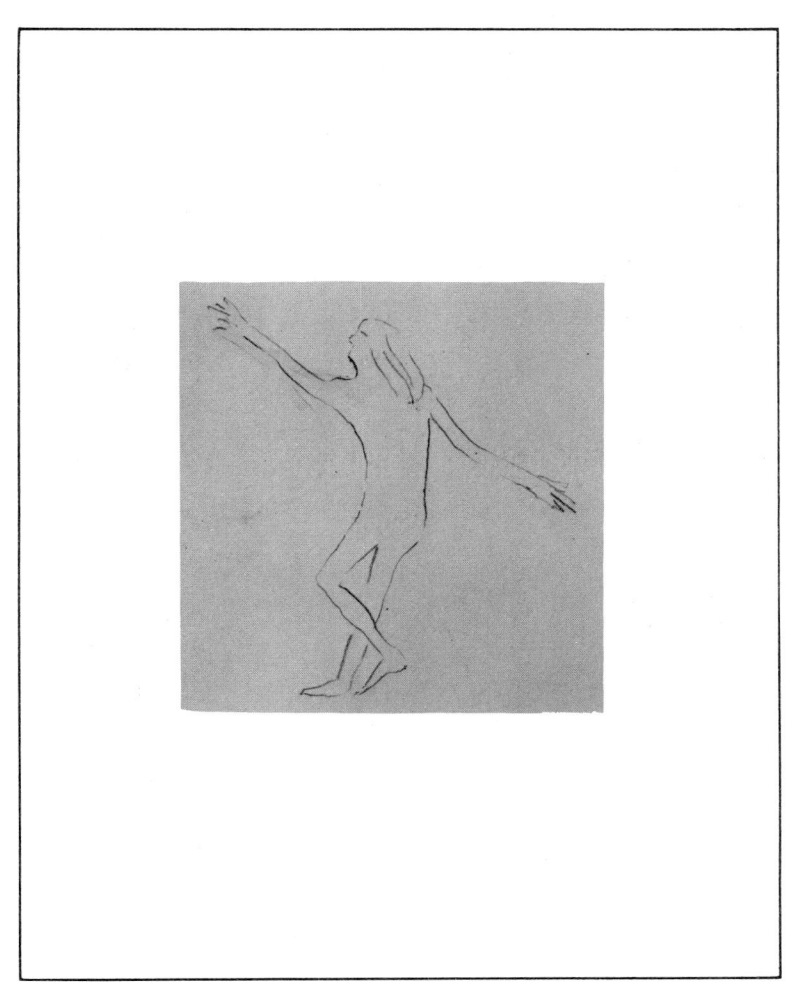

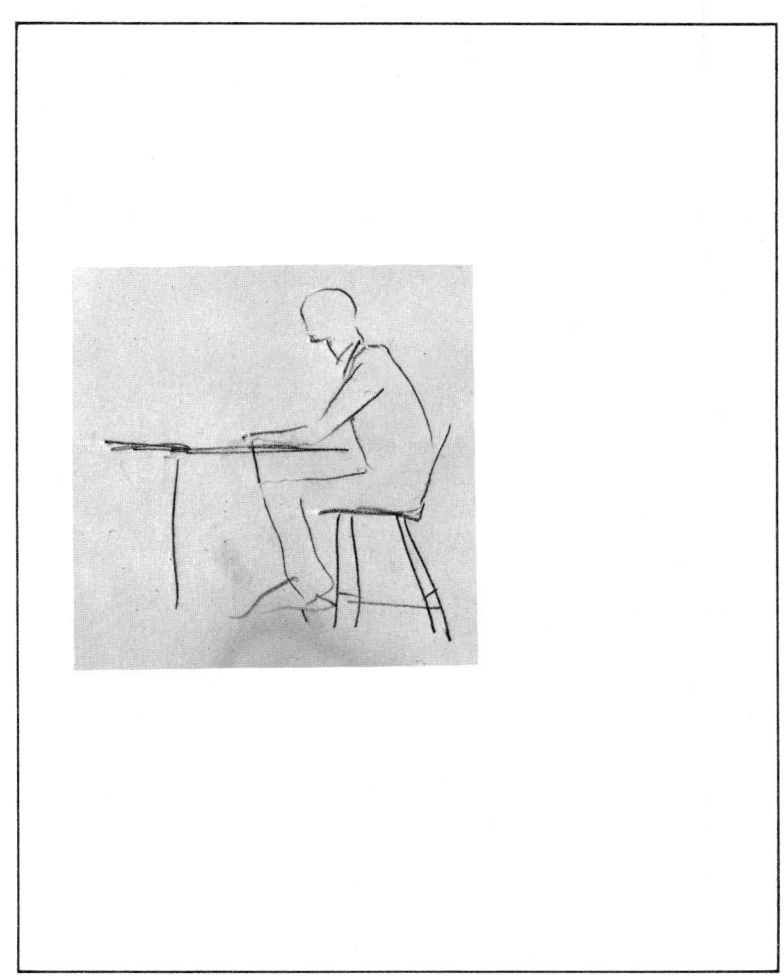

FIGURE-DRAWING CHARACTERISTICS

Structural	Male Female Both	Structural	Male	Female	Structural and Graphic	Male Female Both		Graphic, Global and Height	Male	Female	Body Proportions	Male	Female
Type	0	Omission of Appendages	9	0	Upper and Lower Halves	1	0	Hair Shading	0	7	Head	04	03
Sex Sequence	1	Position of Both Arms	4	0	Four Quarters	4	4	Nudity and Transparency	7	0	Neck	06	04
Posture	3 6	Position of Right Arm	7	6	Relative Size	5		Form	3	3	Shoulders		
Perspective	2 8	Position of Left Arm	2	6	Constant Line Pressure	3	0	Detailing	5	5	Right Arm		
Vertical Midline	4 4	Position of Legs	1	8	Variable Line Pressure	0	1	Identity and Sex	1	3	Left Arm		
Bilateral Symmetry	0 0	Relation of Long Axes	0	1	Line Continuity	2	2	Sophistication	3	3	Chest	05	
Horizontal Midline	0 0	Right and Left Halves	1	0	Body Shading	0	0	Height		04	Girth	05	

GENERAL CHARACTERISTICS OF SUBJECT

IDENTIFICATION
No. 277
Sex M
Marital status S
Age 29 yrs. at
psychological tests

PARENTAL HISTORY
Father
C   H   S   D   O
-   +   (+)   -   -
Mother
C   H   S   D   O
-   -   -   -   ?

PHYSIOLOGICAL AND METABOLIC DATA

	Admission	Initial	Control	Cold pressor change	Exercise change	Smoking change
Systolic pressure	124					
Diastolic pressure	80					
Heart rate	80					

Age 26 yrs.	Height 76 in.	Ponderal index 13.46
	Weight 180 lbs.	Cholesterol 195 mg. per 100 ml.
	Overweight −06 %	Vital capacity liters

HABIT SURVEY
Smoking habits: unknown
Age begun yrs. Inhalation:
Habits of nervous tension: 2, 6

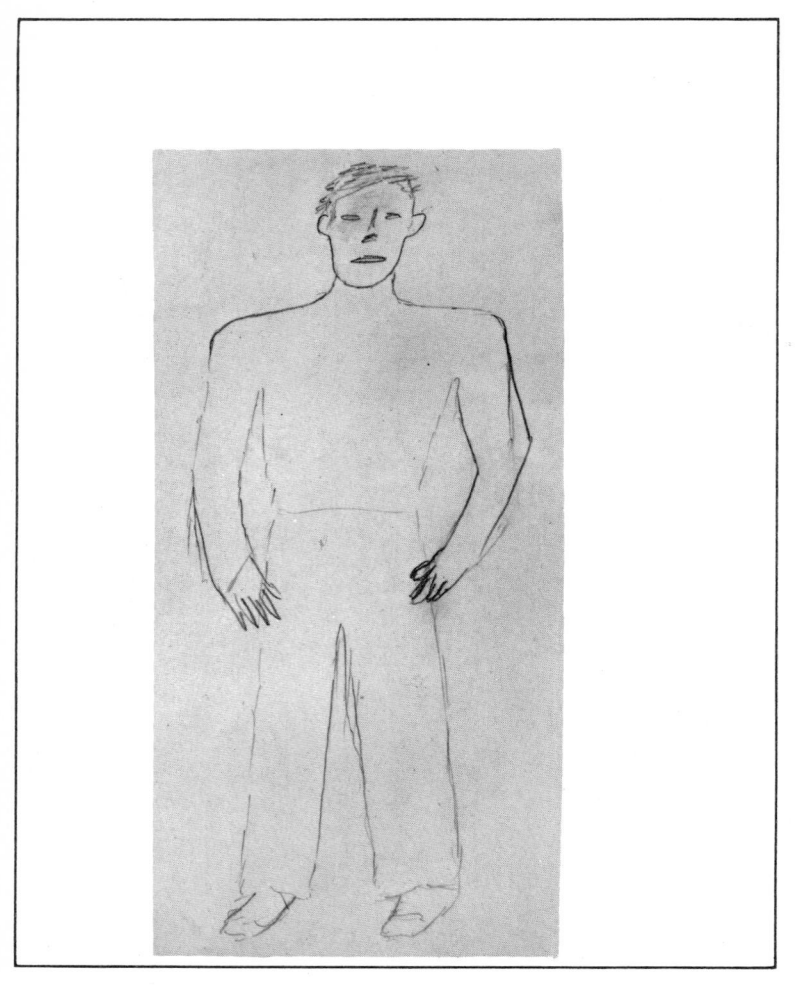

FIGURE-DRAWING CHARACTERISTICS

Structural	Male Female Both	Structural	Male	Female	Structural and Graphic	Male Female Both		Graphic, Global and Height	Male	Female	Body Proportions	Male	Female
Type	0	Omission of Appendages	0		Upper and Lower Halves	3		Hair Shading	3		Head	10	
Sex Sequence	3	Position of Both Arms	0		Four Quarters	4		Nudity and Transparency	3		Neck	08	
Posture	1	Position of Right Arm	5		Relative Size		7	Form	3		Shoulders	11	
Perspective	0	Position of Left Arm	5		Constant Line Pressure	0		Detailing	5		Right Arm	06	
Vertical Midline	0	Position of Legs	6		Variable Line Pressure	3		Identity and Sex	3		Left Arm	06	
Bilateral Symmetry	3	Relation of Long Axes	1		Line Continuity	0		Sophistication	3		Chest	09	
Horizontal Midline	4	Right and Left Halves	1		Body Shading	0		Height	08		Girth	09	

GENERAL CHARACTERISTICS OF SUBJECT

IDENTIFICATION
No. 315
Sex M
Marital status S
Age 24 yrs. at psychological tests

PARENTAL HISTORY				
Father				
C	H	S	D	O
-	+	-	-	?
Mother				
C	H	S	D	O
-	-	-	-	-

PHYSIOLOGICAL AND METABOLIC DATA

	Admission	Initial	Control	Cold pressor change	Exercise change	Smoking change
Systolic pressure	120	94	94	+08	+32	+06
Diastolic pressure	78	54	56	+14	-04	+08
Heart rate	84	68	78	00	+02	+09

	Height 70 in.	Ponderal index 13.15
Age 21 yrs.	Weight 151 lbs.	Cholesterol 152 mg. per 100 ml.
	Overweight -01 %	Vital capacity 3.8 liters

HABIT SURVEY
Smoking habits: nonsmoker
Age begun yrs. Inhalation:
Habits of nervous tension: 5, 9, 17

FIGURE-DRAWING CHARACTERISTICS

Structural	Male Female Both	Structural	Male	Female	Structural and Graphic	Male Female Both		Graphic, Global and Height	Male	Female	Body Proportions	Male	Female
Type	0	Omission of Appendages	0	0	Upper and Lower Halves	0	1	Hair Shading	3	3	Head	08	06
Sex Sequence	0	Position of Both Arms	1	0	Four Quarters	4	4	Nudity and Transparency	7	7	Neck	06	04
Posture	1 1	Position of Right Arm	2	2	Relative Size	0		Form	3	3	Shoulders	10	07
Perspective	0 0	Position of Left Arm	5	2	Constant Line Pressure	0	0	Detailing	3	3	Right Arm	06	04
Vertical Midline	3 0	Position of Legs	6	5	Variable Line Pressure	3	5	Identity and Sex	1	1	Left Arm	08	04
Bilateral Symmetry	3 3	Relation of Long Axes	1	1	Line Continuity	0	2	Sophistication	3	3	Chest	09	06
Horizontal Midline	4 4	Right and Left Halves	1	1	Body Shading	7	4	Height	07	06	Girth	12	08

GENERAL CHARACTERISTICS OF SUBJECT

IDENTIFICATION
No. 435
Sex M
Marital status S
Age 25 yrs. at psychological tests

PARENTAL HISTORY				
Father				
C	H	S	D	O
-	+	-	-	-
Mother				
C	H	S	D	O
-	-	-	-	-

PHYSIOLOGICAL AND METABOLIC DATA

	Admission	Initial	Control	Cold pressor change	Exercise change	Smoking change
Systolic pressure	150	132	120	+08	+38	
Diastolic pressure	76	62	64	+04	-04	
Heart rate	66	78	71	00	+06	

Age 22 yrs.	Height	70	in.	Ponderal index 13.06	
	Weight	154	lbs.	Cholesterol	250 mg. per 100 ml.
	Overweight 00 %			Vital capacity	5.2 liters

HABIT SURVEY
Smoking habits: mixed smoker
Age begun 21 yrs.   Inhalation: yes
Habits of nervous tension: 6, 21

FIGURE-DRAWING CHARACTERISTICS

Structural	Male Female Both	Structural	Male	Female	Structural and Graphic	Male Female Both		Graphic, Global and Height	Male	Female	Body Proportions	Male	Female
Type	0	Omission of Appendages	0	0	Upper and Lower Halves	2	2	Hair Shading	3	3	Head	05	05
Sex Sequence	0	Position of Both Arms	0	0	Four Quarters	0	0	Nudity and Transparency	0	0	Neck	02	06
Posture	2 2	Position of Right Arm	6	6	Relative Size	4		Form	3	3	Shoulders		
Perspective	2 2	Position of Left Arm	6	6	Constant Line Pressure	0	0	Detailing	5	5	Right Arm		
Vertical Midline	4 4	Position of Legs	8	8	Variable Line Pressure	5	5	Identity and Sex	5	3	Left Arm	02	02
Bilateral Symmetry	0 0	Relation of Long Axes	1	1	Line Continuity	0	0	Sophistication	3	3	Chest	03	04
Horizontal Midline	0 0	Right and Left Halves	2	2	Body Shading	0	0	Height	02	03	Girth	03	04

GENERAL CHARACTERISTICS OF SUBJECT

IDENTIFICATION

No. 446

Sex M

Marital status S

Age 23 yrs. at

psychological tests

PARENTAL HISTORY

Father

C	H	S	D	O
-	+	-	-	?

Mother

C	H	S	D	O
-	-	-	-	-

PHYSIOLOGICAL AND METABOLIC DATA

	Admission	Initial	Control	Cold pressor change	Exercise change	Smoking change
Systolic pressure	130	128	105	+04	+25	
Diastolic pressure	70	78	74	+14	+02	
Heart rate	84	72	75	+06	+11	

Age 22 yrs.

Height   72 in.

Weight   177 lbs.

Overweight +09 %

Ponderal index 12.82

Cholesterol   203   mg. per 100 ml.

Vital capacity   5.2   liters

HABIT SURVEY

Smoking habits: moderate cigarette smoker

Age begun 18 yrs.   Inhalation: yes

Habits of nervous tension: 3, 4, 6, 9, 18,

19, 22, 23, 24

Plate 292   DRAWINGS AT AN INTERMEDIATE LEVEL OF SOPHISTICATION   335

FIGURE-DRAWING CHARACTERISTICS

Structural	Male Female Both	Structural	Male	Female	Structural and Graphic	Male Female Both		Graphic, Global and Height	Male	Female	Body Proportions	Male	Female
Type	0	Omission of Appendages	8	7	Upper and Lower Halves	7	3	Hair Shading	2	3	Head	07	03
Sex Sequence	1	Position of Both Arms	4	1	Four Quarters	4	4	Nudity and Transparency	7	7	Neck	07	06
Posture	0	1	Position of Right Arm	7	4	Relative Size	0		Form	3	3	Shoulders		03
Perspective	2	0	Position of Left Arm	4	5	Constant Line Pressure	1	1	Detailing	3	3	Right Arm		04
Vertical Midline	7	0	Position of Legs	1	4	Variable Line Pressure	0	0	Identity and Sex	1	1	Left Arm	06	
Bilateral Symmetry	0	2	Relation of Long Axes	1	1	Line Continuity	0	0	Sophistication	3	3	Chest	09	03
Horizontal Midline	4	4	Right and Left Halves	0	1	Body Shading	7	3	Height		03	Girth	07	04

GENERAL CHARACTERISTICS OF SUBJECT

IDENTIFICATION
No. 522
Sex M
Marital status   M
Age 24 yrs. at
psychological tests

PARENTAL HISTORY
Father
C   H   S   D   O
-     +   -   -   -
Mother
C   H   S   D   O
-     -   -   -   +

PHYSIOLOGICAL AND METABOLIC DATA

	Admission	Initial	Control	Cold pressor change	Exercise change	Smoking change
Systolic pressure	130	140	130	+10	+40	+05
Diastolic pressure	70	90	80	+10	00	+04
Heart rate	72	108	82	-16	+23	+10

	Height 70 in.	Ponderal index 12.61
Age 22 yrs.	Weight 171 lbs.	Cholesterol 222 mg. per 100 ml.
	Overweight +11 %	Vital capacity 5.0 liters

HABIT SURVEY

Smoking habits: mixed smoker

Age begun 15 yrs.   Inhalation: yes

Habits of nervous tension: 4, 5, 6, 9, 19,
22, 23

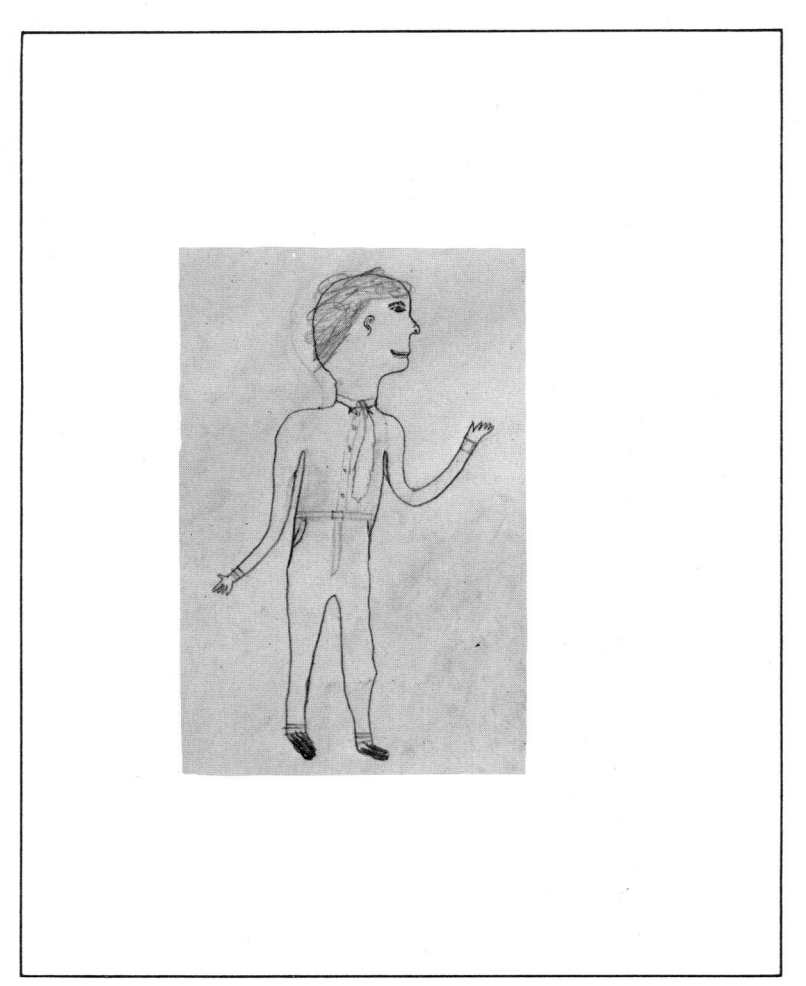

FIGURE-DRAWING CHARACTERISTICS

Structural	Male Female Both	Structural	Male	Female	Structural and Graphic	Male Female Both	Graphic, Global and Height	Male	Female	Body Proportions	Male	Female
Type	0	Omission of Appendages	0	0	Upper and Lower Halves	0 0	Hair Shading	3	3	Head	07	09
Sex Sequence	0	Position of Both Arms	1	0	Four Quarters	4 4	Nudity and Transparency	7	7	Neck	10	08
Posture	1 1	Position of Right Arm	4	2	Relative Size	4	Form	5	5	Shoulders	05	07
Perspective	5 0	Position of Left Arm	3	2	Constant Line Pressure	5 1	Detailing	3	3	Right Arm	04	04
Vertical Midline	3 0	Position of Legs	6	6	Variable Line Pressure	0 0	Identity and Sex	1	1	Left Arm	04	04
Bilateral Symmetry	3 3	Relation of Long Axes	1	1	Line Continuity	4 0	Sophistication	3	3	Chest	03	06
Horizontal Midline	4 4	Right and Left Halves	1	0	Body Shading	4 5	Height	05	06	Girth	05	07

GENERAL CHARACTERISTICS OF SUBJECT

IDENTIFICATION
No. 630
Sex M
Marital status S
Age 24 yrs. at psychological tests

PARENTAL HISTORY
Father
C   H   S   D   O
-   +   -   -   +
Mother
C   H   S   D   O
-   -   -   -   -

PHYSIOLOGICAL AND METABOLIC DATA

	Admission	Initial	Control	Cold pressor change	Exercise change	Smoking change
Systolic pressure	160	128	120	+18	+50	+04
Diastolic pressure	80	72	76	+14	+06	+10
Heart rate	84	72	71	-04	+23	+04

Age 22 yrs.	Height 74 in.	Ponderal index 13.58
	Weight 162 lbs.	Cholesterol 273 mg. per 100 ml.
	Overweight -06 %	Vital capacity 5.5 liters

HABIT SURVEY
Smoking habits: nonsmoker
Age begun   yrs.   Inhalation:
Habits of nervous tension: 5, 6, 9, 19, 21, 23

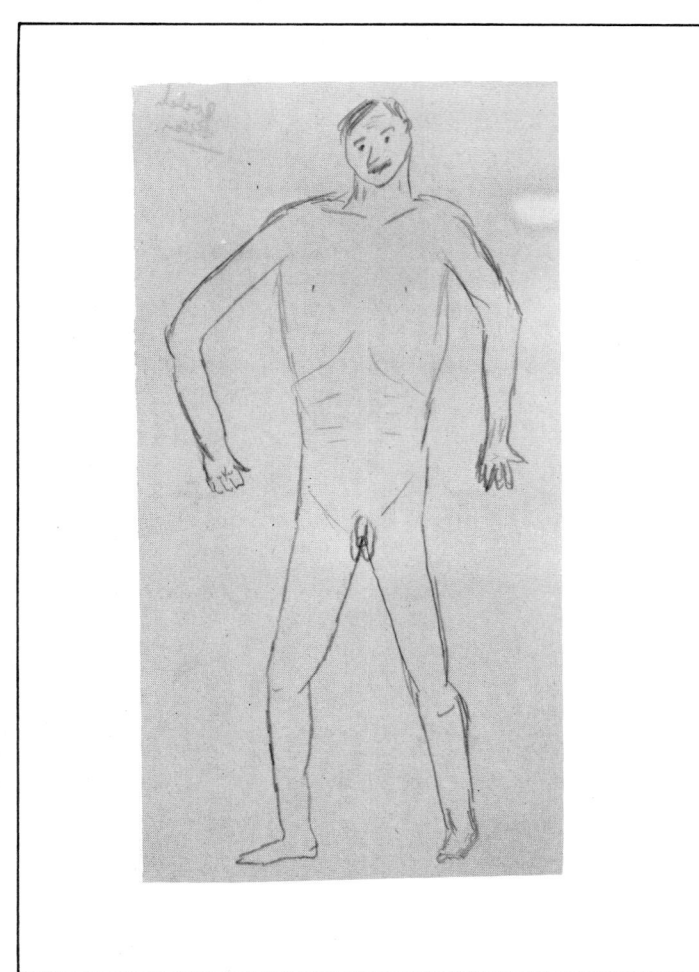

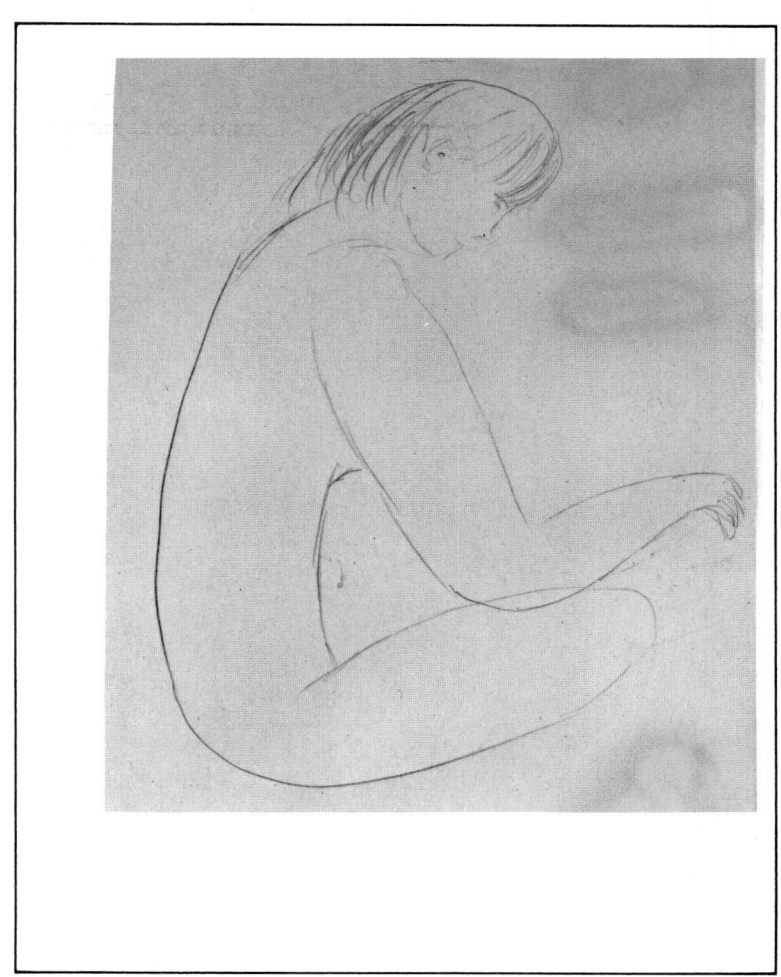

FIGURE-DRAWING CHARACTERISTICS

Structural	Male	Female	Structural	Male	Female	Structural and Graphic	Male	Female	Graphic, Global and Height	Male	Female	Body Proportions	Male	Female
	Both						Both							
Type	0		Omission of Appendages	0	3	Upper and Lower Halves	1	1	Hair Shading	3	2	Head	07	14
Sex Sequence	0		Position of Both Arms	0	2	Four Quarters	4	4	Nudity and Transparency	0	0	Neck	07	
Posture	2	3	Position of Right Arm	5	2	Relative Size	4		Form	3	3	Shoulders	08	
Perspective	0	2	Position of Left Arm	5	7	Constant Line Pressure	0	0	Detailing	3	5	Right Arm	08	14
Vertical Midline	0	4	Position of Legs	8	0	Variable Line Pressure	1	1	Identity and Sex	1	1	Left Arm	07	
Bilateral Symmetry	3	0	Relation of Long Axes	1	0	Line Continuity	0	3	Sophistication	3	3	Chest	08	
Horizontal Midline	0	0	Right and Left Halves	1	1	Body Shading	3	0	Height	08		Girth	08	15

GENERAL CHARACTERISTICS OF SUBJECT

IDENTIFICATION
No. 771
Sex M
Marital status S
Age 25 yrs. at
psychological tests

PARENTAL HISTORY					
Father					
C	H	S	D	O	
−	+	−	?	?	
Mother					
C	H	S	D	O	
−	−	−	−	+	

PHYSIOLOGICAL AND METABOLIC DATA

	Admission	Initial	Control	Cold pressor change	Exercise change	Smoking change
Systolic pressure	125	110	115	+19	+33	+02
Diastolic pressure	80	60	58	+28	−03	+03
Heart rate	80	60	56	+07	+59	+17

Age 22 yrs.	Height 70 in.	Ponderal index 12.77
	Weight 165 lbs.	Cholesterol 300 mg. per 100 ml.
	Overweight +07 %	Vital capacity 5.2 liters

HABIT SURVEY

Smoking habits: light cigarette smoker

Age begun 19 yrs.   Inhalation: yes

Habits of nervous tension: 25

FIGURE-DRAWING CHARACTERISTICS

Structural	Male Female Both		Structural	Male	Female	Structural and Graphic	Male Female Both		Graphic, Global and Height	Male	Female	Body Proportions	Male	Female
Type	0		Omission of Appendages	0	0	Upper and Lower Halves	3	3	Hair Shading	3	3	Head	09	12
Sex Sequence	1		Position of Both Arms	0	0	Four Quarters	4	4	Nudity and Transparency	7	7	Neck	05	08
Posture	1	1	Position of Right Arm	2	2	Relative Size	1		Form	3	3	Shoulders	08	07
Perspective	0	0	Position of Left Arm	2	2	Constant Line Pressure	0	0	Detailing	3	3	Right Arm	06	06
Vertical Midline	3	3	Position of Legs	4	4	Variable Line Pressure	1	4	Identity and Sex	1	1	Left Arm	06	06
Bilateral Symmetry	3	3	Relation of Long Axes	1	1	Line Continuity	0	0	Sophistication	3	3	Chest	07	07
Horizontal Midline	4	4	Right and Left Halves	1	0	Body Shading	1	3	Height	07	07	Girth	06	07

GENERAL CHARACTERISTICS OF SUBJECT

IDENTIFICATION
No. A13
Sex M
Marital status M
Age 23 yrs. at psychological tests

PARENTAL HISTORY				
Father				
C	H	S	D	O
-	+	+	-	+
Mother				
C	H	S	D	O
-	-	-	-	-

PHYSIOLOGICAL AND METABOLIC DATA

	Admission	Initial	Control	Cold pressor change	Exercise change	Smoking change
Systolic pressure	120	130	132	+18	+30	+03
Diastolic pressure	90	66	81	+14	-15	+18
Heart rate	60	61	64	+09	+07	+02

Age 22 yrs.	Height 72 in.	Ponderal index 11.88
	Weight 222 lbs.	Cholesterol 280 mg. per 100 ml.
	Overweight +36 %	Vital capacity liters

HABIT SURVEY

Smoking habits: occasional smoker

Age begun 20 yrs.   Inhalation: sometimes

Habits of nervous tension: 5, 6, 10, 25

STRONG VOCATIONAL INTEREST TEST

Occupation	Artist	Psychologist	Architect	Physician	Osteopath	Dentist	Veterinarian	Mathematician	Physicist	Engineer	Chemist	Production Manager
Standard Score	4	5	5	7	4	4	2	5	5	4	5	2

Occupation	Farmer	Aviator	Carpenter	Printer	Math.-Sci. Teacher	Ind. Arts Teacher	Voc. Agric. Teacher	Policeman	Forest Serv. Man	Y.M.C.A. Phys. Dir.	Personnel Director	Public Administrator
Standard Score	6	6	4	6	6	2	3	4	7	2	2	3

Occupation	Y.M.C.A. Secretary	Soc. Sci. H.S. Teacher	City Sch. Sup't.	Social Worker	Minister	Musician Performer	C.P.A.	Senior C.P.A.	Accountant	Office Man	Purchasing Agent	Banker
Standard Score	2	2	2	2	6	5	3	6	2	4	2	2

Occupation	Mortician	Pharmacist	Sales Manager	Real Est. Manager	Life Ins. Salesman	Advertising Man	Lawyer	Author-Journalist	President Mfg. Co.	Interest Maturity	Occupational Level	Masculinity-Femininity
Standard Score	2	4	2	4	2	3	5	5	2	4	4	6

Plate 296　　　DRAWINGS AT AN INTERMEDIATE LEVEL OF SOPHISTICATION　　　339

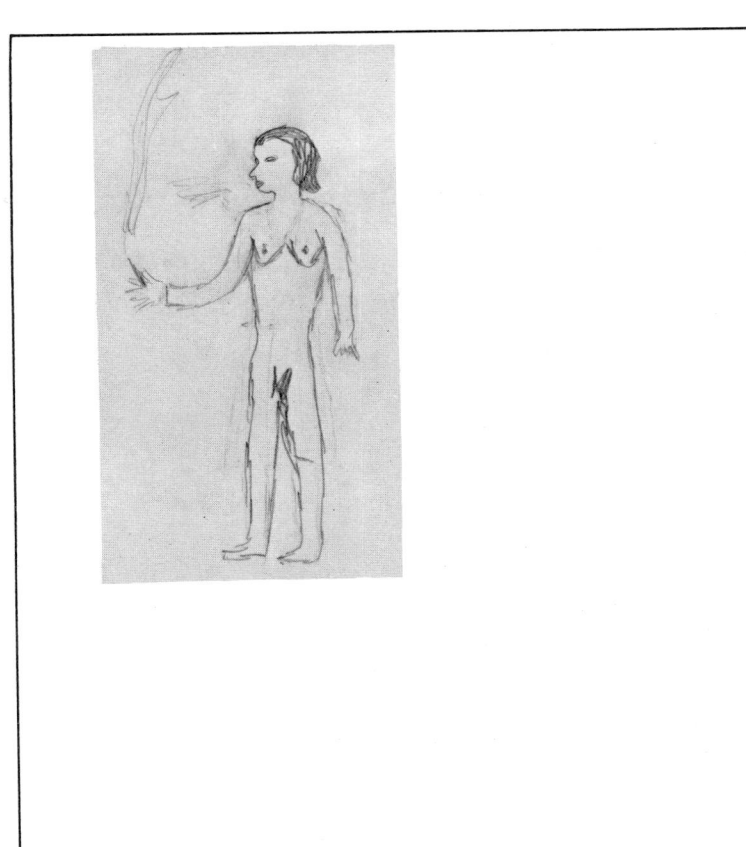

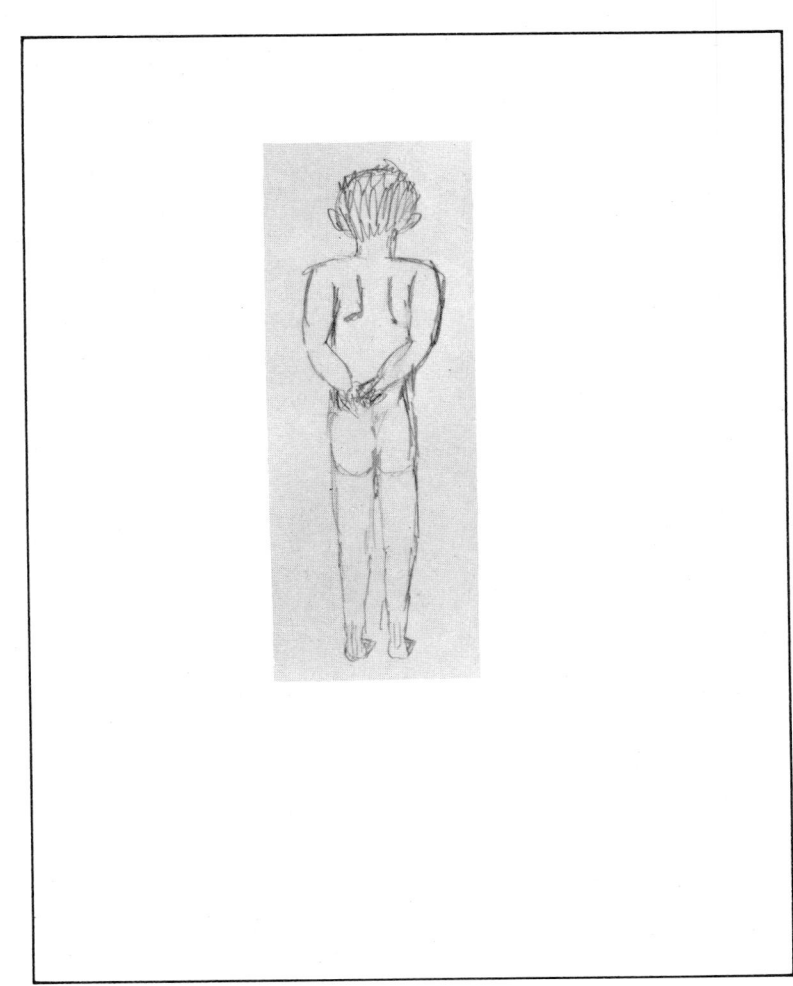

FIGURE-DRAWING CHARACTERISTICS

Structural	Male Female Both		Structural	Male	Female	Structural and Graphic	Male Female Both		Graphic, Global and Height	Male	Female	Body Proportions	Male	Female
Type	0		Omission of Appendages	0	0	Upper and Lower Halves	1	1	Hair Shading	3	1	Head		05
Sex Sequence	1		Position of Both Arms	0	1	Four Quarters	4	4	Nudity and Transparency	0	0	Neck		03
Posture	1	1	Position of Right Arm	5	4	Relative Size	0		Form	1	3	Shoulders	05	04
Perspective	3	5	Position of Left Arm	5	0	Constant Line Pressure	0	0	Detailing	1	3	Right Arm	04	04
Vertical Midline	8	0	Position of Legs	4	4	Variable Line Pressure	2	1	Identity and Sex	3	1	Left Arm	04	02
Bilateral Symmetry	3	3	Relation of Long Axes	1	1	Line Continuity	0	0	Sophistication	3	3	Chest	03	03
Horizontal Midline	0	0	Right and Left Halves	1	2	Body Shading	3	3	Height	05	04	Girth	04	03

GENERAL CHARACTERISTICS OF SUBJECT

IDENTIFICATION
No. A39
Sex M
Marital status M
Age 23 yrs. at
psychological tests

PARENTAL HISTORY				
Father				
C	H	S	D	O
-	+	-	-	-
Mother				
C	H	S	D	O
-	-	-	-	-

PHYSIOLOGICAL AND METABOLIC DATA

	Admission	Initial	Control	Cold pressor change	Exercise change	Smoking change
Systolic pressure	124	132	120	+12	+12	+04
Diastolic pressure	80	64	63	+14	-03	+04
Heart rate	72	80	78	+09	+10	+02

Age 22 yrs.	Height 69 in.	Ponderal index 13.42
	Weight 136 lbs.	Cholesterol 243 mg. per 100 ml.
	Overweight -09 %	Vital capacity liters

HABIT SURVEY

Smoking habits: former smoker

Age begun　　yrs.　　Inhalation: no

Habits of nervous tension: 1, 3, 4, 5, 6, 7, 8, 9, 10, 11, 12, 14, 16, 18, 19, 20, 22, 23, 25

STRONG VOCATIONAL INTEREST TEST

Occupation	Artist	Psychologist	Architect	Physician	Osteopath	Dentist	Veterinarian	Mathematician	Physicist	Engineer	Chemist	Production Manager
Standard Score	34	43	34	49	45	37	12	34	30	38	47	26

Occupation	Farmer	Aviator	Carpenter	Printer	Math.-Sci. Teacher	Ind. Arts Teacher	Voc. Agric. Teacher	Policeman	Forest Serv. Man	Y.M.C.A. Phys. Dir.	Personnel Director	Public Administrator
Standard Score	23	38	11	29	30	05	01	24	14	33	32	49

Occupation	Y.M.C.A. Secretary	Soc. Sci. H.S. Teacher	City Sch. Sup't.	Social Worker	Minister	Musician Performer	C.P.A.	Senior C.P.A.	Accountant	Office Man	Purchasing Agent	Banker
Standard Score	19	33	22	39	60	43	44	46	34	35	28	21

Occupation	Mortician	Pharmacist	Sales Manager	Real Est. Manager	Life Ins. Salesman	Advertising Man	Lawyer	Author-Journalist	President Mfg. Co.	Interest Maturity	Occupational Level	Masculinity-Femininity
Standard Score	19	26	28	30	34	36	42	41	33	53	60	37

FIGURE-DRAWING CHARACTERISTICS

Structural	Male Female Both	Structural	Male	Female	Structural and Graphic	Male Female Both		Graphic, Global and Height	Male	Female	Body Proportions	Male	Female
Type	0	Omission of Appendages	0	0	Upper and Lower Halves	1	1	Hair Shading	1	2	Head	07	06
Sex Sequence	2	Position of Both Arms	1	0	Four Quarters	4	4	Nudity and Transparency	7	7	Neck	06	04
Posture	1 1	Position of Right Arm	5	5	Relative Size	2		Form	3	3	Shoulders	08	07
Perspective	0 0	Position of Left Arm	0	5	Constant Line Pressure	3	3	Detailing	3	3	Right Arm	06	06
Vertical Midline	3 0	Position of Legs	6	6	Variable Line Pressure	0	0	Identity and Sex	1	1	Left Arm	06	05
Bilateral Symmetry	3 3	Relation of Long Axes	1	1	Line Continuity	0	0	Sophistication	3	3	Chest	06	06
Horizontal Midline	4 4	Right and Left Halves	1	3	Body Shading	2	3	Height	07	06	Girth	05	05

GENERAL CHARACTERISTICS OF SUBJECT

IDENTIFICATION
No. A67
Sex M
Marital status M
Age 23 yrs. at
psychological tests

PARENTAL HISTORY
Father
C H S D O
- + - - -
Mother
C H S D O
- - - - -

PHYSIOLOGICAL AND METABOLIC DATA

	Admission	Initial	Control	Cold pressor change	Exercise change	Smoking change
Systolic pressure	134	118	112	+11	+34	+08
Diastolic pressure	76	73	63	+11	-25	+04
Heart rate	72	81	88	+24	+19	+14

Age 23 yrs.	Height 70 in.	Ponderal index 12.82
	Weight 163 lbs.	Cholesterol 280 mg. per 100 ml.
	Overweight +05 %	Vital capacity liters

HABIT SURVEY
Smoking habits: nonsmoker
Age begun yrs. Inhalation:
Habits of nervous tension: 2, 4, 5, 6, 11, 21

STRONG VOCATIONAL INTEREST TEST

Occupation	Artist	Psychologist	Architect	Physician	Osteopath	Dentist	Veterinarian	Mathematician	Physicist	Engineer	Chemist	Production Manager
Standard Score	42	44	41	58	60	45	13	28	27	40	47	33

Occupation	Farmer	Aviator	Carpenter	Printer	Math.-Sci. Teacher	Ind. Arts Teacher	Voc. Agric. Teacher	Policeman	Forest Serv. Man	Y.M.C.A. Phys. Dir.	Personnel Director	Public Administrator
Standard Score	23	38	21	35	34	15	02	32	31	38	46	46

Occupation	Y.M.C.A. Secretary	Soc. Sci. H.S. Teacher	City Sch. Sup't.	Social Worker	Minister	Musician Performer	C.P.A.	Senior C.P.A.	Accountant	Office Man	Purchasing Agent	Banker
Standard Score	27	26	26	43	60	44	24	28	22	28	14	05

Occupation	Mortician	Pharmacist	Sales Manager	Real Est. Manager	Life Ins. Salesman	Advertising Man	Lawyer	Author-Journalist	President Mfg. Co.	Interest Maturity	Occupational Level	Masculinity-Femininity
Standard Score	19	24	25	32	34	40	41	44	33	58	61	36

FIGURE-DRAWING CHARACTERISTICS

Structural	Male Female Both		Structural	Male	Female	Structural and Graphic	Male Female Both		Graphic, Global and Height	Male	Female	Body Proportions	Male	Female
Type	0		Omission of Appendages	0	7	Upper and Lower Halves	1	1	Hair Shading	1	1	Head	09	11
Sex Sequence	0		Position of Both Arms	0	0	Four Quarters	4	4	Nudity and Transparency	7	7	Neck	08	12
Posture	1	1	Position of Right Arm	0	5	Relative Size	4		Form	3	3	Shoulders	07	08
Perspective	0	0	Position of Left Arm	0	5	Constant Line Pressure	0	0	Detailing	3	3	Right Arm	03	
Vertical Midline	3	3	Position of Legs	6	6	Variable Line Pressure	4	5	Identity and Sex	1	1	Left Arm	03	
Bilateral Symmetry	3	4	Relation of Long Axes	3	3	Line Continuity	4	4	Sophistication	3	3	Chest	06	09
Horizontal Midline	4	4	Right and Left Halves	2	3	Body Shading	5	7	Height	06	06	Girth	07	05

GENERAL CHARACTERISTICS OF SUBJECT

IDENTIFICATION
No. C62
Sex M
Marital status S
Age 21 yrs. at
psychological tests

PARENTAL HISTORY				
Father				
C	H	S	D	O
-	+	-	-	+
Mother				
C	H	S	D	O
-	-	-	-	-

PHYSIOLOGICAL AND METABOLIC DATA

	Admission	Initial	Control	Cold pressor change	Exercise change	Smoking change
Systolic pressure	140	150	118	+20	+52	+04
Diastolic pressure	70	75	65	+10	-05	+08
Heart rate	92	96	94	+06	+21	+10

Age 22 yrs.	Height 71 in.	Ponderal index 12.48
	Weight 184 lbs.	Cholesterol 218 mg. per 100 ml.
	Overweight +16 %	Vital capacity 4.6 liters

HABIT SURVEY

Smoking habits: heavy cigarette smoker

Age begun 13 yrs.   Inhalation: yes

Habits of nervous tension: 4, 5, 6, 9, 18

STRONG VOCATIONAL INTEREST TEST

Occupation	Artist	Psychologist	Architect	Physician	Osteopath	Dentist	Veterinarian	Mathematician	Physicist	Engineer	Chemist	Production Manager
Standard Score	16	43	16	52	41	31	22	29	14	20	34	27

Occupation	Farmer	Aviator	Carpenter	Printer	Math.-Sci. Teacher	Ind. Arts Teacher	Voc. Agric. Teacher	Policeman	Forest Serv. Man	Y.M.C.A. Phys. Dir.	Personnel Director	Public Administrator
Standard Score	26	27	10	43	49	13	29	30	18	36	39	48

Occupation	Y.M.C.A. Secretary	Soc. Sci. H.S. Teacher	City Sch. Sup't.	Social Worker	Minister	Musician Performer	C.P.A.	Senior C.P.A.	Accountant	Office Man	Purchasing Agent	Banker
Standard Score	34	47	44	43	62	41	26	44	31	39	23	30

Occupation	Mortician	Pharmacist	Sales Manager	Real Est. Manager	Life Ins. Salesman	Advertising Man	Lawyer	Author- Journalist	President Mfg. Co.	Interest Maturity	Occupational Level	Masculinity- Femininity
Standard Score	28	42	23	30	29	31	39	33	19	58	54	47

FIGURE-DRAWING CHARACTERISTICS

Structural	Male Female Both	Structural	Male	Female	Structural and Graphic	Male Female Both		Graphic, Global and Height	Male	Female	Body Proportions	Male	Female
Type	0	Omission of Appendages	0	0	Upper and Lower Halves	1	1	Hair Shading	2	1	Head	04	05
Sex Sequence	1	Position of Both Arms	0	0	Four Quarters	4	4	Nudity and Transparency	7	7	Neck	05	05
Posture	1	1	Position of Right Arm	0	0	Relative Size	4		Form	3	3	Shoulders	05	05
Perspective	0	0	Position of Left Arm	0	0	Constant Line Pressure	0	0	Detailing	1	1	Right Arm	02	03
Vertical Midline	3	0	Position of Legs	6	4	Variable Line Pressure	1	1	Identity and Sex	1	1	Left Arm	02	02
Bilateral Symmetry	4	4	Relation of Long Axes	1	1	Line Continuity	1	1	Sophistication	3	3	Chest	04	04
Horizontal Midline	6	4	Right and Left Halves	2	2	Body Shading	0	5	Height	03	04	Girth	04	05

GENERAL CHARACTERISTICS OF SUBJECT

IDENTIFICATION
No. D40
Sex M
Marital status M
Age 23 yrs. at
psychological tests

PARENTAL HISTORY				
Father				
C	H	S	D	O
-	+	-	-	+
Mother				
C	H	S	D	O
-	-	-	-	-

PHYSIOLOGICAL AND METABOLIC DATA

	Admission	Initial	Control	Cold pressor change	Exercise change	Smoking change
Systolic pressure	126	115	116	+04	+24	+04
Diastolic pressure	70	72	74	+22	-16	+10
Heart rate	84	72	73	00	+19	+22

Age 24 yrs.   Height 72 in.   Ponderal index 12.77
Weight 179 lbs.   Cholesterol 168 mg. per 100 ml.
Overweight +10 %   Vital capacity 4.7 liters

HABIT SURVEY

Smoking habits: moderate cigarette smoker
Age begun 18 yrs.   Inhalation: yes
Habits of nervous tension: 5, 6, 22

STRONG VOCATIONAL INTEREST TEST

Occupation	Artist	Psychologist	Architect	Physician	Osteopath	Dentist	Veterinarian	Mathematician	Physicist	Engineer	Chemist	Production Manager
Standard Score	12	39	10	40	44	26	22	12	07	22	28	32

Occupation	Farmer	Aviator	Carpenter	Printer	Math.-Sci. Teacher	Ind. Arts Teacher	Voc. Agric. Teacher	Policeman	Forest Serv. Man	Y.M.C.A. Phys. Dir.	Personnel Director	Public Administrator
Standard Score	27	23	14	39	52	19	25	34	21	45	53	51

Occupation	Y.M.C.A. Secretary	Soc. Sci. H.S. Teacher	City Sch. Sup't.	Social Worker	Minister	Musician Performer	C.P.A.	Senior C.P.A.	Accountant	Office Man	Purchasing Agent	Banker
Standard Score	47	55	43	53	63	32	31	44	36	48	21	24

Occupation	Mortician	Pharmacist	Sales Manager	Real Est. Manager	Life Ins. Salesman	Advertising Man	Lawyer	Author- Journalist	President Mfg. Co.	Interest Maturity	Occupational Level	Masculinity- Femininity
Standard Score	31	39	33	31	38	28	32	24	29	66	53	46

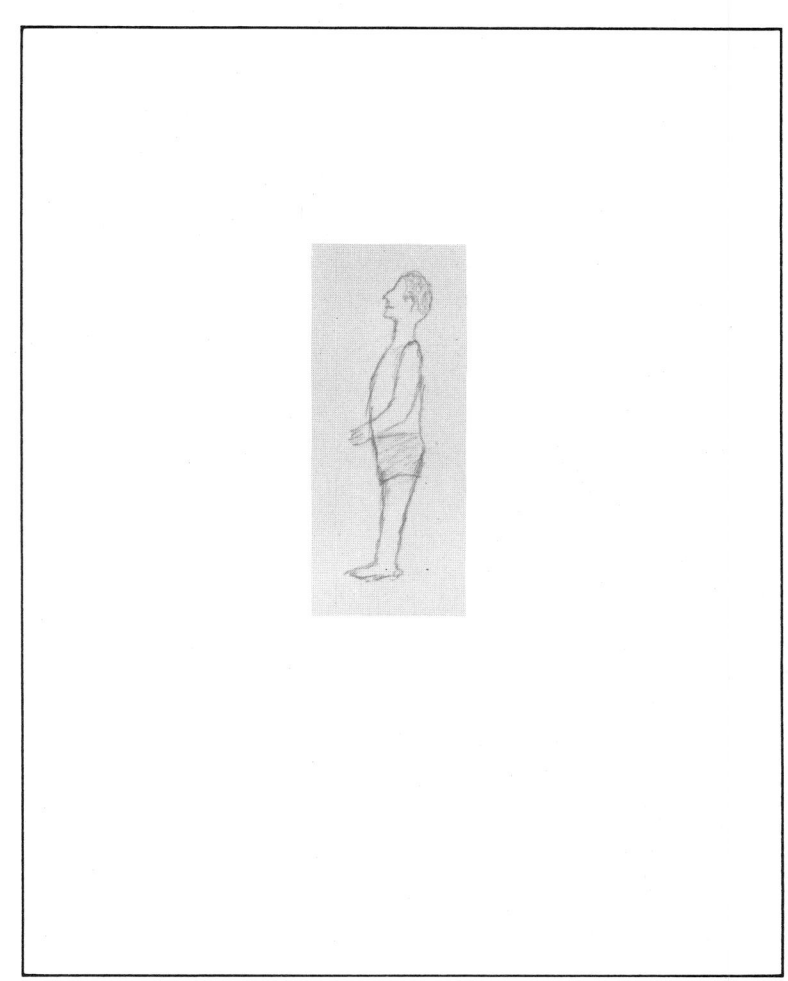

FIGURE-DRAWING CHARACTERISTICS

Structural	Male Female Both	Structural	Male	Female	Structural and Graphic	Male Female Both		Graphic, Global and Height	Male	Female	Body Proportions	Male	Female
Type	0	Omission of Appendages	0	0	Upper and Lower Halves	1	2	Hair Shading	0	3	Head	04	04
Sex Sequence	1	Position of Both Arms	4	4	Four Quarters	4	0	Nudity and Transparency	3	2	Neck	06	04
Posture	1 1	Position of Right Arm	7	7	Relative Size	2		Form	3	3	Shoulders		
Perspective	2 2	Position of Left Arm	4	4	Constant Line Pressure	1	1	Detailing	3	3	Right Arm		
Vertical Midline	4 4	Position of Legs	1	1	Variable Line Pressure	0	0	Identity and Sex	1	1	Left Arm	02	02
Bilateral Symmetry	0 0	Relation of Long Axes	1	1	Line Continuity	0	0	Sophistication	3	3	Chest	03	03
Horizontal Midline	4 4	Right and Left Halves	1	2	Body Shading	2	1	Height	03	03	Girth	04	04

GENERAL CHARACTERISTICS OF SUBJECT

IDENTIFICATION

No. D10
Sex M
Marital status M
Age 22 yrs. at
psychological tests

PARENTAL HISTORY

Father
C   H   S   D   O
-    -   -   -   -
Mother
C   H   S   D   O
-    +   -   -   +

PHYSIOLOGICAL AND METABOLIC DATA

	Admission	Initial	Control	Cold pressor change	Exercise change	Smoking change
Systolic pressure	120	120	120	+05	+40	
Diastolic pressure	80	70	70	+10	-10	
Heart rate	75	68	63	00	+40	

Age 21 yrs.

Height   71   in.
Weight   171   lbs.
Overweight +09 %

Ponderal index 12.79
Cholesterol   226   mg. per 100 ml.
Vital capacity   4.5   liters

HABIT SURVEY

Smoking habits: nonsmoker
   Age begun   yrs.   Inhalation:
Habits of nervous tension: 4, 5, 6, 9, 11, 12, 16, 17

STRONG VOCATIONAL INTEREST TEST

Occupation	Artist	Psychologist	Architect	Physician	Osteopath	Dentist	Veterinarian	Mathematician	Physicist	Engineer	Chemist	Production Manager
Standard Score	29	42	36	66	50	42	31	44	45	53	60	38

Occupation	Farmer	Aviator	Carpenter	Printer	Math.-Sci. Teacher	Ind. Arts Teacher	Voc. Agric. Teacher	Policeman	Forest Serv. Man	Y.M.C.A. Phys. Dir.	Personnel Director	Public Administrator
Standard Score	43	60	30	45	50	26	28	41	40	36	34	50

Occupation	Y.M.C.A. Secretary	Soc. Sci. H.S. Teacher	City Sch. Sup't.	Social Worker	Minister	Musician Performer	C.P.A.	Senior C.P.A.	Accountant	Office Man	Purchasing Agent	Banker
Standard Score	19	24	20	29	63	43	39	58	36	36	23	21

Occupation	Mortician	Pharmacist	Sales Manager	Real Est. Manager	Life Ins. Salesman	Advertising Man	Lawyer	Author-Journalist	President Mfg. Co.	Interest Maturity	Occupational Level	Masculinity-Femininity
Standard Score	22	33	19	23	12	27	32	32	23	53	50	55

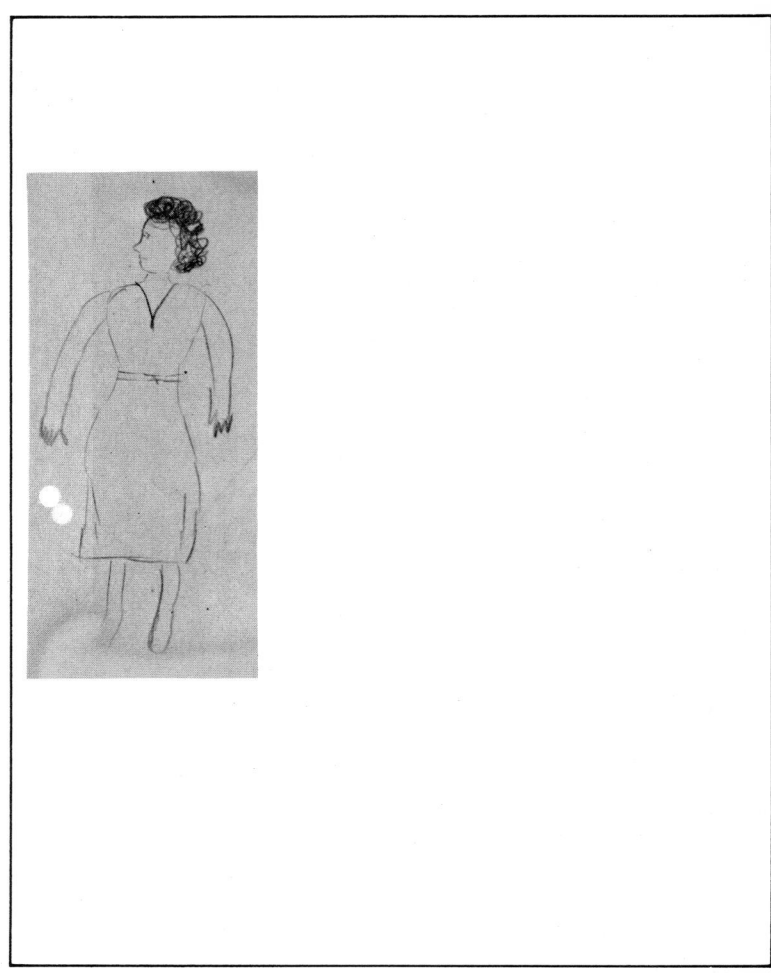

FIGURE-DRAWING CHARACTERISTICS

Structural	Male Female Both	Structural	Male	Female	Structural and Graphic	Male Female Both	Graphic, Global and Height	Male	Female	Body Proportions	Male	Female
Type	0	Omission of Appendages	0	0	Upper and Lower Halves	0	1	Hair Shading	3	3	Head	08	05
Sex Sequence	2	Position of Both Arms	1	1	Four Quarters	4	4	Nudity and Transparency	7	7	Neck	06	04
Posture	1	1	Position of Right Arm	2	0	Relative Size	0		Form	3	3	Shoulders	09	05
Perspective	5	5	Position of Left Arm	2	0	Constant Line Pressure	0	0	Detailing	3	3	Right Arm	04	04
Vertical Midline	3	0	Position of Legs	6	4	Variable Line Pressure	3	1	Identity and Sex	1	1	Left Arm	06	02
Bilateral Symmetry	3	3	Relation of Long Axes	1	1	Line Continuity	0	0	Sophistication	3	3	Chest	05	04
Horizontal Midline	4	4	Right and Left Halves	2	2	Body Shading	6	2	Height	07	04	Girth	08	04

GENERAL CHARACTERISTICS OF SUBJECT

IDENTIFICATION
No. 245
Sex M
Marital status M
Age 29 yrs. at
psychological tests

PARENTAL HISTORY

Father

C	H	S	D	O
-	-	-	-	-

Mother

C	H	S	D	O
-	+	-	-	-

PHYSIOLOGICAL AND METABOLIC DATA

	Admission	Initial	Control	Cold pressor change	Exercise change	Smoking change
Systolic pressure	104					
Diastolic pressure	62					
Heart rate	78					

Age 26 yrs.	Height 70 in.	Ponderal index 13.42
	Weight 142 lbs.	Cholesterol 165 mg. per 100 ml.
	Overweight -10 %	Vital capacity liters

HABIT SURVEY

Smoking habits: unknown

    Age begun yrs.   Inhalation:

Habits of nervous tension:

FIGURE-DRAWING CHARACTERISTICS

Structural	Male Female Both	Structural	Male	Female	Structural and Graphic	Male Female Both		Graphic, Global and Height	Male	Female	Body Proportions	Male	Female
Type	0	Omission of Appendages	0	0	Upper and Lower Halves	0	1	Hair Shading	0	3	Head	08	07
Sex Sequence	0	Position of Both Arms	2	4	Four Quarters	4	4	Nudity and Transparency	7	7	Neck	04	04
Posture	1 1	Position of Right Arm	4	7	Relative Size	0		Form	3	3	Shoulders		
Perspective	2 2	Position of Left Arm	7	5	Constant Line Pressure	5	0	Detailing	3	3	Right Arm	06	
Vertical Midline	4 4	Position of Legs	1	1	Variable Line Pressure	0	3	Identity and Sex	1	1	Left Arm		04
Bilateral Symmetry	0 0	Relation of Long Axes	1	1	Line Continuity	4	2	Sophistication	3	3	Chest	09	05
Horizontal Midline	4 4	Right and Left Halves	1	3	Body Shading	0	0	Height	06	05	Girth	09	06

GENERAL CHARACTERISTICS OF SUBJECT

IDENTIFICATION
No. 328
Sex M
Marital status M
Age 27 yrs. at
psychological tests

PARENTAL HISTORY					
Father					
C	H	S	D	O	
-	-	-	-	+	
Mother					
C	H	S	D	O	
-	+	-	-	-	

PHYSIOLOGICAL AND METABOLIC DATA

	Admission	Initial	Control	Cold pressor change	Exercise change	Smoking change
Systolic pressure	120	122	102	+06	+40	+10
Diastolic pressure	82	66	62	+12	+02	+14
Heart rate	70	102	91	+06	+29	+24

Age 25 yrs.	Height	71 in.	Ponderal index 12.58
	Weight	180 lbs.	Cholesterol 360 mg. per 100 ml.
	Overweight +11 %		Vital capacity 5.9 liters

HABIT SURVEY

Smoking habits: moderate cigarette smoker

Age begun 19 yrs.   Inhalation: yes

Habits of nervous tension: 5, 6, 9, 11, 16, 17, 25

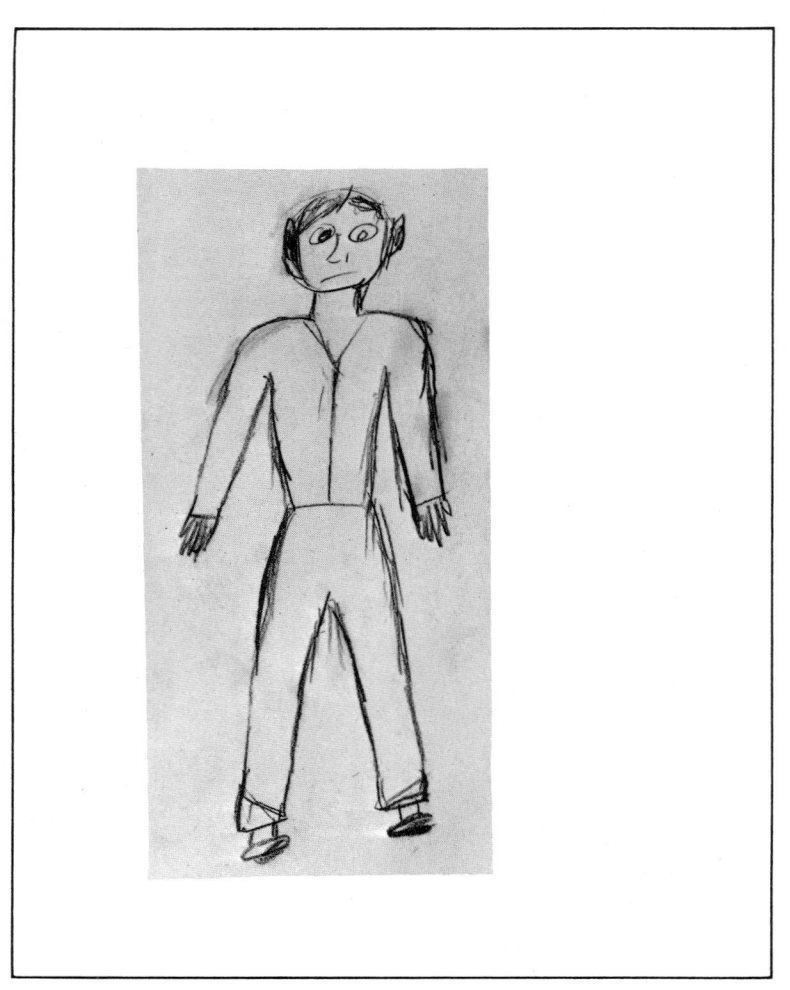

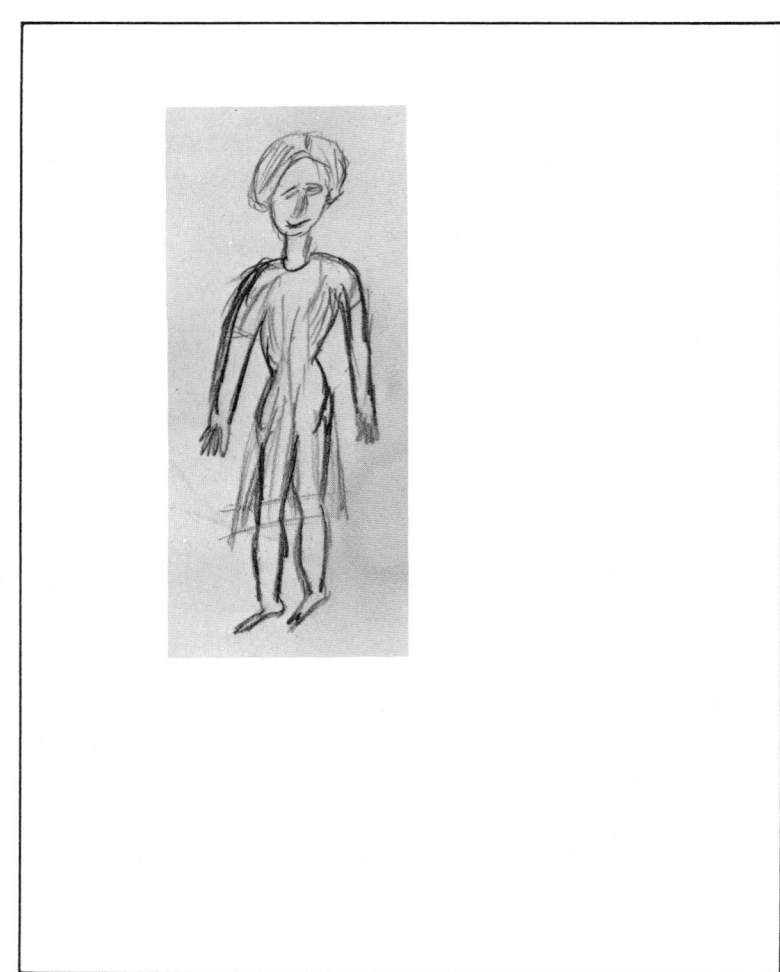

FIGURE-DRAWING CHARACTERISTICS

Structural	Male Female Both		Structural	Male	Female	Structural and Graphic	Male Female Both		Graphic, Global and Height	Male	Female	Body Proportions	Male	Female
Type	0		Omission of Appendages	0	0	Upper and Lower Halves	3	1	Hair Shading	3	3	Head	08	07
Sex Sequence	0		Position of Both Arms	1	1	Four Quarters	4	4	Nudity and Transparency	7	6	Neck	12	10
Posture	1	1	Position of Right Arm	2	2	Relative Size	0		Form	3	3	Shoulders	07	05
Perspective	0	0	Position of Left Arm	0	0	Constant Line Pressure	0	5	Detailing	3	3	Right Arm	04	04
Vertical Midline	3	0	Position of Legs	6	4	Variable Line Pressure	5	0	Identity and Sex	3	3	Left Arm	04	04
Bilateral Symmetry	3	3	Relation of Long Axes	1	1	Line Continuity	0	0	Sophistication	3	3	Chest	05	03
Horizontal Midline	4	0	Right and Left Halves	1	2	Body Shading	0	3	Height	07	05	Girth	05	03

GENERAL CHARACTERISTICS OF SUBJECT

IDENTIFICATION
No. 406
Sex M
Marital status S
Age 29 yrs. at
psychological tests

PARENTAL HISTORY
Father
C H S D O
-   -   -   -   ?
Mother
C H S D O
- + - - -

PHYSIOLOGICAL AND METABOLIC DATA

	Admission	Initial	Control	Cold pressor change	Exercise change	Smoking change
Systolic pressure	110	110	98	+13	+37	
Diastolic pressure	68	68	62	+26	+18	
Heart rate	88	72	66	-04	+17	

Age 27 yrs.

Height	74 in.	Ponderal index 13.63
Weight	160 lbs.	Cholesterol 185 mg. per 100 ml.
Overweight -12 %		Vital capacity 5.6 liters

HABIT SURVEY

Smoking habits: heavy cigarette smoker

Age begun 18 yrs.   Inhalation: yes

Habits of nervous tension: 5, 9, 11, 17, 18, 22

Plate 304   DRAWINGS AT AN INTERMEDIATE LEVEL OF SOPHISTICATION   347

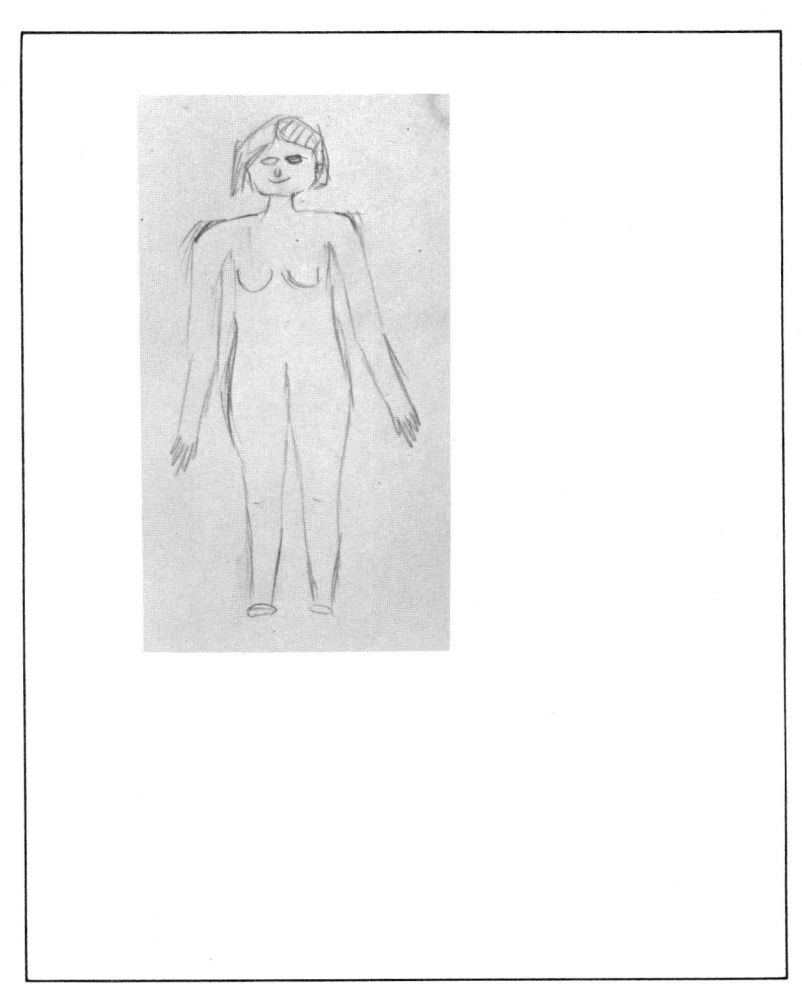

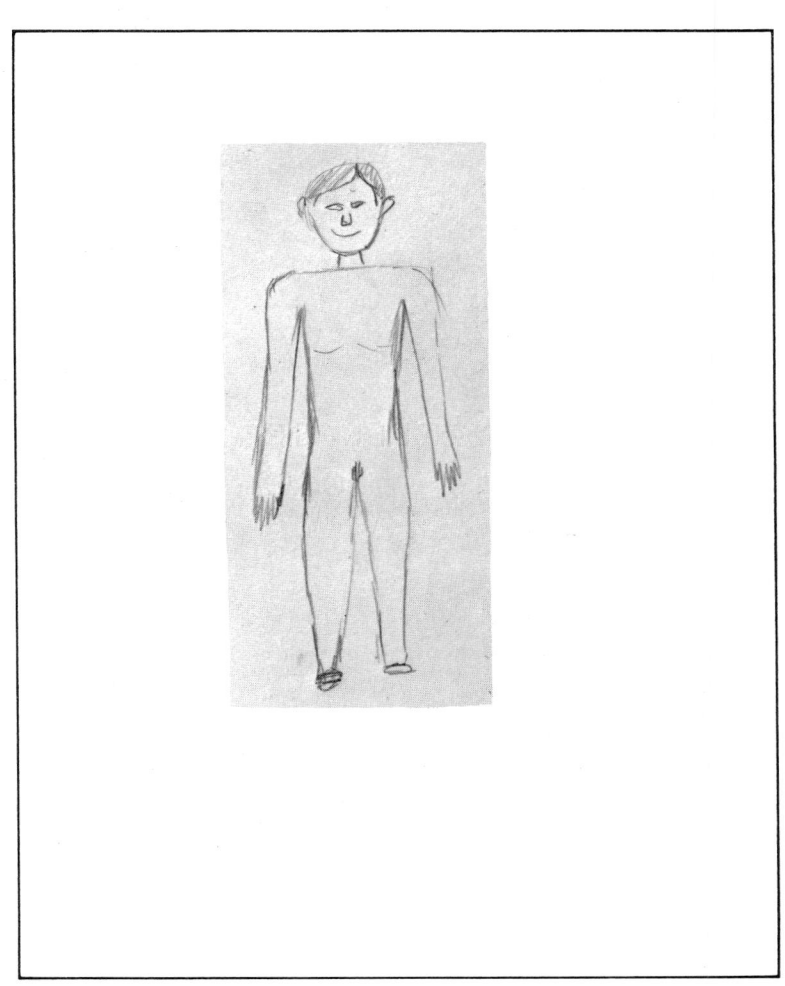

FIGURE-DRAWING CHARACTERISTICS

Structural	Male	Female	Structural	Male	Female	Structural and Graphic	Male	Female	Graphic, Global and Height	Male	Female	Body Proportions	Male	Female
	Both						Both							
Type	0		Omission of Appendages	0	0	Upper and Lower Halves	1	1	Hair Shading	1	3	Head	08	06
Sex Sequence	1		Position of Both Arms	0	1	Four Quarters	4	4	Nudity and Transparency	0	0	Neck	06	06
Posture	1	1	Position of Right Arm	0	0	Relative Size	2		Form	3	3	Shoulders	06	06
Perspective	0	0	Position of Left Arm	0	2	Constant Line Pressure	0	0	Detailing	3	3	Right Arm	06	06
Vertical Midline	0	0	Position of Legs	4	4	Variable Line Pressure	1	1	Identity and Sex	1	1	Left Arm	04	06
Bilateral Symmetry	3	3	Relation of Long Axes	1	1	Line Continuity	0	0	Sophistication	3	3	Chest	05	05
Horizontal Midline	0	0	Right and Left Halves	1	2	Body Shading	0	3	Height	05	05	Girth	05	07

GENERAL CHARACTERISTICS OF SUBJECT

IDENTIFICATION
No. 460
Sex M
Marital status S
Age 26 yrs. at
psychological tests

PARENTAL HISTORY
Father
C   H   S   D   0
-    -   -   -   -
Mother
C   H   S   D   0
-    +   +   -   -

PHYSIOLOGICAL AND METABOLIC DATA

	Admission	Initial	Control	Cold pressor change	Exercise change	Smoking change
Systolic pressure	126	130	100	+18	+30	
Diastolic pressure	70	78	64	+12	-04	
Heart rate	72	64	63	+12	+22	

Age 24 yrs.	Height	74	in.	Ponderal index 13.55
Weight	163	lbs.	Cholesterol	150	mg. per 100 ml.
Overweight -08 %	Vital capacity	5.6	liters

FIGURE-DRAWING CHARACTERISTICS

Structural	Male	Female	Structural	Male	Female	Structural and Graphic	Male	Female	Graphic, Global and Height	Male	Female	Body Proportions	Male	Female
	Both						Both							
Type	0		Omission of Appendages	3	1	Upper and Lower Halves	7	7	Hair Shading	0	3	Head	13	15
Sex Sequence	0		Position of Both Arms	0	6	Four Quarters	4	4	Nudity and Transparency	7	7	Neck	08	08
Posture	0	0	Position of Right Arm	2	8	Relative Size	5		Form	3	3	Shoulders	09	10
Perspective	0	0	Position of Left Arm	2	8	Constant Line Pressure	1	1	Detailing	3	3	Right Arm	08	
Vertical Midline	3	3	Position of Legs	0	0	Variable Line Pressure	0	0	Identity and Sex	3	3	Left Arm	08	
Bilateral Symmetry	5	3	Relation of Long Axes	1	1	Line Continuity	0	3	Sophistication	3	3	Chest	09	09
Horizontal Midline	6	4	Right and Left Halves	1	1	Body Shading	2	2	Height			Girth	12	12

GENERAL CHARACTERISTICS OF SUBJECT

IDENTIFICATION
No. 472
Sex M
Marital status S
Age 26 yrs. at psychological tests

PARENTAL HISTORY
Father
C H S D O
- - - - ?
Mother
C H S D O
- + - - -

PHYSIOLOGICAL AND METABOLIC DATA

	Admission	Initial	Control	Cold pressor change	Exercise change	Smoking change
Systolic pressure	140	116	120	+16	+14	
Diastolic pressure	72	70	72	+16	-02	
Heart rate	72	84	71	+12	+23	

Age 23 yrs.		
Height	78	in.
Weight	208	lbs.
Overweight +07 %		

Ponderal index 13.16	
Cholesterol	172 mg. per 100 ml.
Vital capacity	6.0 liters

HABIT SURVEY
Smoking habits: occasional smoker
Age begun   yrs.   Inhalation: no
Habits of nervous tension: 1, 3, 5, 6, 7, 8, 10, 14, 18, 19, 20, 22, 23, 25

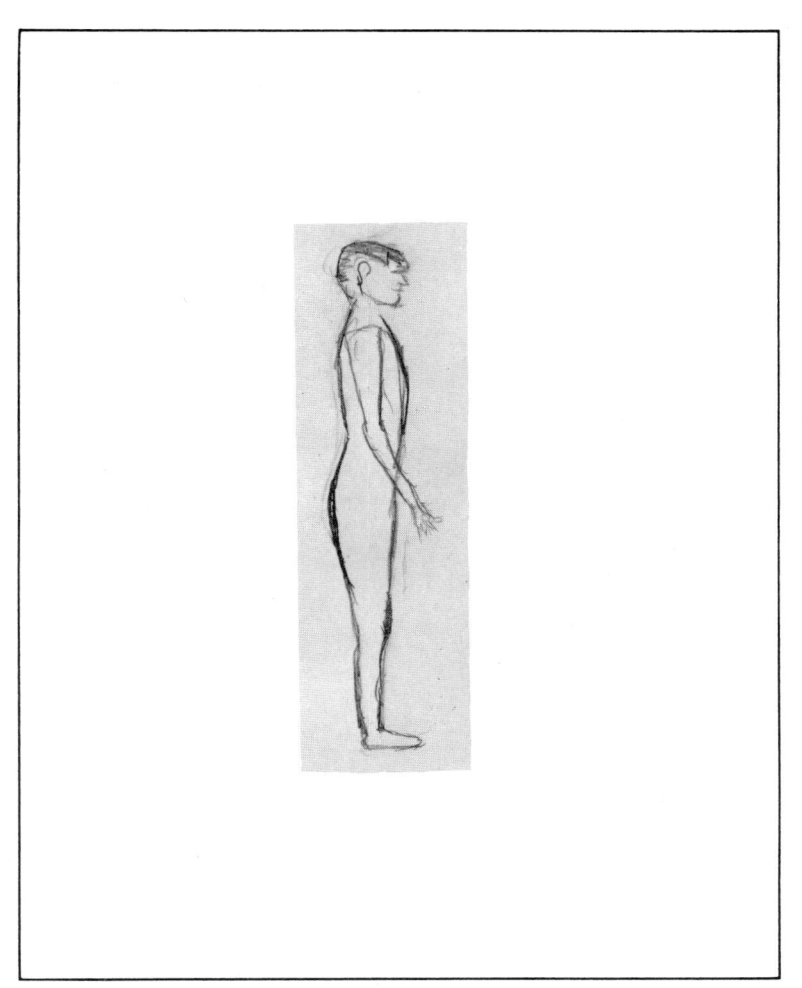
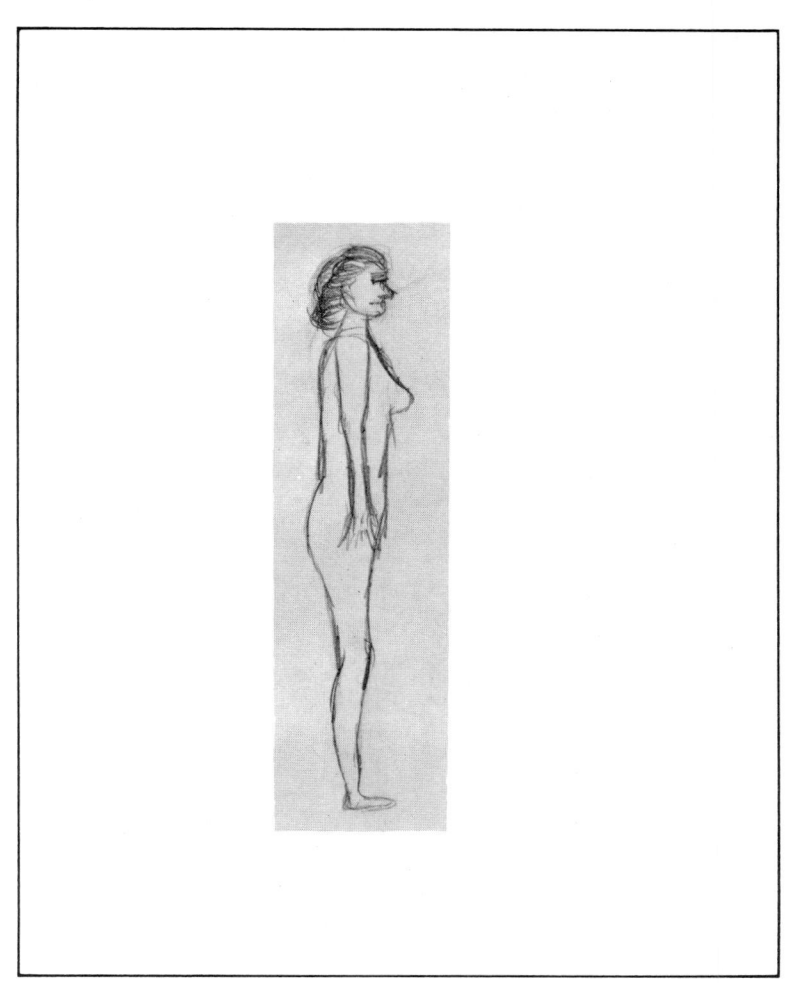

FIGURE-DRAWING CHARACTERISTICS

Structural	Male Female Both		Structural	Male	Female	Structural and Graphic	Male Female Both		Graphic, Global and Height	Male	Female	Body Proportions	Male	Female
Type	0		Omission of Appendages	0	0	Upper and Lower Halves	0	3	Hair Shading	3	3	Head	05	05
Sex Sequence	0		Position of Both Arms	2	2	Four Quarters	4	4	Nudity and Transparency	0	0	Neck	04	06
Posture	1	1	Position of Right Arm	4	0	Relative Size	4		Form	3	3	Shoulders		
Perspective	2	2	Position of Left Arm	7	7	Constant Line Pressure	5	0	Detailing	3	3	Right Arm	04	04
Vertical Midline	4	4	Position of Legs	1	1	Variable Line Pressure	0	5	Identity and Sex	1	1	Left Arm		
Bilateral Symmetry	0	0	Relation of Long Axes	1	1	Line Continuity	0	0	Sophistication	3	3	Chest	04	04
Horizontal Midline	0	0	Right and Left Halves	1	2	Body Shading	0	0	Height	05	06	Girth	04	06

GENERAL CHARACTERISTICS OF SUBJECT

IDENTIFICATION
No. 607
Sex M
Marital status M
Age 24 yrs. at
psychological tests

PARENTAL HISTORY				
Father				
C	H	S	D	O
-	-	-	?	+
Mother				
C	H	S	D	O
-	+	-	?	+

PHYSIOLOGICAL AND METABOLIC DATA

	Admission	Initial	Control	Cold pressor change	Exercise change	Smoking change
Systolic pressure	110	108	108	+12	+20	00
Diastolic pressure	70	60	66	+14	+14	00
Heart rate	80	72	68	00	+20	+12

Age 22 yrs.	Height	70	in.	Ponderal index 12.37
	Weight	181	lbs.	Cholesterol 155 mg. per 100 ml.
	Overweight +18 %			Vital capacity 4.9 liters

HABIT SURVEY

Smoking habits: heavy cigarette smoker

Age begun 15 yrs.   Inhalation: yes

Habits of nervous tension: 1, 2, 3, 4, 5, 6, 8, 9, 11, 16, 17, 22, 25

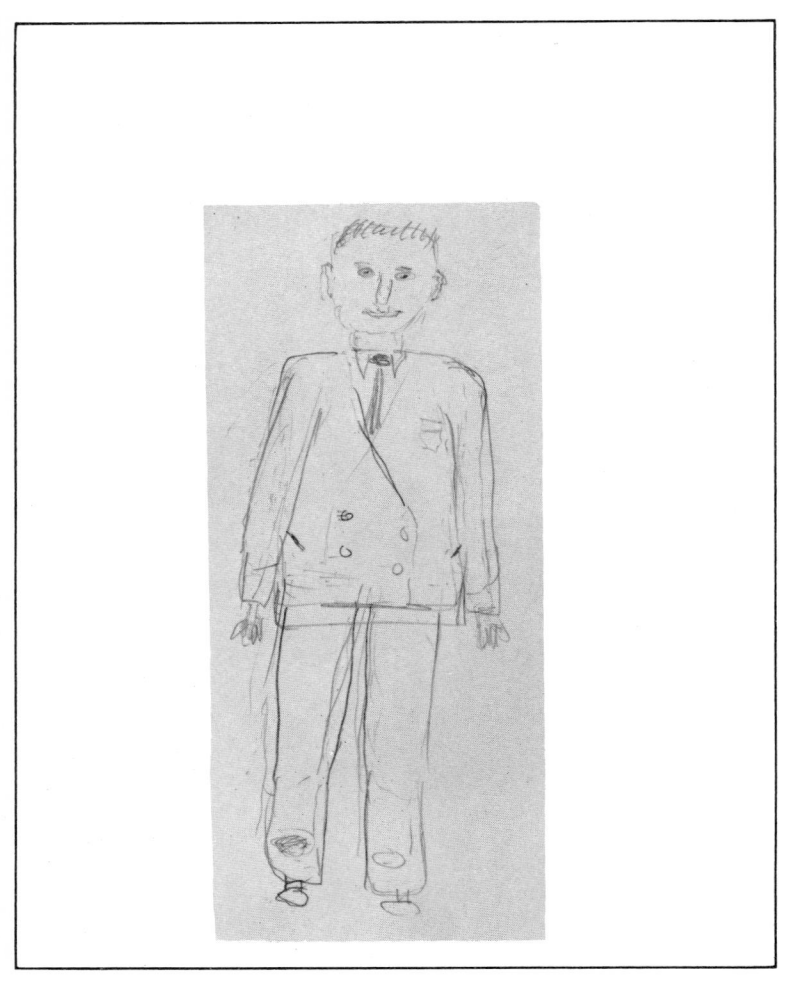

FIGURE-DRAWING CHARACTERISTICS

Structural	Male Female Both	Structural	Male	Female	Structural and Graphic	Male Female Both		Graphic, Global and Height	Male	Female	Body Proportions	Male	Female
Type	0	Omission of Appendages	0	0	Upper and Lower Halves	3	3	Hair Shading	3	3	Head	09	08
Sex Sequence	2	Position of Both Arms	0	0	Four Quarters	4	4	Nudity and Transparency	6	7	Neck	07	08
Posture	1 1	Position of Right Arm	0	0	Relative Size	1		Form	3	3	Shoulders	08	07
Perspective	0 0	Position of Left Arm	0	0	Constant Line Pressure	0	0	Detailing	3	3	Right Arm	06	04
Vertical Midline	3 0	Position of Legs	4	5	Variable Line Pressure	3	3	Identity and Sex	1	1	Left Arm	06	04
Bilateral Symmetry	3 3	Relation of Long Axes	1	1	Line Continuity	1	1	Sophistication	3	3	Chest	07	07
Horizontal Midline	6 4	Right and Left Halves	1	1	Body Shading	7	7	Height	07	07	Girth	11	09

GENERAL CHARACTERISTICS OF SUBJECT

IDENTIFICATION
No. 621
Sex M
Marital status M
Age 26 yrs. at
psychological tests

PARENTAL HISTORY
Father
C   H   S   D   O
-   -   -   -   -
Mother
C   H   S   D   O
-   +   -   -   -

PHYSIOLOGICAL AND METABOLIC DATA

	Admission	Initial	Control	Cold pressor change	Exercise change	Smoking change
Systolic pressure	140	126	126	+08	+14	00
Diastolic pressure	80	74	76	+06	-06	-02
Heart rate	100	88	72	-06	+14	+04

Age 22 yrs.	Height 76 in.	Ponderal index 13.22
	Weight 190 lbs.	Cholesterol 172 mg. per 100 ml.
	Overweight +04 %	Vital capacity liters

HABIT SURVEY
Smoking habits: heavy cigarette smoker
Age begun 22 yrs.   Inhalation: yes
Habits of nervous tension: 6, 16, 19, 22

FIGURE-DRAWING CHARACTERISTICS

Structural	Male Female Both		Structural	Male	Female	Structural and Graphic	Male Female Both		Graphic, Global and Height	Male	Female	Body Proportions	Male	Female
Type	0		Omission of Appendages	7	7	Upper and Lower Halves	1	1	Hair Shading	7	3	Head	05	05
Sex Sequence	1		Position of Both Arms	0	0	Four Quarters	4	4	Nudity and Transparency	7	7	Neck	08	07
Posture	1	1	Position of Right Arm	5	5	Relative Size	3		Form	3	3	Shoulders	07	06
Perspective	0	0	Position of Left Arm	5	5	Constant Line Pressure	5	5	Detailing	3	3	Right Arm		
Vertical Midline	3	1	Position of Legs	4	0	Variable Line Pressure	0	0	Identity and Sex	1	1	Left Arm		
Bilateral Symmetry	4	3	Relation of Long Axes	1	1	Line Continuity	4	4	Sophistication	3	3	Chest	06	05
Horizontal Midline	4	2	Right and Left Halves	3	1	Body Shading	0	3	Height	05	05	Girth	03	05

GENERAL CHARACTERISTICS OF SUBJECT

IDENTIFICATION
No. 667
Sex M
Marital status S
Age 25 yrs. at
psychological tests

PARENTAL HISTORY
Father
C   H   S   D   O
−   −   −   −   ?
Mother
C   H   S   D   O
−   +   −   −   −

PHYSIOLOGICAL AND METABOLIC DATA

	Admission	Initial	Control	Cold pressor change	Exercise change	Smoking change
Systolic pressure	120	126	108	+14	+64	+22
Diastolic pressure	75	64	62	+14	+02	+12
Heart rate	98	68	67	+24	+26	+18

Age 23 yrs.	Height	70	in.	Ponderal index	13.06	
	Weight	154	lbs.	Cholesterol	230	mg. per 100 ml.
	Overweight	−01	%	Vital capacity	4.5	liters

HABIT SURVEY
Smoking habits: heavy cigarette smoker
Age begun 19 yrs.   Inhalation: yes
Habits of nervous tension: 4, 5, 6, 9, 19, 22

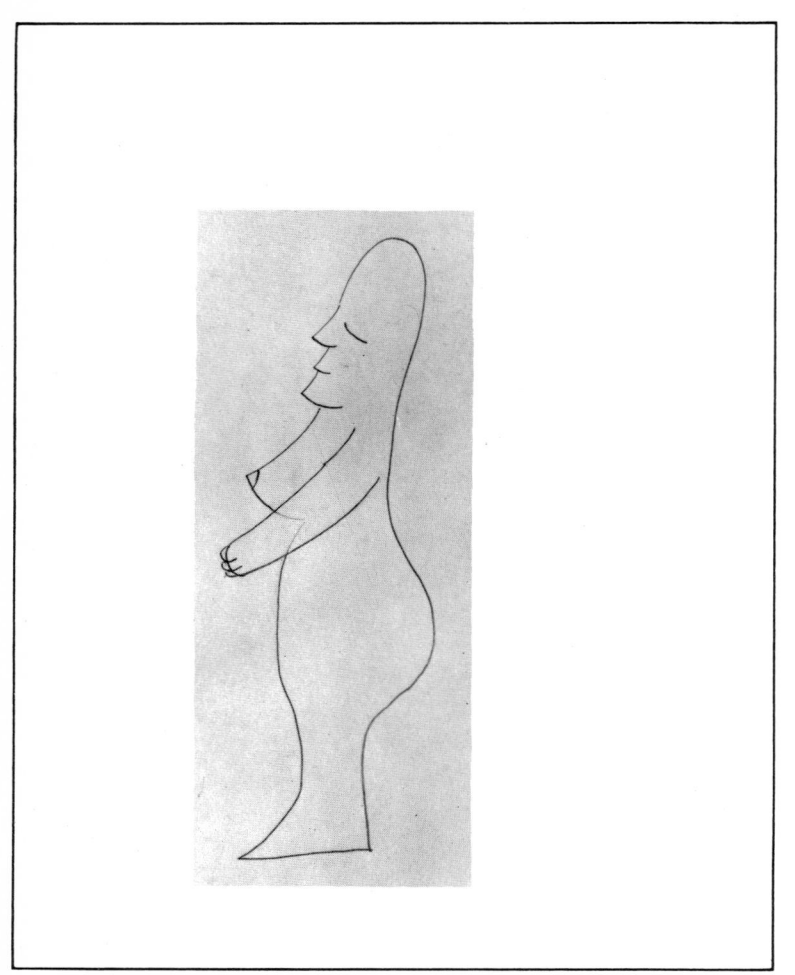

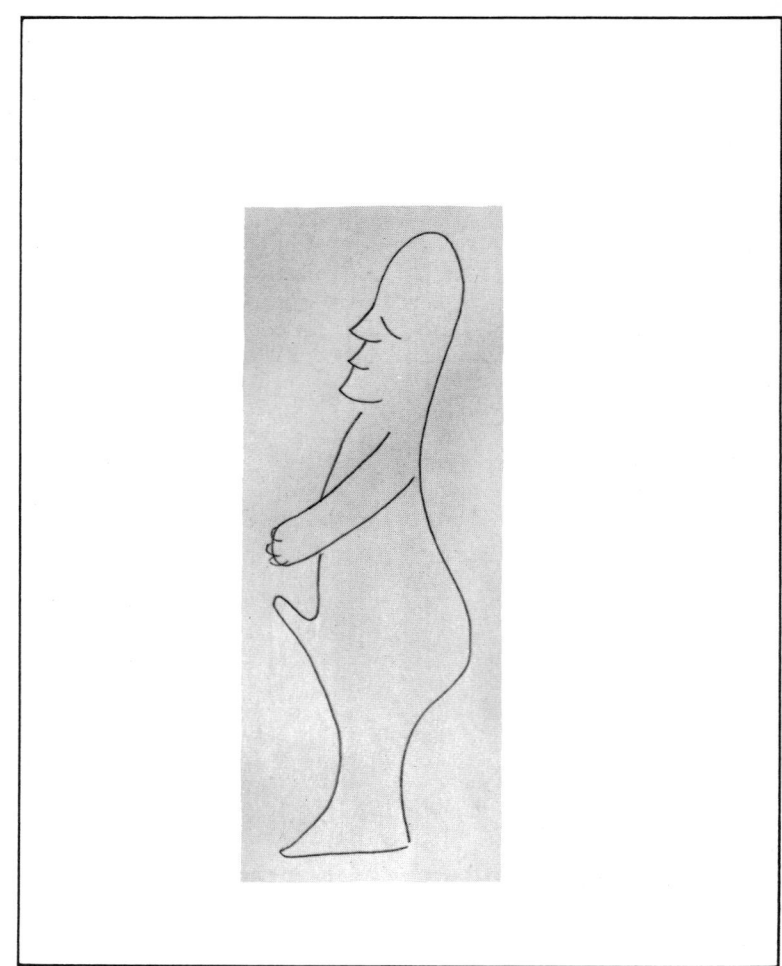

FIGURE-DRAWING CHARACTERISTICS

Structural	Male	Female	Structural	Male	Female	Structural and Graphic	Male	Female	Graphic, Global and Height	Male	Female	Body Proportions	Male	Female
	Both						Both							
Type	0		Omission of Appendages	9	9	Upper and Lower Halves	3	3	Hair Shading	0	0	Head	14	15
Sex Sequence	1		Position of Both Arms	4	4	Four Quarters	4	4	Nudity and Transparency	0	0	Neck		
Posture	1	1	Position of Right Arm	7	7	Relative Size	2		Form	3	3	Shoulders		
Perspective	2	2	Position of Left Arm	4	4	Constant Line Pressure	5	5	Detailing	5	5	Right Arm		
Vertical Midline	4	4	Position of Legs	1	1	Variable Line Pressure	0	0	Identity and Sex	1	1	Left Arm	04	04
Bilateral Symmetry	0	0	Relation of Long Axes	1	1	Line Continuity	4	4	Sophistication	3	3	Chest	07	08
Horizontal Midline	0	0	Right and Left Halves	1	1	Body Shading	0	0	Height	06	06	Girth	09	09

GENERAL CHARACTERISTICS OF SUBJECT

IDENTIFICATION
No. 675
Sex M
Marital status M
Age 25 yrs. at
psychological tests

PARENTAL HISTORY				
Father				
C	H	S	D	O
-	-	-	-	-
Mother				
C	H	S	D	O
-	+	-	-	?

PHYSIOLOGICAL AND METABOLIC DATA

	Admission	Initial	Control	Cold pressor change	Exercise change	Smoking change
Systolic pressure	140	118	112	+22	+56	+02
Diastolic pressure	80	58	62	+18	+10	00
Heart rate	72	72	74	+20	+31	-01

Age 23 yrs.	Height 72 in.		Ponderal index 12.90	
	Weight 174 lbs.		Cholesterol 265 mg. per 100 ml.	
	Overweight +06 %		Vital capacity 4.8 liters	

HABIT SURVEY
Smoking habits: occasional smoker
Age begun 18 yrs.   Inhalation: no
Habits of nervous tension: 2, 6, 25

FIGURE-DRAWING CHARACTERISTICS

Structural	Male Female Both		Structural	Male	Female	Structural and Graphic	Male Female Both		Graphic, Global and Height	Male	Female	Body Proportions	Male	Female
Type	0		Omission of Appendages	0	2	Upper and Lower Halves	1	1	Hair Shading	3	2	Head	05	08
Sex Sequence	0		Position of Both Arms	1	6	Four Quarters	4	4	Nudity and Transparency	3	2	Neck	04	00
Posture	1	1	Position of Right Arm	5	7	Relative Size	4		Form	3	3	Shoulders		
Perspective	1	2	Position of Left Arm	0	7	Constant Line Pressure	0	0	Detailing	3	3	Right Arm	04	
Vertical Midline	0	4	Position of Legs	6	1	Variable Line Pressure	1	1	Identity and Sex	3	1	Left Arm	04	
Bilateral Symmetry	0	0	Relation of Long Axes	1	1	Line Continuity	0	0	Sophistication	3	3	Chest		08
Horizontal Midline	4	2	Right and Left Halves	2	2	Body Shading	0	3	Height	05	07	Girth		08

GENERAL CHARACTERISTICS OF SUBJECT

IDENTIFICATION
No. F14
Sex M
Marital status
Age 23 yrs. at
psychological tests

PARENTAL HISTORY				
Father				
C	H	S	D	O
-	-	-	-	?
Mother				
C	H	S	D	O
-	+	-	-	+

PHYSIOLOGICAL AND METABOLIC DATA

	Admission	Initial	Control	Cold pressor change	Exercise change	Smoking change
Systolic pressure	128	118	106	+04	+28	+06
Diastolic pressure	98	86	80	+06	-02	+08
Heart rate	72	76	74	+08	+12	+08

Age 21 yrs.	Height 68 in.	Ponderal index 12.06
	Weight 179 lbs.	Cholesterol 266 mg. per 100 ml.
	Overweight +23 %	Vital capacity liters

HABIT SURVEY

Smoking habits: nonsmoker

Age begun   yrs.   Inhalation:

Habits of nervous tension: 4, 5, 6, 9, 10, 17, 20, 22

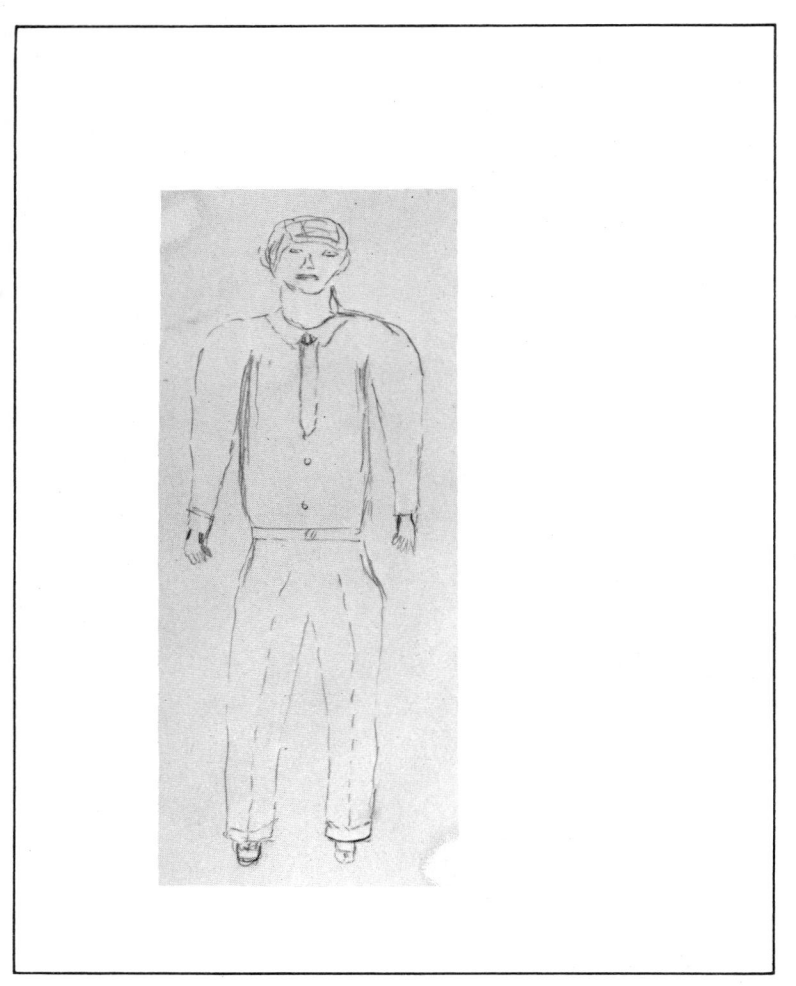

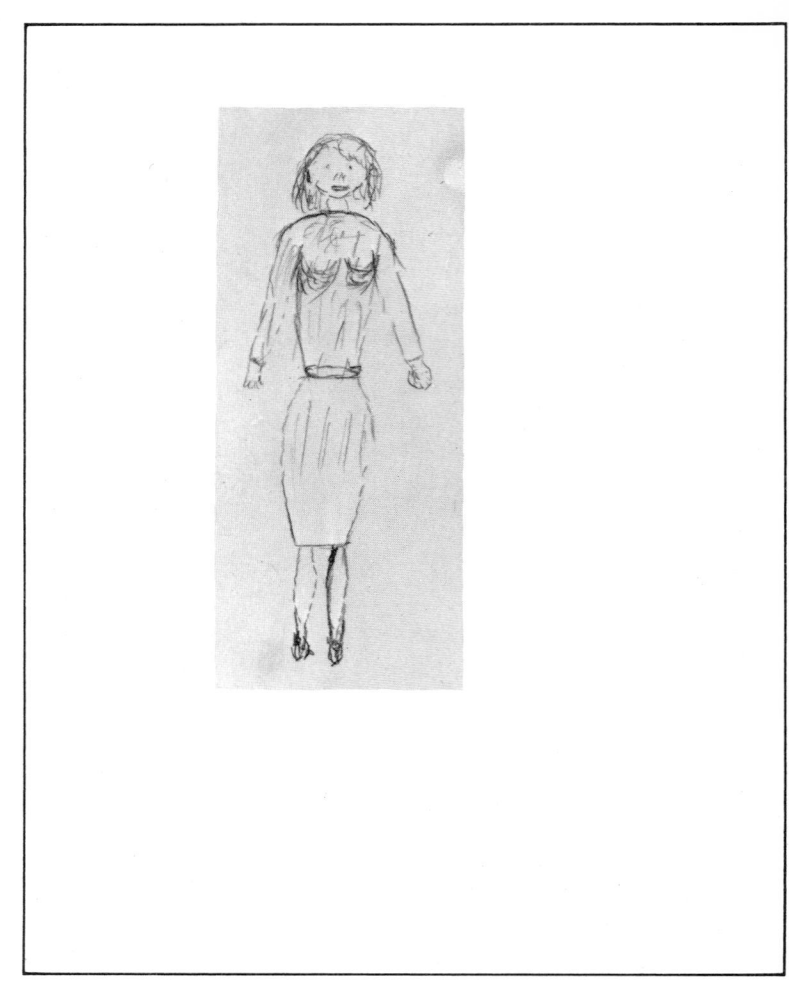

FIGURE-DRAWING CHARACTERISTICS

Structural	Male Female Both		Structural	Male	Female	Structural and Graphic	Male Female Both		Graphic, Global and Height	Male	Female	Body Proportions	Male	Female
Type	0		Omission of Appendages	0	0	Upper and Lower Halves	3	1	Hair Shading	1	3	Head	06	05
Sex Sequence	0		Position of Both Arms	0	0	Four Quarters	4	4	Nudity and Transparency	7	7	Neck	12	05
Posture	1	1	Position of Right Arm	0	1	Relative Size	0		Form	3	3	Shoulders	08	04
Perspective	0	0	Position of Left Arm	0	1	Constant Line Pressure	0	0	Detailing	3	3	Right Arm	06	04
Vertical Midline	3	0	Position of Legs	5	4	Variable Line Pressure	1	2	Identity and Sex	1	1	Left Arm	06	04
Bilateral Symmetry	3	3	Relation of Long Axes	1	1	Line Continuity	0	0	Sophistication	3	3	Chest	06	04
Horizontal Midline	4	4	Right and Left Halves	1	2	Body Shading	7	7	Height	06	05	Girth	07	03

GENERAL CHARACTERISTICS OF SUBJECT

IDENTIFICATION
No. F58
Sex M
Marital status S
Age 25 yrs. at
psychological tests

PARENTAL HISTORY
Father
C   H   S   D   O
–   –   –   –   –
Mother
C   H   S   D   O
–   +   –   –   –

PHYSIOLOGICAL AND METABOLIC DATA

	Admission	Initial	Control	Cold pressor change	Exercise change	Smoking change
Systolic pressure	120	110	108	+02	+20	+04
Diastolic pressure	80	80	76	+08	+10	+01
Heart rate	80	60	63	+08	+16	+20

Age 23 yrs.	Height	72 in.	Ponderal index	13.38	
	Weight	156 lbs.	Cholesterol	190	mg. per 100 ml.
	Overweight –05 %		Vital capacity		liters

HABIT SURVEY
Smoking habits: light cigarette smoker
Age begun 16 yrs.   Inhalation: yes
Habits of nervous tension: 4, 5, 9, 11, 12, 22

STRONG VOCATIONAL INTEREST TEST

Occupation	Artist	Psychologist	Architect	Physician	Osteopath	Dentist	Veterinarian	Mathematician	Physicist	Engineer	Chemist	Production Manager
Standard Score												

Occupation	Farmer	Aviator	Carpenter	Printer	Math.-Sci. Teacher	Ind. Arts Teacher	Voc. Agric. Teacher	Policeman	Forest Serv. Man	Y.M.C.A. Phys. Dir.	Personnel Director	Public Administrator
Standard Score												

Occupation	Y.M.C.A. Secretary	Soc. Sci. H.S. Teacher	City Sch. Sup't.	Social Worker	Minister	Musician Performer	C.P.A.	Senior C.P.A.	Accountant	Office Man	Purchasing Agent	Banker
Standard Score												

Occupation	Mortician	Pharmacist	Sales Manager	Real Est. Manager	Life Ins. Salesman	Advertising Man	Lawyer	Author-Journalist	President Mfg. Co.	Interest Maturity	Occupational Level	Masculinity-Femininity
Standard Score												

FIGURE-DRAWING CHARACTERISTICS

Structural	Male Female Both		Structural	Male	Female	Structural and Graphic	Male Female Both		Graphic, Global and Height	Male	Female	Body Proportions	Male	Female
Type	0		Omission of Appendages	0	2	Upper and Lower Halves	3	0	Hair Shading	3	3	Head	08	06
Sex Sequence	2		Position of Both Arms	0	6	Four Quarters	4	4	Nudity and Transparency	6	0	Neck	07	07
Posture	1	1	Position of Right Arm	0	7	Relative Size	0		Form	3	3	Shoulders	11	
Perspective	0	2	Position of Left Arm	0	7	Constant Line Pressure	0	0	Detailing	3	5	Right Arm	06	
Vertical Midline	3	4	Position of Legs	6	1	Variable Line Pressure	3	4	Identity and Sex	1	1	Left Arm	06	
Bilateral Symmetry	3	0	Relation of Long Axes	1	1	Line Continuity	2	1	Sophistication	3	3	Chest	07	06
Horizontal Midline	4	0	Right and Left Halves	1	1	Body Shading	4	0	Height	08	07	Girth	09	06

GENERAL CHARACTERISTICS OF SUBJECT

IDENTIFICATION
No. F66
Sex M
Marital status M
Age 24 yrs. at
psychological tests

PARENTAL HISTORY				
Father				
C	H	S	D	O
-	-	-	-	-
Mother				
C	H	S	D	O
-	+	-	-	-

PHYSIOLOGICAL AND METABOLIC DATA

	Admission	Initial	Control	Cold pressor change	Exercise change	Smoking change
Systolic pressure	120	130	116	+02	+24	+04
Diastolic pressure	60	80	82	+18	+14	+14
Heart rate	84	64	64	+04	+16	+04

Age 23 yrs.	Height	74 in.	Ponderal index 14.40
	Weight	136 lbs.	Cholesterol 167 mg. per 100 ml.
	Overweight −22 %		Vital capacity liters

HABIT SURVEY

Smoking habits: nonsmoker

Age begun   yrs.   Inhalation:

Habits of nervous tension: 5, 6, 9, 11, 16, 25

STRONG VOCATIONAL INTEREST TEST

Occupation	Artist	Psychologist	Architect	Physician	Osteopath	Dentist	Veterinarian	Mathematician	Physicist	Engineer	Chemist	Production Manager
Standard Score	11	38	14	50	38	26	34	19	12	30	30	33

Occupation	Farmer	Aviator	Carpenter	Printer	Math.-Sci. Teacher	Ind. Arts Teacher	Voc. Agric. Teacher	Policeman	Forest Serv. Man	Y.M.C.A. Phys. Dir.	Personnel Director	Public Administrator
Standard Score	24	26	08	17	42	14	30	31	17	40	41	45

Occupation	Y.M.C.A. Secretary	Soc. Sci. H.S. Teacher	City Sch. Sup't.	Social Worker	Minister	Musician Performer	C.P.A.	Senior C.P.A.	Accountant	Office Man	Purchasing Agent	Banker
Standard Score	30	39	33	42	58	28	34	44	33	36	33	28

Occupation	Mortician	Pharmacist	Sales Manager	Real Est. Manager	Life Ins. Salesman	Advertising Man	Lawyer	Author-Journalist	President Mfg. Co.	Interest Maturity	Occupational Level	Masculinity-Femininity
Standard Score	35	37	42	38	39	27	36	22	34	63	60	52

FIGURE-DRAWING CHARACTERISTICS

Structural	Male	Female	Structural	Male	Female	Structural and Graphic	Male	Female	Graphic, Global and Height	Male	Female	Body Proportions	Male	Female
	Both						Both							
Type	0		Omission of Appendages	0	0	Upper and Lower Halves	0	1	Hair Shading	3	3	Head	07	06
Sex Sequence	0		Position of Both Arms	0	0	Four Quarters	4	4	Nudity and Transparency	7	6	Neck	08	08
Posture	5	2	Position of Right Arm	6	6	Relative Size	0		Form	3	3	Shoulders		
Perspective	2	2	Position of Left Arm	6	6	Constant Line Pressure	0	0	Detailing	5	3	Right Arm		04
Vertical Midline	4	4	Position of Legs	8	8	Variable Line Pressure	5	5	Identity and Sex	3	1	Left Arm	06	04
Bilateral Symmetry	0	0	Relation of Long Axes	1	1	Line Continuity	0	0	Sophistication	3	3	Chest	07	05
Horizontal Midline	4	4	Right and Left Halves	1	1	Body Shading	3	3	Height	07	06	Girth	04	04

GENERAL CHARACTERISTICS OF SUBJECT

IDENTIFICATION
No. G01
Sex M
Marital status M
Age 26 yrs. at
psychological tests

PARENTAL HISTORY
Father
C H S D O
- - - - ?
Mother
C H S D O
- + - - U

PHYSIOLOGICAL AND METABOLIC DATA

	Admission	Initial	Control	Cold pressor change	Exercise change	Smoking change
Systolic pressure	130	130	130	+06	+28	-03
Diastolic pressure	80	98	82	-04	-04	-06
Heart rate	90	66	73	-04	+06	-08

Age 25 yrs.	Height	72 in.	Ponderal index	12.18	
	Weight	206 lbs.	Cholesterol	280	mg. per 100 ml.
	Overweight +23 %		Vital capacity		liters

HABIT SURVEY
Smoking habits: nonsmoker
Age begun   yrs.   Inhalation:
Habits of nervous tension: 25

STRONG VOCATIONAL INTEREST TEST

Occupation	Artist	Psychologist	Architect	Physician	Osteopath	Dentist	Veterinarian	Mathematician	Physicist	Engineer	Chemist	Production Manager
Standard Score	21	34	37	64	49	48	30	34	28	42	43	40

Occupation	Farmer	Aviator	Carpenter	Printer	Math.-Sci. Teacher	Ind. Arts Teacher	Voc. Agric. Teacher	Policeman	Forest Serv. Man	Y.M.C.A. Phys. Dir.	Personnel Director	Public Administrator
Standard Score	39	35	29	38	57	32	38	37	37	44	32	40

Occupation	Y.M.C.A. Secretary	Soc. Sci. H.S. Teacher	City Sch. Sup't.	Social Worker	Minister	Musician Performer	C.P.A.	Senior C.P.A.	Accountant	Office Man	Purchasing Agent	Banker
Standard Score	27	33	34	29	59	44	26	42	32	33	28	24

Occupation	Mortician	Pharmacist	Sales Manager	Real Est. Manager	Life Ins. Salesman	Advertising Man	Lawyer	Author-Journalist	President Mfg. Co.	Interest Maturity	Occupational Level	Masculinity-Femininity
Standard Score	18	35	18	20	18	18	22	22	18	62	58	53

FIGURE-DRAWING CHARACTERISTICS

Structural	Male	Female	Structural	Male	Female	Structural and Graphic	Male	Female	Graphic, Global and Height	Male	Female	Body Proportions	Male	Female
	Both						Both							
Type	0		Omission of Appendages	0	0	Upper and Lower Halves	1	1	Hair Shading	1	5	Head	07	05
Sex Sequence	0		Position of Both Arms	4	4	Four Quarters	4	4	Nudity and Transparency	7	7	Neck	06	06
Posture	1	1	Position of Right Arm	7	7	Relative Size	0		Form	3	3	Shoulders		
Perspective	2	2	Position of Left Arm	4	4	Constant Line Pressure	1	1	Detailing	5	5	Right Arm		
Vertical Midline	4	4	Position of Legs	1	1	Variable Line Pressure	0	0	Identity and Sex	1	1	Left Arm	05	04
Bilateral Symmetry	0	0	Relation of Long Axes	1	1	Line Continuity	0	0	Sophistication	3	3	Chest	07	05
Horizontal Midline	6	4	Right and Left Halves	2	1	Body Shading	0	1	Height	05	04	Girth	08	06

GENERAL CHARACTERISTICS OF SUBJECT

IDENTIFICATION

No. G57
Sex M
Marital status M
Age 22 yrs. at
psychological tests

PARENTAL HISTORY

Father
C H S D O
\- - - - +
Mother
C H S D O
\- + - - -

PHYSIOLOGICAL AND METABOLIC DATA

	Admission	Initial	Control	Cold pressor change	Exercise change	Smoking change
Systolic pressure	120	126	112	+20	+24	+12
Diastolic pressure	60	64	72	+42	−10	+09
Heart rate	74	64	59	+08	+33	+07

Age 21 yrs.
Height 74 in.
Weight 164 lbs.
Overweight −05 %

Ponderal index 13.53
Cholesterol 185 mg. per 100 ml.
Vital capacity liters

HABIT SURVEY

Smoking habits: occasional smoker
Age begun 18 yrs. Inhalation: no
Habits of nervous tension: 3, 5, 6, 9, 11, 12

STRONG VOCATIONAL INTEREST TEST

Occupation	Artist	Psychologist	Architect	Physician	Osteopath	Dentist	Veterinarian	Mathematician	Physicist	Engineer	Chemist	Production Manager
Standard Score	27	22	20	27	61	49	53	19	16	23	29	35

Occupation	Farmer	Aviator	Carpenter	Printer	Math.-Sci. Teacher	Ind. Arts Teacher	Voc. Agric. Teacher	Policeman	Forest Serv. Man	Y.M.C.A. Phys. Dir.	Personnel Director	Public Administrator
Standard Score	52	39	39	44	44	31	42	46	54	55	27	45

Occupation	Y.M.C.A. Secretary	Soc. Sci. H.S. Teacher	City Sch. Sup't.	Social Worker	Minister	Musician Performer	C.P.A.	Senior C.P.A.	Accountant	Office Man	Purchasing Agent	Banker
Standard Score	43	47	32	40	59	44	03	38	23	38	24	39

Occupation	Mortician	Pharmacist	Sales Manager	Real Est. Manager	Life Ins. Salesman	Advertising Man	Lawyer	Author- Journalist	President Mfg. Co.	Interest Maturity	Occupational Level	Masculinity- Femininity
Standard Score	44	34	16	32	29	22	25	29	15	54	42	41

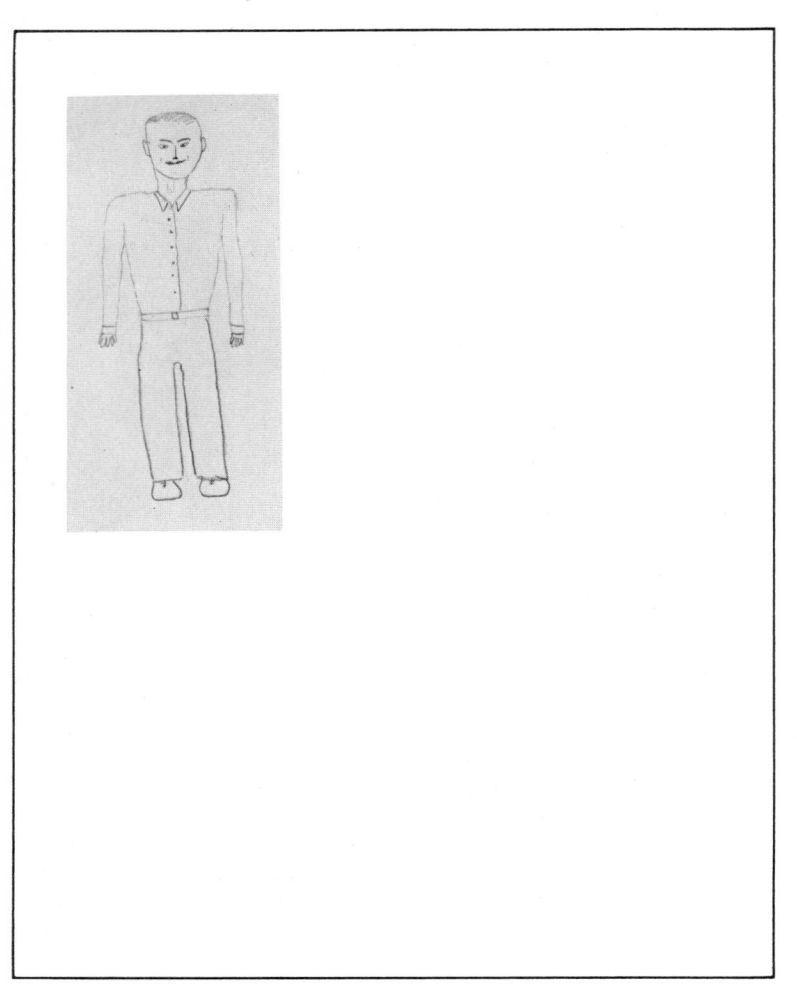

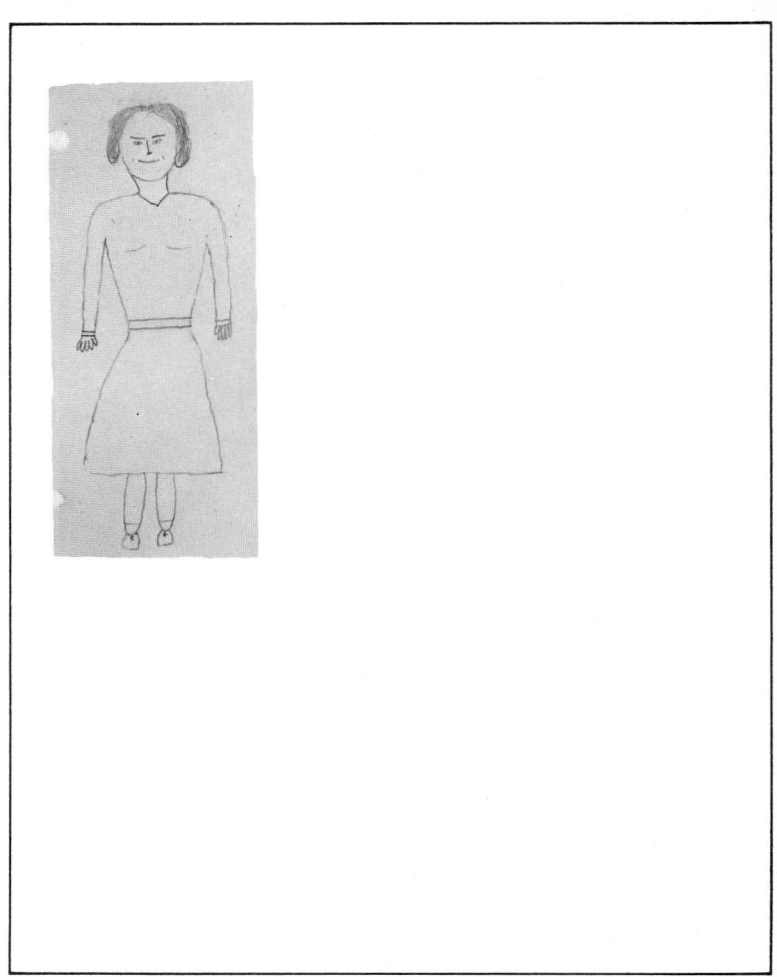

FIGURE-DRAWING CHARACTERISTICS

Structural	Male Female Both	Structural	Male	Female	Structural and Graphic	Male Female Both	Graphic, Global and Height	Male	Female	Body Proportions	Male	Female
Type	0	Omission of Appendages	0	0	Upper and Lower Halves	2 1	Hair Shading	1	2	Head	05	06
Sex Sequence	0	Position of Both Arms	0	0	Four Quarters	0 4	Nudity and Transparency	7	7	Neck	05	05
Posture	1 1	Position of Right Arm	0	0	Relative Size	4	Form	3	3	Shoulders	05	05
Perspective	0 0	Position of Left Arm	0	0	Constant Line Pressure	0 2	Detailing	3	3	Right Arm	03	03
Vertical Midline	3 0	Position of Legs	4	4	Variable Line Pressure	3 0	Identity and Sex	1	1	Left Arm	04	02
Bilateral Symmetry	4 4	Relation of Long Axes	1	1	Line Continuity	2 0	Sophistication	3	3	Chest	04	05
Horizontal Midline	4 4	Right and Left Halves	2	2	Body Shading	0 1	Height	04	04	Girth	04	04

GENERAL CHARACTERISTICS OF SUBJECT

IDENTIFICATION
No. G74
Sex M
Marital status
Age 23 yrs. at psychological tests

PARENTAL HISTORY
Father
C   H   S   D   O
−   −   −   −   −
Mother
C   H   S   D   O
−   +   +   −   −

PHYSIOLOGICAL AND METABOLIC DATA

	Admission	Initial	Control	Cold pressor change	Exercise change	Smoking change
Systolic pressure	134	140	134	+14	+26	+04
Diastolic pressure	72	66	76	+20	−06	−04
Heart rate	82	68	66	+06	+20	−05

Age 22 yrs.   Height 73 in.   Weight 171 lbs.   Overweight +02 %
Ponderal index 13.15   Cholesterol 180 mg. per 100 ml.   Vital capacity liters

HABIT SURVEY
Smoking habits: nonsmoker
Age begun   yrs.   Inhalation:
Habits of nervous tension: 6, 18, 19, 21

STRONG VOCATIONAL INTEREST TEST

Occupation	Artist	Psychologist	Architect	Physician	Osteopath	Dentist	Veterinarian	Mathematician	Physicist	Engineer	Chemist	Production Manager
Standard Score	31	44	31	62	61	46	55	32	31	41	48	28

Occupation	Farmer	Aviator	Carpenter	Printer	Math.-Sci. Teacher	Ind. Arts Teacher	Voc. Agric. Teacher	Policeman	Forest Serv. Man	Y.M.C.A. Phys. Dir.	Personnel Director	Public Administrator
Standard Score	47	46	33	44	49	38	49	39	46	37	31	47

Occupation	Y.M.C.A. Secretary	Soc. Sci. H.S. Teacher	City Sch. Sup't.	Social Worker	Minister	Musician Performer	C.P.A.	Senior C.P.A.	Accountant	Office Man	Purchasing Agent	Banker
Standard Score	31	30	23	39	59	47	14	41	21	28	19	23

Occupation	Mortician	Pharmacist	Sales Manager	Real Est. Manager	Life Ins. Salesman	Advertising Man	Lawyer	Author-Journalist	President Mfg. Co.	Interest Maturity	Occupational Level	Masculinity-Femininity
Standard Score	30	42	22	31	25	26	25	30	25	51	49	52

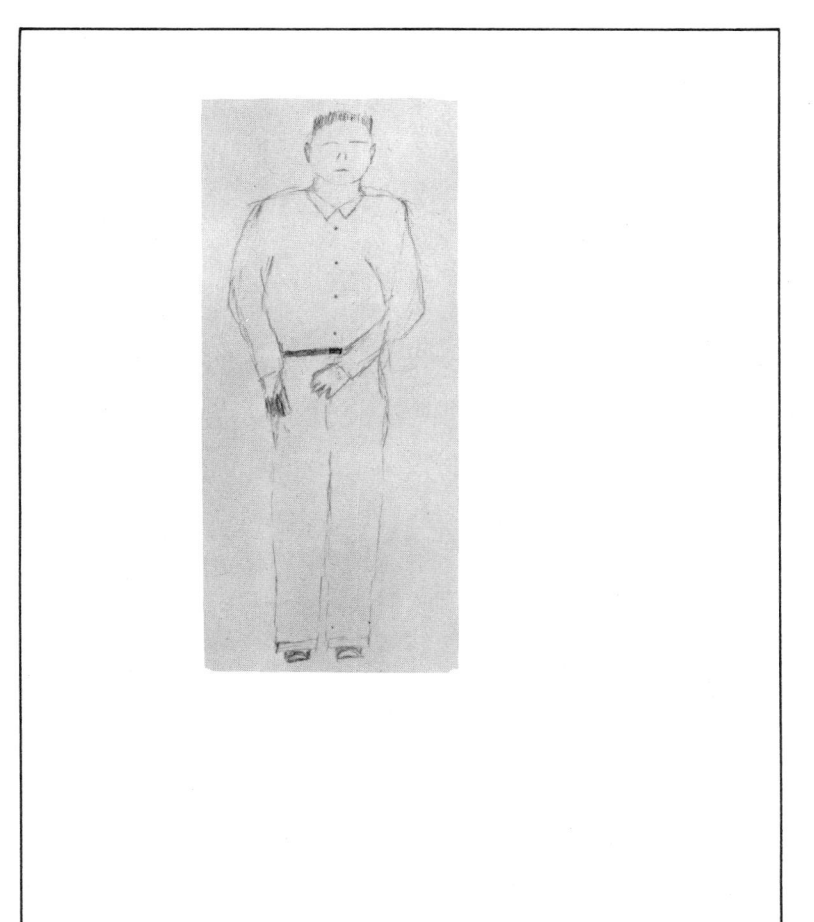

FIGURE-DRAWING CHARACTERISTICS

Structural	Male Female Both	Structural	Male	Female	Structural and Graphic	Male Female Both		Graphic, Global and Height	Male	Female	Body Proportions	Male	Female
Type	0	Omission of Appendages	0	0	Upper and Lower Halves	1	1	Hair Shading	3	3	Head	05	04
Sex Sequence	2	Position of Both Arms	0	0	Four Quarters	4	4	Nudity and Transparency	7	7	Neck	03	02
Posture	1	1	Position of Right Arm	5	0	Relative Size	0		Form	1	3	Shoulders	06	03
Perspective	0	0	Position of Left Arm	5	0	Constant Line Pressure	1	0	Detailing	3	3	Right Arm	04	02
Vertical Midline	3	0	Position of Legs	3	4	Variable Line Pressure	0	1	Identity and Sex	1	1	Left Arm	06	02
Bilateral Symmetry	3	3	Relation of Long Axes	1	1	Line Continuity	0	0	Sophistication	3	3	Chest	05	03
Horizontal Midline	4	4	Right and Left Halves	1	2	Body Shading	4	5	Height	05	04	Girth	07	04

GENERAL CHARACTERISTICS OF SUBJECT

IDENTIFICATION
No. A42
Sex M
Marital status S
Age 23 yrs. at
psychological tests

PARENTAL HISTORY				
Father				
C	H	S	D	O
-	-	-	-	-
Mother				
C	H	S	D	O
-	+	-	-	-

PHYSIOLOGICAL AND METABOLIC DATA

	Admission	Initial	Control	Cold pressor change	Exercise change	Smoking change
Systolic pressure	134	138	124	+22	+22	+04
Diastolic pressure	64	64	42	+23	-22	-03
Heart rate	70	76	68	+04	+09	+04

Age 22 yrs.	Height	73	in.	Ponderal index 13.25	
	Weight	167	lbs.	Cholesterol	222	mg. per 100 ml.
	Overweight -01 %			Vital capacity	liters

HABIT SURVEY

Smoking habits: occasional smoker

Age begun 19 yrs. Inhalation: no

Habits of nervous tension: 5, 6, 18, 25

STRONG VOCATIONAL INTEREST TEST

Occupation	Artist	Psychologist	Architect	Physician	Osteopath	Dentist	Veterinarian	Mathematician	Physicist	Engineer	Chemist	Production Manager
Standard Score	30	29	31	46	52	38	36	23	28	42	40	40

Occupation	Farmer	Aviator	Carpenter	Printer	Math.-Sci. Teacher	Ind. Arts Teacher	Voc. Agric. Teacher	Policeman	Forest Serv. Man	Y.M.C.A. Phys. Dir.	Personnel Director	Public Administrator
Standard Score	50	56	23	29	36	21	37	36	47	34	30	44

Occupation	Y.M.C.A. Secretary	Soc. Sci. H.S. Teacher	City Sch. Sup't.	Social Worker	Minister	Musician Performer	C.P.A.	Senior C.P.A.	Accountant	Office Man	Purchasing Agent	Banker
Standard Score	18	26	20	25	60	30	17	34	17	17	24	18

Occupation	Mortician	Pharmacist	Sales Manager	Real Est. Manager	Life Ins. Salesman	Advertising Man	Lawyer	Author- Journalist	President Mfg. Co.	Interest Maturity	Occupational Level	Masculinity- Femininity
Standard Score	20	24	28	38	28	30	42	34	34	50	61	61

FIGURE-DRAWING CHARACTERISTICS

Structural	Male	Female	Structural	Male	Female	Structural and Graphic	Male	Female	Graphic, Global and Height	Male	Female	Body Proportions	Male	Female
	Both						Both							
Type	0		Omission of Appendages	7	0	Upper and Lower Halves	1	3	Hair Shading	3	1	Head	04	05
Sex Sequence	0		Position of Both Arms	1	4	Four Quarters	4	4	Nudity and Transparency	3	0	Neck	04	03
Posture	1	1	Position of Right Arm	4	7	Relative Size	4		Form	1	3	Shoulders	05	
Perspective	9	2	Position of Left Arm	5	4	Constant Line Pressure	0	0	Detailing	1	1	Right Arm	04	
Vertical Midline	0	4	Position of Legs	4	1	Variable Line Pressure	1	1	Identity and Sex	1	1	Left Arm		04
Bilateral Symmetry	3	0	Relation of Long Axes	1	1	Line Continuity	0	0	Sophistication	3	3	Chest	04	05
Horizontal Midline	4	0	Right and Left Halves	2	2	Body Shading	3	3	Height	04	05	Girth	04	05

GENERAL CHARACTERISTICS OF SUBJECT

IDENTIFICATION	PARENTAL HISTORY
No. A43	Father
Sex M	C H S D O
Marital status S	- - - - ?
Age 22 yrs. at	Mother
psychological tests	C H S D O
	- + - + +

PHYSIOLOGICAL AND METABOLIC DATA

	Admission	Initial	Control	Cold pressor change	Exercise change	Smoking change
Systolic pressure	130	138	142	+14	+24	+05
Diastolic pressure	80	68	76	+16	-14	-03
Heart rate	82	61	55	+08	+13	+01

Age 21 yrs.	Height	74 in.	Ponderal index 12.61
	Weight	202 lbs.	Cholesterol 265 mg. per 100 ml.
	Overweight +17 %		Vital capacity liters

HABIT SURVEY

Smoking habits: mixed smoker

  Age begun 18 yrs.   Inhalation: no

Habits of nervous tension: 4, 5, 18, 19, 21, 22

STRONG VOCATIONAL INTEREST TEST

Occupation	Artist	Psychologist	Architect	Physician	Osteopath	Dentist	Veterinarian	Mathematician	Physicist	Engineer	Chemist	Production Manager
Standard Score	22	41	31	58	54	41	37	26	15	22	35	28

Occupation	Farmer	Aviator	Carpenter	Printer	Math.-Sci. Teacher	Ind. Arts Teacher	Voc. Agric. Teacher	Policeman	Forest Serv. Man	Y.M.C.A. Phys. Dir.	Personnel Director	Public Administrator
Standard Score	35	36	20	47	54	27	42	41	32	45	44	44

Occupation	Y.M.C.A. Secretary	Soc. Sci. H.S. Teacher	City Sch. Sup't.	Social Worker	Minister	Musician Performer	C.P.A.	Senior C.P.A.	Accountant	Office Man	Purchasing Agent	Banker
Standard Score	33	50	40	49	60	50	25	50	36	45	33	32

Occupation	Mortician	Pharmacist	Sales Manager	Real Est. Manager	Life Ins. Salesman	Advertising Man	Lawyer	Author-Journalist	President Mfg. Co.	Interest Maturity	Occupational Level	Masculinity-Femininity
Standard Score	32	45	25	27	26	29	31	26	12	62	47	45

Plate 318   DRAWINGS AT AN INTERMEDIATE LEVEL OF SOPHISTICATION   361

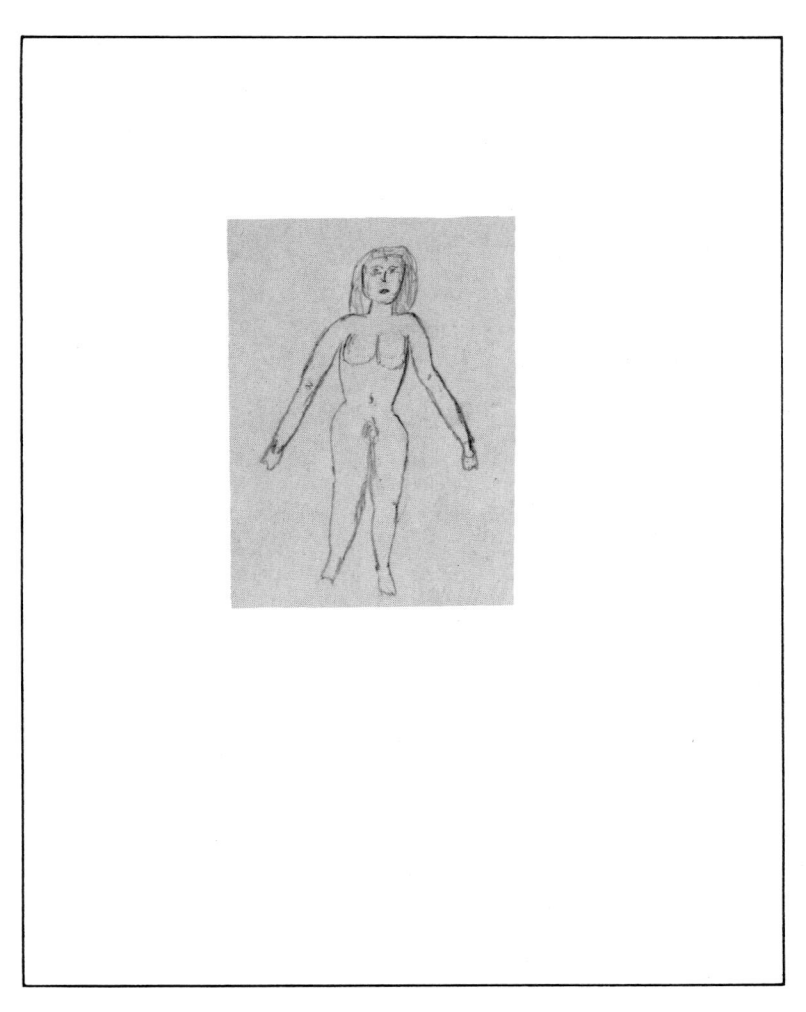

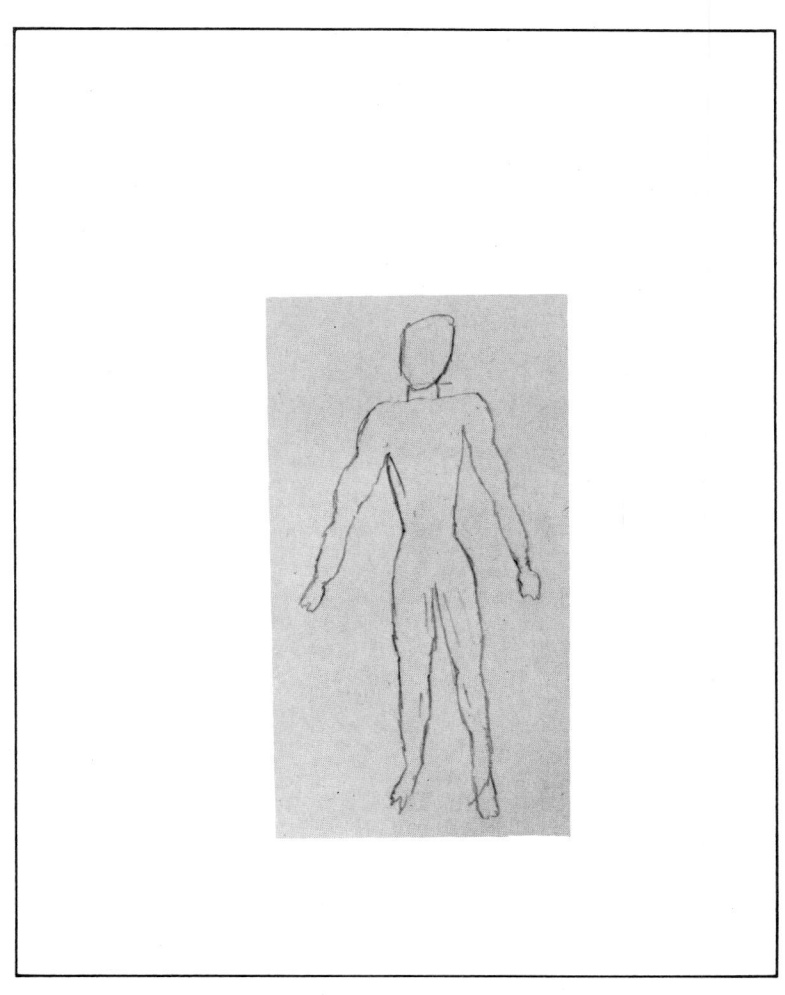

FIGURE-DRAWING CHARACTERISTICS

Structural	Male Female Both		Structural	Male	Female	Structural and Graphic	Male Female Both		Graphic, Global and Height	Male	Female	Body Proportions	Male	Female
Type	0		Omission of Appendages	0	0	Upper and Lower Halves	1	4	Hair Shading	0	2	Head	06	04
Sex Sequence	1		Position of Both Arms	0	1	Four Quarters	4	0	Nudity and Transparency	0	0	Neck	03	04
Posture	1	1	Position of Right Arm	1	1	Relative Size	5		Form	1	3	Shoulders	05	04
Perspective	0	0	Position of Left Arm	1	4	Constant Line Pressure	0	0	Detailing	5	3	Right Arm	04	04
Vertical Midline	0	0	Position of Legs	4	1	Variable Line Pressure	1	2	Identity and Sex	5	1	Left Arm	05	04
Bilateral Symmetry	3	3	Relation of Long Axes	1	3	Line Continuity	0	0	Sophistication	3	3	Chest	03	03
Horizontal Midline	0	0	Right and Left Halves	1	3	Body Shading	2	3	Height	03	06	Girth	03	03

GENERAL CHARACTERISTICS OF SUBJECT

IDENTIFICATION

No. A45

Sex M

Marital status S

Age 22 yrs. at

psychological tests

PARENTAL HISTORY

Father

C H S D O

- - - -

Mother

C H S D O

- + - - ?

PHYSIOLOGICAL AND METABOLIC DATA

	Admission	Initial	Control	Cold pressor change	Exercise change	Smoking change
Systolic pressure	120	137	130	+14	+32	+06
Diastolic pressure	98	72	58	+34	-06	+07
Heart rate	76	76	58	-03	+22	+19

Age 22 yrs.	Height	76	in.	Ponderal index 13.62		
	Weight	174	lbs.	Cholesterol	190	mg. per 100 ml.
	Overweight -05 %			Vital capacity		liters

HABIT SURVEY

Smoking habits: mixed smoker

Age begun 19 yrs.   Inhalation: yes

Habits of nervous tension: 2, 5, 7, 8, 23

STRONG VOCATIONAL INTEREST TEST

Occupation	Artist	Psychologist	Architect	Physician	Osteopath	Dentist	Veterinarian	Mathematician	Physicist	Engineer	Chemist	Production Manager
Standard Score	7	7	7	7	6	5	1	5	7	5	5	4

Occupation	Farmer	Aviator	Carpenter	Printer	Math.-Sci. Teacher	Ind. Arts Teacher	Voc. Agric. Teacher	Policeman	Forest Serv. Man	Y.M.C.A. Phys. Dir.	Personnel Director	Public Administrator
Standard Score	4	4	2	5	4	0	1	3	2	3	4	4

Occupation	Y.M.C.A. Secretary	Soc. Sci. H.S. Teacher	City Sch. Sup't.	Social Worker	Minister	Musician Performer	C.P.A.	Senior C.P.A.	Accountant	Office Man	Purchasing Agent	Banker
Standard Score	3	4	4	5	6	7	4	2	1	2	1	1

Occupation	Mortician	Pharmacist	Sales Manager	Real Est. Manager	Life Ins. Salesman	Advertising Man	Lawyer	Author-Journalist	President Mfg. Co.	Interest Maturity	Occupational Level	Masculinity-Femininity
Standard Score	2	2	2	3	3	5	7	7	4	5	5	3

FIGURE-DRAWING CHARACTERISTICS

Structural	Male	Female	Structural	Male	Female	Structural and Graphic	Male	Female	Graphic, Global and Height	Male	Female	Body Proportions	Male	Female
	Both						Both							
Type	0		Omission of Appendages	7	0	Upper and Lower Halves	0	3	Hair Shading	0	2	Head	08	09
Sex Sequence	0		Position of Both Arms	4	0	Four Quarters	4	4	Nudity and Transparency	7	7	Neck		02
Posture	1	1	Position of Right Arm	7	5	Relative Size		4		Form	1	3	Shoulders		07
Perspective	1	0	Position of Left Arm	5	5	Constant Line Pressure	0	0	Detailing	3	3	Right Arm		08
Vertical Midline	7	0	Position of Legs	2	3	Variable Line Pressure	2	1	Identity and Sex	1	1	Left Arm		08
Bilateral Symmetry	0	3	Relation of Long Axes	1	1	Line Continuity	0	0	Sophistication	3	3	Chest		
Horizontal Midline	0	2	Right and Left Halves	1	1	Body Shading	0	3	Height	06	07	Girth		08

GENERAL CHARACTERISTICS OF SUBJECT

IDENTIFICATION
No. B79
Sex M
Marital status S
Age 23 yrs. at
psychological tests

PARENTAL HISTORY
Father
C H S D O
- - - - +
Mother
C H S D O
- + - - -

PHYSIOLOGICAL AND METABOLIC DATA

	Admission	Initial	Control	Cold pressor change	Exercise change	Smoking change
Systolic pressure	124	132	117	+08	+34	
Diastolic pressure	84	80	68	+14	-07	
Heart rate	80	68	61	+06	+14	

Age 22 yrs.	Height	71	in.	Ponderal index	12.82	
	Weight	170	lbs.	Cholesterol	237	mg. per 100 ml.
	Overweight	+08 %		Vital capacity		liters

HABIT SURVEY

Smoking habits: moderate cigarette smoker

Age begun 21 yrs.   Inhalation: yes

Habits of nervous tension: 3, 4, 5, 7, 8, 18, 22

STRONG VOCATIONAL INTEREST TEST

Occupation	Artist	Psychologist	Architect	Physician	Osteopath	Dentist	Veterinarian	Mathematician	Physicist	Engineer	Chemist	Production Manager
Standard Score	45	54	46	52	36	40	01	45	34	40	46	22

Occupation	Farmer	Aviator	Carpenter	Printer	Math.-Sci. Teacher	Ind. Arts Teacher	Voc. Agric. Teacher	Policeman	Forest Serv. Man	Y.M.C.A. Phys. Dir.	Personnel Director	Public Administrator
Standard Score	13	23	02	27	31	02	-05	11	06	14	36	38

Occupation	Y.M.C.A. Secretary	Soc. Sci. H.S. Teacher	City Sch. Sup't.	Social Worker	Minister	Musician Performer	C.P.A.	Senior C.P.A.	Accountant	Office Man	Purchasing Agent	Banker
Standard Score	16	24	32	34	61	45	40	25	23	24	14	11

Occupation	Mortician	Pharmacist	Sales Manager	Real Est. Manager	Life Ins. Salesman	Advertising Man	Lawyer	Author- Journalist	President Mfg. Co.	Interest Maturity	Occupational Level	Masculinity- Femininity
Standard Score	12	19	28	32	30	47	48	50	34	54	68	41

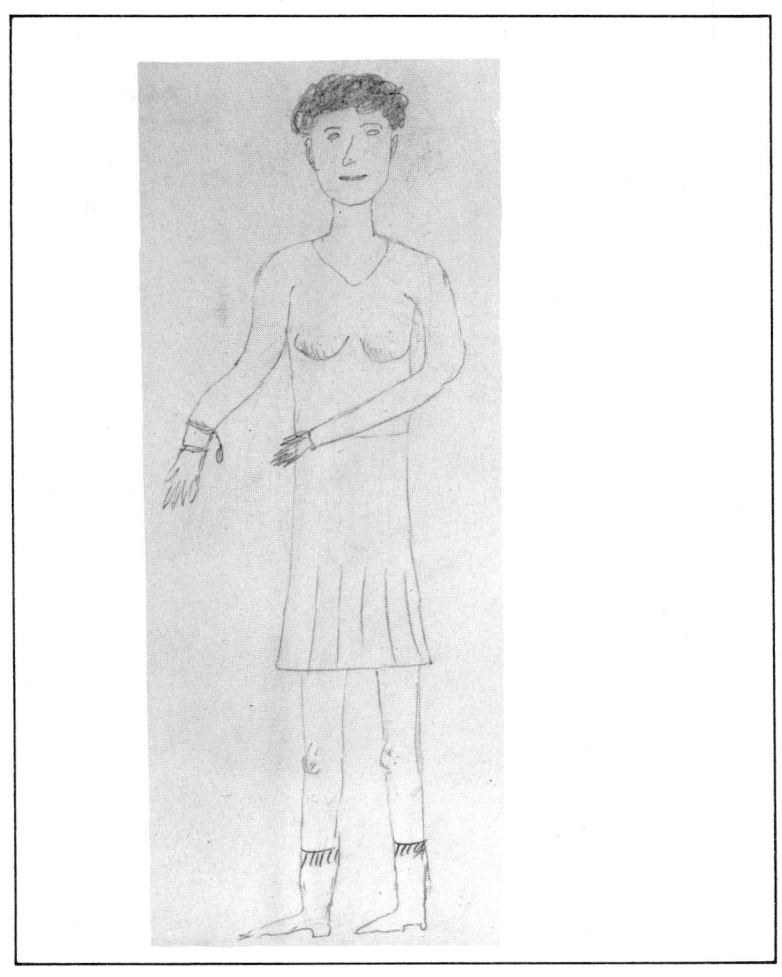

FIGURE-DRAWING CHARACTERISTICS

Structural	Male Female Both		Structural	Male	Female	Structural and Graphic	Male	Female Both		Graphic, Global and Height	Male	Female	Body Proportions	Male	Female
Type	0		Omission of Appendages	7	0	Upper and Lower Halves	3	3		Hair Shading	7	3	Head	09	09
Sex Sequence	0		Position of Both Arms	0	1	Four Quarters	4	4		Nudity and Transparency	7	7	Neck	12	08
Posture	1	1	Position of Right Arm	5	3	Relative Size	4			Form	3	3	Shoulders	09	07
Perspective	0	0	Position of Left Arm	5	5	Constant Line Pressure	1	1		Detailing	1	3	Right Arm	06	06
Vertical Midline	3	0	Position of Legs	5	5	Variable Line Pressure	0	0		Identity and Sex	1	1	Left Arm	08	06
Bilateral Symmetry	2	3	Relation of Long Axes	1	1	Line Continuity	0	0		Sophistication	3	3	Chest	07	06
Horizontal Midline	4	4	Right and Left Halves	3	1	Body Shading	0	3		Height	08	09	Girth	09	08

GENERAL CHARACTERISTICS OF SUBJECT

IDENTIFICATION
No. C22
Sex M
Marital status S
Age 22 yrs. at
psychological tests

PARENTAL HISTORY				
Father				
C	H	S	D	O
-	-	-	-	-
Mother				
C	H	S	D	O
-	+	-	-	+

PHYSIOLOGICAL AND METABOLIC DATA

	Admission	Initial	Control	Cold pressor change	Exercise change	Smoking change
Systolic pressure	130	130	108	+10	+42	-01
Diastolic pressure	85	80	70	+12	00	+09
Heart rate	88	100	86	+04	+19	+04

Age 23 yrs.	Height	73	in.	Ponderal index	13.13	
	Weight	172	lbs.	Cholesterol	202	mg. per 100 ml.
	Overweight +02 %			Vital capacity	5.5	liters

HABIT SURVEY
Smoking habits: occasional smoker
Age begun 19 yrs.   Inhalation: yes
Habits of nervous tension: 5, 9, 14

STRONG VOCATIONAL INTEREST TEST

Occupation	Artist	Psychologist	Architect	Physician	Osteopath	Dentist	Veterinarian	Mathematician	Physicist	Engineer	Chemist	Production Manager
Standard Score	08	25	13	22	28	18	25	22	08	24	28	32

Occupation	Farmer	Aviator	Carpenter	Printer	Math.-Sci. Teacher	Ind. Arts Teacher	Voc. Agric. Teacher	Policeman	Forest Serv. Man	Y.M.C.A. Phys. Dir.	Personnel Director	Public Administrator
Standard Score	27	27	13	26	37	13	29	27	15	19	36	44

Occupation	Y.M.C.A. Secretary	Soc. Sci. H.S. Teacher	City Sch. Sup't.	Social Worker	Minister	Musician Performer	C.P.A.	Senior C.P.A.	Accountant	Office Man	Purchasing Agent	Banker
Standard Score	23	35	22	26	62	26	45	55	56	59	50	52

Occupation	Mortician	Pharmacist	Sales Manager	Real Est. Manager	Life Ins. Salesman	Advertising Man	Lawyer	Author-Journalist	President Mfg. Co.	Interest Maturity	Occupational Level	Masculinity-Femininity
Standard Score	46	45	38	38	32	29	27	24	35	55	58	44

 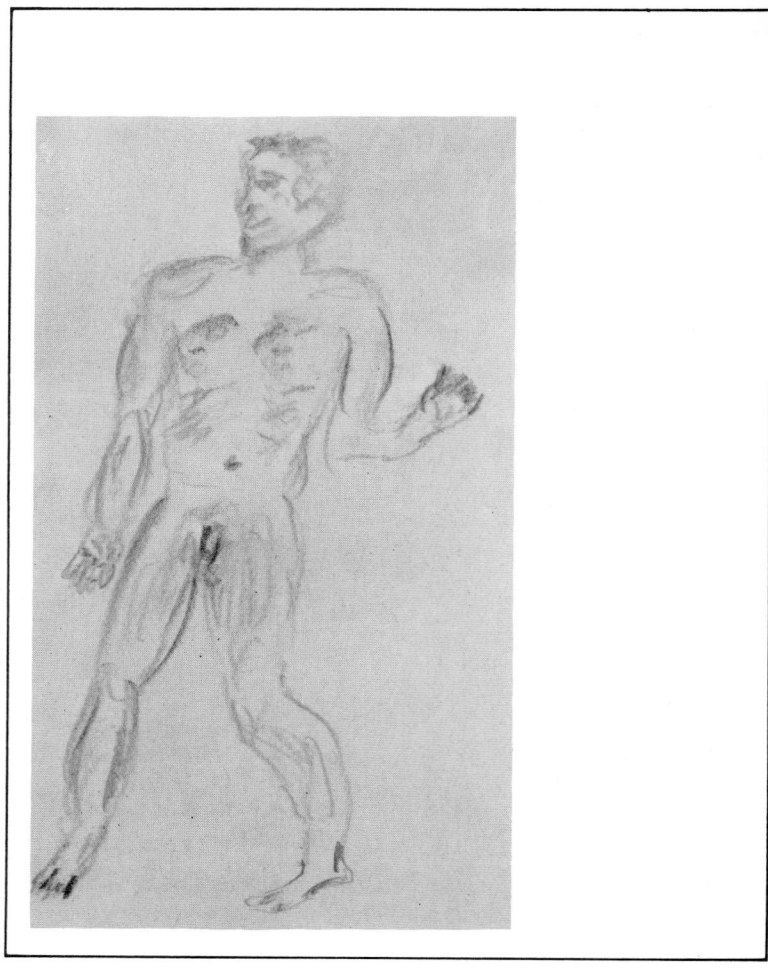

FIGURE-DRAWING CHARACTERISTICS

Structural	Male / Female (Both)	Structural	Male	Female	Structural and Graphic	Male / Female (Both)		Graphic, Global and Height	Male	Female	Body Proportions	Male	Female
Type	0	Omission of Appendages	0	7	Upper and Lower Halves	3	1	Hair Shading	3	3	Head	09	
Sex Sequence	1	Position of Both Arms	1	0	Four Quarters	4	4	Nudity and Transparency	0	0	Neck	07	07
Posture	6 1	Position of Right Arm	0	5	Relative Size	0		Form	1	3	Shoulders	10	09
Perspective	5 0	Position of Left Arm	4	5	Constant Line Pressure	0	1	Detailing	3	3	Right Arm	08	
Vertical Midline	0 0	Position of Legs	8	4	Variable Line Pressure	2	0	Identity and Sex	1	1	Left Arm	06	
Bilateral Symmetry	3 3	Relation of Long Axes	0	1	Line Continuity	0	0	Sophistication	3	3	Chest	08	08
Horizontal Midline	0 0	Right and Left Halves	2	1	Body Shading	3	3	Height	08	07	Girth	08	08

GENERAL CHARACTERISTICS OF SUBJECT

IDENTIFICATION
No. C30
Sex M
Marital status S
Age 22 yrs. at
psychological tests

PARENTAL HISTORY
Father
C H S D O
- - - - +
Mother
C H S D O
- + - - -

PHYSIOLOGICAL AND METABOLIC DATA

	Admission	Initial	Control	Cold pressor change	Exercise change	Smoking change
Systolic pressure	120	130	118	+12	+32	-02
Diastolic pressure	80	70	70	+12	00	+02
Heart rate	80	92	70	-04	+42	+07

Age 23 yrs.	Height 74 in.	Ponderal index 13.21
	Weight 176 lbs.	Cholesterol 186 mg. per 100 ml.
	Overweight +01 %	Vital capacity 5.6 liters

HABIT SURVEY

Smoking habits: occasional smoker

Age begun 19 yrs.   Inhalation: yes

Habits of nervous tension: 2, 5, 6, 10

STRONG VOCATIONAL INTEREST TEST

Occupation	Artist	Psychologist	Architect	Physician	Osteopath	Dentist	Veterinarian	Mathematician	Physicist	Engineer	Chemist	Production Manager
Standard Score	28	39	27	45	51	38	26	12	08	22	25	28

Occupation	Farmer	Aviator	Carpenter	Printer	Math.-Sci. Teacher	Ind. Arts Teacher	Voc. Agric. Teacher	Policeman	Forest Serv. Man	Y.M.C.A. Phys. Dir.	Personnel Director	Public Administrator
Standard Score	37	42	19	44	47	25	36	33	35	52	50	49

Occupation	Y.M.C.A. Secretary	Soc. Sci. H.S. Teacher	City Sch. Sup't.	Social Worker	Minister	Musician Performer	C.P.A.	Senior C.P.A.	Accountant	Office Man	Purchasing Agent	Banker
Standard Score	44	54	35	51	62	47	20	39	19	34	21	12

Occupation	Mortician	Pharmacist	Sales Manager	Real Est. Manager	Life Ins. Salesman	Advertising Man	Lawyer	Author-Journalist	President Mfg. Co.	Interest Maturity	Occupational Level	Masculinity-Femininity
Standard Score	25	34	36	37	38	38	36	31	20	66	54	44

FIGURE-DRAWING CHARACTERISTICS

Structural	Male Female Both		Structural	Male	Female	Structural and Graphic	Male Female Both		Graphic, Global and Height	Male	Female	Body Proportions	Male	Female
Type	0		Omission of Appendages	0	0	Upper and Lower Halves	1	1	Hair Shading	1	3	Head	08	08
Sex Sequence	0		Position of Both Arms	0	1	Four Quarters	4	4	Nudity and Transparency	7	7	Neck	08	08
Posture	1	1	Position of Right Arm	0	0	Relative Size	0		Form	3	3	Shoulders	05	05
Perspective	5	5	Position of Left Arm	0	4	Constant Line Pressure	0	0	Detailing	3	3	Right Arm	04	04
Vertical Midline	3	0	Position of Legs	4	4	Variable Line Pressure	1	1	Identity and Sex	1	1	Left Arm	04	04
Bilateral Symmetry	3	1	Relation of Long Axes	1	1	Line Continuity	0	0	Sophistication	3	3	Chest	04	04
Horizontal Midline	4	4	Right and Left Halves	1	1	Body Shading	1	3	Height	05	05	Girth	05	03

GENERAL CHARACTERISTICS OF SUBJECT

IDENTIFICATION
No. 037
Sex M
Marital status S
Age 26 yrs. at
psychological tests

PARENTAL HISTORY

Father				
C	H	S	D	O
−	−	−	−	+
Mother				
C	H	S	D	O
−	+	−	+	+

PHYSIOLOGICAL AND METABOLIC DATA

	Admission	Initial	Control	Cold pressor change	Exercise change	Smoking change
Systolic pressure	130	130	118	+10	+26	+01
Diastolic pressure	90	75	74	+16	−05	00
Heart rate	82	80	77	+04	+14	+09

Age 24 yrs.

Height	71	in.
Weight	164	lbs.
Overweight	+03	%

Ponderal index 12.98
Cholesterol 180 mg. per 100 ml.
Vital capacity 5.4 liters

HABIT SURVEY

Smoking habits: nonsmoker
Age begun yrs. Inhalation:
Habits of nervous tension: 1, 6, 8, 9, 14, 16, 23

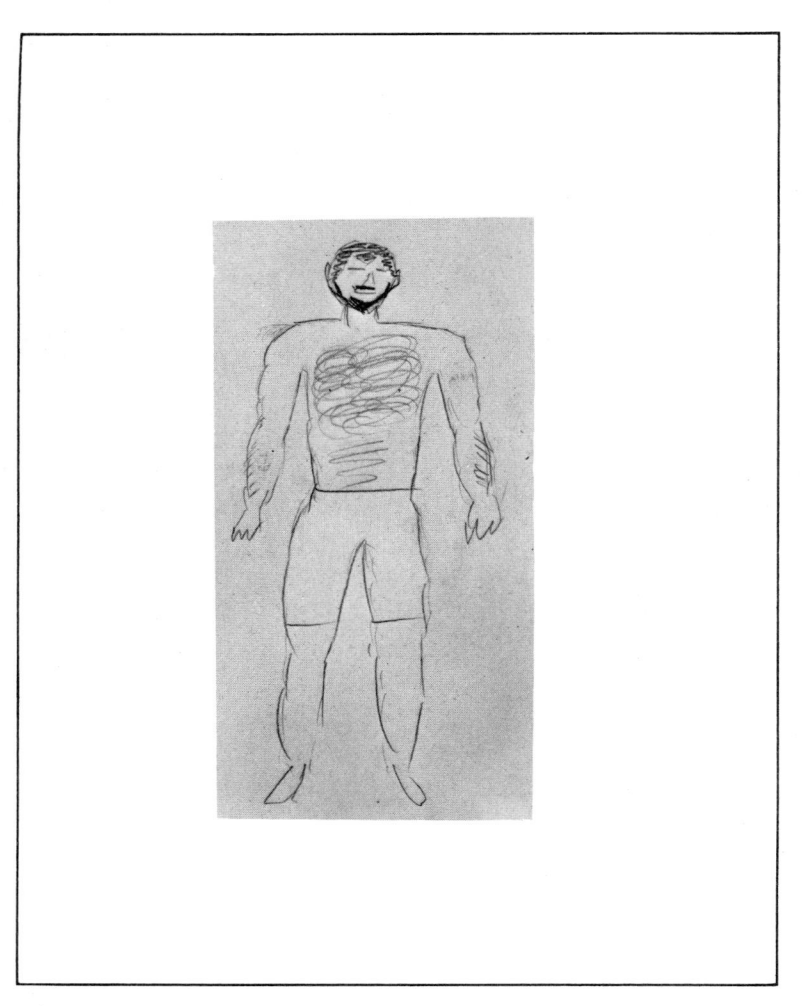

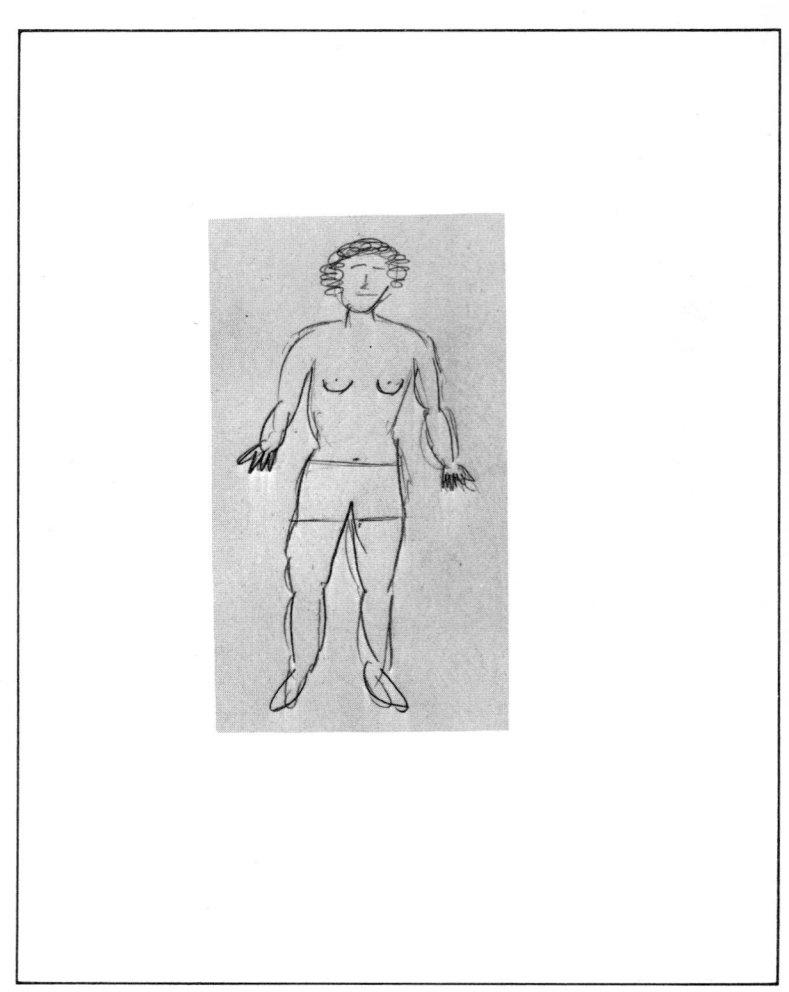

FIGURE-DRAWING CHARACTERISTICS

Structural	Male Female Both	Structural	Male	Female	Structural and Graphic	Male Female Both	Graphic, Global and Height	Male	Female	Body Proportions	Male	Female
Type	0	Omission of Appendages	0	0	Upper and Lower Halves	0	1	Hair Shading	3	3	Head	05	05
Sex Sequence	0	Position of Both Arms	0	0	Four Quarters	4	4	Nudity and Transparency	3	3	Neck	04	03
Posture	1	1	Position of Right Arm	1	1	Relative Size	0	Form	3	3	Shoulders	08	05
Perspective	0	0	Position of Left Arm	1	1	Constant Line Pressure	0	0	Detailing	3	3	Right Arm	04	02
Vertical Midline	0	0	Position of Legs	6	6	Variable Line Pressure	1	4	Identity and Sex	1	1	Left Arm	04	04
Bilateral Symmetry	3	3	Relation of Long Axes	1	1	Line Continuity	0	0	Sophistication	3	3	Chest	05	05
Horizontal Midline	4	4	Right and Left Halves	1	1	Body Shading	1	0	Height	05	05	Girth	06	05

GENERAL CHARACTERISTICS OF SUBJECT

IDENTIFICATION
No. C50
Sex M
Marital status S
Age 21 yrs. at
psychological tests

PARENTAL HISTORY
Father
C   H   S   D   O
-    -   -   -   -
Mother
C   H   S   D   O
-    +   -   -   -

PHYSIOLOGICAL AND METABOLIC DATA

	Admission	Initial	Control	Cold pressor change	Exercise change	Smoking change
Systolic pressure	150	110	118	+02	+52	+04
Diastolic pressure	80	60	62	+16	+08	+08
Heart rate	88	72	64	+12	+41	+12

Age 22 yrs.	Height 73 in.	Ponderal index 13.75
	Weight 150 lbs.	Cholesterol 225 mg. per 100 ml.
	Overweight -11 %	Vital capacity 4.4 liters

HABIT SURVEY

Smoking habits: light cigarette smoker

Age begun 15 yrs.   Inhalation: yes

Habits of nervous tension: 5, 6, 9, 11, 19

STRONG VOCATIONAL INTEREST TEST

Occupation	Artist	Psychologist	Architect	Physician	Osteopath	Dentist	Veterinarian	Mathematician	Physicist	Engineer	Chemist	Production Manager
Standard Score	34	27	32	55	55	53	43	21	24	41	42	34

Occupation	Farmer	Aviator	Carpenter	Printer	Math.-Sci. Teacher	Ind. Arts Teacher	Voc. Agric. Teacher	Policeman	Forest Serv. Man	Y.M.C.A. Phys. Dir.	Personnel Director	Public Administrator
Standard Score	50	60	32	40	33	23	23	34	35	20	18	28

Occupation	Y.M.C.A. Secretary	Soc. Sci. H.S. Teacher	City Sch. Sup't.	Social Worker	Minister	Musician Performer	C.P.A.	Senior C.P.A.	Accountant	Office Man	Purchasing Agent	Banker
Standard Score	05	14	02	20	62	36	22	42	21	27	36	23

Occupation	Mortician	Pharmacist	Sales Manager	Real Est. Manager	Life Ins. Salesman	Advertising Man	Lawyer	Author-Journalist	President Mfg. Co.	Interest Maturity	Occupational Level	Masculinity-Femininity
Standard Score	30	45	29	41	30	33	34	35	36	45	54	60

Plate 324   DRAWINGS AT AN INTERMEDIATE LEVEL OF SOPHISTICATION   367

FIGURE-DRAWING CHARACTERISTICS

Structural	Male Female Both		Structural	Male	Female	Structural and Graphic	Male Female Both		Graphic, Global and Height	Male	Female	Body Proportions	Male	Female
Type	0		Omission of Appendages	0	0	Upper and Lower Halves	1	1	Hair Shading	3	3	Head	06	06
Sex Sequence	1		Position of Both Arms	0	4	Four Quarters	4	4	Nudity and Transparency	7	7	Neck	06	12
Posture	1	1	Position of Right Arm	0	7	Relative Size	4		Form	3	3	Shoulders	07	
Perspective	0	2	Position of Left Arm	0	4	Constant Line Pressure	0	1	Detailing	3	3	Right Arm	04	
Vertical Midline	3	7	Position of Legs	4	1	Variable Line Pressure	2	0	Identity and Sex	1	1	Left Arm	04	04
Bilateral Symmetry	3	0	Relation of Long Axes	1	1	Line Continuity	0	0	Sophistication	3	3	Chest	06	05
Horizontal Midline	6	4	Right and Left Halves	1	2	Body Shading	0	7	Height	05	06	Girth	09	09

GENERAL CHARACTERISTICS OF SUBJECT

IDENTIFICATION
No. D02
Sex M
Marital status S
Age 23 yrs. at
psychological tests

PARENTAL HISTORY
Father
C   H   S   D   O
–   –   –   –   –
Mother
C   H   S   D   O
–   +   –   –   –

PHYSIOLOGICAL AND METABOLIC DATA

	Admission	Initial	Control	Cold pressor change	Exercise change	Smoking change
Systolic pressure	150	125	125	+25	+15	-02
Diastolic pressure	90	55	55	+25	-05	00
Heart rate	72	56	59	+04	+16	+10

Age 22 yrs.	Height	74	in.	Ponderal index 12.71	
	Weight	197	lbs.	Cholesterol	212 mg. per 100 ml.
	Overweight +14 %			Vital capacity	6.1 liters

HABIT SURVEY
Smoking habits: occasional smoker
Age begun 20 yrs.   Inhalation: yes
Habits of nervous tension: 1, 3, 4, 5, 7, 9, 11, 15, 18, 20

STRONG VOCATIONAL INTEREST TEST

Occupation	Artist	Psychologist	Architect	Physician	Osteopath	Dentist	Veterinarian	Mathematician	Physicist	Engineer	Chemist	Production Manager
Standard Score	29	37	29	43	38	29	22	24	14	24	26	27

Occupation	Farmer	Aviator	Carpenter	Printer	Math.-Sci. Teacher	Ind. Arts Teacher	Voc. Agric. Teacher	Policeman	Forest Serv. Man	Y.M.C.A. Phys. Dir.	Personnel Director	Public Administrator
Standard Score	34	39	17	35	40	23	34	31	36	43	47	51

Occupation	Y.M.C.A. Secretary	Soc. Sci. H.S. Teacher	City Sch. Sup't.	Social Worker	Minister	Musician Performer	C.P.A.	Senior C.P.A.	Accountant	Office Man	Purchasing Agent	Banker
Standard Score	40	45	43	45	63	51	13	36	18	27	12	19

Occupation	Mortician	Pharmacist	Sales Manager	Real Est. Manager	Life Ins. Salesman	Advertising Man	Lawyer	Author-Journalist	President Mfg. Co.	Interest Maturity	Occupational Level	Masculinity-Femininity
Standard Score	22	22	31	28	34	38	35	34	22	58	54	40

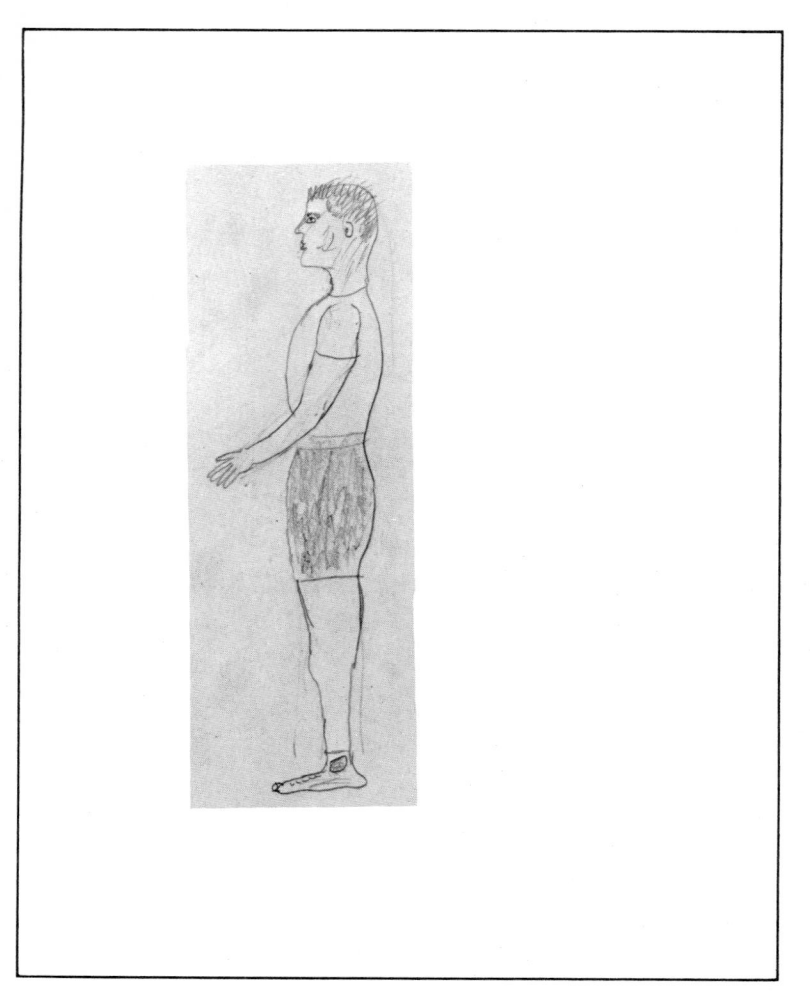

FIGURE-DRAWING CHARACTERISTICS

Structural	Male Female Both	Structural	Male	Female	Structural and Graphic	Male Female Both		Graphic, Global and Height	Male	Female	Body Proportions	Male	Female
Type	0	Omission of Appendages	0	0	Upper and Lower Halves	1	1	Hair Shading	3	3	Head	06	06
Sex Sequence	0	Position of Both Arms	4	4	Four Quarters	4	4	Nudity and Transparency	2	6	Neck	07	07
Posture	1 1	Position of Right Arm	7	7	Relative Size	0		Form	1	3	Shoulders		
Perspective	2 2	Position of Left Arm	4	4	Constant Line Pressure	0	0	Detailing	1	1	Right Arm		
Vertical Midline	4 4	Position of Legs	1	1	Variable Line Pressure	3	1	Identity and Sex	1	1	Left Arm	04	02
Bilateral Symmetry	0 0	Relation of Long Axes	1	1	Line Continuity	2	0	Sophistication	3	3	Chest	07	05
Horizontal Midline	4 4	Right and Left Halves	2	1	Body Shading	6	7	Height	06	04	Girth	05	06

GENERAL CHARACTERISTICS OF SUBJECT

IDENTIFICATION
No.   D14
Sex   M
Marital status   S
Age   22 yrs. at
psychological tests

PARENTAL HISTORY
Father
C   H   S   D   O
-   -   -   -   -
Mother
C   H   S   D   O
-   +   -   +   +

PHYSIOLOGICAL AND METABOLIC DATA

	Admission	Initial	Control	Cold pressor change	Exercise change	Smoking change
Systolic pressure	150	130	126	-04	+54	+08
Diastolic pressure	90	78	72	+13	-04	+06
Heart rate	80	72	77	00	+20	+11

Age 22 yrs.   Height 72 in.   Ponderal index 12.31
Weight 200 lbs.   Cholesterol 240 mg. per 100 ml.
Overweight +23 %   Vital capacity 6.1 liters

HABIT SURVEY

Smoking habits: occasional smoker

Age begun 20 yrs.   Inhalation: yes

Habits of nervous tension: 2, 5, 6, 9, 21

STRONG VOCATIONAL INTEREST TEST

Occupation	Artist	Psychologist	Architect	Physician	Osteopath	Dentist	Veterinarian	Mathematician	Physicist	Engineer	Chemist	Production Manager
Standard Score	29	44	30	59	47	37	33	32	21	32	37	22

Occupation	Farmer	Aviator	Carpenter	Printer	Math.-Sci. Teacher	Ind. Arts Teacher	Voc. Agric. Teacher	Policeman	Forest Serv. Man	Y.M.C.A. Phys. Dir.	Personnel Director	Public Administrator
Standard Score	27	40	06	32	39	12	28	27	22	40	29	46

Occupation	Y.M.C.A. Secretary	Soc. Sci. H.S. Teacher	City Sch. Sup't.	Social Worker	Minister	Musician Performer	C.P.A.	Senior C.P.A.	Accountant	Office Man	Purchasing Agent	Banker
Standard Score	21	33	29	41	63	38	36	42	22	26	21	22

Occupation	Mortician	Pharmacist	Sales Manager	Real Est. Manager	Life Ins. Salesman	Advertising Man	Lawyer	Author-Journalist	President Mfg. Co.	Interest Maturity	Occupational Level	Masculinity-Femininity
Standard Score	27	41	34	40	34	39	43	37	31	55	60	45

FIGURE-DRAWING CHARACTERISTICS

Structural	Male	Female	Structural	Male	Female	Structural and Graphic	Male	Female	Graphic, Global and Height	Male	Female	Body Proportions	Male	Female
		Both						Both						
Type		0	Omission of Appendages	0	0	Upper and Lower Halves	0	1	Hair Shading	3	3	Head	06	06
Sex Sequence		0	Position of Both Arms	0	2	Four Quarters	4	4	Nudity and Transparency	7	7	Neck	02	06
Posture	1	2	Position of Right Arm	0	0	Relative Size		0	Form	3	3	Shoulders	07	
Perspective	0	2	Position of Left Arm	0	7	Constant Line Pressure	0	0	Detailing	3	3	Right Arm	04	04
Vertical Midline	3	4	Position of Legs	6	8	Variable Line Pressure	4	5	Identity and Sex	1	1	Left Arm	04	
Bilateral Symmetry	4	0	Relation of Long Axes	1	1	Line Continuity	4	3	Sophistication	3	3	Chest	04	05
Horizontal Midline	6	4	Right and Left Halves	2	2	Body Shading	2	0	Height	06	06	Girth	06	08

GENERAL CHARACTERISTICS OF SUBJECT

IDENTIFICATION
No. D33
Sex M
Marital status S
Age 21 yrs. at
psychological tests

PARENTAL HISTORY				
Father				
C	H	S	D	O
-	-	-	-	+
Mother				
C	H	S	D	O
-	+	-	-	-

PHYSIOLOGICAL AND METABOLIC DATA

	Admission	Initial	Control	Cold pressor change	Exercise change	Smoking change
Systolic pressure	150	118	116	+12	+24	+06
Diastolic pressure	90	80	78	+20	-02	+04
Heart rate	72	56	50	+04	+09	+04

Age 21 yrs.	Height 68 in.	Ponderal index 13.41	
	Weight 130 lbs.	Cholesterol 205 mg. per 100 ml.	
	Overweight -10 %	Vital capacity liters	

HABIT SURVEY

Smoking habits: mixed smoker

  Age begun 19 yrs.   Inhalation: sometimes

Habits of nervous tension: 4, 5, 6, 9, 16, 19,

25

STRONG VOCATIONAL INTEREST TEST

Occupation	Artist	Psychologist	Architect	Physician	Osteopath	Dentist	Veterinarian	Mathematician	Physicist	Engineer	Chemist	Production Manager
Standard Score	24	44	30	60	56	42	33	24	29	41	44	38

Occupation	Farmer	Aviator	Carpenter	Printer	Math.-Sci. Teacher	Ind. Arts Teacher	Voc. Agric. Teacher	Policeman	Forest Serv. Man	Y.M.C.A. Phys. Dir.	Personnel Director	Public Administrator
Standard Score	45	56	29	45	56	39	46	36	36	43	47	44

Occupation	Y.M.C.A. Secretary	Soc. Sci. H.S. Teacher	City Sch. Sup't.	Social Worker	Minister	Musician Performer	C.P.A.	Senior C.P.A.	Accountant	Office Man	Purchasing Agent	Banker
Standard Score	32	40	30	44	63	48	30	51	29	33	27	18

Occupation	Mortician	Pharmacist	Sales Manager	Real Est. Manager	Life Ins. Salesman	Advertising Man	Lawyer	Author-Journalist	President Mfg. Co.	Interest Maturity	Occupational Level	Masculinity-Femininity
Standard Score	30	34	23	34	26	26	29	24	24	58	48	61

FIGURE-DRAWING CHARACTERISTICS

Structural	Male Female Both		Structural	Male	Female	Structural and Graphic	Male Female Both		Graphic, Global and Height	Male	Female	Body Proportions	Male	Female
Type	0		Omission of Appendages	0	0	Upper and Lower Halves	1	1	Hair Shading	1	1	Head	04	05
Sex Sequence	0		Position of Both Arms	2	2	Four Quarters	4	4	Nudity and Transparency	0	0	Neck	06	05
Posture	1	1	Position of Right Arm	4	4	Relative Size	4		Form	1	1	Shoulders		
Perspective	2	2	Position of Left Arm	7	7	Constant Line Pressure	1	0	Detailing	3	3	Right Arm	04	04
Vertical Midline	4	4	Position of Legs	1	1	Variable Line Pressure	0	3	Identity and Sex	1	1	Left Arm		
Bilateral Symmetry	0	0	Relation of Long Axes	1	1	Line Continuity	0	1	Sophistication	3	3	Chest	06	04
Horizontal Midline	0	0	Right and Left Halves	2	2	Body Shading	0	0	Height	04	05	Girth	04	04

GENERAL CHARACTERISTICS OF SUBJECT

IDENTIFICATION
No. 038
Sex M
Marital status S
Age 25 yrs. at
psychological tests

PARENTAL HISTORY
Father
C   H   S   D   O
-    -   -   -   ?
Mother
C   H   S   D   O
-    +   -   -   -

PHYSIOLOGICAL AND METABOLIC DATA

	Admission	Initial	Control	Cold pressor change	Exercise change	Smoking change
Systolic pressure	125	118	114	+24	+28	+02
Diastolic pressure	85	70	70	+20	-22	+02
Heart rate	75	84	74	+08	+18	+12

Age 22 yrs.	Height 74 in.	Ponderal index 13.53
	Weight 164 lbs.	Cholesterol 206 mg. per 100 ml.
	Overweight -05 %	Vital capacity 4.9 liters

HABIT SURVEY

Smoking habits: heavy cigarette smoker

Age begun 14 yrs.   Inhalation: yes

Habits of nervous tension: 25

STRONG VOCATIONAL INTEREST TEST

Occupation	Artist	Psychologist	Architect	Physician	Osteopath	Dentist	Veterinarian	Mathematician	Physicist	Engineer	Chemist	Production Manager
Standard Score	21	45	21	62	55	39	45	26	21	30	41	27

Occupation	Farmer	Aviator	Carpenter	Printer	Math.-Sci. Teacher	Ind. Arts Teacher	Voc. Agric. Teacher	Policeman	Forest Serv. Man	Y.M.C.A. Phys. Dir.	Personnel Director	Public Administrator
Standard Score	45	44	20	35	53	25	50	39	47	45	39	58

Occupation	Y.M.C.A. Secretary	Soc. Sci. H.S. Teacher	City Sch. Sup't.	Social Worker	Minister	Musician Performer	C.P.A.	Senior C.P.A.	Accountant	Office Man	Purchasing Agent	Banker
Standard Score	36	43	35	50	63	38	19	48	20	25	11	21

Occupation	Mortician	Pharmacist	Sales Manager	Real Est. Manager	Life Ins. Salesman	Advertising Man	Lawyer	Author- Journalist	President Mfg. Co.	Interest Maturity	Occupational Level	Masculinity- Femininity
Standard Score	26	33	19	26	28	24	30	27	15	62	49	52

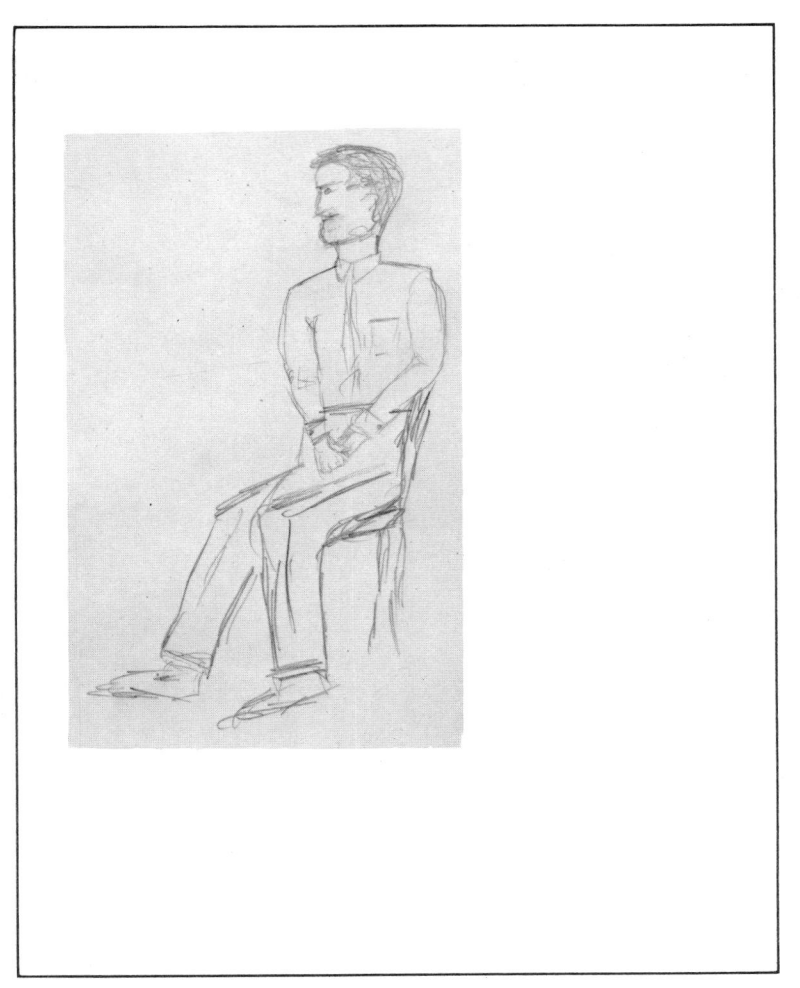

FIGURE-DRAWING CHARACTERISTICS

Structural	Male Female Both		Structural	Male	Female	Structural and Graphic	Male Female Both		Graphic, Global and Height	Male	Female	Body Proportions	Male	Female
Type	0		Omission of Appendages	0	0	Upper and Lower Halves	1	1	Hair Shading	3	3	Head	07	07
Sex Sequence	0		Position of Both Arms	0	1	Four Quarters	4	4	Nudity and Transparency	7	7	Neck	07	05
Posture	3	1	Position of Right Arm	5	4	Relative Size	5		Form	3	3	Shoulders		
Perspective	6	1	Position of Left Arm	5	0	Constant Line Pressure	0	0	Detailing	3	3	Right Arm	04	05
Vertical Midline	7	4	Position of Legs	1	4	Variable Line Pressure	1	3	Identity and Sex	1	1	Left Arm	05	06
Bilateral Symmetry	0	0	Relation of Long Axes	0	1	Line Continuity	0	0	Sophistication	3	3	Chest		
Horizontal Midline	4	4	Right and Left Halves	1	1	Body Shading	7	7	Height		06	Girth		

GENERAL CHARACTERISTICS OF SUBJECT

IDENTIFICATION

No. A21

Sex M

Marital status M

Age 22 yrs. at psychological tests

PARENTAL HISTORY

Father

C	H	S	D	O
-	?	-	-	+

Mother

C	H	S	D	O
-	?	-	-	?

PHYSIOLOGICAL AND METABOLIC DATA

	Admission	Initial	Control	Cold pressor change	Exercise change	Smoking change
Systolic pressure	110	116	110	+12	+38	+04
Diastolic pressure	72	64	64	+16	-02	+06
Heart rate	100	53	58	+02	+13	+12

Age 22 yrs.

Height 70 in.

Weight 165 lbs.

Overweight +07 %

Ponderal index 12.77

Cholesterol 237 mg. per 100 ml.

Vital capacity liters

HABIT SURVEY

Smoking habits: mixed smoker

Age begun 18 yrs.   Inhalation: yes

Habits of nervous tension: 2, 5, 6, 9, 21, 25

STRONG VOCATIONAL INTEREST TEST

Occupation	Artist	Psychologist	Architect	Physician	Osteopath	Dentist	Veterinarian	Mathematician	Physicist	Engineer	Chemist	Production Manager
Standard Score	31	36	39	61	61	46	29	20	22	40	39	39

Occupation	Farmer	Aviator	Carpenter	Printer	Math.-Sci. Teacher	Ind. Arts Teacher	Voc. Agric. Teacher	Policeman	Forest Serv. Man	Y.M.C.A. Phys. Dir.	Personnel Director	Public Administrator
Standard Score	31	48	29	34	40	36	28	36	31	38	38	42

Occupation	Y.M.C.A. Secretary	Soc. Sci. H.S. Teacher	City Sch. Sup't.	Social Worker	Minister	Musician Performer	C.P.A.	Senior C.P.A.	Accountant	Office Man	Purchasing Agent	Banker
Standard Score	22	24	19	36	60	47	13	34	19	28	21	15

Occupation	Mortician	Pharmacist	Sales Manager	Real Est. Manager	Life Ins. Salesman	Advertising Man	Lawyer	Author-Journalist	President Mfg. Co.	Interest Maturity	Occupational Level	Masculinity-Femininity
Standard Score	29	35	27	33	27	32	27	31	37	57	54	45

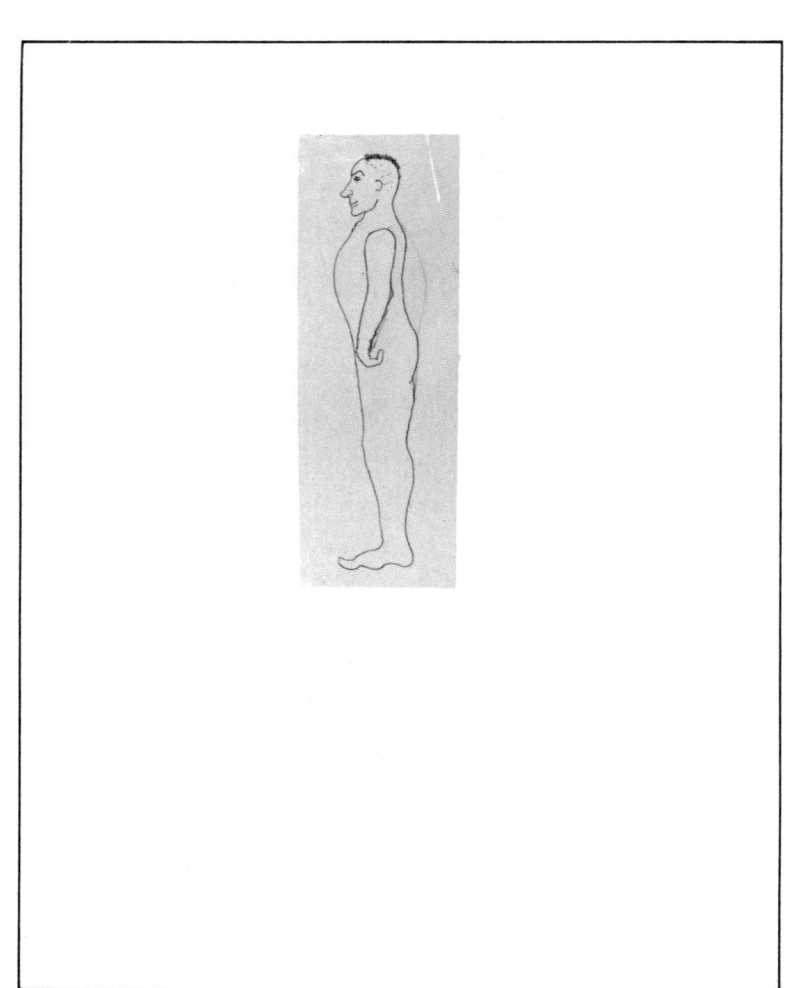

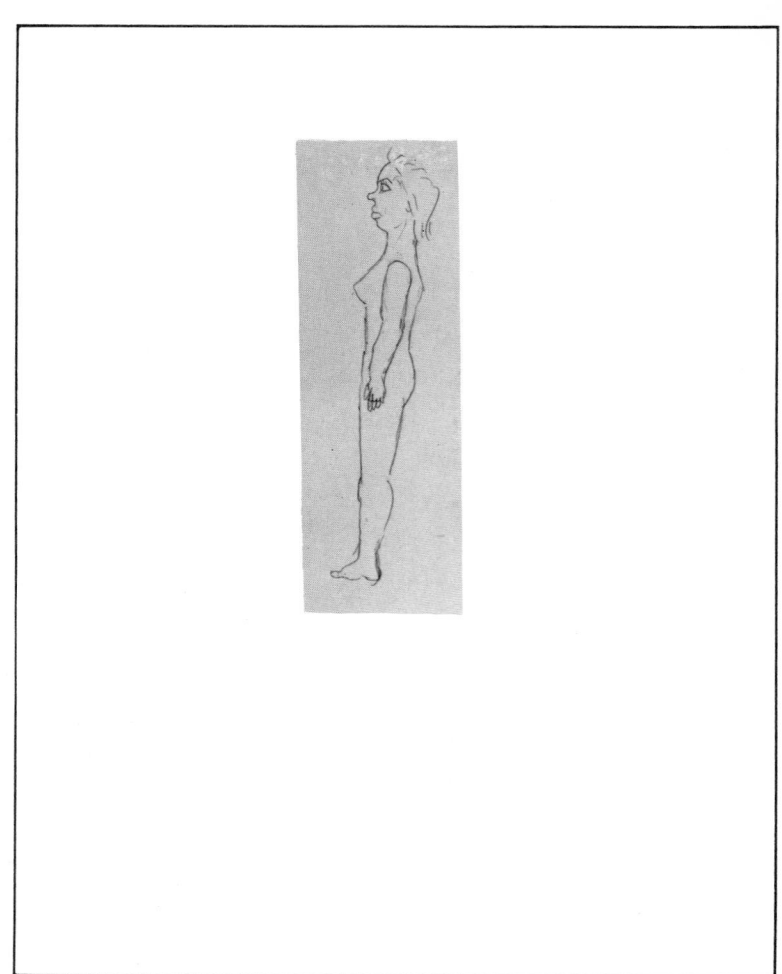

FIGURE-DRAWING CHARACTERISTICS

Structural	Male Female Both	Structural	Male	Female	Structural and Graphic	Male Female Both		Graphic, Global and Height	Male	Female	Body Proportions	Male	Female
Type	0	Omission of Appendages	0	0	Upper and Lower Halves	1	1	Hair Shading	3	7	Head	04	05
Sex Sequence	0	Position of Both Arms	4	4	Four Quarters	4	4	Nudity and Transparency	0	0	Neck	03	07
Posture	1 1	Position of Right Arm	7	7	Relative Size	2		Form	1	1	Shoulders		
Perspective	2 2	Position of Left Arm	0	0	Constant Line Pressure	3	3	Detailing	3	3	Right Arm		
Vertical Midline	4 4	Position of Legs	1	1	Variable Line Pressure	0	0	Identity and Sex	1	1	Left Arm	04	02
Bilateral Symmetry	0 0	Relation of Long Axes	1	1	Line Continuity	4	0	Sophistication	3	3	Chest	05	04
Horizontal Midline	0 0	Right and Left Halves	7	0	Body Shading	0	0	Height	04	04	Girth	05	04

GENERAL CHARACTERISTICS OF SUBJECT

IDENTIFICATION
No. 537
Sex M
Marital status S
Age 24 yrs. at
psychological tests

PARENTAL HISTORY
Father
C   H   S   D   O
-   ?   -   -   +
Mother
C   H   S   D   O
-   -   -   -   -

PHYSIOLOGICAL AND METABOLIC DATA

	Admission	Initial	Control	Cold pressor change	Exercise change	Smoking change
Systolic pressure	120	110	90	00	+30	+07
Diastolic pressure	70	70	50	+10	+10	+06
Heart rate	72	76	73	-02	+24	+11

Age 22 yrs.	Height 72 in.	Ponderal index 13.55
	Weight 150 lbs.	Cholesterol 210 mg. per 100 ml.
	Overweight -08 %	Vital capacity 5.0 liters

HABIT SURVEY

Smoking habits: heavy cigarette smoker

Age begun 16 yrs.   Inhalation: yes

Habits of nervous tension: 4, 5, 6, 22, 23, 25

FIGURE-DRAWING CHARACTERISTICS

Structural	Male — Female (Both)	Structural	Male	Female	Structural and Graphic	Male — Female (Both)		Graphic, Global and Height	Male	Female	Body Proportions	Male	Female
Type	0	Omission of Appendages	0	0	Upper and Lower Halves	3	0	Hair Shading	3	3	Head	12	08
Sex Sequence	0	Position of Both Arms	1	0	Four Quarters	4	4	Nudity and Transparency	7	7	Neck	07	08
Posture	2	1	Position of Right Arm	4	5	Relative Size	0		Form	3	3	Shoulders	09	06
Perspective	0	0	Position of Left Arm	5	5	Constant Line Pressure	0	0	Detailing	3	3	Right Arm	06	04
Vertical Midline	3	3	Position of Legs	8	5	Variable Line Pressure	5	5	Identity and Sex	1	1	Left Arm	04	04
Bilateral Symmetry	2	3	Relation of Long Axes	1	1	Line Continuity	3	3	Sophistication	3	3	Chest	06	04
Horizontal Midline	4	4	Right and Left Halves	1	1	Body Shading	0	1	Height	07	06	Girth	07	03

GENERAL CHARACTERISTICS OF SUBJECT

IDENTIFICATION
No. 726
Sex M
Marital status M
Age 21 yrs. at psychological tests

PARENTAL HISTORY
Father
C H S D O
- ? - - ?
Mother
C H S D O
- - - - -

PHYSIOLOGICAL AND METABOLIC DATA

	Admission	Initial	Control	Cold pressor change	Exercise change	Smoking change
Systolic pressure	140	134	128	+10	+48	
Diastolic pressure	80	68	70	+16	−22	
Heart rate	80	80	68	+04	+26	

Age 20 yrs.

Height	72 in.	Ponderal index	13.00
Weight	170 lbs.	Cholesterol	203 mg. per 100 ml.
Overweight	+06 %	Vital capacity	5.4 liters

HABIT SURVEY

Smoking habits: occasional smoker

Age begun 18 yrs.   Inhalation: no

Habits of nervous tension: 3, 4, 5, 9, 11, 19, 22

FIGURE-DRAWING CHARACTERISTICS

Structural	Male Female Both	Structural	Male	Female	Structural and Graphic	Male Female Both		Graphic, Global and Height	Male	Female	Body Proportions	Male	Female
Type	0	Omission of Appendages	0	0	Upper and Lower Halves	3	3	Hair Shading	3	3	Head	09	12
Sex Sequence	0	Position of Both Arms	4	4	Four Quarters	4	4	Nudity and Transparency	7	7	Neck	08	05
Posture	1 2	Position of Right Arm	7	7	Relative Size	0		Form	3	3	Shoulders		
Perspective	2 2	Position of Left Arm	4	4	Constant Line Pressure	4	4	Detailing	3	3	Right Arm		
Vertical Midline	7 4	Position of Legs	1	8	Variable Line Pressure	0	0	Identity and Sex	1	1	Left Arm	08	08
Bilateral Symmetry	0 0	Relation of Long Axes	1	1	Line Continuity	0	0	Sophistication	3	3	Chest	09	09
Horizontal Midline	4 4	Right and Left Halves	1	0	Body Shading	5	7	Height	08	08	Girth	09	12

GENERAL CHARACTERISTICS OF SUBJECT

IDENTIFICATION
No. 761
Sex M
Marital status S
Age 27 yrs. at psychological tests

PARENTAL HISTORY
Father
C   H   S   D   O
−   ?   −   −   +
Mother
C   H   S   D   O
−   −   −   −   −

PHYSIOLOGICAL AND METABOLIC DATA

	Admission	Initial	Control	Cold pressor change	Exercise change	Smoking change
Systolic pressure	140	124	110	+04	+20	+02
Diastolic pressure	80	62	68	+16	−04	+03
Heart rate	88	88	75	+10	+19	00

Age 26 yrs.	Height 68 in.	Ponderal index 12.83
	Weight 149 lbs.	Cholesterol 222 mg. per 100 ml.
	Overweight −01 %	Vital capacity 4.9 liters

FIGURE-DRAWING CHARACTERISTICS

Structural	Male	Female	Structural	Male	Female	Structural and Graphic	Male	Female	Graphic, Global and Height	Male	Female	Body Proportions	Male	Female
	Both						Both							
Type	0		Omission of Appendages	0	0	Upper and Lower Halves	1	3	Hair Shading	1	5	Head	09	09
Sex Sequence	0		Position of Both Arms	1	2	Four Quarters	4	4	Nudity and Transparency	7	7	Neck	07	07
Posture	2	2	Position of Right Arm	5	2	Relative Size	4		Form	3	3	Shoulders	08	
Perspective	5	2	Position of Left Arm	2	7	Constant Line Pressure	0	0	Detailing	5	5	Right Arm	06	06
Vertical Midline	0	4	Position of Legs	8	8	Variable Line Pressure	3	4	Identity and Sex	3	3	Left Arm	06	
Bilateral Symmetry	3	0	Relation of Long Axes	1	1	Line Continuity	0	0	Sophistication	3	3	Chest	08	07
Horizontal Midline	4	4	Right and Left Halves	1	0	Body Shading	0	3	Height	07	08	Girth	09	09

GENERAL CHARACTERISTICS OF SUBJECT

IDENTIFICATION
No. G39
Sex M
Marital status S
Age 23 yrs. at
psychological tests

PARENTAL HISTORY				
Father				
C	H	S	D	O
-	?	-	-	?
Mother				
C	H	S	D	O
-	-	-	-	+

PHYSIOLOGICAL AND METABOLIC DATA

	Admission	Initial	Control	Cold pressor change	Exercise change	Smoking change
Systolic pressure	140	118	112	+16	+20	+12
Diastolic pressure	70	78	80	+18	-20	+10
Heart rate	72	60	67	+02	+03	+06

Age 22 yrs.	Height	69 in.	Ponderal index 12.61
	Weight	164 lbs.	Cholesterol 210 mg. per 100 ml.
	Overweight +09 %		Vital capacity liters

HABIT SURVEY
Smoking habits: nonsmoker
Age begun yrs. Inhalation:
Habits of nervous tension: 2, 4, 5, 6, 9, 10, 11, 12, 16, 23, 25

STRONG VOCATIONAL INTEREST TEST

Occupation	Artist	Psychologist	Architect	Physician	Osteopath	Dentist	Veterinarian	Mathematician	Physicist	Engineer	Chemist	Production Manager
Standard Score	28	40	35	46	39	28	12	28	22	22	32	22

Occupation	Farmer	Aviator	Carpenter	Printer	Math.-Sci. Teacher	Ind. Arts Teacher	Voc. Agric. Teacher	Policeman	Forest Serv. Man	Y.M.C.A. Phys. Dir.	Personnel Director	Public Administrator
Standard Score	21	23	25	32	42	16	23	27	11	40	39	43

Occupation	Y.M.C.A. Secretary	Soc. Sci. H.S. Teacher	City Sch. Sup't.	Social Worker	Minister	Musician Performer	C.P.A.	Senior C.P.A.	Accountant	Office Man	Purchasing Agent	Banker
Standard Score	42	40	39	46	59	55	38	35	27	35	19	29

Occupation	Mortician	Pharmacist	Sales Manager	Real Est. Manager	Life Ins. Salesman	Advertising Man	Lawyer	Author-Journalist	President Mfg. Co.	Interest Maturity	Occupational Level	Masculinity-Femininity
Standard Score	33	34	28	31	30	35	35	34	23	62	57	31

FIGURE-DRAWING CHARACTERISTICS

Structural	Male Female Both	Structural	Male	Female	Structural and Graphic	Male Female Both		Graphic, Global and Height	Male	Female	Body Proportions	Male	Female
Type	0	Omission of Appendages	0	0	Upper and Lower Halves	1	1	Hair Shading	3	3	Head	08	09
Sex Sequence	2	Position of Both Arms	4	4	Four Quarters	4	4	Nudity and Transparency	7	7	Neck	06	06
Posture	2 2	Position of Right Arm	7	7	Relative Size	0		Form	3	3	Shoulders		
Perspective	2 2	Position of Left Arm	4	4	Constant Line Pressure	0	0	Detailing	3	5	Right Arm		
Vertical Midline	7 4	Position of Legs	8	8	Variable Line Pressure	1	1	Identity and Sex	1	1	Left Arm	04	02
Bilateral Symmetry	0 0	Relation of Long Axes	1	1	Line Continuity	3	3	Sophistication	3	3	Chest	08	05
Horizontal Midline	6 4	Right and Left Halves	2	1	Body Shading	0	0	Height	05	05	Girth	08	07

GENERAL CHARACTERISTICS OF SUBJECT

IDENTIFICATION
No. A06
Sex M
Marital status M
Age 23 yrs. at psychological tests

PARENTAL HISTORY
Father
C   H   S   D   O
-   ?   -   -   ?
Mother
C   H   S   D   O
-   -   -   -   -

PHYSIOLOGICAL AND METABOLIC DATA

	Admission	Initial	Control	Cold pressor change	Exercise change	Smoking change
Systolic pressure	150	122	128	+19	+26	
Diastolic pressure	92	78	82	+15	-08	
Heart rate	100	76	64	-09	+14	

Age 22 yrs.	Height 69 in.	Ponderal index 12.61
	Weight 164 lbs.	Cholesterol 217 mg. per 100 ml.
	Overweight +09 %	Vital capacity liters

HABIT SURVEY
Smoking habits: nonsmoker
Age begun yrs. Inhalation:
Habits of nervous tension: 5, 6, 9, 10, 24

STRONG VOCATIONAL INTEREST TEST

Occupation	Artist	Psychologist	Architect	Physician	Osteopath	Dentist	Veterinarian	Mathematician	Physicist	Engineer	Chemist	Production Manager
Standard Score	3	7	4	7	6	4	3	5	5	4	5	3

Occupation	Farmer	Aviator	Carpenter	Printer	Math.-Sci. Teacher	Ind. Arts Teacher	Voc. Agric. Teacher	Policeman	Forest Serv. Man	Y.M.C.A. Phys. Dir.	Personnel Director	Public Administrator
Standard Score	4	3	2	6	6	2	2	3	5	4	3	6

Occupation	Y.M.C.A. Secretary	Soc. Sci. H.S. Teacher	City Sch. Sup't.	Social Worker	Minister	Musician Performer	C.P.A.	Senior C.P.A.	Accountant	Office Man	Purchasing Agent	Banker
Standard Score	3	5	4	5	6	6	6	7	3	5	2	3

Occupation	Mortician	Pharmacist	Sales Manager	Real Est. Manager	Life Ins. Salesman	Advertising Man	Lawyer	Author-Journalist	President Mfg. Co.	Interest Maturity	Occupational Level	Masculinity-Femininity
Standard Score	3	5	1	4	3	4	4	4	3	6	5	4

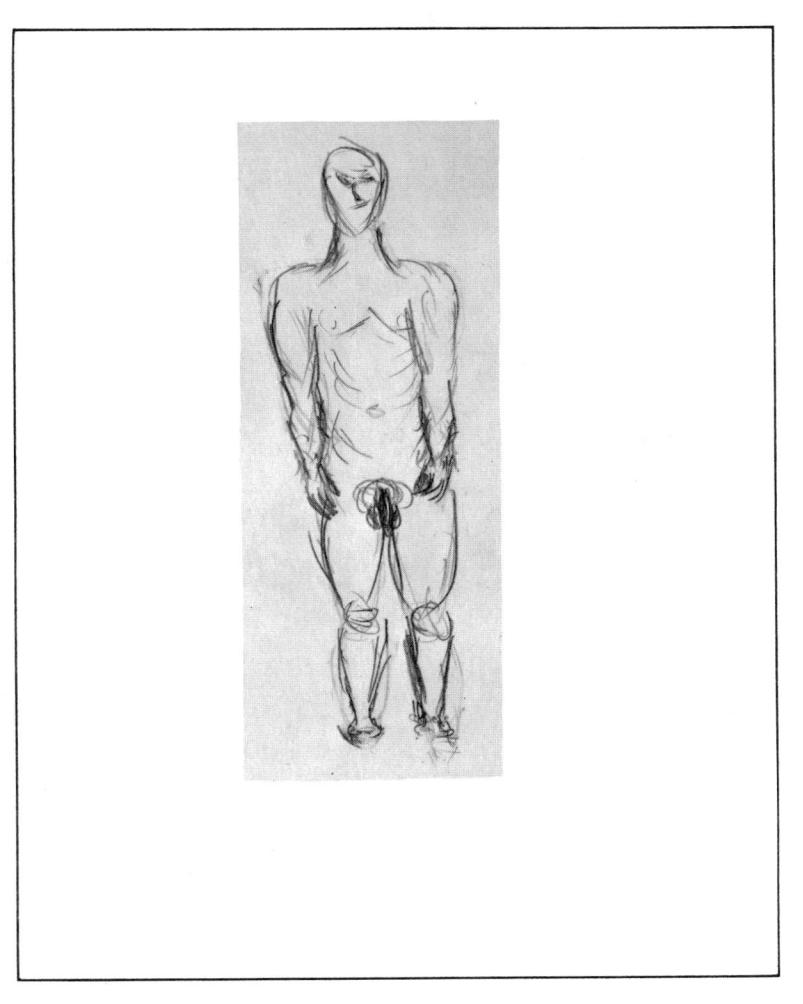

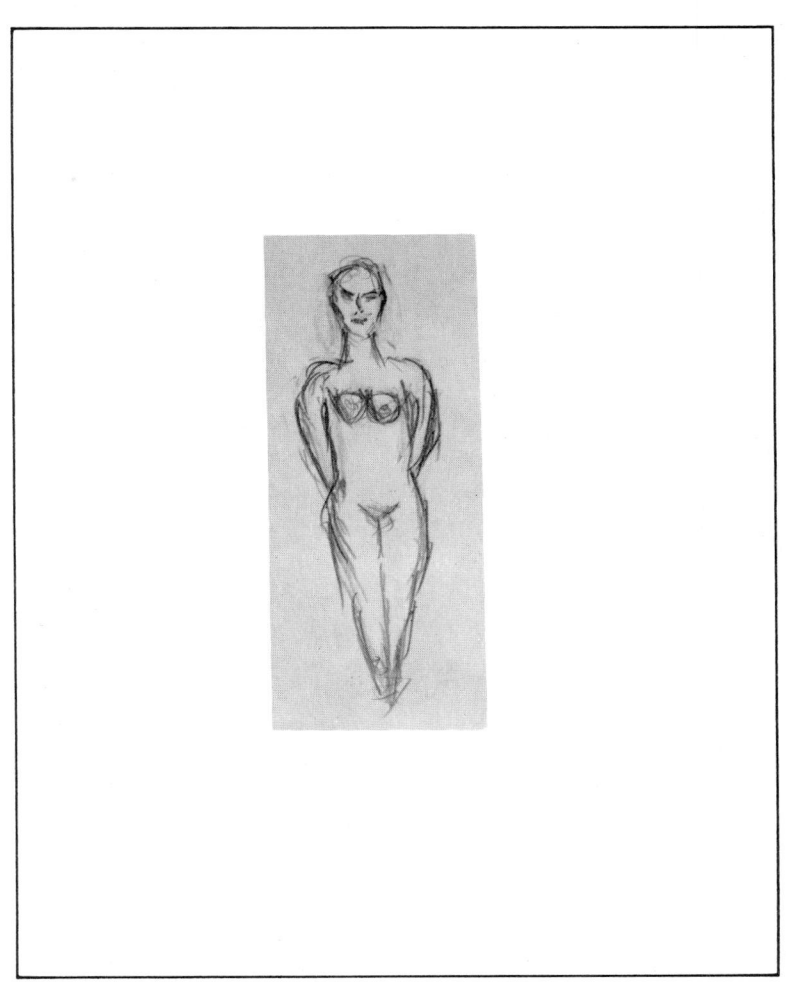

FIGURE-DRAWING CHARACTERISTICS

Structural	Male Female Both		Structural	Male	Female	Structural and Graphic	Male Female Both		Graphic, Global and Height	Male	Female	Body Proportions	Male	Female
Type	0		Omission of Appendages	0	5	Upper and Lower Halves	1	1	Hair Shading	0	3	Head	07	06
Sex Sequence	0		Position of Both Arms	0	6	Four Quarters	4	4	Nudity and Transparency	0	0	Neck	08	08
Posture	1	0	Position of Right Arm	0	8	Relative Size	0		Form	3	3	Shoulders	07	05
Perspective	0	0	Position of Left Arm	0	8	Constant Line Pressure	0	0	Detailing	3	3	Right Arm	06	
Vertical Midline	0	0	Position of Legs	4	2	Variable Line Pressure	5	3	Identity and Sex	1	1	Left Arm	06	
Bilateral Symmetry	3	3	Relation of Long Axes	1	1	Line Continuity	0	0	Sophistication	3	3	Chest	04	04
Horizontal Midline	0	0	Right and Left Halves	1	1	Body Shading	3	3	Height	06		Girth	06	04

GENERAL CHARACTERISTICS OF SUBJECT

IDENTIFICATION
No. A65
Sex M
Marital status S
Age 22 yrs. at
psychological tests

PARENTAL HISTORY					
Father					
C	H	S	D	O	
-	?	-	-	+	
Mother					
C	H	S	D	O	
-	-	-	-	-	

PHYSIOLOGICAL AND METABOLIC DATA

	Admission	Initial	Control	Cold pressor change	Exercise change	Smoking change
Systolic pressure	130	138	120	+36	+38	+07
Diastolic pressure	70	68	64	+36	-02	+10
Heart rate	68	64	51	+25	+25	+02

Age 22 yrs.	Height 72 in.	Ponderal index 12.41
	Weight 195 lbs.	Cholesterol 190 mg. per 100 ml.
	Overweight +20 %	Vital capacity liters

HABIT SURVEY

Smoking habits: occasional smoker

Age begun 18 yrs.   Inhalation:

Habits of nervous tension: 2, 4, 6, 7, 11, 12, 18, 19, 22, 23

STRONG VOCATIONAL INTEREST TEST

Occupation	Artist	Psychologist	Architect	Physician	Osteopath	Dentist	Veterinarian	Mathematician	Physicist	Engineer	Chemist	Production Manager
Standard Score	23	39	27	46	56	34	18	08	12	28	29	40

Occupation	Farmer	Aviator	Carpenter	Printer	Math.-Sci. Teacher	Ind. Arts Teacher	Voc. Agric. Teacher	Policeman	Forest Serv. Man	Y.M.C.A. Phys. Dir.	Personnel Director	Public Administrator
Standard Score	21	37	24	42	39	24	13	46	23	49	63	60

Occupation	Y.M.C.A. Secretary	Soc. Sci. H.S. Teacher	City Sch. Sup't.	Social Worker	Minister	Musician Performer	C.P.A.	Senior C.P.A.	Accountant	Office Man	Purchasing Agent	Banker
Standard Score	42	44	37	57	60	44	28	46	36	43	24	18

Occupation	Mortician	Pharmacist	Sales Manager	Real Est. Manager	Life Ins. Salesman	Advertising Man	Lawyer	Author-Journalist	President Mfg. Co.	Interest Maturity	Occupational Level	Masculinity-Femininity
Standard Score	36	27	28	32	39	35	36	30	33	65	53	41

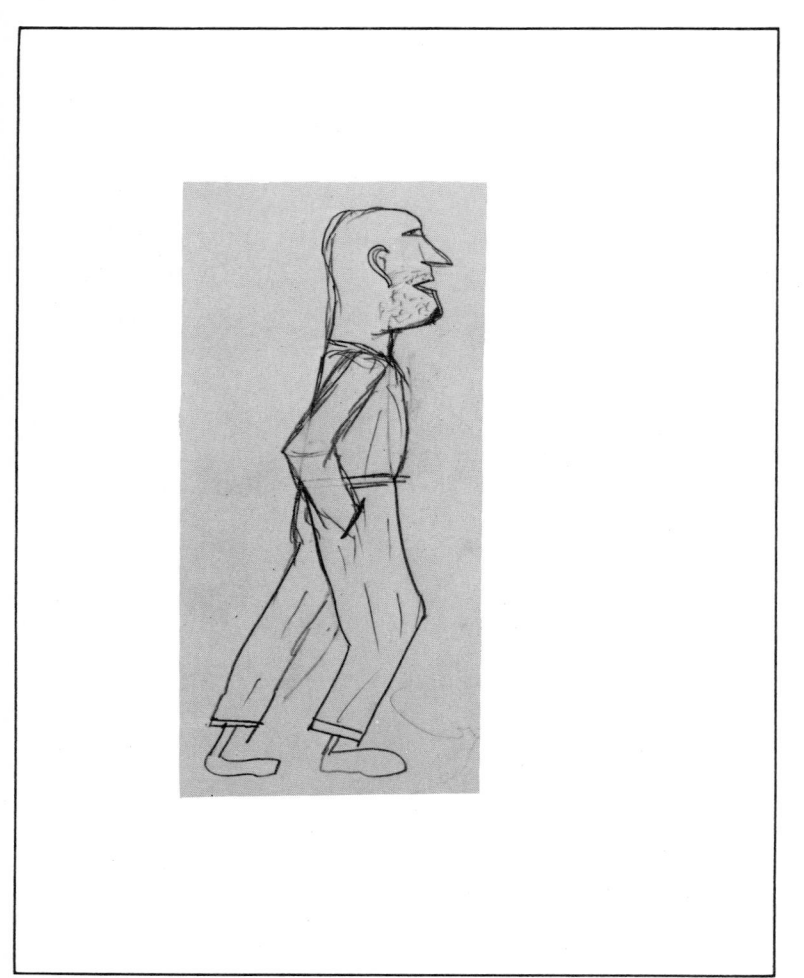

FIGURE-DRAWING CHARACTERISTICS

Structural	Male Female Both		Structural	Male	Female	Structural and Graphic	Male Female Both		Graphic, Global and Height	Male	Female	Body Proportions	Male	Female
Type	0		Omission of Appendages	7	0	Upper and Lower Halves	0	1	Hair Shading	0	3	Head	09	07
Sex Sequence	0		Position of Both Arms	2	2	Four Quarters	4	4	Nudity and Transparency	7	7	Neck	08	04
Posture	2	1	Position of Right Arm	5	0	Relative Size	0		Form	3	3	Shoulders		
Perspective	2	2	Position of Left Arm	7	7	Constant Line Pressure	5	0	Detailing	3	3	Right Arm		06
Vertical Midline	4	4	Position of Legs	8	1	Variable Line Pressure	0	5	Identity and Sex	1	1	Left Arm		
Bilateral Symmetry	0	0	Relation of Long Axes	0	1	Line Continuity	2	4	Sophistication	3	3	Chest	07	04
Horizontal Midline	4	4	Right and Left Halves	1	2	Body Shading	3	0	Height	06	05	Girth	07	05

GENERAL CHARACTERISTICS OF SUBJECT

IDENTIFICATION
No. B77
Sex M
Marital status S
Age 24 yrs. at psychological tests

PARENTAL HISTORY					
Father					
C	H	S	D	O	
–	?	–	–	?	
Mother					
C	H	S	D	O	
–	–	(+)	–	–	

PHYSIOLOGICAL AND METABOLIC DATA

	Admission	Initial	Control	Cold pressor change	Exercise change	Smoking change
Systolic pressure	130	124	114	+40	+66	
Diastolic pressure	68	42	56	+24	-36	
Heart rate	74	82	72	+08	+41	

Age 23 yrs.	Height 71 in.	Ponderal index 13.10
	Weight 159 lbs.	Cholesterol 230 mg. per 100 ml.
	Overweight 00 %	Vital capacity 4.4 liters

HABIT SURVEY

Smoking habits: nonsmoker

Age begun   yrs.   Inhalation:

Habits of nervous tension: 2, 3, 4, 5, 6, 9, 10, 14, 16, 18, 21, 22, 24, 25

STRONG VOCATIONAL INTEREST TEST

Occupation	Artist	Psychologist	Architect	Physician	Osteopath	Dentist	Veterinarian	Mathematician	Physicist	Engineer	Chemist	Production Manager
Standard Score	7	8	6	7	6	4	2	3	4	3	4	2

Occupation	Farmer	Aviator	Carpenter	Printer	Math.-Sci. Teacher	Ind. Arts Teacher	Voc. Agric. Teacher	Policeman	Forest Serv. Man	Y.M.C.A. Phys. Dir.	Personnel Director	Public Administrator
Standard Score	4	3	2	3	4	0	2	2	4	4	5	6

Occupation	Y.M.C.A. Secretary	Soc. Sci. H.S. Teacher	City Sch. Sup't.	Social Worker	Minister	Musician Performer	C.P.A.	Senior C.P.A.	Accountant	Office Man	Purchasing Agent	Banker
Standard Score	3	5	5	7	6	8	5	3	1	2	1	2

Occupation	Mortician	Pharmacist	Sales Manager	Real Est. Manager	Life Ins. Salesman	Advertising Man	Lawyer	Author-Journalist	President Mfg. Co.	Interest Maturity	Occupational Level	Masculinity-Femininity
Standard Score	2	4	3	4	4	6	6	7	4	4	6	3

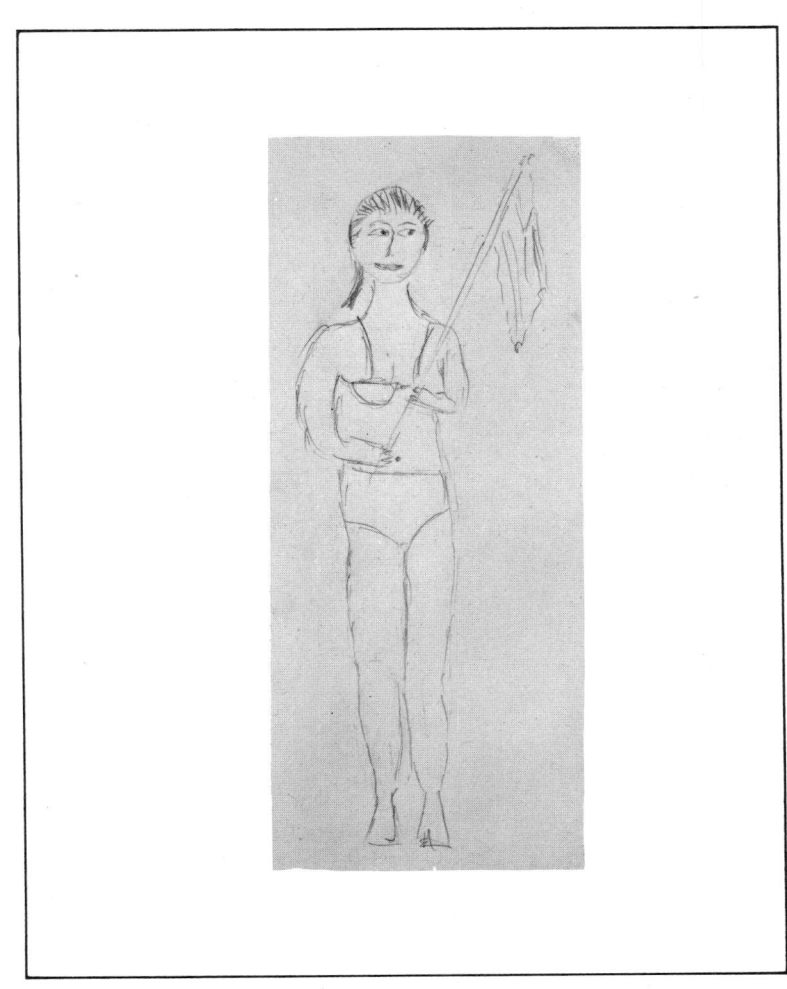

FIGURE-DRAWING CHARACTERISTICS

Structural	Male Female Both	Structural	Male	Female	Structural and Graphic	Male Female Both		Graphic, Global and Height	Male	Female	Body Proportions	Male	Female
Type	0	Omission of Appendages	7	0	Upper and Lower Halves	1	0	Hair Shading	0	3	Head	04	07
Sex Sequence	0	Position of Both Arms	1	0	Four Quarters	4	4	Nudity and Transparency	7	2	Neck	05	10
Posture	4 1	Position of Right Arm	5	5	Relative Size	4		Form	3	5	Shoulders	03	05
Perspective	0 0	Position of Left Arm	2	5	Constant Line Pressure	1	1	Detailing	3	3	Right Arm		04
Vertical Midline	3 0	Position of Legs	7	3	Variable Line Pressure	0	0	Identity and Sex	1	1	Left Arm		
Bilateral Symmetry	3 1	Relation of Long Axes	1	1	Line Continuity	0	0	Sophistication	3	3	Chest	03	05
Horizontal Midline	6 4	Right and Left Halves	1	1	Body Shading	7	0	Height	04	07	Girth	04	06

GENERAL CHARACTERISTICS OF SUBJECT

IDENTIFICATION
No. C44
Sex M
Marital status S
Age 22 yrs. at
psychological tests

PARENTAL HISTORY
Father
C H S D 0
– ? – – ?
Mother
C H S D 0
– – – – –

PHYSIOLOGICAL AND METABOLIC DATA

	Admission	Initial	Control	Cold pressor change	Exercise change	Smoking change
Systolic pressure	140	120	110	+08	+10	+09
Diastolic pressure	85	70	70	+28	–20	+02
Heart rate	84	80	71	+12	+10	–02

Age 23 yrs.	Height 75 in.	Ponderal index 12.82
	Weight 200 lbs.	Cholesterol 154 mg. per 100 ml.
	Overweight +11 %	Vital capacity 5.7 liters

HABIT SURVEY
Smoking habits: mixed smoker
Age begun 19 yrs.   Inhalation: yes
Habits of nervous tension: 1, 2, 3, 4, 5, 6,
8, 9, 11, 12, 14, 16, 18, 19, 23, 25

STRONG VOCATIONAL INTEREST TEST

Occupation	Artist	Psychologist	Architect	Physician	Osteopath	Dentist	Veterinarian	Mathematician	Physicist	Engineer	Chemist	Production Manager
Standard Score	46	45	42	51	32	34	14	44	40	37	52	29

Occupation	Farmer	Aviator	Carpenter	Printer	Math.-Sci. Teacher	Ind. Arts Teacher	Voc. Agric. Teacher	Policeman	Forest Serv. Man	Y.M.C.A. Phys. Dir.	Personnel Director	Public Administrator
Standard Score	41	44	20	40	36	17	24	17	24	18	18	28

Occupation	Y.M.C.A. Secretary	Soc. Sci. H.S. Teacher	City Sch. Sup't.	Social Worker	Minister	Musician Performer	C.P.A.	Senior C.P.A.	Accountant	Office Man	Purchasing Agent	Banker
Standard Score	10	24	19	26	62	54	21	29	16	19	19	14

Occupation	Mortician	Pharmacist	Sales Manager	Real Est. Manager	Life Ins. Salesman	Advertising Man	Lawyer	Author-Journalist	President Mfg. Co.	Interest Maturity	Occupational Level	Masculinity-Femininity
Standard Score	14	28	24	31	20	44	37	46	28	42	55	45

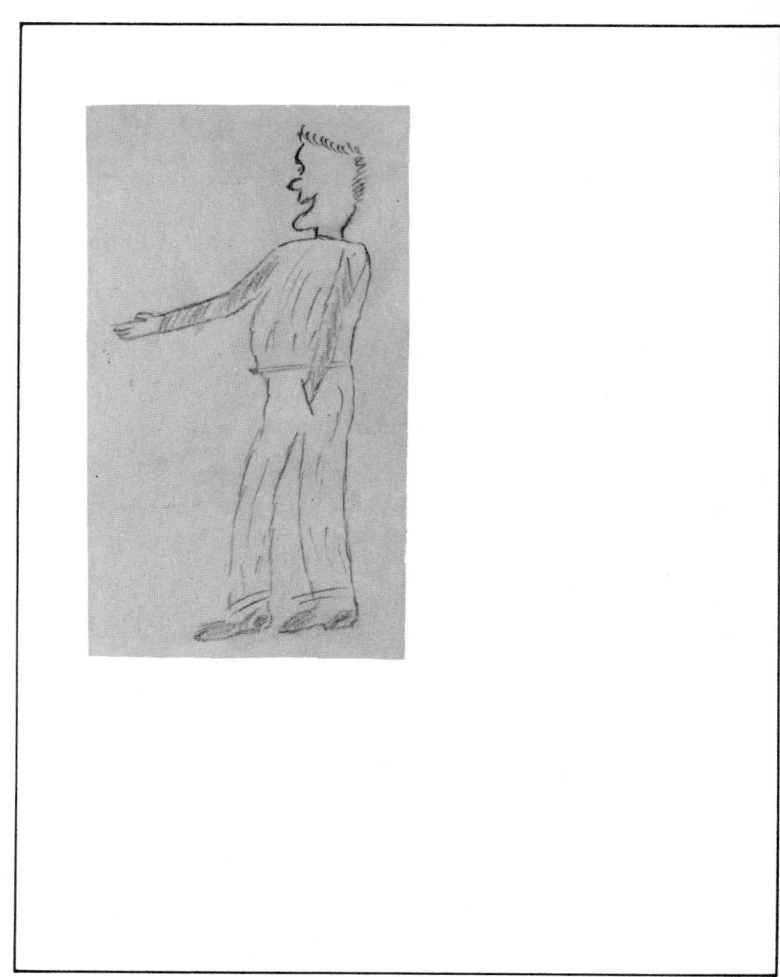

FIGURE-DRAWING CHARACTERISTICS

Structural	Male Female Both	Structural	Male	Female	Structural and Graphic	Male Female Both		Graphic, Global and Height	Male	Female	Body Proportions	Male	Female
Type	0	Omission of Appendages	7	0	Upper and Lower Halves	1	2	Hair Shading	3	3	Head	07	05
Sex Sequence	1	Position of Both Arms	1	4	Four Quarters	4	0	Nudity and Transparency	7	7	Neck	02	02
Posture	1　1	Position of Right Arm	2	7	Relative Size	0		Form	3	3	Shoulders		
Perspective	6　2	Position of Left Arm	0	4	Constant Line Pressure	0	0	Detailing	3	3	Right Arm	04	
Vertical Midline	4　4	Position of Legs	4	4	Variable Line Pressure	5	1	Identity and Sex	1	1	Left Arm		02
Bilateral Symmetry	0　0	Relation of Long Axes	1	1	Line Continuity	0	0	Sophistication	3	3	Chest		04
Horizontal Midline	4　0	Right and Left Halves	2	2	Body Shading	7	7	Height	05	03	Girth		05

GENERAL CHARACTERISTICS OF SUBJECT

IDENTIFICATION
No. 213
Sex M
Marital status M
Age 25 yrs. at
psychological tests

PARENTAL HISTORY
Father
C　H　S　D　O
–　–　–　–　–
Mother
C　H　S　D　O
–　?　–　–　?

PHYSIOLOGICAL AND METABOLIC DATA

	Admission	Initial	Control	Cold pressor change	Exercise change	Smoking change
Systolic pressure	124	128	108	+04	+34	
Diastolic pressure	72	76	70	+12	+02	
Heart rate	68	90	71	+08	+32	

Age 25 yrs.	Height 74 in.	Ponderal index 13.41
	Weight 168 lbs.	Cholesterol 195 mg. per 100 ml.
	Overweight -06 %	Vital capacity 6.5 liters

HABIT SURVEY
Smoking habits: heavy cigarette smoker
Age begun 20 yrs.　Inhalation: yes
Habits of nervous tension: 3, 4, 6, 8,
16, 17, 25

Plate 338   DRAWINGS AT AN INTERMEDIATE LEVEL OF SOPHISTICATION   381

FIGURE-DRAWING CHARACTERISTICS

Structural	Male Female Both	Structural	Male	Female	Structural and Graphic	Male Female Both		Graphic, Global and Height	Male	Female	Body Proportions	Male	Female
Type	0	Omission of Appendages	0		Upper and Lower Halves	1		Hair Shading	1		Head	06	
Sex Sequence	3	Position of Both Arms	0		Four Quarters	4		Nudity and Transparency	7		Neck	08	
Posture	1	Position of Right Arm	2		Relative Size	7		Form	3		Shoulders	06	
Perspective	0	Position of Left Arm	2		Constant Line Pressure	0		Detailing	3		Right Arm	04	
Vertical Midline	3	Position of Legs	6		Variable Line Pressure	1		Identity and Sex	3		Left Arm	02	
Bilateral Symmetry	3	Relation of Long Axes	1		Line Continuity	0		Sophistication	3		Chest	05	
Horizontal Midline	4	Right and Left Halves	1		Body Shading	4		Height	05		Girth	04	

GENERAL CHARACTERISTICS OF SUBJECT

IDENTIFICATION
No. 220
Sex M
Marital status M
Age 27 yrs. at
psychological tests

PARENTAL HISTORY
Father
C   H   S   D   O
-    -   -   -   -
Mother
C   H   S   D   O
-    ?   -   -   -

PHYSIOLOGICAL AND METABOLIC DATA

	Admission	Initial	Control	Cold pressor change	Exercise change	Smoking change
Systolic pressure	100	104	90	+06	+24	
Diastolic pressure	70	66	64	+06	-02	
Heart rate	64	84	70	00	+05	

Age 25 yrs.	Height 69 in.	Ponderal index 12.82
	Weight 156 lbs.	Cholesterol 230 mg. per 100 ml.
	Overweight +02 %	Vital capacity 5.6 liters

HABIT SURVEY

Smoking habits: heavy cigarette smoker

Age begun 20 yrs.   Inhalation: yes

Habits of nervous tension: 1, 4, 5, 6,
8, 11, 16, 17, 18, 23

FIGURE-DRAWING CHARACTERISTICS

Structural	Male Female Both		Structural	Male	Female	Structural and Graphic	Male Female Both		Graphic, Global and Height	Male	Female	Body Proportions	Male	Female
Type	0		Omission of Appendages	8	0	Upper and Lower Halves	0	0	Hair Shading	3	7	Head	06	06
Sex Sequence	0		Position of Both Arms	0	0	Four Quarters	4	4	Nudity and Transparency	7	7	Neck	06	12
Posture	1	1	Position of Right Arm	2	2	Relative Size	0		Form	3	3	Shoulders	08	07
Perspective	5	0	Position of Left Arm	2	2	Constant Line Pressure	1	1	Detailing	3	3	Right Arm	04	04
Vertical Midline	0	0	Position of Legs	6	6	Variable Line Pressure	0	0	Identity and Sex	1	1	Left Arm	04	04
Bilateral Symmetry	3	3	Relation of Long Axes	1	1	Line Continuity	0	0	Sophistication	3	3	Chest	06	05
Horizontal Midline	4	0	Right and Left Halves	0	1	Body Shading	1	1	Height	06	05	Girth	06	05

GENERAL CHARACTERISTICS OF SUBJECT

IDENTIFICATION
No. 414
Sex M
Marital status S
Age 26 yrs. at psychological tests

PARENTAL HISTORY
Father
C H S D O
- - - - ?
Mother
C H S D O
- ? - - +

PHYSIOLOGICAL AND METABOLIC DATA

	Admission	Initial	Control	Cold pressor change	Exercise change	Smoking change
Systolic pressure	126	124	114	+02	+34	
Diastolic pressure	78	82	76	+06	00	
Heart rate	84	104	86	00	+44	

Age 23 yrs.	Height	72 in.	Ponderal index 13.40
	Weight	155 lbs.	Cholesterol 155 mg. per 100 ml.
	Overweight -05 %		Vital capacity 4.8 liters

HABIT SURVEY
Smoking habits: heavy cigarette smoker
Age begun 19 yrs.   Inhalation: yes
Habits of nervous tension: 4, 6, 11, 20

FIGURE-DRAWING CHARACTERISTICS

Structural	Male Female Both		Structural	Male	Female	Structural and Graphic	Male Female Both		Graphic, Global and Height	Male	Female	Body Proportions	Male	Female
Type	0		Omission of Appendages	0	0	Upper and Lower Halves	1	1	Hair Shading	1	1	Head	07	07
Sex Sequence	0		Position of Both Arms	1	0	Four Quarters	4	4	Nudity and Transparency	7	7	Neck	10	06
Posture	1	1	Position of Right Arm	0	0	Relative Size	2		Form	3	3	Shoulders	07	05
Perspective	5	0	Position of Left Arm	5	0	Constant Line Pressure	2	0	Detailing	3	3	Right Arm	04	04
Vertical Midline	3	0	Position of Legs	6	4	Variable Line Pressure	0	3	Identity and Sex	1	1	Left Arm	04	04
Bilateral Symmetry	3	3	Relation of Long Axes	1	1	Line Continuity	1	2	Sophistication	3	3	Chest	05	05
Horizontal Midline	4	4	Right and Left Halves	1	1	Body Shading	0	1	Height	06	06	Girth	08	05

GENERAL CHARACTERISTICS OF SUBJECT

IDENTIFICATION

No. F23
Sex M
Marital status M
Age 24 yrs. at psychological tests

PARENTAL HISTORY

Father
C H S D O
– – – – ?
Mother
C H S D O
– ? – – +

PHYSIOLOGICAL AND METABOLIC DATA

	Admission	Initial	Control	Cold pressor change	Exercise change	Smoking change
Systolic pressure	150	132	112	+28	+26	
Diastolic pressure	88	76	76	+20	+10	
Heart rate	72	72	70	+16	+25	

Age 22 yrs.
Height 70 in.
Weight 159 lbs.
Overweight +03 %
Ponderal index 12.92
Cholesterol 290 mg. per 100 ml.
Vital capacity liters

HABIT SURVEY

Smoking habits: nonsmoker
  Age begun   yrs.   Inhalation:
Habits of nervous tension: 4, 5, 6, 9, 11, 16

STRONG VOCATIONAL INTEREST TEST

Occupation	Artist	Psychologist	Architect	Physician	Osteopath	Dentist	Veterinarian	Mathematician	Physicist	Engineer	Chemist	Production Manager
Standard Score	17	35	20	40	33	25	20	31	22	27	30	25

Occupation	Farmer	Aviator	Carpenter	Printer	Math.-Sci. Teacher	Ind. Arts Teacher	Voc. Agric. Teacher	Policeman	Forest Serv. Man	Y.M.C.A. Phys. Dir.	Personnel Director	Public Administrator
Standard Score	36	24	19	35	47	20	45	37	39	47	39	54

Occupation	Y.M.C.A. Secretary	Soc. Sci. H.S. Teacher	City Sch. Sup't.	Social Worker	Minister	Musician Performer	C.P.A.	Senior C.P.A.	Accountant	Office Man	Purchasing Agent	Banker
Standard Score	53	49	55	42	58	38	29	45	33	39	14	37

Occupation	Mortician	Pharmacist	Sales Manager	Real Est. Manager	Life Ins. Salesman	Advertising Man	Lawyer	Author-Journalist	President Mfg. Co.	Interest Maturity	Occupational Level	Masculinity-Femininity
Standard Score	17	19	21	18	21	23	32	25	15	63	54	45

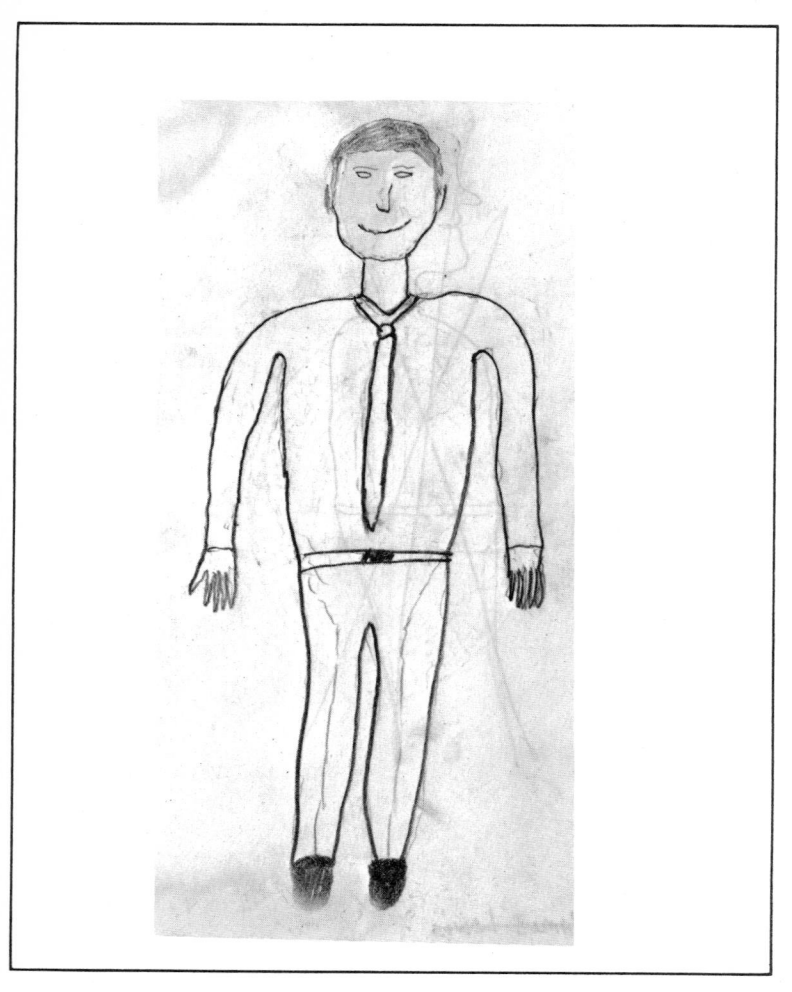

FIGURE-DRAWING CHARACTERISTICS

Structural	Male Female — Both	Structural	Male	Female	Structural and Graphic	Male	Female — Both	Graphic, Global and Height	Male	Female	Body Proportions	Male	Female
Type	0	Omission of Appendages	0	0	Upper and Lower Halves	3	3	Hair Shading	1	1	Head	12	13
Sex Sequence	0	Position of Both Arms	0	0	Four Quarters	4	4	Nudity and Transparency	7	7	Neck	14	16
Posture	1 1	Position of Right Arm	0	0	Relative Size	4		Form	3	3	Shoulders	11	09
Perspective	0 0	Position of Left Arm	0	0	Constant Line Pressure	5	5	Detailing	3	3	Right Arm	06	06
Vertical Midline	3 3	Position of Legs	4	4	Variable Line Pressure	0	0	Identity and Sex	3	3	Left Arm	06	06
Bilateral Symmetry	4 4	Relation of Long Axes	1	1	Line Continuity	4	4	Sophistication	3	3	Chest	09	07
Horizontal Midline	4 4	Right and Left Halves	1	1	Body Shading	4	7	Height	08	09	Girth	09	09

GENERAL CHARACTERISTICS OF SUBJECT

IDENTIFICATION
No. D21
Sex M
Marital status S
Age 22 yrs. at psychological tests

PARENTAL HISTORY
Father
C H S D O
- - - - -
Mother
C H S D O
- ? - - -

PHYSIOLOGICAL AND METABOLIC DATA

	Admission	Initial	Control	Cold pressor change	Exercise change	Smoking change
Systolic pressure	140	120	120	+10	+20	-02
Diastolic pressure	80	70	70	+20	00	+10
Heart rate	82	72	61	-04	+36	+03

Age 21 yrs.	Height 72 in.	Ponderal index 13.61
	Weight 148 lbs.	Cholesterol 193 mg. per 100 ml.
	Overweight -09 %	Vital capacity 4.9 liters

HABIT SURVEY

Smoking habits: mixed smoker
   Age begun 18 yrs.   Inhalation: sometimes
Habits of nervous tension: 1, 3, 4, 5, 6, 9, 11, 12, 19

STRONG VOCATIONAL INTEREST TEST

Occupation	Artist	Psychologist	Architect	Physician	Osteopath	Dentist	Veterinarian	Mathematician	Physicist	Engineer	Chemist	Production Manager
Standard Score	17	32	16	42	29	26	38	22	14	27	32	26

Occupation	Farmer	Aviator	Carpenter	Printer	Math.-Sci. Teacher	Ind. Arts Teacher	Voc. Agric. Teacher	Policeman	Forest Serv. Man	Y.M.C.A. Phys. Dir.	Personnel Director	Public Administrator
Standard Score	31	36	07	26	36	07	31	25	21	31	38	37

Occupation	Y.M.C.A. Secretary	Soc. Sci. H.S. Teacher	City Sch. Sup't.	Social Worker	Minister	Musician Performer	C.P.A.	Senior C.P.A.	Accountant	Office Man	Purchasing Agent	Banker
Standard Score	21	28	22	32	63	37	29	45	24	36	32	28

Occupation	Mortician	Pharmacist	Sales Manager	Real Est. Manager	Life Ins. Salesman	Advertising Man	Lawyer	Author-Journalist	President Mfg. Co.	Interest Maturity	Occupational Level	Masculinity-Femininity
Standard Score	34	48	44	46	41	38	33	28	36	54	58	48

Plate 342   DRAWINGS AT AN INTERMEDIATE LEVEL OF SOPHISTICATION   385

FIGURE-DRAWING CHARACTERISTICS

Structural	Male	Female	Structural	Male	Female	Structural and Graphic	Male	Female	Graphic, Global and Height	Male	Female	Body Proportions	Male	Female
	Both						Both							
Type	0		Omission of Appendages	0	0	Upper and Lower Halves	0	1	Hair Shading	1	1	Head	12	04
Sex Sequence	0		Position of Both Arms	0	2	Four Quarters	4	4	Nudity and Transparency	7	7	Neck	10	04
Posture	1	1	Position of Right Arm	2	5	Relative Size	0		Form	5	3	Shoulders	06	
Perspective	0	2	Position of Left Arm	2	7	Constant Line Pressure	0	0	Detailing	3	3	Right Arm	05	02
Vertical Midline	3	4	Position of Legs	6	1	Variable Line Pressure	2	3	Identity and Sex	1	1	Left Arm	04	
Bilateral Symmetry	2	0	Relation of Long Axes	1	1	Line Continuity	4	4	Sophistication	3	3	Chest	04	02
Horizontal Midline	4	4	Right and Left Halves	1	3	Body Shading	0	0	Height	06	03	Girth	02	02

GENERAL CHARACTERISTICS OF SUBJECT

IDENTIFICATION
No. E61
Sex M
Marital status M
Age 21 yrs. at
psychological tests

PARENTAL HISTORY				
Father				
C	H	S	D	O
-	-	-	-	+
Mother				
C	H	S	D	O
-	?	-	-	+

PHYSIOLOGICAL AND METABOLIC DATA

	Admission	Initial	Control	Cold pressor change	Exercise change	Smoking change
Systolic pressure	130	128	110	+06	+48	+04
Diastolic pressure	70	60	66	-04	-14	+06
Heart rate	70	80	83	+08	+17	+07

Age 21 yrs.	Height 69 in.	Ponderal index 12.66
	Weight 162 lbs.	Cholesterol 260 mg. per 100 ml.
	Overweight +09 %	Vital capacity 4.5 liters

HABIT SURVEY
Smoking habits: former smoker
Age begun 17 yrs.   Inhalation:
Habits of nervous tension: 2, 4, 5, 6, 9, 10, 14, 16, 17, 19, 22

STRONG VOCATIONAL INTEREST TEST

Occupation	Artist	Psychologist	Architect	Physician	Osteopath	Dentist	Veterinarian	Mathematician	Physicist	Engineer	Chemist	Production Manager
Standard Score	31	45	33	58	44	44	23	36	31	31	42	28

Occupation	Farmer	Aviator	Carpenter	Printer	Math.-Sci. Teacher	Ind. Arts Teacher	Voc. Agric. Teacher	Policeman	Forest Serv. Man	Y.M.C.A. Phys. Dir.	Personnel Director	Public Administrator
Standard Score	31	21	09	24	35	10	18	17	04	32	25	34

Occupation	Y.M.C.A. Secretary	Soc. Sci. H.S. Teacher	City Sch. Sup't.	Social Worker	Minister	Musician Performer	C.P.A.	Senior C.P.A.	Accountant	Office Man	Purchasing Agent	Banker
Standard Score	27	25	35	32	64	40	39	34	19	25	19	16

Occupation	Mortician	Pharmacist	Sales Manager	Real Est. Manager	Life Ins. Salesman	Advertising Man	Lawyer	Author-Journalist	President Mfg. Co.	Interest Maturity	Occupational Level	Masculinity-Femininity
Standard Score	29	37	29	26	32	38	40	38	34	53	65	37

FIGURE-DRAWING CHARACTERISTICS

Structural	Male Female Both	Structural	Male	Female	Structural and Graphic	Male Female Both		Graphic, Global and Height	Male	Female	Body Proportions	Male	Female
Type	0	Omission of Appendages	0	0	Upper and Lower Halves	2	1	Hair Shading	3	3	Head		07
Sex Sequence	0	Position of Both Arms	1	0	Four Quarters	4	4	Nudity and Transparency	3	6	Neck		12
Posture	1 1	Position of Right Arm	2	2	Relative Size	4		Form	3	3	Shoulders	05	08
Perspective	0 0	Position of Left Arm	0	2	Constant Line Pressure	1	1	Detailing	3	3	Right Arm	02	04
Vertical Midline	0 0	Position of Legs	6	6	Variable Line Pressure	0	0	Identity and Sex	3	3	Left Arm	02	06
Bilateral Symmetry	1 3	Relation of Long Axes	1	1	Line Continuity	0	0	Sophistication	3	3	Chest	05	07
Horizontal Midline	4 4	Right and Left Halves	1	3	Body Shading	5	5	Height	04	06	Girth	05	06

GENERAL CHARACTERISTICS OF SUBJECT

IDENTIFICATION
No. 456
Sex M
Marital status M
Age 24 yrs. at
psychological tests

PARENTAL HISTORY
Father
C   H   S   D   O
-   -   +   -   -
Mother
C   H   S   D   O
-   -   -   -   +

PHYSIOLOGICAL AND METABOLIC DATA

	Admission	Initial	Control	Cold pressor change	Exercise change	Smoking change
Systolic pressure	124	112	94	+10	+40	
Diastolic pressure	76	70	64	+16	+06	
Heart rate	60	60	61	00	+17	

Age 22 yrs.	Height 73 in.	Ponderal index 12.55
	Weight 197 lbs.	Cholesterol 250 mg. per 100 ml.
	Overweight +17 %	Vital capacity 5.4 liters

HABIT SURVEY
Smoking habits: moderate cigarette smoker
Age begun 19 yrs.   Inhalation: yes
Habits of nervous tension: 4, 5, 6, 7, 9, 10,
16, 19

Plate 344   DRAWINGS AT AN INTERMEDIATE LEVEL OF SOPHISTICATION   387

FIGURE-DRAWING CHARACTERISTICS

Structural	Male	Female	Structural	Male	Female	Structural and Graphic	Male	Female	Graphic, Global and Height	Male	Female	Body Proportions	Male	Female
	Both						Both							
Type	0		Omission of Appendages	0	7	Upper and Lower Halves	3	3	Hair Shading	3	3	Head	16	07
Sex Sequence	0		Position of Both Arms	0	6	Four Quarters	4	4	Nudity and Transparency	7	7	Neck	12	
Posture	1	1	Position of Right Arm	5	8	Relative Size	0		Form	3	3	Shoulders	07	05
Perspective	0	7	Position of Left Arm	5	8	Constant Line Pressure	0	3	Detailing	3	3	Right Arm	05	
Vertical Midline	0	0	Position of Legs	6	4	Variable Line Pressure	1	0	Identity and Sex	1	1	Left Arm	04	
Bilateral Symmetry	2	3	Relation of Long Axes	1	1	Line Continuity	1	0	Sophistication	3	3	Chest	06	04
Horizontal Midline	4	4	Right and Left Halves	1	1	Body Shading	0	2	Height	07	06	Girth	06	04

GENERAL CHARACTERISTICS OF SUBJECT

IDENTIFICATION

No. G75

Sex M

Marital status M

Age 25 yrs. at psychological tests

PARENTAL HISTORY

Father

C	H	S	D	O
–	–	+	–	–

Mother

C	H	S	D	O
–	–	–	–	–

PHYSIOLOGICAL AND METABOLIC DATA

	Admission	Initial	Control	Cold pressor change	Exercise change	Smoking change
Systolic pressure	122	130	118	+22	+26	
Diastolic pressure	70	68	68	+26	–10	
Heart rate	84	61	53	–14	+25	

Age 26 yrs.

Height 70 in.   Ponderal index 13.03

Weight 155 lbs.   Cholesterol 212 mg. per 100 ml.

Overweight –02 %   Vital capacity liters

HABIT SURVEY

Smoking habits: nonsmoker

Age begun yrs.   Inhalation:

Habits of nervous tension: 6

STRONG VOCATIONAL INTEREST TEST

Occupation	Artist	Psychologist	Architect	Physician	Osteopath	Dentist	Veterinarian	Mathematician	Physicist	Engineer	Chemist	Production Manager
Standard Score	24	38	29	47	35	32	40	34	24	31	27	25

Occupation	Farmer	Aviator	Carpenter	Printer	Math.-Sci. Teacher	Ind. Arts Teacher	Voc. Agric. Teacher	Policeman	Forest Serv. Man	Y.M.C.A. Phys. Dir.	Personnel Director	Public Administrator
Standard Score	51	41	26	29	44	33	54	31	44	36	28	42

Occupation	Y.M.C.A. Secretary	Soc. Sci. H.S. Teacher	City Sch. Sup't.	Social Worker	Minister	Musician Performer	C.P.A.	Senior C.P.A.	Accountant	Office Man	Purchasing Agent	Banker
Standard Score	29	39	35	36	59	39	20	39	16	22	21	27

Occupation	Mortician	Pharmacist	Sales Manager	Real Est. Manager	Life Ins. Salesman	Advertising Man	Lawyer	Author-Journalist	President Mfg. Co.	Interest Maturity	Occupational Level	Masculinity-Femininity
Standard Score	24	25	24	33	24	21	29	26	16	52	53	52

FIGURE-DRAWING CHARACTERISTICS

Structural	Male Female Both	Structural	Male	Female	Structural and Graphic	Male Female Both		Graphic, Global and Height	Male	Female	Body Proportions	Male	Female
Type	0	Omission of Appendages	0	0	Upper and Lower Halves	2	2	Hair Shading	0	3	Head	03	03
Sex Sequence	2	Position of Both Arms	0	0	Four Quarters	0	1	Nudity and Transparency	7	7	Neck	06	06
Posture	1 1	Position of Right Arm	2	2	Relative Size	3		Form	3	3	Shoulders	02	02
Perspective	0 0	Position of Left Arm	2	2	Constant Line Pressure	5	5	Detailing	1	3	Right Arm	00	00
Vertical Midline	3 0	Position of Legs	6	6	Variable Line Pressure	0	0	Identity and Sex	1	1	Left Arm	00	00
Bilateral Symmetry	5 5	Relation of Long Axes	1	1	Line Continuity	4	4	Sophistication	3	3	Chest	02	02
Horizontal Midline	4 4	Right and Left Halves	9	9	Body Shading	4	4	Height	02	02	Girth	02	02

GENERAL CHARACTERISTICS OF SUBJECT

IDENTIFICATION
No. 450
Sex F
Marital status S
Age 25 yrs. at
psychological tests

PARENTAL HISTORY
Father
C H S D O
- - - + ?
Mother
C H S D O
- - + - -

PHYSIOLOGICAL AND METABOLIC DATA

	Admission	Initial	Control	Cold pressor change	Exercise change	Smoking change
Systolic pressure	110	92	100	+08	+26	
Diastolic pressure	60	62	62	+12	+02	
Heart rate	108	78	81	-06	+49	

Age 23 yrs.
Height 68 in.
Weight 140 lbs.
Overweight -01 %
Ponderal index 13.10
Cholesterol 250 mg. per 100 ml.
Vital capacity 3.4 liters

HABIT SURVEY
Smoking habits: occasional smoker
Age begun 21 yrs.   Inhalation: yes
Habits of nervous tension: 5, 14, 16

Plate 346   **DRAWINGS AT AN INTERMEDIATE LEVEL OF SOPHISTICATION**   389

FIGURE-DRAWING CHARACTERISTICS

Structural	Male Female Both	Structural	Male	Female	Structural and Graphic	Male Female Both		Graphic, Global and Height	Male	Female	Body Proportions	Male	Female
Type	0	Omission of Appendages	7	0	Upper and Lower Halves	0	3	Hair Shading	7	3	Head	09	07
Sex Sequence	0	Position of Both Arms	1	0	Four Quarters	4	4	Nudity and Transparency	7	7	Neck	03	05
Posture	1 1	Position of Right Arm	2	5	Relative Size	0		Form	3	3	Shoulders		06
Perspective	6 0	Position of Left Arm	5	5	Constant Line Pressure	0	0	Detailing	1	1	Right Arm	04	04
Vertical Midline	7 0	Position of Legs	4	6	Variable Line Pressure	1	1	Identity and Sex	1	1	Left Arm		04
Bilateral Symmetry	0 3	Relation of Long Axes	1	1	Line Continuity	0	0	Sophistication	3	3	Chest		07
Horizontal Midline	4 4	Right and Left Halves	1	1	Body Shading	4	7	Height	07	07	Girth		06

GENERAL CHARACTERISTICS OF SUBJECT

IDENTIFICATION
No. 666
Sex M
Marital status M
Age 26 yrs. at psychological tests

PARENTAL HISTORY
Father
C   H   S   D   O
-    -   -   -   -
Mother
C   H   S   D   O
-    -   +   -   ?

PHYSIOLOGICAL AND METABOLIC DATA

	Admission	Initial	Control	Cold pressor change	Exercise change	Smoking change
Systolic pressure	130	112	104	+28	+24	-04
Diastolic pressure	80	62	58	+24	+02	+04
Heart rate	100	64	62	+10	+21	+02

Age 24 yrs.	Height 72 in.	Ponderal index 13.48
	Weight 152 lbs.	Cholesterol 177 mg. per 100 ml.
	Overweight -08 %	Vital capacity 4.8 liters

HABIT SURVEY
Smoking habits: moderate cigarette smoker
Age begun 22 yrs.   Inhalation: yes
Habits of nervous tension: 3, 5, 6, 15, 25

FIGURE-DRAWING CHARACTERISTICS

Structural	Male Female Both		Structural	Male	Female	Structural and Graphic	Male Female Both		Graphic, Global and Height	Male	Female	Body Proportions	Male	Female
Type	0		Omission of Appendages	0	0	Upper and Lower Halves	1	1	Hair Shading	1	3	Head	07	06
Sex Sequence	0		Position of Both Arms	4	4	Four Quarters	4	4	Nudity and Transparency	7	7	Neck	06	06
Posture	1	2	Position of Right Arm	7	7	Relative Size	2		Form	3	3	Shoulders		
Perspective	2	2	Position of Left Arm	4	3	Constant Line Pressure	1	0	Detailing	3	3	Right Arm		
Vertical Midline	7	4	Position of Legs	1	8	Variable Line Pressure	0	1	Identity and Sex	1	1	Left Arm	04	04
Bilateral Symmetry	0	0	Relation of Long Axes	1	1	Line Continuity	0	0	Sophistication	3	3	Chest	06	04
Horizontal Midline	4	4	Right and Left Halves	2	2	Body Shading	4	6	Height	05	05	Girth	05	05

GENERAL CHARACTERISTICS OF SUBJECT

IDENTIFICATION
No.   F29
Sex   M
Marital status   S
Age   23   yrs. at
psychological tests

PARENTAL HISTORY
Father
C   H   S   D   O
–   –   –   –   ?
Mother
C   H   S   D   O
–   –   +   –   ?

PHYSIOLOGICAL AND METABOLIC DATA

	Admission	Initial	Control	Cold pressor change	Exercise change	Smoking change
Systolic pressure	122	112	106	+22	+48	+07
Diastolic pressure	84	70	76	+20	+24	+05
Heart rate	76	68	68	+20	+52	+17

Age 21 yrs.	Height 69 in.	Ponderal index 13.17
	Weight 144 lbs.	Cholesterol 266 mg. per 100 ml.
	Overweight –03 %	Vital capacity liters

HABIT SURVEY
Smoking habits: light cigarette smoker
Age begun 19 yrs.   Inhalation: yes
Habits of nervous tension: 4, 6, 25

STRONG VOCATIONAL INTEREST TEST

Occupation	Artist	Psychologist	Architect	Physician	Osteopath	Dentist	Veterinarian	Mathematician	Physicist	Engineer	Chemist	Production Manager
Standard Score	31	62	45	58	40	39	15	45	46	54	56	37

Occupation	Farmer	Aviator	Carpenter	Printer	Math.-Sci. Teacher	Ind. Arts Teacher	Voc. Agric. Teacher	Policeman	Forest Serv. Man	Y.M.C.A. Phys. Dir.	Personnel Director	Public Administrator
Standard Score	36	45	31	46	55	43	37	24	29	29	39	42

Occupation	Y.M.C.A. Secretary	Soc. Sci. H.S. Teacher	City Sch. Sup't.	Social Worker	Minister	Musician Performer	C.P.A.	Senior C.P.A.	Accountant	Office Man	Purchasing Agent	Banker
Standard Score	21	31	34	37	58	45	28	45	28	23	20	10

Occupation	Mortician	Pharmacist	Sales Manager	Real Est. Manager	Life Ins. Salesman	Advertising Man	Lawyer	Author-Journalist	President Mfg. Co.	Interest Maturity	Occupational Level	Masculinity-Femininity
Standard Score	11	28	16	18	10	32	24	33	20	56	56	54

Plate 348   **DRAWINGS AT AN INTERMEDIATE LEVEL OF SOPHISTICATION**   391

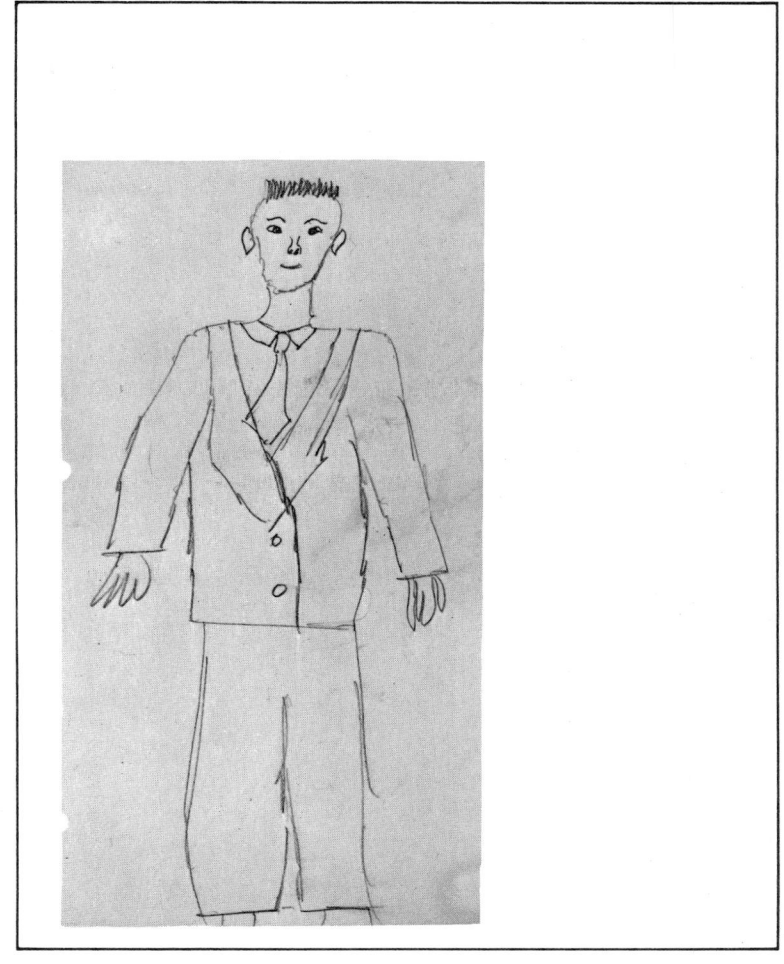

FIGURE-DRAWING CHARACTERISTICS

Structural	Male Female		Structural	Male	Female	Structural and Graphic	Male Female		Graphic, Global and Height	Male	Female	Body Proportions	Male	Female
	Both						Both							
Type	0		Omission of Appendages	8	0	Upper and Lower Halves	7	0	Hair Shading	3	3	Head	09	05
Sex Sequence	1		Position of Both Arms	0	4	Four Quarters	4	4	Nudity and Transparency	7	2	Neck	10	10
Posture	0	1	Position of Right Arm	2	7	Relative Size	5		Form	3	3	Shoulders	09	
Perspective	0	2	Position of Left Arm	2	4	Constant Line Pressure	3	0	Detailing	1	1	Right Arm	06	
Vertical Midline	3	4	Position of Legs	4	1	Variable Line Pressure	0	3	Identity and Sex	1	1	Left Arm	06	06
Bilateral Symmetry	3	0	Relation of Long Axes	1	1	Line Continuity	0	0	Sophistication	3	3	Chest	08	08
Horizontal Midline	6	0	Right and Left Halves	1	2	Body Shading	0	3	Height		07	Girth	12	08

GENERAL CHARACTERISTICS OF SUBJECT

IDENTIFICATION
No. 258
Sex M
Marital status   S
Age 27 yrs. at
psychological tests

PARENTAL HISTORY				
Father				
C	H	S	D	O
-	-	(+)	-	-
Mother				
C	H	S	D	O
-	-	-	-	-

PHYSIOLOGICAL AND METABOLIC DATA

	Admission	Initial	Control	Cold pressor change	Exercise change	Smoking change
Systolic pressure	98	102	100	+18	+48	
Diastolic pressure	60	54	52	+18	+02	
Heart rate	76	84	81	-06	+34	

Age 25 yrs.	Height 70 in.	Ponderal index 13.06
	Weight 154 lbs.	Cholesterol 250 mg. per 100 ml.
	Overweight -02%	Vital capacity 4.2 liters

HABIT SURVEY

Smoking habits: heavy cigarette smoker

Age begun 16 yrs.   Inhalation: yes

Habits of nervous tension: 1, 4, 5, 23

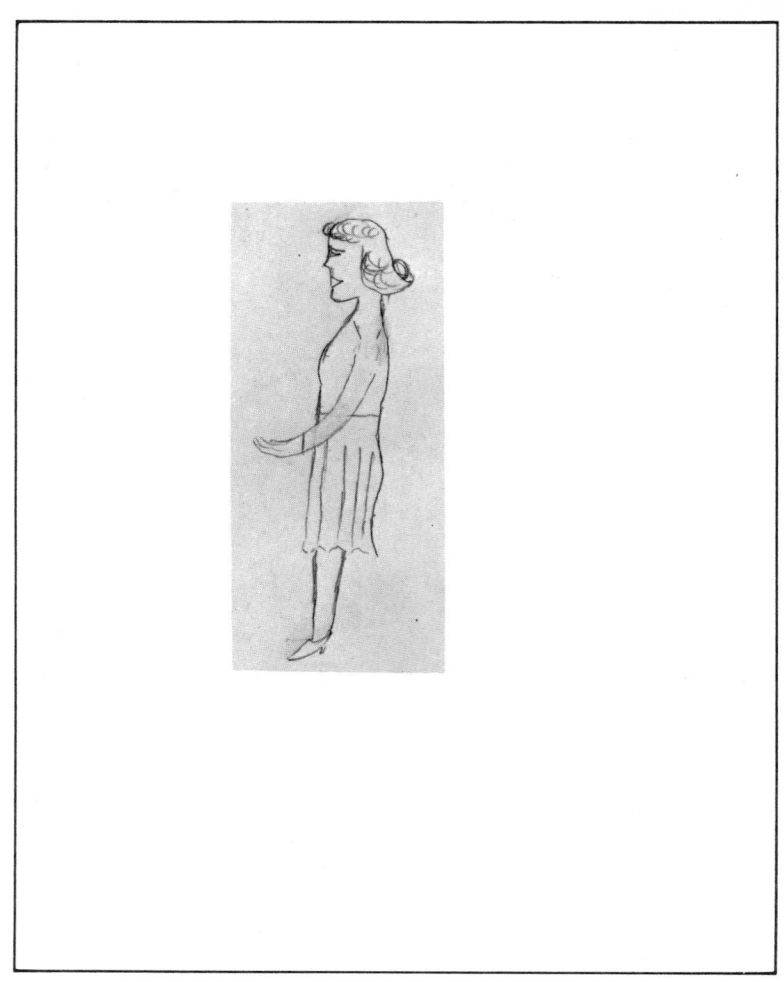

FIGURE-DRAWING CHARACTERISTICS

Structural	Male Both	Female	Structural	Male	Female	Structural and Graphic	Male Both	Female	Graphic, Global and Height	Male	Female	Body Proportions	Male	Female
Type	0		Omission of Appendages	0	0	Upper and Lower Halves	1	1	Hair Shading	1	1	Head	07	07
Sex Sequence	0		Position of Both Arms	0	4	Four Quarters	4	4	Nudity and Transparency	7	7	Neck	06	04
Posture	1	1	Position of Right Arm	0	7	Relative Size	0		Form	3	3	Shoulders	07	
Perspective	0	2	Position of Left Arm	0	4	Constant Line Pressure	3	0	Detailing	3	3	Right Arm	04	
Vertical Midline	3	4	Position of Legs	2	1	Variable Line Pressure	0	3	Identity and Sex	1	1	Left Arm	04	04
Bilateral Symmetry	3	0	Relation of Long Axes	1	1	Line Continuity	0	0	Sophistication	3	3	Chest	05	04
Horizontal Midline	6	4	Right and Left Halves	1	2	Body Shading	0	2	Height	05	04	Girth	07	06

GENERAL CHARACTERISTICS OF SUBJECT

IDENTIFICATION
No. 307
Sex M
Marital status M
Age 26 yrs. at psychological tests

PARENTAL HISTORY					
Father					
C	H	S	D	O	
-	-	(+)	+	+	
Mother					
C	H	S	D	O	
-	-	-	-	?	

PHYSIOLOGICAL AND METABOLIC DATA

	Admission	Initial	Control	Cold pressor change	Exercise change	Smoking change
Systolic pressure	108	124	114	+08	+28	
Diastolic pressure	54	68	70	+24	-08	
Heart rate	72	80	65	-06	+21	

Age 24 yrs.	Height 70 in.	Ponderal index 13.65
	Weight 135 lbs.	Cholesterol 195 mg. per 100 ml.
	Overweight -13 %	Vital capacity 4.0 liters

HABIT SURVEY
Smoking habits: moderate cigarette smoker
Age begun 18 yrs.   Inhalation: yes
Habits of nervous tension: 4, 9, 17, 18,
21, 22

Plate 350   **DRAWINGS AT AN INTERMEDIATE LEVEL OF SOPHISTICATION**   393

FIGURE-DRAWING CHARACTERISTICS

Structural	Male Female Both		Structural	Male	Female	Structural and Graphic	Male Female Both		Graphic, Global and Height	Male	Female	Body Proportions	Male	Female
Type	0		Omission of Appendages	0	0	Upper and Lower Halves	2	1	Hair Shading	0	3	Head	04	10
Sex Sequence	2		Position of Both Arms	1	4	Four Quarters	4	4	Nudity and Transparency	6	7	Neck	02	06
Posture	1	1	Position of Right Arm	5	7	Relative Size	4		Form	3	3	Shoulders	04	
Perspective	0	2	Position of Left Arm	0	2	Constant Line Pressure	0	0	Detailing	3	3	Right Arm	04	
Vertical Midline	3	4	Position of Legs	4	1	Variable Line Pressure	3	1	Identity and Sex	1	1	Left Arm	02	04
Bilateral Symmetry	3	0	Relation of Long Axes	1	3	Line Continuity	0	0	Sophistication	3	3	Chest	04	06
Horizontal Midline	4	4	Right and Left Halves	1	0	Body Shading	4	6	Height	03	06	Girth	05	07

GENERAL CHARACTERISTICS OF SUBJECT

IDENTIFICATION
No. 334
Sex M
Marital status S
Age 23 yrs. at
psychological tests

PARENTAL HISTORY
Father
C H S D O
- - ? - +
Mother
C H S D O
- - - - +

PHYSIOLOGICAL AND METABOLIC DATA

	Admission	Initial	Control	Cold pressor change	Exercise change	Smoking change
Systolic pressure	118	110	96	+16	+34	
Diastolic pressure	60	62	60	+10	+02	
Heart rate	76	72	65	+06	+14	

Age 21 yrs.	Height 73 in.	Ponderal index 13.00
	Weight 177 lbs.	Cholesterol 243 mg. per 100 ml.
	Overweight +06 %	Vital capacity 4.8 liters

HABIT SURVEY
Smoking habits: nonsmoker
Age begun   yrs.   Inhalation:
Habits of nervous tension: 5, 6, 11, 19

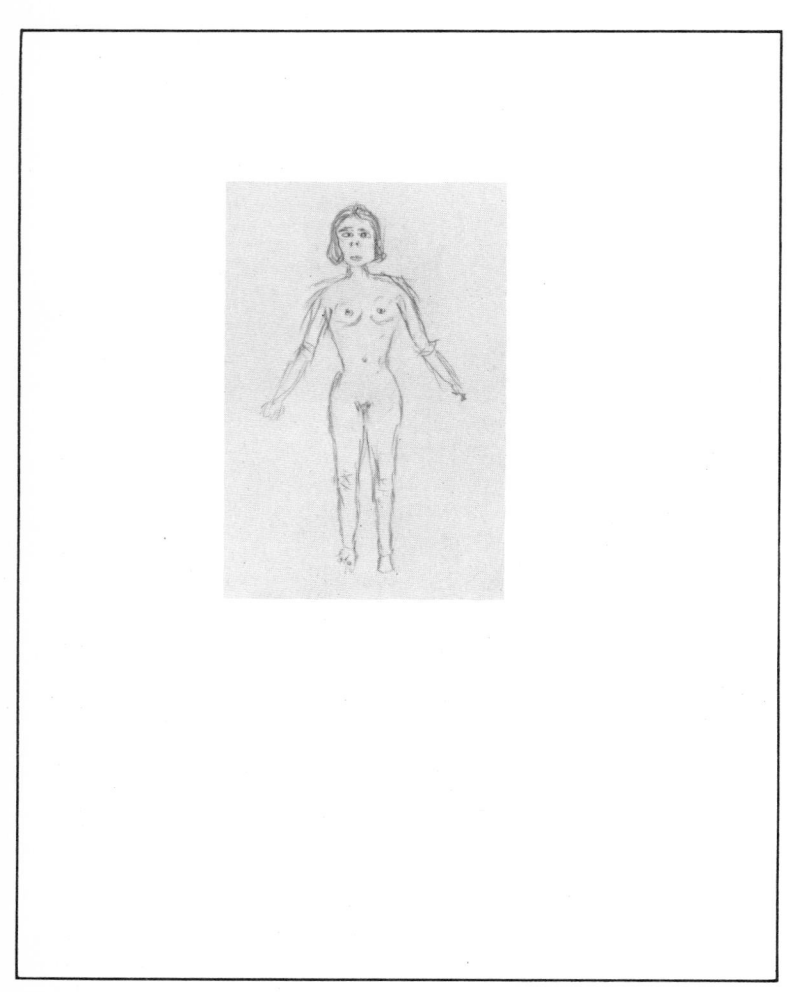

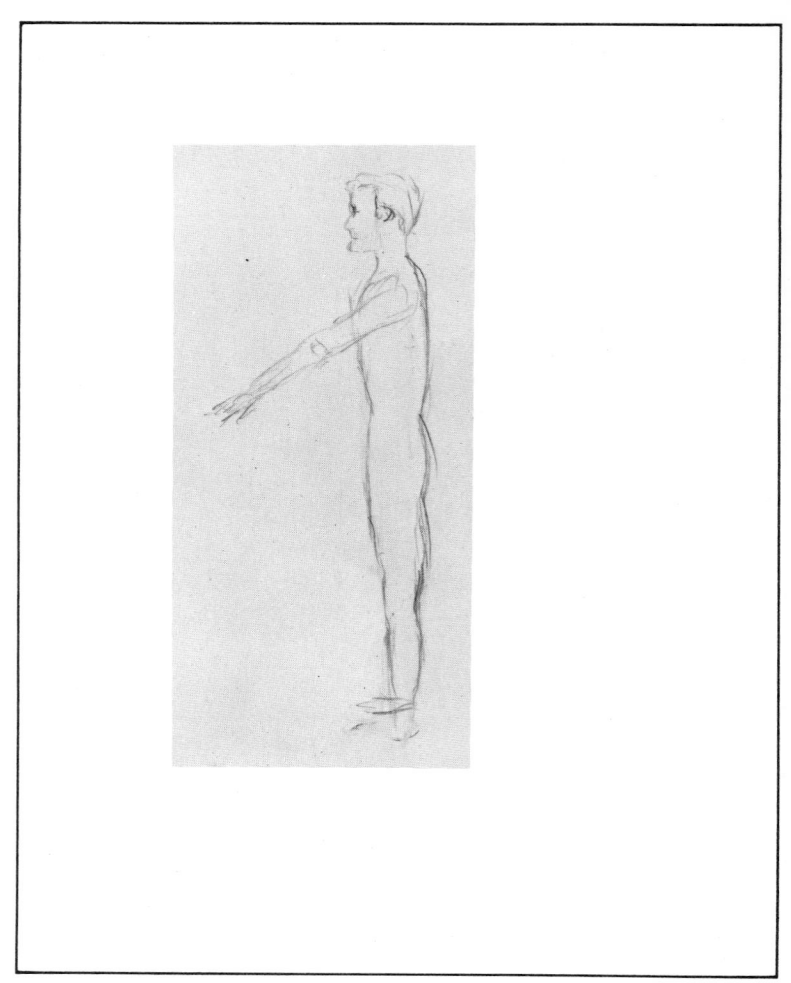

FIGURE-DRAWING CHARACTERISTICS

Structural	Male Female Both		Structural	Male	Female	Structural and Graphic	Male Female Both		Graphic, Global and Height	Male	Female	Body Proportions	Male	Female
Type	0		Omission of Appendages	0	0	Upper and Lower Halves	1	1	Hair Shading	3	2	Head	06	04
Sex Sequence	1		Position of Both Arms	4	0	Four Quarters	4	4	Nudity and Transparency	0	0	Neck	06	02
Posture	1	1	Position of Right Arm	7	2	Relative Size	0		Form	3	3	Shoulders		04
Perspective	2	0	Position of Left Arm	2	2	Constant Line Pressure	0	1	Detailing	3	3	Right Arm		02
Vertical Midline	4	0	Position of Legs	1	4	Variable Line Pressure	1	0	Identity and Sex	1	1	Left Arm	04	02
Bilateral Symmetry	0	3	Relation of Long Axes	1	1	Line Continuity	0	0	Sophistication	3	3	Chest	05	03
Horizontal Midline	0	0	Right and Left Halves	0	1	Body Shading	1	3	Height	05	03	Girth	04	03

GENERAL CHARACTERISTICS OF SUBJECT

IDENTIFICATION
No. C03
Sex M
Marital status S
Age 23 yrs. at psychological tests

PARENTAL HISTORY				
Father				
C	H	S	D	O
–	–	?	–	–
Mother				
C	H	S	D	O
–	–	–	–	?

PHYSIOLOGICAL AND METABOLIC DATA

	Admission	Initial	Control	Cold pressor change	Exercise change	Smoking change
Systolic pressure	130	120	120	+12	+60	00
Diastolic pressure	80	70	70	+25	–30	+06
Heart rate	80	68	57	+12	+18	+15

Age 23 yrs.	Height 68 in. Weight 150 lbs. Overweight +02 %	Ponderal index 12.81 Cholesterol 218 mg. per 100 ml. Vital capacity 4.5 liters

HABIT SURVEY
Smoking habits: heavy cigarette smoker
Age begun 19 yrs.   Inhalation: yes
Habits of nervous tension: 3, 4, 5, 16, 17, 21, 22, 24

FIGURE-DRAWING CHARACTERISTICS

Structural	Male Female Both	Structural	Male	Female	Structural and Graphic	Male Female Both		Graphic, Global and Height	Male	Female	Body Proportions	Male	Female
Type	0	Omission of Appendages	0	0	Upper and Lower Halves	0	1	Hair Shading	2	3	Head	09	08
Sex Sequence	2	Position of Both Arms	4	1	Four Quarters	4	4	Nudity and Transparency	7	7	Neck	08	05
Posture	1 1	Position of Right Arm	7	2	Relative Size	0		Form	1	1	Shoulders		04
Perspective	2 0	Position of Left Arm	4	5	Constant Line Pressure	1	0	Detailing	3	3	Right Arm		04
Vertical Midline	4 0	Position of Legs	1	4	Variable Line Pressure	0	2	Identity and Sex	1	1	Left Arm	04	03
Bilateral Symmetry	0 3	Relation of Long Axes	1	1	Line Continuity	0	0	Sophistication	3	3	Chest	06	05
Horizontal Midline	6 4	Right and Left Halves	1	0	Body Shading	0	7	Height	06	05	Girth	08	05

GENERAL CHARACTERISTICS OF SUBJECT

IDENTIFICATION
No. 714
Sex M
Marital status S
Age 24 yrs. at
psychological tests

PARENTAL HISTORY
Father
C   H   S   D   O
-   -   -   -   -
Mother
C   H   S   D   O
-   -   ?   -   -

PHYSIOLOGICAL AND METABOLIC DATA

	Admission	Initial	Control	Cold pressor change	Exercise change	Smoking change
Systolic pressure	120	122	122	+08	+30	+03
Diastolic pressure	78	62	66	+12	+02	+06
Heart rate	70	68	56	+22	+23	+05

Age 21 yrs.	Height 76 in.	Ponderal index 13.26
	Weight 188 lbs.	Cholesterol 222 mg. per 100 ml.
	Overweight +03 %	Vital capacity 6.6 liters

HABIT SURVEY
Smoking habits: nonsmoker
Age begun   yrs.   Inhalation:
Habits of nervous tension: 2, 4, 5, 6, 9, 18,
20, 21

FIGURE-DRAWING CHARACTERISTICS

Structural	Male Female Both	Structural	Male	Female	Structural and Graphic	Male Female Both		Graphic, Global and Height	Male	Female	Body Proportions	Male	Female
Type	0	Omission of Appendages	0	0	Upper and Lower Halves	1	3	Hair Shading	1	5	Head	06	07
Sex Sequence	0	Position of Both Arms	0	0	Four Quarters	4	4	Nudity and Transparency	7	7	Neck	06	06
Posture	1	1	Position of Right Arm	0	0	Relative Size	4		Form	3	3	Shoulders	06	07
Perspective	0	0	Position of Left Arm	0	0	Constant Line Pressure	1	0	Detailing	1	1	Right Arm	04	04
Vertical Midline	3	0	Position of Legs	6	6	Variable Line Pressure	0	1	Identity and Sex	1	1	Left Arm	04	04
Bilateral Symmetry	3	3	Relation of Long Axes	1	1	Line Continuity	0	0	Sophistication	3	3	Chest	05	05
Horizontal Midline	4	4	Right and Left Halves	1	1	Body Shading	4	6	Height	05	06	Girth	07	04

GENERAL CHARACTERISTICS OF SUBJECT

IDENTIFICATION
No. E65
Sex M
Marital status S
Age 21 yrs. at psychological tests

PARENTAL HISTORY
Father
C H S D O
– – – – ?
Mother
C H S D O
– – ? – –

PHYSIOLOGICAL AND METABOLIC DATA

	Admission	Initial	Control	Cold pressor change	Exercise change	Smoking change
Systolic pressure	110	100	102	+16	+26	00
Diastolic pressure	70	68	68	+22	-19	-06
Heart rate	68	68	70	+04	-02	+05

Age 19 yrs.	Height 70 in.	Ponderal index 13.54
	Weight 138 lbs.	Cholesterol 205 mg. per 100 ml.
	Overweight -08 %	Vital capacity 4.0 liters

HABIT SURVEY
Smoking habits: nonsmoker
Age begun yrs. Inhalation:
Habits of nervous tension: 6, 11

Plate 354   DRAWINGS AT AN INTERMEDIATE LEVEL OF SOPHISTICATION   397

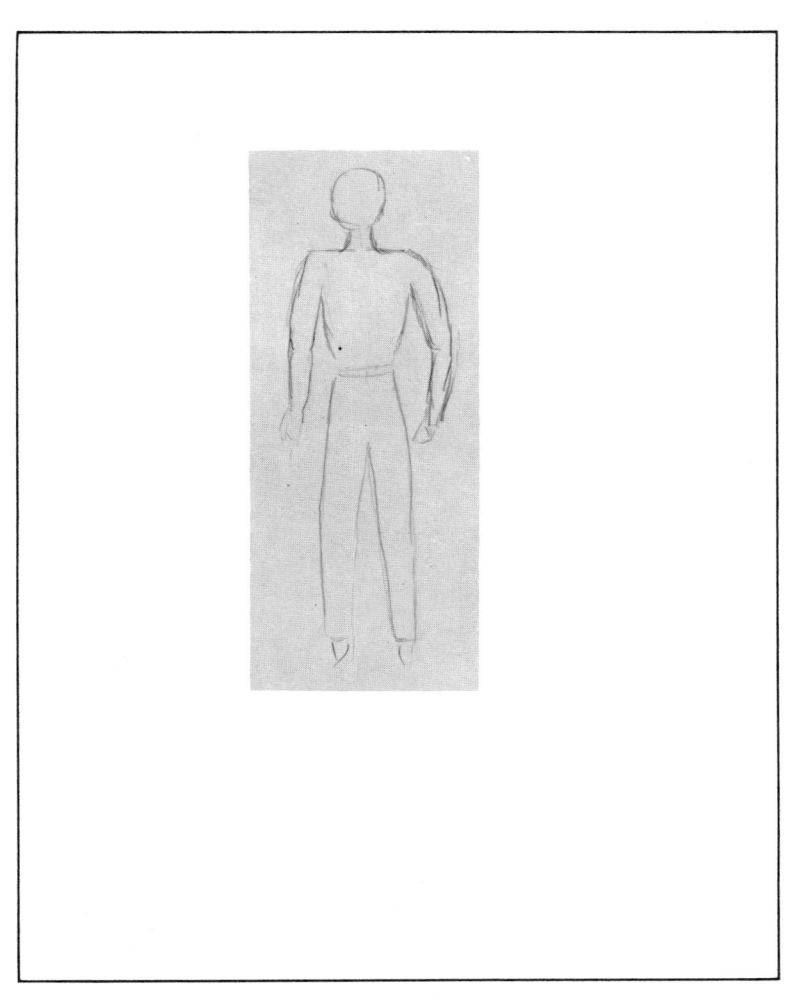

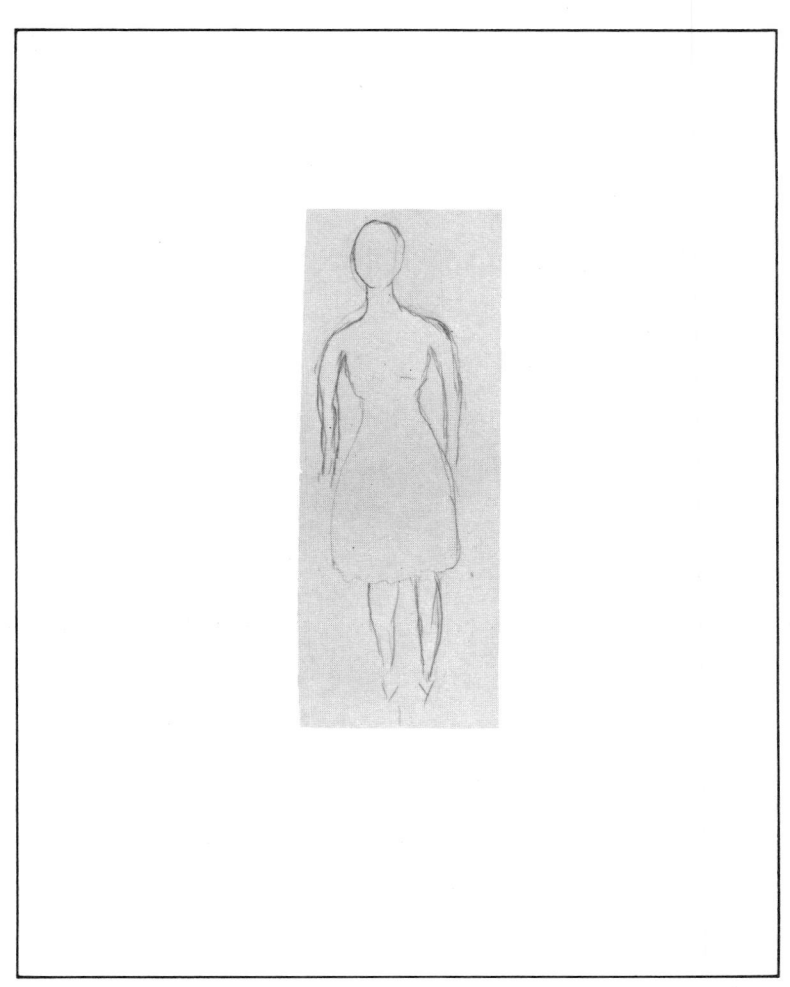

FIGURE-DRAWING CHARACTERISTICS

Structural	Male Female Both		Structural	Male	Female	Structural and Graphic	Male	Female	Graphic, Global and Height	Male	Female	Body Proportions	Male	Female
Type	0		Omission of Appendages	0	7	Upper and Lower Halves	1	1	Hair Shading	0	0	Head	05	05
Sex Sequence	0		Position of Both Arms	1	0	Four Quarters	4	4	Nudity and Transparency	7	7	Neck	06	08
Posture	1	1	Position of Right Arm	0	0	Relative Size	0		Form	3	3	Shoulders	04	05
Perspective	0	0	Position of Left Arm	5	0	Constant Line Pressure	0	0	Detailing	5	5	Right Arm	04	
Vertical Midline	0	0	Position of Legs	4	4	Variable Line Pressure	2	2	Identity and Sex	1	1	Left Arm	04	
Bilateral Symmetry	3	3	Relation of Long Axes	1	1	Line Continuity	0	0	Sophistication	3	3	Chest	04	04
Horizontal Midline	4	0	Right and Left Halves	1	1	Body Shading	0	0	Height	05	05	Girth	03	03

GENERAL CHARACTERISTICS OF SUBJECT

IDENTIFICATION
No. 611
Sex F
Marital status S
Age 31 yrs. at
psychological tests

PARENTAL HISTORY				
Father				
C	H	S	D	O
–	–	(?)	–	–
Mother				
C	H	S	D	O
–	–	–	–	?

PHYSIOLOGICAL AND METABOLIC DATA

	Admission	Initial	Control	Cold pressor change	Exercise change	Smoking change
Systolic pressure	112	110	104	+06	+38	+09
Diastolic pressure	72	74	70	+18	+04	+06
Heart rate	80	80	83	00	+32	+16

Age 28 yrs.	Height 68 in.	Ponderal index 13.91
	Weight 117 lbs.	Cholesterol 222 mg. per 100 ml.
	Overweight –19 %	Vital capacity liters

HABIT SURVEY
Smoking habits: light cigarette smoker
Age begun 16 yrs.   Inhalation: yes
Habits of nervous tension: 4, 5, 6, 9, 14

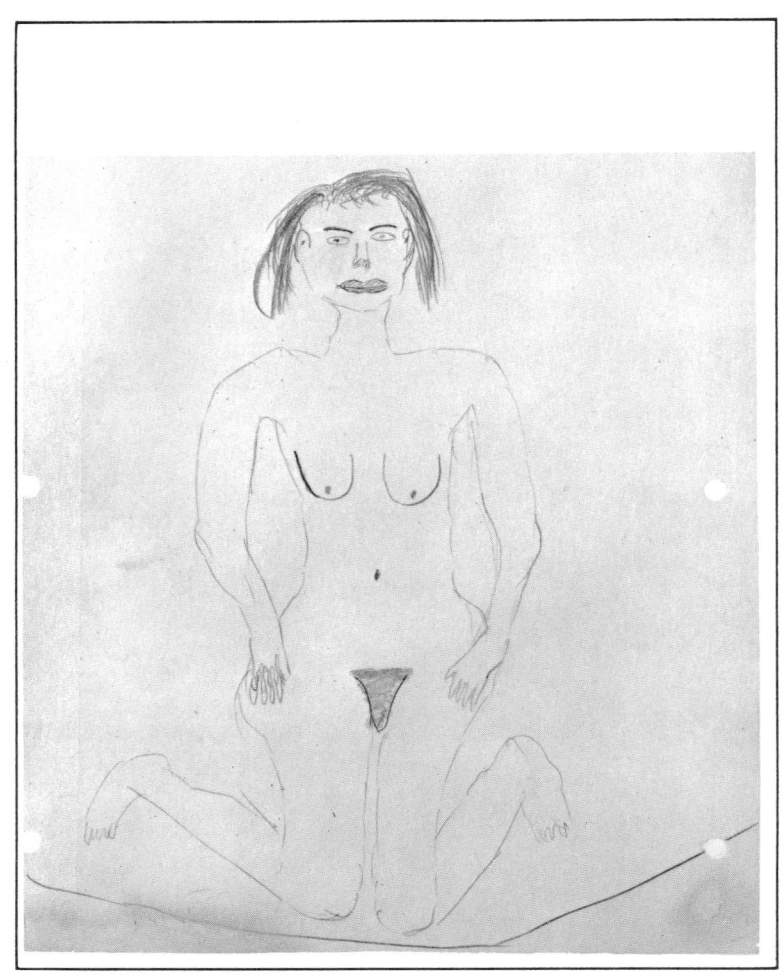
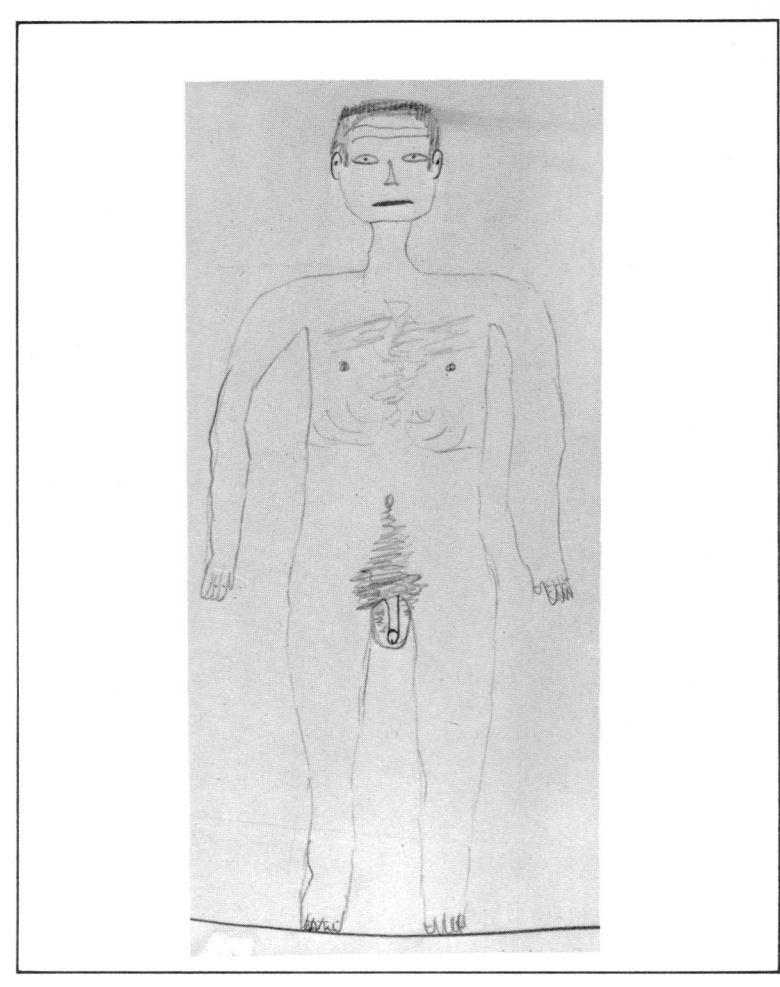

FIGURE-DRAWING CHARACTERISTICS

Structural	Male Female Both		Structural	Male	Female	Structural and Graphic	Male Female Both		Graphic, Global and Height	Male	Female	Body Proportions	Male	Female
Type	0		Omission of Appendages	0	0	Upper and Lower Halves	3	3	Hair Shading	3	3	Head	09	11
Sex Sequence	1		Position of Both Arms	0	0	Four Quarters	4	4	Nudity and Transparency	0	0	Neck	16	14
Posture	1	8	Position of Right Arm	0	5	Relative Size	5		Form	3	3	Shoulders	11	11
Perspective	0	0	Position of Left Arm	0	5	Constant Line Pressure	0	1	Detailing	3	3	Right Arm	08	08
Vertical Midline	0	0	Position of Legs	5	9	Variable Line Pressure	1	0	Identity and Sex	1	1	Left Arm	08	08
Bilateral Symmetry	3	3	Relation of Long Axes	1	1	Line Continuity	0	0	Sophistication	3	3	Chest	08	09
Horizontal Midline	0	0	Right and Left Halves	0	1	Body Shading	3	2	Height	09		Girth	11	09

GENERAL CHARACTERISTICS OF SUBJECT

IDENTIFICATION

No. B13
Sex M
Marital status S
Age 22 yrs. at
psychological tests

PARENTAL HISTORY

Father
C H S D O
- - - + ?

Mother
C H S D O
- - - + +

PHYSIOLOGICAL AND METABOLIC DATA

	Admission	Initial	Control	Cold pressor change	Exercise change	Smoking change
Systolic pressure	126	144	117	+11	+33	+04
Diastolic pressure	76	74	66	+09	-02	+05
Heart rate	76	80	64	+12	+43	+08

Age 21 yrs.

Height 73 in.
Weight 197 lbs.
Overweight +18 %

Ponderal index 12.54
Cholesterol 222 mg. per 100 ml.
Vital capacity 4.9 liters

HABIT SURVEY

Smoking habits: mixed smoker

Age begun 15 yrs.   Inhalation: sometimes

Habits of nervous tension: 4, 5, 6, 15, 22

STRONG VOCATIONAL INTEREST TEST

Occupation	Artist	Psychologist	Architect	Physician	Osteopath	Dentist	Veterinarian	Mathematician	Physicist	Engineer	Chemist	Production Manager
Standard Score	39	53	41	55	31	25	08	38	25	22	36	16

Occupation	Farmer	Aviator	Carpenter	Printer	Math.-Sci. Teacher	Ind. Arts Teacher	Voc. Agric. Teacher	Policeman	Forest Serv. Man	Y.M.C.A. Phys. Dir.	Personnel Director	Public Administrator
Standard Score	25	24	11	35	42	08	20	22	24	39	44	48

Occupation	Y.M.C.A. Secretary	Soc. Sci. H.S. Teacher	City Sch. Sup't.	Social Worker	Minister	Musician Performer	C.P.A.	Senior C.P.A.	Accountant	Office Man	Purchasing Agent	Banker
Standard Score	35	45	43	55	61	64	33	41	20	27	06	18

Occupation	Mortician	Pharmacist	Sales Manager	Real Est. Manager	Life Ins. Salesman	Advertising Man	Lawyer	Author-Journalist	President Mfg. Co.	Interest Maturity	Occupational Level	Masculinity-Femininity
Standard Score	16	23	22	28	28	42	40	41	17	58	56	33

Plate 356   DRAWINGS AT AN INTERMEDIATE LEVEL OF SOPHISTICATION   399

FIGURE-DRAWING CHARACTERISTICS

Structural	Male Female Both		Structural	Male	Female	Structural and Graphic	Male Female Both		Graphic, Global and Height	Male	Female	Body Proportions	Male	Female
Type	0		Omission of Appendages	0	0	Upper and Lower Halves	3	1	Hair Shading	2	2	Head	09	08
Sex Sequence	0		Position of Both Arms	1	0	Four Quarters	4	4	Nudity and Transparency	7	7	Neck	14	06
Posture	1	1	Position of Right Arm	4	5	Relative Size	0		Form	3	3	Shoulders	08	07
Perspective	0	0	Position of Left Arm	5	5	Constant Line Pressure	0	0	Detailing	3	3	Right Arm		05
Vertical Midline	3	3	Position of Legs	4	4	Variable Line Pressure	1	5	Identity and Sex	3	1	Left Arm	06	04
Bilateral Symmetry	1	2	Relation of Long Axes	3	1	Line Continuity	0	0	Sophistication	3	3	Chest	07	06
Horizontal Midline	6	4	Right and Left Halves	0	1	Body Shading	0	3	Height	08	06	Girth	09	09

GENERAL CHARACTERISTICS OF SUBJECT

IDENTIFICATION
No. 524
Sex M
Marital status S
Age 24 yrs. at psychological tests

PARENTAL HISTORY				
Father				
C	H	S	D	O
-	-	-	+	?
Mother				
C	H	S	D	O
-	-	-	-	-

PHYSIOLOGICAL AND METABOLIC DATA						
	Admission	Initial	Control	Cold pressor change	Exercise change	Smoking change
Systolic pressure	120	114	104	+02	+32	
Diastolic pressure	70	60	60	+16	-18	
Heart rate	88	84	83	+20	+20	

Age 24 yrs.	Height 72 in.	Ponderal index 12.85
	Weight 176 lbs.	Cholesterol 210 mg. per 100 ml.
	Overweight +07 %	Vital capacity 5.4 liters

HABIT SURVEY
Smoking habits: heavy cigarette smoker
Age begun 18 yrs.   Inhalation: yes
Habits of nervous tension: 1, 3, 4, 5, 8, 11, 22

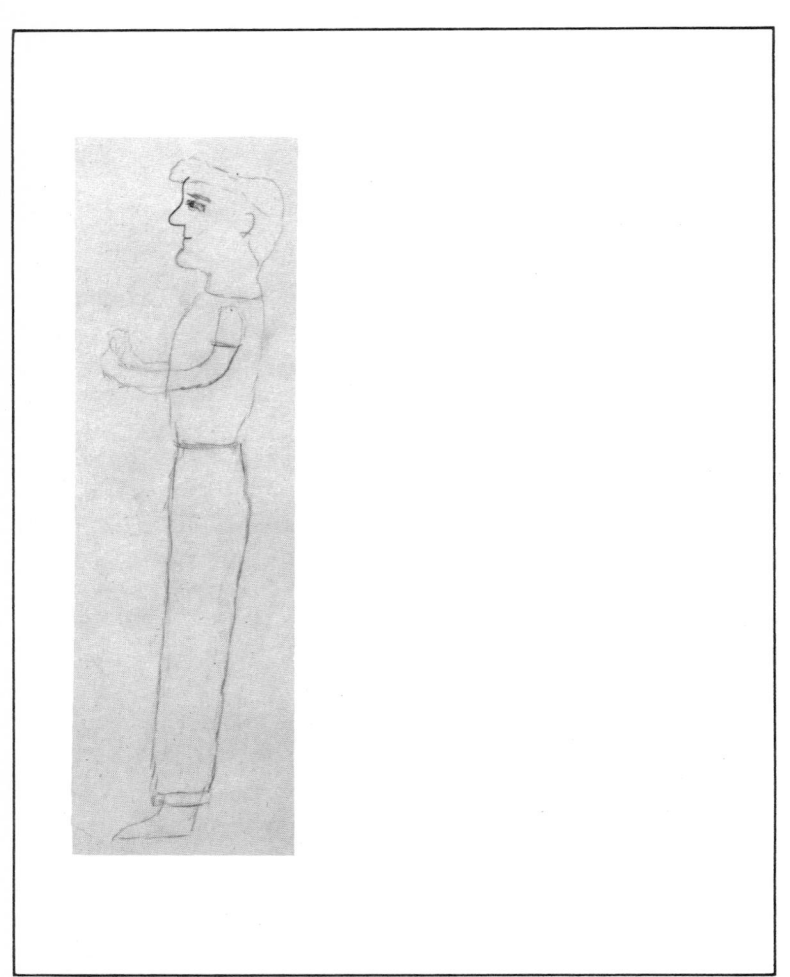

FIGURE-DRAWING CHARACTERISTICS

Structural	Male Female Both		Structural	Male	Female	Structural and Graphic	Male Female Both		Graphic, Global and Height	Male	Female	Body Proportions	Male	Female
Type	0		Omission of Appendages	0	0	Upper and Lower Halves	1	0	Hair Shading	5	5	Head	08	07
Sex Sequence	0		Position of Both Arms	4	4	Four Quarters	4	4	Nudity and Transparency	7	7	Neck	06	08
Posture	1	1	Position of Right Arm	7	7	Relative Size	4		Form	3	3	Shoulders		
Perspective	2	2	Position of Left Arm	4	4	Constant Line Pressure	0	1	Detailing	3	3	Right Arm		
Vertical Midline	4	4	Position of Legs	1	1	Variable Line Pressure	1	0	Identity and Sex	1	1	Left Arm	04	05
Bilateral Symmetry	0	0	Relation of Long Axes	1	1	Line Continuity	0	0	Sophistication	3	3	Chest	06	06
Horizontal Midline	4	4	Right and Left Halves	2	2	Body Shading	4	0	Height	07	08	Girth	05	05

GENERAL CHARACTERISTICS OF SUBJECT

IDENTIFICATION
No. 583
Sex M
Marital status S
Age 24 yrs. at
psychological tests

PARENTAL HISTORY

Father

C	H	S	D	O
–	–	–	+	–

Mother

C	H	S	D	O
–	–	–	–	+

PHYSIOLOGICAL AND METABOLIC DATA

	Admission	Initial	Control	Cold pressor change	Exercise change	Smoking change
Systolic pressure						
Diastolic pressure						
Heart rate						

	Height	in.	Ponderal index	
Age 24 yrs.	Weight	lbs.	Cholesterol 210	mg. per 100 ml.
	Overweight	%	Vital capacity	liters

HABIT SURVEY

Smoking habits: heavy cigarette smoker

Age begun 22 yrs.　　Inhalation: yes

Habits of nervous tension: 17, 25

FIGURE-DRAWING CHARACTERISTICS

Structural	Male Female		Structural	Male	Female	Structural and Graphic	Male	Female	Graphic, Global and Height	Male	Female	Body Proportions	Male	Female
	Both						Both							
Type	0		Omission of Appendages	0	0	Upper and Lower Halves	1	1	Hair Shading	5	2	Head	07	06
Sex Sequence	0		Position of Both Arms	4	4	Four Quarters	4	4	Nudity and Transparency	7	7	Neck	06	05
Posture	1	1	Position of Right Arm	7	7	Relative Size	0		Form	3	3	Shoulders		
Perspective	2	2	Position of Left Arm	4	4	Constant Line Pressure	0	0	Detailing	3	3	Right Arm		
Vertical Midline	4	4	Position of Legs	4	4	Variable Line Pressure	4	4	Identity and Sex	1	1	Left Arm	04	02
Bilateral Symmetry	0	0	Relation of Long Axes	1	1	Line Continuity	0	0	Sophistication	3	3	Chest	06	04
Horizontal Midline	4	4	Right and Left Halves	1	2	Body Shading	0	6	Height	05	05	Girth	05	04

GENERAL CHARACTERISTICS OF SUBJECT

IDENTIFICATION

No. A34

Sex M

Marital status S

Age 23 yrs. at psychological tests

PARENTAL HISTORY

Father

C   H   S   D   O

−   −   −   +   −

Mother

C   H   S   D   O

−   −   −   −   −

PHYSIOLOGICAL AND METABOLIC DATA

	Admission	Initial	Control	Cold pressor change	Exercise change	Smoking change
Systolic pressure	120	124	123	+06	+17	+10
Diastolic pressure	80	68	69	+13	−07	+06
Heart rate	82	69	81	+18	−02	+08

Age 22 yrs.

Height 72 in.   Ponderal index 12.79

Weight 178 lbs.   Cholesterol 273 mg. per 100 ml.

Overweight +09 %   Vital capacity   liters

HABIT SURVEY

Smoking habits: heavy cigarette smoker

   Age begun 17 yrs.   Inhalation: yes

Habits of nervous tension: 5, 6, 9, 16

STRONG VOCATIONAL INTEREST TEST

Occupation	Artist	Psychologist	Architect	Physician	Osteopath	Dentist	Veterinarian	Mathematician	Physicist	Engineer	Chemist	Production Manager
Standard Score	3	5	3	7	6	3	4	2	2	3	3	4

Occupation	Farmer	Aviator	Carpenter	Printer	Math.-Sci. Teacher	Ind. Arts Teacher	Voc. Agric. Teacher	Policeman	Forest Serv. Man	Y.M.C.A. Phys. Dir.	Personnel Director	Public Administrator
Standard Score	6	4	2	4	1	1	3	3	4	4	4	6

Occupation	Y.M.C.A. Secretary	Soc. Sci. H.S. Teacher	City Sch. Sup't.	Social Worker	Minister	Musician Performer	C.P.A.	Senior C.P.A.	Accountant	Office Man	Purchasing Agent	Banker
Standard Score	3	5	3	5	6	5	3	4	2	3	2	2

Occupation	Mortician	Pharmacist	Sales Manager	Real Est. Manager	Life Ins. Salesman	Advertising Man	Lawyer	Author-Journalist	President Mfg. Co.	Interest Maturity	Occupational Level	Masculinity-Femininity
Standard Score	3	3	3	5	4	4	6	4	3	6	5	5

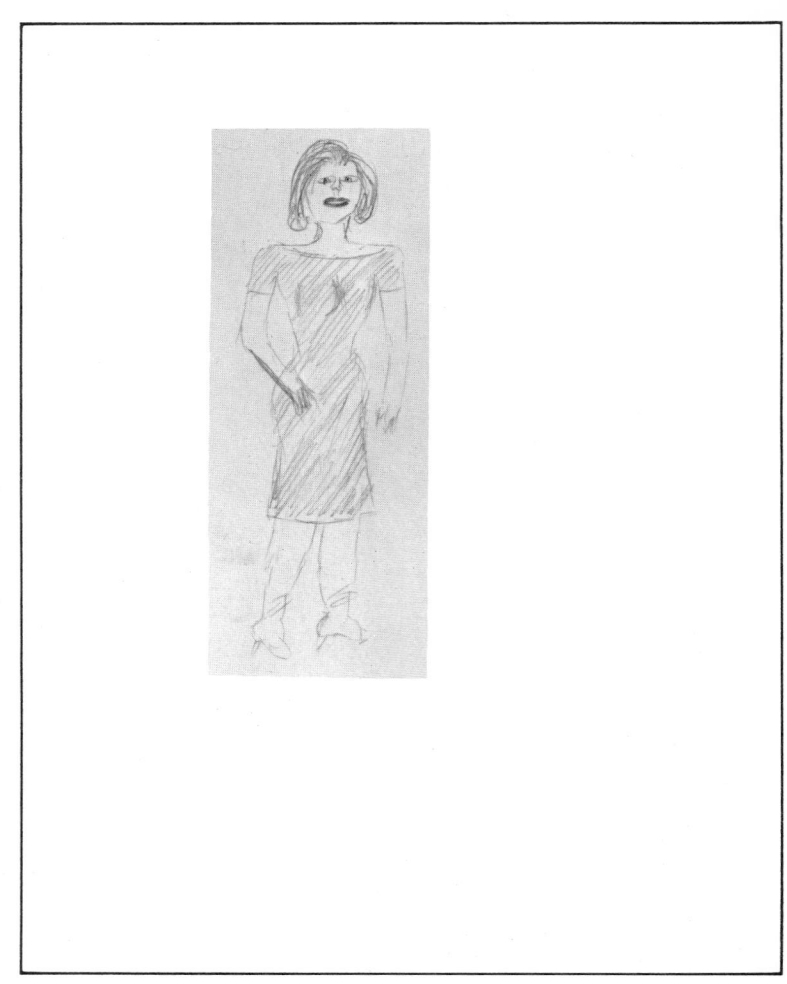

FIGURE-DRAWING CHARACTERISTICS

Structural	Male Female Both		Structural	Male	Female	Structural and Graphic	Male Female Both		Graphic, Global and Height	Male	Female	Body Proportions	Male	Female
Type	0		Omission of Appendages	0	0	Upper and Lower Halves	1	1	Hair Shading	3	3	Head	06	06
Sex Sequence	0		Position of Both Arms	1	1	Four Quarters	4	4	Nudity and Transparency	7	7	Neck	06	06
Posture	1	1	Position of Right Arm	3	5	Relative Size	1		Form	3	3	Shoulders	07	06
Perspective	0	0	Position of Left Arm	5	0	Constant Line Pressure	1	1	Detailing	3	3	Right Arm	04	04
Vertical Midline	0	0	Position of Legs	4	4	Variable Line Pressure	0	0	Identity and Sex	1	1	Left Arm	04	04
Bilateral Symmetry	3	3	Relation of Long Axes	1	1	Line Continuity	0	0	Sophistication	3	3	Chest	06	05
Horizontal Midline	4	0	Right and Left Halves	1	2	Body Shading	7	3	Height	05	05	Girth	06	03

GENERAL CHARACTERISTICS OF SUBJECT

IDENTIFICATION
No. D12
Sex M
Marital status S
Age 22 yrs. at psychological tests

PARENTAL HISTORY
Father
C   H   S   D   O
–   –   –   +   ?
Mother
C   H   S   D   O
–   –   –   –   –

PHYSIOLOGICAL AND METABOLIC DATA

	Admission	Initial	Control	Cold pressor change	Exercise change	Smoking change
Systolic pressure	120	140	120	+05	+40	+16
Diastolic pressure	70	70	70	+10	00	+14
Heart rate	74	100	86	+08	+21	+12

Age 21 yrs.	Height 73 in.	Ponderal index 13.35
	Weight 164 lbs.	Cholesterol 233 mg. per 100 ml.
	Overweight –02 %	Vital capacity 5.2 liters

HABIT SURVEY

Smoking habits: former smoker

Age begun 16 yrs.   Inhalation: yes

Habits of nervous tension: 4, 5, 6

STRONG VOCATIONAL INTEREST TEST

Occupation	Artist	Psychologist	Architect	Physician	Osteopath	Dentist	Veterinarian	Mathematician	Physicist	Engineer	Chemist	Production Manager
Standard Score	37	53	39	58	52	42	25	33	39	40	51	32

Occupation	Farmer	Aviator	Carpenter	Printer	Math.-Sci. Teacher	Ind. Arts Teacher	Voc. Agric. Teacher	Policeman	Forest Serv. Man	Y.M.C.A. Phys. Dir.	Personnel Director	Public Administrator
Standard Score	36	46	18	40	38	15	23	25	28	24	39	49

Occupation	Y.M.C.A. Secretary	Soc. Sci. H.S. Teacher	City Sch. Sup't.	Social Worker	Minister	Musician Performer	C.P.A.	Senior C.P.A.	Accountant	Office Man	Purchasing Agent	Banker
Standard Score	17	26	23	39	63	46	34	36	18	25	21	18

Occupation	Mortician	Pharmacist	Sales Manager	Real Est. Manager	Life Ins. Salesman	Advertising Man	Lawyer	Author-Journalist	President Mfg. Co.	Interest Maturity	Occupational Level	Masculinity-Femininity
Standard Score	22	34	28	38	27	37	47	41	33	50	58	52

FIGURE-DRAWING CHARACTERISTICS

Structural	Male Female Both	Structural	Male	Female	Structural and Graphic	Male Female Both		Graphic, Global and Height	Male	Female	Body Proportions	Male	Female
Type	0	Omission of Appendages	0	0	Upper and Lower Halves	1	0	Hair Shading	3	3	Head	07	06
Sex Sequence	2	Position of Both Arms	0	0	Four Quarters	4	4	Nudity and Transparency	7	7	Neck	06	06
Posture	1 1	Position of Right Arm	2	2	Relative Size	3		Form	3	3	Shoulders	05	05
Perspective	0 5	Position of Left Arm	2	2	Constant Line Pressure	0	5	Detailing	1	1	Right Arm	04	04
Vertical Midline	3 3	Position of Legs	6	5	Variable Line Pressure	5	0	Identity and Sex	1	1	Left Arm	04	04
Bilateral Symmetry	3 3	Relation of Long Axes	1	1	Line Continuity	2	3	Sophistication	3	3	Chest	04	03
Horizontal Midline	4 4	Right and Left Halves	1	1	Body Shading	6	6	Height	05	06	Girth	03	04

GENERAL CHARACTERISTICS OF SUBJECT

IDENTIFICATION
No. 729
Sex M
Marital status S
Age 24 yrs. at psychological tests

PARENTAL HISTORY
Father
C   H   S   D   O
–   –   –   ?   –
Mother
C   H   S   D   O
–   –   –   –   –

PHYSIOLOGICAL AND METABOLIC DATA

	Admission	Initial	Control	Cold pressor change	Exercise change	Smoking change
Systolic pressure	118	120	108	+14	+34	+05
Diastolic pressure	75	74	68	+18	+02	+06
Heart rate	76	72	88	+16	+32	–02

Age 21 yrs.	Height	70 in.	Ponderal index 11.78
	Weight	210 lbs.	Cholesterol 237 mg. per 100 ml.
	Overweight +37 %		Vital capacity 5.1 liters

HABIT SURVEY
Smoking habits: heavy cigarette smoker
Age begun 18 yrs.   Inhalation: sometimes
Habits of nervous tension: 2, 4, 5, 6, 9, 11, 16, 22, 23, 25

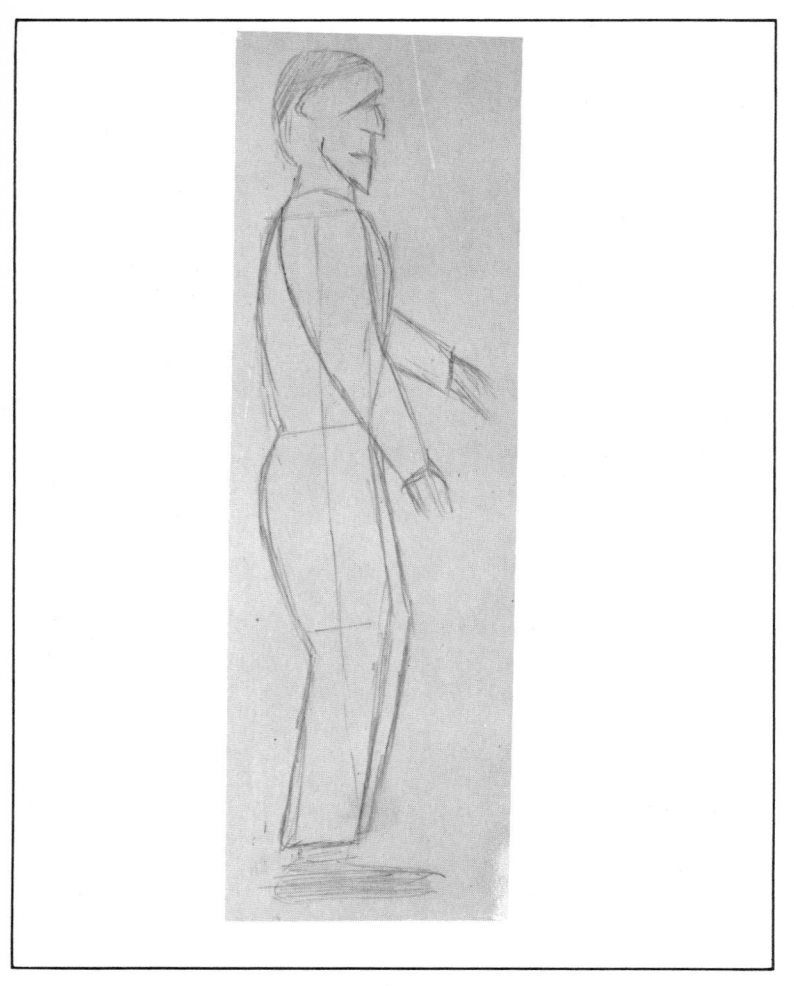

FIGURE-DRAWING CHARACTERISTICS

Structural	Male	Female	Structural	Male	Female	Structural and Graphic	Male	Female	Graphic, Global and Height	Male	Female	Body Proportions	Male	Female
	Both						Both							
Type	0		Omission of Appendages	7	4	Upper and Lower Halves	0	7	Hair Shading	2	3	Head	11	11
Sex Sequence	0		Position of Both Arms	2	2	Four Quarters	4	4	Nudity and Transparency	7	7	Neck	06	10
Posture	1	0	Position of Right Arm	4	4	Relative Size	5		Form	3	3	Shoulders		
Perspective	2	2	Position of Left Arm	7	7	Constant Line Pressure	2	2	Detailing	3	3	Right Arm	08	
Vertical Midline	4	4	Position of Legs	1	0	Variable Line Pressure	0	0	Identity and Sex	1	1	Left Arm		
Bilateral Symmetry	0	0	Relation of Long Axes	1	1	Line Continuity	0	0	Sophistication	3	3	Chest	09	07
Horizontal Midline	2	4	Right and Left Halves	1	2	Body Shading	0	4	Height	09		Girth	07	06

GENERAL CHARACTERISTICS OF SUBJECT

IDENTIFICATION

No. A76

Sex M

Marital status S

Age 22 yrs. at

psychological tests

PARENTAL HISTORY

Father

C H S D O

- - - ? +

Mother

C H S D O

- - - - ?

PHYSIOLOGICAL AND METABOLIC DATA

	Admission	Initial	Control	Cold pressor change	Exercise change	Smoking change
Systolic pressure	140	136	121	+14	+33	
Diastolic pressure	90	62	53	+37	-15	
Heart rate		80	74	+10	+13	

Age 22 yrs.

Height 72 in.

Weight 151 lbs.

Overweight -07 %

Ponderal index 13.52

Cholesterol 237 mg. per 100 ml.

Vital capacity liters

HABIT SURVEY

Smoking habits: moderate cigarette smoker

Age begun 17 yrs.   Inhalation: yes

Habits of nervous tension: 6, 9, 10, 25

STRONG VOCATIONAL INTEREST TEST

Occupation	Artist	Psychologist	Architect	Physician	Osteopath	Dentist	Veterinarian	Mathematician	Physicist	Engineer	Chemist	Production Manager
Standard Score	34	55	44	61	48	44	21	34	39	54	57	42

Occupation	Farmer	Aviator	Carpenter	Printer	Math.-Sci. Teacher	Ind. Arts Teacher	Voc. Agric. Teacher	Policeman	Forest Serv. Man	Y.M.C.A. Phys. Dir.	Personnel Director	Public Administrator
Standard Score	31	55	27	36	42	27	23	32	43	42	58	58

Occupation	Y.M.C.A. Secretary	Soc. Sci. H.S. Teacher	City Sch. Sup't.	Social Worker	Minister	Musician Performer	C.P.A.	Senior C.P.A.	Accountant	Office Man	Purchasing Agent	Banker
Standard Score	20	30	27	47	60	50	40	49	29	26	22	05

Occupation	Mortician	Pharmacist	Sales Manager	Real Est. Manager	Life Ins. Salesman	Advertising Man	Lawyer	Author-Journalist	President Mfg. Co.	Interest Maturity	Occupational Level	Masculinity-Femininity
Standard Score	19	26	29	29	25	34	41	35	38	58	58	49

Plate 362   DRAWINGS AT AN INTERMEDIATE LEVEL OF SOPHISTICATION   405

FIGURE-DRAWING CHARACTERISTICS

Structural	Male Female Both	Structural	Male	Female	Structural and Graphic	Male Female Both		Graphic, Global and Height	Male	Female	Body Proportions	Male	Female
Type	0	Omission of Appendages	0	0	Upper and Lower Halves	1	1	Hair Shading	0	3	Head	05	05
Sex Sequence	1	Position of Both Arms	4	0	Four Quarters	4	4	Nudity and Transparency	7	7	Neck	04	08
Posture	5	1	Position of Right Arm	6	5	Relative Size	0		Form	3	3	Shoulders		05
Perspective	9	0	Position of Left Arm	6	5	Constant Line Pressure	0	0	Detailing	3	3	Right Arm		04
Vertical Midline	4	3	Position of Legs	8	2	Variable Line Pressure	5	5	Identity and Sex	1	1	Left Arm		04
Bilateral Symmetry	0	3	Relation of Long Axes	1	1	Line Continuity	0	0	Sophistication	3	3	Chest	06	06
Horizontal Midline	4	4	Right and Left Halves	1	1	Body Shading	0	3	Height	04	04	Girth	05	07

GENERAL CHARACTERISTICS OF SUBJECT

IDENTIFICATION
No. O20
Sex M
Marital status M
Age 23 yrs. at
psychological tests

PARENTAL HISTORY
Father
C   H   S   D   O
–   –   –   ?   +
Mother
C   H   S   D   O
–   –   –   –   –

PHYSIOLOGICAL AND METABOLIC DATA

	Admission	Initial	Control	Cold pressor change	Exercise change	Smoking change
Systolic pressure	150	120	126	–01	+24	+18
Diastolic pressure	90	70	70	+22	–12	+02
Heart rate	72	52	52	+12	+16	+09

Age 21 yrs.	Height	71	in.	Ponderal index	12.77	
	Weight	172	lbs.	Cholesterol	215	mg. per 100 ml.
	Overweight +10 %			Vital capacity	5.0	liters

HABIT SURVEY

Smoking habits: nonsmoker

Age begun   yrs.   Inhalation:

Habits of nervous tension: 3, 4, 5, 9, 10, 22

STRONG VOCATIONAL INTEREST TEST

Occupation	Artist	Psychologist	Architect	Physician	Osteopath	Dentist	Veterinarian	Mathematician	Physicist	Engineer	Chemist	Production Manager
Standard Score	34	46	42	58	54	52	20	38	44	49	47	35

Occupation	Farmer	Aviator	Carpenter	Printer	Math.-Sci. Teacher	Ind. Arts Teacher	Voc. Agric. Teacher	Policeman	Forest Serv. Man	Y.M.C.A. Phys. Dir.	Personnel Director	Public Administrator
Standard Score	34	38	25	33	41	27	25	21	20	34	35	35

Occupation	Y.M.C.A. Secretary	Soc. Sci. H.S. Teacher	City Sch. Sup't.	Social Worker	Minister	Musician Performer	C.P.A.	Senior C.P.A.	Accountant	Office Man	Purchasing Agent	Banker
Standard Score	17	22	26	31	64	45	28	31	22	26	20	13

Occupation	Mortician	Pharmacist	Sales Manager	Real Est. Manager	Life Ins. Salesman	Advertising Man	Lawyer	Author-Journalist	President Mfg. Co.	Interest Maturity	Occupational Level	Masculinity-Femininity
Standard Score	24	33	19	29	26	31	30	35	37	52	61	43

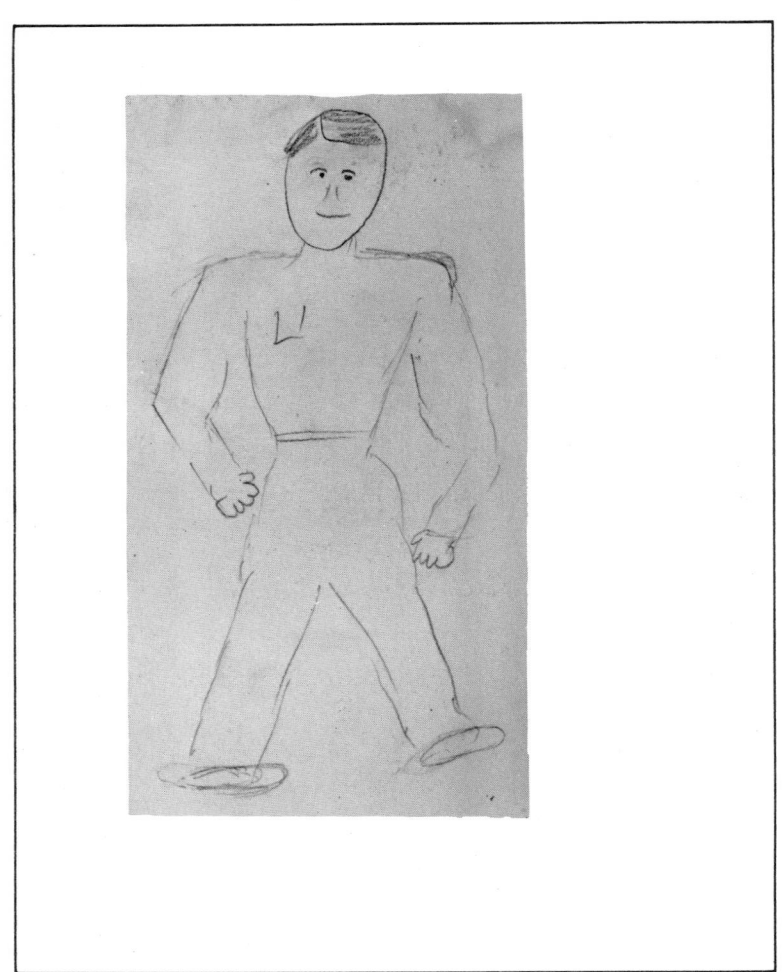

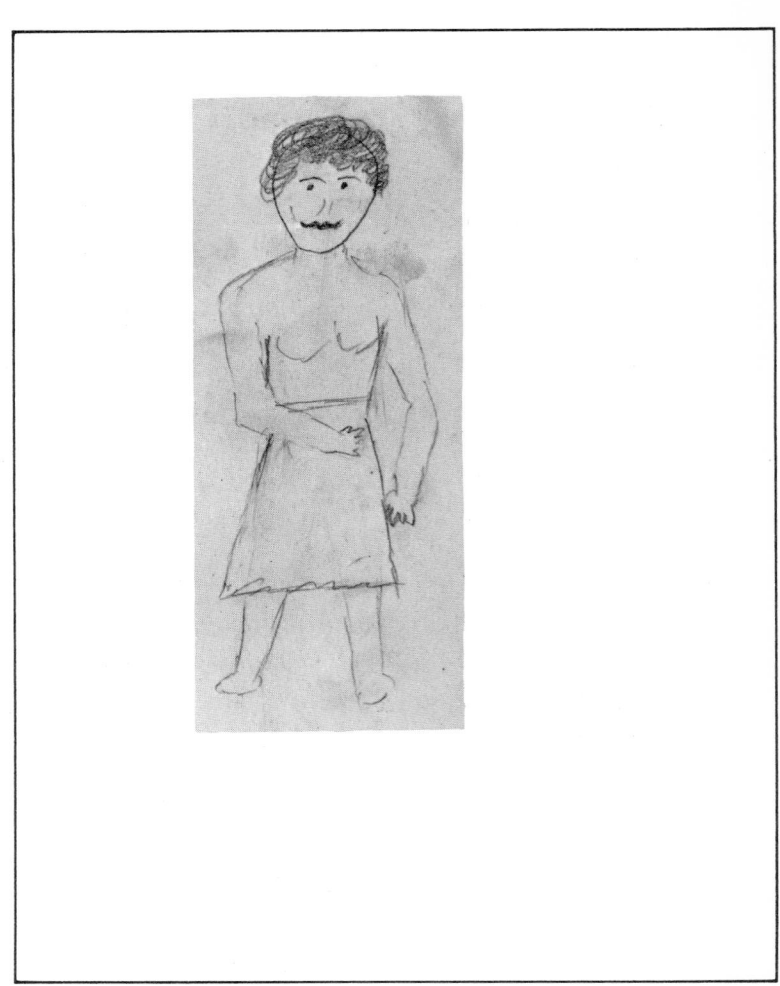

FIGURE-DRAWING CHARACTERISTICS

Structural	Male Female Both	Structural	Male	Female	Structural and Graphic	Male Female Both		Graphic, Global and Height	Male	Female	Body Proportions	Male	Female
Type	0	Omission of Appendages	0	0	Upper and Lower Halves	1	1	Hair Shading	2	3	Head	12	11
Sex Sequence	0	Position of Both Arms	0	0	Four Quarters	4	4	Nudity and Transparency	7	3	Neck	05	04
Posture	2 1	Position of Right Arm	5	5	Relative Size	0		Form	3	3	Shoulders	11	07
Perspective	0 0	Position of Left Arm	5	5	Constant Line Pressure	0	0	Detailing	5	5	Right Arm	06	06
Vertical Midline	0 0	Position of Legs	8	6	Variable Line Pressure	3	2	Identity and Sex	1	1	Left Arm	08	06
Bilateral Symmetry	3 2	Relation of Long Axes	1	1	Line Continuity	0	0	Sophistication	3	3	Chest	07	05
Horizontal Midline	4 4	Right and Left Halves	1	1	Body Shading	0	0	Height	07	06	Girth	06	06

GENERAL CHARACTERISTICS OF SUBJECT

IDENTIFICATION
No. 541
Sex M
Marital status S
Age 24 yrs. at
psychological tests

PARENTAL HISTORY
Father
C   H   S   D   O
-   -   -   -   -
Mother
C   H   S   D   O
-   -   -   ?   +

PHYSIOLOGICAL AND METABOLIC DATA

	Admission	Initial	Control	Cold pressor change	Exercise change	Smoking change
Systolic pressure	125	120	110	+10	+20	
Diastolic pressure	60	70	70	00	00	
Heart rate	70	68	67	+08	+08	

	Height	72 in.	Ponderal index 12.87
Age 22 yrs.	Weight	175 lbs.	Cholesterol 197 mg. per 100 ml.
	Overweight +07 %		Vital capacity 5.6 liters

HABIT SURVEY
Smoking habits: nonsmoker
Age begun yrs. Inhalation:
Habits of nervous tension: 2, 4, 5, 6, 9,
10, 17

Plate 364   DRAWINGS AT AN INTERMEDIATE LEVEL OF SOPHISTICATION   407

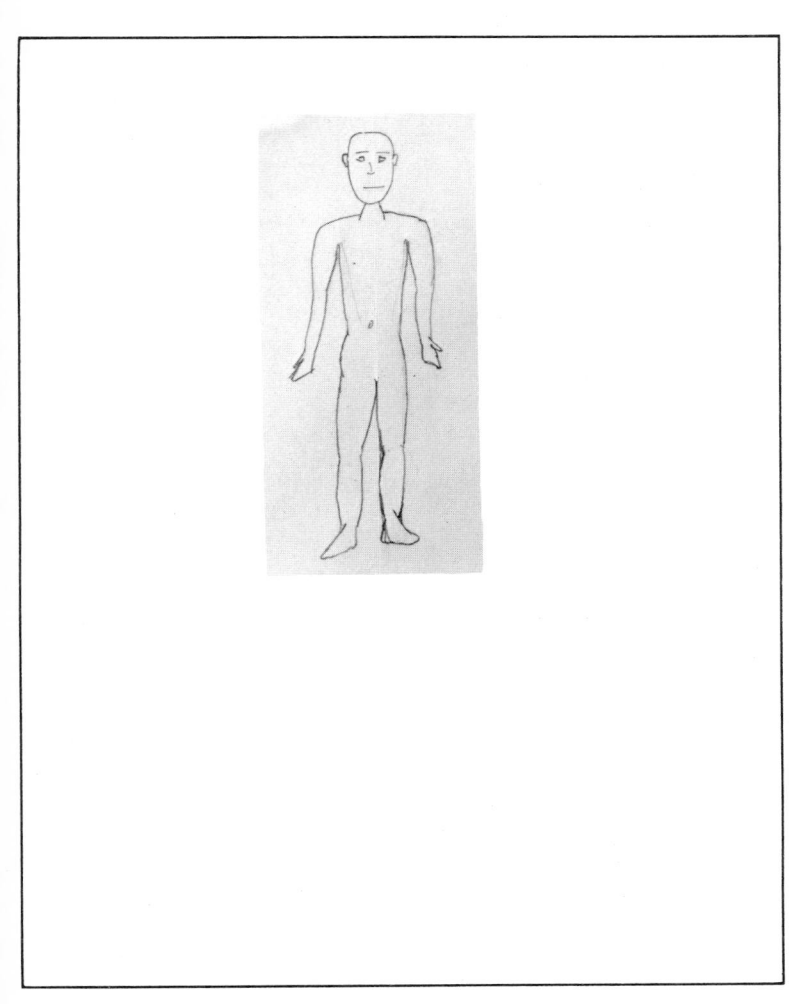

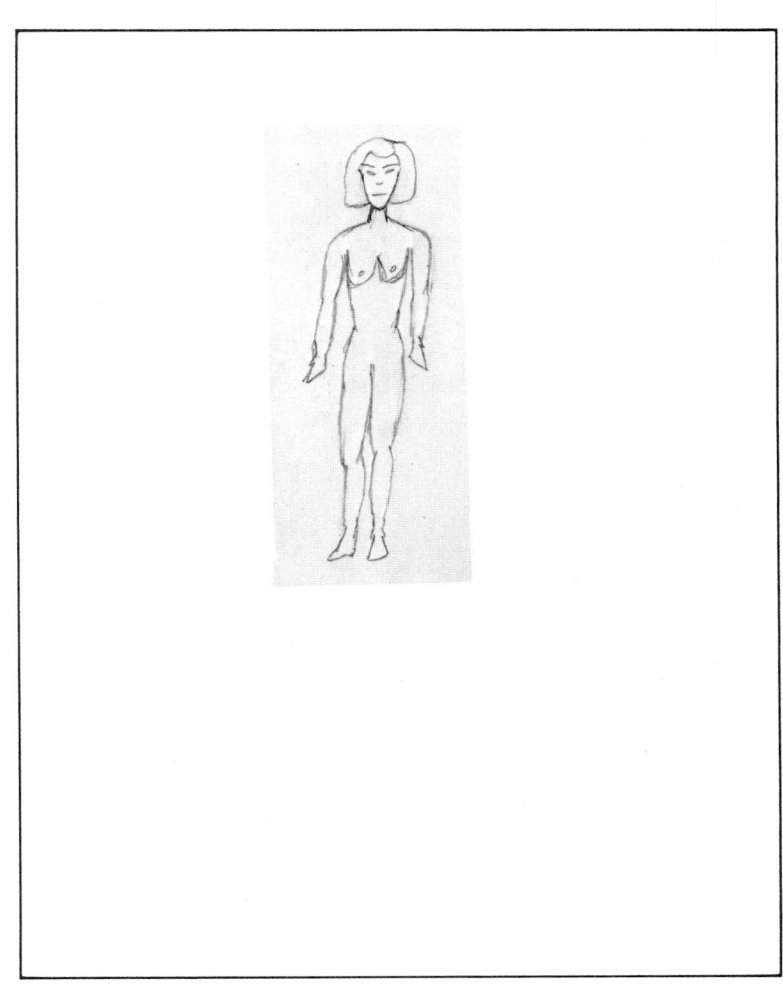

FIGURE-DRAWING CHARACTERISTICS

Structural	Male Female Both		Structural	Male	Female	Structural and Graphic	Male Female Both		Graphic, Global and Height	Male	Female	Body Proportions	Male	Female
Type	0		Omission of Appendages	0	0	Upper and Lower Halves	1	1	Hair Shading	0	5	Head	06	05
Sex Sequence	0		Position of Both Arms	0	0	Four Quarters	4	4	Nudity and Transparency	0	0	Neck	03	04
Posture	1	1	Position of Right Arm	0	0	Relative Size	2		Form	1	1	Shoulders	04	04
Perspective	0	0	Position of Left Arm	0	0	Constant Line Pressure	0	0	Detailing	5	3	Right Arm	03	02
Vertical Midline	0	0	Position of Legs	4	4	Variable Line Pressure	5	5	Identity and Sex	1	1	Left Arm	03	02
Bilateral Symmetry	3	3	Relation of Long Axes	1	1	Line Continuity	2	0	Sophistication	3	3	Chest	03	03
Horizontal Midline	0	0	Right and Left Halves	1	1	Body Shading	0	1	Height	04	04	Girth	03	02

GENERAL CHARACTERISTICS OF SUBJECT

IDENTIFICATION

No. F07

Sex M

Marital status S

Age 23 yrs. at

psychological tests

PARENTAL HISTORY

Father

C	H	S	D	O
–	–	–	–	?

Mother

C	H	S	D	O
–	–	–	?	+

PHYSIOLOGICAL AND METABOLIC DATA

	Admission	Initial	Control	Cold pressor change	Exercise change	Smoking change
Systolic pressure	130	110	104	+16	+36	00
Diastolic pressure	84	86	80	+08	+10	+10
Heart rate	72	92	85	+08	+18	+17

Age 21 yrs.

Height 72 in.   Ponderal index 12.52

Weight 190 lbs.   Cholesterol 188 mg. per 100 ml.

Overweight +17 %   Vital capacity   liters

HABIT SURVEY

Smoking habits: occasional smoker

Age begun 20 yrs.   Inhalation: no

Habits of nervous tension: 4, 5, 19

STRONG VOCATIONAL INTEREST TEST

Occupation	Artist	Psychologist	Architect	Physician	Osteopath	Dentist	Veterinarian	Mathematician	Physicist	Engineer	Chemist	Production Manager
Standard Score	23	42	36	56	56	43	34	23	33	53	50	44

Occupation	Farmer	Aviator	Carpenter	Printer	Math.-Sci. Teacher	Ind. Arts Teacher	Voc. Agric. Teacher	Policeman	Forest Serv. Man	Y.M.C.A. Phys. Dir.	Personnel Director	Public Administrator
Standard Score	43	69	32	42	43	39	34	38	43	33	41	47

Occupation	Y.M.C.A. Secretary	Soc. Sci. H.S. Teacher	City Sch. Sup't.	Social Worker	Minister	Musician Performer	C.P.A.	Senior C.P.A.	Accountant	Office Man	Purchasing Agent	Banker
Standard Score	20	20	13	32	58	35	23	48	18	19	27	08

Occupation	Mortician	Pharmacist	Sales Manager	Real Est. Manager	Life Ins. Salesman	Advertising Man	Lawyer	Author- Journalist	President Mfg. Co.	Interest Maturity	Occupational Level	Masculinity- Femininity
Standard Score	26	26	27	30	22	26	28	28	30	54	53	68

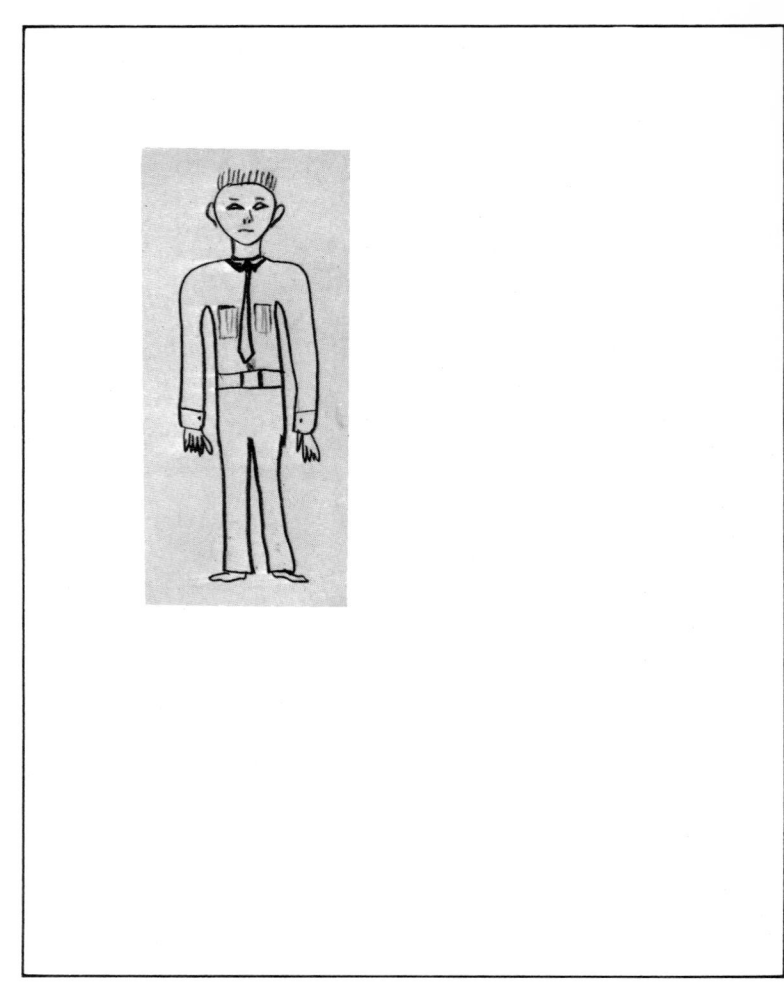

FIGURE-DRAWING CHARACTERISTICS

Structural	Male Female Both	Structural	Male	Female	Structural and Graphic	Male Female Both		Graphic, Global and Height	Male	Female	Body Proportions	Male	Female
Type	0	Omission of Appendages	0	0	Upper and Lower Halves	1	1	Hair Shading	7	3	Head	05	07
Sex Sequence	1	Position of Both Arms	0	1	Four Quarters	4	4	Nudity and Transparency	7	7	Neck	05	06
Posture	1 1	Position of Right Arm	0	0	Relative Size	4		Form	3	3	Shoulders	05	06
Perspective	0 0	Position of Left Arm	0	5	Constant Line Pressure	5	0	Detailing	3	3	Right Arm	04	04
Vertical Midline	3 0	Position of Legs	4	0	Variable Line Pressure	0	2	Identity and Sex	1	1	Left Arm	04	05
Bilateral Symmetry	4 3	Relation of Long Axes	1	1	Line Continuity	4	2	Sophistication	3	3	Chest	03	05
Horizontal Midline	4 0	Right and Left Halves	2	2	Body Shading	5	1	Height	04	05	Girth	04	04

GENERAL CHARACTERISTICS OF SUBJECT

IDENTIFICATION
No. 571
Sex M
Marital status S
Age 24 yrs. at
psychological tests

PARENTAL HISTORY
Father
C   H   S   D   O
-   -   -   -   +
Mother
C   H   S   D   O
-   -   -   -   +

PHYSIOLOGICAL AND METABOLIC DATA

	Admission	Initial	Control	Cold pressor change	Exercise change	Smoking change
Systolic pressure	112	128	112	+16	+22	+04
Diastolic pressure	60	74	64	+20	+10	-04
Heart rate	72	80	79	-04	+17	+01

Age 21 yrs.	Height 72 in.	Ponderal index 13.52
	Weight 151 lbs.	Cholesterol 185 mg. per 100 ml.
	Overweight -07 %	Vital capacity liters

HABIT SURVEY

Smoking habits: heavy cigarette smoker

   Age begun 15 yrs.   Inhalation: yes

Habits of nervous tension: 4, 5, 6, 12, 18, 21, 22

Plate 366   DRAWINGS AT AN INTERMEDIATE LEVEL OF SOPHISTICATION   409

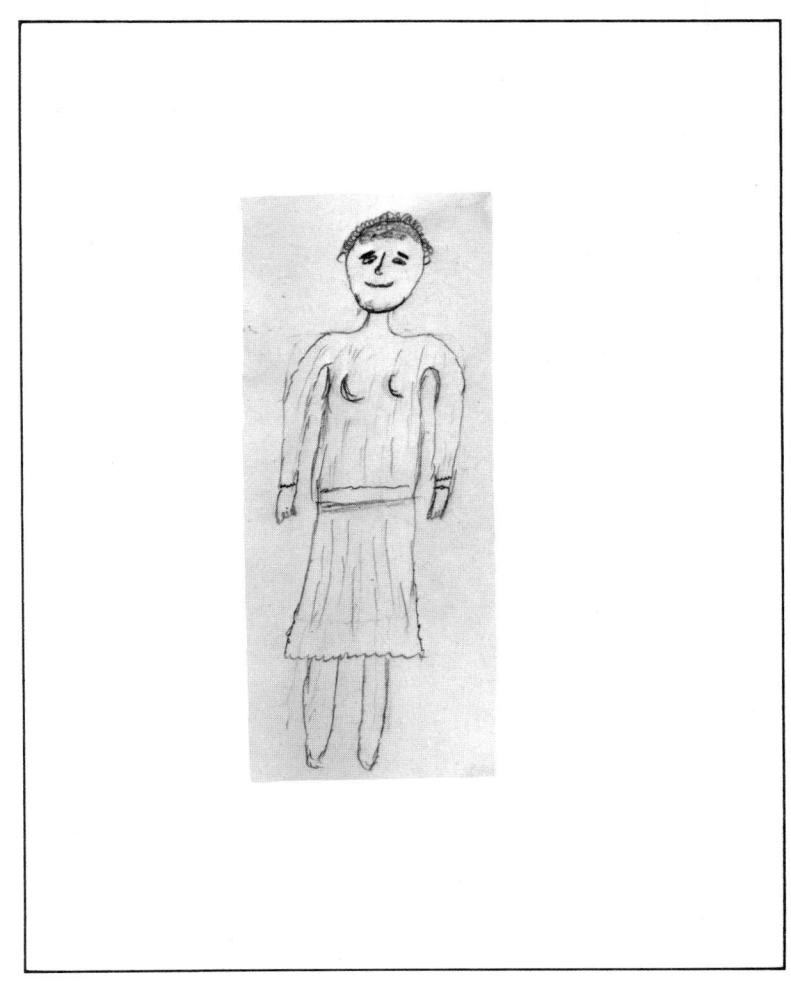

FIGURE-DRAWING CHARACTERISTICS

Structural	Male Female Both		Structural	Male	Female	Structural and Graphic	Male Female Both		Graphic, Global and Height	Male	Female	Body Proportions	Male	Female
Type	0		Omission of Appendages	0	0	Upper and Lower Halves	3	0	Hair Shading	1	3	Head		07
Sex Sequence	0		Position of Both Arms	0	0	Four Quarters	4	4	Nudity and Transparency	7	7	Neck		06
Posture	1	1	Position of Right Arm	5	0	Relative Size	0		Form	3	3	Shoulders	09	06
Perspective	0	0	Position of Left Arm	5	0	Constant Line Pressure	0	0	Detailing	3	3	Right Arm	06	04
Vertical Midline	3	0	Position of Legs	5	4	Variable Line Pressure	1	1	Identity and Sex	3	3	Left Arm	06	04
Bilateral Symmetry	2	2	Relation of Long Axes	1	1	Line Continuity	0	0	Sophistication	3	3	Chest	06	05
Horizontal Midline	4	4	Right and Left Halves	1	1	Body Shading	5	3	Height	06	05	Girth	08	06

GENERAL CHARACTERISTICS OF SUBJECT

IDENTIFICATION
No. F41
Sex M
Marital status S
Age 24 yrs. at
psychological tests

PARENTAL HISTORY				
Father				
C	H	S	D	O
-	-	-	-	+
Mother				
C	H	S	D	O
-	-	-	-	+

PHYSIOLOGICAL AND METABOLIC DATA

	Admission	Initial	Control	Cold pressor change	Exercise change	Smoking change
Systolic pressure	130	92	84	+06	+22	00
Diastolic pressure	68	66	62	+12	+10	00
Heart rate	68	60	58	00	+14	+03

Age 22 yrs.	Height 68 in.	Ponderal index 12.30
	Weight 169 lbs.	Cholesterol 204 mg. per 100 ml.
	Overweight +16 %	Vital capacity liters

HABIT SURVEY

Smoking habits: pipe smoker

Age begun 19* yrs.   Inhalation: no

Habits of nervous tension: 11, 16, 21

* "plus a lot of behind the barn cigarettes when I was a kid."

STRONG VOCATIONAL INTEREST TEST

Occupation	Artist	Psychologist	Architect	Physician	Osteopath	Dentist	Veterinarian	Mathematician	Physicist	Engineer	Chemist	Production Manager
Standard Score	30	42	31	58	49	40	21	25	15	23	28	30

Occupation	Farmer	Aviator	Carpenter	Printer	Math.-Sci. Teacher	Ind. Arts Teacher	Voc. Agric. Teacher	Policeman	Forest Serv. Man	Y.M.C.A. Phys. Dir.	Personnel Director	Public Administrator
Standard Score	22	26	11	38	40	10	17	31	24	42	38	45

Occupation	Y.M.C.A. Secretary	Soc. Sci. H.S. Teacher	City Sch. Sup't.	Social Worker	Minister	Musician Performer	C.P.A.	Senior C.P.A.	Accountant	Office Man	Purchasing Agent	Banker
Standard Score	39	48	44	51	58	56	31	39	23	33	16	26

Occupation	Mortician	Pharmacist	Sales Manager	Real Est. Manager	Life Ins. Salesman	Advertising Man	Lawyer	Author- Journalist	President Mfg. Co.	Interest Maturity	Occupational Level	Masculinity- Femininity
Standard Score	32	33	22	30	31	32	39	36	22	62	54	32

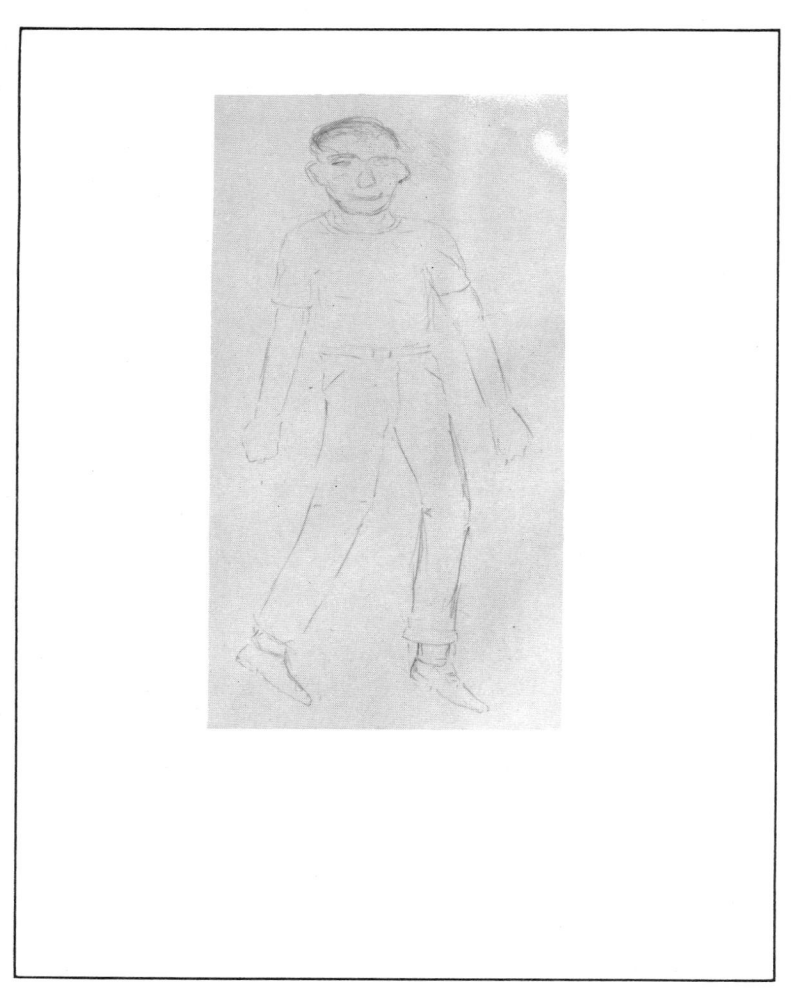

FIGURE-DRAWING CHARACTERISTICS

Structural	Male Female Both		Structural	Male	Female	Structural and Graphic	Male	Female	Graphic, Global and Height	Male	Female	Body Proportions	Male	Female
Type	0		Omission of Appendages	0	0	Upper and Lower Halves	1	1	Hair Shading	3	5	Head	07	07
Sex Sequence	0		Position of Both Arms	0	0	Four Quarters	4	4	Nudity and Transparency	7	7	Neck	04	06
Posture	2	1	Position of Right Arm	2	2	Relative Size	3		Form	3	3	Shoulders	07	06
Perspective	0	0	Position of Left Arm	2	2	Constant Line Pressure	1	0	Detailing	3	3	Right Arm	06	05
Vertical Midline	3	0	Position of Legs	8	5	Variable Line Pressure	0	1	Identity and Sex	1	1	Left Arm	06	06
Bilateral Symmetry	3	3	Relation of Long Axes	1	1	Line Continuity	0	0	Sophistication	3	3	Chest	05	06
Horizontal Midline	4	4	Right and Left Halves	1	1	Body Shading	3	3	Height	06	06	Girth	07	07

GENERAL CHARACTERISTICS OF SUBJECT

IDENTIFICATION
No. G09
Sex M
Marital status M
Age 23 yrs. at
psychological tests

PARENTAL HISTORY
Father
C H S D O
- - - - +
Mother
C H S D O
- - - - +

PHYSIOLOGICAL AND METABOLIC DATA

	Admission	Initial	Control	Cold pressor change	Exercise change	Smoking change
Systolic pressure	125	110	102	+16	+48	+04
Diastolic pressure	80	72	80	+14	-12	+04
Heart rate	80	64	61	+32	+12	+10

Age 22 yrs.	Height 71 in.	Ponderal index 13.27
	Weight 153 lbs.	Cholesterol 210 mg. per 100 ml.
	Overweight -03 %	Vital capacity liters

HABIT SURVEY

Smoking habits: nonsmoker

Age begun yrs. Inhalation:

Habits of nervous tension: 1, 4, 6, 9, 11, 14, 16, 17, 21, 25

STRONG VOCATIONAL INTEREST TEST

Occupation	Artist	Psychologist	Architect	Physician	Osteopath	Dentist	Veterinarian	Mathematician	Physicist	Engineer	Chemist	Production Manager
Standard Score	40	49	50	59	35	46	12	54	55	51	59	32

Occupation	Farmer	Aviator	Carpenter	Printer	Math.-Sci. Teacher	Ind. Arts Teacher	Voc. Agric. Teacher	Policeman	Forest Serv. Man	Y.M.C.A. Phys. Dir.	Personnel Director	Public Administrator
Standard Score	31	36	22	36	44	22	22	24	22	22	23	36

Occupation	Y.M.C.A. Secretary	Soc. Sci. H.S. Teacher	City Sch. Sup't.	Social Worker	Minister	Musician Performer	C.P.A.	Senior C.P.A.	Accountant	Office Man	Purchasing Agent	Banker
Standard Score	20	25	32	30	59	50	32	34	21	17	11	15

Occupation	Mortician	Pharmacist	Sales Manager	Real Est. Manager	Life Ins. Salesman	Advertising Man	Lawyer	Author-Journalist	President Mfg. Co.	Interest Maturity	Occupational Level	Masculinity-Femininity
Standard Score	08	17	15	19	13	29	31	38	33	51	60	48

FIGURE-DRAWING CHARACTERISTICS

Structural	Male	Female	Structural	Male	Female	Structural and Graphic	Male	Female	Graphic, Global and Height	Male	Female	Body Proportions	Male	Female
	Both						Both							
Type	0		Omission of Appendages	0	0	Upper and Lower Halves	1	1	Hair Shading	3	3	Head	07	07
Sex Sequence	1		Position of Both Arms	1	1	Four Quarters	4	4	Nudity and Transparency	7	7	Neck	04	04
Posture	1	1	Position of Right Arm	2	3	Relative Size	2		Form	3	1	Shoulders	07	
Perspective	0	1	Position of Left Arm	0	5	Constant Line Pressure	0	0	Detailing	3	3	Right Arm	04	04
Vertical Midline	3	4	Position of Legs	6	1	Variable Line Pressure	3	1	Identity and Sex	1	1	Left Arm	04	04
Bilateral Symmetry	3	0	Relation of Long Axes	1	1	Line Continuity	0	0	Sophistication	3	3	Chest	07	
Horizontal Midline	6	4	Right and Left Halves	1	1	Body Shading	7	3	Height	06	06	Girth	09	

GENERAL CHARACTERISTICS OF SUBJECT

IDENTIFICATION

No. B38

Sex M

Marital status S

Age 21 yrs. at

psychological tests

PARENTAL HISTORY

Father

C   H   S   D   O

–   –   –   –   +

Mother

C   H   S   D   O

–   –   –   –   +

PHYSIOLOGICAL AND METABOLIC DATA

	Admission	Initial	Control	Cold pressor change	Exercise change	Smoking change
Systolic pressure		124	122	+20	+30	+02
Diastolic pressure		62	64	+36	-04	+02
Heart rate		88	71	+15	+26	-02

Age 21 yrs.	Height	72 in.	Ponderal index 12.83
	Weight	177 lbs.	Cholesterol 175 mg. per 100 ml.
	Overweight +09 %		Vital capacity 6.6 liters

HABIT SURVEY

Smoking habits: nonsmoker

Age begun   yrs.   Inhalation:

Habits of nervous tension: 4, 5, 6, 9, 10, 14,

16, 21, 23

STRONG VOCATIONAL INTEREST TEST

Occupation	Artist	Psychologist	Architect	Physician	Osteopath	Dentist	Veterinarian	Mathematician	Physicist	Engineer	Chemist	Production Manager
Standard Score	37	56	41	55	39	30	07	29	24	31	38	27

Occupation	Farmer	Aviator	Carpenter	Printer	Math.-Sci. Teacher	Ind. Arts Teacher	Voc. Agric. Teacher	Policeman	Forest Serv. Man	Y.M.C.A. Phys. Dir.	Personnel Director	Public Administrator
Standard Score	16	34	02	32	33	02	12	25	24	47	57	60

Occupation	Y.M.C.A. Secretary	Soc. Sci. H.S. Teacher	City Sch. Sup't.	Social Worker	Minister	Musician Performer	C.P.A.	Senior C.P.A.	Accountant	Office Man	Purchasing Agent	Banker
Standard Score	35	42	44	58	61	59	46	45	25	33	21	14

Occupation	Mortician	Pharmacist	Sales Manager	Real Est. Manager	Life Ins. Salesman	Advertising Man	Lawyer	Author-Journalist	President Mfg. Co.	Interest Maturity	Occupational Level	Masculinity-Femininity
Standard Score	23	31	41	34	39	46	49	40	32	61	61	35

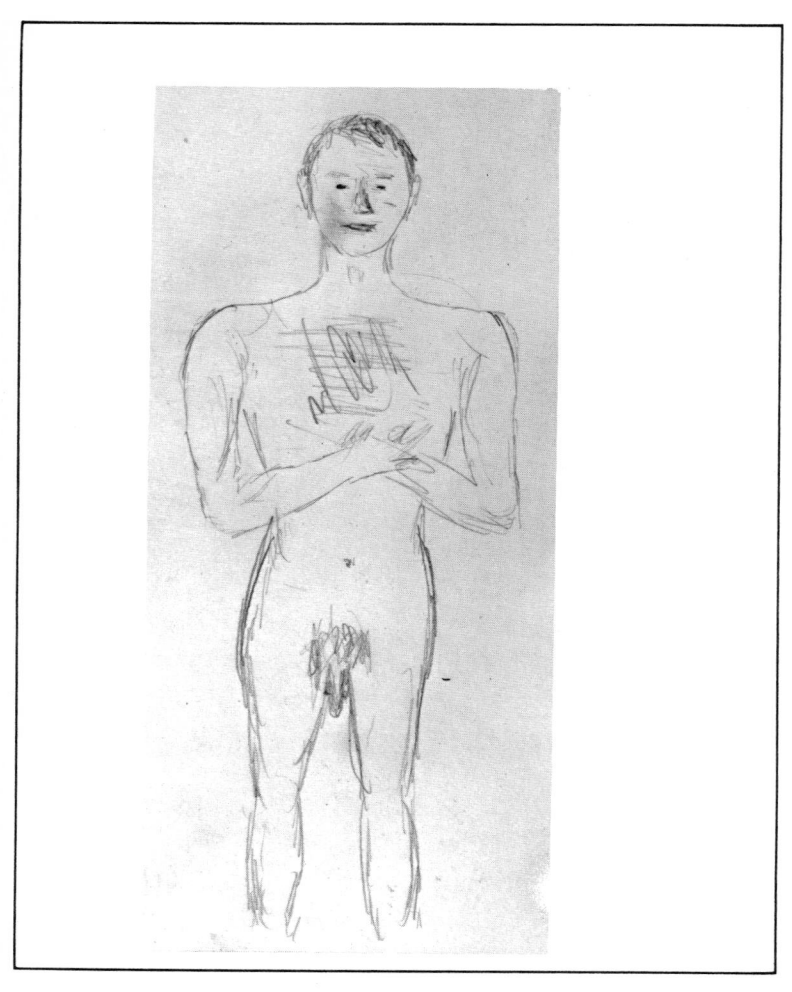

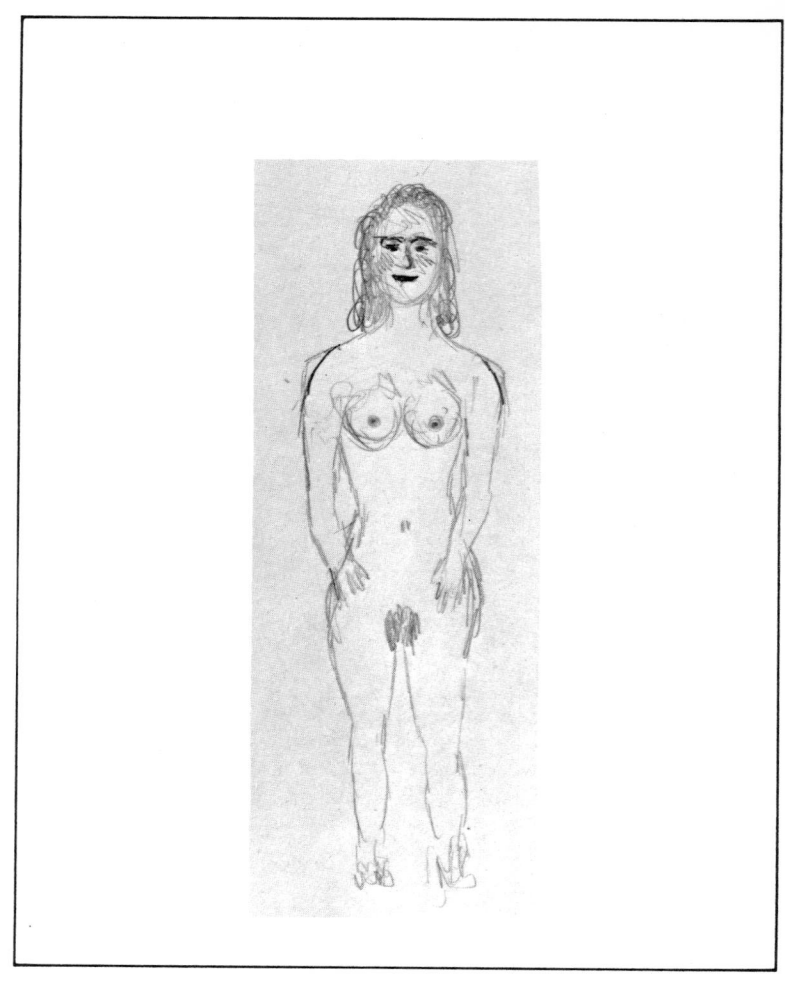

FIGURE-DRAWING CHARACTERISTICS

Structural	Male Female Both	Structural	Male	Female	Structural and Graphic	Male Female Both	Graphic, Global and Height	Male	Female	Body Proportions	Male	Female
Type	0	Omission of Appendages	4	0	Upper and Lower Halves	7	3	Hair Shading	3	3	Head	11	09
Sex Sequence	0	Position of Both Arms	0	0	Four Quarters	4	4	Nudity and Transparency	0	0	Neck	10	08
Posture	0	1	Position of Right Arm	5	5	Relative Size	0	Form	1	1	Shoulders	13	07
Perspective	0	0	Position of Left Arm	5	5	Constant Line Pressure	0	0	Detailing	3	3	Right Arm	10	06
Vertical Midline	0	0	Position of Legs	5	4	Variable Line Pressure	1	3	Identity and Sex	1	1	Left Arm	08	06
Bilateral Symmetry	3	4	Relation of Long Axes	1	1	Line Continuity	0	0	Sophistication	3	3	Chest	09	06
Horizontal Midline	0	0	Right and Left Halves	1	1	Body Shading	3	3	Height		07	Girth	09	06

GENERAL CHARACTERISTICS OF SUBJECT

IDENTIFICATION	PARENTAL HISTORY
No. B41	Father
Sex M	C H S D O
Marital status S	- - - - +
Age 20 yrs. at	Mother
psychological tests	C H S D O
	- - - - +

PHYSIOLOGICAL AND METABOLIC DATA

	Admission	Initial	Control	Cold pressor change	Exercise change	Smoking change
Systolic pressure	130	144	134	+12	+40	+12
Diastolic pressure	70	62	70	+16	00	00
Heart rate	78	80	75	+07	+25	+13

Age 19 yrs.   Height 68 in.   Weight 182 lbs.   Overweight +28 %

Ponderal index 11.99   Cholesterol 193 mg. per 100 ml.   Vital capacity 5.0 liters

HABIT SURVEY

Smoking habits: light cigarette smoker

Age begun 16 yrs.   Inhalation: no

Habits of nervous tension: 5, 6, 10, 16, 19, 24, 25

STRONG VOCATIONAL INTEREST TEST

Occupation	Artist	Psychologist	Architect	Physician	Osteopath	Dentist	Veterinarian	Mathematician	Physicist	Engineer	Chemist	Production Manager
Standard Score	33	62	35	59	49	30	12	28	25	31	40	28

Occupation	Farmer	Aviator	Carpenter	Printer	Math.-Sci. Teacher	Ind. Arts Teacher	Voc. Agric. Teacher	Policeman	Forest Serv. Man	Y.M.C.A. Phys. Dir.	Personnel Director	Public Administrator
Standard Score	16	25	00	32	40	08	16	23	20	42	50	57

Occupation	Y.M.C.A. Secretary	Soc. Sci. H.S. Teacher	City Sch. Sup't.	Social Worker	Minister	Musician Performer	C.P.A.	Senior C.P.A.	Accountant	Office Man	Purchasing Agent	Banker
Standard Score	37	45	49	60	61	50	42	40	21	24	13	11

Occupation	Mortician	Pharmacist	Sales Manager	Real Est. Manager	Life Ins. Salesman	Advertising Man	Lawyer	Author-Journalist	President Mfg. Co.	Interest Maturity	Occupational Level	Masculinity-Femininity
Standard Score	18	28	29	31	34	43	48	41	31	61	62	42

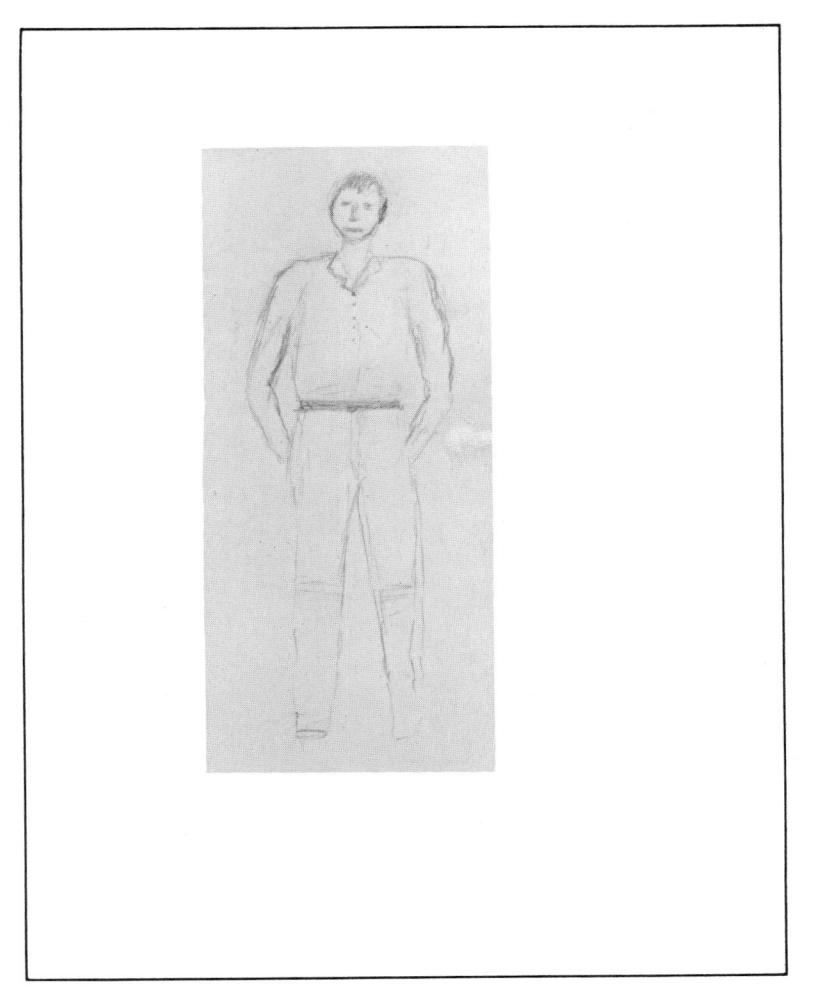

FIGURE-DRAWING CHARACTERISTICS

Structural	Male Female Both	Structural	Male	Female	Structural and Graphic	Male Female Both		Graphic, Global and Height	Male	Female	Body Proportions	Male	Female
Type	0	Omission of Appendages	7	7	Upper and Lower Halves	1	0	Hair Shading	3	3	Head	05	05
Sex Sequence	0	Position of Both Arms	0	0	Four Quarters	4	4	Nudity and Transparency	6	7	Neck	04	05
Posture	1 1	Position of Right Arm	5	5	Relative Size	0		Form	1	1	Shoulders	06	05
Perspective	0 0	Position of Left Arm	5	5	Constant Line Pressure	1	1	Detailing	3	3	Right Arm		04
Vertical Midline	3 0	Position of Legs	6	1	Variable Line Pressure	0	0	Identity and Sex	1	1	Left Arm		04
Bilateral Symmetry	3 3	Relation of Long Axes	1	1	Line Continuity	0	0	Sophistication	3	3	Chest	05	04
Horizontal Midline	4 4	Right and Left Halves	1	1	Body Shading	6	7	Height	06	05	Girth	06	03

GENERAL CHARACTERISTICS OF SUBJECT

IDENTIFICATION
No. B71
Sex F
Marital status S
Age 22 yrs. at
psychological tests

PARENTAL HISTORY
Father
C H S D O
- - - - +
Mother
C H S D O
- - - - ?

PHYSIOLOGICAL AND METABOLIC DATA

	Admission	Initial	Control	Cold pressor change	Exercise change	Smoking change
Systolic pressure	110	108	100	+22	+38	00
Diastolic pressure	64	58	60	+18	-08	-02
Heart rate	80	96	75	+24	+34	+04

Age 22 yrs.
Height 66 in.
Weight 146 lbs.
Overweight +10 %
Ponderal index 12.52
Cholesterol 278 mg. per 100 ml.
Vital capacity 3.6 liters

HABIT SURVEY

Smoking habits: nonsmoker

Age begun yrs. Inhalation:

Habits of nervous tension: 25

STRONG VOCATIONAL INTEREST TEST

Occupation	Artist	Psychologist	Architect	Physician	Osteopath	Dentist	Veterinarian	Mathematician	Physicist	Engineer	Chemist	Production Manager
Standard Score	37	40	42	54	51	46	23	26	25	38	41	27

Occupation	Farmer	Aviator	Carpenter	Printer	Math.-Sci. Teacher	Ind. Arts Teacher	Voc. Agric. Teacher	Policeman	Forest Serv. Man	Y.M.C.A. Phys. Dir.	Personnel Director	Public Administrator
Standard Score	41	48	15	37	39	16	28	32	38	42	44	45

Occupation	Y.M.C.A. Secretary	Soc. Sci. H.S. Teacher	City Sch. Sup't.	Social Worker	Minister	Musician Performer	C.P.A.	Senior C.P.A.	Accountant	Office Man	Purchasing Agent	Banker
Standard Score	32	33	28	37	61	48	18	39	18	29	13	14

Occupation	Mortician	Pharmacist	Sales Manager	Real Est. Manager	Life Ins. Salesman	Advertising Man	Lawyer	Author- Journalist	President Mfg. Co.	Interest Maturity	Occupational Level	Masculinity- Femininity
Standard Score	25	19	24	31	30	33	38	35	25	56	55	40

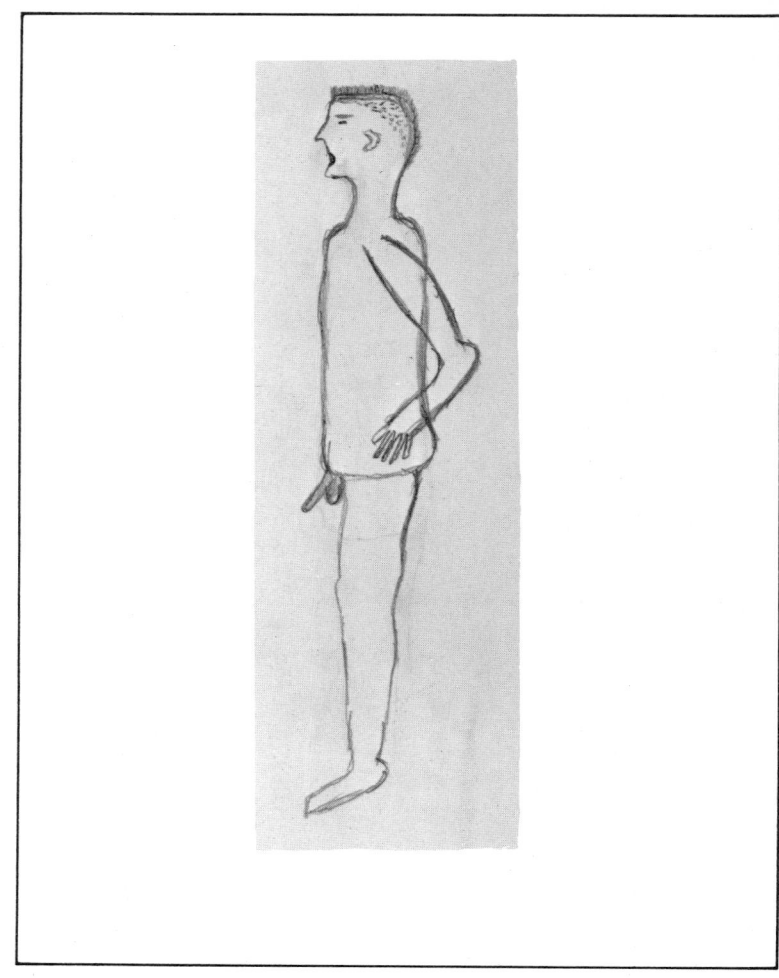

FIGURE-DRAWING CHARACTERISTICS

Structural	Male Female Both		Structural	Male	Female	Structural and Graphic	Male Female Both		Graphic, Global and Height	Male	Female	Body Proportions	Male	Female
Type	0		Omission of Appendages	0	0	Upper and Lower Halves	1	1	Hair Shading	3	1	Head	07	09
Sex Sequence	1		Position of Both Arms	4	4	Four Quarters	4	4	Nudity and Transparency	4	9	Neck	14	08
Posture	1	1	Position of Right Arm	7	7	Relative Size	1		Form	3	3	Shoulders		
Perspective	2	2	Position of Left Arm	5	5	Constant Line Pressure	0	0	Detailing	3	3	Right Arm		
Vertical Midline	4	4	Position of Legs	1	1	Variable Line Pressure	4	3	Identity and Sex	1	1	Left Arm	06	06
Bilateral Symmetry	0	0	Relation of Long Axes	1	1	Line Continuity	0	0	Sophistication	3	3	Chest	06	07
Horizontal Midline	6	6	Right and Left Halves	1	1	Body Shading	2	0	Height	07	07	Girth	07	07

GENERAL CHARACTERISTICS OF SUBJECT

IDENTIFICATION
No. C16
Sex M
Marital status S
Age 22 yrs. at
psychological tests

PARENTAL HISTORY
Father
C   H   S   D   O
-   -   -   -   +
Mother
C   H   S   D   O
-   -   -   -   ?

PHYSIOLOGICAL AND METABOLIC DATA

	Admission	Initial	Control	Cold pressor change	Exercise change	Smoking change
Systolic pressure	110	100	102	+18	+58	
Diastolic pressure	50	70	70	+05	-05	
Heart rate	90	84	77	+08	+38	

Age 23 yrs.	Height 66 in.	Ponderal index 12.62
	Weight 143 lbs.	Cholesterol 212 mg. per 100 ml.
	Overweight +02 %	Vital capacity 4.6 liters

HABIT SURVEY
Smoking habits: former smoker
Age begun 15 yrs.   Inhalation:
Habits of nervous tension: 3, 5, 6, 18, 19,
23, 24

FIGURE-DRAWING CHARACTERISTICS

Structural	Male	Female	Structural	Male	Female	Structural and Graphic	Male	Female	Graphic, Global and Height	Male	Female	Body Proportions	Male	Female
	Both						Both							
Type	0		Omission of Appendages	0	0	Upper and Lower Halves	0	1	Hair Shading	3	3	Head	06	09
Sex Sequence	0		Position of Both Arms	2	2	Four Quarters	4	4	Nudity and Transparency	7	7	Neck	04	08
Posture	2	2	Position of Right Arm	6	6	Relative Size	1		Form	5	5	Shoulders		
Perspective	2	2	Position of Left Arm	7	7	Constant Line Pressure	1	1	Detailing	3	3	Right Arm	04	03
Vertical Midline	4	4	Position of Legs	8	8	Variable Line Pressure	0	0	Identity and Sex	1	1	Left Arm		
Bilateral Symmetry	0	0	Relation of Long Axes	1	1	Line Continuity	0	0	Sophistication	3	3	Chest	06	05
Horizontal Midline	4	4	Right and Left Halves	1	1	Body Shading	7	7	Height	05	05	Girth	05	08

GENERAL CHARACTERISTICS OF SUBJECT

IDENTIFICATION

No. D13
Sex M
Marital status M
Age 22 yrs. at psychological tests

PARENTAL HISTORY

Father
C H S D O
– – – – +

Mother
C H S D O
– – – – ?

PHYSIOLOGICAL AND METABOLIC DATA

	Admission	Initial	Control	Cold pressor change	Exercise change	Smoking change
Systolic pressure	140	122	120	+08	+30	+02
Diastolic pressure	80	70	72	+02	-12	+04
Heart rate	84	84	75	+04	+40	+13

Age 22 yrs.
Height 70 in.
Weight 160 lbs.
Overweight +04 %

Ponderal index 12.89
Cholesterol 202 mg. per 100 ml.
Vital capacity 5.4 liters

HABIT SURVEY

Smoking habits: former smoker
Age begun 14 yrs.   Inhalation:
Habits of nervous tension: 4, 5, 17, 20

STRONG VOCATIONAL INTEREST TEST

Occupation	Artist	Psychologist	Architect	Physician	Osteopath	Dentist	Veterinarian	Mathematician	Physicist	Engineer	Chemist	Production Manager
Standard Score	22	26	24	34	43	36	18	19	22	41	45	49

Occupation	Farmer	Aviator	Carpenter	Printer	Math.-Sci. Teacher	Ind. Arts Teacher	Voc. Agric. Teacher	Policeman	Forest Serv. Man	Y.M.C.A. Phys. Dir.	Personnel Director	Public Administrator
Standard Score	33	44	29	39	40	22	11	34	27	25	38	40

Occupation	Y.M.C.A. Secretary	Soc. Sci. H.S. Teacher	City Sch. Sup't.	Social Worker	Minister	Musician Performer	C.P.A.	Senior C.P.A.	Accountant	Office Man	Purchasing Agent	Banker
Standard Score	24	33	15	28	63	28	32	40	36	39	41	22

Occupation	Mortician	Pharmacist	Sales Manager	Real Est. Manager	Life Ins. Salesman	Advertising Man	Lawyer	Author-Journalist	President Mfg. Co.	Interest Maturity	Occupational Level	Masculinity-Femininity
Standard Score	27	38	30	35	25	29	32	31	41	55	55	53

FIGURE-DRAWING CHARACTERISTICS

Structural	Male Female Both		Structural	Male	Female	Structural and Graphic	Male Female Both		Graphic, Global and Height	Male	Female	Body Proportions	Male	Female
Type	0		Omission of Appendages	0	0	Upper and Lower Halves	0	3	Hair Shading	1	3	Head	08	10
Sex Sequence	2		Position of Both Arms	1	0	Four Quarters	4	4	Nudity and Transparency	7	7	Neck	07	06
Posture	1	1	Position of Right Arm	4	0	Relative Size	4		Form	3	5	Shoulders	08	07
Perspective	0	0	Position of Left Arm	0	0	Constant Line Pressure	0	0	Detailing	1	3	Right Arm	06	06
Vertical Midline	3	0	Position of Legs	5	5	Variable Line Pressure	4	5	Identity and Sex	1	3	Left Arm	06	06
Bilateral Symmetry	2	3	Relation of Long Axes	1	1	Line Continuity	2	3	Sophistication	3	3	Chest	06	05
Horizontal Midline	6	4	Right and Left Halves	1	1	Body Shading	5	6	Height	06	08	Girth	08	06

GENERAL CHARACTERISTICS OF SUBJECT

IDENTIFICATION
No. E53
Sex M
Marital status M
Age 22 yrs. at psychological tests

PARENTAL HISTORY				
Father				
C	H	S	D	O
–	–	–	–	+
Mother				
C	H	S	D	O
–	–	–	–	?

PHYSIOLOGICAL AND METABOLIC DATA

	Admission	Initial	Control	Cold pressor change	Exercise change	Smoking change
Systolic pressure	90	135	105	+12	+35	–01
Diastolic pressure	60	80	70	+10	–10	+09
Heart rate	72	96	89	+04	+08	00

Age 22 yrs.	Height 73 in.	Ponderal index 12.61
	Weight 194 lbs.	Cholesterol 200 mg. per 100 ml.
	Overweight +15 %	Vital capacity 5.4 liters

HABIT SURVEY

Smoking habits: nonsmoker

Age begun   yrs.   Inhalation:

Habits of nervous tension: 5, 6, 8, 9, 10, 14, 19, 23

STRONG VOCATIONAL INTEREST TEST

Occupation	Artist	Psychologist	Architect	Physician	Osteopath	Dentist	Veterinarian	Mathematician	Physicist	Engineer	Chemist	Production Manager
Standard Score	37	50	41	57	40	30	11	37	27	28	41	22

Occupation	Farmer	Aviator	Carpenter	Printer	Math.-Sci. Teacher	Ind. Arts Teacher	Voc. Agric. Teacher	Policeman	Forest Serv. Man	Y.M.C.A. Phys. Dir.	Personnel Director	Public Administrator
Standard Score	26	40	03	36	37	11	14	24	20	38	45	45

Occupation	Y.M.C.A. Secretary	Soc. Sci. H.S. Teacher	City Sch. Sup't.	Social Worker	Minister	Musician Performer	C.P.A.	Senior C.P.A.	Accountant	Office Man	Purchasing Agent	Banker
Standard Score	27	38	36	46	64	54	31	40	19	32	14	13

Occupation	Mortician	Pharmacist	Sales Manager	Real Est. Manager	Life Ins. Salesman	Advertising Man	Lawyer	Author-Journalist	President Mfg. Co.	Interest Maturity	Occupational Level	Masculinity-Femininity
Standard Score	17	28	28	32	28	42	44	39	24	58	60	41

Plate 374　　DRAWINGS AT AN INTERMEDIATE LEVEL OF SOPHISTICATION　　417

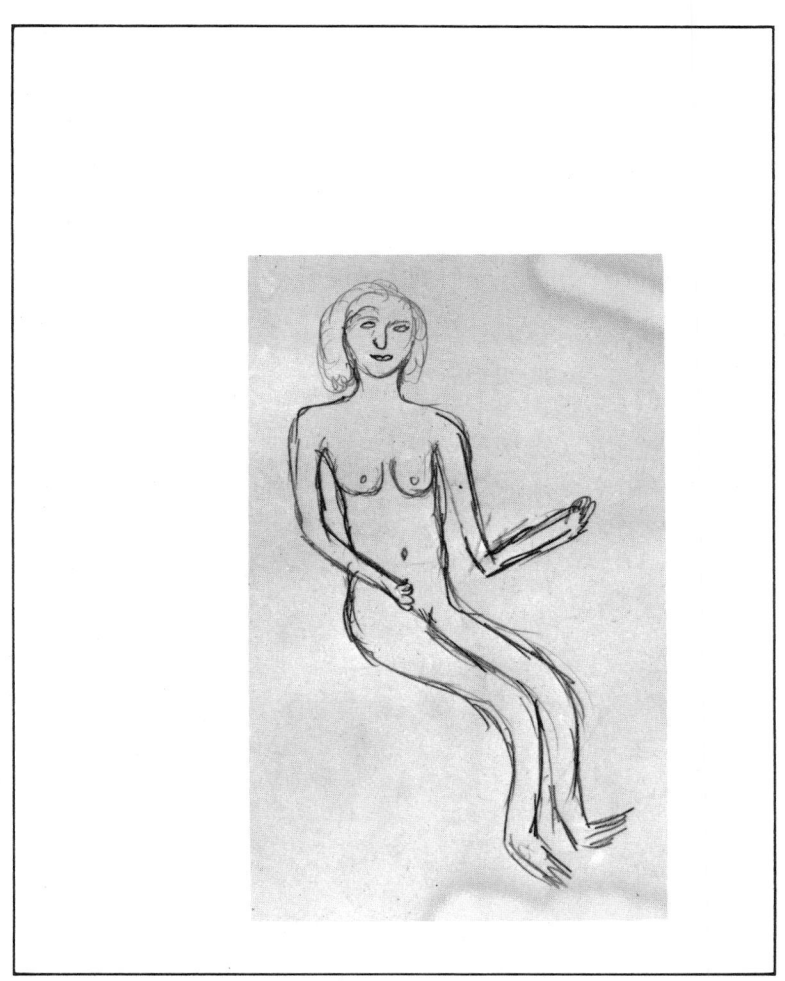

FIGURE-DRAWING CHARACTERISTICS

Structural	Male Female Both		Structural	Male	Female	Structural and Graphic	Male Female Both		Graphic, Global and Height	Male	Female	Body Proportions	Male	Female
Type	0		Omission of Appendages	0	0	Upper and Lower Halves	3	3	Hair Shading	3	3	Head	11	07
Sex Sequence	0		Position of Both Arms	2	1	Four Quarters	4	4	Nudity and Transparency	2	0	Neck	12	08
Posture	5	3	Position of Right Arm	4	5	Relative Size	5		Form	3	3	Shoulders		06
Perspective	2	9	Position of Left Arm	7	4	Constant Line Pressure	0	5	Detailing	3	3	Right Arm	06	06
Vertical Midline	4	0	Position of Legs	8	2	Variable Line Pressure	5	0	Identity and Sex	1	1	Left Arm		06
Bilateral Symmetry	0	3	Relation of Long Axes	1	0	Line Continuity	0	0	Sophistication	3	3	Chest	07	05
Horizontal Midline	4	0	Right and Left Halves	1	3	Body Shading	0	1	Height			Girth	07	06

GENERAL CHARACTERISTICS OF SUBJECT

IDENTIFICATION
No. 332
Sex M
Marital status   M
Age 26 yrs. at
psychological tests

PARENTAL HISTORY				
Father				
C	H	S	D	O
-	-	-	-	?
Mother				
C	H	S	D	O
-	-	-	-	+

PHYSIOLOGICAL AND METABOLIC DATA

	Admission	Initial	Control	Cold pressor change	Exercise change	Smoking change
Systolic pressure	124	132	120	+02	+44	-10
Diastolic pressure	68	64	66	+06	-02	+12
Heart rate	80	72	67	00	+10	-02

Age 23 yrs.	Height 73 in.	Ponderal index 12.77
	Weight 187 lbs.	Cholesterol 197 mg. per 100 ml.
	Overweight +11 %	Vital capacity 6.7 liters

HABIT SURVEY

Smoking habits: pipe smoker

　Age begun 22 yrs.　　Inhalation: no

Habits of nervous tension: 2, 5, 6, 9, 10,
12, 14, 16, 25

FIGURE-DRAWING CHARACTERISTICS

Structural	Male Female Both		Structural	Male	Female	Structural and Graphic	Male	Female Both	Graphic, Global and Height	Male	Female	Body Proportions	Male	Female
Type	0		Omission of Appendages	0	0	Upper and Lower Halves	3	1	Hair Shading	1	1	Head	08	07
Sex Sequence	2		Position of Both Arms	2	2	Four Quarters	4	4	Nudity and Transparency	7	7	Neck	06	06
Posture	2	1	Position of Right Arm	4	0	Relative Size	0		Form	3	3	Shoulders		
Perspective	2	2	Position of Left Arm	7	7	Constant Line Pressure	1	0	Detailing	3	3	Right Arm	06	04
Vertical Midline	4	4	Position of Legs	8	4	Variable Line Pressure	0	3	Identity and Sex	1	1	Left Arm		
Bilateral Symmetry	0	0	Relation of Long Axes	1	1	Line Continuity	4	0	Sophistication	3	3	Chest	09	07
Horizontal Midline	4	4	Right and Left Halves	2	1	Body Shading	0	4	Height	07	06	Girth	09	07

GENERAL CHARACTERISTICS OF SUBJECT

IDENTIFICATION
No. 429
Sex M
Marital status S
Age 23 yrs. at
psychological tests

PARENTAL HISTORY				
Father				
C	H	S	D	O
–	–	–	–	?
Mother				
C	H	S	D	O
–	–	–	–	+

PHYSIOLOGICAL AND METABOLIC DATA

	Admission	Initial	Control	Cold pressor change	Exercise change	Smoking change
Systolic pressure	125	110	84	+08	+26	
Diastolic pressure	80	60	62	+10	–07	
Heart rate	70	40	39	+08	+20	

Age 20 yrs.	Height	68	in.	Ponderal index 13.16
	Weight	138	lbs.	Cholesterol 237 mg. per 100 ml.
	Overweight –04 %			Vital capacity 5.4 liters

HABIT SURVEY

Smoking habits: former smoker

    Age begun 16 yrs.   Inhalation:

Habits of nervous tension: 3, 5, 6, 9, 10, 19

Plate 376   DRAWINGS AT AN INTERMEDIATE LEVEL OF SOPHISTICATION   419

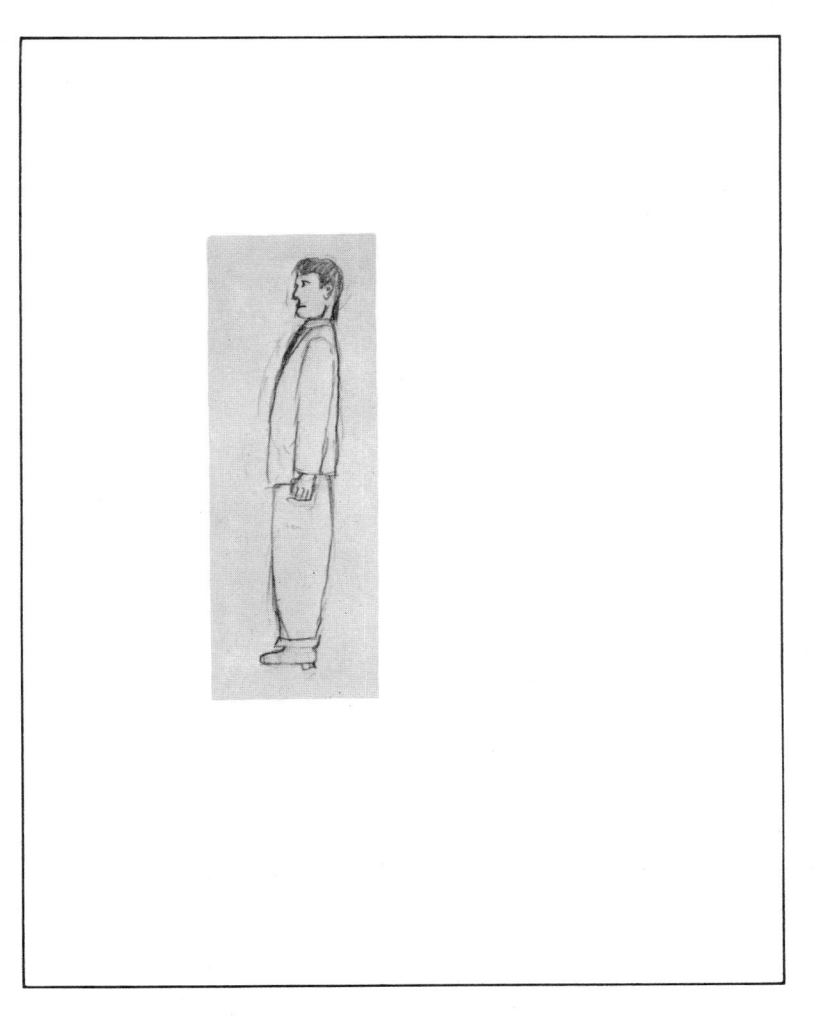

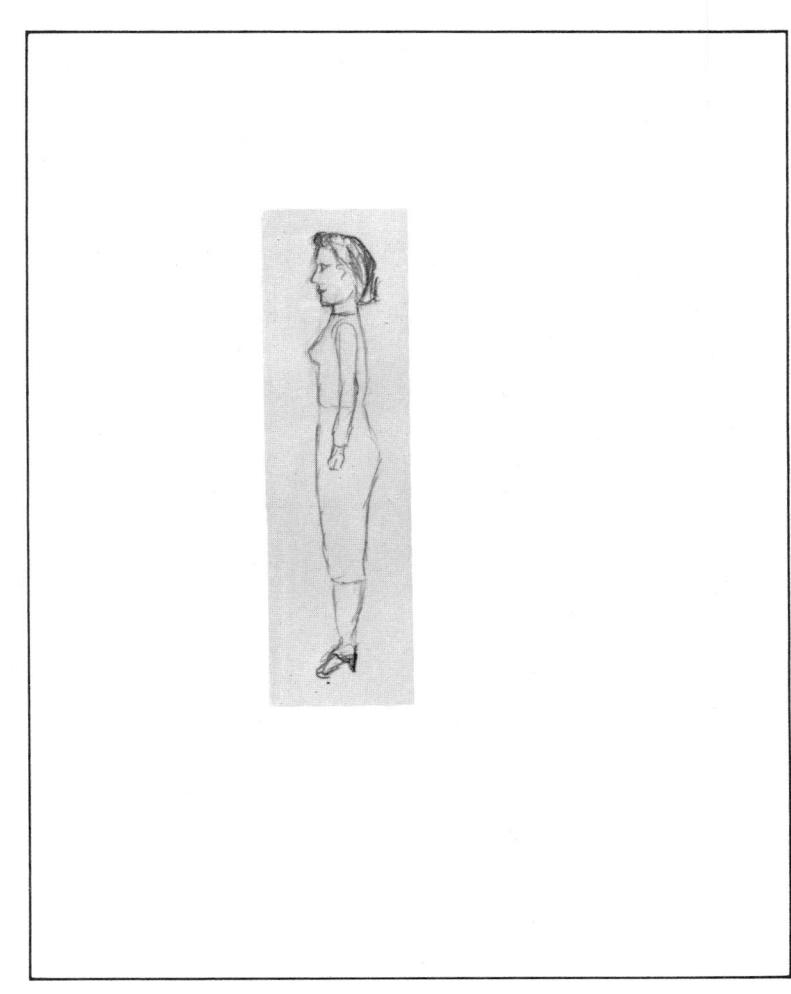

FIGURE-DRAWING CHARACTERISTICS

Structural	Male Female Both	Structural	Male	Female	Structural and Graphic	Male Female Both		Graphic, Global and Height	Male	Female	Body Proportions	Male	Female
Type	0	Omission of Appendages	0	0	Upper and Lower Halves	1	1	Hair Shading	1	2	Head	04	06
Sex Sequence	0	Position of Both Arms	4	4	Four Quarters	4	4	Nudity and Transparency	7	7	Neck	01	03
Posture	1	1	Position of Right Arm	7	7	Relative Size	4		Form	3	1	Shoulders		
Perspective	2	2	Position of Left Arm	0	0	Constant Line Pressure	0	0	Detailing	3	3	Right Arm		
Vertical Midline	7	4	Position of Legs	1	1	Variable Line Pressure	4	4	Identity and Sex	1	1	Left Arm	04	03
Bilateral Symmetry	0	0	Relation of Long Axes	1	1	Line Continuity	0	0	Sophistication	3	3	Chest	04	03
Horizontal Midline	6	4	Right and Left Halves	2	2	Body Shading	4	4	Height	04	04	Girth	05	04

GENERAL CHARACTERISTICS OF SUBJECT

IDENTIFICATION
No. G54
Sex M
Marital status S
Age 22 yrs. at
psychological tests

PARENTAL HISTORY				
Father				
C	H	S	D	O
-	-	-	-	?
Mother				
C	H	S	D	O
-	-	-	-	+

PHYSIOLOGICAL AND METABOLIC DATA

	Admission	Initial	Control	Cold pressor change	Exercise change	Smoking change
Systolic pressure	140	130	122	+22	+38	+05
Diastolic pressure	80	78	72	+10	+06	+14
Heart rate	80	80	81	+12	+24	+10

Age 22 yrs.	Height 67 in.	Ponderal index 12.62
	Weight 150 lbs.	Cholesterol 222 mg. per 100 ml.
	Overweight +06 %	Vital capacity liters

HABIT SURVEY

Smoking habits: occasional smoker

Age begun 16 yrs.   Inhalation: yes

Habits of nervous tension: 2, 4, 5, 6, 9, 11, 14, 16, 17, 18

STRONG VOCATIONAL INTEREST TEST

Occupation	Artist	Psychologist	Architect	Physician	Osteopath	Dentist	Veterinarian	Mathematician	Physicist	Engineer	Chemist	Production Manager
Standard Score	38	27	34	43	41	38	13	26	27	41	35	28

Occupation	Farmer	Aviator	Carpenter	Printer	Math.-Sci. Teacher	Ind. Arts Teacher	Voc. Agric. Teacher	Policeman	Forest Serv. Man	Y.M.C.A. Phys. Dir.	Personnel Director	Public Administrator
Standard Score	30	46	14	32	21	04	01	24	17	23	26	25

Occupation	Y.M.C.A. Secretary	Soc. Sci. H.S. Teacher	City Sch. Sup't.	Social Worker	Minister	Musician Performer	C.P.A.	Senior C.P.A.	Accountant	Office Man	Purchasing Agent	Banker
Standard Score	05	10	04	20	59	36	40	28	25	29	28	18

Occupation	Mortician	Pharmacist	Sales Manager	Real Est. Manager	Life Ins. Salesman	Advertising Man	Lawyer	Author-Journalist	President Mfg. Co.	Interest Maturity	Occupational Level	Masculinity-Femininity
Standard Score	22	35	34	45	35	43	40	44	40	43	61	47

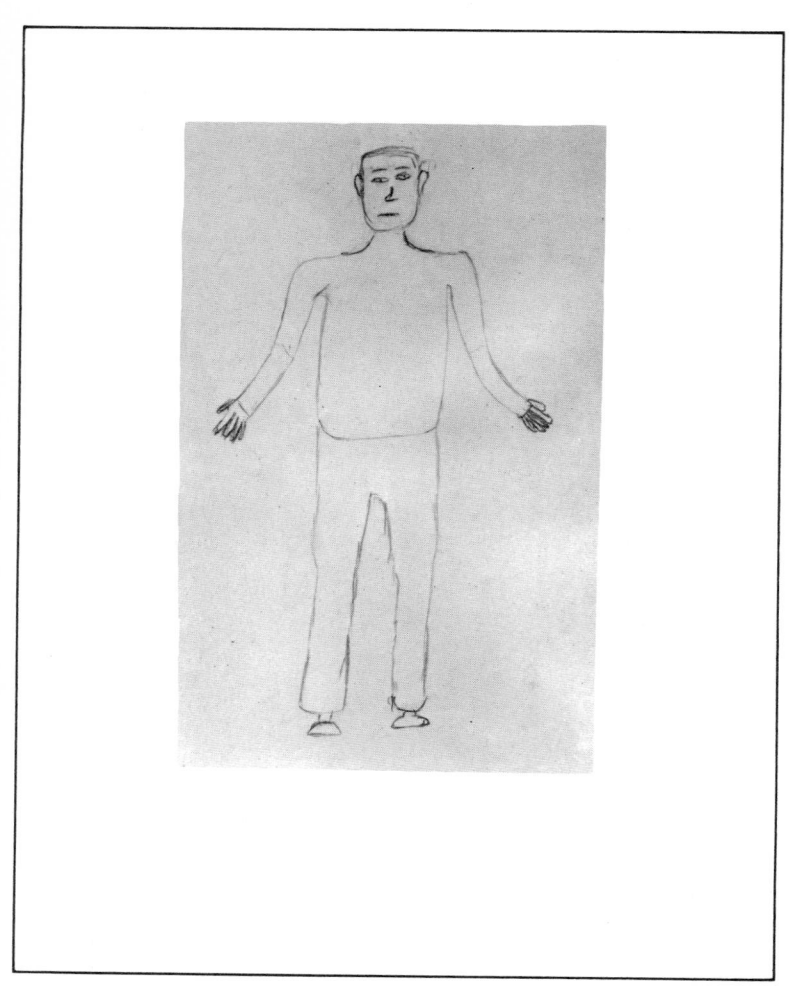

FIGURE-DRAWING CHARACTERISTICS

Structural	Male Female Both		Structural	Male	Female	Structural and Graphic	Male Female Both		Graphic, Global and Height	Male	Female	Body Proportions	Male	Female
Type	0		Omission of Appendages	0	0	Upper and Lower Halves	1	1	Hair Shading	3	3	Head	06	06
Sex Sequence	0		Position of Both Arms	0	0	Four Quarters	4	4	Nudity and Transparency	7	3	Neck	06	08
Posture	1	1	Position of Right Arm	3	5	Relative Size	0		Form	3	3	Shoulders	07	05
Perspective	0	0	Position of Left Arm	3	5	Constant Line Pressure	0	0	Detailing	3	3	Right Arm	04	04
Vertical Midline	0	0	Position of Legs	5	4	Variable Line Pressure	2	2	Identity and Sex	1	1	Left Arm	04	04
Bilateral Symmetry	3	3	Relation of Long Axes	1	1	Line Continuity	0	0	Sophistication	3	3	Chest	06	04
Horizontal Midline	4	4	Right and Left Halves	0	1	Body Shading	0	0	Height	06	04	Girth	07	03

GENERAL CHARACTERISTICS OF SUBJECT

IDENTIFICATION

No. C80

Sex M

Marital status S

Age 22 yrs. at

psychological tests

PARENTAL HISTORY

Father

C   H   S   D   O

–   –   –   –   ?

Mother

C   H   S   D   O

–   –   –   –   +

PHYSIOLOGICAL AND METABOLIC DATA

	Admission	Initial	Control	Cold pressor change	Exercise change	Smoking change
Systolic pressure	126	114	112	+08	+50	+06
Diastolic pressure	80	64	70	+14	−26	+07
Heart rate	84	76	74	+06	+33	+08

Age 22 yrs.

Height 74 in.   Ponderal index 12.82

Weight 192 lbs.   Cholesterol 255 mg. per 100 ml.

Overweight +11 %   Vital capacity 4.9 liters

HABIT SURVEY

Smoking habits: nonsmoker

Age begun   yrs.   Inhalation:

Habits of nervous tension: 5, 23

STRONG VOCATIONAL INTEREST TEST

Occupation	Artist	Psychologist	Architect	Physician	Osteopath	Dentist	Veterinarian	Mathematician	Physicist	Engineer	Chemist	Production Manager
Standard Score	26	49	32	52	32	30	12	45	34	40	46	27

Occupation	Farmer	Aviator	Carpenter	Printer	Math.-Sci. Teacher	Ind. Arts Teacher	Voc. Agric. Teacher	Policeman	Forest Serv. Man	Y.M.C.A. Phys. Dir.	Personnel Director	Public Administrator
Standard Score	34	38	17	37	47	21	28	28	21	30	44	47

Occupation	Y.M.C.A. Secretary	Soc. Sci. H.S. Teacher	City Sch. Sup't.	Social Worker	Minister	Musician Performer	C.P.A.	Senior C.P.A.	Accountant	Office Man	Purchasing Agent	Banker
Standard Score	32	36	39	41	62	40	34	47	26	33	18	26

Occupation	Mortician	Pharmacist	Sales Manager	Real Est. Manager	Life Ins. Salesman	Advertising Man	Lawyer	Author-Journalist	President Mfg. Co.	Interest Maturity	Occupational Level	Masculinity-Femininity
Standard Score	06	18	23	24	16	29	38	35	18	56	55	52

FIGURE-DRAWING CHARACTERISTICS

Structural	Male Female Both		Structural	Male	Female	Structural and Graphic	Male Female Both		Graphic, Global and Height	Male	Female	Body Proportions	Male	Female
Type	0		Omission of Appendages	0	6	Upper and Lower Halves	0	3	Hair Shading	3	3	Head	09	06
Sex Sequence	0		Position of Both Arms	1	0	Four Quarters	4	4	Nudity and Transparency	7	7	Neck	14	02
Posture	1	1	Position of Right Arm	5	2	Relative Size	0		Form	1	1	Shoulders		
Perspective	1	1	Position of Left Arm	2	2	Constant Line Pressure	0	1	Detailing	3	3	Right Arm	08	
Vertical Midline	4	3	Position of Legs	4	1	Variable Line Pressure	2	0	Identity and Sex	1	1	Left Arm	07	
Bilateral Symmetry	0	0	Relation of Long Axes	1	1	Line Continuity	0	0	Sophistication	3	3	Chest		
Horizontal Midline	4	4	Right and Left Halves	1	1	Body Shading	3	7	Height	08	05	Girth		

GENERAL CHARACTERISTICS OF SUBJECT

IDENTIFICATION
No. C75
Sex M
Marital status S
Age 21 yrs. at
psychological tests

PARENTAL HISTORY
Father
C H S D O
- - - - +
Mother
C H S D O
- - - - -

PHYSIOLOGICAL AND METABOLIC DATA

	Admission	Initial	Control	Cold pressor change	Exercise change	Smoking change
Systolic pressure	130	110	108	00	+22	-04
Diastolic pressure	70	70	68	+15	-08	-04
Heart rate	76	76	75	+08	+22	+07

Age 21 yrs.	Height	72 in.	Ponderal index 13.56
	Weight	150 lbs.	Cholesterol 180 mg. per 100 ml.
	Overweight -07 %		Vital capacity 4.9 liters

HABIT SURVEY
Smoking habits: former smoker
Age begun yrs. Inhalation:
Habits of nervous tension: 5, 6, 9, 14, 21, 22

FIGURE-DRAWING CHARACTERISTICS

Structural	Male Female Both	Structural	Male	Female	Structural and Graphic	Male Female Both		Graphic, Global and Height	Male	Female	Body Proportions	Male	Female
Type	0	Omission of Appendages	0	0	Upper and Lower Halves	3	3	Hair Shading	7	5	Head		10
Sex Sequence	2	Position of Both Arms	1	0	Four Quarters	4	4	Nudity and Transparency	7	7	Neck		10
Posture	1 1	Position of Right Arm	2	5	Relative Size	4		Form	3	3	Shoulders	07	06
Perspective	0 0	Position of Left Arm	1	5	Constant Line Pressure	0	0	Detailing	3	3	Right Arm	05	06
Vertical Midline	3 3	Position of Legs	6	6	Variable Line Pressure	5	1	Identity and Sex	1	1	Left Arm	06	05
Bilateral Symmetry	2 2	Relation of Long Axes	1	1	Line Continuity	1	0	Sophistication	3	3	Chest	05	06
Horizontal Midline	4 4	Right and Left Halves	1	1	Body Shading	0	2	Height	06	07	Girth	07	11

GENERAL CHARACTERISTICS OF SUBJECT

IDENTIFICATION
No. 549
Sex F
Marital status S
Age 23 yrs. at
psychological tests

PARENTAL HISTORY
Father
C   H · S   D   O
–   –   –   –   +
Mother
C   H   S   D   O
–   –   –   –   –

PHYSIOLOGICAL AND METABOLIC DATA

	Admission	Initial	Control	Cold pressor change	Exercise change	Smoking change
Systolic pressure	120	90	90	+10	+30	–02
Diastolic pressure	70	60	70	+10	–20	00
Heart rate	76	76	73	+10	+42	+14

Age 21 yrs.
Height 68 in.
Weight 175 lbs.
Overweight +24 %
Ponderal index 12.16
Cholesterol 190 mg. per 100 ml.
Vital capacity 3.6 liters

HABIT SURVEY
Smoking habits: nonsmoker
Age begun   yrs.   Inhalation:
Habits of nervous tension: 5, 6, 9, 22

Plate 380   DRAWINGS AT AN INTERMEDIATE LEVEL OF SOPHISTICATION   423

FIGURE-DRAWING CHARACTERISTICS

Structural	Male	Female	Structural	Male	Female	Structural and Graphic	Male	Female	Graphic, Global and Height	Male	Female	Body Proportions	Male	Female
	Both						Both							
Type	0		Omission of Appendages	0	0	Upper and Lower Halves	1	0	Hair Shading	3	3	Head	05	07
Sex Sequence	0		Position of Both Arms	1	1	Four Quarters	4	4	Nudity and Transparency	7	7	Neck	06	07
Posture	2	1	Position of Right Arm	2	2	Relative Size	4		Form	3	3	Shoulders		05
Perspective	1	9	Position of Left Arm	0	5	Constant Line Pressure	1	0	Detailing	3	3	Right Arm	04	04
Vertical Midline	7	0	Position of Legs	8	8	Variable Line Pressure	0	1	Identity and Sex	1	1	Left Arm	04	04
Bilateral Symmetry	0	3	Relation of Long Axes	1	1	Line Continuity	0	0	Sophistication	3	3	Chest		05
Horizontal Midline	4	4	Right and Left Halves	2	2	Body Shading	0	3	Height	04	05	Girth		05

GENERAL CHARACTERISTICS OF SUBJECT

IDENTIFICATION
No.   F50
Sex M
Marital status   S
Age 23 yrs. at
psychological tests

PARENTAL HISTORY				
Father				
C	H	S	D	O
−	−	−	−	+
Mother				
C	H	S	D	O
−	−	−	−	−

PHYSIOLOGICAL AND METABOLIC DATA

	Admission	Initial	Control	Cold pressor change	Exercise change	Smoking change
Systolic pressure	150	130	132	+10	+28	00
Diastolic pressure	90	90	92	+12	+08	00
Heart rate	80	88	77	+12	+23	−01

Age 21 yrs.	Height 70 in.	Ponderal index 13.23
	Weight 148 lbs.	Cholesterol 234 mg. per 100 ml.
	Overweight −03 %	Vital capacity liters

HABIT SURVEY

Smoking habits: nonsmoker

Age begun   yrs.   Inhalation:

Habits of nervous tension: 2, 4, 5, 6, 9, 14, 16, 17

STRONG VOCATIONAL INTEREST TEST

Occupation	Artist	Psychologist	Architect	Physician	Osteopath	Dentist	Veterinarian	Mathematician	Physicist	Engineer	Chemist	Production Manager
Standard Score	36	50	40	53	56	45	12	33	38	42	52	32

Occupation	Farmer	Aviator	Carpenter	Printer	Math.-Sci. Teacher	Ind. Arts Teacher	Voc. Agric. Teacher	Policeman	Forest Serv. Man	Y.M.C.A. Phys. Dir.	Personnel Director	Public Administrator
Standard Score	33	39	21	42	48	24	25	29	27	45	43	42

Occupation	Y.M.C.A. Secretary	Soc. Sci. H.S. Teacher	City Sch. Sup't.	Social Worker	Minister	Musician Performer	C.P.A.	Senior C.P.A.	Accountant	Office Man	Purchasing Agent	Banker
Standard Score	35	34	36	39	58	54	34	33	25	26	21	09

Occupation	Mortician	Pharmacist	Sales Manager	Real Est. Manager	Life Ins. Salesman	Advertising Man	Lawyer	Author-Journalist	President Mfg. Co.	Interest Maturity	Occupational Level	Masculinity-Femininity
Standard Score	17	24	23	29	27	33	36	37	26	57	61	40

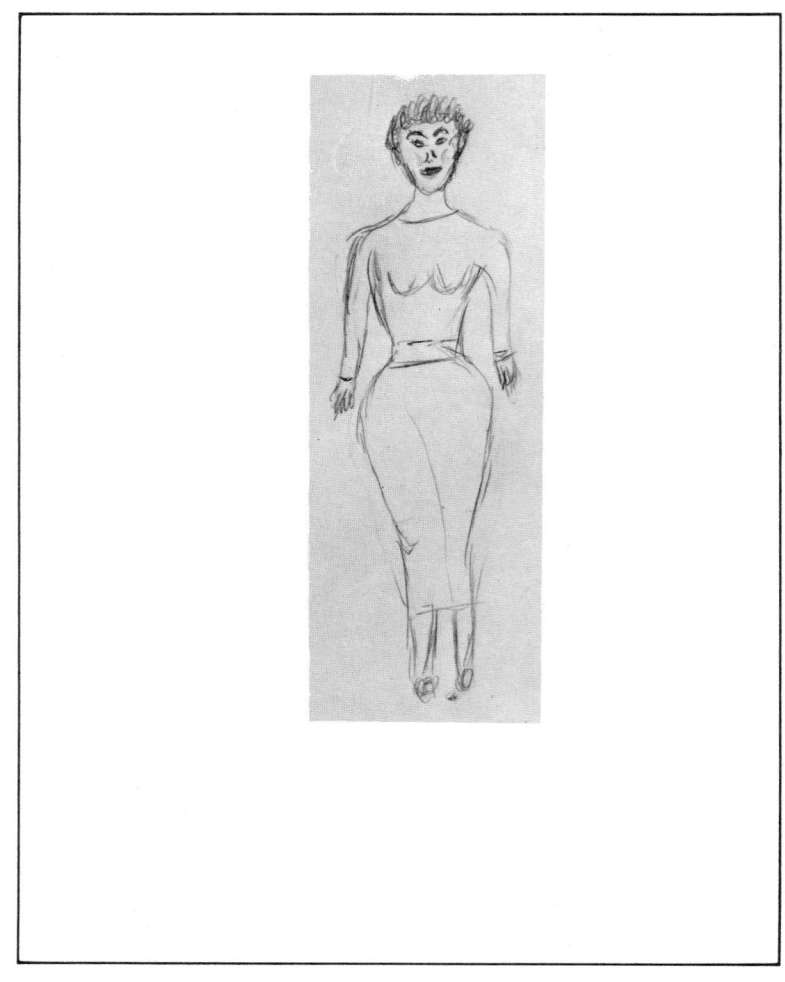

FIGURE-DRAWING CHARACTERISTICS

Structural	Male	Female	Structural	Male	Female	Structural and Graphic	Male	Female	Graphic, Global and Height	Male	Female	Body Proportions	Male	Female
	Both						Both							
Type	0		Omission of Appendages	0	0	Upper and Lower Halves	1	1	Hair Shading	3	3	Head	05	07
Sex Sequence	0		Position of Both Arms	1	0	Four Quarters	4	4	Nudity and Transparency	7	7	Neck	05	05
Posture	1	1	Position of Right Arm	5	0	Relative Size	4		Form	3	3	Shoulders		06
Perspective	6	0	Position of Left Arm	3	0	Constant Line Pressure	2	0	Detailing	3	3	Right Arm	04	04
Vertical Midline	7	0	Position of Legs	4	4	Variable Line Pressure	0	1	Identity and Sex	1	1	Left Arm	04	03
Bilateral Symmetry	0	3	Relation of Long Axes	1	1	Line Continuity	0	0	Sophistication	3	3	Chest		05
Horizontal Midline	4	4	Right and Left Halves	1	3	Body Shading	4	3	Height	04	06	Girth		05

GENERAL CHARACTERISTICS OF SUBJECT

IDENTIFICATION
No. A25
Sex M
Marital status S
Age 22 yrs. at
psychological tests

PARENTAL HISTORY				
Father				
C	H	S	D	O
–	–	–	–	+
Mother				
C	H	S	D	O
–	–	–	–	–

PHYSIOLOGICAL AND METABOLIC DATA

	Admission	Initial	Control	Cold pressor change	Exercise change	Smoking change
Systolic pressure	118	140	133	+39	+37	
Diastolic pressure	72	72	62	+35	-04	
Heart rate	71	82	69	+11	+22	

Age 22 yrs.	Height	72	in.	Ponderal index 13.00
	Weight	170	lbs.	Cholesterol 230 mg. per 100 ml.
	Overweight +04 %			Vital capacity liters

HABIT SURVEY

Smoking habits: nonsmoker

Age begun   yrs.   Inhalation:

Habits of nervous tension: 4, 5, 9, 16, 18

STRONG VOCATIONAL INTEREST TEST

Occupation	Artist	Psychologist	Architect	Physician	Osteopath	Dentist	Veterinarian	Mathematician	Physicist	Engineer	Chemist	Production Manager
Standard Score	25	19	28	43	35	40	27	23	24	44	37	41

Occupation	Farmer	Aviator	Carpenter	Printer	Math.-Sci. Teacher	Ind. Arts Teacher	Voc. Agric. Teacher	Policeman	Forest Serv. Man	Y.M.C.A. Phys. Dir.	Personnel Director	Public Administrator
Standard Score	37	43	22	25	29	13	26	30	32	19	28	37

Occupation	Y.M.C.A. Secretary	Soc. Sci. H.S. Teacher	City Sch. Sup't.	Social Worker	Minister	Musician Performer	C.P.A.	Senior C.P.A.	Accountant	Office Man	Purchasing Agent	Banker
Standard Score	15	16	15	15	60	26	32	34	31	25	38	30

Occupation	Mortician	Pharmacist	Sales Manager	Real Est. Manager	Life Ins. Salesman	Advertising Man	Lawyer	Author-Journalist	President Mfg. Co.	Interest Maturity	Occupational Level	Masculinity-Femininity
Standard Score	25	28	32	35	21	29	25	30	38	50	61	58

FIGURE-DRAWING CHARACTERISTICS

Structural	Male	Female	Structural	Male	Female	Structural and Graphic	Male	Female	Graphic, Global and Height	Male	Female	Body Proportions	Male	Female
		Both						Both						
Type		0	Omission of Appendages	0	0	Upper and Lower Halves	0	1	Hair Shading	3	3	Head	05	07
Sex Sequence		2	Position of Both Arms	0	0	Four Quarters	4	4	Nudity and Transparency	7	7	Neck	06	06
Posture	1	2	Position of Right Arm	0	2	Relative Size		0	Form	1	3	Shoulders	07	05
Perspective	0	0	Position of Left Arm	0	2	Constant Line Pressure	1	1	Detailing	3	3	Right Arm	06	04
Vertical Midline	3	0	Position of Legs	5	8	Variable Line Pressure	0	0	Identity and Sex	1	1	Left Arm	06	04
Bilateral Symmetry	4	3	Relation of Long Axes	1	1	Line Continuity	0	0	Sophistication	3	3	Chest	06	05
Horizontal Midline	6	4	Right and Left Halves	1	1	Body Shading	0	1	Height	06	06	Girth	08	04

GENERAL CHARACTERISTICS OF SUBJECT

IDENTIFICATION

No. B44

Sex M

Marital status S

Age 21 yrs. at psychological tests

PARENTAL HISTORY

Father

C	H	S	D	O
-	-	-	-	+

Mother

C	H	S	D	O
-	-	-	-	-

PHYSIOLOGICAL AND METABOLIC DATA

	Admission	Initial	Control	Cold pressor change	Exercise change	Smoking change
Systolic pressure	122	132	126	+08	+18	-02
Diastolic pressure	84	78	82	+04	-10	+08
Heart rate	88	86	81	-16	+28	+11

Age 20 yrs.

Height 77 in.
Weight 184 lbs.
Overweight -01 %

Ponderal index 13.53
Cholesterol 142 mg. per 100 ml.
Vital capacity 5.4 liters

HABIT SURVEY

Smoking habits: occasional smoker

Age begun 15 yrs.   Inhalation: yes

Habits of nervous tension: 4, 6, 11

STRONG VOCATIONAL INTEREST TEST

Occupation	Artist	Psychologist	Architect	Physician	Osteopath	Dentist	Veterinarian	Mathematician	Physicist	Engineer	Chemist	Production Manager
Standard Score	22	38	21	43	44	28	26	18	17	29	26	31

Occupation	Farmer	Aviator	Carpenter	Printer	Math.-Sci. Teacher	Ind. Arts Teacher	Voc. Agric. Teacher	Policeman	Forest Serv. Man	Y.M.C.A. Phys. Dir.	Personnel Director	Public Administrator
Standard Score	30	38	16	39	35	12	18	38	27	41	39	45

Occupation	Y.M.C.A. Secretary	Soc. Sci. H.S. Teacher	City Sch. Sup't.	Social Worker	Minister	Musician Performer	C.P.A.	Senior C.P.A.	Accountant	Office Man	Purchasing Agent	Banker
Standard Score	36	33	28	42	61	36	29	45	26	36	21	22

Occupation	Mortician	Pharmacist	Sales Manager	Real Est. Manager	Life Ins. Salesman	Advertising Man	Lawyer	Author-Journalist	President Mfg. Co.	Interest Maturity	Occupational Level	Masculinity-Femininity
Standard Score	27	32	37	39	37	36	36	32	33	57	53	53

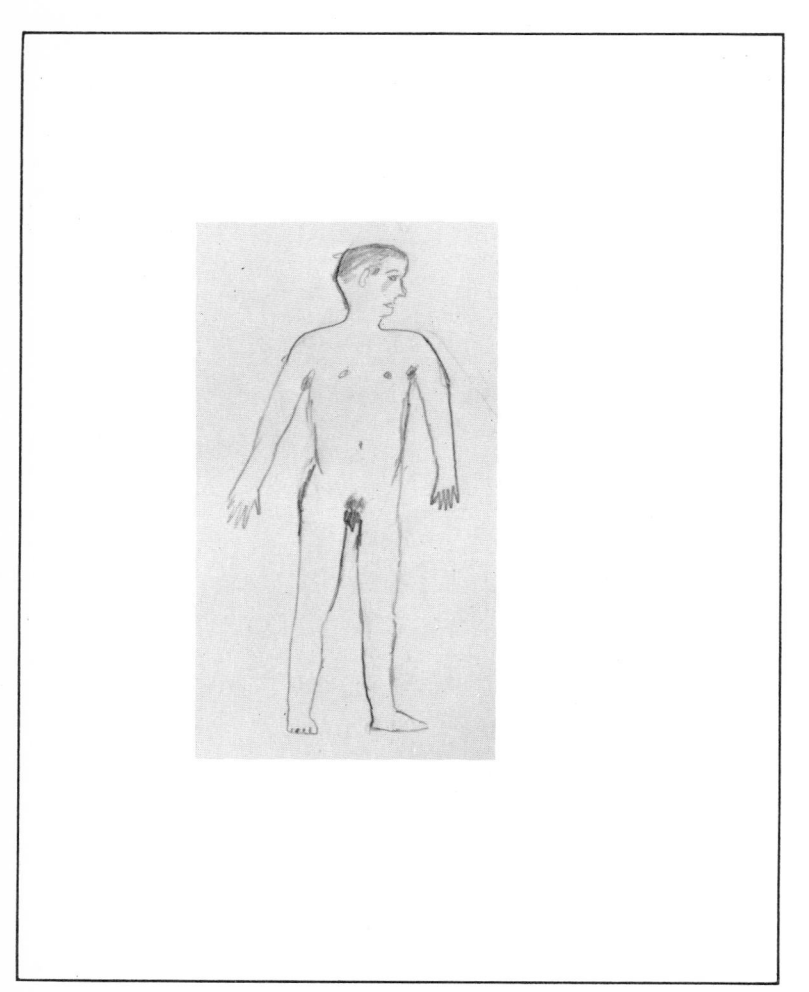

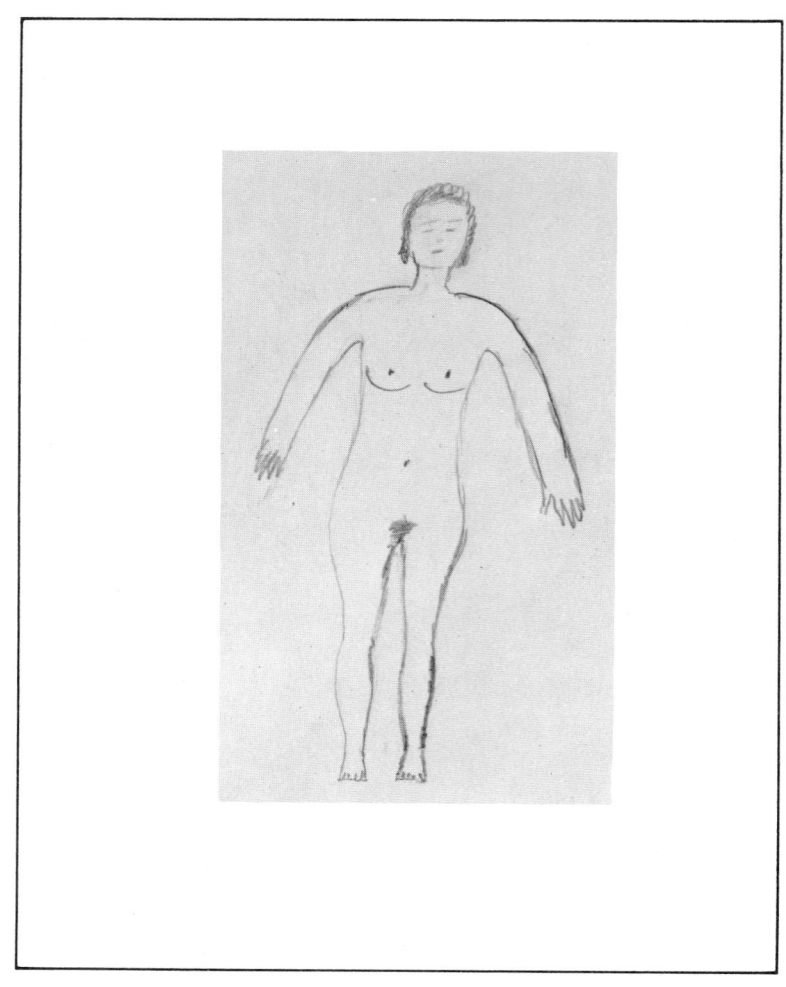

FIGURE-DRAWING CHARACTERISTICS

Structural	Male Female Both	Structural	Male	Female	Structural and Graphic	Male Female Both		Graphic, Global and Height	Male	Female	Body Proportions	Male	Female
Type	0	Omission of Appendages	0	0	Upper and Lower Halves	0	0	Hair Shading	3	3	Head	05	06
Sex Sequence	0	Position of Both Arms	1	0	Four Quarters	4	4	Nudity and Transparency	0	0	Neck	04	07
Posture	1	1	Position of Right Arm	2	2	Relative Size	4		Form	1	3	Shoulders	05	06
Perspective	5	0	Position of Left Arm	1	2	Constant Line Pressure	0	0	Detailing	3	3	Right Arm	04	04
Vertical Midline	0	0	Position of Legs	6	4	Variable Line Pressure	4	3	Identity and Sex	1	1	Left Arm	04	05
Bilateral Symmetry	3	3	Relation of Long Axes	1	1	Line Continuity	1	1	Sophistication	3	3	Chest	04	06
Horizontal Midline	0	0	Right and Left Halves	1	0	Body Shading	3	2	Height	05	06	Girth	05	07

GENERAL CHARACTERISTICS OF SUBJECT

IDENTIFICATION
No. B76
Sex M
Marital status M
Age 23 yrs. at
psychological tests

PARENTAL HISTORY
Father
C H S D O
- - - - +
Mother
C H S D O
- - - - -

PHYSIOLOGICAL AND METABOLIC DATA

	Admission	Initial	Control	Cold pressor change	Exercise change	Smoking change
Systolic pressure	120	132	126	+13	+28	+04
Diastolic pressure	90	60	63	+20	-13	+05
Heart rate		68	63	+10	+16	+11

Age 22 yrs.	Height 78 in.	Ponderal index 13.38
	Weight 198 lbs.	Cholesterol 217 mg. per 100 ml.
	Overweight +03 %	Vital capacity 6.6 liters

HABIT SURVEY
Smoking habits: heavy cigarette smoker
Age begun 17 yrs.   Inhalation: yes
Habits of nervous tension: 5, 8, 9, 22, 24

STRONG VOCATIONAL INTEREST TEST

Occupation	Artist	Psychologist	Architect	Physician	Osteopath	Dentist	Veterinarian	Mathematician	Physicist	Engineer	Chemist	Production Manager
Standard Score	33	39	29	47	39	33	33	22	14	20	27	22

Occupation	Farmer	Aviator	Carpenter	Printer	Math.-Sci. Teacher	Ind. Arts Teacher	Voc. Agric. Teacher	Policeman	Forest Serv. Man	Y.M.C.A. Phys. Dir.	Personnel Director	Public Administrator
Standard Score	37	37	16	38	38	15	37	32	35	44	39	46

Occupation	Y.M.C.A. Secretary	Soc. Sci. H.S. Teacher	City Sch. Sup't.	Social Worker	Minister	Musician Performer	C.P.A.	Senior C.P.A.	Accountant	Office Man	Purchasing Agent	Banker
Standard Score	37	50	43	46	61	51	16	34	13	28	12	23

Occupation	Mortician	Pharmacist	Sales Manager	Real Est. Manager	Life Ins. Salesman	Advertising Man	Lawyer	Author-Journalist	President Mfg. Co.	Interest Maturity	Occupational Level	Masculinity-Femininity
Standard Score	22	25	23	34	33	34	40	38	15	56	49	46

Plate 384   DRAWINGS AT AN INTERMEDIATE LEVEL OF SOPHISTICATION   427

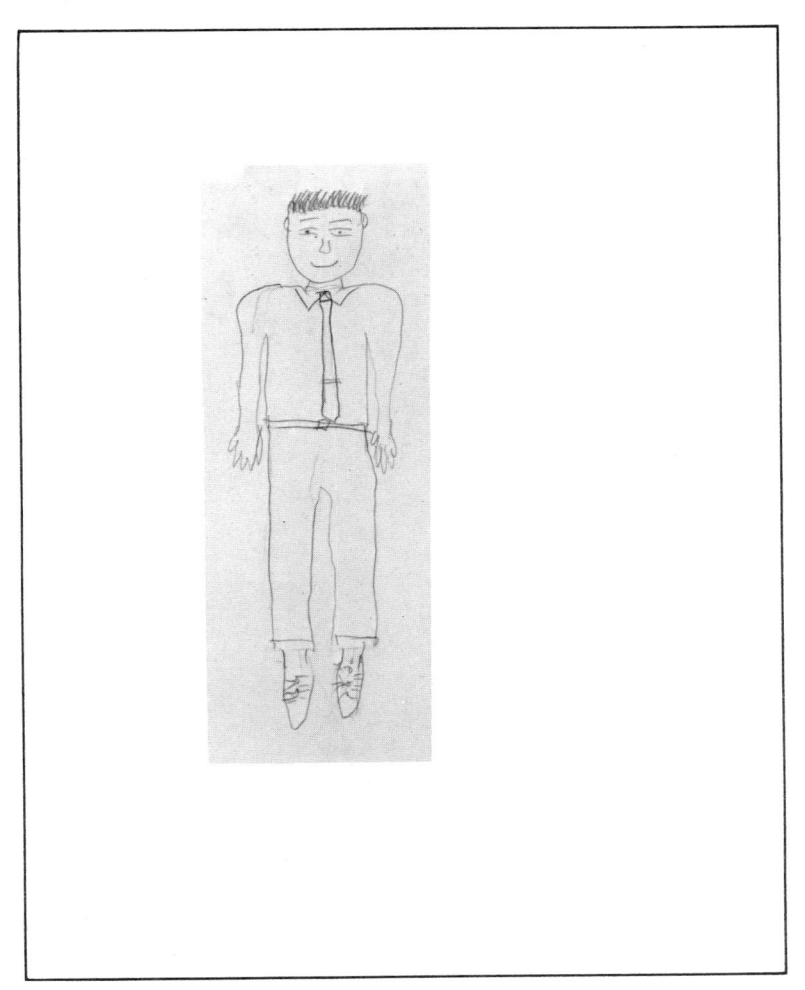

FIGURE-DRAWING CHARACTERISTICS

Structural	Male Female Both		Structural	Male	Female	Structural and Graphic	Male Female Both		Graphic, Global and Height	Male	Female	Body Proportions	Male	Female
Type	0		Omission of Appendages	0	0	Upper and Lower Halves	1	1	Hair Shading	3	5	Head	06	06
Sex Sequence	0		Position of Both Arms	0	0	Four Quarters	4	4	Nudity and Transparency	7	3	Neck	03	02
Posture	1	1	Position of Right Arm	0	0	Relative Size	0		Form	3	3	Shoulders	06	05
Perspective	0	0	Position of Left Arm	0	0	Constant Line Pressure	0	3	Detailing	3	3	Right Arm	04	02
Vertical Midline	3	0	Position of Legs	4	4	Variable Line Pressure	1	0	Identity and Sex	1	1	Left Arm	04	02
Bilateral Symmetry	2	2	Relation of Long Axes	1	1	Line Continuity	3	2	Sophistication	3	3	Chest	04	03
Horizontal Midline	4	4	Right and Left Halves	1	1	Body Shading	0	4	Height	05	04	Girth	06	03

GENERAL CHARACTERISTICS OF SUBJECT

IDENTIFICATION

No. C24

Sex M

Marital status S

Age 21 yrs. at

psychological tests

PARENTAL HISTORY

Father

C H S D O

- - - - +

Mother

C H S D O

- - - - -

PHYSIOLOGICAL AND METABOLIC DATA

	Admission	Initial	Control	Cold pressor change	Exercise change	Smoking change
Systolic pressure	110	118	118	+10	+22	+05
Diastolic pressure	70	70	70	+06	-20	+08
Heart rate	84	80	70	-04	+24	+06

Age 21 yrs.

Height	70 in.	Ponderal index 12.99
Weight	157 lbs.	Cholesterol 200 mg. per 100 ml.
Overweight +03 %		Vital capacity 4.7 liters

HABIT SURVEY

Smoking habits: moderate cigarette smoker

Age begun 16 yrs.   Inhalation: yes

Habits of nervous tension: 4, 5, 6, 11

STRONG VOCATIONAL INTEREST TEST

Occupation	Artist	Psychologist	Architect	Physician	Osteopath	Dentist	Veterinarian	Mathematician	Physicist	Engineer	Chemist	Production Manager
Standard Score	33	58	32	62	51	41	30	29	27	35	48	27

Occupation	Farmer	Aviator	Carpenter	Printer	Math.-Sci. Teacher	Ind. Arts Teacher	Voc. Agric. Teacher	Policeman	Forest Serv. Man	Y.M.C.A. Phys. Dir.	Personnel Director	Public Administrator
Standard Score	33	35	08	35	48	15	35	24	27	40	40	45

Occupation	Y.M.C.A. Secretary	Soc. Sci. H.S. Teacher	City Sch. Sup't.	Social Worker	Minister	Musician Performer	C.P.A.	Senior C.P.A.	Accountant	Office Man	Purchasing Agent	Banker
Standard Score	29	41	34	46	62	47	31	40	15	20	16	10

Occupation	Mortician	Pharmacist	Sales Manager	Real Est. Manager	Life Ins. Salesman	Advertising Man	Lawyer	Author- Journalist	President Mfg. Co.	Interest Maturity	Occupational Level	Masculinity- Femininity
Standard Score	16	31	29	28	30	37	39	38	29	56	59	48

FIGURE-DRAWING CHARACTERISTICS

Structural	Male Female Both	Structural	Male	Female	Structural and Graphic	Male Female Both		Graphic, Global and Height	Male	Female	Body Proportions	Male	Female
Type	0	Omission of Appendages	0	0	Upper and Lower Halves	1	1	Hair Shading	1	3	Head	08	06
Sex Sequence	0	Position of Both Arms	0	0	Four Quarters	4	4	Nudity and Transparency	7	7	Neck	02	04
Posture	1	1	Position of Right Arm	5	5	Relative Size	0		Form	3	3	Shoulders	06	04
Perspective	0	0	Position of Left Arm	5	5	Constant Line Pressure	0	0	Detailing	3	1	Right Arm	04	02
Vertical Midline	3	0	Position of Legs	4	4	Variable Line Pressure	1	3	Identity and Sex	1	1	Left Arm	04	02
Bilateral Symmetry	3	3	Relation of Long Axes	1	1	Line Continuity	2	0	Sophistication	3	3	Chest	05	04
Horizontal Midline	2	4	Right and Left Halves	1	1	Body Shading	2	7	Height	05	04	Girth	05	04

GENERAL CHARACTERISTICS OF SUBJECT

IDENTIFICATION
No. O28
Sex M
Marital status M
Age 26 yrs. at
psychological tests

PARENTAL HISTORY
Father
C H S D O
- - - - +
Mother
C H S D O
- - - - -

PHYSIOLOGICAL AND METABOLIC DATA

	Admission	Initial	Control	Cold pressor change	Exercise change	Smoking change
Systolic pressure	130	120	120	-02	+30	
Diastolic pressure	85	80	75	00	-20	
Heart rate	80	80	67	-12	+10	

Age 23 yrs.

Height 72 in.   Ponderal index 12.17
Weight 207 lbs.   Cholesterol 212 mg. per 100 ml.
Overweight +26 %   Vital capacity 5.8 liters

HABIT SURVEY
Smoking habits: nonsmoker
Age begun yrs. Inhalation:
Habits of nervous tension: 1, 4, 6, 9, 16

STRONG VOCATIONAL INTEREST TEST

Occupation	Artist	Psychologist	Architect	Physician	Osteopath	Dentist	Veterinarian	Mathematician	Physicist	Engineer	Chemist	Production Manager
Standard Score	27	40	36	57	49	40	31	29	28	44	47	42

Occupation	Farmer	Aviator	Carpenter	Printer	Math.-Sci. Teacher	Ind. Arts Teacher	Voc. Agric. Teacher	Policeman	Forest Serv. Man	Y.M.C.A. Phys. Dir.	Personnel Director	Public Administrator
Standard Score	41	49	36	39	50	38	45	38	44	41	40	46

Occupation	Y.M.C.A. Secretary	Soc. Sci. H.S. Teacher	City Sch. Sup't.	Social Worker	Minister	Musician Performer	C.P.A.	Senior C.P.A.	Accountant	Office Man	Purchasing Agent	Banker
Standard Score	27	29	27	37	62	44	22	50	29	29	22	16

Occupation	Mortician	Pharmacist	Sales Manager	Real Est. Manager	Life Ins. Salesman	Advertising Man	Lawyer	Author-Journalist	President Mfg. Co.	Interest Maturity	Occupational Level	Masculinity-Femininity
Standard Score	21	20	19	25	19	22	22	24	23	61	53	56

Plate 386   DRAWINGS AT AN INTERMEDIATE LEVEL OF SOPHISTICATION   429

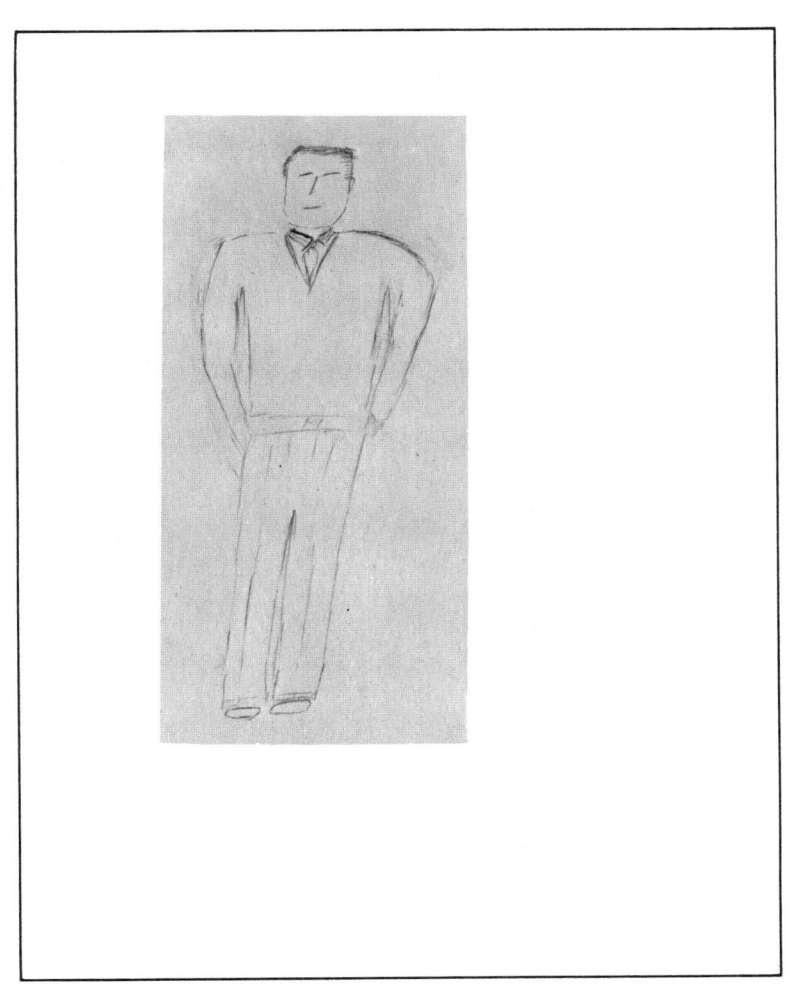

FIGURE-DRAWING CHARACTERISTICS

Structural	Male	Female	Structural	Male	Female	Structural and Graphic	Male	Female	Graphic, Global and Height	Male	Female	Body Proportions	Male	Female
	Both						Both							
Type	0		Omission of Appendages	7	7	Upper and Lower Halves	1	1	Hair Shading	3	3	Head	06	05
Sex Sequence	0		Position of Both Arms	0	0	Four Quarters	4	4	Nudity and Transparency	7	7	Neck	03	02
Posture	1	1	Position of Right Arm	5	5	Relative Size	0		Form	3	3	Shoulders	08	06
Perspective	0	0	Position of Left Arm	5	5	Constant Line Pressure	1	1	Detailing	3	3	Right Arm		
Vertical Midline	1	0	Position of Legs	3	3	Variable Line Pressure	0	0	Identity and Sex	1	1	Left Arm		03
Bilateral Symmetry	2	3	Relation of Long Axes	1	1	Line Continuity	0	0	Sophistication	3	3	Chest	06	05
Horizontal Midline	4	0	Right and Left Halves	1	2	Body Shading	6	3	Height	06	05	Girth	07	04

GENERAL CHARACTERISTICS OF SUBJECT

IDENTIFICATION
No. C58
Sex M
Marital status S
Age 23 yrs. at psychological tests

PARENTAL HISTORY					
Father					
C	H	S	D	O	
–	–	–	–	+	
Mother					
C	H	S	D	O	
–	–	–	–	–	

PHYSIOLOGICAL AND METABOLIC DATA

	Admission	Initial	Control	Cold pressor change	Exercise change	Smoking change
Systolic pressure	110	112	108	+18	+22	00
Diastolic pressure	70	60	58	+12	–08	00
Heart rate	56	72	63	–12	+14	–03

Age 23 yrs.	Height	74	in.	Ponderal index	13.10	
	Weight	180	lbs.	Cholesterol	200	mg. per 100 ml.
	Overweight +03 %			Vital capacity	5.9	liters

HABIT SURVEY
Smoking habits: former smoker
Age begun   yrs.   Inhalation: no
Habits of nervous tension: 4, 5

STRONG VOCATIONAL INTEREST TEST

Occupation	Artist	Psychologist	Architect	Physician	Osteopath	Dentist	Veterinarian	Mathematician	Physicist	Engineer	Chemist	Production Manager
Standard Score	21	36	19	37	47	23	32	12	04	11	13	25

Occupation	Farmer	Aviator	Carpenter	Printer	Math.-Sci. Teacher	Ind. Arts Teacher	Voc. Agric. Teacher	Policeman	Forest Serv. Man	Y.M.C.A. Phys. Dir.	Personnel Director	Public Administrator
Standard Score	30	29	11	27	31	11	32	36	22	46	53	51

Occupation	Y.M.C.A. Secretary	Soc. Sci. H.S. Teacher	City Sch. Sup't.	Social Worker	Minister	Musician Performer	C.P.A.	Senior C.P.A.	Accountant	Office Man	Purchasing Agent	Banker
Standard Score	42	50	40	50	62	37	28	38	27	42	21	30

Occupation	Mortician	Pharmacist	Sales Manager	Real Est. Manager	Life Ins. Salesman	Advertising Man	Lawyer	Author-Journalist	President Mfg. Co.	Interest Maturity	Occupational Level	Masculinity-Femininity
Standard Score	41	28	35	40	46	38	39	30	19	59	56	41

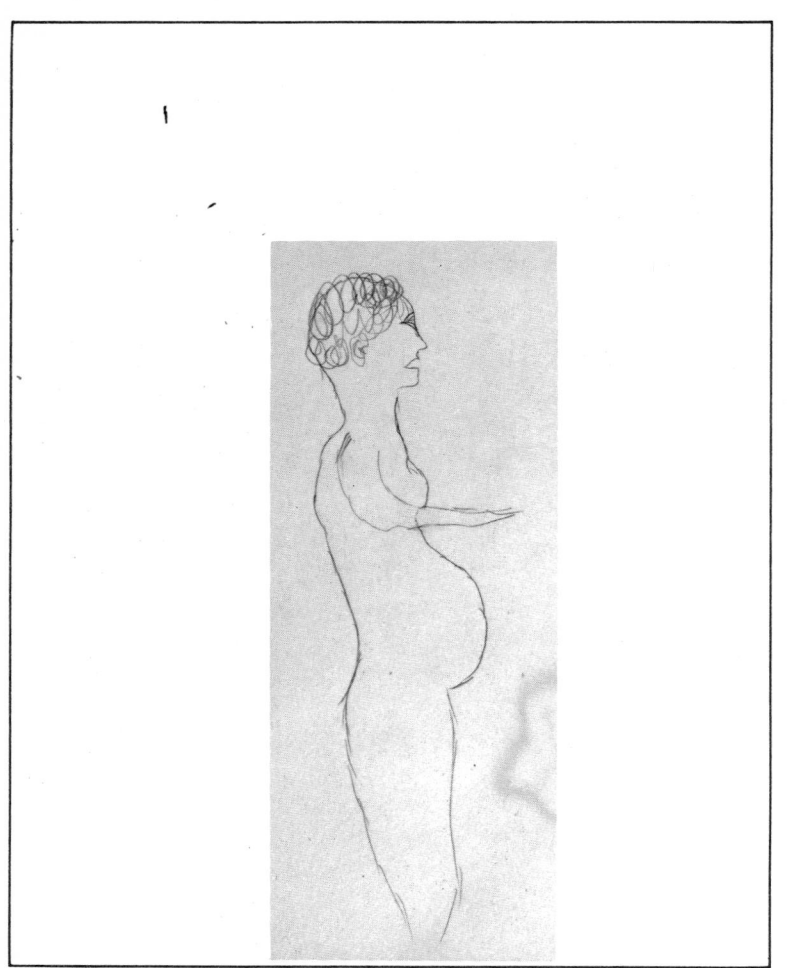

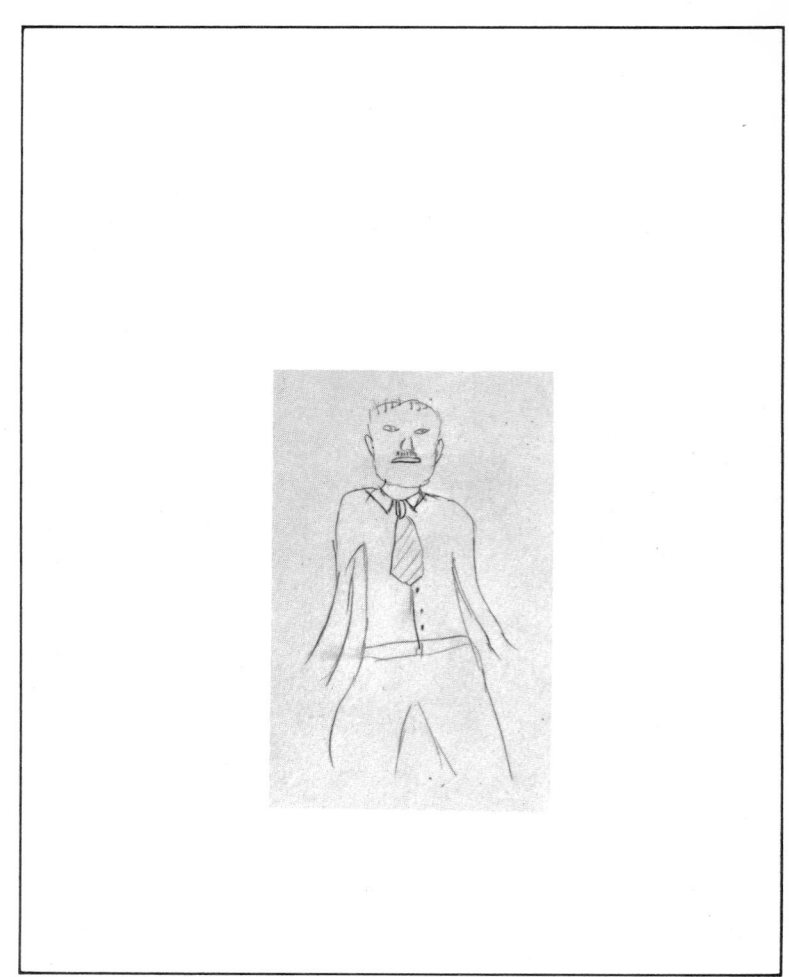

FIGURE-DRAWING CHARACTERISTICS

Structural	Male Female Both	Structural	Male	Female	Structural and Graphic	Male Female Both		Graphic, Global and Height	Male	Female	Body Proportions	Male	Female
Type	0	Omission of Appendages	4	4	Upper and Lower Halves	3	7	Hair Shading	7	3	Head	07	09
Sex Sequence	1	Position of Both Arms	0	2	Four Quarters	4	4	Nudity and Transparency	7	0	Neck	04	12
Posture	0 0	Position of Right Arm	8	4	Relative Size	4		Form	3	5	Shoulders	05	
Perspective	0 2	Position of Left Arm	8	7	Constant Line Pressure	1	0	Detailing	3	5	Right Arm		
Vertical Midline	3 4	Position of Legs	0	0	Variable Line Pressure	0	1	Identity and Sex	1	1	Left Arm		
Bilateral Symmetry	1 0	Relation of Long Axes	1	1	Line Continuity	0	0	Sophistication	3	3	Chest	04	07
Horizontal Midline	4 0	Right and Left Halves	0	0	Body Shading	0	0	Height			Girth	06	10

GENERAL CHARACTERISTICS OF SUBJECT

IDENTIFICATION
No. 320
Sex M
Marital status S
Age 25 yrs. at
psychological tests

PARENTAL HISTORY
Father
C   H   S   D   O
-   -   -   -   -
Mother
C   H   S   D   O
-   -   -   -   +

PHYSIOLOGICAL AND METABOLIC DATA

	Admission	Initial	Control	Cold pressor change	Exercise change	Smoking change
Systolic pressure	106	112	102	+04	+30	-02
Diastolic pressure	64	74	74	+02	00	00
Heart rate	64	72	61	00	+27	+01

Age 23 yrs.	Height 70 in.	Ponderal index 13.32
	Weight 145 lbs.	Cholesterol 195 mg. per 100 ml.
	Overweight -06 %	Vital capacity 4.5 liters

HABIT SURVEY
Smoking habits: mixed smoker
Age begun 18 yrs.   Inhalation: no
Habits of nervous tension: 4, 21, 25

Plate 388   DRAWINGS AT AN INTERMEDIATE LEVEL OF SOPHISTICATION   431

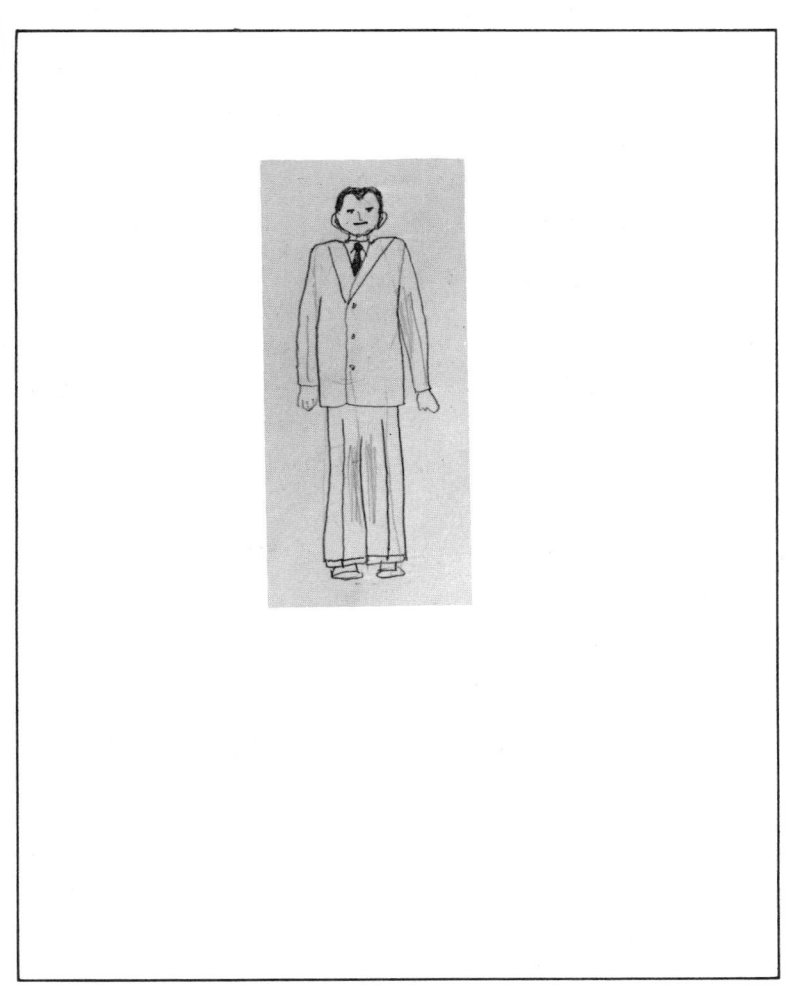

FIGURE-DRAWING CHARACTERISTICS

Structural	Male	Female	Structural	Male	Female	Structural and Graphic	Male	Female	Graphic, Global and Height	Male	Female	Body Proportions	Male	Female
	Both						Both							
Type	0		Omission of Appendages	0	0	Upper and Lower Halves	1	1	Hair Shading	3	3	Head	04	03
Sex Sequence	0		Position of Both Arms	1	0	Four Quarters	4	4	Nudity and Transparency	7	7	Neck	04	04
Posture	1	1	Position of Right Arm	0	2	Relative Size	0		Form	3	3	Shoulders	04	04
Perspective	0	0	Position of Left Arm	2	2	Constant Line Pressure	4	0	Detailing	3	3	Right Arm	04	02
Vertical Midline	3	3	Position of Legs	2	4	Variable Line Pressure	0	5	Identity and Sex	1	1	Left Arm	04	02
Bilateral Symmetry	3	3	Relation of Long Axes	1	1	Line Continuity	4	4	Sophistication	3	3	Chest	03	03
Horizontal Midline	6	4	Right and Left Halves	1	2	Body Shading	7	6	Height	04	04	Girth	05	04

GENERAL CHARACTERISTICS OF SUBJECT

IDENTIFICATION
No. 506
Sex F
Marital status S
Age 23 yrs. at psychological tests

PARENTAL HISTORY				
Father				
C	H	S	D	O
–	–	–	–	–
Mother				
C	H	S	D	O
–	–	–	–	+

PHYSIOLOGICAL AND METABOLIC DATA

	Admission	Initial	Control	Cold pressor change	Exercise change	Smoking change
Systolic pressure	122	110	110	+10	+40	
Diastolic pressure	80	60	70	+20	00	
Heart rate	80	88	88	–16	+55	

Age 21 yrs.	Height 69 in.	Ponderal index 13.55
	Weight 132 lbs.	Cholesterol 210 mg. per 100 ml.
	Overweight –08 %	Vital capacity 3.2 liters

HABIT SURVEY

Smoking habits: nonsmoker

Age begun   yrs.   Inhalation:

Habits of nervous tension: 1, 4, 5, 22

FIGURE-DRAWING CHARACTERISTICS

Structural	Male Female Both		Structural	Male	Female	Structural and Graphic	Male Female Both		Graphic, Global and Height	Male	Female	Body Proportions	Male	Female
Type	0		Omission of Appendages	0	0	Upper and Lower Halves	0	0	Hair Shading	7	3	Head	05	05
Sex Sequence	0		Position of Both Arms	1	1	Four Quarters	4	4	Nudity and Transparency	7	7	Neck	08	07
Posture	2	1	Position of Right Arm	2	5	Relative Size	2		Form	3	3	Shoulders		
Perspective	6	6	Position of Left Arm	5	2	Constant Line Pressure	5	0	Detailing	3	3	Right Arm	05	04
Vertical Midline	4	4	Position of Legs	8	5	Variable Line Pressure	0	4	Identity and Sex	1	1	Left Arm	04	04
Bilateral Symmetry	0	0	Relation of Long Axes	1	1	Line Continuity	2	1	Sophistication	3	3	Chest		
Horizontal Midline	4	4	Right and Left Halves	1	1	Body Shading	4	4	Height	05	05	Girth		

GENERAL CHARACTERISTICS OF SUBJECT

IDENTIFICATION
No. 656
Sex M
Marital status S
Age 24 yrs. at
psychological tests

PARENTAL HISTORY
Father
C   H   S   D   O
−   −   −   −   −
Mother
C   H   S   D   O
−   −   −   −   +

PHYSIOLOGICAL AND METABOLIC DATA

	Admission	Initial	Control	Cold pressor change	Exercise change	Smoking change
Systolic pressure	155	142	134	+18	+68	−03
Diastolic pressure	80	72	74	+14	+02	+15
Heart rate		108	90	−14	+21	+11

Age 21 yrs.   Height 78 in.   Ponderal index 13.95
Weight 175 lbs.   Cholesterol 167 mg. per 100 ml.
Overweight −09 %   Vital capacity   liters

HABIT SURVEY
Smoking habits: nonsmoker
Age begun   yrs.   Inhalation:
Habits of nervous tension: 1, 4, 5, 6, 9, 11, 22, 23

Plate 390   DRAWINGS AT AN INTERMEDIATE LEVEL OF SOPHISTICATION   433

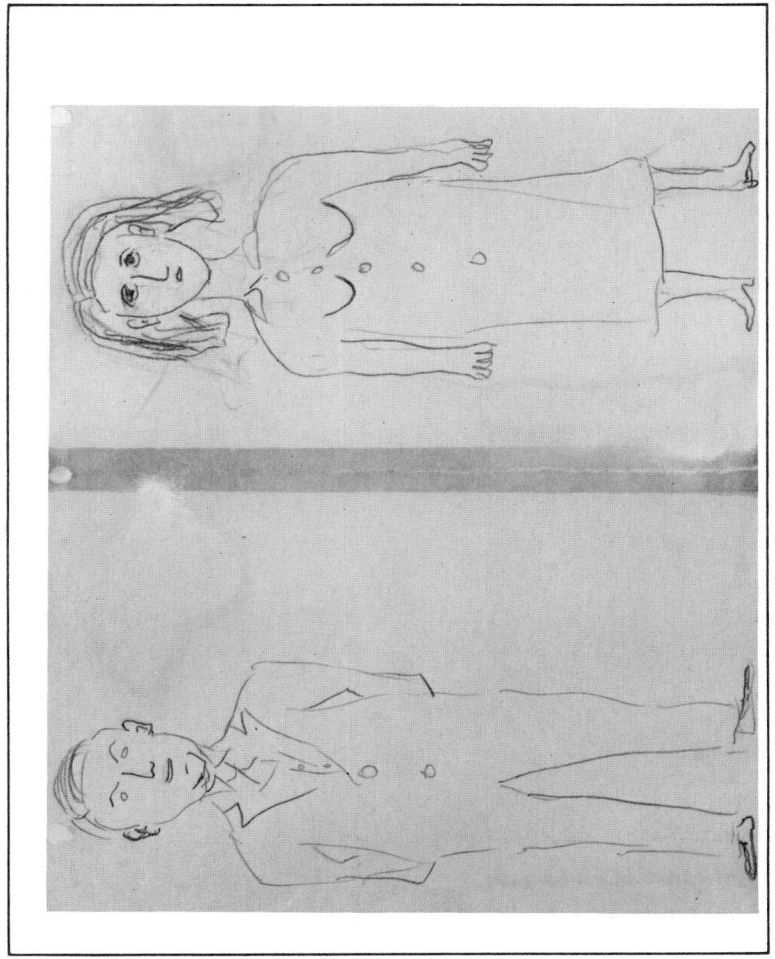

FIGURE-DRAWING CHARACTERISTICS

Structural	Male	Female	Structural	Male	Female	Structural and Graphic	Male	Female	Graphic, Global and Height	Male	Female	Body Proportions	Male	Female
	Both						Both							
Type	0		Omission of Appendages	2	0	Upper and Lower Halves	0	0	Hair Shading	3	3	Head	12	11
Sex Sequence	2		Position of Both Arms	6	0	Four Quarters	4	4	Nudity and Transparency	7	7	Neck	07	12
Posture	1	1	Position of Right Arm	8	0	Relative Size	2		Form	3	3	Shoulders	09	09
Perspective	0	0	Position of Left Arm	8	0	Constant Line Pressure	0	0	Detailing	3	3	Right Arm		04
Vertical Midline	3	3	Position of Legs	5	6	Variable Line Pressure	2	3	Identity and Sex	1	1	Left Arm		04
Bilateral Symmetry	3	3	Relation of Long Axes	2	2	Line Continuity	2	2	Sophistication	3	3	Chest	07	08
Horizontal Midline	0	0	Right and Left Halves	9	9	Body Shading	0	1	Height	07	07	Girth	11	11

GENERAL CHARACTERISTICS OF SUBJECT

IDENTIFICATION
No. F59
Sex M
Marital status S
Age 29 yrs. at
psychological tests

PARENTAL HISTORY
Father
C H S D O
– – – – –
Mother
C H S D O
– – – – +

PHYSIOLOGICAL AND METABOLIC DATA

	Admission	Initial	Control	Cold pressor change	Exercise change	Smoking change
Systolic pressure	130					+06
Diastolic pressure	80					+02
Heart rate	84					+14

Age 24 yrs.	Height	70 in.	Ponderal index 12.59
	Weight	172 lbs.	Cholesterol 258 mg. per 100 ml.
	Overweight +10 %		Vital capacity liters

HABIT SURVEY

Smoking habits: moderate cigarette smoker

Age begun 18 yrs.   Inhalation: yes

Habits of nervous tension:

FIGURE-DRAWING CHARACTERISTICS

Structural	Male Female Both		Structural	Male	Female	Structural and Graphic	Male Female Both		Graphic, Global and Height	Male	Female	Body Proportions	Male	Female
Type	0		Omission of Appendages	0	0	Upper and Lower Halves	0	0	Hair Shading	3	3	Head	06	07
Sex Sequence	0		Position of Both Arms	4	0	Four Quarters	4	4	Nudity and Transparency	6	6	Neck	05	04
Posture	2	1	Position of Right Arm	7	2	Relative Size	2		Form	3	3	Shoulders		05
Perspective	2	0	Position of Left Arm	4	2	Constant Line Pressure	0	0	Detailing	3	3	Right Arm		04
Vertical Midline	4	3	Position of Legs	8	4	Variable Line Pressure	4	4	Identity and Sex	1	1	Left Arm	04	04
Bilateral Symmetry	0	3	Relation of Long Axes	1	1	Line Continuity	1	4	Sophistication	3	3	Chest	07	04
Horizontal Midline	4	4	Right and Left Halves	0	0	Body Shading	0	6	Height	05	06	Girth	06	05

GENERAL CHARACTERISTICS OF SUBJECT

IDENTIFICATION
No. E60
Sex M
Marital status S
Age 23 yrs. at
psychological tests

PARENTAL HISTORY
Father
C H S D O
- - - - -
Mother
C H S D O
- - - - +

PHYSIOLOGICAL AND METABOLIC DATA

	Admission	Initial	Control	Cold pressor change	Exercise change	Smoking change
Systolic pressure	120	120	114	+07	+24	+22
Diastolic pressure	70	60	68	-08	-12	+19
Heart rate	70	76	70	+12	+24	+12

Age 22 yrs.	Height 68 in.	Ponderal index 12.85
	Weight 148 lbs.	Cholesterol 184 mg. per 100 ml.
	Overweight +01 %	Vital capacity 4.7 liters

HABIT SURVEY

Smoking habits: moderate cigarette smoker

Age begun   yrs.   Inhalation:

Habits of nervous tension:

STRONG VOCATIONAL INTEREST TEST

Occupation	Artist	Psychologist	Architect	Physician	Osteopath	Dentist	Veterinarian	Mathematician	Physicist	Engineer	Chemist	Production Manager
Standard Score	30	37	23	43	41	28	23	22	22	35	35	35

Occupation	Farmer	Aviator	Carpenter	Printer	Math.-Sci. Teacher	Ind. Arts Teacher	Voc. Agric. Teacher	Policeman	Forest Serv. Man	Y.M.C.A. Phys. Dir.	Personnel Director	Public Administrator
Standard Score	25	29	11	21	21	-08	06	32	27	30	44	54

Occupation	Y.M.C.A. Secretary	Soc. Sci. H.S. Teacher	City Sch. Sup't.	Social Worker	Minister	Musician Performer	C.P.A.	Senior C.P.A.	Accountant	Office Man	Purchasing Agent	Banker
Standard Score	32	27	35	42	64	30	35	32	23	22	20	17

Occupation	Mortician	Pharmacist	Sales Manager	Real Est. Manager	Life Ins. Salesman	Advertising Man	Lawyer	Author-Journalist	President Mfg. Co.	Interest Maturity	Occupational Level	Masculinity-Femininity
Standard Score	23	27	37	32	42	36	47	40	43	56	62	47

Plate 392   **DRAWINGS AT AN INTERMEDIATE LEVEL OF SOPHISTICATION**   435

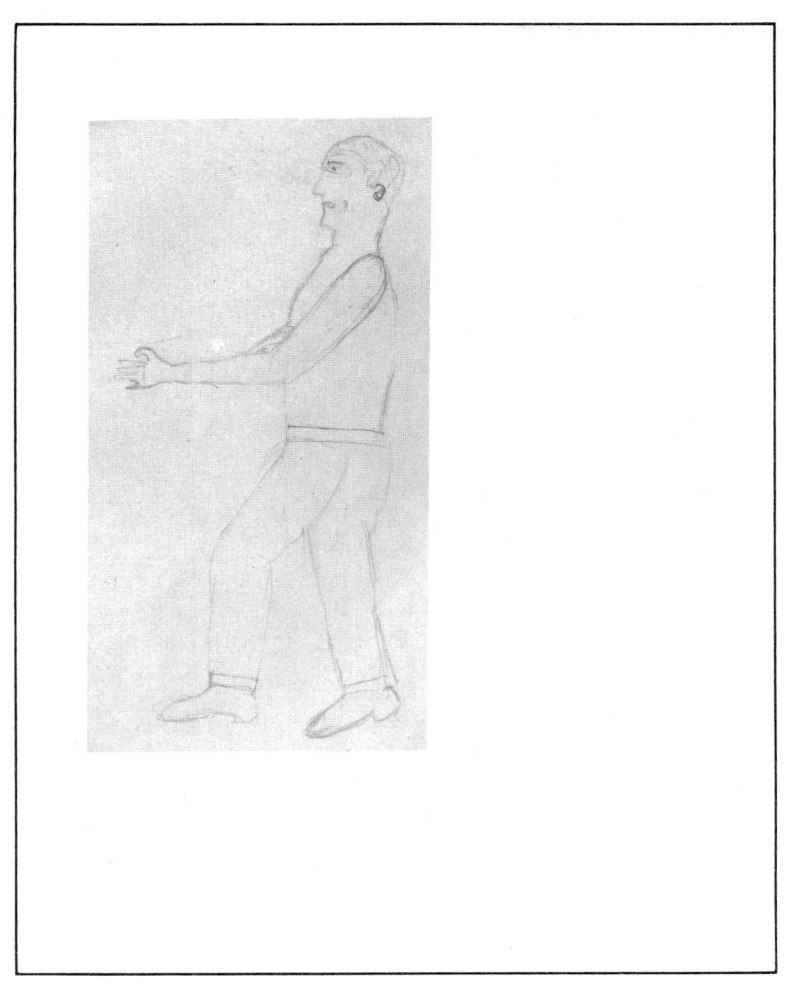

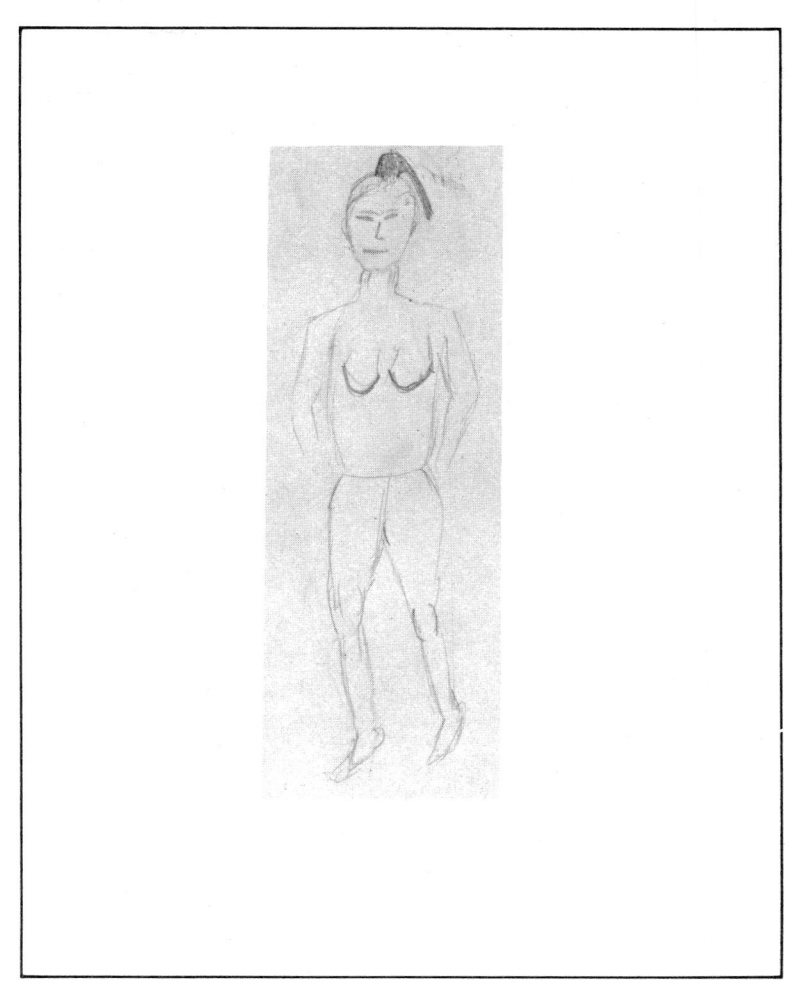

FIGURE-DRAWING CHARACTERISTICS

Structural	Male Female Both		Structural	Male	Female	Structural and Graphic	Male Female Both		Graphic, Global and Height	Male	Female	Body Proportions	Male	Female
Type	0		Omission of Appendages	0	2	Upper and Lower Halves	1	1	Hair Shading	1	1	Head	07	08
Sex Sequence	2		Position of Both Arms	4	6	Four Quarters	4	4	Nudity and Transparency	3	3	Neck	06	10
Posture	2	2	Position of Right Arm	7	8	Relative Size	2		Form	3	3	Shoulders		06
Perspective	2	0	Position of Left Arm	4	5	Constant Line Pressure	1	1	Detailing	3	3	Right Arm		
Vertical Midline	4	1	Position of Legs	8	8	Variable Line Pressure	0	0	Identity and Sex	1	1	Left Arm	08	
Bilateral Symmetry	0	3	Relation of Long Axes	1	1	Line Continuity	0	0	Sophistication	3	3	Chest	08	05
Horizontal Midline	4	4	Right and Left Halves	2	1	Body Shading	0	3	Height	06	06	Girth	07	05

GENERAL CHARACTERISTICS OF SUBJECT

IDENTIFICATION
No. 462
Sex M
Marital status M
Age 24 yrs. at
psychological tests

PARENTAL HISTORY				
Father				
C	H	S	D	O
–	–	–	–	?
Mother				
C	H	S	D	O
–	–	–	–	?

PHYSIOLOGICAL AND METABOLIC DATA

	Admission	Initial	Control	Cold pressor change	Exercise change	Smoking change
Systolic pressure	140	110	104	+20	+36	
Diastolic pressure	84	72	70	+30	+10	
Heart rate	64	72	63	+14	+12	

Age 22 yrs.	Height	71 in.	Ponderal index 12.69
	Weight	175 lbs.	Cholesterol 250 mg. per 100 ml.
	Overweight +11 %		Vital capacity 5.0 liters

HABIT SURVEY
Smoking habits: nonsmoker
Age begun   yrs.   Inhalation:
Habits of nervous tension: 4, 5, 6, 9, 11,
17

FIGURE-DRAWING CHARACTERISTICS

Structural	Male Female Both	Structural	Male	Female	Structural and Graphic	Male Female Both		Graphic, Global and Height	Male	Female	Body Proportions	Male	Female
Type	0	Omission of Appendages	0		Upper and Lower Halves	3		Hair Shading	0		Head	09	
Sex Sequence	3	Position of Both Arms	4		Four Quarters	4		Nudity and Transparency	7		Neck	12	
Posture	1	Position of Right Arm	7		Relative Size	7		Form	3		Shoulders		
Perspective	2	Position of Left Arm	4		Constant Line Pressure	1		Detailing	3		Right Arm		
Vertical Midline	4	Position of Legs	6		Variable Line Pressure	0		Identity and Sex	3		Left Arm	10	
Bilateral Symmetry	0	Relation of Long Axes	1		Line Continuity	0		Sophistication	3		Chest	13	
Horizontal Midline	4	Right and Left Halves	1		Body Shading	7		Height	08		Girth	12	

GENERAL CHARACTERISTICS OF SUBJECT

IDENTIFICATION
No. 747
Sex M
Marital status S
Age 24 yrs. at
psychological tests

PARENTAL HISTORY
Father
C   H   S   D   O
-   -   -   -   ?
Mother
C   H   S   D   O
-   -   -   -   ?

PHYSIOLOGICAL AND METABOLIC DATA

	Admission	Initial	Control	Cold pressor change	Exercise change	Smoking change
Systolic pressure	120	120	114	00	+14	-02
Diastolic pressure	80	70	68	+08	+06	+05
Heart rate	76	72	70	+08	+33	00

Age 23 yrs.

Height 70 in.
Weight 164 lbs.
Overweight +06 %

Ponderal index 12.80
Cholesterol 230 mg. per 100 ml.
Vital capacity 4.3 liters

HABIT SURVEY
Smoking habits: nonsmoker
Age begun   yrs.   Inhalation:
Habits of nervous tension: 5, 11, 15, 21

FIGURE-DRAWING CHARACTERISTICS

Structural	Male	Female	Structural	Male	Female	Structural and Graphic	Male	Female	Graphic, Global and Height	Male	Female	Body Proportions	Male	Female
	Both						Both							
Type	0		Omission of Appendages	0	0	Upper and Lower Halves	3	3	Hair Shading	3	3	Head	06	05
Sex Sequence	2		Position of Both Arms	0	0	Four Quarters	4	4	Nudity and Transparency	7	7	Neck		01
Posture	1	1	Position of Right Arm	4	4	Relative Size	0		Form	1	3	Shoulders	06	04
Perspective	0	0	Position of Left Arm	4	4	Constant Line Pressure	0	0	Detailing	3	3	Right Arm	05	04
Vertical Midline	3	0	Position of Legs	4	4	Variable Line Pressure	1	4	Identity and Sex	1	1	Left Arm	04	04
Bilateral Symmetry	3	3	Relation of Long Axes	1	1	Line Continuity	0	0	Sophistication	3	3	Chest	05	04
Horizontal Midline	6	0	Right and Left Halves	1	1	Body Shading	4	1	Height	05	04	Girth	07	03

GENERAL CHARACTERISTICS OF SUBJECT

IDENTIFICATION	PARENTAL HISTORY
No. G50	Father
Sex M	C H S D O
Marital status S	− − − − ?
Age 23 yrs. at	Mother
psychological tests	C H S D O
	− − − − ?

PHYSIOLOGICAL AND METABOLIC DATA

	Admission	Initial	Control	Cold pressor change	Exercise change	Smoking change
Systolic pressure	146	120	114	+20	+36	00
Diastolic pressure	90	88	92	+08	00	00
Heart rate	88	60	69	+12	+08	00

Age 22 yrs.	Height 70 in.	Ponderal index 12.50
	Weight 176 lbs.	Cholesterol 222 mg. per 100 ml.
	Overweight +14 %	Vital capacity liters

HABIT SURVEY

Smoking habits: mixed smoker

Age begun 18 yrs.   Inhalation: yes

Habits of nervous tension: 2, 4, 6, 11, 16, 25

STRONG VOCATIONAL INTEREST TEST

Occupation	Artist	Psychologist	Architect	Physician	Osteopath	Dentist	Veterinarian	Mathematician	Physicist	Engineer	Chemist	Production Manager
Standard Score	27	32	28	45	38	27	25	23	18	24	23	25

Occupation	Farmer	Aviator	Carpenter	Printer	Math.-Sci. Teacher	Ind. Arts Teacher	Voc. Agric. Teacher	Policeman	Forest Serv. Man	Y.M.C.A. Phys. Dir.	Personnel Director	Public Administrator
Standard Score	19	19	08	13	27	13	24	21	11	37	29	29

Occupation	Y.M.C.A. Secretary	Soc. Sci. H.S. Teacher	City Sch. Sup't.	Social Worker	Minister	Musician Performer	C.P.A.	Senior C.P.A.	Accountant	Office Man	Purchasing Agent	Banker
Standard Score	34	26	32	36	59	37	20	22	12	24	17	23

Occupation	Mortician	Pharmacist	Sales Manager	Real Est. Manager	Life Ins. Salesman	Advertising Man	Lawyer	Author-Journalist	President Mfg. Co.	Interest Maturity	Occupational Level	Masculinity-Femininity
Standard Score	37	34	42	45	48	37	32	32	42	55	63	37

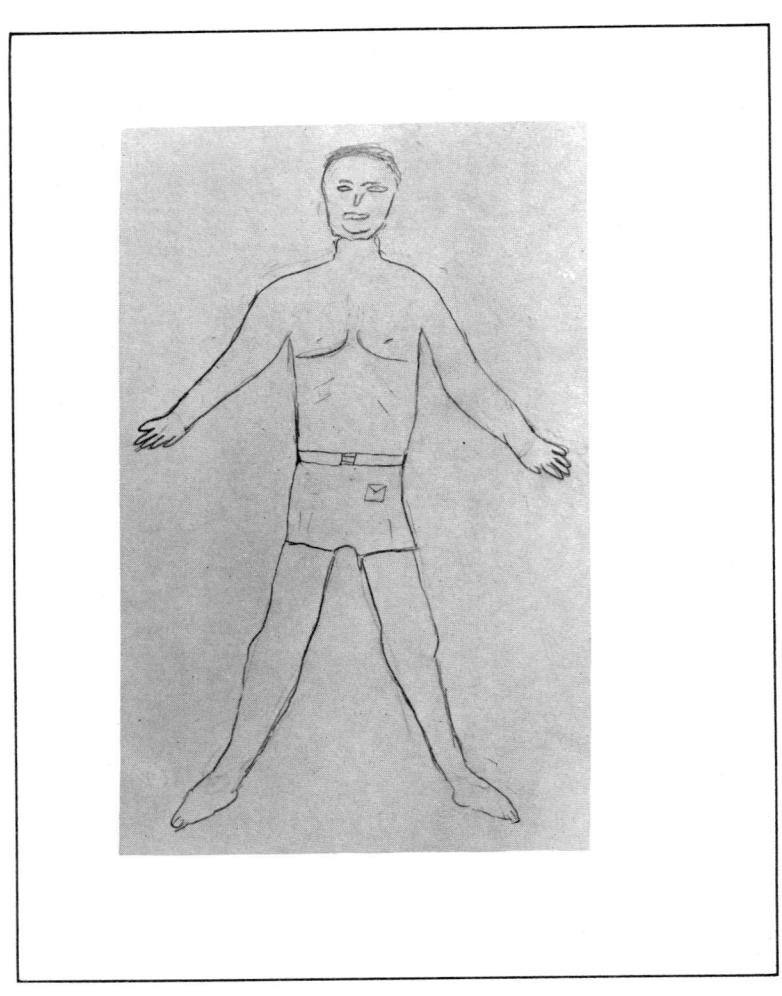

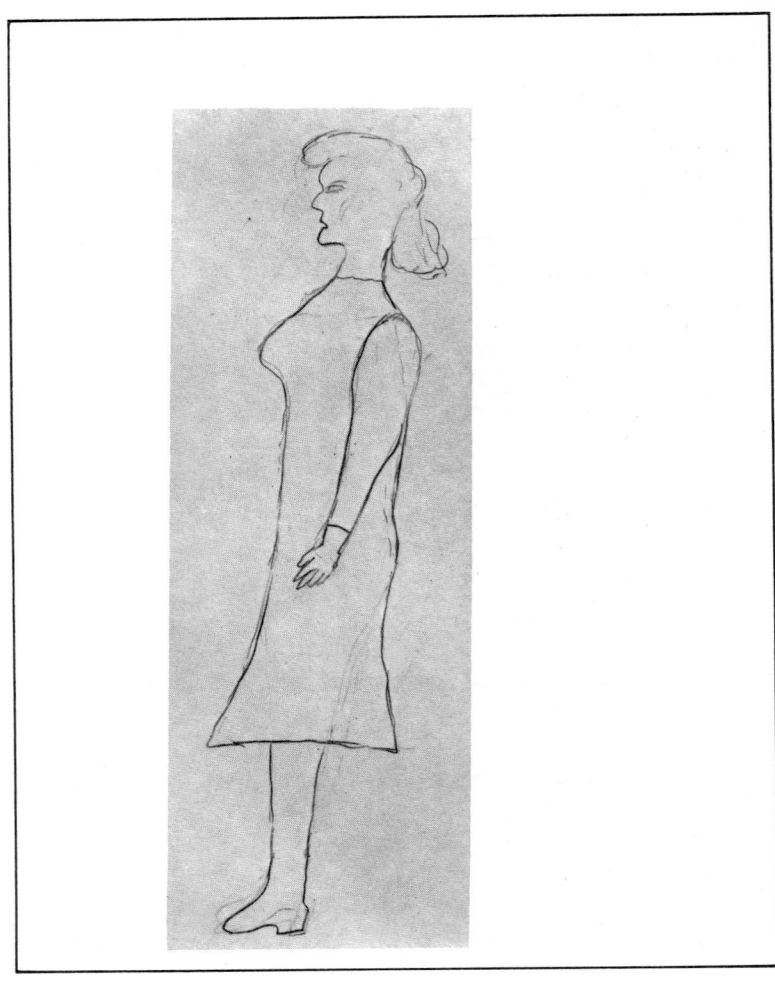

FIGURE-DRAWING CHARACTERISTICS

Structural	Male Female Both		Structural	Male	Female	Structural and Graphic	Male Female Both		Graphic, Global and Height	Male	Female	Body Proportions	Male	Female
Type	0		Omission of Appendages	0	0	Upper and Lower Halves	1	3	Hair Shading	3	5	Head	07	09
Sex Sequence	0		Position of Both Arms	0	4	Four Quarters	4	4	Nudity and Transparency	3	6	Neck	06	08
Posture	1	1	Position of Right Arm	2	7	Relative Size	4		Form	3	3	Shoulders	07	
Perspective	0	2	Position of Left Arm	2	0	Constant Line Pressure	0	0	Detailing	3	5	Right Arm	04	
Vertical Midline	0	4	Position of Legs	6	1	Variable Line Pressure	3	5	Identity and Sex	1	1	Left Arm	06	06
Bilateral Symmetry	2	0	Relation of Long Axes	1	1	Line Continuity	1	1	Sophistication	3	3	Chest	06	10
Horizontal Midline	4	0	Right and Left Halves	1	2	Body Shading	3	0	Height	07	08	Girth	07	11

GENERAL CHARACTERISTICS OF SUBJECT

IDENTIFICATION
No. B11
Sex M
Marital status S
Age 22 yrs. at
psychological tests

PARENTAL HISTORY					
Father					
C	H	S	D	O	
–	–	–	–	?	
Mother					
C	H	S	D	O	
–	–	–	–	?	

PHYSIOLOGICAL AND METABOLIC DATA						
	Admission	Initial	Control	Cold pressor change	Exercise change	Smoking change
Systolic pressure	128	116	112	+22	+46	+03
Diastolic pressure	70	70	58	+26	+02	–01
Heart rate	72	88	74	+16	+30	+01
Age 22 yrs.	Height 68 in.			Ponderal index 13.03		
	Weight 142 lbs.			Cholesterol 186 mg. per 100 ml.		
	Overweight –03 %			Vital capacity 5.4 liters		

HABIT SURVEY
Smoking habits: nonsmoker
Age begun   yrs.   Inhalation:
Habits of nervous tension: 3, 4, 5, 6, 11, 18,
21, 22, 23, 24

STRONG VOCATIONAL INTEREST TEST

Occupation	Artist	Psychologist	Architect	Physician	Osteopath	Dentist	Veterinarian	Mathematician	Physicist	Engineer	Chemist	Production Manager
Standard Score	27	38	28	48	41	44	30	25	18	24	28	32

Occupation	Farmer	Aviator	Carpenter	Printer	Math.-Sci. Teacher	Ind. Arts Teacher	Voc. Agric. Teacher	Policeman	Forest Serv. Man	Y.M.C.A. Phys. Dir.	Personnel Director	Public Administrator
Standard Score	33	27	10	39	36	13	26	33	27	44	37	45

Occupation	Y.M.C.A. Secretary	Soc. Sci. H.S. Teacher	City Sch. Sup't.	Social Worker	Minister	Musician Performer	C.P.A.	Senior C.P.A.	Accountant	Office Man	Purchasing Agent	Banker
Standard Score	33	41	40	36	61	40	23	34	25	34	28	28

Occupation	Mortician	Pharmacist	Sales Manager	Real Est. Manager	Life Ins. Salesman	Advertising Man	Lawyer	Author- Journalist	President Mfg. Co.	Interest Maturity	Occupational Level	Masculinity- Femininity
Standard Score	29	35	36	29	36	37	34	36	27	55	59	47

FIGURE-DRAWING CHARACTERISTICS

Structural	Male Female Both		Structural	Male	Female	Structural and Graphic	Male Female Both		Graphic, Global and Height	Male	Female	Body Proportions	Male	Female
Type	0		Omission of Appendages	0	0	Upper and Lower Halves	2	2	Hair Shading	3	5	Head	05	04
Sex Sequence	1		Position of Both Arms	0	0	Four Quarters	0	4	Nudity and Transparency	7	7	Neck	04	04
Posture	1	1	Position of Right Arm	0	1	Relative Size	3		Form	3	3	Shoulders	03	04
Perspective	0	0	Position of Left Arm	0	1	Constant Line Pressure	0	0	Detailing	3	3	Right Arm	02	02
Vertical Midline	0	0	Position of Legs	4	6	Variable Line Pressure	1	3	Identity and Sex	1	1	Left Arm	02	02
Bilateral Symmetry	3	3	Relation of Long Axes	1	1	Line Continuity	0	0	Sophistication	3	3	Chest	02	03
Horizontal Midline	4	4	Right and Left Halves	2	1	Body Shading	4	5	Height	04	04	Girth	03	03

GENERAL CHARACTERISTICS OF SUBJECT

IDENTIFICATION
No. C43
Sex M
Marital status S
Age 21 yrs. at psychological tests

PARENTAL HISTORY
Father
C H S D O
- - - - ?
Mother
C H S D O
- - - - ?

PHYSIOLOGICAL AND METABOLIC DATA

	Admission	Initial	Control	Cold pressor change	Exercise change	Smoking change
Systolic pressure	130					
Diastolic pressure	70					
Heart rate	80					

Age 21 yrs.   Height 72 in.   Weight 193 lbs.   Overweight +19 %   Ponderal index 12.46   Cholesterol 263 mg. per 100 ml.   Vital capacity 4.7 liters

HABIT SURVEY
Smoking habits: nonsmoker
Age begun yrs.   Inhalation:
Habits of nervous tension: 12, 14, 15, 16, 19, 21, 25

STRONG VOCATIONAL INTEREST TEST

Occupation	Artist	Psychologist	Architect	Physician	Osteopath	Dentist	Veterinarian	Mathematician	Physicist	Engineer	Chemist	Production Manager
Standard Score	17	41	19	47	56	36	24	15	14	24	33	36

Occupation	Farmer	Aviator	Carpenter	Printer	Math.-Sci. Teacher	Ind. Arts Teacher	Voc. Agric. Teacher	Policeman	Forest Serv. Man	Y.M.C.A. Phys. Dir.	Personnel Director	Public Administrator
Standard Score	26	40	31	55	52	34	30	46	20	51	56	56

Occupation	Y.M.C.A. Secretary	Soc. Sci. H.S. Teacher	City Sch. Sup't.	Social Worker	Minister	Musician Performer	C.P.A.	Senior C.P.A.	Accountant	Office Man	Purchasing Agent	Banker
Standard Score	47	56	35	58	62	48	29	47	37	52	28	24

Occupation	Mortician	Pharmacist	Sales Manager	Real Est. Manager	Life Ins. Salesman	Advertising Man	Lawyer	Author-Journalist	President Mfg. Co.	Interest Maturity	Occupational Level	Masculinity-Femininity
Standard Score	49	48	37	40	40	35	31	24	31	68	46	47

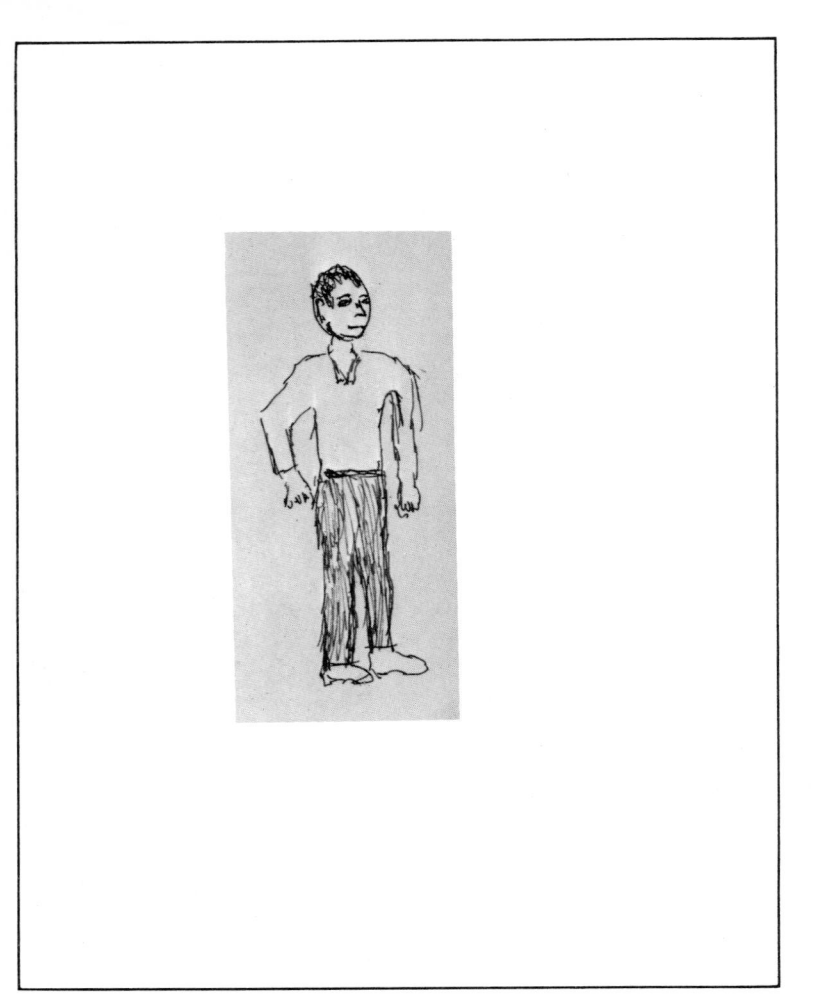

FIGURE-DRAWING CHARACTERISTICS

Structural	Male Female Both	Structural	Male	Female	Structural and Graphic	Male Female Both		Graphic, Global and Height	Male	Female	Body Proportions	Male	Female
Type	0	Omission of Appendages	0	0	Upper and Lower Halves	1	1	Hair Shading	3	3	Head	05	05
Sex Sequence	0	Position of Both Arms	1	0	Four Quarters	4	4	Nudity and Transparency	7	7	Neck	05	05
Posture	1	1	Position of Right Arm	5	0	Relative Size	0		Form	3	3	Shoulders	04	04
Perspective	1	1	Position of Left Arm	0	0	Constant Line Pressure	3	3	Detailing	3	3	Right Arm	04	02
Vertical Midline	0	0	Position of Legs	4	4	Variable Line Pressure	0	0	Identity and Sex	1	1	Left Arm	04	02
Bilateral Symmetry	2	3	Relation of Long Axes	1	1	Line Continuity	0	0	Sophistication	3	3	Chest	03	03
Horizontal Midline	4	4	Right and Left Halves	1	1	Body Shading	2	5	Height	04	03	Girth	04	04

GENERAL CHARACTERISTICS OF SUBJECT

IDENTIFICATION		PARENTAL HISTORY				
No. C72		Father				
Sex M		C H S D O				
Marital status S		– – – – ?				
Age 20 yrs. at		Mother				
psychological tests		C H S D O				
		– – – – ?				

PHYSIOLOGICAL AND METABOLIC DATA

	Admission	Initial	Control	Cold pressor change	Exercise change	Smoking change
Systolic pressure	116	122	118	+04	+34	+01
Diastolic pressure	76	68	58	+10	00	–04
Heart rate	68	64	63	–04	+31	+03

Age 22 yrs.	Height 70 in.	Ponderal index 13.06
	Weight 154 lbs.	Cholesterol 206 mg. per 100 ml.
	Overweight 00 %	Vital capacity 4.8 liters

HABIT SURVEY

Smoking habits: nonsmoker

Age begun   yrs.   Inhalation:

Habits of nervous tension: 5, 8, 9

STRONG VOCATIONAL INTEREST TEST

Occupation	Artist	Psychologist	Architect	Physician	Osteopath	Dentist	Veterinarian	Mathematician	Physicist	Engineer	Chemist	Production Manager
Standard Score	44	56	50	55	32	32	21	45	35	32	55	13

Occupation	Farmer	Aviator	Carpenter	Printer	Math.-Sci. Teacher	Ind. Arts Teacher	Voc. Agric. Teacher	Policeman	Forest Serv. Man	Y.M.C.A. Phys. Dir.	Personnel Director	Public Administrator
Standard Score	41	31	24	40	39	16	35	20	34	21	28	45

Occupation	Y.M.C.A. Secretary	Soc. Sci. H.S. Teacher	City Sch. Sup't.	Social Worker	Minister	Musician Performer	C.P.A.	Senior C.P.A.	Accountant	Office Man	Purchasing Agent	Banker
Standard Score	27	37	32	42	62	55	29	35	15	20	09	14

Occupation	Mortician	Pharmacist	Sales Manager	Real Est. Manager	Life Ins. Salesman	Advertising Man	Lawyer	Author-Journalist	President Mfg. Co.	Interest Maturity	Occupational Level	Masculinity-Femininity
Standard Score	05	14	15	23	16	35	35	42	15	53	54	37

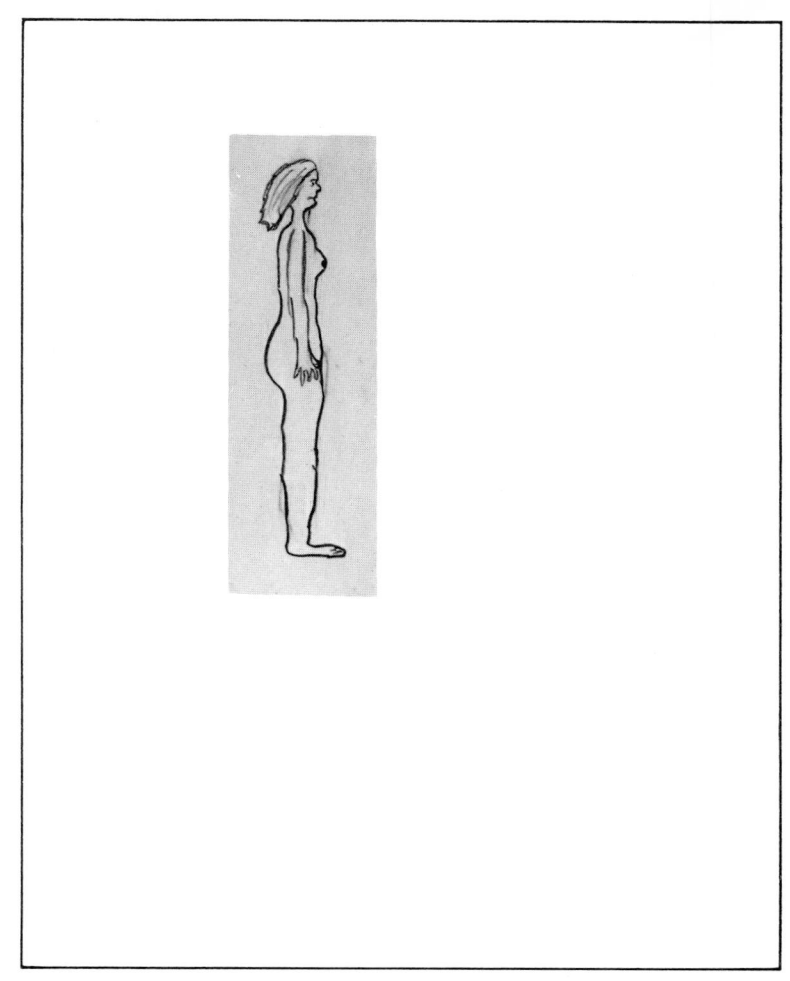

FIGURE-DRAWING CHARACTERISTICS

Structural	Male Female (Both)		Structural	Male	Female	Structural and Graphic	Male Female (Both)		Graphic, Global and Height	Male	Female	Body Proportions	Male	Female
Type	0		Omission of Appendages	0	0	Upper and Lower Halves	1	1	Hair Shading	7	1	Head	05	04
Sex Sequence	2		Position of Both Arms	0	2	Four Quarters	4	4	Nudity and Transparency	3	0	Neck	02	05
Posture	1	1	Position of Right Arm	2	0	Relative Size	0		Form	3	3	Shoulders	05	
Perspective	0	2	Position of Left Arm	2	7	Constant Line Pressure	0	5	Detailing	1	3	Right Arm	04	02
Vertical Midline	0	4	Position of Legs	5	1	Variable Line Pressure	5	0	Identity and Sex	1	1	Left Arm	04	
Bilateral Symmetry	3	0	Relation of Long Axes	1	1	Line Continuity	0	3	Sophistication	3	3	Chest	04	02
Horizontal Midline	4	0	Right and Left Halves	1	2	Body Shading	7	0	Height	05	04	Girth	06	03

GENERAL CHARACTERISTICS OF SUBJECT

IDENTIFICATION
No. D20
Sex M
Marital status S
Age 23 yrs. at psychological tests

PARENTAL HISTORY
Father
C H S D O
- - - - ?
Mother
C H S D O
- - - - ?

PHYSIOLOGICAL AND METABOLIC DATA

	Admission	Initial	Control	Cold pressor change	Exercise change	Smoking change
Systolic pressure	140	140	110	+30	+52	+14
Diastolic pressure	80	62	70	+10	-12	+08
Heart rate	80	88	88	+08	+21	+17

Age 23 yrs.	Height 71 in.	Ponderal index 12.46
	Weight 185 lbs.	Cholesterol 208 mg. per 100 ml.
	Overweight +16 %	Vital capacity 5.2 liters

HABIT SURVEY

Smoking habits: moderate cigarette smoker

Age begun 18 yrs.   Inhalation: sometimes

Habits of nervous tension: 4, 5, 6, 9, 11, 16, 18, 21, 22

STRONG VOCATIONAL INTEREST TEST

Occupation	Artist	Psychologist	Architect	Physician	Osteopath	Dentist	Veterinarian	Mathematician	Physicist	Engineer	Chemist	Production Manager
Standard Score	42	23	33	31	29	32	22	26	17	24	33	25

Occupation	Farmer	Aviator	Carpenter	Printer	Math.-Sci. Teacher	Ind. Arts Teacher	Voc. Agric. Teacher	Policeman	Forest Serv. Man	Y.M.C.A. Phys. Dir.	Personnel Director	Public Administrator
Standard Score	31	37	14	34	12	-10	-07	27	20	18	18	24

Occupation	Y.M.C.A. Secretary	Soc. Sci. H.S. Teacher	City Sch. Sup't.	Social Worker	Minister	Musician Performer	C.P.A.	Senior C.P.A.	Accountant	Office Man	Purchasing Agent	Banker
Standard Score	05	25	13	21	63	35	36	28	17	25	28	26

Occupation	Mortician	Pharmacist	Sales Manager	Real Est. Manager	Life Ins. Salesman	Advertising Man	Lawyer	Author-Journalist	President Mfg. Co.	Interest Maturity	Occupational Level	Masculinity-Femininity
Standard Score	22	27	33	48	39	49	58	51	34	44	55	44

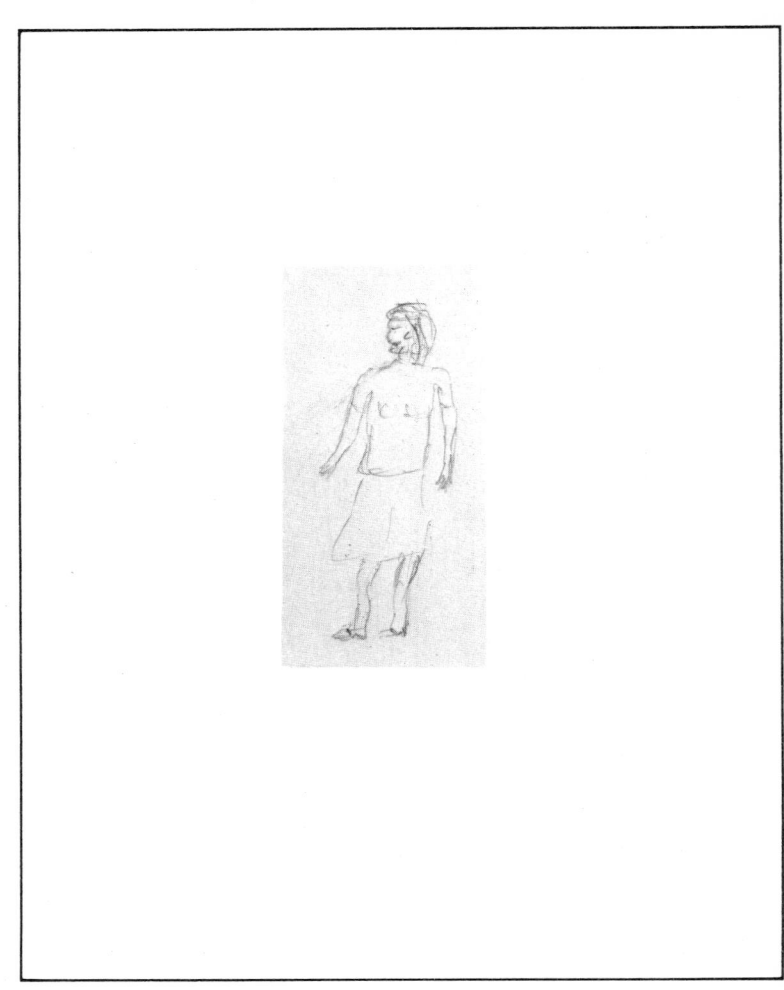

FIGURE-DRAWING CHARACTERISTICS

Structural	Male	Female	Structural	Male	Female	Structural and Graphic	Male	Female	Graphic, Global and Height	Male	Female	Body Proportions	Male	Female
	Both						Both							
Type	0		Omission of Appendages	0	0	Upper and Lower Halves	1	1	Hair Shading	3	3	Head	04	04
Sex Sequence	0		Position of Both Arms	1	1	Four Quarters	4	4	Nudity and Transparency	7	7	Neck	04	03
Posture	1	1	Position of Right Arm	2	3	Relative Size	0		Form	3	3	Shoulders	04	03
Perspective	0	5	Position of Left Arm	5	0	Constant Line Pressure	1	1	Detailing	3	5	Right Arm	03	02
Vertical Midline	3	0	Position of Legs	6	5	Variable Line Pressure	0	0	Identity and Sex	1	3	Left Arm	04	02
Bilateral Symmetry	2	2	Relation of Long Axes	1	1	Line Continuity	0	0	Sophistication	3	3	Chest	04	03
Horizontal Midline	4	4	Right and Left Halves	2	1	Body Shading	6	1	Height	04	03	Girth	05	04

GENERAL CHARACTERISTICS OF SUBJECT

IDENTIFICATION
No. D64
Sex M
Marital status S
Age 22 yrs. at
psychological tests

PARENTAL HISTORY					
Father					
C	H	S	D	O	
–	–	–	–	?	
Mother					
C	H	S	D	O	
–	–	–	–	?	

PHYSIOLOGICAL AND METABOLIC DATA

	Admission	Initial	Control	Cold pressor change	Exercise change	Smoking change
Systolic pressure	120	116	112	+06	+40	+02
Diastolic pressure	60	50	68	–08	–19	00
Heart rate	74	64	65	–04	+21	–17

Age 22 yrs.			
Height 70 in.	Ponderal index 13.54		
Weight 138 lbs.	Cholesterol 200 mg. per 100 ml.		
Overweight –17 %	Vital capacity 4.7 liters		

HABIT SURVEY

Smoking habits: nonsmoker

Age begun   yrs.   Inhalation:

Habits of nervous tension: 4, 5, 16, 21, 23

STRONG VOCATIONAL INTEREST TEST

Occupation	Artist	Psychologist	Architect	Physician	Osteopath	Dentist	Veterinarian	Mathematician	Physicist	Engineer	Chemist	Production Manager
Standard Score	42	43	38	56	57	48	22	35	35	29	48	14

Occupation	Farmer	Aviator	Carpenter	Printer	Math.-Sci. Teacher	Ind. Arts Teacher	Voc. Agric. Teacher	Policeman	Forest Serv. Man	Y.M.C.A. Phys. Dir.	Personnel Director	Public Administrator
Standard Score	26	24	14	30	36	07	08	17	12	22	23	34

Occupation	Y.M.C.A. Secretary	Soc. Sci. H.S. Teacher	City Sch. Sup't.	Social Worker	Minister	Musician Performer	C.P.A.	Senior C.P.A.	Accountant	Office Man	Purchasing Agent	Banker
Standard Score	18	30	26	35	63	46	36	28	25	31	05	18

Occupation	Mortician	Pharmacist	Sales Manager	Real Est. Manager	Life Ins. Salesman	Advertising Man	Lawyer	Author-Journalist	President Mfg. Co.	Interest Maturity	Occupational Level	Masculinity-Femininity
Standard Score	26	30	08	30	30	33	42	44	26	53	61	27

Plate 400   DRAWINGS AT AN INTERMEDIATE LEVEL OF SOPHISTICATION   443

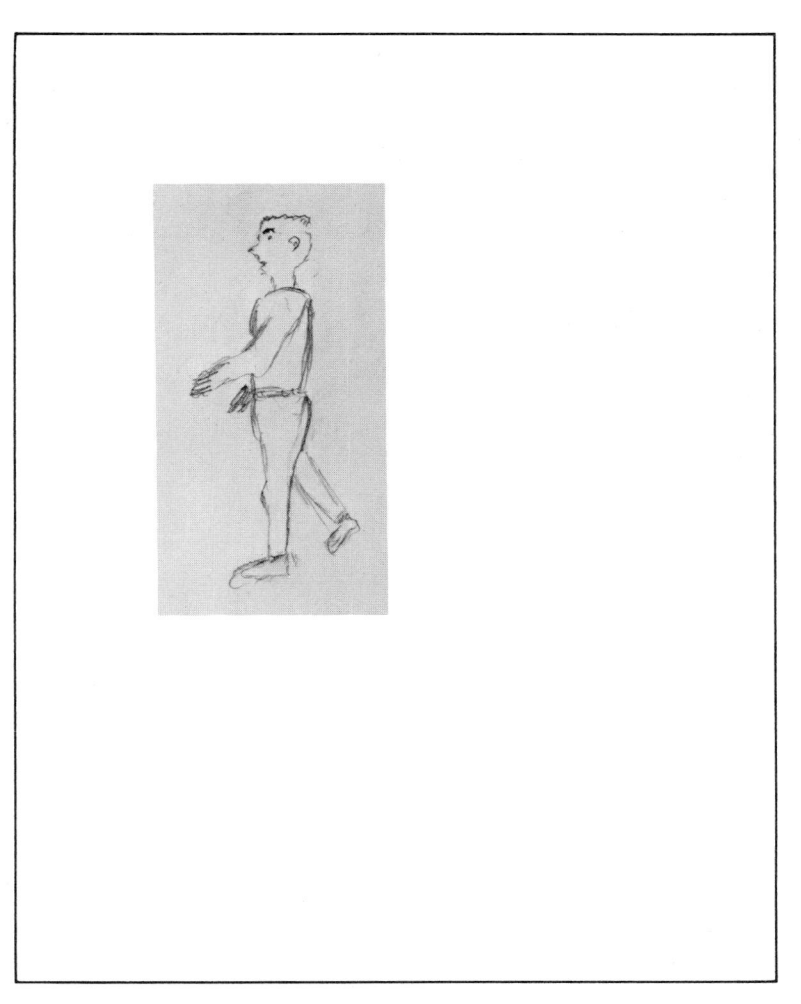

FIGURE-DRAWING CHARACTERISTICS

Structural	Male Female Both		Structural	Male	Female	Structural and Graphic	Male Female Both		Graphic, Global and Height	Male	Female	Body Proportions	Male	Female
Type	0		Omission of Appendages	0	0	Upper and Lower Halves	1	1	Hair Shading	5	3	Head	04	04
Sex Sequence	0		Position of Both Arms	4	4	Four Quarters	4	4	Nudity and Transparency	9	7	Neck	05	04
Posture	2	2	Position of Right Arm	7	7	Relative Size	0		Form	3	3	Shoulders		
Perspective	2	2	Position of Left Arm	4	4	Constant Line Pressure	0	1	Detailing	3	3	Right Arm		
Vertical Midline	4	4	Position of Legs	8	8	Variable Line Pressure	1	0	Identity and Sex	1	1	Left Arm	02	02
Bilateral Symmetry	0	0	Relation of Long Axes	1	1	Line Continuity	0	0	Sophistication	3	3	Chest	04	02
Horizontal Midline	4	4	Right and Left Halves	2	2	Body Shading	4	4	Height	03	03	Girth	04	02

GENERAL CHARACTERISTICS OF SUBJECT

IDENTIFICATION

No. E44
Sex M
Marital status M
Age 21 yrs. at
psychological tests

PARENTAL HISTORY

Father
C   H   S   D   O
–   –   –   –   ?

Mother
C   H   S   D   O
–   –   –   –   ?

PHYSIOLOGICAL AND METABOLIC DATA

	Admission	Initial	Control	Cold pressor change	Exercise change	Smoking change
Systolic pressure	100	118	105	+05	+25	+07
Diastolic pressure	60	62	60	+12	–15	+12
Heart rate	72	60	70	–04	+18	+25

Age 21 yrs.	Height 70 in.	Ponderal index 12.73
	Weight 166 lbs.	Cholesterol 284 mg. per 100 ml.
	Overweight +08 %	Vital capacity 3.9 liters

HABIT SURVEY

Smoking habits: heavy cigarette smoker
Age begun 18 yrs.   Inhalation: yes
Habits of nervous tension: 4, 5, 6, 10, 16, 23

STRONG VOCATIONAL INTEREST TEST

Occupation	Artist	Psychologist	Architect	Physician	Osteopath	Dentist	Veterinarian	Mathematician	Physicist	Engineer	Chemist	Production Manager
Standard Score	39	62	46	64	39	37	15	38	35	40	49	30

Occupation	Farmer	Aviator	Carpenter	Printer	Math.-Sci. Teacher	Ind. Arts Teacher	Voc. Agric. Teacher	Policeman	Forest Serv. Man	Y.M.C.A. Phys. Dir.	Personnel Director	Public Administrator
Standard Score	28	43	18	43	43	23	34	27	27	36	47	51

Occupation	Y.M.C.A. Secretary	Soc. Sci. H.S. Teacher	City Sch. Sup't.	Social Worker	Minister	Musician Performer	C.P.A.	Senior C.P.A.	Accountant	Office Man	Purchasing Agent	Banker
Standard Score	26	34	36	49	64	56	39	43	22	21	17	12

Occupation	Mortician	Pharmacist	Sales Manager	Real Est. Manager	Life Ins. Salesman	Advertising Man	Lawyer	Author-Journalist	President Mfg. Co.	Interest Maturity	Occupational Level	Masculinity-Femininity
Standard Score	11	31	25	28	24	42	42	42	30	56	56	48

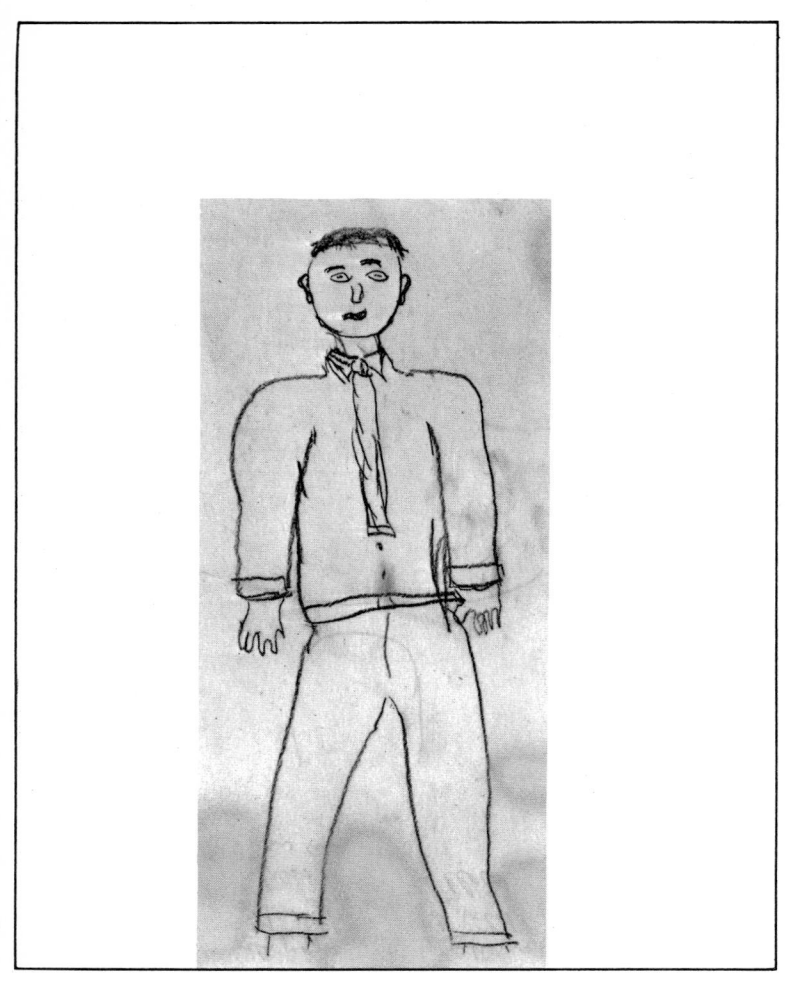

FIGURE-DRAWING CHARACTERISTICS

Structural	Male Female — Both	Structural	Male	Female	Structural and Graphic	Male Female — Both		Graphic, Global and Height	Male	Female	Body Proportions	Male	Female
Type	0	Omission of Appendages	8	0	Upper and Lower Halves	7	3	Hair Shading	3	3	Head	09	10
Sex Sequence	2	Position of Both Arms	0	4	Four Quarters	4	4	Nudity and Transparency	7	7	Neck	10	10
Posture	0 1	Position of Right Arm	0	7	Relative Size	0		Form	3	3	Shoulders	09	
Perspective	0 2	Position of Left Arm	0	0	Constant Line Pressure	5	5	Detailing	3	3	Right Arm	06	
Vertical Midline	3 4	Position of Legs	6	1	Variable Line Pressure	0	0	Identity and Sex	1	1	Left Arm	06	04
Bilateral Symmetry	3 0	Relation of Long Axes	1	1	Line Continuity	3	0	Sophistication	3	3	Chest	06	10
Horizontal Midline	4 0	Right and Left Halves	1	1	Body Shading	0	0	Height		07	Girth	09	15

GENERAL CHARACTERISTICS OF SUBJECT

IDENTIFICATION
No. 270
Sex M
Marital status S
Age 25 yrs. at
psychological tests

PARENTAL HISTORY
Father
C   H   S   D   O
–   –   –   –   ?
Mother
C   H   S   D   O
–   –   –   –

PHYSIOLOGICAL AND METABOLIC DATA

	Admission	Initial	Control	Cold pressor change	Exercise change	Smoking change
Systolic pressure	142	130	118	+08	+48	
Diastolic pressure	80	78	64	+08	+04	
Heart rate	92	84	75	+06	+19	

Age 21 yrs.	Height	70 in.	Ponderal index	13.45
	Weight	141 lbs.	Cholesterol	305 mg. per 100 ml.
	Overweight –08 %		Vital capacity	3.7 liters

HABIT SURVEY

Smoking habits: nonsmoker

   Age begun   yrs.   Inhalation:

Habits of nervous tension: 5, 8, 21, 25

Plate 402   DRAWINGS AT AN INTERMEDIATE LEVEL OF SOPHISTICATION   445

FIGURE-DRAWING CHARACTERISTICS

Structural	Male Female Both		Structural	Male	Female	Structural and Graphic	Male Female Both		Graphic, Global and Height	Male	Female	Body Proportions	Male	Female
Type	0		Omission of Appendages	0	0	Upper and Lower Halves	0	1	Hair Shading	9	5	Head	08	06
Sex Sequence	0		Position of Both Arms	1	0	Four Quarters	4	4	Nudity and Transparency	7	7	Neck	06	06
Posture	1	1	Position of Right Arm	5	0	Relative Size	0		Form	1	3	Shoulders		03
Perspective	6	5	Position of Left Arm	0	0	Constant Line Pressure	5	5	Detailing	1	5	Right Arm	06	02
Vertical Midline	7	0	Position of Legs	2	4	Variable Line Pressure	0	0	Identity and Sex	1	1	Left Arm	04	02
Bilateral Symmetry	0	3	Relation of Long Axes	1	1	Line Continuity	4	4	Sophistication	3	3	Chest		02
Horizontal Midline	4	4	Right and Left Halves	2	2	Body Shading	4	0	Height	04	03	Girth		03

GENERAL CHARACTERISTICS OF SUBJECT

IDENTIFICATION

No. 367

Sex M

Marital status S

Age 23 yrs. at

psychological tests

PARENTAL HISTORY

Father

C   H   S   D   O

–   –   –   –   ?

Mother

C   H   S   D   O

–   –   –   –   –

PHYSIOLOGICAL AND METABOLIC DATA

	Admission	Initial	Control	Cold pressor change	Exercise change	Smoking change
Systolic pressure	130	102	96	+04	+32	
Diastolic pressure	64	46	48	+18	00	
Heart rate	56	60	52	+12	+08	

Age 22 yrs.   Height 71 in.   Weight 166 lbs.   Overweight +05 %

Ponderal index 12.92   Cholesterol 265 mg. per 100 ml.   Vital capacity 4.8 liters

HABIT SURVEY

Smoking habits: mixed smoker

Age begun 20 yrs.   Inhalation: yes

Habits of nervous tension: 6

FIGURE-DRAWING CHARACTERISTICS

Structural	Male Female Both	Structural	Male	Female	Structural and Graphic	Male Female Both		Graphic, Global and Height	Male	Female	Body Proportions	Male	Female
Type	0	Omission of Appendages	0	1	Upper and Lower Halves	2	2	Hair Shading	3	1	Head	05	04
Sex Sequence	0	Position of Both Arms	4	6	Four Quarters	1	4	Nudity and Transparency	7	7	Neck	04	08
Posture	1 0	Position of Right Arm	7	7	Relative Size	4		Form	3	3	Shoulders		
Perspective	2 2	Position of Left Arm	4	7	Constant Line Pressure	3	0	Detailing	3	3	Right Arm		
Vertical Midline	7 4	Position of Legs	1	0	Variable Line Pressure	0	3	Identity and Sex	1	1	Left Arm	02	
Bilateral Symmetry	0 0	Relation of Long Axes	1	1	Line Continuity	0	0	Sophistication	3	3	Chest	04	03
Horizontal Midline	4 0	Right and Left Halves	4	3	Body Shading	4	0	Height	03		Girth	04	02

GENERAL CHARACTERISTICS OF SUBJECT

IDENTIFICATION
No. 470
Sex M
Marital status S
Age 23 yrs. at
psychological tests

PARENTAL HISTORY
Father
C   H   S   D   O
-   -   -   -   ?
Mother
C   H   S   D   O
-   -   -   -   -

PHYSIOLOGICAL AND METABOLIC DATA

	Admission	Initial	Control	Cold pressor change	Exercise change	Smoking change
Systolic pressure	140	132	106	+09	+44	
Diastolic pressure	84	76	74	+12	-02	
Heart rate	88	72	63	+06	+23	

	Height 68 in.	Ponderal index 13.16
Age 21 yrs.	Weight 138 lbs.	Cholesterol 317 mg. per 100 ml.
	Overweight -05 %	Vital capacity 3.8 liters

HABIT SURVEY
Smoking habits: moderate cigarette smoker
Age begun 18 yrs.   Inhalation: yes
Habits of nervous tension: 4, 5, 21

Plate 404   DRAWINGS AT AN INTERMEDIATE LEVEL OF SOPHISTICATION   447

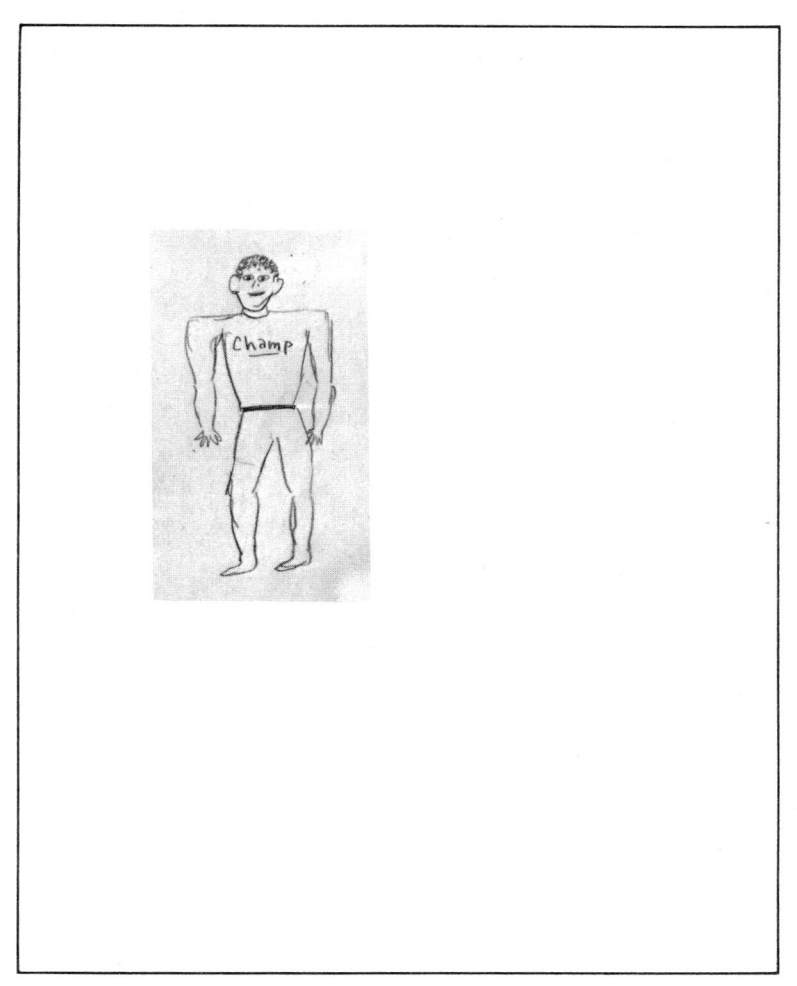

FIGURE-DRAWING CHARACTERISTICS

Structural	Male Female Both		Structural	Male	Female	Structural and Graphic	Male Female Both		Graphic, Global and Height	Male	Female	Body Proportions	Male	Female
Type	0		Omission of Appendages	0	0	Upper and Lower Halves	1	1	Hair Shading	2	2	Head	04	06
Sex Sequence	2		Position of Both Arms	0	1	Four Quarters	4	4	Nudity and Transparency	2	7	Neck	01	04
Posture	1	1	Position of Right Arm	0	0	Relative Size	4		Form	1	3	Shoulders	06	04
Perspective	0	0	Position of Left Arm	0	2	Constant Line Pressure	0	0	Detailing	3	3	Right Arm	02	02
Vertical Midline	0	2	Position of Legs	6	5	Variable Line Pressure	5	5	Identity and Sex	1	1	Left Arm	02	02
Bilateral Symmetry	3	3	Relation of Long Axes	1	1	Line Continuity	0	0	Sophistication	3	3	Chest	03	04
Horizontal Midline	4	4	Right and Left Halves	2	3	Body Shading	4	2	Height	03	04	Girth	03	04

GENERAL CHARACTERISTICS OF SUBJECT

IDENTIFICATION
No. 557
Sex M
Marital status S
Age 24 yrs. at psychological tests

PARENTAL HISTORY				
Father				
C	H	S	D	O
-	-	-	-	?
Mother				
C	H	S	D	O
-	-	-	-	-

PHYSIOLOGICAL AND METABOLIC DATA

	Admission	Initial	Control	Cold pressor change	Exercise change	Smoking change
Systolic pressure	120	114	108	+06	+14	
Diastolic pressure	70	64	64	+06	+02	
Heart rate	64	66	79	+04	00	

Age 22 yrs.	Height	70 in.	Ponderal index 12.97
	Weight	157 lbs.	Cholesterol 217 mg. per 100 ml.
	Overweight +02 %		Vital capacity 4.2 liters

HABIT SURVEY
Smoking habits: light cigarette smoker
Age begun 17 yrs.   Inhalation: yes
Habits of nervous tension: 25

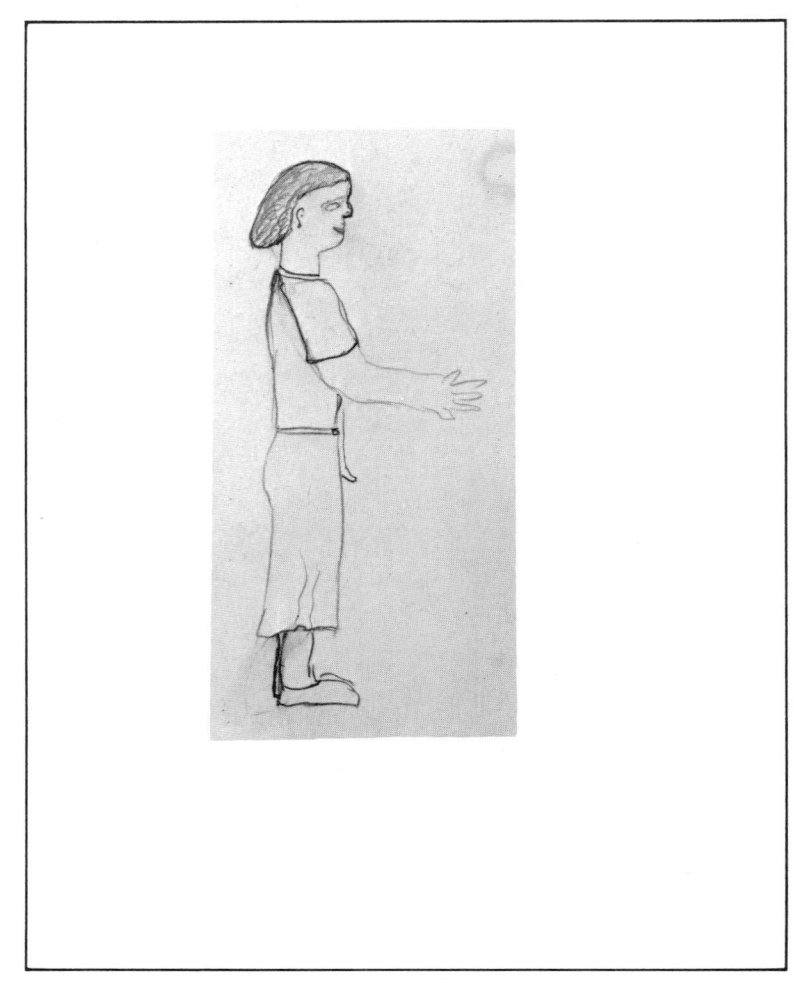

FIGURE-DRAWING CHARACTERISTICS

Structural	Male Female Both		Structural	Male	Female	Structural and Graphic	Male Female Both		Graphic, Global and Height	Male	Female	Body Proportions	Male	Female
Type	0		Omission of Appendages	0	0	Upper and Lower Halves	0	1	Hair Shading	2	1	Head	07	06
Sex Sequence	0		Position of Both Arms	2	2	Four Quarters	4	4	Nudity and Transparency	7	7	Neck	06	06
Posture	1	1	Position of Right Arm	4	4	Relative Size	0		Form	3	3	Shoulders		
Perspective	2	2	Position of Left Arm	7	7	Constant Line Pressure	0	0	Detailing	3	3	Right Arm	04	04
Vertical Midline	7	4	Position of Legs	1	1	Variable Line Pressure	5	4	Identity and Sex	3	3	Left Arm		
Bilateral Symmetry	0	0	Relation of Long Axes	1	1	Line Continuity	2	2	Sophistication	3	3	Chest	05	05
Horizontal Midline	4	4	Right and Left Halves	2	2	Body Shading	0	2	Height	06	05	Girth	06	06

GENERAL CHARACTERISTICS OF SUBJECT

IDENTIFICATION
No. F37
Sex M
Marital status M
Age 24 yrs. at
psychological tests

PARENTAL HISTORY
Father
C   H   S   D   O
-    -   -   -   ?
Mother
C   H   S   D   O
-    -   -   -   -

PHYSIOLOGICAL AND METABOLIC DATA

	Admission	Initial	Control	Cold pressor change	Exercise change	Smoking change
Systolic pressure	110	90	92	+10	+32	+10
Diastolic pressure	70	68	68	+10	+22	+02
Heart rate	76	64	72	-04	-02	+11

Age 22 yrs.	Height 75 in.	Ponderal index 13.54
	Weight 170 lbs.	Cholesterol 224 mg. per 100 ml.
	Overweight -04 %	Vital capacity liters

HABIT SURVEY
Smoking habits: former smoker
Age begun 4* yrs.   Inhalation:
Habits of nervous tension: 1, 2, 3, 5, 22
* "habitual smoker at age 4. Freshman year in college I smoked a pipe for a short period."

STRONG VOCATIONAL INTEREST TEST

Occupation	Artist	Psychologist	Architect	Physician	Osteopath	Dentist	Veterinarian	Mathematician	Physicist	Engineer	Chemist	Production Manager
Standard Score	36	54	41	65	58	45	31	31	35	44	48	35

Occupation	Farmer	Aviator	Carpenter	Printer	Math.-Sci. Teacher	Ind. Arts Teacher	Voc. Agric. Teacher	Policeman	Forest Serv. Man	Y.M.C.A. Phys. Dir.	Personnel Director	Public Administrator
Standard Score	37	43	36	49	49	43	35	36	40	47	44	52

Occupation	Y.M.C.A. Secretary	Soc. Sci. H.S. Teacher	City Sch. Sup't.	Social Worker	Minister	Musician Performer	C.P.A.	Senior C.P.A.	Accountant	Office Man	Purchasing Agent	Banker
Standard Score	38	33	33	53	58	58	18	35	17	28	14	13

Occupation	Mortician	Pharmacist	Sales Manager	Real Est. Manager	Life Ins. Salesman	Advertising Man	Lawyer	Author-Journalist	President Mfg. Co.	Interest Maturity	Occupational Level	Masculinity-Femininity
Standard Score	24	28	20	25	24	34	29	36	27	61	52	40

Plate 406   DRAWINGS AT AN INTERMEDIATE LEVEL OF SOPHISTICATION   449

FIGURE-DRAWING CHARACTERISTICS

Structural	Male Female Both	Structural	Male	Female	Structural and Graphic	Male Female Both		Graphic, Global and Height	Male	Female	Body Proportions	Male	Female
Type	0	Omission of Appendages	0	0	Upper and Lower Halves	1	1	Hair Shading	3	3	Head	07	09
Sex Sequence	0	Position of Both Arms	0	1	Four Quarters	4	4	Nudity and Transparency	7	7	Neck	07	03
Posture	1	1	Position of Right Arm	0	1	Relative Size	1		Form	3	3	Shoulders	05	06
Perspective	0	0	Position of Left Arm	0	0	Constant Line Pressure	0	2	Detailing	3	3	Right Arm	02	02
Vertical Midline	0	0	Position of Legs	4	6	Variable Line Pressure	1	0	Identity and Sex	1	1	Left Arm	02	02
Bilateral Symmetry	2	3	Relation of Long Axes	1	1	Line Continuity	2	2	Sophistication	3	3	Chest	03	04
Horizontal Midline	4	4	Right and Left Halves	1	1	Body Shading	1	4	Height	04	04	Girth	05	05

GENERAL CHARACTERISTICS OF SUBJECT

IDENTIFICATION
No. G34
Sex M
Marital status M
Age 22 yrs. at
psychological tests

PARENTAL HISTORY
Father
C   H   S   D   O
–   –   –   –   ?
Mother
C   H   S   D   O
–   –   –   –   –

PHYSIOLOGICAL AND METABOLIC DATA

	Admission	Initial	Control	Cold pressor change	Exercise change	Smoking change
Systolic pressure	130	118	110	+20	+30	+10
Diastolic pressure	80	74	70	+28	00	+09
Heart rate	78	76	82	+18	+18	+20

Age 21 yrs.	Height 69 in.	Ponderal index 13.42
	Weight 136 lbs.	Cholesterol 210 mg. per 100 ml.
	Overweight –09 %	Vital capacity liters

HABIT SURVEY

Smoking habits: mixed smoker

Age begun 18 yrs.   Inhalation: yes

Habits of nervous tension: 3, 4, 5, 8, 9, 11, 23

STRONG VOCATIONAL INTEREST TEST

Occupation	Artist	Psychologist	Architect	Physician	Osteopath	Dentist	Veterinarian	Mathematician	Physicist	Engineer	Chemist	Production Manager
Standard Score	30	32	32	63	60	48	33	37	40	50	53	42

Occupation	Farmer	Aviator	Carpenter	Printer	Math.-Sci. Teacher	Ind. Arts Teacher	Voc. Agric. Teacher	Policeman	Forest Serv. Man	Y.M.C.A. Phys. Dir.	Personnel Director	Public Administrator
Standard Score	35	48	35	37	44	20	17	46	32	33	21	37

Occupation	Y.M.C.A. Secretary	Soc. Sci. H.S. Teacher	City Sch. Sup't.	Social Worker	Minister	Musician Performer	C.P.A.	Senior C.P.A.	Accountant	Office Man	Purchasing Agent	Banker
Standard Score	09	17	20	22	59	35	34	43	37	40	32	31

Occupation	Mortician	Pharmacist	Sales Manager	Real Est. Manager	Life Ins. Salesman	Advertising Man	Lawyer	Author-Journalist	President Mfg. Co.	Interest Maturity	Occupational Level	Masculinity-Femininity
Standard Score	27	43	19	32	20	21	35	32	32	50	57	52

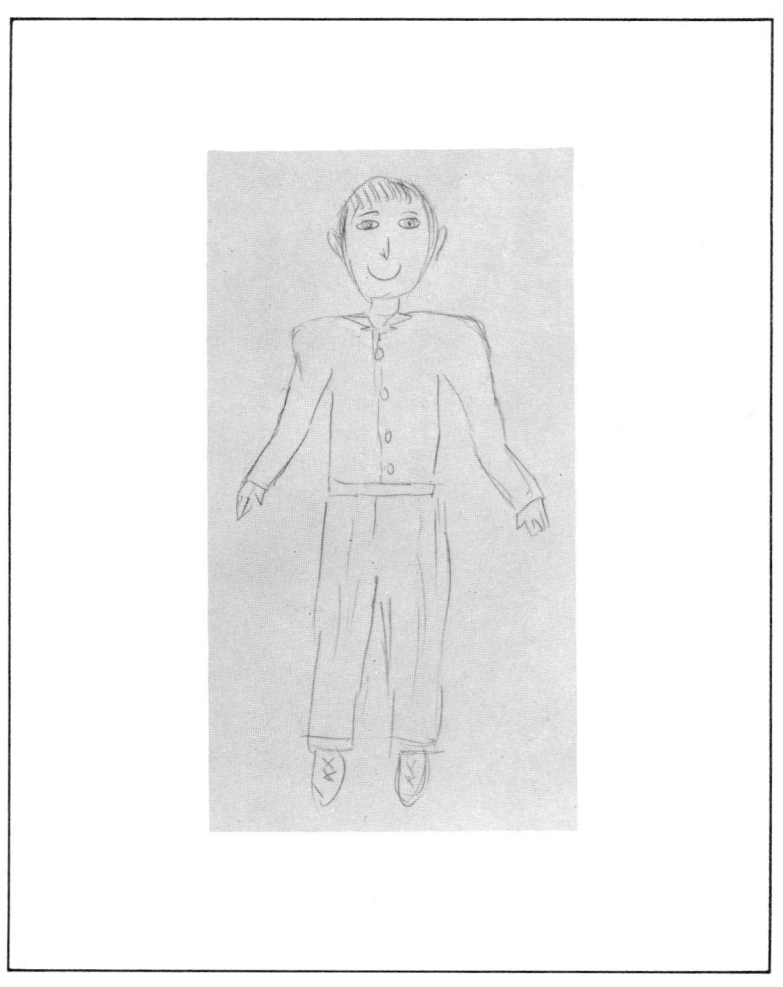

FIGURE-DRAWING CHARACTERISTICS

Structural	Male Female Both	Structural	Male	Female	Structural and Graphic	Male Female Both		Graphic, Global and Height	Male	Female	Body Proportions	Male	Female
Type	0	Omission of Appendages	0	0	Upper and Lower Halves	0	1	Hair Shading	3	2	Head	09	09
Sex Sequence	1	Position of Both Arms	0	0	Four Quarters	4	4	Nudity and Transparency	7	7	Neck	05	05
Posture	1 1	Position of Right Arm	2	2	Relative Size	2		Form	3	3	Shoulders	07	06
Perspective	0 0	Position of Left Arm	2	2	Constant Line Pressure	0	1	Detailing	3	3	Right Arm	04	04
Vertical Midline	3 0	Position of Legs	4	4	Variable Line Pressure	1	0	Identity and Sex	1	1	Left Arm	06	04
Bilateral Symmetry	3 3	Relation of Long Axes	1	1	Line Continuity	0	0	Sophistication	3	3	Chest	05	05
Horizontal Midline	4 4	Right and Left Halves	1	1	Body Shading	2	2	Height	06	06	Girth	06	06

GENERAL CHARACTERISTICS OF SUBJECT

IDENTIFICATION

No. A08

Sex F

Marital status M

Age 22 yrs. at psychological tests

PARENTAL HISTORY

Father

C   H   S   D   O

–   –   –   –   ?

Mother

C   H   S   D   O

–   –   –   –   –

PHYSIOLOGICAL AND METABOLIC DATA

	Admission	Initial	Control	Cold pressor change	Exercise change	Smoking change
Systolic pressure	110	116	114	+12	+38	+02
Diastolic pressure	80	64	63	+10	+07	+10
Heart rate	72	98	93	+06	+32	+12

Age 21 yrs.   Height 63 in.   Ponderal index 12.86

Weight 118 lbs.   Cholesterol 222 mg. per 100 ml.

Overweight –04 %   Vital capacity   liters

HABIT SURVEY

Smoking habits: moderate cigarette smoker

Age begun 17 yrs.   Inhalation: yes

Habits of nervous tension: 4, 8, 9, 10, 17, 25

STRONG VOCATIONAL INTEREST TEST

Occupation	Artist	Psychologist	Architect	Physician	Osteopath	Dentist	Veterinarian	Mathematician	Physicist	Engineer	Chemist	Production Manager
Standard Score	48	57	52	66	49	47	23	42	39	38	54	26

Occupation	Farmer	Aviator	Carpenter	Printer	Math.-Sci. Teacher	Ind. Arts Teacher	Voc. Agric. Teacher	Policeman	Forest Serv. Man	Y.M.C.A. Phys. Dir.	Personnel Director	Public Administrator
Standard Score	37	40	24	44	48	31	33	24	37	35	39	46

Occupation	Y.M.C.A. Secretary	Soc. Sci. H.S. Teacher	City Sch. Sup't.	Social Worker	Minister	Musician Performer	C.P.A.	Senior C.P.A.	Accountant	Office Man	Purchasing Agent	Banker
Standard Score	28	36	35	47	60	65	25	38	18	22	16	10

Occupation	Mortician	Pharmacist	Sales Manager	Real Est. Manager	Life Ins. Salesman	Advertising Man	Lawyer	Author-Journalist	President Mfg. Co.	Interest Maturity	Occupational Level	Masculinity-Femininity
Standard Score	17	31	15	22	17	39	31	43	22	54	54	33

FIGURE-DRAWING CHARACTERISTICS

Structural	Male Female Both		Structural	Male	Female	Structural and Graphic	Male Female Both		Graphic, Global and Height	Male	Female	Body Proportions	Male	Female
Type	0		Omission of Appendages	0	0	Upper and Lower Halves	1	1	Hair Shading	1	2	Head	07	09
Sex Sequence	0		Position of Both Arms	4	1	Four Quarters	4	4	Nudity and Transparency	3	3	Neck	06	07
Posture	1	1	Position of Right Arm	7	4	Relative Size	4		Form	3	3	Shoulders		06
Perspective	2	0	Position of Left Arm	4	0	Constant Line Pressure	0	1	Detailing	1	3	Right Arm		06
Vertical Midline	4	0	Position of Legs	1	4	Variable Line Pressure	2	0	Identity and Sex	1	1	Left Arm	04	04
Bilateral Symmetry	0	3	Relation of Long Axes	1	1	Line Continuity	0	0	Sophistication	3	3	Chest	06	05
Horizontal Midline	4	4	Right and Left Halves	2	2	Body Shading	5	2	Height	05	06	Girth	06	06

GENERAL CHARACTERISTICS OF SUBJECT

IDENTIFICATION	PARENTAL HISTORY
No. A36	Father
Sex M	C H S D O
Marital status S	- - - - ?
Age 23 yrs. at	Mother
psychological tests	C H S D O
	- - - - -

PHYSIOLOGICAL AND METABOLIC DATA

	Admission	Initial	Control	Cold pressor change	Exercise change	Smoking change
Systolic pressure	95	132	116	+14	+42	+01
Diastolic pressure	68	60	54	+13	-12	+04
Heart rate	72		61	+03	+27	+01

Age 22 yrs.	Height 74 in.	Ponderal index 13.81
	Weight 154 lbs.	Cholesterol 185 mg. per 100 ml.
	Overweight -11 %	Vital capacity liters

HABIT SURVEY

Smoking habits: nonsmoker

  Age begun   yrs.   Inhalation:

Habits of nervous tension: 25

STRONG VOCATIONAL INTEREST TEST

Occupation	Artist	Psychologist	Architect	Physician	Osteopath	Dentist	Veterinarian	Mathematician	Physicist	Engineer	Chemist	Production Manager
Standard Score	3	6	2	5	4	3	2	3	2	3	4	5

Occupation	Farmer	Aviator	Carpenter	Printer	Math.-Sci. Teacher	Ind. Arts Teacher	Voc. Agric. Teacher	Policeman	Forest Serv. Man	Y.M.C.A. Phys. Dir.	Personnel Director	Public Administrator
Standard Score	4	5	2	5	5	0	1	2	2	2	4	5

Occupation	Y.M.C.A. Secretary	Soc. Sci. H.S. Teacher	City Sch. Sup't.	Social Worker	Minister	Musician Performer	C.P.A.	Senior C.P.A.	Accountant	Office Man	Purchasing Agent	Banker
Standard Score	2	4	3	4	6	6	5	6	2	4	3	2

Occupation	Mortician	Pharmacist	Sales Manager	Real Est. Manager	Life Ins. Salesman	Advertising Man	Lawyer	Author-Journalist	President Mfg. Co.	Interest Maturity	Occupational Level	Masculinity-Femininity
Standard Score	3	3	4	5	4	5	7	6	4	5	5	4

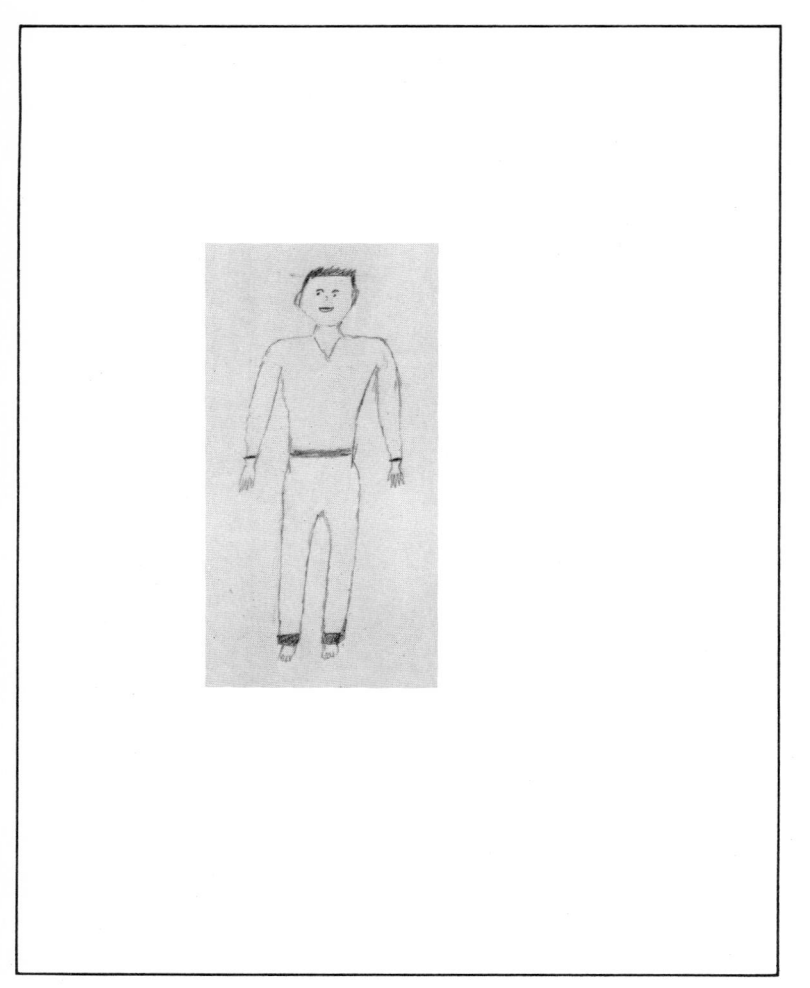

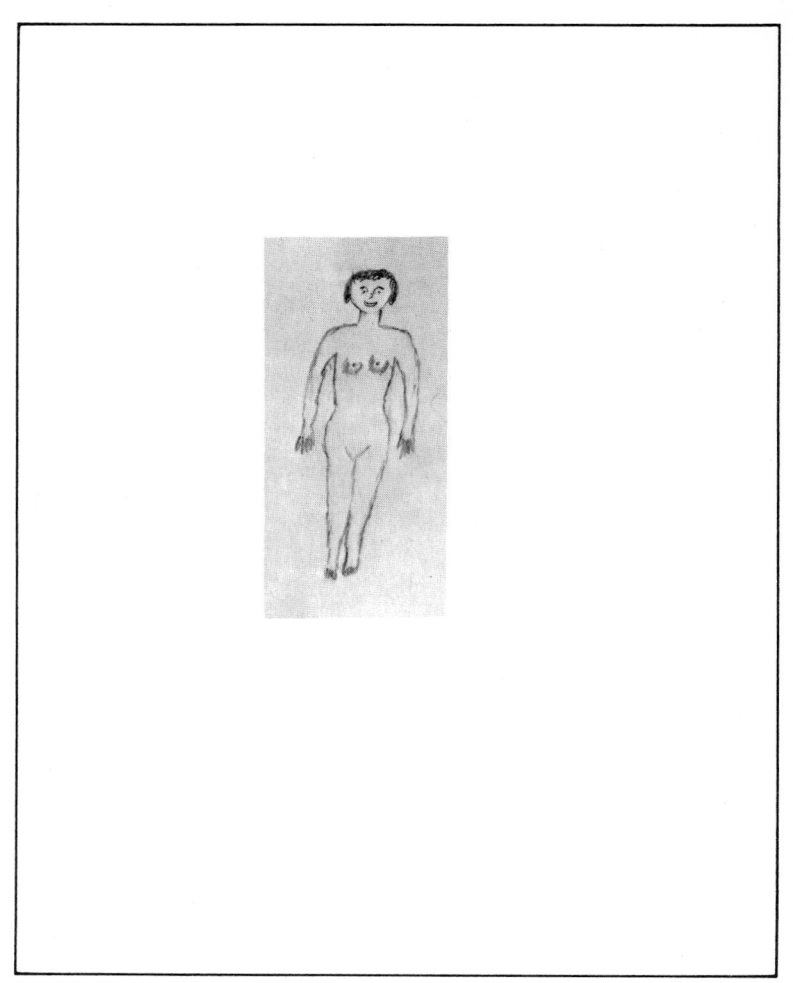

FIGURE-DRAWING CHARACTERISTICS

Structural	Male Female Both		Structural	Male	Female	Structural and Graphic	Male Female Both		Graphic, Global and Height	Male	Female	Body Proportions	Male	Female
Type	0		Omission of Appendages	0	0	Upper and Lower Halves	1	1	Hair Shading	3	3	Head	04	03
Sex Sequence	0		Position of Both Arms	0	0	Four Quarters	4	4	Nudity and Transparency	7	0	Neck	04	04
Posture	1	1	Position of Right Arm	0	0	Relative Size	0		Form	1	1	Shoulders	05	03
Perspective	0	0	Position of Left Arm	0	0	Constant Line Pressure	0	0	Detailing	3	3	Right Arm	04	02
Vertical Midline	0	0	Position of Legs	4	2	Variable Line Pressure	1	1	Identity and Sex	1	1	Left Arm	04	02
Bilateral Symmetry	4	3	Relation of Long Axes	1	1	Line Continuity	0	0	Sophistication	3	3	Chest	04	03
Horizontal Midline	4	0	Right and Left Halves	1	2	Body Shading	4	3	Height	04	03	Girth	04	03

GENERAL CHARACTERISTICS OF SUBJECT

IDENTIFICATION
No. A70
Sex M
Marital status S
Age 23 yrs. at psychological tests

PARENTAL HISTORY
Father
C H S D O
- - - - ?
Mother
C H S D O
- - - - -

PHYSIOLOGICAL AND METABOLIC DATA

	Admission	Initial	Control	Cold pressor change	Exercise change	Smoking change
Systolic pressure	145	128	125	+12	+31	+06
Diastolic pressure	80	66	61	+16	+07	+06
Heart rate	72	84	71	+06	+24	+05

Age 22 yrs.	Height 74 in.	Ponderal index 13.01
	Weight 184 lbs.	Cholesterol 217 mg. per 100 ml.
	Overweight +06 %	Vital capacity liters

HABIT SURVEY
Smoking habits: nonsmoker
Age begun yrs. Inhalation:
Habits of nervous tension: 4, 5, 6, 9, 11, 16, 21

STRONG VOCATIONAL INTEREST TEST

Occupation	Artist	Psychologist	Architect	Physician	Osteopath	Dentist	Veterinarian	Mathematician	Physicist	Engineer	Chemist	Production Manager
Standard Score	34	29	37	58	55	49	49	19	14	28	35	35

Occupation	Farmer	Aviator	Carpenter	Printer	Math.-Sci. Teacher	Ind. Arts Teacher	Voc. Agric. Teacher	Policeman	Forest Serv. Man	Y.M.C.A. Phys. Dir.	Personnel Director	Public Administrator
Standard Score	46	43	26	31	36	29	36	31	37	40	28	33

Occupation	Y.M.C.A. Secretary	Soc. Sci. H.S. Teacher	City Sch. Sup't.	Social Worker	Minister	Musician Performer	C.P.A.	Senior C.P.A.	Accountant	Office Man	Purchasing Agent	Banker
Standard Score	27	33	24	36	60	50	22	39	18	34	21	22

Occupation	Mortician	Pharmacist	Sales Manager	Real Est. Manager	Life Ins. Salesman	Advertising Man	Lawyer	Author-Journalist	President Mfg. Co.	Interest Maturity	Occupational Level	Masculinity-Femininity
Standard Score	29	34	24	40	32	35	30	33	31	54	55	48

Plate 410   **DRAWINGS AT AN INTERMEDIATE LEVEL OF SOPHISTICATION**   453

FIGURE-DRAWING CHARACTERISTICS

Structural	Male Female Both	Structural	Male	Female	Structural and Graphic	Male Female Both	Graphic, Global and Height	Male	Female	Body Proportions	Male	Female
Type	0	Omission of Appendages	0	0	Upper and Lower Halves	0	0	Hair Shading	3	3	Head	07	09
Sex Sequence	1	Position of Both Arms	0	0	Four Quarters	4	4	Nudity and Transparency	7	7	Neck	06	10
Posture	1	1	Position of Right Arm	0	0	Relative Size	4		Form	3	3	Shoulders	09	06
Perspective	0	0	Position of Left Arm	0	0	Constant Line Pressure	0	0	Detailing	3	3	Right Arm	06	04
Vertical Midline	3	0	Position of Legs	4	4	Variable Line Pressure	1	1	Identity and Sex	1	1	Left Arm	06	04
Bilateral Symmetry	3	3	Relation of Long Axes	1	1	Line Continuity	0	0	Sophistication	3	3	Chest	06	05
Horizontal Midline	4	4	Right and Left Halves	1	1	Body Shading	7	7	Height	07	08	Girth	06	05

GENERAL CHARACTERISTICS OF SUBJECT

IDENTIFICATION
No. B04
Sex M
Marital status S
Age 22 yrs. at psychological tests

PARENTAL HISTORY
Father
C H S D O
-   -   -   -   ?
Mother
C H S D O
-   -   -   -   -

PHYSIOLOGICAL AND METABOLIC DATA

	Admission	Initial	Control	Cold pressor change	Exercise change	Smoking change
Systolic pressure	114	124	116	+18	+40	-06
Diastolic pressure	58	56	52	+32	-08	00
Heart rate	72	76	64	+05	+19	+03

Age 22 yrs. Height 73 in. Weight 176 lbs. Overweight +05 %
Ponderal index 13.04 Cholesterol 200 mg. per 100 ml. Vital capacity 4.6 liters

HABIT SURVEY
Smoking habits: heavy cigarette smoker
Age begun 19 yrs.   Inhalation: yes
Habits of nervous tension: 1, 5, 11

STRONG VOCATIONAL INTEREST TEST

Occupation	Artist	Psychologist	Architect	Physician	Osteopath	Dentist	Veterinarian	Mathematician	Physicist	Engineer	Chemist	Production Manager
Standard Score	20	26	26	37	27	30	25	32	19	30	30	29

Occupation	Farmer	Aviator	Carpenter	Printer	Math.-Sci. Teacher	Ind. Arts Teacher	Voc. Agric. Teacher	Policeman	Forest Serv. Man	Y.M.C.A. Phys. Dir.	Personnel Director	Public Administrator
Standard Score	28	25	10	28	36	01	23	21	17	19	25	30

Occupation	Y.M.C.A. Secretary	Soc. Sci. H.S. Teacher	City Sch. Sup't.	Social Worker	Minister	Musician Performer	C.P.A.	Senior C.P.A.	Accountant	Office Man	Purchasing Agent	Banker
Standard Score	19	28	23	21	61	27	47	45	42	38	43	39

Occupation	Mortician	Pharmacist	Sales Manager	Real Est. Manager	Life Ins. Salesman	Advertising Man	Lawyer	Author-Journalist	President Mfg. Co.	Interest Maturity	Occupational Level	Masculinity-Femininity
Standard Score	34	36	40	40	33	30	36	30	36	52	62	48

FIGURE-DRAWING CHARACTERISTICS

Structural	Male Female Both		Structural	Male	Female	Structural and Graphic	Male Female Both		Graphic, Global and Height	Male	Female	Body Proportions	Male	Female
Type	0		Omission of Appendages	0	0	Upper and Lower Halves	3	3	Hair Shading	3	3	Head	09	09
Sex Sequence	2		Position of Both Arms	0	4	Four Quarters	4	4	Nudity and Transparency	7	7	Neck	07	08
Posture	1	1	Position of Right Arm	0	7	Relative Size	0		Form	3	3	Shoulders	13	
Perspective	0	2	Position of Left Arm	0	0	Constant Line Pressure	5	0	Detailing	1	3	Right Arm	10	
Vertical Midline	3	4	Position of Legs	4	1	Variable Line Pressure	0	1	Identity and Sex	1	1	Left Arm	10	06
Bilateral Symmetry	5	0	Relation of Long Axes	1	1	Line Continuity	4	0	Sophistication	3	3	Chest	09	07
Horizontal Midline	4	0	Right and Left Halves	1	2	Body Shading	4	0	Height	08	08	Girth	10	08

GENERAL CHARACTERISTICS OF SUBJECT

IDENTIFICATION
No. B14
Sex M
Marital status S
Age 23 yrs. at
psychological tests

PARENTAL HISTORY
Father
C   H   S   D   O
–   –   –   –   ?
Mother
C   H   S   D   O
–   –   –   –   –

PHYSIOLOGICAL AND METABOLIC DATA

	Admission	Initial	Control	Cold pressor change	Exercise change	Smoking change
Systolic pressure	120	126	116	+20	+22	00
Diastolic pressure	80	70	76	+26	–06	00
Heart rate	72	84	63	+02	+31	+02

Age 23 yrs.	Height 70 in.	Ponderal index 12.61
	Weight 171 lbs.	Cholesterol 325 mg. per 100 ml.
	Overweight +10 %	Vital capacity 5.4 liters

HABIT SURVEY

Smoking habits: nonsmoker

  Age begun   yrs.   Inhalation:

Habits of nervous tension: 2, 4, 5, 6, 9, 16

STRONG VOCATIONAL INTEREST TEST

Occupation	Artist	Psychologist	Architect	Physician	Osteopath	Dentist	Veterinarian	Mathematician	Physicist	Engineer	Chemist	Production Manager
Standard Score	12	22	06	25	33	14	29	03	–10	08	08	27

Occupation	Farmer	Aviator	Carpenter	Printer	Math.-Sci. Teacher	Ind. Arts Teacher	Voc. Agric. Teacher	Policeman	Forest Serv. Man	Y.M.C.A. Phys. Dir.	Personnel Director	Public Administrator
Standard Score	27	29	07	28	32	09	25	38	18	47	38	42

Occupation	Y.M.C.A. Secretary	Soc. Sci. H.S. Teacher	City Sch. Sup't.	Social Worker	Minister	Musician Performer	C.P.A.	Senior C.P.A.	Accountant	Office Man	Purchasing Agent	Banker
Standard Score	37	49	34	42	61	23	29	39	29	42	32	31

Occupation	Mortician	Pharmacist	Sales Manager	Real Est. Manager	Life Ins. Salesman	Advertising Man	Lawyer	Author-Journalist	President Mfg. Co.	Interest Maturity	Occupational Level	Masculinity-Femininity
Standard Score	44	48	56	51	55	40	36	25	32	63	56	43

FIGURE-DRAWING CHARACTERISTICS

Structural	Male	Female	Structural	Male	Female	Structural and Graphic	Male	Female	Graphic, Global and Height	Male	Female	Body Proportions	Male	Female
	Both						Both							
Type	0		Omission of Appendages	0	0	Upper and Lower Halves	1	3	Hair Shading	2	2	Head	07	09
Sex Sequence	0		Position of Both Arms	0	0	Four Quarters	4	4	Nudity and Transparency	7	7	Neck	04	04
Posture	1	1	Position of Right Arm	0	0	Relative Size	0		Form	3	3	Shoulders	10	07
Perspective	0	0	Position of Left Arm	0	0	Constant Line Pressure	1	1	Detailing	3	3	Right Arm	07	05
Vertical Midline	3	0	Position of Legs	6	6	Variable Line Pressure	0	0	Identity and Sex	1	1	Left Arm	06	04
Bilateral Symmetry	1	1	Relation of Long Axes	1	1	Line Continuity	0	0	Sophistication	3	3	Chest	08	05
Horizontal Midline	4	4	Right and Left Halves	1	1	Body Shading	0	1	Height	07	06	Girth	09	05

GENERAL CHARACTERISTICS OF SUBJECT

IDENTIFICATION
No. B36
Sex M
Marital status S
Age 22 yrs. at
psychological tests

PARENTAL HISTORY				
Father				
C	H	S	D	0
-	-	-	-	?
Mother				
C	H	S	D	0
-	-	-	-	-

PHYSIOLOGICAL AND METABOLIC DATA

	Admission	Initial	Control	Cold pressor change	Exercise change	Smoking change
Systolic pressure	120	128	122	+06	+16	+09
Diastolic pressure	70	68	72	+12	-32	+07
Heart rate	78	56	51	+17	+05	+13

Age 22 yrs.	Height 74 in.	Ponderal index 13.14
	Weight 178 lbs.	Cholesterol 212 mg. per 100 ml.
	Overweight +03 %	Vital capacity 5.3 liters

HABIT SURVEY

Smoking habits: mixed smoker

   Age begun 16 yrs.   Inhalation: yes

Habits of nervous tension: 4, 5, 6, 9, 11, 12

STRONG VOCATIONAL INTEREST TEST

Occupation	Artist	Psychologist	Architect	Physician	Osteopath	Dentist	Veterinarian	Mathematician	Physicist	Engineer	Chemist	Production Manager
Standard Score	39	36	33	54	55	37	30	19	14	17	20	22

Occupation	Farmer	Aviator	Carpenter	Printer	Math.-Sci. Teacher	Ind. Arts Teacher	Voc. Agric. Teacher	Policeman	Forest Serv. Man	Y.M.C.A. Phys. Dir.	Personnel Director	Public Administrator
Standard Score	23	28	03	30	25	01	17	32	19	45	36	40

Occupation	Y.M.C.A. Secretary	Soc. Sci. H.S. Teacher	City Sch. Sup't.	Social Worker	Minister	Musician Performer	C.P.A.	Senior C.P.A.	Accountant	Office Man	Purchasing Agent	Banker
Standard Score	33	41	32	50	61	54	32	30	14	30	14	30

Occupation	Mortician	Pharmacist	Sales Manager	Real Est. Manager	Life Ins. Salesman	Advertising Man	Lawyer	Author-Journalist	President Mfg. Co.	Interest Maturity	Occupational Level	Masculinity-Femininity
Standard Score	39	41	35	40	47	43	53	46	26	53	60	30

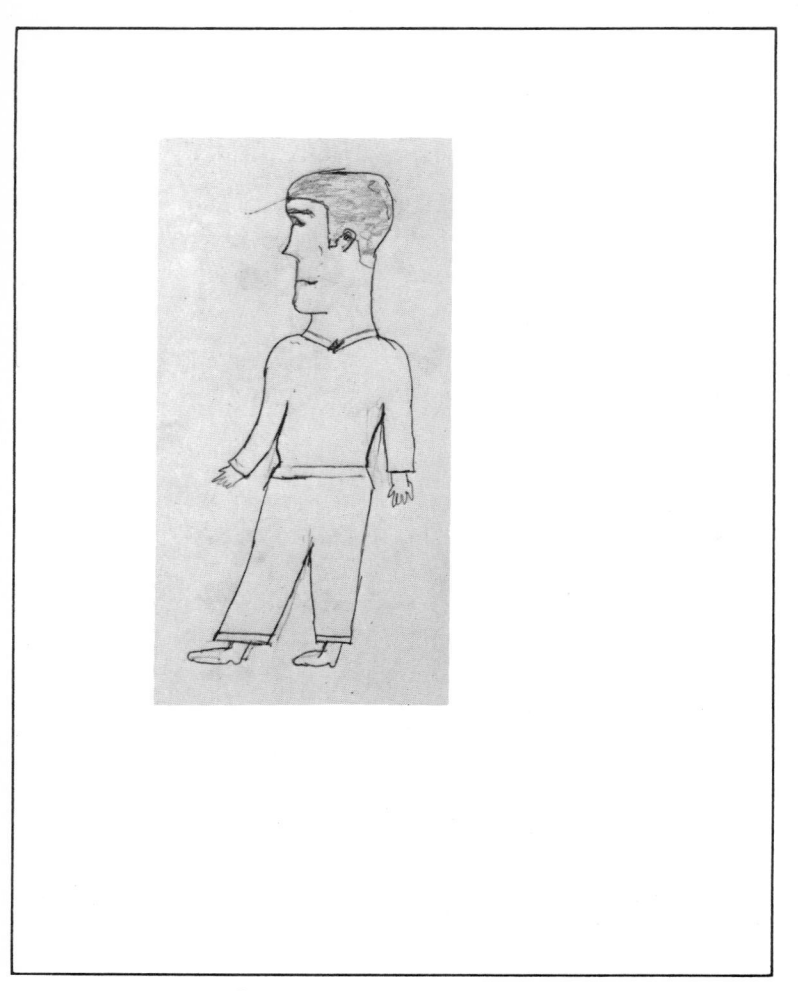

FIGURE-DRAWING CHARACTERISTICS

Structural	Male Female Both		Structural	Male	Female	Structural and Graphic	Male Female Both		Graphic, Global and Height	Male	Female	Body Proportions	Male	Female
Type	0		Omission of Appendages	0	0	Upper and Lower Halves	1	0	Hair Shading	1	1	Head	12	09
Sex Sequence	0		Position of Both Arms	1	4	Four Quarters	4	4	Nudity and Transparency	7	7	Neck	07	08
Posture	1	1	Position of Right Arm	4	7	Relative Size	4		Form	3	3	Shoulders	05	
Perspective	5	2	Position of Left Arm	0	4	Constant Line Pressure	0	0	Detailing	3	3	Right Arm	03	
Vertical Midline	0	4	Position of Legs	5	6	Variable Line Pressure	5	5	Identity and Sex	1	1	Left Arm	04	02
Bilateral Symmetry	3	0	Relation of Long Axes	1	1	Line Continuity	2	2	Sophistication	3	3	Chest	04	06
Horizontal Midline	4	4	Right and Left Halves	2	2	Body Shading	0	2	Height	05	05	Girth	05	06

GENERAL CHARACTERISTICS OF SUBJECT

IDENTIFICATION
No. B67
Sex M
Marital status S
Age 22 yrs. at psychological tests

PARENTAL HISTORY
Father
C   H   S   D   O
-   -   -   -   ?
Mother
C   H   S   D   O
-   -   -   -   -

PHYSIOLOGICAL AND METABOLIC DATA

	Admission	Initial	Control	Cold pressor change	Exercise change	Smoking change
Systolic pressure	110	122	116	+08	+18	+12
Diastolic pressure	74	76	70	+08	-06	+10
Heart rate	60	70	64	+06	+15	+08

Age 22 yrs.	Height	75 in.		Ponderal index	12.56	
	Weight	213 lbs.		Cholesterol	225	mg. per 100 ml.
	Overweight +20 %			Vital capacity	6.4	liters

HABIT SURVEY

Smoking habits: nonsmoker

Age begun   yrs.   Inhalation:

Habits of nervous tension: 1, 4, 5, 6, 9, 10, 16, 20, 21, 22, 24

STRONG VOCATIONAL INTEREST TEST

Occupation	Artist	Psychologist	Architect	Physician	Osteopath	Dentist	Veterinarian	Mathematician	Physicist	Engineer	Chemist	Production Manager
Standard Score	22	30	09	38	52	19	31	-08	-02	-07	03	15

Occupation	Farmer	Aviator	Carpenter	Printer	Math.-Sci. Teacher	Ind. Arts Teacher	Voc. Agric. Teacher	Policeman	Forest Serv. Man	Y.M.C.A. Phys. Dir.	Personnel Director	Public Administrator
Standard Score	12	12	-10	12	28	-10	19	22	08	50	42	46

Occupation	Y.M.C.A. Secretary	Soc. Sci. H.S. Teacher	City Sch. Sup't.	Social Worker	Minister	Musician Performer	C.P.A.	Senior C.P.A.	Accountant	Office Man	Purchasing Agent	Banker
Standard Score	47	55	47	52	61	35	27	24	15	34	16	26

Occupation	Mortician	Pharmacist	Sales Manager	Real Est. Manager	Life Ins. Salesman	Advertising Man	Lawyer	Author-Journalist	President Mfg. Co.	Interest Maturity	Occupational Level	Masculinity-Femininity
Standard Score	49	46	52	52	68	46	49	36	37	63	69	26

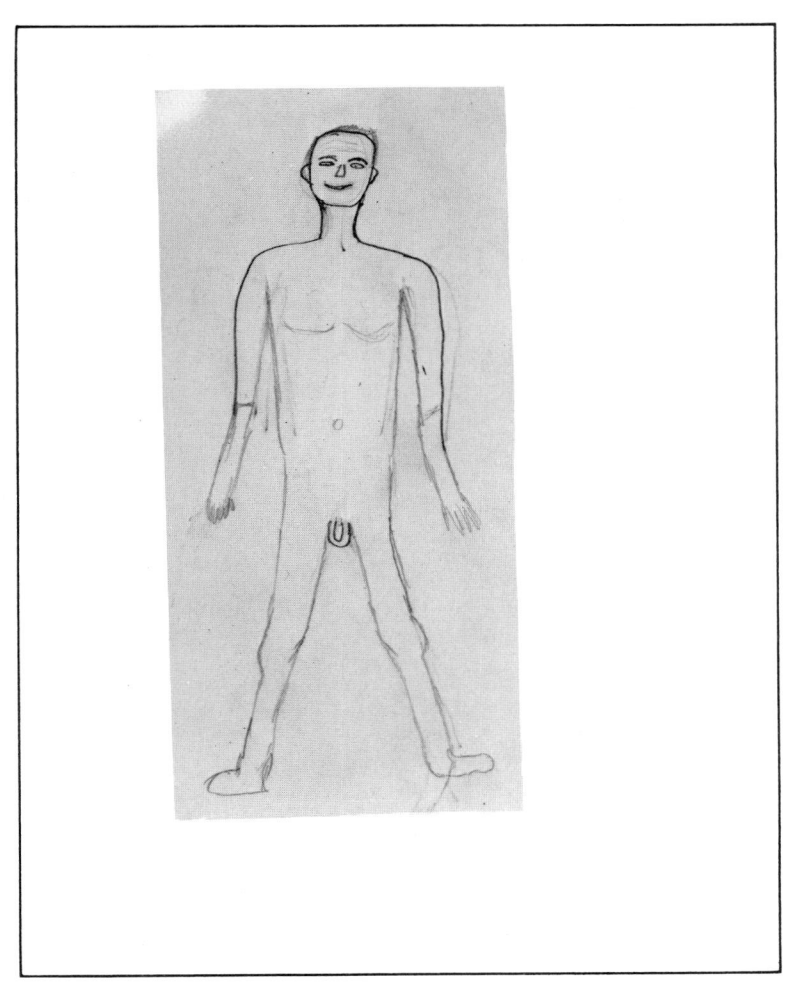

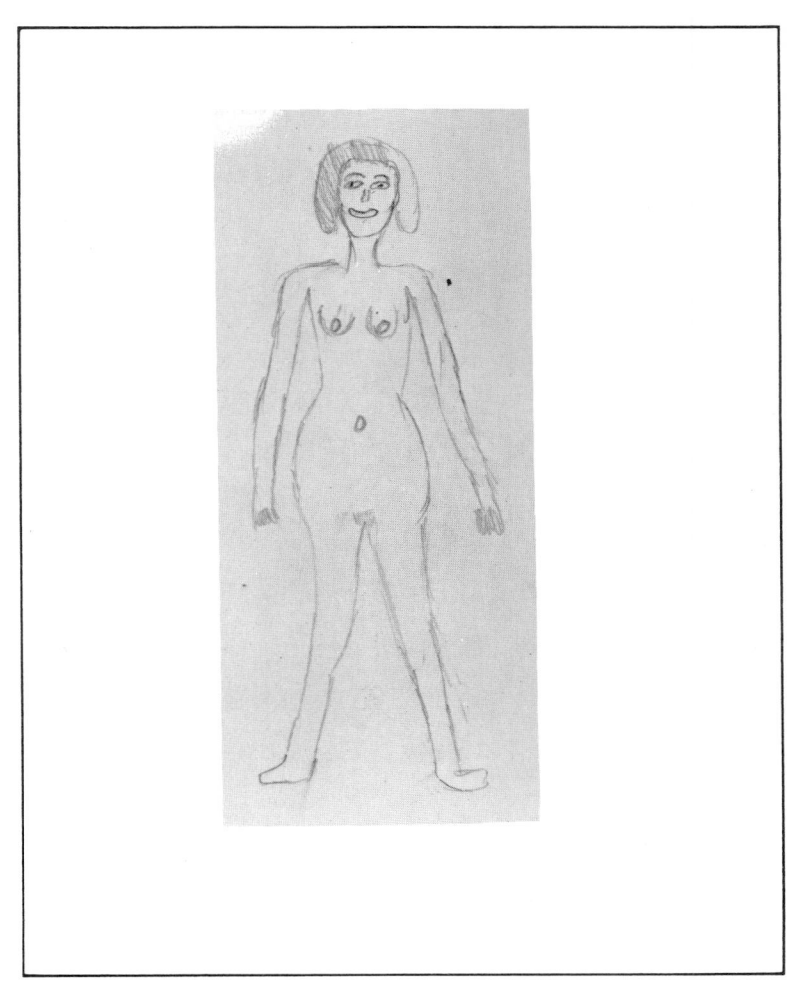

FIGURE-DRAWING CHARACTERISTICS

Structural	Male Female Both	Structural	Male	Female	Structural and Graphic	Male Female Both		Graphic, Global and Height	Male	Female	Body Proportions	Male	Female
Type	0	Omission of Appendages	0	0	Upper and Lower Halves	1	1	Hair Shading	3	3	Head	06	07
Sex Sequence	0	Position of Both Arms	0	0	Four Quarters	4	4	Nudity and Transparency	0	0	Neck	12	08
Posture	1 1	Position of Right Arm	0	0	Relative Size	1		Form	3	3	Shoulders	07	06
Perspective	0 0	Position of Left Arm	0	0	Constant Line Pressure	0	1	Detailing	3	3	Right Arm	06	06
Vertical Midline	0 0	Position of Legs	6	6	Variable Line Pressure	4	0	Identity and Sex	1	1	Left Arm	06	06
Bilateral Symmetry	3 3	Relation of Long Axes	1	1	Line Continuity	0	0	Sophistication	3	3	Chest	06	05
Horizontal Midline	0 0	Right and Left Halves	1	1	Body Shading	1	3	Height	07	06	Girth	07	05

GENERAL CHARACTERISTICS OF SUBJECT

IDENTIFICATION				
No. D30				
Sex M				
Marital status S				
Age 21 yrs. at				
psychological tests				

PARENTAL HISTORY				
Father				
C	H	S	D	0
-	-	-	-	?
Mother				
C	H	S	D	0
-	-	-	-	-

PHYSIOLOGICAL AND METABOLIC DATA

	Admission	Initial	Control	Cold pressor change	Exercise change	Smoking change
Systolic pressure	130	118	106	+10	+32	+12
Diastolic pressure	60	62	68	+07	-20	+08
Heart rate	74	76	64	-04	+30	+16

Age 21 yrs.	Height 74 in.	Ponderal index 13.86
	Weight 152 lbs.	Cholesterol 122 mg. per 100 ml.
	Overweight -12 %	Vital capacity 5.4 liters

HABIT SURVEY

Smoking habits: heavy cigarette smoker

Age begun 16 yrs.   Inhalation: yes

Habits of nervous tension: 2, 4, 5, 6, 9, 10, 12, 14, 16, 22

STRONG VOCATIONAL INTEREST TEST

Occupation	Artist	Psychologist	Architect	Physician	Osteopath	Dentist	Veterinarian	Mathematician	Physicist	Engineer	Chemist	Production Manager
Standard Score	32	46	40	59	41	41	13	44	39	42	51	33

Occupation	Farmer	Aviator	Carpenter	Printer	Math.-Sci. Teacher	Ind. Arts Teacher	Voc. Agric. Teacher	Policeman	Forest Serv. Man	Y.M.C.A. Phys. Dir.	Personnel Director	Public Administrator
Standard Score	33	34	25	29	43	21	26	24	26	28	33	42

Occupation	Y.M.C.A. Secretary	Soc. Sci. H.S. Teacher	City Sch. Sup't.	Social Worker	Minister	Musician Performer	C.P.A.	Senior C.P.A.	Accountant	Office Man	Purchasing Agent	Banker
Standard Score	27	30	35	34	63	46	33	38	23	23	14	19

Occupation	Mortician	Pharmacist	Sales Manager	Real Est. Manager	Life Ins. Salesman	Advertising Man	Lawyer	Author-Journalist	President Mfg. Co.	Interest Maturity	Occupational Level	Masculinity-Femininity
Standard Score	16	16	19	22	21	26	36	34	33	54	59	44

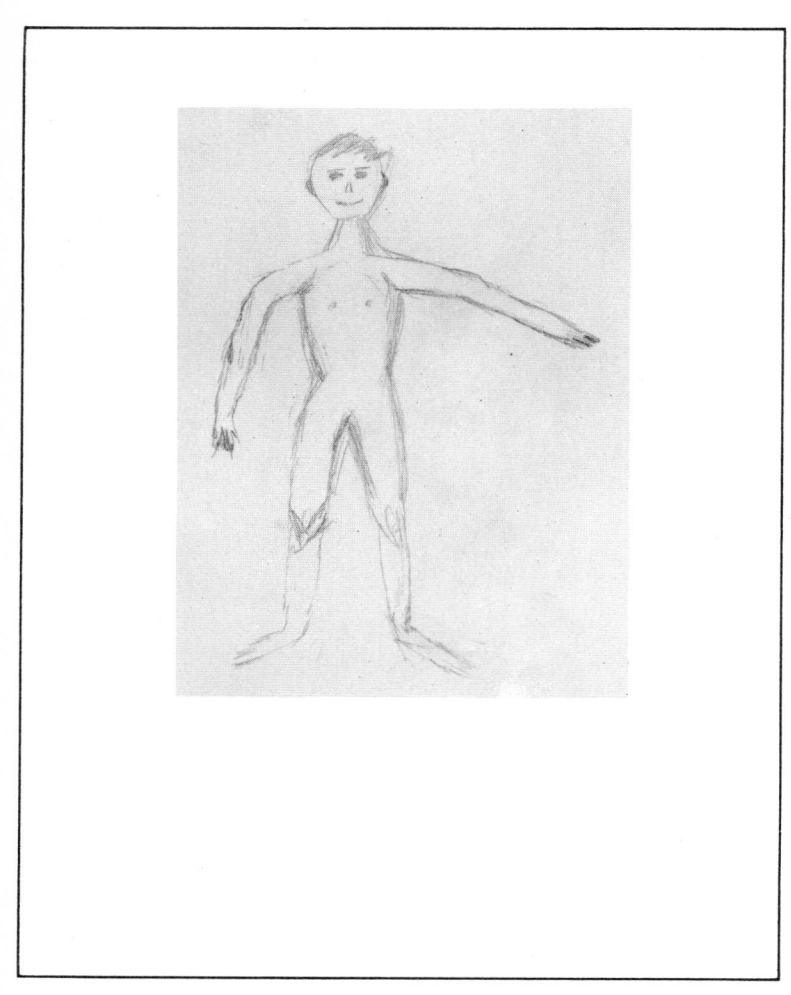

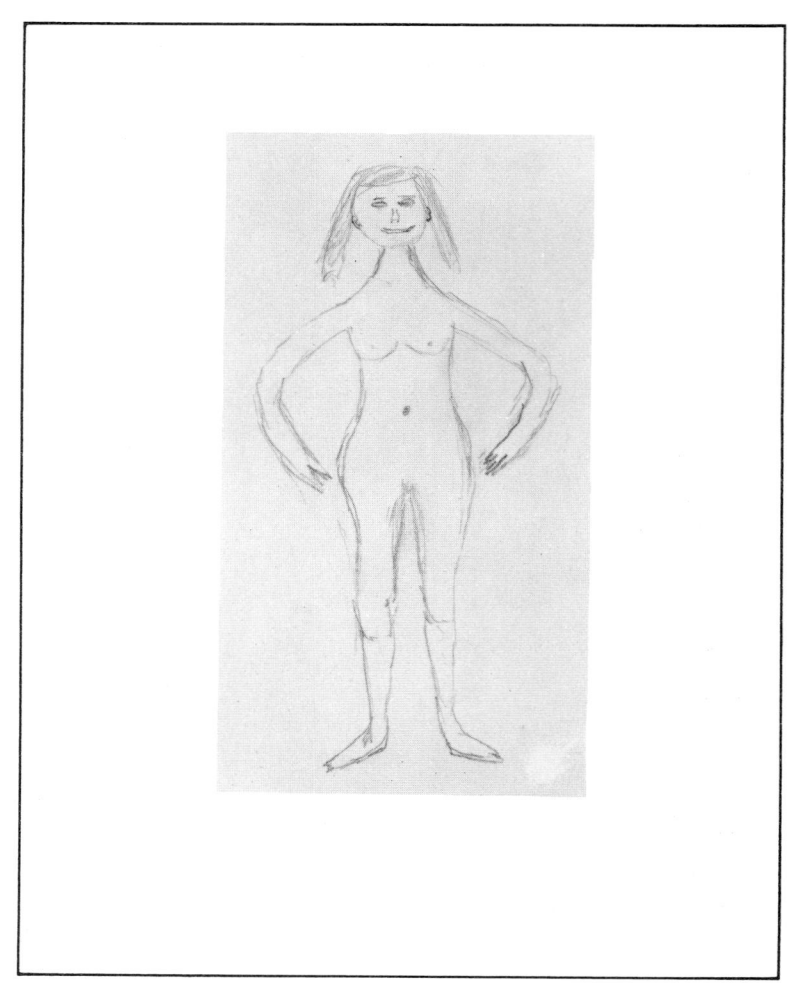

FIGURE-DRAWING CHARACTERISTICS

Structural	Male Female Both	Structural	Male	Female	Structural and Graphic	Male Female Both		Graphic, Global and Height	Male	Female	Body Proportions	Male	Female
Type	0	Omission of Appendages	0	0	Upper and Lower Halves	1	1	Hair Shading	3	3	Head	07	07
Sex Sequence	0	Position of Both Arms	0	0	Four Quarters	4	4	Nudity and Transparency	0	0	Neck	09	09
Posture	1 1	Position of Right Arm	2	5	Relative Size	4		Form	3	3	Shoulders	04	05
Perspective	0 0	Position of Left Arm	2	5	Constant Line Pressure	0	0	Detailing	3	3	Right Arm	04	04
Vertical Midline	0 0	Position of Legs	6	4	Variable Line Pressure	1	1	Identity and Sex	3	3	Left Arm	04	04
Bilateral Symmetry	3 3	Relation of Long Axes	1	1	Line Continuity	0	0	Sophistication	3	3	Chest	04	05
Horizontal Midline	0 0	Right and Left Halves	1	1	Body Shading	3	3	Height	05	06	Girth	04	06

GENERAL CHARACTERISTICS OF SUBJECT

IDENTIFICATION

No. E17
Sex F
Marital status M
Age 26 yrs. at
psychological tests

PARENTAL HISTORY

Father
C H S D O
- - - - ?
Mother
C H S D O
- - - - -

PHYSIOLOGICAL AND METABOLIC DATA

	Admission	Initial	Control	Cold pressor change	Exercise change	Smoking change
Systolic pressure	120	102	98	-02	+52	
Diastolic pressure	80	62	62	+28	-02	
Heart rate	76	60	64	00	+43	

Age 23 yrs.
Height 68 in.
Weight 132 lbs.
Overweight -07 %
Ponderal index 13.36
Cholesterol 230 mg. per 100 ml.
Vital capacity 3.5 liters

HABIT SURVEY

Smoking habits: nonsmoker
Age begun   yrs.   Inhalation:
Habits of nervous tension: 1, 8, 10, 23

STRONG VOCATIONAL INTEREST TEST

Occupation	Artist	Psychologist	Architect	Physician	Osteopath	Dentist	Veterinarian	Mathematician	Physicist	Engineer	Chemist	Production Manager
Standard Score	49	41	45	56	50	42	19	35	25	23	39	15

Occupation	Farmer	Aviator	Carpenter	Printer	Math.-Sci. Teacher	Ind. Arts Teacher	Voc. Agric. Teacher	Policeman	Forest Serv. Man	Y.M.C.A. Phys. Dir.	Personnel Director	Public Administrator
Standard Score	25	21	11	35	31	01	10	20	20	35	28	40

Occupation	Y.M.C.A. Secretary	Soc. Sci. H.S. Teacher	City Sch. Sup't.	Social Worker	Minister	Musician Performer	C.P.A.	Senior C.P.A.	Accountant	Office Man	Purchasing Agent	Banker
Standard Score	31	38	32	43	64	58	41	28	15	24	10	18

Occupation	Mortician	Pharmacist	Sales Manager	Real Est. Manager	Life Ins. Salesman	Advertising Man	Lawyer	Author-Journalist	President Mfg. Co.	Interest Maturity	Occupational Level	Masculinity-Femininity
Standard Score	21	26	23	34	34	44	50	50	28	56	61	18

Plate 416   **DRAWINGS AT AN INTERMEDIATE LEVEL OF SOPHISTICATION**   459

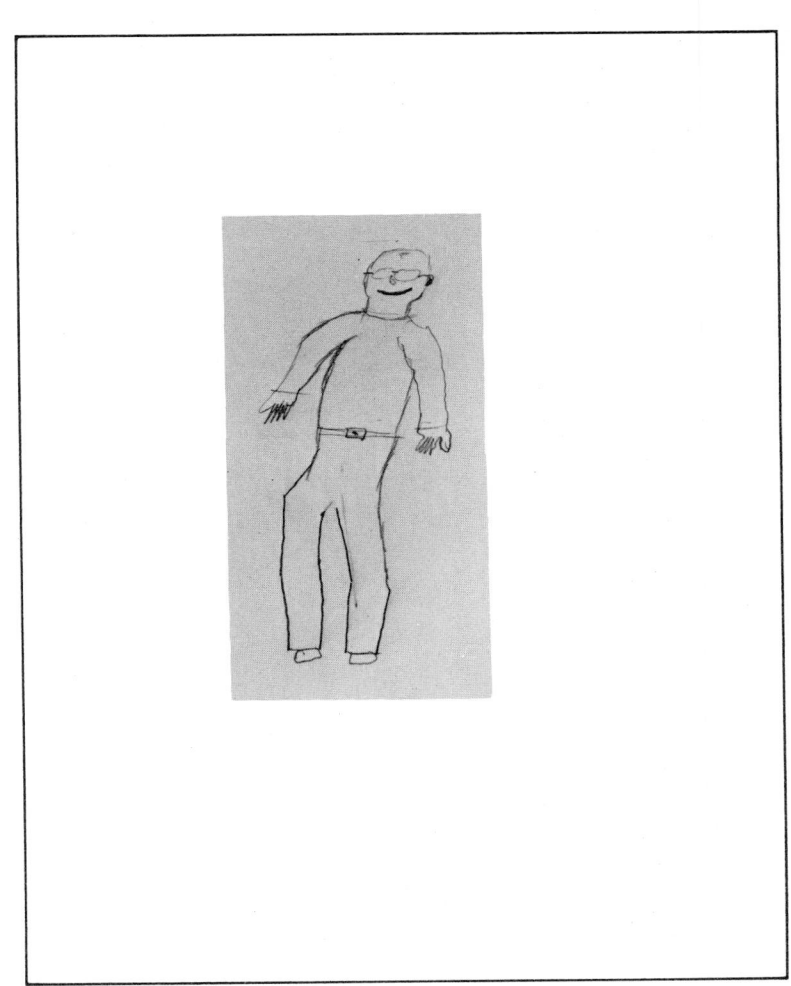

FIGURE-DRAWING CHARACTERISTICS

Structural	Male Female Both		Structural	Male	Female	Structural and Graphic	Male Female Both		Graphic, Global and Height	Male	Female	Body Proportions	Male	Female
Type	0		Omission of Appendages	0	0	Upper and Lower Halves	1	1	Hair Shading	0	3	Head	04	04
Sex Sequence	1		Position of Both Arms	0	0	Four Quarters	4	4	Nudity and Transparency	7	3	Neck	05	00
Posture	1	1	Position of Right Arm	2	2	Relative Size	0		Form	5	5	Shoulders	04	
Perspective	0	9	Position of Left Arm	2	2	Constant Line Pressure	0	0	Detailing	3	5	Right Arm	02	02
Vertical Midline	0	4	Position of Legs	4	4	Variable Line Pressure	4	4	Identity and Sex	3	3	Left Arm	02	02
Bilateral Symmetry	2	0	Relation of Long Axes	0	1	Line Continuity	0	0	Sophistication	3	3	Chest	03	
Horizontal Midline	4	4	Right and Left Halves	1	1	Body Shading	0	0	Height	04	03	Girth	04	

GENERAL CHARACTERISTICS OF SUBJECT

IDENTIFICATION

No. E43

Sex M

Marital status S

Age 22 yrs. at

psychological tests

PARENTAL HISTORY

Father

C   H   S   D   O

–   –   –   –   ?

Mother

C   H   S   D   O

–   –   –   –   –

PHYSIOLOGICAL AND METABOLIC DATA

	Admission	Initial	Control	Cold pressor change	Exercise change	Smoking change
Systolic pressure	120	140	138	+18	+32	
Diastolic pressure	65	68	80	+35	+10	
Heart rate	72	72	61	00	+33	

Age 22 yrs.   Height 72 in.   Weight 184 lbs.   Overweight +13 %

Ponderal index 12.65   Cholesterol 250 mg. per 100 ml.   Vital capacity 4.6 liters

HABIT SURVEY

Smoking habits: nonsmoker

Age begun   yrs.   Inhalation:

Habits of nervous tension: 2, 5, 6, 9, 10, 14, 16, 18, 21, 22, 23, 24

STRONG VOCATIONAL INTEREST TEST

Occupation	Artist	Psychologist	Architect	Physician	Osteopath	Dentist	Veterinarian	Mathematician	Physicist	Engineer	Chemist	Production Manager
Standard Score	28	50	29	49	42	27	18	21	21	30	38	38

Occupation	Farmer	Aviator	Carpenter	Printer	Math.-Sci. Teacher	Ind. Arts Teacher	Voc. Agric. Teacher	Policeman	Forest Serv. Man	Y.M.C.A. Phys. Dir.	Personnel Director	Public Administrator
Standard Score	25	39	09	33	40	16	16	27	19	39	46	45

Occupation	Y.M.C.A. Secretary	Soc. Sci. H.S. Teacher	City Sch. Sup't.	Social Worker	Minister	Musician Performer	C.P.A.	Senior C.P.A.	Accountant	Office Man	Purchasing Agent	Banker
Standard Score	30	38	32	48	64	48	35	37	27	31	20	12

Occupation	Mortician	Pharmacist	Sales Manager	Real Est. Manager	Life Ins. Salesman	Advertising Man	Lawyer	Author-Journalist	President Mfg. Co.	Interest Maturity	Occupational Level	Masculinity-Femininity
Standard Score	29	34	38	37	38	42	38	35	40	59	61	41

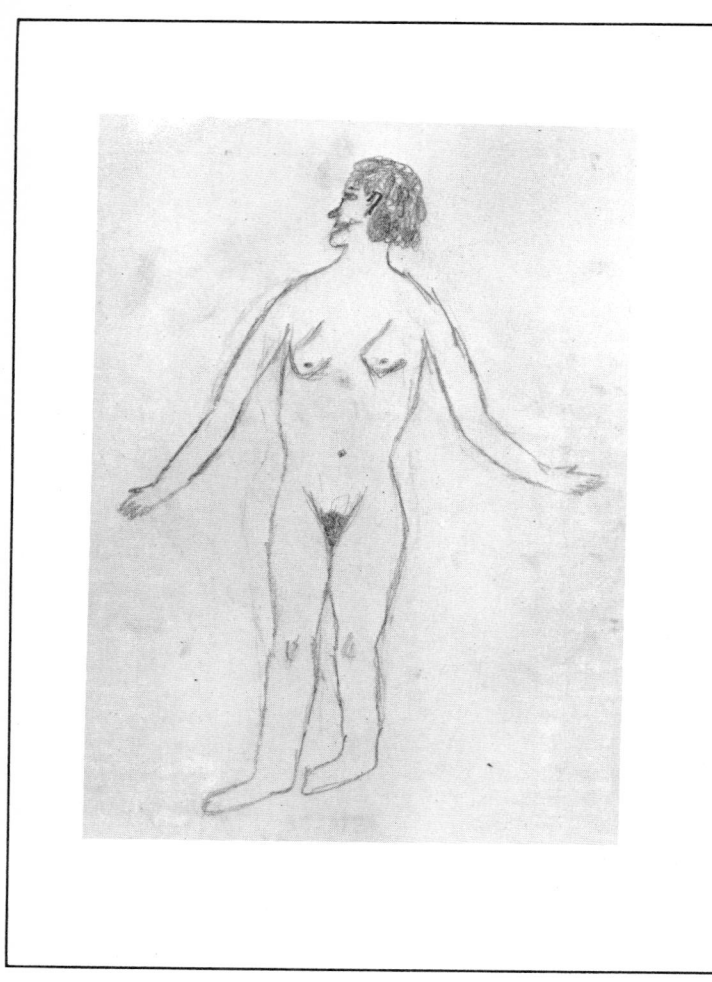

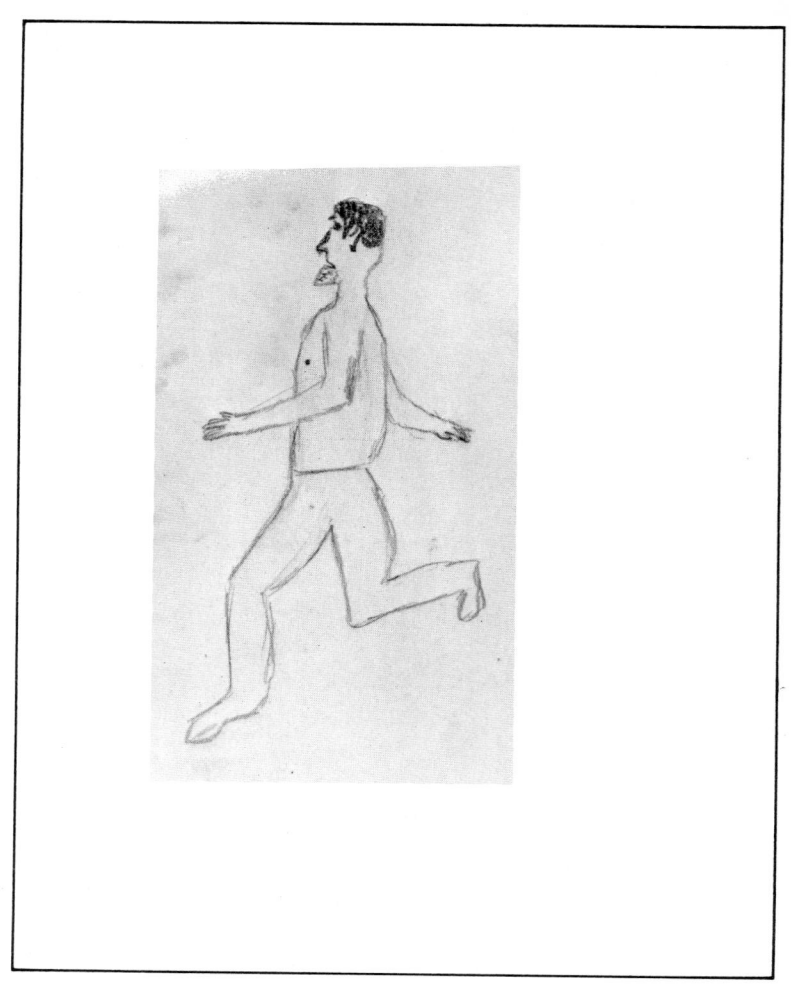

FIGURE-DRAWING CHARACTERISTICS

Structural	Male	Female	Structural	Male	Female	Structural and Graphic	Male	Female	Graphic, Global and Height	Male	Female	Body Proportions	Male	Female
	Both						Both							
Type	0		Omission of Appendages	0	0	Upper and Lower Halves	1	0	Hair Shading	3	3	Head	07	07
Sex Sequence	1		Position of Both Arms	4	0	Four Quarters	4	4	Nudity and Transparency	9	0	Neck	06	04
Posture	5	1	Position of Right Arm	7	2	Relative Size	4		Form	3	3	Shoulders		06
Perspective	2	5	Position of Left Arm	6	2	Constant Line Pressure	0	0	Detailing	3	3	Right Arm		06
Vertical Midline	4	0	Position of Legs	8	4	Variable Line Pressure	1	1	Identity and Sex	1	1	Left Arm	04	06
Bilateral Symmetry	0	3	Relation of Long Axes	1	1	Line Continuity	0	0	Sophistication	3	3	Chest	06	07
Horizontal Midline	4	0	Right and Left Halves	1	1	Body Shading	0	3	Height	05	07	Girth	06	07

GENERAL CHARACTERISTICS OF SUBJECT

IDENTIFICATION
No. E82
Sex M
Marital status S
Age 22 yrs. at
psychological tests

PARENTAL HISTORY
Father
C H S D O
- - - - ?
Mother
C H S D O
- - - - -

PHYSIOLOGICAL AND METABOLIC DATA

	Admission	Initial	Control	Cold pressor change	Exercise change	Smoking change
Systolic pressure	140	118	116	+12	+14	00
Diastolic pressure	80	75	72	+18	-17	+01
Heart rate	70	68	58	+04	+28	+14

Age 22 yrs.	Height 73 in.	Ponderal index 12.48
	Weight 200 lbs.	Cholesterol 225 mg. per 100 ml.
	Overweight +19 %	Vital capacity 6.0 liters

HABIT SURVEY

Smoking habits: nonsmoker

Age begun   yrs.   Inhalation:

Habits of nervous tension: 8, 24

STRONG VOCATIONAL INTEREST TEST

Occupation	Artist	Psychologist	Architect	Physician	Osteopath	Dentist	Veterinarian	Mathematician	Physicist	Engineer	Chemist	Production Manager
Standard Score	47	48	43	65	51	48	36	40	31	28	41	18

Occupation	Farmer	Aviator	Carpenter	Printer	Math.-Sci. Teacher	Ind. Arts Teacher	Voc. Agric. Teacher	Policeman	Forest Serv. Man	Y.M.C.A. Phys. Dir.	Personnel Director	Public Administrator
Standard Score	40	33	19	35	37	17	35	24	25	36	21	33

Occupation	Y.M.C.A. Secretary	Soc. Sci. H.S. Teacher	City Sch. Sup't.	Social Worker	Minister	Musician Performer	C.P.A.	Senior C.P.A.	Accountant	Office Man	Purchasing Agent	Banker
Standard Score	25	34	30	36	64	56	30	31	08	15	06	17

Occupation	Mortician	Pharmacist	Sales Manager	Real Est. Manager	Life Ins. Salesman	Advertising Man	Lawyer	Author-Journalist	President Mfg. Co.	Interest Maturity	Occupational Level	Masculinity-Femininity
Standard Score	18	25	16	30	28	31	37	42	17	49	49	36

FIGURE-DRAWING CHARACTERISTICS

Structural	Male Female Both	Structural	Male	Female	Structural and Graphic	Male Female Both		Graphic, Global and Height	Male	Female	Body Proportions	Male	Female
Type	0	Omission of Appendages	0	0	Upper and Lower Halves	1	0	Hair Shading	1	3	Head	05	07
Sex Sequence	0	Position of Both Arms	4	4	Four Quarters	4	4	Nudity and Transparency	7	7	Neck	06	08
Posture	1	1	Position of Right Arm	7	7	Relative Size	4		Form	3	3	Shoulders		
Perspective	2	2	Position of Left Arm	4	4	Constant Line Pressure	1	1	Detailing	3	3	Right Arm		
Vertical Midline	7	4	Position of Legs	1	4	Variable Line Pressure	0	0	Identity and Sex	1	1	Left Arm	04	06
Bilateral Symmetry	0	0	Relation of Long Axes	1	1	Line Continuity	0	0	Sophistication	3	3	Chest	05	05
Horizontal Midline	4	4	Right and Left Halves	2	1	Body Shading	4	0	Height	04	06	Girth	06	08

GENERAL CHARACTERISTICS OF SUBJECT

IDENTIFICATION
No. 310
Sex M
Marital status M
Age 25 yrs. at
psychological tests

PARENTAL HISTORY
Father
C   H   S   D   O
–   –   –   –   –
Mother
C   H   S   D   O
–   –   –   –   ?

PHYSIOLOGICAL AND METABOLIC DATA

	Admission	Initial	Control	Cold pressor change	Exercise change	Smoking change
Systolic pressure	124	108	100	+12	+36	+02
Diastolic pressure	76	60	62	+10	-02	+08
Heart rate	70	60	59	+06	+39	-02

Age 23 yrs.	Height 72 in.	Ponderal index 13.29
	Weight 159 lbs.	Cholesterol 215 mg. per 100 ml.
	Overweight -03 %	Vital capacity 4.6 liters

HABIT SURVEY
Smoking habits: nonsmoker
Age begun   yrs.   Inhalation:
Habits of nervous tension: 2, 4, 5, 6, 9, 23

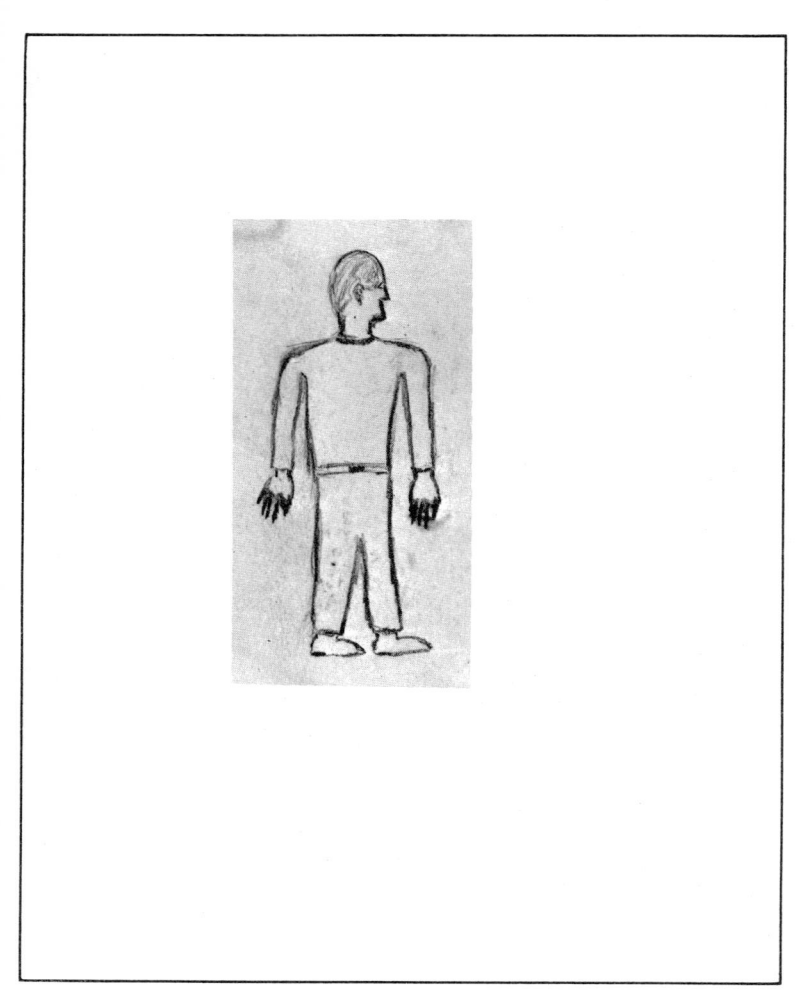

FIGURE-DRAWING CHARACTERISTICS

Structural	Male Female Both		Structural	Male	Female	Structural and Graphic	Male Female Both		Graphic, Global and Height	Male	Female	Body Proportions	Male	Female
Type	0		Omission of Appendages	0	0	Upper and Lower Halves	1	3	Hair Shading	1	3	Head	06	06
Sex Sequence	0		Position of Both Arms	0	2	Four Quarters	4	4	Nudity and Transparency	7	7	Neck	06	04
Posture	1	1	Position of Right Arm	0	0	Relative Size	4		Form	3	3	Shoulders	06	
Perspective	5	2	Position of Left Arm	0	7	Constant Line Pressure	0	0	Detailing	3	3	Right Arm	04	04
Vertical Midline	0	4	Position of Legs	4	1	Variable Line Pressure	5	3	Identity and Sex	1	1	Left Arm	04	
Bilateral Symmetry	5	0	Relation of Long Axes	1	1	Line Continuity	0	0	Sophistication	3	3	Chest	04	04
Horizontal Midline	4	4	Right and Left Halves	1	2	Body Shading	4	2	Height	04	05	Girth	05	05

GENERAL CHARACTERISTICS OF SUBJECT

IDENTIFICATION
No.   317
Sex   M
Marital status   S
Age   24   yrs. at
psychological tests

PARENTAL HISTORY
Father
C   H   S   D   O
-    -   -   -   -
Mother
C   H   S   D   O
-    -   -   -   ?

PHYSIOLOGICAL AND METABOLIC DATA

	Admission	Initial	Control	Cold pressor change	Exercise change	Smoking change
Systolic pressure	124	114	106	+06	+42	
Diastolic pressure	68	64	62	+06	-04	
Heart rate	68	76	71	-04	+18	

Age 22 yrs.	Height 71 in.	Ponderal index 14.09
	Weight 128 lbs.	Cholesterol 182 mg. per 100 ml.
	Overweight -19 %	Vital capacity 4.5 liters

HABIT SURVEY

Smoking habits: nonsmoker

   Age begun   yrs.   Inhalation:

Habits of nervous tension: 1, 2, 4, 5, 6, 7,

8, 9, 11, 12, 13, 14, 21, 25

Plate 420　　DRAWINGS AT AN INTERMEDIATE LEVEL OF SOPHISTICATION　　463

FIGURE-DRAWING CHARACTERISTICS

Structural	Male Female Both	Structural	Male	Female	Structural and Graphic	Male Female Both		Graphic, Global and Height	Male	Female	Body Proportions	Male	Female
Type	0	Omission of Appendages	0	0	Upper and Lower Halves	1	1	Hair Shading	1	1	Head	06	05
Sex Sequence	0	Position of Both Arms	0	0	Four Quarters	4	4	Nudity and Transparency	7	7	Neck	06	04
Posture	1	1	Position of Right Arm	2	2	Relative Size	0		Form	1	1	Shoulders	05	05
Perspective	0	0	Position of Left Arm	4	2	Constant Line Pressure	0	1	Detailing	3	3	Right Arm	04	04
Vertical Midline	3	0	Position of Legs	6	6	Variable Line Pressure	1	0	Identity and Sex	1	1	Left Arm	04	04
Bilateral Symmetry	3	3	Relation of Long Axes	1	1	Line Continuity	0	0	Sophistication	3	3	Chest	04	04
Horizontal Midline	4	4	Right and Left Halves	1	1	Body Shading	0	3	Height	06	05	Girth	05	03

GENERAL CHARACTERISTICS OF SUBJECT

<table>
<tr><td rowspan="2">IDENTIFICATION</td><td rowspan="2">PARENTAL HISTORY</td><td colspan="7">PHYSIOLOGICAL AND METABOLIC DATA</td><td rowspan="2">HABIT SURVEY</td></tr>
</table>

IDENTIFICATION

No. 425

Sex M

Marital status　S

Age 29　yrs. at

psychological tests

PARENTAL HISTORY

Father

C　H　S　D　0

–　–　–　–　–

Mother

C　H　S　D　0

–　–　–　–　?

PHYSIOLOGICAL AND METABOLIC DATA

	Admission	Initial	Control	Cold pressor change	Exercise change	Smoking change
Systolic pressure	126	120	110	+10	+40	
Diastolic pressure	80	82	70	00	+05	
Heart rate	88	84	65	+02	+32	

Age 27　yrs.　　Height　71　in.　　Ponderal index　12.72

Weight　174　lbs.　　Cholesterol　308　mg. per 100 ml.

Overweight　+07　%　　Vital capacity　4.8　liters

HABIT SURVEY

Smoking habits: heavy cigarette smoker

Age begun　18　yrs.　　Inhalation: sometimes

Habits of nervous tension: 4, 5, 6, 9

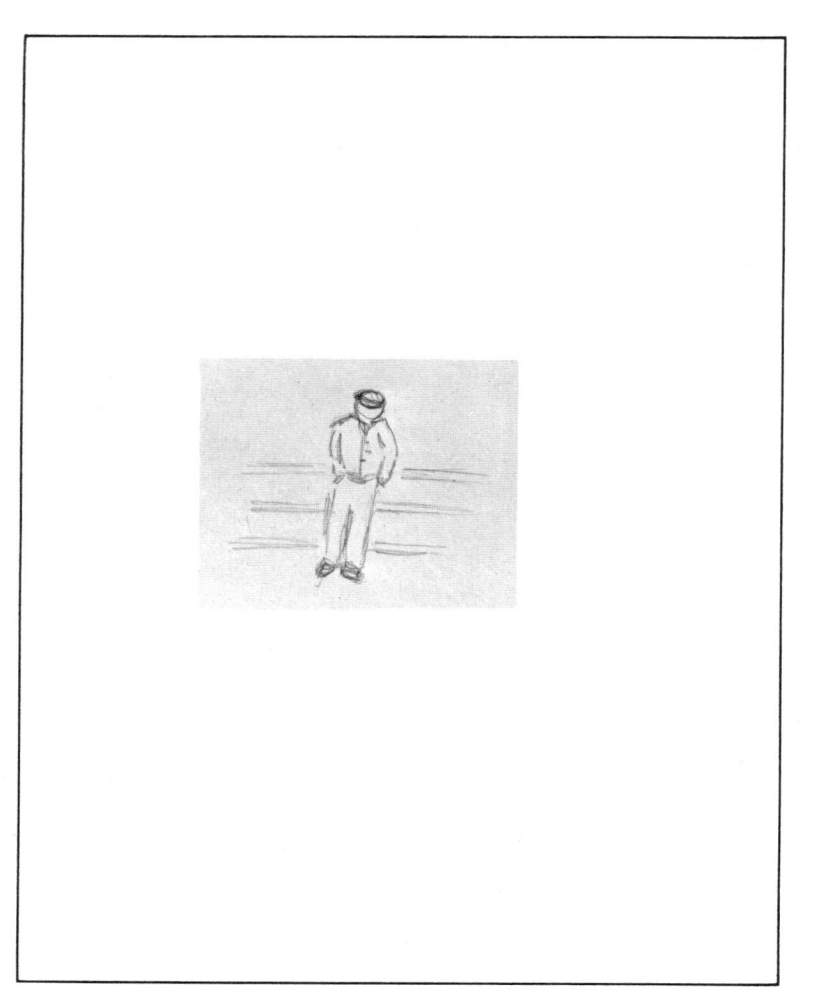

FIGURE-DRAWING CHARACTERISTICS

Structural	Male Female Both		Structural	Male	Female	Structural and Graphic	Male Female Both		Graphic, Global and Height	Male	Female	Body Proportions	Male	Female
Type	0		Omission of Appendages	7	7	Upper and Lower Halves	1	3	Hair Shading	0	0	Head		02
Sex Sequence	2		Position of Both Arms	0	0	Four Quarters	4	4	Nudity and Transparency	7	7	Neck		
Posture	1	1	Position of Right Arm	9	0	Relative Size	4		Form	3	3	Shoulders	02	02
Perspective	0	5	Position of Left Arm	5	0	Constant Line Pressure	1	1	Detailing	3	3	Right Arm		
Vertical Midline	3	3	Position of Legs	3	2	Variable Line Pressure	0	0	Identity and Sex	3	3	Left Arm		02
Bilateral Symmetry	3	3	Relation of Long Axes	1	1	Line Continuity	0	0	Sophistication	3	3	Chest	01	02
Horizontal Midline	4	0	Right and Left Halves	2	2	Body Shading	4	6	Height	02	02	Girth	02	03

GENERAL CHARACTERISTICS OF SUBJECT

IDENTIFICATION
No. 461
Sex M
Marital status S
Age 27 yrs. at
psychological tests

PARENTAL HISTORY
Father
C H S D O
- - - - -
Mother
C H S D O
- - - - ?

PHYSIOLOGICAL AND METABOLIC DATA

	Admission	Initial	Control	Cold pressor change	Exercise change	Smoking change
Systolic pressure	130	114	112	+14	+42	
Diastolic pressure	65	62	70	+14	00	
Heart rate	72	60	56	+06	+23	

Age 24 yrs.	Height 71 in.	Ponderal index 12.97
	Weight 164 lbs.	Cholesterol 237 mg. per 100 ml.
	Overweight +02 %	Vital capacity 4.3 liters

HABIT SURVEY
Smoking habits: pipe smoker
Age begun 20 yrs.   Inhalation: no
Habits of nervous tension: 5, 7, 8, 21, 23, 25

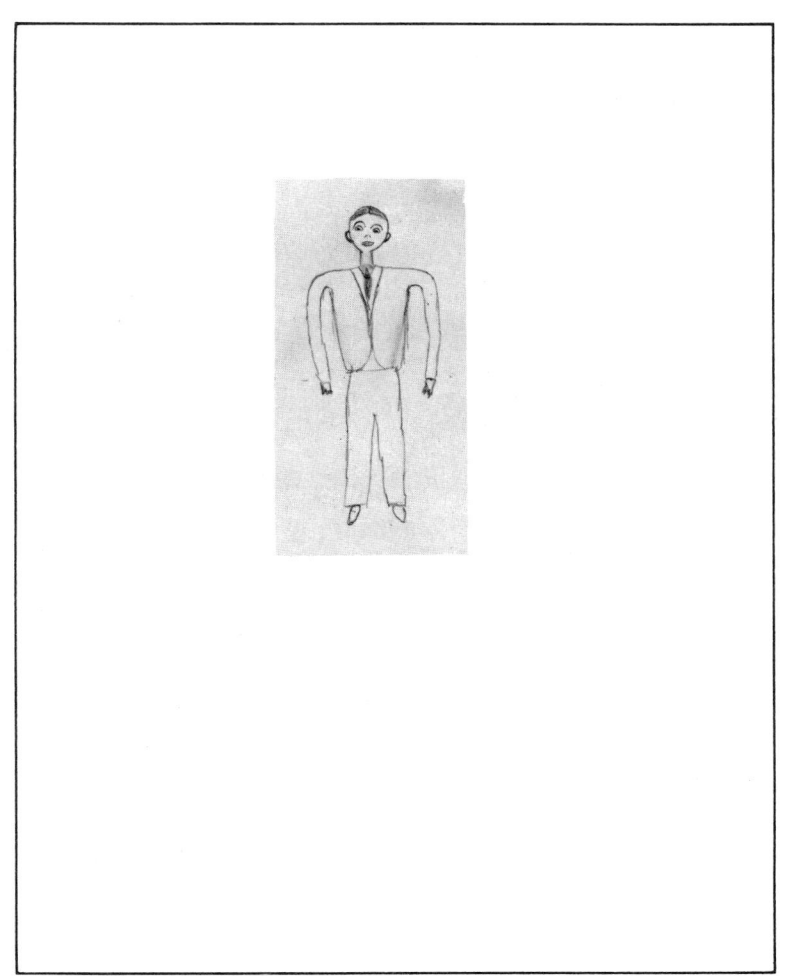

FIGURE-DRAWING CHARACTERISTICS

Structural	Male Female Both	Structural	Male	Female	Structural and Graphic	Male Female Both		Graphic, Global and Height	Male	Female	Body Proportions	Male	Female
Type	0	Omission of Appendages	0	0	Upper and Lower Halves	2	1	Hair Shading	2	3	Head	04	04
Sex Sequence	0	Position of Both Arms	0	1	Four Quarters	4	4	Nudity and Transparency	7	7	Neck	06	04
Posture	1 1	Position of Right Arm	0	5	Relative Size	0		Form	3	3	Shoulders	03	03
Perspective	0 0	Position of Left Arm	0	0	Constant Line Pressure	3	3	Detailing	3	3	Right Arm	02	02
Vertical Midline	3 0	Position of Legs	4	3	Variable Line Pressure	0	0	Identity and Sex	1	1	Left Arm	02	00
Bilateral Symmetry	3 3	Relation of Long Axes	1	1	Line Continuity	0	1	Sophistication	3	3	Chest	03	02
Horizontal Midline	4 4	Right and Left Halves	1	1	Body Shading	4	5	Height	03	03	Girth	03	01

GENERAL CHARACTERISTICS OF SUBJECT

IDENTIFICATION
No. 579
Sex M
Marital status S
Age 25 yrs. at
psychological tests

PARENTAL HISTORY				
Father				
C	H	S	D	0
-	-	-	-	-
Mother				
C	H	S	D	0
-	-	-	-	?

PHYSIOLOGICAL AND METABOLIC DATA

	Admission	Initial	Control	Cold pressor change	Exercise change	Smoking change
Systolic pressure	140	132	116	+04	+16	-02
Diastolic pressure	90	72	70	+20	-10	-02
Heart rate	78	72	64	+36	+19	+07

Age 25 yrs.	Height	76 in.	Ponderal index 13.08	
	Weight	196 lbs.	Cholesterol	mg. per 100 ml.
	Overweight +04 %		Vital capacity	liters

HABIT SURVEY

Smoking habits: heavy cigarette smoker

Age begun 17 yrs.   Inhalation: yes

Habits of nervous tension: 5, 6, 11, 22

FIGURE-DRAWING CHARACTERISTICS

Structural	Male Female Both		Structural	Male	Female	Structural and Graphic	Male	Female Both		Graphic, Global and Height	Male	Female	Body Proportions	Male	Female
Type	0		Omission of Appendages	7	7	Upper and Lower Halves	1		1	Hair Shading	1	3	Head	06	06
Sex Sequence	0		Position of Both Arms	1	0	Four Quarters	4		4	Nudity and Transparency	7	7	Neck	12	08
Posture	1	1	Position of Right Arm	0	5	Relative Size	0			Form	1	1	Shoulders	07	06
Perspective	5	5	Position of Left Arm	5	5	Constant Line Pressure	0		0	Detailing	3	3	Right Arm	06	
Vertical Midline	3	0	Position of Legs	6	4	Variable Line Pressure	1		2	Identity and Sex	1	1	Left Arm		
Bilateral Symmetry	3	3	Relation of Long Axes	1	1	Line Continuity	0		0	Sophistication	3	3	Chest	06	06
Horizontal Midline	4	4	Right and Left Halves	1	1	Body Shading	0		1	Height	07	06	Girth	06	07

GENERAL CHARACTERISTICS OF SUBJECT

IDENTIFICATION
No. 665
Sex M
Marital status S
Age 23 yrs. at
psychological tests

PARENTAL HISTORY
Father
C   H   S   D   O
–   –   –   –   –
Mother
C   H   S   D   O
–   –   –   –   ?

PHYSIOLOGICAL AND METABOLIC DATA

	Admission	Initial	Control	Cold pressor change	Exercise change	Smoking change
Systolic pressure	110	116	112	+22	+26	+08
Diastolic pressure	68	70	70	+28	–18	+14
Heart rate	72	60	64	+20	+19	+08

Age 21 yrs.	Height	71 in.	Ponderal index	13.92	
	Weight	133 lbs.	Cholesterol	167	mg. per 100 ml.
	Overweight –15 %		Vital capacity	4.6	liters

HABIT SURVEY

Smoking habits: nonsmoker

Age begun   yrs.   Inhalation:

Habits of nervous tension: 4, 5, 6, 9, 11, 17, 19, 21, 22

Plate 424   **DRAWINGS AT AN INTERMEDIATE LEVEL OF SOPHISTICATION**   467

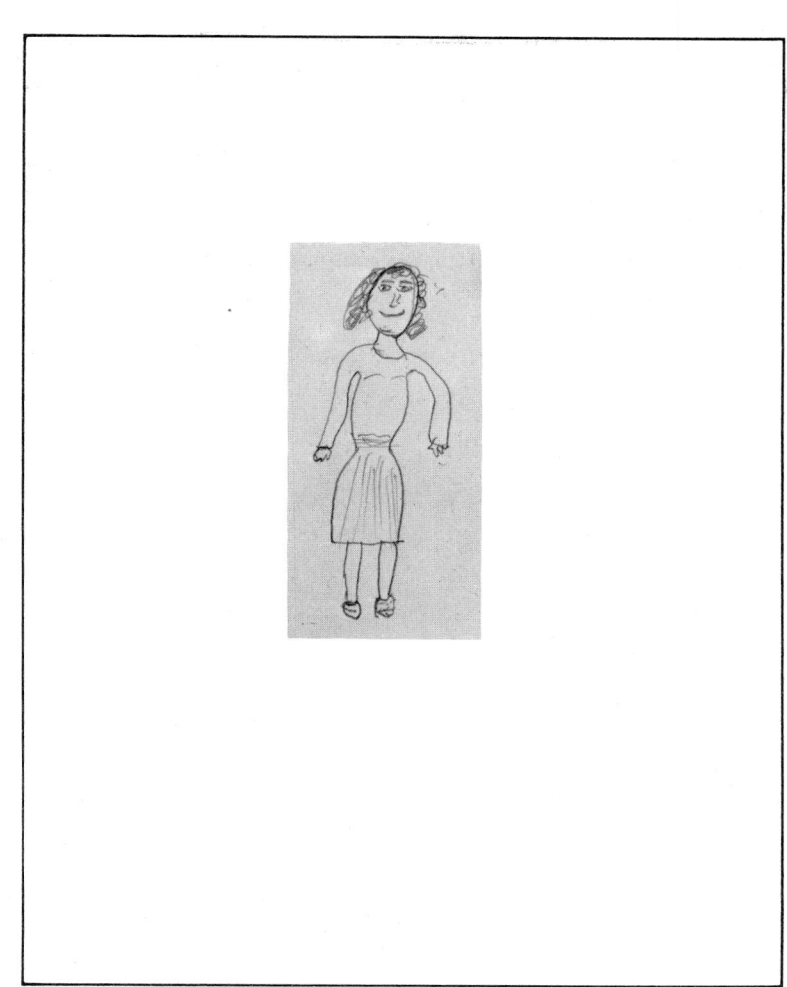

FIGURE-DRAWING CHARACTERISTICS

Structural	Male Female Both	Structural	Male	Female	Structural and Graphic	Male Female Both		Graphic, Global and Height	Male	Female	Body Proportions	Male	Female
Type	0	Omission of Appendages	0	0	Upper and Lower Halves	1	1	Hair Shading	1	3	Head	05	06
Sex Sequence	0	Position of Both Arms	2	1	Four Quarters	4	4	Nudity and Transparency	7	7	Neck	07	04
Posture	1 1	Position of Right Arm	4	0	Relative Size	4		Form	3	3	Shoulders		03
Perspective	2 0	Position of Left Arm	7	2	Constant Line Pressure	0	0	Detailing	1	3	Right Arm	02	02
Vertical Midline	7 0	Position of Legs	1	4	Variable Line Pressure	5	5	Identity and Sex	1	1	Left Arm		02
Bilateral Symmetry	0 2	Relation of Long Axes	1	1	Line Continuity	2	3	Sophistication	3	3	Chest	03	02
Horizontal Midline	4 4	Right and Left Halves	1	1	Body Shading	7	7	Height	03	03	Girth	03	02

GENERAL CHARACTERISTICS OF SUBJECT

IDENTIFICATION
No. 749
Sex M
Marital status M
Age 25 yrs. at
psychological tests

PARENTAL HISTORY
Father
C   H   S   D   0
-    -   -   -   -
Mother
C   H   S   D   0
-    -   -   -   ?

PHYSIOLOGICAL AND METABOLIC DATA

	Admission	Initial	Control	Cold pressor change	Exercise change	Smoking change
Systolic pressure	122	114	108	+22	+56	
Diastolic pressure	78	62	58	+10	-10	
Heart rate	80	80	85	+16	+40	

Age 23 yrs.	Height 71 in.	Ponderal index 13.98
	Weight 131 lbs.	Cholesterol 177 mg. per 100 ml.
	Overweight -18 %	Vital capacity 4.7 liters

HABIT SURVEY
Smoking habits: nonsmoker
Age begun   yrs.   Inhalation:
Habits of nervous tension: 4, 5, 6, 9, 21

FIGURE-DRAWING CHARACTERISTICS

Structural	Male Female / Both		Structural	Male	Female	Structural and Graphic	Male Female / Both		Graphic, Global and Height	Male	Female	Body Proportions	Male	Female
Type	0		Omission of Appendages	0	0	Upper and Lower Halves	1	3	Hair Shading	7	3	Head	06	07
Sex Sequence	2		Position of Both Arms	4	1	Four Quarters	4	4	Nudity and Transparency	0	0	Neck	06	05
Posture	2	2	Position of Right Arm	7	5	Relative Size	4		Form	3	3	Shoulders		
Perspective	2	1	Position of Left Arm	4	4	Constant Line Pressure	1	1	Detailing	5	5	Right Arm		06
Vertical Midline	4	4	Position of Legs	8	8	Variable Line Pressure	0	0	Identity and Sex	1	1	Left Arm	04	06
Bilateral Symmetry	0	0	Relation of Long Axes	1	1	Line Continuity	0	0	Sophistication	3	3	Chest	06	
Horizontal Midline	0	0	Right and Left Halves	1	1	Body Shading	0	1	Height	05	06	Girth	04	

GENERAL CHARACTERISTICS OF SUBJECT

IDENTIFICATION
No. A31
Sex M
Marital status S
Age 24 yrs. at
psychological tests

PARENTAL HISTORY
Father
C H S D O
- - - - -
Mother
C H S D O
- - - - ?

PHYSIOLOGICAL AND METABOLIC DATA

	Admission	Initial	Control	Cold pressor change	Exercise change	Smoking change
Systolic pressure	160	140	133	+28	+41	
Diastolic pressure	80	72	71	+38	-13	
Heart rate	90	72	68	+02	+09	

Age 23 yrs.	Height 71 in.	Ponderal index 12.74
	Weight 173 lbs.	Cholesterol 258 mg. per 100 ml.
	Overweight +09 %	Vital capacity liters

HABIT SURVEY
Smoking habits: nonsmoker
Age begun   yrs.   Inhalation:
Habits of nervous tension: 2, 5, 6, 10

STRONG VOCATIONAL INTEREST TEST

Occupation	Artist	Psychologist	Architect	Physician	Osteopath	Dentist	Veterinarian	Mathematician	Physicist	Engineer	Chemist	Production Manager
Standard Score	2	4	3	6	6	4	2	2	3	4	4	6

Occupation	Farmer	Aviator	Carpenter	Printer	Math.-Sci. Teacher	Ind. Arts Teacher	Voc. Agric. Teacher	Policeman	Forest Serv. Man	Y.M.C.A. Phys. Dir.	Personnel Director	Public Administrator
Standard Score	6	6	4	5	5	2	1	4	4	4	4	6

Occupation	Y.M.C.A. Secretary	Soc. Sci. H.S. Teacher	City Sch. Sup't.	Social Worker	Minister	Musician Performer	C.P.A.	Senior C.P.A.	Accountant	Office Man	Purchasing Agent	Banker
Standard Score	3	3	2	3	6	4	3	5	4	4	2	2

Occupation	Mortician	Pharmacist	Sales Manager	Real Est. Manager	Life Ins. Salesman	Advertising Man	Lawyer	Author- Journalist	President Mfg. Co.	Interest Maturity	Occupational Level	Masculinity- Femininity
Standard Score	2	3	3	4	2	3	3	3	4	5	4	5

FIGURE-DRAWING CHARACTERISTICS

Structural	Male Female Both	Structural	Male	Female	Structural and Graphic	Male Female Both		Graphic, Global and Height	Male	Female	Body Proportions	Male	Female
Type	0	Omission of Appendages	0	0	Upper and Lower Halves	1	1	Hair Shading	1	1	Head	07	05
Sex Sequence	0	Position of Both Arms	0	0	Four Quarters	4	4	Nudity and Transparency	7	7	Neck	07	07
Posture	1 1	Position of Right Arm	0	0	Relative Size	0		Form	3	3	Shoulders	08	04
Perspective	0 0	Position of Left Arm	0	0	Constant Line Pressure	0	0	Detailing	3	3	Right Arm	06	04
Vertical Midline	3 0	Position of Legs	4	4	Variable Line Pressure	4	1	Identity and Sex	1	3	Left Arm	06	04
Bilateral Symmetry	3 2	Relation of Long Axes	1	1	Line Continuity	0	0	Sophistication	3	3	Chest	05	03
Horizontal Midline	4 0	Right and Left Halves	3	3	Body Shading	4	5	Height	05	04	Girth	06	03

GENERAL CHARACTERISTICS OF SUBJECT

IDENTIFICATION
No. D08
Sex M
Marital status S
Age 22 yrs. at
psychological tests

PARENTAL HISTORY				
Father				
C	H	S	D	O
-	-	-	-	-
Mother				
C	H	S	D	O
-	-	-	-	?

PHYSIOLOGICAL AND METABOLIC DATA

	Admission	Initial	Control	Cold pressor change	Exercise change	Smoking change
Systolic pressure	120	120	110	+20	+30	+08
Diastolic pressure	72	70	70	+10	-20	-04
Heart rate	78	80	67	-04	+42	00

Age 21 yrs.	Height 70 in.	Ponderal index 13.75
	Weight 132 lbs.	Cholesterol 222 mg. per 100 ml.
	Overweight -14 %	Vital capacity 4.5 liters

HABIT SURVEY

Smoking habits: nonsmoker

Age begun   yrs.   Inhalation:

Habits of nervous tension: 4, 5, 6, 19, 22

STRONG VOCATIONAL INTEREST TEST

Occupation	Artist	Psychologist	Architect	Physician	Osteopath	Dentist	Veterinarian	Mathematician	Physicist	Engineer	Chemist	Production Manager
Standard Score	50	72	47	72	53	47	24	41	35	29	47	27

Occupation	Farmer	Aviator	Carpenter	Printer	Math.-Sci. Teacher	Ind. Arts Teacher	Voc. Agric. Teacher	Policeman	Forest Serv. Man	Y.M.C.A. Phys. Dir.	Personnel Director	Public Administrator
Standard Score	21	27	09	29	38	11	20	15	14	31	36	46

Occupation	Y.M.C.A. Secretary	Soc. Sci. H.S. Teacher	City Sch. Sup't.	Social Worker	Minister	Musician Performer	C.P.A.	Senior C.P.A.	Accountant	Office Man	Purchasing Agent	Banker
Standard Score	19	37	45	52	63	65	40	26	09	15	08	14

Occupation	Mortician	Pharmacist	Sales Manager	Real Est. Manager	Life Ins. Salesman	Advertising Man	Lawyer	Author-Journalist	President Mfg. Co.	Interest Maturity	Occupational Level	Masculinity-Femininity
Standard Score	25	42	33	36	35	51	53	51	42	47	65	33

FIGURE-DRAWING CHARACTERISTICS

Structural	Male Female Both	Structural	Male	Female	Structural and Graphic	Male Female Both	Graphic, Global and Height	Male	Female	Body Proportions	Male	Female
Type	0	Omission of Appendages	0	0	Upper and Lower Halves	0 3	Hair Shading	0	3	Head		04
Sex Sequence	1	Position of Both Arms	4	4	Four Quarters	4 4	Nudity and Transparency	7	7	Neck		01
Posture	1 2	Position of Right Arm	7	7	Relative Size	0	Form	3	3	Shoulders		
Perspective	9 2	Position of Left Arm	0	4	Constant Line Pressure	3 5	Detailing	5	3	Right Arm		
Vertical Midline	7 4	Position of Legs	2	8	Variable Line Pressure	0 0	Identity and Sex	1	1	Left Arm	02	02
Bilateral Symmetry	0 0	Relation of Long Axes	1	1	Line Continuity	0 4	Sophistication	3	3	Chest		03
Horizontal Midline	6 0	Right and Left Halves	0	2	Body Shading	4 0	Height		02	Girth		05

GENERAL CHARACTERISTICS OF SUBJECT

IDENTIFICATION
No. D41
Sex M
Marital status S
Age 22 yrs. at
psychological tests

PARENTAL HISTORY				
Father				
C	H	S	D	0
–	–	–	–	–
Mother				
C	H	S	D	0
–	–	–	–	?

PHYSIOLOGICAL AND METABOLIC DATA

	Admission	Initial	Control	Cold pressor change	Exercise change	Smoking change
Systolic pressure	140	110	110	+10	+30	+03
Diastolic pressure	80	60	60	+30	–10	–02
Heart rate	72	76	68	–04	+34	+01

Age 22 yrs.	Height 74 in.	Ponderal index 13.41
	Weight 168 lbs.	Cholesterol 233 mg. per 100 ml.
	Overweight –03 %	Vital capacity 4.3 liters

HABIT SURVEY

Smoking habits: pipe smoker

  Age begun 15 yrs.   Inhalation: no

Habits of nervous tension: 4, 5, 9, 11

STRONG VOCATIONAL INTEREST TEST

Occupation	Artist	Psychologist	Architect	Physician	Osteopath	Dentist	Veterinarian	Mathematician	Physicist	Engineer	Chemist	Production Manager
Standard Score	47	44	56	63	46	50	32	39	41	42	52	25

Occupation	Farmer	Aviator	Carpenter	Printer	Math.-Sci. Teacher	Ind. Arts Teacher	Voc. Agric. Teacher	Policeman	Forest Serv. Man	Y.M.C.A. Phys. Dir.	Personnel Director	Public Administrator
Standard Score	44	36	26	38	37	27	31	21	24	31	18	27

Occupation	Y.M.C.A. Secretary	Soc. Sci. H.S. Teacher	City Sch. Sup't.	Social Worker	Minister	Musician Performer	C.P.A.	Senior C.P.A.	Accountant	Office Man	Purchasing Agent	Banker
Standard Score	20	18	13	23	63	48	24	34	17	21	15	09

Occupation	Mortician	Pharmacist	Sales Manager	Real Est. Manager	Life Ins. Salesman	Advertising Man	Lawyer	Author-Journalist	President Mfg. Co.	Interest Maturity	Occupational Level	Masculinity-Femininity
Standard Score	17	34	20	26	17	35	25	39	30	47	58	44

Plate 428   DRAWINGS AT AN INTERMEDIATE LEVEL OF SOPHISTICATION   471

FIGURE-DRAWING CHARACTERISTICS

Structural	Male Female Both		Structural	Male	Female	Structural and Graphic	Male	Female Both		Graphic, Global and Height	Male	Female	Body Proportions	Male	Female
Type	0		Omission of Appendages	0	0	Upper and Lower Halves	2	1		Hair Shading	1	1	Head	05	05
Sex Sequence	0		Position of Both Arms	0	0	Four Quarters	4	4		Nudity and Transparency	7	7	Neck	04	06
Posture	1	1	Position of Right Arm	5	2	Relative Size	4			Form	3	3	Shoulders	04	04
Perspective	5	5	Position of Left Arm	5	2	Constant Line Pressure	5	5		Detailing	3	3	Right Arm	02	02
Vertical Midline	1	3	Position of Legs	6	4	Variable Line Pressure	0	0		Identity and Sex	1	1	Left Arm	02	02
Bilateral Symmetry	3	3	Relation of Long Axes	1	1	Line Continuity	4	4		Sophistication	3	3	Chest	03	03
Horizontal Midline	4	4	Right and Left Halves	1	2	Body Shading	3	1		Height	04	04	Girth	03	03

GENERAL CHARACTERISTICS OF SUBJECT

IDENTIFICATION
No.   274
Sex M
Marital status   M
Age 27 yrs. at
psychological tests

PARENTAL HISTORY				
Father				
C	H	S	D	O
–	–	–	–	–
Mother				
C	H	S	D	O
–	–	–	–	–

PHYSIOLOGICAL AND METABOLIC DATA

	Admission	Initial	Control	Cold pressor change	Exercise change	Smoking change
Systolic pressure	128	150	122	+02	+50	
Diastolic pressure	72	76	70	+22	–14	
Heart rate	96	90	91	–06	+09	

Age 24 yrs.	Height 68 in.	Ponderal index 13.16
	Weight 138 lbs.	Cholesterol 177 mg. per 100 ml.
	Overweight –07 %	Vital capacity 4.8 liters

HABIT SURVEY

Smoking habits: heavy cigarette smoker

Age begun 17 yrs.   Inhalation: yes

Habits of nervous tension: 6, 11, 14, 21

FIGURE-DRAWING CHARACTERISTICS

Structural	Male Female Both	Structural	Male	Female	Structural and Graphic	Male Female Both		Graphic, Global and Height	Male	Female	Body Proportions	Male	Female
Type	0	Omission of Appendages	0	0	Upper and Lower Halves	3	0	Hair Shading	0	3	Head		
Sex Sequence	0	Position of Both Arms	4	4	Four Quarters	4	4	Nudity and Transparency	7	7	Neck		
Posture	2 1	Position of Right Arm	7	7	Relative Size	4		Form	3	3	Shoulders		
Perspective	2 2	Position of Left Arm	4	4	Constant Line Pressure	0	0	Detailing	3	3	Right Arm		
Vertical Midline	4 4	Position of Legs	8	4	Variable Line Pressure	1	3	Identity and Sex	1	1	Left Arm	06	06
Bilateral Symmetry	0 0	Relation of Long Axes	1	1	Line Continuity	2	2	Sophistication	3	3	Chest	06	09
Horizontal Midline	0 4	Right and Left Halves	0	1	Body Shading	0	0	Height	07	09	Girth	06	10

GENERAL CHARACTERISTICS OF SUBJECT

IDENTIFICATION
No. 303
Sex M
Marital status M
Age 26 yrs. at
psychological tests

PARENTAL HISTORY				
Father				
C	H	S	D	O
–	–	–	–	–
Mother				
C	H	S	D	O
–	–	–	–	–

PHYSIOLOGICAL AND METABOLIC DATA

	Admission	Initial	Control	Cold pressor change	Exercise change	Smoking change
Systolic pressure	114	118	108	+08	+46	–02
Diastolic pressure	56	54	60	+20	+04	+02
Heart rate	64	102	81	00	+37	+04

Age 24 yrs.	Height 70 in.	Ponderal index 12.95
	Weight 158 lbs.	Cholesterol 250 mg. per 100 ml.
	Overweight +01 %	Vital capacity 6.2 liters

HABIT SURVEY
Smoking habits: pipe smoker
Age begun 17 yrs.   Inhalation: no
Habits of nervous tension: 4, 5, 6, 8, 10, 12, 24

Plate 430   **DRAWINGS AT AN INTERMEDIATE LEVEL OF SOPHISTICATION**   473

FIGURE-DRAWING CHARACTERISTICS

Structural	Male Female Both		Structural	Male	Female	Structural and Graphic	Male Female Both		Graphic, Global and Height	Male	Female	Body Proportions	Male	Female
Type	0		Omission of Appendages	7	0	Upper and Lower Halves	3	3	Hair Shading	0	5	Head	05	06
Sex Sequence	0		Position of Both Arms	0	0	Four Quarters	4	4	Nudity and Transparency	7	7	Neck	08	12
Posture	1	1	Position of Right Arm	5	5	Relative Size	2		Form	1	3	Shoulders	06	06
Perspective	0	0	Position of Left Arm	5	5	Constant Line Pressure	1	1	Detailing	3	5	Right Arm		04
Vertical Midline	3	0	Position of Legs	4	4	Variable Line Pressure	0	0	Identity and Sex	1	3	Left Arm		04
Bilateral Symmetry	3	3	Relation of Long Axes	1	1	Line Continuity	2	2	Sophistication	3	3	Chest	05	05
Horizontal Midline	4	4	Right and Left Halves	2	1	Body Shading	0	0	Height	06	06	Girth	07	05

GENERAL CHARACTERISTICS OF SUBJECT

IDENTIFICATION
No. 344
Sex M
Marital status   M
Age 26 yrs. at psychological tests

PARENTAL HISTORY				
Father				
C	H	S	D	O
-	-	-	-	-
Mother				
C	H	S	D	O
-	-	-	-	-

PHYSIOLOGICAL AND METABOLIC DATA

	Admission	Initial	Control	Cold pressor change	Exercise change	Smoking change
Systolic pressure	118	116	108	+12	+36	+02
Diastolic pressure	70	72	70	+10	-10	+06
Heart rate	84	72	73	+16	+27	+07

Age 24 yrs.	Height 72 in.	Ponderal index 13.15
	Weight 164 lbs.	Cholesterol 378 mg. per 100 ml.
	Overweight -01 %	Vital capacity 4.2 liters

HABIT SURVEY
Smoking habits: heavy cigarette smoker
Age begun   yrs.   Inhalation:
Habits of nervous tension:

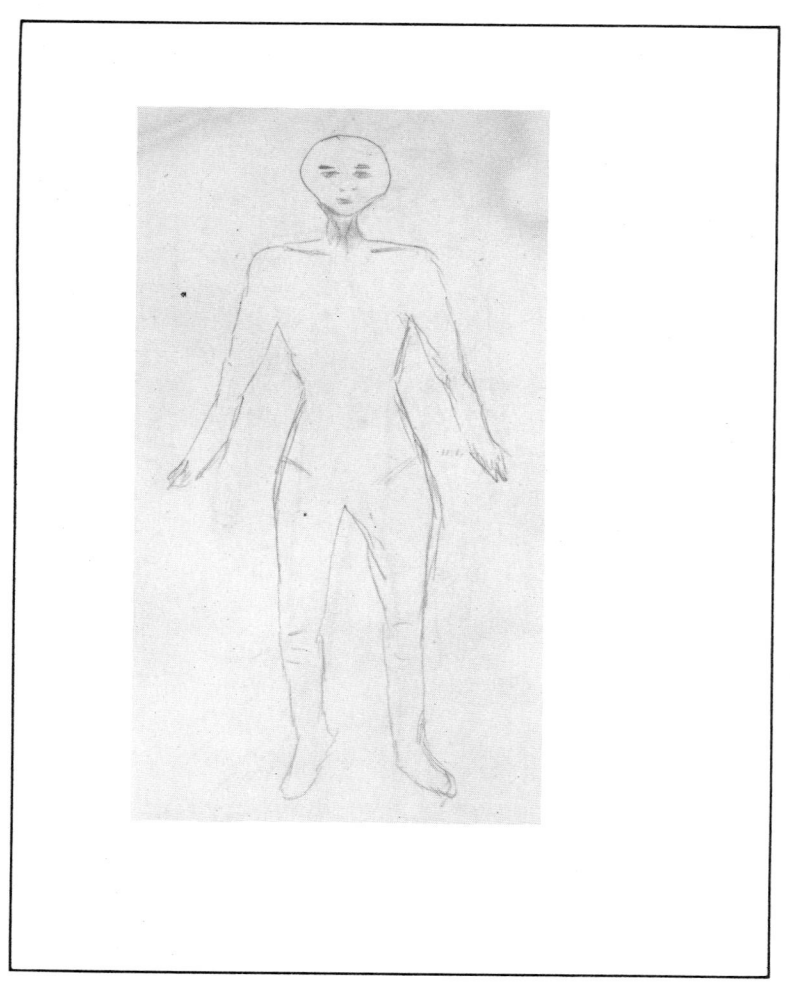

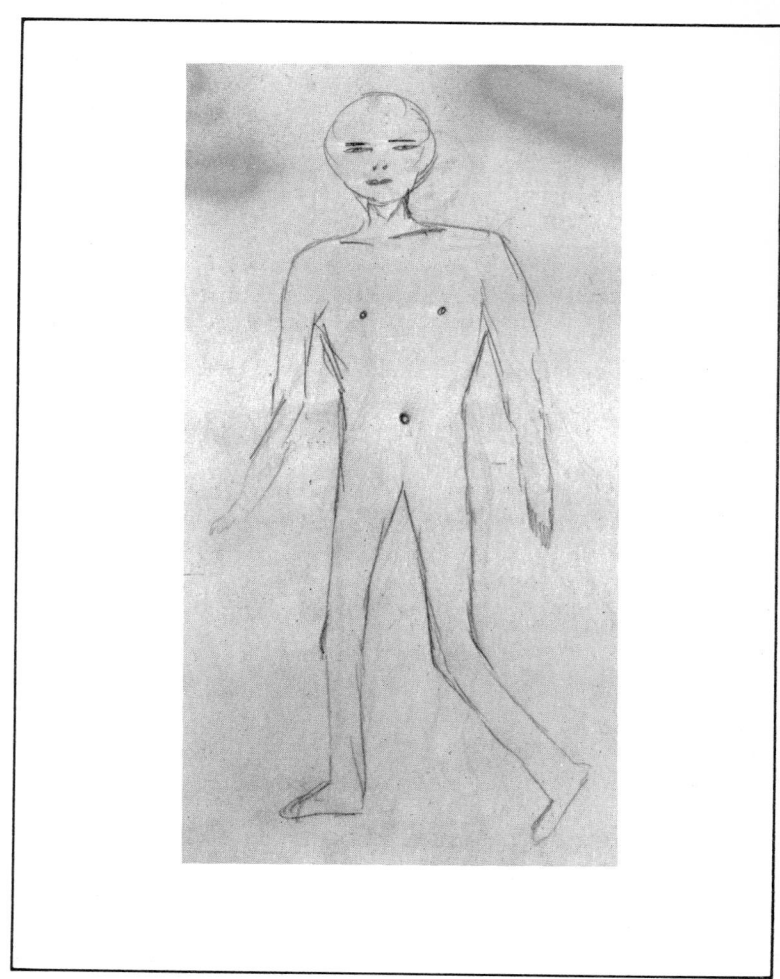

FIGURE-DRAWING CHARACTERISTICS

Structural	Male Female Both		Structural	Male	Female	Structural and Graphic	Male	Female Both	Graphic, Global and Height	Male	Female	Body Proportions	Male	Female
Type	0		Omission of Appendages	0	0	Upper and Lower Halves	1	1	Hair Shading	0	0	Head	09	06
Sex Sequence	1		Position of Both Arms	0	0	Four Quarters	4	4	Nudity and Transparency	0	0	Neck	08	08
Posture	2	1	Position of Right Arm	6	2	Relative Size	0		Form	3	3	Shoulders	09	07
Perspective	0	0	Position of Left Arm	6	2	Constant Line Pressure	0	0	Detailing	5	5	Right Arm	08	06
Vertical Midline	0	0	Position of Legs	8	6	Variable Line Pressure	1	1	Identity and Sex	3	3	Left Arm	08	06
Bilateral Symmetry	3	3	Relation of Long Axes	1	1	Line Continuity	0	0	Sophistication	3	3	Chest	08	06
Horizontal Midline	0	0	Right and Left Halves	0	1	Body Shading	1	3	Height	08	07	Girth	07	06

GENERAL CHARACTERISTICS OF SUBJECT

IDENTIFICATION
No. 369
Sex F
Marital status S
Age 23 yrs. at
psychological tests

PARENTAL HISTORY				
Father				
C	H	S	D	O
-	-	-	-	-
Mother				
C	H	S	D	O
-	-	-	-	-

PHYSIOLOGICAL AND METABOLIC DATA

	Admission	Initial	Control	Cold pressor change	Exercise change	Smoking change
Systolic pressure	100	114	108	+16	+32	
Diastolic pressure	60	76	68	+14	+02	
Heart rate	84	102	87	+12	+49	

Age 20 yrs.   Height 62 in.   Ponderal index 12.60

Weight 119 lbs.   Cholesterol 280 mg. per 100 ml.

Overweight 00 %   Vital capacity 2.6 liters

HABIT SURVEY

Smoking habits: heavy cigarette smoker

Age begun 16 yrs.   Inhalation: yes

Habits of nervous tension: 1, 3, 4, 7, 8, 10, 14, 15, 16, 23

Plate 432   DRAWINGS AT AN INTERMEDIATE LEVEL OF SOPHISTICATION   475

FIGURE-DRAWING CHARACTERISTICS

Structural	Male Female Both	Structural	Male	Female	Structural and Graphic	Male Female Both		Graphic, Global and Height	Male	Female	Body Proportions	Male	Female
Type	0	Omission of Appendages	0	0	Upper and Lower Halves	3	3	Hair Shading	7	5	Head	10	12
Sex Sequence	0	Position of Both Arms	1	4	Four Quarters	4	4	Nudity and Transparency	7	7	Neck	10	12
Posture	1 5	Position of Right Arm	2	7	Relative Size	4		Form	3	3	Shoulders	11	
Perspective	0 2	Position of Left Arm	4	4	Constant Line Pressure	0	0	Detailing	3	3	Right Arm	08	
Vertical Midline	0 4	Position of Legs	6	8	Variable Line Pressure	5	3	Identity and Sex	1	1	Left Arm	08	08
Bilateral Symmetry	3 0	Relation of Long Axes	1	1	Line Continuity	0	0	Sophistication	3	3	Chest	09	08
Horizontal Midline	4 0	Right and Left Halves	1	1	Body Shading	0	0	Height	08	09	Girth	09	10

GENERAL CHARACTERISTICS OF SUBJECT

IDENTIFICATION
No. 375
Sex M
Marital status S
Age 25 yrs. at psychological tests

PARENTAL HISTORY
Father
C H S D O
- - - - -
Mother
C H S D O
- - - - -

PHYSIOLOGICAL AND METABOLIC DATA

	Admission	Initial	Control	Cold pressor change	Exercise change	Smoking change
Systolic pressure	150	134	124	+10	+32	
Diastolic pressure	90	78	76	+04	00	
Heart rate	92	92	81	+04	+14	

Age 22 yrs.	Height	72 in.	Ponderal index 12.87
	Weight	175 lbs.	Cholesterol 208 mg. per 100 ml.
	Overweight +07 %		Vital capacity 5.1 liters

HABIT SURVEY

Smoking habits: moderate cigarette smoker

Age begun 19 yrs.   Inhalation: yes

Habits of nervous tension: 4, 5, 6, 11, 16, 25

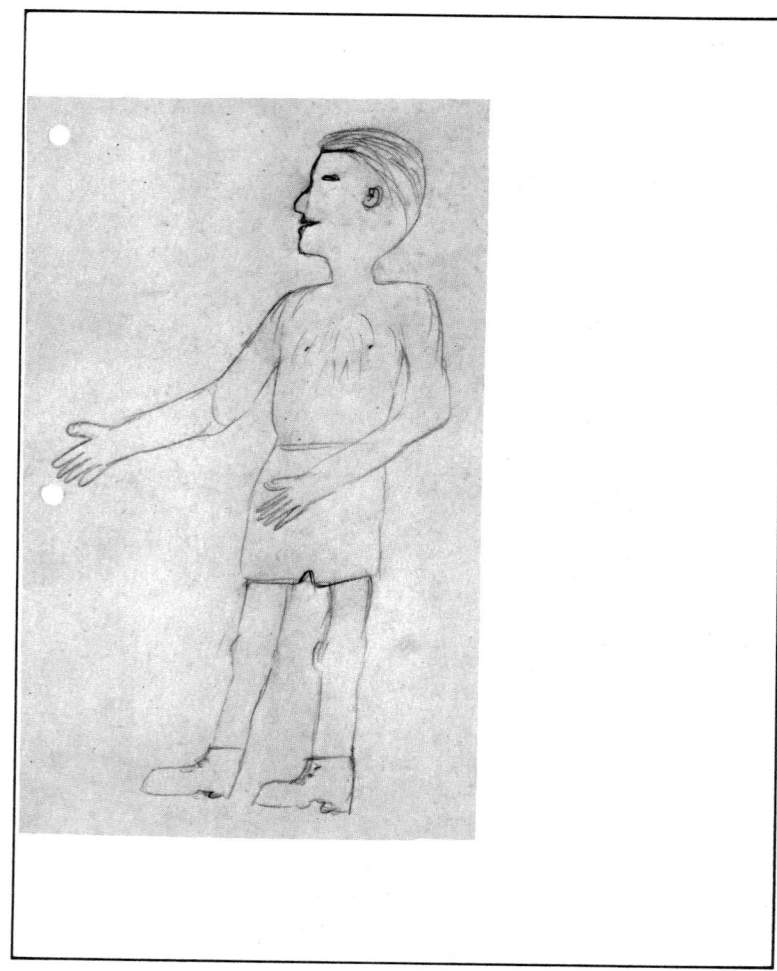

FIGURE-DRAWING CHARACTERISTICS

Structural	Male	Female	Structural	Male	Female	Structural and Graphic	Male	Female	Graphic, Global and Height	Male	Female	Body Proportions	Male	Female
	Both						Both							
Type	0		Omission of Appendages	0	0	Upper and Lower Halves	1	3	Hair Shading	1	1	Head	10	13
Sex Sequence	1		Position of Both Arms	1	0	Four Quarters	4	4	Nudity and Transparency	3	7	Neck	08	10
Posture	1	1	Position of Right Arm	2	2	Relative Size	4		Form	3	3	Shoulders		11
Perspective	6	0	Position of Left Arm	5	2	Constant Line Pressure	0	1	Detailing	3	5	Right Arm	06	06
Vertical Midline	0	3	Position of Legs	5	3	Variable Line Pressure	3	0	Identity and Sex	1	3	Left Arm	06	08
Bilateral Symmetry	0	3	Relation of Long Axes	1	1	Line Continuity	0	0	Sophistication	3	3	Chest		10
Horizontal Midline	4	4	Right and Left Halves	1	1	Body Shading	1	4	Height	07	09	Girth		11

GENERAL CHARACTERISTICS OF SUBJECT

IDENTIFICATION
No. 381
Sex M
Marital status S
Age 24 yrs. at
psychological tests

PARENTAL HISTORY
Father
C   H   S   D   O
-     -   -   -   -
Mother
C   H   S   D   O
-     -   -   -   -

PHYSIOLOGICAL AND METABOLIC DATA

	Admission	Initial	Control	Cold pressor change	Exercise change	Smoking change
Systolic pressure	125	120	108	+18	+46	
Diastolic pressure	80	73	68	+28	-04	
Heart rate	74	80	77	00	+26	

Age 24 yrs.	Height	71	in.	Ponderal index	13.30	
	Weight	152	lbs.	Cholesterol	230	mg. per 100 ml.
	Overweight	-05	%	Vital capacity	4.9	liters

HABIT SURVEY
Smoking habits: former smoker
Age begun   yrs.   Inhalation:
Habits of nervous tension: 5, 6, 10, 14

Plate 434   DRAWINGS AT AN INTERMEDIATE LEVEL OF SOPHISTICATION   477

FIGURE-DRAWING CHARACTERISTICS

Structural	Male Female Both	Structural	Male	Female	Structural and Graphic	Male Female Both		Graphic, Global and Height	Male	Female	Body Proportions	Male	Female
Type	0	Omission of Appendages	1	0	Upper and Lower Halves	7	3	Hair Shading	7	3	Head	23	16
Sex Sequence	2	Position of Both Arms	6	0	Four Quarters	4	4	Nudity and Transparency	9	7	Neck	24	12
Posture	0 1	Position of Right Arm	8	2	Relative Size	5		Form	3	3	Shoulders	18	11
Perspective	9 0	Position of Left Arm	8	2	Constant Line Pressure	5	0	Detailing	5	5	Right Arm		06
Vertical Midline	0 0	Position of Legs	0	4	Variable Line Pressure	0	5	Identity and Sex	3	3	Left Arm		08
Bilateral Symmetry	9 3	Relation of Long Axes	1	1	Line Continuity	4	2	Sophistication	3	3	Chest	15	08
Horizontal Midline	9 0	Right and Left Halves	1	1	Body Shading	0	0	Height		08	Girth		06

GENERAL CHARACTERISTICS OF SUBJECT

IDENTIFICATION
No. 413
Sex M
Marital status M
Age 26 yrs. at
psychological tests

PARENTAL HISTORY
Father
C   H   S   D   O
-    -   -   -   -
Mother
C   H   S   D   O
-    -   -   -   -

PHYSIOLOGICAL AND METABOLIC DATA

	Admission	Initial	Control	Cold pressor change	Exercise change	Smoking change
Systolic pressure	128	120	122	+32	+24	
Diastolic pressure	75	80	75	+30	-05	
Heart rate	84	76	81	+06	+13	

Age 24 yrs.	Height 69 in.	Ponderal index 13.29
	Weight 140 lbs.	Cholesterol 243 mg. per 100 ml.
	Overweight -08 %	Vital capacity 4.8 liters

HABIT SURVEY
Smoking habits: light cigarette smoker
Age begun 15 yrs.   Inhalation: yes
Habits of nervous tension: 1, 4, 5, 8, 14, 17

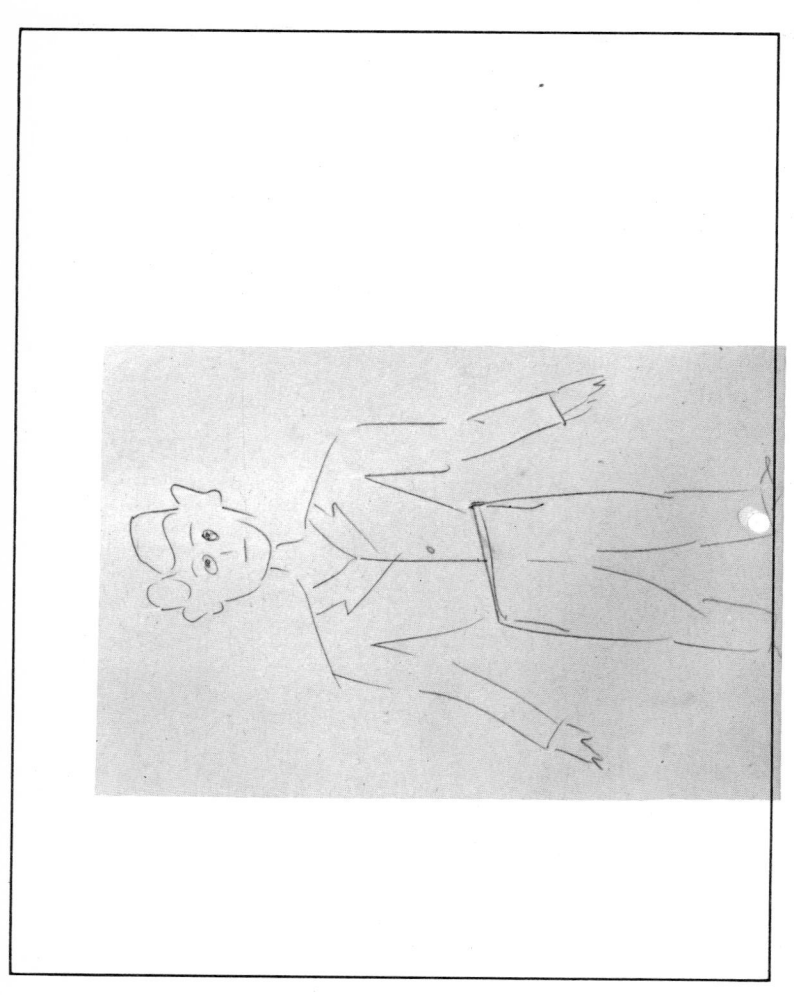

FIGURE-DRAWING CHARACTERISTICS

Structural	Male Female Both	Structural	Male	Female	Structural and Graphic	Male Female Both		Graphic, Global and Height	Male	Female	Body Proportions	Male	Female
Type	0	Omission of Appendages	8	0	Upper and Lower Halves	7	3	Hair Shading	5	5	Head	09	11
Sex Sequence	0	Position of Both Arms	0	0	Four Quarters	4	4	Nudity and Transparency	7	7	Neck	12	12
Posture	0 1	Position of Right Arm	2	2	Relative Size	2		Form	3	3	Shoulders	11	08
Perspective	0 0	Position of Left Arm	2	2	Constant Line Pressure	3	3	Detailing	3	3	Right Arm	06	04
Vertical Midline	3 0	Position of Legs	6	6	Variable Line Pressure	0	0	Identity and Sex	1	1	Left Arm	06	06
Bilateral Symmetry	3 3	Relation of Long Axes	2	2	Line Continuity	2	2	Sophistication	3	3	Chest	08	07
Horizontal Midline	4 4	Right and Left Halves	1	1	Body Shading	0	0	Height	06	06	Girth	07	08

GENERAL CHARACTERISTICS OF SUBJECT

IDENTIFICATION
No. 419
Sex M
Marital status M
Age 25 yrs. at
psychological tests

PARENTAL HISTORY
Father
C H S D O
- - - - -
Mother
C H S D O
- - - - -

PHYSIOLOGICAL AND METABOLIC DATA

	Admission	Initial	Control	Cold pressor change	Exercise change	Smoking change
Systolic pressure	100	114	108	+02	+38	
Diastolic pressure	60	74	64	+10	00	
Heart rate	84	96	82	+06	+18	

Age 22 yrs.	Height 72 in.	Ponderal index 13.43
	Weight 154 lbs.	Cholesterol 230 mg. per 100 ml.
	Overweight −06 %	Vital capacity 3.9 liters

HABIT SURVEY
Smoking habits: nonsmoker
Age begun yrs. Inhalation:
Habits of nervous tension: 3, 4, 5, 9, 20, 21

Plate 436   **DRAWINGS AT AN INTERMEDIATE LEVEL OF SOPHISTICATION**   479

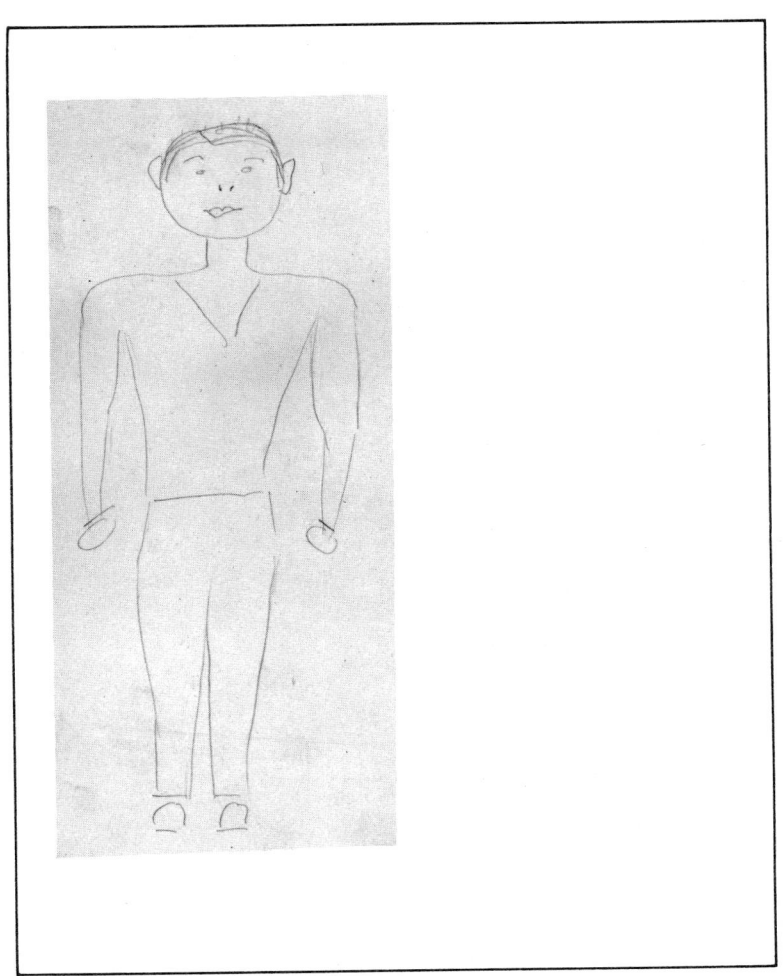

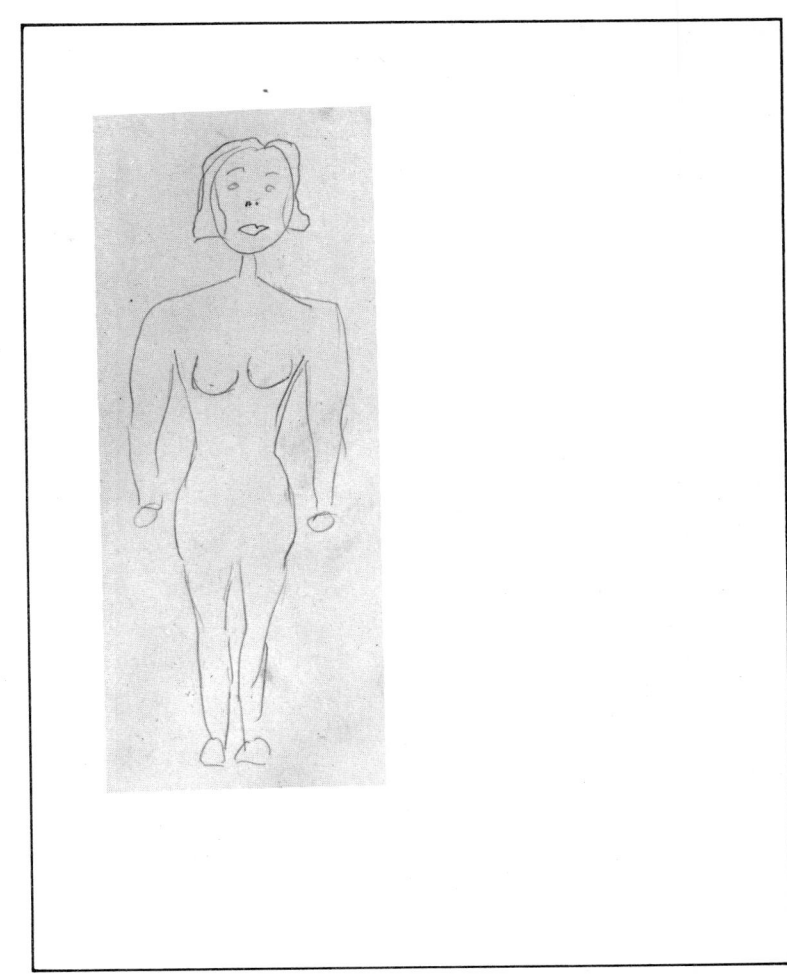

FIGURE-DRAWING CHARACTERISTICS

Structural	Male Female Both		Structural	Male	Female	Structural and Graphic	Male Female Both		Graphic, Global and Height	Male	Female	Body Proportions	Male	Female
Type	0		Omission of Appendages	0	0	Upper and Lower Halves	1	1	Hair Shading	3	5	Head	09	09
Sex Sequence	0		Position of Both Arms	0	0	Four Quarters	4	4	Nudity and Transparency	7	0	Neck	10	08
Posture	1	1	Position of Right Arm	0	0	Relative Size	0		Form	3	3	Shoulders	11	08
Perspective	0	0	Position of Left Arm	0	0	Constant Line Pressure	1	1	Detailing	3	3	Right Arm	06	06
Vertical Midline	0	0	Position of Legs	4	3	Variable Line Pressure	0	0	Identity and Sex	1	1	Left Arm	06	06
Bilateral Symmetry	3	3	Relation of Long Axes	1	1	Line Continuity	3	0	Sophistication	3	3	Chest	08	06
Horizontal Midline	4	0	Right and Left Halves	2	2	Body Shading	0	0	Height	07	06	Girth	07	05

GENERAL CHARACTERISTICS OF SUBJECT

IDENTIFICATION
No. 421
Sex M
Marital status S
Age 28 yrs. at
psychological tests

PARENTAL HISTORY
Father
C   H   S   D   O
-    -   -   -   -
Mother
C   H   S   D   O
-    -   -   -   -

PHYSIOLOGICAL AND METABOLIC DATA

	Admission	Initial	Control	Cold pressor change	Exercise change	Smoking change
Systolic pressure	148	120	118	+07	+22	
Diastolic pressure	80	70	68	+08	-10	
Heart rate	80	76	71	+06	+17	

Age 25 yrs.	Height 72 in.	Ponderal index 12.71
	Weight 182 lbs.	Cholesterol 355 mg. per 100 ml.
	Overweight +09 %	Vital capacity 5.7 liters

HABIT SURVEY
Smoking habits: moderate cigarette smoker
Age begun 18 yrs.   Inhalation: yes
Habits of nervous tension: 5, 6, 9, 11, 17

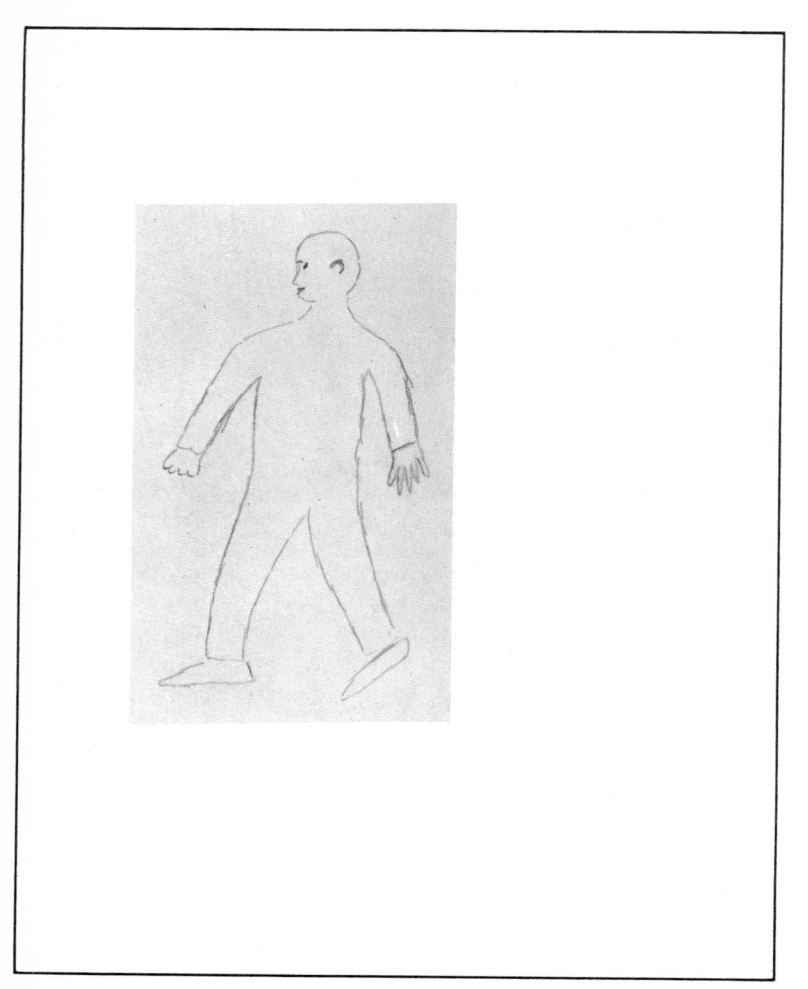

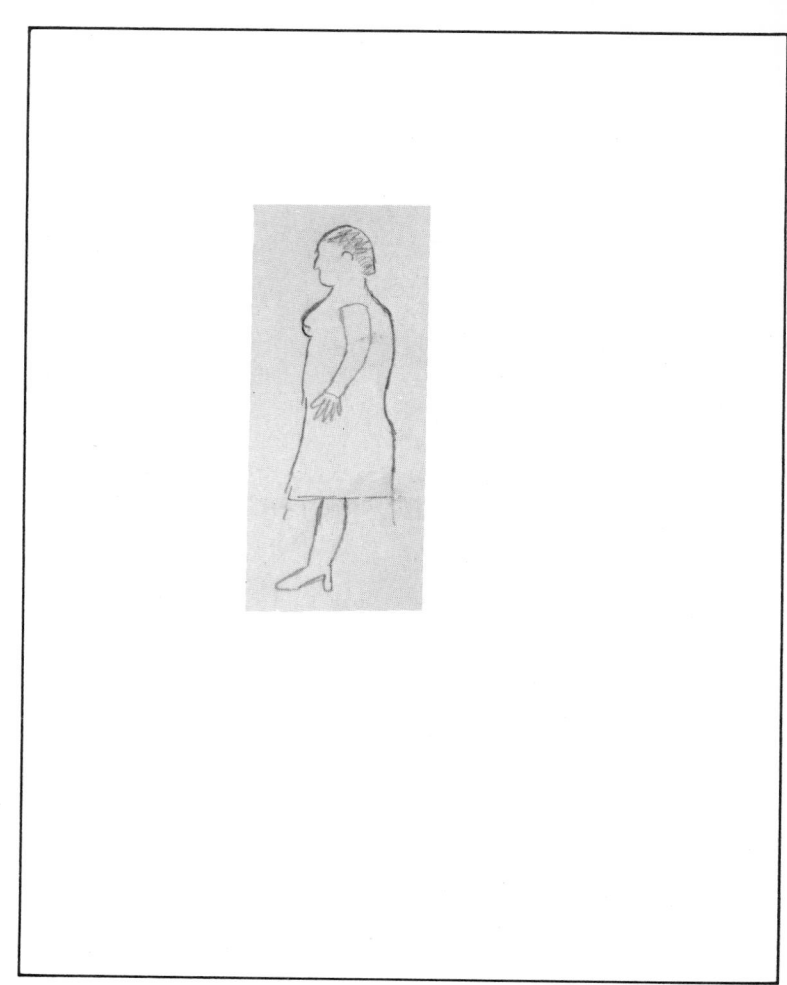

FIGURE-DRAWING CHARACTERISTICS

Structural	Male Female Both		Structural	Male	Female	Structural and Graphic	Male Female Both		Graphic, Global and Height	Male	Female	Body Proportions	Male	Female
Type	0		Omission of Appendages	0	0	Upper and Lower Halves	1	1	Hair Shading	0	1	Head	06	05
Sex Sequence	0		Position of Both Arms	0	4	Four Quarters	4	4	Nudity and Transparency	7	7	Neck	04	02
Posture	2	1	Position of Right Arm	2	7	Relative Size	0		Form	3	3	Shoulders	06	
Perspective	5	2	Position of Left Arm	2	5	Constant Line Pressure	0	0	Detailing	5	5	Right Arm	04	
Vertical Midline	0	4	Position of Legs	8	1	Variable Line Pressure	1	5	Identity and Sex	3	1	Left Arm	02	02
Bilateral Symmetry	3	0	Relation of Long Axes	1	1	Line Continuity	0	0	Sophistication	3	3	Chest	05	05
Horizontal Midline	0	0	Right and Left Halves	1	2	Body Shading	0	0	Height	05	03	Girth	06	08

GENERAL CHARACTERISTICS OF SUBJECT

<table>
<tr><td colspan="2">IDENTIFICATION</td><td colspan="2">PARENTAL HISTORY</td><td colspan="7">PHYSIOLOGICAL AND METABOLIC DATA</td><td colspan="2">HABIT SURVEY</td></tr>
</table>

IDENTIFICATION

No. 424
Sex M
Marital status M
Age 26 yrs. at
psychological tests

PARENTAL HISTORY

Father
C H S D O
- - - - -

Mother
C H S D O
- - - - -

PHYSIOLOGICAL AND METABOLIC DATA

	Admission	Initial	Control	Cold pressor change	Exercise change	Smoking change
Systolic pressure	140	122	120	+16	+34	
Diastolic pressure	84	76	70	+14	-00	
Heart rate	108	102	94	+06	+21	

Age 24 yrs.
Height 71 in.
Weight 146 lbs.
Overweight -09 %

Ponderal index 13.48
Cholesterol 222 mg. per 100 ml.
Vital capacity 4.9 liters

HABIT SURVEY

Smoking habits: unknown
　Age begun　yrs.　Inhalation:
Habits of nervous tension:

Plate 438   **DRAWINGS AT AN INTERMEDIATE LEVEL OF SOPHISTICATION**   481

FIGURE-DRAWING CHARACTERISTICS

Structural	Male Female Both	Structural	Male	Female	Structural and Graphic	Male Female Both		Graphic, Global and Height	Male	Female	Body Proportions	Male	Female
Type	0	Omission of Appendages	0	0	Upper and Lower Halves	1	3	Hair Shading	5	5	Head	12	13
Sex Sequence	0	Position of Both Arms	4	4	Four Quarters	4	4	Nudity and Transparency	7	7	Neck	04	10
Posture	2 2	Position of Right Arm	7	7	Relative Size	4		Form	3	3	Shoulders		
Perspective	2 2	Position of Left Arm	2	2	Constant Line Pressure	1	0	Detailing	5	5	Right Arm		
Vertical Midline	4 4	Position of Legs	8	8	Variable Line Pressure	0	1	Identity and Sex	1	1	Left Arm	06	06
Bilateral Symmetry	0 0	Relation of Long Axes	1	1	Line Continuity	0	0	Sophistication	3	3	Chest	10	10
Horizontal Midline	4 4	Right and Left Halves	1	2	Body Shading	0	0	Height	07	08	Girth	10	10

GENERAL CHARACTERISTICS OF SUBJECT

IDENTIFICATION
No. 427
Sex M
Marital status M
Age 25 yrs. at
psychological tests

PARENTAL HISTORY
Father
C H S D O
- - - - -
Mother
C H S D O
- - - - -

PHYSIOLOGICAL AND METABOLIC DATA

	Admission	Initial	Control	Cold pressor change	Exercise change	Smoking change
Systolic pressure	128	114	100	+26	+10	
Diastolic pressure	68	62	60	+28	+10	
Heart rate	88	68	77	+28	+23	

Age 22 yrs.	Height 67 in.	Ponderal index 12.50	
	Weight 154 lbs.	Cholesterol 298 mg. per 100 ml.	
	Overweight +08 %	Vital capacity 3.7 liters	

HABIT SURVEY
Smoking habits: unknown
Age begun   yrs.   Inhalation:
Habits of nervous tension:

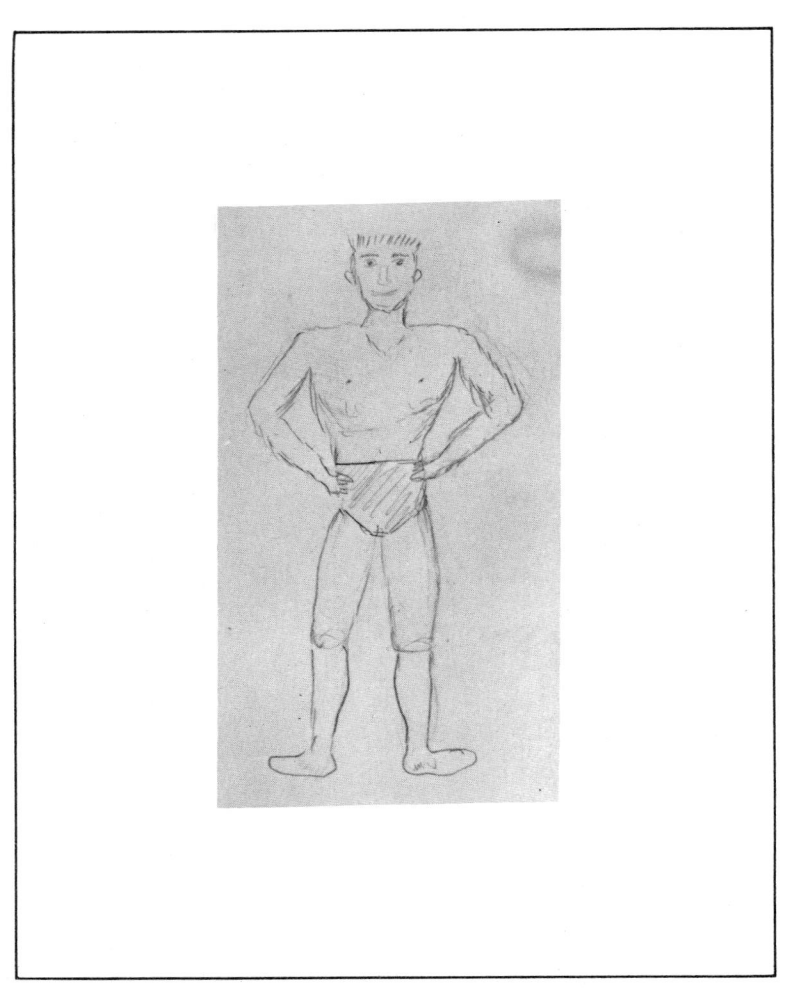

FIGURE-DRAWING CHARACTERISTICS

Structural	Male Female		Structural	Male	Female	Structural and Graphic	Male	Female	Graphic, Global and Height	Male	Female	Body Proportions	Male	Female
	Both						Both							
Type	0		Omission of Appendages	0	0	Upper and Lower Halves	0	3	Hair Shading	7	3	Head	06	07
Sex Sequence	0		Position of Both Arms	0	1	Four Quarters	4	4	Nudity and Transparency	3	2	Neck	08	08
Posture	1	1	Position of Right Arm	5	2	Relative Size	4		Form	3	3	Shoulders	07	06
Perspective	0	0	Position of Left Arm	5	5	Constant Line Pressure	0	0	Detailing	3	3	Right Arm	04	04
Vertical Midline	0	0	Position of Legs	6	5	Variable Line Pressure	1	3	Identity and Sex	1	1	Left Arm	04	04
Bilateral Symmetry	3	3	Relation of Long Axes	1	1	Line Continuity	0	0	Sophistication	3	3	Chest	07	07
Horizontal Midline	4	0	Right and Left Halves	1	1	Body Shading	3	3	Height	05	07	Girth	05	07

GENERAL CHARACTERISTICS OF SUBJECT

IDENTIFICATION
No. 431
Sex M
Marital status S
Age 28 yrs. at
psychological tests

PARENTAL HISTORY				
Father				
C	H	S	D	O
-	-	-	-	-
Mother				
C	H	S	D	O
-	-	-	-	-

PHYSIOLOGICAL AND METABOLIC DATA

	Admission	Initial	Control	Cold pressor change	Exercise change	Smoking change
Systolic pressure	120	120	108	+22	+30	
Diastolic pressure	80	72	68	+20	-16	
Heart rate	60	80	77	00	+06	

Age 25 yrs.	Height 68 in.	Ponderal index 13.10
	Weight 140 lbs.	Cholesterol 222 mg. per 100 ml.
	Overweight -06 %	Vital capacity 4.8 liters

Plate 440   DRAWINGS AT AN INTERMEDIATE LEVEL OF SOPHISTICATION   483

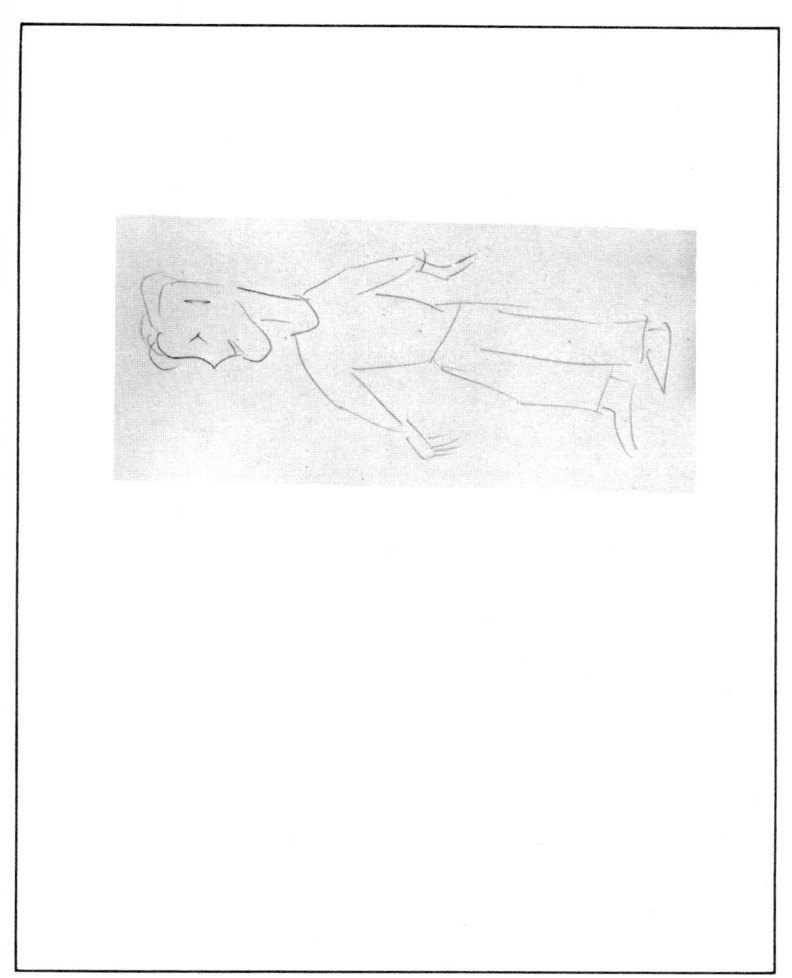

FIGURE-DRAWING CHARACTERISTICS

Structural	Male Female Both		Structural	Male	Female	Structural and Graphic	Male Female Both		Graphic, Global and Height	Male	Female	Body Proportions	Male	Female
Type	0		Omission of Appendages	0	7	Upper and Lower Halves	0	0	Hair Shading	7	5	Head	09	07
Sex Sequence	0		Position of Both Arms	0	2	Four Quarters	4	4	Nudity and Transparency	7	7	Neck	14	14
Posture	1	1	Position of Right Arm	2	5	Relative Size	0		Form	3	3	Shoulders		
Perspective	6	9	Position of Left Arm	2	7	Constant Line Pressure	0	0	Detailing	5	5	Right Arm	04	
Vertical Midline	4	4	Position of Legs	5	4	Variable Line Pressure	1	1	Identity and Sex	1	1	Left Arm	02	
Bilateral Symmetry	0	0	Relation of Long Axes	2	2	Line Continuity	2	2	Sophistication	3	3	Chest		06
Horizontal Midline	4	4	Right and Left Halves	4	4	Body Shading	0	0	Height	05	04	Girth		04

GENERAL CHARACTERISTICS OF SUBJECT

IDENTIFICATION
No. 440
Sex M
Marital status S
Age 29 yrs. at
psychological tests

PARENTAL HISTORY				
Father				
C	H	S	D	O
-	-	-	-	-
Mother				
C	H	S	D	O
-	-	-	-	-

PHYSIOLOGICAL AND METABOLIC DATA

	Admission	Initial	Control	Cold pressor change	Exercise change	Smoking change
Systolic pressure	132	106	102	+14	+20	
Diastolic pressure	72	56	66	+08	-02	
Heart rate	80	76	71	+08	+12	

Age 26 yrs.	Height	73	in.	Ponderal index	13.45	
	Weight	160	lbs.	Cholesterol	273	mg. per 100 ml.
	Overweight	-08	%	Vital capacity	4.7	liters

HABIT SURVEY

Smoking habits: nonsmoker

Age begun   yrs.   Inhalation:

Habits of nervous tension: 2, 5, 6, 9, 11, 14, 16, 21

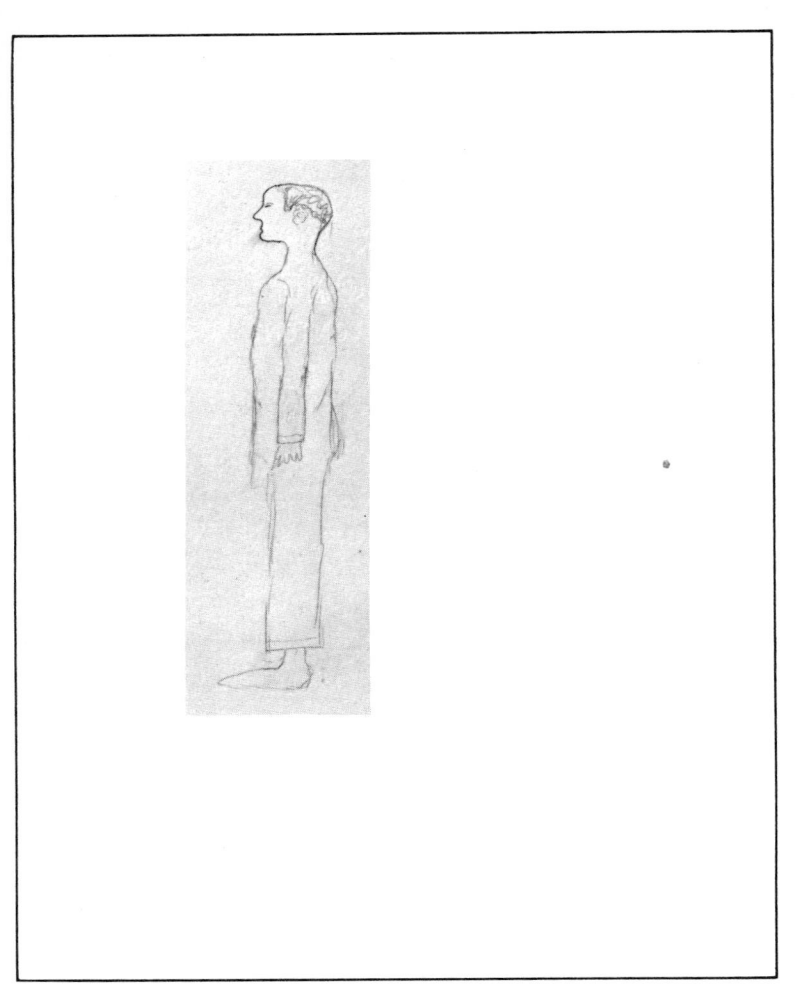

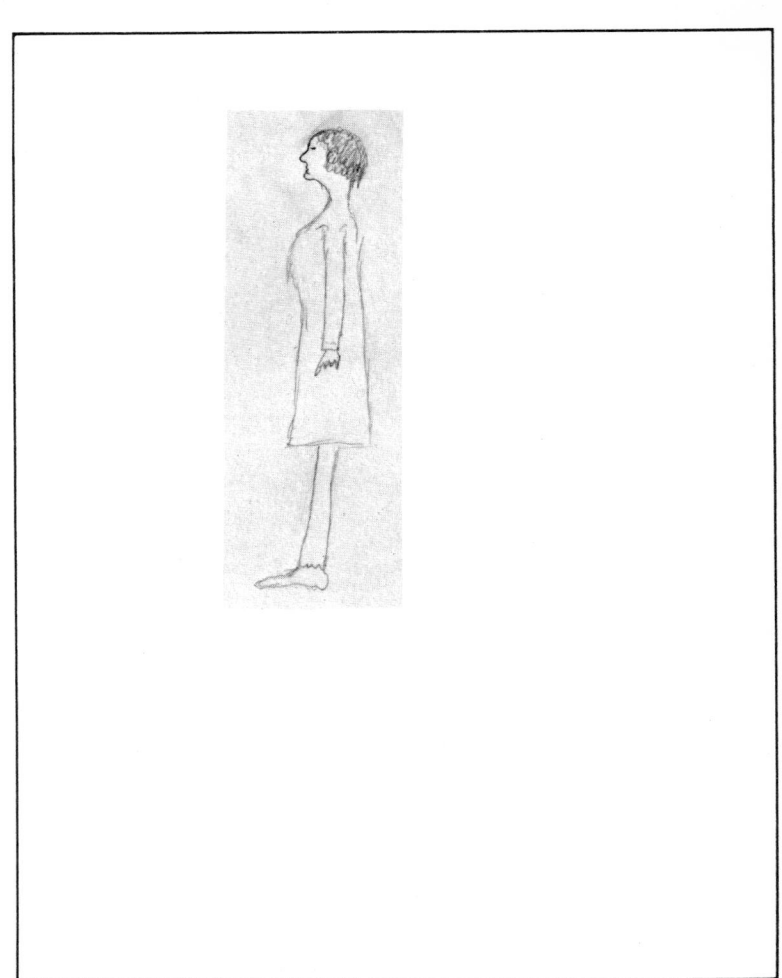

FIGURE-DRAWING CHARACTERISTICS

Structural	Male Female Both		Structural	Male	Female	Structural and Graphic	Male Female Both		Graphic, Global and Height	Male	Female	Body Proportions	Male	Female
Type	0		Omission of Appendages	0	0	Upper and Lower Halves	1	1	Hair Shading	1	3	Head	05	04
Sex Sequence	0		Position of Both Arms	4	4	Four Quarters	4	4	Nudity and Transparency	7	7	Neck	06	08
Posture	1	1	Position of Right Arm	7	7	Relative Size	0		Form	3	3	Shoulders		
Perspective	2	2	Position of Left Arm	0	0	Constant Line Pressure	0	0	Detailing	5	5	Right Arm		
Vertical Midline	4	4	Position of Legs	1	1	Variable Line Pressure	3	3	Identity and Sex	3	3	Left Arm	04	02
Bilateral Symmetry	0	0	Relation of Long Axes	1	1	Line Continuity	0	0	Sophistication	3	3	Chest	06	04
Horizontal Midline	0	0	Right and Left Halves	2	2	Body Shading	0	0	Height	05	04	Girth	06	06

GENERAL CHARACTERISTICS OF SUBJECT

IDENTIFICATION
No. 471
Sex M
Marital status M
Age 25 yrs. at
psychological tests

PARENTAL HISTORY				
Father				
C	H	S	D	O
-	-	-	-	-
Mother				
C	H	S	D	O
-	-	-	-	-

PHYSIOLOGICAL AND METABOLIC DATA

	Admission	Initial	Control	Cold pressor change	Exercise change	Smoking change
Systolic pressure	104	120	100	+15	+30	
Diastolic pressure	68	80	60	+14	+10	
Heart rate	72	72	71	+06	+03	

Age 23 yrs.	Height 72 in.	Ponderal index 12.85
	Weight 176 lbs.	Cholesterol 237 mg. per 100 ml.
	Overweight +07 %	Vital capacity 4.4 liters

HABIT SURVEY

Smoking habits: nonsmoker

  Age begun   yrs.   Inhalation:

Habits of nervous tension: 3, 4, 5, 6, 9, 19, 23

FIGURE-DRAWING CHARACTERISTICS

Structural	Male Female Both		Structural	Male	Female	Structural and Graphic	Male Female Both		Graphic, Global and Height	Male	Female	Body Proportions	Male	Female
Type	0		Omission of Appendages	0	8	Upper and Lower Halves	0	7	Hair Shading	3	3	Head	14	13
Sex Sequence	0		Position of Both Arms	0	1	Four Quarters	4	4	Nudity and Transparency	7	7	Neck	12	14
Posture	1	1	Position of Right Arm	5	2	Relative Size	1		Form	3	3	Shoulders	12	12
Perspective	0	0	Position of Left Arm	5	5	Constant Line Pressure	0	0	Detailing	3	3	Right Arm	08	10
Vertical Midline	3	0	Position of Legs	4	4	Variable Line Pressure	4	1	Identity and Sex	1	1	Left Arm	08	08
Bilateral Symmetry	3	3	Relation of Long Axes	1	1	Line Continuity	2	0	Sophistication	3	3	Chest	11	09
Horizontal Midline	4	4	Right and Left Halves	1	1	Body Shading	6	3	Height	09	10	Girth	14	12

GENERAL CHARACTERISTICS OF SUBJECT

IDENTIFICATION
No. 519
Sex M
Marital status S
Age 23 yrs. at
psychological tests

PARENTAL HISTORY				
Father				
C	H	S	D	O
-	-	-	-	-
Mother				
C	H	S	D	O
-	-	-	-	-

PHYSIOLOGICAL AND METABOLIC DATA

	Admission	Initial	Control	Cold pressor change	Exercise change	Smoking change
Systolic pressure	125	124	124	+12	+30	+04
Diastolic pressure	60	80	80	+16	-10	+12
Heart rate	78	80	72	+08	+28	+10

Age 22 yrs.

Height	75 in.	Ponderal index 13.67
Weight	165 lbs.	Cholesterol 222 mg. per 100 ml.
Overweight -07 %		Vital capacity 4.3 liters

HABIT SURVEY
Smoking habits: pipe smoker
Age begun 18 yrs.   Inhalation: no
Habits of nervous tension: 3, 25

FIGURE-DRAWING CHARACTERISTICS

Structural	Male Female Both		Structural	Male	Female	Structural and Graphic	Male Female Both		Graphic, Global and Height	Male	Female	Body Proportions	Male	Female
Type	0		Omission of Appendages	0	0	Upper and Lower Halves	1	1	Hair Shading	2	3	Head	04	05
Sex Sequence	1		Position of Both Arms	0	1	Four Quarters	4	4	Nudity and Transparency	7	7	Neck	05	05
Posture	1	1	Position of Right Arm	0	3	Relative Size	4		Form	3	3	Shoulders	03	04
Perspective	0	0	Position of Left Arm	0	5	Constant Line Pressure	0	0	Detailing	3	3	Right Arm	02	03
Vertical Midline	3	0	Position of Legs	4	4	Variable Line Pressure	1	1	Identity and Sex	1	1	Left Arm	02	04
Bilateral Symmetry	3	3	Relation of Long Axes	1	1	Line Continuity	0	0	Sophistication	3	3	Chest	02	04
Horizontal Midline	6	4	Right and Left Halves	1	2	Body Shading	0	3	Height	03	03	Girth	03	03

GENERAL CHARACTERISTICS OF SUBJECT

IDENTIFICATION
No. 525
Sex M
Marital status S
Age 25 yrs. at
psychological tests

PARENTAL HISTORY					
Father					
C	H	S	D	O	
-	-	-	-	-	
Mother					
C	H	S	D	O	
-	-	-	-	-	

PHYSIOLOGICAL AND METABOLIC DATA

	Admission	Initial	Control	Cold pressor change	Exercise change	Smoking change
Systolic pressure	150	146	120	-12	+24	-01
Diastolic pressure	70	74	72	+08	00	+04
Heart rate	104	78	56	+18	+09	+03

Age 24 yrs.	Height 74 in.	Ponderal index 13.11
	Weight 180 lbs.	Cholesterol 210 mg. per 100 ml.
	Overweight +02 %	Vital capacity liters

HABIT SURVEY

Smoking habits: nonsmoker

Age begun   yrs.   Inhalation:

Habits of nervous tension: 3, 4, 5, 8, 9, 14, 17, 18, 21, 24, 25

Plate 444   DRAWINGS AT AN INTERMEDIATE LEVEL OF SOPHISTICATION   487

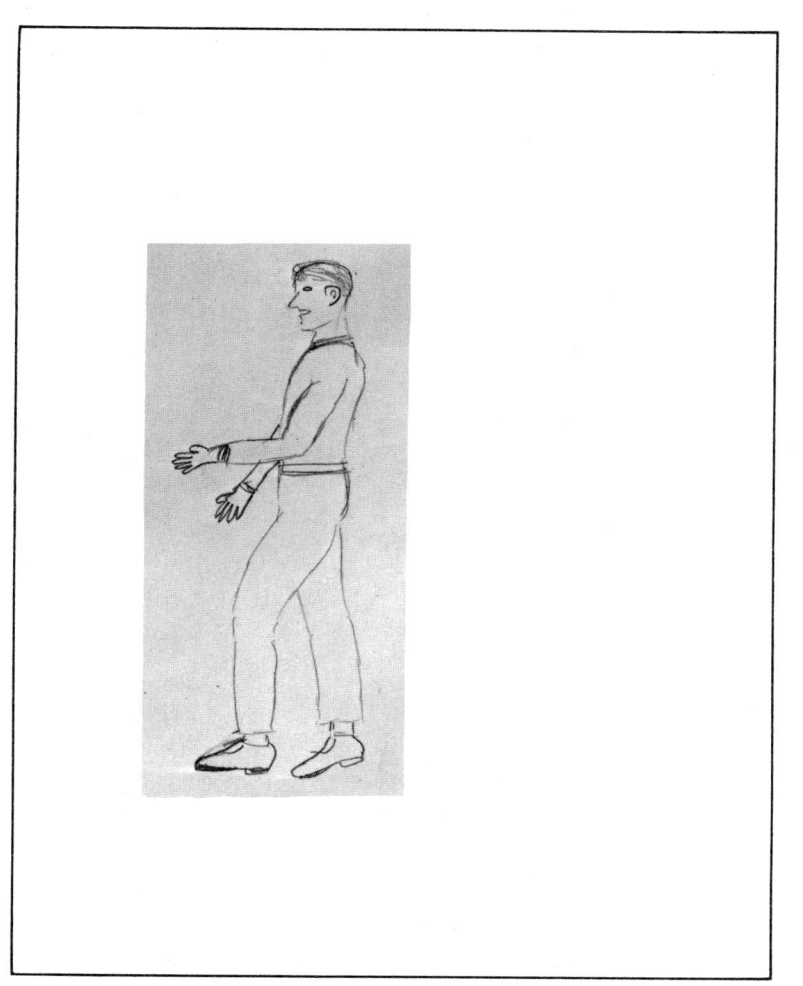

FIGURE-DRAWING CHARACTERISTICS

Structural	Male Female Both	Structural	Male	Female	Structural and Graphic	Male Female Both	Graphic, Global and Height	Male	Female	Body Proportions	Male	Female
Type	0	Omission of Appendages	0	0	Upper and Lower Halves	0	3	Hair Shading	2	3	Head	05	07
Sex Sequence	0	Position of Both Arms	4	4	Four Quarters	4	4	Nudity and Transparency	7	7	Neck	04	07
Posture	2	2	Position of Right Arm	7	7	Relative Size	4		Form	1	1	Shoulders		
Perspective	2	2	Position of Left Arm	4	4	Constant Line Pressure	0	0	Detailing	3	3	Right Arm		
Vertical Midline	4	4	Position of Legs	8	8	Variable Line Pressure	4	4	Identity and Sex	1	1	Left Arm	04	05
Bilateral Symmetry	0	0	Relation of Long Axes	1	1	Line Continuity	0	0	Sophistication	3	3	Chest	05	05
Horizontal Midline	4	4	Right and Left Halves	2	2	Body Shading	0	0	Height	05	06	Girth	05	06

GENERAL CHARACTERISTICS OF SUBJECT

IDENTIFICATION
No. 534
Sex M
Marital status S
Age 25 yrs. at
psychological tests

PARENTAL HISTORY
Father
C   H   S   D   O
–   –   –   –   –
Mother
C   H   S   D   O
–   –   –   –   –

PHYSIOLOGICAL AND METABOLIC DATA

	Admission	Initial	Control	Cold pressor change	Exercise change	Smoking change
Systolic pressure	124	100	90	+10	+10	
Diastolic pressure	82	60	70	+10	00	
Heart rate	72	60	61	+02	+07	

Age 23 yrs.

Height 74 in.
Weight 197 lbs.
Overweight +13 %

Ponderal index 12.72
Cholesterol 258 mg. per 100 ml.
Vital capacity 5.7 liters

HABIT SURVEY
Smoking habits: nonsmoker
Age begun   yrs.   Inhalation:
Habits of nervous tension: 4, 5, 11, 16, 22

FIGURE-DRAWING CHARACTERISTICS

Structural	Male	Female	Structural	Male	Female	Structural and Graphic	Male	Female	Graphic, Global and Height	Male	Female	Body Proportions	Male	Female
	Both						Both							
Type	0		Omission of Appendages	2	7	Upper and Lower Halves	4	4	Hair Shading	0	1	Head	03	
Sex Sequence	0		Position of Both Arms	4	6	Four Quarters	3	3	Nudity and Transparency	7	7	Neck	06	
Posture	1	1	Position of Right Arm	7	7	Relative Size	4		Form	3	3	Shoulders		
Perspective	8	4	Position of Left Arm	4	7	Constant Line Pressure	0	0	Detailing	5	5	Right Arm		
Vertical Midline	4	4	Position of Legs	4	5	Variable Line Pressure	3	3	Identity and Sex	3	3	Left Arm	02	
Bilateral Symmetry	0	0	Relation of Long Axes	1	1	Line Continuity	0	0	Sophistication	3	3	Chest		
Horizontal Midline	0	0	Right and Left Halves	4	4	Body Shading	0	0	Height	03	04	Girth		

GENERAL CHARACTERISTICS OF SUBJECT

IDENTIFICATION
No. 546
Sex M
Marital status M
Age 24 yrs. at psychological tests

PARENTAL HISTORY				
Father				
C	H	S	D	O
–	–	–	–	–
Mother				
C	H	S	D	O
–	–	–	–	–

PHYSIOLOGICAL AND METABOLIC DATA

	Admission	Initial	Control	Cold pressor change	Exercise change	Smoking change
Systolic pressure	120	126	120	+14	+22	
Diastolic pressure	76	78	72	+06	+06	
Heart rate	70	76	77	+12	+20	

Age 22 yrs.	Height 68 in.	Ponderal index 12.42
	Weight 164 lbs.	Cholesterol 230 mg. per 100 ml.
	Overweight +12 %	Vital capacity 3.8 liters

HABIT SURVEY
Smoking habits: former smoker
Age begun 17 yrs.   Inhalation:
Habits of nervous tension: 5, 18, 23

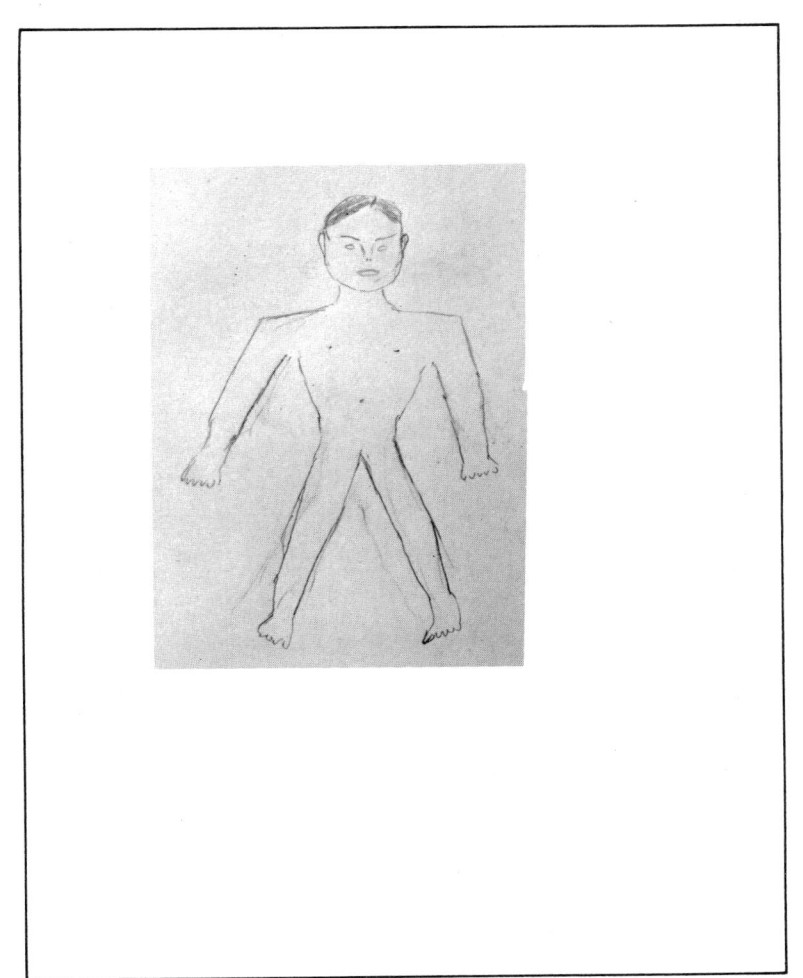

FIGURE-DRAWING CHARACTERISTICS

Structural	Male Female Both	Structural	Male	Female	Structural and Graphic	Male Female Both		Graphic, Global and Height	Male	Female	Body Proportions	Male	Female
Type	0	Omission of Appendages	0	0	Upper and Lower Halves	1	1	Hair Shading	2	2	Head	07	07
Sex Sequence	0	Position of Both Arms	0	0	Four Quarters	4	4	Nudity and Transparency	0	0	Neck	06	06
Posture	1 1	Position of Right Arm	2	2	Relative Size	2		Form	3	3	Shoulders	08	05
Perspective	0 0	Position of Left Arm	2	2	Constant Line Pressure	0	0	Detailing	5	5	Right Arm	04	03
Vertical Midline	0 0	Position of Legs	6	2	Variable Line Pressure	2	2	Identity and Sex	1	1	Left Arm	04	03
Bilateral Symmetry	4 4	Relation of Long Axes	1	1	Line Continuity	0	3	Sophistication	3	3	Chest	06	05
Horizontal Midline	0 0	Right and Left Halves	1	1	Body Shading	0	0	Height	04	04	Girth	04	04

GENERAL CHARACTERISTICS OF SUBJECT

IDENTIFICATION
No. 559
Sex M
Marital status M
Age 25 yrs. at psychological tests

PARENTAL HISTORY
Father
C H S D O
- - - - -
Mother
C H S D O
- - - - -

PHYSIOLOGICAL AND METABOLIC DATA

	Admission	Initial	Control	Cold pressor change	Exercise change	Smoking change
Systolic pressure	140	100	100	+10	+30	
Diastolic pressure	92	70	70	+10	00	
Heart rate	72	68	68	+02	+03	

Age 24 yrs.

Height 72 in.
Weight 173 lbs.
Overweight +05 %

Ponderal index 12.92
Cholesterol 265 mg. per 100 ml.
Vital capacity 5.0 liters

HABIT SURVEY

Smoking habits: heavy cigarette smoker

Age begun 18 yrs. Inhalation: yes

Habits of nervous tension: 6

FIGURE-DRAWING CHARACTERISTICS

Structural	Male Female Both	Structural	Male	Female	Structural and Graphic	Male Female Both		Graphic, Global and Height	Male	Female	Body Proportions	Male	Female
Type	0	Omission of Appendages	0	0	Upper and Lower Halves	3	3	Hair Shading	3	1	Head	11	09
Sex Sequence	1	Position of Both Arms	2	1	Four Quarters	4	4	Nudity and Transparency	7	7	Neck	16	16
Posture	1	1	Position of Right Arm	4	4	Relative Size	2		Form	3	3	Shoulders		
Perspective	2	6	Position of Left Arm	7	2	Constant Line Pressure	0	0	Detailing	3	3	Right Arm	08	08
Vertical Midline	7	4	Position of Legs	1	6	Variable Line Pressure	1	1	Identity and Sex	1	1	Left Arm		06
Bilateral Symmetry	0	0	Relation of Long Axes	1	1	Line Continuity	0	0	Sophistication	3	3	Chest	11	
Horizontal Midline	4	0	Right and Left Halves	2	1	Body Shading	0	3	Height	09	09	Girth	09	

GENERAL CHARACTERISTICS OF SUBJECT

<table>
<tr><th>IDENTIFICATION</th></tr>
<tr><td>No. 574</td></tr>
<tr><td>Sex M</td></tr>
<tr><td>Marital status S</td></tr>
<tr><td>Age 23 yrs. at</td></tr>
<tr><td>psychological tests</td></tr>
</table>

PARENTAL HISTORY
Father
C　H　S　D　O
-　-　-　-　-
Mother
C　H　S　D　O
-　-　-　-　-

PHYSIOLOGICAL AND METABOLIC DATA

	Admission	Initial	Control	Cold pressor change	Exercise change	Smoking change
Systolic pressure	135	114	94	+16	+36	+08
Diastolic pressure	80	72	74	+14	-12	00
Heart rate	68	70	65	+06	+08	+06

Age 21 yrs.	Height 68 in.	Ponderal index 12.53
	Weight 160 lbs.	Cholesterol 222 mg. per 100 ml.
	Overweight +10 %	Vital capacity 5.0 liters

HABIT SURVEY

Smoking habits: nonsmoker

Age begun　yrs.　Inhalation:

Habits of nervous tension: 5, 6, 16, 21, 25

Plate 448   DRAWINGS AT AN INTERMEDIATE LEVEL OF SOPHISTICATION   491

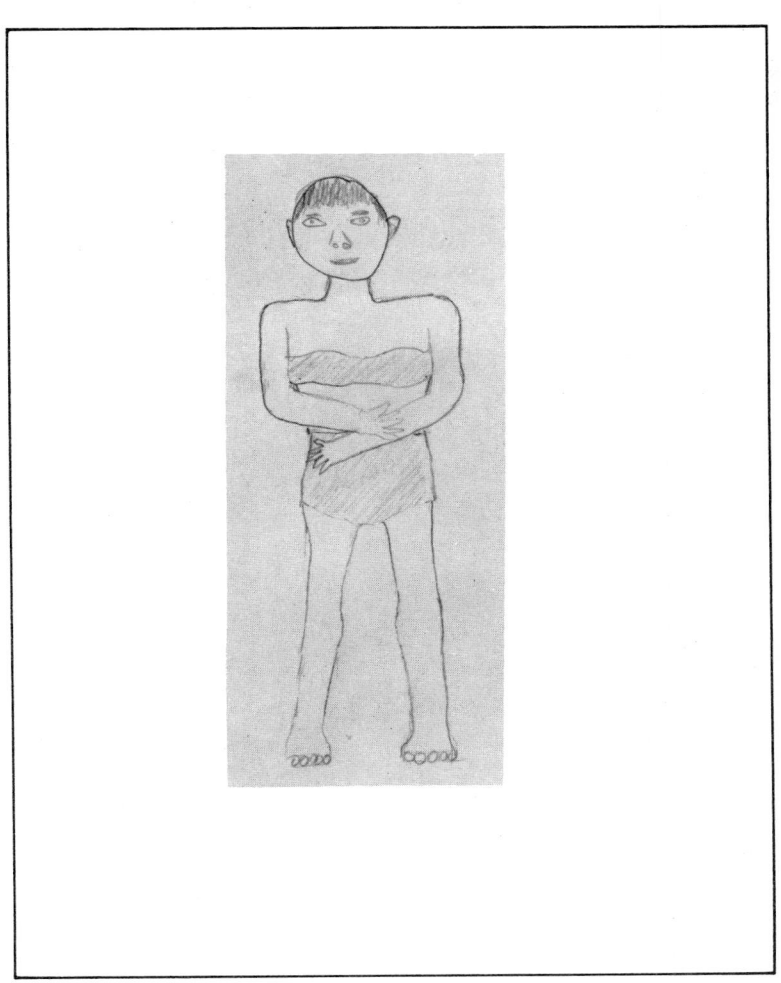

FIGURE-DRAWING CHARACTERISTICS

Structural	Male	Female	Structural	Male	Female	Structural and Graphic	Male	Female	Graphic, Global and Height	Male	Female	Body Proportions	Male	Female
	Both						Both							
Type	0		Omission of Appendages	0	0	Upper and Lower Halves	3	1	Hair Shading	1	2	Head	08	08
Sex Sequence	0		Position of Both Arms	0	0	Four Quarters	4	4	Nudity and Transparency	7	2	Neck	10	07
Posture	1	1	Position of Right Arm	5	5	Relative Size	0		Form	3	3	Shoulders	09	08
Perspective	0	0	Position of Left Arm	5	5	Constant Line Pressure	0	0	Detailing	3	3	Right Arm	04	04
Vertical Midline	3	0	Position of Legs	6	6	Variable Line Pressure	3	4	Identity and Sex	3	3	Left Arm	04	06
Bilateral Symmetry	2	2	Relation of Long Axes	1	1	Line Continuity	2	0	Sophistication	3	3	Chest	09	07
Horizontal Midline	4	4	Right and Left Halves	1	1	Body Shading	4	3	Height	08	06	Girth	10	08

GENERAL CHARACTERISTICS OF SUBJECT

IDENTIFICATION
No. 609
Sex M
Marital status S
Age 24 yrs. at
psychological tests

PARENTAL HISTORY
Father
C   H   S   D   O
-    -   -   -   -
Mother
C   H   S   D   O
-    -   -   -   -

PHYSIOLOGICAL AND METABOLIC DATA

	Admission	Initial	Control	Cold pressor change	Exercise change	Smoking change
Systolic pressure	120	122	122	+04	+26	+02
Diastolic pressure	80	80	84	+06	-06	+04
Heart rate	64	68	74	00	+17	+07

Age 21 yrs.	Height	75	in.	Ponderal index	13.33	
	Weight	178	lbs.	Cholesterol	197	mg. per 100 ml.
	Overweight +01 %			Vital capacity	5.8	liters

HABIT SURVEY
Smoking habits: occasional smoker
Age begun 15 yrs.   Inhalation: yes
Habits of nervous tension: 5, 6, 9, 11

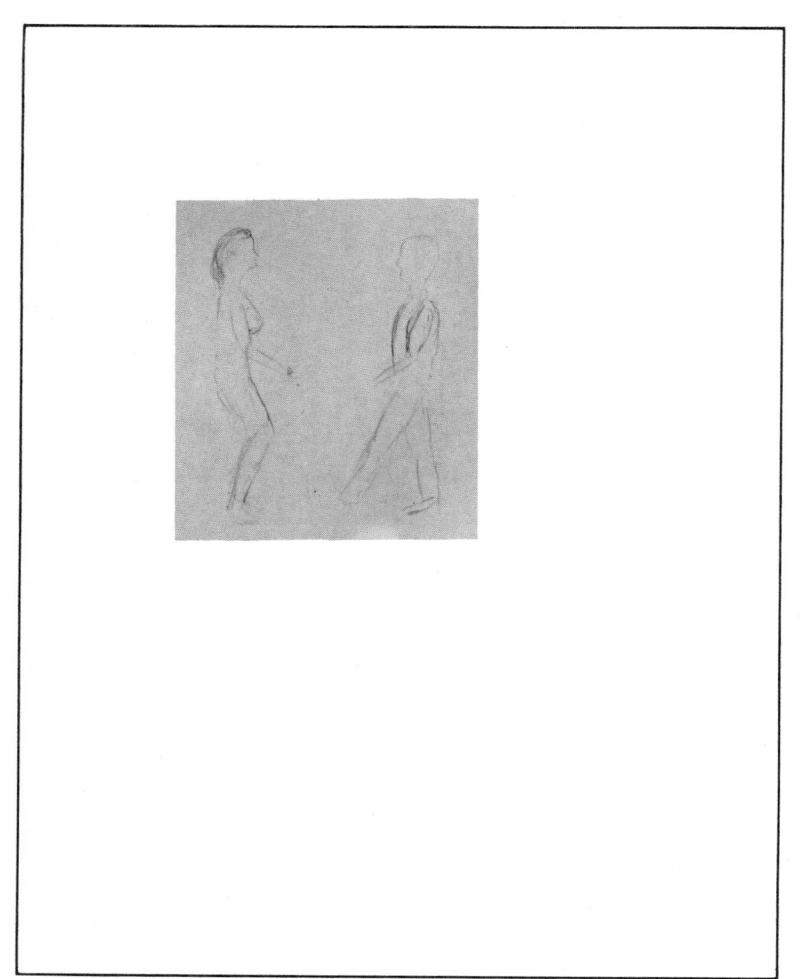

FIGURE-DRAWING CHARACTERISTICS

Structural	Male Female Both		Structural	Male	Female	Structural and Graphic	Male Female Both		Graphic, Global and Height	Male	Female	Body Proportions	Male	Female
Type	0		Omission of Appendages	6	0	Upper and Lower Halves	1	1	Hair Shading	0	3	Head	03	03
Sex Sequence	2		Position of Both Arms	4	2	Four Quarters	4	4	Nudity and Transparency	0	0	Neck	05	05
Posture	2	8	Position of Right Arm	7	4	Relative Size	3		Form	3	3	Shoulders		
Perspective	2	2	Position of Left Arm	4	7	Constant Line Pressure	0	0	Detailing	5	5	Right Arm		02
Vertical Midline	4	4	Position of Legs	8	1	Variable Line Pressure	1	1	Identity and Sex	3	1	Left Arm	02	
Bilateral Symmetry	0	0	Relation of Long Axes	1	1	Line Continuity	0	0	Sophistication	3	3	Chest	03	02
Horizontal Midline	0	0	Right and Left Halves	9	9	Body Shading	0	0	Height	02	03	Girth	02	03

GENERAL CHARACTERISTICS OF SUBJECT

IDENTIFICATION

No. 634
Sex M
Marital status S
Age 26 yrs. at
psychological tests

PARENTAL HISTORY

Father
C   H   S   D   O
–   –   –   –   –
Mother
C   H   S   D   O
–   –   –   –   –

PHYSIOLOGICAL AND METABOLIC DATA

	Admission	Initial	Control	Cold pressor change	Exercise change	Smoking change
Systolic pressure	150	122	118	+10	+36	+08
Diastolic pressure	78	74	66	+12	+06	00
Heart rate	72	68	66	+12	+22	+09

Age 23 yrs.
Height 71 in.
Weight 166 lbs.
Overweight +04 %
Ponderal index 12.91
Cholesterol 230 mg. per 100 ml.
Vital capacity 5.2 liters

HABIT SURVEY

Smoking habits: heavy cigarette smoker
Age begun   yrs.   Inhalation:
Habits of nervous tension:

FIGURE-DRAWING CHARACTERISTICS

Structural	Male Female Both		Structural	Male	Female	Structural and Graphic	Male Female Both		Graphic, Global and Height	Male	Female	Body Proportions	Male	Female
Type	0		Omission of Appendages	0	7	Upper and Lower Halves	1	0	Hair Shading	3	3	Head	08	06
Sex Sequence	0		Position of Both Arms	0	0	Four Quarters	4	4	Nudity and Transparency	7	7	Neck	12	06
Posture	1	1	Position of Right Arm	5	5	Relative Size	0		Form	3	3	Shoulders	08	04
Perspective	0	0	Position of Left Arm	5	5	Constant Line Pressure	5	5	Detailing	3	3	Right Arm	04	02
Vertical Midline	3	3	Position of Legs	6	4	Variable Line Pressure	0	0	Identity and Sex	1	1	Left Arm	04	02
Bilateral Symmetry	2	3	Relation of Long Axes	1	1	Line Continuity	4	3	Sophistication	3	3	Chest	05	04
Horizontal Midline	4	4	Right and Left Halves	1	1	Body Shading	0	5	Height	05	04	Girth	06	03

GENERAL CHARACTERISTICS OF SUBJECT

<table>
<tr><td>IDENTIFICATION</td><td>PARENTAL HISTORY</td><td colspan="7">PHYSIOLOGICAL AND METABOLIC DATA</td><td>HABIT SURVEY</td></tr>
</table>

IDENTIFICATION	PARENTAL HISTORY
No. 639	Father
Sex M	C H S D O
Marital status M	– – – – –
Age 25 yrs. at	Mother
psychological tests	C H S D O
	– – – – –

PHYSIOLOGICAL AND METABOLIC DATA

	Admission	Initial	Control	Cold pressor change	Exercise change	Smoking change
Systolic pressure	122	124	108	+02	+12	–02
Diastolic pressure	80	78	72	+20	+18	+02
Heart rate	76	68	67	+16	+07	+11

Age 22 yrs.   Height 74 in.   Weight 175 lbs.   Overweight +01 %

Ponderal index 13.24   Cholesterol 222 mg. per 100 ml.   Vital capacity 6.5 liters

HABIT SURVEY

Smoking habits: mixed smoker

Age begun 20 yrs.   Inhalation: yes

Habits of nervous tension: 1, 2, 3, 4, 5, 17, 21, 22, 25

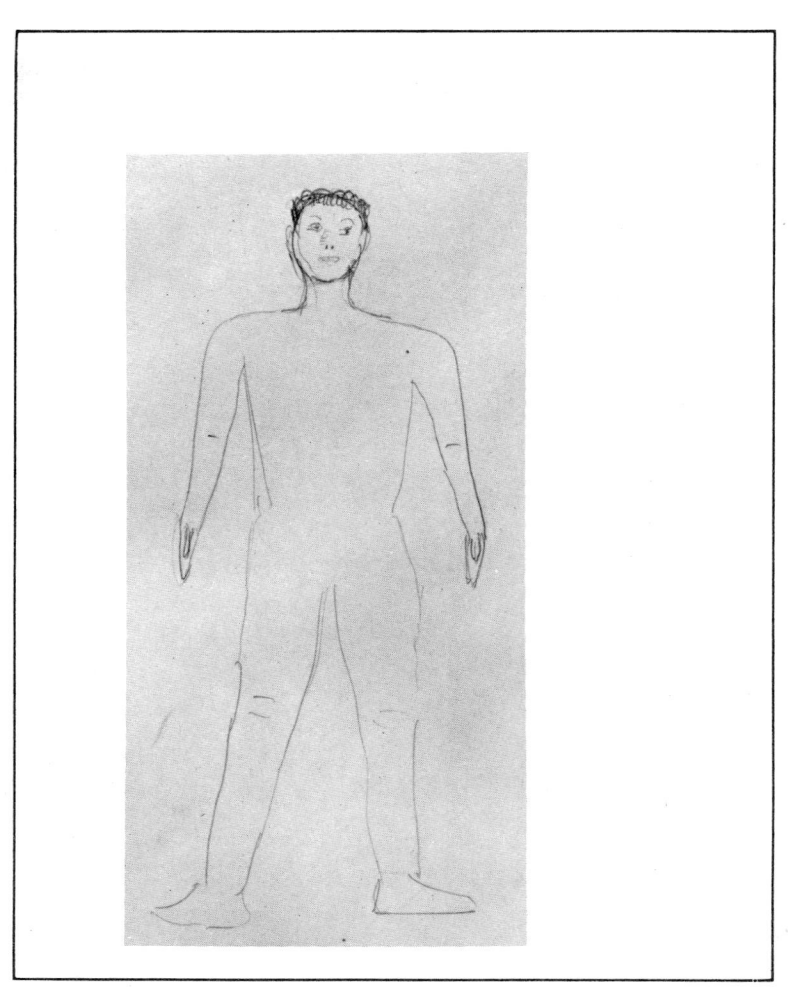

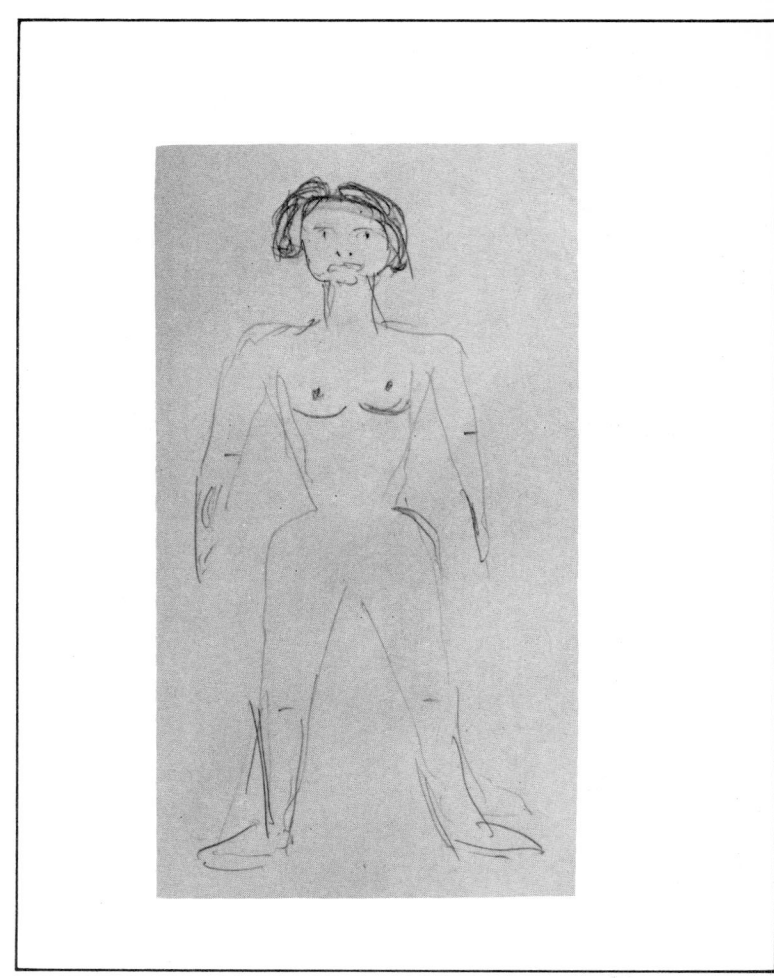

FIGURE-DRAWING CHARACTERISTICS

Structural	Male Female Both	Structural	Male	Female	Structural and Graphic	Male Female Both		Graphic, Global and Height	Male	Female	Body Proportions	Male	Female
Type	0	Omission of Appendages	0	0	Upper and Lower Halves	3	3	Hair Shading	3	3	Head	07	07
Sex Sequence	0	Position of Both Arms	0	0	Four Quarters	4	4	Nudity and Transparency	0	0	Neck	10	12
Posture	1 1	Position of Right Arm	2	2	Relative Size	0		Form	3	3	Shoulders	10	09
Perspective	0 0	Position of Left Arm	2	2	Constant Line Pressure	0	0	Detailing	3	3	Right Arm	06	06
Vertical Midline	0 0	Position of Legs	6	6	Variable Line Pressure	2	2	Identity and Sex	1	1	Left Arm	06	06
Bilateral Symmetry	3 3	Relation of Long Axes	1	1	Line Continuity	1	0	Sophistication	3	3	Chest	08	08
Horizontal Midline	0 0	Right and Left Halves	1	1	Body Shading	3	3	Height	07	07	Girth	09	05

GENERAL CHARACTERISTICS OF SUBJECT

IDENTIFICATION
No. 640
Sex M
Marital status M
Age 25 yrs. at
psychological tests

PARENTAL HISTORY
Father
C H S D O
- - - - -
Mother
C H S D O
- - - - -

PHYSIOLOGICAL AND METABOLIC DATA

	Admission	Initial	Control	Cold pressor change	Exercise change	Smoking change
Systolic pressure	120	144	128	+06	+48	+01
Diastolic pressure	80	84	82	+12	+06	00
Heart rate	76	96	87	+10	+20	+02

Age 23 yrs.

Height 74 in.
Weight 184 lbs.
Overweight +05 %

Ponderal index 13.01
Cholesterol 210 mg. per 100 ml.
Vital capacity liters

HABIT SURVEY

Smoking habits: occasional smoker
  Age begun 22 yrs.   Inhalation: no
Habits of nervous tension: 2, 5, 9, 16

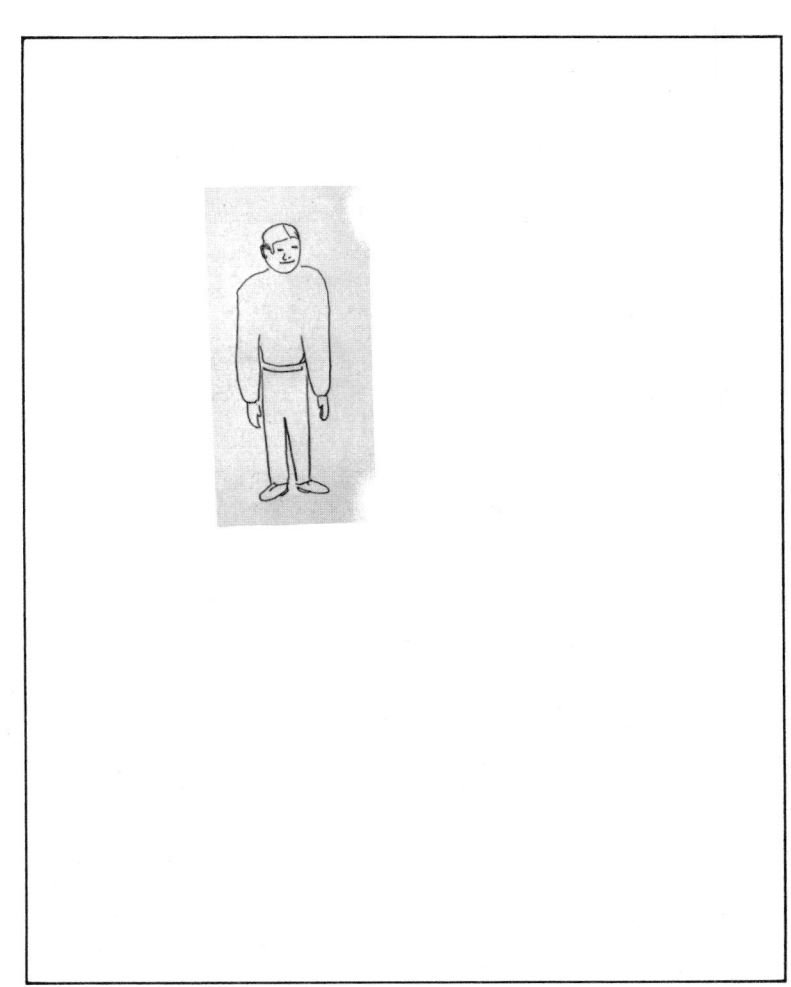

FIGURE-DRAWING CHARACTERISTICS

Structural	Male Female Both	Structural	Male	Female	Structural and Graphic	Male Female Both		Graphic, Global and Height	Male	Female	Body Proportions	Male	Female
Type	0	Omission of Appendages	0	0	Upper and Lower Halves	2	2	Hair Shading	5	9	Head	04	03
Sex Sequence	1	Position of Both Arms	0	0	Four Quarters	0	0	Nudity and Transparency	7	7	Neck	00	00
Posture	1 1	Position of Right Arm	0	0	Relative Size	0		Form	3	3	Shoulders	03	02
Perspective	0 0	Position of Left Arm	0	0	Constant Line Pressure	5	0	Detailing	3	3	Right Arm	04	02
Vertical Midline	0 0	Position of Legs	4	5	Variable Line Pressure	0	5	Identity and Sex	1	1	Left Arm	04	02
Bilateral Symmetry	3 3	Relation of Long Axes	1	1	Line Continuity	4	4	Sophistication	3	3	Chest	02	01
Horizontal Midline	4 4	Right and Left Halves	2	2	Body Shading	0	0	Height	03	02	Girth	02	01

GENERAL CHARACTERISTICS OF SUBJECT

IDENTIFICATION
No. 715
Sex M
Marital status S
Age 23 yrs. at
psychological tests

PARENTAL HISTORY
Father
C   H   S   D   O
-   -   -   -   -
Mother
C   H   S   D   O
-   -   -   -   -

PHYSIOLOGICAL AND METABOLIC DATA

	Admission	Initial	Control	Cold pressor change	Exercise change	Smoking change
Systolic pressure	124	128	124	+10	+34	+07
Diastolic pressure	76	64	60	+10	-12	+13
Heart rate	80	68	67	00	+19	+06

Age 23 yrs.	Height	74 in.		Ponderal index 12.94
	Weight	187 lbs.		Cholesterol 190 mg. per 100 ml.
	Overweight +07 %			Vital capacity 6.7 liters

HABIT SURVEY

Smoking habits: nonsmoker

Age begun   yrs.   Inhalation:

Habits of nervous tension: 2, 5, 8, 11, 16

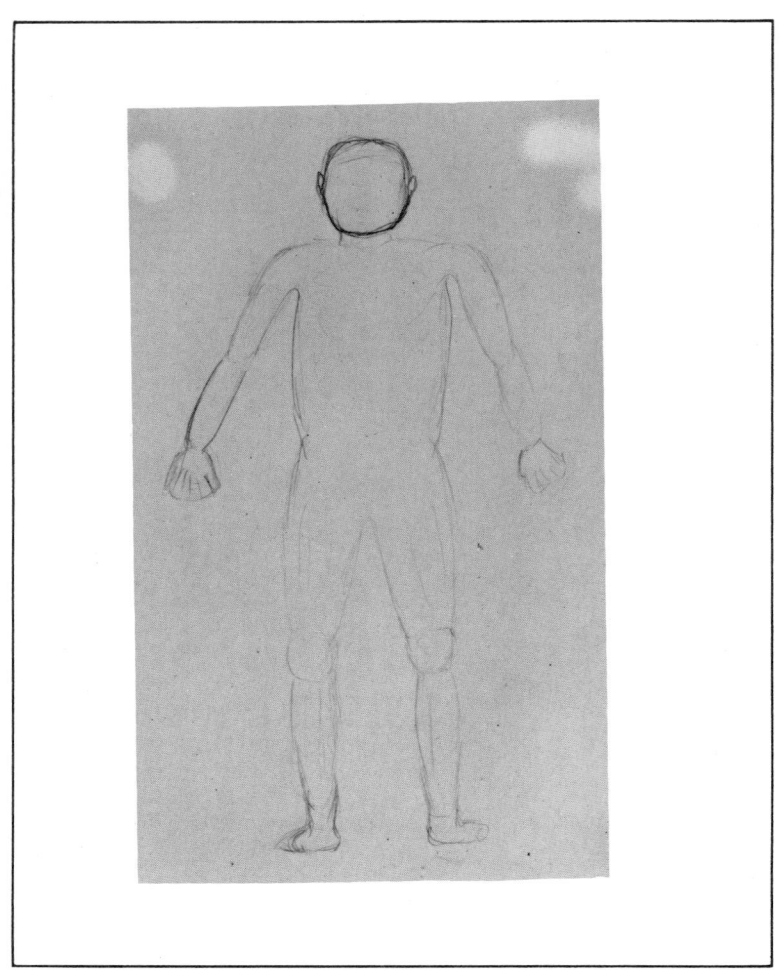

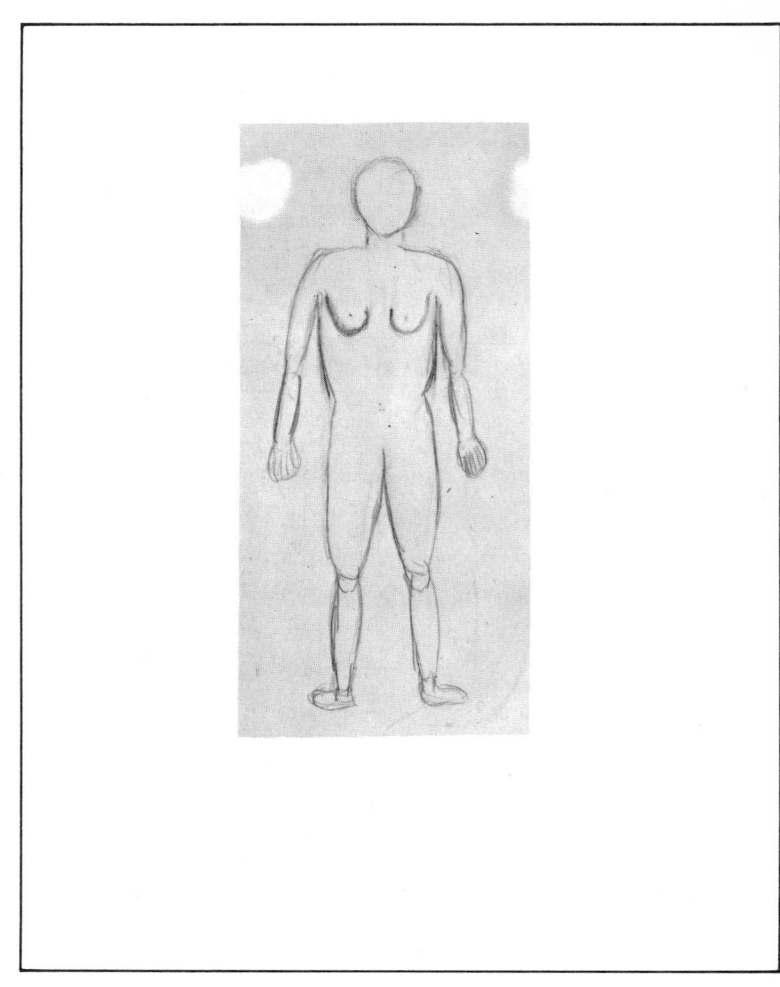

FIGURE-DRAWING CHARACTERISTICS

Structural	Male Female Both		Structural	Male	Female	Structural and Graphic	Male Female Both		Graphic, Global and Height	Male	Female	Body Proportions	Male	Female
Type	0		Omission of Appendages	0	0	Upper and Lower Halves	0	1	Hair Shading	9	9	Head	08	06
Sex Sequence	0		Position of Both Arms	0	0	Four Quarters	4	4	Nudity and Transparency	0	0	Neck	03	05
Posture	1	1	Position of Right Arm	2	1	Relative Size	0		Form	3	1	Shoulders	09	06
Perspective	0	0	Position of Left Arm	2	1	Constant Line Pressure	0	0	Detailing	5	3	Right Arm	06	06
Vertical Midline	0	0	Position of Legs	6	6	Variable Line Pressure	3	3	Identity and Sex	5	1	Left Arm	06	04
Bilateral Symmetry	2	3	Relation of Long Axes	1	1	Line Continuity	0	0	Sophistication	3	3	Chest	07	06
Horizontal Midline	0	0	Right and Left Halves	1	1	Body Shading	3	3	Height	07	06	Girth	09	06

GENERAL CHARACTERISTICS OF SUBJECT

IDENTIFICATION
No. 716
Sex M
Marital status S
Age 25 yrs. at
psychological tests

PARENTAL HISTORY				
Father				
C	H	S	D	O
–	–	–	–	–
Mother				
C	H	S	D	O
–	–	–	–	–

PHYSIOLOGICAL AND METABOLIC DATA

	Admission	Initial	Control	Cold pressor change	Exercise change	Smoking change
Systolic pressure	138	116	110	+28	+34	+05
Diastolic pressure	84	56	70	+32	–10	+03
Heart rate	80	60	58	+16	+17	+05

Age 23 yrs.	Height 72 in.	Ponderal index 12.93
	Weight 173 lbs.	Cholesterol 217 mg. per 100 ml.
	Overweight +05 %	Vital capacity 4.5 liters

HABIT SURVEY
Smoking habits: nonsmoker
Age begun   yrs.   Inhalation:
Habits of nervous tension: 5

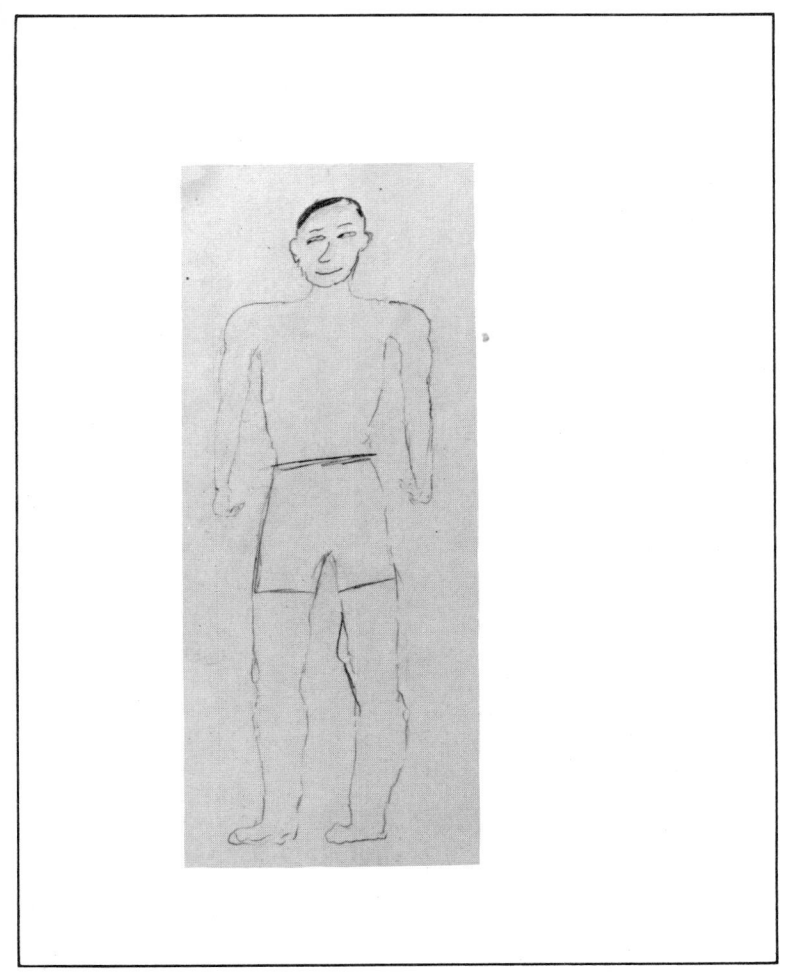

FIGURE-DRAWING CHARACTERISTICS

Structural	Male Female Both		Structural	Male	Female	Structural and Graphic	Male	Female Both	Graphic, Global and Height	Male	Female	Body Proportions	Male	Female
Type	0		Omission of Appendages	0	0	Upper and Lower Halves	3	3	Hair Shading	2	3	Head	07	05
Sex Sequence	0		Position of Both Arms	0	2	Four Quarters	4	4	Nudity and Transparency	3	0	Neck	05	02
Posture	1	1	Position of Right Arm	0	4	Relative Size	0		Form	3	0	Shoulders	08	
Perspective	0	2	Position of Left Arm	0	7	Constant Line Pressure	0	0	Detailing	5	5	Right Arm	05	04
Vertical Midline	0	4	Position of Legs	4	1	Variable Line Pressure	1	1	Identity and Sex	3	1	Left Arm	04	
Bilateral Symmetry	3	0	Relation of Long Axes	1	1	Line Continuity	0	0	Sophistication	3	3	Chest	06	05
Horizontal Midline	4	0	Right and Left Halves	1	1	Body Shading	0	0	Height	06	04	Girth	06	05

GENERAL CHARACTERISTICS OF SUBJECT

IDENTIFICATION
No. F32
Sex M
Marital status
Age 25 yrs. at
psychological tests

PARENTAL HISTORY
Father
C H S D O
- - - - -
Mother
C H S D O
- - - - -

PHYSIOLOGICAL AND METABOLIC DATA

	Admission	Initial	Control	Cold pressor change	Exercise change	Smoking change
Systolic pressure	160	122	110	+08	+38	+09
Diastolic pressure	74	70	76	+16	+14	+09
Heart rate	72	64	60	-04	+24	+21

Age 23 yrs.	Height 72 in.	Ponderal index 13.36
	Weight 157 lbs.	Cholesterol 177 mg. per 100 ml.
	Overweight -04 %	Vital capacity liters

HABIT SURVEY
Smoking habits: former smoker
Age begun 15 yrs.   Inhalation:
Habits of nervous tension: 5, 6, 11

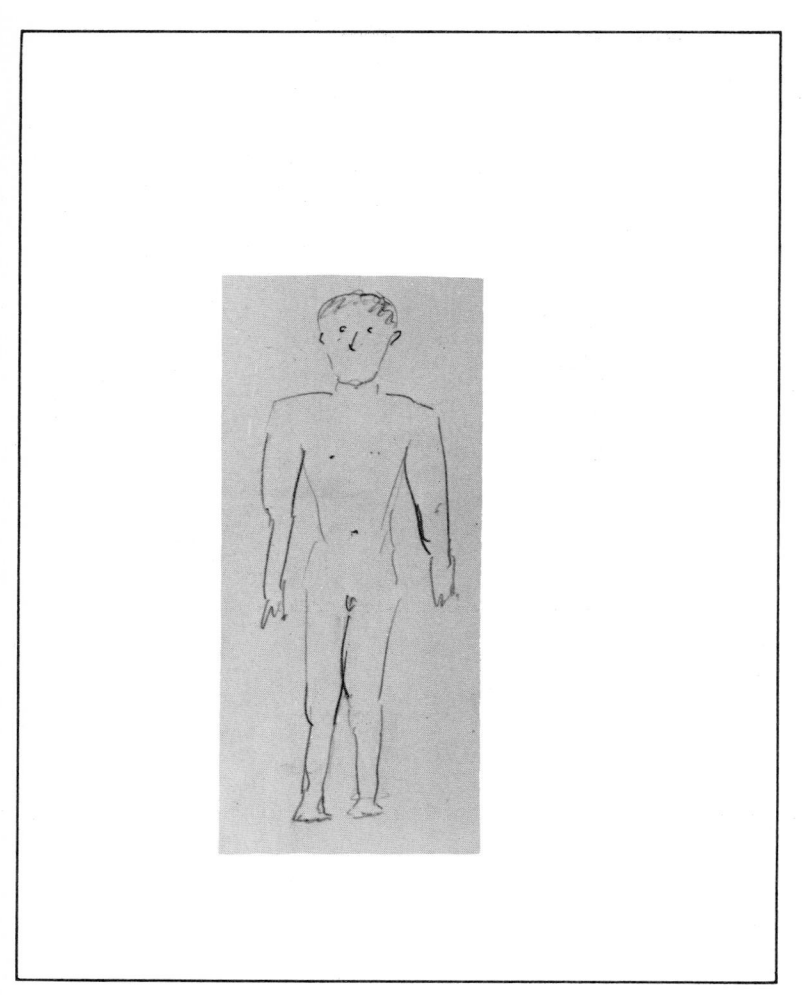

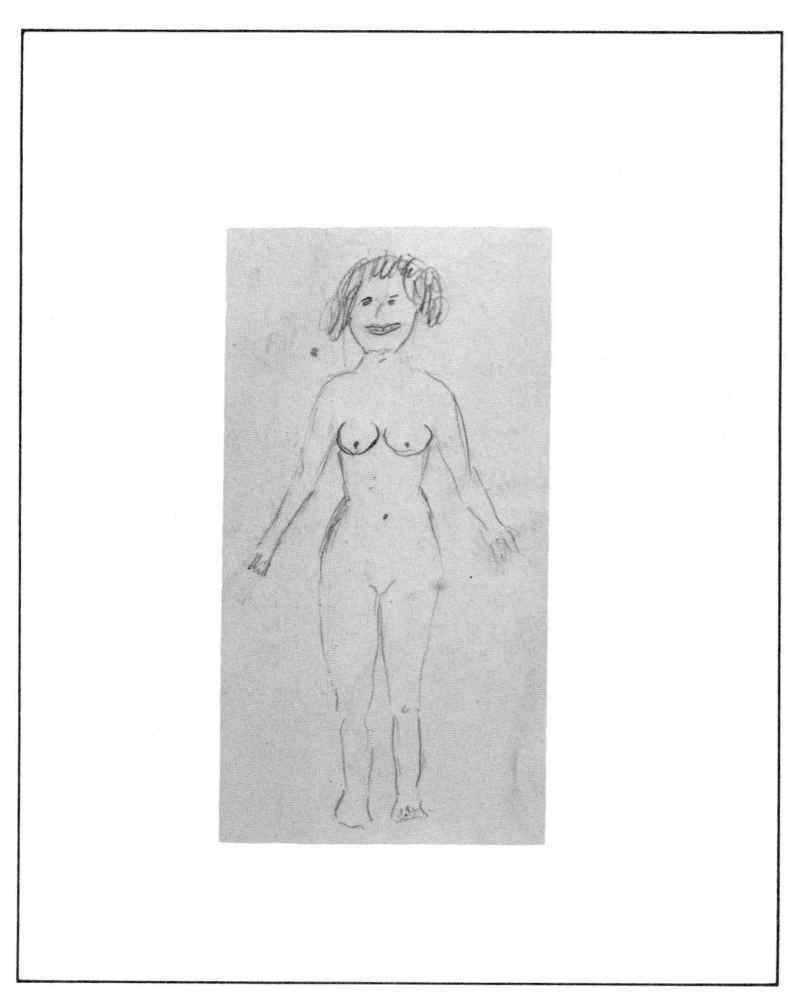

FIGURE-DRAWING CHARACTERISTICS

Structural	Male	Female	Structural	Male	Female	Structural and Graphic	Male	Female	Graphic, Global and Height	Male	Female	Body Proportions	Male	Female
	Both						Both							
Type	0		Omission of Appendages	0	0	Upper and Lower Halves	3	3	Hair Shading	3	3	Head	07	07
Sex Sequence	2		Position of Both Arms	0	0	Four Quarters	4	4	Nudity and Transparency	0	0	Neck	03	05
Posture	1	1	Position of Right Arm	0	2	Relative Size	4		Form	3	3	Shoulders	06	05
Perspective	0	0	Position of Left Arm	1	2	Constant Line Pressure	0	1	Detailing	5	5	Right Arm	04	04
Vertical Midline	0	0	Position of Legs	4	4	Variable Line Pressure	2	0	Identity and Sex	1	1	Left Arm	04	04
Bilateral Symmetry	3	3	Relation of Long Axes	1	1	Line Continuity	2	0	Sophistication	3	3	Chest	04	04
Horizontal Midline	0	0	Right and Left Halves	1	1	Body Shading	0	0	Height	05	06	Girth	03	05

GENERAL CHARACTERISTICS OF SUBJECT

IDENTIFICATION
No. F36
Sex M
Marital status S
Age 24 yrs. at
psychological tests

PARENTAL HISTORY
Father
C H S D O
- - - - -
Mother
C H S D O
- - - - -

PHYSIOLOGICAL AND METABOLIC DATA

	Admission	Initial	Control	Cold pressor change	Exercise change	Smoking change
Systolic pressure	140	130	116	+28	+44	+20
Diastolic pressure	86	76	76	+38	+14	+13
Heart rate	76	72	73	+20	+22	+34

Age 22 yrs.	Height 71 in.	Ponderal index 13.20
	Weight 156 lbs.	Cholesterol 203 mg. per 100 ml.
	Overweight -01 %	Vital capacity liters

HABIT SURVEY

Smoking habits: light cigarette smoker

Age begun 19 yrs.   Inhalation: yes

Habits of nervous tension: 4, 5, 6, 9, 11, 21, 22

STRONG VOCATIONAL INTEREST TEST

Occupation	Artist	Psychologist	Architect	Physician	Osteopath	Dentist	Veterinarian	Mathematician	Physicist	Engineer	Chemist	Production Manager
Standard Score	37	36	43	52	37	44	16	42	39	42	51	28

Occupation	Farmer	Aviator	Carpenter	Printer	Math.-Sci. Teacher	Ind. Arts Teacher	Voc. Agric. Teacher	Policeman	Forest Serv. Man	Y.M.C.A. Phys. Dir.	Personnel Director	Public Administrator
Standard Score	37	37	29	45	45	22	19	29	28	34	28	29

Occupation	Y.M.C.A. Secretary	Soc. Sci. H.S. Teacher	City Sch. Sup't.	Social Worker	Minister	Musician Performer	C.P.A.	Senior C.P.A.	Accountant	Office Man	Purchasing Agent	Banker
Standard Score	26	33	31	29	58	54	24	34	25	32	18	22

Occupation	Mortician	Pharmacist	Sales Manager	Real Est. Manager	Life Ins. Salesman	Advertising Man	Lawyer	Author-Journalist	President Mfg. Co.	Interest Maturity	Occupational Level	Masculinity-Femininity
Standard Score	11	14	10	19	14	29	31	36	23	52	53	42

Plate 456   DRAWINGS AT AN INTERMEDIATE LEVEL OF SOPHISTICATION   499

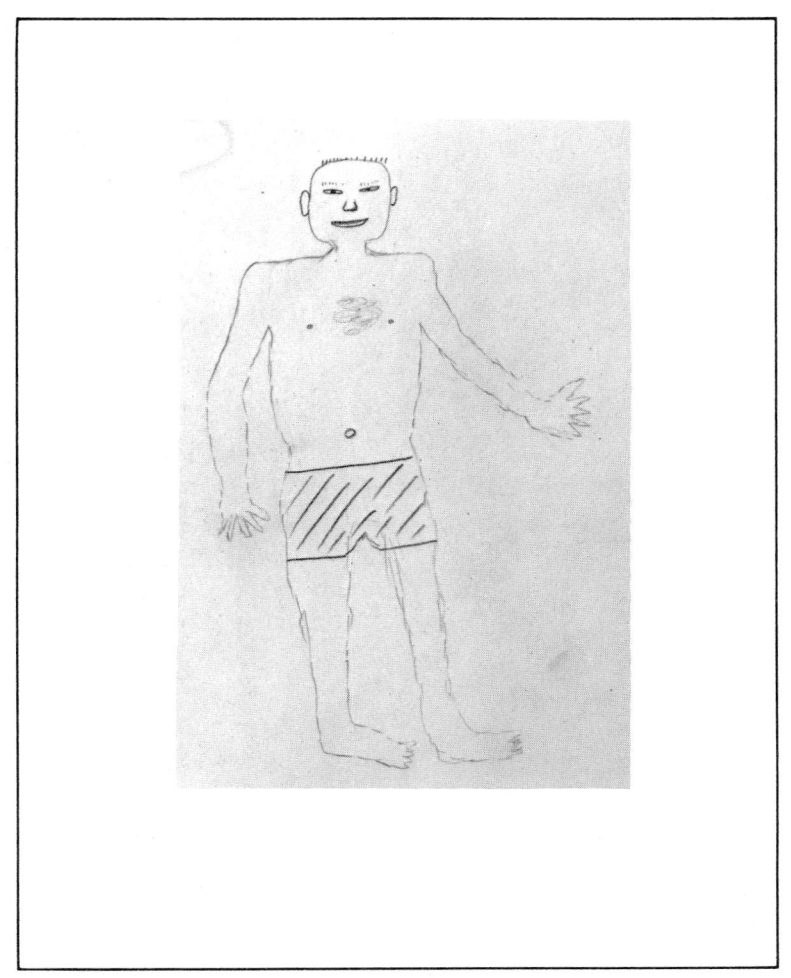

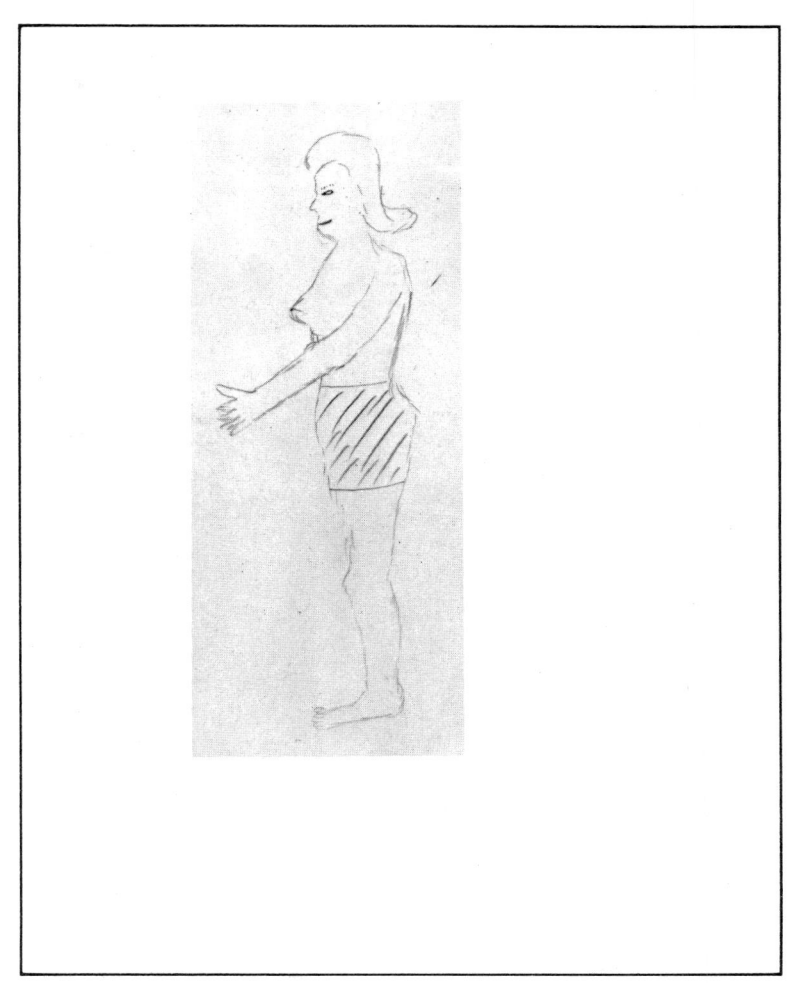

FIGURE-DRAWING CHARACTERISTICS

Structural	Male Female Both		Structural	Male	Female	Structural and Graphic	Male Female Both		Graphic, Global and Height	Male	Female	Body Proportions	Male	Female
Type	0		Omission of Appendages	0	0	Upper and Lower Halves	1	1	Hair Shading	7	5	Head	07	07
Sex Sequence	0		Position of Both Arms	1	4	Four Quarters	4	4	Nudity and Transparency	3	3	Neck	04	02
Posture	1	1	Position of Right Arm	5	7	Relative Size	2		Form	3	3	Shoulders	07	
Perspective	0	2	Position of Left Arm	2	4	Constant Line Pressure	0	1	Detailing	3	3	Right Arm	06	
Vertical Midline	0	4	Position of Legs	5	1	Variable Line Pressure	1	0	Identity and Sex	1	1	Left Arm	06	04
Bilateral Symmetry	3	0	Relation of Long Axes	1	1	Line Continuity	0	0	Sophistication	3	3	Chest	07	07
Horizontal Midline	4	4	Right and Left Halves	1	2	Body Shading	1	0	Height	06	06	Girth	08	06

GENERAL CHARACTERISTICS OF SUBJECT

IDENTIFICATION
No. F57
Sex M
Marital status   S
Age 24 yrs. at
psychological tests

PARENTAL HISTORY
Father
C   H   S   D   0
-    -   -   -   -
Mother
C   H   S   D   0
-    -   -   -   -

PHYSIOLOGICAL AND METABOLIC DATA

	Admission	Initial	Control	Cold pressor change	Exercise change	Smoking change
Systolic pressure	140	100	92	+18	+28	+03
Diastolic pressure	70	74	70	+20	+08	+04
Heart rate	76	68	65	-16	+24	+13

Age 22 yrs.	Height 69 in.	Ponderal index 12.41
	Weight 172 lbs.	Cholesterol 190 mg. per 100 ml.
	Overweight +15 %	Vital capacity liters

HABIT SURVEY

Smoking habits: pipe smoker

Age begun 22 yrs.   Inhalation: no

Habits of nervous tension: 4, 5, 6, 8, 9, 11, 15, 19, 22

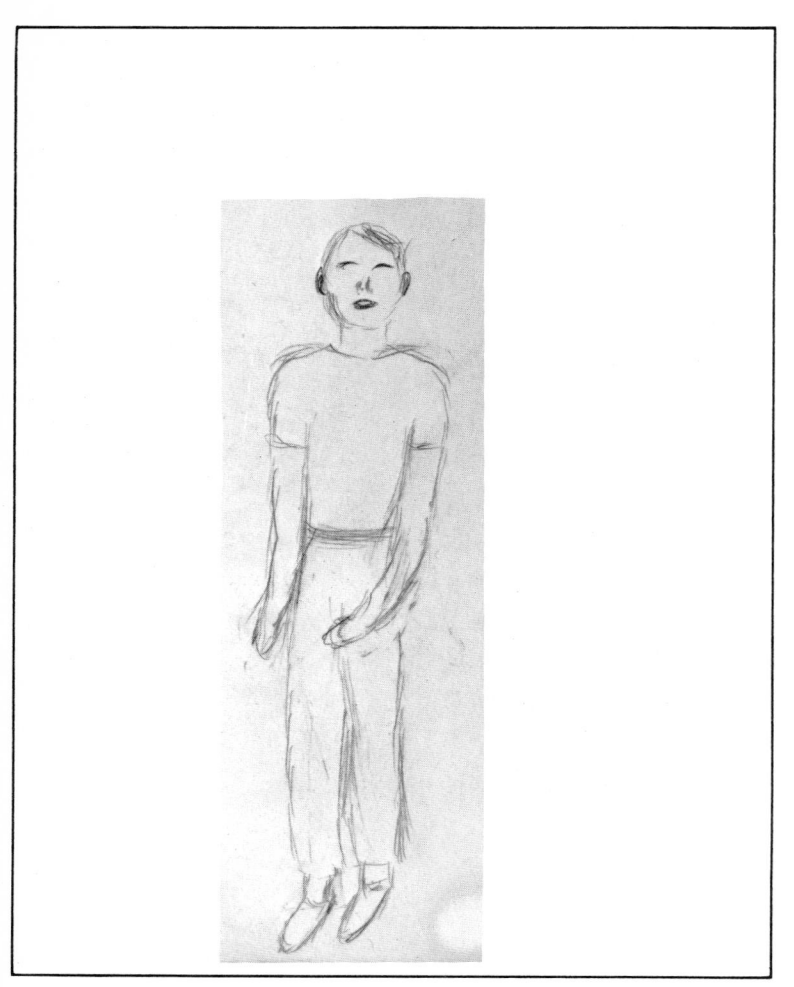

FIGURE-DRAWING CHARACTERISTICS

Structural	Male Female Both	Structural	Male	Female	Structural and Graphic	Male Female Both		Graphic, Global and Height	Male	Female	Body Proportions	Male	Female
Type	0	Omission of Appendages	0	0	Upper and Lower Halves	3	3	Hair Shading	3	3	Head	09	09
Sex Sequence	0	Position of Both Arms	1	0	Four Quarters	4	4	Nudity and Transparency	7	7	Neck	07	08
Posture	1 1	Position of Right Arm	0	5	Relative Size	2		Form	3	3	Shoulders	07	
Perspective	0 1	Position of Left Arm	5	5	Constant Line Pressure	2	0	Detailing	5	3	Right Arm	06	06
Vertical Midline	0 4	Position of Legs	4	4	Variable Line Pressure	0	1	Identity and Sex	3	1	Left Arm	06	
Bilateral Symmetry	3 0	Relation of Long Axes	1	1	Line Continuity	0	0	Sophistication	3	3	Chest	05	
Horizontal Midline	4 0	Right and Left Halves	1	0	Body Shading	4	0	Height	07	07	Girth	05	

GENERAL CHARACTERISTICS OF SUBJECT

IDENTIFICATION
No. F69
Sex M
Marital status S
Age 24 yrs. at psychological tests

PARENTAL HISTORY
Father
C H S D O
- - - - -
Mother
C H S D O
- - - - -

PHYSIOLOGICAL AND METABOLIC DATA

	Admission	Initial	Control	Cold pressor change	Exercise change	Smoking change
Systolic pressure	140	110	98	+16	+22	+12
Diastolic pressure	70	74	72	+18	+12	00
Heart rate	90	76	69	-04	+21	+14

Age 22 yrs.	Height 74 in.	Ponderal index 13.78
	Weight 155 lbs.	Cholesterol 203 mg. per 100 ml.
	Overweight -10 %	Vital capacity liters

HABIT SURVEY
Smoking habits: occasional smoker
Age begun 18 yrs.   Inhalation: yes
Habits of nervous tension: 4, 5, 6, 9, 11, 17, 21, 23

FIGURE-DRAWING CHARACTERISTICS

Structural	Male Female Both		Structural	Male	Female	Structural and Graphic	Male Female Both		Graphic, Global and Height	Male	Female	Body Proportions	Male	Female
Type	0		Omission of Appendages	0	0	Upper and Lower Halves	1	1	Hair Shading	7	2	Head	07	06
Sex Sequence	0		Position of Both Arms	1	1	Four Quarters	4	4	Nudity and Transparency	7	7	Neck	03	05
Posture	1	1	Position of Right Arm	4	4	Relative Size	0		Form	3	3	Shoulders	07	05
Perspective	1	1	Position of Left Arm	5	5	Constant Line Pressure	1	1	Detailing	3	3	Right Arm	04	02
Vertical Midline	7	4	Position of Legs	4	4	Variable Line Pressure	0	0	Identity and Sex	1	1	Left Arm	04	04
Bilateral Symmetry	0	0	Relation of Long Axes	1	1	Line Continuity	0	0	Sophistication	3	3	Chest		
Horizontal Midline	6	0	Right and Left Halves	2	2	Body Shading	2	3	Height	05	04	Girth		

GENERAL CHARACTERISTICS OF SUBJECT

IDENTIFICATION
No.   G06
Sex   M
Marital status   M
Age   23   yrs. at
psychological tests

PARENTAL HISTORY
Father
C   H   S   D   O
–   –   –   –   –
Mother
C   H   S   D   O
–   –   –   –   –

PHYSIOLOGICAL AND METABOLIC DATA

	Admission	Initial	Control	Cold pressor change	Exercise change	Smoking change
Systolic pressure	130	130	114	+08	+46	+05
Diastolic pressure	70	84	78	+18	–08	+08
Heart rate	80	76	77	+08	+34	+03

Age 22 yrs.	Height 70 in.	Ponderal index 12.80
	Weight 164 lbs.	Cholesterol 210 mg. per 100 ml.
	Overweight +06 %	Vital capacity liters

HABIT SURVEY

Smoking habits: pipe smoker

Age begun   20 yrs.   Inhalation: no

Habits of nervous tension: 2, 4, 5, 6, 9, 11, 22, 23

STRONG VOCATIONAL INTEREST TEST

Occupation	Artist	Psychologist	Architect	Physician	Osteopath	Dentist	Veterinarian	Mathematician	Physicist	Engineer	Chemist	Production Manager
Standard Score	25	49	31	47	40	27	16	37	34	38	44	35

Occupation	Farmer	Aviator	Carpenter	Printer	Math.-Sci. Teacher	Ind. Arts Teacher	Voc. Agric. Teacher	Policeman	Forest Serv. Man	Y.M.C.A. Phys. Dir.	Personnel Director	Public Administrator
Standard Score	38	38	25	37	45	25	34	32	33	32	52	57

Occupation	Y.M.C.A. Secretary	Soc. Sci. H.S. Teacher	City Sch. Sup't.	Social Worker	Minister	Musician Performer	C.P.A.	Senior C.P.A.	Accountant	Office Man	Purchasing Agent	Banker
Standard Score	32	37	36	40	59	46	33	44	32	35	26	30

Occupation	Mortician	Pharmacist	Sales Manager	Real Est. Manager	Life Ins. Salesman	Advertising Man	Lawyer	Author-Journalist	President Mfg. Co.	Interest Maturity	Occupational Level	Masculinity-Femininity
Standard Score	23	25	24	26	20	33	38	36	24	56	52	48

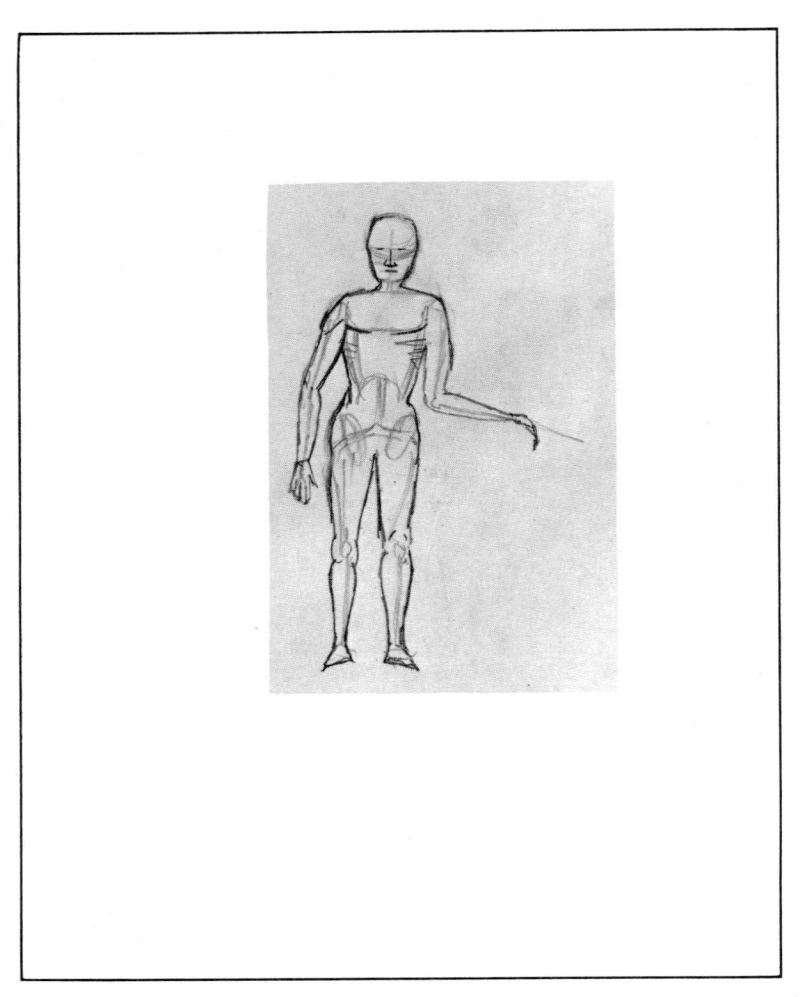

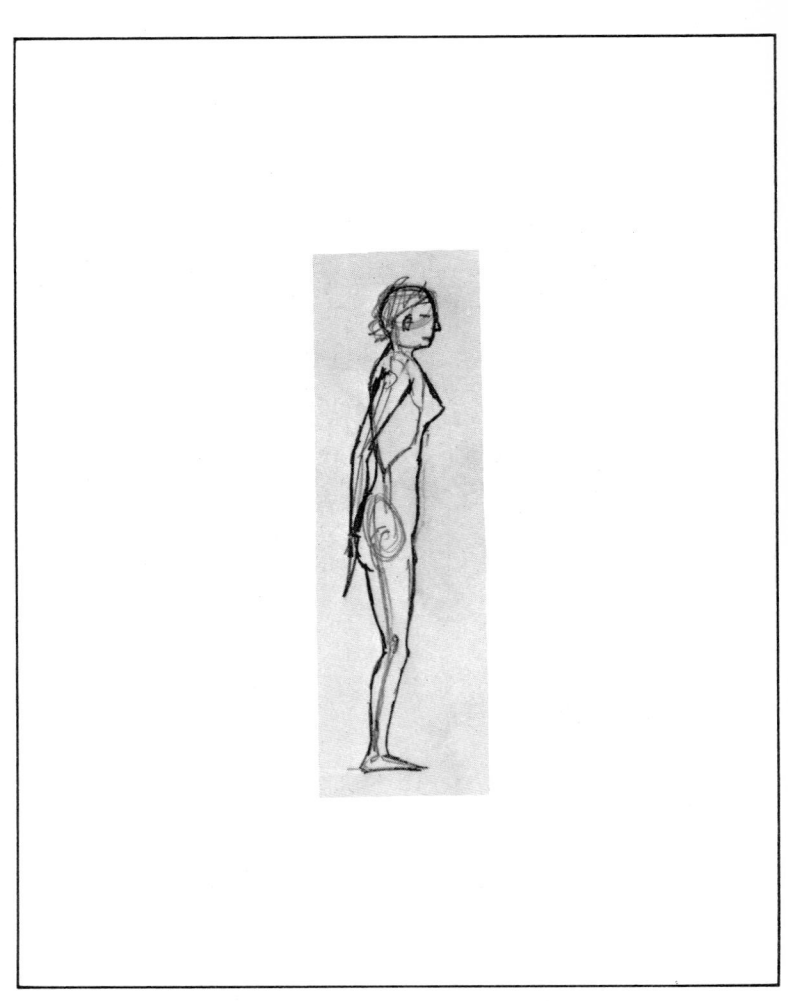

FIGURE-DRAWING CHARACTERISTICS

Structural	Male	Female	Structural	Male	Female	Structural and Graphic	Male	Female	Graphic, Global and Height	Male	Female	Body Proportions	Male	Female
	Both						Both							
Type	0		Omission of Appendages	0	0	Upper and Lower Halves	1	3	Hair Shading	0	3	Head	05	05
Sex Sequence	0		Position of Both Arms	1	2	Four Quarters	4	4	Nudity and Transparency	0	0	Neck	02	02
Posture	1	1	Position of Right Arm	0	5	Relative Size	4		Form	1	1	Shoulders	04	
Perspective	0	2	Position of Left Arm	4	7	Constant Line Pressure	0	3	Detailing	3	3	Right Arm	04	06
Vertical Midline	0	4	Position of Legs	4	1	Variable Line Pressure	4	0	Identity and Sex	1	1	Left Arm	04	
Bilateral Symmetry	3	0	Relation of Long Axes	1	1	Line Continuity	0	0	Sophistication	3	3	Chest	03	04
Horizontal Midline	0	0	Right and Left Halves	1	1	Body Shading	0	0	Height	04	05	Girth	03	04

GENERAL CHARACTERISTICS OF SUBJECT

IDENTIFICATION
No. G13
Sex M
Marital status S
Age 24 yrs. at psychological tests

PARENTAL HISTORY					
Father					
C	H	S	D	O	
-	-	-	-	-	
Mother					
C	H	S	D	O	
-	-	-	-	-	

PHYSIOLOGICAL AND METABOLIC DATA

	Admission	Initial	Control	Cold pressor change	Exercise change	Smoking change
Systolic pressure	140	130	118	+32	+32	+02
Diastolic pressure	70	70	60	+40	00	+04
Heart rate	78	56	59	+04	+13	+02

Age 23 yrs.	Height 69 in.	Ponderal index 12.30
	Weight 177 lbs.	Cholesterol 203 mg. per 100 ml.
	Overweight +17 %	Vital capacity liters

HABIT SURVEY

Smoking habits: pipe smoker

Age begun 22 yrs.   Inhalation: sometimes

Habits of nervous tension: 5, 6, 14

STRONG VOCATIONAL INTEREST TEST

Occupation	Artist	Psychologist	Architect	Physician	Osteopath	Dentist	Veterinarian	Mathematician	Physicist	Engineer	Chemist	Production Manager
Standard Score	48	56	50	71	50	51	25	43	46	51	57	31

Occupation	Farmer	Aviator	Carpenter	Printer	Math.-Sci. Teacher	Ind. Arts Teacher	Voc. Agric. Teacher	Policeman	Forest Serv. Man	Y.M.C.A. Phys. Dir.	Personnel Director	Public Administrator
Standard Score	39	47	31	33	43	29	24	29	39	26	26	42

Occupation	Y.M.C.A. Secretary	Soc. Sci. H.S. Teacher	City Sch. Sup't.	Social Worker	Minister	Musician Performer	C.P.A.	Senior C.P.A.	Accountant	Office Man	Purchasing Agent	Banker
Standard Score	17	21	26	36	59	55	23	32	08	11	11	03

Occupation	Mortician	Pharmacist	Sales Manager	Real Est. Manager	Life Ins. Salesman	Advertising Man	Lawyer	Author-Journalist	President Mfg. Co.	Interest Maturity	Occupational Level	Masculinity-Femininity
Standard Score	10	28	16	24	16	30	37	41	32	52	58	50

Plate 460   **DRAWINGS AT AN INTERMEDIATE LEVEL OF SOPHISTICATION**   503

FIGURE-DRAWING CHARACTERISTICS

Structural	Male Female Both		Structural	Male	Female	Structural and Graphic	Male Female Both		Graphic, Global and Height	Male	Female	Body Proportions	Male	Female
Type	0		Omission of Appendages	0	0	Upper and Lower Halves	1	1	Hair Shading	7	2	Head	08	05
Sex Sequence	0		Position of Both Arms	0	2	Four Quarters	4	4	Nudity and Transparency	7	7	Neck	05	06
Posture	1	1	Position of Right Arm	0	4	Relative Size	0		Form	3	3	Shoulders	07	
Perspective	0	2	Position of Left Arm	0	7	Constant Line Pressure	0	0	Detailing	3	3	Right Arm	06	02
Vertical Midline	3	4	Position of Legs	4	1	Variable Line Pressure	1	2	Identity and Sex	1	1	Left Arm	06	
Bilateral Symmetry	3	0	Relation of Long Axes	1	1	Line Continuity	0	0	Sophistication	3	3	Chest	06	03
Horizontal Midline	4	0	Right and Left Halves	1	2	Body Shading	0	0	Height	07	05	Girth	07	04

GENERAL CHARACTERISTICS OF SUBJECT

IDENTIFICATION
No. G25
Sex M
Marital status S
Age 22 yrs. at
psychological tests

PARENTAL HISTORY
Father
C H S D 0
-   -   -   -   -
Mother
C H S D 0
-   -   -   -   -

PHYSIOLOGICAL AND METABOLIC DATA

	Admission	Initial	Control	Cold pressor change	Exercise change	Smoking change
Systolic pressure	135	130	114	+12	+46	+04
Diastolic pressure	70	64	70	+22	-12	+02
Heart rate	82	96	83	+02	+34	+11

Age 21 yrs.	Height 72 in.	Ponderal index 12.79
	Weight 178 lbs.	Cholesterol 317 mg. per 100 ml.
	Overweight +10 %	Vital capacity liters

HABIT SURVEY

Smoking habits: light cigarette smoker

Age begun 17 yrs.   Inhalation: yes

Habits of nervous tension: 1, 4, 5, 6, 9, 17, 18, 23

STRONG VOCATIONAL INTEREST TEST

Occupation	Artist	Psychologist	Architect	Physician	Osteopath	Dentist	Veterinarian	Mathematician	Physicist	Engineer	Chemist	Production Manager
Standard Score	27	24	26	42	39	45	31	34	25	29	27	17

Occupation	Farmer	Aviator	Carpenter	Printer	Math.-Sci. Teacher	Ind. Arts Teacher	Voc. Agric. Teacher	Policeman	Forest Serv. Man	Y.M.C.A. Phys. Dir.	Personnel Director	Public Administrator
Standard Score	28	15	09	24	30	-06	11	16	04	10	02	17

Occupation	Y.M.C.A. Secretary	Soc. Sci. H.S. Teacher	City Sch. Sup't.	Social Worker	Minister	Musician Performer	C.P.A.	Senior C.P.A.	Accountant	Office Man	Purchasing Agent	Banker
Standard Score	04	27	26	16	59	22	41	25	25	31	35	44

Occupation	Mortician	Pharmacist	Sales Manager	Real Est. Manager	Life Ins. Salesman	Advertising Man	Lawyer	Author-Journalist	President Mfg. Co.	Interest Maturity	Occupational Level	Masculinity-Femininity
Standard Score	30	42	25	39	33	28	45	37	33	46	68	37

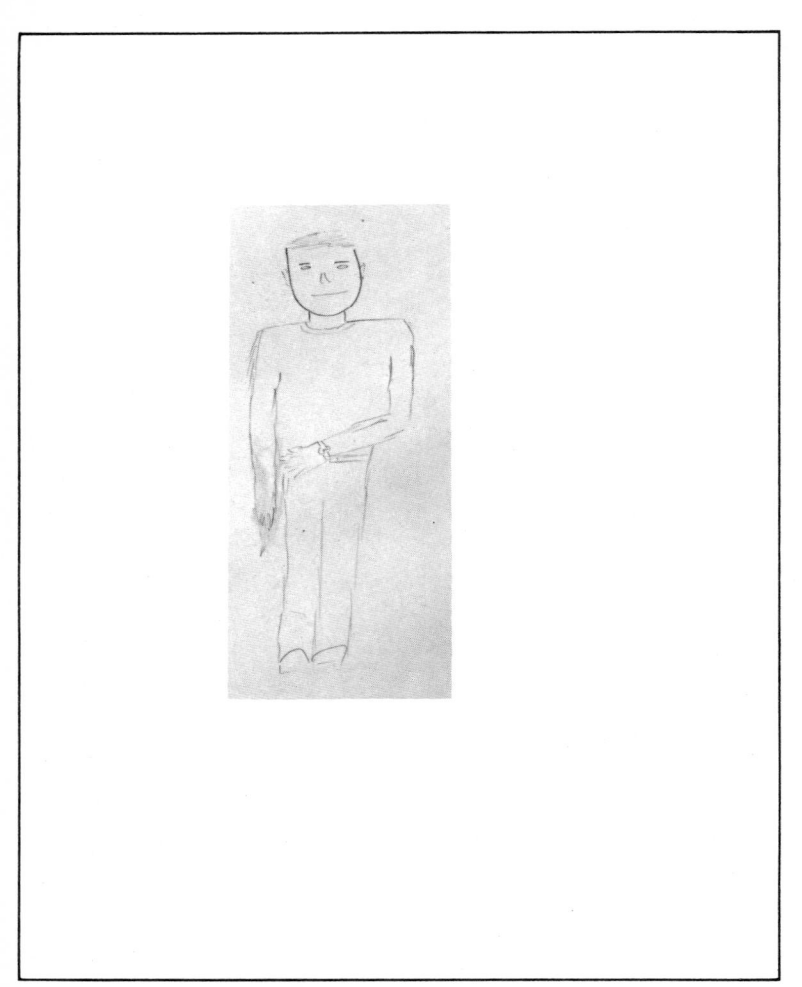

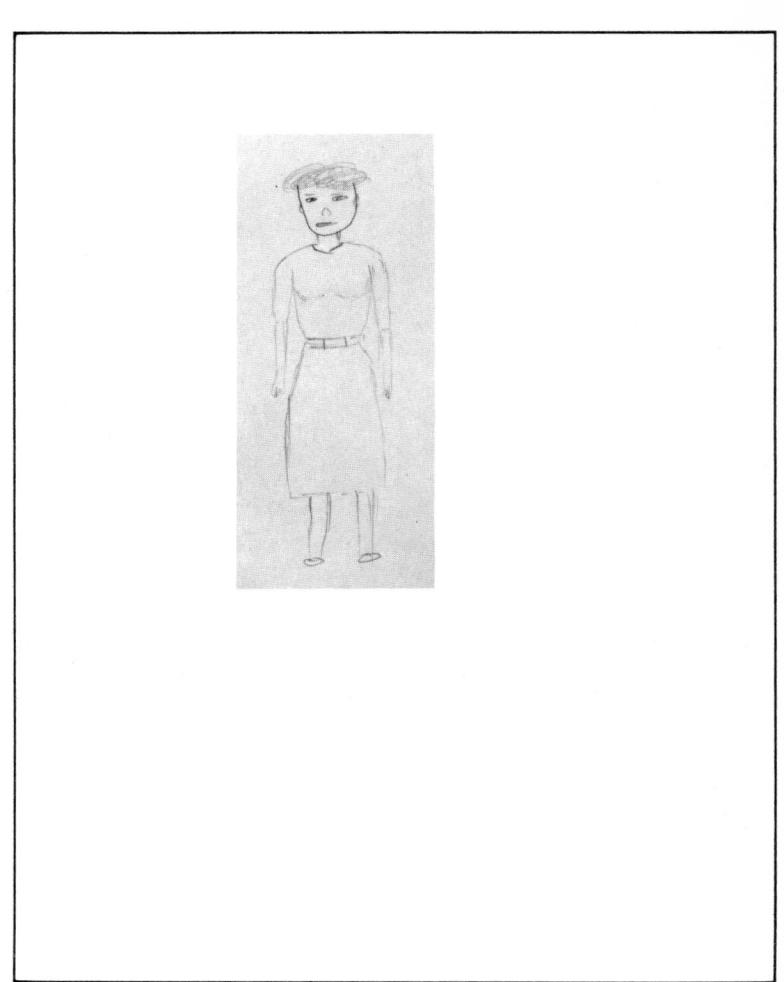

FIGURE-DRAWING CHARACTERISTICS

Structural	Male	Female	Structural	Male	Female	Structural and Graphic	Male	Female	Graphic, Global and Height	Male	Female	Body Proportions	Male	Female
	Both						Both							
Type	0		Omission of Appendages	0	0	Upper and Lower Halves	1	1	Hair Shading	3	3	Head	06	05
Sex Sequence	0		Position of Both Arms	1	0	Four Quarters	4	4	Nudity and Transparency	7	7	Neck	03	03
Posture	1	1	Position of Right Arm	0	0	Relative Size	0		Form	3	3	Shoulders	06	04
Perspective	0	0	Position of Left Arm	5	0	Constant Line Pressure	0	0	Detailing	5	3	Right Arm	04	02
Vertical Midline	0	0	Position of Legs	2	4	Variable Line Pressure	1	1	Identity and Sex	1	1	Left Arm	05	03
Bilateral Symmetry	2	3	Relation of Long Axes	1	1	Line Continuity	0	0	Sophistication	3	3	Chest	05	03
Horizontal Midline	4	4	Right and Left Halves	1	1	Body Shading	0	1	Height	04	04	Girth	05	04

GENERAL CHARACTERISTICS OF SUBJECT

IDENTIFICATION
No. G29
Sex M
Marital status S
Age 23 yrs. at
psychological tests

PARENTAL HISTORY
Father
C H S D O
-    -   -   -   -
Mother
C H S D O
-    -   -   -   -

PHYSIOLOGICAL AND METABOLIC DATA

	Admission	Initial	Control	Cold pressor change	Exercise change	Smoking change
Systolic pressure	126	118	124	+16	+18	+08
Diastolic pressure	80	86	72	+12	-04	+02
Heart rate	82	72	69	-04	+10	+10

Age 23 yrs.	Height 66 in.	Ponderal index 12.72
	Weight 140 lbs.	Cholesterol 258 mg. per 100 ml.
	Overweight 00 %	Vital capacity liters

HABIT SURVEY

Smoking habits: pipe smoker

Age begun 19 yrs. Inhalation: no

Habits of nervous tension: 5, 25

STRONG VOCATIONAL INTEREST TEST

Occupation	Artist	Psychologist	Architect	Physician	Osteopath	Dentist	Veterinarian	Mathematician	Physicist	Engineer	Chemist	Production Manager
Standard Score	48	55	43	65	38	35	20	46	36	30	48	15

Occupation	Farmer	Aviator	Carpenter	Printer	Math.-Sci. Teacher	Ind. Arts Teacher	Voc. Agric. Teacher	Policeman	Forest Serv. Man	Y.M.C.A. Phys. Dir.	Personnel Director	Public Administrator
Standard Score	29	30	04	31	33	02	26	15	24	28	31	43

Occupation	Y.M.C.A. Secretary	Soc. Sci. H.S. Teacher	City Sch. Sup't.	Social Worker	Minister	Musician Performer	C.P.A.	Senior C.P.A.	Accountant	Office Man	Purchasing Agent	Banker
Standard Score	21	27	38	41	59	54	34	30	09	16	08	14

Occupation	Mortician	Pharmacist	Sales Manager	Real Est. Manager	Life Ins. Salesman	Advertising Man	Lawyer	Author-Journalist	President Mfg. Co.	Interest Maturity	Occupational Level	Masculinity-Femininity
Standard Score	14	23	28	29	28	45	55	51	25	48	60	37

Plate 462   DRAWINGS AT AN INTERMEDIATE LEVEL OF SOPHISTICATION   505

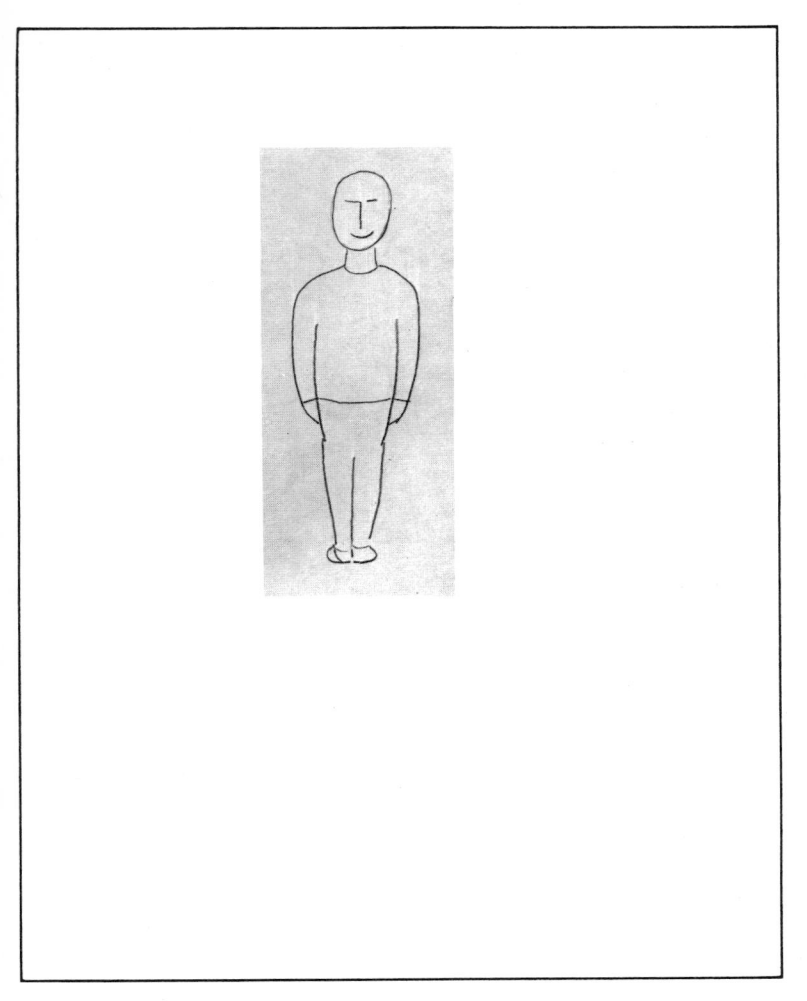

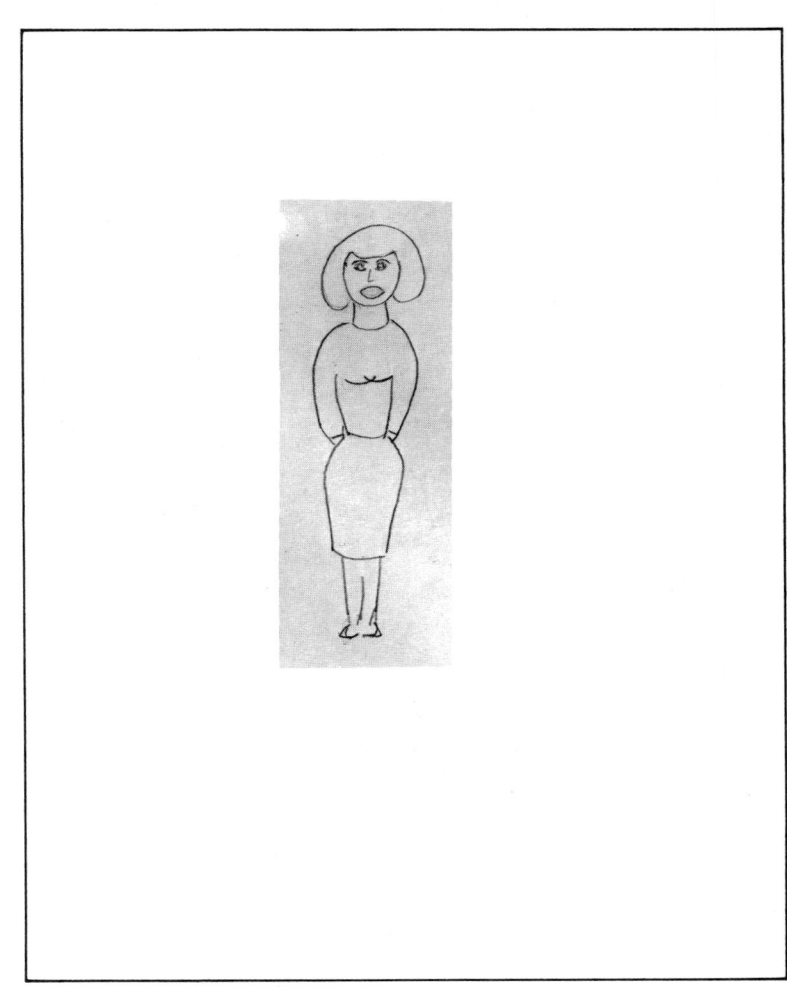

FIGURE-DRAWING CHARACTERISTICS

Structural	Male Female Both	Structural	Male	Female	Structural and Graphic	Male Female Both	Graphic, Global and Height	Male	Female	Body Proportions	Male	Female
Type	0	Omission of Appendages	0	7	Upper and Lower Halves	1	1	Hair Shading	0	5	Head	06	05
Sex Sequence	0	Position of Both Arms	0	0	Four Quarters	4	4	Nudity and Transparency	7	7	Neck	06	06
Posture	1	1	Position of Right Arm	0	5	Relative Size	4		Form	3	3	Shoulders	05	04
Perspective	0	0	Position of Left Arm	0	5	Constant Line Pressure	5	5	Detailing	5	3	Right Arm	03	02
Vertical Midline	0	0	Position of Legs	2	2	Variable Line Pressure	0	0	Identity and Sex	3	1	Left Arm	03	02
Bilateral Symmetry	5	5	Relation of Long Axes	1	1	Line Continuity	4	4	Sophistication	3	3	Chest	04	03
Horizontal Midline	4	4	Right and Left Halves	1	2	Body Shading	0	1	Height	04	04	Girth	04	02

GENERAL CHARACTERISTICS OF SUBJECT

IDENTIFICATION
No. G38
Sex M
Marital status S
Age 23 yrs. at
psychological tests

PARENTAL HISTORY
Father
C H S D O
- - - - -
Mother
C H S D O
- - - - -

PHYSIOLOGICAL AND METABOLIC DATA

	Admission	Initial	Control	Cold pressor change	Exercise change	Smoking change
Systolic pressure	118	124	118	+20	+22	+04
Diastolic pressure	70	82	68	+22	-02	+08
Heart rate	86	76	69	+06	+28	+06

Age 22 yrs.	Height 71 in.	Ponderal index 13.05
	Weight 161 lbs.	Cholesterol 217 mg. per 100 ml.
	Overweight +02 %	Vital capacity liters

HABIT SURVEY
Smoking habits: heavy cigarette smoker
Age begun 18 yrs.   Inhalation: no
Habits of nervous tension: 21, 25

STRONG VOCATIONAL INTEREST TEST

Occupation	Artist	Psychologist	Architect	Physician	Osteopath	Dentist	Veterinarian	Mathematician	Physicist	Engineer	Chemist	Production Manager
Standard Score	33	47	38	50	35	34	23	29	28	33	37	31

Occupation	Farmer	Aviator	Carpenter	Printer	Math.-Sci. Teacher	Ind. Arts Teacher	Voc. Agric. Teacher	Policeman	Forest Serv. Man	Y.M.C.A. Phys. Dir.	Personnel Director	Public Administrator
Standard Score	36	39	19	34	31	18	26	27	24	24	33	39

Occupation	Y.M.C.A. Secretary	Soc. Sci. H.S. Teacher	City Sch. Sup't.	Social Worker	Minister	Musician Performer	C.P.A.	Senior C.P.A.	Accountant	Office Man	Purchasing Agent	Banker
Standard Score	22	23	27	38	59	47	37	40	22	28	22	22

Occupation	Mortician	Pharmacist	Sales Manager	Real Est. Manager	Life Ins. Salesman	Advertising Man	Lawyer	Author-Journalist	President Mfg. Co.	Interest Maturity	Occupational Level	Masculinity-Femininity
Standard Score	21	26	29	35	29	39	41	37	33	51	57	51

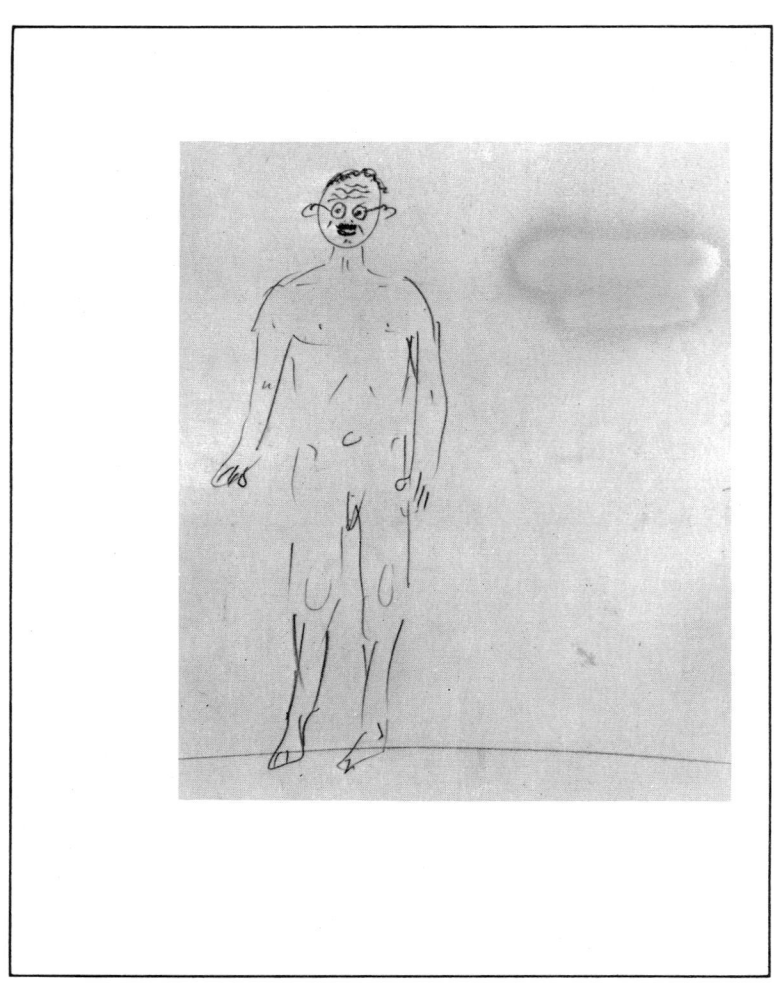

FIGURE-DRAWING CHARACTERISTICS

Structural	Male	Female	Structural	Male	Female	Structural and Graphic	Male	Female	Graphic, Global and Height	Male	Female	Body Proportions	Male	Female
	Both						Both							
Type	0		Omission of Appendages	0	0	Upper and Lower Halves	1	0	Hair Shading	3	3	Head	06	07
Sex Sequence	0		Position of Both Arms	0	0	Four Quarters	4	4	Nudity and Transparency	0	0	Neck	08	12
Posture	1	1	Position of Right Arm	1	0	Relative Size	4		Form	3	3	Shoulders	06	
Perspective	0	1	Position of Left Arm	1	0	Constant Line Pressure	0	0	Detailing	3	1	Right Arm	04	04
Vertical Midline	0	4	Position of Legs	4	4	Variable Line Pressure	1	2	Identity and Sex	1	1	Left Arm	05	04
Bilateral Symmetry	2	0	Relation of Long Axes	1	1	Line Continuity	1	1	Sophistication	3	3	Chest	05	
Horizontal Midline	0	0	Right and Left Halves	1	2	Body Shading	3	7	Height	06	06	Girth		

GENERAL CHARACTERISTICS OF SUBJECT

IDENTIFICATION
No. G70
Sex M
Marital status S
Age 23 yrs. at
psychological tests

PARENTAL HISTORY
Father
C H S D O
- - - - -
Mother
C H S D O
- - - - -

PHYSIOLOGICAL AND METABOLIC DATA

	Admission	Initial	Control	Cold pressor change	Exercise change	Smoking change
Systolic pressure	105	112	100	+14	+40	-01
Diastolic pressure	60	64	62	+16	+10	-01
Heart rate	68	84	70	+12	+07	+01

Age 22 yrs.	Height 74 in.	Ponderal index 13.01
	Weight 184 lbs.	Cholesterol 222 mg. per 100 ml.
	Overweight +06 %	Vital capacity liters

HABIT SURVEY

Smoking habits: heavy cigarette smoker

   Age begun 18 yrs.   Inhalation: yes

Habits of nervous tension: 1, 2, 3, 4, 5, 6,

7, 10, 18, 19, 22, 25

STRONG VOCATIONAL INTEREST TEST

Occupation	Artist	Psychologist	Architect	Physician	Osteopath	Dentist	Veterinarian	Mathematician	Physicist	Engineer	Chemist	Production Manager
Standard Score	56	44	57	55	41	49	20	48	55	60	62	27

Occupation	Farmer	Aviator	Carpenter	Printer	Math.-Sci. Teacher	Ind. Arts Teacher	Voc. Agric. Teacher	Policeman	Forest Serv. Man	Y.M.C.A. Phys. Dir.	Personnel Director	Public Administrator
Standard Score	46	55	37	42	29	28	18	20	31	09	18	25

Occupation	Y.M.C.A. Secretary	Soc. Sci. H.S. Teacher	City Sch. Sup't.	Social Worker	Minister	Musician Performer	C.P.A.	Senior C.P.A.	Accountant	Office Man	Purchasing Agent	Banker
Standard Score	-04	01	-07	13	59	45	24	28	05	08	21	07

Occupation	Mortician	Pharmacist	Sales Manager	Real Est. Manager	Life Ins. Salesman	Advertising Man	Lawyer	Author-Journalist	President Mfg. Co.	Interest Maturity	Occupational Level	Masculinity-Femininity
Standard Score	08	17	15	29	13	39	38	50	44	36	55	57

Plate 464   **DRAWINGS AT AN INTERMEDIATE LEVEL OF SOPHISTICATION**   507

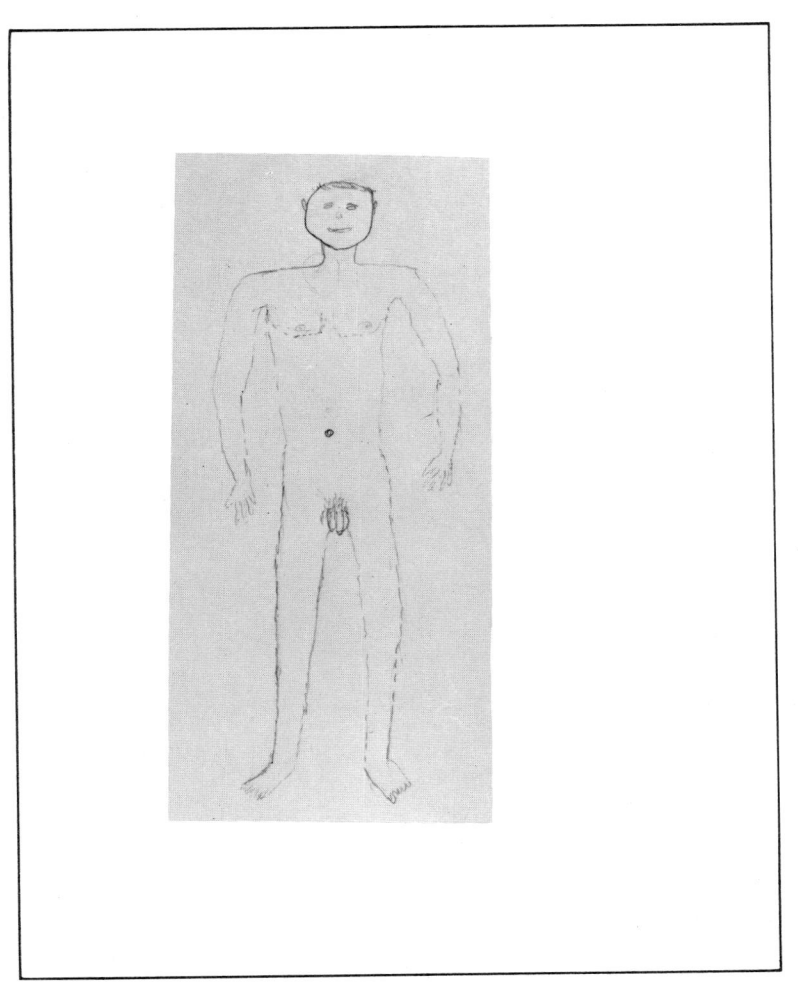

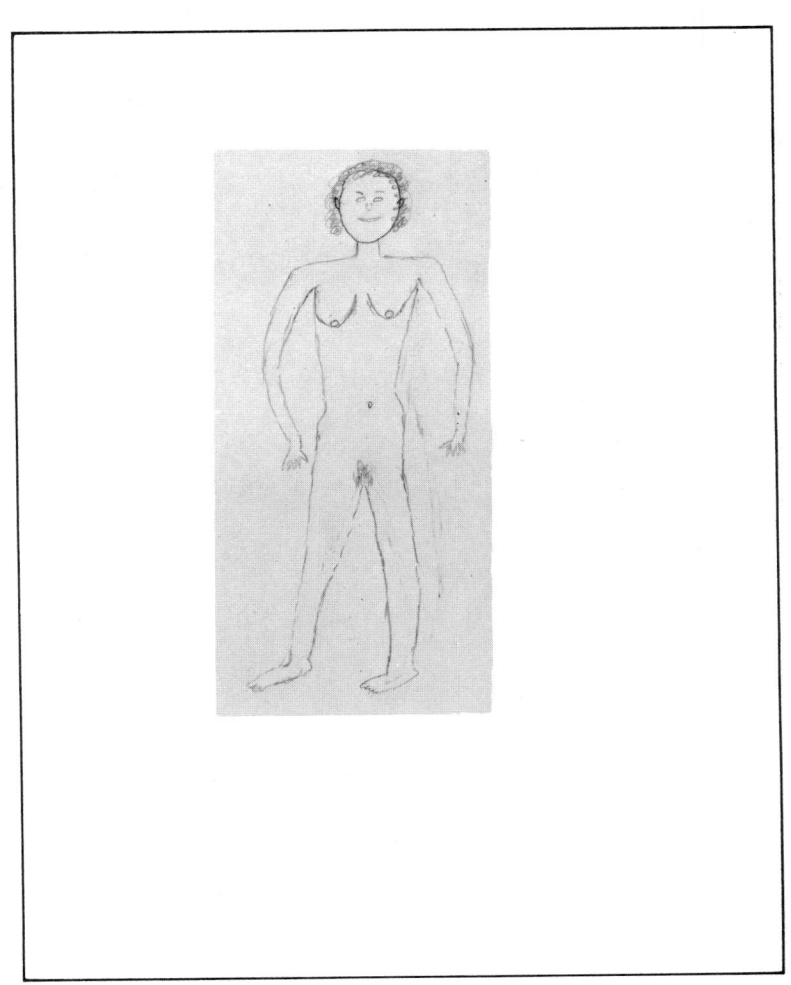

FIGURE-DRAWING CHARACTERISTICS

Structural	Male Female		Structural	Male	Female	Structural and Graphic	Male Female		Graphic, Global and Height	Male	Female	Body Proportions	Male	Female
	Both						Both							
Type	0		Omission of Appendages	0	0	Upper and Lower Halves	0	1	Hair Shading	3	3	Head	05	06
Sex Sequence	0		Position of Both Arms	0	0	Four Quarters	4	4	Nudity and Transparency	0	0	Neck	06	04
Posture	1	1	Position of Right Arm	5	5	Relative Size	0		Form	3	3	Shoulders	07	06
Perspective	0	0	Position of Left Arm	5	5	Constant Line Pressure	0	0	Detailing	3	3	Right Arm	06	04
Vertical Midline	0	0	Position of Legs	6	6	Variable Line Pressure	2	1	Identity and Sex	1	1	Left Arm	06	04
Bilateral Symmetry	3	3	Relation of Long Axes	1	1	Line Continuity	0	0	Sophistication	3	3	Chest	06	05
Horizontal Midline	0	0	Right and Left Halves	1	1	Body Shading	2	2	Height	06	05	Girth	06	05

GENERAL CHARACTERISTICS OF SUBJECT

IDENTIFICATION

No. A09

Sex M

Marital status S

Age 23 yrs. at psychological tests

PARENTAL HISTORY

Father

C H S D O

- - - - -

Mother

C H S D O

- - - - -

PHYSIOLOGICAL AND METABOLIC DATA

	Admission	Initial	Control	Cold pressor change	Exercise change	Smoking change
Systolic pressure	120	136	125	+04	+35	
Diastolic pressure	80	62	61	+13	-03	
Heart rate	82	60	56	-16	+09	

Age 22 yrs. Height 71 in. Weight 168 lbs. Overweight +06 %

Ponderal index 12.86 Cholesterol 190 mg. per 100 ml. Vital capacity   liters

HABIT SURVEY

Smoking habits: nonsmoker

Age begun * yrs.   Inhalation:

Habits of nervous tension: 3, 4, 5, 9, 10, 11, 14, 16, 22, 25

* smoked for two months at age 9

STRONG VOCATIONAL INTEREST TEST

Occupation	Artist	Psychologist	Architect	Physician	Osteopath	Dentist	Veterinarian	Mathematician	Physicist	Engineer	Chemist	Production Manager
Standard Score	31	31	32	52	43	44	37	30	28	38	43	29

Occupation	Farmer	Aviator	Carpenter	Printer	Math.-Sci. Teacher	Ind. Arts Teacher	Voc. Agric. Teacher	Policeman	Forest Serv. Man	Y.M.C.A. Phys. Dir.	Personnel Director	Public Administrator
Standard Score	45	47	25	33	35	18	35	38	35	35	29	36

Occupation	Y.M.C.A. Secretary	Soc. Sci. H.S. Teacher	City Sch. Sup't.	Social Worker	Minister	Musician Performer	C.P.A.	Senior C.P.A.	Accountant	Office Man	Purchasing Agent	Banker
Standard Score	17	26	16	26	60	42	25	43	29	35	33	28

Occupation	Mortician	Pharmacist	Sales Manager	Real Est. Manager	Life Ins. Salesman	Advertising Man	Lawyer	Author-Journalist	President Mfg. Co.	Interest Maturity	Occupational Level	Masculinity-Femininity
Standard Score	26	35	29	36	31	30	34	31	33	51	54	48

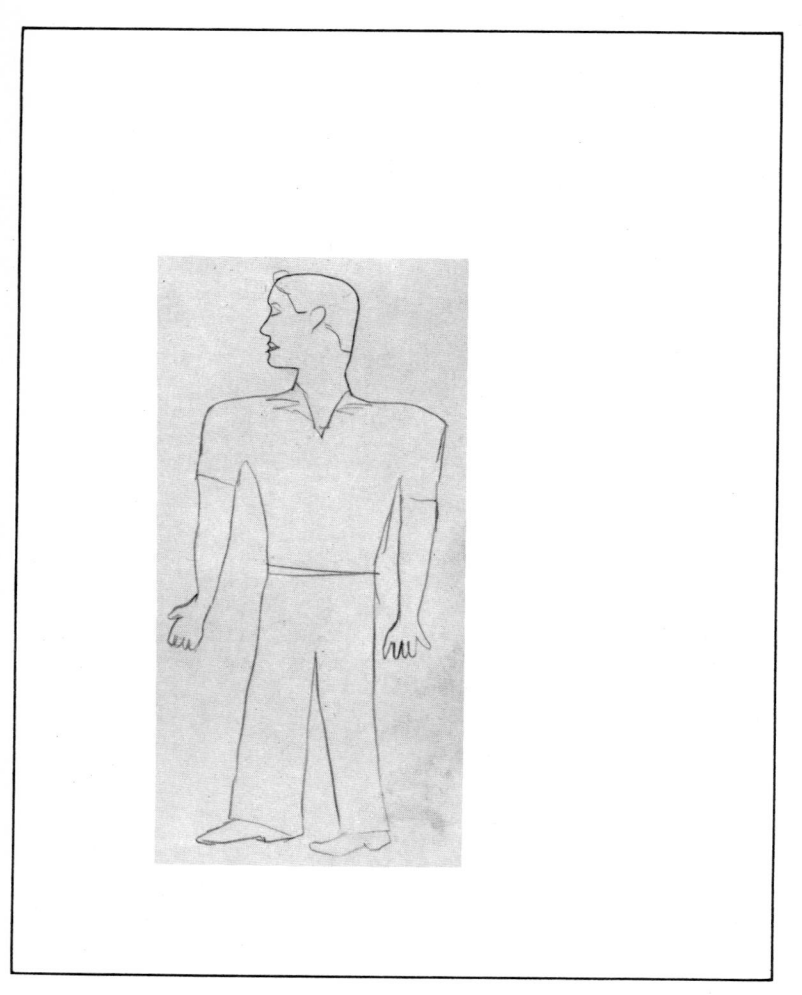

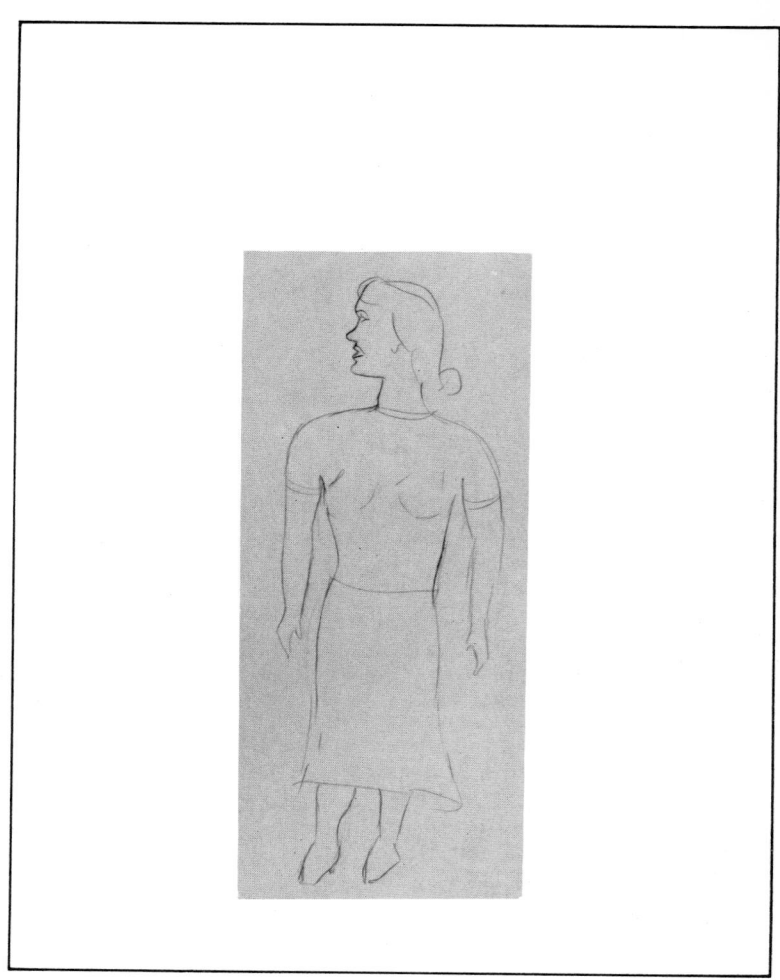

FIGURE-DRAWING CHARACTERISTICS

Structural	Male Female Both		Structural	Male	Female	Structural and Graphic	Male Female Both		Graphic, Global and Height	Male	Female	Body Proportions	Male	Female
Type	0		Omission of Appendages	0	0	Upper and Lower Halves	3	3	Hair Shading	5	5	Head	07	07
Sex Sequence	0		Position of Both Arms	0	0	Four Quarters	4	4	Nudity and Transparency	7	7	Neck	06	08
Posture	1	1	Position of Right Arm	0	0	Relative Size	2		Form	3	3	Shoulders	10	08
Perspective	5	5	Position of Left Arm	0	0	Constant Line Pressure	0	0	Detailing	5	3	Right Arm	06	06
Vertical Midline	0	0	Position of Legs	4	4	Variable Line Pressure	1	1	Identity and Sex	1	1	Left Arm	06	06
Bilateral Symmetry	3	3	Relation of Long Axes	1	1	Line Continuity	2	1	Sophistication	3	3	Chest	06	06
Horizontal Midline	4	4	Right and Left Halves	1	1	Body Shading	0	1	Height	06	06	Girth	07	07

GENERAL CHARACTERISTICS OF SUBJECT

IDENTIFICATION
No. A22
Sex M
Marital status S
Age 22 yrs. at psychological tests

PARENTAL HISTORY				
Father				
C	H	S	D	O
-	-	-	-	-
Mother				
C	H	S	D	O
-	-	-	-	-

PHYSIOLOGICAL AND METABOLIC DATA

	Admission	Initial	Control	Cold pressor change	Exercise change	Smoking change
Systolic pressure	120	134	128	+12	+24	+06
Diastolic pressure	68	58	54	+35	-10	+07
Heart rate	72	72	65	+04	+08	-01

Age 22 yrs.	Height 72 in.	Ponderal index 12.95
	Weight 172 lbs.	Cholesterol 197 mg. per 100 ml.
	Overweight +06 %	Vital capacity liters

HABIT SURVEY

Smoking habits: nonsmoker

   Age begun   yrs.   Inhalation:

Habits of nervous tension: 1, 4, 5, 6, 9, 11, 17, 18, 21, 23

STRONG VOCATIONAL INTEREST TEST

Occupation	Artist	Psychologist	Architect	Physician	Osteopath	Dentist	Veterinarian	Mathematician	Physicist	Engineer	Chemist	Production Manager
Standard Score	49	42	44	62	54	52	12	43	39	41	52	23

Occupation	Farmer	Aviator	Carpenter	Printer	Math.-Sci. Teacher	Ind. Arts Teacher	Voc. Agric. Teacher	Policeman	Forest Serv. Man	Y.M.C.A. Phys. Dir.	Personnel Director	Public Administrator
Standard Score	30	34	18	36	35	15	11	20	20	28	24	30

Occupation	Y.M.C.A. Secretary	Soc. Sci. H.S. Teacher	City Sch. Sup't.	Social Worker	Minister	Musician Performer	C.P.A.	Senior C.P.A.	Accountant	Office Man	Purchasing Agent	Banker
Standard Score	26	26	28	27	60	55	22	22	12	24	10	13

Occupation	Mortician	Pharmacist	Sales Manager	Real Est. Manager	Life Ins. Salesman	Advertising Man	Lawyer	Author-Journalist	President Mfg. Co.	Interest Maturity	Occupational Level	Masculinity-Femininity
Standard Score	30	29	20	27	26	39	35	45	32	51	65	30

Plate 466   DRAWINGS AT AN INTERMEDIATE LEVEL OF SOPHISTICATION   509

FIGURE-DRAWING CHARACTERISTICS

Structural	Male	Female	Structural	Male	Female	Structural and Graphic	Male	Female	Graphic, Global and Height	Male	Female	Body Proportions	Male	Female
	Both						Both							
Type	0		Omission of Appendages	0	7	Upper and Lower Halves	1	3	Hair Shading	3	3	Head	09	09
Sex Sequence	2		Position of Both Arms	0	0	Four Quarters	4	4	Nudity and Transparency	6	6	Neck	08	12
Posture	2	1	Position of Right Arm	2	5	Relative Size	2		Form	3	3	Shoulders	09	07
Perspective	0	0	Position of Left Arm	2	5	Constant Line Pressure	0	0	Detailing	1	3	Right Arm	06	05
Vertical Midline	3	0	Position of Legs	8	5	Variable Line Pressure	3	1	Identity and Sex	1	1	Left Arm	05	04
Bilateral Symmetry	3	3	Relation of Long Axes	1	1	Line Continuity	0	0	Sophistication	3	3	Chest	09	06
Horizontal Midline	4	4	Right and Left Halves	1	1	Body Shading	3	3	Height	07	07	Girth	09	06

GENERAL CHARACTERISTICS OF SUBJECT

IDENTIFICATION
No. A23
Sex M
Marital status M
Age 23 yrs. at
psychological tests

PARENTAL HISTORY				
Father				
C	H	S	D	O
-	-	-	-	-
Mother				
C	H	S	D	O
-	-	-	-	-

PHYSIOLOGICAL AND METABOLIC DATA

	Admission	Initial	Control	Cold pressor change	Exercise change	Smoking change
Systolic pressure	134	120	127	+22	+09	+03
Diastolic pressure	66	58	67	+18	-15	+07
Heart rate	72	80	66	+15	+13	+10

Age 22 yrs.	Height	74 in.	Ponderal index	13.36	
	Weight	170 lbs.	Cholesterol	190	mg. per 100 ml.
	Overweight -02 %		Vital capacity		liters

HABIT SURVEY

Smoking habits: light cigarette smoker

Age begun 18 yrs.   Inhalation: sometimes

Habits of nervous tension: 2, 3, 4, 5, 6, 9, 10, 12, 15, 16, 22

STRONG VOCATIONAL INTEREST TEST

Occupation	Artist	Psychologist	Architect	Physician	Osteopath	Dentist	Veterinarian	Mathematician	Physicist	Engineer	Chemist	Production Manager
Standard Score	23	36	14	43	52	26	32	10	04	21	29	36

Occupation	Farmer	Aviator	Carpenter	Printer	Math.-Sci. Teacher	Ind. Arts Teacher	Voc. Agric. Teacher	Policeman	Forest Serv. Man	Y.M.C.A. Phys. Dir.	Personnel Director	Public Administrator
Standard Score	32	46	08	34	34	13	33	32	29	47	49	51

Occupation	Y.M.C.A. Secretary	Soc. Sci. H.S. Teacher	City Sch. Sup't.	Social Worker	Minister	Musician Performer	C.P.A.	Senior C.P.A.	Accountant	Office Man	Purchasing Agent	Banker
Standard Score	34	48	27	48	60	37	19	38	25	37	31	22

Occupation	Mortician	Pharmacist	Sales Manager	Real Est. Manager	Life Ins. Salesman	Advertising Man	Lawyer	Author-Journalist	President Mfg. Co.	Interest Maturity	Occupational Level	Masculinity-Femininity
Standard Score	37	35	44	46	44	39	38	31	29	56	56	49

FIGURE-DRAWING CHARACTERISTICS

Structural	Male Female Both		Structural	Male	Female	Structural and Graphic	Male Female Both		Graphic, Global and Height	Male	Female	Body Proportions	Male	Female
Type	0		Omission of Appendages	3	1	Upper and Lower Halves	3	3	Hair Shading	0	3	Head	09	11
Sex Sequence	1		Position of Both Arms	0	6	Four Quarters	4	4	Nudity and Transparency	3	3	Neck	12	12
Posture	0	0	Position of Right Arm	5	8	Relative Size	4		Form	5	3	Shoulders	07	08
Perspective	0	0	Position of Left Arm	5	8	Constant Line Pressure	0	0	Detailing	3	3	Right Arm	04	
Vertical Midline	0	0	Position of Legs	2	4	Variable Line Pressure	4	5	Identity and Sex	1	1	Left Arm	06	
Bilateral Symmetry	3	3	Relation of Long Axes	1	1	Line Continuity	0	0	Sophistication	3	3	Chest	05	05
Horizontal Midline	4	4	Right and Left Halves	1	0	Body Shading	5	7	Height			Girth	07	07

GENERAL CHARACTERISTICS OF SUBJECT

IDENTIFICATION
No. A26
Sex M
Marital status S
Age 23 yrs. at
psychological tests

PARENTAL HISTORY
Father
C   H   S   D   O
-    -   -   -   -
Mother
C   H   S   D   O
-    -   -   -   -

PHYSIOLOGICAL AND METABOLIC DATA

	Admission	Initial	Control	Cold pressor change	Exercise change	Smoking change
Systolic pressure	120	126	134	+16	+24	
Diastolic pressure	80	66	74	+13	-10	
Heart rate	72	80	85	+10	+14	

Age 22 yrs.	Height	74	in.	Ponderal index	13.13	
	Weight	179	lbs.	Cholesterol	258	mg. per 100 ml.
	Overweight	+03	%	Vital capacity		liters

HABIT SURVEY

Smoking habits: heavy cigarette smoker

Age begun 13 yrs.   Inhalation: yes

Habits of nervous tension: 2, 3, 5, 8, 9, 19, 23, 25

STRONG VOCATIONAL INTEREST TEST

Occupation	Artist	Psychologist	Architect	Physician	Osteopath	Dentist	Veterinarian	Mathematician	Physicist	Engineer	Chemist	Production Manager
Standard Score	6	7	5	7	6	4	2	4	2	2	4	2

Occupation	Farmer	Aviator	Carpenter	Printer	Math.-Sci. Teacher	Ind. Arts Teacher	Voc. Agric. Teacher	Policeman	Forest Serv. Man	Y.M.C.A. Phys. Dir.	Personnel Director	Public Administrator
Standard Score	5	4	2	5	6	1	3	2	2	5	4	6

Occupation	Y.M.C.A. Secretary	Soc. Sci. H.S. Teacher	City Sch. Sup't.	Social Worker	Minister	Musician Performer	C.P.A.	Senior C.P.A.	Accountant	Office Man	Purchasing Agent	Banker
Standard Score	4	6	5	6	6	8	4	4	2	3	1	2

Occupation	Mortician	Pharmacist	Sales Manager	Real Est. Manager	Life Ins. Salesman	Advertising Man	Lawyer	Author-Journalist	President Mfg. Co.	Interest Maturity	Occupational Level	Masculinity-Femininity
Standard Score	2	3	2	4	3	5	5	6	2	5	4	2

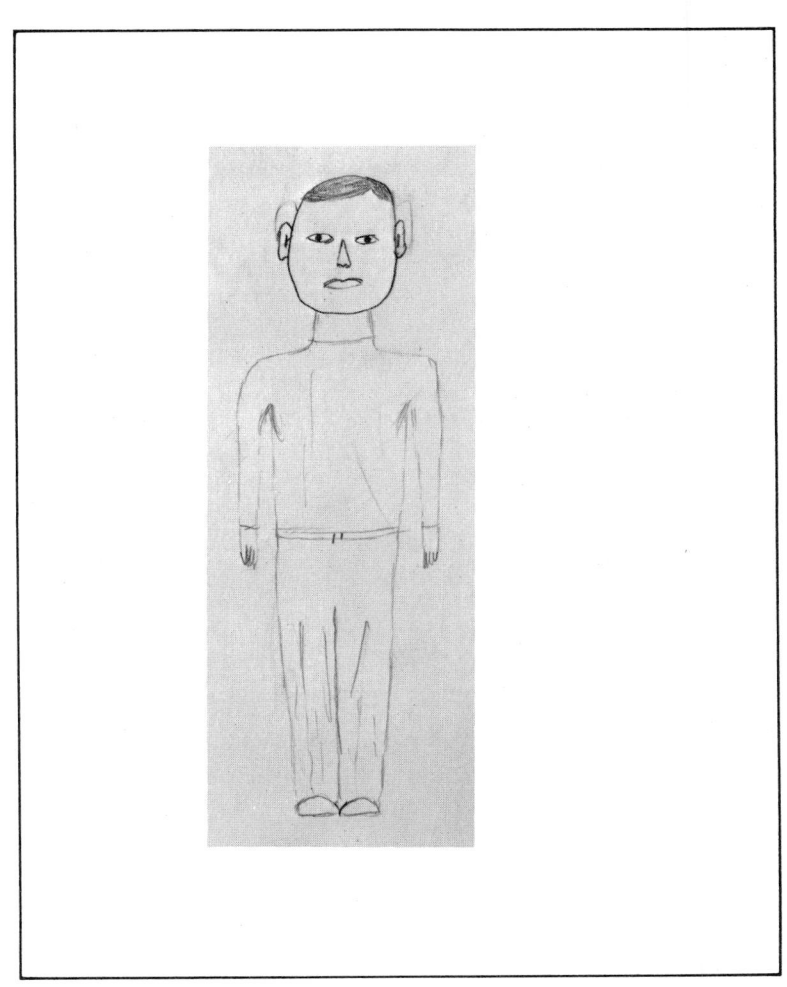

FIGURE-DRAWING CHARACTERISTICS

Structural	Male Female Both		Structural	Male	Female	Structural and Graphic	Male Female Both		Graphic, Global and Height	Male	Female	Body Proportions	Male	Female
Type	0		Omission of Appendages	0	0	Upper and Lower Halves	0	1	Hair Shading	1	2	Head	11	07
Sex Sequence	1		Position of Both Arms	0	0	Four Quarters	4	4	Nudity and Transparency	7	7	Neck	12	07
Posture	1	1	Position of Right Arm	0	0	Relative Size	0		Form	3	3	Shoulders	07	06
Perspective	0	0	Position of Left Arm	0	0	Constant Line Pressure	0	0	Detailing	3	3	Right Arm	04	02
Vertical Midline	0	0	Position of Legs	2	2	Variable Line Pressure	3	2	Identity and Sex	1	1	Left Arm	04	02
Bilateral Symmetry	5	5	Relation of Long Axes	1	1	Line Continuity	0	0	Sophistication	3	3	Chest	06	05
Horizontal Midline	4	4	Right and Left Halves	1	1	Body Shading	3	1	Height	06	06	Girth	08	05

GENERAL CHARACTERISTICS OF SUBJECT

IDENTIFICATION
No. A64
Sex M
Marital status S
Age 22 yrs. at
psychological tests

PARENTAL HISTORY
Father
C H S D O
– – – – –
Mother
C H S D O
– – – – –

PHYSIOLOGICAL AND METABOLIC DATA

	Admission	Initial	Control	Cold pressor change	Exercise change	Smoking change
Systolic pressure	130	132	123	+12	+19	
Diastolic pressure	80	62	67	+08	–12	
Heart rate	80	80	74	+06	+14	

Height	72 in.
Age 21 yrs. Weight	176 lbs.
Overweight	+09 %

Ponderal index	12.86
Cholesterol	197 mg. per 100 ml.
Vital capacity	liters

HABIT SURVEY
Smoking habits: nonsmoker
Age begun yrs. Inhalation:
Habits of nervous tension: 4, 5, 6

STRONG VOCATIONAL INTEREST TEST

Occupation	Artist	Psychologist	Architect	Physician	Osteopath	Dentist	Veterinarian	Mathematician	Physicist	Engineer	Chemist	Production Manager
Standard Score	4	7	5	5	2	2	1	3	4	5	5	5

Occupation	Farmer	Aviator	Carpenter	Printer	Math.-Sci. Teacher	Ind. Arts Teacher	Voc. Agric. Teacher	Policeman	Forest Serv. Man	Y.M.C.A. Phys. Dir.	Personnel Director	Public Administrator
Standard Score	3	6	2	5	4	0		4	2	4	0	7

Occupation	Y.M.C.A. Secretary	Soc. Sci. H.S. Teacher	City Sch. Sup't.	Social Worker	Minister	Musician Performer	C.P.A.	Senior C.P.A.	Accountant	Office Man	Purchasing Agent	Banker
Standard Score	3	4	2	6	6	6	7	6	3	4	3	1

Occupation	Mortician	Pharmacist	Sales Manager	Real Est. Manager	Life Ins. Salesman	Advertising Man	Lawyer	Author-Journalist	President Mfg. Co.	Interest Maturity	Occupational Level	Masculinity-Femininity
Standard Score	2	2	5	5	4	6	7	6	5	5	5	4

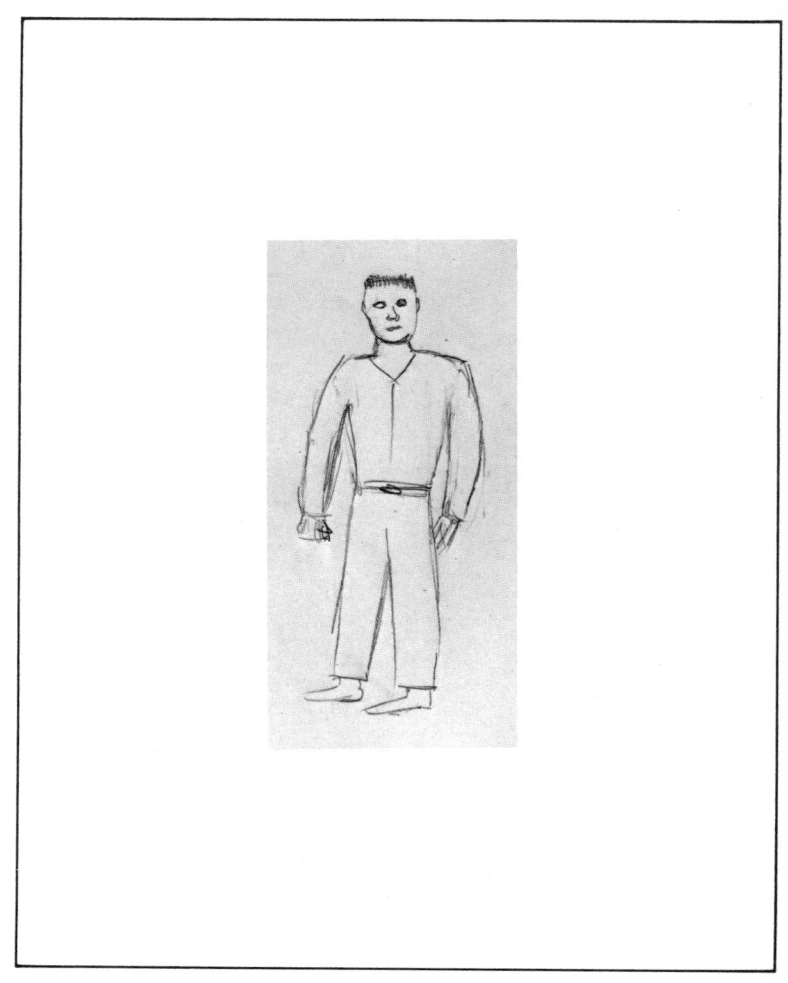

FIGURE-DRAWING CHARACTERISTICS

Structural	Male Female Both		Structural	Male	Female	Structural and Graphic	Male Female Both		Graphic, Global and Height	Male	Female	Body Proportions	Male	Female
Type	0		Omission of Appendages	0	0	Upper and Lower Halves	0	3	Hair Shading	3	3	Head	05	04
Sex Sequence	1		Position of Both Arms	1	1	Four Quarters	4	4	Nudity and Transparency	7	7	Neck	04	04
Posture	1	1	Position of Right Arm	0	2	Relative Size	2		Form	3	3	Shoulders	05	
Perspective	0	1	Position of Left Arm	5	5	Constant Line Pressure	3	0	Detailing	3	3	Right Arm	04	04
Vertical Midline	3	4	Position of Legs	4	4	Variable Line Pressure	0	1	Identity and Sex	1	1	Left Arm	04	04
Bilateral Symmetry	3	0	Relation of Long Axes	1	1	Line Continuity	0	0	Sophistication	3	3	Chest	04	
Horizontal Midline	4	4	Right and Left Halves	1	0	Body Shading	4	0	Height	04	04	Girth	04	

GENERAL CHARACTERISTICS OF SUBJECT

IDENTIFICATION

No. B23

Sex M

Marital status S

Age 22 yrs. at psychological tests

PARENTAL HISTORY

Father

C   H   S   D   O

–   –   –   –   –

Mother

C   H   S   D   O

–   –   –   –   –

PHYSIOLOGICAL AND METABOLIC DATA

	Admission	Initial	Control	Cold pressor change	Exercise change	Smoking change
Systolic pressure	120	120	112	+21	+36	−04
Diastolic pressure	76	64	55	+24	−01	+06
Heart rate	80	72	59	−09	+19	−01

Age 22 yrs.

Height 72 in.

Weight 188 lbs.

Overweight +15 %

Ponderal index 12.57

Cholesterol 186 mg. per 100 ml.

Vital capacity 6.2 liters

HABIT SURVEY

Smoking habits: occasional smoker

Age begun 19 yrs.   Inhalation:

Habits of nervous tension: 4, 6, 25

STRONG VOCATIONAL INTEREST TEST

Occupation	Artist	Psychologist	Architect	Physician	Osteopath	Dentist	Veterinarian	Mathematician	Physicist	Engineer	Chemist	Production Manager
Standard Score	16	35	31	57	52	42	35	25	26	44	40	38

Occupation	Farmer	Aviator	Carpenter	Printer	Math.-Sci. Teacher	Ind. Arts Teacher	Voc. Agric. Teacher	Policeman	Forest Serv. Man	Y.M.C.A. Phys. Dir.	Personnel Director	Public Administrator
Standard Score	43	57	35	48	51	43	36	46	39	41	34	43

Occupation	Y.M.C.A. Secretary	Soc. Sci. H.S. Teacher	City Sch. Sup't.	Social Worker	Minister	Musician Performer	C.P.A.	Senior C.P.A.	Accountant	Office Man	Purchasing Agent	Banker
Standard Score	24	29	23	31	61	34	22	51	32	34	24	17

Occupation	Mortician	Pharmacist	Sales Manager	Real Est. Manager	Life Ins. Salesman	Advertising Man	Lawyer	Author-Journalist	President Mfg. Co.	Interest Maturity	Occupational Level	Masculinity-Femininity
Standard Score	30	32	21	28	22	20	23	22	22	58	50	65

FIGURE-DRAWING CHARACTERISTICS

Structural	Male Female Both		Structural	Male	Female	Structural and Graphic	Male Female Both		Graphic, Global and Height	Male	Female	Body Proportions	Male	Female
Type	0		Omission of Appendages	7	0	Upper and Lower Halves	3	3	Hair Shading	3	3	Head	09	09
Sex Sequence	0		Position of Both Arms	0	0	Four Quarters	4	4	Nudity and Transparency	7	7	Neck	08	06
Posture	3	2	Position of Right Arm	5	5	Relative Size	0		Form	3	3	Shoulders	10	07
Perspective	9	0	Position of Left Arm	5	5	Constant Line Pressure	0	0	Detailing	3	3	Right Arm		06
Vertical Midline	3	0	Position of Legs	7	8	Variable Line Pressure	1	2	Identity and Sex	1	1	Left Arm	08	04
Bilateral Symmetry	1	3	Relation of Long Axes	0	1	Line Continuity	0	0	Sophistication	3	3	Chest	07	06
Horizontal Midline	4	2	Right and Left Halves	0	1	Body Shading	0	3	Height		06	Girth	09	07

GENERAL CHARACTERISTICS OF SUBJECT

IDENTIFICATION
No. B24
Sex M
Marital status S
Age 22 yrs. at
psychological tests

PARENTAL HISTORY				
Father				
C	H	S	D	0
-	-	-	-	-
Mother				
C	H	S	D	0
-	-	-	-	-

PHYSIOLOGICAL AND METABOLIC DATA

	Admission	Initial	Control	Cold pressor change	Exercise change	Smoking change
Systolic pressure	145	124	114	+18	+28	+12
Diastolic pressure	70	72	70	+16	-14	+12
Heart rate	76	92	85	+16	+24	+22

Age 21 yrs.	Height	74 in.	Ponderal index	13.50	
	Weight	165 lbs.	Cholesterol	170	mg. per 100 ml.
	Overweight	-04 %	Vital capacity	5.5	liters

HABIT SURVEY

Smoking habits: mixed smoker

  Age begun 15 yrs.   Inhalation: sometimes

Habits of nervous tension: 1, 4, 5, 6, 14, 16, 23

STRONG VOCATIONAL INTEREST TEST

Occupation	Artist	Psychologist	Architect	Physician	Osteopath	Dentist	Veterinarian	Mathematician	Physicist	Engineer	Chemist	Production Manager
Standard Score	46	41	47	60	39	49	29	45	41	40	47	22

Occupation	Farmer	Aviator	Carpenter	Printer	Math.-Sci. Teacher	Ind. Arts Teacher	Voc. Agric. Teacher	Policeman	Forest Serv. Man	Y.M.C.A. Phys. Dir.	Personnel Director	Public Administrator
Standard Score	23	25	11	25	26	04	13	15	00	11	07	21

Occupation	Y.M.C.A. Secretary	Soc. Sci. H.S. Teacher	City Sch. Sup't.	Social Worker	Minister	Musician Performer	C.P.A.	Senior C.P.A.	Accountant	Office Man	Purchasing Agent	Banker
Standard Score	-08	09	16	20	61	43	36	21	12	20	22	20

Occupation	Mortician	Pharmacist	Sales Manager	Real Est. Manager	Life Ins. Salesman	Advertising Man	Lawyer	Author-Journalist	President Mfg. Co.	Interest Maturity	Occupational Level	Masculinity-Femininity
Standard Score	33	45	27	37	29	43	44	49	43	39	64	39

FIGURE-DRAWING CHARACTERISTICS

Structural	Male Female Both		Structural	Male	Female	Structural and Graphic	Male Female Both		Graphic, Global and Height	Male	Female	Body Proportions	Male	Female
Type	0		Omission of Appendages	0	0	Upper and Lower Halves	0	3	Hair Shading	3	3	Head	09	09
Sex Sequence	0		Position of Both Arms	1	1	Four Quarters	4	4	Nudity and Transparency	7	7	Neck	08	14
Posture	1	1	Position of Right Arm	4	4	Relative Size	4		Form	3	3	Shoulders	09	07
Perspective	0	0	Position of Left Arm	0	0	Constant Line Pressure	1	1	Detailing	3	3	Right Arm	06	06
Vertical Midline	3	3	Position of Legs	6	5	Variable Line Pressure	0	0	Identity and Sex	1	1	Left Arm	06	06
Bilateral Symmetry	3	3	Relation of Long Axes	1	1	Line Continuity	0	0	Sophistication	3	3	Chest	07	06
Horizontal Midline	4	4	Right and Left Halves	1	1	Body Shading	2	1	Height	07	08	Girth	08	07

GENERAL CHARACTERISTICS OF SUBJECT

IDENTIFICATION
No. B32
Sex M
Marital status S
Age 23 yrs. at
psychological tests

PARENTAL HISTORY				
Father				
C	H	S	D	O
–	–	–	–	–
Mother				
C	H	S	D	O
–	–	–	–	–

PHYSIOLOGICAL AND METABOLIC DATA

	Admission	Initial	Control	Cold pressor change	Exercise change	Smoking change
Systolic pressure	135	116	106	+09	+38	+08
Diastolic pressure	65	65	64	+12	–16	+08
Heart rate	78	71	65	–03	+26	+05

Age 22 yrs.	Height 74 in.	Ponderal index 13.58
	Weight 162 lbs.	Cholesterol 248 mg. per 100 ml.
	Overweight –06 %	Vital capacity 5.0 liters

HABIT SURVEY

Smoking habits: nonsmoker

Age begun   yrs.   Inhalation:

Habits of nervous tension: 3, 5, 9, 14, 16, 25

STRONG VOCATIONAL INTEREST TEST

Occupation	Artist	Psychologist	Architect	Physician	Osteopath	Dentist	Veterinarian	Mathematician	Physicist	Engineer	Chemist	Production Manager
Standard Score	40	44	41	65	67	61	30	42	48	43	53	28

Occupation	Farmer	Aviator	Carpenter	Printer	Math.-Sci. Teacher	Ind. Arts Teacher	Voc. Agric. Teacher	Policeman	Forest Serv. Man	Y.M.C.A. Phys. Dir.	Personnel Director	Public Administrator
Standard Score	45	42	45	48	53	42	32	36	34	35	23	36

Occupation	Y.M.C.A. Secretary	Soc. Sci. H.S. Teacher	City Sch. Sup't.	Social Worker	Minister	Musician Performer	C.P.A.	Senior C.P.A.	Accountant	Office Man	Purchasing Agent	Banker
Standard Score	30	36	32	37	61	50	13	33	11	24	02	14

Occupation	Mortician	Pharmacist	Sales Manager	Real Est. Manager	Life Ins. Salesman	Advertising Man	Lawyer	Author-Journalist	President Mfg. Co.	Interest Maturity	Occupational Level	Masculinity-Femininity
Standard Score	23	28	03	19	16	19	29	35	20	54	50	41

Plate 472   DRAWINGS AT AN INTERMEDIATE LEVEL OF SOPHISTICATION   515

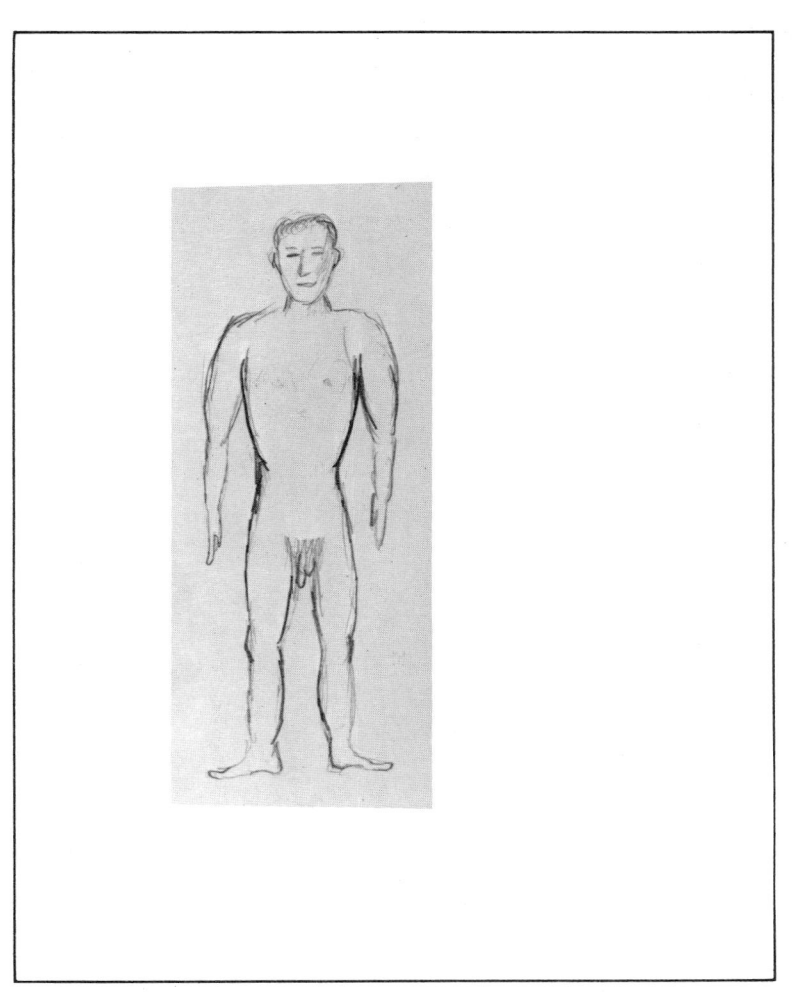

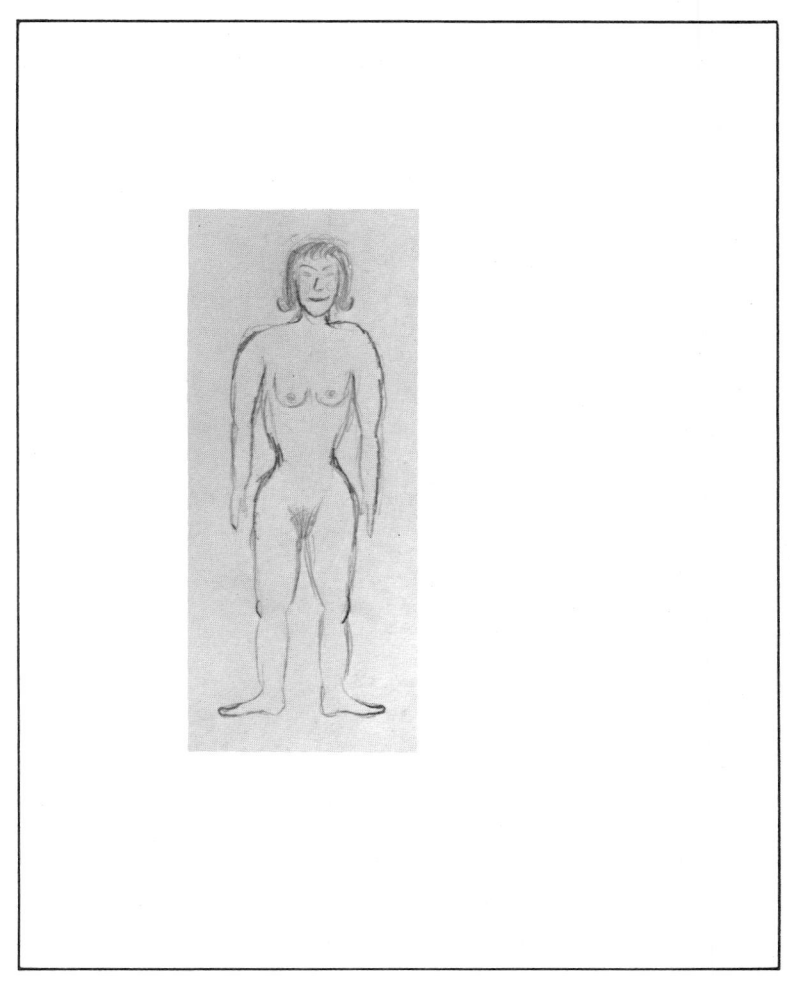

FIGURE-DRAWING CHARACTERISTICS

Structural	Male Female Both		Structural	Male	Female	Structural and Graphic	Male	Female Both		Graphic, Global and Height	Male	Female	Body Proportions	Male	Female
Type	0		Omission of Appendages	0	0	Upper and Lower Halves	0	0		Hair Shading	3	3	Head	06	05
Sex Sequence	0		Position of Both Arms	0	0	Four Quarters	4	4		Nudity and Transparency	0	0	Neck	04	04
Posture	1	1	Position of Right Arm	0	0	Relative Size	0			Form	3	3	Shoulders	06	05
Perspective	0	0	Position of Left Arm	0	0	Constant Line Pressure	0	0		Detailing	3	3	Right Arm	06	04
Vertical Midline	0	0	Position of Legs	5	5	Variable Line Pressure	4	1		Identity and Sex	1	1	Left Arm	06	04
Bilateral Symmetry	4	4	Relation of Long Axes	1	1	Line Continuity	0	0		Sophistication	3	3	Chest	05	04
Horizontal Midline	0	0	Right and Left Halves	2	2	Body Shading	3	3		Height	06	05	Girth	05	04

GENERAL CHARACTERISTICS OF SUBJECT

IDENTIFICATION

No. B35
Sex M
Marital status S
Age 21 yrs. at
psychological tests

PARENTAL HISTORY

Father
C   H   S   D   O
-    -   -   -   -
Mother
C   H   S   D   O
-    -   -   -   -

PHYSIOLOGICAL AND METABOLIC DATA

	Admission	Initial	Control	Cold pressor change	Exercise change	Smoking change
Systolic pressure	94	112	108	+12	+34	+05
Diastolic pressure	56	56	66	+08	-08	+04
Heart rate	80	72	63	+12	+40	+09

Age 21 yrs.
Height 72 in.
Weight 173 lbs.
Overweight +07 %
Ponderal index 12.93
Cholesterol 205 mg. per 100 ml.
Vital capacity 4.8 liters

HABIT SURVEY

Smoking habits: occasional smoker
Age begun 21 yrs.   Inhalation: no
Habits of nervous tension: 25

STRONG VOCATIONAL INTEREST TEST

Occupation	Artist	Psychologist	Architect	Physician	Osteopath	Dentist	Veterinarian	Mathematician	Physicist	Engineer	Chemist	Production Manager
Standard Score	30	52	32	64	60	48	47	27	23	32	45	30

Occupation	Farmer	Aviator	Carpenter	Printer	Math.-Sci. Teacher	Ind. Arts Teacher	Voc. Agric. Teacher	Policeman	Forest Serv. Man	Y.M.C.A. Phys. Dir.	Personnel Director	Public Administrator
Standard Score	46	45	21	47	52	29	48	41	50	55	43	56

Occupation	Y.M.C.A. Secretary	Soc. Sci. H.S. Teacher	City Sch. Sup't.	Social Worker	Minister	Musician Performer	C.P.A.	Senior C.P.A.	Accountant	Office Man	Purchasing Agent	Banker
Standard Score	39	48	39	51	61	51	24	45	24	33	14	15

Occupation	Mortician	Pharmacist	Sales Manager	Real Est. Manager	Life Ins. Salesman	Advertising Man	Lawyer	Author-Journalist	President Mfg. Co.	Interest Maturity	Occupational Level	Masculinity-Femininity
Standard Score	22	38	16	23	24	29	33	33	15	58	49	47

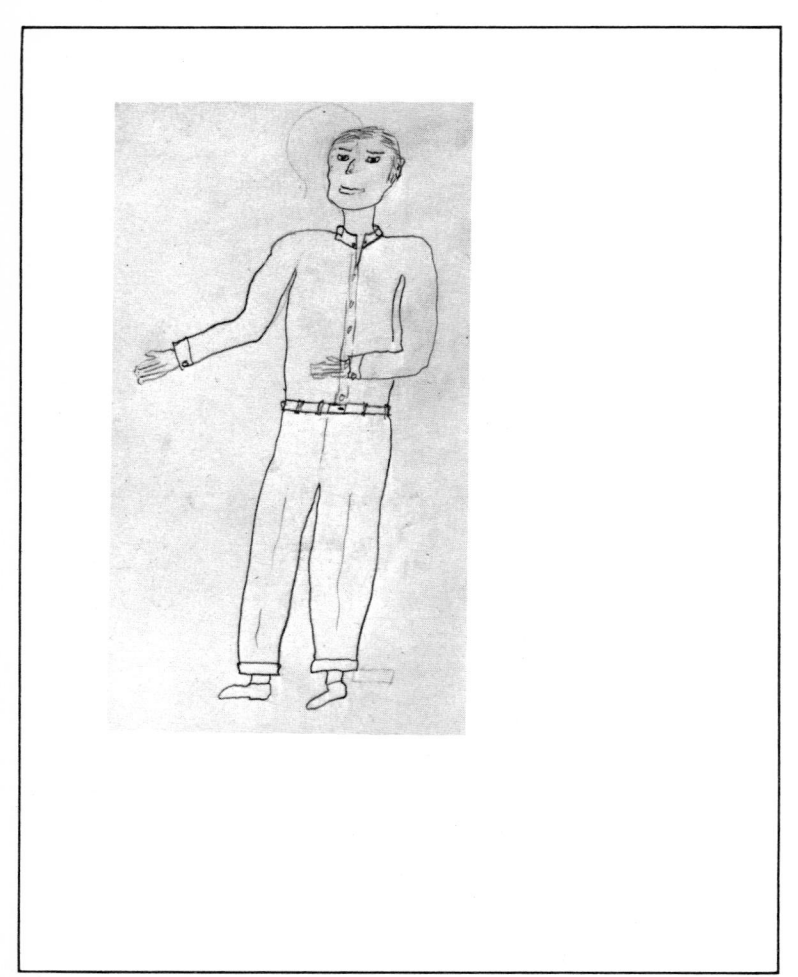

FIGURE-DRAWING CHARACTERISTICS

Structural	Male Female Both	Structural	Male	Female	Structural and Graphic	Male Female Both	Graphic, Global and Height	Male	Female	Body Proportions	Male	Female
Type	0	Omission of Appendages	0	8	Upper and Lower Halves	1	0	Hair Shading	3	3	Head	06	06
Sex Sequence	0	Position of Both Arms	1	1	Four Quarters	4	4	Nudity and Transparency	7	7	Neck	08	08
Posture	2	0	Position of Right Arm	3	2	Relative Size	0		Form	3	3	Shoulders	06	05
Perspective	0	0	Position of Left Arm	5	0	Constant Line Pressure	0	1	Detailing	3	3	Right Arm	04	04
Vertical Midline	3	0	Position of Legs	8	4	Variable Line Pressure	5	0	Identity and Sex	1	1	Left Arm	04	04
Bilateral Symmetry	3	3	Relation of Long Axes	1	1	Line Continuity	4	0	Sophistication	3	3	Chest	05	04
Horizontal Midline	4	0	Right and Left Halves	1	1	Body Shading	2	1	Height	06	05	Girth	06	05

GENERAL CHARACTERISTICS OF SUBJECT

IDENTIFICATION
No. B40
Sex M
Marital status S
Age 22 yrs. at
psychological tests

PARENTAL HISTORY
Father
C   H   S   D   O
-    -   -   -   -
Mother
C   H   S   D   O
-    -   -   -   -

PHYSIOLOGICAL AND METABOLIC DATA

	Admission	Initial	Control	Cold pressor change	Exercise change	Smoking change
Systolic pressure	120	122	108	+14	+32	+06
Diastolic pressure	72	58	50	+12	-08	+12
Heart rate	64	63	64	+10	+24	+02

Age 22 yrs.	Height 71 in.	Ponderal index 13.25
	Weight 154 lbs.	Cholesterol 200 mg. per 100 ml.
	Overweight -03 %	Vital capacity 5.2 liters

HABIT SURVEY
Smoking habits: heavy cigarette smoker
Age begun 16 yrs.   Inhalation: yes
Habits of nervous tension: 4, 5, 6, 11, 18, 22

Plate 474   DRAWINGS AT AN INTERMEDIATE LEVEL OF SOPHISTICATION   517

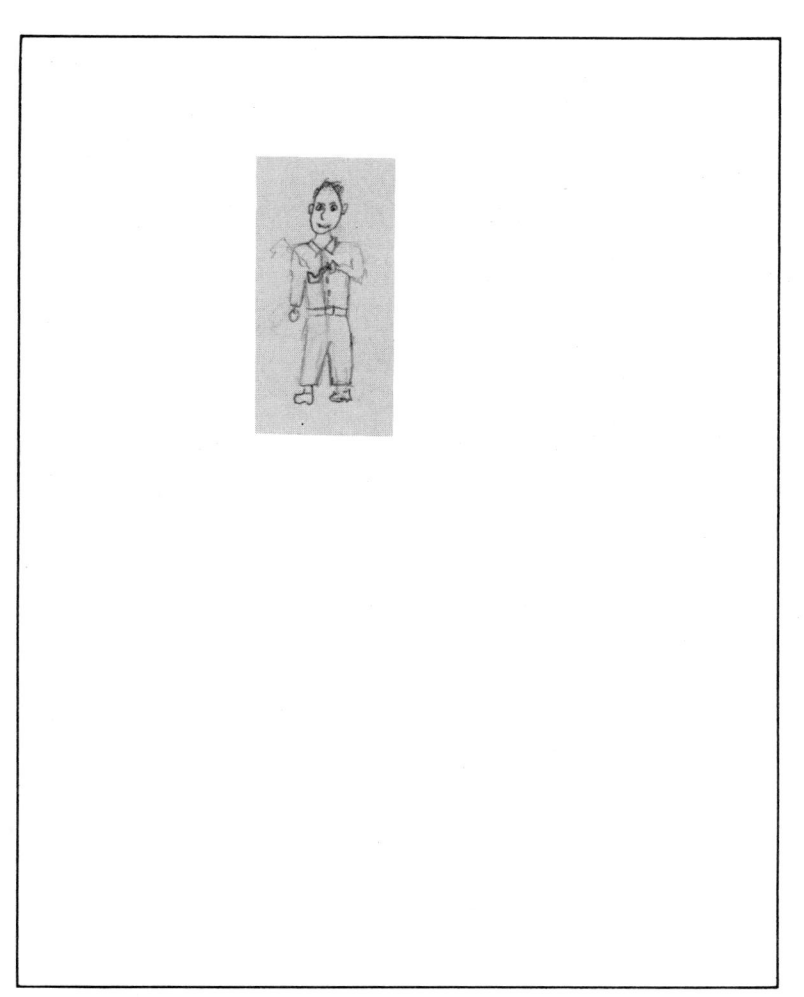

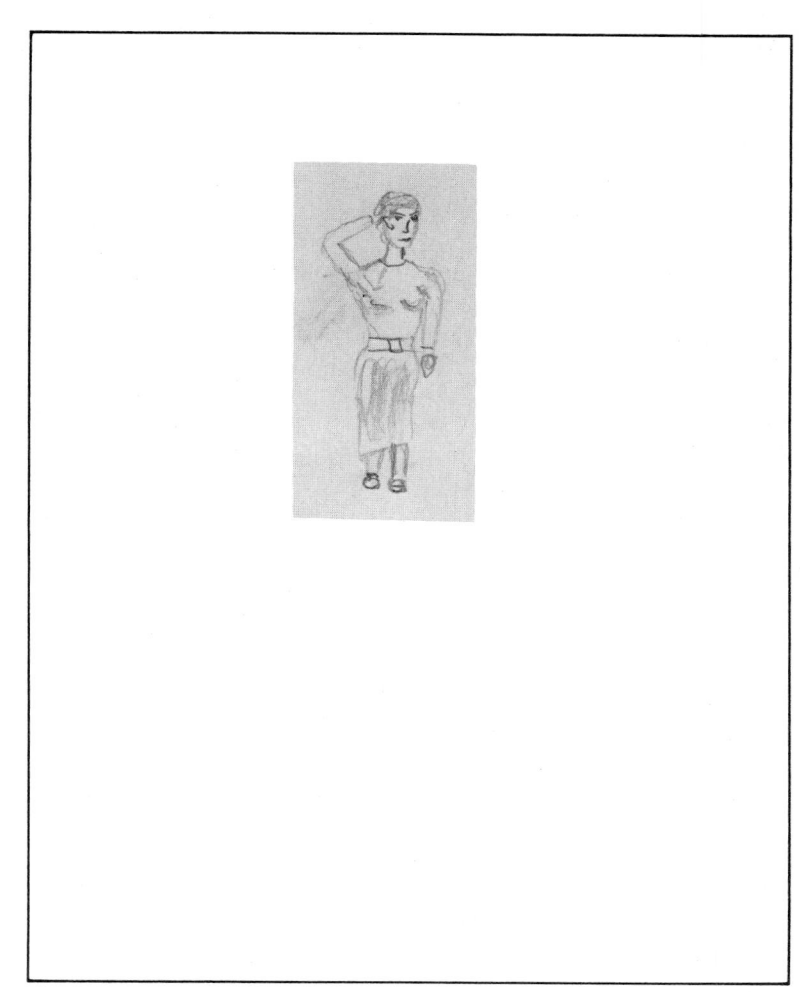

FIGURE-DRAWING CHARACTERISTICS

Structural	Male Female Both		Structural	Male	Female	Structural and Graphic	Male	Female Both	Graphic, Global and Height	Male	Female	Body Proportions	Male	Female
Type	0		Omission of Appendages	0	7	Upper and Lower Halves	2	2	Hair Shading	3	2	Head	04	04
Sex Sequence	0		Position of Both Arms	1	1	Four Quarters	0	4	Nudity and Transparency	6	7	Neck	02	04
Posture	1	1	Position of Right Arm	0	5	Relative Size	4		Form	3	3	Shoulders	02	03
Perspective	0	0	Position of Left Arm	5	0	Constant Line Pressure	0	0	Detailing	3	3	Right Arm	00	02
Vertical Midline	3	0	Position of Legs	5	4	Variable Line Pressure	3	1	Identity and Sex	1	1	Left Arm	00	02
Bilateral Symmetry	3	3	Relation of Long Axes	1	1	Line Continuity	0	0	Sophistication	3	3	Chest	02	03
Horizontal Midline	4	4	Right and Left Halves	2	1	Body Shading	0	3	Height	02	03	Girth	02	03

GENERAL CHARACTERISTICS OF SUBJECT

IDENTIFICATION
No. B45
Sex M
Marital status S
Age 23 yrs. at
psychological tests

PARENTAL HISTORY
Father
C   H   S   D   O
-    -   -   -   -
Mother
C   H   S   D   O
-    -   -   -   -

PHYSIOLOGICAL AND METABOLIC DATA

	Admission	Initial	Control	Cold pressor change	Exercise change	Smoking change
Systolic pressure	120	134	126	+12	+32	-06
Diastolic pressure	65	56	60	+08	-30	-06
Heart rate	60	72	60	+02	+23	+03

Age 23 yrs.	Height	73 in.	Ponderal index	12.74	
	Weight	188 lbs.	Cholesterol	248	mg. per 100 ml.
	Overweight +11 %		Vital capacity		liters

HABIT SURVEY

Smoking habits: pipe smoker

Age begun 22* yrs.   Inhalation: no

Habits of nervous tension: 1, 2, 4, 5, 6, 7, 8,
11, 12, 16, 17, 18, 19, 22, 23, 24

* smoked cigarettes from age 6 to 10
years

STRONG VOCATIONAL INTEREST TEST

Occupation	Artist	Psychologist	Architect	Physician	Osteopath	Dentist	Veterinarian	Mathematician	Physicist	Engineer	Chemist	Production Manager
Standard Score	37	44	34	50	49	32	16	31	34	42	40	35

Occupation	Farmer	Aviator	Carpenter	Printer	Math.-Sci. Teacher	Ind. Arts Teacher	Voc. Agric. Teacher	Policeman	Forest Serv. Man	Y.M.C.A. Phys. Dir.	Personnel Director	Public Administrator
Standard Score	23	33	16	17	29	09	08	29	28	42	39	52

Occupation	Y.M.C.A. Secretary	Soc. Sci. H.S. Teacher	City Sch. Sup't.	Social Worker	Minister	Musician Performer	C.P.A.	Senior C.P.A.	Accountant	Office Man	Purchasing Agent	Banker
Standard Score	32	28	37	46	61	40	36	32	23	21	09	13

Occupation	Mortician	Pharmacist	Sales Manager	Real Est. Manager	Life Ins. Salesman	Advertising Man	Lawyer	Author-Journalist	President Mfg. Co.	Interest Maturity	Occupational Level	Masculinity-Femininity
Standard Score	20	20	30	30	40	34	46	40	35	58	65	38

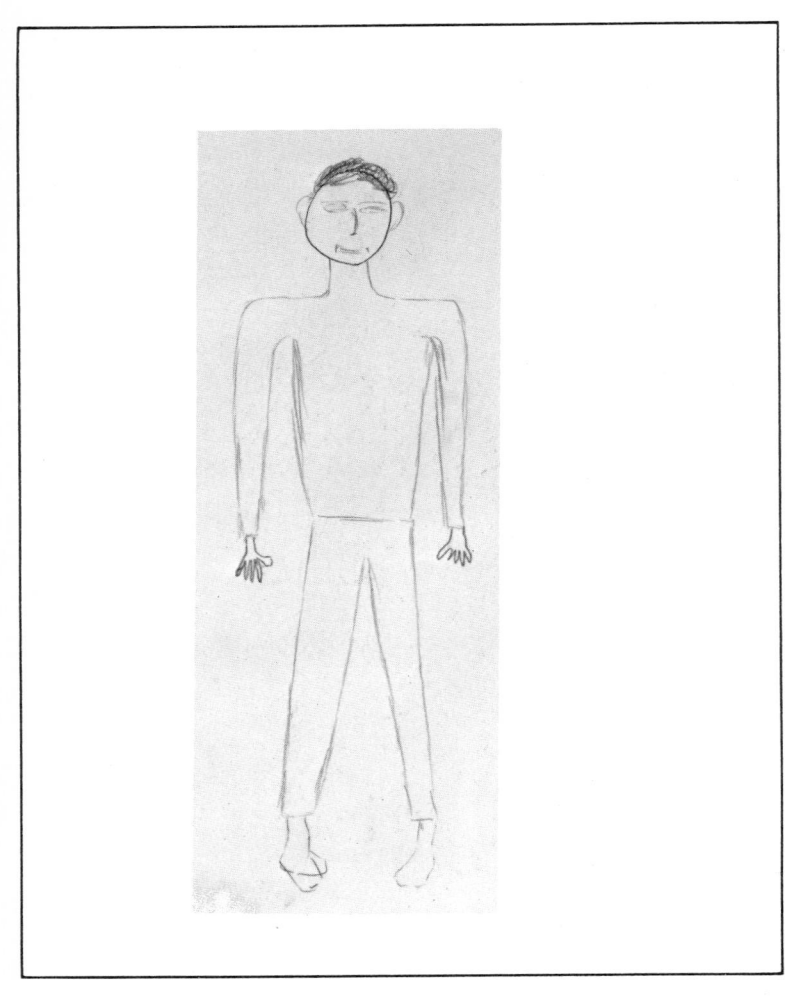

FIGURE-DRAWING CHARACTERISTICS

Structural	Male Female Both		Structural	Male	Female	Structural and Graphic	Male	Female Both		Graphic, Global and Height	Male	Female	Body Proportions	Male	Female
Type	0		Omission of Appendages	0	0	Upper and Lower Halves	3	3		Hair Shading	3	3	Head	08	09
Sex Sequence	0		Position of Both Arms	0	0	Four Quarters	4	4		Nudity and Transparency	7	7	Neck	10	07
Posture	1	1	Position of Right Arm	0	0	Relative Size	2			Form	3	3	Shoulders	09	09
Perspective	0	0	Position of Left Arm	0	0	Constant Line Pressure	0	0		Detailing	5	3	Right Arm	06	06
Vertical Midline	0	0	Position of Legs	6	6	Variable Line Pressure	3	1		Identity and Sex	3	1	Left Arm	06	06
Bilateral Symmetry	3	3	Relation of Long Axes	1	1	Line Continuity	0	0		Sophistication	3	3	Chest	06	06
Horizontal Midline	4	4	Right and Left Halves	1	1	Body Shading	0	1		Height	07	08	Girth	06	05

GENERAL CHARACTERISTICS OF SUBJECT

IDENTIFICATION
No. B54
Sex M
Marital status S
Age 23 yrs. at
psychological tests

PARENTAL HISTORY				
Father				
C	H	S	D	O
-	-	-	-	-
Mother				
C	H	S	D	O
-	-	-	-	-

PHYSIOLOGICAL AND METABOLIC DATA

	Admission	Initial	Control	Cold pressor change	Exercise change	Smoking change
Systolic pressure	120	116	108	+16	+40	
Diastolic pressure	70	54	58	+26	-36	
Heart rate	60	58	43	+02	+23	

Age 22 yrs.	Height	76 in.	Ponderal index	13.64	
	Weight	173 lbs.	Cholesterol	186	mg. per 100 ml.
	Overweight	-05 %	Vital capacity		liters

HABIT SURVEY

Smoking habits: nonsmoker

Age begun   yrs.   Inhalation:

Habits of nervous tension: 1, 3, 4, 5, 8, 11, 12, 14, 19, 21, 22

STRONG VOCATIONAL INTEREST TEST

Occupation	Artist	Psychologist	Architect	Physician	Osteopath	Dentist	Veterinarian	Mathematician	Physicist	Engineer	Chemist	Production Manager
Standard Score	14	30	15	24	19	13	15	22	11	24	19	41

Occupation	Farmer	Aviator	Carpenter	Printer	Math.-Sci. Teacher	Ind. Arts Teacher	Voc. Agric. Teacher	Policeman	Forest Serv. Man	Y.M.C.A. Phys. Dir.	Personnel Director	Public Administrator
Standard Score	30	34	11	25	33	15	40	38	28	34	49	44

Occupation	Y.M.C.A. Secretary	Soc. Sci. H.S. Teacher	City Sch. Sup't.	Social Worker	Minister	Musician Performer	C.P.A.	Senior C.P.A.	Accountant	Office Man	Purchasing Agent	Banker
Standard Score	35	43	43	38	61	38	32	38	32	38	32	39

Occupation	Mortician	Pharmacist	Sales Manager	Real Est. Manager	Life Ins. Salesman	Advertising Man	Lawyer	Author-Journalist	President Mfg. Co.	Interest Maturity	Occupational Level	Masculinity-Femininity
Standard Score	24	25	41	38	36	36	39	27	26	54	56	52

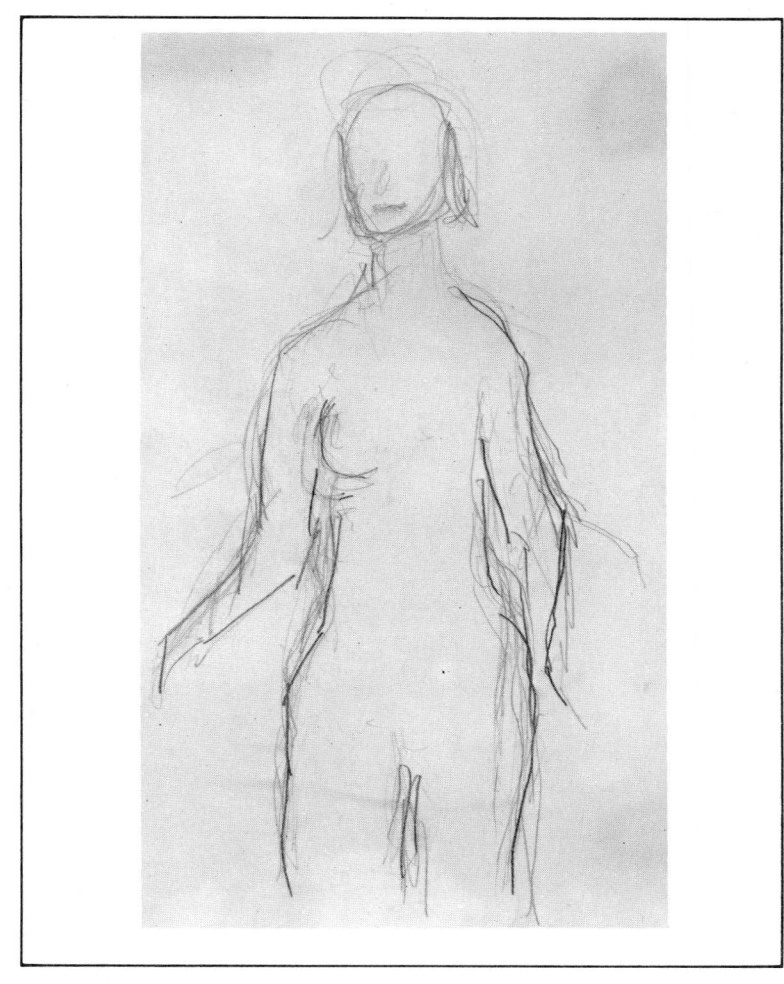

FIGURE-DRAWING CHARACTERISTICS

Structural	Male Female Both	Structural	Male	Female	Structural and Graphic	Male Female Both		Graphic, Global and Height	Male	Female	Body Proportions	Male	Female
Type	0	Omission of Appendages	4	1	Upper and Lower Halves	0	7	Hair Shading	0	0	Head	13	12
Sex Sequence	2	Position of Both Arms	0	6	Four Quarters	4	4	Nudity and Transparency	9	0	Neck	16	16
Posture	0 0	Position of Right Arm	5	4	Relative Size	5		Form	1	1	Shoulders	12	10
Perspective	0 0	Position of Left Arm	5	8	Constant Line Pressure	0	0	Detailing	5	5	Right Arm	10	10
Vertical Midline	0 0	Position of Legs	0	0	Variable Line Pressure	4	4	Identity and Sex	3	3	Left Arm		
Bilateral Symmetry	2 1	Relation of Long Axes	1	1	Line Continuity	1	1	Sophistication	3	3	Chest	08	08
Horizontal Midline	0 0	Right and Left Halves	1	1	Body Shading	0	0	Height			Girth	12	08

GENERAL CHARACTERISTICS OF SUBJECT

IDENTIFICATION
No. B58
Sex M
Marital status S
Age 22 yrs. at
psychological tests

PARENTAL HISTORY
Father
C   H   S   D   O
-   -   -   -   -
Mother
C   H   S   D   O
-   -   -   -   -

PHYSIOLOGICAL AND METABOLIC DATA

	Admission	Initial	Control	Cold pressor change	Exercise change	Smoking change
Systolic pressure	120	120	110	+16	+34	+06
Diastolic pressure	80	68	64	+12	-20	+04
Heart rate	70	66	62	+14	+11	+02

Age 22 yrs.	Height 70 in.	Ponderal index 13.67
	Weight 134 lbs.	Cholesterol 212 mg. per 100 ml.
	Overweight -13 %	Vital capacity 4.4 liters

HABIT SURVEY

Smoking habits: nonsmoker

Age begun   yrs.   Inhalation:

Habits of nervous tension: 1, 2, 3, 5, 6, 7, 9, 16, 25

STRONG VOCATIONAL INTEREST TEST

Occupation	Artist	Psychologist	Architect	Physician	Osteopath	Dentist	Veterinarian	Mathematician	Physicist	Engineer	Chemist	Production Manager
Standard Score	47	51	49	43	33	33	-07	45	39	35	46	26

Occupation	Farmer	Aviator	Carpenter	Printer	Math.-Sci. Teacher	Ind. Arts Teacher	Voc. Agric. Teacher	Policeman	Forest Serv. Man	Y.M.C.A. Phys. Dir.	Personnel Director	Public Administrator
Standard Score	16	24	16	31	28	05	00	13	10	21	29	39

Occupation	Y.M.C.A. Secretary	Soc. Sci. H.S. Teacher	City Sch. Sup't.	Social Worker	Minister	Musician Performer	C.P.A.	Senior C.P.A.	Accountant	Office Man	Purchasing Agent	Banker
Standard Score	19	25	30	36	61	57	40	29	25	25	16	21

Occupation	Mortician	Pharmacist	Sales Manager	Real Est. Manager	Life Ins. Salesman	Advertising Man	Lawyer	Author-Journalist	President Mfg. Co.	Interest Maturity	Occupational Level	Masculinity-Femininity
Standard Score	18	20	30	33	30	47	48	51	37	52	62	25

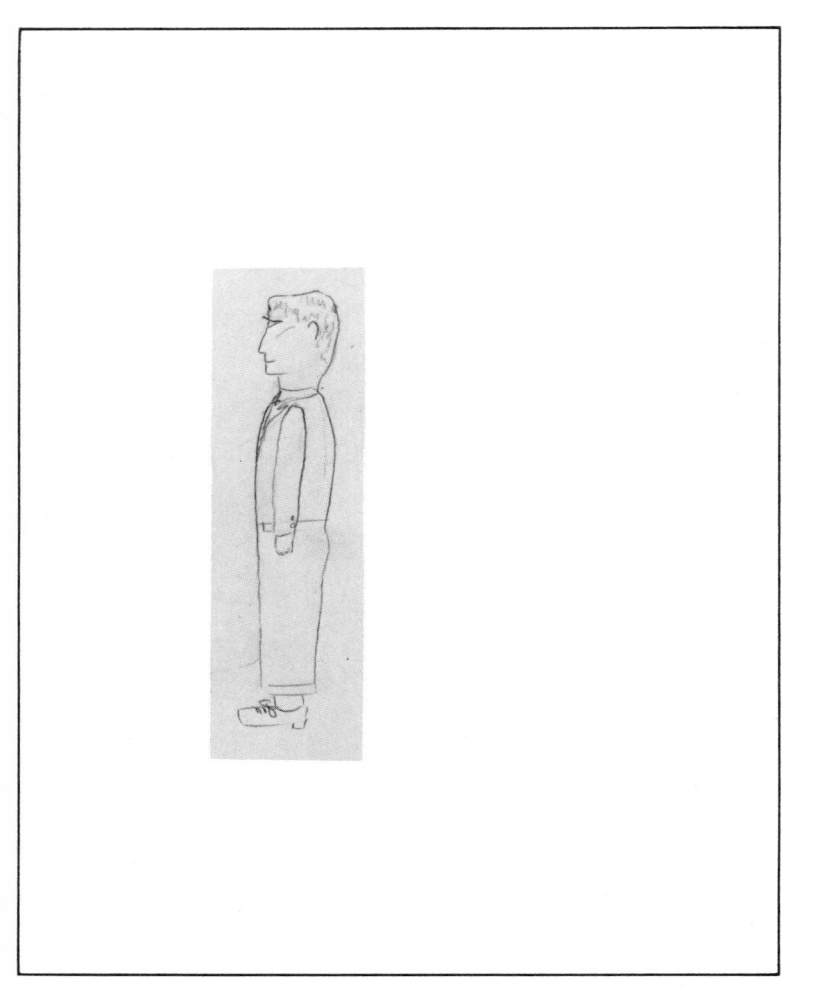

FIGURE-DRAWING CHARACTERISTICS

Structural	Male Female Both	Structural	Male	Female	Structural and Graphic	Male Female Both		Graphic, Global and Height	Male	Female	Body Proportions	Male	Female
Type	0	Omission of Appendages	0	0	Upper and Lower Halves	0	3	Hair Shading	1	5	Head	06	04
Sex Sequence	0	Position of Both Arms	4	0	Four Quarters	4	4	Nudity and Transparency	7	7	Neck	05	04
Posture	1 1	Position of Right Arm	7	2	Relative Size	0		Form	3	1	Shoulders		04
Perspective	2 0	Position of Left Arm	0	2	Constant Line Pressure	0	0	Detailing	3	3	Right Arm		02
Vertical Midline	7 3	Position of Legs	1	4	Variable Line Pressure	4	3	Identity and Sex	1	1	Left Arm	04	02
Bilateral Symmetry	0 3	Relation of Long Axes	1	1	Line Continuity	4	4	Sophistication	3	3	Chest	05	04
Horizontal Midline	4 4	Right and Left Halves	2	1	Body Shading	0	0	Height	04	04	Girth	05	05

GENERAL CHARACTERISTICS OF SUBJECT

IDENTIFICATION
No. B69
Sex M
Marital status S
Age 21 yrs. at
psychological tests

PARENTAL HISTORY
Father
C   H   S   D   O
-   -   -   -   -
Mother
C   H   S   D   O
-   -   -   -   -

PHYSIOLOGICAL AND METABOLIC DATA

	Admission	Initial	Control	Cold pressor change	Exercise change	Smoking change
Systolic pressure	122	120	118	+32	+40	+12
Diastolic pressure	80	70	68	+16	-04	+06
Heart rate	80	84	70	+34	+41	+16

Age 21 yrs.   Height 73 in.   Weight 157 lbs.   Overweight -06 %   Ponderal index 13.54   Cholesterol 193 mg. per 100 ml.   Vital capacity 5.7 liters

HABIT SURVEY
Smoking habits: pipe smoker
Age begun 17 yrs.   Inhalation: no
Habits of nervous tension: 5, 6, 11, 25

STRONG VOCATIONAL INTEREST TEST

Occupation	Artist	Psychologist	Architect	Physician	Osteopath	Dentist	Veterinarian	Mathematician	Physicist	Engineer	Chemist	Production Manager
Standard Score	28	41	31	46	29	32	19	26	16	21	29	23

Occupation	Farmer	Aviator	Carpenter	Printer	Math.-Sci. Teacher	Ind. Arts Teacher	Voc. Agric. Teacher	Policeman	Forest Serv. Man	Y.M.C.A. Phys. Dir.	Personnel Director	Public Administrator
Standard Score	34	29	14	40	40	13	24	27	24	31	32	43

Occupation	Y.M.C.A. Secretary	Soc. Sci. H.S. Teacher	City Sch. Sup't.	Social Worker	Minister	Musician Performer	C.P.A.	Senior C.P.A.	Accountant	Office Man	Purchasing Agent	Banker
Standard Score	32	42	35	42	61	46	27	39	22	35	21	29

Occupation	Mortician	Pharmacist	Sales Manager	Real Est. Manager	Life Ins. Salesman	Advertising Man	Lawyer	Author- Journalist	President Mfg. Co.	Interest Maturity	Occupational Level	Masculinity- Femininity
Standard Score	23	32	25	30	24	38	38	37	23	57	54	41

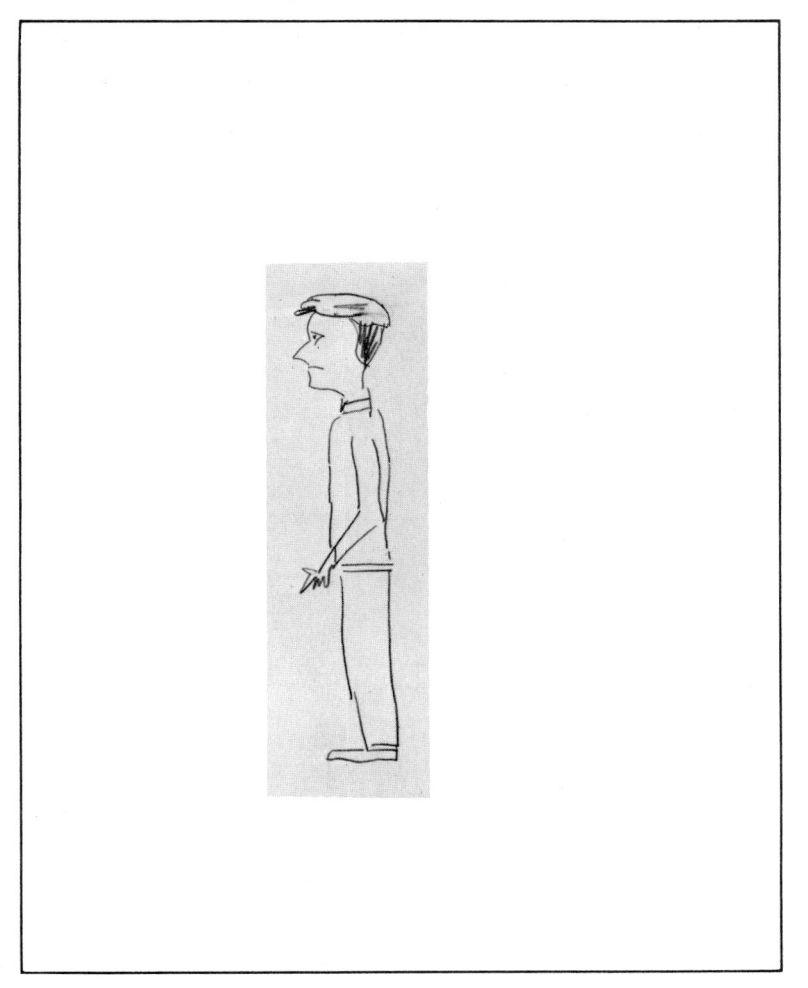

FIGURE-DRAWING CHARACTERISTICS

Structural	Male Female Both		Structural	Male	Female	Structural and Graphic	Male Female Both		Graphic, Global and Height	Male	Female	Body Proportions	Male	Female
Type	0		Omission of Appendages	0	0	Upper and Lower Halves	3	3	Hair Shading	1	3	Head	07	09
Sex Sequence	0		Position of Both Arms	4	4	Four Quarters	4	4	Nudity and Transparency	7	3	Neck	05	07
Posture	1	1	Position of Right Arm	7	7	Relative Size	4		Form	1	3	Shoulders		
Perspective	2	2	Position of Left Arm	4	4	Constant Line Pressure	5	5	Detailing	3	3	Right Arm		
Vertical Midline	4	4	Position of Legs	1	1	Variable Line Pressure	0	0	Identity and Sex	1	1	Left Arm	05	06
Bilateral Symmetry	0	0	Relation of Long Axes	1	1	Line Continuity	3	4	Sophistication	3	3	Chest	04	06
Horizontal Midline	6	4	Right and Left Halves	2	1	Body Shading	0	4	Height	05	06	Girth	04	04

GENERAL CHARACTERISTICS OF SUBJECT

IDENTIFICATION
No. B73
Sex M
Marital status M
Age 26 yrs. at
psychological tests

PARENTAL HISTORY				
Father				
C	H	S	D	O
-	-	-	-	-
Mother				
C	H	S	D	O
-	-	-	-	-

PHYSIOLOGICAL AND METABOLIC DATA

	Admission	Initial	Control	Cold pressor change	Exercise change	Smoking change
Systolic pressure	125	124	120	+14	+36	+10
Diastolic pressure	85	78	78	+10	-32	+24
Heart rate	68	72	70	+28	+30	+03

Age 26 yrs.	Height 70 in.	Ponderal index 12.80
	Weight 164 lbs.	Cholesterol 240 mg. per 100 ml.
	Overweight +04 %	Vital capacity 4.8 liters

HABIT SURVEY

Smoking habits: light cigarette smoker

Age begun 17 yrs.   Inhalation: yes

Habits of nervous tension: 4, 5, 6, 18, 24

STRONG VOCATIONAL INTEREST TEST

Occupation	Artist	Psychologist	Architect	Physician	Osteopath	Dentist	Veterinarian	Mathematician	Physicist	Engineer	Chemist	Production Manager
Standard Score	37	47	42	56	44	44	27	45	47	59	59	35

Occupation	Farmer	Aviator	Carpenter	Printer	Math.-Sci. Teacher	Ind. Arts Teacher	Voc. Agric. Teacher	Policeman	Forest Serv. Man	Y.M.C.A. Phys. Dir.	Personnel Director	Public Administrator
Standard Score	47	53	32	32	42	35	41	29	39	28	34	46

Occupation	Y.M.C.A. Secretary	Soc. Sci. H.S. Teacher	City Sch. Sup't.	Social Worker	Minister	Musician Performer	C.P.A.	Senior C.P.A.	Accountant	Office Man	Purchasing Agent	Banker
Standard Score	17	23	23	31	61	41	21	34	15	16	18	10

Occupation	Mortician	Pharmacist	Sales Manager	Real Est. Manager	Life Ins. Salesman	Advertising Man	Lawyer	Author-Journalist	President Mfg. Co.	Interest Maturity	Occupational Level	Masculinity-Femininity
Standard Score	11	26	16	22	17	30	31	38	32	50	54	54

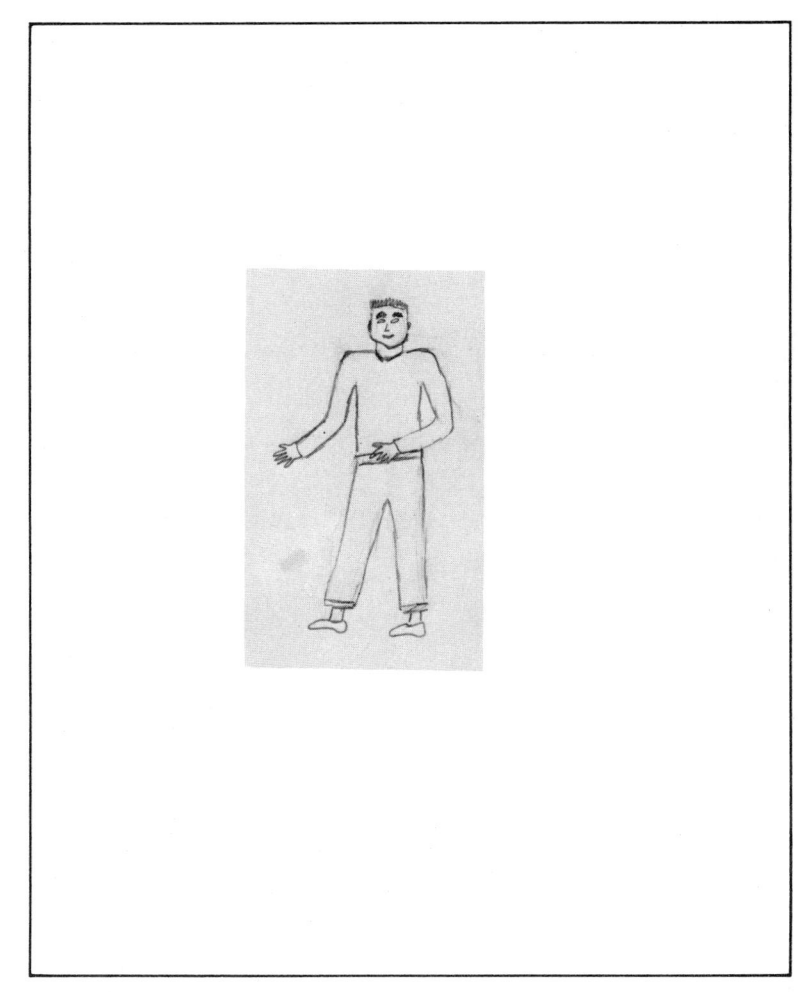

FIGURE-DRAWING CHARACTERISTICS

Structural	Male	Female	Structural	Male	Female	Structural and Graphic	Male	Female	Graphic, Global and Height	Male	Female	Body Proportions	Male	Female
	Both						Both							
Type	0		Omission of Appendages	0	0	Upper and Lower Halves	1	1	Hair Shading	3	5	Head	04	03
Sex Sequence	1		Position of Both Arms	1	0	Four Quarters	4	4	Nudity and Transparency	7	7	Neck	02	03
Posture	1	1	Position of Right Arm	2	2	Relative Size	0		Form	1	3	Shoulders	04	03
Perspective	0	0	Position of Left Arm	5	2	Constant Line Pressure	0	0	Detailing	3	3	Right Arm	02	02
Vertical Midline	0	0	Position of Legs	5	5	Variable Line Pressure	4	3	Identity and Sex	1	1	Left Arm	02	02
Bilateral Symmetry	3	3	Relation of Long Axes	1	1	Line Continuity	2	2	Sophistication	3	3	Chest	03	02
Horizontal Midline	4	4	Right and Left Halves	1	1	Body Shading	0	4	Height	03	03	Girth	04	01

GENERAL CHARACTERISTICS OF SUBJECT

IDENTIFICATION

No. B48
Sex F
Marital status S
Age 23 yrs. at psychological tests

PARENTAL HISTORY

Father
C   H   S   D   O
-   -   -   -   -

Mother
C   H   S   D   O
-   -   -   -   -

PHYSIOLOGICAL AND METABOLIC DATA

	Admission	Initial	Control	Cold pressor change	Exercise change	Smoking change
Systolic pressure	100	117	106	+16	+30	
Diastolic pressure	60	56	60	+18	-08	
Heart rate	78	84	87	+18	+17	

Age 23 yrs.   Height 60 in.   Ponderal index 12.45
Weight 112 lbs.   Cholesterol 186 mg. per 100 ml.
Overweight -03 %   Vital capacity liters

HABIT SURVEY

Smoking habits: nonsmoker
Age begun yrs.   Inhalation:
Habits of nervous tension: 1, 3, 4, 5, 6, 8, 11, 12, 14, 16, 19, 22, 23

STRONG VOCATIONAL INTEREST TEST

Occupation	Artist	Psychologist	Architect	Physician	Osteopath	Dentist	Veterinarian	Mathematician	Physicist	Engineer	Chemist	Production Manager
Standard Score	49	35	44	51	41	38	18	35	27	26	31	16

Occupation	Farmer	Aviator	Carpenter	Printer	Math.-Sci. Teacher	Ind. Arts Teacher	Voc. Agric. Teacher	Policeman	Forest Serv. Man	Y.M.C.A. Phys. Dir.	Personnel Director	Public Administrator
Standard Score	21	14	10	25	19	-05	05	15	16	22	08	30

Occupation	Y.M.C.A. Secretary	Soc. Sci. H.S. Teacher	City Sch. Sup't.	Social Worker	Minister	Musician Performer	C.P.A.	Senior C.P.A.	Accountant	Office Man	Purchasing Agent	Banker
Standard Score	16	22	27	30	61	49	40	17	19	21	11	26

Occupation	Mortician	Pharmacist	Sales Manager	Real Est. Manager	Life Ins. Salesman	Advertising Man	Lawyer	Author-Journalist	President Mfg. Co.	Interest Maturity	Occupational Level	Masculinity-Femininity
Standard Score	25	30	25	38	31	43	50	52	38	48	65	16

Plate 480   **DRAWINGS AT AN INTERMEDIATE LEVEL OF SOPHISTICATION**   523

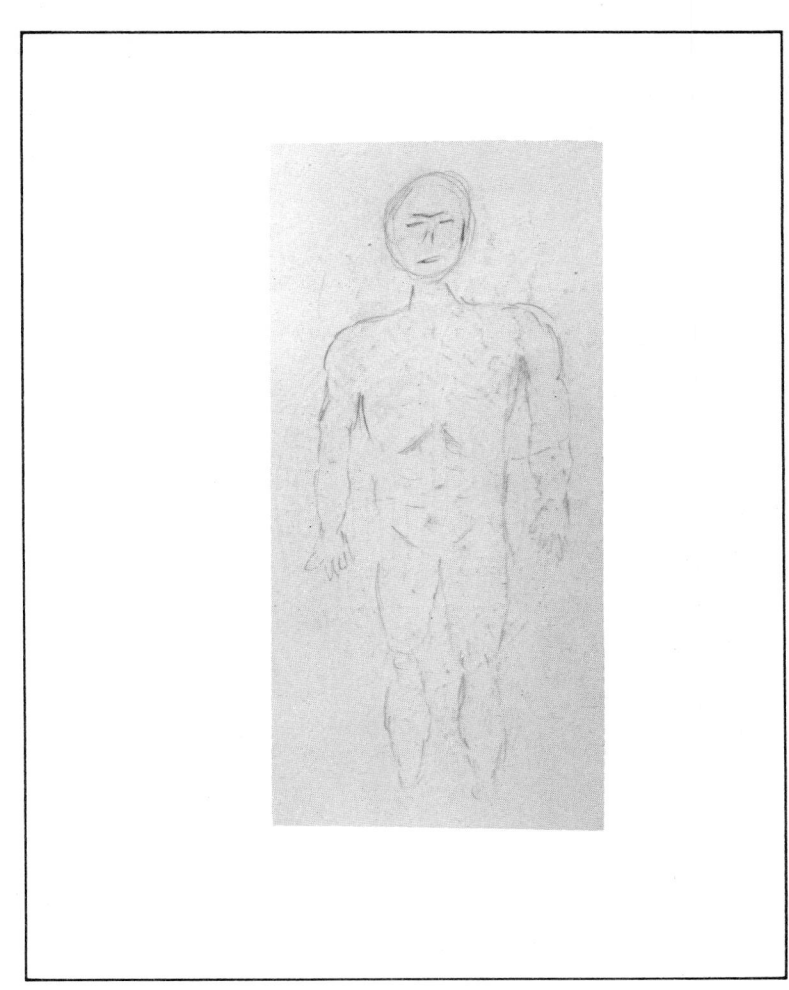

FIGURE-DRAWING CHARACTERISTICS

Structural	Male Female Both		Structural	Male	Female	Structural and Graphic	Male Female Both		Graphic, Global and Height	Male	Female	Body Proportions	Male	Female
Type	0		Omission of Appendages	8	0	Upper and Lower Halves	0	0	Hair Shading	7	3	Head	09	07
Sex Sequence	1		Position of Both Arms	0	1	Four Quarters	4	4	Nudity and Transparency	0	7	Neck	08	04
Posture	0	1	Position of Right Arm	0	5	Relative Size	0		Form	3	3	Shoulders	09	06
Perspective	0	0	Position of Left Arm	0	4	Constant Line Pressure	1	0	Detailing	5	5	Right Arm	06	04
Vertical Midline	0	0	Position of Legs	4	4	Variable Line Pressure	0	4	Identity and Sex	1	1	Left Arm	06	04
Bilateral Symmetry	3	3	Relation of Long Axes	1	1	Line Continuity	0	0	Sophistication	3	3	Chest	07	05
Horizontal Midline	0	2	Right and Left Halves	3	1	Body Shading	3	1	Height		06	Girth	08	07

GENERAL CHARACTERISTICS OF SUBJECT

IDENTIFICATION

No. C36
Sex M
Marital status S
Age 22 yrs. at
psychological tests

PARENTAL HISTORY

Father
C H S D O
–   –   –   –   –
Mother
C H S D O
–   –   –   –   –

PHYSIOLOGICAL AND METABOLIC DATA

	Admission	Initial	Control	Cold pressor change	Exercise change	Smoking change
Systolic pressure	118	130	130	+10	+30	+04
Diastolic pressure	70	70	70	00	–05	+02
Heart rate	64	72	63	+08	+40	+06

Age 23 yrs.
Height 71 in.
Weight 165 lbs.
Overweight +04 %
Ponderal index 12.96
Cholesterol 236 mg. per 100 ml.
Vital capacity 5.8 liters

HABIT SURVEY

Smoking habits: occasional smoker
Age begun   yrs.   Inhalation: no
Habits of nervous tension: 4, 5, 6, 9, 10, 25

STRONG VOCATIONAL INTEREST TEST

Occupation	Artist	Psychologist	Architect	Physician	Osteopath	Dentist	Veterinarian	Mathematician	Physicist	Engineer	Chemist	Production Manager
Standard Score	35	28	36	53	52	40	37	25	26	38	36	28

Occupation	Farmer	Aviator	Carpenter	Printer	Math.-Sci. Teacher	Ind. Arts Teacher	Voc. Agric. Teacher	Policeman	Forest Serv. Man	Y.M.C.A. Phys. Dir.	Personnel Director	Public Administrator
Standard Score	45	47	28	28	30	24	29	35	36	35	21	36

Occupation	Y.M.C.A. Secretary	Soc. Sci. H.S. Teacher	City Sch. Sup't.	Social Worker	Minister	Musician Performer	C.P.A.	Senior C.P.A.	Accountant	Office Man	Purchasing Agent	Banker
Standard Score	14	25	13	26	62	38	20	32	08	19	18	15

Occupation	Mortician	Pharmacist	Sales Manager	Real Est. Manager	Life Ins. Salesman	Advertising Man	Lawyer	Author-Journalist	President Mfg. Co.	Interest Maturity	Occupational Level	Masculinity-Femininity
Standard Score	18	34	28	36	28	31	36	36	36	49	57	51

FIGURE-DRAWING CHARACTERISTICS

Structural	Male	Female	Structural	Male	Female	Structural and Graphic	Male	Female	Graphic, Global and Height	Male	Female	Body Proportions	Male	Female
	Both						Both							
Type	0		Omission of Appendages	0	0	Upper and Lower Halves	1	1	Hair Shading	7	1	Head	05	04
Sex Sequence	0		Position of Both Arms	1	1	Four Quarters	4	4	Nudity and Transparency	3	9	Neck	06	06
Posture	1	1	Position of Right Arm	5	5	Relative Size	2		Form	3	3	Shoulders	06	05
Perspective	5	5	Position of Left Arm	3	3	Constant Line Pressure	0	0	Detailing	3	3	Right Arm	04	04
Vertical Midline	1	0	Position of Legs	5	5	Variable Line Pressure	1	1	Identity and Sex	1	1	Left Arm	05	04
Bilateral Symmetry	3	3	Relation of Long Axes	1	1	Line Continuity	0	0	Sophistication	3	3	Chest	04	03
Horizontal Midline	0	0	Right and Left Halves	1	1	Body Shading	3	1	Height	05	05	Girth	04	03

GENERAL CHARACTERISTICS OF SUBJECT

IDENTIFICATION
No. C84
Sex M
Marital status S
Age 23 yrs. at
psychological tests

PARENTAL HISTORY
Father
C   H   S   D   O
-    -   -   -   -
Mother
C   H   S   D   O
-    -   -   -   -

PHYSIOLOGICAL AND METABOLIC DATA

	Admission	Initial	Control	Cold pressor change	Exercise change	Smoking change
Systolic pressure	120	130	110	+24	+44	+08
Diastolic pressure	80	70	70	+26	00	+05
Heart rate	80	92	83	+30	+26	+02

Age 22 yrs.	Height 70 in.	Ponderal index 12.84
	Weight 162 lbs.	Cholesterol 177 mg. per 100 ml.
	Overweight +05 %	Vital capacity 4.7 liters

HABIT SURVEY

Smoking habits: nonsmoker

Age begun   yrs.   Inhalation:

Habits of nervous tension: 4, 5, 9, 11, 16, 23

Plate 482   **DRAWINGS AT AN INTERMEDIATE LEVEL OF SOPHISTICATION**   525

FIGURE-DRAWING CHARACTERISTICS

Structural	Male Female Both		Structural	Male	Female	Structural and Graphic	Male Female Both		Graphic, Global and Height	Male	Female	Body Proportions	Male	Female
Type	0		Omission of Appendages	0	0	Upper and Lower Halves	1	1	Hair Shading	0	3	Head	05	05
Sex Sequence	0		Position of Both Arms	1	0	Four Quarters	4	4	Nudity and Transparency	7	7	Neck	04	04
Posture	1	1	Position of Right Arm	0	2	Relative Size	0		Form	3	3	Shoulders	07	03
Perspective	0	0	Position of Left Arm	1	2	Constant Line Pressure	3	0	Detailing	1	1	Right Arm	04	02
Vertical Midline	3	0	Position of Legs	4	6	Variable Line Pressure	0	5	Identity and Sex	1	1	Left Arm	04	02
Bilateral Symmetry	3	5	Relation of Long Axes	1	1	Line Continuity	4	4	Sophistication	3	3	Chest	05	02
Horizontal Midline	6	4	Right and Left Halves	2	3	Body Shading	2	7	Height	05	03	Girth	07	02

GENERAL CHARACTERISTICS OF SUBJECT

IDENTIFICATION
No. D55
Sex M
Marital status S
Age 22 yrs. at
psychological tests

PARENTAL HISTORY
Father
C   H   S   D   O
-    -   -   -   -
Mother
C   H   S   D   O
-    -   -   -   -

PHYSIOLOGICAL AND METABOLIC DATA

	Admission	Initial	Control	Cold pressor change	Exercise change	Smoking change
Systolic pressure	110	100	108	+01	+22	-04
Diastolic pressure	70	60	70	-02	-08	00
Heart rate	72	68	67	00	+12	+05

Age 22 yrs.	Height 70 in.	Ponderal index 13.75	
	Weight 132 lbs.	Cholesterol 229 mg. per 100 ml.	
	Overweight -14 %	Vital capacity liters	

HABIT SURVEY

Smoking habits: nonsmoker

Age begun   yrs.   Inhalation:

Habits of nervous tension: 4, 5, 6, 16, 25

STRONG VOCATIONAL INTEREST TEST

Occupation	Artist	Psychologist	Architect	Physician	Osteopath	Dentist	Veterinarian	Mathematician	Physicist	Engineer	Chemist	Production Manager
Standard Score	30	29	30	53	44	41	40	19	15	31	31	22

Occupation	Farmer	Aviator	Carpenter	Printer	Math.-Sci. Teacher	Ind. Arts Teacher	Voc. Agric. Teacher	Policeman	Forest Serv. Man	Y.M.C.A. Phys. Dir.	Personnel Director	Public Administrator
Standard Score	46	47	29	43	36	22	36	37	35	31	33	36

Occupation	Y.M.C.A. Secretary	Soc. Sci. H.S. Teacher	City Sch. Sup't.	Social Worker	Minister	Musician Performer	C.P.A.	Senior C.P.A.	Accountant	Office Man	Purchasing Agent	Banker
Standard Score	24	28	14	31	63	37	24	41	19	31	22	27

Occupation	Mortician	Pharmacist	Sales Manager	Real Est. Manager	Life Ins. Salesman	Advertising Man	Lawyer	Author-Journalist	President Mfg. Co.	Interest Maturity	Occupational Level	Masculinity-Femininity
Standard Score	30	32	22	33	27	31	33	35	23	51	46	58

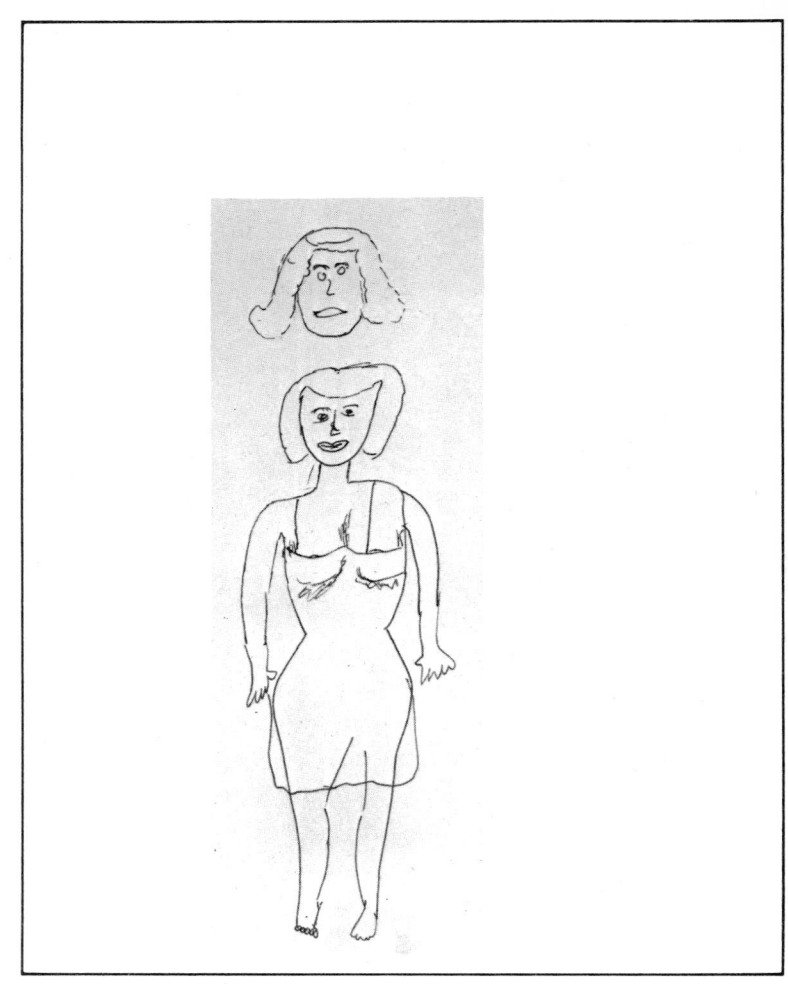

FIGURE-DRAWING CHARACTERISTICS

Structural	Male Female Both	Structural	Male	Female	Structural and Graphic	Male Female Both	Graphic, Global and Height	Male	Female	Body Proportions	Male	Female
Type	0	Omission of Appendages	0	0	Upper and Lower Halves	0	3	Hair Shading	0	5	Head	11	07
Sex Sequence	0	Position of Both Arms	0	0	Four Quarters	4	4	Nudity and Transparency	7	6	Neck	16	06
Posture	1	1	Position of Right Arm	0	0	Relative Size	0	Form	3	3	Shoulders	08	07
Perspective	0	0	Position of Left Arm	0	0	Constant Line Pressure	0	3	Detailing	1	3	Right Arm	06	05
Vertical Midline	3	0	Position of Legs	4	4	Variable Line Pressure	1	0	Identity and Sex	1	1	Left Arm	06	04
Bilateral Symmetry	1	2	Relation of Long Axes	1	1	Line Continuity	4	4	Sophistication	3	3	Chest	06	06
Horizontal Midline	4	0	Right and Left Halves	1	1	Body Shading	0	1	Height	08	06	Girth	08	05

GENERAL CHARACTERISTICS OF SUBJECT

IDENTIFICATION
No. E21
Sex M
Marital status S
Age 22 yrs. at
psychological tests

PARENTAL HISTORY
Father
C H S D O
- - - - -
Mother
C H S D O
- - - - -

PHYSIOLOGICAL AND METABOLIC DATA

	Admission	Initial	Control	Cold pressor change	Exercise change	Smoking change
Systolic pressure	120	117	110	+18	+32	+07
Diastolic pressure	80	66	70	+28	-12	+04
Heart rate	72	76	67	00	+33	+15

Age 22 yrs.	Height 70 in.	Ponderal index 12.39
	Weight 180 lbs.	Cholesterol 200 mg. per 100 ml.
	Overweight +17 %	Vital capacity 4.5 liters

HABIT SURVEY

Smoking habits: mixed smoker

Age begun 18 yrs.   Inhalation: yes

Habits of nervous tension: 2, 5, 6, 9

STRONG VOCATIONAL INTEREST TEST

Occupation	Artist	Psychologist	Architect	Physician	Osteopath	Dentist	Veterinarian	Mathematician	Physicist	Engineer	Chemist	Production Manager
Standard Score	34	38	31	42	46	37	07	25	19	31	41	30

Occupation	Farmer	Aviator	Carpenter	Printer	Math.-Sci. Teacher	Ind. Arts Teacher	Voc. Agric. Teacher	Policeman	Forest Serv. Man	Y.M.C.A. Phys. Dir.	Personnel Director	Public Administrator
Standard Score	27	35	07	33	23	-07	02	24	20	18	36	46

Occupation	Y.M.C.A. Secretary	Soc. Sci. H.S. Teacher	City Sch. Sup't.	Social Worker	Minister	Musician Performer	C.P.A.	Senior C.P.A.	Accountant	Office Man	Purchasing Agent	Banker
Standard Score	18	32	19	29	64	34	33	29	21	30	17	20

Occupation	Mortician	Pharmacist	Sales Manager	Real Est. Manager	Life Ins. Salesman	Advertising Man	Lawyer	Author-Journalist	President Mfg. Co.	Interest Maturity	Occupational Level	Masculinity-Femininity
Standard Score	18	11	20	36	27	41	48	46	27	51	62	41

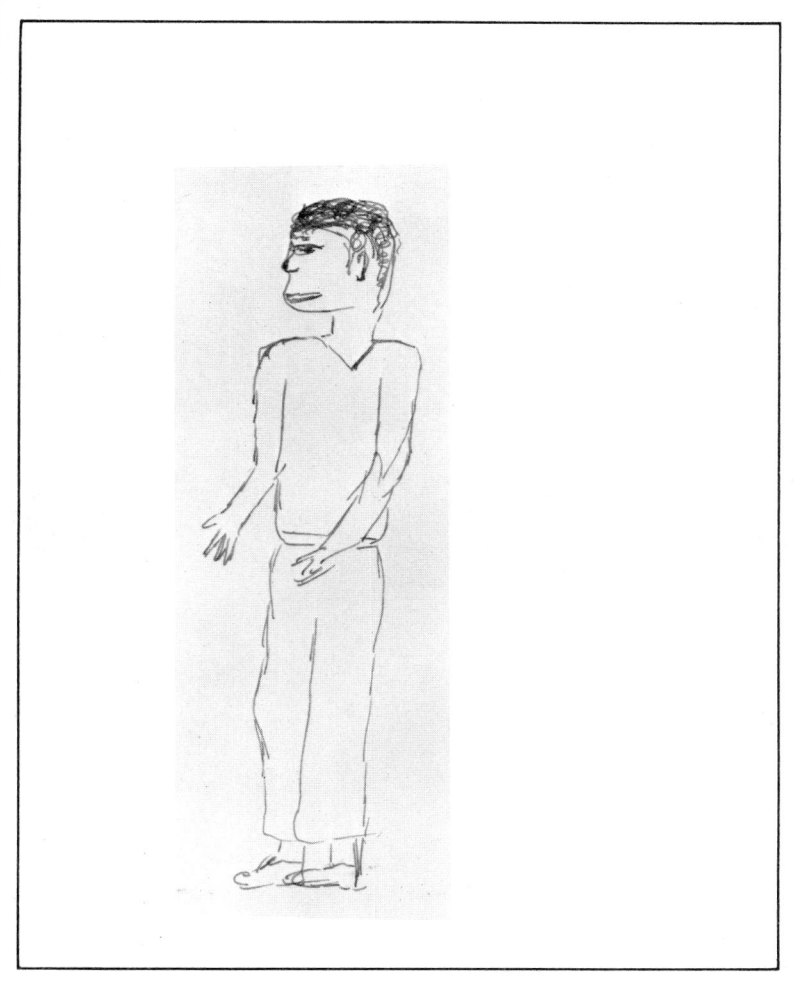

FIGURE-DRAWING CHARACTERISTICS

Structural	Male Female Both	Structural	Male	Female	Structural and Graphic	Male Female Both		Graphic, Global and Height	Male	Female	Body Proportions	Male	Female
Type	0	Omission of Appendages	0	7	Upper and Lower Halves	3	3	Hair Shading	3	3	Head	09	07
Sex Sequence	0	Position of Both Arms	1	0	Four Quarters	4	4	Nudity and Transparency	7	7	Neck	10	10
Posture	1 1	Position of Right Arm	4	5	Relative Size	0		Form	3	3	Shoulders		05
Perspective	6 5	Position of Left Arm	5	5	Constant Line Pressure	3	3	Detailing	3	3	Right Arm	04	05
Vertical Midline	4 0	Position of Legs	1	2	Variable Line Pressure	0	0	Identity and Sex	1	1	Left Arm	06	04
Bilateral Symmetry	0 3	Relation of Long Axes	1	1	Line Continuity	0	0	Sophistication	3	3	Chest		04
Horizontal Midline	4 0	Right and Left Halves	1	1	Body Shading	0	5	Height	07	06	Girth		

GENERAL CHARACTERISTICS OF SUBJECT

IDENTIFICATION

No. E73

Sex M

Marital status S

Age 22 yrs. at psychological tests

PARENTAL HISTORY

Father

C   H   S   D   O

–   –   –   –   –

Mother

C   H   S   D   O

–   –   –   –   –

PHYSIOLOGICAL AND METABOLIC DATA

	Admission	Initial	Control	Cold pressor change	Exercise change	Smoking change
Systolic pressure	100	120	116	+06	+14	00
Diastolic pressure	50	72	80	+02	–20	00
Heart rate	76	80	82	+12	+19	+15

Age 22 yrs.

Height 73 in.   Ponderal index 13.85

Weight 146 lbs.   Cholesterol 230 mg. per 100 ml.

Overweight –13 %   Vital capacity 4.9 liters

HABIT SURVEY

Smoking habits: heavy cigarette smoker

Age begun 18 yrs.   Inhalation: yes

Habits of nervous tension:

STRONG VOCATIONAL INTEREST TEST

Occupation	Artist	Psychologist	Architect	Physician	Osteopath	Dentist	Veterinarian	Mathematician	Physicist	Engineer	Chemist	Production Manager
Standard Score	40	53	44	57	49	46	08	43	45	48	58	29

Occupation	Farmer	Aviator	Carpenter	Printer	Math.-Sci. Teacher	Ind. Arts Teacher	Voc. Agric. Teacher	Policeman	Forest Serv. Man	Y.M.C.A. Phys. Dir.	Personnel Director	Public Administrator
Standard Score	32	42	28	51	46	19	11	26	16	23	36	39

Occupation	Y.M.C.A. Secretary	Soc. Sci. H.S. Teacher	City Sch. Sup't.	Social Worker	Minister	Musician Performer	C.P.A.	Senior C.P.A.	Accountant	Office Man	Purchasing Agent	Banker
Standard Score	16	26	22	36	64	51	42	41	31	33	13	13

Occupation	Mortician	Pharmacist	Sales Manager	Real Est. Manager	Life Ins. Salesman	Advertising Man	Lawyer	Author- Journalist	President Mfg. Co.	Interest Maturity	Occupational Level	Masculinity- Femininity
Standard Score	11	19	07	26	17	33	39	41	25	55	54	42

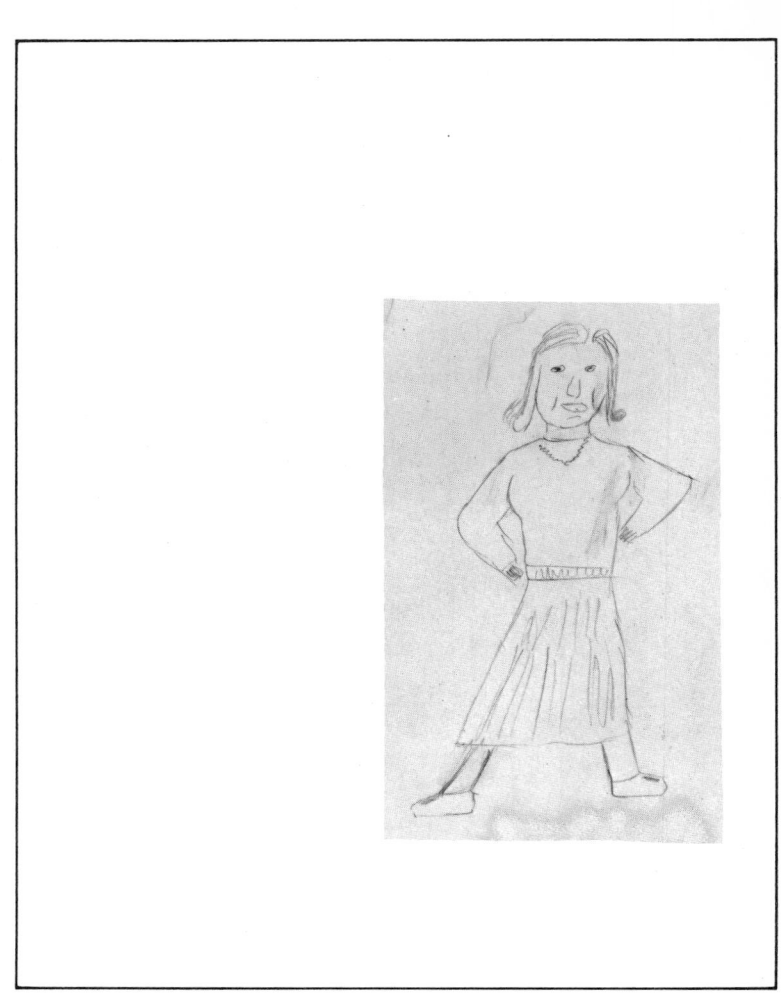

FIGURE-DRAWING CHARACTERISTICS

Structural	Male Female Both	Structural	Male	Female	Structural and Graphic	Male Female Both		Graphic, Global and Height	Male	Female	Body Proportions	Male	Female
Type	0	Omission of Appendages	7	7	Upper and Lower Halves	1	3	Hair Shading	7	3	Head	04	08
Sex Sequence	0	Position of Both Arms	0	0	Four Quarters	4	4	Nudity and Transparency	7	7	Neck	04	04
Posture	1	1	Position of Right Arm	5	5	Relative Size	4		Form	1	3	Shoulders	04	05
Perspective	0	0	Position of Left Arm	5	5	Constant Line Pressure	1	1	Detailing	3	3	Right Arm	02	
Vertical Midline	3	0	Position of Legs	6	6	Variable Line Pressure	0	0	Identity and Sex	1	1	Left Arm		
Bilateral Symmetry	3	3	Relation of Long Axes	1	1	Line Continuity	1	0	Sophistication	3	3	Chest	04	06
Horizontal Midline	4	4	Right and Left Halves	2	4	Body Shading	3	2	Height	03	05	Girth	04	06

GENERAL CHARACTERISTICS OF SUBJECT

IDENTIFICATION
No. 407
Sex M
Marital status S
Age 23 yrs. at psychological tests

PARENTAL HISTORY
Father
C H S D O
U U U U U
Mother
C H S D O
U U U U U

PHYSIOLOGICAL AND METABOLIC DATA

	Admission	Initial	Control	Cold pressor change	Exercise change	Smoking change
Systolic pressure	140	136	128	+21	+46	
Diastolic pressure	65	68	68	+08	-02	
Heart rate	72	90	83	00	+17	

Age 22 yrs.	Height 74 in.	Ponderal index 13.23
	Weight 175 lbs.	Cholesterol 237 mg. per 100 ml.
	Overweight +01 %	Vital capacity 5.6 liters

HABIT SURVEY
Smoking habits: heavy cigarette smoker
Age begun 16 yrs.   Inhalation: yes
Habits of nervous tension: 4, 5, 6, 9, 10, 22

Plate 486   DRAWINGS AT AN INTERMEDIATE LEVEL OF SOPHISTICATION   529

FIGURE-DRAWING CHARACTERISTICS

Structural	Male Female Both	Structural	Male	Female	Structural and Graphic	Male Female Both		Graphic, Global and Height	Male	Female	Body Proportions	Male	Female
Type	0	Omission of Appendages	0	0	Upper and Lower Halves	1	1	Hair Shading	1	1	Head	09	06
Sex Sequence	2	Position of Both Arms	4	4	Four Quarters	4	4	Nudity and Transparency	7	7	Neck	10	07
Posture	1	1	Position of Right Arm	7	7	Relative Size	0		Form	1	3	Shoulders		
Perspective	2	2	Position of Left Arm	0	0	Constant Line Pressure	1	1	Detailing	3	3	Right Arm		
Vertical Midline	7	4	Position of Legs	1	1	Variable Line Pressure	0	0	Identity and Sex	1	1	Left Arm	06	04
Bilateral Symmetry	0	0	Relation of Long Axes	1	1	Line Continuity	0	0	Sophistication	3	3	Chest	06	04
Horizontal Midline	4	4	Right and Left Halves	1	2	Body Shading	7	2	Height	06	04	Girth	07	06

GENERAL CHARACTERISTICS OF SUBJECT

IDENTIFICATION
No. 553
Sex M
Marital status S
Age 23 yrs. at psychological tests

PARENTAL HISTORY				
Father				
C	H	S	D	O
U	U	U	U	U
Mother				
C	H	S	D	O
U	U	U	U	U

PHYSIOLOGICAL AND METABOLIC DATA

	Admission	Initial	Control	Cold pressor change	Exercise change	Smoking change
Systolic pressure	132	120	115	+18	+35	+04
Diastolic pressure	70	70	68	+18	00	+08
Heart rate	100	80	79	00	+15	+12

	Height 76 in.		Ponderal index 13.75	
Age 21 yrs.	Weight 169 lbs.		Cholesterol 203 mg. per 100 ml.	
	Overweight -07 %		Vital capacity 5.8 liters	

HABIT SURVEY

Smoking habits: moderate cigarette smoker

Age begun 17 yrs.   Inhalation: yes

Habits of nervous tension: 4, 5, 9, 11, 17, 22

FIGURE-DRAWING CHARACTERISTICS

Structural	Male Female Both		Structural	Male	Female	Structural and Graphic	Male Female Both		Graphic, Global and Height	Male	Female	Body Proportions	Male	Female
Type	0		Omission of Appendages	0	0	Upper and Lower Halves	3	3	Hair Shading	1	7	Head	06	09
Sex Sequence	0		Position of Both Arms	1	1	Four Quarters	4	4	Nudity and Transparency	7	7	Neck	08	07
Posture	1	1	Position of Right Arm	5	0	Relative Size	4		Form	1	3	Shoulders	08	09
Perspective	0	0	Position of Left Arm	4	2	Constant Line Pressure	5	0	Detailing	3	3	Right Arm	04	06
Vertical Midline	3	0	Position of Legs	4	4	Variable Line Pressure	0	4	Identity and Sex	1	1	Left Arm	04	07
Bilateral Symmetry	3	3	Relation of Long Axes	1	1	Line Continuity	3	0	Sophistication	3	3	Chest	06	07
Horizontal Midline	6	4	Right and Left Halves	3	3	Body Shading	0	3	Height	06	08	Girth	09	07

GENERAL CHARACTERISTICS OF SUBJECT

IDENTIFICATION
No. 502
Sex M
Marital status S
Age 24 yrs. at
psychological tests

PARENTAL HISTORY				
Father				
C	H	S	D	O
U	U	U	U	U
Mother				
C	H	S	D	O
-	-	-	-	-

PHYSIOLOGICAL AND METABOLIC DATA

	Admission	Initial	Control	Cold pressor change	Exercise change	Smoking change
Systolic pressure	120	112	102	+20	+33	+06
Diastolic pressure	70	78	72	+10	-06	+02
Heart rate	72	76	75	-04	+05	+02

Age 22 yrs.	Height 74 in.	Ponderal index 13.63
	Weight 160 lbs.	Cholesterol 222 mg. per 100 ml.
	Overweight -08 %	Vital capacity 5.6 liters

HABIT SURVEY

Smoking habits: nonsmoker

Age begun   yrs.   Inhalation:

Habits of nervous tension: 5, 6, 16, 17, 23

VIII. MIXED INTERMEDIATE AND MODERATELY SOPHISTICATED DRAWINGS

In this section, represented by twenty-eight subjects, one drawing of each pair is intermediate in level of sophistication and the other is moderately sophisticated.

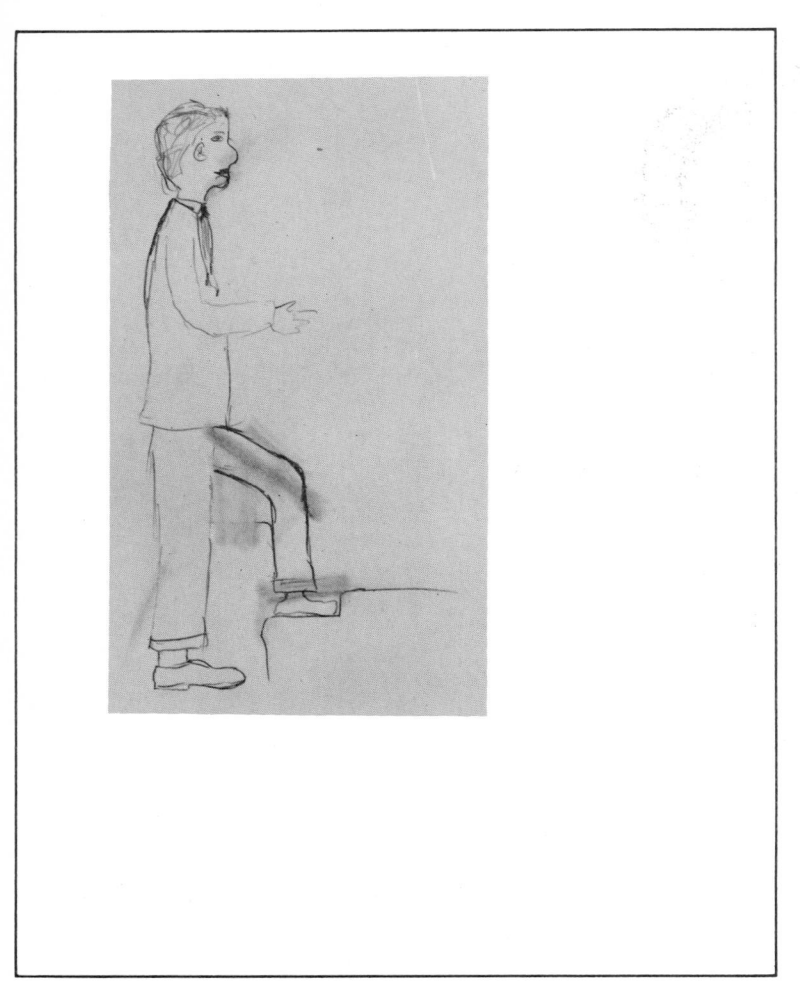

FIGURE-DRAWING CHARACTERISTICS

Structural	Male Female Both	Structural	Male	Female	Structural and Graphic	Male Female Both	Graphic, Global and Height	Male	Female	Body Proportions	Male	Female
Type	0	Omission of Appendages	0	7	Upper and Lower Halves	1	1	Hair Shading	3	2	Head	06	06
Sex Sequence	0	Position of Both Arms	2	0	Four Quarters	4	4	Nudity and Transparency	7	7	Neck	06	04
Posture	2	1	Position of Right Arm	4	5	Relative Size	0		Form	3	1	Shoulders		07
Perspective	2	0	Position of Left Arm	7	5	Constant Line Pressure	0	0	Detailing	3	1	Right Arm	04	
Vertical Midline	7	0	Position of Legs	8	4	Variable Line Pressure	3	3	Identity and Sex	1	1	Left Arm		
Bilateral Symmetry	0	3	Relation of Long Axes	1	1	Line Continuity	0	0	Sophistication	3	2	Chest	05	05
Horizontal Midline	6	4	Right and Left Halves	2	2	Body Shading	4	3	Height	06	05	Girth	06	05

GENERAL CHARACTERISTICS OF SUBJECT

IDENTIFICATION
No. G69
Sex M
Marital status M
Age 23 yrs. at
psychological tests

PARENTAL HISTORY					
Father					
	C	H	S	D	O
	+	+	-	-	-
Mother					
	C	H	S	D	O
	-	+	-	-	-

PHYSIOLOGICAL AND METABOLIC DATA

	Admission	Initial	Control	Cold pressor change	Exercise change	Smoking change
Systolic pressure		122	112	+06	+22	+07
Diastolic pressure		70	72	+12	00	+16
Heart rate		64	58	+12	+29	+07

Age 22 yrs.	Height	72 in.	Ponderal index 12.72
	Weight	181 lbs.	Cholesterol 190 mg. per 100 ml.
	Overweight +11 %		Vital capacity liters

HABIT SURVEY

Smoking habits: former smoker

Age begun   yrs.   Inhalation:

Habits of nervous tension: 1, 3, 4, 5, 6, 9, 11, 15, 16, 17, 22, 23, 25

STRONG VOCATIONAL INTEREST TEST

Occupation	Artist	Psychologist	Architect	Physician	Osteopath	Dentist	Veterinarian	Mathematician	Physicist	Engineer	Chemist	Production Manager
Standard Score	51	44	52	65	58	48	23	35	35	39	47	27

Occupation	Farmer	Aviator	Carpenter	Printer	Math.-Sci. Teacher	Ind. Arts Teacher	Voc. Agric. Teacher	Policeman	Forest Serv. Man	Y.M.C.A. Phys. Dir.	Personnel Director	Public Administrator
Standard Score	32	38	32	39	27	21	14	25	27	20	26	36

Occupation	Y.M.C.A. Secretary	Soc. Sci. H.S. Teacher	City Sch. Sup't.	Social Worker	Minister	Musician Performer	C.P.A.	Senior C.P.A.	Accountant	Office Man	Purchasing Agent	Banker
Standard Score	12	24	23	35	59	50	26	22	18	24	14	20

Occupation	Mortician	Pharmacist	Sales Manager	Real Est. Manager	Life Ins. Salesman	Advertising Man	Lawyer	Author-Journalist	President Mfg. Co.	Interest Maturity	Occupational Level	Masculinity-Femininity
Standard Score	24	26	16	32	23	39	39	48	35	54	58	33

Plate 489   **MIXED INTERMEDIATE AND MODERATELY SOPHISTICATED DRAWINGS**   533

FIGURE-DRAWING CHARACTERISTICS

Structural	Male Female Both	Structural	Male	Female	Structural and Graphic	Male Female Both		Graphic, Global and Height	Male	Female	Body Proportions	Male	Female
Type	0	Omission of Appendages	0	0	Upper and Lower Halves	3	3	Hair Shading	1	1	Head	09	09
Sex Sequence	2	Position of Both Arms	0	4	Four Quarters	4	4	Nudity and Transparency	7	7	Neck	08	12
Posture	1 1	Position of Right Arm	0	7	Relative Size	0		Form	3	1	Shoulders	10	
Perspective	0 2	Position of Left Arm	0	0	Constant Line Pressure	0	0	Detailing	3	3	Right Arm	06	
Vertical Midline	3 4	Position of Legs	4	1	Variable Line Pressure	1	1	Identity and Sex	1	1	Left Arm	06	05
Bilateral Symmetry	4 0	Relation of Long Axes	1	1	Line Continuity	0	0	Sophistication	3	2	Chest	08	05
Horizontal Midline	4 4	Right and Left Halves	9	9	Body Shading	4	6	Height	08	07	Girth	09	04

GENERAL CHARACTERISTICS OF SUBJECT

IDENTIFICATION
No. 732
Sex M
Marital status   S
Age 22 yrs. at
psychological tests

PARENTAL HISTORY
Father
C   H   S   D   O
+   -   -   -   -
Mother
C   H   S   D   O
-   -   -   -   ?

PHYSIOLOGICAL AND METABOLIC DATA

	Admission	Initial	Control	Cold pressor change	Exercise change	Smoking change
Systolic pressure	132	122	94	+16	+20	+03
Diastolic pressure	70	64	54	+20	-10	+02
Heart rate	72	68	63	+52	+18	00

Age 20 yrs.	Height	76	in.	Ponderal index	13.64	
	Weight	173	lbs.	Cholesterol	177	mg. per 100 ml.
	Overweight	-04	%	Vital capacity	6.2	liters

HABIT SURVEY

Smoking habits: nonsmoker

Age begun   yrs.   Inhalation:

Habits of nervous tension: 5, 6, 9, 17, 25

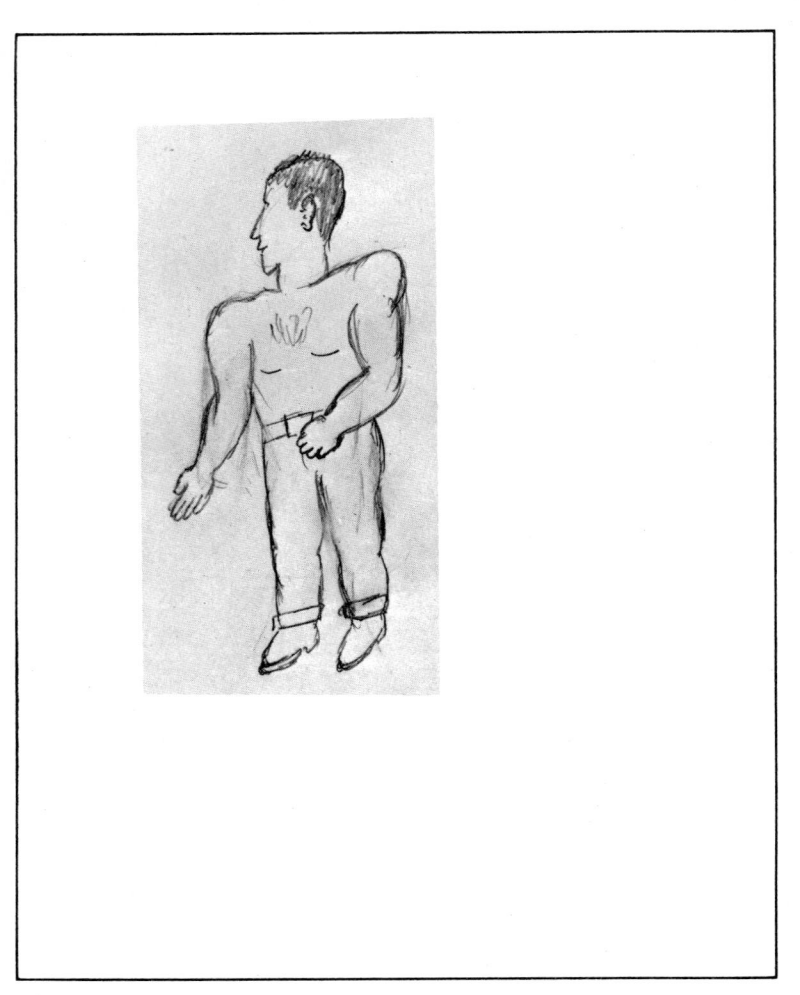

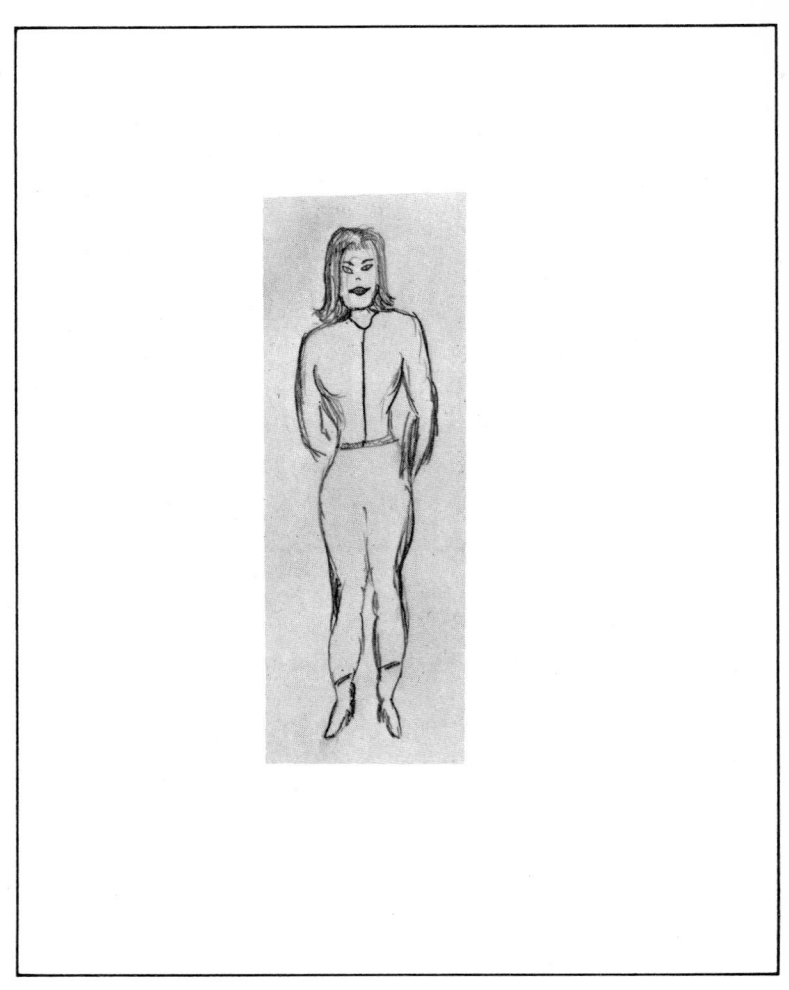

FIGURE-DRAWING CHARACTERISTICS

Structural	Male	Female	Structural	Male	Female	Structural and Graphic	Male	Female	Graphic, Global and Height	Male	Female	Body Proportions	Male	Female
	Both						Both							
Type		0	Omission of Appendages	0	7	Upper and Lower Halves	1	1	Hair Shading	3	2	Head	09	06
Sex Sequence		0	Position of Both Arms	1	0	Four Quarters	4	4	Nudity and Transparency	3	6	Neck	07	02
Posture	1	1	Position of Right Arm	4	8	Relative Size		0	Form	3	1	Shoulders		05
Perspective	6	0	Position of Left Arm	5	5	Constant Line Pressure	4	0	Detailing	1	1	Right Arm	04	
Vertical Midline	5	3	Position of Legs	4	4	Variable Line Pressure	0	1	Identity and Sex	1	1	Left Arm	06	
Bilateral Symmetry	0	3	Relation of Long Axes	1	1	Line Continuity	0	0	Sophistication	3	2	Chest		04
Horizontal Midline	4	4	Right and Left Halves	1	1	Body Shading	1	1	Height	05	05	Girth		03

GENERAL CHARACTERISTICS OF SUBJECT

IDENTIFICATION
No. G26
Sex M
Marital status S
Age 22 yrs. at
psychological tests

PARENTAL HISTORY				
Father				
C	H	S	D	O
+	-	-	-	?
Mother				
C	H	S	D	O
-	-	-	?	+

PHYSIOLOGICAL AND METABOLIC DATA

	Admission	Initial	Control	Cold pressor change	Exercise change	Smoking change
Systolic pressure	120	132	122	+16	+16	+02
Diastolic pressure	70	72	80	-10	-06	+02
Heart rate	80	76	69	+08	+13	+08

Age 22 yrs.	Height 68 in.	Ponderal index 12.48
	Weight 162 lbs.	Cholesterol 258 mg. per 100 ml.
	Overweight +11 %	Vital capacity liters

HABIT SURVEY

Smoking habits: nonsmoker

Age begun   yrs.   Inhalation:

Habits of nervous tension: 2, 3, 4, 5, 14, 16, 17, 18, 22, 23

STRONG VOCATIONAL INTEREST TEST

Occupation	Artist	Psychologist	Architect	Physician	Osteopath	Dentist	Veterinarian	Mathematician	Physicist	Engineer	Chemist	Production Manager
Standard Score	38	58	39	68	55	41	27	37	39	44	57	35

Occupation	Farmer	Aviator	Carpenter	Printer	Math.-Sci. Teacher	Ind. Arts Teacher	Voc. Agric. Teacher	Policeman	Forest Serv. Man	Y.M.C.A. Phys. Dir.	Personnel Director	Public Administrator
Standard Score	32	56	26	42	45	25	26	38	34	47	37	50

Occupation	Y.M.C.A. Secretary	Soc. Sci. H.S. Teacher	City Sch. Sup't.	Social Worker	Minister	Musician Performer	C.P.A.	Senior C.P.A.	Accountant	Office Man	Purchasing Agent	Banker
Standard Score	26	31	23	45	59	54	37	47	26	24	20	13

Occupation	Mortician	Pharmacist	Sales Manager	Real Est. Manager	Life Ins. Salesman	Advertising Man	Lawyer	Author-Journalist	President Mfg. Co.	Interest Maturity	Occupational Level	Masculinity-Femininity
Standard Score	21	31	26	25	24	34	39	37	25	54	53	52

Plate 491   **MIXED INTERMEDIATE AND MODERATELY SOPHISTICATED DRAWINGS**   535

FIGURE-DRAWING CHARACTERISTICS

Structural	Male Female Both	Structural	Male	Female	Structural and Graphic	Male Female Both		Graphic, Global and Height	Male	Female	Body Proportions	Male	Female
Type	0	Omission of Appendages	7	0	Upper and Lower Halves	0	1	Hair Shading	0	5	Head	12	07
Sex Sequence	1	Position of Both Arms	0	1	Four Quarters	4	4	Nudity and Transparency	7	7	Neck	00	02
Posture	1 1	Position of Right Arm	5	0	Relative Size	0		Form	3	3	Shoulders	08	02
Perspective	0 0	Position of Left Arm	5	1	Constant Line Pressure	4	5	Detailing	1	3	Right Arm		02
Vertical Midline	3 0	Position of Legs	2	4	Variable Line Pressure	0	0	Identity and Sex	3	3	Left Arm		03
Bilateral Symmetry	2 3	Relation of Long Axes	1	1	Line Continuity	2	2	Sophistication	2	3	Chest		03
Horizontal Midline	0 4	Right and Left Halves	2	2	Body Shading	2	0	Height	06	04	Girth	09	02

GENERAL CHARACTERISTICS OF SUBJECT

IDENTIFICATION
No. G37
Sex M
Marital status S
Age 24 yrs. at
psychological tests

PARENTAL HISTORY					
Father					
C	H	S	D	O	
+	+	-	-	?	
Mother					
C	H	S	D	O	
-	-	-	-	-	

PHYSIOLOGICAL AND METABOLIC DATA

	Admission	Initial	Control	Cold pressor change	Exercise change	Smoking change
Systolic pressure	118	120	122	+24	+40	+08
Diastolic pressure	70	78	76	+28	00	+02
Heart rate	76	72	73	+14	+09	+03

Age 23 yrs.	Height	73 in.	Ponderal index 13.90
	Weight	145 lbs.	Cholesterol 188 mg. per 100 ml.
	Overweight -14 %		Vital capacity liters

HABIT SURVEY

Smoking habits: heavy cigarette smoker

Age begun 17 yrs.   Inhalation: yes

Habits of nervous tension: 4, 5, 20

STRONG VOCATIONAL INTEREST TEST

Occupation	Artist	Psychologist	Architect	Physician	Osteopath	Dentist	Veterinarian	Mathematician	Physicist	Engineer	Chemist	Production Manager
Standard Score	25	43	30	45	30	24	15	35	20	22	32	21

Occupation	Farmer	Aviator	Carpenter	Printer	Math.-Sci. Teacher	Ind. Arts Teacher	Voc. Agric. Teacher	Policeman	Forest Serv. Man	Y.M.C.A. Phys. Dir.	Personnel Director	Public Administrator
Standard Score	29	28	06	39	44	12	32	26	13	28	47	39

Occupation	Y.M.C.A. Secretary	Soc. Sci. H.S. Teacher	City Sch. Sup't.	Social Worker	Minister	Musician Performer	C.P.A.	Senior C.P.A.	Accountant	Office Man	Purchasing Agent	Banker
Standard Score	32	38	37	39	59	40	31	45	27	34	28	25

Occupation	Mortician	Pharmacist	Sales Manager	Real Est. Manager	Life Ins. Salesman	Advertising Man	Lawyer	Author-Journalist	President Mfg. Co.	Interest Maturity	Occupational Level	Masculinity-Femininity
Standard Score	18	29	36	35	32	40	36	35	20	52	54	48

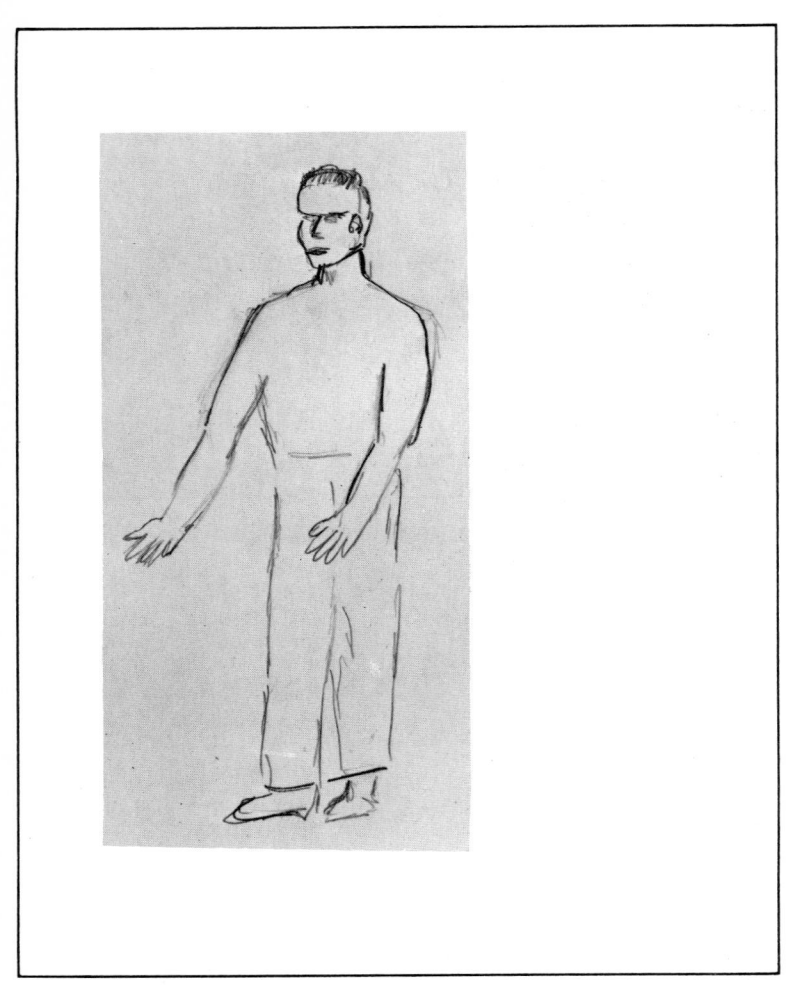

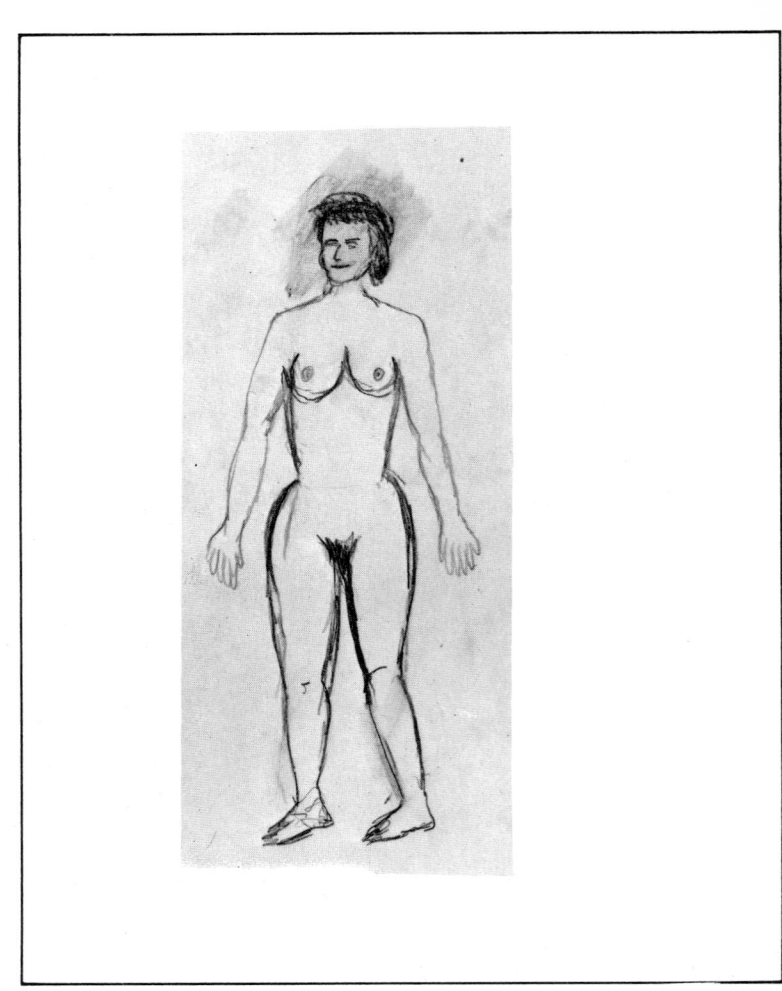

FIGURE-DRAWING CHARACTERISTICS

Structural	Male Female Both		Structural	Male	Female	Structural and Graphic	Male Female Both		Graphic, Global and Height	Male	Female	Body Proportions	Male	Female
Type	0		Omission of Appendages	0	0	Upper and Lower Halves	0	0	Hair Shading	3	3	Head	08	06
Sex Sequence	0		Position of Both Arms	1	0	Four Quarters	4	4	Nudity and Transparency	3	0	Neck	06	04
Posture	1	1	Position of Right Arm	2	1	Relative Size	2		Form	1	1	Shoulders		06
Perspective	1	0	Position of Left Arm	5	1	Constant Line Pressure	0	0	Detailing	3	1	Right Arm	06	06
Vertical Midline	7	0	Position of Legs	4	5	Variable Line Pressure	5	5	Identity and Sex	1	1	Left Arm	06	06
Bilateral Symmetry	0	3	Relation of Long Axes	1	1	Line Continuity	1	1	Sophistication	3	2	Chest		05
Horizontal Midline	4	0	Right and Left Halves	1	1	Body Shading	2	3	Height	07	07	Girth		06

GENERAL CHARACTERISTICS OF SUBJECT

IDENTIFICATION
No. G71
Sex M
Marital status S
Age 21 yrs. at psychological tests

PARENTAL HISTORY				
Father				
C	H	S	D	O
+	-	-	-	-
Mother				
C	H	S	D	O
-	-	-	-	+

PHYSIOLOGICAL AND METABOLIC DATA

	Admission	Initial	Control	Cold pressor change	Exercise change	Smoking change
Systolic pressure		130	110	+12	+30	+05
Diastolic pressure		50	60	+20	-10	+08
Heart rate		60	54	-08	+07	+16

Age 20 yrs.	Height 72 in.	Ponderal index 13.07
	Weight 167 lbs.	Cholesterol 298 mg. per 100 ml.
	Overweight +04 %	Vital capacity liters

HABIT SURVEY

Smoking habits: light cigarette smoker

Age begun 18 yrs.   Inhalation: yes

Habits of nervous tension: 5, 6, 9, 18

STRONG VOCATIONAL INTEREST TEST

Occupation	Artist	Psychologist	Architect	Physician	Osteopath	Dentist	Veterinarian	Mathematician	Physicist	Engineer	Chemist	Production Manager
Standard Score	29	55	33	52	45	32	14	25	19	31	42	38

Occupation	Farmer	Aviator	Carpenter	Printer	Math.-Sci. Teacher	Ind. Arts Teacher	Voc. Agric. Teacher	Policeman	Forest Serv. Man	Y.M.C.A. Phys. Dir.	Personnel Director	Public Administrator
Standard Score	17	33	11	31	40	11	11	26	19	36	56	53

Occupation	Y.M.C.A. Secretary	Soc. Sci. H.S. Teacher	City Sch. Sup't.	Social Worker	Minister	Musician Performer	C.P.A.	Senior C.P.A.	Accountant	Office Man	Purchasing Agent	Banker
Standard Score	33	45	43	53	59	48	45	47	33	34	22	18

Occupation	Mortician	Pharmacist	Sales Manager	Real Est. Manager	Life Ins. Salesman	Advertising Man	Lawyer	Author-Journalist	President Mfg. Co.	Interest Maturity	Occupational Level	Masculinity-Femininity
Standard Score	22	28	33	35	32	38	45	37	41	63	59	44

Plate 493   **MIXED INTERMEDIATE AND MODERATELY SOPHISTICATED DRAWINGS**   537

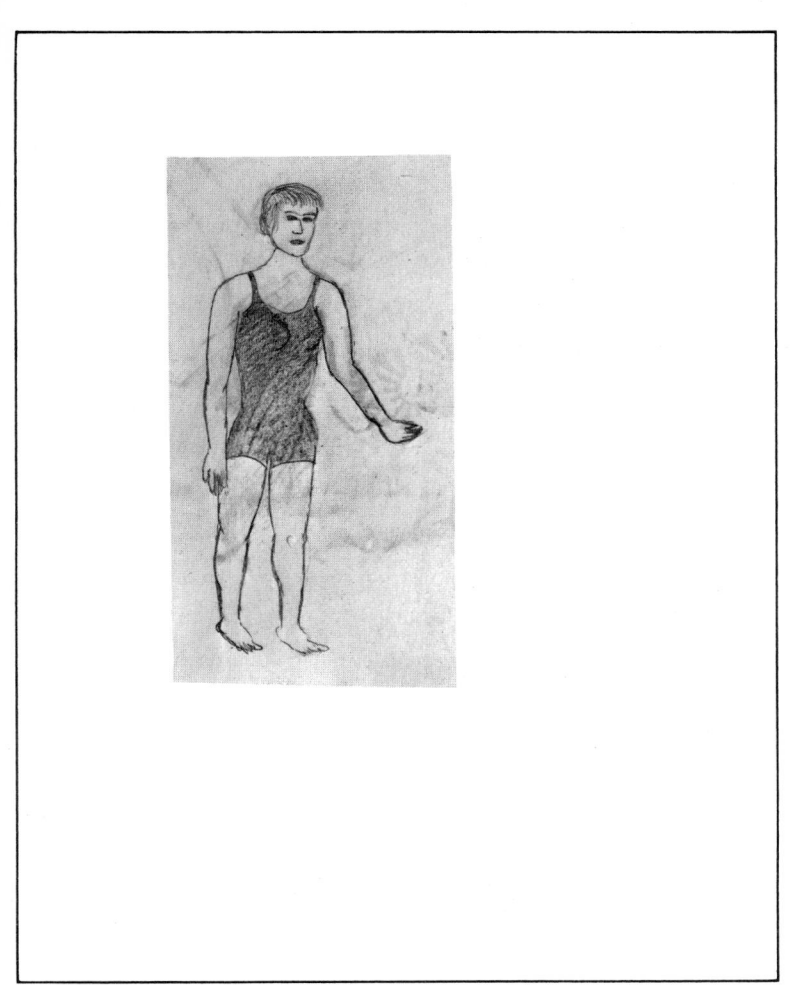

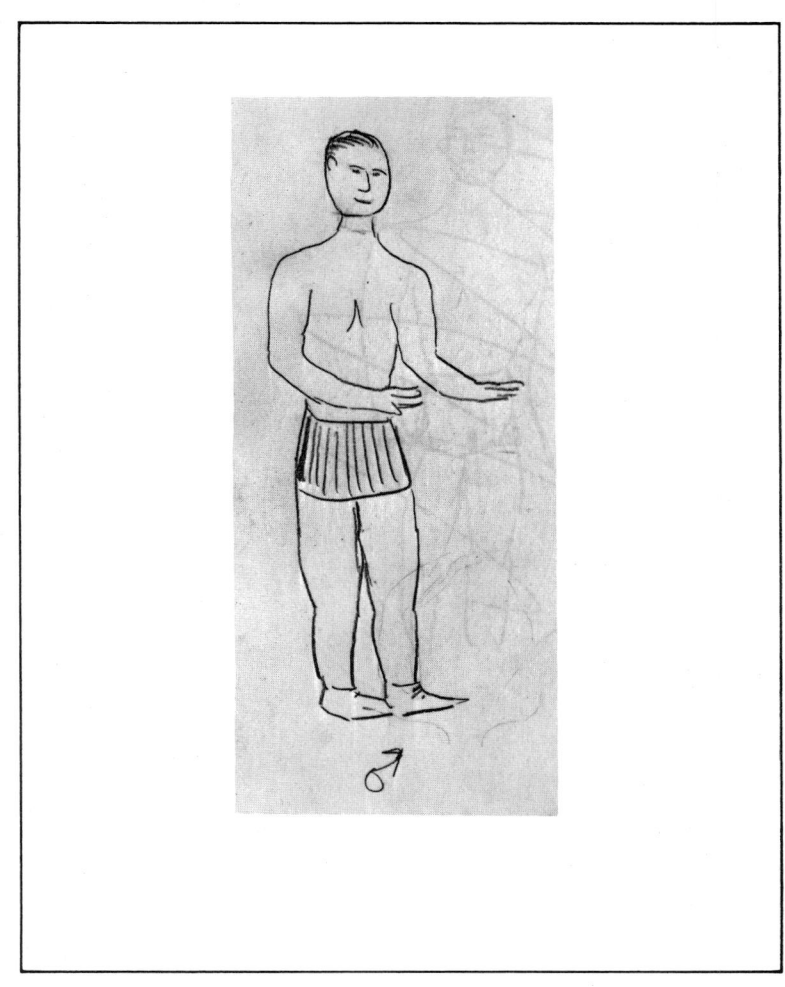

FIGURE-DRAWING CHARACTERISTICS

Structural	Male Female Both	Structural	Male	Female	Structural and Graphic	Male Female Both		Graphic, Global and Height	Male	Female	Body Proportions	Male	Female
Type	0	Omission of Appendages	0	0	Upper and Lower Halves	1	1	Hair Shading	1	2	Head	06	05
Sex Sequence	1	Position of Both Arms	1	1	Four Quarters	4	4	Nudity and Transparency	3	2	Neck	07	04
Posture	1 2	Position of Right Arm	5	0	Relative Size	0		Form	1	1	Shoulders	06	
Perspective	1 1	Position of Left Arm	3	4	Constant Line Pressure	5	0	Detailing	3	1	Right Arm	05	04
Vertical Midline	4 4	Position of Legs	4	8	Variable Line Pressure	0	5	Identity and Sex	1	1	Left Arm	04	04
Bilateral Symmetry	0 0	Relation of Long Axes	1	1	Line Continuity	3	1	Sophistication	3	2	Chest	04	
Horizontal Midline	4 0	Right and Left Halves	1	2	Body Shading	0	3	Height	06	05	Girth	05	

GENERAL CHARACTERISTICS OF SUBJECT

IDENTIFICATION
No. C46
Sex M
Marital status S
Age 22 yrs. at
psychological tests

PARENTAL HISTORY				
Father				
C	H	S	D	O
+	-	-	-	+
Mother				
C	H	S	D	O
-	-	-	-	-

PHYSIOLOGICAL AND METABOLIC DATA

	Admission	Initial	Control	Cold pressor change	Exercise change	Smoking change
Systolic pressure	120	100	104	-04	+46	00
Diastolic pressure	80	50	54	+31	-04	+02
Heart rate	72	60	59	+16	+32	+06

Age 22 yrs.	Height 72 in.	Ponderal index 12.74
	Weight 180 lbs.	Cholesterol 345 mg. per 100 ml.
	Overweight +10 %	Vital capacity 5.6 liters

HABIT SURVEY
Smoking habits: light cigarette smoker
Age begun 18 yrs.   Inhalation: yes
Habits of nervous tension: 4, 5, 9, 11, 14,
21, 22

STRONG VOCATIONAL INTEREST TEST

Occupation	Artist	Psychologist	Architect	Physician	Osteopath	Dentist	Veterinarian	Mathematician	Physicist	Engineer	Chemist	Production Manager
Standard Score	24	39	23	40	35	26	25	10	01	13	16	35

Occupation	Farmer	Aviator	Carpenter	Printer	Math.-Sci. Teacher	Ind. Arts Teacher	Voc. Agric. Teacher	Policeman	Forest Serv. Man	Y.M.C.A. Phys. Dir.	Personnel Director	Public Administrator
Standard Score	31	28	11	32	32	19	33	32	23	46	50	50

Occupation	Y.M.C.A. Secretary	Soc. Sci. H.S. Teacher	City Sch. Sup't.	Social Worker	Minister	Musician Performer	C.P.A.	Senior C.P.A.	Accountant	Office Man	Purchasing Agent	Banker
Standard Score	41	51	38	52	62	49	26	40	26	39	31	26

Occupation	Mortician	Pharmacist	Sales Manager	Real Est. Manager	Life Ins. Salesman	Advertising Man	Lawyer	Author-Journalist	President Mfg. Co.	Interest Maturity	Occupational Level	Masculinity-Femininity
Standard Score	34	38	39	40	39	46	35	34	24	59	54	43

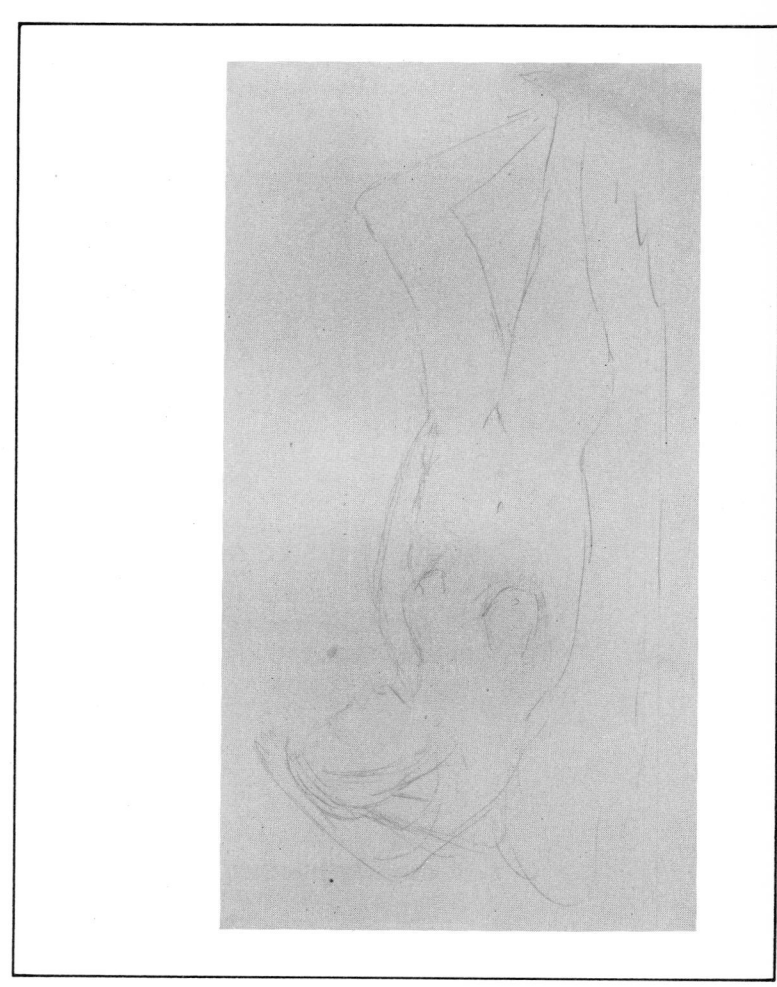

FIGURE-DRAWING CHARACTERISTICS

Structural	Male Female Both		Structural	Male	Female	Structural and Graphic	Male	Female Both		Graphic, Global and Height	Male	Female	Body Proportions	Male	Female
Type	0		Omission of Appendages	0	6	Upper and Lower Halves	1	3		Hair Shading	7	3	Head	11	10
Sex Sequence	0		Position of Both Arms	0	2	Four Quarters	4	4		Nudity and Transparency	7	0	Neck	04	
Posture	1	7	Position of Right Arm	0	5	Relative Size	5			Form	3	3	Shoulders	12	
Perspective	0	6	Position of Left Arm	0	5	Constant Line Pressure	1	1		Detailing	3	3	Right Arm	06	
Vertical Midline	3	4	Position of Legs	5	5	Variable Line Pressure	0	0		Identity and Sex	1	1	Left Arm	06	
Bilateral Symmetry	5	0	Relation of Long Axes	1	0	Line Continuity	4	0		Sophistication	3	2	Chest	09	
Horizontal Midline	6	0	Right and Left Halves	1	9	Body Shading	0	1		Height	08		Girth	10	

GENERAL CHARACTERISTICS OF SUBJECT

IDENTIFICATION
No. E25
Sex M
Marital status S
Age 22 yrs. at
psychological tests

PARENTAL HISTORY					
Father					
C	H	S	D	O	
+	+	-	-	+	
Mother					
C	H	S	D	O	
-	+	-	-	-	

PHYSIOLOGICAL AND METABOLIC DATA

	Admission	Initial	Control	Cold pressor change	Exercise change	Smoking change
Systolic pressure	100	130	114	+06	+34	+07
Diastolic pressure	70	70	78	+08	-26	+15
Heart rate	80	80	70	+04	+18	+30

Age 22 yrs.	Height	74 in.	Ponderal index 13.60	
	Weight	161 lbs.	Cholesterol 183 mg. per 100 ml.	
	Overweight -07 %		Vital capacity 5.5 liters	

HABIT SURVEY

Smoking habits: light cigarette smoker

Age begun 20 yrs.   Inhalation: yes

Habits of nervous tension: 4, 11, 19

STRONG VOCATIONAL INTEREST TEST

Occupation	Artist	Psychologist	Architect	Physician	Osteopath	Dentist	Veterinarian	Mathematician	Physicist	Engineer	Chemist	Production Manager
Standard Score	47	41	53	50	31	35	08	49	42	42	47	22

Occupation	Farmer	Aviator	Carpenter	Printer	Math.-Sci. Teacher	Ind. Arts Teacher	Voc. Agric. Teacher	Policeman	Forest Serv. Man	Y.M.C.A. Phys. Dir.	Personnel Director	Public Administrator
Standard Score	28	39	20	30	28	10	20	16	19	16	25	35

Occupation	Y.M.C.A. Secretary	Soc. Sci. H.S. Teacher	City Sch. Sup't.	Social Worker	Minister	Musician Performer	C.P.A.	Senior C.P.A.	Accountant	Office Man	Purchasing Agent	Banker
Standard Score	08	19	22	24	64	44	40	40	19	24	21	20

Occupation	Mortician	Pharmacist	Sales Manager	Real Est. Manager	Life Ins. Salesman	Advertising Man	Lawyer	Author-Journalist	President Mfg. Co.	Interest Maturity	Occupational Level	Masculinity-Femininity
Standard Score	19	27	26	34	24	42	43	47	35	45	61	41

FIGURE-DRAWING CHARACTERISTICS

Structural	Male	Female	Structural	Male	Female	Structural and Graphic	Male	Female	Graphic, Global and Height	Male	Female	Body Proportions	Male	Female
	Both						Both							
Type	0		Omission of Appendages	0	2	Upper and Lower Halves	0	0	Hair Shading	5	1	Head	09	08
Sex Sequence	1		Position of Both Arms	4	6	Four Quarters	4	4	Nudity and Transparency	7	7	Neck	10	08
Posture	1	1	Position of Right Arm	7	8	Relative Size	0		Form	3	3	Shoulders		06
Perspective	2	5	Position of Left Arm	4	8	Constant Line Pressure	0	0	Detailing	1	3	Right Arm		
Vertical Midline	7	0	Position of Legs	1	4	Variable Line Pressure	4	3	Identity and Sex	1	1	Left Arm	06	
Bilateral Symmetry	0	3	Relation of Long Axes	1	1	Line Continuity	1	4	Sophistication	2	3	Chest	07	07
Horizontal Midline	4	4	Right and Left Halves	1	3	Body Shading	4	4	Height	08	07	Girth	06	06

GENERAL CHARACTERISTICS OF SUBJECT

IDENTIFICATION
No. E31
Sex M
Marital status S
Age 22 yrs. at psychological tests

PARENTAL HISTORY					
Father					
C	H	S	D	O	
-	-	-	-	-	
Mother					
C	H	S	D	O	
+	-	-	-	-	

PHYSIOLOGICAL AND METABOLIC DATA

	Admission	Initial	Control	Cold pressor change	Exercise change	Smoking change
Systolic pressure		108	106	+08	+24	
Diastolic pressure		60	66	+16	-11	
Heart rate		68	65	00	+26	

Age 22 yrs.	
Height 72 in.	Ponderal index 13.46
Weight 153 lbs.	Cholesterol 184 mg. per 100 ml.
Overweight -06 %	Vital capacity 5.7 liters

HABIT SURVEY

Smoking habits: heavy cigarette smoker

Age begun 15 yrs.   Inhalation: yes

Habits of nervous tension: 1, 4, 5, 9, 11, 15, 16, 17, 18, 20, 21, 23

STRONG VOCATIONAL INTEREST TEST

Occupation	Artist	Psychologist	Architect	Physician	Osteopath	Dentist	Veterinarian	Mathematician	Physicist	Engineer	Chemist	Production Manager
Standard Score	45	44	46	56	41	40	22	41	23	19	30	06

Occupation	Farmer	Aviator	Carpenter	Printer	Math.-Sci. Teacher	Ind. Arts Teacher	Voc. Agric. Teacher	Policeman	Forest Serv. Man	Y.M.C.A. Phys. Dir.	Personnel Director	Public Administrator
Standard Score	28	21	10	35	37	06	20	20	08	25	26	33

Occupation	Y.M.C.A. Secretary	Soc. Sci. H.S. Teacher	City Sch. Sup't.	Social Worker	Minister	Musician Performer	C.P.A.	Senior C.P.A.	Accountant	Office Man	Purchasing Agent	Banker
Standard Score	22	34	36	38	64	58	34	28	16	27	08	26

Occupation	Mortician	Pharmacist	Sales Manager	Real Est. Manager	Life Ins. Salesman	Advertising Man	Lawyer	Author-Journalist	President Mfg. Co.	Interest Maturity	Occupational Level	Masculinity-Femininity
Standard Score	27	31	20	38	34	43	46	47	25	51	58	23

FIGURE-DRAWING CHARACTERISTICS

Structural	Male Female Both	Structural	Male	Female	Structural and Graphic	Male Female Both	Graphic, Global and Height	Male	Female	Body Proportions	Male	Female
Type	0	Omission of Appendages	0	4	Upper and Lower Halves	0 7	Hair Shading	0	0	Head	09	08
Sex Sequence	2	Position of Both Arms	0	1	Four Quarters	4 4	Nudity and Transparency	7	7	Neck		10
Posture	1 0	Position of Right Arm	5	2	Relative Size	4	Form	3	3	Shoulders	11	13
Perspective	0 0	Position of Left Arm	5	5	Constant Line Pressure	1 1	Detailing	3	3	Right Arm	08	
Vertical Midline	3 3	Position of Legs	5	0	Variable Line Pressure	0 0	Identity and Sex	1	1	Left Arm	08	
Bilateral Symmetry	3 3	Relation of Long Axes	1	1	Line Continuity	0 0	Sophistication	3	2	Chest	11	09
Horizontal Midline	4 0	Right and Left Halves	0	1	Body Shading	4 3	Height	08		Girth	12	08

GENERAL CHARACTERISTICS OF SUBJECT

IDENTIFICATION
No. 219
Sex M
Marital status M
Age 29 yrs. at
psychological tests

PARENTAL HISTORY
Father
C H S D O
– ? – – ?
Mother
C H S D O
(+) + (+) – +

PHYSIOLOGICAL AND METABOLIC DATA

	Admission	Initial	Control	Cold pressor change	Exercise change	Smoking change
Systolic pressure	110	112	106	+04	+22	
Diastolic pressure	74	72	66	+04	+02	
Heart rate	88	88	81	00	+07	

Age 26 yrs.	Height 77 in.	Ponderal index 13.61	
	Weight 181 lbs.	Cholesterol 237 mg. per 100 ml.	
	Overweight –08 %	Vital capacity 6.7 liters	

HABIT SURVEY
Smoking habits: mixed smoker
Age begun 13 yrs.   Inhalation: yes
Habits of nervous tension: 2, 4, 6, 10
16, 22, 25

Plate 497   **MIXED INTERMEDIATE AND MODERATELY SOPHISTICATED DRAWINGS**   541

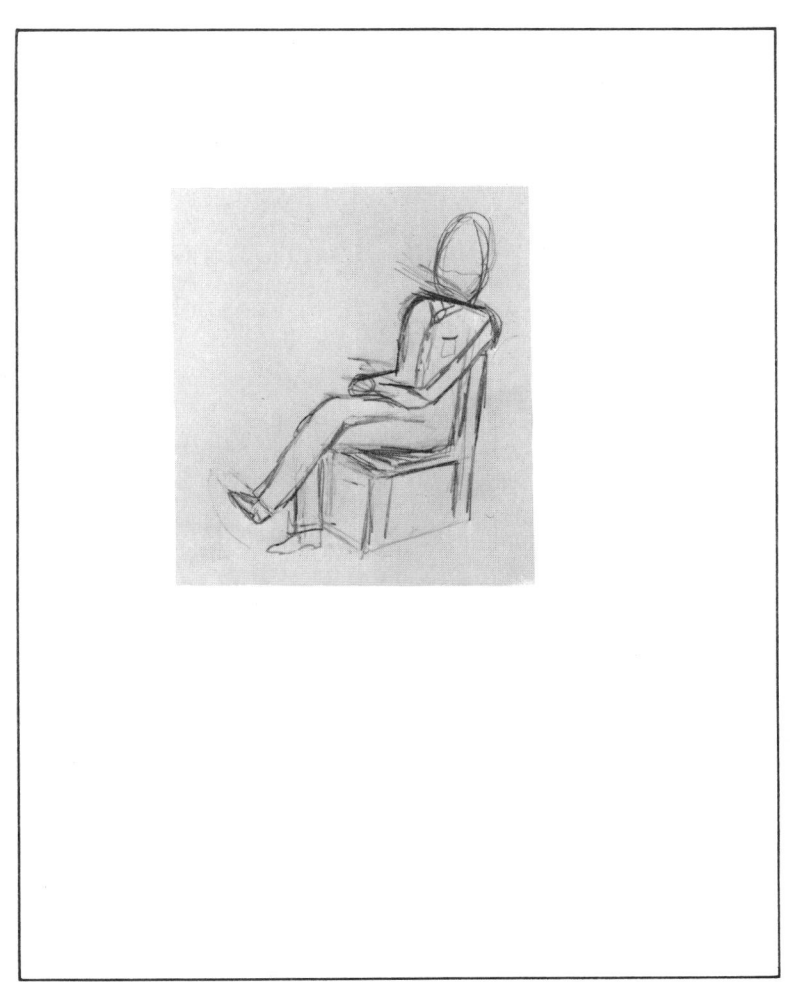

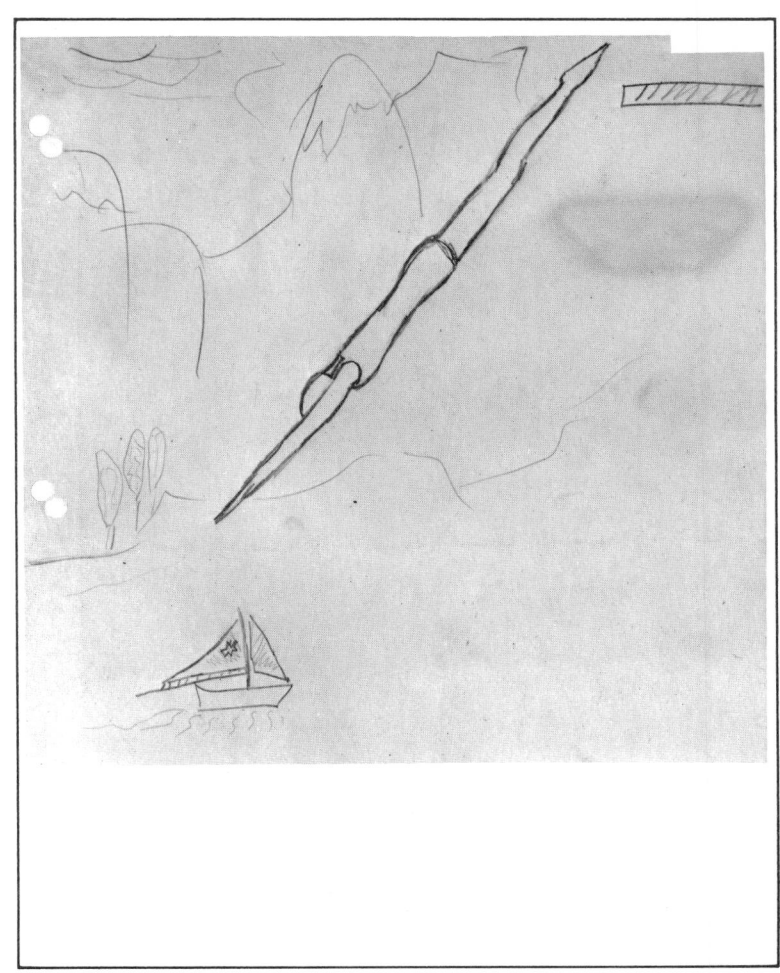

FIGURE-DRAWING CHARACTERISTICS

Structural	Male	Female	Structural	Male	Female	Structural and Graphic	Male	Female	Graphic, Global and Height	Male	Female	Body Proportions	Male	Female
	Both						Both							
Type	0		Omission of Appendages	0	0	Upper and Lower Halves	1	2	Hair Shading	0	0	Head		
Sex Sequence	0		Position of Both Arms	4	4	Four Quarters	4	4	Nudity and Transparency	7	2	Neck		
Posture	3	6	Position of Right Arm	7	7	Relative Size	5		Form	3	1	Shoulders		
Perspective	1	2	Position of Left Arm	9	2	Constant Line Pressure	0	4	Detailing	5	5	Right Arm		
Vertical Midline	7	4	Position of Legs	7	8	Variable Line Pressure	5	0	Identity and Sex	3	1	Left Arm	04	04
Bilateral Symmetry	0	0	Relation of Long Axes	0	3	Line Continuity	0	0	Sophistication	3	2	Chest		02
Horizontal Midline	0	0	Right and Left Halves	3	0	Body Shading	0	0	Height		05	Girth		03

GENERAL CHARACTERISTICS OF SUBJECT

<table>
<tr><th colspan="2">IDENTIFICATION</th><th colspan="2">PARENTAL HISTORY</th><th colspan="7">PHYSIOLOGICAL AND METABOLIC DATA</th><th colspan="2">HABIT SURVEY</th></tr>
</table>

IDENTIFICATION

No. A80
Sex M
Marital status M
Age 22 yrs. at
psychological tests

PARENTAL HISTORY

Father

C	H	S	D	O
?	–	–	–	?

Mother

C	H	S	D	O
–	+	–	–	+

PHYSIOLOGICAL AND METABOLIC DATA

	Admission	Initial	Control	Cold pressor change	Exercise change	Smoking change
Systolic pressure	132	130	118	+14	+37	+04
Diastolic pressure	70	70	60	+24	+10	+04
Heart rate	64	80	81	+07	+30	–08

Age 21 yrs.

Height 72 in.
Weight 161 lbs.
Overweight –01 %

Ponderal index 13.24
Cholesterol 250 mg. per 100 ml.
Vital capacity liters

HABIT SURVEY

Smoking habits: nonsmoker
Age begun   yrs.   Inhalation:
Habits of nervous tension: 1, 4, 5, 8, 10, 15, 18, 19, 22

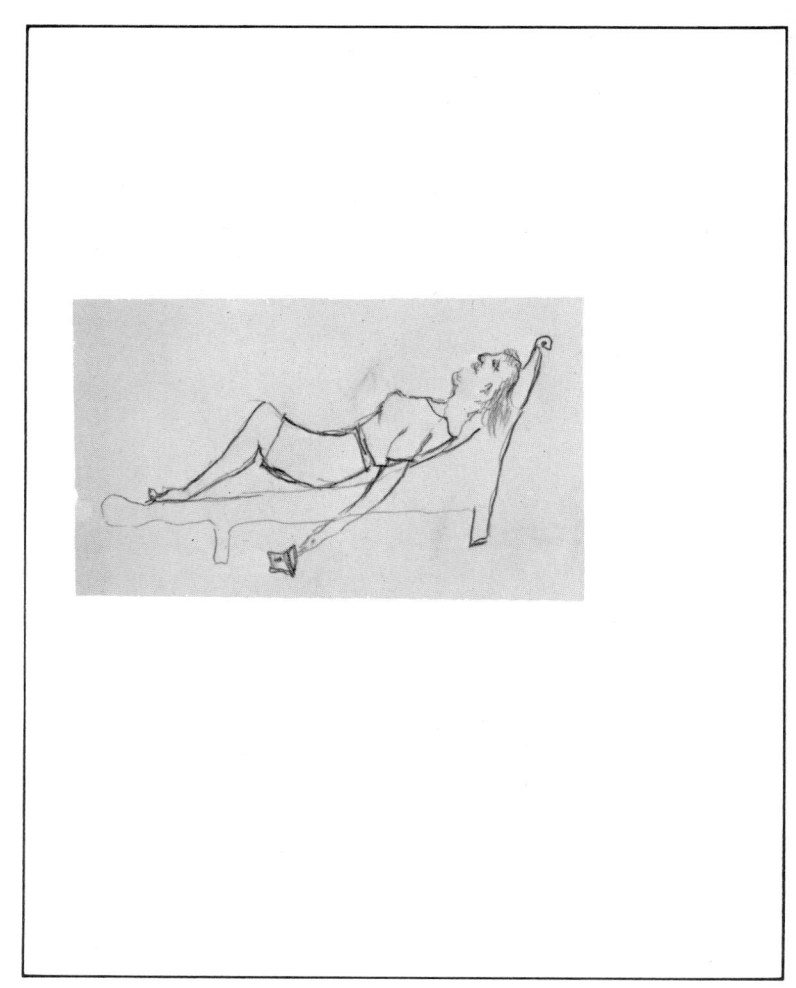

FIGURE-DRAWING CHARACTERISTICS

Structural	Male Female Both		Structural	Male	Female	Structural and Graphic	Male Female Both		Graphic, Global and Height	Male	Female	Body Proportions	Male	Female
Type	0		Omission of Appendages	0	0	Upper and Lower Halves	1	1	Hair Shading	3	3	Head	04	05
Sex Sequence	0		Position of Both Arms	4	4	Four Quarters	4	4	Nudity and Transparency	6	7	Neck	02	06
Posture	1	7	Position of Right Arm	7	7	Relative Size	4		Form	1	1	Shoulders		
Perspective	2	2	Position of Left Arm	4	2	Constant Line Pressure	3	0	Detailing	1	3	Right Arm		
Vertical Midline	4	4	Position of Legs	1	1	Variable Line Pressure	0	3	Identity and Sex	1	1	Left Arm	02	04
Bilateral Symmetry	0	0	Relation of Long Axes	1	0	Line Continuity	0	1	Sophistication	3	2	Chest	03	04
Horizontal Midline	4	4	Right and Left Halves	2	1	Body Shading	0	5	Height	02		Girth	03	04

GENERAL CHARACTERISTICS OF SUBJECT

IDENTIFICATION
No. 756
Sex M
Marital status S
Age 23 yrs. at psychological tests

PARENTAL HISTORY
Father
C H S D O
- (+) - - ?
Mother
C H S D O
- + - - ?

PHYSIOLOGICAL AND METABOLIC DATA

	Admission	Initial	Control	Cold pressor change	Exercise change	Smoking change
Systolic pressure	130	124	118	+08	+16	
Diastolic pressure	70	60	60	+18	-10	
Heart rate	68	64	57	-08	+01	

Age 23 yrs.	Height 74 in.	Ponderal index 13.41
	Weight 168 lbs.	Cholesterol 197 mg. per 100 ml.
	Overweight -04 %	Vital capacity 5.5 liters

HABIT SURVEY
Smoking habits: nonsmoker
Age begun yrs. Inhalation:
Habits of nervous tension: 2, 5, 6, 8, 23

FIGURE-DRAWING CHARACTERISTICS

Structural	Male	Female	Structural	Male	Female	Structural and Graphic	Male	Female	Graphic, Global and Height	Male	Female	Body Proportions	Male	Female
	\multicolumn{2}{c}{Both}					\multicolumn{2}{c}{Both}						
Type	\multicolumn{2}{c}{0}		Omission of Appendages	0	3	Upper and Lower Halves	2	2	Hair Shading	3	2	Head	02	03
Sex Sequence	\multicolumn{2}{c}{2}		Position of Both Arms	1	0	Four Quarters	0	4	Nudity and Transparency	7	0	Neck	03	04
Posture	1	0	Position of Right Arm	4	2	Relative Size	\multicolumn{2}{c}{4}		Form	3	3	Shoulders	01	03
Perspective	5	5	Position of Left Arm	0	2	Constant Line Pressure	0	5	Detailing	3	3	Right Arm	02	02
Vertical Midline	0	0	Position of Legs	6	2	Variable Line Pressure	2	0	Identity and Sex	3	1	Left Arm	02	02
Bilateral Symmetry	2	1	Relation of Long Axes	3	1	Line Continuity	1	4	Sophistication	3	2	Chest	01	02
Horizontal Midline	4	0	Right and Left Halves	2	0	Body Shading	0	0	Height	02		Girth	01	02

GENERAL CHARACTERISTICS OF SUBJECT

IDENTIFICATION

No. E71

Sex M

Marital status S

Age 21 yrs. at

psychological tests

PARENTAL HISTORY

Father

C   H   S   D   O

−   +   −   −   ?

Mother

C   H   S   D   O

−   ?   −   −   −

PHYSIOLOGICAL AND METABOLIC DATA

	Admission	Initial	Control	Cold pressor change	Exercise change	Smoking change
Systolic pressure	136	100	100	+18	+36	−01
Diastolic pressure	76	60	62	+24	−22	00
Heart rate	80	68	70	+16	+16	+02

Age 21 yrs.   Height 70 in.   Weight 120 lbs.   Overweight −22 %

Ponderal index 14.20   Cholesterol 178 mg. per 100 ml.   Vital capacity   liters

HABIT SURVEY

Smoking habits: heavy cigarette smoker

Age begun 18 yrs.   Inhalation: yes

Habits of nervous tension: 2, 5, 6, 23

STRONG VOCATIONAL INTEREST TEST

Occupation	Artist	Psychologist	Architect	Physician	Osteopath	Dentist	Veterinarian	Mathematician	Physicist	Engineer	Chemist	Production Manager
Standard Score	47	58	50	70	48	48	23	48	49	46	54	23

Occupation	Farmer	Aviator	Carpenter	Printer	Math.-Sci. Teacher	Ind. Arts Teacher	Voc. Agric. Teacher	Policeman	Forest Serv. Man	Y.M.C.A. Phys. Dir.	Personnel Director	Public Administrator
Standard Score	39	48	24	37	41	22	33	25	39	30	35	48

Occupation	Y.M.C.A. Secretary	Soc. Sci. H.S. Teacher	City Sch. Sup't.	Social Worker	Minister	Musician Performer	C.P.A.	Senior C.P.A.	Accountant	Office Man	Purchasing Agent	Banker
Standard Score	20	27	35	39	64	56	34	39	10	11	07	09

Occupation	Mortician	Pharmacist	Sales Manager	Real Est. Manager	Life Ins. Salesman	Advertising Man	Lawyer	Author-Journalist	President Mfg. Co.	Interest Maturity	Occupational Level	Masculinity-Femininity
Standard Score	01	17	13	19	15	34	49	48	24	52	58	53

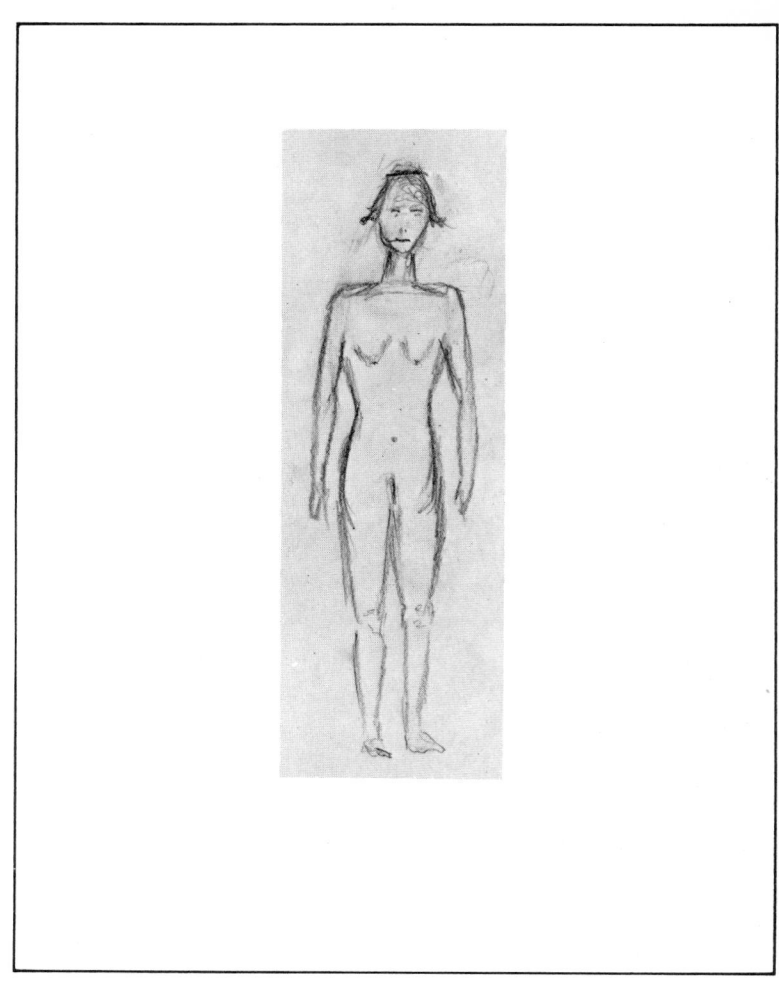

FIGURE-DRAWING CHARACTERISTICS

Structural	Male Female Both	Structural	Male	Female	Structural and Graphic	Male Female Both		Graphic, Global and Height	Male	Female	Body Proportions	Male	Female
Type	0	Omission of Appendages	0	0	Upper and Lower Halves	1	1	Hair Shading	3	3	Head	08	07
Sex Sequence	0	Position of Both Arms	1	0	Four Quarters	4	4	Nudity and Transparency	0	0	Neck	08	10
Posture	1 1	Position of Right Arm	2	0	Relative Size	0		Form	1	1	Shoulders		05
Perspective	9 0	Position of Left Arm	4	0	Constant Line Pressure	0	0	Detailing	5	1	Right Arm	06	06
Vertical Midline	4 0	Position of Legs	6	4	Variable Line Pressure	4	4	Identity and Sex	3	1	Left Arm	06	06
Bilateral Symmetry	0 5	Relation of Long Axes	1	1	Line Continuity	0	0	Sophistication	3	2	Chest		05
Horizontal Midline	2 0	Right and Left Halves	1	1	Body Shading	3	3	Height	07	06	Girth		05

GENERAL CHARACTERISTICS OF SUBJECT

IDENTIFICATION
No. 528
Sex M
Marital status S
Age 24 yrs. at psychological tests

PARENTAL HISTORY
Father
C H S D O
- ? + - -
Mother
C H S D O
- ? - - -

PHYSIOLOGICAL AND METABOLIC DATA

	Admission	Initial	Control	Cold pressor change	Exercise change	Smoking change
Systolic pressure	145	116	105	-08	+27	
Diastolic pressure	86	72	68	+12	+06	
Heart rate	74	68	65	00	+18	

Age 21 yrs.	Height 74 in.	Ponderal index 13.25
	Weight 174 lbs.	Cholesterol 234 mg. per 100 ml.
	Overweight +01 %	Vital capacity 5.0 liters

HABIT SURVEY
Smoking habits: nonsmoker
Age begun yrs.   Inhalation:
Habits of nervous tension: 5, 6, 9, 25

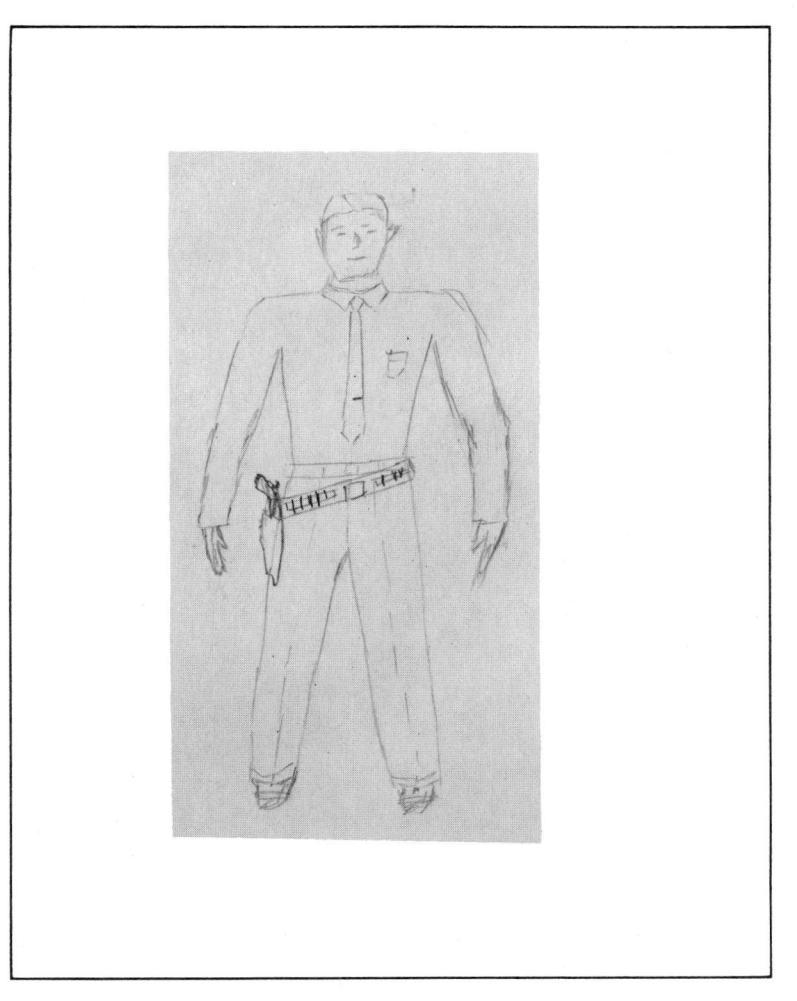

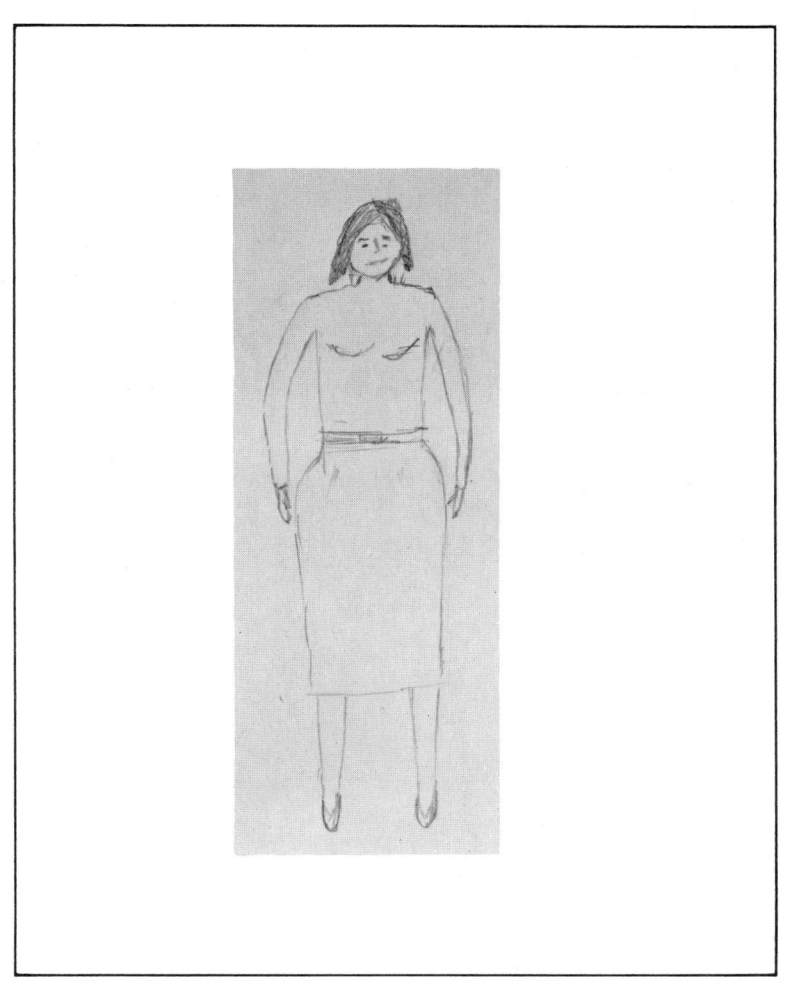

FIGURE-DRAWING CHARACTERISTICS

Structural	Male Female Both	Structural	Male	Female	Structural and Graphic	Male Female Both		Graphic, Global and Height	Male	Female	Body Proportions	Male	Female
Type	0	Omission of Appendages	0	0	Upper and Lower Halves	0	0	Hair Shading	5	3	Head	06	06
Sex Sequence	0	Position of Both Arms	0	0	Four Quarters	4	4	Nudity and Transparency	7	7	Neck	05	03
Posture	1 1	Position of Right Arm	2	5	Relative Size	2		Form	1	3	Shoulders	09	05
Perspective	0 0	Position of Left Arm	2	5	Constant Line Pressure	2	2	Detailing	3	3	Right Arm	06	06
Vertical Midline	3 0	Position of Legs	6	6	Variable Line Pressure	0	0	Identity and Sex	1	1	Left Arm	06	06
Bilateral Symmetry	4 4	Relation of Long Axes	1	1	Line Continuity	0	0	Sophistication	2	3	Chest	07	05
Horizontal Midline	4 4	Right and Left Halves	1	1	Body Shading	6	7	Height	06	06	Girth	07	07

GENERAL CHARACTERISTICS OF SUBJECT

IDENTIFICATION
No. A77
Sex M
Marital status S
Age 24 yrs. at
psychological tests

PARENTAL HISTORY
Father
C   H   S   D   O
–   ?   –   –   –
Mother
C   H   S   D   O
–   –   –   –   –

PHYSIOLOGICAL AND METABOLIC DATA

	Admission	Initial	Control	Cold pressor change	Exercise change	Smoking change
Systolic pressure	125	138	126	+08	+32	00
Diastolic pressure	80	72	79	+04	–13	+10
Heart rate	80	69	48	+01	+22	+03

Age 24 yrs.   Height 72 in.   Ponderal index 12.31
Weight 200 lbs.   Cholesterol 273 mg. per 100 ml.
Overweight +21 %   Vital capacity   liters

HABIT SURVEY

Smoking habits: nonsmoker

Age begun   yrs.   Inhalation:

Habits of nervous tension: 5, 6, 16, 25

STRONG VOCATIONAL INTEREST TEST

Occupation	Artist	Psychologist	Architect	Physician	Osteopath	Dentist	Veterinarian	Mathematician	Physicist	Engineer	Chemist	Production Manager
Standard Score	23	36	30	51	50	48	42	38	37	55	57	40

Occupation	Farmer	Aviator	Carpenter	Printer	Math.-Sci. Teacher	Ind. Arts Teacher	Voc. Agric. Teacher	Policeman	Forest Serv. Man	Y.M.C.A. Phys. Dir.	Personnel Director	Public Administrator
Standard Score	53	62	44	51	50	38	41	49	48	33	29	49

Occupation	Y.M.C.A. Secretary	Soc. Sci. H.S. Teacher	City Sch. Sup't.	Social Worker	Minister	Musician Performer	C.P.A.	Senior C.P.A.	Accountant	Office Man	Purchasing Agent	Banker
Standard Score	10	28	15	25	60	24	29	56	36	41	33	23

Occupation	Mortician	Pharmacist	Sales Manager	Real Est. Manager	Life Ins. Salesman	Advertising Man	Lawyer	Author-Journalist	President Mfg. Co.	Interest Maturity	Occupational Level	Masculinity-Femininity
Standard Score	22	31	14	22	09	19	30	28	24	50	49	64

FIGURE-DRAWING CHARACTERISTICS

Structural	Male Female Both	Structural	Male	Female	Structural and Graphic	Male Female Both	Graphic, Global and Height	Male	Female	Body Proportions	Male	Female
Type	0	Omission of Appendages	0	0	Upper and Lower Halves	3 1	Hair Shading	1	5	Head	07	07
Sex Sequence	0	Position of Both Arms	0	4	Four Quarters	4 4	Nudity and Transparency	7	7	Neck	06	06
Posture	1 1	Position of Right Arm	5	7	Relative Size	0	Form	3	3	Shoulders	07	
Perspective	0 2	Position of Left Arm	5	4	Constant Line Pressure	0 0	Detailing	3	5	Right Arm	04	
Vertical Midline	3 4	Position of Legs	6	1	Variable Line Pressure	5 5	Identity and Sex	1	1	Left Arm	04	02
Bilateral Symmetry	4 0	Relation of Long Axes	1	1	Line Continuity	0 2	Sophistication	2	3	Chest	05	06
Horizontal Midline	4 4	Right and Left Halves	1	2	Body Shading	0 0	Height	06	05	Girth	06	05

GENERAL CHARACTERISTICS OF SUBJECT

IDENTIFICATION
No. 362
Sex M
Marital status M
Age 28 yrs. at
psychological tests

PARENTAL HISTORY
Father
C   H   S   D   O
-    -   -   (+)   +
Mother
C   H   S   D   O
-    -   -   -   +

PHYSIOLOGICAL AND METABOLIC DATA

	Admission	Initial	Control	Cold pressor change	Exercise change	Smoking change
Systolic pressure	150	126	112	+08	+44	00
Diastolic pressure	60	68	62	+02	+02	+04
Heart rate	84	78	79	+04	+28	00

Age 24 yrs.

Height   73   in.   Ponderal index 12.98
Weight   178 lbs.   Cholesterol   295   mg. per 100 ml.
Overweight +04 %   Vital capacity 5.1   liters

HABIT SURVEY
Smoking habits: mixed smoker
Age begun 16 yrs.   Inhalation: yes
Habits of nervous tension: 4, 5, 6, 9, 11,
16, 21, 23, 24

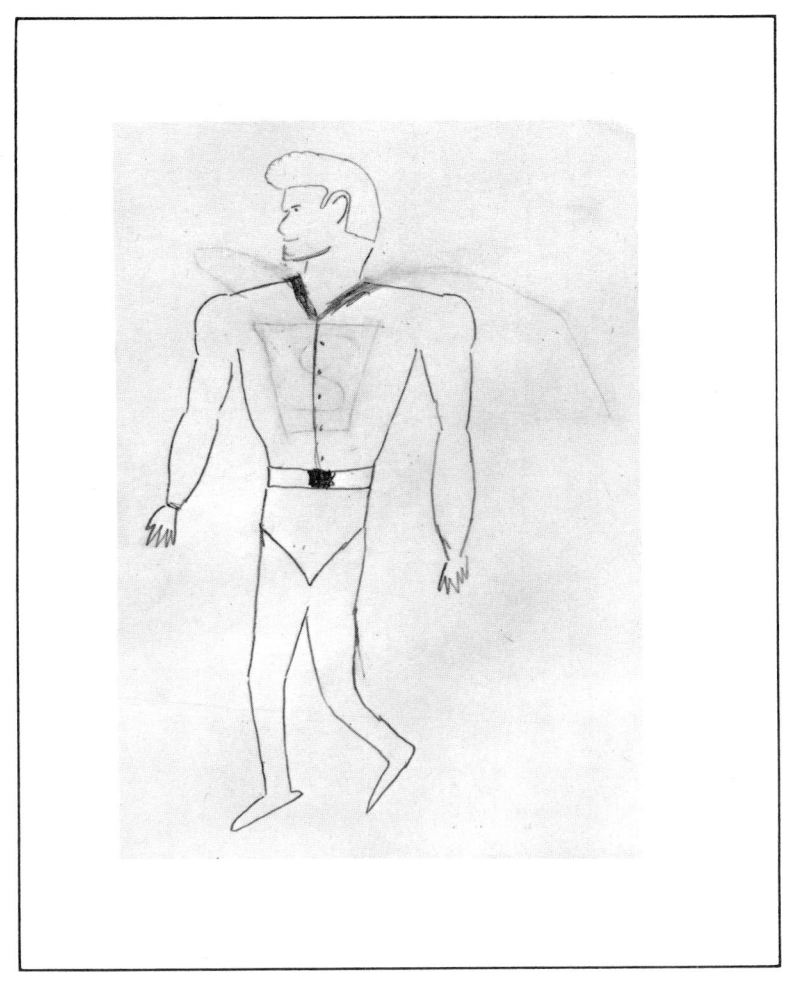

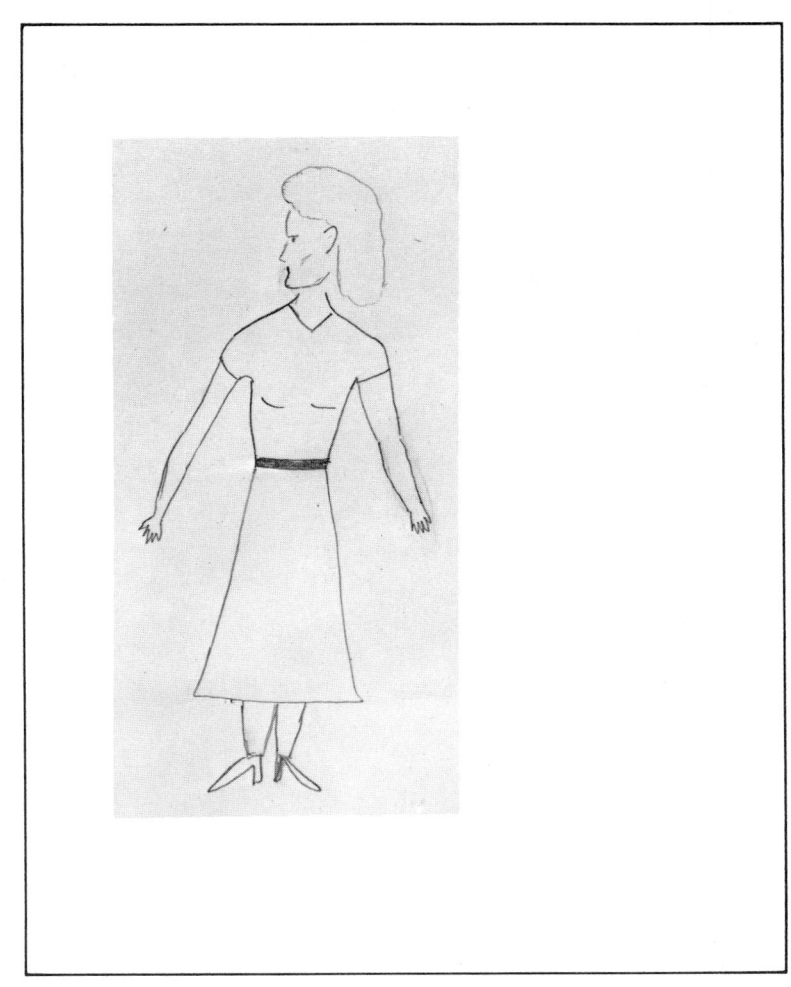

FIGURE-DRAWING CHARACTERISTICS

Structural	Male Female Both		Structural	Male	Female	Structural and Graphic	Male Female Both		Graphic, Global and Height	Male	Female	Body Proportions	Male	Female
Type	0		Omission of Appendages	0	0	Upper and Lower Halves	0	0	Hair Shading	5	5	Head	08	08
Sex Sequence	0		Position of Both Arms	0	0	Four Quarters	4	4	Nudity and Transparency	2	7	Neck	08	06
Posture	2	1	Position of Right Arm	2	2	Relative Size	0		Form	3	3	Shoulders	11	06
Perspective	5	5	Position of Left Arm	2	2	Constant Line Pressure	5	5	Detailing	3	3	Right Arm	06	06
Vertical Midline	3	0	Position of Legs	8	2	Variable Line Pressure	0	0	Identity and Sex	1	1	Left Arm	06	04
Bilateral Symmetry	4	4	Relation of Long Axes	1	1	Line Continuity	3	3	Sophistication	2	3	Chest	08	05
Horizontal Midline	4	4	Right and Left Halves	1	2	Body Shading	4	5	Height	07	06	Girth	06	05

GENERAL CHARACTERISTICS OF SUBJECT

IDENTIFICATION
No. G18
Sex M
Marital status S
Age 22 yrs. at
psychological tests

PARENTAL HISTORY				
Father				
C	H	S	D	O
–	–	–	–	+
Mother				
C	H	S	D	O
–	–	–	+	+

PHYSIOLOGICAL AND METABOLIC DATA

	Admission	Initial	Control	Cold pressor change	Exercise change	Smoking change
Systolic pressure	135	132	122	+20	+48	00
Diastolic pressure	80	82	84	+24	–10	+03
Heart rate	82	56	54	+06	+29	+03

Age 21 yrs.	Height 73 in. Weight 191 lbs. Overweight +14 %	Ponderal index 12.68 Cholesterol 203 mg. per 100 ml. Vital capacity liters

HABIT SURVEY
Smoking habits: pipe smoker
Age begun 16 yrs.   Inhalation: no
Habits of nervous tension: 4, 5, 11, 18

STRONG VOCATIONAL INTEREST TEST

Occupation	Artist	Psychologist	Architect	Physician	Osteopath	Dentist	Veterinarian	Mathematician	Physicist	Engineer	Chemist	Production Manager
Standard Score	33	47	39	62	51	42	22	35	39	52	51	39

Occupation	Farmer	Aviator	Carpenter	Printer	Math.-Sci. Teacher	Ind. Arts Teacher	Voc. Agric. Teacher	Policeman	Forest Serv. Man	Y.M.C.A. Phys. Dir.	Personnel Director	Public Administrator
Standard Score	25	46	31	39	38	32	28	36	27	34	35	48

Occupation	Y.M.C.A. Secretary	Soc. Sci. H.S. Teacher	City Sch. Sup't.	Social Worker	Minister	Musician Performer	C.P.A.	Senior C.P.A.	Accountant	Office Man	Purchasing Agent	Banker
Standard Score	16	21	23	35	59	39	30	40	24	25	30	12

Occupation	Mortician	Pharmacist	Sales Manager	Real Est. Manager	Life Ins. Salesman	Advertising Man	Lawyer	Author- Journalist	President Mfg. Co.	Interest Maturity	Occupational Level	Masculinity- Femininity
Standard Score	25	29	23	27	21	35	32	37	36	53	57	49

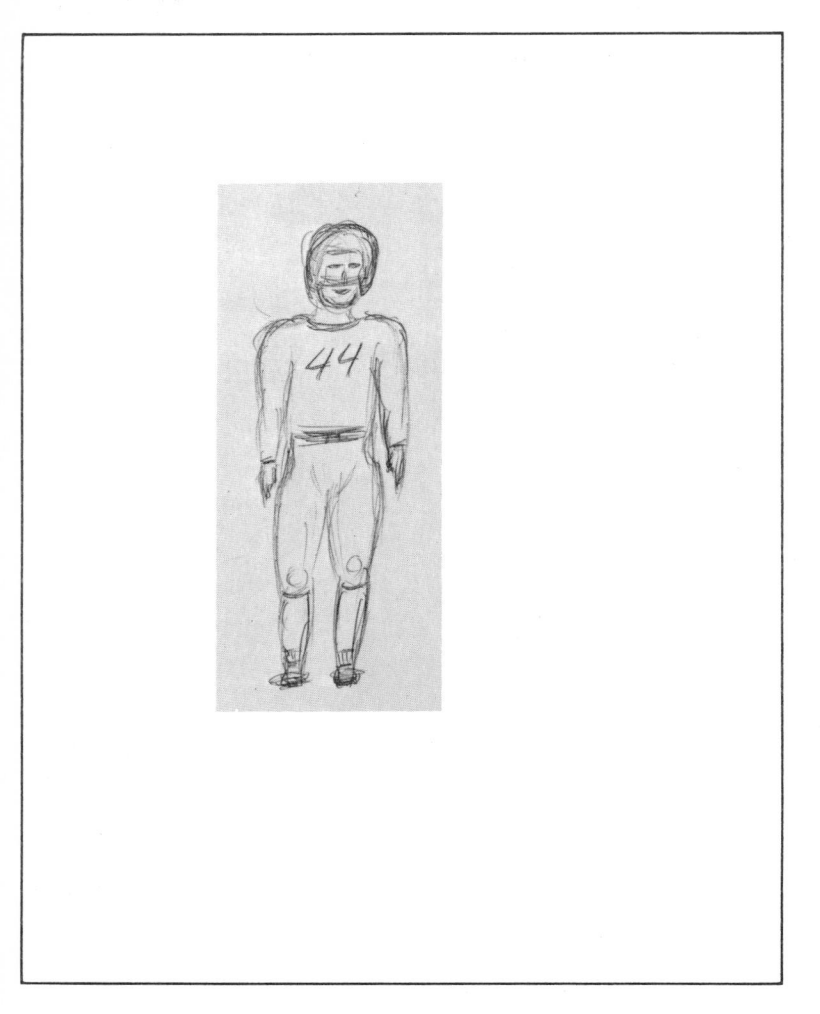

FIGURE-DRAWING CHARACTERISTICS

Structural	Male	Female	Structural	Male	Female	Structural and Graphic	Male	Female	Graphic, Global and Height	Male	Female	Body Proportions	Male	Female
	Both						Both							
Type	0		Omission of Appendages	0	0	Upper and Lower Halves	1	2	Hair Shading	0	3	Head	06	04
Sex Sequence	0		Position of Both Arms	0	4	Four Quarters	4	4	Nudity and Transparency	7	0	Neck	05	02
Posture	1	8	Position of Right Arm	0	7	Relative Size	5		Form	1	3	Shoulders	06	
Perspective	0	2	Position of Left Arm	0	2	Constant Line Pressure	0	0	Detailing	1	5	Right Arm	04	
Vertical Midline	0	4	Position of Legs	4	1	Variable Line Pressure	1	2	Identity and Sex	1	3	Left Arm	04	03
Bilateral Symmetry	4	0	Relation of Long Axes	1	0	Line Continuity	0	0	Sophistication	2	3	Chest	04	04
Horizontal Midline	4	0	Right and Left Halves	1	1	Body Shading	6	0	Height	05		Girth	05	04

GENERAL CHARACTERISTICS OF SUBJECT

IDENTIFICATION
No. A72
Sex M
Marital status S
Age 23 yrs. at
psychological tests

PARENTAL HISTORY
Father
C H S D O
- - - - +
Mother
C H S D O
- - - - -

PHYSIOLOGICAL AND METABOLIC DATA

	Admission	Initial	Control	Cold pressor change	Exercise change	Smoking change
Systolic pressure	112	124	111	+20	+22	+04
Diastolic pressure	60	70	60	+31	-42	-02
Heart rate	84	72	64	+10	+47	+06

Age 22 yrs.	Height	69	in.	Ponderal index 13.22	
	Weight	142	lbs.	Cholesterol	250 mg. per 100 ml.
	Overweight -05 %			Vital capacity	liters

HABIT SURVEY

Smoking habits: occasional smoker

Age begun 18 yrs.   Inhalation: no

Habits of nervous tension: 2, 3, 4, 5, 6, 9, 10, 18, 22, 23, 24, 25

STRONG VOCATIONAL INTEREST TEST

Occupation	Artist	Psychologist	Architect	Physician	Osteopath	Dentist	Veterinarian	Mathematician	Physicist	Engineer	Chemist	Production Manager
Standard Score	29	35	30	48	41	38	08	26	21	31	35	35

Occupation	Farmer	Aviator	Carpenter	Printer	Math.-Sci. Teacher	Ind. Arts Teacher	Voc. Agric. Teacher	Policeman	Forest Serv. Man	Y.M.C.A. Phys. Dir.	Personnel Director	Public Administrator
Standard Score	22	25	02	20	32	09	10	24	08	40	36	36

Occupation	Y.M.C.A. Secretary	Soc. Sci. H.S. Teacher	City Sch. Sup't.	Social Worker	Minister	Musician Performer	C.P.A.	Senior C.P.A.	Accountant	Office Man	Purchasing Agent	Banker
Standard Score	29	28	32	32	60	36	28	30	22	30	27	19

Occupation	Mortician	Pharmacist	Sales Manager	Real Est. Manager	Life Ins. Salesman	Advertising Man	Lawyer	Author-Journalist	President Mfg. Co.	Interest Maturity	Occupational Level	Masculinity-Femininity
Standard Score	26	32	29	30	32	35	40	35	39	54	66	45

FIGURE-DRAWING CHARACTERISTICS

Structural	Male Female Both		Structural	Male	Female	Structural and Graphic	Male Female Both		Graphic, Global and Height	Male	Female	Body Proportions	Male	Female
Type	0		Omission of Appendages	0	3	Upper and Lower Halves	1	1	Hair Shading	3	3	Head	06	06
Sex Sequence	0		Position of Both Arms	1	4	Four Quarters	4	4	Nudity and Transparency	7	6	Neck	05	06
Posture	1	0	Position of Right Arm	2	7	Relative Size	2		Form	1	1	Shoulders	07	
Perspective	0	2	Position of Left Arm	0	4	Constant Line Pressure	1	0	Detailing	1	3	Right Arm	07	
Vertical Midline	3	4	Position of Legs	4	1	Variable Line Pressure	0	3	Identity and Sex	1	1	Left Arm	06	04
Bilateral Symmetry	3	0	Relation of Long Axes	1	1	Line Continuity	0	0	Sophistication	2	3	Chest	05	04
Horizontal Midline	4	4	Right and Left Halves	2	2	Body Shading	7	3	Height	05		Girth	06	05

GENERAL CHARACTERISTICS OF SUBJECT

IDENTIFICATION
No. 057
Sex M
Marital status M
Age 25 yrs. at
psychological tests

PARENTAL HISTORY
Father
C H S D O
- - - - +
Mother
C H S D O
- - - - -

PHYSIOLOGICAL AND METABOLIC DATA

	Admission	Initial	Control	Cold pressor change	Exercise change	Smoking change
Systolic pressure	120	122	112	+18	+28	+02
Diastolic pressure	80	64	64	+20	-26	+04
Heart rate	72	65	57	+18	+08	+16

Age 22 yrs.	Height 74 in.	Ponderal index 12.82
	Weight 192 lbs.	Cholesterol 248 mg. per 100 ml.
	Overweight +11 %	Vital capacity 5.3 liters

HABIT SURVEY

Smoking habits: mixed smoker

  Age begun 18 yrs.   Inhalation: yes

Habits of nervous tension: 5, 14, 15, 18

STRONG VOCATIONAL INTEREST TEST

Occupation	Artist	Psychologist	Architect	Physician	Osteopath	Dentist	Veterinarian	Mathematician	Physicist	Engineer	Chemist	Production Manager
Standard Score	26	39	27	47	41	26	27	24	22	33	39	46

Occupation	Farmer	Aviator	Carpenter	Printer	Math.-Sci. Teacher	Ind. Arts Teacher	Voc. Agric. Teacher	Policeman	Forest Serv. Man	Y.M.C.A. Phys. Dir.	Personnel Director	Public Administrator
Standard Score	40	50	21	35	38	36	42	29	32	35	39	45

Occupation	Y.M.C.A. Secretary	Soc. Sci. H.S. Teacher	City Sch. Sup't.	Social Worker	Minister	Musician Performer	C.P.A.	Senior C.P.A.	Accountant	Office Man	Purchasing Agent	Banker
Standard Score	23	32	20	33	61	36	17	34	17	25	22	18

Occupation	Mortician	Pharmacist	Sales Manager	Real Est. Manager	Life Ins. Salesman	Advertising Man	Lawyer	Author-Journalist	President Mfg. Co.	Interest Maturity	Occupational Level	Masculinity-Femininity
Standard Score	18	25	32	28	24	32	27	33	32	51	56	53

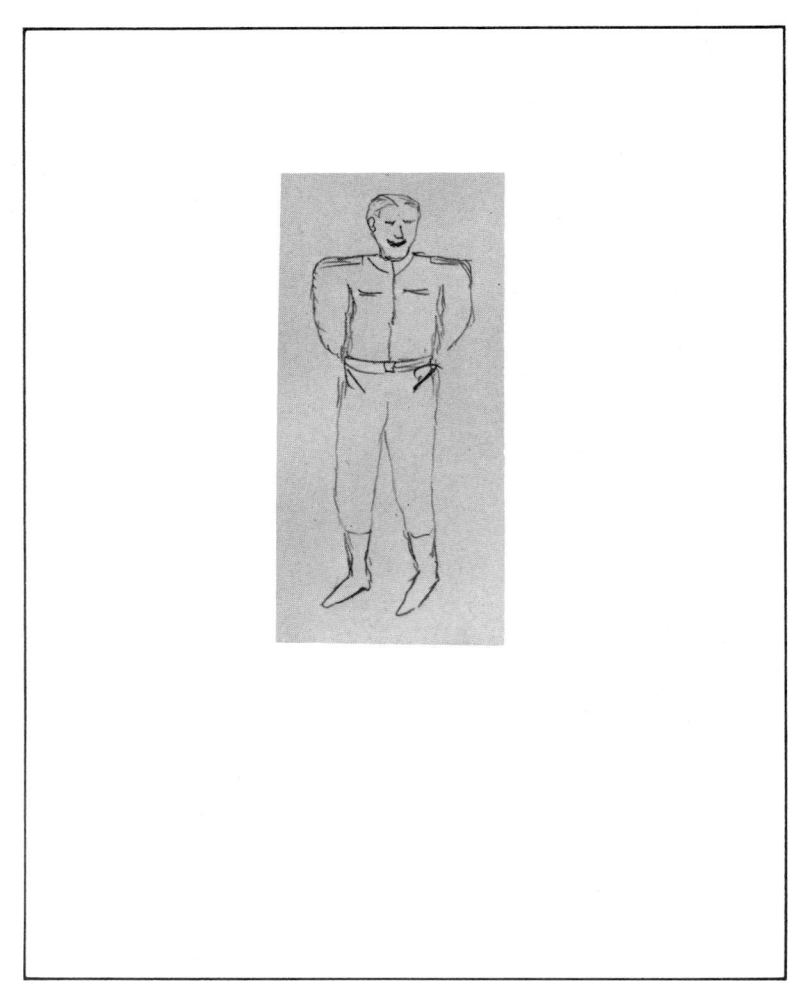

FIGURE-DRAWING CHARACTERISTICS

Structural	Male Female Both		Structural	Male	Female	Structural and Graphic	Male Female Both		Graphic, Global and Height	Male	Female	Body Proportions	Male	Female
Type	0		Omission of Appendages	2	0	Upper and Lower Halves	1	2	Hair Shading	1	5	Head	05	03
Sex Sequence	1		Position of Both Arms	6	4	Four Quarters	4	0	Nudity and Transparency	7	7	Neck	00	
Posture	1	1	Position of Right Arm	8	7	Relative Size	0		Form	1	3	Shoulders	06	
Perspective	0	2	Position of Left Arm	8	4	Constant Line Pressure	0	1	Detailing	3	3	Right Arm		
Vertical Midline	3	4	Position of Legs	6	1	Variable Line Pressure	1	0	Identity and Sex	1	1	Left Arm		04
Bilateral Symmetry	3	0	Relation of Long Axes	1	1	Line Continuity	0	0	Sophistication	2	3	Chest	04	03
Horizontal Midline	4	4	Right and Left Halves	1	2	Body Shading	4	2	Height	04	03	Girth	05	04

GENERAL CHARACTERISTICS OF SUBJECT

IDENTIFICATION
No. 326
Sex M
Marital status S
Age 25 yrs. at
psychological tests

PARENTAL HISTORY
Father
C   H   S   D   O
–   –   –   –   –
Mother
C   H   S   D   O
–   –   –   –   +

PHYSIOLOGICAL AND METABOLIC DATA

	Admission	Initial	Control	Cold pressor change	Exercise change	Smoking change
Systolic pressure	122	116	114	+04	+32	–04
Diastolic pressure	70	64	64	+06	–02	00
Heart rate	72	78	75	00	+05	00

Age 24 yrs.	Height	72	in.	Ponderal index	13.38	
	Weight	156	lbs.	Cholesterol	250	mg. per 100 ml.
	Overweight	–05 %		Vital capacity	4.9	liters

HABIT SURVEY
Smoking habits: heavy cigarette smoker
Age begun 20 yrs.   Inhalation: yes
Habits of nervous tension: 2, 5, 6, 10

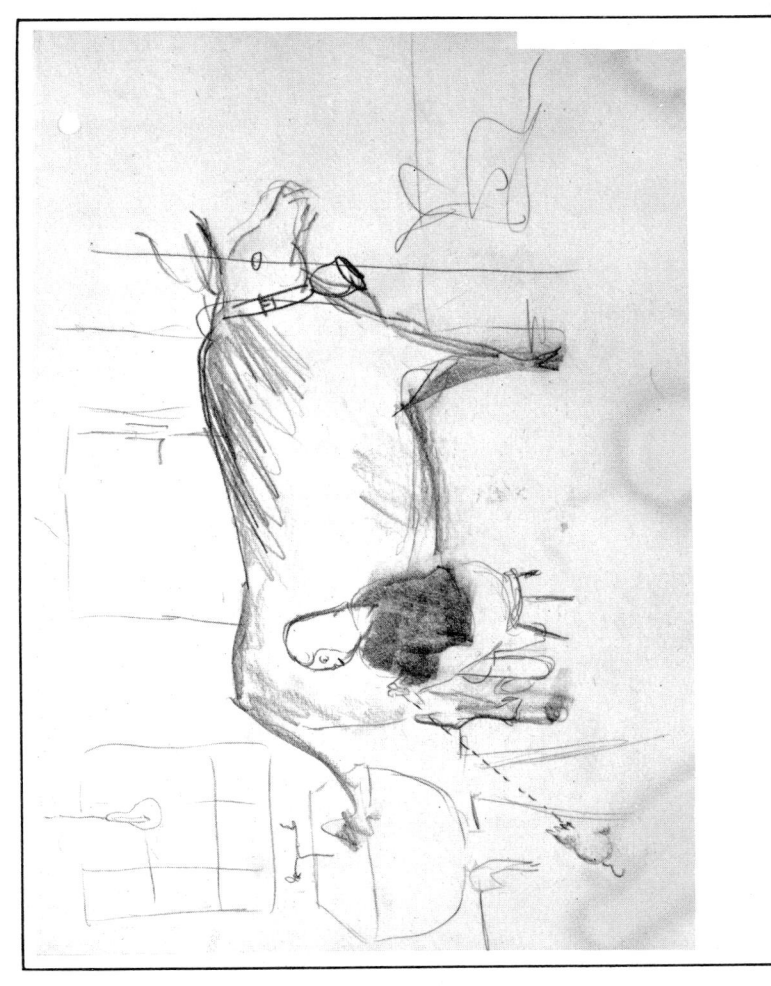

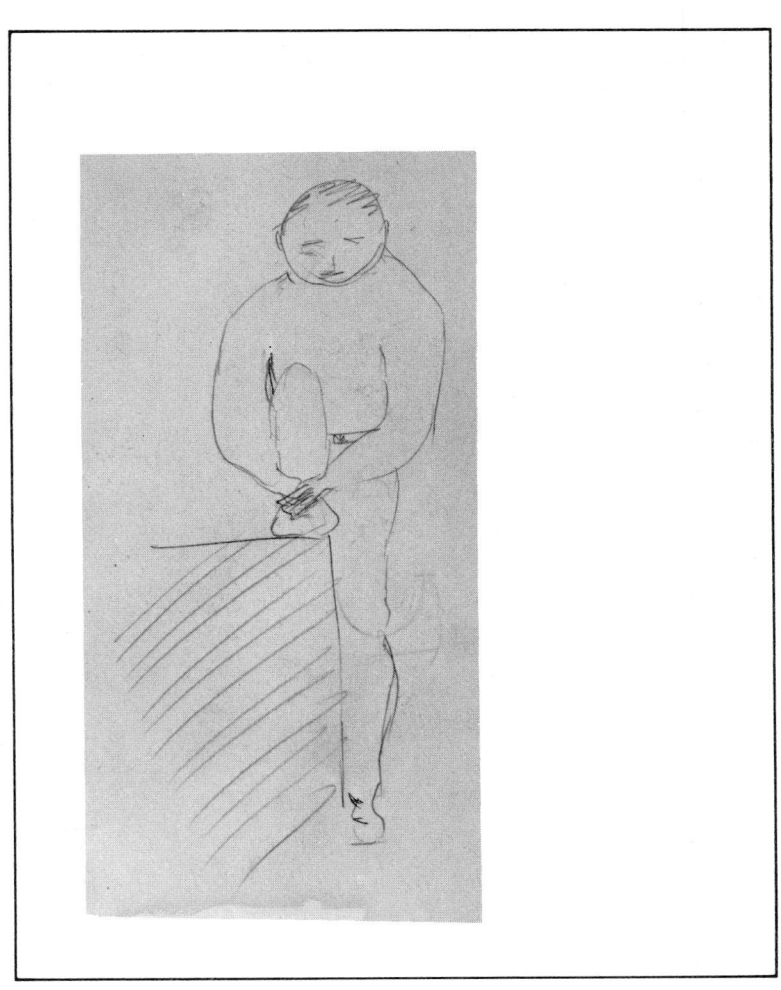

FIGURE-DRAWING CHARACTERISTICS

Structural	Male Female Both		Structural	Male	Female	Structural and Graphic	Male Female Both		Graphic, Global and Height	Male	Female	Body Proportions	Male	Female
Type	0		Omission of Appendages	0	6	Upper and Lower Halves	0	0	Hair Shading	7	5	Head		05
Sex Sequence	1		Position of Both Arms	0	4	Four Quarters	4	4	Nudity and Transparency	7	7	Neck		
Posture	9	3	Position of Right Arm	5	7	Relative Size	0		Form	3	3	Shoulders	08	
Perspective	0	8	Position of Left Arm	5	7	Constant Line Pressure	0	0	Detailing	5	3	Right Arm	06	
Vertical Midline	0	4	Position of Legs	9	9	Variable Line Pressure	1	1	Identity and Sex	3	1	Left Arm	06	
Bilateral Symmetry	1	0	Relation of Long Axes	1	0	Line Continuity	1	0	Sophistication	3	2	Chest	05	
Horizontal Midline	4	4	Right and Left Halves	1	2	Body Shading	0	1	Height	07		Girth		

GENERAL CHARACTERISTICS OF SUBJECT

IDENTIFICATION

No. F08

Sex F

Marital status S

Age 24 yrs. at

psychological tests

PARENTAL HISTORY

Father

C   H   S   D   O

–   –   –   –   –

Mother

C   H   S   D   O

–   –   –   –   +

PHYSIOLOGICAL AND METABOLIC DATA

	Admission	Initial	Control	Cold pressor change	Exercise change	Smoking change
Systolic pressure	104	96	90	+10	+20	–04
Diastolic pressure	58	78	70	+14	00	+12
Heart rate	68	80	71	–16	+08	+14

Age 22 yrs.

Height 70 in.   Ponderal index 12.01

Weight 198 lbs.   Cholesterol 196 mg. per 100 ml.

Overweight +33 %   Vital capacity   liters

HABIT SURVEY

Smoking habits: nonsmoker

Age begun   yrs.   Inhalation:

Habits of nervous tension: 6, 8, 16, 17

STRONG VOCATIONAL INTEREST TEST

Occupation	Artist	Psychologist	Architect	Physician	Osteopath	Dentist	Veterinarian	Mathematician	Physicist	Engineer	Chemist	Production Manager
Standard Score	51	47	48	58	51	41	24	40	38	36	42	26

Occupation	Farmer	Aviator	Carpenter	Printer	Math.-Sci. Teacher	Ind. Arts Teacher	Voc. Agric. Teacher	Policeman	Forest Serv. Man	Y.M.C.A. Phys. Dir.	Personnel Director	Public Administrator
Standard Score	35	35	25	32	31	19	22	24	31	40	36	42

Occupation	Y.M.C.A. Secretary	Soc. Sci. H.S. Teacher	City Sch. Sup't.	Social Worker	Minister	Musician Performer	C.P.A.	Senior C.P.A.	Accountant	Office Man	Purchasing Agent	Banker
Standard Score	32	27	29	44	58	59	20	24	11	18	09	10

Occupation	Mortician	Pharmacist	Sales Manager	Real Est. Manager	Life Ins. Salesman	Advertising Man	Lawyer	Author-Journalist	President Mfg. Co.	Interest Maturity	Occupational Level	Masculinity-Femininity
Standard Score	21	19	20	29	29	40	39	48	27	53	57	33

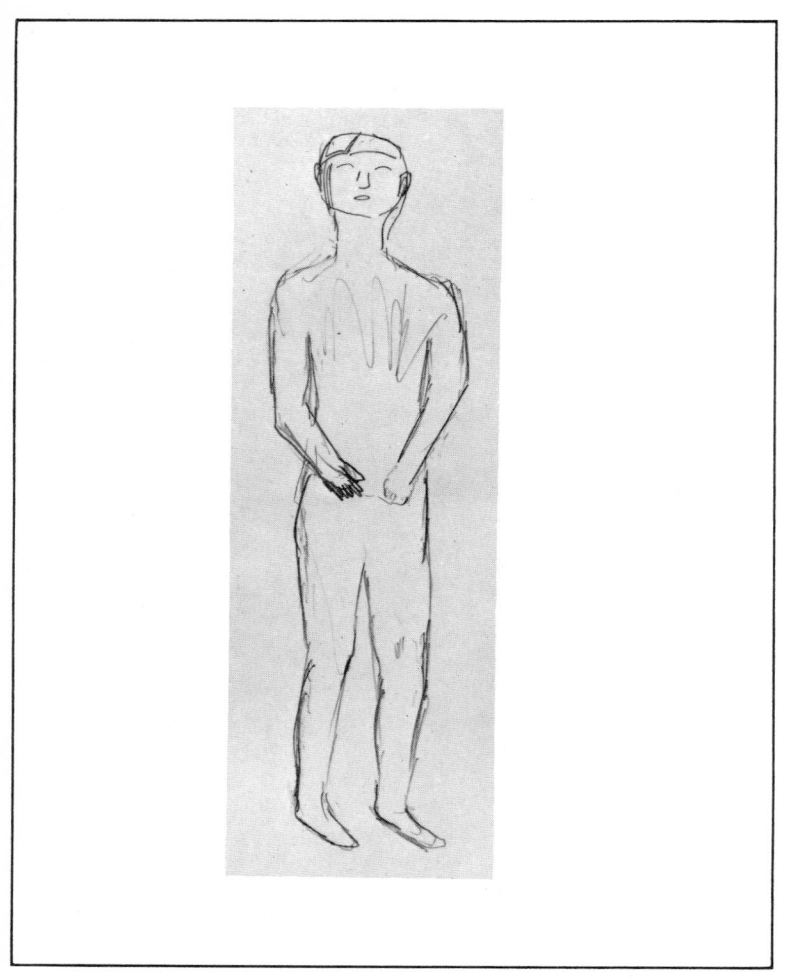

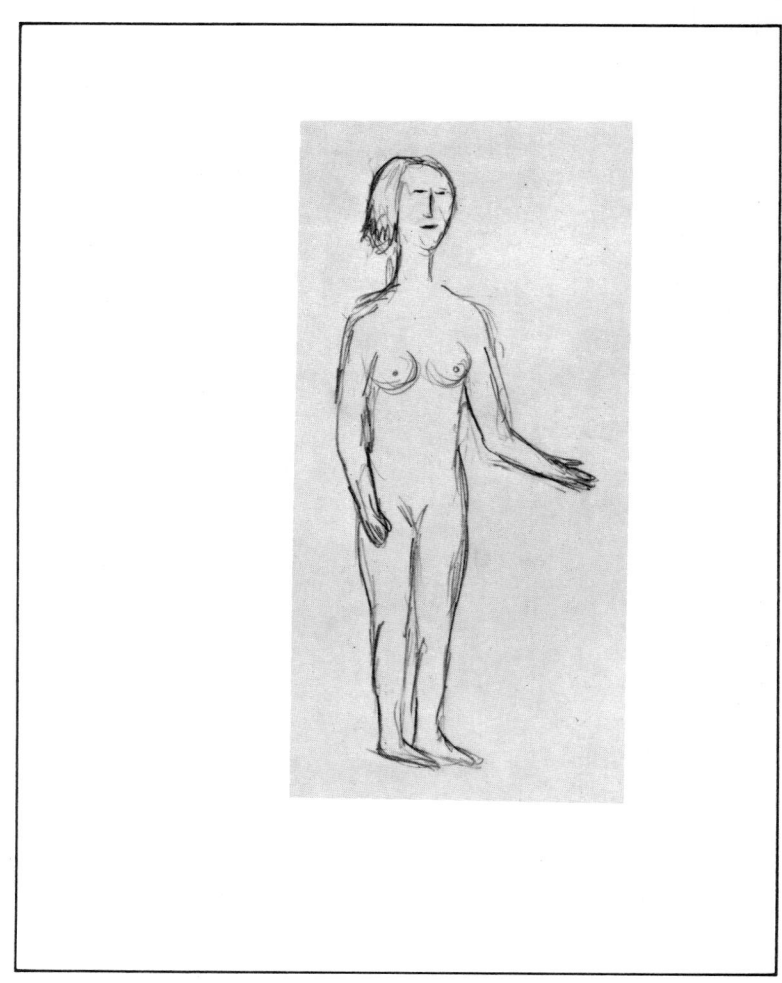

FIGURE-DRAWING CHARACTERISTICS

Structural	Male Female Both	Structural	Male	Female	Structural and Graphic	Male Female Both	Graphic, Global and Height	Male	Female	Body Proportions	Male	Female
Type	0	Omission of Appendages	0	0	Upper and Lower Halves	0	1	Hair Shading	5	2	Head	07	07
Sex Sequence	2	Position of Both Arms	0	1	Four Quarters	4	4	Nudity and Transparency	0	0	Neck	12	12
Posture	1	1	Position of Right Arm	5	0	Relative Size	0	Form	3	3	Shoulders	07	06
Perspective	9	9	Position of Left Arm	5	4	Constant Line Pressure	0	0	Detailing	5	3	Right Arm	06	06
Vertical Midline	0	0	Position of Legs	4	4	Variable Line Pressure	5	5	Identity and Sex	3	1	Left Arm	06	06
Bilateral Symmetry	3	3	Relation of Long Axes	1	1	Line Continuity	0	0	Sophistication	3	2	Chest	05	05
Horizontal Midline	0	0	Right and Left Halves	1	3	Body Shading	3	3	Height	07	06	Girth	06	06

GENERAL CHARACTERISTICS OF SUBJECT

IDENTIFICATION
No. A32
Sex M
Marital status S
Age 24 yrs. at
psychological tests

PARENTAL HISTORY

Father

C   H   S   D   O

–   –   –   –   –

Mother

C   H   S   D   O

–   –   –   –   +

PHYSIOLOGICAL AND METABOLIC DATA

	Admission	Initial	Control	Cold pressor change	Exercise change	Smoking change
Systolic pressure	104	112	120	+05	+22	+07
Diastolic pressure	64	48	58	+15	+02	+02
Heart rate	74	57	56	+04	+34	+15

Age 23 yrs.

Height 71 in.
Weight 167 lbs.
Overweight +05 %

Ponderal index 12.89
Cholesterol 210 mg. per 100 ml.
Vital capacity liters

HABIT SURVEY

Smoking habits: occasional smoker

Age begun 20 yrs.   Inhalation: yes

Habits of nervous tension: 3, 9, 17, 23, 25

STRONG VOCATIONAL INTEREST TEST

Occupation	Artist	Psychologist	Architect	Physician	Osteopath	Dentist	Veterinarian	Mathematician	Physicist	Engineer	Chemist	Production Manager
Standard Score	7	7	8	7	4	4	2	5	7	4	5	2

Occupation	Farmer	Aviator	Carpenter	Printer	Math.-Sci. Teacher	Ind. Arts Teacher	Voc. Agric. Teacher	Policeman	Forest Serv. Man	Y.M.C.A. Phys. Dir.	Personnel Director	Public Administrator
Standard Score	6	4	3	5	4	1	2	2	2	2	2	3

Occupation	Y.M.C.A. Secretary	Soc. Sci. H.S. Teacher	City Sch. Sup't.	Social Worker	Minister	Musician Performer	C.P.A.	Senior C.P.A.	Accountant	Office Man	Purchasing Agent	Banker
Standard Score	2	2	2	2	6	7	4	3	1	2	1	1

Occupation	Mortician	Pharmacist	Sales Manager	Real Est. Manager	Life Ins. Salesman	Advertising Man	Lawyer	Author-Journalist	President Mfg. Co.	Interest Maturity	Occupational Level	Masculinity-Femininity
Standard Score	2	2	2	4	2	5	5	7	3	3	5	4

Plate 509   MIXED INTERMEDIATE AND MODERATELY SOPHISTICATED DRAWINGS   553

FIGURE-DRAWING CHARACTERISTICS

Structural	Male Female Both		Structural	Male	Female	Structural and Graphic	Male Female Both		Graphic, Global and Height	Male	Female	Body Proportions	Male	Female
Type	0		Omission of Appendages	7	8	Upper and Lower Halves	1	1	Hair Shading	0	0	Head	08	07
Sex Sequence	0		Position of Both Arms	0	0	Four Quarters	4	4	Nudity and Transparency	9	7	Neck	08	06
Posture	1	0	Position of Right Arm	5	1	Relative Size	0		Form	1	3	Shoulders	06	05
Perspective	0	0	Position of Left Arm	5	1	Constant Line Pressure	1	1	Detailing	1	1	Right Arm		04
Vertical Midline	3	0	Position of Legs	6	0	Variable Line Pressure	0	0	Identity and Sex	1	1	Left Arm	04	04
Bilateral Symmetry	2	3	Relation of Long Axes	1	1	Line Continuity	0	0	Sophistication	2	3	Chest	05	05
Horizontal Midline	4	4	Right and Left Halves	1	1	Body Shading	3	6	Height	06		Girth		06

GENERAL CHARACTERISTICS OF SUBJECT

IDENTIFICATION

No. A49
Sex M
Marital status S
Age 23 yrs. at
psychological tests

PARENTAL HISTORY

Father

C H S D O
- - - - ?

Mother

C H S D O
- - - - ?

PHYSIOLOGICAL AND METABOLIC DATA

	Admission	Initial	Control	Cold pressor change	Exercise change	Smoking change
Systolic pressure	134	122	120	+15	+42	+05
Diastolic pressure	84	80	78	+15	-21	+11
Heart rate	100	64	60	+14	+33	00

Age 22 yrs.

Height 74 in.
Weight 198 lbs.
Overweight +14 %

Ponderal index 12.69
Cholesterol 160 mg. per 100 ml.
Vital capacity liters

HABIT SURVEY

Smoking habits: nonsmoker

Age begun yrs.   Inhalation:

Habits of nervous tension: 5, 25

STRONG VOCATIONAL INTEREST TEST

Occupation	Artist	Psychologist	Architect	Physician	Osteopath	Dentist	Veterinarian	Mathematician	Physicist	Engineer	Chemist	Production Manager
Standard Score	2	5	3	2	5	4	2	3	4	4	4	4

Occupation	Farmer	Aviator	Carpenter	Printer	Math.-Sci. Teacher	Ind. Arts Teacher	Voc. Agric. Teacher	Policeman	Forest Serv. Man	Y.M.C.A. Phys. Dir.	Personnel Director	Public Administrator
Standard Score	5	4	3	7	7	4	4	5	4	5	6	6

Occupation	Y.M.C.A. Secretary	Soc. Sci. H.S. Teacher	City Sch. Sup't.	Social Worker	Minister	Musician Performer	C.P.A.	Senior C.P.A.	Accountant	Office Man	Purchasing Agent	Banker
Standard Score	5	6	5	5	6	6	3	7	5	6	0	2

Occupation	Mortician	Pharmacist	Sales Manager	Real Est. Manager	Life Ins. Salesman	Advertising Man	Lawyer	Author-Journalist	President Mfg. Co.	Interest Maturity	Occupational Level	Masculinity-Femininity
Standard Score	2	3	2	3	2	3	3	2	2	7	4	4

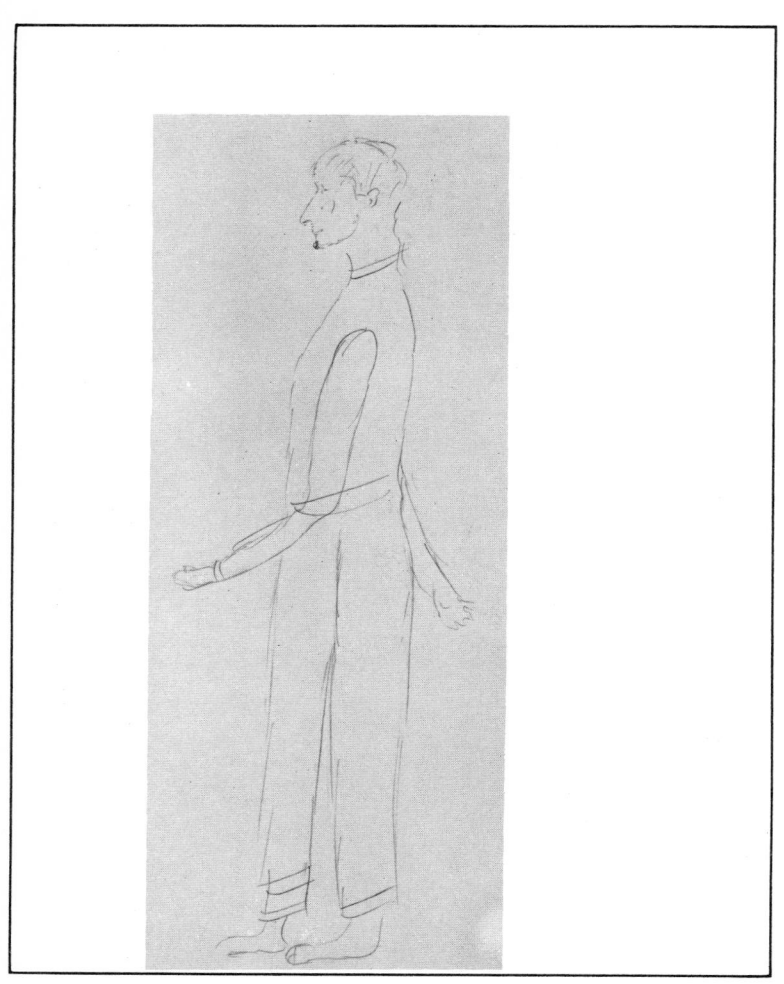

FIGURE-DRAWING CHARACTERISTICS

Structural	Male Female Both	Structural	Male	Female	Structural and Graphic	Male Female Both		Graphic, Global and Height	Male	Female	Body Proportions	Male	Female
Type	0	Omission of Appendages	0	0	Upper and Lower Halves	3	3	Hair Shading	7	3	Head	09	09
Sex Sequence	2	Position of Both Arms	4	4	Four Quarters	4	4	Nudity and Transparency	7	7	Neck	12	14
Posture	1 1	Position of Right Arm	7	7	Relative Size	2		Form	3	1	Shoulders		
Perspective	9 2	Position of Left Arm	4	4	Constant Line Pressure	0	3	Detailing	3	1	Right Arm		
Vertical Midline	9 4	Position of Legs	4	1	Variable Line Pressure	1	0	Identity and Sex	3	1	Left Arm	08	08
Bilateral Symmetry	0 0	Relation of Long Axes	1	1	Line Continuity	0	0	Sophistication	3	2	Chest	09	08
Horizontal Midline	4 4	Right and Left Halves	1	2	Body Shading	0	6	Height	08	08	Girth	09	11

GENERAL CHARACTERISTICS OF SUBJECT

IDENTIFICATION
No. 548
Sex M
Marital status S
Age 23 yrs. at
psychological tests

PARENTAL HISTORY
Father
C　H　S　D　O
–　–　–　–　?
Mother
C　H　S　D　O
–　–　–　–　–

PHYSIOLOGICAL AND METABOLIC DATA

	Admission	Initial	Control	Cold pressor change	Exercise change	Smoking change
Systolic pressure	130	130	120	+10	+30	+07
Diastolic pressure	74	80	80	00	–10	+04
Heart rate	72	76	59	+16	+12	+04

Age 21 yrs.	Height	75 in.	Ponderal index	13.07
	Weight	189 lbs.	Cholesterol	155 mg. per 100 ml.
	Overweight	+07 %	Vital capacity	5.0 liters

HABIT SURVEY
Smoking habits: nonsmoker
Age begun   yrs.   Inhalation:
Habits of nervous tension: 5, 6, 9, 18, 21

Plate 511   **MIXED INTERMEDIATE AND MODERATELY SOPHISTICATED DRAWINGS**   555

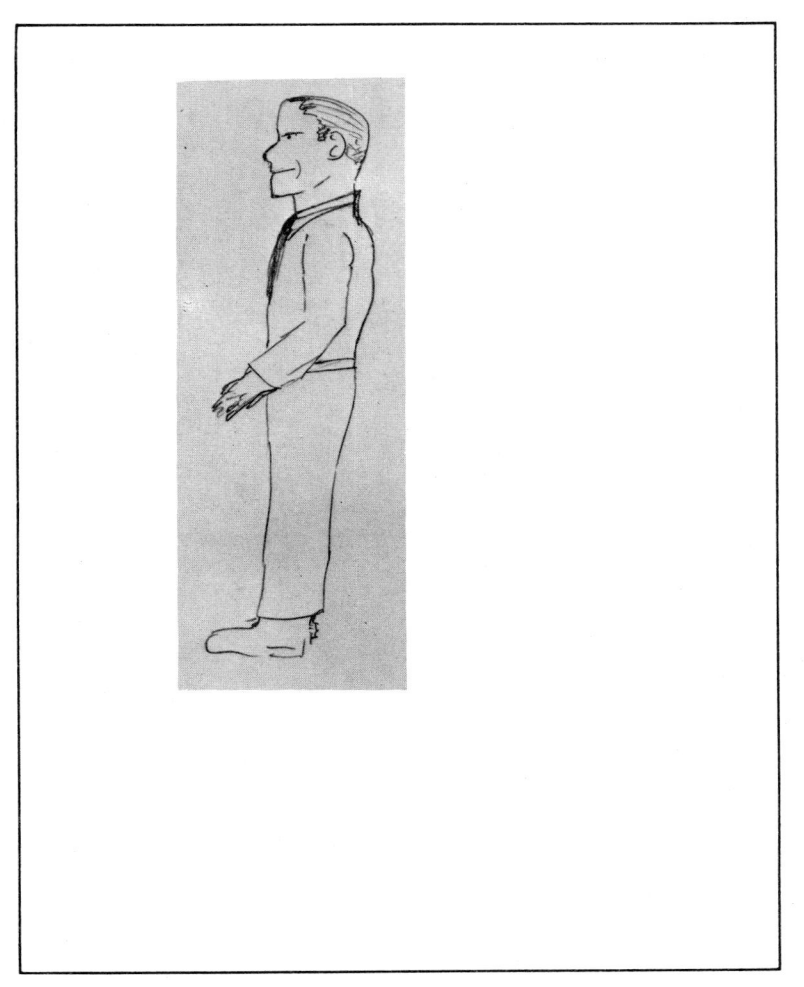

FIGURE-DRAWING CHARACTERISTICS

Structural	Male	Female	Structural	Male	Female	Structural and Graphic	Male	Female	Graphic, Global and Height	Male	Female	Body Proportions	Male	Female
	Both						Both							
Type	0		Omission of Appendages	0	0	Upper and Lower Halves	1	1	Hair Shading	1	2	Head	08	07
Sex Sequence	0		Position of Both Arms	4	4	Four Quarters	4	4	Nudity and Transparency	7	7	Neck	06	08
Posture	1	1	Position of Right Arm	7	7	Relative Size	2		Form	1	3	Shoulders		
Perspective	2	2	Position of Left Arm	4	4	Constant Line Pressure	5	0	Detailing	3	3	Right Arm		
Vertical Midline	7	4	Position of Legs	1	1	Variable Line Pressure	0	5	Identity and Sex	1	1	Left Arm	06	06
Bilateral Symmetry	0	0	Relation of Long Axes	1	1	Line Continuity	2	2	Sophistication	2	3	Chest	07	06
Horizontal Midline	4	0	Right and Left Halves	2	2	Body Shading	4	4	Height	06	06	Girth	07	07

GENERAL CHARACTERISTICS OF SUBJECT

IDENTIFICATION
No. G46
Sex M
Marital status M
Age 30 yrs. at
psychological tests

PARENTAL HISTORY
Father
C   H   S   D   O
-    -   -   -   ?
Mother
C   H   S   D   O
-    -   -   -   -

PHYSIOLOGICAL AND METABOLIC DATA

	Admission	Initial	Control	Cold pressor change	Exercise change	Smoking change
Systolic pressure	130	128	120	+14	+40	
Diastolic pressure	82	72	70	+20	00	
Heart rate	80	64	63	+14	+16	

Age 29 yrs.	Height	68 in.	Ponderal index 12.76
	Weight	151 lbs.	Cholesterol 230 mg. per 100 ml.
	Overweight -01 %		Vital capacity liters

HABIT SURVEY
Smoking habits: nonsmoker
Age begun   yrs.   Inhalation:
Habits of nervous tension: 5, 6, 19

STRONG VOCATIONAL INTEREST TEST

Occupation	Artist	Psychologist	Architect	Physician	Osteopath	Dentist	Veterinarian	Mathematician	Physicist	Engineer	Chemist	Production Manager
Standard Score	42	41	45	65	46	50	34	45	46	50	53	34

Occupation	Farmer	Aviator	Carpenter	Printer	Math.-Sci. Teacher	Ind. Arts Teacher	Voc. Agric. Teacher	Policeman	Forest Serv. Man	Y.M.C.A. Phys. Dir.	Personnel Director	Public Administrator
Standard Score	41	42	11	21	35	14	23	20	32	21	15	35

Occupation	Y.M.C.A. Secretary	Soc. Sci. H.S. Teacher	City Sch. Sup't.	Social Worker	Minister	Musician Performer	C.P.A.	Senior C.P.A.	Accountant	Office Man	Purchasing Agent	Banker
Standard Score	01	11	23	19	59	36	29	24	11	13	21	17

Occupation	Mortician	Pharmacist	Sales Manager	Real Est. Manager	Life Ins. Salesman	Advertising Man	Lawyer	Author- Journalist	President Mfg. Co.	Interest Maturity	Occupational Level	Masculinity- Femininity
Standard Score	13	31	24	30	21	33	39	42	40	45	69	50

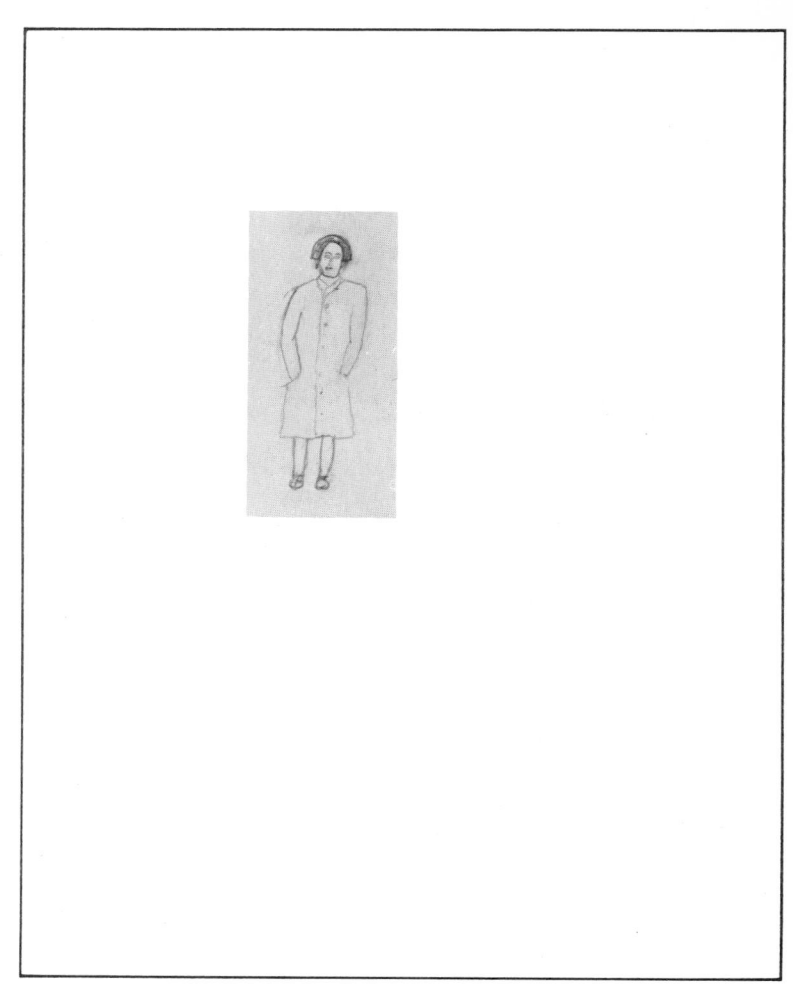

FIGURE-DRAWING CHARACTERISTICS

Structural	Male Female Both		Structural	Male	Female	Structural and Graphic	Male Female Both		Graphic, Global and Height	Male	Female	Body Proportions	Male	Female
Type	0		Omission of Appendages	0	7	Upper and Lower Halves	1	2	Hair Shading	2	2	Head	04	03
Sex Sequence	0		Position of Both Arms	0	0	Four Quarters	4	0	Nudity and Transparency	7	7	Neck	02	00
Posture	1	1	Position of Right Arm	0	5	Relative Size	0		Form	3	3	Shoulders	04	03
Perspective	0	0	Position of Left Arm	0	5	Constant Line Pressure	0	0	Detailing	3	3	Right Arm	02	
Vertical Midline	3	3	Position of Legs	5	4	Variable Line Pressure	1	1	Identity and Sex	1	5	Left Arm	02	
Bilateral Symmetry	3	3	Relation of Long Axes	1	1	Line Continuity	1	1	Sophistication	2	3	Chest	03	02
Horizontal Midline	0	0	Right and Left Halves	2	2	Body Shading	2	0	Height	03	02	Girth	05	04

GENERAL CHARACTERISTICS OF SUBJECT

IDENTIFICATION
No. 775
Sex M
Marital status S
Age 21 yrs. at
psychological tests

PARENTAL HISTORY				
Father				
C	H	S	D	O
–	–	–	–	–
Mother				
C	H	S	D	O
–	–	–	–	–

PHYSIOLOGICAL AND METABOLIC DATA

	Admission	Initial	Control	Cold pressor change	Exercise change	Smoking change
Systolic pressure	130	110	106	+21	+24	+03
Diastolic pressure	80	62	66	+26	-14	+02
Heart rate	82	68	69	+04	+19	+08

Age 21 yrs.	Height	72	in.	Ponderal index 13.31	
	Weight	158	lbs.	Cholesterol	222 mg. per 100 ml.
	Overweight -02 %			Vital capacity 6.1	liters

HABIT SURVEY

Smoking habits: occasional smoker

  Age begun 18 yrs.   Inhalation: yes

Habits of nervous tension: 4, 5, 11, 16, 17, 21, 23

FIGURE-DRAWING CHARACTERISTICS

Structural	Male Female Both	Structural	Male	Female	Structural and Graphic	Male Female Both		Graphic, Global and Height	Male	Female	Body Proportions	Male	Female
Type	0	Omission of Appendages	0	0	Upper and Lower Halves	0	3	Hair Shading	5	3	Head	07	06
Sex Sequence	0	Position of Both Arms	4	0	Four Quarters	4	4	Nudity and Transparency	7	7	Neck	08	07
Posture	2 1	Position of Right Arm	7	0	Relative Size	2		Form	1	1	Shoulders		06
Perspective	2 0	Position of Left Arm	0	0	Constant Line Pressure	2	2	Detailing	3	3	Right Arm		04
Vertical Midline	4 3	Position of Legs	8	6	Variable Line Pressure	0	0	Identity and Sex	1	1	Left Arm	06	04
Bilateral Symmetry	0 3	Relation of Long Axes	1	1	Line Continuity	2	0	Sophistication	2	3	Chest	07	06
Horizontal Midline	4 4	Right and Left Halves	1	0	Body Shading	0	3	Height	06	06	Girth	06	07

GENERAL CHARACTERISTICS OF SUBJECT

IDENTIFICATION	PARENTAL HISTORY
No. F04	Father
Sex M	C H S D O
Marital status M	- - - - -
Age 25 yrs. at	Mother
psychological tests	C H S D O
	- - - - -

PHYSIOLOGICAL AND METABOLIC DATA

	Admission	Initial	Control	Cold pressor change	Exercise change	Smoking change
Systolic pressure	126	132	120	+14	+32	+05
Diastolic pressure	84	52	62	+18	-04	00
Heart rate	70	64	68	+08	+07	+01

Age 22 yrs.	Height 74 in.	Ponderal index 13.03
	Weight 183 lbs.	Cholesterol 224 mg. per 100 ml.
	Overweight +06 %	Vital capacity liters

HABIT SURVEY

Smoking habits: pipe smoker

  Age begun 15 yrs.   Inhalation: no

Habits of nervous tension: 1, 4, 11, 16

STRONG VOCATIONAL INTEREST TEST

Occupation	Artist	Psychologist	Architect	Physician	Osteopath	Dentist	Veterinarian	Mathematician	Physicist	Engineer	Chemist	Production Manager
Standard Score	35	38	38	62	55	46	26	25	19	29	34	27

Occupation	Farmer	Aviator	Carpenter	Printer	Math.-Sci. Teacher	Ind. Arts Teacher	Voc. Agric. Teacher	Policeman	Forest Serv. Man	Y.M.C.A. Phys. Dir.	Personnel Director	Public Administrator
Standard Score	33	36	09	30	37	19	30	33	31	43	34	44

Occupation	Y.M.C.A. Secretary	Soc. Sci. H.S. Teacher	City Sch. Sup't.	Social Worker	Minister	Musician Performer	C.P.A.	Senior C.P.A.	Accountant	Office Man	Purchasing Agent	Banker
Standard Score	32	38	32	40	58	48	25	29	12	18	14	23

Occupation	Mortician	Pharmacist	Sales Manager	Real Est. Manager	Life Ins. Salesman	Advertising Man	Lawyer	Author-Journalist	President Mfg. Co.	Interest Maturity	Occupational Level	Masculinity-Femininity
Standard Score	19	28	22	29	30	35	40	39	22	56	61	44

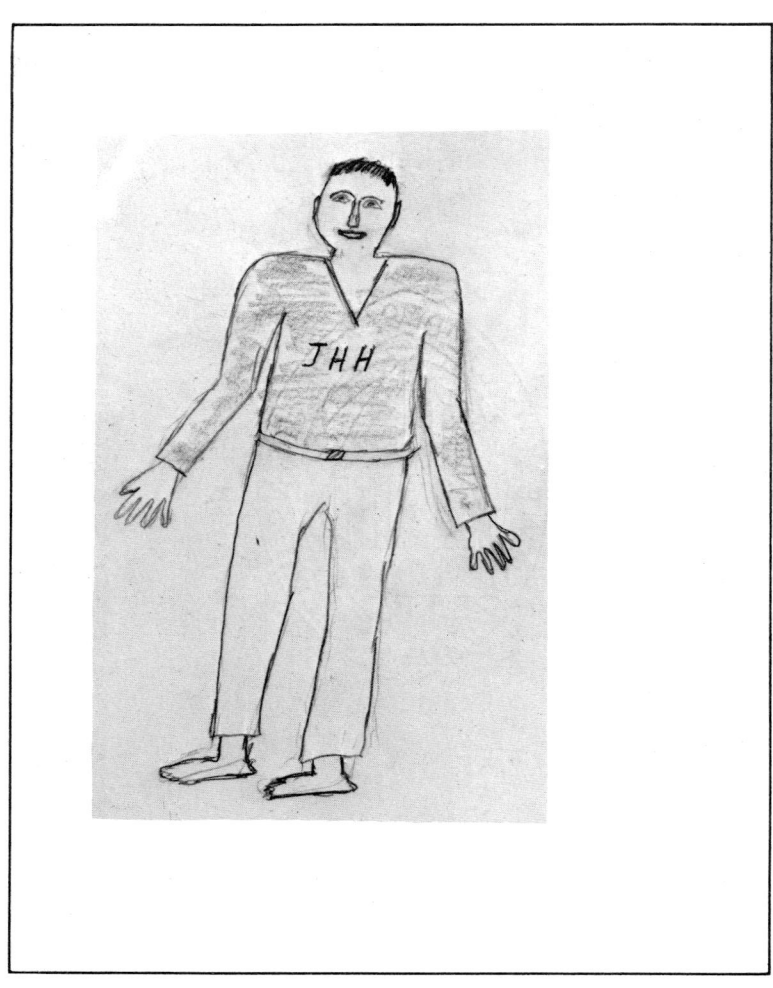

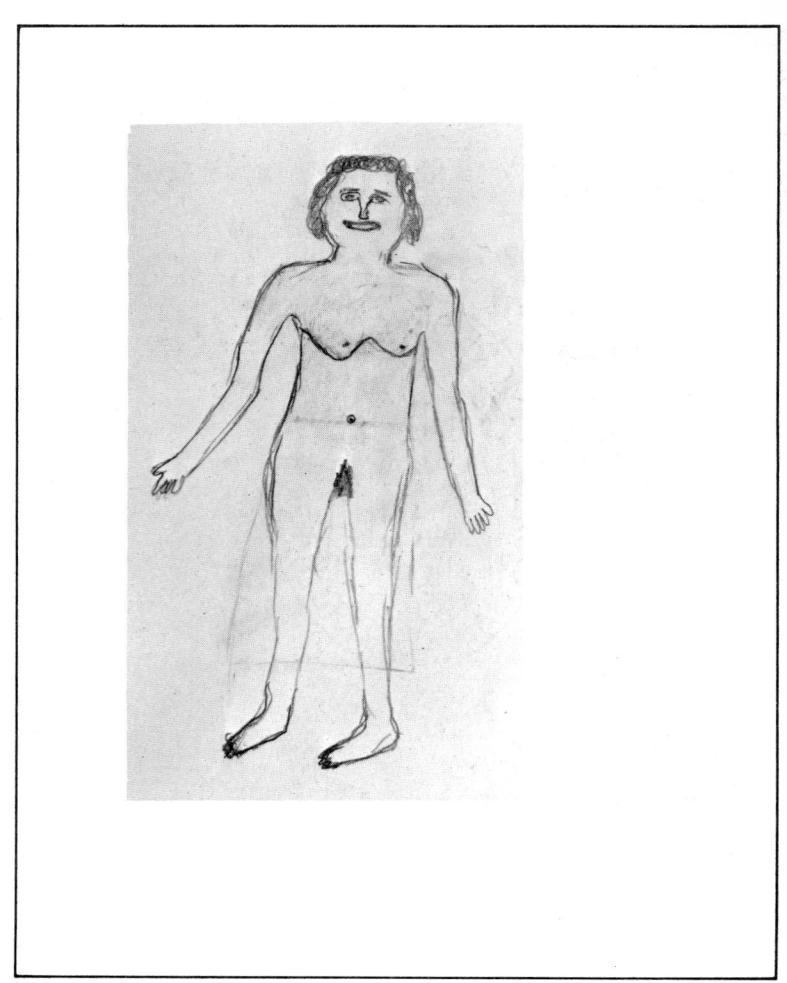

FIGURE-DRAWING CHARACTERISTICS

Structural	Male Female Both	Structural	Male	Female	Structural and Graphic	Male Female Both	Graphic, Global and Height	Male	Female	Body Proportions	Male	Female
Type	0	Omission of Appendages	0	0	Upper and Lower Halves	1 1	Hair Shading	3	3	Head	07	07
Sex Sequence	0	Position of Both Arms	0	0	Four Quarters	4 4	Nudity and Transparency	7	0	Neck	03	04
Posture	1 1	Position of Right Arm	3	3	Relative Size	0	Form	1	3	Shoulders	08	07
Perspective	0 0	Position of Left Arm	3	3	Constant Line Pressure	3 0	Detailing	1	3	Right Arm	06	06
Vertical Midline	0 0	Position of Legs	6	6	Variable Line Pressure	0 4	Identity and Sex	1	1	Left Arm	08	06
Bilateral Symmetry	3 3	Relation of Long Axes	1	1	Line Continuity	1 0	Sophistication	2	3	Chest	07	06
Horizontal Midline	4 0	Right and Left Halves	1	1	Body Shading	1 3	Height	06	06	Girth	10	08

GENERAL CHARACTERISTICS OF SUBJECT

IDENTIFICATION
No. C21
Sex M
Marital status S
Age 23 yrs. at
psychological tests

PARENTAL HISTORY
Father
C H S D 0
- - - - -
Mother
C H S D 0
- - - - -

PHYSIOLOGICAL AND METABOLIC DATA

	Admission	Initial	Control	Cold pressor change	Exercise change	Smoking change
Systolic pressure	120	135	122	+15	+38	+06
Diastolic pressure	80	75	72	+15	-07	+10
Heart rate	68	72	68	+16	+26	+16

Age 23 yrs.	Height 72 in.	Ponderal index 13.36
	Weight 157 lbs.	Cholesterol 208 mg. per 100 ml.
	Overweight -04 %	Vital capacity 5.4 liters

HABIT SURVEY

Smoking habits: heavy cigarette smoker

Age begun 18 yrs.   Inhalation: yes

Habits of nervous tension: 3, 4, 5, 6, 11, 14, 17, 19, 22, 24, 25

STRONG VOCATIONAL INTEREST TEST

Occupation	Artist	Psychologist	Architect	Physician	Osteopath	Dentist	Veterinarian	Mathematician	Physicist	Engineer	Chemist	Production Manager
Standard Score	30	51	26	55	49	29	25	27	22	27	39	29

Occupation	Farmer	Aviator	Carpenter	Printer	Math.-Sci. Teacher	Ind. Arts Teacher	Voc. Agric. Teacher	Policeman	Forest Serv. Man	Y.M.C.A. Phys. Dir.	Personnel Director	Public Administrator
Standard Score	21	32	02	28	34	01	19	32	31	43	45	57

Occupation	Y.M.C.A. Secretary	Soc. Sci. H.S. Teacher	City Sch. Sup't.	Social Worker	Minister	Musician Performer	C.P.A.	Senior C.P.A.	Accountant	Office Man	Purchasing Agent	Banker
Standard Score	34	44	49	55	62	40	40	36	20	27	20	20

Occupation	Mortician	Pharmacist	Sales Manager	Real Est. Manager	Life Ins. Salesman	Advertising Man	Lawyer	Author-Journalist	President Mfg. Co.	Interest Maturity	Occupational Level	Masculinity-Femininity
Standard Score	29	36	32	37	43	41	56	43	31	56	62	36

Plate 515   **MIXED INTERMEDIATE AND MODERATELY SOPHISTICATED DRAWINGS**   559

FIGURE-DRAWING CHARACTERISTICS

Structural	Male Female Both	Structural	Male	Female	Structural and Graphic	Male Female Both		Graphic, Global and Height	Male	Female	Body Proportions	Male	Female
Type	0	Omission of Appendages	0	9	Upper and Lower Halves	1	1	Hair Shading	3	3	Head	06	06
Sex Sequence	0	Position of Both Arms	1	0	Four Quarters	4	4	Nudity and Transparency	7	7	Neck	10	10
Posture	1	1	Position of Right Arm	2	5	Relative Size	4		Form	3	1	Shoulders	02	
Perspective	9	0	Position of Left Arm	5	5	Constant Line Pressure	1	1	Detailing	3	1	Right Arm	03	
Vertical Midline	7	3	Position of Legs	2	4	Variable Line Pressure	0	0	Identity and Sex	1	1	Left Arm	04	
Bilateral Symmetry	2	3	Relation of Long Axes	1	1	Line Continuity	2	2	Sophistication	3	2	Chest	05	04
Horizontal Midline	6	4	Right and Left Halves	1	2	Body Shading	6	7	Height	04	05	Girth	06	02

GENERAL CHARACTERISTICS OF SUBJECT

IDENTIFICATION
No. E27
Sex F
Marital status S
Age 22 yrs. at psychological tests

PARENTAL HISTORY
Father
C H S D O
-   -   -   -   -
Mother
C H S D O
-   -   -   -   -

PHYSIOLOGICAL AND METABOLIC DATA

	Admission	Initial	Control	Cold pressor change	Exercise change	Smoking change
Systolic pressure	120	120	105	-10	+45	
Diastolic pressure	80	60	70	+12	-15	
Heart rate	80	68	68	+08	+42	

Age 21 yrs.	Height 64 in.	Ponderal index 12.65
	Weight 130 lbs.	Cholesterol 210 mg. per 100 ml.
	Overweight +03 %	Vital capacity liters

HABIT SURVEY
Smoking habits: nonsmoker
Age begun yrs.   Inhalation:
Habits of nervous tension: 5, 6, 9, 10, 16

STRONG VOCATIONAL INTEREST TEST

Occupation	Artist	Psychologist	Architect	Physician	Osteopath	Dentist	Veterinarian	Mathematician	Physicist	Engineer	Chemist	Production Manager
Standard Score	44	41	44	39	24	32	06	30	19	25	29	19

Occupation	Farmer	Aviator	Carpenter	Printer	Math.-Sci. Teacher	Ind. Arts Teacher	Voc. Agric. Teacher	Policeman	Forest Serv. Man	Y.M.C.A. Phys. Dir.	Personnel Director	Public Administrator
Standard Score	26	23	12	36	26	02	11	17	23	32	41	37

Occupation	Y.M.C.A. Secretary	Soc. Sci. H.S. Teacher	City Sch. Sup't.	Social Worker	Minister	Musician Performer	C.P.A.	Senior C.P.A.	Accountant	Office Man	Purchasing Agent	Banker
Standard Score	37	37	34	44	64	54	33	29	17	26	14	21

Occupation	Mortician	Pharmacist	Sales Manager	Real Est. Manager	Life Ins. Salesman	Advertising Man	Lawyer	Author-Journalist	President Mfg. Co.	Interest Maturity	Occupational Level	Masculinity-Femininity
Standard Score	19	22	30	36	32	51	44	47	22	53	58	29

IX. MIXED INTERMEDIATE AND MOST SOPHISTICATED DRAWINGS

In this section, represented by three subjects, one drawing of each pair is intermediate in level of sophistication and the other is most sophisticated.

FIGURE-DRAWING CHARACTERISTICS

Structural	Male Female Both	Structural	Male	Female	Structural and Graphic	Male Female Both		Graphic, Global and Height	Male	Female	Body Proportions	Male	Female
Type	0	Omission of Appendages	0	8	Upper and Lower Halves	0	3	Hair Shading	3	5	Head	07	12
Sex Sequence	0	Position of Both Arms	4	4	Four Quarters	4	4	Nudity and Transparency	7	7	Neck	02	06
Posture	1　1	Position of Right Arm	7	7	Relative Size	4		Form	1	3	Shoulders		
Perspective	2　2	Position of Left Arm	4	0	Constant Line Pressure	0	1	Detailing	1	3	Right Arm		
Vertical Midline	7　4	Position of Legs	1	1	Variable Line Pressure	1	0	Identity and Sex	1	1	Left Arm	06	06
Bilateral Symmetry	0　0	Relation of Long Axes	1	1	Line Continuity	0	0	Sophistication	1	3	Chest	08	07
Horizontal Midline	6　4	Right and Left Halves	1	1	Body Shading	6	2	Height	05		Girth	09	06

GENERAL CHARACTERISTICS OF SUBJECT

IDENTIFICATION

No. G14

Sex M

Marital status S

Age 23 yrs. at

psychological tests

PARENTAL HISTORY

Father

C	H	S	D	O
+	-	-	-	?

Mother

C	H	S	D	O
-	+	-	-	+

PHYSIOLOGICAL AND METABOLIC DATA

	Admission	Initial	Control	Cold pressor change	Exercise change	Smoking change
Systolic pressure	125	142	140	+26	+40	+09
Diastolic pressure	75	68	64	+34	+06	+11
Heart rate	64	80	64	+10	+33	+04

Age 22 yrs.

Height 74 in.

Weight 206 lbs.

Overweight +19 %

Ponderal index 12.52

Cholesterol 288 mg. per 100 ml.

Vital capacity liters

HABIT SURVEY

Smoking habits: occasional smoker

Age begun 20 yrs.　Inhalation: no

Habits of nervous tension: 4, 6, 9, 16, 25

STRONG VOCATIONAL INTEREST TEST

Occupation	Artist	Psychologist	Architect	Physician	Osteopath	Dentist	Veterinarian	Mathematician	Physicist	Engineer	Chemist	Production Manager
Standard Score	39	42	46	65	47	44	33	35	36	38	46	28

Occupation	Farmer	Aviator	Carpenter	Printer	Math.-Sci. Teacher	Ind. Arts Teacher	Voc. Agric. Teacher	Policeman	Forest Serv. Man	Y.M.C.A. Phys. Dir.	Personnel Director	Public Administrator
Standard Score	48	44	20	29	44	20	37	27	36	36	30	37

Occupation	Y.M.C.A. Secretary	Soc. Sci. H.S. Teacher	City Sch. Sup't.	Social Worker	Minister	Musician Performer	C.P.A.	Senior C.P.A.	Accountant	Office Man	Purchasing Agent	Banker
Standard Score	21	29	28	31	59	53	27	38	17	24	21	20

Occupation	Mortician	Pharmacist	Sales Manager	Real Est. Manager	Life Ins. Salesman	Advertising Man	Lawyer	Author-Journalist	President Mfg. Co.	Interest Maturity	Occupational Level	Masculinity-Femininity
Standard Score	18	31	23	29	21	32	35	34	26	51	57	50

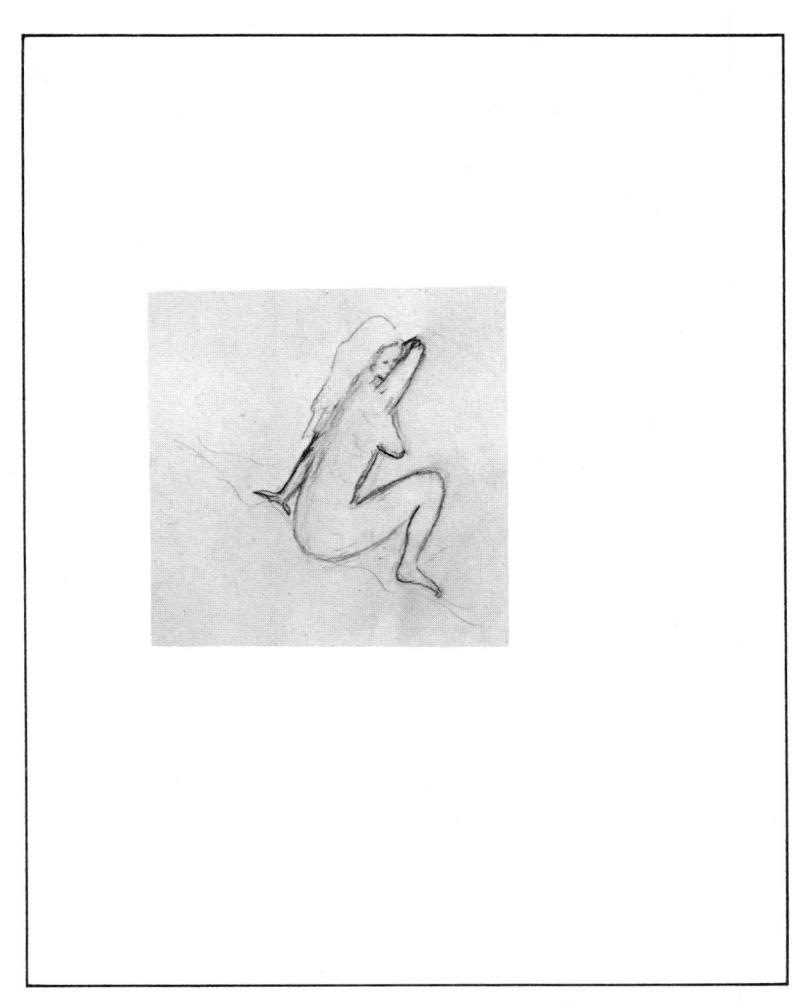

FIGURE-DRAWING CHARACTERISTICS

Structural	Male Female Both	Structural	Male	Female	Structural and Graphic	Male Female Both		Graphic, Global and Height	Male	Female	Body Proportions	Male	Female
Type	0	Omission of Appendages	0	2	Upper and Lower Halves	1	1	Hair Shading	3	5	Head	04	
Sex Sequence	0	Position of Both Arms	0	6	Four Quarters	4	4	Nudity and Transparency	2	0	Neck	05	
Posture	1 3	Position of Right Arm	2	2	Relative Size	5		Form	1	3	Shoulders	05	
Perspective	0 9	Position of Left Arm	2	7	Constant Line Pressure	0	0	Detailing	1	3	Right Arm	02	
Vertical Midline	0 4	Position of Legs	6	1	Variable Line Pressure	5	2	Identity and Sex	1	1	Left Arm	02	
Bilateral Symmetry	4 0	Relation of Long Axes	1	0	Line Continuity	2	0	Sophistication	1	3	Chest	05	04
Horizontal Midline	4 0	Right and Left Halves	1	1	Body Shading	4	0	Height	04		Girth	03	05

GENERAL CHARACTERISTICS OF SUBJECT

IDENTIFICATION

No. D62

Sex M

Marital status S

Age 22 yrs. at
psychological tests

PARENTAL HISTORY

Father

C	H	S	D	O
-	-	-	-	?

Mother

C	H	S	D	O
-	+	-	-	?

PHYSIOLOGICAL AND METABOLIC DATA

	Admission	Initial	Control	Cold pressor change	Exercise change	Smoking change
Systolic pressure	120	128	126	+04	+39	+06
Diastolic pressure	80	62	70	+12	-02	-02
Heart rate	80	80	71	+12	+44	+12

Age 22 yrs.	Height	71	in.	Ponderal index	13.47	
	Weight	146	lbs.	Cholesterol	205	mg. per 100 ml.
	Overweight	-08 %		Vital capacity	4.5	liters

HABIT SURVEY

Smoking habits: occasional smoker

   Age begun 20 yrs.   Inhalation: yes

Habits of nervous tension: 3, 4, 5, 8, 9, 11,

14, 18, 23

STRONG VOCATIONAL INTEREST TEST

Occupation	Artist	Psychologist	Architect	Physician	Osteopath	Dentist	Veterinarian	Mathematician	Physicist	Engineer	Chemist	Production Manager
Standard Score	53	52	46	58	46	42	08	48	40	35	51	17

Occupation	Farmer	Aviator	Carpenter	Printer	Math.-Sci. Teacher	Ind. Arts Teacher	Voc. Agric. Teacher	Policeman	Forest Serv. Man	Y.M.C.A. Phys. Dir.	Personnel Director	Public Administrator
Standard Score	21	26	01	23	27	-05	-09	12	13	23	24	36

Occupation	Y.M.C.A. Secretary	Soc. Sci. H.S. Teacher	City Sch. Sup't.	Social Worker	Minister	Musician Performer	C.P.A.	Senior C.P.A.	Accountant	Office Man	Purchasing Agent	Banker
Standard Score	16	27	31	36	63	53	39	21	12	10	07	12

Occupation	Mortician	Pharmacist	Sales Manager	Real Est. Manager	Life Ins. Salesman	Advertising Man	Lawyer	Author-Journalist	President Mfg. Co.	Interest Maturity	Occupational Level	Masculinity-Femininity
Standard Score	11	18	24	33	35	48	56	57	36	50	72	27

FIGURE-DRAWING CHARACTERISTICS

Structural	Male Female Both	Structural	Male	Female	Structural and Graphic	Male Female Both	Graphic, Global and Height	Male	Female	Body Proportions	Male	Female
Type	0	Omission of Appendages	3	0	Upper and Lower Halves	9 1	Hair Shading	7	2	Head	20	14
Sex Sequence	1	Position of Both Arms	4	4	Four Quarters	4 4	Nudity and Transparency	7	7	Neck		14
Posture	9 1	Position of Right Arm	7	7	Relative Size	5	Form	3	1	Shoulders		
Perspective	9 2	Position of Left Arm	4	4	Constant Line Pressure	5 0	Detailing	3	1	Right Arm		
Vertical Midline	7 4	Position of Legs	9	1	Variable Line Pressure	0 3	Identity and Sex	3	1	Left Arm	08	05
Bilateral Symmetry	9 0	Relation of Long Axes	0	1	Line Continuity	3 2	Sophistication	3	1	Chest	19	08
Horizontal Midline	9 0	Right and Left Halves	1	1	Body Shading	4 7	Height		08	Girth		06

GENERAL CHARACTERISTICS OF SUBJECT

IDENTIFICATION
No. E35
Sex M
Marital status S
Age 23 yrs. at psychological tests

PARENTAL HISTORY				
Father				
C	H	S	D	O
-	-	+	-	-
Mother				
C	H	S	D	O
-	-	-	-	-

PHYSIOLOGICAL AND METABOLIC DATA

	Admission	Initial	Control	Cold pressor change	Exercise change	Smoking change
Systolic pressure	120	140	120	+12	+42	+07
Diastolic pressure	90	68	70	+07	-18	+02
Heart rate	78	120	88	+20	+32	-01

Age 23 yrs.

Height 74 in.   Ponderal index 13.94
Weight 150 lbs.   Cholesterol 176 mg. per 100 ml.
Overweight -14 %   Vital capacity 4.3 liters

HABIT SURVEY

Smoking habits: nonsmoker

Age begun   yrs.   Inhalation:

Habits of nervous tension: 4, 5, 6, 11, 12, 16

STRONG VOCATIONAL INTEREST TEST

Occupation	Artist	Psychologist	Architect	Physician	Osteopath	Dentist	Veterinarian	Mathematician	Physicist	Engineer	Chemist	Production Manager
Standard Score	30	45	31	43	30	29	08	32	25	42	45	31

Occupation	Farmer	Aviator	Carpenter	Printer	Math.-Sci. Teacher	Ind. Arts Teacher	Voc. Agric. Teacher	Policeman	Forest Serv. Man	Y.M.C.A. Phys. Dir.	Personnel Director	Public Administrator
Standard Score	19	38	10	32	33	04	01	36	22	41	42	51

Occupation	Y.M.C.A. Secretary	Soc. Sci. H.S. Teacher	City Sch. Sup't.	Social Worker	Minister	Musician Performer	C.P.A.	Senior C.P.A.	Accountant	Office Man	Purchasing Agent	Banker
Standard Score	23	29	28	40	64	42	43	41	32	37	28	16

Occupation	Mortician	Pharmacist	Sales Manager	Real Est. Manager	Life Ins. Salesman	Advertising Man	Lawyer	Author-Journalist	President Mfg. Co.	Interest Maturity	Occupational Level	Masculinity-Femininity
Standard Score	17	26	33	31	31	40	44	39	30	56	60	45

X. MODERATELY SOPHISTICATED DRAWINGS

In this section, the drawings by 238 subjects show a definite attempt at role assignment with regard to age, activity, occupation, and so on, through adequate detailing, shaping, and clothing. Continuity of outline (i.e., integration of parts) is attempted. The end product is, however, less deliberate, the outlines less decisive and/or skillful, and the head and/or hand treatment is less sophisticated than in drawings of the most sophisticated group.

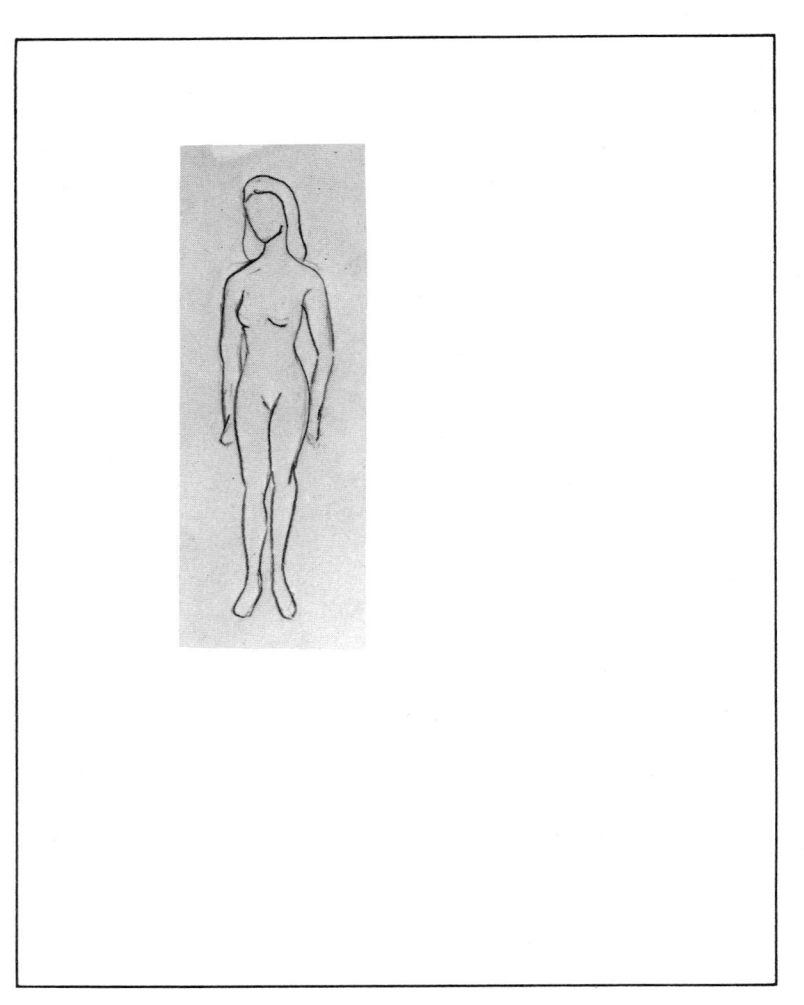

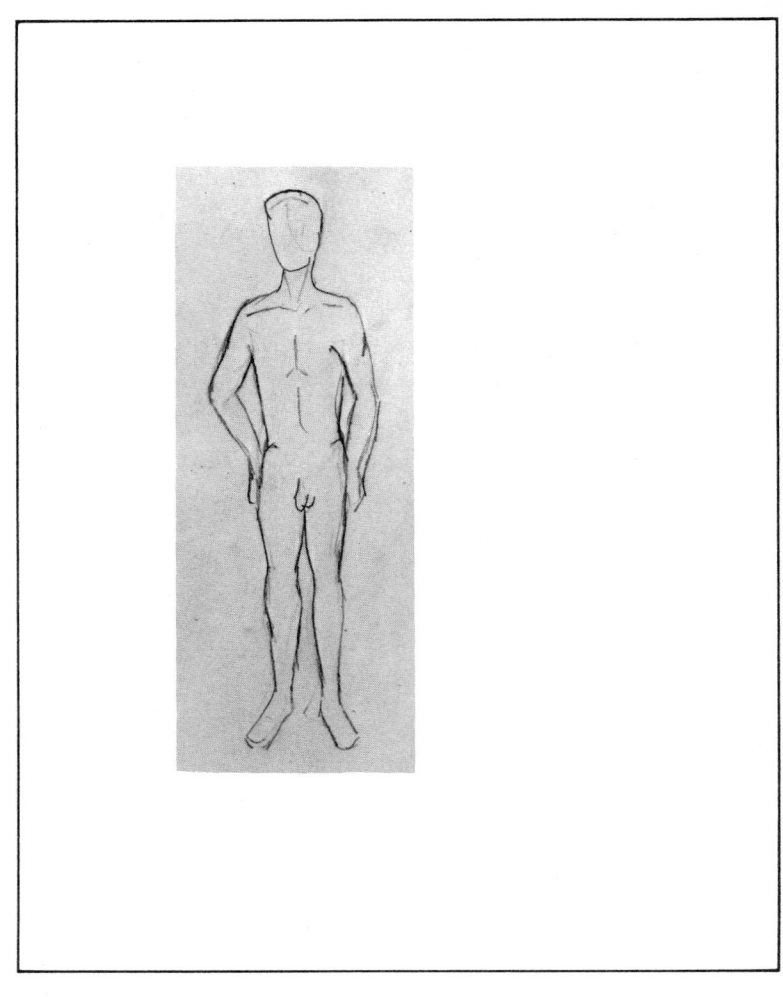

FIGURE-DRAWING CHARACTERISTICS

Structural	Male Female Both		Structural	Male	Female	Structural and Graphic	Male Female Both		Graphic, Global and Height	Male	Female	Body Proportions	Male	Female
Type	0		Omission of Appendages	0	0	Upper and Lower Halves	1	1	Hair Shading	5	5	Head	06	05
Sex Sequence	1		Position of Both Arms	0	1	Four Quarters	4	4	Nudity and Transparency	0	0	Neck	07	04
Posture	1	1	Position of Right Arm	5	0	Relative Size	0		Form	1	1	Shoulders	05	
Perspective	0	1	Position of Left Arm	5	5	Constant Line Pressure	0	0	Detailing	3	3	Right Arm	04	04
Vertical Midline	0	4	Position of Legs	4	4	Variable Line Pressure	4	5	Identity and Sex	1	1	Left Arm	04	04
Bilateral Symmetry	3	0	Relation of Long Axes	1	1	Line Continuity	1	3	Sophistication	2	2	Chest	04	
Horizontal Midline	0	0	Right and Left Halves	2	2	Body Shading	1	0	Height	06	04	Girth	04	

GENERAL CHARACTERISTICS OF SUBJECT

IDENTIFICATION
No. F38
Sex F
Marital status S
Age 25 yrs. at
psychological tests

PARENTAL HISTORY				
Father				
C	H	S	D	O
(+)	-	-	-	-
Mother				
C	H	S	D	O
+	-	-	-	-

PHYSIOLOGICAL AND METABOLIC DATA

	Admission	Initial	Control	Cold pressor change	Exercise change	Smoking change
Systolic pressure	108	116	106	+06	+24	+06
Diastolic pressure	64	86	82	+12	+10	+06
Heart rate	70	72	73	+04	+27	+10

Age 23 yrs.	Height	66	in.	Ponderal index	13.02	
	Weight	130	lbs.	Cholesterol	222	mg. per 100 ml.
	Overweight	-03	%	Vital capacity		liters

HABIT SURVEY
Smoking habits: former smoker
Age begun 17 yrs.   Inhalation: yes
Habits of nervous tension: 2, 4, 5, 6, 9, 11,
16, 17, 23

STRONG VOCATIONAL INTEREST TEST

Occupation	Artist	Psychologist	Architect	Physician	Osteopath	Dentist	Veterinarian	Mathematician	Physicist	Engineer	Chemist	Production Manager
Standard Score	57	52	57	65	48	41	23	36	30	32	45	17

Occupation	Farmer	Aviator	Carpenter	Printer	Math.-Sci. Teacher	Ind. Arts Teacher	Voc. Agric. Teacher	Policeman	Forest Serv. Man	Y.M.C.A. Phys. Dir.	Personnel Director	Public Administrator
Standard Score	27	37	23	43	29	14	15	23	27	30	24	34

Occupation	Y.M.C.A. Secretary	Soc. Sci. H.S. Teacher	City Sch. Sup't.	Social Worker	Minister	Musician Performer	C.P.A.	Senior C.P.A.	Accountant	Office Man	Purchasing Agent	Banker
Standard Score	22	27	21	44	58	64	29	35	12	20	06	09

Occupation	Mortician	Pharmacist	Sales Manager	Real Est. Manager	Life Ins. Salesman	Advertising Man	Lawyer	Author-Journalist	President Mfg. Co.	Interest Maturity	Occupational Level	Masculinity-Femininity
Standard Score	20	24	18	30	29	48	40	51	24	55	56	28

FIGURE-DRAWING CHARACTERISTICS

Structural	Male Female Both		Structural	Male	Female	Structural and Graphic	Male Female Both		Graphic, Global and Height	Male	Female	Body Proportions	Male	Female
Type	0		Omission of Appendages	6	4	Upper and Lower Halves	1	1	Hair Shading	2	5	Head	06	05
Sex Sequence	1		Position of Both Arms	0	0	Four Quarters	4	4	Nudity and Transparency	7	7	Neck	07	05
Posture	1	0	Position of Right Arm	5	5	Relative Size	5		Form	3	1	Shoulders	07	05
Perspective	0	0	Position of Left Arm	5	5	Constant Line Pressure	0	0	Detailing	3	3	Right Arm		
Vertical Midline	3	0	Position of Legs	3	4	Variable Line Pressure	2	2	Identity and Sex	1	1	Left Arm		
Bilateral Symmetry	3	3	Relation of Long Axes	1	1	Line Continuity	0	0	Sophistication	2	2	Chest	06	04
Horizontal Midline	2	4	Right and Left Halves	1	2	Body Shading	2	2	Height	05		Girth	08	04

GENERAL CHARACTERISTICS OF SUBJECT

IDENTIFICATION
No. C27
Sex F
Marital status S
Age 22 yrs. at psychological tests

PARENTAL HISTORY				
Father				
C	H	S	D	O
?	–	–	–	+
Mother				
C	H	S	D	O
+	+	–	–	?

PHYSIOLOGICAL AND METABOLIC DATA

	Admission	Initial	Control	Cold pressor change	Exercise change	Smoking change
Systolic pressure	120	112	102	+04	+36	–03
Diastolic pressure	60	58	60	+18	–04	00
Heart rate	68	84	71	+12	+40	–01

Age 22 yrs.	Height	70	in.	Ponderal index 13.28	
	Weight	146	lbs.	Cholesterol 200	mg. per 100 ml.
	Overweight +02 %			Vital capacity 3.8	liters

HABIT SURVEY
Smoking habits: nonsmoker
Age begun   yrs.   Inhalation:
Habits of nervous tension: 5, 6

STRONG VOCATIONAL INTEREST TEST

Occupation	Artist	Psychologist	Architect	Physician	Osteopath	Dentist	Veterinarian	Mathematician	Physicist	Engineer	Chemist	Production Manager
Standard Score	37	44	42	58	47	30	19	29	22	25	36	23

Occupation	Farmer	Aviator	Carpenter	Printer	Math.-Sci. Teacher	Ind. Arts Teacher	Voc. Agric. Teacher	Policeman	Forest Serv. Man	Y.M.C.A. Phys. Dir.	Personnel Director	Public Administrator
Standard Score	27	26	11	27	34	15	22	21	23	34	44	42

Occupation	Y.M.C.A. Secretary	Soc. Sci. H.S. Teacher	City Sch. Sup't.	Social Worker	Minister	Musician Performer	C.P.A.	Senior C.P.A.	Accountant	Office Man	Purchasing Agent	Banker
Standard Score	27	34	34	44	62	50	33	38	20	30	17	21

Occupation	Mortician	Pharmacist	Sales Manager	Real Est. Manager	Life Ins. Salesman	Advertising Man	Lawyer	Author-Journalist	President Mfg. Co.	Interest Maturity	Occupational Level	Masculinity-Femininity
Standard Score	32	37	29	35	34	38	41	36	32	58	60	31

FIGURE-DRAWING CHARACTERISTICS

Structural	Male Female Both	Structural	Male	Female	Structural and Graphic	Male Female Both		Graphic, Global and Height	Male	Female	Body Proportions	Male	Female
Type	0	Omission of Appendages	0	0	Upper and Lower Halves	1	1	Hair Shading	3	7	Head	04	03
Sex Sequence	1	Position of Both Arms	1	4	Four Quarters	4	4	Nudity and Transparency	7	6	Neck	02	02
Posture	1 1	Position of Right Arm	0	7	Relative Size	4		Form	1	1	Shoulders	04	
Perspective	1 2	Position of Left Arm	4	4	Constant Line Pressure	0	0	Detailing	3	3	Right Arm	02	
Vertical Midline	3 4	Position of Legs	4	1	Variable Line Pressure	5	2	Identity and Sex	1	1	Left Arm	02	03
Bilateral Symmetry	3 0	Relation of Long Axes	1	1	Line Continuity	2	0	Sophistication	2	2	Chest	03	04
Horizontal Midline	4 0	Right and Left Halves	2	2	Body Shading	2	4	Height	03	04	Girth	03	03

GENERAL CHARACTERISTICS OF SUBJECT

IDENTIFICATION
No. A58
Sex M
Marital status S
Age 24 yrs. at
psychological tests

PARENTAL HISTORY				
Father				
C	H	S	D	O
(?)	-	-	-	-
Mother				
C	H	S	D	O
+	-	-	-	-

PHYSIOLOGICAL AND METABOLIC DATA

	Admission	Initial	Control	Cold pressor change	Exercise change	Smoking change
Systolic pressure	140	118	115	+24	+21	+06
Diastolic pressure	85	62	74	+27	-18	+22
Heart rate	94	68	67	+16	+17	+01

Age 23 yrs.
Height 70 in.   Ponderal index 13.21
Weight 149 lbs.   Cholesterol 222 mg. per 100 ml.
Overweight -04 %   Vital capacity liters

HABIT SURVEY

Smoking habits: light cigarette smoker
Age begun 20 yrs.   Inhalation: yes
Habits of nervous tension: 5, 6, 11

STRONG VOCATIONAL INTEREST TEST

Occupation	Artist	Psychologist	Architect	Physician	Osteopath	Dentist	Veterinarian	Mathematician	Physicist	Engineer	Chemist	Production Manager
Standard Score	3	7	3	7	7	4	2	2	2	4	4	5

Occupation	Farmer	Aviator	Carpenter	Printer	Math.-Sci. Teacher	Ind. Arts Teacher	Voc. Agric. Teacher	Policeman	Forest Serv. Man	Y.M.C.A. Phys. Dir.	Personnel Director	Public Administrator
Standard Score	4	5	2	5	6	1	2	4	3	5	7	7

Occupation	Y.M.C.A. Secretary	Soc. Sci. H.S. Teacher	City Sch. Sup't.	Social Worker	Minister	Musician Performer	C.P.A.	Senior C.P.A.	Accountant	Office Man	Purchasing Agent	Banker
Standard Score	5	7	4	7	6	6	4	6	3	5	2	1

Occupation	Mortician	Pharmacist	Sales Manager	Real Est. Manager	Life Ins. Salesman	Advertising Man	Lawyer	Author- Journalist	President Mfg. Co.	Interest Maturity	Occupational Level	Masculinity- Femininity
Standard Score	3	4	3	5	5	5	4	4	4	7	5	5

Plate 522   **MODERATELY SOPHISTICATED DRAWINGS**   569

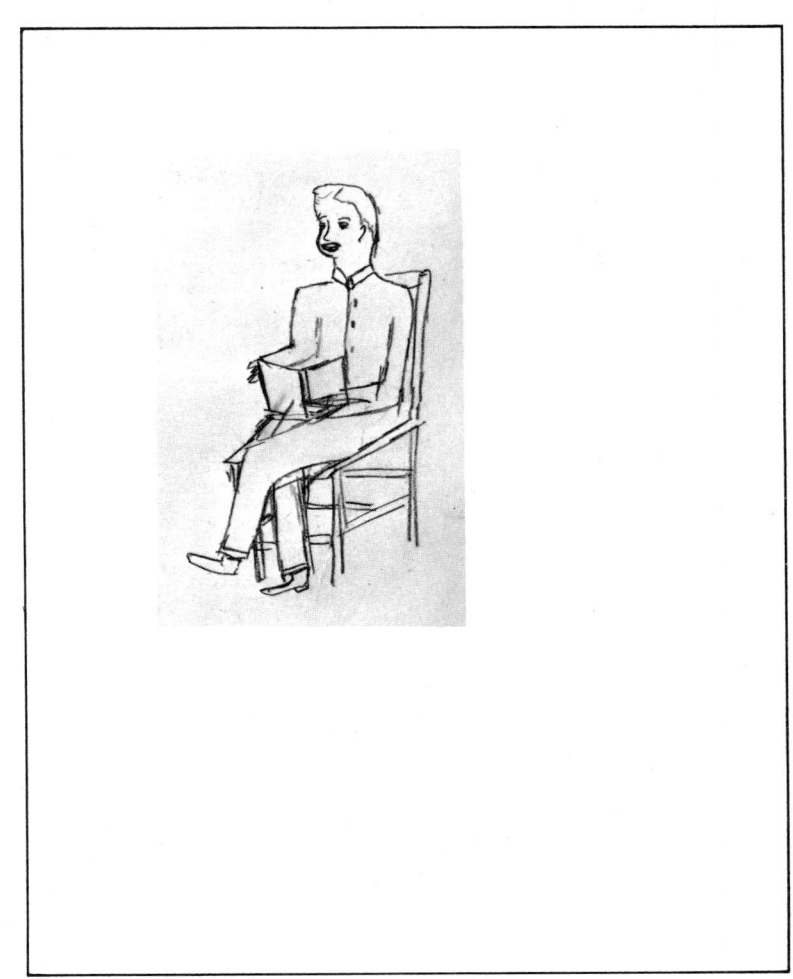

FIGURE-DRAWING CHARACTERISTICS

Structural	Male Female Both	Structural	Male	Female	Structural and Graphic	Male Female Both		Graphic, Global and Height	Male	Female	Body Proportions	Male	Female
Type	0	Omission of Appendages	7	0	Upper and Lower Halves	1	1	Hair Shading	5	5	Head	06	05
Sex Sequence	1	Position of Both Arms	0	0	Four Quarters	4	4	Nudity and Transparency	7	7	Neck	08	04
Posture	3 1	Position of Right Arm	4	5	Relative Size	0		Form	3	3	Shoulders	04	04
Perspective	9 1	Position of Left Arm	4	5	Constant Line Pressure	5	0	Detailing	3	3	Right Arm	02	02
Vertical Midline	3 7	Position of Legs	7	5	Variable Line Pressure	0	3	Identity and Sex	1	1	Left Arm	04	02
Bilateral Symmetry	0 0	Relation of Long Axes	0	1	Line Continuity	0	0	Sophistication	2	2	Chest	03	
Horizontal Midline	2 2	Right and Left Halves	1	2	Body Shading	0	3	Height		04	Girth		

GENERAL CHARACTERISTICS OF SUBJECT

IDENTIFICATION
No. 436
Sex M
Marital status S
Age 25 yrs. at psychological tests

PARENTAL HISTORY
Father
C   H   S   D   O
(+) (+)   -   -   ?
Mother
C   H   S   D   O
?   -   -   -   +

PHYSIOLOGICAL AND METABOLIC DATA

	Admission	Initial	Control	Cold pressor change	Exercise change	Smoking change
Systolic pressure	124	142	130	+14	+24	00
Diastolic pressure	80	80	74	+16	00	+14
Heart rate	72	90	88	+06	00	00

Age 22 yrs.	Height 72 in.	Ponderal index 12.71
	Weight 182 lbs.	Cholesterol 210 mg. per 100 ml.
	Overweight +12 %	Vital capacity 5.2 liters

HABIT SURVEY
Smoking habits: occasional smoker
Age begun   yrs.   Inhalation: no
Habits of nervous tension: 3, 4, 5, 6, 17

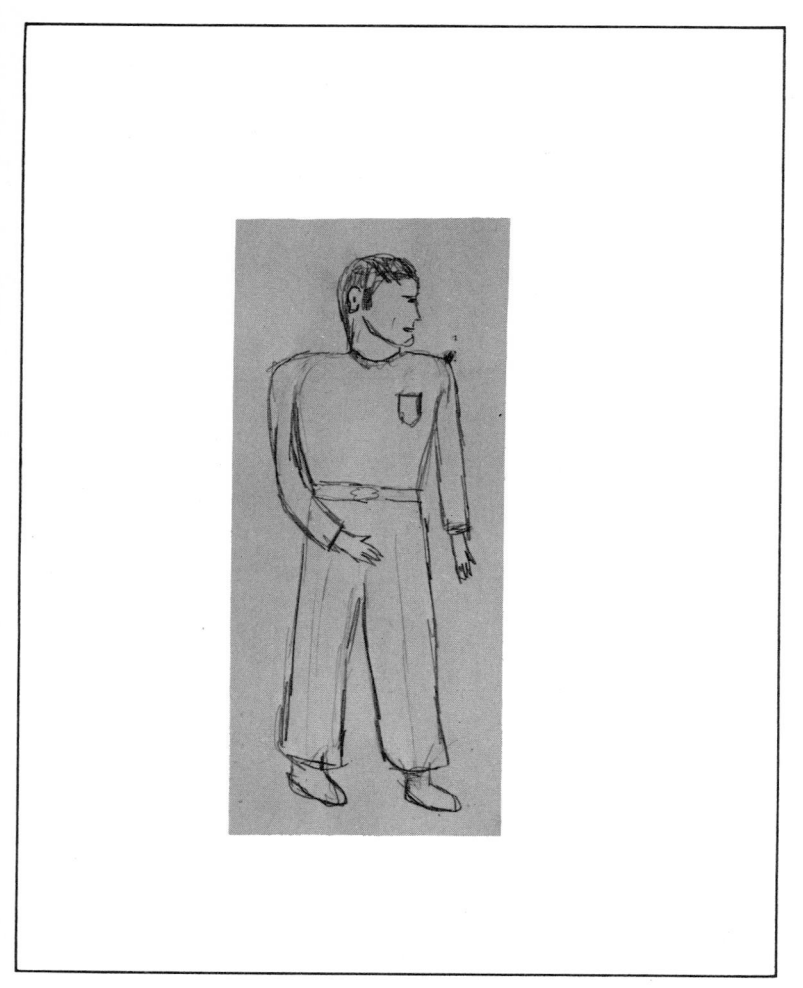

FIGURE-DRAWING CHARACTERISTICS

Structural	Male Female Both		Structural	Male	Female	Structural and Graphic	Male Female Both		Graphic, Global and Height	Male	Female	Body Proportions	Male	Female
Type	0		Omission of Appendages	0	0	Upper and Lower Halves	3	3	Hair Shading	3	5	Head	07	07
Sex Sequence	0		Position of Both Arms	1	0	Four Quarters	4	4	Nudity and Transparency	7	7	Neck	08	08
Posture	1	1	Position of Right Arm	5	5	Relative Size	4		Form	1	1	Shoulders	07	05
Perspective	5	0	Position of Left Arm	0	5	Constant Line Pressure	0	0	Detailing	1	1	Right Arm	06	06
Vertical Midline	0	0	Position of Legs	5	4	Variable Line Pressure	5	5	Identity and Sex	1	1	Left Arm	04	06
Bilateral Symmetry	3	5	Relation of Long Axes	1	1	Line Continuity	0	0	Sophistication	2	2	Chest	07	05
Horizontal Midline	4	4	Right and Left Halves	1	1	Body Shading	2	3	Height	06	07	Girth	07	05

GENERAL CHARACTERISTICS OF SUBJECT

IDENTIFICATION
No. 214
Sex M
Marital status M
Age 24 yrs. at psychological tests

PARENTAL HISTORY					
Father					
C	H	S	D	O	
?	–	–	–	–	
Mother					
C	H	S	D	O	
(+)	+	–	–	+	

PHYSIOLOGICAL AND METABOLIC DATA

	Admission	Initial	Control	Cold pressor change	Exercise change	Smoking change
Systolic pressure	108					
Diastolic pressure	72					
Heart rate	76					

Age 20 yrs.	Height 72 in.	Ponderal index 12.57
	Weight 188 lbs.	Cholesterol 237 mg. per 100 ml.
	Overweight +17 %	Vital capacity liters

HABIT SURVEY
Smoking habits: unknown
Age begun yrs.   Inhalation:
Habits of nervous tension:

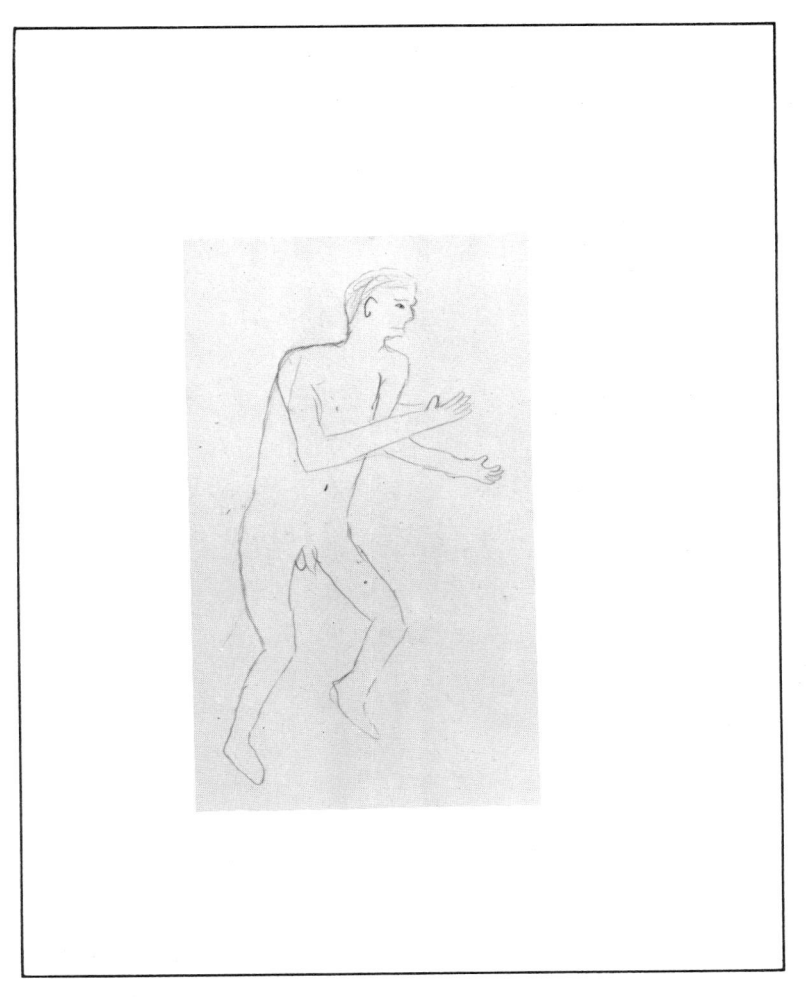

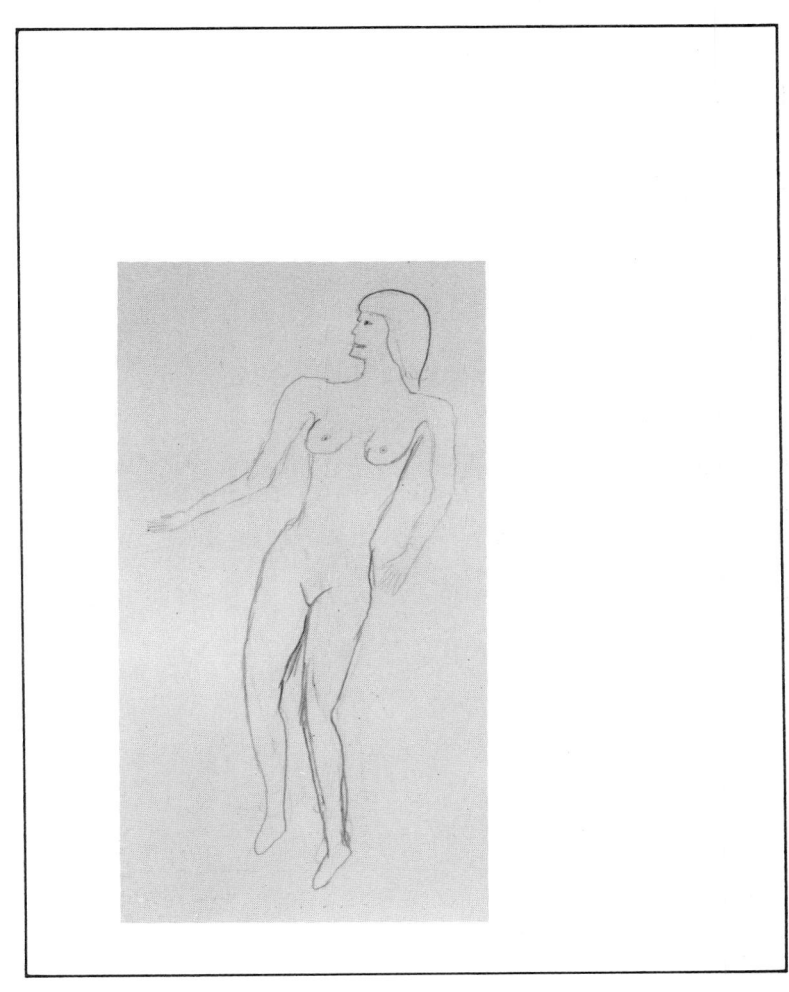

FIGURE-DRAWING CHARACTERISTICS

Structural	Male	Female	Structural	Male	Female	Structural and Graphic	Male	Female	Graphic, Global and Height	Male	Female	Body Proportions	Male	Female
	Both						Both							
Type	0		Omission of Appendages	0	0	Upper and Lower Halves	3	3	Hair Shading	3	5	Head	05	05
Sex Sequence	0		Position of Both Arms	0	1	Four Quarters	4	4	Nudity and Transparency	0	0	Neck	04	06
Posture	6	6	Position of Right Arm	6	3	Relative Size		5	Form	1	3	Shoulders		06
Perspective	6	5	Position of Left Arm	6	5	Constant Line Pressure	1	0	Detailing	3	3	Right Arm	06	06
Vertical Midline	4	0	Position of Legs	8	8	Variable Line Pressure	0	3	Identity and Sex	1	1	Left Arm		04
Bilateral Symmetry	0	3	Relation of Long Axes	0	0	Line Continuity	0	0	Sophistication	2	2	Chest		05
Horizontal Midline	0	0	Right and Left Halves	2	1	Body Shading	0	0	Height	05	06	Girth		05

GENERAL CHARACTERISTICS OF SUBJECT

IDENTIFICATION

No. D69

Sex M

Marital status M

Age 23 yrs. at

psychological tests

PARENTAL HISTORY

Father

C	H	S	D	O
+	-	-	-	+

Mother

C	H	S	D	O
-	-	-	-	-

PHYSIOLOGICAL AND METABOLIC DATA

	Admission	Initial	Control	Cold pressor change	Exercise change	Smoking change
Systolic pressure	120	120	118	+17	+14	+10
Diastolic pressure	80	62	60	+25	-05	+06
Heart rate	68	64	65	+12	+23	+08

Age 23 yrs.

Height 73 in.

Weight 158 lbs.

Overweight -06 %

Ponderal index 13.49

Cholesterol 190 mg. per 100 ml.

Vital capacity 5.1 liters

HABIT SURVEY

Smoking habits: former smoker

Age begun 16 yrs. Inhalation:

Habits of nervous tension: 1, 3, 4, 6, 7, 8, 22

STRONG VOCATIONAL INTEREST TEST

Occupation	Artist	Psychologist	Architect	Physician	Osteopath	Dentist	Veterinarian	Mathematician	Physicist	Engineer	Chemist	Production Manager
Standard Score	51	58	57	65	38	41	23	48	47	42	59	18

Occupation	Farmer	Aviator	Carpenter	Printer	Math.-Sci. Teacher	Ind. Arts Teacher	Voc. Agric. Teacher	Policeman	Forest Serv. Man	Y.M.C.A. Phys. Dir.	Personnel Director	Public Administrator
Standard Score	41	34	28	45	46	21	29	21	41	29	31	42

Occupation	Y.M.C.A. Secretary	Soc. Sci. H.S. Teacher	City Sch. Sup't.	Social Worker	Minister	Musician Performer	C.P.A.	Senior C.P.A.	Accountant	Office Man	Purchasing Agent	Banker
Standard Score	22	29	28	41	63	61	33	39	13	21	09	13

Occupation	Mortician	Pharmacist	Sales Manager	Real Est. Manager	Life Ins. Salesman	Advertising Man	Lawyer	Author-Journalist	President Mfg. Co.	Interest Maturity	Occupational Level	Masculinity-Femininity
Standard Score	05	23	13	19	12	34	33	43	17	51	55	41

FIGURE-DRAWING CHARACTERISTICS

Structural	Male Female Both		Structural	Male	Female	Structural and Graphic	Male Female Both		Graphic, Global and Height	Male	Female	Body Proportions	Male	Female
Type	0		Omission of Appendages	0	5	Upper and Lower Halves	1	1	Hair Shading	6	3	Head	05	05
Sex Sequence	2		Position of Both Arms	1	6	Four Quarters	4	4	Nudity and Transparency	7	2	Neck	10	06
Posture	1	0	Position of Right Arm	2	2	Relative Size	0		Form	1	1	Shoulders	05	04
Perspective	0	0	Position of Left Arm	4	2	Constant Line Pressure	0	1	Detailing	1	1	Right Arm	04	
Vertical Midline	3	0	Position of Legs	6	4	Variable Line Pressure	1	0	Identity and Sex	1	1	Left Arm	02	
Bilateral Symmetry	3	3	Relation of Long Axes	1	1	Line Continuity	0	0	Sophistication	2	2	Chest	04	04
Horizontal Midline	4	4	Right and Left Halves	1	1	Body Shading	7	3	Height	05	04	Girth	04	04

GENERAL CHARACTERISTICS OF SUBJECT

IDENTIFICATION
No. 203
Sex M
Marital status S
Age 30 yrs. at psychological tests

PARENTAL HISTORY				
Father				
C	H	S	D	O
+	-	-	-	-
Mother				
C	H	S	D	O
-	+	-	-	-

PHYSIOLOGICAL AND METABOLIC DATA

	Admission	Initial	Control	Cold pressor change	Exercise change	Smoking change
Systolic pressure	110	132	116	+10	+22	
Diastolic pressure	70	80	74	+06	-14	
Heart rate	64	84	75	-06	+08	

Age 27 yrs.	Height 69 in.	Ponderal index 13.29
	Weight 140 lbs.	Cholesterol 237 mg. per 100 ml.
	Overweight -09 %	Vital capacity 4.4 liters

HABIT SURVEY
Smoking habits: heavy cigarette smoker
Age begun 16 yrs.   Inhalation: yes
Habits of nervous tension: 2, 3, 4, 5, 6, 11, 15, 16, 17, 21, 25

FIGURE-DRAWING CHARACTERISTICS

Structural	Male Female Both		Structural	Male	Female	Structural and Graphic	Male Female Both		Graphic, Global and Height	Male	Female	Body Proportions	Male	Female
Type	0		Omission of Appendages	0	0	Upper and Lower Halves	1	1	Hair Shading	1	1	Head	08	10
Sex Sequence	2		Position of Both Arms	1	1	Four Quarters	4	4	Nudity and Transparency	7	7	Neck	08	04
Posture	1	1	Position of Right Arm	4	3	Relative Size	0		Form	1	1	Shoulders	08	
Perspective	5	1	Position of Left Arm	5	0	Constant Line Pressure	0	0	Detailing	1	3	Right Arm	04	04
Vertical Midline	7	4	Position of Legs	4	4	Variable Line Pressure	1	1	Identity and Sex	1	1	Left Arm	06	06
Bilateral Symmetry	3	0	Relation of Long Axes	3	1	Line Continuity	0	2	Sophistication	2	2	Chest	07	
Horizontal Midline	0	4	Right and Left Halves	1	1	Body Shading	6	1	Height	07	06	Girth	08	

GENERAL CHARACTERISTICS OF SUBJECT

<table>
<tr><th>IDENTIFICATION</th><th>PARENTAL HISTORY</th><th colspan="7">PHYSIOLOGICAL AND METABOLIC DATA</th><th>HABIT SURVEY</th></tr>
<tr>
<td>No. 239
Sex M
Marital status S
Age 28 yrs. at
psychological tests</td>
<td>Father
C   H   S   D   O
+   U   –   –   U
Mother
C   H   S   D   O
–   –   –   –   U</td>
<td colspan="7">

	Admission	Initial	Control	Cold pressor change	Exercise change	Smoking change
Systolic pressure	114					
Diastolic pressure	70					
Heart rate	92					

Age 25 yrs.   Height 69 in.   Ponderal index 12.36
           Weight 174 lbs.   Cholesterol 183 mg. per 100 ml.
           Overweight +14 %   Vital capacity liters
</td>
<td>Smoking habits: unknown
    Age begun   yrs.   Inhalation:
    Habits of nervous tension:</td>
</tr>
</table>

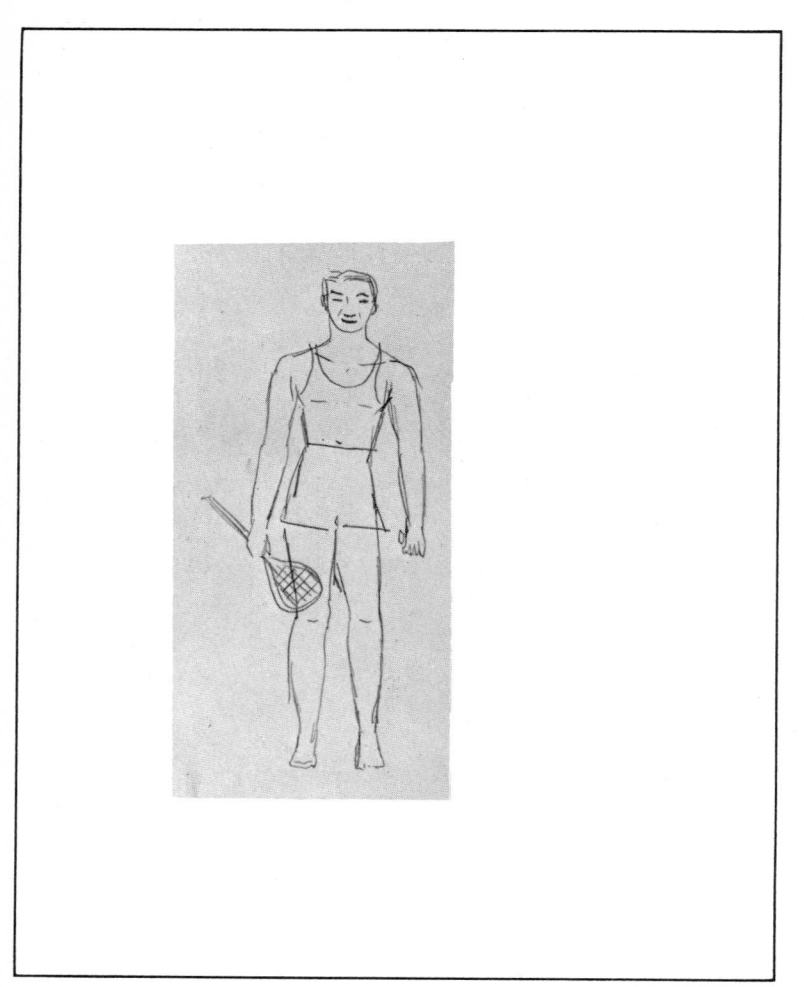

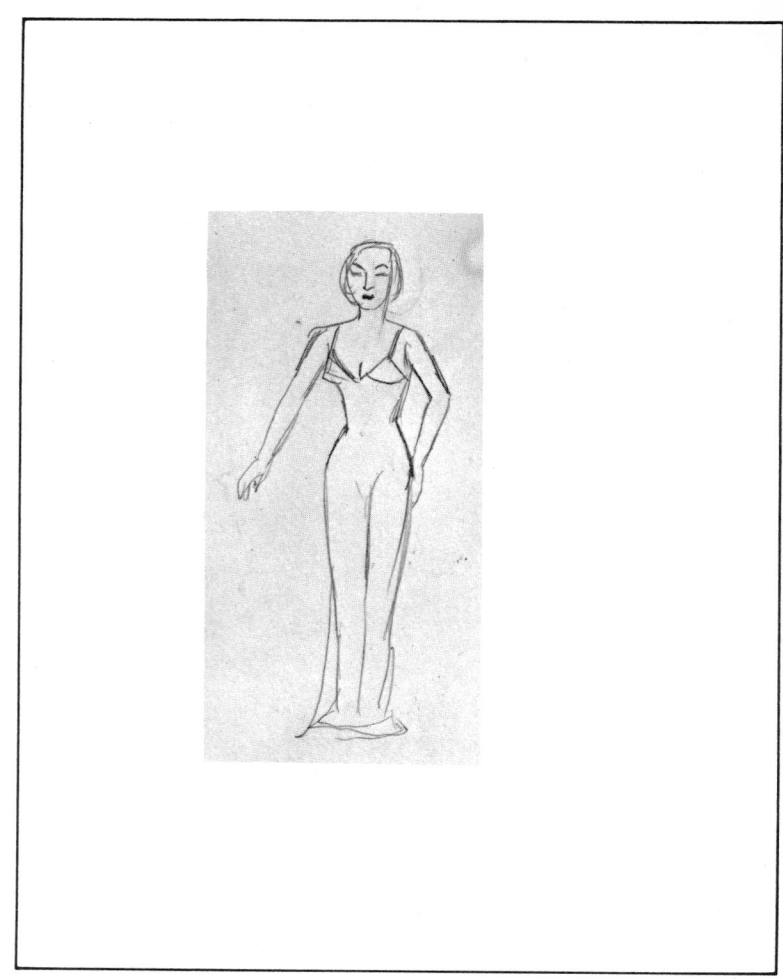

FIGURE-DRAWING CHARACTERISTICS

Structural	Male Female Both	Structural	Male	Female	Structural and Graphic	Male Both	Female	Graphic, Global and Height	Male	Female	Body Proportions	Male	Female
Type	0	Omission of Appendages	0	8	Upper and Lower Halves	0	0	Hair Shading	1	1	Head	05	05
Sex Sequence	0	Position of Both Arms	0	1	Four Quarters	4	4	Nudity and Transparency	2	6	Neck	04	04
Posture	1 1	Position of Right Arm	0	2	Relative Size	2		Form	1	1	Shoulders	05	
Perspective	0 9	Position of Left Arm	0	5	Constant Line Pressure	0	0	Detailing	3	3	Right Arm	04	04
Vertical Midline	0 0	Position of Legs	4	2	Variable Line Pressure	3	3	Identity and Sex	1	1	Left Arm	04	04
Bilateral Symmetry	3 3	Relation of Long Axes	1	1	Line Continuity	0	0	Sophistication	2	2	Chest	04	
Horizontal Midline	4 0	Right and Left Halves	1	1	Body Shading	3	3	Height	05	05	Girth	04	03

GENERAL CHARACTERISTICS OF SUBJECT

IDENTIFICATION
No. 305
Sex M
Marital status S
Age 24 yrs. at
psychological tests

PARENTAL HISTORY
Father
C H S D O
+ + - - +
Mother
C H S D O
- - - - -

PHYSIOLOGICAL AND METABOLIC DATA

	Admission	Initial	Control	Cold pressor change	Exercise change	Smoking change
Systolic pressure	134	133	114	00	+36	+04
Diastolic pressure	72	70	74	+14	00	00
Heart rate	84	78	70	+02	+12	+01

Age 22 yrs.	Height 75 in.	Ponderal index 13.81
	Weight 160 lbs.	Cholesterol 160 mg. per 100 ml.
	Overweight -10 %	Vital capacity 4.4 liters

HABIT SURVEY

Smoking habits: occasional smoker

  Age begun 18 yrs.   Inhalation: no

Habits of nervous tension: 3, 5, 7, 9,

11, 12, 22

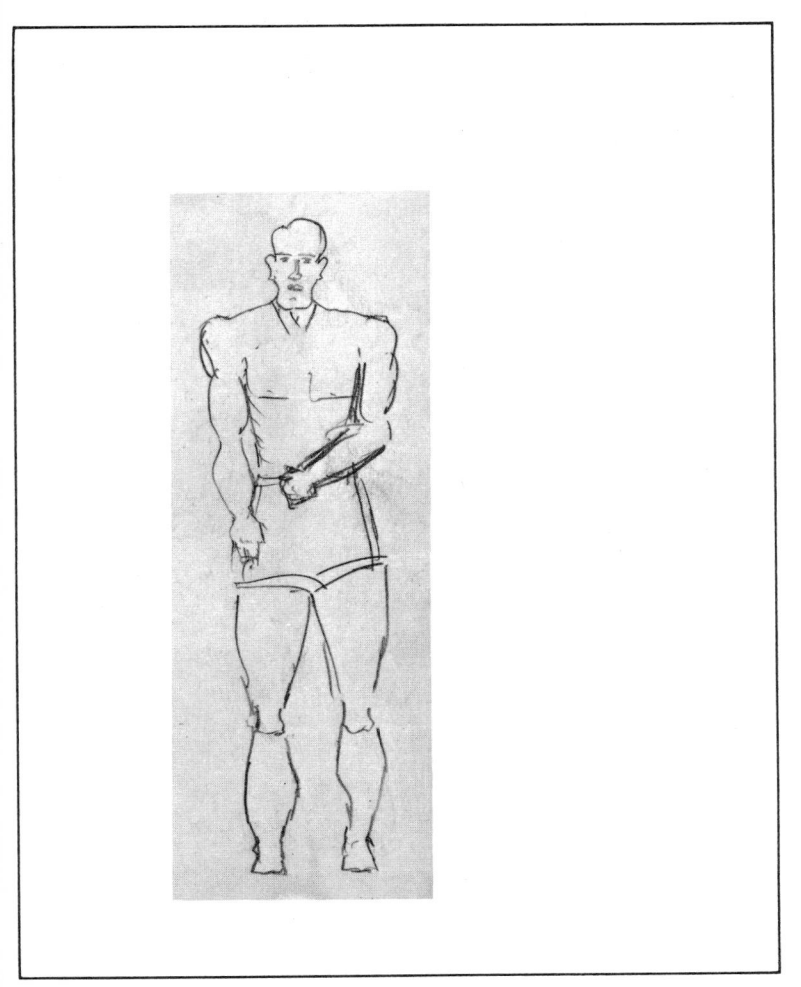

FIGURE-DRAWING CHARACTERISTICS

Structural	Male Female Both		Structural	Male	Female	Structural and Graphic	Male Female Both		Graphic, Global and Height	Male	Female	Body Proportions	Male	Female
Type	0		Omission of Appendages	0	0	Upper and Lower Halves	3	0	Hair Shading	5	5	Head	07	06
Sex Sequence	0		Position of Both Arms	1	1	Four Quarters	4	4	Nudity and Transparency	3	2	Neck		06
Posture	1	1	Position of Right Arm	0	0	Relative Size	0		Form	1	1	Shoulders	07	06
Perspective	0	0	Position of Left Arm	5	5	Constant Line Pressure	0	0	Detailing	3	3	Right Arm	06	04
Vertical Midline	0	0	Position of Legs	6	4	Variable Line Pressure	5	1	Identity and Sex	1	1	Left Arm	06	04
Bilateral Symmetry	3	3	Relation of Long Axes	1	1	Line Continuity	2	0	Sophistication	2	2	Chest	05	05
Horizontal Midline	4	4	Right and Left Halves	2	2	Body Shading	3	3	Height	07	05	Girth	06	06

GENERAL CHARACTERISTICS OF SUBJECT

IDENTIFICATION
No. 337
Sex M
Marital status M
Age 28 yrs. at
psychological tests

PARENTAL HISTORY				
Father				
C	H	S	D	O
+	?	+	-	+
Mother				
C	H	S	D	O
-	-	-	-	+

PHYSIOLOGICAL AND METABOLIC DATA

	Admission	Initial	Control	Cold pressor change	Exercise change	Smoking change
Systolic pressure	154	158	130	+03	+44	-08
Diastolic pressure	86	80	74	+02	00	+04
Heart rate	88	96	91	00	+20	+10

Age 26 yrs.

Height	75	in.
Weight	200	lbs.
Overweight+08 %		

Ponderal index 12.82

Cholesterol 330 mg. per 100 ml.

Vital capacity 6.1 liters

HABIT SURVEY

Smoking habits: moderate cigarette smoker

Age begun 18 yrs.   Inhalation: yes

Habits of nervous tension: 2, 5, 6, 11

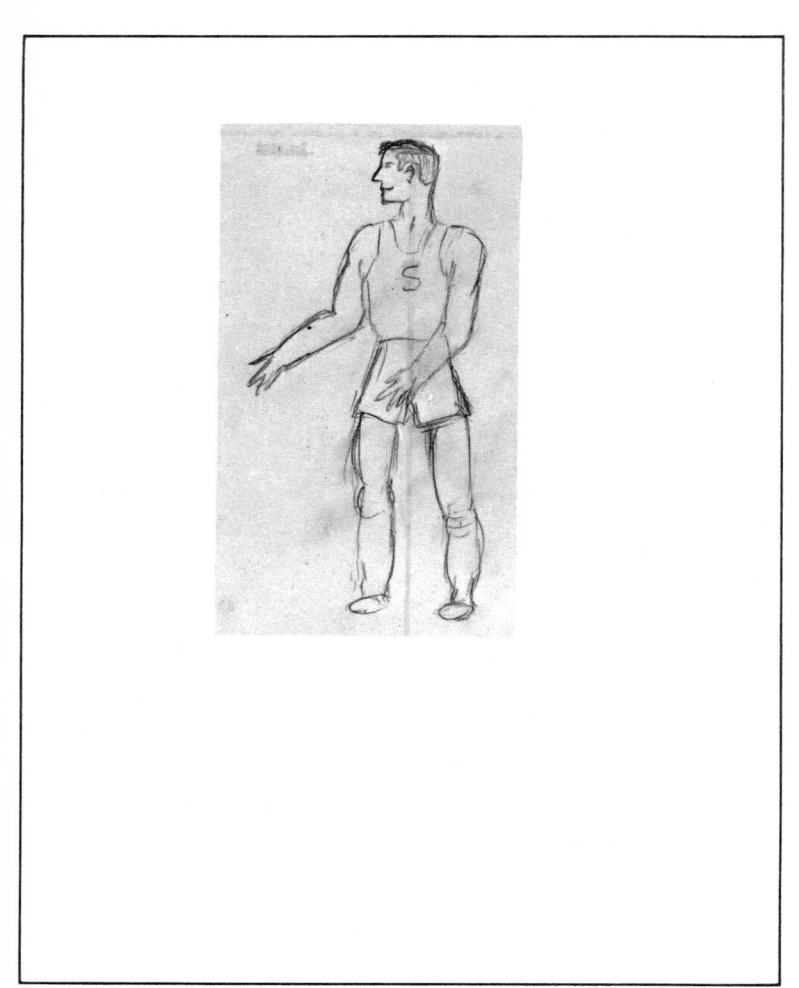

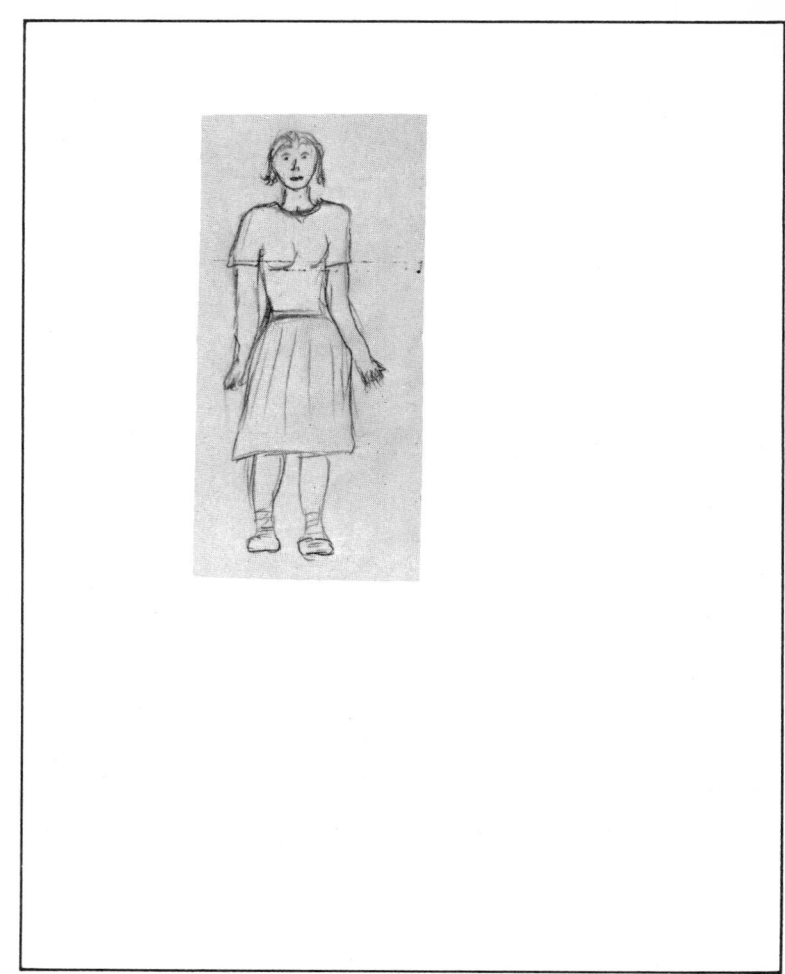

FIGURE-DRAWING CHARACTERISTICS

Structural	Male Female Both		Structural	Male	Female	Structural and Graphic	Male Female Both		Graphic, Global and Height	Male	Female	Body Proportions	Male	Female
Type	0		Omission of Appendages	0	0	Upper and Lower Halves	1	1	Hair Shading	3	3	Head	05	04
Sex Sequence	0		Position of Both Arms	0	0	Four Quarters	4	4	Nudity and Transparency	2	7	Neck	07	06
Posture	1	1	Position of Right Arm	4	0	Relative Size	0		Form	3	3	Shoulders	05	04
Perspective	5	0	Position of Left Arm	5	0	Constant Line Pressure	0	0	Detailing	3	3	Right Arm	04	04
Vertical Midline	0	0	Position of Legs	6	4	Variable Line Pressure	3	3	Identity and Sex	1	1	Left Arm	04	04
Bilateral Symmetry	3	3	Relation of Long Axes	1	1	Line Continuity	0	0	Sophistication	2	2	Chest	04	03
Horizontal Midline	4	4	Right and Left Halves	0	2	Body Shading	3	3	Height	05	04	Girth	04	04

GENERAL CHARACTERISTICS OF SUBJECT

IDENTIFICATION

No.   356

Sex   M

Marital status   S

Age   25 yrs. at

psychological tests

PARENTAL HISTORY

Father

C	H	S	D	O
+	+	-	(+)	+

Mother

C	H	S	D	O
-	-	-	-	-

PHYSIOLOGICAL AND METABOLIC DATA

	Admission	Initial	Control	Cold pressor change	Exercise change	Smoking change
Systolic pressure	130	124	104	+12	+28	+08
Diastolic pressure	80	70	72	+22	-02	+04
Heart rate	64	66	53	+18	+18	-01

Age 23 yrs.

Height	72 in.	Ponderal index 13.00
Weight	170 lbs.	Cholesterol 215 mg. per 100 ml.
Overweight +04 %		Vital capacity 5.5 liters

HABIT SURVEY

Smoking habits: nonsmoker

Age begun   yrs.   Inhalation:

Habits of nervous tension: 4, 5, 11, 22

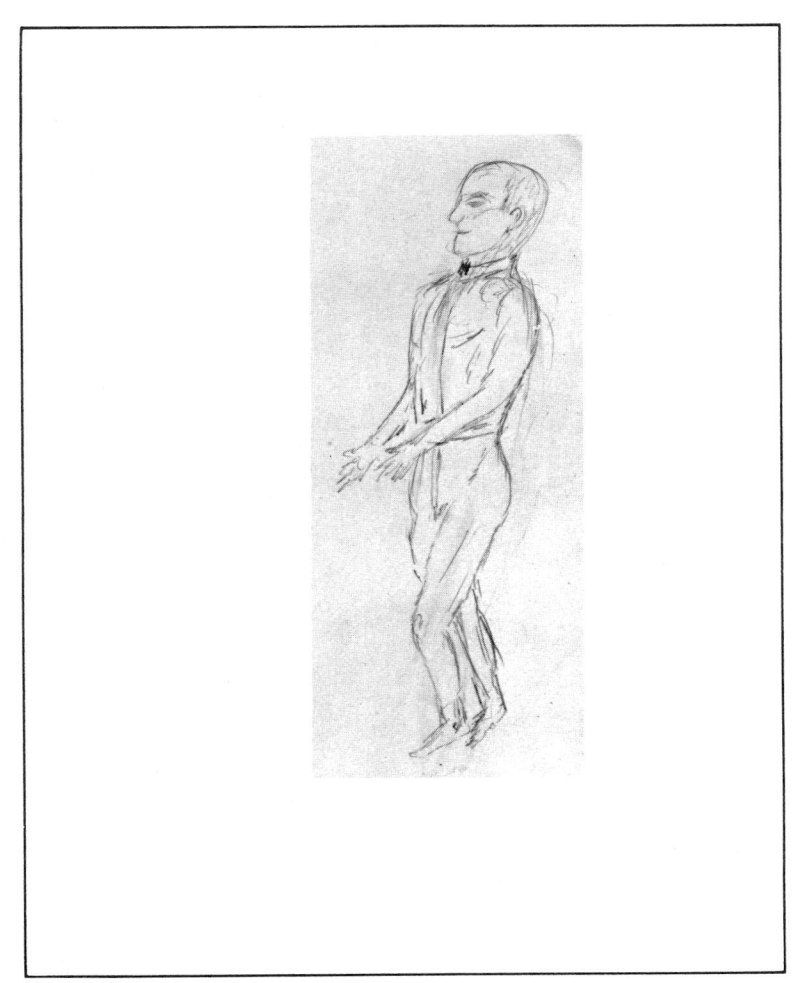

FIGURE-DRAWING CHARACTERISTICS

Structural	Male Female Both	Structural	Male	Female	Structural and Graphic	Male Female Both		Graphic, Global and Height	Male	Female	Body Proportions	Male	Female
Type	0	Omission of Appendages	0	0	Upper and Lower Halves	1	1	Hair Shading	1	3	Head	08	08
Sex Sequence	0	Position of Both Arms	4	1	Four Quarters	4	4	Nudity and Transparency	7	7	Neck	04	06
Posture	2 1	Position of Right Arm	7	5	Relative Size	2		Form	3	3	Shoulders		07
Perspective	6 0	Position of Left Arm	4	4	Constant Line Pressure	0	0	Detailing	3	3	Right Arm		06
Vertical Midline	7 1	Position of Legs	8	5	Variable Line Pressure	1	1	Identity and Sex	1	1	Left Arm	06	06
Bilateral Symmetry	0 3	Relation of Long Axes	1	1	Line Continuity	0	0	Sophistication	2	2	Chest		06
Horizontal Midline	4 4	Right and Left Halves	3	0	Body Shading	7	7	Height	06	06	Girth		06

GENERAL CHARACTERISTICS OF SUBJECT

IDENTIFICATION
No. 366
Sex M
Marital status S
Age 25 yrs. at
psychological tests

PARENTAL HISTORY				
Father				
C	H	S	D	O
+	+	-	-	?
Mother				
C	H	S	D	O
-	U	+	-	-

PHYSIOLOGICAL AND METABOLIC DATA

	Admission	Initial	Control	Cold pressor change	Exercise change	Smoking change
Systolic pressure	112	112	105	+06	+21	
Diastolic pressure	70	76	74	+08	00	
Heart rate	80	60	60	+06	+22	

Age 24 yrs.

Height 67 in.
Weight 134 lbs.
Overweight -07 %

Ponderal index 13.09
Cholesterol 235 mg. per 100 ml.
Vital capacity 4.7 liters

HABIT SURVEY

Smoking habits: occasional smoker
  Age begun 20 yrs.   Inhalation: yes
Habits of nervous tension: 4, 5, 6, 10, 14,
21, 23

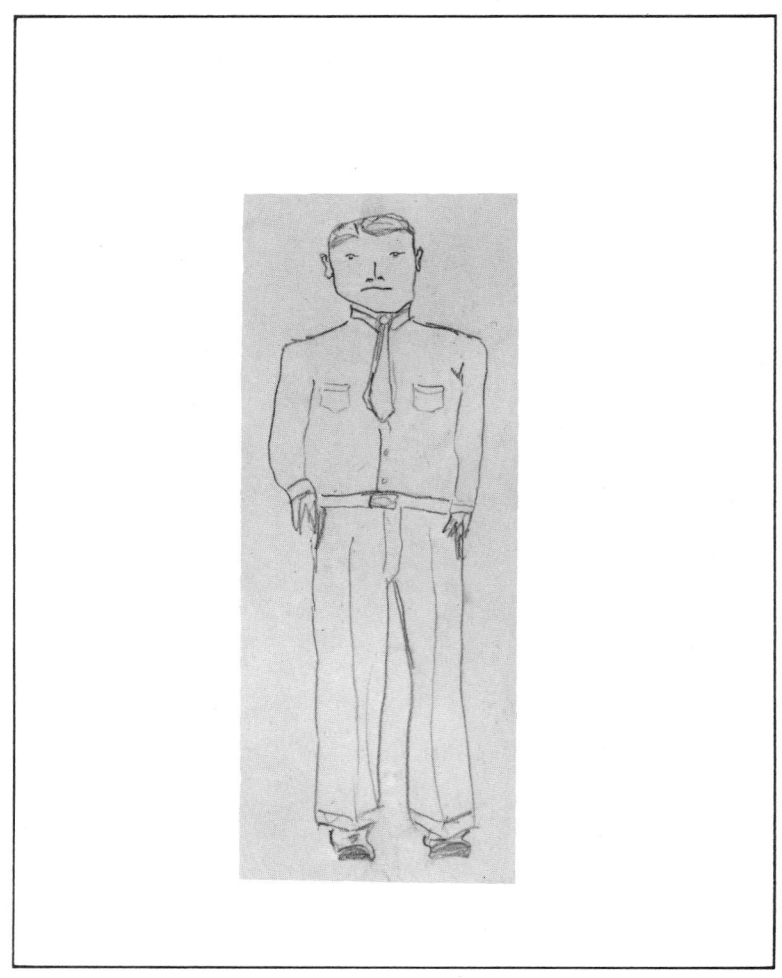

FIGURE-DRAWING CHARACTERISTICS

Structural	Male Female Both	Structural	Male	Female	Structural and Graphic	Male Female Both		Graphic, Global and Height	Male	Female	Body Proportions	Male	Female
Type	0	Omission of Appendages	0	0	Upper and Lower Halves	3	3	Hair Shading	1	5	Head	08	07
Sex Sequence	1	Position of Both Arms	0	1	Four Quarters	4	4	Nudity and Transparency	7	7	Neck	04	04
Posture	1 1	Position of Right Arm	0	2	Relative Size	0		Form	1	1	Shoulders	08	07
Perspective	0 0	Position of Left Arm	0	0	Constant Line Pressure	3	0	Detailing	3	3	Right Arm	04	04
Vertical Midline	3 3	Position of Legs	5	4	Variable Line Pressure	0	1	Identity and Sex	1	1	Left Arm	04	04
Bilateral Symmetry	3 3	Relation of Long Axes	1	1	Line Continuity	2	2	Sophistication	2	2	Chest	07	05
Horizontal Midline	4 4	Right and Left Halves	1	1	Body Shading	7	0	Height	06	06	Girth	08	06

GENERAL CHARACTERISTICS OF SUBJECT

IDENTIFICATION
No. 410
Sex M
Marital status M
Age 29 yrs. at
psychological tests

PARENTAL HISTORY				
Father				
C	H	S	D	O
+	?	+	-	-
Mother				
C	H	S	D	O
-	?	-	-	-

PHYSIOLOGICAL AND METABOLIC DATA

	Admission	Initial	Control	Cold pressor change	Exercise change	Smoking change
Systolic pressure	122	122	120	+11	+26	
Diastolic pressure	70	56	62	+22	-02	
Heart rate	72	66	54	+04	+18	

Age 26 yrs.

Height	73	in.	Ponderal index	12.95	
Weight	179	lbs.	Cholesterol	258	mg. per 100 ml.
Overweight +03 %			Vital capacity	6.3	liters

HABIT SURVEY

Smoking habits: occasional smoker

   Age begun 17 yrs.   Inhalation: no

Habits of nervous tension: 2, 5, 6, 24

FIGURE-DRAWING CHARACTERISTICS

Structural	Male	Female	Structural	Male	Female	Structural and Graphic	Male	Female	Graphic, Global and Height	Male	Female	Body Proportions	Male	Female
	Both						Both							
Type	0		Omission of Appendages	0	0	Upper and Lower Halves	3	0	Hair Shading	3	3	Head	10	09
Sex Sequence	0		Position of Both Arms	4	4	Four Quarters	4	4	Nudity and Transparency	7	7	Neck	08	08
Posture	2	2	Position of Right Arm	7	7	Relative Size	0		Form	1	1	Shoulders		
Perspective	2	2	Position of Left Arm	4	4	Constant Line Pressure	0	0	Detailing	1	1	Right Arm		
Vertical Midline	7	4	Position of Legs	8	8	Variable Line Pressure	1	3	Identity and Sex	1	1	Left Arm	04	04
Bilateral Symmetry	0	0	Relation of Long Axes	1	1	Line Continuity	0	0	Sophistication	2	2	Chest	06	05
Horizontal Midline	4	4	Right and Left Halves	2	2	Body Shading	6	7	Height	07	06	Girth	06	05

GENERAL CHARACTERISTICS OF SUBJECT

IDENTIFICATION
No. 451
Sex M
Marital status M
Age 27 yrs. at
psychological tests

PARENTAL HISTORY				
Father				
C	H	S	D	O
+	-	+	-	-
Mother				
C	H	S	D	O
-	-	-	-	-

PHYSIOLOGICAL AND METABOLIC DATA

	Admission	Initial	Control	Cold pressor change	Exercise change	Smoking change
Systolic pressure	124	126	112	+08	+18	+02
Diastolic pressure	70	76	74	+12	00	+02
Heart rate	80	108	103	+04	+22	+04

Age 25 yrs.	Height 67 in.	Ponderal index 12.07
	Weight 171 lbs.	Cholesterol 273 mg. per 100 ml.
	Overweight +18 %	Vital capacity 4.8 liters

HABIT SURVEY
Smoking habits: occasional smoker
Age begun 16 yrs.   Inhalation: no
Habits of nervous tension: 4, 5, 6, 11, 16, 23

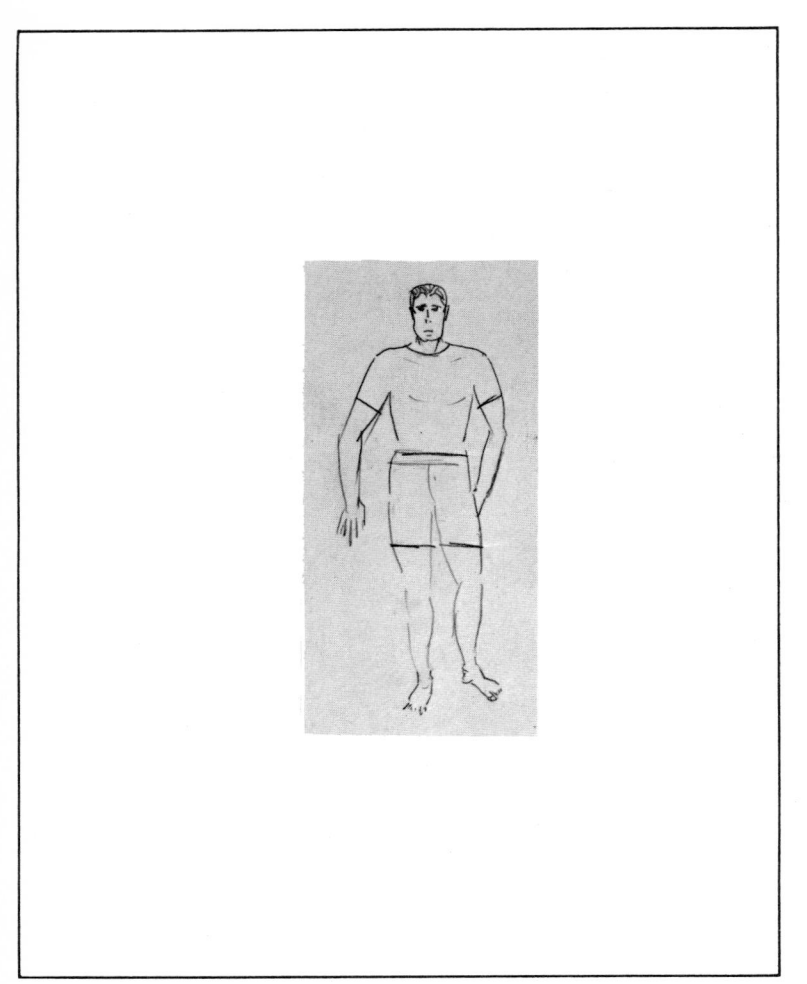

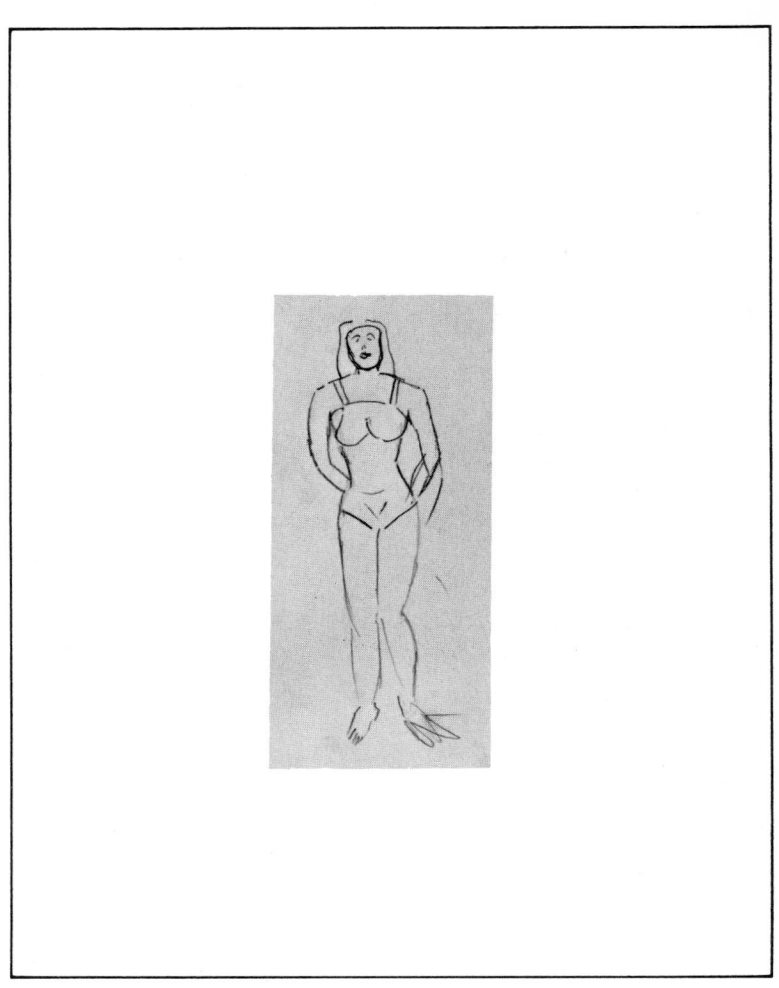

FIGURE-DRAWING CHARACTERISTICS

Structural	Male	Female	Structural	Male	Female	Structural and Graphic	Male	Female	Graphic, Global and Height	Male	Female	Body Proportions	Male	Female
	Both						Both							
Type	0		Omission of Appendages	7	7	Upper and Lower Halves	0	3	Hair Shading	1	5	Head	04	04
Sex Sequence	0		Position of Both Arms	1	0	Four Quarters	4	4	Nudity and Transparency	2	2	Neck	02	02
Posture	2	1	Position of Right Arm	2	5	Relative Size	2		Form	1	1	Shoulders	04	04
Perspective	0	0	Position of Left Arm	5	5	Constant Line Pressure	0	0	Detailing	1	3	Right Arm	04	
Vertical Midline	3	0	Position of Legs	8	2	Variable Line Pressure	3	3	Identity and Sex	1	1	Left Arm		
Bilateral Symmetry	3	3	Relation of Long Axes	1	1	Line Continuity	1	0	Sophistication	2	2	Chest	04	04
Horizontal Midline	4	0	Right and Left Halves	3	1	Body Shading	5	3	Height	04	04	Girth	04	03

GENERAL CHARACTERISTICS OF SUBJECT

IDENTIFICATION
No. 458
Sex M
Marital status M
Age 30 yrs. at
psychological tests

PARENTAL HISTORY				
Father				
C	H	S	D	O
+	-	-	-	?
Mother				
C	H	S	D	O
-	-	-	-	-

PHYSIOLOGICAL AND METABOLIC DATA

	Admission	Initial	Control	Cold pressor change	Exercise change	Smoking change
Systolic pressure	130	112	106	+04	+26	
Diastolic pressure	84	74	76	+10	-04	
Heart rate	84	80	81	+06	+26	

	Height 68 in.	Ponderal index 12.85
Age 27 yrs.	Weight 148 lbs.	Cholesterol 308 mg. per 100 ml.
	Overweight -01 %	Vital capacity 4.0 liters

HABIT SURVEY
Smoking habits: light cigarette smoker
Age begun 18 yrs.   Inhalation: yes
Habits of nervous tension: 3, 4, 5, 6, 11,
19, 22

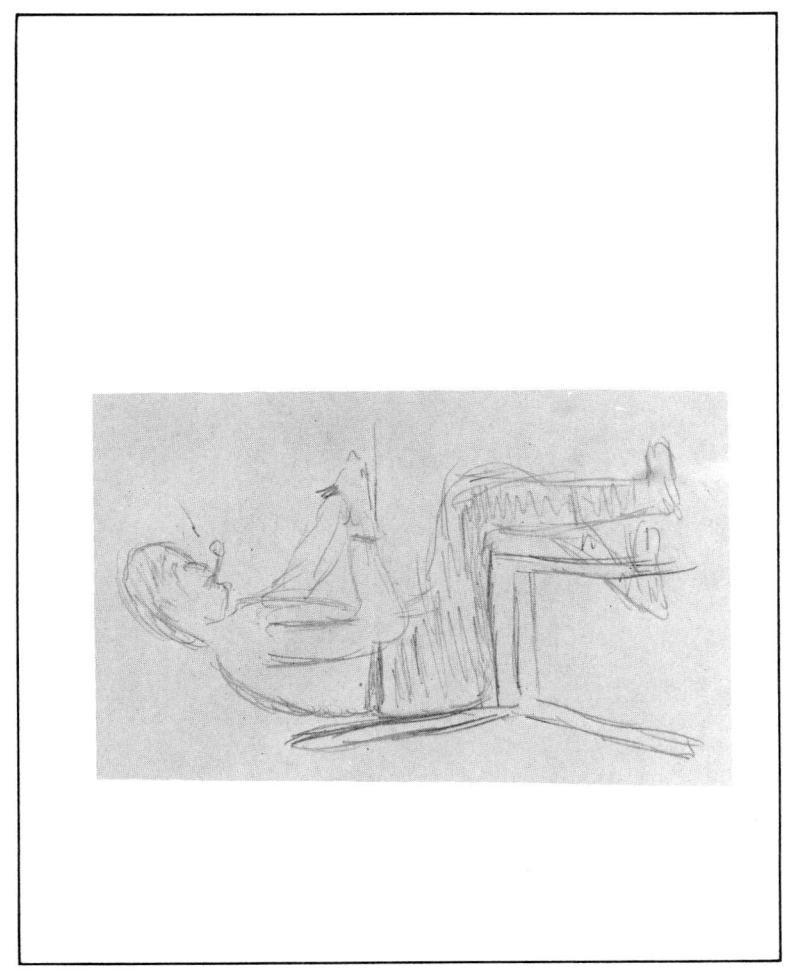

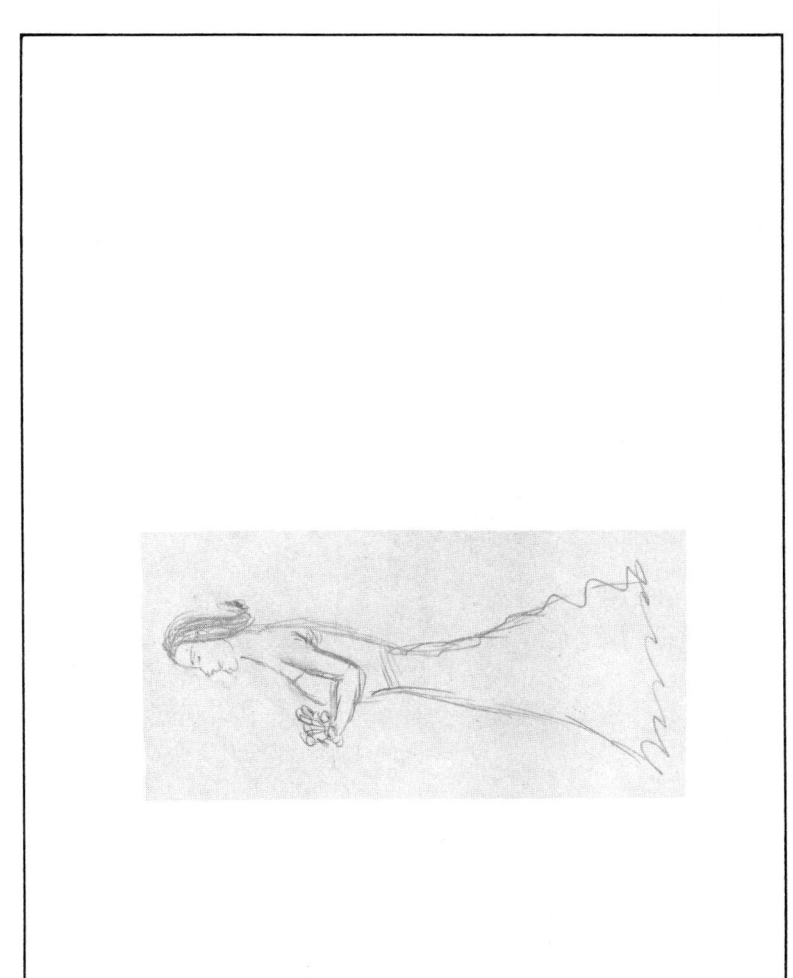

FIGURE-DRAWING CHARACTERISTICS

Structural	Male Female — Both		Structural	Male	Female	Structural and Graphic	Male Female — Both		Graphic, Global and Height	Male	Female	Body Proportions	Male	Female
Type	0		Omission of Appendages	0	8	Upper and Lower Halves	3	3	Hair Shading	3	3	Head	08	05
Sex Sequence	0		Position of Both Arms	2	4	Four Quarters	4	4	Nudity and Transparency	7	7	Neck		08
Posture	3	1	Position of Right Arm	4	7	Relative Size	5		Form	3	3	Shoulders		
Perspective	2	2	Position of Left Arm	7	4	Constant Line Pressure	1	0	Detailing	3	3	Right Arm	06	
Vertical Midline	4	4	Position of Legs	1	0	Variable Line Pressure	0	1	Identity and Sex	1	1	Left Arm		02
Bilateral Symmetry	0	0	Relation of Long Axes	0	2	Line Continuity	0	0	Sophistication	2	2	Chest	09	04
Horizontal Midline	4	4	Right and Left Halves	2	2	Body Shading	6	4	Height		05	Girth	08	04

GENERAL CHARACTERISTICS OF SUBJECT

<table>
<tr><th colspan="2">IDENTIFICATION</th><th colspan="2">PARENTAL HISTORY</th><th colspan="7">PHYSIOLOGICAL AND METABOLIC DATA</th><th colspan="2">HABIT SURVEY</th></tr>
</table>

IDENTIFICATION

No. 529

Sex M

Marital status S

Age 24 yrs. at

psychological tests

PARENTAL HISTORY

Father

C	H	S	D	O
+	-	-	+	?

Mother

C	H	S	D	O
-	(+)	+	-	+

PHYSIOLOGICAL AND METABOLIC DATA

	Admission	Initial	Control	Cold pressor change	Exercise change	Smoking change
Systolic pressure	120	132	124	+18	+36	+06
Diastolic pressure	75	84	80	+16	-04	+12
Heart rate	64	68	66	-04	+25	+08

Age 23 yrs.	Height	72 in.	Ponderal index 12.85
	Weight	176 lbs.	Cholesterol 237 mg. per 100 ml.
	Overweight +01 %		Vital capacity 5.7 liters

HABIT SURVEY

Smoking habits: occasional smoker

   Age begun 20 yrs.   Inhalation: no

Habits of nervous tension: 4, 5, 6, 8,

11, 16

FIGURE-DRAWING CHARACTERISTICS

Structural	Male	Female	Structural	Male	Female	Structural and Graphic	Male	Female	Graphic, Global and Height	Male	Female	Body Proportions	Male	Female
	Both						Both							
Type	0		Omission of Appendages	0	7	Upper and Lower Halves	1	1	Hair Shading	0	3	Head	05	04
Sex Sequence	1		Position of Both Arms	1	2	Four Quarters	4	4	Nudity and Transparency	7	0	Neck	05	06
Posture	1	1	Position of Right Arm	2	5	Relative Size	2		Form	1	1	Shoulders	05	
Perspective	0	6	Position of Left Arm	0	7	Constant Line Pressure	0	0	Detailing	3	3	Right Arm	03	04
Vertical Midline	3	4	Position of Legs	4	2	Variable Line Pressure	5	4	Identity and Sex	1	1	Left Arm	02	
Bilateral Symmetry	3	0	Relation of Long Axes	1	1	Line Continuity	0	0	Sophistication	2	2	Chest	04	
Horizontal Midline	4	0	Right and Left Halves	1	1	Body Shading	7	3	Height	04	04	Girth	05	

GENERAL CHARACTERISTICS OF SUBJECT

IDENTIFICATION
No. 543
Sex M
Marital status S
Age 24 yrs. at
psychological tests

PARENTAL HISTORY
Father
C   H   S   D   O
+   -   -   -   -
Mother
C   H   S   D   O
-    -   -   -   -

PHYSIOLOGICAL AND METABOLIC DATA

	Admission	Initial	Control	Cold pressor change	Exercise change	Smoking change
Systolic pressure	154	128	124	+16	+51	
Diastolic pressure	80	72	80	+04	-10	
Heart rate	84	68	73	+10	+20	

	Height 72 in.	Ponderal index 12.61
Age 21 yrs.	Weight 186 lbs.	Cholesterol 237 mg. per 100 ml.
	Overweight +15 %	Vital capacity 5.2 liters

HABIT SURVEY
Smoking habits: heavy cigarette smoker
Age begun 16 yrs.   Inhalation: yes
Habits of nervous tension: 2, 5, 9, 11, 18,
22, 24

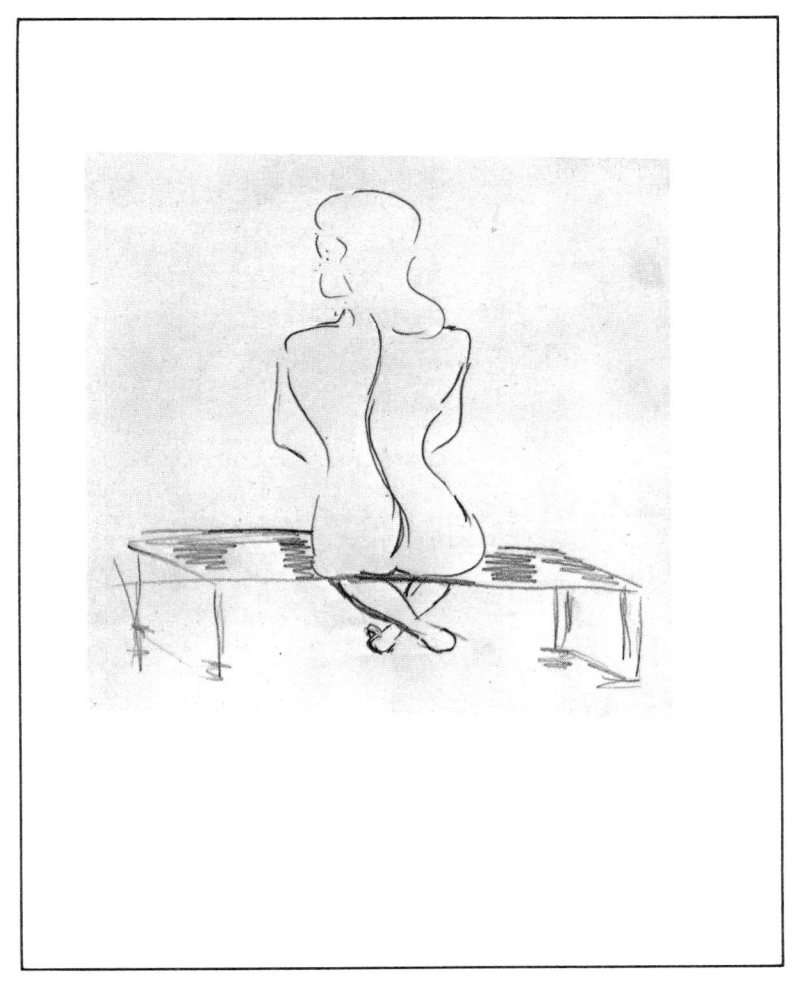

FIGURE-DRAWING CHARACTERISTICS

Structural	Male Female Both	Structural	Male	Female	Structural and Graphic	Male Female Both		Graphic, Global and Height	Male	Female	Body Proportions	Male	Female
Type	0	Omission of Appendages	0	2	Upper and Lower Halves	3	1	Hair Shading	7	5	Head	10	08
Sex Sequence	1	Position of Both Arms	1	6	Four Quarters	4	4	Nudity and Transparency	7	0	Neck	12	08
Posture	1　3	Position of Right Arm	4	8	Relative Size	5		Form	3	1	Shoulders	13	07
Perspective	0　7	Position of Left Arm	0	8	Constant Line Pressure	0	0	Detailing	1	3	Right Arm	07	
Vertical Midline	1　8	Position of Legs	5	7	Variable Line Pressure	5	5	Identity and Sex	1	1	Left Arm	06	
Bilateral Symmetry	3　3	Relation of Long Axes	1	0	Line Continuity	1	2	Sophistication	2	2	Chest	09	07
Horizontal Midline	4　0	Right and Left Halves	0	1	Body Shading	7	0	Height	07		Girth	07	06

GENERAL CHARACTERISTICS OF SUBJECT

IDENTIFICATION
No. 551
Sex M
Marital status M
Age 24 yrs. at psychological tests

PARENTAL HISTORY				
Father				
C	H	S	D	O
+	-	-	-	?
Mother				
C	H	S	D	O
-	-	-	-	-

PHYSIOLOGICAL AND METABOLIC DATA

	Admission	Initial	Control	Cold pressor change	Exercise change	Smoking change
Systolic pressure	130	120	106	+03	+44	+08
Diastolic pressure	76	56	60	+12	00	+14
Heart rate	64	48	47	00	+13	+21

Age 22 yrs.	Height	70	in.	Ponderal index 12.33	
	Weight	183	lbs.	Cholesterol	237 mg. per 100 ml.
	Overweight +19 %			Vital capacity	5.0 liters

HABIT SURVEY

Smoking habits: moderate cigarette smoker

Age begun 18 yrs.   Inhalation: yes

Habits of nervous tension: 4, 5, 6, 9, 11, 16, 17, 18, 23

FIGURE-DRAWING CHARACTERISTICS

Structural	Male Female Both	Structural	Male	Female	Structural and Graphic	Male Female Both	Graphic, Global and Height	Male	Female	Body Proportions	Male	Female
Type	0	Omission of Appendages	0	7	Upper and Lower Halves	1	2	Hair Shading	3	3	Head	06	04
Sex Sequence	0	Position of Both Arms	0	0	Four Quarters	4	0	Nudity and Transparency	7	7	Neck	05	05
Posture	1	1	Position of Right Arm	0	5	Relative Size	0		Form	1	1	Shoulders	05	04
Perspective	0	0	Position of Left Arm	0	5	Constant Line Pressure	0	0	Detailing	1	1	Right Arm	04	
Vertical Midline	3	3	Position of Legs	4	5	Variable Line Pressure	1	5	Identity and Sex	1	1	Left Arm	02	
Bilateral Symmetry	3	3	Relation of Long Axes	1	1	Line Continuity	0	0	Sophistication	2	2	Chest	04	03
Horizontal Midline	4	4	Right and Left Halves	1	2	Body Shading	6	7	Height	04	03	Girth	04	03

GENERAL CHARACTERISTICS OF SUBJECT

IDENTIFICATION
No. 575
Sex M
Marital status S
Age 26 yrs. at
psychological tests

PARENTAL HISTORY
Father
C   H   S   D   O
+   -   -   -   +
Mother
C   H   S   D   O
-   -   -   -   +

PHYSIOLOGICAL AND METABOLIC DATA

	Admission	Initial	Control	Cold pressor change	Exercise change	Smoking change
Systolic pressure	120	110	100	+30	+40	
Diastolic pressure	75	70	70	+10	+10	
Heart rate	72	80	71	+06	+44	

Age 24 yrs.	Height 67 in.	Ponderal index 11.93
	Weight 177 lbs.	Cholesterol 258 mg. per 100 ml.
	Overweight +23 %	Vital capacity 3.6 liters

HABIT SURVEY

Smoking habits: pipe and cigar smoker

Age begun 18 yrs.   Inhalation: no

Habits of nervous tension: 4, 5

FIGURE-DRAWING CHARACTERISTICS

Structural	Male Female Both	Structural	Male	Female	Structural and Graphic	Male Female Both		Graphic, Global and Height	Male	Female	Body Proportions	Male	Female
Type	0	Omission of Appendages	3	3	Upper and Lower Halves	7	7	Hair Shading	3	3	Head	14	15
Sex Sequence	1	Position of Both Arms	1	1	Four Quarters	4	4	Nudity and Transparency	7	7	Neck	05	12
Posture	0 0	Position of Right Arm	2	5	Relative Size	5		Form	3	3	Shoulders	13	11
Perspective	0 0	Position of Left Arm	0	4	Constant Line Pressure	0	1	Detailing	3	3	Right Arm	08	08
Vertical Midline	3 1	Position of Legs	0	0	Variable Line Pressure	1	0	Identity and Sex	1	1	Left Arm	10	08
Bilateral Symmetry	3 3	Relation of Long Axes	1	1	Line Continuity	0	0	Sophistication	2	2	Chest	10	09
Horizontal Midline	6 4	Right and Left Halves	0	0	Body Shading	0	1	Height			Girth	12	09

GENERAL CHARACTERISTICS OF SUBJECT

IDENTIFICATION
No. 604
Sex M
Marital status S
Age 25 yrs. at psychological tests

PARENTAL HISTORY				
Father				
C	H	S	D	O
+	+	-	-	+
Mother				
C	H	S	D	O
-	-	-	-	-

PHYSIOLOGICAL AND METABOLIC DATA

	Admission	Initial	Control	Cold pressor change	Exercise change	Smoking change
Systolic pressure	154	122	118	+20	+32	+06
Diastolic pressure	80	78	76	+18	+04	+06
Heart rate	72	72	73	00	+27	+19

Age 22 yrs.	Height 72 in.	Ponderal index 12.41
	Weight 195 lbs.	Cholesterol 150 mg. per 100 ml.
	Overweight +20 %	Vital capacity 6.0 liters

HABIT SURVEY
Smoking habits: light cigarette smoker
Age begun yrs. Inhalation:
Habits of nervous tension:

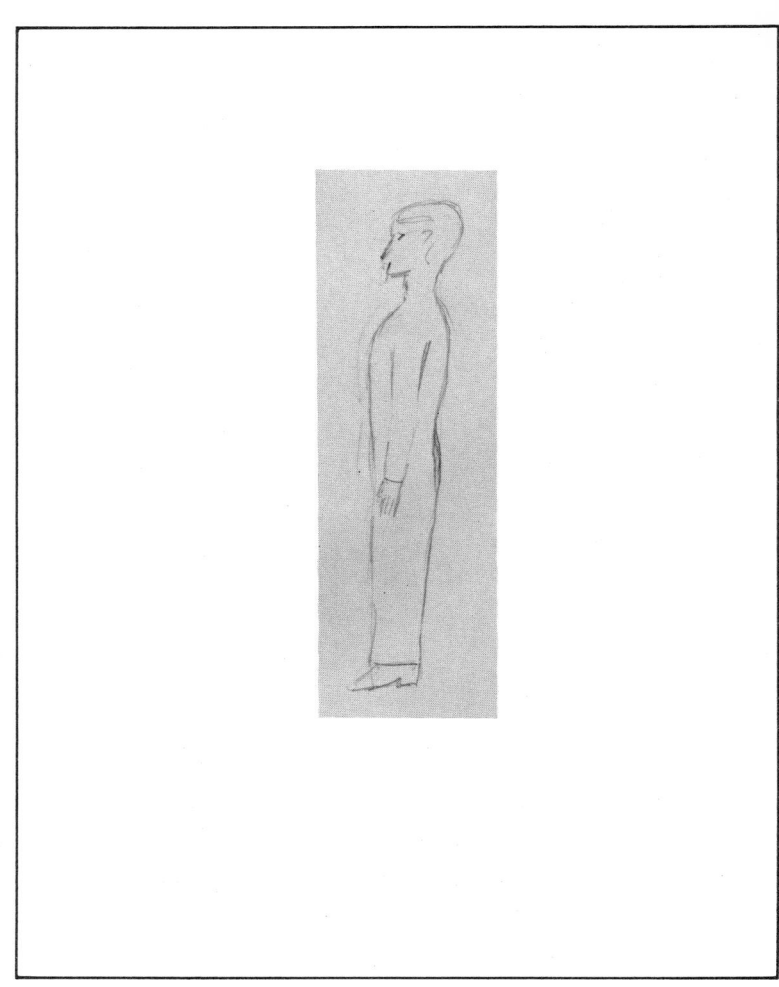

FIGURE-DRAWING CHARACTERISTICS

Structural	Male Female Both	Structural	Male	Female	Structural and Graphic	Male Female Both		Graphic, Global and Height	Male	Female	Body Proportions	Male	Female
Type	0	Omission of Appendages	0	0	Upper and Lower Halves	1	1	Hair Shading	7	5	Head	05	05
Sex Sequence	1	Position of Both Arms	4	4	Four Quarters	4	4	Nudity and Transparency	7	7	Neck	08	07
Posture	1	1	Position of Right Arm	7	7	Relative Size	1		Form	1	1	Shoulders		
Perspective	2	2	Position of Left Arm	0	0	Constant Line Pressure	0	0	Detailing	5	5	Right Arm		
Vertical Midline	4	4	Position of Legs	1	1	Variable Line Pressure	2	3	Identity and Sex	1	1	Left Arm	04	04
Bilateral Symmetry	0	0	Relation of Long Axes	1	1	Line Continuity	0	0	Sophistication	2	2	Chest	05	05
Horizontal Midline	0	0	Right and Left Halves	1	0	Body Shading	0	0	Height	05	05	Girth	05	05

GENERAL CHARACTERISTICS OF SUBJECT

IDENTIFICATION
No. 606
Sex M
Marital status S
Age 25 yrs. at
psychological tests

PARENTAL HISTORY
Father
C H S D O
+   -   -   -   ?
Mother
C H S D O
-   +   -   -   -

PHYSIOLOGICAL AND METABOLIC DATA

	Admission	Initial	Control	Cold pressor change	Exercise change	Smoking change
Systolic pressure	170	152	140	+10	+42	-08
Diastolic pressure	88	70	84	+06	-04	+04
Heart rate	110	100	91	+04	+45	+09

Age 22 yrs.	Height	67 in.	Ponderal index	12.98	
	Weight	137 lbs.	Cholesterol	298	mg. per 100 ml.
	Overweight	-04 %	Vital capacity	4.3	liters

HABIT SURVEY
Smoking habits: nonsmoker
Age begun   yrs.   Inhalation:
Habits of nervous tension: 1, 5, 6, 8, 11

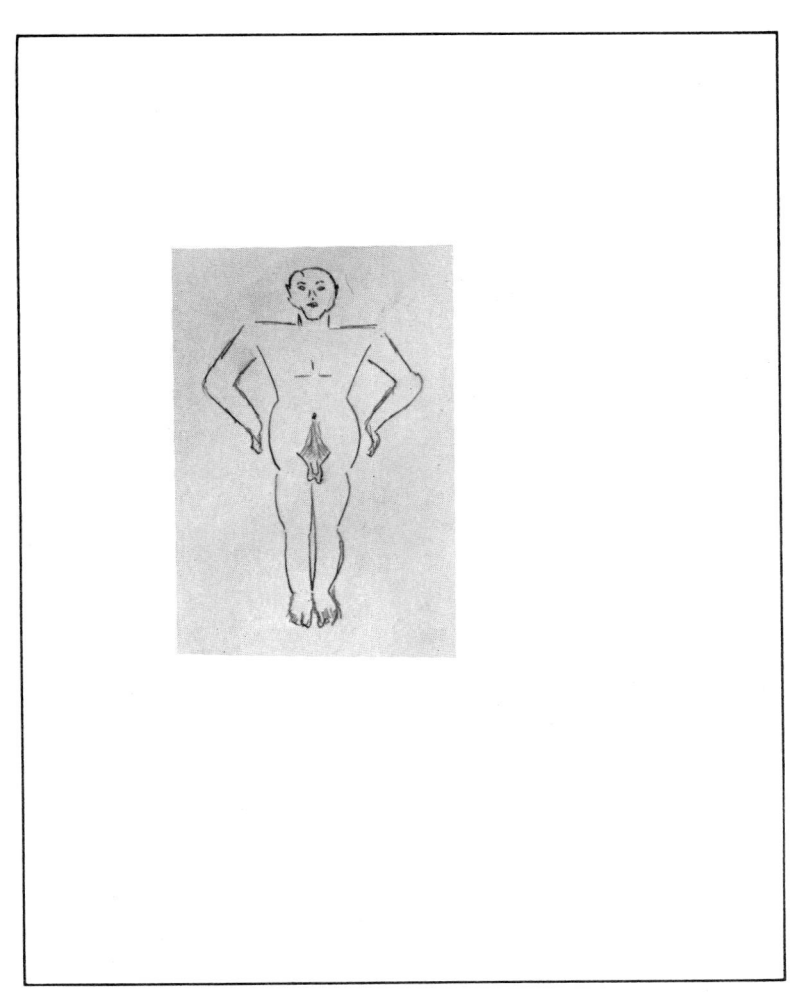

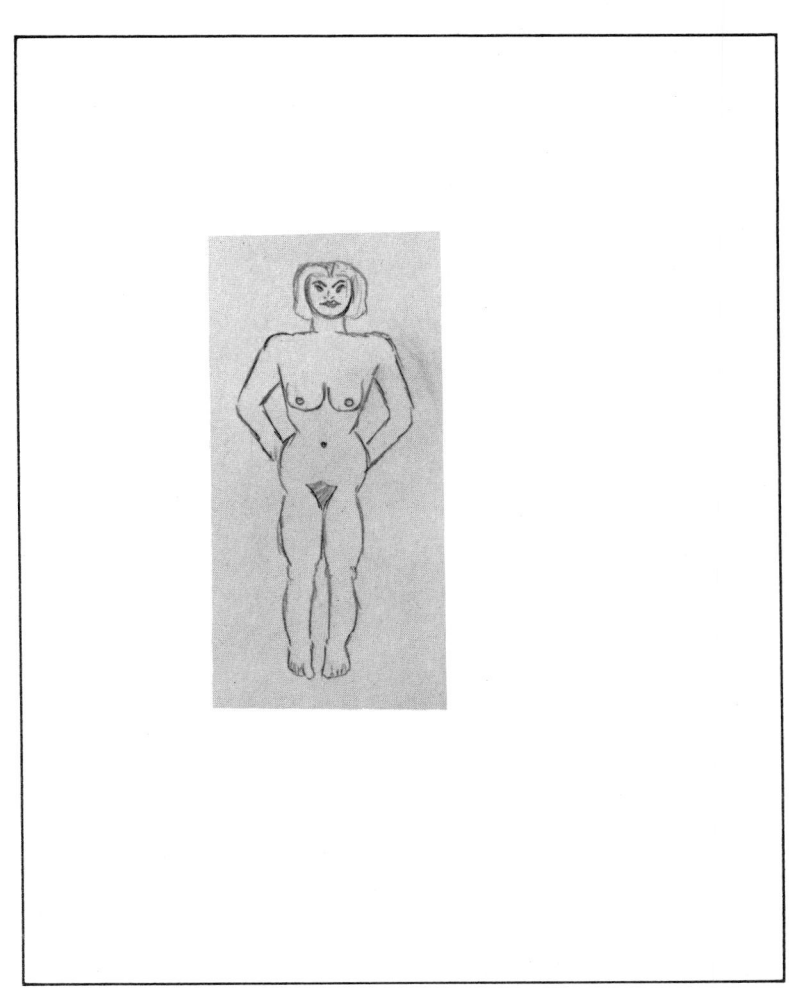

FIGURE-DRAWING CHARACTERISTICS

Structural	Male Female Both	Structural	Male	Female	Structural and Graphic	Male Female Both		Graphic, Global and Height	Male	Female	Body Proportions	Male	Female
Type	0	Omission of Appendages	0	7	Upper and Lower Halves	1	1	Hair Shading	0	1	Head	04	04
Sex Sequence	0	Position of Both Arms	0	0	Four Quarters	4	4	Nudity and Transparency	0	0	Neck	03	04
Posture	1	1	Position of Right Arm	5	5	Relative Size	4		Form	1	1	Shoulders	05	05
Perspective	0	0	Position of Left Arm	5	5	Constant Line Pressure	5	5	Detailing	1	1	Right Arm	04	
Vertical Midline	0	0	Position of Legs	2	4	Variable Line Pressure	0	0	Identity and Sex	1	1	Left Arm	04	
Bilateral Symmetry	5	5	Relation of Long Axes	1	1	Line Continuity	2	0	Sophistication	2	2	Chest	04	04
Horizontal Midline	0	0	Right and Left Halves	1	1	Body Shading	3	2	Height	03	04	Girth	04	03

GENERAL CHARACTERISTICS OF SUBJECT

IDENTIFICATION
No. 660
Sex M
Marital status S
Age 24 yrs. at
psychological tests

PARENTAL HISTORY
Father
C H S D O
+ - - - ?
Mother
C H S D O
- + - - +

PHYSIOLOGICAL AND METABOLIC DATA

	Admission	Initial	Control	Cold pressor change	Exercise change	Smoking change
Systolic pressure	120	128	126	+20	+42	00
Diastolic pressure	80	80	74	+16	-12	-01
Heart rate	80	76	73	+12	+24	-01

Age 21 yrs.	Height 70 in.	Ponderal index 11.78
	Weight 210 lbs.	Cholesterol 217 mg. per 100 ml.
	Overweight +37 %	Vital capacity 5.0 liters

HABIT SURVEY
Smoking habits: pipe smoker
Age begun 16 yrs.   Inhalation: sometimes
Habits of nervous tension: 5, 6, 9, 10, 14,
16, 18, 19, 22, 25

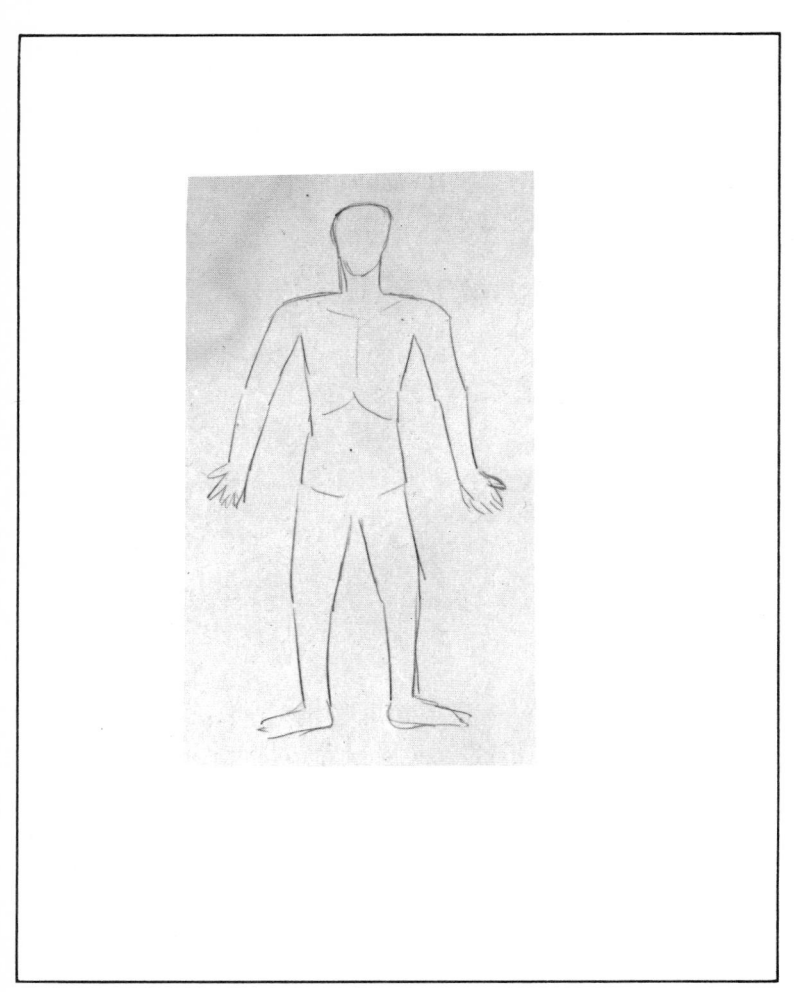

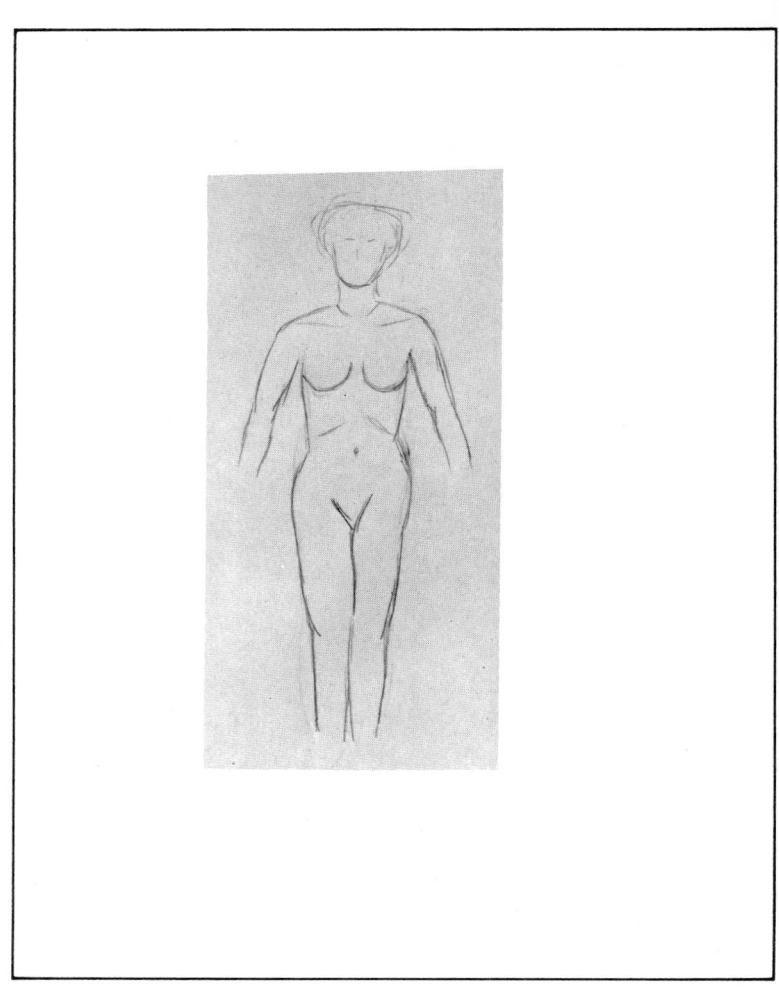

FIGURE-DRAWING CHARACTERISTICS

Structural	Male Female Both		Structural	Male	Female	Structural and Graphic	Male Female Both		Graphic, Global and Height	Male	Female	Body Proportions	Male	Female
Type	0		Omission of Appendages	0	1	Upper and Lower Halves	1	1	Hair Shading	0	7	Head	06	06
Sex Sequence	0		Position of Both Arms	0	6	Four Quarters	4	4	Nudity and Transparency	0	0	Neck	06	07
Posture	1	0	Position of Right Arm	2	8	Relative Size	4		Form	1	1	Shoulders	07	06
Perspective	0	0	Position of Left Arm	2	8	Constant Line Pressure	0	0	Detailing	5	3	Right Arm	04	
Vertical Midline	0	0	Position of Legs	6	2	Variable Line Pressure	1	5	Identity and Sex	1	1	Left Arm	04	
Bilateral Symmetry	4	4	Relation of Long Axes	1	1	Line Continuity	1	0	Sophistication	2	2	Chest	05	05
Horizontal Midline	2	2	Right and Left Halves	1	1	Body Shading	3	3	Height	05		Girth	05	06

GENERAL CHARACTERISTICS OF SUBJECT

IDENTIFICATION
No. 662
Sex M
Marital status M
Age 25 yrs. at
psychological tests

PARENTAL HISTORY
Father
C   H   S   D   O
+   ?   −   −   ?
Mother
C   H   S   D   O
−   −   −   −   −

PHYSIOLOGICAL AND METABOLIC DATA

	Admission	Initial	Control	Cold pressor change	Exercise change	Smoking change
Systolic pressure	120	132	118	+08	+36	+04
Diastolic pressure	80	64	58	+10	+08	+04
Heart rate	68	72	66	+08	+14	+07

Age 23 yrs.	Height 73 in.	Ponderal index 13.08
	Weight 174 lbs.	Cholesterol 177 mg. per 100 ml.
	Overweight +03 %	Vital capacity liters

HABIT SURVEY
Smoking habits: heavy cigarette smoker
Age begun 16 yrs.   Inhalation: yes
Habits of nervous tension: 2, 4, 6, 11, 12

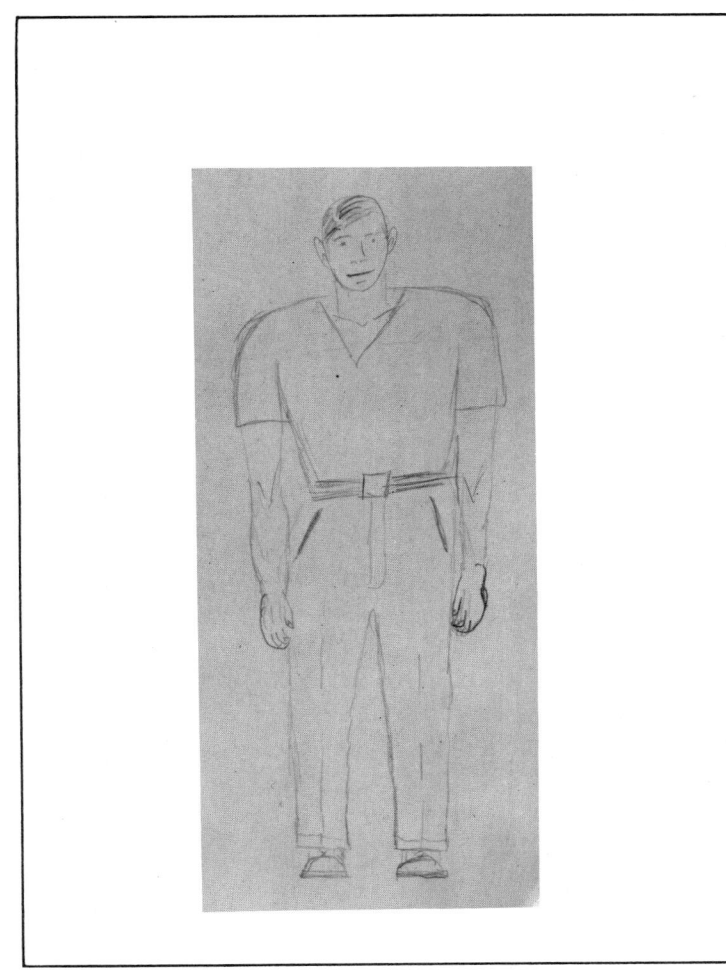

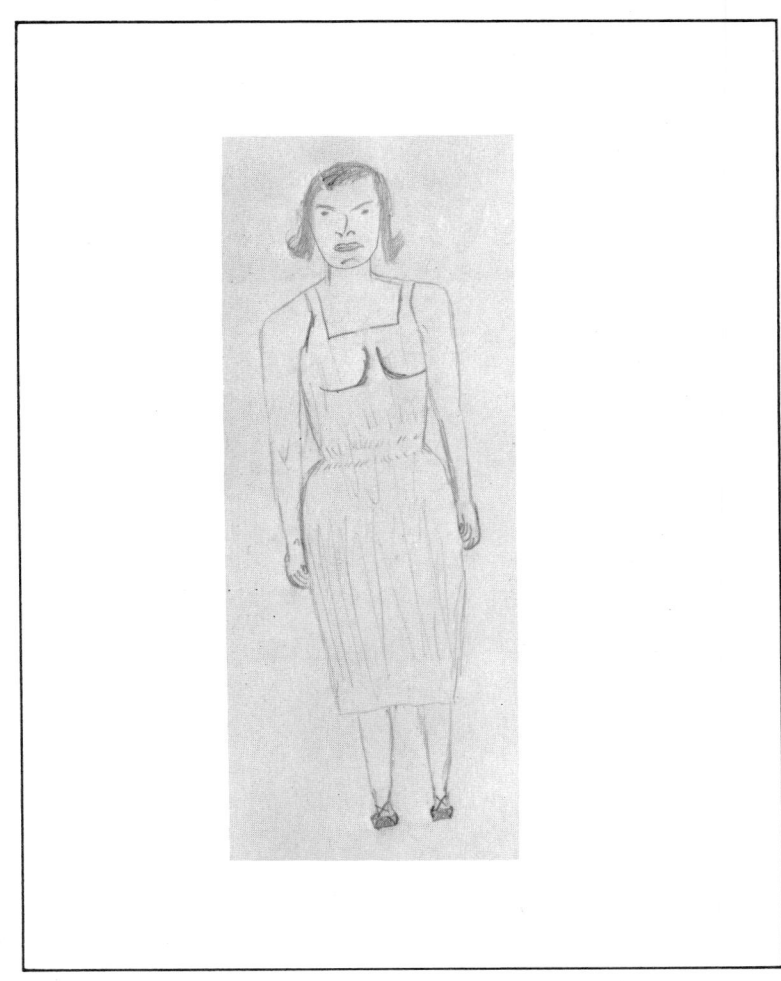

FIGURE-DRAWING CHARACTERISTICS

Structural	Male Female Both		Structural	Male	Female	Structural and Graphic	Male Female Both		Graphic, Global and Height	Male	Female	Body Proportions	Male	Female
Type	0		Omission of Appendages	0	0	Upper and Lower Halves	3	0	Hair Shading	1	3	Head	07	09
Sex Sequence	2		Position of Both Arms	0	0	Four Quarters	4	4	Nudity and Transparency	7	7	Neck	10	06
Posture	1	1	Position of Right Arm	0	0	Relative Size	0		Form	1	1	Shoulders	10	07
Perspective	0	0	Position of Left Arm	0	0	Constant Line Pressure	0	0	Detailing	1	1	Right Arm	08	06
Vertical Midline	3	0	Position of Legs	5	4	Variable Line Pressure	3	3	Identity and Sex	1	1	Left Arm	08	06
Bilateral Symmetry	3	3	Relation of Long Axes	1	1	Line Continuity	0	0	Sophistication	2	2	Chest	09	06
Horizontal Midline	4	3	Right and Left Halves	1	1	Body Shading	7	7	Height	07	07	Girth	09	07

GENERAL CHARACTERISTICS OF SUBJECT

IDENTIFICATION
No. 702
Sex M
Marital status S
Age 23 yrs. at psychological tests

PARENTAL HISTORY				
Father				
C	H	S	D	O
+	−	−	−	?
Mother				
C	H	S	D	O
−	−	−	−	?

PHYSIOLOGICAL AND METABOLIC DATA

	Admission	Initial	Control	Cold pressor change	Exercise change	Smoking change
Systolic pressure	120	114	106	+08	+30	+03
Diastolic pressure	80	78	74	+16	+12	−01
Heart rate	80	64	73	+16	+16	−04

Age 22 yrs.	Height 69 in.	Ponderal index 13.09
	Weight 146 lbs.	Cholesterol 237 mg. per 100 ml.
	Overweight −03 %	Vital capacity 4.8 liters

HABIT SURVEY

Smoking habits: nonsmoker

Age begun   yrs.   Inhalation:

Habits of nervous tension: 4, 5, 6, 9, 11, 22

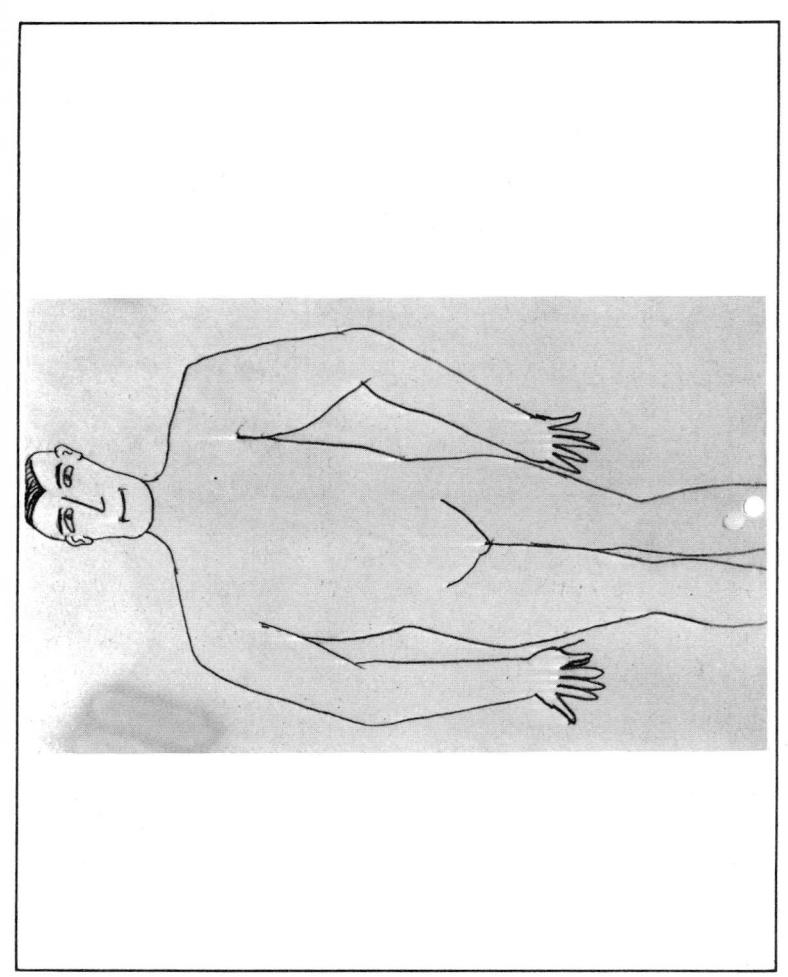
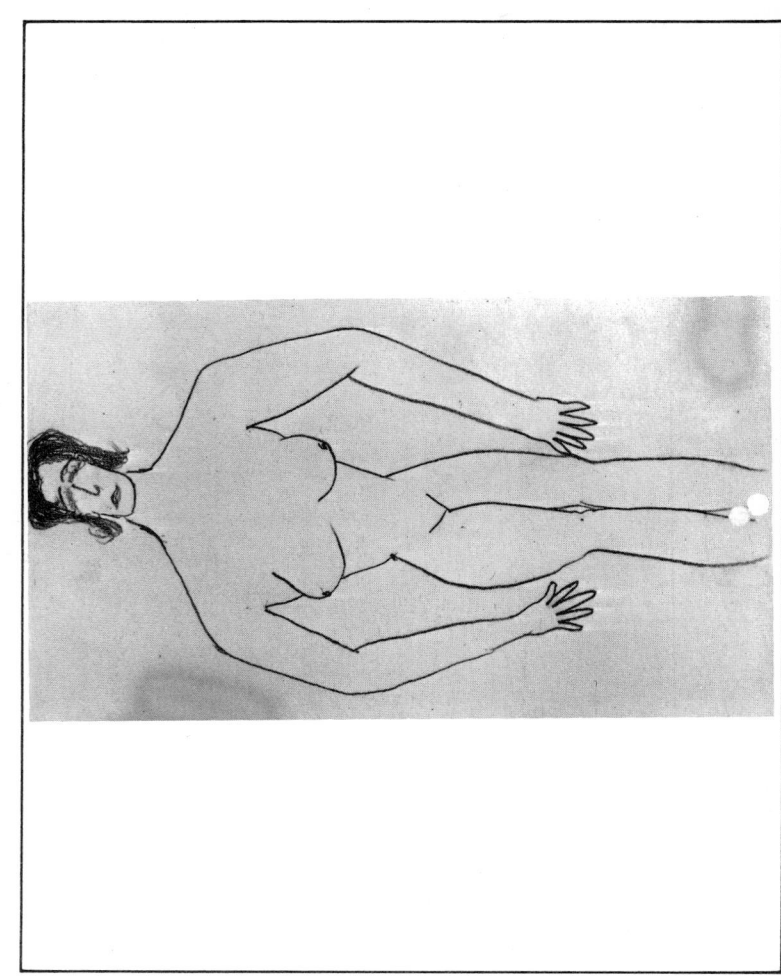

FIGURE-DRAWING CHARACTERISTICS

Structural	Male Female Both	Structural	Male	Female	Structural and Graphic	Male Female Both		Graphic, Global and Height	Male	Female	Body Proportions	Male	Female
Type	0	Omission of Appendages	3	3	Upper and Lower Halves	9	9	Hair Shading	1	3	Head	10	08
Sex Sequence	0	Position of Both Arms	0	0	Four Quarters	4	4	Nudity and Transparency	0	0	Neck	07	07
Posture	0 0	Position of Right Arm	5	5	Relative Size	5		Form	1	1	Shoulders	13	12
Perspective	0 0	Position of Left Arm	5	5	Constant Line Pressure	5	5	Detailing	3	3	Right Arm	10	08
Vertical Midline	0 0	Position of Legs	2	2	Variable Line Pressure	0	0	Identity and Sex	1	1	Left Arm	10	10
Bilateral Symmetry	2 2	Relation of Long Axes	2	2	Line Continuity	4	4	Sophistication	2	2	Chest	09	09
Horizontal Midline	0 0	Right and Left Halves	1	0	Body Shading	0	0	Height			Girth	11	06

GENERAL CHARACTERISTICS OF SUBJECT

IDENTIFICATION
No. 724
Sex M
Marital status S
Age 21 yrs. at psychological tests

PARENTAL HISTORY
Father
C   H   S   D   O
+   -   -   -   -
Mother
C   H   S   D   O
-   +   -   -   ?

PHYSIOLOGICAL AND METABOLIC DATA

	Admission	Initial	Control	Cold pressor change	Exercise change	Smoking change
Systolic pressure	170	127	118	+26	+12	+13
Diastolic pressure	100	76	66	+20	-06	+09
Heart rate	100	68	63	+32	+20	+31

Age 21 yrs.

Height 69 in.   Ponderal index 13.58

Weight 131 lbs.   Cholesterol 222 mg. per 100 ml.

Overweight -12 %   Vital capacity 3.8 liters

HABIT SURVEY

Smoking habits: heavy cigarette smoker

Age begun 15 yrs.   Inhalation: yes

Habits of nervous tension: 3, 4, 5, 6, 9, 18, 19, 20, 21, 22, 24

Plate 544　　　**MODERATELY SOPHISTICATED DRAWINGS**　　　591

FIGURE-DRAWING CHARACTERISTICS

Structural	Male Female Both	Structural	Male	Female	Structural and Graphic	Male Female Both		Graphic, Global and Height	Male	Female	Body Proportions	Male	Female
Type	0	Omission of Appendages	0	7	Upper and Lower Halves	1	1	Hair Shading	0	3	Head	05	04
Sex Sequence	0	Position of Both Arms	0	1	Four Quarters	4	4	Nudity and Transparency	7	7	Neck	06	04
Posture	1　1	Position of Right Arm	5	5	Relative Size	3		Form	3	3	Shoulders	05	04
Perspective	0　0	Position of Left Arm	5	2	Constant Line Pressure	5	5	Detailing	3	3	Right Arm	03	
Vertical Midline	3　0	Position of Legs	6	4	Variable Line Pressure	0	0	Identity and Sex	1	1	Left Arm	03	
Bilateral Symmetry	5　3	Relation of Long Axes	1	1	Line Continuity	4	4	Sophistication	2	2	Chest	04	04
Horizontal Midline	4　4	Right and Left Halves	1	1	Body Shading	0	2	Height	03	04	Girth	04	03

GENERAL CHARACTERISTICS OF SUBJECT

IDENTIFICATION
No. 733
Sex M
Marital status S
Age 23 yrs. at
psychological tests

PARENTAL HISTORY				
Father				
C	H	S	D	O
+	-	-	-	-
Mother				
C	H	S	D	O
-	+	-	-	-

PHYSIOLOGICAL AND METABOLIC DATA

	Admission	Initial	Control	Cold pressor change	Exercise change	Smoking change
Systolic pressure	160	126	118	+28	+12	
Diastolic pressure	100	62	76	+30	-12	
Heart rate	80	64	62	+32	+32	

Age 21 yrs.	Height 71 in.	Ponderal index 12.35
	Weight 190 lbs.	Cholesterol 203 mg. per 100 ml.
	Overweight +21 %	Vital capacity 4.8 liters

HABIT SURVEY

Smoking habits: nonsmoker

Age begun   yrs.   Inhalation:

Habits of nervous tension: 2, 6, 16

FIGURE-DRAWING CHARACTERISTICS

Structural	Male Female Both	Structural	Male	Female	Structural and Graphic	Male Female Both		Graphic, Global and Height	Male	Female	Body Proportions	Male	Female
Type	0	Omission of Appendages	7	7	Upper and Lower Halves	3	0	Hair Shading	3	3	Head	05	06
Sex Sequence	0	Position of Both Arms	2	1	Four Quarters	4	4	Nudity and Transparency	7	7	Neck	04	04
Posture	1 2	Position of Right Arm	5	0	Relative Size	0		Form	1	1	Shoulders		
Perspective	2 1	Position of Left Arm	7	5	Constant Line Pressure	1	1	Detailing	1	1	Right Arm		04
Vertical Midline	7 7	Position of Legs	1	8	Variable Line Pressure	0	0	Identity and Sex	1	3	Left Arm		
Bilateral Symmetry	0 0	Relation of Long Axes	1	1	Line Continuity	0	0	Sophistication	2	2	Chest	06	
Horizontal Midline	0 0	Right and Left Halves	2	1	Body Shading	7	4	Height	05	05	Girth	06	

GENERAL CHARACTERISTICS OF SUBJECT

IDENTIFICATION
No. 745
Sex M
Marital status   S
Age 23 yrs. at
psychological tests

PARENTAL HISTORY
Father
C   H   S   D   O
+   +   –   –   –
Mother
C   H   S   D   O
–   –   –   –   ?

PHYSIOLOGICAL AND METABOLIC DATA

	Admission	Initial	Control	Cold pressor change	Exercise change	Smoking change
Systolic pressure	118	104	100	+24	+24	+12
Diastolic pressure	64	54	54	+32	–04	+10
Heart rate	72	68	65	+18	+10	+23

Age 23 yrs.	Height 74 in.	Ponderal index 13.53
	Weight 164 lbs.	Cholesterol 210 mg. per 100 ml.
	Overweight –06 %	Vital capacity 5.6 liters

HABIT SURVEY
Smoking habits: mixed smoker
Age begun 20 yrs.   Inhalation: sometimes
Habits of nervous tension: 2, 5, 6, 9, 11,
15, 17, 21, 22

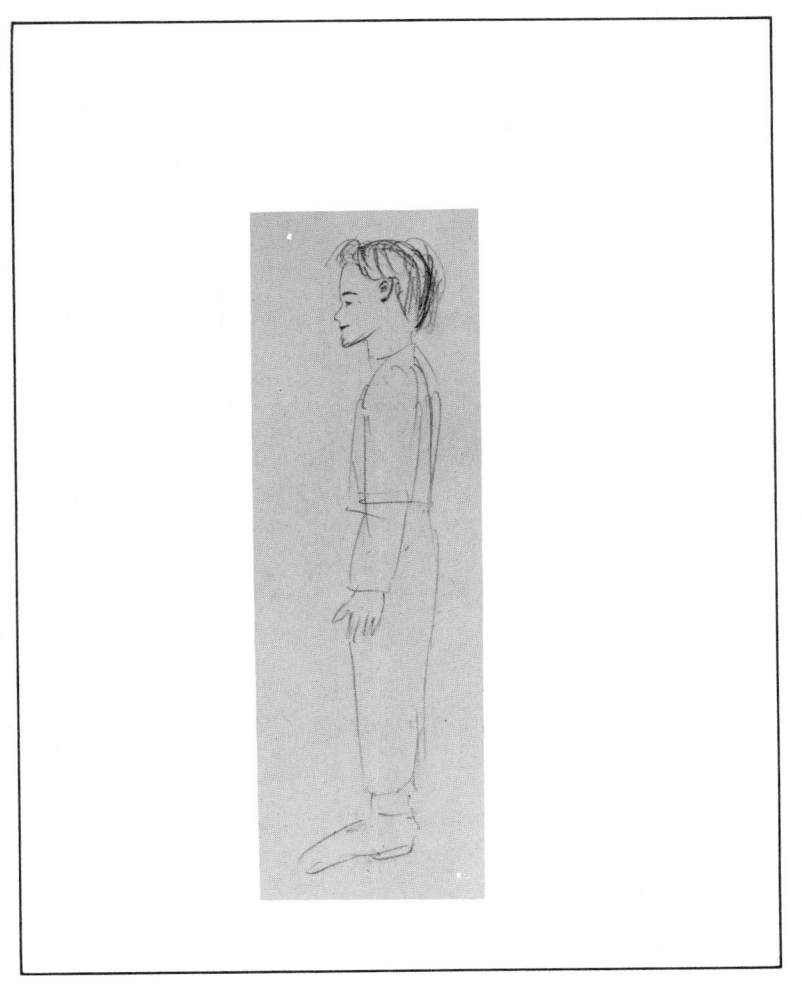

FIGURE-DRAWING CHARACTERISTICS

Structural	Male Female Both	Structural	Male	Female	Structural and Graphic	Male Female Both	Graphic, Global and Height	Male	Female	Body Proportions	Male	Female
Type	0	Omission of Appendages	0	0	Upper and Lower Halves	3 3	Hair Shading	3	3	Head	09	07
Sex Sequence	2	Position of Both Arms	4	4	Four Quarters	4 4	Nudity and Transparency	7	7	Neck	08	07
Posture	1 1	Position of Right Arm	7	7	Relative Size	4	Form	1	1	Shoulders		
Perspective	2 2	Position of Left Arm	0	0	Constant Line Pressure	1 1	Detailing	3	1	Right Arm		
Vertical Midline	4 4	Position of Legs	1	1	Variable Line Pressure	0 0	Identity and Sex	1	1	Left Arm	06	06
Bilateral Symmetry	0 0	Relation of Long Axes	1	1	Line Continuity	0 0	Sophistication	2	2	Chest	06	05
Horizontal Midline	4 4	Right and Left Halves	0	0	Body Shading	0 6	Height	06	07	Girth	05	05

GENERAL CHARACTERISTICS OF SUBJECT

IDENTIFICATION
No. 754
Sex M
Marital status S
Age 23 yrs. at
psychological tests

PARENTAL HISTORY
Father
C   H   S   D   O
+   +   −   −   +
Mother
C   H   S   D   O
−   −   −   −   +

PHYSIOLOGICAL AND METABOLIC DATA

	Admission	Initial	Control	Cold pressor change	Exercise change	Smoking change
Systolic pressure	120	122	114	+18	+30	+04
Diastolic pressure	80	74	68	+20	+02	+08
Heart rate	80	80	78	+32	+10	+06

Age 22 yrs.	Height 74 in.	Ponderal index 13.01
	Weight 184 lbs.	Cholesterol 210 mg. per 100 ml.
	Overweight +06 %	Vital capacity 6.1 liters

HABIT SURVEY
Smoking habits: nonsmoker
Age begun 17 yrs.   Inhalation:
Habits of nervous tension: 4, 5, 6, 9, 11, 17

FIGURE-DRAWING CHARACTERISTICS

Structural	Male Female Both	Structural	Male	Female	Structural and Graphic	Male Female Both		Graphic, Global and Height	Male	Female	Body Proportions	Male	Female
Type	0	Omission of Appendages	0	0	Upper and Lower Halves	3	1	Hair Shading	3	1	Head	11	07
Sex Sequence	0	Position of Both Arms	1	4	Four Quarters	4	4	Nudity and Transparency	7	7	Neck	08	06
Posture	1 2	Position of Right Arm	2	7	Relative Size	0		Form	3	3	Shoulders	09	
Perspective	5 2	Position of Left Arm	5	4	Constant Line Pressure	0	0	Detailing	3	3	Right Arm	07	
Vertical Midline	3 4	Position of Legs	6	8	Variable Line Pressure	4	5	Identity and Sex	1	1	Left Arm	08	05
Bilateral Symmetry	3 0	Relation of Long Axes	1	1	Line Continuity	0	1	Sophistication	2	2	Chest	10	07
Horizontal Midline	4 4	Right and Left Halves	1	1	Body Shading	4	1	Height	08	07	Girth	11	07

GENERAL CHARACTERISTICS OF SUBJECT

IDENTIFICATION
No. 774
Sex M
Marital status S
Age 21 yrs. at
psychological tests

PARENTAL HISTORY
Father
C   H   S   D   O
+   ?   -   +   +
Mother
C   H   S   D   O
-    ?   -   -   -

PHYSIOLOGICAL AND METABOLIC DATA

	Admission	Initial	Control	Cold pressor change	Exercise change	Smoking change
Systolic pressure	126	112	106	+14	+34	+10
Diastolic pressure	74	78	72	+18	+16	+20
Heart rate	92	84	81	+12	+19	+08

Age 21 yrs.	Height	69 in.	Ponderal index	12.02
	Weight	189 lbs.	Cholesterol	234 mg. per 100 ml.
	Overweight +27 %		Vital capacity	3.9 liters

HABIT SURVEY
Smoking habits: mixed smoker
Age begun 18 yrs.   Inhalation: sometimes
Habits of nervous tension: 5, 6, 9, 18, 19, 21, 23

FIGURE-DRAWING CHARACTERISTICS

Structural	Male Female Both	Structural	Male	Female	Structural and Graphic	Male Female Both	Graphic, Global and Height	Male	Female	Body Proportions	Male	Female
Type	0	Omission of Appendages	0	7	Upper and Lower Halves	1 1	Hair Shading	3	3	Head	06	06
Sex Sequence	0	Position of Both Arms	0	0	Four Quarters	4 4	Nudity and Transparency	7	7	Neck	03	03
Posture	1 1	Position of Right Arm	0	5	Relative Size	0	Form	1	1	Shoulders	06	04
Perspective	0 0	Position of Left Arm	0	5	Constant Line Pressure	0 0	Detailing	1	1	Right Arm	06	
Vertical Midline	3 3	Position of Legs	2	2	Variable Line Pressure	1 1	Identity and Sex	1	1	Left Arm	06	
Bilateral Symmetry	4 3	Relation of Long Axes	1	1	Line Continuity	0 0	Sophistication	2	2	Chest	05	03
Horizontal Midline	4 4	Right and Left Halves	0	1	Body Shading	7 7	Height	06	06	Girth	07	02

GENERAL CHARACTERISTICS OF SUBJECT

IDENTIFICATION

No. F06

Sex M

Marital status S

Age 24 yrs. at psychological tests

PARENTAL HISTORY

Father

C	H	S	D	O
+	-	-	-	+

Mother

C	H	S	D	O
-	-	-	-	-

PHYSIOLOGICAL AND METABOLIC DATA

	Admission	Initial	Control	Cold pressor change	Exercise change	Smoking change
Systolic pressure	130	104	102	+08	+30	00
Diastolic pressure	78	70	68	+12	+20	00
Heart rate	68	68	65	-08	+09	+02

Age 22 yrs.	Height 70 in.	Ponderal index 13.06
	Weight 154 lbs.	Cholesterol 222 mg. per 100 ml.
	Overweight 00 %	Vital capacity liters

HABIT SURVEY

Smoking habits: nonsmoker

Age begun   yrs.   Inhalation:

Habits of nervous tension: 5, 6, 10, 14, 17, 18, 21, 25

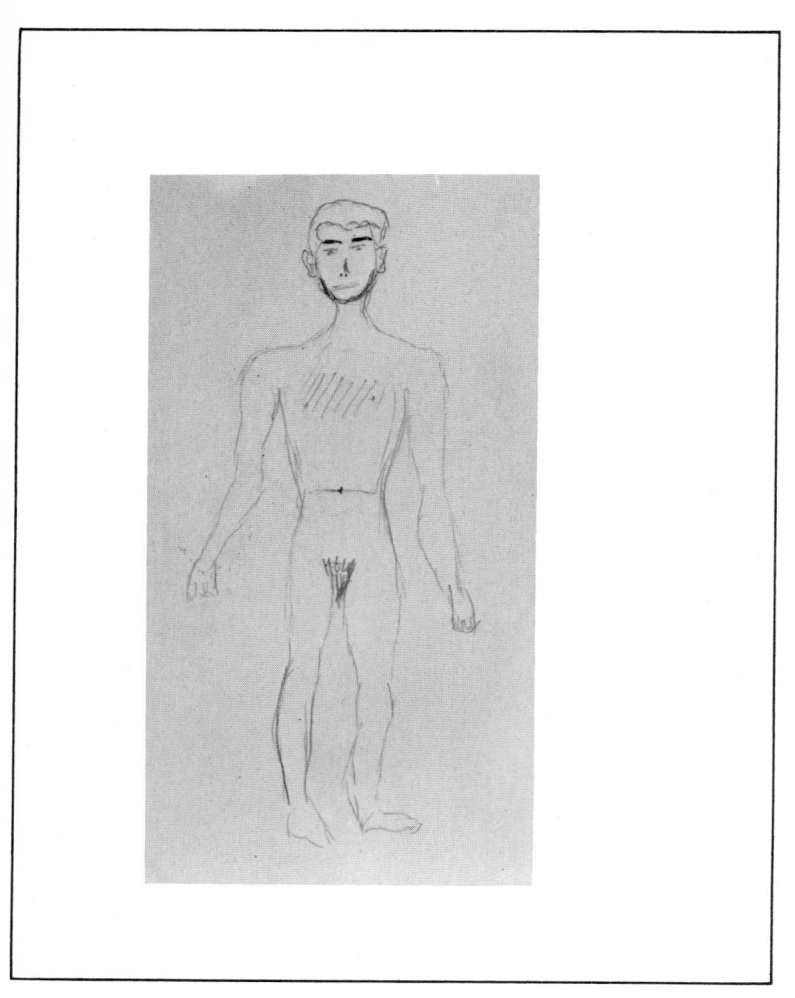

FIGURE-DRAWING CHARACTERISTICS

Structural	Male	Female	Structural	Male	Female	Structural and Graphic	Male	Female	Graphic, Global and Height	Male	Female	Body Proportions	Male	Female
	Both						Both							
Type	0		Omission of Appendages	0	7	Upper and Lower Halves	3	0	Hair Shading	5	1	Head	07	07
Sex Sequence	0		Position of Both Arms	1	0	Four Quarters	4	4	Nudity and Transparency	0	0	Neck	12	12
Posture	1	1	Position of Right Arm	1	0	Relative Size	1		Form	3	3	Shoulders	08	06
Perspective	0	0	Position of Left Arm	0	0	Constant Line Pressure	0	1	Detailing	3	3	Right Arm	06	06
Vertical Midline	0	0	Position of Legs	4	4	Variable Line Pressure	1	0	Identity and Sex	1	1	Left Arm	06	
Bilateral Symmetry	3	3	Relation of Long Axes	1	1	Line Continuity	0	0	Sophistication	2	2	Chest	06	05
Horizontal Midline	2	0	Right and Left Halves	1	1	Body Shading	3	3	Height	06	06	Girth	05	06

GENERAL CHARACTERISTICS OF SUBJECT

IDENTIFICATION
No. F15
Sex F
Marital status S
Age 26 yrs. at
psychological tests

PARENTAL HISTORY				
Father				
C	H	S	D	O
+	+	−	−	?
Mother				
C	H	S	D	O
−	−	−	−	−

PHYSIOLOGICAL AND METABOLIC DATA

	Admission	Initial	Control	Cold pressor change	Exercise change	Smoking change
Systolic pressure	120	110	102	+08	+12	+12
Diastolic pressure	78	68	70	+12	00	+06
Heart rate	80	68	80	−04	−04	+12

Age 24 yrs.	Height	69	in.	Ponderal index	12.83	
	Weight	156	lbs.	Cholesterol	204	mg. per 100 ml.
	Overweight +07 %			Vital capacity		liters

HABIT SURVEY
Smoking habits: nonsmoker
Age begun   yrs.   Inhalation:
Habits of nervous tension:

STRONG VOCATIONAL INTEREST TEST

Occupation	Artist	Psychologist	Architect	Physician	Osteopath	Dentist	Veterinarian	Mathematician	Physicist	Engineer	Chemist	Production Manager
Standard Score	49	49	52	58	36	35	31	43	32	28	41	10

Occupation	Farmer	Aviator	Carpenter	Printer	Math.-Sci. Teacher	Ind. Arts Teacher	Voc. Agric. Teacher	Policeman	Forest Serv. Man	Y.M.C.A. Phys. Dir.	Personnel Director	Public Administrator
Standard Score	43	37	21	36	36	16	38	20	41	31	21	38

Occupation	Y.M.C.A. Secretary	Soc. Sci. H.S. Teacher	City Sch. Sup't.	Social Worker	Minister	Musician Performer	C.P.A.	Senior C.P.A.	Accountant	Office Man	Purchasing Agent	Banker
Standard Score	20	32	31	35	58	57	24	33	16	17	06	20

Occupation	Mortician	Pharmacist	Sales Manager	Real Est. Manager	Life Ins. Salesman	Advertising Man	Lawyer	Author-Journalist	President Mfg. Co.	Interest Maturity	Occupational Level	Masculinity-Femininity
Standard Score	07	23	20	27	22	38	41	45	25	50	52	32

Plate 550　　　MODERATELY SOPHISTICATED DRAWINGS　　　597

FIGURE-DRAWING CHARACTERISTICS

Structural	Male Female Both	Structural	Male	Female	Structural and Graphic	Male Female Both		Graphic, Global and Height	Male	Female	Body Proportions	Male	Female
Type	0	Omission of Appendages	2	2	Upper and Lower Halves	3	3	Hair Shading	3	1	Head	13	07
Sex Sequence	1	Position of Both Arms	6	6	Four Quarters	4	4	Nudity and Transparency	7	7	Neck	14	08
Posture	3　4	Position of Right Arm	7	7	Relative Size	0		Form	3	1	Shoulders		
Perspective	1　9	Position of Left Arm	7	7	Constant Line Pressure	0	0	Detailing	3	1	Right Arm		
Vertical Midline	7　4	Position of Legs	4	1	Variable Line Pressure	5	5	Identity and Sex	1	1	Left Arm		
Bilateral Symmetry	0　0	Relation of Long Axes	0	1	Line Continuity	1	1	Sophistication	2	2	Chest		06
Horizontal Midline	0　4	Right and Left Halves	1	0	Body Shading	1	7	Height		07	Girth		05

GENERAL CHARACTERISTICS OF SUBJECT

IDENTIFICATION
No.　F17
Sex　M
Marital status　M
Age　24　yrs. at
psychological tests

PARENTAL HISTORY
Father
C　H　S　D　O
+　+　−　−　+
Mother
C　H　S　D　O
−　−　−　−　?

PHYSIOLOGICAL AND METABOLIC DATA

	Admission	Initial	Control	Cold pressor change	Exercise change	Smoking change
Systolic pressure	120	130	130	+12	+18	00
Diastolic pressure	80	80	80	+10	00	+01
Heart rate	78	80	86	+08	+02	+08

Age 22 yrs.	Height　72　in.	Ponderal index　11.48
	Weight　247　lbs.	Cholesterol　234　mg. per 100 ml.
	Overweight +52 %	Vital capacity　　liters

HABIT SURVEY

Smoking habits:　pipe smoker

Age begun 20　yrs.　Inhalation: no

Habits of nervous tension: 5, 6, 9, 25

STRONG VOCATIONAL INTEREST TEST

Occupation	Artist	Psychologist	Architect	Physician	Osteopath	Dentist	Veterinarian	Mathematician	Physicist	Engineer	Chemist	Production Manager
Standard Score	38	41	43	59	50	50	36	32	31	42	48	32

Occupation	Farmer	Aviator	Carpenter	Printer	Math.-Sci. Teacher	Ind. Arts Teacher	Voc. Agric. Teacher	Policeman	Forest Serv. Man	Y.M.C.A. Phys. Dir.	Personnel Director	Public Administrator
Standard Score	38	46	31	35	33	29	30	32	42	36	30	42

Occupation	Y.M.C.A. Secretary	Soc. Sci. H.S. Teacher	City Sch. Sup't.	Social Worker	Minister	Musician Performer	C.P.A.	Senior C.P.A.	Accountant	Office Man	Purchasing Agent	Banker
Standard Score	21	23	22	33	58	44	21	37	15	19	22	13

Occupation	Mortician	Pharmacist	Sales Manager	Real Est. Manager	Life Ins. Salesman	Advertising Man	Lawyer	Author-Journalist	President Mfg. Co.	Interest Maturity	Occupational Level	Masculinity-Femininity
Standard Score	25	26	25	30	29	31	39	37	33	54	57	50

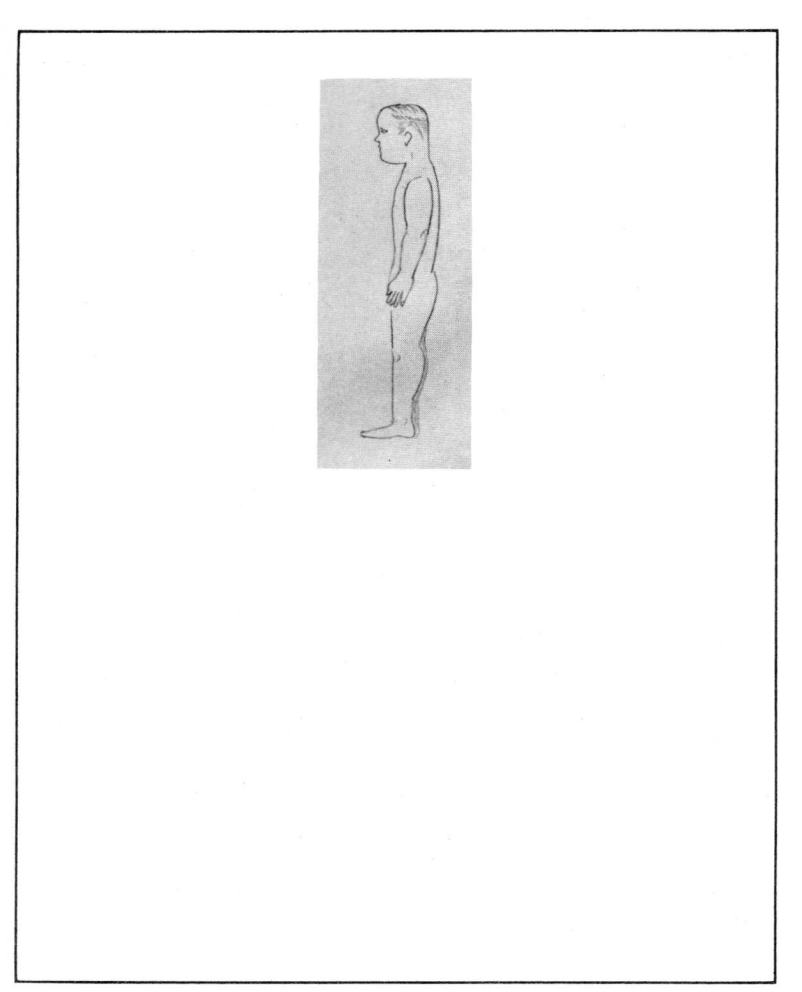

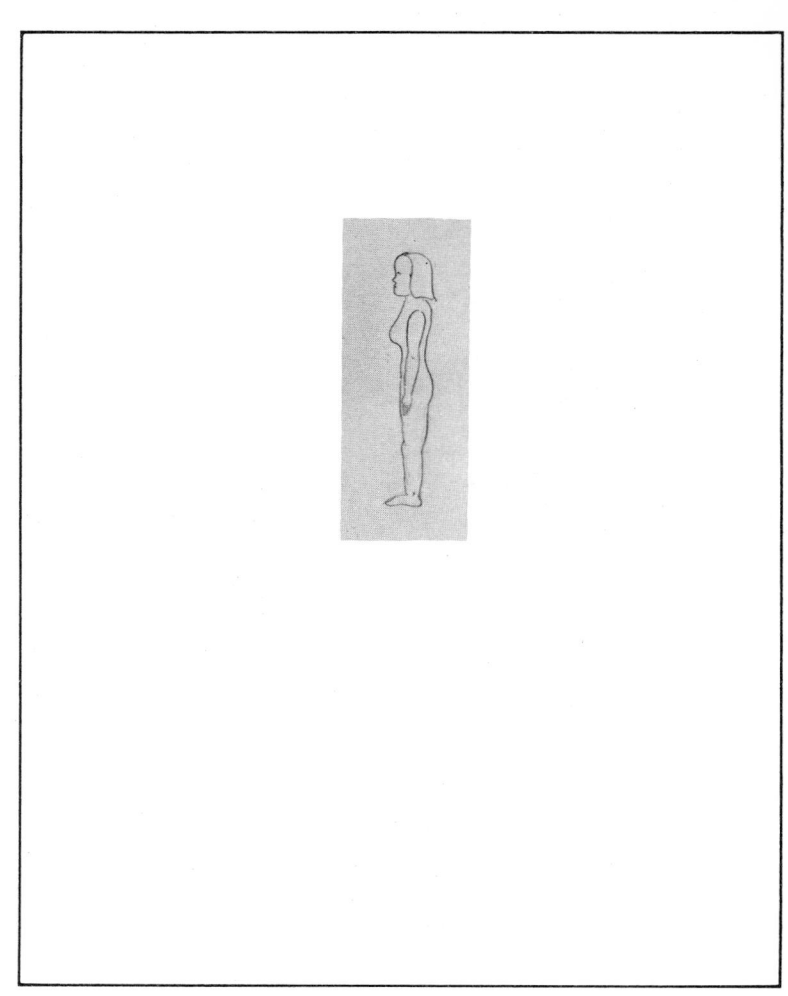

FIGURE-DRAWING CHARACTERISTICS

Structural	Male Female Both	Structural	Male	Female	Structural and Graphic	Male Female Both	Graphic, Global and Height	Male	Female	Body Proportions	Male	Female
Type	0	Omission of Appendages	0	0	Upper and Lower Halves	2 2	Hair Shading	2	5	Head	04	03
Sex Sequence	0	Position of Both Arms	4	4	Four Quarters	4 4	Nudity and Transparency	0	0	Neck	02	00
Posture	1 1	Position of Right Arm	7	7	Relative Size	0	Form	1	1	Shoulders		
Perspective	2 2	Position of Left Arm	0	0	Constant Line Pressure	0 0	Detailing	3	3	Right Arm		
Vertical Midline	4 4	Position of Legs	1	1	Variable Line Pressure	1 1	Identity and Sex	1	1	Left Arm	02	02
Bilateral Symmetry	0 0	Relation of Long Axes	1	1	Line Continuity	3 3	Sophistication	2	2	Chest	03	02
Horizontal Midline	0 0	Right and Left Halves	3	3	Body Shading	3 3	Height	03	02	Girth	03	02

GENERAL CHARACTERISTICS OF SUBJECT

IDENTIFICATION
No. G05
Sex M
Marital status S
Age 23 yrs. at
psychological tests

PARENTAL HISTORY
Father
C H S D O
+ + - - -
Mother
C H S D O
- - - - -

PHYSIOLOGICAL AND METABOLIC DATA

	Admission	Initial	Control	Cold pressor change	Exercise change	Smoking change
Systolic pressure	110	110	118	+12	+32	+04
Diastolic pressure	70	60	68	+20	-08	+05
Heart rate	80	80	66	+04	+10	+02

Age 23 yrs.	Height 71 in.	Ponderal index 13.20
	Weight 156 lbs.	Cholesterol 243 mg. per 100 ml.
	Overweight -02 %	Vital capacity liters

HABIT SURVEY

Smoking habits: nonsmoker

Age begun   yrs.   Inhalation:

Habits of nervous tension: 1, 4, 5, 6, 9, 10, 23

STRONG VOCATIONAL INTEREST TEST

Occupation	Artist	Psychologist	Architect	Physician	Osteopath	Dentist	Veterinarian	Mathematician	Physicist	Engineer	Chemist	Production Manager
Standard Score	32	60	40	65	45	42	14	41	36	38	46	28

Occupation	Farmer	Aviator	Carpenter	Printer	Math.-Sci. Teacher	Ind. Arts Teacher	Voc. Agric. Teacher	Policeman	Forest Serv. Man	Y.M.C.A. Phys. Dir.	Personnel Director	Public Administrator
Standard Score	28	33	16	36	53	21	32	32	30	42	44	54

Occupation	Y.M.C.A. Secretary	Soc. Sci. H.S. Teacher	City Sch. Sup't.	Social Worker	Minister	Musician Performer	C.P.A.	Senior C.P.A.	Accountant	Office Man	Purchasing Agent	Banker
Standard Score	41	43	49	51	59	53	35	44	25	25	09	16

Occupation	Mortician	Pharmacist	Sales Manager	Real Est. Manager	Life Ins. Salesman	Advertising Man	Lawyer	Author-Journalist	President Mfg. Co.	Interest Maturity	Occupational Level	Masculinity-Femininity
Standard Score	17	23	14	19	19	29	38	35	18	61	57	44

Plate 552   MODERATELY SOPHISTICATED DRAWINGS   599

FIGURE-DRAWING CHARACTERISTICS

Structural	Male Female Both	Structural	Male	Female	Structural and Graphic	Male Female Both		Graphic, Global and Height	Male	Female	Body Proportions	Male	Female
Type	0	Omission of Appendages	0	0	Upper and Lower Halves	1	1	Hair Shading	5	2	Head	06	06
Sex Sequence	0	Position of Both Arms	2	2	Four Quarters	4	4	Nudity and Transparency	7	7	Neck	06	05
Posture	1	2	Position of Right Arm	5	5	Relative Size	4		Form	1	1	Shoulders		
Perspective	6	9	Position of Left Arm	7	7	Constant Line Pressure	0	0	Detailing	1	1	Right Arm		04
Vertical Midline	7	4	Position of Legs	7	8	Variable Line Pressure	1	3	Identity and Sex	1	1	Left Arm		
Bilateral Symmetry	0	0	Relation of Long Axes	1	1	Line Continuity	0	0	Sophistication	2	2	Chest		
Horizontal Midline	6	0	Right and Left Halves	1	2	Body Shading	7	7	Height	05	05	Girth		

GENERAL CHARACTERISTICS OF SUBJECT

IDENTIFICATION
No. G16
Sex M
Marital status S
Age 22 yrs. at psychological tests

PARENTAL HISTORY

Father

C	H	S	D	O
+	?	-	-	-

Mother

C	H	S	D	O
-	-	-	-	-

PHYSIOLOGICAL AND METABOLIC DATA

	Admission	Initial	Control	Cold pressor change	Exercise change	Smoking change
Systolic pressure	130	125	122	+12	+20	+10
Diastolic pressure	77	70	70	+12	00	+16
Heart rate	88	76	73	-04	+21	+11

Age 21 yrs.

Height 69 in. Weight 166 lbs. Overweight +11 %

Ponderal index 12.55 Cholesterol 203 mg. per 100 ml. Vital capacity liters

HABIT SURVEY

Smoking habits: nonsmoker

Age begun   yrs.   Inhalation:

Habits of nervous tension: 3, 4, 5, 6, 7, 8, 9, 11, 17, 18, 22, 23

STRONG VOCATIONAL INTEREST TEST

Occupation	Artist	Psychologist	Architect	Physician	Osteopath	Dentist	Veterinarian	Mathematician	Physicist	Engineer	Chemist	Production Manager
Standard Score	41	37	43	60	45	42	29	38	34	42	46	26

Occupation	Farmer	Aviator	Carpenter	Printer	Math.-Sci. Teacher	Ind. Arts Teacher	Voc. Agric. Teacher	Policeman	Forest Serv. Man	Y.M.C.A. Phys. Dir.	Personnel Director	Public Administrator
Standard Score	41	44	09	17	30	09	23	15	38	24	19	40

Occupation	Y.M.C.A. Secretary	Soc. Sci. H.S. Teacher	City Sch. Sup't.	Social Worker	Minister	Musician Performer	C.P.A.	Senior C.P.A.	Accountant	Office Man	Purchasing Agent	Banker
Standard Score	17	18	23	23	59	36	27	29	10	14	11	18

Occupation	Mortician	Pharmacist	Sales Manager	Real Est. Manager	Life Ins. Salesman	Advertising Man	Lawyer	Author-Journalist	President Mfg. Co.	Interest Maturity	Occupational Level	Masculinity-Femininity
Standard Score	17	14	24	31	26	33	40	42	30	51	65	45

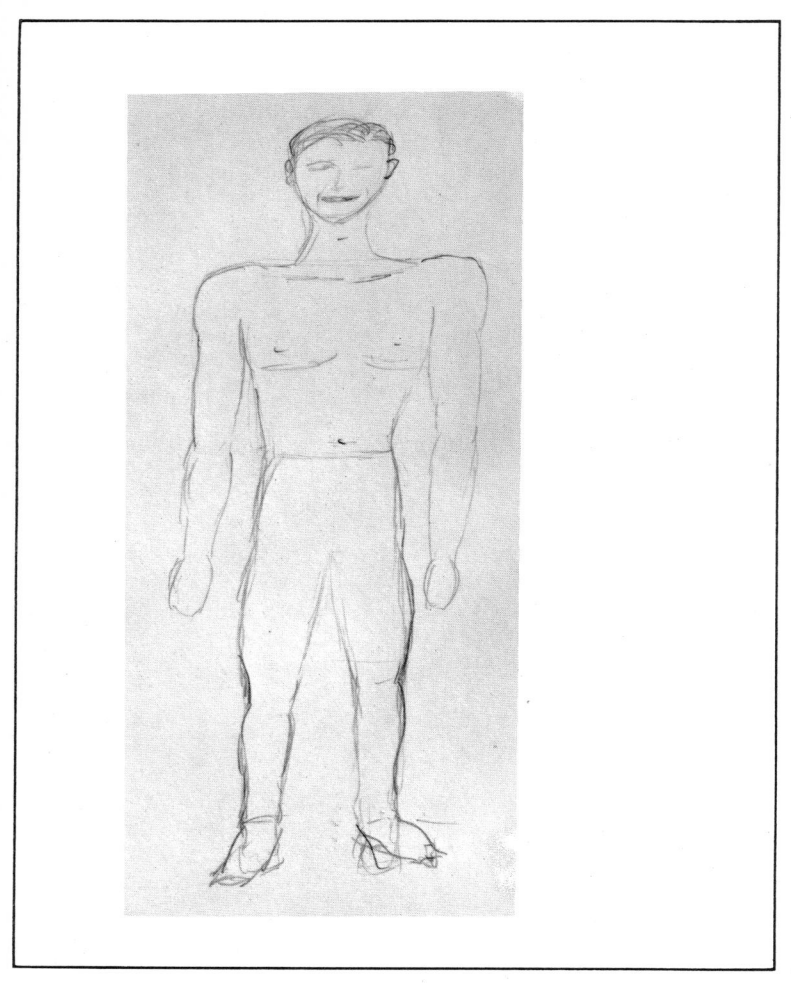

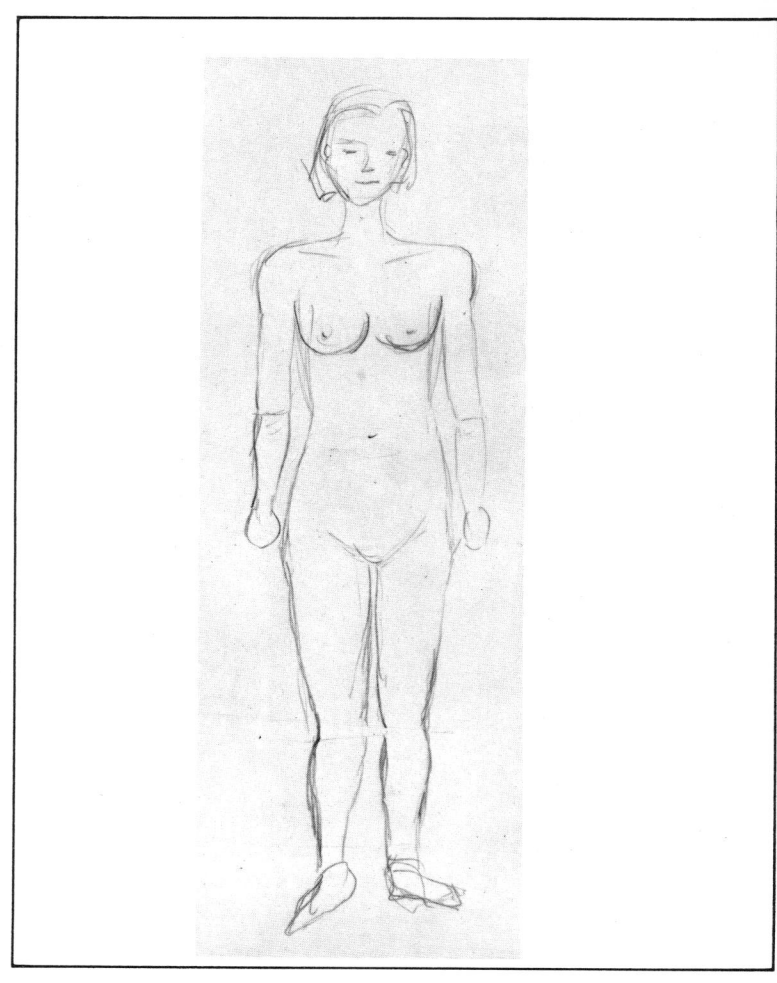

FIGURE-DRAWING CHARACTERISTICS

Structural	Male Female Both	Structural	Male	Female	Structural and Graphic	Male Female Both		Graphic, Global and Height	Male	Female	Body Proportions	Male	Female
Type	0	Omission of Appendages	0	0	Upper and Lower Halves	0	3	Hair Shading	3	3	Head	08	09
Sex Sequence	0	Position of Both Arms	0	0	Four Quarters	4	4	Nudity and Transparency	3	0	Neck	14	10
Posture	1 1	Position of Right Arm	0	0	Relative Size	4		Form	1	1	Shoulders	11	08
Perspective	0 0	Position of Left Arm	0	0	Constant Line Pressure	0	0	Detailing	3	3	Right Arm	08	07
Vertical Midline	0 0	Position of Legs	6	4	Variable Line Pressure	3	2	Identity and Sex	1	1	Left Arm	08	07
Bilateral Symmetry	3 3	Relation of Long Axes	1	1	Line Continuity	0	0	Sophistication	2	2	Chest	09	07
Horizontal Midline	4 0	Right and Left Halves	1	1	Body Shading	1	3	Height	08	09	Girth	08	08

GENERAL CHARACTERISTICS OF SUBJECT

IDENTIFICATION
No. G27
Sex M
Marital status S
Age 23 yrs. at psychological tests

PARENTAL HISTORY				
Father				
C	H	S	D	O
+	-	-	-	-
Mother				
C	H	S	D	O
-	-	-	-	-

PHYSIOLOGICAL AND METABOLIC DATA

	Admission	Initial	Control	Cold pressor change	Exercise change	Smoking change
Systolic pressure	105	118	112	+24	+26	00
Diastolic pressure	70	72	72	+22	-10	+03
Heart rate	68	72	63	+04	+01	+10

Age 22 yrs.	Height	71 in.	Ponderal index	12.57
	Weight	180 lbs.	Cholesterol	150 mg. per 100 ml.
	Overweight +14 %		Vital capacity	liters

HABIT SURVEY

Smoking habits: nonsmoker

Age begun   yrs.   Inhalation:

Habits of nervous tension: 5, 23, 25

STRONG VOCATIONAL INTEREST TEST

Occupation	Artist	Psychologist	Architect	Physician	Osteopath	Dentist	Veterinarian	Mathematician	Physicist	Engineer	Chemist	Production Manager
Standard Score	40	36	42	51	41	42	29	32	30	36	39	22

Occupation	Farmer	Aviator	Carpenter	Printer	Math.-Sci. Teacher	Ind. Arts Teacher	Voc. Agric. Teacher	Policeman	Forest Serv. Man	Y.M.C.A. Phys. Dir.	Personnel Director	Public Administrator
Standard Score	43	31	30	36	37	21	24	31	31	30	30	30

Occupation	Y.M.C.A. Secretary	Soc. Sci. H.S. Teacher	City Sch. Sup't.	Social Worker	Minister	Musician Performer	C.P.A.	Senior C.P.A.	Accountant	Office Man	Purchasing Agent	Banker
Standard Score	22	28	25	31	59	49	13	27	13	29	15	22

Occupation	Mortician	Pharmacist	Sales Manager	Real Est. Manager	Life Ins. Salesman	Advertising Man	Lawyer	Author- Journalist	President Mfg. Co.	Interest Maturity	Occupational Level	Masculinity- Femininity
Standard Score	20	23	20	28	27	35	31	37	24	51	54	35

Plate 554　　　　　　**MODERATELY SOPHISTICATED DRAWINGS**　　　　　601

FIGURE-DRAWING CHARACTERISTICS

Structural	Male Female Both		Structural	Male	Female	Structural and Graphic	Male Female Both		Graphic, Global and Height	Male	Female	Body Proportions	Male	Female
Type	0		Omission of Appendages	0	0	Upper and Lower Halves	1	0	Hair Shading	5	5	Head	06	07
Sex Sequence	0		Position of Both Arms	0	0	Four Quarters	4	4	Nudity and Transparency	7	7	Neck	07	04
Posture	1	1	Position of Right Arm	5	5	Relative Size	4		Form	1	1	Shoulders	07	07
Perspective	0	0	Position of Left Arm	5	5	Constant Line Pressure	0	0	Detailing	3	3	Right Arm	04	04
Vertical Midline	3	0	Position of Legs	4	4	Variable Line Pressure	1	1	Identity and Sex	1	1	Left Arm	05	04
Bilateral Symmetry	3	3	Relation of Long Axes	1	1	Line Continuity	0	0	Sophistication	2	2	Chest	05	06
Horizontal Midline	4	4	Right and Left Halves	1	1	Body Shading	2	1	Height	06	06	Girth	05	04

GENERAL CHARACTERISTICS OF SUBJECT

IDENTIFICATION
No. G52
Sex M
Marital status S
Age 23 yrs. at
psychological tests

PARENTAL HISTORY				
Father				
C	H	S	D	O
+	-	-	-	-
Mother				
C	H	S	D	O
-	(+)	-	-	-

PHYSIOLOGICAL AND METABOLIC DATA

	Admission	Initial	Control	Cold pressor change	Exercise change	Smoking change
Systolic pressure	120	124	108	+24	+32	+02
Diastolic pressure	70	64	66	+28	-08	+06
Heart rate	72	68	63	+28	+17	+04

Age 22 yrs.	Height	72 in.		Ponderal index 13.79	
	Weight	142 lbs.		Cholesterol	210 mg. per 100 ml.
	Overweight	-13 %		Vital capacity	liters

HABIT SURVEY

Smoking habits: heavy cigarette smoker

　Age begun 15 yrs.　　Inhalation: yes

Habits of nervous tension: 1, 4, 5, 6, 8, 11, 20, 21, 22

STRONG VOCATIONAL INTEREST TEST

Occupation	Artist	Psychologist	Architect	Physician	Osteopath	Dentist	Veterinarian	Mathematician	Physicist	Engineer	Chemist	Production Manager
Standard Score	25	44	30	55	39	38	37	38	34	44	48	27

Occupation	Farmer	Aviator	Carpenter	Printer	Math.-Sci. Teacher	Ind. Arts Teacher	Voc. Agric. Teacher	Policeman	Forest Serv. Man	Y.M.C.A. Phys. Dir.	Personnel Director	Public Administrator
Standard Score	42	50	23	29	45	28	45	29	22	31	31	36

Occupation	Y.M.C.A. Secretary	Soc. Sci. H.S. Teacher	City Sch. Sup't.	Social Worker	Minister	Musician Performer	C.P.A.	Senior C.P.A.	Accountant	Office Man	Purchasing Agent	Banker
Standard Score	16	22	19	27	59	40	33	48	27	28	29	23

Occupation	Mortician	Pharmacist	Sales Manager	Real Est. Manager	Life Ins. Salesman	Advertising Man	Lawyer	Author-Journalist	President Mfg. Co.	Interest Maturity	Occupational Level	Masculinity-Femininity
Standard Score	26	36	29	37	23	27	30	29	32	47	54	57

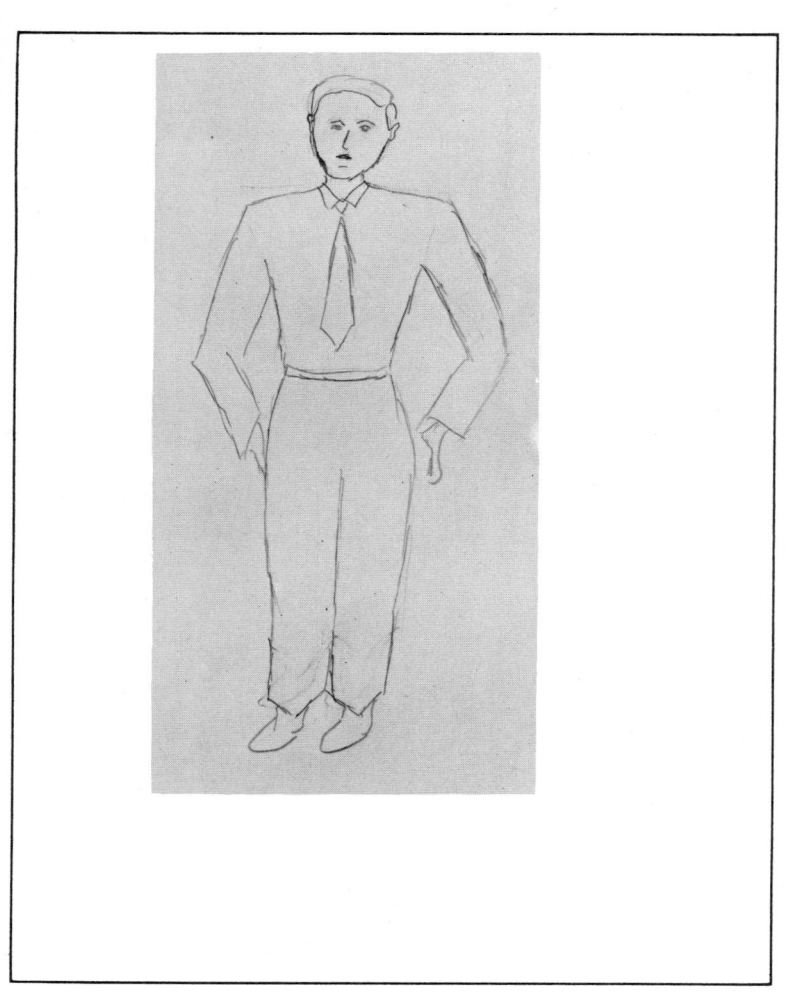

FIGURE-DRAWING CHARACTERISTICS

Structural	Male Female Both		Structural	Male	Female	Structural and Graphic	Male	Female Both		Graphic, Global and Height	Male	Female	Body Proportions	Male	Female
Type	0		Omission of Appendages	0	7	Upper and Lower Halves	1	1		Hair Shading	5	5	Head	07	09
Sex Sequence	0		Position of Both Arms	0	0	Four Quarters	4	4		Nudity and Transparency	7	7	Neck	04	03
Posture	1	1	Position of Right Arm	5	5	Relative Size	2			Form	1	1	Shoulders	08	08
Perspective	0	0	Position of Left Arm	5	5	Constant Line Pressure	0	0		Detailing	3	3	Right Arm	06	
Vertical Midline	3	0	Position of Legs	2	4	Variable Line Pressure	1	1		Identity and Sex	1	1	Left Arm	06	
Bilateral Symmetry	3	3	Relation of Long Axes	1	1	Line Continuity	0	0		Sophistication	2	2	Chest	06	06
Horizontal Midline	4	4	Right and Left Halves	1	1	Body Shading	0	1		Height	07	07	Girth	07	07

GENERAL CHARACTERISTICS OF SUBJECT

IDENTIFICATION
No. G72
Sex M
Marital status S
Age 25 yrs. at
psychological tests

PARENTAL HISTORY				
Father				
C	H	S	D	O
+	+	–	–	?
Mother				
C	H	S	D	O
–	–	–	–	–

PHYSIOLOGICAL AND METABOLIC DATA

	Admission	Initial	Control	Cold pressor change	Exercise change	Smoking change
Systolic pressure	138	116	110	+02	+24	–02
Diastolic pressure	98	70	76	+04	00	+01
Heart rate	72	68	69	–02	+07	+09

Age 24 yrs.	Height 69 in.	Ponderal index 13.07
	Weight 147 lbs.	Cholesterol 203 mg. per 100 ml.
	Overweight –03 %	Vital capacity liters

HABIT SURVEY
Smoking habits: heavy cigarette smoker
Age begun 19 yrs.   Inhalation: yes
Habits of nervous tension: 5, 9, 11, 16, 19,
22

STRONG VOCATIONAL INTEREST TEST

Occupation	Artist	Psychologist	Architect	Physician	Osteopath	Dentist	Veterinarian	Mathematician	Physicist	Engineer	Chemist	Production Manager
Standard Score	14	44	11	55	52	26	37	18	05	12	27	26

Occupation	Farmer	Aviator	Carpenter	Printer	Math.-Sci. Teacher	Ind. Arts Teacher	Voc. Agric. Teacher	Policeman	Forest Serv. Man	Y.M.C.A. Phys. Dir.	Personnel Director	Public Administrator
Standard Score	27	36	02	32	48	15	43	35	24	57	49	56

Occupation	Y.M.C.A. Secretary	Soc. Sci. H.S. Teacher	City Sch. Sup't.	Social Worker	Minister	Musician Performer	C.P.A.	Senior C.P.A.	Accountant	Office Man	Purchasing Agent	Banker
Standard Score	48	62	50	60	59	48	25	50	24	39	22	30

Occupation	Mortician	Pharmacist	Sales Manager	Real Est. Manager	Life Ins. Salesman	Advertising Man	Lawyer	Author- Journalist	President Mfg. Co.	Interest Maturity	Occupational Level	Masculinity- Femininity
Standard Score	34	37	32	31	37	31	40	28	16	61	52	46

Plate 556   **MODERATELY SOPHISTICATED DRAWINGS**   603

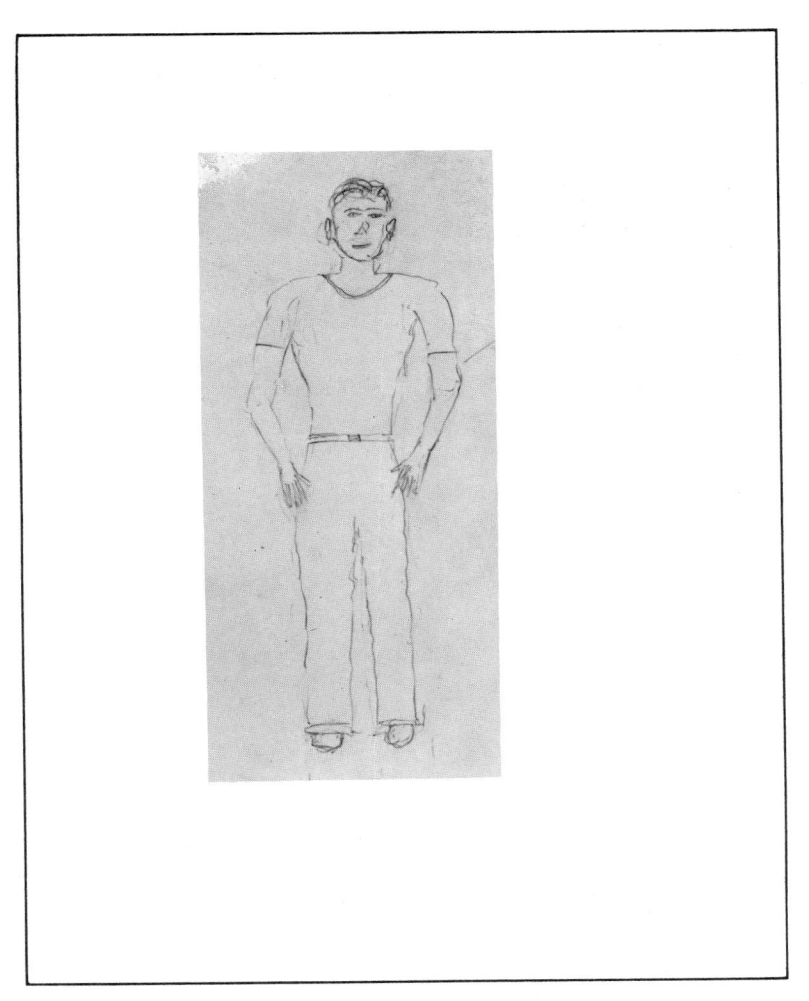

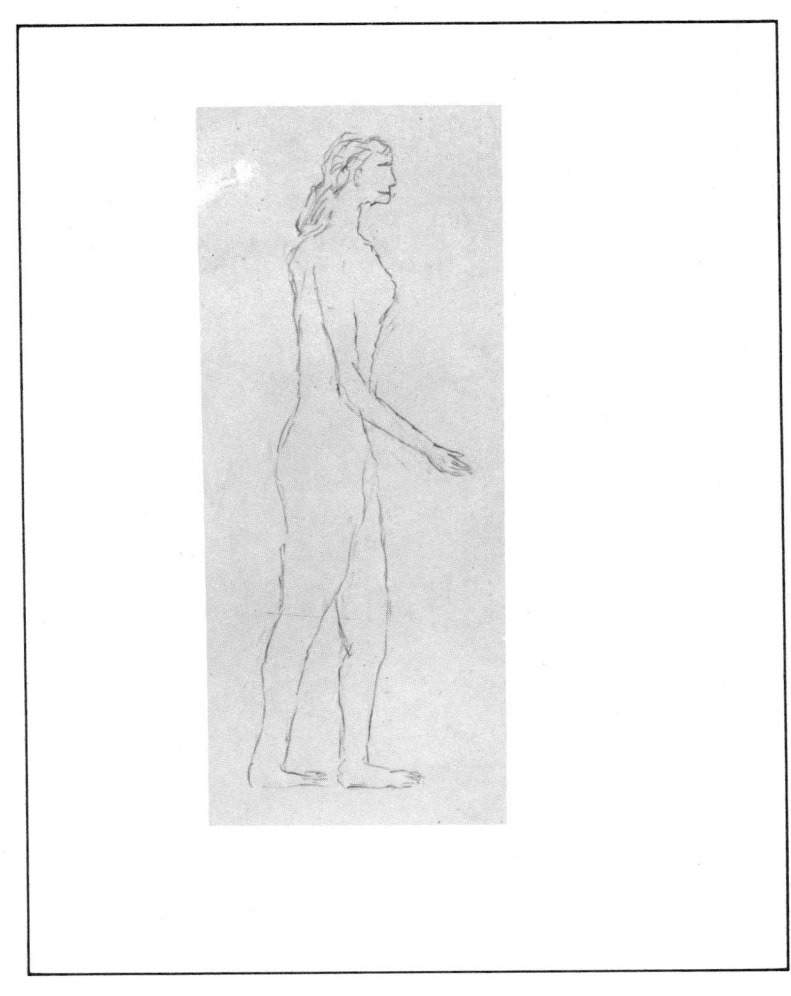

FIGURE-DRAWING CHARACTERISTICS

Structural	Male Female Both		Structural	Male	Female	Structural and Graphic	Male Female Both		Graphic, Global and Height	Male	Female	Body Proportions	Male	Female
Type	0		Omission of Appendages	0	0	Upper and Lower Halves	1	1	Hair Shading	3	2	Head	06	05
Sex Sequence	0		Position of Both Arms	0	2	Four Quarters	4	4	Nudity and Transparency	7	0	Neck	06	08
Posture	1	2	Position of Right Arm	5	4	Relative Size	4		Form	1	1	Shoulders	07	
Perspective	0	2	Position of Left Arm	5	7	Constant Line Pressure	1	1	Detailing	3	3	Right Arm	05	06
Vertical Midline	0	4	Position of Legs	4	8	Variable Line Pressure	0	0	Identity and Sex	1	1	Left Arm	04	
Bilateral Symmetry	3	0	Relation of Long Axes	1	1	Line Continuity	0	0	Sophistication	2	2	Chest	06	05
Horizontal Midline	4	0	Right and Left Halves	1	2	Body Shading	0	0	Height	06	07	Girth	05	06

GENERAL CHARACTERISTICS OF SUBJECT

IDENTIFICATION
No. A05
Sex M
Marital status S
Age 22 yrs. at
psychological tests

PARENTAL HISTORY
Father
C H S D O
+ − − − +
Mother
C H S D O
− − − − ?

PHYSIOLOGICAL AND METABOLIC DATA

	Admission	Initial	Control	Cold pressor change	Exercise change	Smoking change
Systolic pressure	120	122	114	+09	+34	+08
Diastolic pressure	70	62	56	+14	+19	+09
Heart rate	72	64	68	+02	+34	+01

Age 21 yrs.	Height 70 in.	Ponderal index 12.43
	Weight 178 lbs.	Cholesterol 222 mg. per 100 ml.
	Overweight +16 %	Vital capacity liters

HABIT SURVEY
Smoking habits: nonsmoker
Age begun yrs. Inhalation:
Habits of nervous tension: 4, 5, 6, 8, 16

STRONG VOCATIONAL INTEREST TEST

Occupation	Artist	Psychologist	Architect	Physician	Osteopath	Dentist	Veterinarian	Mathematician	Physicist	Engineer	Chemist	Production Manager
Standard Score	47	44	41	53	39	33	20	35	28	35	39	21

Occupation	Farmer	Aviator	Carpenter	Printer	Math.-Sci. Teacher	Ind. Arts Teacher	Voc. Agric. Teacher	Policeman	Forest Serv. Man	Y.M.C.A. Phys. Dir.	Personnel Director	Public Administrator
Standard Score	19	25	02	19	19	−02	−08	20	17	25	28	36

Occupation	Y.M.C.A. Secretary	Soc. Sci. H.S. Teacher	City Sch. Sup't.	Social Worker	Minister	Musician Performer	C.P.A.	Senior C.P.A.	Accountant	Office Man	Purchasing Agent	Banker
Standard Score	20	18	28	36	60	43	33	23	12	20	16	14

Occupation	Mortician	Pharmacist	Sales Manager	Real Est. Manager	Life Ins. Salesman	Advertising Man	Lawyer	Author-Journalist	President Mfg. Co.	Interest Maturity	Occupational Level	Masculinity-Femininity
Standard Score	24	26	33	38	39	48	55	52	35	50	67	33

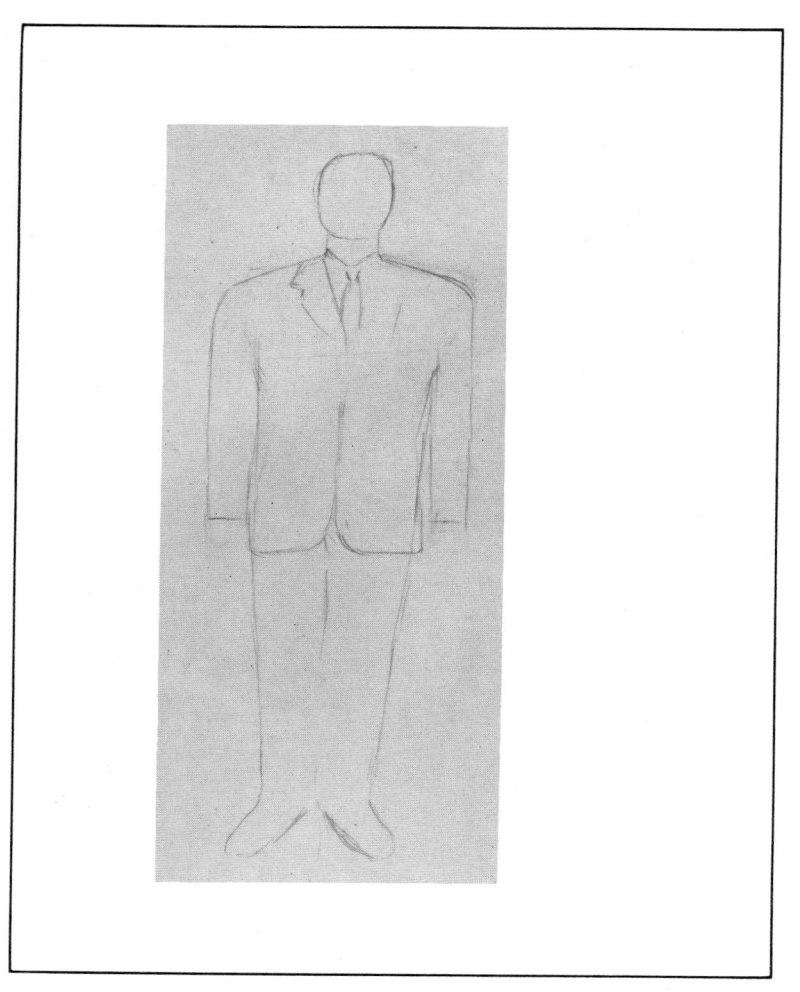

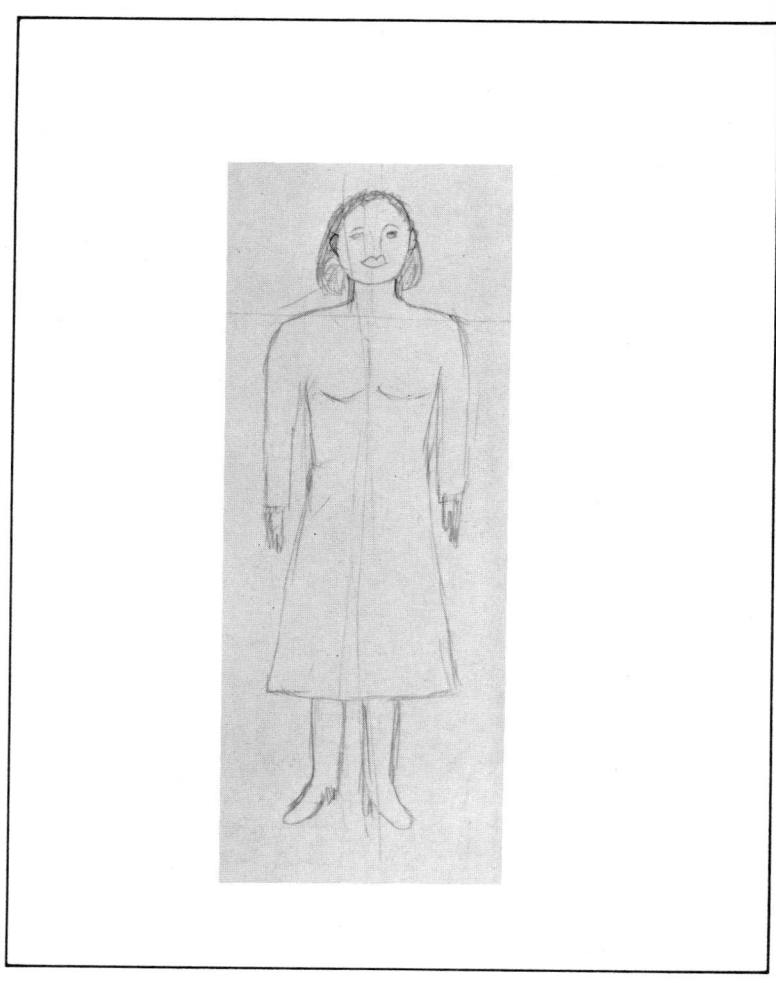

FIGURE-DRAWING CHARACTERISTICS

Structural	Male	Female	Structural	Male	Female	Structural and Graphic	Male	Female	Graphic, Global and Height	Male	Female	Body Proportions	Male	Female
	Both						Both							
Type	0		Omission of Appendages	7	0	Upper and Lower Halves	3	3	Hair Shading	0	3	Head	07	07
Sex Sequence	0		Position of Both Arms	0	0	Four Quarters	4	4	Nudity and Transparency	7	7	Neck	07	06
Posture	1	1	Position of Right Arm	0	0	Relative Size	0		Form	1	1	Shoulders	10	07
Perspective	0	0	Position of Left Arm	0	0	Constant Line Pressure	1	1	Detailing	5	3	Right Arm	06	06
Vertical Midline	3	1	Position of Legs	2	4	Variable Line Pressure	0	0	Identity and Sex	1	1	Left Arm	06	05
Bilateral Symmetry	4	4	Relation of Long Axes	1	1	Line Continuity	0	0	Sophistication	2	2	Chest	08	06
Horizontal Midline	6	0	Right and Left Halves	1	1	Body Shading	0	1	Height	07	06	Girth	10	07

GENERAL CHARACTERISTICS OF SUBJECT

IDENTIFICATION

No. A20

Sex M

Marital status S

Age 23 yrs. at psychological tests

PARENTAL HISTORY

Father

	C	H	S	D	O
	+	+	-	-	+

Mother

	C	H	S	D	O
	-	-	-	-	-

PHYSIOLOGICAL AND METABOLIC DATA

	Admission	Initial	Control	Cold pressor change	Exercise change	Smoking change
Systolic pressure	120	124	117	+26	+53	+09
Diastolic pressure	80	70	64	+12	+08	+13
Heart rate	81	65	70	+11	+30	-10

Age 22 yrs.

Height 71 in.
Weight 163 lbs.
Overweight +03 %

Ponderal index 13.00
Cholesterol 258 mg. per 100 ml.
Vital capacity liters

HABIT SURVEY

Smoking habits: pipe smoker

  Age begun 19 yrs.   Inhalation: no

Habits of nervous tension: 4, 6, 21

STRONG VOCATIONAL INTEREST TEST

Occupation	Artist	Psychologist	Architect	Physician	Osteopath	Dentist	Veterinarian	Mathematician	Physicist	Engineer	Chemist	Production Manager
Standard Score	25	24	38	43	27	38	19	36	31	47	42	34

Occupation	Farmer	Aviator	Carpenter	Printer	Math.-Sci. Teacher	Ind. Arts Teacher	Voc. Agric. Teacher	Policeman	Forest Serv. Man	Y.M.C.A. Phys. Dir.	Personnel Director	Public Administrator
Standard Score	36	27	20	25	34	13	14	27	28	16	25	36

Occupation	Y.M.C.A. Secretary	Soc. Sci. H.S. Teacher	City Sch. Sup't.	Social Worker	Minister	Musician Performer	C.P.A.	Senior C.P.A.	Accountant	Office Man	Purchasing Agent	Banker
Standard Score	14	25	26	17	60	24	34	42	36	34	29	30

Occupation	Mortician	Pharmacist	Sales Manager	Real Est. Manager	Life Ins. Salesman	Advertising Man	Lawyer	Author-Journalist	President Mfg. Co.	Interest Maturity	Occupational Level	Masculinity-Femininity
Standard Score	17	24	23	24	20	27	36	32	33	54	63	53

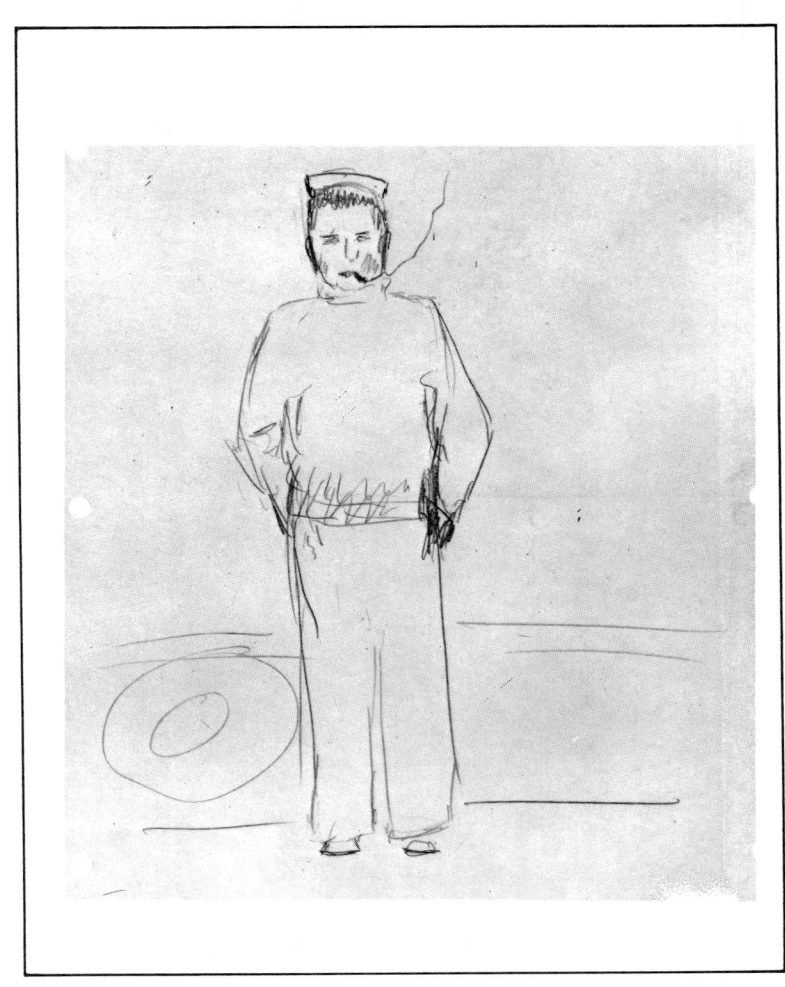

FIGURE-DRAWING CHARACTERISTICS

Structural	Male Female Both	Structural	Male	Female	Structural and Graphic	Male Female Both		Graphic, Global and Height	Male	Female	Body Proportions	Male	Female
Type	0	Omission of Appendages	7	7	Upper and Lower Halves	0	0	Hair Shading	3	2	Head	08	06
Sex Sequence	1	Position of Both Arms	0	0	Four Quarters	4	4	Nudity and Transparency	7	7	Neck	03	01
Posture	1 1	Position of Right Arm	5	5	Relative Size	0		Form	1	1	Shoulders	07	05
Perspective	0 0	Position of Left Arm	5	5	Constant Line Pressure	0	0	Detailing	1	3	Right Arm		
Vertical Midline	0 0	Position of Legs	4	4	Variable Line Pressure	4	4	Identity and Sex	1	1	Left Arm		06
Bilateral Symmetry	3 2	Relation of Long Axes	1	1	Line Continuity	1	1	Sophistication	2	2	Chest		06
Horizontal Midline	4 0	Right and Left Halves	1	2	Body Shading	4	3	Height	07	05	Girth		09

GENERAL CHARACTERISTICS OF SUBJECT

IDENTIFICATION

No. A27

Sex F

Marital status S

Age 21 yrs. at

psychological tests

PARENTAL HISTORY

Father

C	H	S	D	O
+	?	-	-	?

Mother

C	H	S	D	O
-	?	-	-	-

PHYSIOLOGICAL AND METABOLIC DATA

	Admission	Initial	Control	Cold pressor change	Exercise change	Smoking change
Systolic pressure	108	110	112	+16	+42	+02
Diastolic pressure	70	64	66	+21	-08	+01
Heart rate	102	84	64	+10	+18	+06

Age 20 yrs.   Height 63 in.   Ponderal index 12.28

Weight 135 lbs.   Cholesterol 190 mg. per 100 ml.

Overweight +11 %   Vital capacity   liters

HABIT SURVEY

Smoking habits: light cigarette smoker

Age begun 16 yrs.   Inhalation: sometimes

Habits of nervous tension: 3, 4, 5, 6, 9, 10, 16, 19, 21

STRONG VOCATIONAL INTEREST TEST

Occupation	Artist	Psychologist	Architect	Physician	Osteopath	Dentist	Veterinarian	Mathematician	Physicist	Engineer	Chemist	Production Manager
Standard Score	6	6	7	7	4	4	2	6	7	5	6	4

Occupation	Farmer	Aviator	Carpenter	Printer	Math.-Sci. Teacher	Ind. Arts Teacher	Voc. Agric. Teacher	Policeman	Forest Serv. Man	Y.M.C.A. Phys. Dir.	Personnel Director	Public Administrator
Standard Score	6	5	2	4	4	0	2		2	2	5	4

Occupation	Y.M.C.A. Secretary	Soc. Sci. H.S. Teacher	City Sch. Sup't.	Social Worker	Minister	Musician Performer	C.P.A.	Senior C.P.A.	Accountant	Office Man	Purchasing Agent	Banker
Standard Score	1	1	1	2	6	6	6	4	2	2	2	1

Occupation	Mortician	Pharmacist	Sales Manager	Real Est. Manager	Life Ins. Salesman	Advertising Man	Lawyer	Author-Journalist	President Mfg. Co.	Interest Maturity	Occupational Level	Masculinity-Femininity
Standard Score	1	2	2	4	2	5	6	7	4	3	5	3

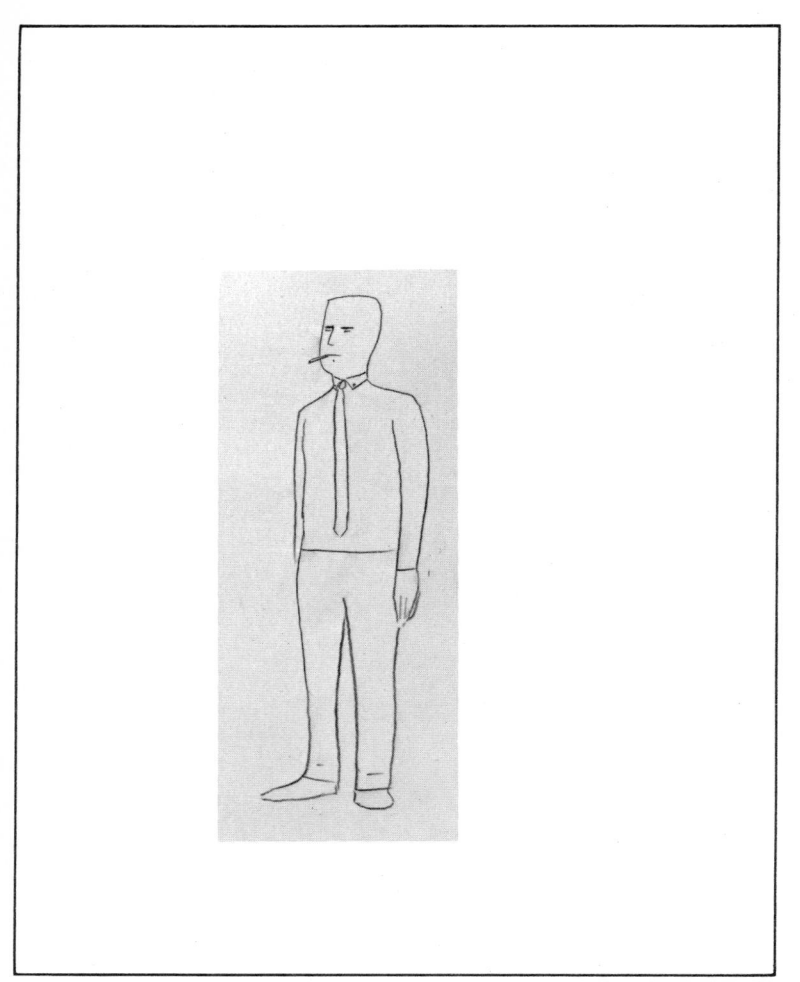

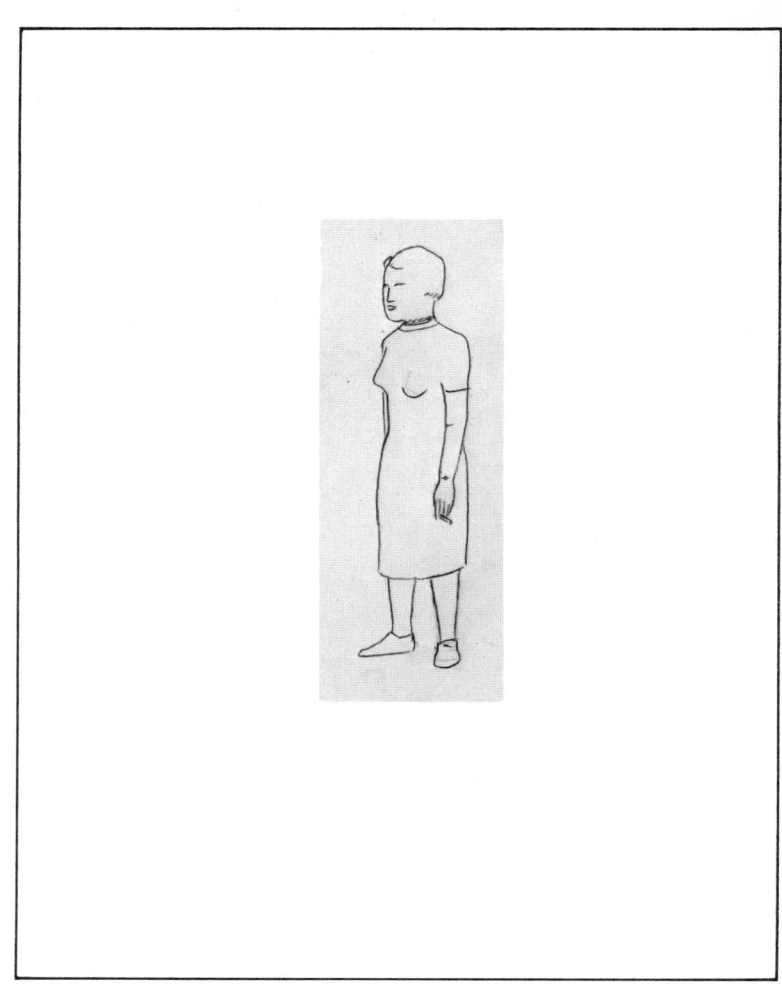

FIGURE-DRAWING CHARACTERISTICS

Structural	Male Female Both	Structural	Male	Female	Structural and Graphic	Male Female Both	Graphic, Global and Height	Male	Female	Body Proportions	Male	Female
Type	0	Omission of Appendages	0	0	Upper and Lower Halves	3	1	Hair Shading	0	5	Head	06	05
Sex Sequence	0	Position of Both Arms	4	4	Four Quarters	4	4	Nudity and Transparency	7	7	Neck	03	00
Posture	1	1 ·	Position of Right Arm	7	7	Relative Size	0		Form	1	1	Shoulders		
Perspective	1	1	Position of Left Arm	0	0	Constant Line Pressure	5	5	Detailing	3	3	Right Arm		
Vertical Midline	7	4	Position of Legs	4	4	Variable Line Pressure	0	0	Identity and Sex	1	1	Left Arm	04	04
Bilateral Symmetry	0	0	Relation of Long Axes	1	1	Line Continuity	4	4	Sophistication	2	2	Chest		
Horizontal Midline	4	0	Right and Left Halves	1	0	Body Shading	0	1	Height	05	04	Girth		

GENERAL CHARACTERISTICS OF SUBJECT

IDENTIFICATION
No. B52
Sex M
Marital status S
Age 22 yrs. at
psychological tests

PARENTAL HISTORY
Father
C   H   S   D   O
+   -   -   -   -
Mother
C   H   S   D   O
-    -   -   -   -

PHYSIOLOGICAL AND METABOLIC DATA

	Admission	Initial	Control	Cold pressor change	Exercise change	Smoking change
Systolic pressure	120	114	114	+16	+36	+08
Diastolic pressure	80	66	72	+18	-18	+02
Heart rate	92	76	65	+06	+38	+03

Age 22 yrs.	Height 64 in.	Ponderal index 12.70
	Weight 128 lbs.	Cholesterol 225 mg. per 100 ml.
	Overweight -02 %	Vital capacity 3.6 liters

HABIT SURVEY
Smoking habits: heavy cigarette smoker
Age begun 18 yrs.   Inhalation: yes
Habits of nervous tension: 1, 3, 4, 5, 7, 8,
9, 10, 17, 22

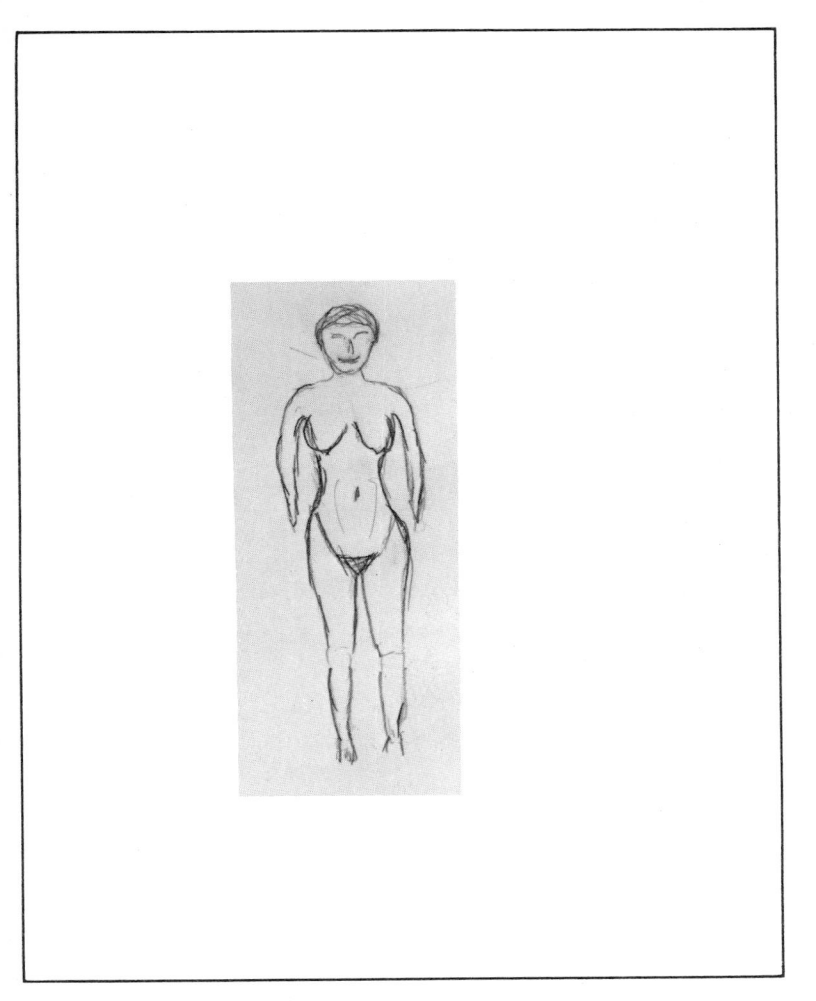

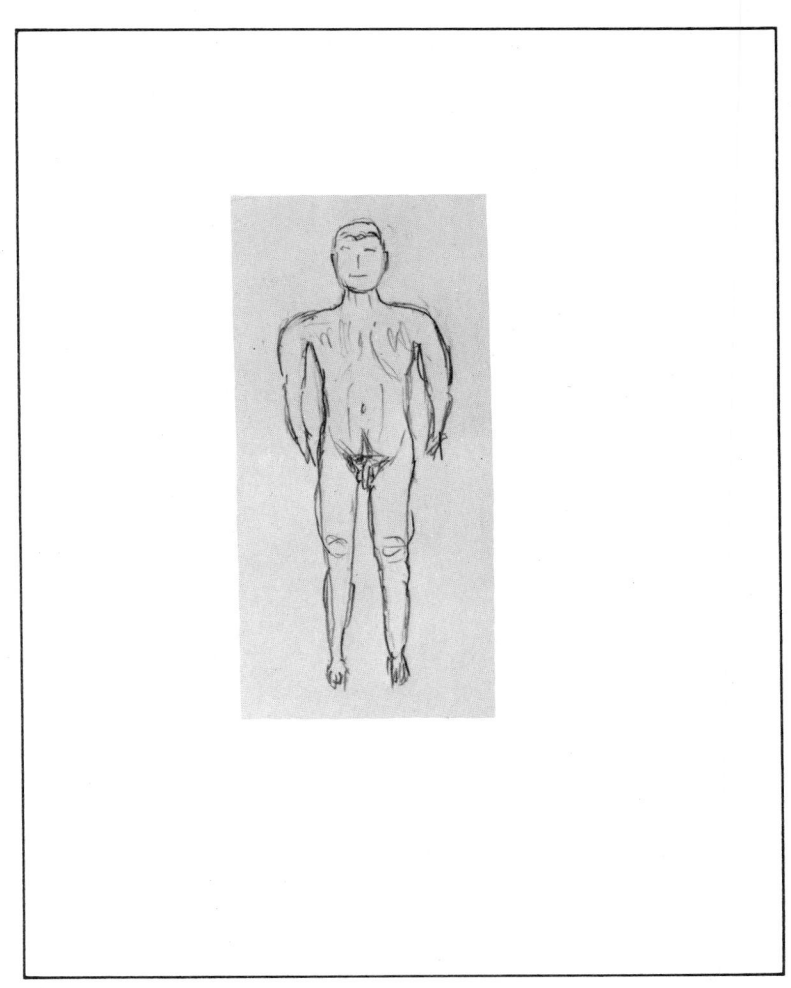

FIGURE-DRAWING CHARACTERISTICS

Structural	Male Female Both	Structural	Male	Female	Structural and Graphic	Male Female Both	Graphic, Global and Height	Male	Female	Body Proportions	Male	Female
Type	0	Omission of Appendages	7	6	Upper and Lower Halves	1 3	Hair Shading	5	2	Head	05	05
Sex Sequence	1	Position of Both Arms	0	0	Four Quarters	4 4	Nudity and Transparency	0	0	Neck	04	02
Posture	1 1	Position of Right Arm	0	0	Relative Size	2	Form	3	3	Shoulders	06	04
Perspective	0 0	Position of Left Arm	0	0	Constant Line Pressure	0 0	Detailing	3	3	Right Arm	02	02
Vertical Midline	0 0	Position of Legs	4	4	Variable Line Pressure	5 4	Identity and Sex	1	1	Left Arm	02	02
Bilateral Symmetry	3 3	Relation of Long Axes	1	1	Line Continuity	0 0	Sophistication	2	2	Chest	04	05
Horizontal Midline	0 0	Right and Left Halves	1	1	Body Shading	3 3	Height	05	04	Girth	05	04

GENERAL CHARACTERISTICS OF SUBJECT

IDENTIFICATION
No. B75
Sex M
Marital status S
Age 24 yrs. at
psychological tests

PARENTAL HISTORY
Father
C   H   S   D   O
+   -   -   -   ?
Mother
C   H   S   D   O
-   -   -   -   +

PHYSIOLOGICAL AND METABOLIC DATA

	Admission	Initial	Control	Cold pressor change	Exercise change	Smoking change
Systolic pressure	130	114	120	+12	+36	+03
Diastolic pressure	76	70	78	+21	-30	+10
Heart rate	92	72	57	+01	+58	+06

Age 22 yrs.   Height 68 in.   Weight 156 lbs.   Overweight +07 %

Ponderal index 12.64   Cholesterol 256 mg. per 100 ml.   Vital capacity 4.5 liters

HABIT SURVEY

Smoking habits: pipe smoker

Age begun 17 yrs.   Inhalation: no

Habits of nervous tension: 2, 4, 5, 22, 25

STRONG VOCATIONAL INTEREST TEST

Occupation	Artist	Psychologist	Architect	Physician	Osteopath	Dentist	Veterinarian	Mathematician	Physicist	Engineer	Chemist	Production Manager
Standard Score	4	8	5	8	7	4	2	5	7	4	6	4

Occupation	Farmer	Aviator	Carpenter	Printer	Math.-Sci. Teacher	Ind. Arts Teacher	Voc. Agric. Teacher	Policeman	Forest Serv. Man	Y.M.C.A. Phys. Dir.	Personnel Director	Public Administrator
Standard Score	4	5	3	7	7	2	3	3	5	6	7	7

Occupation	Y.M.C.A. Secretary	Soc. Sci. H.S. Teacher	City Sch. Sup't.	Social Worker	Minister	Musician Performer	C.P.A.	Senior C.P.A.	Accountant	Office Man	Purchasing Agent	Banker
Standard Score	5	6	5	7	6	7	4	6	2	2	1	1

Occupation	Mortician	Pharmacist	Sales Manager	Real Est. Manager	Life Ins. Salesman	Advertising Man	Lawyer	Author-Journalist	President Mfg. Co.	Interest Maturity	Occupational Level	Masculinity-Femininity
Standard Score	2	4	2	3	2	5	4	5	3	6	4	4

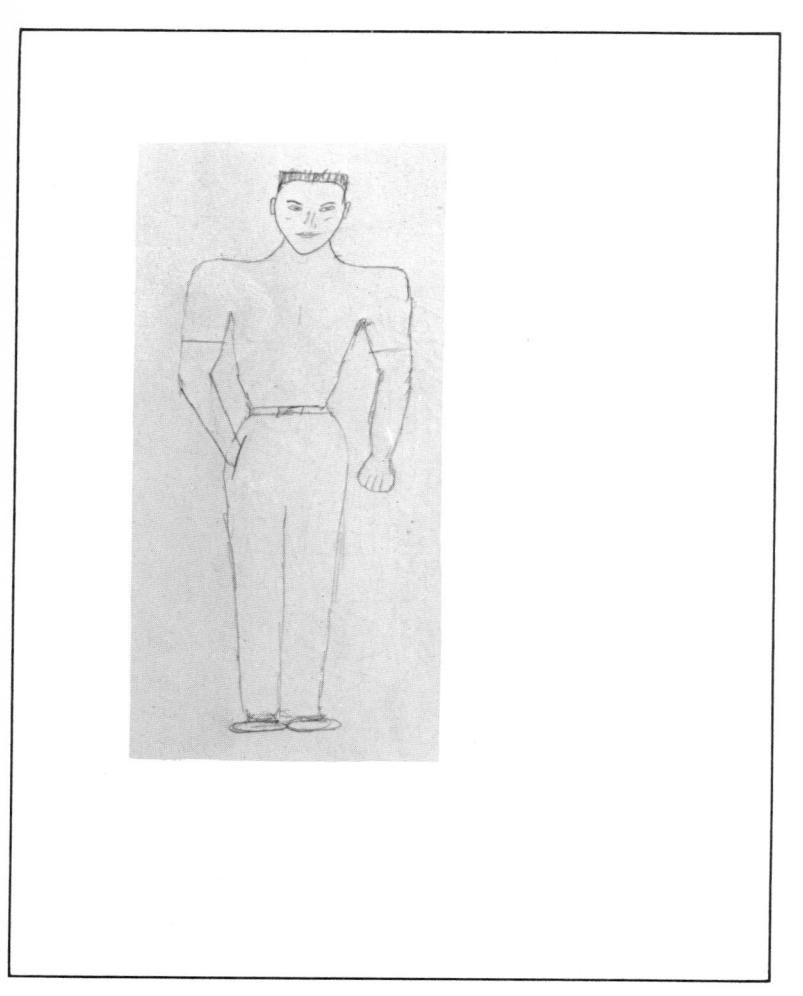

FIGURE-DRAWING CHARACTERISTICS

Structural	Male Female Both	Structural	Male	Female	Structural and Graphic	Male Female Both		Graphic, Global and Height	Male	Female	Body Proportions	Male	Female
Type	0	Omission of Appendages	7	0	Upper and Lower Halves	1	1	Hair Shading	3	1	Head	06	07
Sex Sequence	0	Position of Both Arms	1	0	Four Quarters	4	4	Nudity and Transparency	7	7	Neck	04	04
Posture	1 1	Position of Right Arm	5	0	Relative Size	2		Form	3	1	Shoulders	09	07
Perspective	0 0	Position of Left Arm	0	0	Constant Line Pressure	2	2	Detailing	3	1	Right Arm	06	04
Vertical Midline	0 3	Position of Legs	2	4	Variable Line Pressure	0	0	Identity and Sex	1	1	Left Arm	06	04
Bilateral Symmetry	4 3	Relation of Long Axes	1	1	Line Continuity	0	0	Sophistication	2	2	Chest	06	05
Horizontal Midline	4 4	Right and Left Halves	1	2	Body Shading	1	1	Height	06	06	Girth	05	05

GENERAL CHARACTERISTICS OF SUBJECT

IDENTIFICATION
No. C15
Sex M
Marital status S
Age 22 yrs. at psychological tests

PARENTAL HISTORY				
Father				
C	H	S	D	O
+	U	–	–	?
Mother				
C	H	S	D	O
–	–	–	–	?

PHYSIOLOGICAL AND METABOLIC DATA

	Admission	Initial	Control	Cold pressor change	Exercise change	Smoking change
Systolic pressure	130	124	118	+20	+20	+09
Diastolic pressure	70	60	60	+30	+18	+03
Heart rate	81	80	79	–12	+15	+13
Age 22 yrs.	Height 74 in.		Ponderal index 13.53			
	Weight 164 lbs.		Cholesterol 160 mg. per 100 ml.			
	Overweight –05 %		Vital capacity 4.9 liters			

HABIT SURVEY
Smoking habits: heavy cigarette smoker
Age begun 19 yrs. Inhalation: yes
Habits of nervous tension: 1, 4, 5, 6, 8, 9, 11, 17, 19, 21, 22, 23

STRONG VOCATIONAL INTEREST TEST

Occupation	Artist	Psychologist	Architect	Physician	Osteopath	Dentist	Veterinarian	Mathematician	Physicist	Engineer	Chemist	Production Manager
Standard Score	31	50	34	47	35	24	04	32	23	29	35	24

Occupation	Farmer	Aviator	Carpenter	Printer	Math.-Sci. Teacher	Ind. Arts Teacher	Voc. Agric. Teacher	Policeman	Forest Serv. Man	Y.M.C.A. Phys. Dir.	Personnel Director	Public Administrator
Standard Score	09	26	–10	17	24	–10	01	12	00	22	44	48

Occupation	Y.M.C.A. Secretary	Soc. Sci. H.S. Teacher	City Sch. Sup't.	Social Worker	Minister	Musician Performer	C.P.A.	Senior C.P.A.	Accountant	Office Man	Purchasing Agent	Banker
Standard Score	13	26	31	38	62	38	50	31	24	22	23	22

Occupation	Mortician	Pharmacist	Sales Manager	Real Est. Manager	Life Ins. Salesman	Advertising Man	Lawyer	Author-Journalist	President Mfg. Co.	Interest Maturity	Occupational Level	Masculinity-Femininity
Standard Score	25	34	45	41	46	55	60	47	41	53	72	40

Plate 562　　　MODERATELY SOPHISTICATED DRAWINGS　　　609

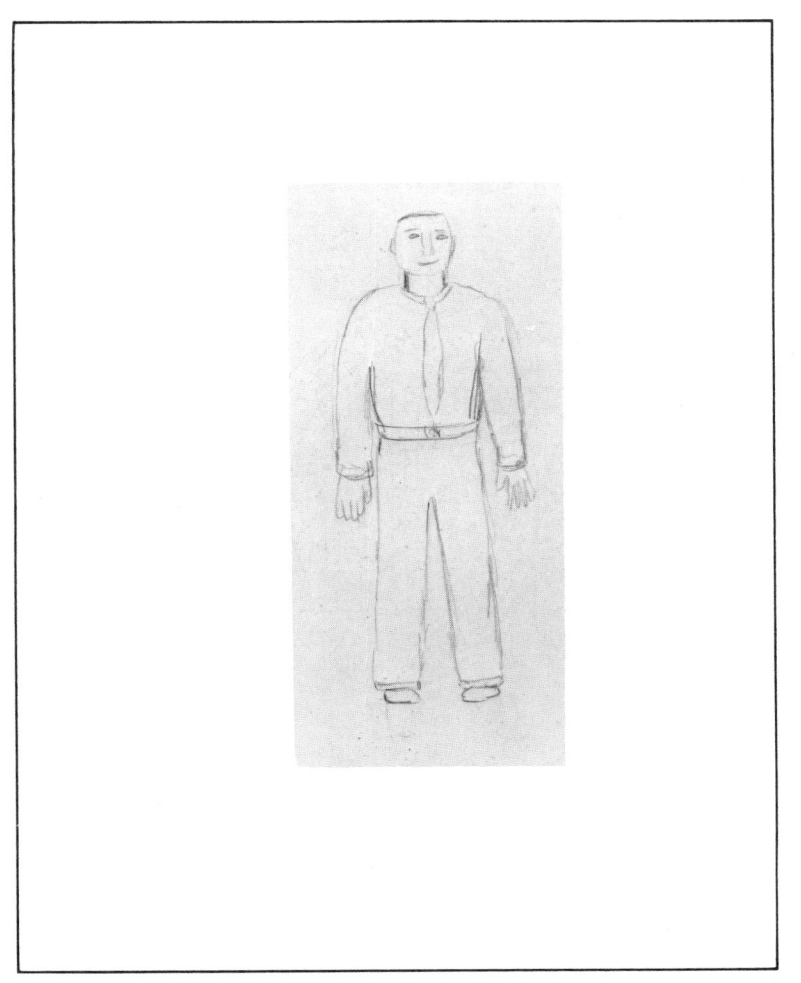

FIGURE-DRAWING CHARACTERISTICS

Structural	Male Female Both		Structural	Male	Female	Structural and Graphic	Male Female Both		Graphic, Global and Height	Male	Female	Body Proportions	Male	Female
Type	0		Omission of Appendages	0	0	Upper and Lower Halves	1	1	Hair Shading	0	3	Head	05	04
Sex Sequence	0		Position of Both Arms	0	0	Four Quarters	4	4	Nudity and Transparency	7	7	Neck	06	04
Posture	1	1	Position of Right Arm	0	5	Relative Size	0		Form	1	1	Shoulders	06	04
Perspective	0	0	Position of Left Arm	0	5	Constant Line Pressure	1	1	Detailing	3	3	Right Arm	05	02
Vertical Midline	3	0	Position of Legs	5	4	Variable Line Pressure	0	0	Identity and Sex	1	1	Left Arm	04	02
Bilateral Symmetry	4	5	Relation of Long Axes	1	1	Line Continuity	0	0	Sophistication	2	2	Chest	05	03
Horizontal Midline	4	4	Right and Left Halves	3	1	Body Shading	0	5	Height	05	04	Girth	06	03

GENERAL CHARACTERISTICS OF SUBJECT

IDENTIFICATION

No. C18

Sex M

Marital status S

Age 20 yrs. at

psychological tests

PARENTAL HISTORY

Father

	C	H	S	D	O
	+	-	-	-	?

Mother

	C	H	S	D	O
	-	-	-	-	-

PHYSIOLOGICAL AND METABOLIC DATA

	Admission	Initial	Control	Cold pressor change	Exercise change	Smoking change
Systolic pressure	120	110	104	+26	+58	+08
Diastolic pressure	70	78	76	+16	-24	+11
Heart rate	80	60	53	+08	+54	+01

Age 22 yrs.

Height 72 in.　　Ponderal index 13.04

Weight 168 lbs.　　Cholesterol 255 mg. per 100 ml.

Overweight +03 %　　Vital capacity 4.4 liters

HABIT SURVEY

Smoking habits: nonsmoker

Age begun yrs. Inhalation:

Habits of nervous tension: 5, 6, 11

STRONG VOCATIONAL INTEREST TEST

Occupation	Artist	Psychologist	Architect	Physician	Osteopath	Dentist	Veterinarian	Mathematician	Physicist	Engineer	Chemist	Production Manager
Standard Score	12	35	15	45	38	25	29	21	14	24	33	32

Occupation	Farmer	Aviator	Carpenter	Printer	Math.-Sci. Teacher	Ind. Arts Teacher	Voc. Agric. Teacher	Policeman	Forest Serv. Man	Y.M.C.A. Phys. Dir.	Personnel Director	Public Administrator
Standard Score	35	36	18	36	45	18	37	35	23	37	44	50

Occupation	Y.M.C.A. Secretary	Soc. Sci. H.S. Teacher	City Sch. Sup't.	Social Worker	Minister	Musician Performer	C.P.A.	Senior C.P.A.	Accountant	Office Man	Purchasing Agent	Banker
Standard Score	37	43	31	39	62	29	34	52	34	35	33	35

Occupation	Mortician	Pharmacist	Sales Manager	Real Est. Manager	Life Ins. Salesman	Advertising Man	Lawyer	Author-Journalist	President Mfg. Co.	Interest Maturity	Occupational Level	Masculinity-Femininity
Standard Score	29	38	36	33	28	27	34	23	29	57	52	58

FIGURE-DRAWING CHARACTERISTICS

Structural	Male Female Both	Structural	Male	Female	Structural and Graphic	Male Female Both	Graphic, Global and Height	Male	Female	Body Proportions	Male	Female
Type	0	Omission of Appendages	0	0	Upper and Lower Halves	3 3	Hair Shading	0	3	Head	09	09
Sex Sequence	0	Position of Both Arms	0	0	Four Quarters	4 4	Nudity and Transparency	7	7	Neck	06	08
Posture	1 1	Position of Right Arm	5	5	Relative Size	0	Form	3	1	Shoulders	09	08
Perspective	0 0	Position of Left Arm	5	5	Constant Line Pressure	4 0	Detailing	1	1	Right Arm	06	06
Vertical Midline	3 3	Position of Legs	4	4	Variable Line Pressure	0 3	Identity and Sex	1	1	Left Arm	06	04
Bilateral Symmetry	5 5	Relation of Long Axes	1	1	Line Continuity	3 3	Sophistication	2	2	Chest	07	07
Horizontal Midline	4 4	Right and Left Halves	1	1	Body Shading	7 3	Height	07	06	Girth	11	06

GENERAL CHARACTERISTICS OF SUBJECT

IDENTIFICATION
No. D31
Sex M
Marital status S
Age 22 yrs. at psychological tests

PARENTAL HISTORY
Father
C   H   S   D   O
+   -   -   -   ?
Mother
C   H   S   D   O
-    +   -   -   -

PHYSIOLOGICAL AND METABOLIC DATA

	Admission	Initial	Control	Cold pressor change	Exercise change	Smoking change
Systolic pressure	128	140	124	+07	+28	+02
Diastolic pressure	80	76	75	+19	-23	00
Heart rate	82	80	81	+04	+39	+08

Age 22 yrs.	Height 70 in.	Ponderal index 13.01
	Weight 156 lbs.	Cholesterol 266 mg. per 100 ml.
	Overweight +01 %	Vital capacity 5.0 liters

HABIT SURVEY
Smoking habits: nonsmoker
Age begun   yrs.   Inhalation:
Habits of nervous tension: 4, 5, 6, 9, 11, 14, 15, 16, 25

STRONG VOCATIONAL INTEREST TEST

Occupation	Artist	Psychologist	Architect	Physician	Osteopath	Dentist	Veterinarian	Mathematician	Physicist	Engineer	Chemist	Production Manager
Standard Score	42	42	53	66	45	53	37	45	48	49	54	32

Occupation	Farmer	Aviator	Carpenter	Printer	Math.-Sci. Teacher	Ind. Arts Teacher	Voc. Agric. Teacher	Policeman	Forest Serv. Man	Y.M.C.A. Phys. Dir.	Personnel Director	Public Administrator
Standard Score	45	54	40	47	46	35	40	31	34	33	19	24

Occupation	Y.M.C.A. Secretary	Soc. Sci. H.S. Teacher	City Sch. Sup't.	Social Worker	Minister	Musician Performer	C.P.A.	Senior C.P.A.	Accountant	Office Man	Purchasing Agent	Banker
Standard Score	09	20	12	26	63	62	25	44	22	25	21	16

Occupation	Mortician	Pharmacist	Sales Manager	Real Est. Manager	Life Ins. Salesman	Advertising Man	Lawyer	Author-Journalist	President Mfg. Co.	Interest Maturity	Occupational Level	Masculinity-Femininity
Standard Score	18	40	22	30	17	32	25	35	31	49	48	53

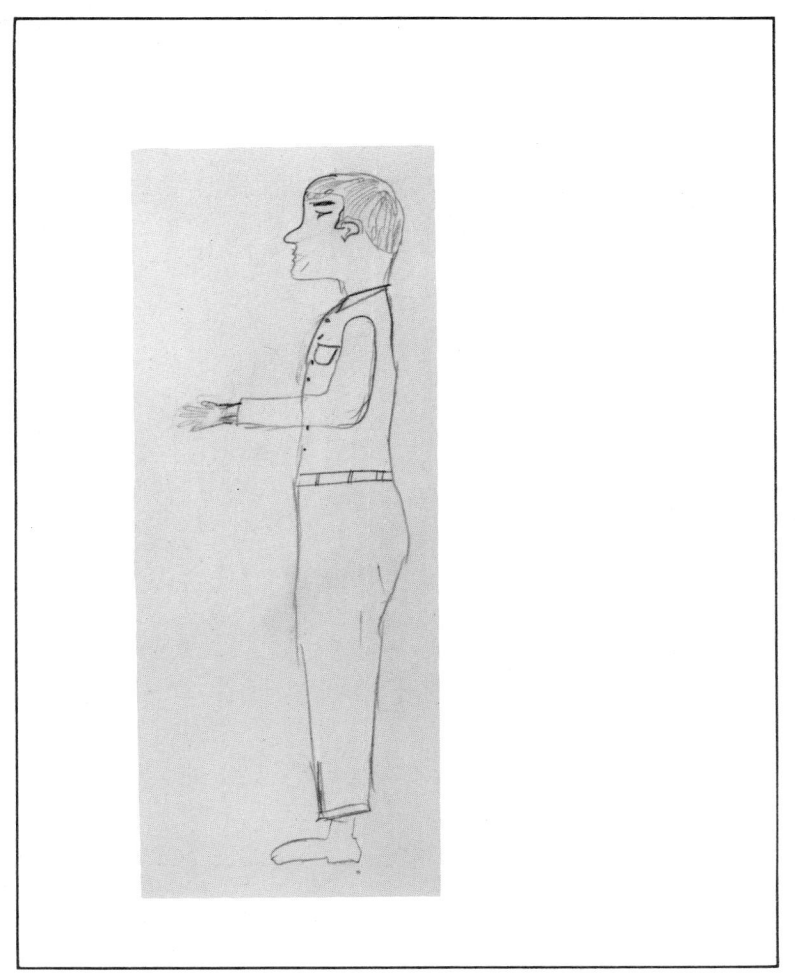

FIGURE-DRAWING CHARACTERISTICS

Structural	Male	Female	Structural	Male	Female	Structural and Graphic	Male	Female	Graphic, Global and Height	Male	Female	Body Proportions	Male	Female
		Both						Both						
Type		0	Omission of Appendages	0	0	Upper and Lower Halves	3	1	Hair Shading	1	2	Head	09	11
Sex Sequence		0	Position of Both Arms	4	4	Four Quarters	4	4	Nudity and Transparency	7	7	Neck	06	14
Posture	1	1	Position of Right Arm	7	7	Relative Size		4	Form	3	1	Shoulders		
Perspective	2	2	Position of Left Arm	4	4	Constant Line Pressure	0	0	Detailing	1	1	Right Arm		
Vertical Midline	7	4	Position of Legs	1	1	Variable Line Pressure	2	2	Identity and Sex	1	1	Left Arm	06	07
Bilateral Symmetry	0	0	Relation of Long Axes	1	1	Line Continuity	0	0	Sophistication	2	2	Chest	06	07
Horizontal Midline	4	4	Right and Left Halves	2	1	Body Shading	0	0	Height	07	08	Girth	07	07

GENERAL CHARACTERISTICS OF SUBJECT

IDENTIFICATION

No. D45

Sex M

Marital status S

Age 22 yrs. at
psychological tests

PARENTAL HISTORY

Father

C	H	S	D	O
+	-	-	-	+

Mother

C	H	S	D	O
-	-	-	-	?

PHYSIOLOGICAL AND METABOLIC DATA

	Admission	Initial	Control	Cold pressor change	Exercise change	Smoking change
Systolic pressure	150	110	106	+17	+34	-02
Diastolic pressure	90	60	60	+20	-10	00
Heart rate	72	72	64	+08	+39	+04

Age 22 yrs.

Height	74 in.	Ponderal index 13.36
Weight	170 lbs.	Cholesterol 199 mg. per 100 ml.
Overweight -02 %		Vital capacity 5.2 liters

HABIT SURVEY

Smoking habits: nonsmoker

  Age begun yrs.   Inhalation:

Habits of nervous tension: 4, 5, 6, 9, 14, 16,
17, 19, 21

STRONG VOCATIONAL INTEREST TEST

Occupation	Artist	Psychologist	Architect	Physician	Osteopath	Dentist	Veterinarian	Mathematician	Physicist	Engineer	Chemist	Production Manager
Standard Score	44	54	42	62	58	48	34	28	29	35	46	32

Occupation	Farmer	Aviator	Carpenter	Printer	Math.-Sci. Teacher	Ind. Arts Teacher	Voc. Agric. Teacher	Policeman	Forest Serv. Man	Y.M.C.A. Phys. Dir.	Personnel Director	Public Administrator
Standard Score	36	45	30	36	42	35	34	27	34	33	37	42

Occupation	Y.M.C.A. Secretary	Soc. Sci. H.S. Teacher	City Sch. Sup't.	Social Worker	Minister	Musician Performer	C.P.A.	Senior C.P.A.	Accountant	Office Man	Purchasing Agent	Banker
Standard Score	23	34	25	45	63	63	18	31	17	23	18	13

Occupation	Mortician	Pharmacist	Sales Manager	Real Est. Manager	Life Ins. Salesman	Advertising Man	Lawyer	Author-Journalist	President Mfg. Co.	Interest Maturity	Occupational Level	Masculinity-Femininity
Standard Score	28	36	23	32	26	36	33	38	26	54	53	33

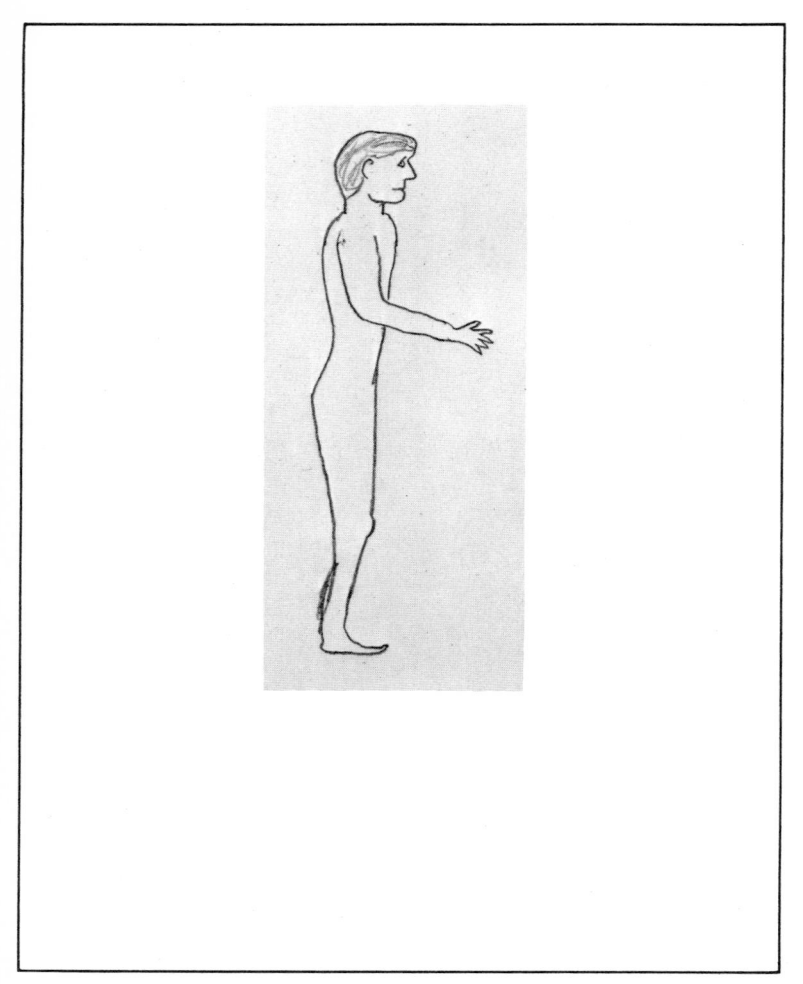

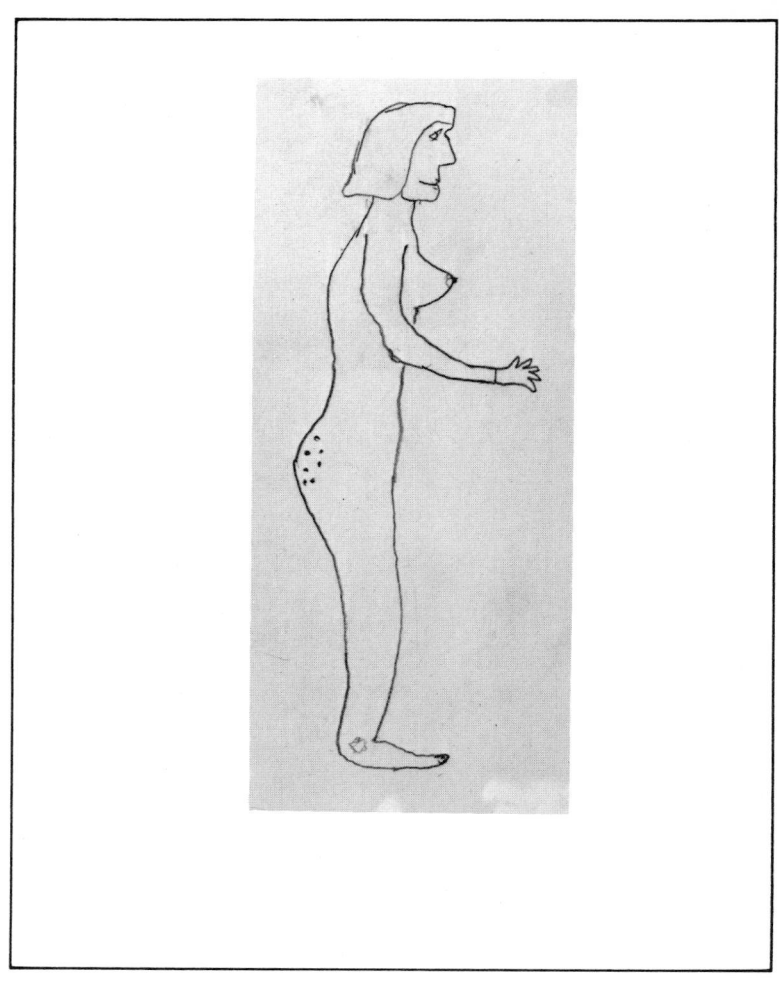

FIGURE-DRAWING CHARACTERISTICS

Structural	Male Female Both	Structural	Male	Female	Structural and Graphic	Male Female Both		Graphic, Global and Height	Male	Female	Body Proportions	Male	Female
Type	0	Omission of Appendages	0	0	Upper and Lower Halves	1	1	Hair Shading	1	5	Head	05	07
Sex Sequence	0	Position of Both Arms	2	2	Four Quarters	4	4	Nudity and Transparency	0	0	Neck	04	07
Posture	1 1	Position of Right Arm	4	4	Relative Size	4		Form	1	1	Shoulders		
Perspective	2 2	Position of Left Arm	7	7	Constant Line Pressure	5	5	Detailing	3	3	Right Arm	04	06
Vertical Midline	4 4	Position of Legs	1	1	Variable Line Pressure	0	0	Identity and Sex	1	1	Left Arm		
Bilateral Symmetry	0 0	Relation of Long Axes	1	1	Line Continuity	4	4	Sophistication	2	2	Chest	05	06
Horizontal Midline	0 0	Right and Left Halves	1	1	Body Shading	0	3	Height	05	07	Girth	04	06

GENERAL CHARACTERISTICS OF SUBJECT

IDENTIFICATION
No. D50
Sex M
Marital status S
Age 21 yrs. at
psychological tests

PARENTAL HISTORY
Father
C   H   S   D   O
+   +   -   +   +
Mother
C   H   S   D   O
-   -   -   -   -

PHYSIOLOGICAL AND METABOLIC DATA

	Admission	Initial	Control	Cold pressor change	Exercise change	Smoking change
Systolic pressure	180	150	135	-01	+45	+02
Diastolic pressure	110	90	85	+16	-15	+10
Heart rate	80	68	65	+04	+16	+21

Age 21 yrs.
Height 71 in.
Weight 169 lbs.
Overweight +08 %
Ponderal index 12.84
Cholesterol 259 mg. per 100 ml.
Vital capacity 4.5 liters

HABIT SURVEY

Smoking habits: occasional smoker

Age begun 17 yrs.   Inhalation: yes

Habits of nervous tension: 1, 3, 7, 8, 25

STRONG VOCATIONAL INTEREST TEST

Occupation	Artist	Psychologist	Architect	Physician	Osteopath	Dentist	Veterinarian	Mathematician	Physicist	Engineer	Chemist	Production Manager
Standard Score	50	49	47	53	35	36	-09	37	31	38	42	26

Occupation	Farmer	Aviator	Carpenter	Printer	Math.-Sci. Teacher	Ind. Arts Teacher	Voc. Agric. Teacher	Policeman	Forest Serv. Man	Y.M.C.A. Phys. Dir.	Personnel Director	Public Administrator
Standard Score	16	33	03	28	22	-05	00	14	15	22	38	43

Occupation	Y.M.C.A. Secretary	Soc. Sci. H.S. Teacher	City Sch. Sup't.	Social Worker	Minister	Musician Performer	C.P.A.	Senior C.P.A.	Accountant	Office Man	Purchasing Agent	Banker
Standard Score	17	22	30	36	63	49	46	26	15	17	12	11

Occupation	Mortician	Pharmacist	Sales Manager	Real Est. Manager	Life Ins. Salesman	Advertising Man	Lawyer	Author-Journalist	President Mfg. Co.	Interest Maturity	Occupational Level	Masculinity-Femininity
Standard Score	11	14	32	36	29	54	59	54	34	51	66	36

Plate 566 **MODERATELY SOPHISTICATED DRAWINGS** 613

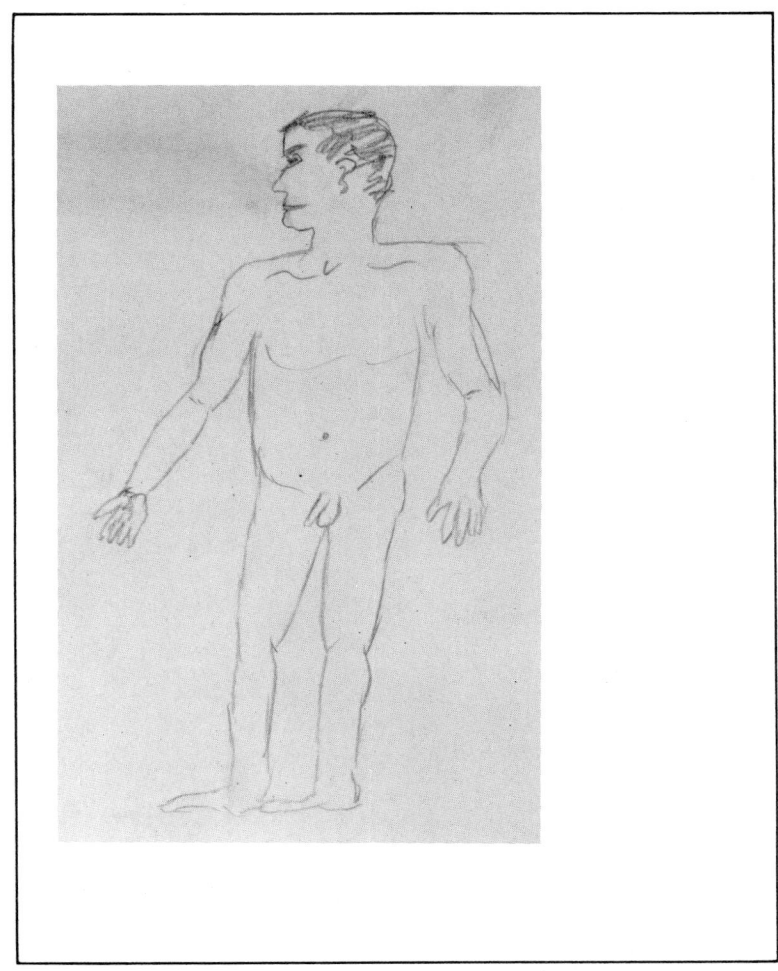

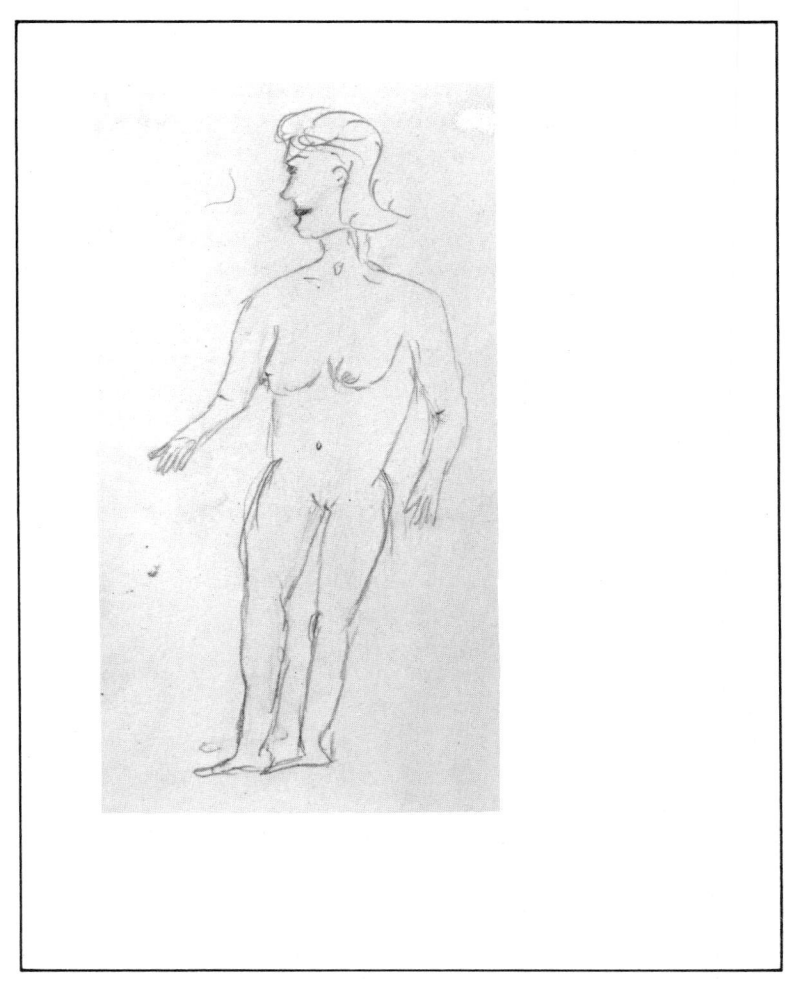

FIGURE-DRAWING CHARACTERISTICS

Structural	Male Female Both		Structural	Male	Female	Structural and Graphic	Male Female Both		Graphic, Global and Height	Male	Female	Body Proportions	Male	Female
Type	0		Omission of Appendages	0	0	Upper and Lower Halves	1	1	Hair Shading	3	3	Head	10	09
Sex Sequence	0		Position of Both Arms	1	1	Four Quarters	4	4	Nudity and Transparency	0	0	Neck	08	08
Posture	1	1	Position of Right Arm	2	3	Relative Size	0		Form	1	1	Shoulders	09	
Perspective	5	6	Position of Left Arm	5	5	Constant Line Pressure	0	0	Detailing	3	3	Right Arm	07	04
Vertical Midline	0	4	Position of Legs	4	4	Variable Line Pressure	1	1	Identity and Sex	1	1	Left Arm	06	05
Bilateral Symmetry	3	0	Relation of Long Axes	1	1	Line Continuity	0	0	Sophistication	2	2	Chest	08	
Horizontal Midline	0	0	Right and Left Halves	1	1	Body Shading	3	1	Height	07	07	Girth	09	

GENERAL CHARACTERISTICS OF SUBJECT

IDENTIFICATION
No. D68
Sex M
Marital status S
Age 23 yrs. at
psychological tests

PARENTAL HISTORY
Father
C H S D O
+ - - - -
Mother
C H S D O
- - - - -

PHYSIOLOGICAL AND METABOLIC DATA

	Admission	Initial	Control	Cold pressor change	Exercise change	Smoking change
Systolic pressure	150	128	104	+07	+26	+02
Diastolic pressure	90	62	70	+02	-08	+04
Heart rate	90	104	74	+08	+33	-03

Age 23 yrs.	Height	68 in.	Ponderal index 13.18
	Weight	137 lbs.	Cholesterol 205 mg. per 100 ml.
	Overweight -07 %		Vital capacity 4.2 liters

HABIT SURVEY
Smoking habits: nonsmoker
Age begun yrs. Inhalation:
Habits of nervous tension: 5, 6, 11

STRONG VOCATIONAL INTEREST TEST

Occupation	Artist	Psychologist	Architect	Physician	Osteopath	Dentist	Veterinarian	Mathematician	Physicist	Engineer	Chemist	Production Manager
Standard Score	39	57	36	60	50	37	23	23	18	16	36	21

Occupation	Farmer	Aviator	Carpenter	Printer	Math.-Sci. Teacher	Ind. Arts Teacher	Voc. Agric. Teacher	Policeman	Forest Serv. Man	Y.M.C.A. Phys. Dir.	Personnel Director	Public Administrator
Standard Score	20	25	04	42	37	08	25	24	20	49	44	55

Occupation	Y.M.C.A. Secretary	Soc. Sci. H.S. Teacher	City Sch. Sup't.	Social Worker	Minister	Musician Performer	C.P.A.	Senior C.P.A.	Accountant	Office Man	Purchasing Agent	Banker
Standard Score	47	51	41	62	63	61	27	35	12	29	11	14

Occupation	Mortician	Pharmacist	Sales Manager	Real Est. Manager	Life Ins. Salesman	Advertising Man	Lawyer	Author-Journalist	President Mfg. Co.	Interest Maturity	Occupational Level	Masculinity-Femininity
Standard Score	32	31	28	28	35	46	47	44	27	61	57	29

FIGURE-DRAWING CHARACTERISTICS

Structural	Male Female Both	Structural	Male	Female	Structural and Graphic	Male Female Both		Graphic, Global and Height	Male	Female	Body Proportions	Male	Female
Type	0	Omission of Appendages	7	0	Upper and Lower Halves	0	1	Hair Shading	1	3	Head	09	07
Sex Sequence	0	Position of Both Arms	1	0	Four Quarters	4	4	Nudity and Transparency	7	7	Neck	10	05
Posture	1　1	Position of Right Arm	5	0	Relative Size	0		Form	1	3	Shoulders	10	05
Perspective	0　0	Position of Left Arm	0	0	Constant Line Pressure	0	1	Detailing	1	1	Right Arm		04
Vertical Midline	3　0	Position of Legs	6	4	Variable Line Pressure	1	0	Identity and Sex	1	1	Left Arm	08	02
Bilateral Symmetry	3　3	Relation of Long Axes	1	1	Line Continuity	0	0	Sophistication	2	2	Chest	07	05
Horizontal Midline	4　4	Right and Left Halves	1	1	Body Shading	7	7	Height	07	04	Girth	09	05

GENERAL CHARACTERISTICS OF SUBJECT

IDENTIFICATION
No.　E02
Sex　M
Marital status　S
Age　22 yrs. at psychological tests

PARENTAL HISTORY				
Father				
C	H	S	D	O
+	+	-	-	+
Mother				
C	H	S	D	O
-	-	-	-	-

PHYSIOLOGICAL AND METABOLIC DATA

	Admission	Initial	Control	Cold pressor change	Exercise change	Smoking change
Systolic pressure	120	100	104	+16	+26	00
Diastolic pressure	62	65	62	+16	-06	-02
Heart rate	72	64	62	+12	+09	-01

Age 22 yrs.	Height	71	in.	Ponderal index	13.34	
	Weight	151	lbs.	Cholesterol	184	mg. per 100 ml.
	Overweight	-04	%	Vital capacity	4.8	liters

HABIT SURVEY
Smoking habits:　nonsmoker
Age begun　yrs.　Inhalation:
Habits of nervous tension:　5, 6, 9

STRONG VOCATIONAL INTEREST TEST

Occupation	Artist	Psychologist	Architect	Physician	Osteopath	Dentist	Veterinarian	Mathematician	Physicist	Engineer	Chemist	Production Manager
Standard Score	43	37	43	37	24	30	07	47	42	39	46	22

Occupation	Farmer	Aviator	Carpenter	Printer	Math.-Sci. Teacher	Ind. Arts Teacher	Voc. Agric. Teacher	Policeman	Forest Serv. Man	Y.M.C.A. Phys. Dir.	Personnel Director	Public Administrator
Standard Score	30	42	19	39	27	13	17	19	12	05	18	19

Occupation	Y.M.C.A. Secretary	Soc. Sci. H.S. Teacher	City Sch. Sup't.	Social Worker	Minister	Musician Performer	C.P.A.	Senior C.P.A.	Accountant	Office Man	Purchasing Agent	Banker
Standard Score	05	17	11	19	64	43	35	30	22	20	24	18

Occupation	Mortician	Pharmacist	Sales Manager	Real Est. Manager	Life Ins. Salesman	Advertising Man	Lawyer	Author-Journalist	President Mfg. Co.	Interest Maturity	Occupational Level	Masculinity-Femininity
Standard Score	15	20	29	39	24	45	36	45	27	44	58	47

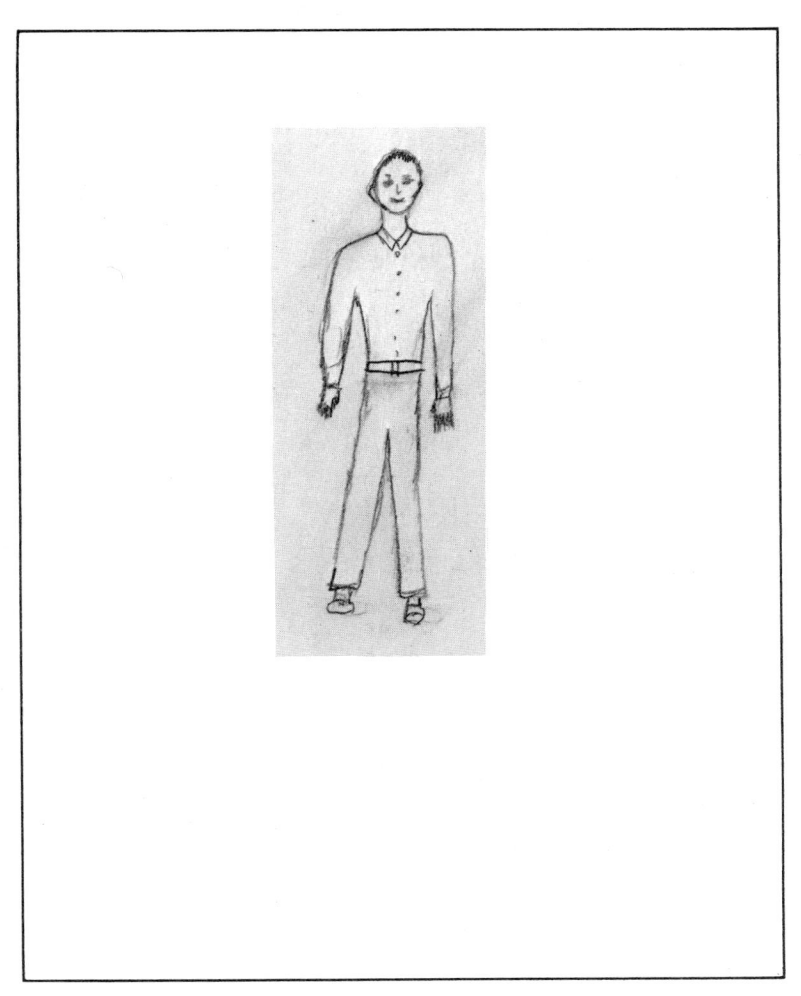

FIGURE-DRAWING CHARACTERISTICS

Structural	Male	Female	Structural	Male	Female	Structural and Graphic	Male	Female	Graphic, Global and Height	Male	Female	Body Proportions	Male	Female
	Both						Both							
Type	0		Omission of Appendages	0	0	Upper and Lower Halves	1	1	Hair Shading	1	3	Head	05	07
Sex Sequence	0		Position of Both Arms	0	4	Four Quarters	4	4	Nudity and Transparency	7	0	Neck	07	04
Posture	1	1	Position of Right Arm	0	7	Relative Size	4		Form	1	1	Shoulders	04	
Perspective	0	2	Position of Left Arm	0	0	Constant Line Pressure	3	0	Detailing	1	1	Right Arm	04	
Vertical Midline	3	4	Position of Legs	5	1	Variable Line Pressure	0	5	Identity and Sex	1	1	Left Arm	04	04
Bilateral Symmetry	3	0	Relation of Long Axes	1	1	Line Continuity	0	0	Sophistication	2	2	Chest	03	04
Horizontal Midline	4	0	Right and Left Halves	0	0	Body Shading	0	1	Height	05	05	Girth	03	03

GENERAL CHARACTERISTICS OF SUBJECT

IDENTIFICATION

No. E04

Sex M

Marital status S

Age 22 yrs. at

psychological tests

PARENTAL HISTORY

Father

C H S D O

+ – – – –

Mother

C H S D O

– – – – +

PHYSIOLOGICAL AND METABOLIC DATA

	Admission	Initial	Control	Cold pressor change	Exercise change	Smoking change
Systolic pressure	90	110	100	+10	+50	
Diastolic pressure	60	62	68	+16	–18	
Heart rate	72	72	62	00	+32	

Age 22 yrs.   Height 70 in.   Ponderal index 13.31

Weight 146 lbs.   Cholesterol 210 mg. per 100 ml.

Overweight –05 %   Vital capacity 4.3 liters

HABIT SURVEY

Smoking habits: occasional smoker

Age begun   yrs.   Inhalation:

Habits of nervous tension: 5, 9, 11, 19, 25

STRONG VOCATIONAL INTEREST TEST

Occupation	Artist	Psychologist	Architect	Physician	Osteopath	Dentist	Veterinarian	Mathematician	Physicist	Engineer	Chemist	Production Manager
Standard Score	48	56	51	65	46	46	19	41	48	50	53	29

Occupation	Farmer	Aviator	Carpenter	Printer	Math.-Sci. Teacher	Ind. Arts Teacher	Voc. Agric. Teacher	Policeman	Forest Serv. Man	Y.M.C.A. Phys. Dir.	Personnel Director	Public Administrator
Standard Score	45	58	35	51	47	33	31	34	44	32	36	45

Occupation	Y.M.C.A. Secretary	Soc. Sci. H.S. Teacher	City Sch. Sup't.	Social Worker	Minister	Musician Performer	C.P.A.	Senior C.P.A.	Accountant	Office Man	Purchasing Agent	Banker
Standard Score	21	29	25	41	64	67	22	38	14	18	09	03

Occupation	Mortician	Pharmacist	Sales Manager	Real Est. Manager	Life Ins. Salesman	Advertising Man	Lawyer	Author-Journalist	President Mfg. Co.	Interest Maturity	Occupational Level	Masculinity-Femininity
Standard Score	07	20	09	24	14	33	38	44	24	52	49	51

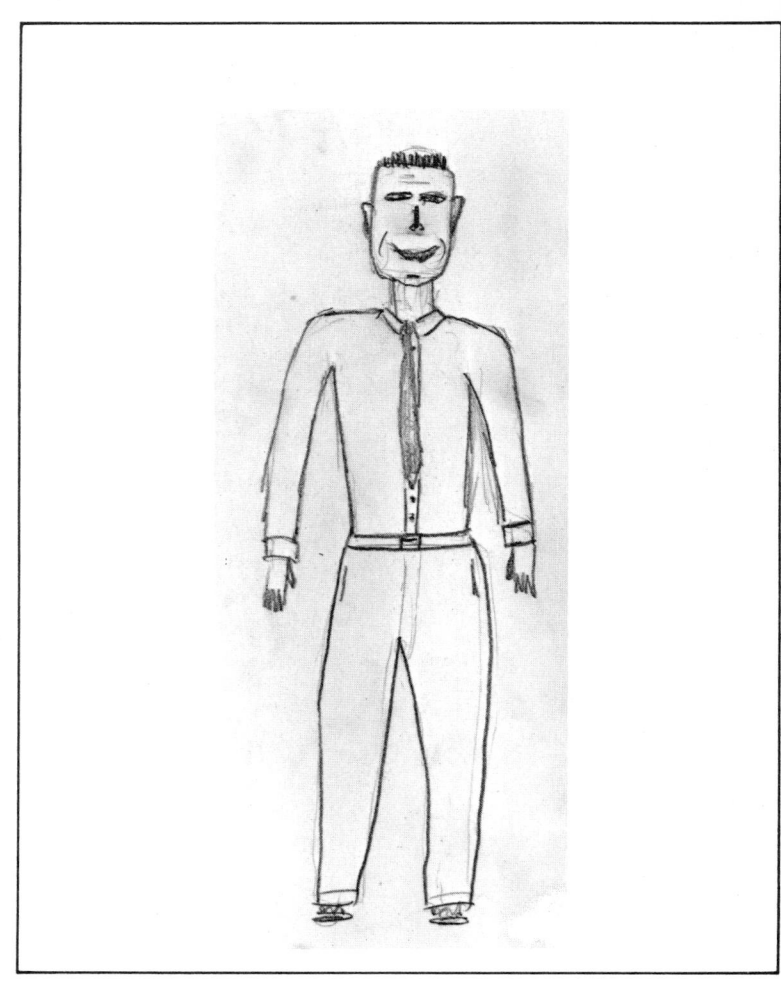

FIGURE-DRAWING CHARACTERISTICS

Structural	Male	Female	Structural	Male	Female	Structural and Graphic	Male	Female	Graphic, Global and Height	Male	Female	Body Proportions	Male	Female
	Both						Both							
Type	0		Omission of Appendages	0	0	Upper and Lower Halves	3	0	Hair Shading	3	3	Head	10	09
Sex Sequence	1		Position of Both Arms	0	2	Four Quarters	4	4	Nudity and Transparency	7	7	Neck	12	10
Posture	1	1	Position of Right Arm	0	4	Relative Size	0		Form	1	1	Shoulders	08	
Perspective	0	2	Position of Left Arm	0	7	Constant Line Pressure	5	3	Detailing	1	1	Right Arm	06	06
Vertical Midline	3	4	Position of Legs	5	1	Variable Line Pressure	0	0	Identity and Sex	1	1	Left Arm	06	
Bilateral Symmetry	3	0	Relation of Long Axes	1	1	Line Continuity	2	2	Sophistication	2	2	Chest	06	05
Horizontal Midline	4	4	Right and Left Halves	3	0	Body Shading	4	6	Height	08	07	Girth	07	07

GENERAL CHARACTERISTICS OF SUBJECT

IDENTIFICATION
No. E62
Sex M
Marital status M
Age 22 yrs. at
psychological tests

PARENTAL HISTORY					
Father					
C	H	S	D	O	
+	+	-	-	+	
Mother					
C	H	S	D	O	
-	-	-	-	-	

PHYSIOLOGICAL AND METABOLIC DATA

	Admission	Initial	Control	Cold pressor change	Exercise change	Smoking change
Systolic pressure	120	110	118	-02	+21	+01
Diastolic pressure	80	60	70	+30	-18	-10
Heart rate	76	64	54	-04	+32	+11

Age 22 yrs.	Height	69	in.	Ponderal index	12.99	
	Weight	150	lbs.	Cholesterol	200	mg. per 100 ml.
	Overweight	00	%	Vital capacity	4.9	liters

HABIT SURVEY

Smoking habits: heavy cigarette smoker

Age begun 13 yrs.　　Inhalation: yes

Habits of nervous tension: 5, 21, 24

STRONG VOCATIONAL INTEREST TEST

Occupation	Artist	Psychologist	Architect	Physician	Osteopath	Dentist	Veterinarian	Mathematician	Physicist	Engineer	Chemist	Production Manager
Standard Score	24	41	25	57	49	38	27	21	17	27	30	32

Occupation	Farmer	Aviator	Carpenter	Printer	Math.-Sci. Teacher	Ind. Arts Teacher	Voc. Agric. Teacher	Policeman	Forest Serv. Man	Y.M.C.A. Phys. Dir.	Personnel Director	Public Administrator
Standard Score	30	40	15	33	43	20	34	29	28	44	43	46

Occupation	Y.M.C.A. Secretary	Soc. Sci. H.S. Teacher	City Sch. Sup't.	Social Worker	Minister	Musician Performer	C.P.A.	Senior C.P.A.	Accountant	Office Man	Purchasing Agent	Banker
Standard Score	29	44	35	44	64	46	32	42	25	34	25	27

Occupation	Mortician	Pharmacist	Sales Manager	Real Est. Manager	Life Ins. Salesman	Advertising Man	Lawyer	Author-Journalist	President Mfg. Co.	Interest Maturity	Occupational Level	Masculinity-Femininity
Standard Score	28	30	33	34	33	34	38	29	30	57	57	49

Plate 570　　　　MODERATELY SOPHISTICATED DRAWINGS　　　　617

FIGURE-DRAWING CHARACTERISTICS

Structural	Male Female Both	Structural	Male	Female	Structural and Graphic	Male Female Both		Graphic, Global and Height	Male	Female	Body Proportions	Male	Female
Type	0	Omission of Appendages	0	7	Upper and Lower Halves	1	1	Hair Shading	3	3	Head	12	11
Sex Sequence	2	Position of Both Arms	4	4	Four Quarters	4	4	Nudity and Transparency	7	2	Neck	07	08
Posture	1　1	Position of Right Arm	7	7	Relative Size	2		Form	3	1	Shoulders		
Perspective	2　2	Position of Left Arm	4	5	Constant Line Pressure	0	0	Detailing	3	1	Right Arm		
Vertical Midline	4　4	Position of Legs	1	1	Variable Line Pressure	1	1	Identity and Sex	1	1	Left Arm	06	
Bilateral Symmetry	0　0	Relation of Long Axes	1	1	Line Continuity	0	0	Sophistication	2	2	Chest	07	06
Horizontal Midline	0　4	Right and Left Halves	9	9	Body Shading	4	5	Height	06	06	Girth	09	07

GENERAL CHARACTERISTICS OF SUBJECT

IDENTIFICATION
No. 207
Sex M
Marital status S
Age 23 yrs. at
psychological tests

PARENTAL HISTORY
Father
C　H　S　D　O
–　–　(+)　–　?
Mother
C　H　S　D　O
+　–　–　–　?

PHYSIOLOGICAL AND METABOLIC DATA

	Admission	Initial	Control	Cold pressor change	Exercise change	Smoking change
Systolic pressure	132	130	118	+06	+66	
Diastolic pressure	60	64	70	+16	00	
Heart rate	72	86	70	+08	+24	

Age 20 yrs.	Height	70 in.	Ponderal index 11.72
	Weight	213 lbs.	Cholesterol 252 mg. per 100 ml.
	Overweight +40 %		Vital capacity 3.4 liters

HABIT SURVEY
Smoking habits: heavy cigarette smoker
Age begun 17 yrs.　　Inhalation: yes
Habits of nervous tension: 6, 8, 10, 16

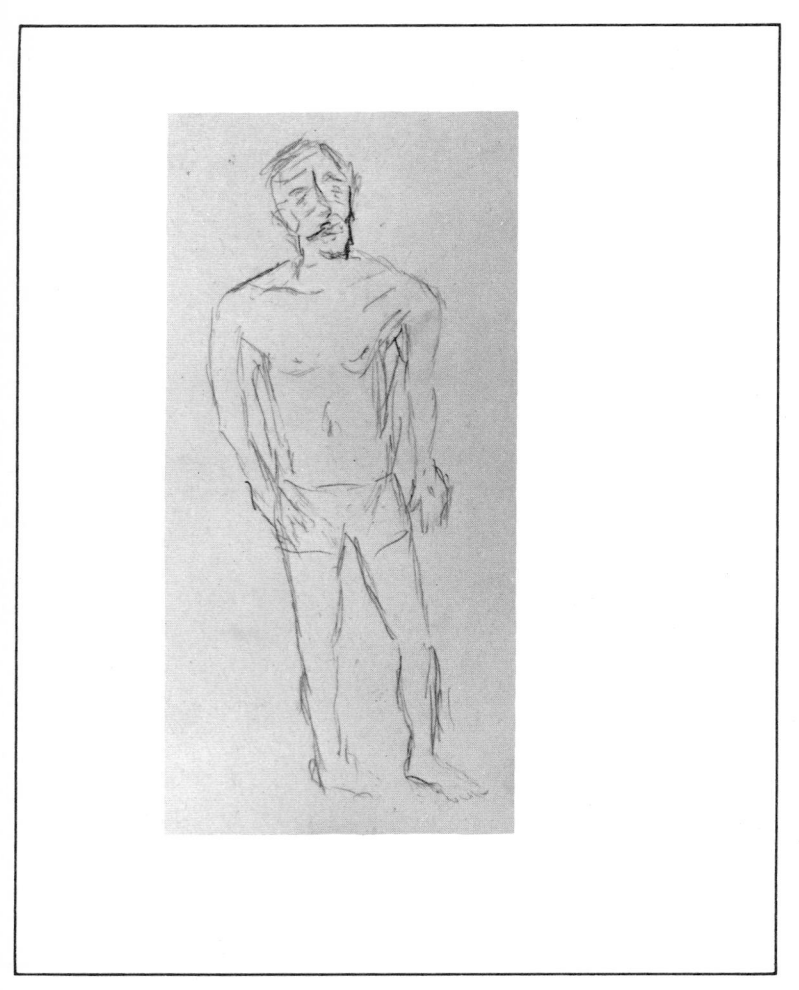

FIGURE-DRAWING CHARACTERISTICS

Structural	Male Female Both		Structural	Male	Female	Structural and Graphic	Male Female Both		Graphic, Global and Height	Male	Female	Body Proportions	Male	Female
Type	0		Omission of Appendages	0	8	Upper and Lower Halves	1	7	Hair Shading	3	3	Head	09	13
Sex Sequence	0		Position of Both Arms	1	0	Four Quarters	4	4	Nudity and Transparency	3	0	Neck	05	06
Posture	1	1	Position of Right Arm	5	5	Relative Size	4		Form	3	3	Shoulders	09	09
Perspective	0	9	Position of Left Arm	0	5	Constant Line Pressure	0	0	Detailing	3	3	Right Arm	06	08
Vertical Midline	0	0	Position of Legs	6	5	Variable Line Pressure	1	1	Identity and Sex	1	1	Left Arm	06	08
Bilateral Symmetry	3	3	Relation of Long Axes	1	1	Line Continuity	0	0	Sophistication	2	2	Chest	06	08
Horizontal Midline	4	0	Right and Left Halves	1	1	Body Shading	3	3	Height	07	09	Girth	07	09

GENERAL CHARACTERISTICS OF SUBJECT

IDENTIFICATION
No. 569
Sex M
Marital status M
Age 24 yrs. at
psychological tests

PARENTAL HISTORY				
Father				
C	H	S	D	O
-	-	-	-	-
Mother				
C	H	S	D	O
+	+	-	-	-

PHYSIOLOGICAL AND METABOLIC DATA

	Admission	Initial	Control	Cold pressor change	Exercise change	Smoking change
Systolic pressure	110	110	110	+10	+50	00
Diastolic pressure	70	70	70	+10	00	00
Heart rate	80	64	69	00	+24	+04

	Height	72 in.	Ponderal index 14.18
Age 22 yrs.	Weight	131 lbs.	Cholesterol 230 mg. per 100 ml.
	Overweight −20 %		Vital capacity 3.2 liters

HABIT SURVEY

Smoking habits: mixed smoker

  Age begun 17 yrs.   Inhalation: yes

Habits of nervous tension: 3, 5, 6, 9, 11, 16, 18, 19, 22

FIGURE-DRAWING CHARACTERISTICS

Structural	Male Female Both		Structural	Male	Female	Structural and Graphic	Male Female Both		Graphic, Global and Height	Male	Female	Body Proportions	Male	Female
Type	0		Omission of Appendages	0	0	Upper and Lower Halves	1	1	Hair Shading	7	7	Head	06	07
Sex Sequence	0		Position of Both Arms	4	4	Four Quarters	4	4	Nudity and Transparency	7	7	Neck	05	08
Posture	1	1	Position of Right Arm	7	7	Relative Size	4		Form	3	3	Shoulders		
Perspective	2	2	Position of Left Arm	4	3	Constant Line Pressure	4	5	Detailing	3	3	Right Arm		
Vertical Midline	4	4	Position of Legs	1	1	Variable Line Pressure	0	0	Identity and Sex	1	1	Left Arm	02	02
Bilateral Symmetry	0	0	Relation of Long Axes	1	1	Line Continuity	3	3	Sophistication	2	2	Chest	03	04
Horizontal Midline	4	4	Right and Left Halves	4	4	Body Shading	0	0	Height	04	04	Girth	04	03

GENERAL CHARACTERISTICS OF SUBJECT

IDENTIFICATION

No. F26

Sex M

Marital status M

Age 25 yrs. at

psychological tests

PARENTAL HISTORY

Father

C   H   S   D   O

−   +   −   −   −

Mother

C   H   S   D   O

+   ?   −   −   −

PHYSIOLOGICAL AND METABOLIC DATA

	Admission	Initial	Control	Cold pressor change	Exercise change	Smoking change
Systolic pressure	125	130	116	+04	+36	+08
Diastolic pressure	80	82	80	+10	+10	+02
Heart rate	84	88	79	+04	+11	−03

Age 22 yrs.

Height   73   in.

Weight   175   lbs.

Overweight +04 %

Ponderal index 13.06

Cholesterol   214   mg. per 100 ml.

Vital capacity   liters

HABIT SURVEY

Smoking habits: nonsmoker

Age begun   yrs.   Inhalation:

Habits of nervous tension: 4, 5, 8, 11, 16

STRONG VOCATIONAL INTEREST TEST

Occupation	Artist	Psychologist	Architect	Physician	Osteopath	Dentist	Veterinarian	Mathematician	Physicist	Engineer	Chemist	Production Manager
Standard Score	38	50	45	58	49	36	25	27	27	30	34	30

Occupation	Farmer	Aviator	Carpenter	Printer	Math.-Sci. Teacher	Ind. Arts Teacher	Voc. Agric. Teacher	Policeman	Forest Serv. Man	Y.M.C.A. Phys. Dir.	Personnel Director	Public Administrator
Standard Score	25	28	18	29	33	22	25	26	32	44	50	54

Occupation	Y.M.C.A. Secretary	Soc. Sci. H.S. Teacher	City Sch. Sup't.	Social Worker	Minister	Musician Performer	C.P.A.	Senior C.P.A.	Accountant	Office Man	Purchasing Agent	Banker
Standard Score	38	37	44	52	58	53	24	33	13	18	08	13

Occupation	Mortician	Pharmacist	Sales Manager	Real Est. Manager	Life Ins. Salesman	Advertising Man	Lawyer	Author-Journalist	President Mfg. Co.	Interest Maturity	Occupational Level	Masculinity-Femininity
Standard Score	29	27	25	22	31	38	38	39	34	61	60	32

FIGURE-DRAWING CHARACTERISTICS

Structural	Male Female Both	Structural	Male	Female	Structural and Graphic	Male Female Both		Graphic, Global and Height	Male	Female	Body Proportions	Male	Female
Type	0	Omission of Appendages	7	7	Upper and Lower Halves	0	1	Hair Shading	3	2	Head	06	06
Sex Sequence	0	Position of Both Arms	0	0	Four Quarters	4	4	Nudity and Transparency	7	7	Neck	06	06
Posture	1 1	Position of Right Arm	5	5	Relative Size	0		Form	1	1	Shoulders	07	05
Perspective	0 0	Position of Left Arm	5	5	Constant Line Pressure	0	0	Detailing	1	3	Right Arm		04
Vertical Midline	1 0	Position of Legs	4	1	Variable Line Pressure	4	4	Identity and Sex	1	1	Left Arm		
Bilateral Symmetry	3 3	Relation of Long Axes	1	1	Line Continuity	0	0	Sophistication	2	2	Chest	06	04
Horizontal Midline	4 0	Right and Left Halves	1	1	Body Shading	6	1	Height	07	05	Girth	06	04

GENERAL CHARACTERISTICS OF SUBJECT

IDENTIFICATION	PARENTAL HISTORY
No. G68	Father
Sex M	C H S D O
Marital status M	- - - - -
Age 26 yrs. at	Mother
psychological tests	C H S D O
	+ + ? ? +

PHYSIOLOGICAL AND METABOLIC DATA

	Admission	Initial	Control	Cold pressor change	Exercise change	Smoking change
Systolic pressure	130	120	110	+20	+66	-03
Diastolic pressure	60	64	68	+20	-10	-08
Heart rate	80	60	53	+18	+20	+02

Age 25 yrs.	Height 68 in.	Ponderal index 12.64
	Weight 156 lbs.	Cholesterol 167 mg. per 100 ml.
	Overweight +05 %	Vital capacity liters

HABIT SURVEY

Smoking habits: nonsmoker

   Age begun   yrs.   Inhalation:

Habits of nervous tension: 4, 5, 6, 8, 9, 16

STRONG VOCATIONAL INTEREST TEST

Occupation	Artist	Psychologist	Architect	Physician	Osteopath	Dentist	Veterinarian	Mathematician	Physicist	Engineer	Chemist	Production Manager
Standard Score	33	-10	41	63	46	44	21	35	25	32	41	26

Occupation	Farmer	Aviator	Carpenter	Printer	Math.-Sci. Teacher	Ind. Arts Teacher	Voc. Agric. Teacher	Policeman	Forest Serv. Man	Y.M.C.A. Phys. Dir.	Personnel Director	Public Administrator
Standard Score	23	31	14	40	48	20	25	28	22	36	40	42

Occupation	Y.M.C.A. Secretary	Soc. Sci. H.S. Teacher	City Sch. Sup't.	Social Worker	Minister	Musician Performer	C.P.A.	Senior C.P.A.	Accountant	Office Man	Purchasing Agent	Banker
Standard Score	30	41	42	48	59	60	33	45	31	37	25	22

Occupation	Mortician	Pharmacist	Sales Manager	Real Est. Manager	Life Ins. Salesman	Advertising Man	Lawyer	Author-Journalist	President Mfg. Co.	Interest Maturity	Occupational Level	Masculinity-Femininity
Standard Score	26	34	26	28	28	34	32	34	24	59	56	37

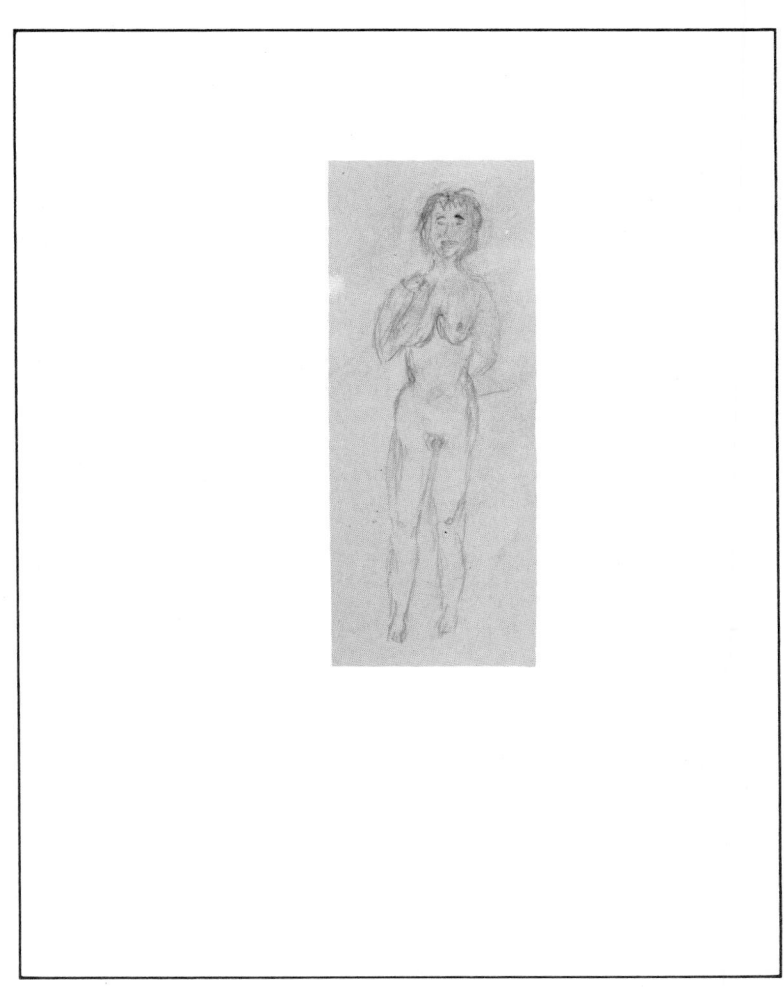

FIGURE-DRAWING CHARACTERISTICS

Structural	Male Female Both		Structural	Male	Female	Structural and Graphic	Male Female Both		Graphic, Global and Height	Male	Female	Body Proportions	Male	Female
Type	0		Omission of Appendages	0	7	Upper and Lower Halves	1	1	Hair Shading	3	3	Head	04	05
Sex Sequence	0		Position of Both Arms	4	2	Four Quarters	4	4	Nudity and Transparency	5	0	Neck		05
Posture	1	1	Position of Right Arm	7	5	Relative Size	4		Form	1	1	Shoulders		04
Perspective	2	0	Position of Left Arm	5	8	Constant Line Pressure	1	1	Detailing	3	3	Right Arm		04
Vertical Midline	4	0	Position of Legs	1	4	Variable Line Pressure	0	0	Identity and Sex	1	1	Left Arm	04	
Bilateral Symmetry	0	3	Relation of Long Axes	1	1	Line Continuity	0	0	Sophistication	2	2	Chest	05	03
Horizontal Midline	4	0	Right and Left Halves	1	3	Body Shading	0	3	Height	04	04	Girth	04	04

GENERAL CHARACTERISTICS OF SUBJECT

IDENTIFICATION
No. D42
Sex M
Marital status S
Age 23 yrs. at psychological tests

PARENTAL HISTORY					
Father					
C	H	S	D	O	
-	-	-	-	+	
Mother					
C	H	S	D	O	
+	-	-	-	-	

PHYSIOLOGICAL AND METABOLIC DATA

	Admission	Initial	Control	Cold pressor change	Exercise change	Smoking change
Systolic pressure	120	105	110	+12	+28	+06
Diastolic pressure	80	70	70	+22	00	+04
Heart rate	76	72	70	+16	+15	+09

Age 23 yrs.	Height	72	in.	Ponderal index	12.59	
	Weight	187	lbs.	Cholesterol	225	mg. per 100 ml.
	Overweight +14 %			Vital capacity	4.8	liters

HABIT SURVEY

Smoking habits: heavy cigarette smoker

Age begun 19 yrs.   Inhalation: yes

Habits of nervous tension: 4, 6, 8, 11, 16, 19

STRONG VOCATIONAL INTEREST TEST

Occupation	Artist	Psychologist	Architect	Physician	Osteopath	Dentist	Veterinarian	Mathematician	Physicist	Engineer	Chemist	Production Manager
Standard Score	46	54	47	72	64	50	30	27	25	26	35	22

Occupation	Farmer	Aviator	Carpenter	Printer	Math.-Sci. Teacher	Ind. Arts Teacher	Voc. Agric. Teacher	Policeman	Forest Serv. Man	Y.M.C.A. Phys. Dir.	Personnel Director	Public Administrator
Standard Score	26	34	09	28	34	10	20	22	27	37	40	49

Occupation	Y.M.C.A. Secretary	Soc. Sci. H.S. Teacher	City Sch. Sup't.	Social Worker	Minister	Musician Performer	C.P.A.	Senior C.P.A.	Accountant	Office Man	Purchasing Agent	Banker
Standard Score	27	38	34	51	63	58	25	29	05	16	07	08

Occupation	Mortician	Pharmacist	Sales Manager	Real Est. Manager	Life Ins. Salesman	Advertising Man	Lawyer	Author-Journalist	President Mfg. Co.	Interest Maturity	Occupational Level	Masculinity-Femininity
Standard Score	27	37	28	36	37	45	51	44	31	57	63	35

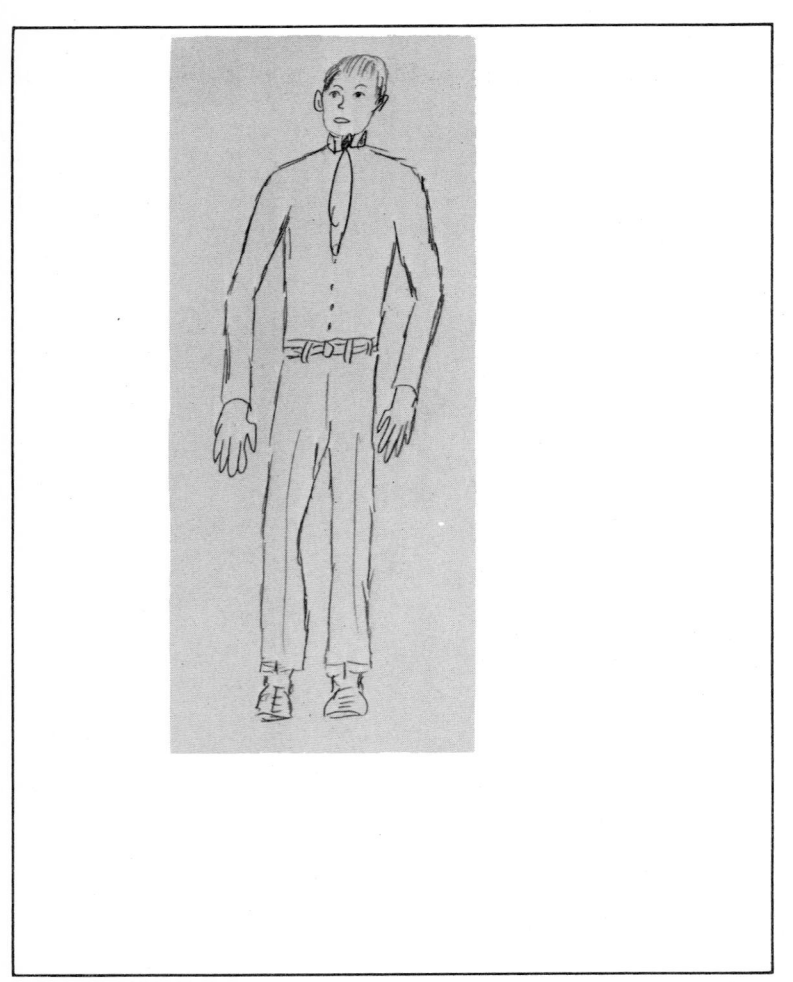

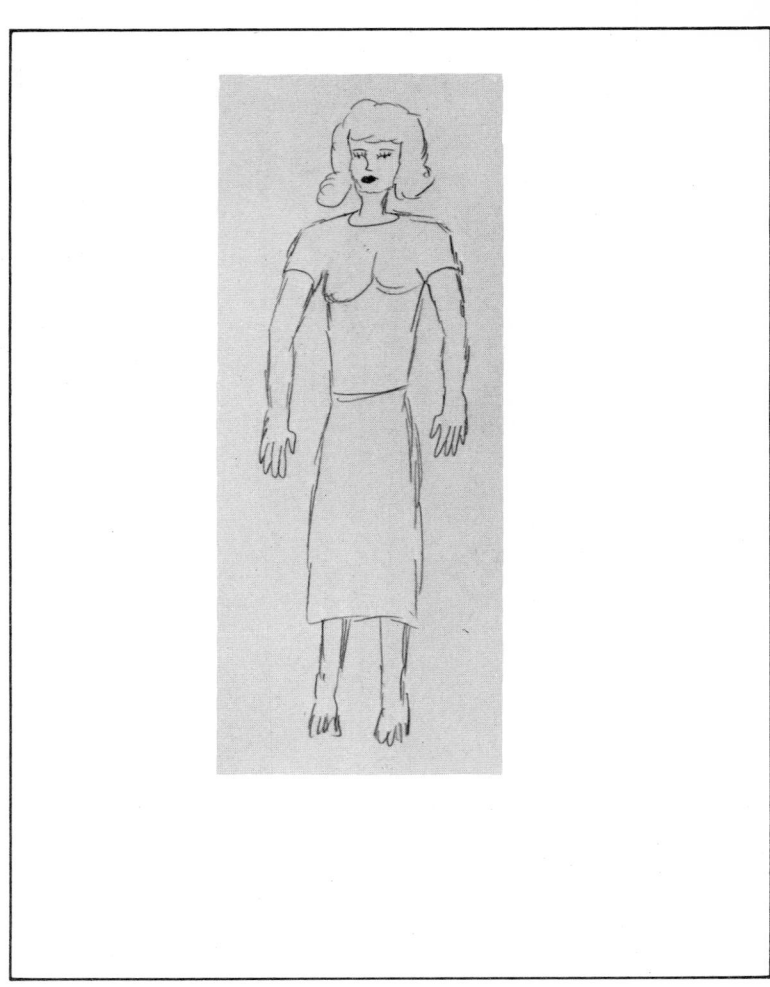

FIGURE-DRAWING CHARACTERISTICS

Structural	Male Female Both		Structural	Male	Female	Structural and Graphic	Male Female Both		Graphic, Global and Height	Male	Female	Body Proportions	Male	Female
Type	0		Omission of Appendages	0	0	Upper and Lower Halves	1	1	Hair Shading	3	5	Head	06	06
Sex Sequence	0		Position of Both Arms	0	0	Four Quarters	4	4	Nudity and Transparency	7	7	Neck	04	06
Posture	1	1	Position of Right Arm	5	0	Relative Size	1		Form	1	1	Shoulders	06	06
Perspective	0	0	Position of Left Arm	5	0	Constant Line Pressure	3	3	Detailing	1	3	Right Arm	06	06
Vertical Midline	3	0	Position of Legs	4	4	Variable Line Pressure	0	0	Identity and Sex	1	1	Left Arm	06	04
Bilateral Symmetry	3	3	Relation of Long Axes	1	1	Line Continuity	0	0	Sophistication	2	2	Chest	05	05
Horizontal Midline	4	4	Right and Left Halves	1	1	Body Shading	6	1	Height	07	06	Girth	06	05

GENERAL CHARACTERISTICS OF SUBJECT

IDENTIFICATION
No. E46
Sex M
Marital status S
Age 26 yrs. at
psychological tests

PARENTAL HISTORY				
Father				
C	H	S	D	O
-	-	-	-	-
Mother				
C	H	S	D	O
+	-	-	-	-

PHYSIOLOGICAL AND METABOLIC DATA

	Admission	Initial	Control	Cold pressor change	Exercise change	Smoking change
Systolic pressure	130	121	118	-10	+14	+28
Diastolic pressure	50	70	68	-08	-28	+24
Heart rate	76	64	56	+08	+19	+12

Age 26 yrs.	Height 69 in.	Ponderal index 12.71
	Weight 160 lbs.	Cholesterol 202 mg. per 100 ml.
	Overweight +04 %	Vital capacity 5.0 liters

HABIT SURVEY
Smoking habits: occasional smoker
Age begun 15 yrs.   Inhalation: yes
Habits of nervous tension: 4, 5, 11, 25

Plate 576   MODERATELY SOPHISTICATED DRAWINGS   623

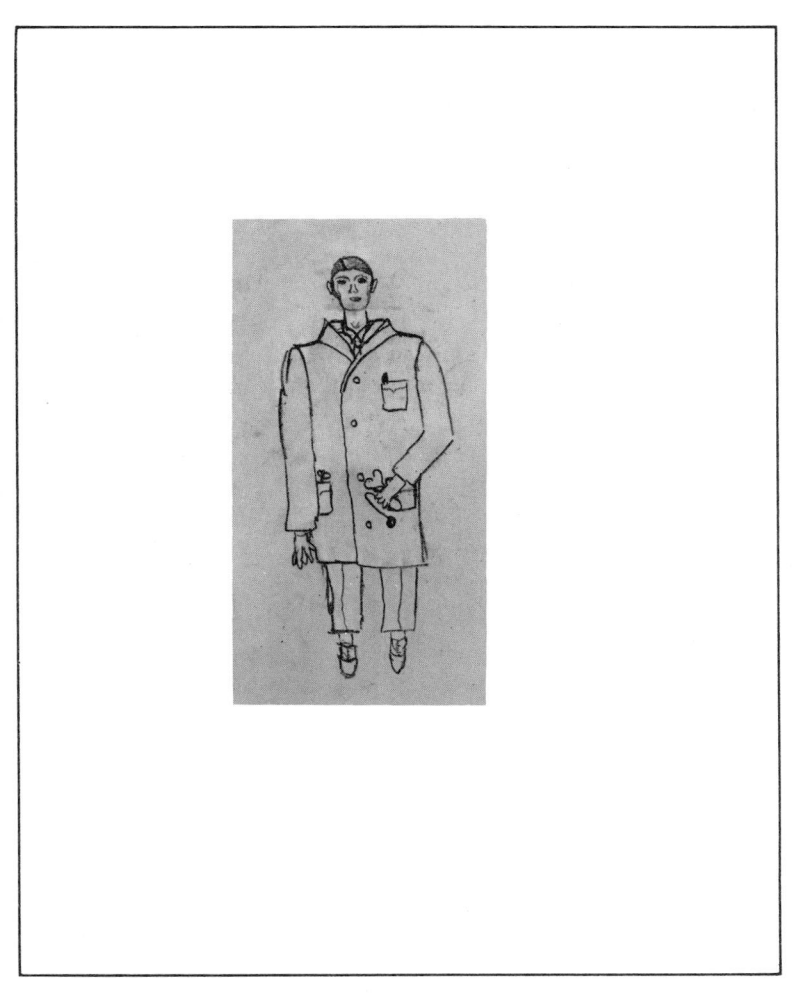

FIGURE-DRAWING CHARACTERISTICS

Structural	Male Female Both	Structural	Male	Female	Structural and Graphic	Male Female Both		Graphic, Global and Height	Male	Female	Body Proportions	Male	Female
Type	0	Omission of Appendages	0	7	Upper and Lower Halves	1	1	Hair Shading	1	1	Head	04	04
Sex Sequence	2	Position of Both Arms	1	0	Four Quarters	4	4	Nudity and Transparency	7	7	Neck	08	06
Posture	1 1	Position of Right Arm	0	5	Relative Size	0		Form	3	1	Shoulders	06	03
Perspective	0 0	Position of Left Arm	5	5	Constant Line Pressure	0	0	Detailing	3	3	Right Arm	06	02
Vertical Midline	3 0	Position of Legs	4	4	Variable Line Pressure	5	5	Identity and Sex	1	1	Left Arm	04	
Bilateral Symmetry	3 3	Relation of Long Axes	1	1	Line Continuity	2	3	Sophistication	2	2	Chest	05	03
Horizontal Midline	0 4	Right and Left Halves	1	1	Body Shading	6	3	Height	04	03	Girth	07	02

GENERAL CHARACTERISTICS OF SUBJECT

IDENTIFICATION
No. 237
Sex M
Marital status S
Age 28 yrs. at
psychological tests

PARENTAL HISTORY
Father
C   H   S   D   O
(+)   -   -   -   -
Mother
C   H   S   D   O
-    +   -   -   -

PHYSIOLOGICAL AND METABOLIC DATA

	Admission	Initial	Control	Cold pressor change	Exercise change	Smoking change
Systolic pressure	120	116	114	+05	+36	
Diastolic pressure	80	76	78	+08	+06	
Heart rate	72	68	58	-04	+23	

Age 24 yrs.	Height 75 in.	Ponderal index 13.67
	Weight 165 lbs.	Cholesterol 240 mg. per 100 ml.
	Overweight -09 %	Vital capacity liters

HABIT SURVEY
Smoking habits: nonsmoker
Age begun   yrs.   Inhalation:
Habits of nervous tension: 4, 5, 9, 11,
23

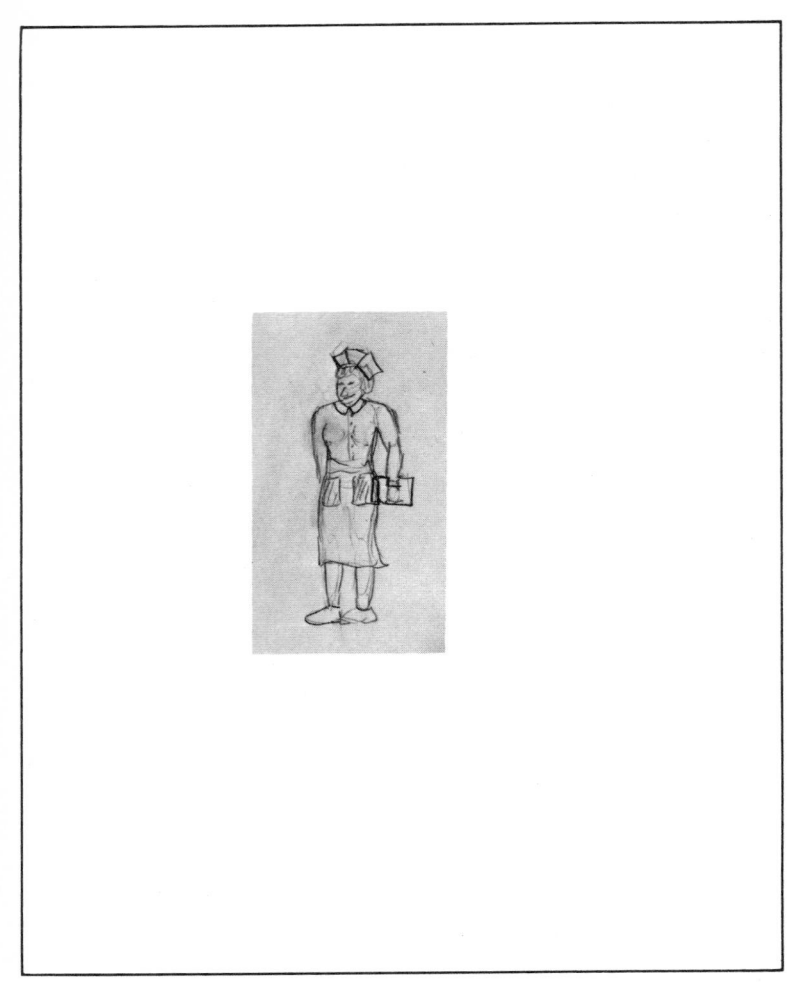

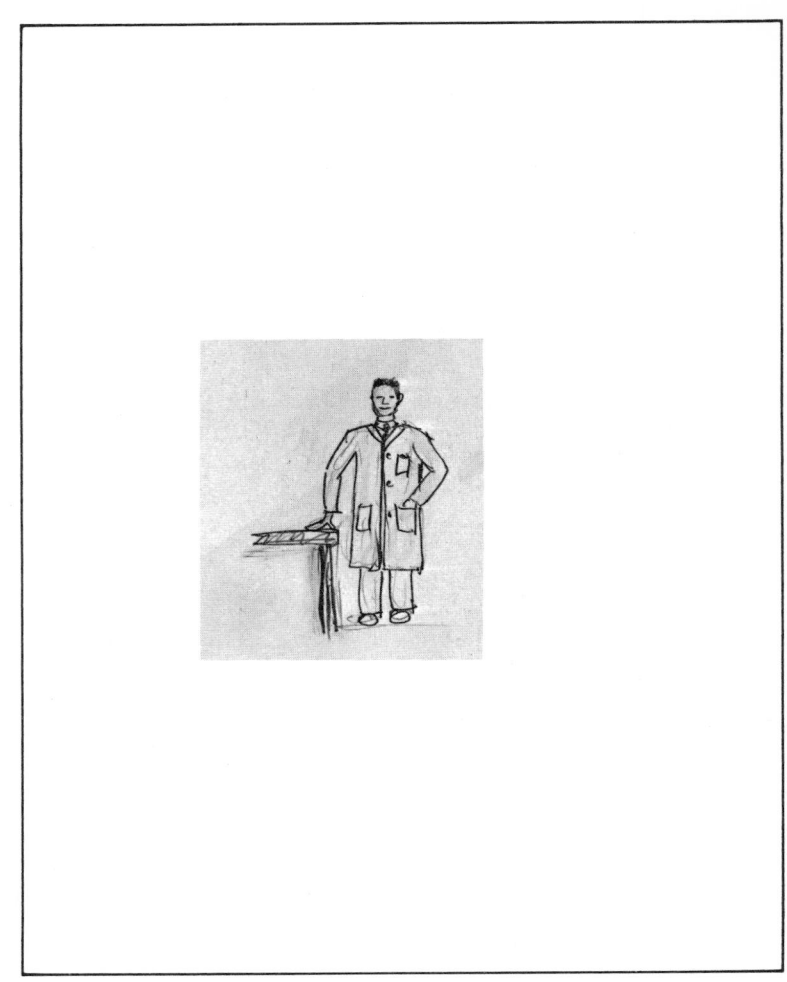

FIGURE-DRAWING CHARACTERISTICS

Structural	Male Female Both	Structural	Male	Female	Structural and Graphic	Male Female Both		Graphic, Global and Height	Male	Female	Body Proportions	Male	Female
Type	0	Omission of Appendages	7	7	Upper and Lower Halves	0	1	Hair Shading	3	3	Head	03	03
Sex Sequence	1	Position of Both Arms	1	4	Four Quarters	4	4	Nudity and Transparency	6	6	Neck	02	00
Posture	1 1	Position of Right Arm	2	7	Relative Size	4		Form	3	3	Shoulders	03	
Perspective	0 1	Position of Left Arm	5	0	Constant Line Pressure	5	0	Detailing	3	3	Right Arm	02	
Vertical Midline	3 7	Position of Legs	4	4	Variable Line Pressure	0	5	Identity and Sex	1	1	Left Arm		02
Bilateral Symmetry	3 0	Relation of Long Axes	1	1	Line Continuity	2	0	Sophistication	2	2	Chest	03	
Horizontal Midline	0 2	Right and Left Halves	1	1	Body Shading	4	3	Height	02	02	Girth	04	

GENERAL CHARACTERISTICS OF SUBJECT

IDENTIFICATION

No. 378

Sex M

Marital status S

Age 24 yrs. at
psychological tests

PARENTAL HISTORY

Father

C	H	S	D	O
(+)	-	-	-	?

Mother

C	H	S	D	O
-	+	-	(?)	+

PHYSIOLOGICAL AND METABOLIC DATA

	Admission	Initial	Control	Cold pressor change	Exercise change	Smoking change
Systolic pressure	130	118	108	00	+38	
Diastolic pressure	75	68	64	+06	-02	
Heart rate	72	66	63	00	+24	

Age 23 yrs.

Height   72 in.   Ponderal index 13.07

Weight   167 lbs.   Cholesterol   230   mg. per 100 ml.

Overweight +02 %   Vital capacity   5.1   liters

HABIT SURVEY

Smoking habits: pipe smoker

Age begun 18 yrs.   Inhalation: yes

Habits of nervous tension: 5, 6, 9

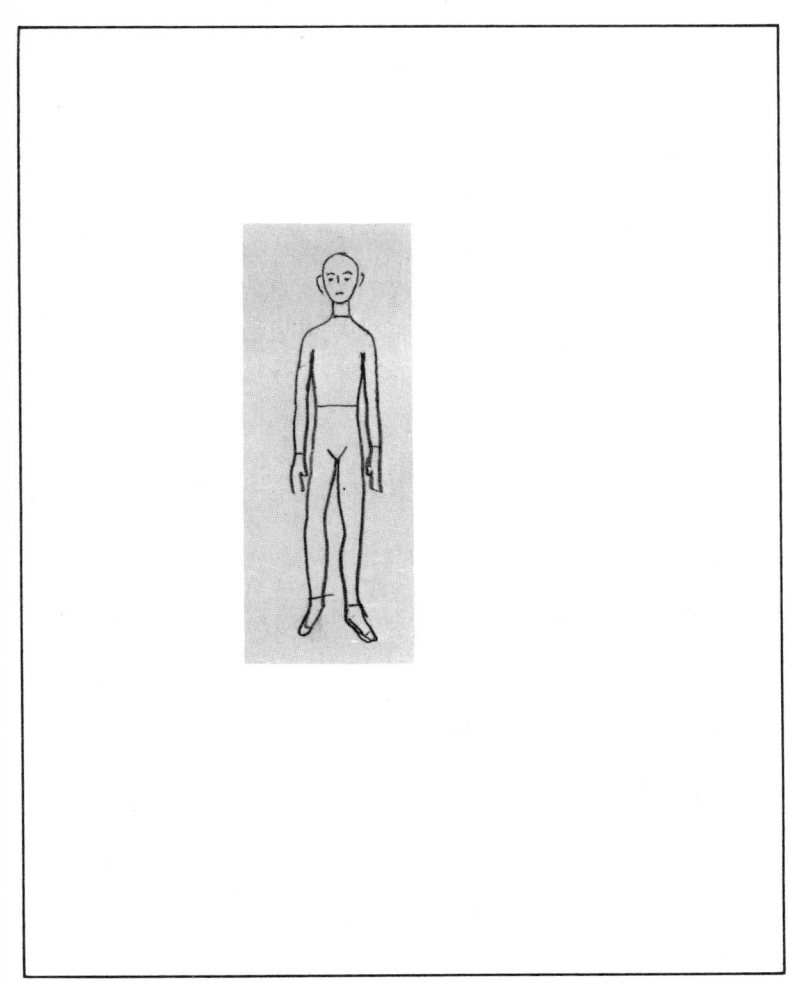

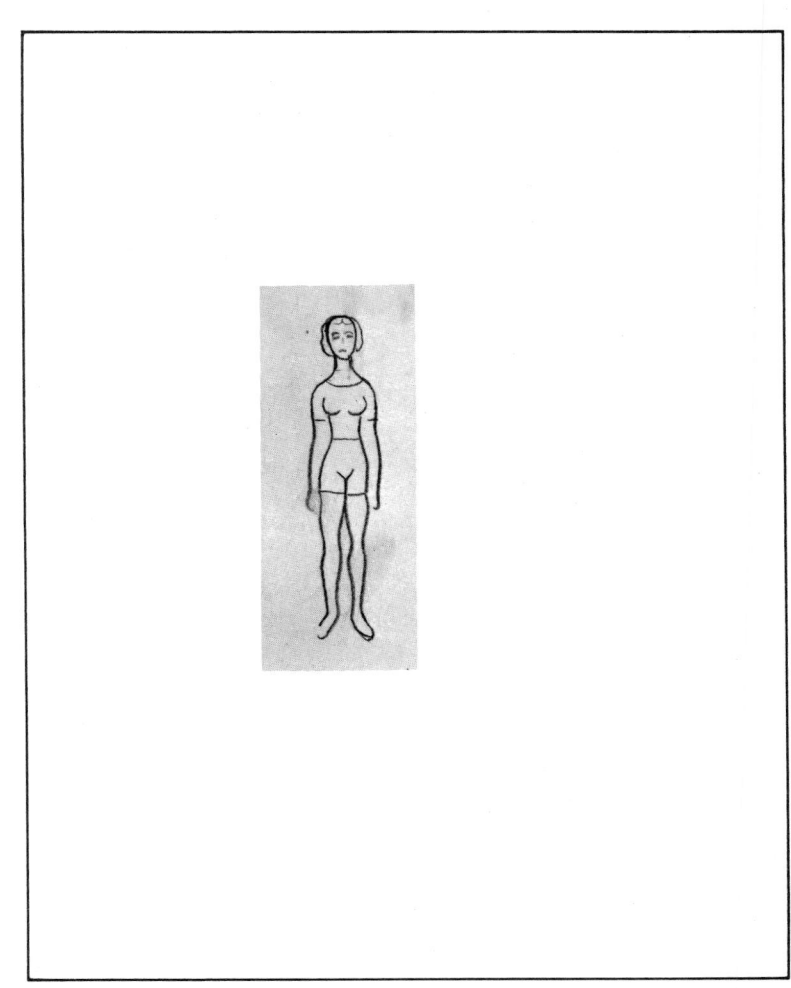

FIGURE-DRAWING CHARACTERISTICS

Structural	Male Female		Structural	Male	Female	Structural and Graphic	Male	Female	Graphic, Global and Height	Male	Female	Body Proportions	Male	Female
	Both						Both							
Type	0		Omission of Appendages	0	0	Upper and Lower Halves	1	1	Hair Shading	0	5	Head	04	03
Sex Sequence	0		Position of Both Arms	0	0	Four Quarters	4	4	Nudity and Transparency	2	2	Neck	04	04
Posture	1	1	Position of Right Arm	0	0	Relative Size	0		Form	1	1	Shoulders	02	02
Perspective	0	0	Position of Left Arm	0	0	Constant Line Pressure	5	5	Detailing	3	3	Right Arm	04	02
Vertical Midline	0	0	Position of Legs	4	4	Variable Line Pressure	0	0	Identity and Sex	3	1	Left Arm	04	02
Bilateral Symmetry	5	5	Relation of Long Axes	1	1	Line Continuity	4	4	Sophistication	2	2	Chest	02	02
Horizontal Midline	4	4	Right and Left Halves	2	2	Body Shading	2	3	Height	04	03	Girth	02	02

GENERAL CHARACTERISTICS OF SUBJECT

IDENTIFICATION
No. 478
Sex M
Marital status S
Age 26 yrs. at
psychological tests

PARENTAL HISTORY
Father
C H S D O
(+) - - - ?
Mother
C H S D O
- - - - -

PHYSIOLOGICAL AND METABOLIC DATA

	Admission	Initial	Control	Cold pressor change	Exercise change	Smoking change
Systolic pressure	130	122	108	+08	+34	-04
Diastolic pressure	88	72	68	+12	+02	+12
Heart rate	100	114	103	00	+04	+04

Age 22 yrs.	Height 66 in.	Ponderal index 12.59
	Weight 144 lbs.	Cholesterol 200 mg. per 100 ml.
	Overweight +04 %	Vital capacity 4.0 liters

HABIT SURVEY

Smoking habits: light cigarette smoker

  Age begun 21 yrs.   Inhalation: no

Habits of nervous tension: 1, 4, 5, 9, 11,

  14, 17, 21, 22

FIGURE-DRAWING CHARACTERISTICS

Structural	Male Female Both	Structural	Male	Female	Structural and Graphic	Male Female Both		Graphic, Global and Height	Male	Female	Body Proportions	Male	Female
Type	0	Omission of Appendages	7	0	Upper and Lower Halves	3	3	Hair Shading	5	3	Head	09	04
Sex Sequence	0	Position of Both Arms	4	4	Four Quarters	4	4	Nudity and Transparency	7	2	Neck	07	01
Posture	1 9	Position of Right Arm	7	7	Relative Size	0		Form	1	1	Shoulders		
Perspective	2 1	Position of Left Arm	5	2	Constant Line Pressure	1	0	Detailing	1	1	Right Arm		
Vertical Midline	7 4	Position of Legs	1	9	Variable Line Pressure	0	3	Identity and Sex	1	1	Left Arm		04
Bilateral Symmetry	0 0	Relation of Long Axes	1	0	Line Continuity	0	0	Sophistication	2	2	Chest	07	
Horizontal Midline	6 4	Right and Left Halves	2	1	Body Shading	4	0	Height	07		Girth	07	

GENERAL CHARACTERISTICS OF SUBJECT

IDENTIFICATION
No. 773
Sex M
Marital status S
Age 22 yrs. at
psychological tests

PARENTAL HISTORY				
Father				
C	H	S	D	O
(+)	-	-	-	-
Mother				
C	H	S	D	O
-	-	-	-	+

PHYSIOLOGICAL AND METABOLIC DATA

	Admission	Initial	Control	Cold pressor change	Exercise change	Smoking change
Systolic pressure	110	104	98	+04	+34	+01
Diastolic pressure	60	52	56	+10	-08	+03
Heart rate	92	88	84	-20	+27	+26

Age 22 yrs.
Height 70 in.
Weight 152 lbs.
Overweight -01 %

Ponderal index 13.11
Cholesterol 222 mg. per 100 ml.
Vital capacity 5.6 liters

HABIT SURVEY
Smoking habits: heavy cigarette smoker
Age begun 14 yrs.   Inhalation: yes
Habits of nervous tension: 6

Plate 580 **MODERATELY SOPHISTICATED DRAWINGS** 627

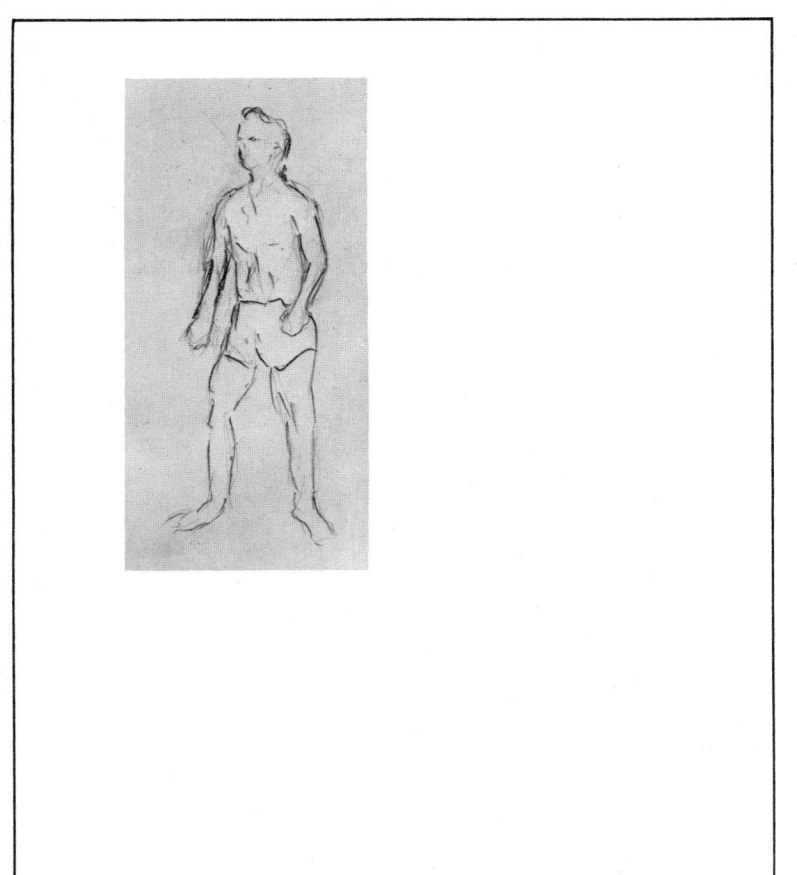

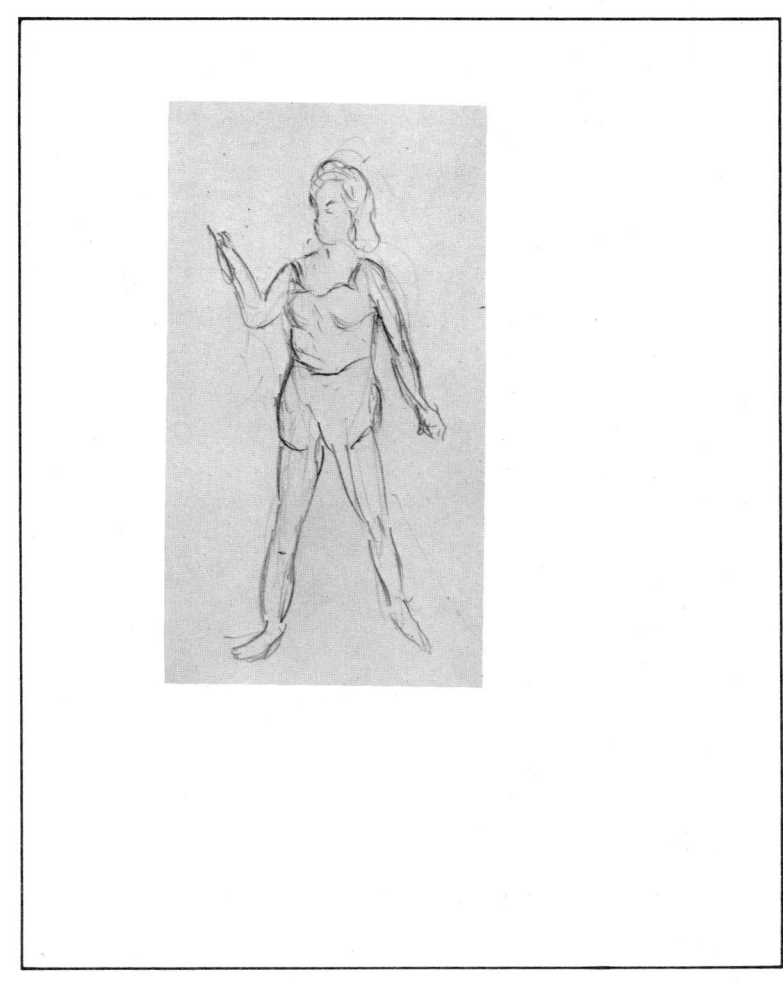

FIGURE-DRAWING CHARACTERISTICS

Structural	Male Female Both	Structural	Male	Female	Structural and Graphic	Male Female Both		Graphic, Global and Height	Male	Female	Body Proportions	Male	Female
Type	0	Omission of Appendages	0	0	Upper and Lower Halves	1	1	Hair Shading	3	2	Head	04	05
Sex Sequence	0	Position of Both Arms	1	1	Four Quarters	4	4	Nudity and Transparency	3	2	Neck	04	03
Posture	1 2	Position of Right Arm	1	4	Relative Size	4		Form	1	1	Shoulders		
Perspective	1 1	Position of Left Arm	5	2	Constant Line Pressure	0	0	Detailing	3	3	Right Arm	02	
Vertical Midline	3 4	Position of Legs	6	8	Variable Line Pressure	5	3	Identity and Sex	1	1	Left Arm	02	04
Bilateral Symmetry	0 0	Relation of Long Axes	1	1	Line Continuity	0	0	Sophistication	2	2	Chest		
Horizontal Midline	4 4	Right and Left Halves	2	2	Body Shading	3	3	Height	04	05	Girth		

GENERAL CHARACTERISTICS OF SUBJECT

IDENTIFICATION
No. G44
Sex M
Marital status S
Age 22 yrs. at
psychological tests

PARENTAL HISTORY				
Father				
C	H	S	D	0
(+)	-	-	-	?
Mother				
C	H	S	D	0
-	+	-	-	+

PHYSIOLOGICAL AND METABOLIC DATA

	Admission	Initial	Control	Cold pressor change	Exercise change	Smoking change
Systolic pressure	120	134	120	+08	+40	+07
Diastolic pressure	78	80	70	+20	+10	00
Heart rate	80	72	65	+04	+29	+07

Age 21 yrs.

Height 73 in. Ponderal index 12.92
Weight 180 lbs. Cholesterol 190 mg. per 100 ml.
Overweight +08 % Vital capacity liters

HABIT SURVEY

Smoking habits: nonsmoker
Age begun yrs. Inhalation:
Habits of nervous tension: 4, 5, 11, 16, 25

STRONG VOCATIONAL INTEREST TEST

Occupation	Artist	Psychologist	Architect	Physician	Osteopath	Dentist	Veterinarian	Mathematician	Physicist	Engineer	Chemist	Production Manager
Standard Score	31	42	34	52	49	33	27	19	14	15	22	23

Occupation	Farmer	Aviator	Carpenter	Printer	Math.-Sci. Teacher	Ind. Arts Teacher	Voc. Agric. Teacher	Policeman	Forest Serv. Man	Y.M.C.A. Phys. Dir.	Personnel Director	Public Administrator
Standard Score	35	27	16	40	46	19	28	34	28	49	45	45

Occupation	Y.M.C.A. Secretary	Soc. Sci. H.S. Teacher	City Sch. Sup't.	Social Worker	Minister	Musician Performer	C.P.A.	Senior C.P.A.	Accountant	Office Man	Purchasing Agent	Banker
Standard Score	44	54	46	53	59	60	26	38	24	35	16	28

Occupation	Mortician	Pharmacist	Sales Manager	Real Est. Manager	Life Ins. Salesman	Advertising Man	Lawyer	Author-Journalist	President Mfg. Co.	Interest Maturity	Occupational Level	Masculinity-Femininity
Standard Score	29	28	27	32	33	38	38	35	16	62	52	34

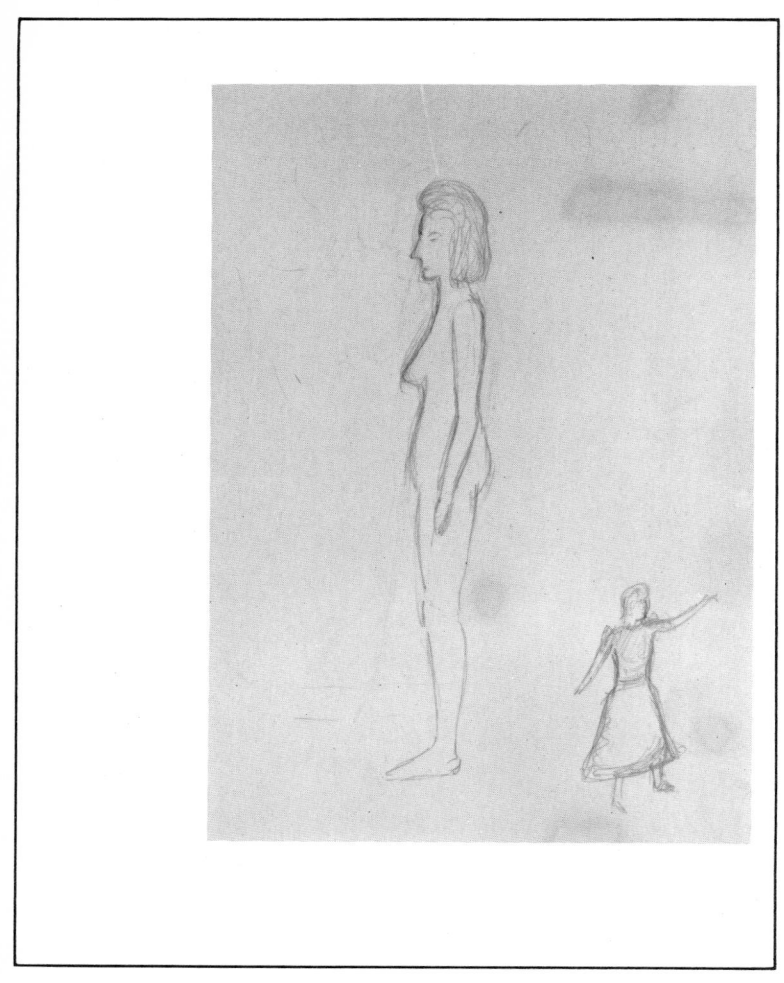

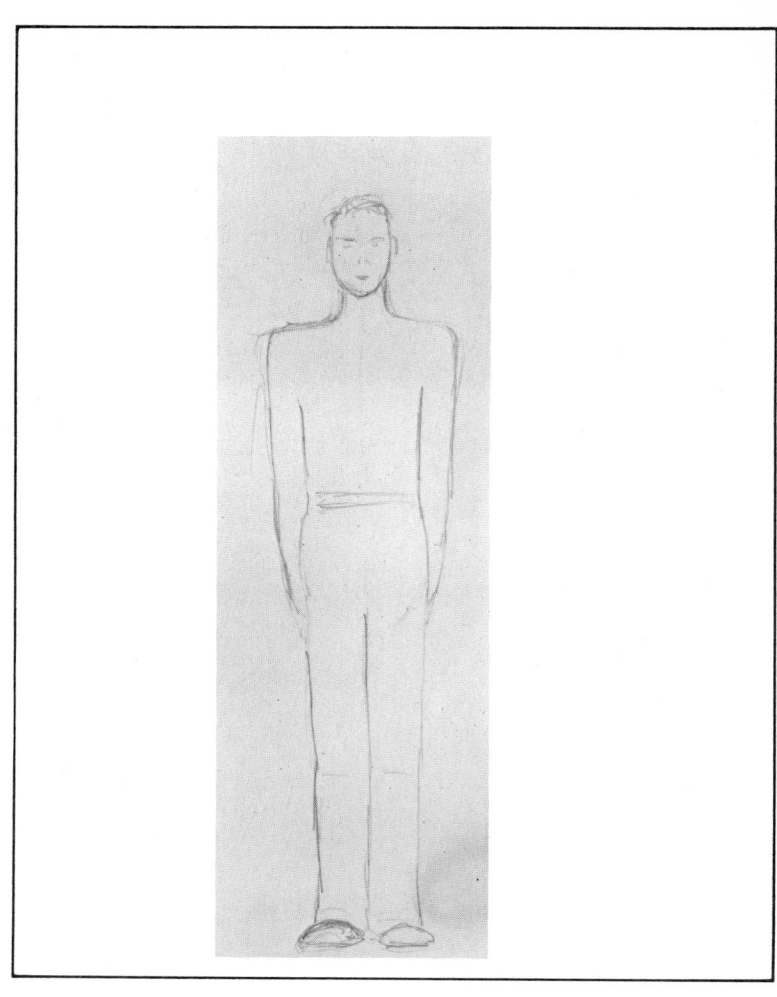

FIGURE-DRAWING CHARACTERISTICS

Structural	Male Female Both	Structural	Male	Female	Structural and Graphic	Male Female Both		Graphic, Global and Height	Male	Female	Body Proportions	Male	Female
Type	0	Omission of Appendages	0	0	Upper and Lower Halves	3	0	Hair Shading	3	3	Head	07	06
Sex Sequence	1	Position of Both Arms	0	4	Four Quarters	4	4	Nudity and Transparency	3	0	Neck	07	07
Posture	1 1	Position of Right Arm	0	7	Relative Size	0		Form	1	1	Shoulders	07	
Perspective	0 2	Position of Left Arm	0	0	Constant Line Pressure	0	0	Detailing	3	3	Right Arm	08	
Vertical Midline	0 4	Position of Legs	2	1	Variable Line Pressure	1	1	Identity and Sex	1	1	Left Arm	07	06
Bilateral Symmetry	4 0	Relation of Long Axes	1	1	Line Continuity	0	0	Sophistication	2	2	Chest	05	03
Horizontal Midline	4 0	Right and Left Halves	1	3	Body Shading	6	0	Height	08	06	Girth	06	05

GENERAL CHARACTERISTICS OF SUBJECT

IDENTIFICATION

No. C71

Sex M

Marital status S

Age 23 yrs. at

psychological tests

PARENTAL HISTORY

Father

C	H	S	D	O
(+)	-	-	-	-

Mother

C	H	S	D	O
-	-	-	-	-

PHYSIOLOGICAL AND METABOLIC DATA

	Admission	Initial	Control	Cold pressor change	Exercise change	Smoking change
Systolic pressure	100	130	120	00	+30	+10
Diastolic pressure	60	70	70	+05	-05	+04
Heart rate	60	72	74	+12	+18	+03

Age 23 yrs.

Height 73 in.

Weight 162 lbs.

Overweight -04 %

Ponderal index 13.39

Cholesterol 218 mg. per 100 ml.

Vital capacity 5.5 liters

HABIT SURVEY

Smoking habits: nonsmoker

Age begun yrs. Inhalation:

Habits of nervous tension: 1, 2, 3, 4, 5, 6

STRONG VOCATIONAL INTEREST TEST

Occupation	Artist	Psychologist	Architect	Physician	Osteopath	Dentist	Veterinarian	Mathematician	Physicist	Engineer	Chemist	Production Manager
Standard Score	31	37	37	39	46	35	16	22	22	35	36	35

Occupation	Farmer	Aviator	Carpenter	Printer	Math.-Sci. Teacher	Ind. Arts Teacher	Voc. Agric. Teacher	Policeman	Forest Serv. Man	Y.M.C.A. Phys. Dir.	Personnel Director	Public Administrator
Standard Score	34	43	30	40	38	29	12	36	28	34	44	48

Occupation	Y.M.C.A. Secretary	Soc. Sci. H.S. Teacher	City Sch. Sup't.	Social Worker	Minister	Musician Performer	C.P.A.	Senior C.P.A.	Accountant	Office Man	Purchasing Agent	Banker
Standard Score	29	32	21	40	62	43	25	44	32	42	26	17

Occupation	Mortician	Pharmacist	Sales Manager	Real Est. Manager	Life Ins. Salesman	Advertising Man	Lawyer	Author-Journalist	President Mfg. Co.	Interest Maturity	Occupational Level	Masculinity-Femininity
Standard Score	36	28	30	35	33	34	29	30	36	60	54	40

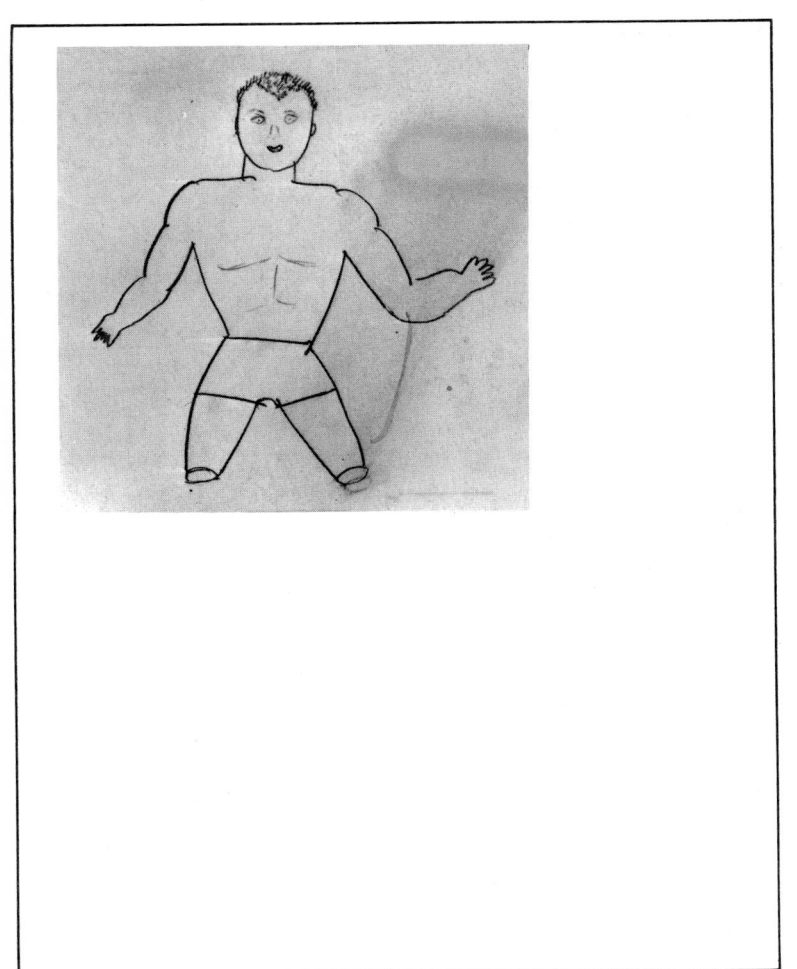

FIGURE-DRAWING CHARACTERISTICS

Structural	Male Female Both		Structural	Male	Female	Structural and Graphic	Male Female Both		Graphic, Global and Height	Male	Female	Body Proportions	Male	Female
Type	0		Omission of Appendages	3	0	Upper and Lower Halves	2	1	Hair Shading	3	3	Head	08	08
Sex Sequence	0		Position of Both Arms	0	4	Four Quarters	4	4	Nudity and Transparency	3	6	Neck	04	02
Posture	0	1	Position of Right Arm	2	7	Relative Size	5		Form	3	1	Shoulders	07	
Perspective	0	2	Position of Left Arm	2	4	Constant Line Pressure	5	0	Detailing	3	1	Right Arm	04	
Vertical Midline	0	4	Position of Legs	0	7	Variable Line Pressure	0	1	Identity and Sex	1	1	Left Arm	04	04
Bilateral Symmetry	3	0	Relation of Long Axes	1	1	Line Continuity	2	0	Sophistication	2	2	Chest	07	06
Horizontal Midline	4	4	Right and Left Halves	1	2	Body Shading	1	7	Height		06	Girth	05	06

GENERAL CHARACTERISTICS OF SUBJECT

IDENTIFICATION
No. 211
Sex M
Marital status M
Age 28 yrs. at
psychological tests

PARENTAL HISTORY
Father
C H S D O
? - - - ?
Mother
C H S D O
? ? - - -

PHYSIOLOGICAL AND METABOLIC DATA

	Admission	Initial	Control	Cold pressor change	Exercise change	Smoking change
Systolic pressure	152	154	144	+04	+76	
Diastolic pressure	82	80	78	+08	+12	
Heart rate	72	84	86	+06	+34	

Age 25 yrs.	Height 76 in.	Ponderal index 12.95
	Weight 202 lbs.	Cholesterol 223 mg. per 100 ml.
	Overweight +07%	Vital capacity 6.4 liters

HABIT SURVEY
Smoking habits: former smoker
Age begun yrs. Inhalation:
Habits of nervous tension: 2, 4, 6

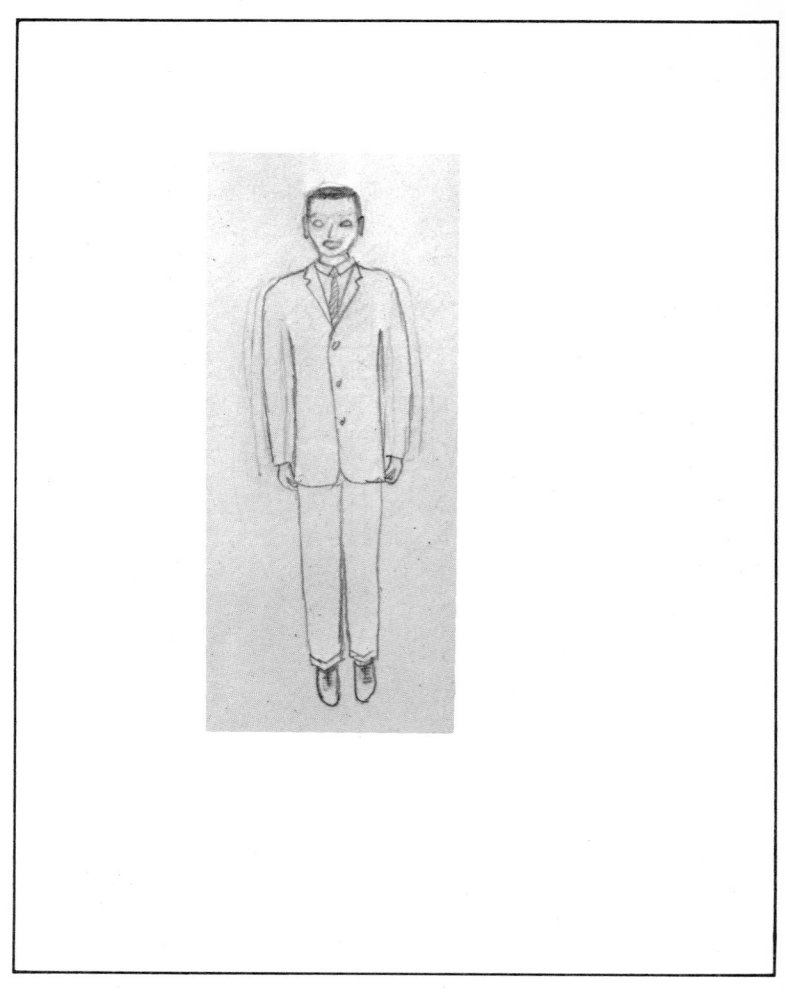

FIGURE-DRAWING CHARACTERISTICS

Structural	Male	Female	Structural	Male	Female	Structural and Graphic	Male	Female	Graphic, Global and Height	Male	Female	Body Proportions	Male	Female
	Both						Both							
Type	0		Omission of Appendages	0	7	Upper and Lower Halves	1	1	Hair Shading	1	5	Head	05	07
Sex Sequence	1		Position of Both Arms	0	4	Four Quarters	4	4	Nudity and Transparency	7	6	Neck	04	04
Posture	1	2	Position of Right Arm	0	7	Relative Size	4		Form	1	1	Shoulders	05	
Perspective	0	1	Position of Left Arm	0	5	Constant Line Pressure	3	0	Detailing	1	1	Right Arm	04	
Vertical Midline	3	4	Position of Legs	2	8	Variable Line Pressure	0	2	Identity and Sex	1	1	Left Arm	04	06
Bilateral Symmetry	3	0	Relation of Long Axes	1	1	Line Continuity	2	4	Sophistication	2	2	Chest	04	
Horizontal Midline	6	4	Right and Left Halves	1	1	Body Shading	0	5	Height	05	06	Girth	05	

GENERAL CHARACTERISTICS OF SUBJECT

IDENTIFICATION
No. E26
Sex M
Marital status S
Age 22 yrs. at
psychological tests

PARENTAL HISTORY
Father
C H S D O
? - - - -
Mother
C H S D O
? - - - -

PHYSIOLOGICAL AND METABOLIC DATA

	Admission	Initial	Control	Cold pressor change	Exercise change	Smoking change
Systolic pressure	110	108	106	+06	+24	+15
Diastolic pressure	70	70	68	+14	+02	+14
Heart rate	80	72	72	+20	-01	+09

Age 21 yrs.	Height	68	in.	Ponderal index	13.03	
	Weight	142	lbs.	Cholesterol	168	mg. per 100 ml.
	Overweight	-02	%	Vital capacity	5.0	liters

HABIT SURVEY

Smoking habits: nonsmoker

Age begun　yrs.　Inhalation:

Habits of nervous tension: 1, 3, 4, 5, 6, 10, 14, 16, 21, 22, 23

STRONG VOCATIONAL INTEREST TEST

Occupation	Artist	Psychologist	Architect	Physician	Osteopath	Dentist	Veterinarian	Mathematician	Physicist	Engineer	Chemist	Production Manager
Standard Score	42	52	39	65	46	45	19	48	48	41	56	29

Occupation	Farmer	Aviator	Carpenter	Printer	Math.-Sci. Teacher	Ind. Arts Teacher	Voc. Agric. Teacher	Policeman	Forest Serv. Man	Y.M.C.A. Phys. Dir.	Personnel Director	Public Administrator
Standard Score	36	38	29	49	42	26	24	31	20	27	18	30

Occupation	Y.M.C.A. Secretary	Soc. Sci. H.S. Teacher	City Sch. Sup't.	Social Worker	Minister	Musician Performer	C.P.A.	Senior C.P.A.	Accountant	Office Man	Purchasing Agent	Banker
Standard Score	18	25	27	30	64	50	28	34	13	25	10	14

Occupation	Mortician	Pharmacist	Sales Manager	Real Est. Manager	Life Ins. Salesman	Advertising Man	Lawyer	Author-Journalist	President Mfg. Co.	Interest Maturity	Occupational Level	Masculinity-Femininity
Standard Score	14	26	08	19	14	30	39	42	26	48	53	48

Plate 584   **MODERATELY SOPHISTICATED DRAWINGS**   631

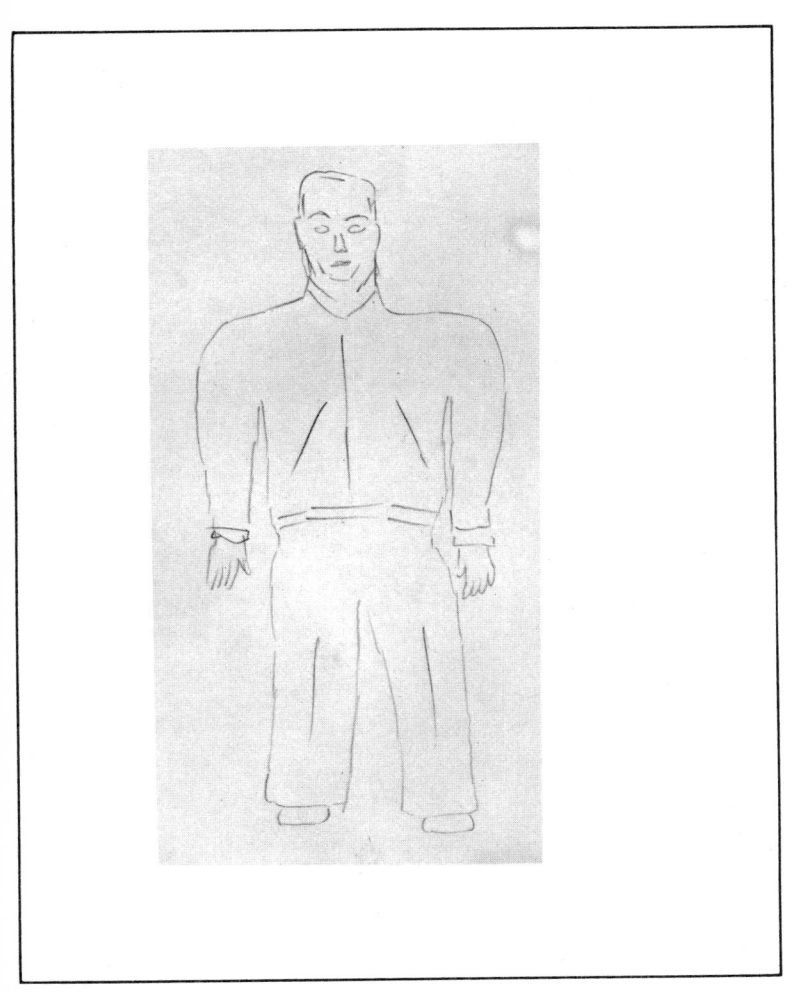

FIGURE-DRAWING CHARACTERISTICS

Structural	Male Female Both		Structural	Male	Female	Structural and Graphic	Male Female Both		Graphic, Global and Height	Male	Female	Body Proportions	Male	Female
Type	0		Omission of Appendages	0	0	Upper and Lower Halves	0	1	Hair Shading	5	5	Head	09	09
Sex Sequence	2		Position of Both Arms	0	0	Four Quarters	4	4	Nudity and Transparency	7	7	Neck	10	04
Posture	1	1	Position of Right Arm	0	2	Relative Size	0		Form	3	3	Shoulders	12	07
Perspective	0	0	Position of Left Arm	0	2	Constant Line Pressure	1	1	Detailing	3	3	Right Arm	06	04
Vertical Midline	3	3	Position of Legs	6	6	Variable Line Pressure	0	0	Identity and Sex	1	1	Left Arm	06	04
Bilateral Symmetry	3	3	Relation of Long Axes	1	1	Line Continuity	0	0	Sophistication	2	2	Chest	08	06
Horizontal Midline	4	0	Right and Left Halves	1	1	Body Shading	2	1	Height	07	06	Girth	10	08

GENERAL CHARACTERISTICS OF SUBJECT

IDENTIFICATION
No. 443
Sex M
Marital status S
Age 26 yrs. at
psychological tests

PARENTAL HISTORY				
Father				
C	H	S	D	O
?	−	−	−	?
Mother				
C	H	S	D	O
(?)	−	−	−	−

PHYSIOLOGICAL AND METABOLIC DATA

	Admission	Initial	Control	Cold pressor change	Exercise change	Smoking change
Systolic pressure	130	118	110	+14	+26	
Diastolic pressure	78	62	66	+24	−02	
Heart rate	88	84	75	+12	+25	

Age 23 yrs.	Height 68 in.	Ponderal index 12.42
	Weight 164 lbs.	Cholesterol 217 mg. per 100 ml.
	Overweight +12 %	Vital capacity 5.0 liters

HABIT SURVEY
Smoking habits: nonsmoker
Age begun   yrs.   Inhalation:
Habits of nervous tension: 5, 6

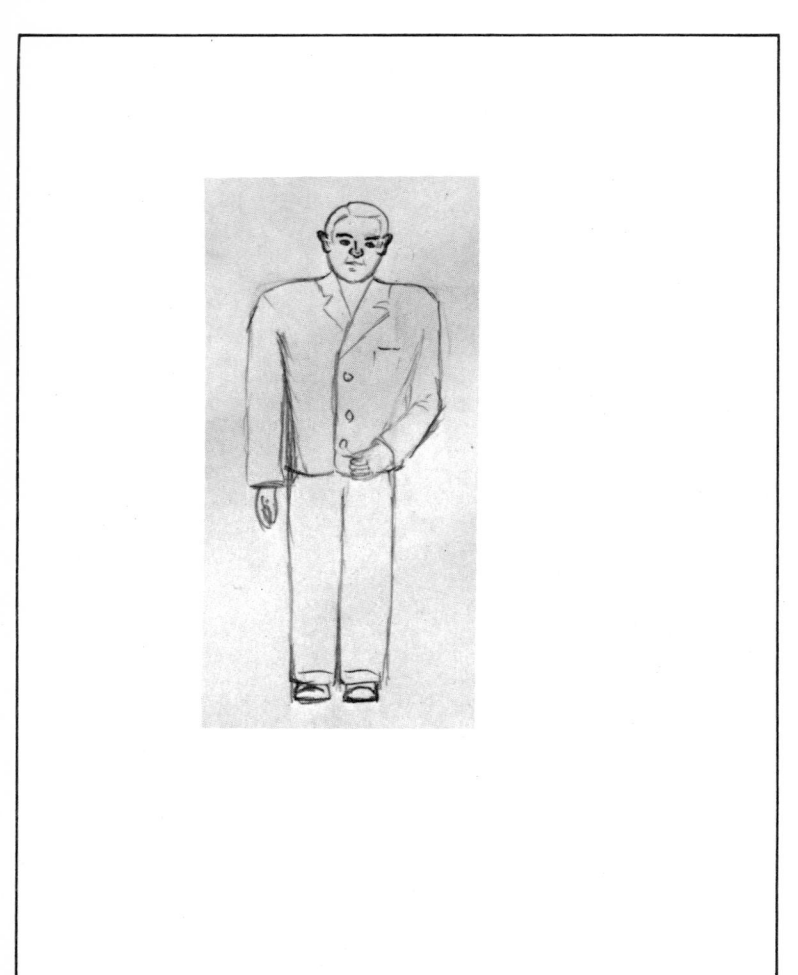

FIGURE-DRAWING CHARACTERISTICS

Structural	Male Female Both		Structural	Male	Female	Structural and Graphic	Male Female Both		Graphic, Global and Height	Male	Female	Body Proportions	Male	Female
Type	0		Omission of Appendages	0	0	Upper and Lower Halves	1	1	Hair Shading	5	3	Head	06	05
Sex Sequence	2		Position of Both Arms	1	1	Four Quarters	4	4	Nudity and Transparency	7	7	Neck	01	01
Posture	1	1	Position of Right Arm	0	0	Relative Size	0		Form	1	1	Shoulders	07	04
Perspective	0	0	Position of Left Arm	5	5	Constant Line Pressure	0	0	Detailing	3	1	Right Arm	06	04
Vertical Midline	3	0	Position of Legs	2	4	Variable Line Pressure	5	5	Identity and Sex	1	1	Left Arm	05	04
Bilateral Symmetry	3	3	Relation of Long Axes	1	1	Line Continuity	0	0	Sophistication	2	2	Chest	06	04
Horizontal Midline	6	4	Right and Left Halves	1	1	Body Shading	1	7	Height	05	04	Girth	06	04

GENERAL CHARACTERISTICS OF SUBJECT

IDENTIFICATION
No. 672
Sex M
Marital status M
Age 28 yrs. at
psychological tests

PARENTAL HISTORY

Father					
C	H	S	D	O
?	-	-	-	-
Mother					
C	H	S	D	O
(?)	-	-	-	+

PHYSIOLOGICAL AND METABOLIC DATA

	Admission	Initial	Control	Cold pressor change	Exercise change	Smoking change
Systolic pressure	120	116	116	+36	+44	
Diastolic pressure	70	70	70	+26	+16	
Heart rate	80	76	77	+16	+08	

Age 25 yrs.	Height	74	in.	Ponderal index 13.31	
	Weight	172	lbs.	Cholesterol	172	mg. per 100 ml.
	Overweight −04 %			Vital capacity	5.5	liters

HABIT SURVEY

Smoking habits: former smoker

  Age begun 14 yrs.   Inhalation:

Habits of nervous tension: 1, 2, 3, 5, 6, 7,

11, 18, 19, 21, 24

FIGURE-DRAWING CHARACTERISTICS

Structural	Male Female Both		Structural	Male	Female	Structural and Graphic	Male Female Both		Graphic, Global and Height	Male	Female	Body Proportions	Male	Female
Type	0		Omission of Appendages	7	0	Upper and Lower Halves	7	0	Hair Shading	3	2	Head	09	07
Sex Sequence	0		Position of Both Arms	0	0	Four Quarters	4	4	Nudity and Transparency	7	7	Neck	05	04
Posture	1	1	Position of Right Arm	5	5	Relative Size	0		Form	1	1	Shoulders	09	06
Perspective	0	0	Position of Left Arm	5	5	Constant Line Pressure	0	0	Detailing	3	3	Right Arm		04
Vertical Midline	0	0	Position of Legs	5	4	Variable Line Pressure	1	1	Identity and Sex	1	1	Left Arm		05
Bilateral Symmetry	3	3	Relation of Long Axes	1	1	Line Continuity	0	0	Sophistication	2	2	Chest	07	05
Horizontal Midline	4	4	Right and Left Halves	3	1	Body Shading	6	6	Height	08	06	Girth	07	04

GENERAL CHARACTERISTICS OF SUBJECT

IDENTIFICATION
No. 631
Sex M
Marital status S
Age 25 yrs. at
psychological tests

PARENTAL HISTORY
Father
C H S D O
(?) - - -
Mother
C H S D O
? + - - +

PHYSIOLOGICAL AND METABOLIC DATA

	Admission	Initial	Control	Cold pressor change	Exercise change	Smoking change
Systolic pressure	120	118	114	+30	+52	+02
Diastolic pressure	80	62	68	+24	00	-02
Heart rate	80	64	65	+06	+46	+07

Age 22 yrs.	Height	70 in.	Ponderal index	12.69	
	Weight	168 lbs.	Cholesterol	203	mg. per 100 ml.
	Overweight +09 %		Vital capacity	5.3	liters

HABIT SURVEY
Smoking habits: heavy cigarette smoker
Age begun 18 yrs.   Inhalation: yes
Habits of nervous tension: 2, 3, 4, 5, 6, 9,
11, 16, 18, 21, 22, 23, 24

FIGURE-DRAWING CHARACTERISTICS

Structural	Male Female Both		Structural	Male	Female	Structural and Graphic	Male Female Both		Graphic, Global and Height	Male	Female	Body Proportions	Male	Female
Type	0		Omission of Appendages	3	3	Upper and Lower Halves	7	7	Hair Shading	3	3	Head	12	12
Sex Sequence	1		Position of Both Arms	2	2	Four Quarters	4	4	Nudity and Transparency	7	6	Neck	12	08
Posture	0	0	Position of Right Arm	6	4	Relative Size	5		Form	3	3	Shoulders		
Perspective	2	2	Position of Left Arm	7	7	Constant Line Pressure	5	0	Detailing	1	1	Right Arm	08	06
Vertical Midline	7	4	Position of Legs	0	0	Variable Line Pressure	0	5	Identity and Sex	1	1	Left Arm		
Bilateral Symmetry	0	0	Relation of Long Axes	1	1	Line Continuity	0	0	Sophistication	2	2	Chest	13	10
Horizontal Midline	4	0	Right and Left Halves	2	2	Body Shading	4	2	Height			Girth	12	11

GENERAL CHARACTERISTICS OF SUBJECT

<table>
<tr><th colspan="2">IDENTIFICATION</th><th colspan="2">PARENTAL HISTORY</th><th colspan="7">PHYSIOLOGICAL AND METABOLIC DATA</th><th colspan="2">HABIT SURVEY</th></tr>
</table>

IDENTIFICATION	PARENTAL HISTORY	PHYSIOLOGICAL AND METABOLIC DATA						HABIT SURVEY

IDENTIFICATION

No. 267
Sex M
Marital status S
Age 24 yrs. at
psychological tests

PARENTAL HISTORY

Father

C	H	S	D	O
?	-	-	-	+

Mother

C	H	S	D	O
-	-	-	-	-

PHYSIOLOGICAL AND METABOLIC DATA

	Admission	Initial	Control	Cold pressor change	Exercise change	Smoking change
Systolic pressure	120					
Diastolic pressure	70					
Heart rate	72					

Age 20 yrs.

Height   71   in.
Weight   151 lbs.
Overweight -03 %

Ponderal index   13.33
Cholesterol   165 mg. per 100 ml.
Vital capacity   liters

HABIT SURVEY

Smoking habits: heavy cigarette smoker
  Age begun 16 yrs.   Inhalation: yes
Habits of nervous tension: 5, 6

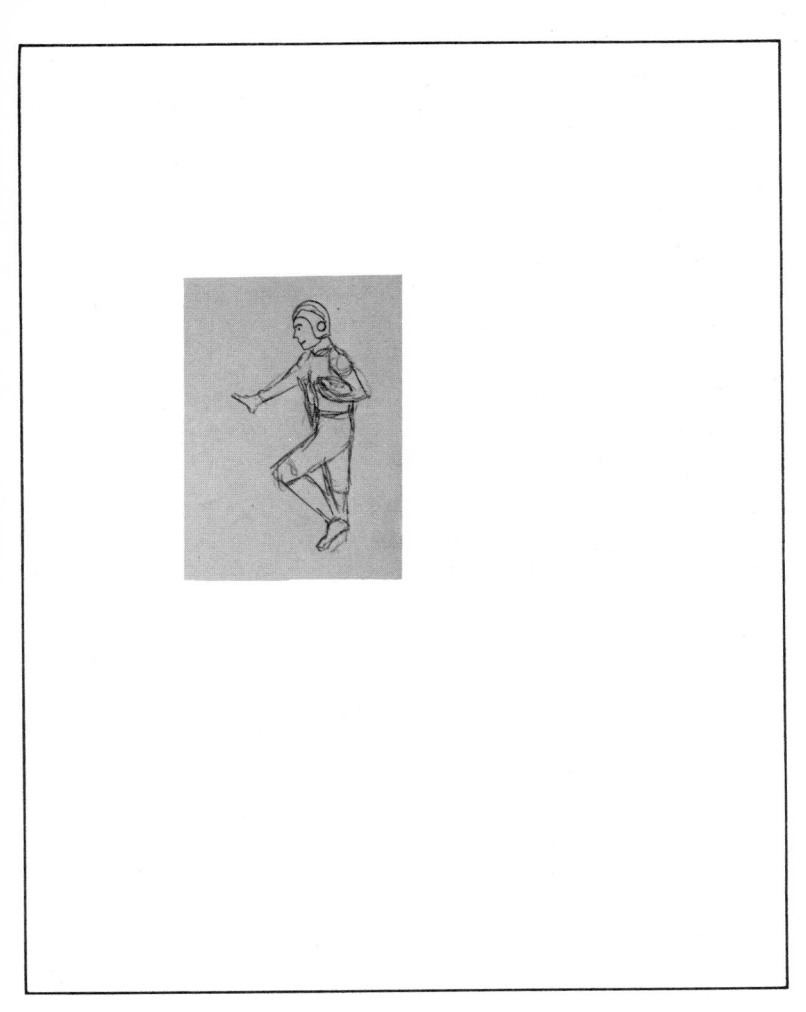

FIGURE-DRAWING CHARACTERISTICS

Structural	Male Female Both	Structural	Male	Female	Structural and Graphic	Male Female Both		Graphic, Global and Height	Male	Female	Body Proportions	Male	Female
Type	0	Omission of Appendages	0	7	Upper and Lower Halves	2	1	Hair Shading	0	3	Head	03	03
Sex Sequence	0	Position of Both Arms	1	0	Four Quarters	0	4	Nudity and Transparency	7	7	Neck	02	04
Posture	5	1	Position of Right Arm	2	2	Relative Size	4		Form	3	3	Shoulders		02
Perspective	2	0	Position of Left Arm	5	2	Constant Line Pressure	0	0	Detailing	3	3	Right Arm	02	
Vertical Midline	4	0	Position of Legs	8	4	Variable Line Pressure	1	3	Identity and Sex	1	1	Left Arm	02	02
Bilateral Symmetry	0	3	Relation of Long Axes	0	1	Line Continuity	0	0	Sophistication	2	2	Chest		02
Horizontal Midline	4	4	Right and Left Halves	2	2	Body Shading	7	2	Height	02	03	Girth	03	02

GENERAL CHARACTERISTICS OF SUBJECT

IDENTIFICATION
No. 374
Sex M
Marital status S
Age 25 yrs. at
psychological tests

PARENTAL HISTORY				
Father				
C	H	S	D	O
?	–	–	–	–
Mother				
C	H	S	D	O
–	–	–	–	–

PHYSIOLOGICAL AND METABOLIC DATA

	Admission	Initial	Control	Cold pressor change	Exercise change	Smoking change
Systolic pressure	140	130	112	+14	+12	
Diastolic pressure	64	72	68	+06	+02	
Heart rate	96	90	79	+14	+09	

Age 23 yrs.	Height 78 in.	Ponderal index 13.10	
	Weight 211 lbs.	Cholesterol 258 mg. per 100 ml.	
	Overweight +08 %	Vital capacity 5.6 liters	

HABIT SURVEY
Smoking habits: heavy cigarette smoker
Age begun 19 yrs.   Inhalation: yes
Habits of nervous tension: 5, 6, 11

FIGURE-DRAWING CHARACTERISTICS

Structural	Male	Female	Structural	Male	Female	Structural and Graphic	Male	Female	Graphic, Global and Height	Male	Female	Body Proportions	Male	Female
	Both						Both							
Type	0		Omission of Appendages	7	7	Upper and Lower Halves	1	1	Hair Shading	3	0	Head	05	06
Sex Sequence	1		Position of Both Arms	0	0	Four Quarters	4	4	Nudity and Transparency	7	7	Neck	04	06
Posture	1	1	Position of Right Arm	5	5	Relative Size	4		Form	1	1	Shoulders	06	05
Perspective	0	5	Position of Left Arm	5	5	Constant Line Pressure	0	0	Detailing	1	1	Right Arm		
Vertical Midline	3	3	Position of Legs	4	4	Variable Line Pressure	4	2	Identity and Sex	1	1	Left Arm	04	04
Bilateral Symmetry	3	3	Relation of Long Axes	1	1	Line Continuity	0	0	Sophistication	2	2	Chest	05	05
Horizontal Midline	6	4	Right and Left Halves	2	0	Body Shading	7	7	Height	05	05	Girth	06	04

GENERAL CHARACTERISTICS OF SUBJECT

IDENTIFICATION
No. 566
Sex M
Marital status S
Age 27 yrs. at psychological tests

PARENTAL HISTORY
Father
C   H   S   D   O
?   -   -   -   ?
Mother
C   H   S   D   O
-   -   -   -   -

PHYSIOLOGICAL AND METABOLIC DATA

	Admission	Initial	Control	Cold pressor change	Exercise change	Smoking change
Systolic pressure	135	120	112	+16	+38	+04
Diastolic pressure	80	74	70	+22	+14	00
Heart rate	74	60	56	00	+21	-04

Age 26 yrs.	Height 75 in.	Ponderal index 13.31
	Weight 179 lbs.	Cholesterol 222 mg. per 100 ml.
	Overweight -04 %	Vital capacity 6.2 liters

HABIT SURVEY
Smoking habits: former smoker
Age begun   yrs.   Inhalation:
Habits of nervous tension:

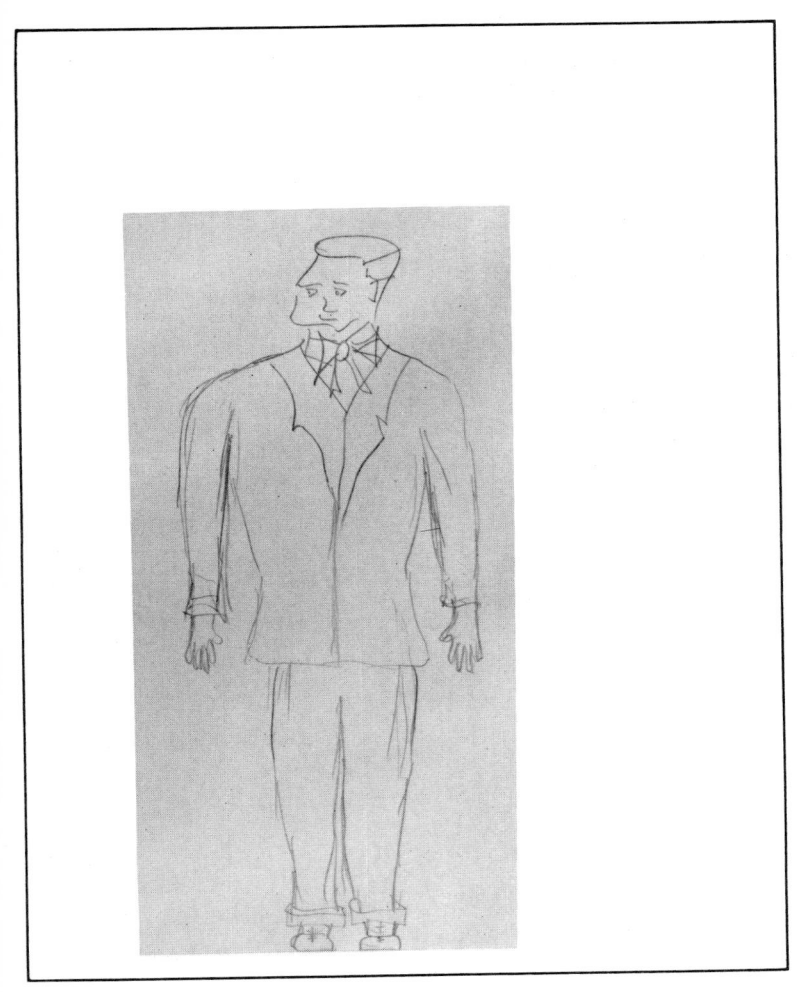

FIGURE-DRAWING CHARACTERISTICS

Structural	Male Female Both	Structural	Male	Female	Structural and Graphic	Male Female Both		Graphic, Global and Height	Male	Female	Body Proportions	Male	Female
Type	0	Omission of Appendages	0	0	Upper and Lower Halves	3	3	Hair Shading	5	5	Head	07	11
Sex Sequence	0	Position of Both Arms	0	4	Four Quarters	4	4	Nudity and Transparency	7	7	Neck	07	05
Posture	1 1	Position of Right Arm	0	7	Relative Size	0		Form	3	3	Shoulders	11	
Perspective	0 2	Position of Left Arm	0	4	Constant Line Pressure	0	0	Detailing	3	3	Right Arm	06	
Vertical Midline	3 4	Position of Legs	4	1	Variable Line Pressure	1	2	Identity and Sex	1	1	Left Arm	06	06
Bilateral Symmetry	2 0	Relation of Long Axes	1	1	Line Continuity	0	0	Sophistication	2	2	Chest	09	06
Horizontal Midline	6 0	Right and Left Halves	1	0	Body Shading	3	0	Height	07	06	Girth	09	04

GENERAL CHARACTERISTICS OF SUBJECT

IDENTIFICATION

No. 608

Sex M

Marital status S

Age 24 yrs. at psychological tests

PARENTAL HISTORY

Father

C	H	S	D	O
?	+	-	+	?

Mother

C	H	S	D	O
-	-	-	-	-

PHYSIOLOGICAL AND METABOLIC DATA

	Admission	Initial	Control	Cold pressor change	Exercise change	Smoking change
Systolic pressure	128	120	118	+02	+20	
Diastolic pressure	80	78	70	+08	+04	
Heart rate	80	60	58	00	+05	

Age 22 yrs.   Height 77 in.   Ponderal index 13.28

Weight 195 lbs.   Cholesterol 243 mg. per 100 ml.

Overweight +04 %   Vital capacity 5.5 liters

HABIT SURVEY

Smoking habits: nonsmoker

Age begun   yrs.   Inhalation:

Habits of nervous tension: 2, 5, 6, 11

FIGURE-DRAWING CHARACTERISTICS

Structural	Male Female Both		Structural	Male	Female	Structural and Graphic	Male Female Both		Graphic, Global and Height	Male	Female	Body Proportions	Male	Female
Type	0		Omission of Appendages	2	0	Upper and Lower Halves	3	3	Hair Shading	7	5	Head	07	09
Sex Sequence	0		Position of Both Arms	4	4	Four Quarters	4	4	Nudity and Transparency	7	7	Neck	05	05
Posture	1	2	Position of Right Arm	8	7	Relative Size	0		Form	1	1	Shoulders	09	
Perspective	0	2	Position of Left Arm	0	4	Constant Line Pressure	1	0	Detailing	3	3	Right Arm		
Vertical Midline	3	4	Position of Legs	3	8	Variable Line Pressure	0	1	Identity and Sex	1	1	Left Arm	06	06
Bilateral Symmetry	3	0	Relation of Long Axes	1	1	Line Continuity	0	0	Sophistication	2	2	Chest	07	06
Horizontal Midline	4	4	Right and Left Halves	1	1	Body Shading	6	4	Height	07	06	Girth	10	05

GENERAL CHARACTERISTICS OF SUBJECT

IDENTIFICATION
No. 651
Sex M
Marital status S
Age 24 yrs. at
psychological tests

PARENTAL HISTORY				
Father				
C	H	S	D	O
?	(+)	-	-	-
Mother				
C	H	S	D	O
-	-	-	-	-

PHYSIOLOGICAL AND METABOLIC DATA

	Admission	Initial	Control	Cold pressor change	Exercise change	Smoking change
Systolic pressure	110	118	104	+02	+44	+06
Diastolic pressure	72	74	70	+12	-02	+04
Heart rate	72	56	55	+08	+29	+16

Age 23 yrs.

Height	68 in.	Ponderal index	12.19	
Weight	174 lbs.	Cholesterol	298	mg. per 100 ml.
Overweight +18 %		Vital capacity	4.5	liters

HABIT SURVEY
Smoking habits: heavy cigarette smoker
Age begun 16 yrs.   Inhalation: yes
Habits of nervous tension: 2, 6, 10, 21, 25

Plate 592   **MODERATELY SOPHISTICATED DRAWINGS**   639

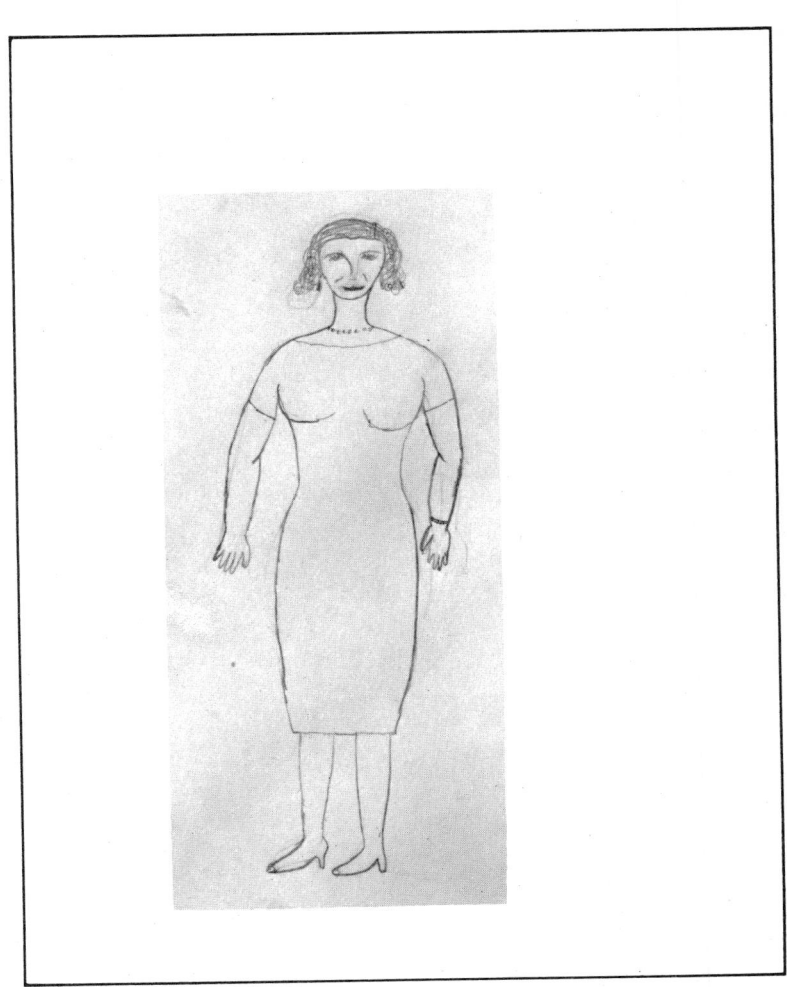

FIGURE-DRAWING CHARACTERISTICS

Structural	Male Female Both	Structural	Male	Female	Structural and Graphic	Male Female Both		Graphic, Global and Height	Male	Female	Body Proportions	Male	Female
Type	0	Omission of Appendages	0	0	Upper and Lower Halves	3	3	Hair Shading	3	3	Head	07	06
Sex Sequence	2	Position of Both Arms	1	1	Four Quarters	4	4	Nudity and Transparency	7	7	Neck	07	08
Posture	1 1	Position of Right Arm	0	2	Relative Size	3		Form	3	3	Shoulders	08	07
Perspective	0 0	Position of Left Arm	5	5	Constant Line Pressure	0	0	Detailing	1	1	Right Arm	06	05
Vertical Midline	3 0	Position of Legs	4	4	Variable Line Pressure	1	5	Identity and Sex	1	1	Left Arm	04	05
Bilateral Symmetry	3 3	Relation of Long Axes	1	1	Line Continuity	0	1	Sophistication	2	2	Chest	06	07
Horizontal Midline	4 0	Right and Left Halves	1	1	Body Shading	2	1	Height	06	07	Girth	08	07

GENERAL CHARACTERISTICS OF SUBJECT

IDENTIFICATION
No. 671
Sex M
Marital status S
Age 24 yrs. at psychological tests

PARENTAL HISTORY
Father
C   H   S   D   O
?   -   -   -   +
Mother
C   H   S   D   O
-    -   -   -   ?

PHYSIOLOGICAL AND METABOLIC DATA

	Admission	Initial	Control	Cold pressor change	Exercise change	Smoking change
Systolic pressure	108	106	106	+10	+42	+01
Diastolic pressure	70	66	72	+28	-10	00
Heart rate	80	56	52	-08	+23	-01

Age 22 yrs.

Height   68 in.
Weight   148 lbs.
Overweight +01 %

Ponderal index 12.85
Cholesterol   222   mg. per 100 ml.
Vital capacity 4.3   liters

HABIT SURVEY

Smoking habits: occasional smoker

Age begun 15 yrs.   Inhalation: no

Habits of nervous tension: 5, 15, 25

FIGURE-DRAWING CHARACTERISTICS

Structural	Male Female Both	Structural	Male	Female	Structural and Graphic	Male Female Both		Graphic, Global and Height	Male	Female	Body Proportions	Male	Female
Type	0	Omission of Appendages	0	0	Upper and Lower Halves	0	0	Hair Shading	3	2	Head	10	10
Sex Sequence	0	Position of Both Arms	1	0	Four Quarters	4	4	Nudity and Transparency	6	7	Neck	07	12
Posture	1	1	Position of Right Arm	5	2	Relative Size	2		Form	3	3	Shoulders	06	06
Perspective	0	0	Position of Left Arm	2	2	Constant Line Pressure	0	0	Detailing	3	3	Right Arm	06	08
Vertical Midline	0	0	Position of Legs	4	4	Variable Line Pressure	1	1	Identity and Sex	1	1	Left Arm	08	06
Bilateral Symmetry	3	3	Relation of Long Axes	1	1	Line Continuity	2	2	Sophistication	2	2	Chest	05	06
Horizontal Midline	4	4	Right and Left Halves	1	0	Body Shading	3	3	Height	07	07	Girth	07	06

GENERAL CHARACTERISTICS OF SUBJECT

IDENTIFICATION

No. F42

Sex F

Marital status S

Age 24 yrs. at

psychological tests

PARENTAL HISTORY

Father

	C	H	S	D	O
?	-	-	-	+

Mother

	C	H	S	D	O
	-	+	-	-	+

PHYSIOLOGICAL AND METABOLIC DATA

	Admission	Initial	Control	Cold pressor change	Exercise change	Smoking change
Systolic pressure	140	112	106	+04	+34	+26
Diastolic pressure	90	80	78	+10	+10	+20
Heart rate	90	88	92	-04	+15	+23

Age 22 yrs.

Height	68 in.	Ponderal index 13.10
Weight	140 lbs.	Cholesterol 224 mg. per 100 ml.
Overweight -01 %		Vital capacity liters

HABIT SURVEY

Smoking habits: former smoker

Age begun 20 yrs.   Inhalation:

Habits of nervous tension: 2, 3, 4, 5, 6, 10,

18, 19, 22, 23

STRONG VOCATIONAL INTEREST TEST

Occupation	Artist	Psychologist	Architect	Physician	Osteopath	Dentist	Veterinarian	Mathematician	Physicist	Engineer	Chemist	Production Manager
Standard Score	48	47	47	68	53	48	23	39	39	38	49	22

Occupation	Farmer	Aviator	Carpenter	Printer	Math.-Sci. Teacher	Ind. Arts Teacher	Voc. Agric. Teacher	Policeman	Forest Serv. Man	Y.M.C.A. Phys. Dir.	Personnel Director	Public Administrator
Standard Score	27	29	17	32	39	18	17	20	22	44	33	34

Occupation	Y.M.C.A. Secretary	Soc. Sci. H.S. Teacher	City Sch. Sup't.	Social Worker	Minister	Musician Performer	C.P.A.	Senior C.P.A.	Accountant	Office Man	Purchasing Agent	Banker
Standard Score	33	29	32	44	58	58	27	27	15	24	11	09

Occupation	Mortician	Pharmacist	Sales Manager	Real Est. Manager	Life Ins. Salesman	Advertising Man	Lawyer	Author-Journalist	President Mfg. Co.	Interest Maturity	Occupational Level	Masculinity-Femininity
Standard Score	22	25	25	31	35	37	38	43	33	55	60	26

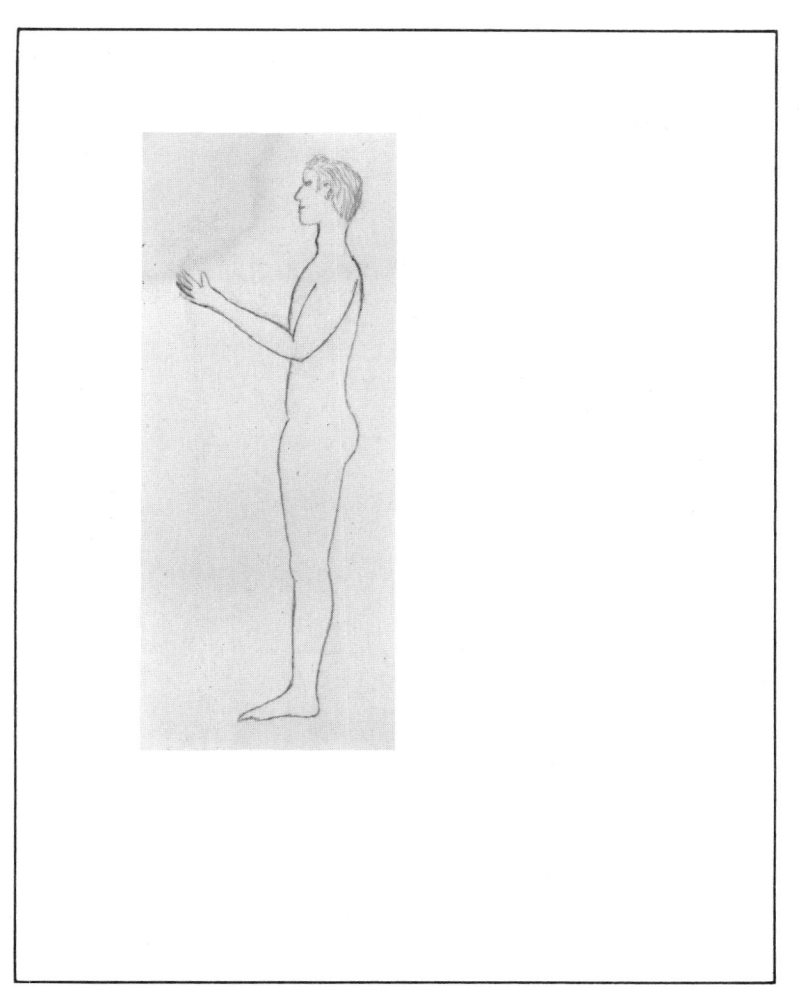

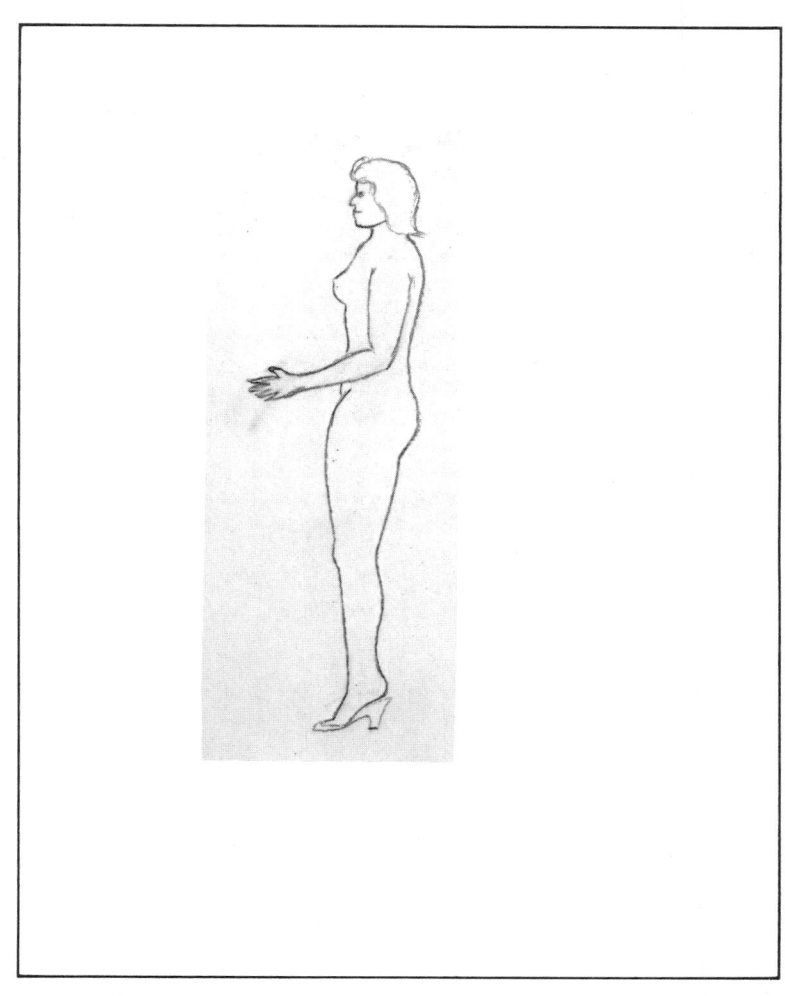

FIGURE-DRAWING CHARACTERISTICS

Structural	Male Female Both		Structural	Male	Female	Structural and Graphic	Male Female Both		Graphic, Global and Height	Male	Female	Body Proportions	Male	Female
Type	0		Omission of Appendages	0	0	Upper and Lower Halves	1	1	Hair Shading	3	5	Head	05	05
Sex Sequence	0		Position of Both Arms	4	4	Four Quarters	4	4	Nudity and Transparency	0	0	Neck	08	02
Posture	1	1	Position of Right Arm	7	7	Relative Size	2		Form	1	1	Shoulders		
Perspective	2	2	Position of Left Arm	4	4	Constant Line Pressure	3	3	Detailing	3	3	Right Arm		
Vertical Midline	4	4	Position of Legs	1	1	Variable Line Pressure	0	0	Identity and Sex	1	1	Left Arm	04	04
Bilateral Symmetry	0	0	Relation of Long Axes	1	1	Line Continuity	4	4	Sophistication	2	2	Chest	05	05
Horizontal Midline	0	0	Right and Left Halves	2	2	Body Shading	0	0	Height	06	06	Girth	04	06

GENERAL CHARACTERISTICS OF SUBJECT

IDENTIFICATION

No. F56

Sex M

Marital status M

Age 24 yrs. at psychological tests

PARENTAL HISTORY

Father

C	H	S	D	O
?	+	-	-	-

Mother

C	H	S	D	O
-	-	-	-	+

PHYSIOLOGICAL AND METABOLIC DATA

	Admission	Initial	Control	Cold pressor change	Exercise change	Smoking change
Systolic pressure	120	120	106	+02	+24	00
Diastolic pressure	70	82	76	+14	+12	+04
Heart rate	72	64	60	00	+15	-03

Age 22 yrs.

Height	68 in.	Ponderal index	13.10
Weight	140 lbs.	Cholesterol	275 mg. per 100 ml.
Overweight	-04 %	Vital capacity	liters

HABIT SURVEY

Smoking habits: pipe smoker

  Age begun 19 yrs.   Inhalation: sometimes

Habits of nervous tension: 4, 9, 11, 16

STRONG VOCATIONAL INTEREST TEST

Occupation	Artist	Psychologist	Architect	Physician	Osteopath	Dentist	Veterinarian	Mathematician	Physicist	Engineer	Chemist	Production Manager
Standard Score	35	40	45	52	30	38	24	48	46	43	50	27

Occupation	Farmer	Aviator	Carpenter	Printer	Math.-Sci. Teacher	Ind. Arts Teacher	Voc. Agric. Teacher	Policeman	Forest Serv. Man	Y.M.C.A. Phys. Dir.	Personnel Director	Public Administrator
Standard Score	40	39	21	33	42	21	34	20	22	21	22	30

Occupation	Y.M.C.A. Secretary	Soc. Sci. H.S. Teacher	City Sch. Sup't.	Social Worker	Minister	Musician Performer	C.P.A.	Senior C.P.A.	Accountant	Office Man	Purchasing Agent	Banker
Standard Score	10	20	19	23	58	46	36	41	23	22	20	24

Occupation	Mortician	Pharmacist	Sales Manager	Real Est. Manager	Life Ins. Salesman	Advertising Man	Lawyer	Author-Journalist	President Mfg. Co.	Interest Maturity	Occupational Level	Masculinity-Femininity
Standard Score	19	27	20	22	15	27	28	33	26	45	55	44

FIGURE-DRAWING CHARACTERISTICS

Structural	Male Female Both		Structural	Male	Female	Structural and Graphic	Male Female Both		Graphic, Global and Height	Male	Female	Body Proportions	Male	Female
Type	0		Omission of Appendages	7	0	Upper and Lower Halves	0	3	Hair Shading	3	3	Head	07	07
Sex Sequence	2		Position of Both Arms	0	1	Four Quarters	4	4	Nudity and Transparency	7	7	Neck	12	07
Posture	1	1	Position of Right Arm	5	2	Relative Size	4		Form	3	3	Shoulders	07	06
Perspective	0	0	Position of Left Arm	5	0	Constant Line Pressure	0	0	Detailing	3	3	Right Arm		06
Vertical Midline	3	3	Position of Legs	6	4	Variable Line Pressure	1	1	Identity and Sex	1	1	Left Arm	06	06
Bilateral Symmetry	2	3	Relation of Long Axes	1	1	Line Continuity	0	0	Sophistication	2	2	Chest	06	05
Horizontal Midline	6	0	Right and Left Halves	1	1	Body Shading	7	7	Height	06	07	Girth	08	05

GENERAL CHARACTERISTICS OF SUBJECT

IDENTIFICATION
No. G19
Sex F
Marital status S
Age 25 yrs. at
psychological tests

PARENTAL HISTORY				
Father				
C	H	S	D	O
?	+	-	-	+
Mother				
C	H	S	D	O
-	-	-	-	-

PHYSIOLOGICAL AND METABOLIC DATA

	Admission	Initial	Control	Cold pressor change	Exercise change	Smoking change
Systolic pressure	130	98	102	+14	+40	+23
Diastolic pressure	60	58	74	+14	-02	+25
Heart rate	84	64	62	+08	+22	+43

Age 25 yrs.

Height 69 in.
Weight 137 lbs.
Overweight -07 %

Ponderal index 13.37
Cholesterol 167 mg. per 100 ml.
Vital capacity liters

HABIT SURVEY
Smoking habits: light cigarette smoker
Age begun 20 yrs.   Inhalation: yes
Habits of nervous tension: 1, 2, 5, 6, 9, 11, 25

FIGURE-DRAWING CHARACTERISTICS

Structural	Male Female Both		Structural	Male	Female	Structural and Graphic	Male Female Both		Graphic, Global and Height	Male	Female	Body Proportions	Male	Female
Type	0		Omission of Appendages	7	0	Upper and Lower Halves	3	3	Hair Shading	7	3	Head	04	
Sex Sequence	1		Position of Both Arms	4	2	Four Quarters	4	4	Nudity and Transparency	7	0	Neck	02	
Posture	2	3	Position of Right Arm	7	5	Relative Size	4		Form	1	1	Shoulders		
Perspective	2	2	Position of Left Arm	5	7	Constant Line Pressure	4	0	Detailing	1	3	Right Arm		
Vertical Midline	7	4	Position of Legs	8	1	Variable Line Pressure	0	4	Identity and Sex	1	1	Left Arm	04	
Bilateral Symmetry	0	0	Relation of Long Axes	1	0	Line Continuity	0	1	Sophistication	2	2	Chest	06	
Horizontal Midline	4	0	Right and Left Halves	1	1	Body Shading	6	0	Height	04		Girth	06	

GENERAL CHARACTERISTICS OF SUBJECT

IDENTIFICATION
No. A41
Sex F
Marital status S
Age 26 yrs. at
psychological tests

PARENTAL HISTORY
Father
C   H   S   D   O
?   -   -   +   +
Mother
C   H   S   D   O
-   -   -   -   -

PHYSIOLOGICAL AND METABOLIC DATA

	Admission	Initial	Control	Cold pressor change	Exercise change	Smoking change
Systolic pressure	104	120	111	+14	+26	+08
Diastolic pressure	64	76	70	+18	-14	+03
Heart rate	92	76	65	+12	+24	+20

Age 25 yrs.	Height	68	in.	Ponderal index	12.85	
	Weight	148	lbs.	Cholesterol	222	mg. per 100 ml.
	Overweight +03 %			Vital capacity		liters

HABIT SURVEY

Smoking habits: heavy cigarette smoker

Age begun 20 yrs.   Inhalation: yes

Habits of nervous tension: 2, 5, 6, 23

STRONG VOCATIONAL INTEREST TEST

Occupation	Artist	Psychologist	Architect	Physician	Osteopath	Dentist	Veterinarian	Mathematician	Physicist	Engineer	Chemist	Production Manager
Standard Score	6	7	8	8	6	4	2	4	5	4	5	3

Occupation	Farmer	Aviator	Carpenter	Printer	Math.-Sci. Teacher	Ind. Arts Teacher	Voc. Agric. Teacher	Policeman	Forest Serv. Man	Y.M.C.A. Phys. Dir.	Personnel Director	Public Administrator
Standard Score	6	5	3	6	6	2	3	3	4	4	6	6

Occupation	Y.M.C.A. Secretary	Soc. Sci. H.S. Teacher	City Sch. Sup't.	Social Worker	Minister	Musician Performer	C.P.A.	Senior C.P.A.	Accountant	Office Man	Purchasing Agent	Banker
Standard Score	3	3	4	6	6	8	3	5	2	2	2	1

Occupation	Mortician	Pharmacist	Sales Manager	Real Est. Manager	Life Ins. Salesman	Advertising Man	Lawyer	Author-Journalist	President Mfg. Co.	Interest Maturity	Occupational Level	Masculinity-Femininity
Standard Score	2	3	2	4	2	5	4	5	3	6	4	3

FIGURE-DRAWING CHARACTERISTICS

Structural	Male	Female	Structural	Male	Female	Structural and Graphic	Male	Female	Graphic, Global and Height	Male	Female	Body Proportions	Male	Female
		Both						Both						
Type		0	Omission of Appendages	0	0	Upper and Lower Halves	3	3	Hair Shading	7	2	Head	16	09
Sex Sequence		1	Position of Both Arms	1	0	Four Quarters	4	4	Nudity and Transparency	7	7	Neck	16	02
Posture	1	1	Position of Right Arm	4	0	Relative Size		0	Form	3	3	Shoulders		
Perspective	6	1	Position of Left Arm	0	0	Constant Line Pressure	0	0	Detailing	3	3	Right Arm	08	06
Vertical Midline	7	4	Position of Legs	1	2	Variable Line Pressure	3	1	Identity and Sex	1	1	Left Arm	08	06
Bilateral Symmetry	0	0	Relation of Long Axes	1	1	Line Continuity	1	2	Sophistication	2	2	Chest		
Horizontal Midline	4	4	Right and Left Halves	1	2	Body Shading	3	1	Height	09	06	Girth		

GENERAL CHARACTERISTICS OF SUBJECT

IDENTIFICATION
No. A71
Sex M
Marital status M
Age 23 yrs. at
psychological tests

PARENTAL HISTORY
Father
C H S D O
? – – – –
Mother
C H S D O
– – – – –

PHYSIOLOGICAL AND METABOLIC DATA

	Admission	Initial	Control	Cold pressor change	Exercise change	Smoking change
Systolic pressure	124	126	121	+22	+40	+06
Diastolic pressure	76	62	71	+16	−27	+08
Heart rate	80	64	52	+24	+19	+06

Age 22 yrs.	Height	73 in.	Ponderal index 13.54	
	Weight	157 lbs.	Cholesterol	210 mg. per 100 ml.
	Overweight −07 %		Vital capacity	liters

HABIT SURVEY

Smoking habits: heavy cigarette smoker

Age begun 12 yrs.   Inhalation: yes

Habits of nervous tension: 5, 6, 18, 19

STRONG VOCATIONAL INTEREST TEST

Occupation	Artist	Psychologist	Architect	Physician	Osteopath	Dentist	Veterinarian	Mathematician	Physicist	Engineer	Chemist	Production Manager
Standard Score	33	51	31	59	41	29	25	29	22	32	41	29

Occupation	Farmer	Aviator	Carpenter	Printer	Math.-Sci. Teacher	Ind. Arts Teacher	Voc. Agric. Teacher	Policeman	Forest Serv. Man	Y.M.C.A. Phys. Dir.	Personnel Director	Public Administrator
Standard Score	26	35	05	20	29	−08	21	20	22	28	40	49

Occupation	Y.M.C.A. Secretary	Soc. Sci. H.S. Teacher	City Sch. Sup't.	Social Worker	Minister	Musician Performer	C.P.A.	Senior C.P.A.	Accountant	Office Man	Purchasing Agent	Banker
Standard Score	17	28	37	44	60	37	47	36	18	21	21	18

Occupation	Mortician	Pharmacist	Sales Manager	Real Est. Manager	Life Ins. Salesman	Advertising Man	Lawyer	Author-Journalist	President Mfg. Co.	Interest Maturity	Occupational Level	Masculinity-Femininity
Standard Score	25	37	41	43	38	45	54	43	37	51	65	45

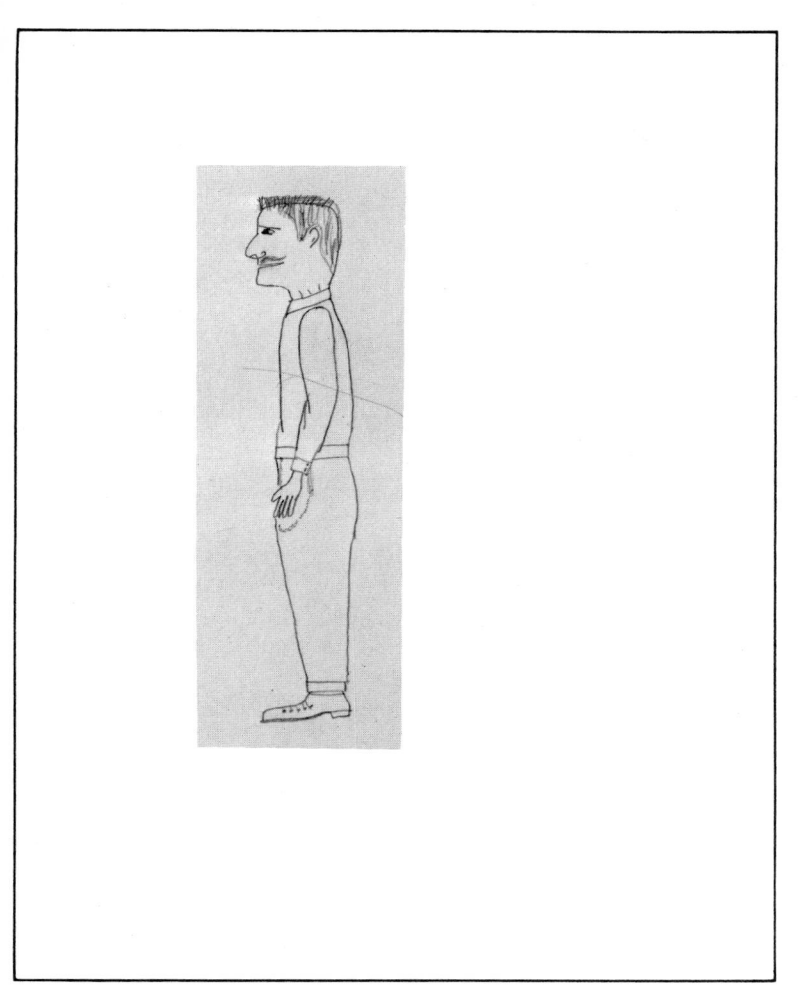

FIGURE-DRAWING CHARACTERISTICS

Structural	Male Female Both	Structural	Male	Female	Structural and Graphic	Male Female Both		Graphic, Global and Height	Male	Female	Body Proportions	Male	Female
Type	0	Omission of Appendages	0	0	Upper and Lower Halves	1	0	Hair Shading	3	1	Head	07	05
Sex Sequence	0	Position of Both Arms	4	4	Four Quarters	4	4	Nudity and Transparency	7	7	Neck	05	03
Posture	1 1	Position of Right Arm	7	7	Relative Size	0		Form	1	1	Shoulders		
Perspective	2 2	Position of Left Arm	0	4	Constant Line Pressure	0	0	Detailing	3	1	Right Arm		
Vertical Midline	4 7	Position of Legs	1	1	Variable Line Pressure	5	4	Identity and Sex	1	1	Left Arm	04	04
Bilateral Symmetry	0 0	Relation of Long Axes	1	1	Line Continuity	4	0	Sophistication	2	2	Chest	05	04
Horizontal Midline	4 4	Right and Left Halves	2	2	Body Shading	0	4	Height	05	05	Girth	06	03

GENERAL CHARACTERISTICS OF SUBJECT

IDENTIFICATION	PARENTAL HISTORY
No. B72	Father
Sex M	C H S D O
Marital status S	? - - - -
Age 22 yrs. at	Mother
psychological tests	C H S D O
	- - - - -

PHYSIOLOGICAL AND METABOLIC DATA

	Admission	Initial	Control	Cold pressor change	Exercise change	Smoking change
Systolic pressure	120	126	124	+10	+20	-01
Diastolic pressure	80	58	70	+30	00	-02
Heart rate	64	58	47	+14	+30	+07

Age 22 yrs.	Height 74 in.	Ponderal index 13.60
	Weight 161 lbs.	Cholesterol 215 mg. per 100 ml.
	Overweight -07 %	Vital capacity liters

HABIT SURVEY

Smoking habits: occasional smoker

Age begun 18 yrs.   Inhalation: no

Habits of nervous tension: 2, 4, 5, 8, 9, 11, 16, 25

STRONG VOCATIONAL INTEREST TEST

Occupation	Artist	Psychologist	Architect	Physician	Osteopath	Dentist	Veterinarian	Mathematician	Physicist	Engineer	Chemist	Production Manager
Standard Score	30	49	27	63	53	37	35	27	29	36	48	38

Occupation	Farmer	Aviator	Carpenter	Printer	Math.-Sci. Teacher	Ind. Arts Teacher	Voc. Agric. Teacher	Policeman	Forest Serv. Man	Y.M.C.A. Phys. Dir.	Personnel Director	Public Administrator
Standard Score	41	53	24	41	52	33	44	30	36	44	48	46

Occupation	Y.M.C.A. Secretary	Soc. Sci. H.S. Teacher	City Sch. Sup't.	Social Worker	Minister	Musician Performer	C.P.A.	Senior C.P.A.	Accountant	Office Man	Purchasing Agent	Banker
Standard Score	34	40	29	45	61	48	18	41	16	24	17	10

Occupation	Mortician	Pharmacist	Sales Manager	Real Est. Manager	Life Ins. Salesman	Advertising Man	Lawyer	Author-Journalist	President Mfg. Co.	Interest Maturity	Occupational Level	Masculinity-Femininity
Standard Score	18	29	31	29	29	30	36	31	33	55	52	60

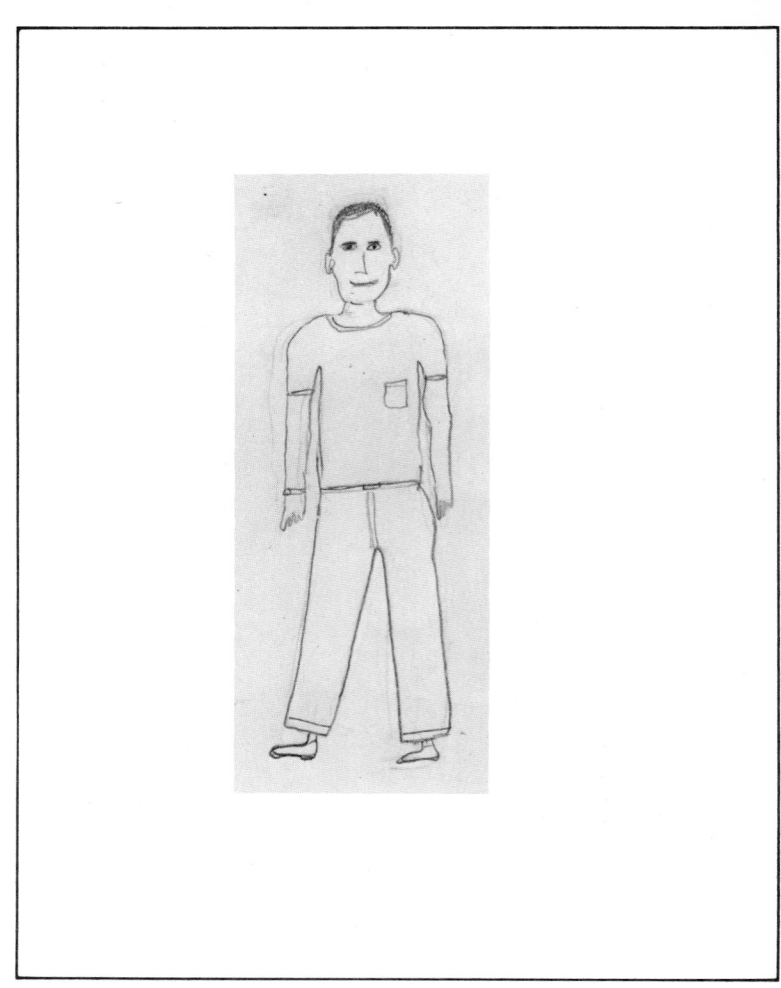

FIGURE-DRAWING CHARACTERISTICS

Structural	Male Female / Both		Structural	Male	Female	Structural and Graphic	Male	Female / Both		Graphic, Global and Height	Male	Female	Body Proportions	Male	Female
Type	0		Omission of Appendages	0	0	Upper and Lower Halves	1	1		Hair Shading	3	3	Head	08	07
Sex Sequence	1		Position of Both Arms	0	0	Four Quarters	4	4		Nudity and Transparency	7	7	Neck	04	05
Posture	1	1	Position of Right Arm	0	5	Relative Size	4			Form	3	3	Shoulders	06	06
Perspective	0	0	Position of Left Arm	0	5	Constant Line Pressure	0	0		Detailing	1	1	Right Arm	04	04
Vertical Midline	3	0	Position of Legs	6	4	Variable Line Pressure	5	5		Identity and Sex	1	1	Left Arm	04	04
Bilateral Symmetry	3	3	Relation of Long Axes	1	1	Line Continuity	3	4		Sophistication	2	2	Chest	04	06
Horizontal Midline	4	4	Right and Left Halves	1	1	Body Shading	0	5		Height	05	06	Girth	06	05

GENERAL CHARACTERISTICS OF SUBJECT

IDENTIFICATION
No. D63
Sex M
Marital status S
Age 22 yrs. at
psychological tests

PARENTAL HISTORY				
Father				
C	H	S	D	O
?	-	-	-	+
Mother				
C	H	S	D	O
-	-	-	-	+

PHYSIOLOGICAL AND METABOLIC DATA

	Admission	Initial	Control	Cold pressor change	Exercise change	Smoking change
Systolic pressure	142	128	116	+06	+22	+12
Diastolic pressure	76	70	76	+22	-14	+08
Heart rate	80	80	68	+08	+11	+21

Age 22 yrs.	Height 74 in.	Ponderal index 12.42
	Weight 212 lbs.	Cholesterol 263 mg. per 100 ml.
	Overweight +23 %	Vital capacity 5.4 liters

HABIT SURVEY

Smoking habits: occasional smoker

Age begun 18 yrs.   Inhalation: yes

Habits of nervous tension: 1, 4, 5, 6, 8, 9, 10, 11, 16, 18, 21, 22

STRONG VOCATIONAL INTEREST TEST

Occupation	Artist	Psychologist	Architect	Physician	Osteopath	Dentist	Veterinarian	Mathematician	Physicist	Engineer	Chemist	Production Manager
Standard Score	39	58	40	63	47	37	24	38	28	32	46	22

Occupation	Farmer	Aviator	Carpenter	Printer	Math.-Sci. Teacher	Ind. Arts Teacher	Voc. Agric. Teacher	Policeman	Forest Serv. Man	Y.M.C.A. Phys. Dir.	Personnel Director	Public Administrator
Standard Score	23	25	10	29	35	02	20	23	23	35	40	51

Occupation	Y.M.C.A. Secretary	Soc. Sci. H.S. Teacher	City Sch. Sup't.	Social Worker	Minister	Musician Performer	C.P.A.	Senior C.P.A.	Accountant	Office Man	Purchasing Agent	Banker
Standard Score	29	35	40	51	63	47	47	36	19	19	17	21

Occupation	Mortician	Pharmacist	Sales Manager	Real Est. Manager	Life Ins. Salesman	Advertising Man	Lawyer	Author-Journalist	President Mfg. Co.	Interest Maturity	Occupational Level	Masculinity-Femininity
Standard Score	25	38	30	35	33	40	48	43	30	54	63	33

FIGURE-DRAWING CHARACTERISTICS

Structural	Male Female Both		Structural	Male	Female	Structural and Graphic	Male Female Both		Graphic, Global and Height	Male	Female	Body Proportions	Male	Female
Type	0		Omission of Appendages	0	0	Upper and Lower Halves	1	1	Hair Shading	1	1	Head	04	05
Sex Sequence	0		Position of Both Arms	4	4	Four Quarters	4	4	Nudity and Transparency	7	7	Neck	06	04
Posture	1	1	Position of Right Arm	7	7	Relative Size	2		Form	1	1	Shoulders		
Perspective	2	2	Position of Left Arm	4	0	Constant Line Pressure	0	0	Detailing	3	3	Right Arm		
Vertical Midline	4	4	Position of Legs	1	1	Variable Line Pressure	3	3	Identity and Sex	1	1	Left Arm	04	02
Bilateral Symmetry	0	0	Relation of Long Axes	1	1	Line Continuity	0	0	Sophistication	2	2	Chest	05	03
Horizontal Midline	6	4	Right and Left Halves	3	0	Body Shading	4	2	Height	04	04	Girth	05	03

GENERAL CHARACTERISTICS OF SUBJECT

IDENTIFICATION
No. 309
Sex M
Marital status S
Age 26 yrs. at psychological tests

PARENTAL HISTORY
Father
C H S D O
- ? - + +
Mother
C H S D O
? - - - -

PHYSIOLOGICAL AND METABOLIC DATA

	Admission	Initial	Control	Cold pressor change	Exercise change	Smoking change
Systolic pressure	140	126	114	+22	+28	
Diastolic pressure	78	76	74	+08	00	
Heart rate	80	84	73	+02	+18	

Age 24 yrs.	Height 69 in.	Ponderal index 12.43
	Weight 171 lbs.	Cholesterol 258 mg. per 100 ml.
	Overweight +12 %	Vital capacity 5.2 liters

HABIT SURVEY
Smoking habits: nonsmoker
Age begun   yrs.   Inhalation:
Habits of nervous tension: 6, 9, 10, 14, 15

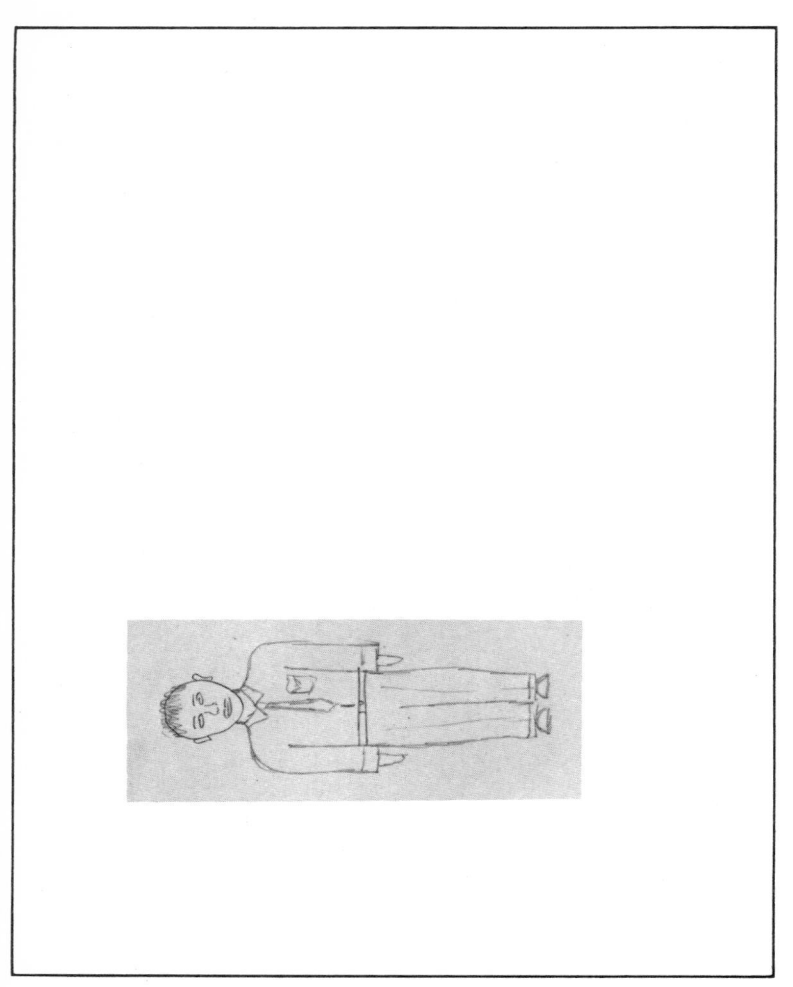

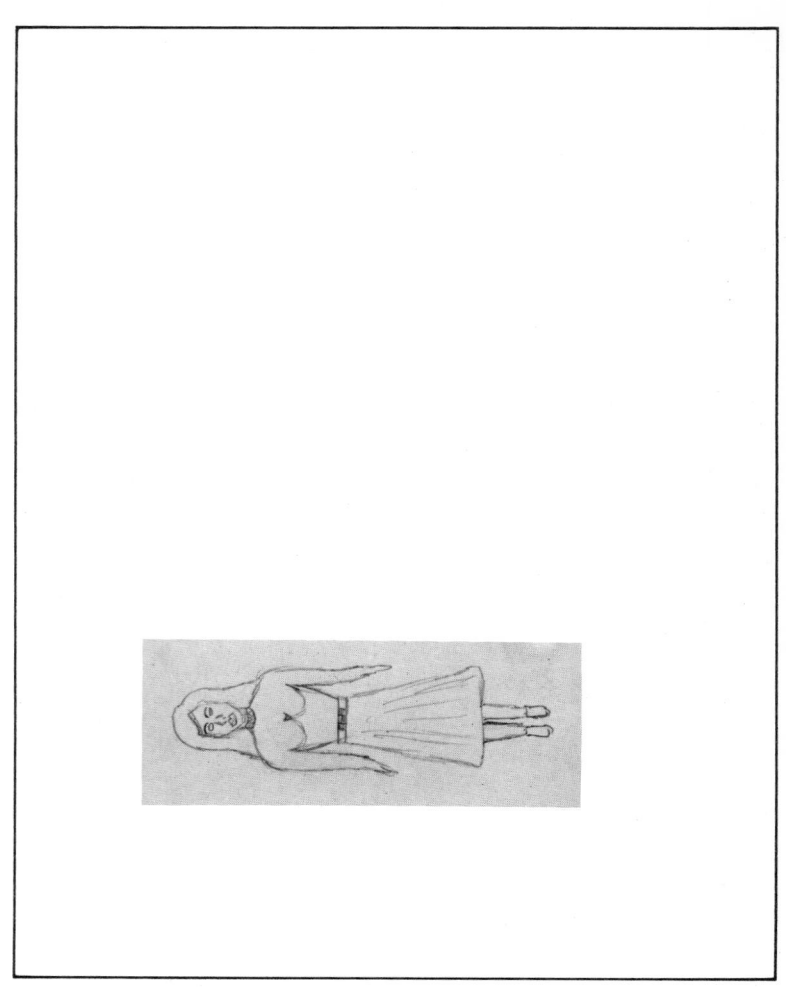

FIGURE-DRAWING CHARACTERISTICS

Structural	Male Female Both	Structural	Male	Female	Structural and Graphic	Male Female Both		Graphic, Global and Height	Male	Female	Body Proportions	Male	Female
Type	0	Omission of Appendages	0	0	Upper and Lower Halves	1	1	Hair Shading	3	5	Head	06	05
Sex Sequence	0	Position of Both Arms	0	0	Four Quarters	4	4	Nudity and Transparency	7	7	Neck	04	04
Posture	1 1	Position of Right Arm	0	0	Relative Size	2		Form	1	1	Shoulders	05	04
Perspective	0 0	Position of Left Arm	0	0	Constant Line Pressure	2	0	Detailing	3	3	Right Arm	02	02
Vertical Midline	3 0	Position of Legs	2	4	Variable Line Pressure	0	1	Identity and Sex	1	1	Left Arm	02	02
Bilateral Symmetry	5 5	Relation of Long Axes	2	2	Line Continuity	0	0	Sophistication	2	2	Chest	04	03
Horizontal Midline	4 4	Right and Left Halves	2	2	Body Shading	6	7	Height	04	03	Girth	05	03

GENERAL CHARACTERISTICS OF SUBJECT

IDENTIFICATION
No. 459
Sex M
Marital status M
Age 24 yrs. at
psychological tests

PARENTAL HISTORY
Father
C   H   S   D   O
–   –   –   –   +
Mother
C   H   S   D   O
?   –   –   –   +

PHYSIOLOGICAL AND METABOLIC DATA

	Admission	Initial	Control	Cold pressor change	Exercise change	Smoking change
Systolic pressure	130	120	104	+14	+32	+04
Diastolic pressure	70	56	52	+28	00	+08
Heart rate	78	88	64	+24	+47	+16

Age 22 yrs.	Height 74 in.	Ponderal index 13.93
	Weight 150 lbs.	Cholesterol 155 mg. per 100 ml.
	Overweight –13 %	Vital capacity 6.0 liters

HABIT SURVEY
Smoking habits: occasional smoker
Age begun 18 yrs.   Inhalation: yes
Habits of nervous tension: 4, 5, 6, 8, 11, 16, 19, 22

Plate 602　　　　MODERATELY SOPHISTICATED DRAWINGS　　　　649

FIGURE-DRAWING CHARACTERISTICS

Structural	Male Female Both	Structural	Male	Female	Structural and Graphic	Male Female Both	Graphic, Global and Height	Male	Female	Body Proportions	Male	Female
Type	0	Omission of Appendages	0	0	Upper and Lower Halves	2 2	Hair Shading	5	5	Head	04	05
Sex Sequence	1	Position of Both Arms	1	1	Four Quarters	0 0	Nudity and Transparency	7	7	Neck	03	03
Posture	1 1	Position of Right Arm	4	4	Relative Size	0	Form	3	3	Shoulders	05	04
Perspective	0 0	Position of Left Arm	0	5	Constant Line Pressure	0 0	Detailing	1	1	Right Arm	02	02
Vertical Midline	3 0	Position of Legs	4	4	Variable Line Pressure	1 2	Identity and Sex	1	1	Left Arm	02	02
Bilateral Symmetry	3 3	Relation of Long Axes	1	1	Line Continuity	0 0	Sophistication	2	2	Chest	03	03
Horizontal Midline	6 4	Right and Left Halves	2	2	Body Shading	6 3	Height	03	03	Girth	04	03

GENERAL CHARACTERISTICS OF SUBJECT

IDENTIFICATION
No. 511
Sex M
Marital status S
Age 23 yrs. at psychological tests

PARENTAL HISTORY
Father
C　H　S　D　O
-　+　(+)　-　+
Mother
C　H　S　D　O
?　-　-　-　-

PHYSIOLOGICAL AND METABOLIC DATA

	Admission	Initial	Control	Cold pressor change	Exercise change	Smoking change
Systolic pressure	120	114	100	00	+20	-06
Diastolic pressure	70	68	60	+10	00	+04
Heart rate	72	78	73	+10	+15	00

Age 21 yrs.	Height 72 in.	Ponderal index 13.26
	Weight 160 lbs.	Cholesterol 222 mg. per 100 ml.
	Overweight -01 %	Vital capacity 5.1 liters

HABIT SURVEY
Smoking habits: nonsmoker
Age begun　yrs.　Inhalation:
Habits of nervous tension: 4, 5, 6, 9, 11, 17, 18

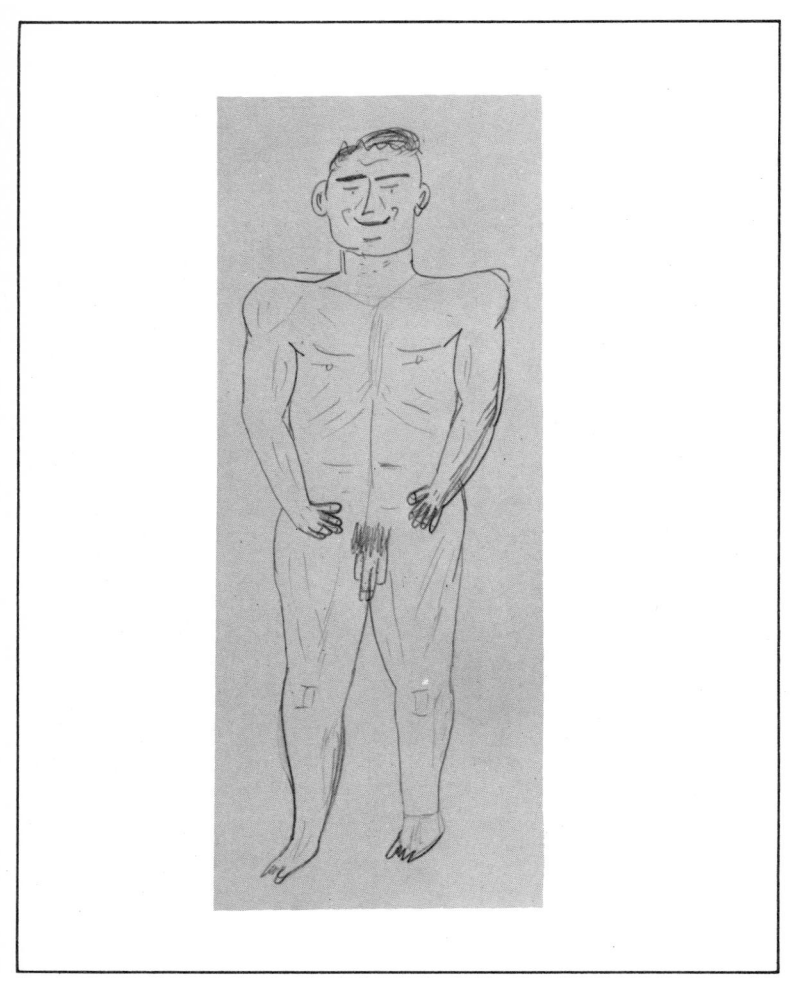

FIGURE-DRAWING CHARACTERISTICS

Structural	Male Female Both	Structural	Male	Female	Structural and Graphic	Male Female Both		Graphic, Global and Height	Male	Female	Body Proportions	Male	Female
Type	0	Omission of Appendages	0	0	Upper and Lower Halves	0	1	Hair Shading	3	5	Head	09	11
Sex Sequence	0	Position of Both Arms	0	4	Four Quarters	4	4	Nudity and Transparency	0	0	Neck	10	07
Posture	1 1	Position of Right Arm	5	7	Relative Size	0		Form	1	1	Shoulders	11	
Perspective	0 2	Position of Left Arm	5	4	Constant Line Pressure	0	0	Detailing	1	3	Right Arm	06	
Vertical Midline	0 4	Position of Legs	5	1	Variable Line Pressure	5	4	Identity and Sex	1	1	Left Arm	06	05
Bilateral Symmetry	3 0	Relation of Long Axes	1	1	Line Continuity	1	1	Sophistication	2	2	Chest	08	04
Horizontal Midline	0 0	Right and Left Halves	1	4	Body Shading	3	0	Height	08	06	Girth	10	04

GENERAL CHARACTERISTICS OF SUBJECT

IDENTIFICATION
No. 610
Sex M
Marital status M
Age 26 yrs. at
psychological tests

PARENTAL HISTORY				
Father				
C	H	S	D	O
-	+	(+)	-	+
Mother				
C	H	S	D	O
?	+	-	-	+

PHYSIOLOGICAL AND METABOLIC DATA

	Admission	Initial	Control	Cold pressor change	Exercise change	Smoking change
Systolic pressure	130	116	110	+20	+48	+01
Diastolic pressure	82	74	76	+20	+02	+04
Heart rate	80	72	66	+08		+11

Age 23 yrs.	Height 68 in.	Ponderal index 12.69
	Weight 154 lbs.	Cholesterol 243 mg. per 100 ml.
	Overweight +05 %	Vital capacity 4.6 liters

HABIT SURVEY
Smoking habits: light cigarette smoker
Age begun 18 yrs.   Inhalation: yes
Habits of nervous tension: 5, 6

Plate 604   MODERATELY SOPHISTICATED DRAWINGS   651

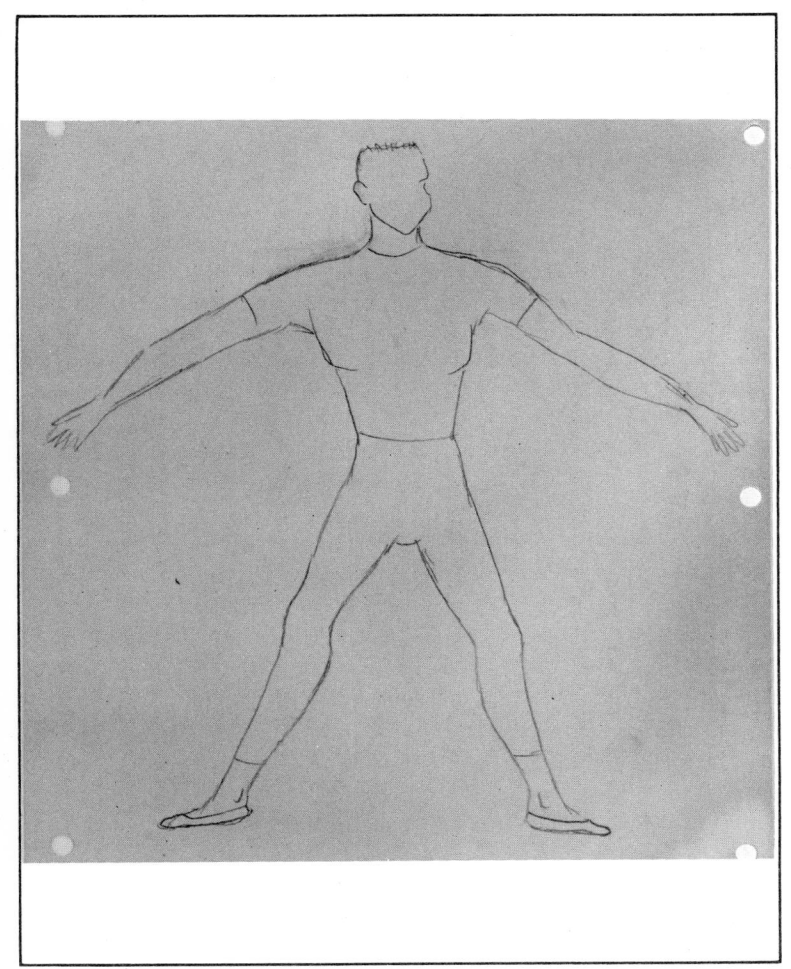

FIGURE-DRAWING CHARACTERISTICS

Structural	Male Female Both	Structural	Male	Female	Structural and Graphic	Male Female Both		Graphic, Global and Height	Male	Female	Body Proportions	Male	Female
Type	0	Omission of Appendages	0	0	Upper and Lower Halves	0	0	Hair Shading	7	7	Head	07	07
Sex Sequence	0	Position of Both Arms	0	6	Four Quarters	4	4	Nudity and Transparency	2	2	Neck	06	07
Posture	1 1	Position of Right Arm	2	6	Relative Size	1		Form	1	1	Shoulders	09	
Perspective	0 9	Position of Left Arm	2	6	Constant Line Pressure	0	0	Detailing	5	3	Right Arm	06	08
Vertical Midline	0 0	Position of Legs	6	7	Variable Line Pressure	3	1	Identity and Sex	1	1	Left Arm	06	08
Bilateral Symmetry	4 0	Relation of Long Axes	1	1	Line Continuity	0	0	Sophistication	2	2	Chest	07	
Horizontal Midline	4 0	Right and Left Halves	0	1	Body Shading	3	1	Height	07	07	Girth	06	05

GENERAL CHARACTERISTICS OF SUBJECT

IDENTIFICATION
No. 637
Sex F
Marital status M
Age 25 yrs. at
psychological tests

PARENTAL HISTORY				
Father				
C	H	S	D	O
–	U	–	–	–
Mother				
C	H	S	D	O
?	–	–	–	+

PHYSIOLOGICAL AND METABOLIC DATA

	Admission	Initial	Control	Cold pressor change	Exercise change	Smoking change
Systolic pressure	110	98	96	+16	+46	+06
Diastolic pressure	80	64	62	+12	+12	+04
Heart rate	80	84	81	00	+39	+03

Age 24 yrs.		
Height 69 in.	Ponderal index 12.99	
Weight 150 lbs.	Cholesterol 273 mg. per 100 ml.	
Overweight +03 %	Vital capacity 3.9 liters	

HABIT SURVEY

Smoking habits: nonsmoker

Age begun   yrs.   Inhalation:

Habits of nervous tension: 1, 2, 3, 5, 6, 7, 8, 9, 10, 11, 14, 15, 16, 18

FIGURE-DRAWING CHARACTERISTICS

Structural	Male Female Both	Structural	Male	Female	Structural and Graphic	Male Female Both	Graphic, Global and Height	Male	Female	Body Proportions	Male	Female
Type	0	Omission of Appendages	0	7	Upper and Lower Halves	9 9	Hair Shading	0	1	Head	04	04
Sex Sequence	2	Position of Both Arms	0	6	Four Quarters	4 4	Nudity and Transparency	7	7	Neck	02	03
Posture	1 1	Position of Right Arm	0	8	Relative Size	3	Form	3	3	Shoulders	04	03
Perspective	0 0	Position of Left Arm	0	8	Constant Line Pressure	1 1	Detailing	3	3	Right Arm	04	
Vertical Midline	3 0	Position of Legs	2	2	Variable Line Pressure	0 0	Identity and Sex	1	1	Left Arm	02	
Bilateral Symmetry	3 3	Relation of Long Axes	1	1	Line Continuity	0 0	Sophistication	2	2	Chest	03	03
Horizontal Midline	6 4	Right and Left Halves	1	1	Body Shading	3 7	Height	03	03	Girth	04	03

GENERAL CHARACTERISTICS OF SUBJECT

IDENTIFICATION
No. 642
Sex F
Marital status S
Age 24 yrs. at
psychological tests

PARENTAL HISTORY
Father
C   H   S   D   O
-    -   -   -   -
Mother
C   H   S   D   O
?   -   -   -   -

PHYSIOLOGICAL AND METABOLIC DATA

	Admission	Initial	Control	Cold pressor change	Exercise change	Smoking change
Systolic pressure	100	110	100	+14	+42	+02
Diastolic pressure	70	68	70	+20	+08	+02
Heart rate	80	96	78	-20	+37	+04

Age 21 yrs.	Height 62 in.	Ponderal index 12.11
	Weight 134 lbs.	Cholesterol 222 mg. per 100 ml.
	Overweight +12 %	Vital capacity 3.5 liters

HABIT SURVEY
Smoking habits: moderate cigarette smoker
Age begun 17 yrs.   Inhalation: yes
Habits of nervous tension: 5, 10, 19, 21

Plate 606　　　MODERATELY SOPHISTICATED DRAWINGS　　　653

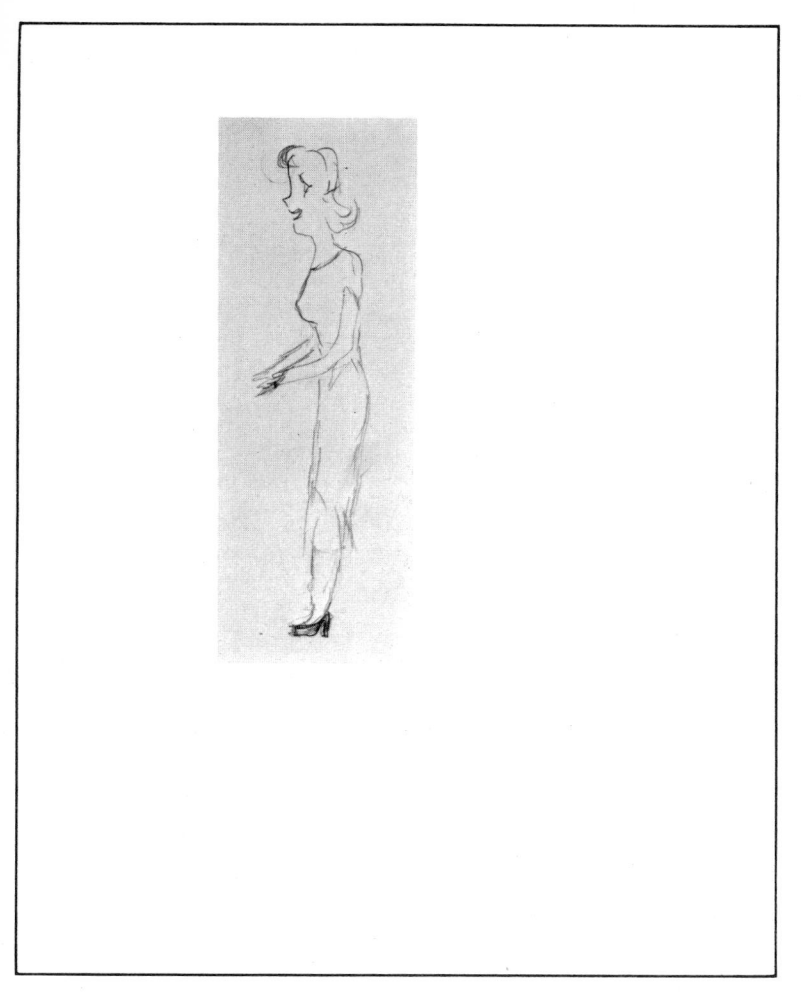

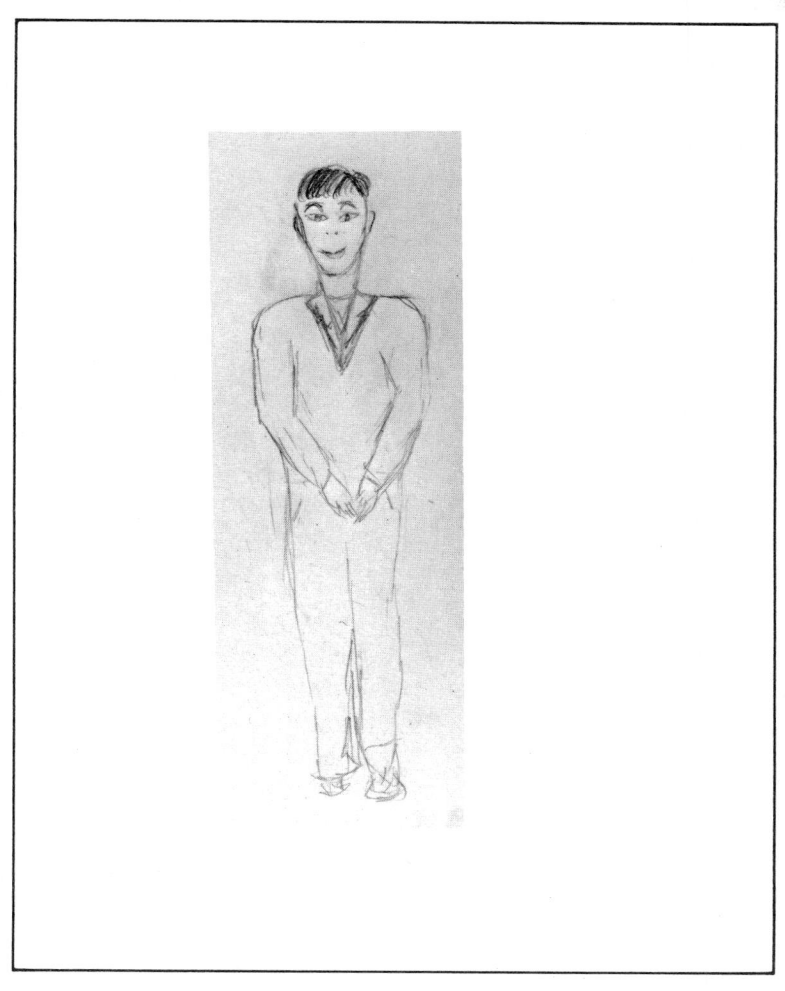

FIGURE-DRAWING CHARACTERISTICS

Structural	Male Female Both	Structural	Male	Female	Structural and Graphic	Male Female Both		Graphic, Global and Height	Male	Female	Body Proportions	Male	Female
Type	0	Omission of Appendages	0	0	Upper and Lower Halves	0	1	Hair Shading	3	7	Head	09	06
Sex Sequence	1	Position of Both Arms	0	4	Four Quarters	4	4	Nudity and Transparency	7	6	Neck	08	06
Posture	1　1	Position of Right Arm	5	7	Relative Size	0		Form	3	1	Shoulders	06	
Perspective	0　2	Position of Left Arm	5	4	Constant Line Pressure	1	0	Detailing	3	3	Right Arm	06	
Vertical Midline	0　4	Position of Legs	2	1	Variable Line Pressure	0	2	Identity and Sex	1	1	Left Arm	06	04
Bilateral Symmetry	3　0	Relation of Long Axes	1	1	Line Continuity	0	0	Sophistication	2	2	Chest	04	04
Horizontal Midline	0　0	Right and Left Halves	1	2	Body Shading	1	6	Height	06	05	Girth	07	04

GENERAL CHARACTERISTICS OF SUBJECT

IDENTIFICATION
No. B28
Sex F
Marital status S
Age 21 yrs. at
psychological tests

PARENTAL HISTORY
Father
C　H　S　D　O
-　-　-　-　?
Mother
C　H　S　D　O
?　?　-　-　?

PHYSIOLOGICAL AND METABOLIC DATA

	Admission	Initial	Control	Cold pressor change	Exercise change	Smoking change
Systolic pressure	100	104	102	+08	+40	-11
Diastolic pressure	60	72	74	+08	-10	00
Heart rate	70	68	60	+04	+27	+02

Age 21 yrs.	Height 65 in.	Ponderal index 13.18
	Weight 120 lbs.	Cholesterol 263 mg. per 100 ml.
	Overweight -07 %	Vital capacity 3.6 liters

HABIT SURVEY

Smoking habits: moderate cigarette smoker

　Age begun 21 yrs.　　Inhalation: yes

Habits of nervous tension: 2, 3, 4, 5, 10, 13,
16, 23

STRONG VOCATIONAL INTEREST TEST

Occupation	Artist	Psychologist	Architect	Physician	Osteopath	Dentist	Veterinarian	Mathematician	Physicist	Engineer	Chemist	Production Manager
Standard Score	49	23	39	35	37	38	14	29	21	23	24	17

Occupation	Farmer	Aviator	Carpenter	Printer	Math.-Sci. Teacher	Ind. Arts Teacher	Voc. Agric. Teacher	Policeman	Forest Serv. Man	Y.M.C.A. Phys. Dir.	Personnel Director	Public Administrator
Standard Score	20	11	06	13	15	-02	02	09	-07	17	12	15

Occupation	Y.M.C.A. Secretary	Soc. Sci. H.S. Teacher	City Sch. Sup't.	Social Worker	Minister	Musician Performer	C.P.A.	Senior C.P.A.	Accountant	Office Man	Purchasing Agent	Banker
Standard Score	17	18	19	19	61	39	28	05	10	16	23	19

Occupation	Mortician	Pharmacist	Sales Manager	Real Est. Manager	Life Ins. Salesman	Advertising Man	Lawyer	Author- Journalist	President Mfg. Co.	Interest Maturity	Occupational Level	Masculinity- Femininity
Standard Score	32	36	36	51	48	47	53	53	42	41	67	23

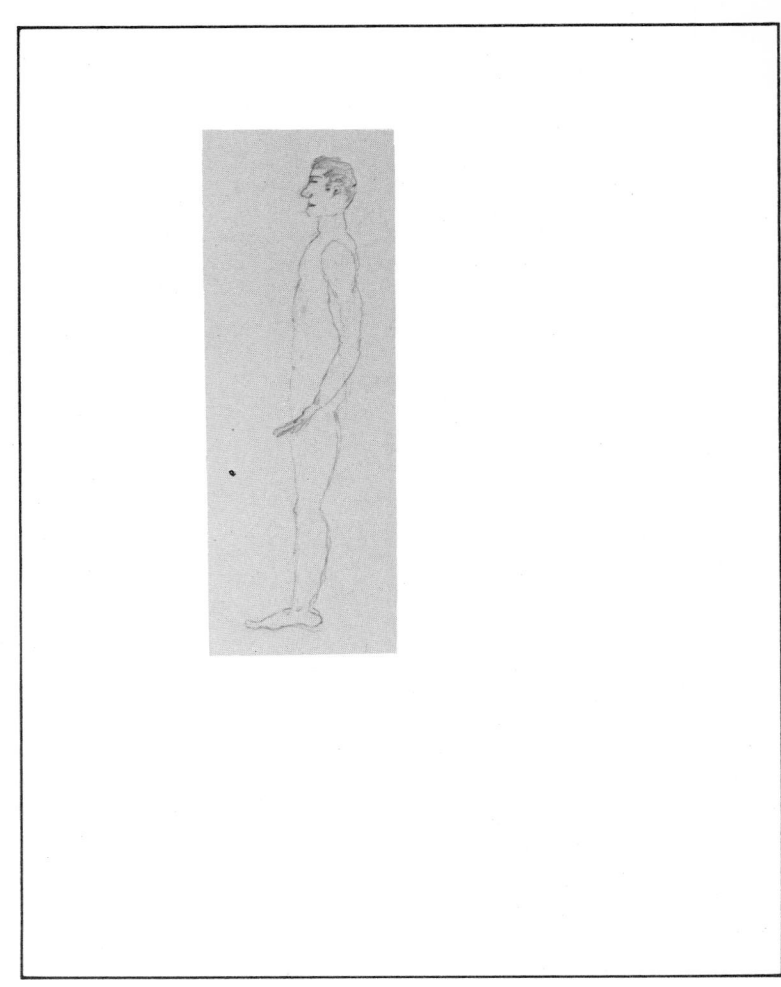

FIGURE-DRAWING CHARACTERISTICS

Structural	Male Female Both	Structural	Male	Female	Structural and Graphic	Male Female Both		Graphic, Global and Height	Male	Female	Body Proportions	Male	Female
Type	0	Omission of Appendages	0	0	Upper and Lower Halves	1	1	Hair Shading	3	3	Head	04	03
Sex Sequence	1	Position of Both Arms	4	4	Four Quarters	4	4	Nudity and Transparency	0	0	Neck	04	03
Posture	1 1	Position of Right Arm	7	7	Relative Size	0		Form	1	1	Shoulders		
Perspective	2 2	Position of Left Arm	5	5	Constant Line Pressure	1	0	Detailing	3	3	Right Arm		
Vertical Midline	4 4	Position of Legs	1	1	Variable Line Pressure	0	1	Identity and Sex	1	1	Left Arm	04	03
Bilateral Symmetry	0 0	Relation of Long Axes	1	1	Line Continuity	0	0	Sophistication	2	2	Chest	03	03
Horizontal Midline	0 0	Right and Left Halves	2	2	Body Shading	3	3	Height	05	04	Girth	03	03

GENERAL CHARACTERISTICS OF SUBJECT

IDENTIFICATION
No. C12
Sex M
Marital status S
Age 22 yrs. at
psychological tests

PARENTAL HISTORY
Father
C   H   S   D   0
–   –   –   –   –
Mother
C   H   S   D   0
?   –   –   –   –

PHYSIOLOGICAL AND METABOLIC DATA

	Admission	Initial	Control	Cold pressor change	Exercise change	Smoking change
Systolic pressure	110	100	100	+08	+20	+06
Diastolic pressure	60	60	60	+35	-10	+06
Heart rate	80	60	57	-04	+14	-09

Age 22 yrs.	Height	72 in.	Ponderal index	13.43	
	Weight	154 lbs.	Cholesterol	225	mg. per 100 ml.
	Overweight	-06 %	Vital capacity	4.5	liters

HABIT SURVEY
Smoking habits: occasional smoker
Age begun 18 yrs.   Inhalation: no
Habits of nervous tension: 4, 5, 11, 16, 25

STRONG VOCATIONAL INTEREST TEST

Occupation	Artist	Psychologist	Architect	Physician	Osteopath	Dentist	Veterinarian	Mathematician	Physicist	Engineer	Chemist	Production Manager
Standard Score	42	51	44	68	55	53	29	38	44	49	57	36

Occupation	Farmer	Aviator	Carpenter	Printer	Math.-Sci. Teacher	Ind. Arts Teacher	Voc. Agric. Teacher	Policeman	Forest Serv. Man	Y.M.C.A. Phys. Dir.	Personnel Director	Public Administrator
Standard Score	41	47	20	36	42	19	32	33	42	41	42	46

Occupation	Y.M.C.A. Secretary	Soc. Sci. H.S. Teacher	City Sch. Sup't.	Social Worker	Minister	Musician Performer	C.P.A.	Senior C.P.A.	Accountant	Office Man	Purchasing Agent	Banker
Standard Score	23	25	31	32	62	45	27	35	19	25	18	15

Occupation	Mortician	Pharmacist	Sales Manager	Real Est. Manager	Life Ins. Salesman	Advertising Man	Lawyer	Author-Journalist	President Mfg. Co.	Interest Maturity	Occupational Level	Masculinity-Femininity
Standard Score	19	24	20	23	18	36	40	41	27	51	59	51

Plate 608   MODERATELY SOPHISTICATED DRAWINGS   655

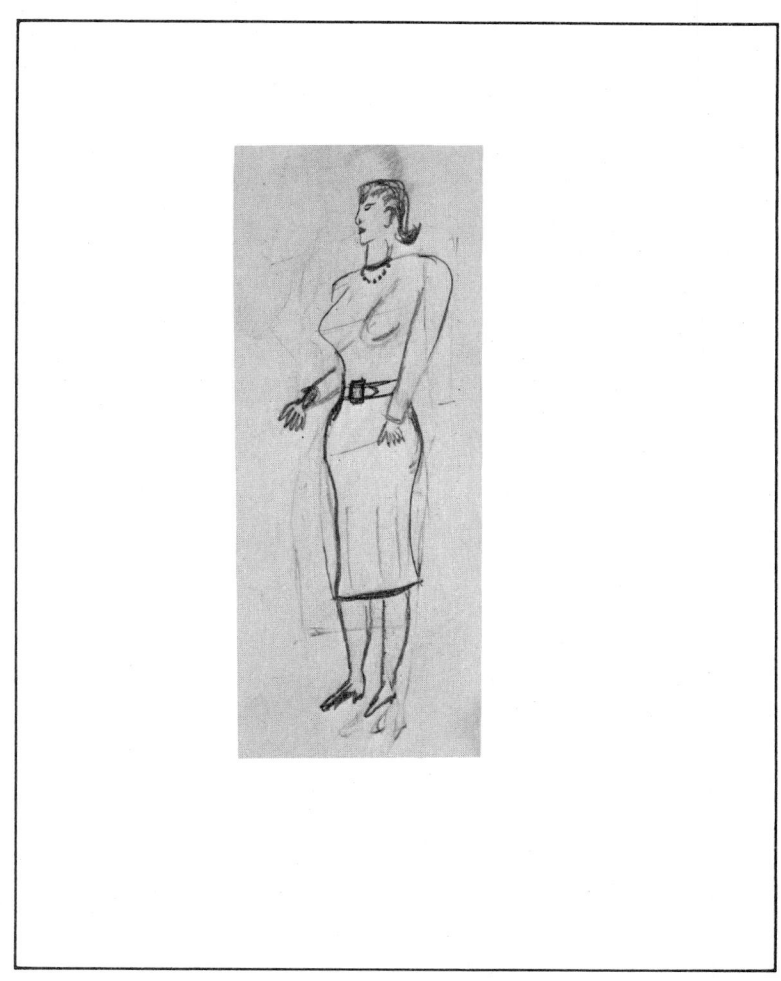

FIGURE-DRAWING CHARACTERISTICS

Structural	Male Female Both	Structural	Male	Female	Structural and Graphic	Male Female Both	Graphic, Global and Height	Male	Female	Body Proportions	Male	Female
Type	0	Omission of Appendages	0	0	Upper and Lower Halves	1 1	Hair Shading	3	3	Head	05	05
Sex Sequence	0	Position of Both Arms	0	4	Four Quarters	4 4	Nudity and Transparency	7	7	Neck	04	06
Posture	1 1	Position of Right Arm	0	7	Relative Size	4	Form	1	1	Shoulders	06	
Perspective	0 6	Position of Left Arm	0	0	Constant Line Pressure	0 0	Detailing	1	1	Right Arm	06	
Vertical Midline	3 4	Position of Legs	2	4	Variable Line Pressure	2 4	Identity and Sex	1	1	Left Arm	06	04
Bilateral Symmetry	5 0	Relation of Long Axes	1	1	Line Continuity	0 3	Sophistication	2	2	Chest	04	
Horizontal Midline	6 4	Right and Left Halves	2	1	Body Shading	3 7	Height	05	05	Girth	05	

GENERAL CHARACTERISTICS OF SUBJECT

IDENTIFICATION
No. C65
Sex M
Marital status S
Age 22 yrs. at psychological tests

PARENTAL HISTORY
Father
C H S D O
- - - - +
Mother
C H S D O
? - - - -

PHYSIOLOGICAL AND METABOLIC DATA

	Admission	Initial	Control	Cold pressor change	Exercise change	Smoking change
Systolic pressure	200	150	130	+30	+50	-05
Diastolic pressure	80	70	70	+35	-10	-06
Heart rate	88	88	77	+20	+28	+02

Age 23 yrs.
Height 70 in.
Weight 187 lbs.
Overweight +21 %
Ponderal index 12.24
Cholesterol 240 mg. per 100 ml.
Vital capacity 6.1 liters

HABIT SURVEY

Smoking habits: occasional smoker
Age begun 20 yrs.   Inhalation: no
Habits of nervous tension: 4, 5, 11, 18, 19

STRONG VOCATIONAL INTEREST TEST

Occupation	Artist	Psychologist	Architect	Physician	Osteopath	Dentist	Veterinarian	Mathematician	Physicist	Engineer	Chemist	Production Manager
Standard Score	35	53	38	73	52	48	36	45	46	49	65	32

Occupation	Farmer	Aviator	Carpenter	Printer	Math.-Sci. Teacher	Ind. Arts Teacher	Voc. Agric. Teacher	Policeman	Forest Serv. Man	Y.M.C.A. Phys. Dir.	Personnel Director	Public Administrator
Standard Score	48	54	26	47	57	32	40	35	43	41	31	42

Occupation	Y.M.C.A. Secretary	Soc. Sci. H.S. Teacher	City Sch. Sup't.	Social Worker	Minister	Musician Performer	C.P.A.	Senior C.P.A.	Accountant	Office Man	Purchasing Agent	Banker
Standard Score	22	28	23	32	62	43	21	46	18	22	18	10

Occupation	Mortician	Pharmacist	Sales Manager	Real Est. Manager	Life Ins. Salesman	Advertising Man	Lawyer	Author-Journalist	President Mfg. Co.	Interest Maturity	Occupational Level	Masculinity-Femininity
Standard Score	13	27	18	16	14	22	27	34	17	50	50	60

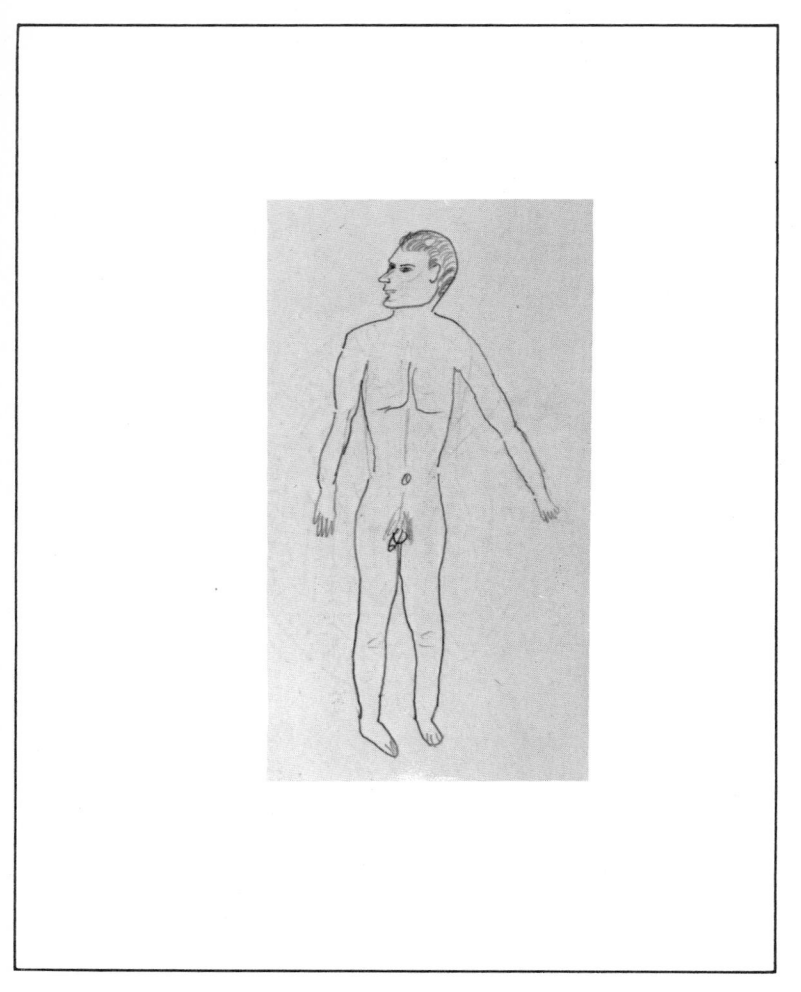
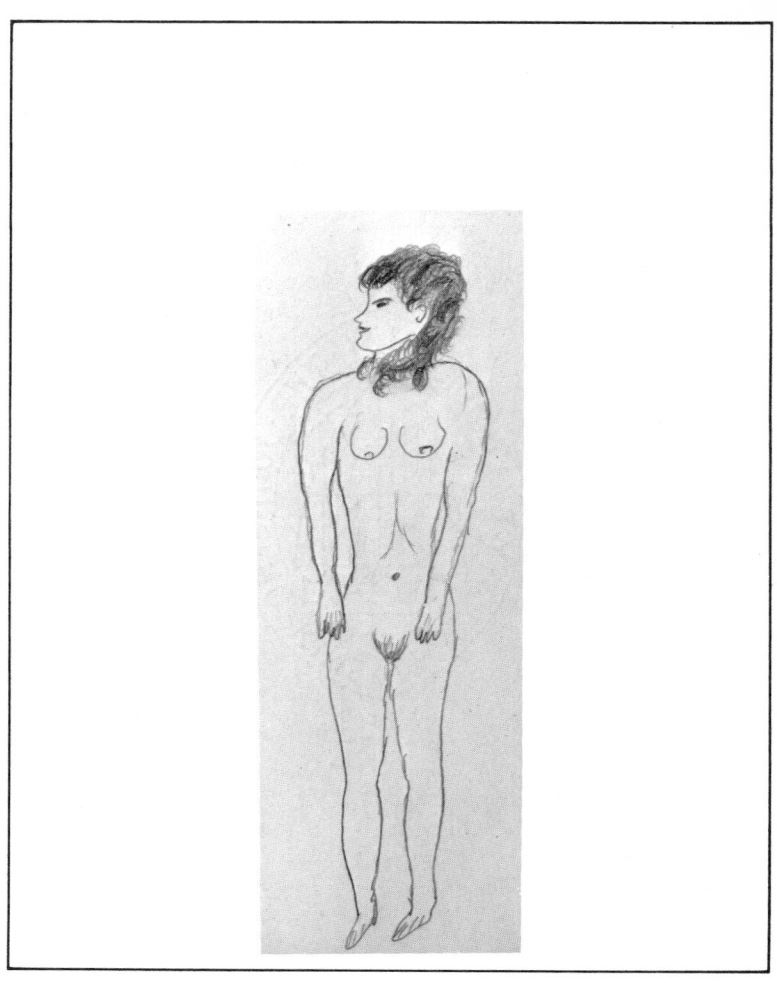

FIGURE-DRAWING CHARACTERISTICS

Structural	Male Female Both		Structural	Male	Female	Structural and Graphic	Male Female Both		Graphic, Global and Height	Male	Female	Body Proportions	Male	Female
Type	0		Omission of Appendages	0	0	Upper and Lower Halves	0	3	Hair Shading	1	3	Head	06	08
Sex Sequence	0		Position of Both Arms	1	0	Four Quarters	4	4	Nudity and Transparency	0	0	Neck	03	04
Posture	1	1	Position of Right Arm	0	0	Relative Size	4		Form	1	3	Shoulders	05	07
Perspective	5	5	Position of Left Arm	2	0	Constant Line Pressure	0	0	Detailing	1	1	Right Arm	04	06
Vertical Midline	0	0	Position of Legs	4	4	Variable Line Pressure	4	5	Identity and Sex	1	1	Left Arm	04	06
Bilateral Symmetry	3	3	Relation of Long Axes	1	1	Line Continuity	3	3	Sophistication	2	2	Chest	04	05
Horizontal Midline	0	0	Right and Left Halves	3	3	Body Shading	3	3	Height	05	07	Girth	04	05

GENERAL CHARACTERISTICS OF SUBJECT

IDENTIFICATION	PARENTAL HISTORY
No. D19	Father
Sex M	C H S D O
Marital status S	- + - - +
Age 22 yrs. at	Mother
psychological tests	C H S D O
	? - - - -

PHYSIOLOGICAL AND METABOLIC DATA

	Admission	Initial	Control	Cold pressor change	Exercise change	Smoking change
Systolic pressure	120	132	116	+04	+48	00
Diastolic pressure	74	89	64	+16	-02	00
Heart rate	74	88	71	-12	+44	+05

Age 22 yrs.	Height	71	in.	Ponderal index	13.22	
	Weight	155	lbs.	Cholesterol	200	mg. per 100 ml.
	Overweight	-02	%	Vital capacity	4.6	liters

HABIT SURVEY

Smoking habits: mixed smoker

Age begun 18 yrs.   Inhalation: yes

Habits of nervous tension: 3, 4, 5, 6, 8, 9, 16, 17, 18, 19, 21, 23

STRONG VOCATIONAL INTEREST TEST

Occupation	Artist	Psychologist	Architect	Physician	Osteopath	Dentist	Veterinarian	Mathematician	Physicist	Engineer	Chemist	Production Manager
Standard Score	42	47	46	39	28	28	01	37	27	26	34	17

Occupation	Farmer	Aviator	Carpenter	Printer	Math.-Sci. Teacher	Ind. Arts Teacher	Voc. Agric. Teacher	Policeman	Forest Serv. Man	Y.M.C.A. Phys. Dir.	Personnel Director	Public Administrator
Standard Score	21	23	05	29	31	09	16	15	15	22	36	41

Occupation	Y.M.C.A. Secretary	Soc. Sci. H.S. Teacher	City Sch. Sup't.	Social Worker	Minister	Musician Performer	C.P.A.	Senior C.P.A.	Accountant	Office Man	Purchasing Agent	Banker
Standard Score	24	34	37	42	63	58	40	32	22	25	17	20

Occupation	Mortician	Pharmacist	Sales Manager	Real Est. Manager	Life Ins. Salesman	Advertising Man	Lawyer	Author-Journalist	President Mfg. Co.	Interest Maturity	Occupational Level	Masculinity-Femininity
Standard Score	12	14	25	34	29	42	49	45	26	52	61	31

FIGURE-DRAWING CHARACTERISTICS

Structural	Male Female Both		Structural	Male	Female	Structural and Graphic	Male Female Both		Graphic, Global and Height	Male	Female	Body Proportions	Male	Female
Type	0		Omission of Appendages	0	0	Upper and Lower Halves	1	3	Hair Shading	3	3	Head	07	08
Sex Sequence	0		Position of Both Arms	4	0	Four Quarters	4	4	Nudity and Transparency	0	7	Neck	04	08
Posture	9	1	Position of Right Arm	7	5	Relative Size	4		Form	1	1	Shoulders		07
Perspective	2	0	Position of Left Arm	9	5	Constant Line Pressure	3	1	Detailing	3	3	Right Arm		04
Vertical Midline	4	0	Position of Legs	1	4	Variable Line Pressure	0	0	Identity and Sex	1	1	Left Arm	04	04
Bilateral Symmetry	0	5	Relation of Long Axes	0	1	Line Continuity	0	0	Sophistication	2	2	Chest	08	06
Horizontal Midline	0	4	Right and Left Halves	0	1	Body Shading	1	3	Height		07	Girth	06	06

GENERAL CHARACTERISTICS OF SUBJECT

IDENTIFICATION
No. E07
Sex M
Marital status M
Age 23 yrs. at
psychological tests

PARENTAL HISTORY				
Father				
C	H	S	D	O
–	–	–	–	+
Mother				
C	H	S	D	O
?	U	–	U	–

PHYSIOLOGICAL AND METABOLIC DATA

	Admission	Initial	Control	Cold pressor change	Exercise change	Smoking change
Systolic pressure	110	118	105	-02	+73	
Diastolic pressure	60	58	68	+08	-17	
Heart rate	92	80	74	00	+41	

Age 22 yrs.	Height	70 in.	Ponderal index	13.38	
	Weight	143 lbs.	Cholesterol	250	mg. per 100 ml.
	Overweight	-07 %	Vital capacity	4.5	liters

HABIT SURVEY

Smoking habits: pipe smoker

  Age begun 19 yrs.   Inhalation: no

Habits of nervous tension: 5, 6, 7, 8, 9, 10,

14, 19, 22, 25

STRONG VOCATIONAL INTEREST TEST

Occupation	Artist	Psychologist	Architect	Physician	Osteopath	Dentist	Veterinarian	Mathematician	Physicist	Engineer	Chemist	Production Manager
Standard Score	24	52	27	47	46	31	13	24	21	27	36	25

Occupation	Farmer	Aviator	Carpenter	Printer	Math.-Sci. Teacher	Ind. Arts Teacher	Voc. Agric. Teacher	Policeman	Forest Serv. Man	Y.M.C.A. Phys. Dir.	Personnel Director	Public Administrator
Standard Score	21	25	16	40	48	23	24	29	18	45	50	52

Occupation	Y.M.C.A. Secretary	Soc. Sci. H.S. Teacher	City Sch. Sup't.	Social Worker	Minister	Musician Performer	C.P.A.	Senior C.P.A.	Accountant	Office Man	Purchasing Agent	Banker
Standard Score	52	48	47	57	64	47	26	31	23	28	07	18

Occupation	Mortician	Pharmacist	Sales Manager	Real Est. Manager	Life Ins. Salesman	Advertising Man	Lawyer	Author-Journalist	President Mfg. Co.	Interest Maturity	Occupational Level	Masculinity-Femininity
Standard Score	26	28	25	30	33	31	34	31	24	65	57	36

FIGURE-DRAWING CHARACTERISTICS

Structural	Male Female Both	Structural	Male	Female	Structural and Graphic	Male Female Both		Graphic, Global and Height	Male	Female	Body Proportions	Male	Female
Type	0	Omission of Appendages	0	0	Upper and Lower Halves	1	1	Hair Shading	2	3	Head	06	06
Sex Sequence	0	Position of Both Arms	0	1	Four Quarters	4	4	Nudity and Transparency	7	7	Neck	06	06
Posture	1 1	Position of Right Arm	0	4	Relative Size	1		Form	1	1	Shoulders	06	05
Perspective	0 0	Position of Left Arm	0	5	Constant Line Pressure	1	1	Detailing	1	3	Right Arm	04	04
Vertical Midline	3 3	Position of Legs	4	4	Variable Line Pressure	0	0	Identity and Sex	1	1	Left Arm	04	04
Bilateral Symmetry	3 3	Relation of Long Axes	1	1	Line Continuity	0	0	Sophistication	2	2	Chest	05	04
Horizontal Midline	6 4	Right and Left Halves	2	2	Body Shading	4	5	Height	05	05	Girth	07	03

GENERAL CHARACTERISTICS OF SUBJECT

IDENTIFICATION
No. E09
Sex M
Marital status S
Age 22 yrs. at
psychological tests

PARENTAL HISTORY
Father
C   H   S   D   O
-   -   -   -   ?
Mother
C   H   S   D   O
?   -   -   -   ?

PHYSIOLOGICAL AND METABOLIC DATA

	Admission	Initial	Control	Cold pressor change	Exercise change	Smoking change
Systolic pressure	110	142	118	+17	+80	
Diastolic pressure	80	58	60	+12	-15	
Heart rate	80	84	82	00	+45	

Age 21 yrs.	Height 73 in.	Ponderal index 13.27
	Weight 166 lbs.	Cholesterol 199 mg. per 100 ml.
	Overweight -01 %	Vital capacity 4.7 liters

HABIT SURVEY
Smoking habits: nonsmoker
Age begun   yrs.   Inhalation:
Habits of nervous tension: 8, 16, 19, 22

STRONG VOCATIONAL INTEREST TEST

Occupation	Artist	Psychologist	Architect	Physician	Osteopath	Dentist	Veterinarian	Mathematician	Physicist	Engineer	Chemist	Production Manager
Standard Score	27	40	27	59	47	37	29	29	21	26	28	22

Occupation	Farmer	Aviator	Carpenter	Printer	Math.-Sci. Teacher	Ind. Arts Teacher	Voc. Agric. Teacher	Policeman	Forest Serv. Man	Y.M.C.A. Phys. Dir.	Personnel Director	Public Administrator
Standard Score	23	26	10	25	42	10	24	26	20	43	40	43

Occupation	Y.M.C.A. Secretary	Soc. Sci. H.S. Teacher	City Sch. Sup't.	Social Worker	Minister	Musician Performer	C.P.A.	Senior C.P.A.	Accountant	Office Man	Purchasing Agent	Banker
Standard Score	42	39	51	46	64	46	31	32	17	26	11	24

Occupation	Mortician	Pharmacist	Sales Manager	Real Est. Manager	Life Ins. Salesman	Advertising Man	Lawyer	Author-Journalist	President Mfg. Co.	Interest Maturity	Occupational Level	Masculinity-Femininity
Standard Score	27	30	32	35	36	36	42	34	30	60	60	38

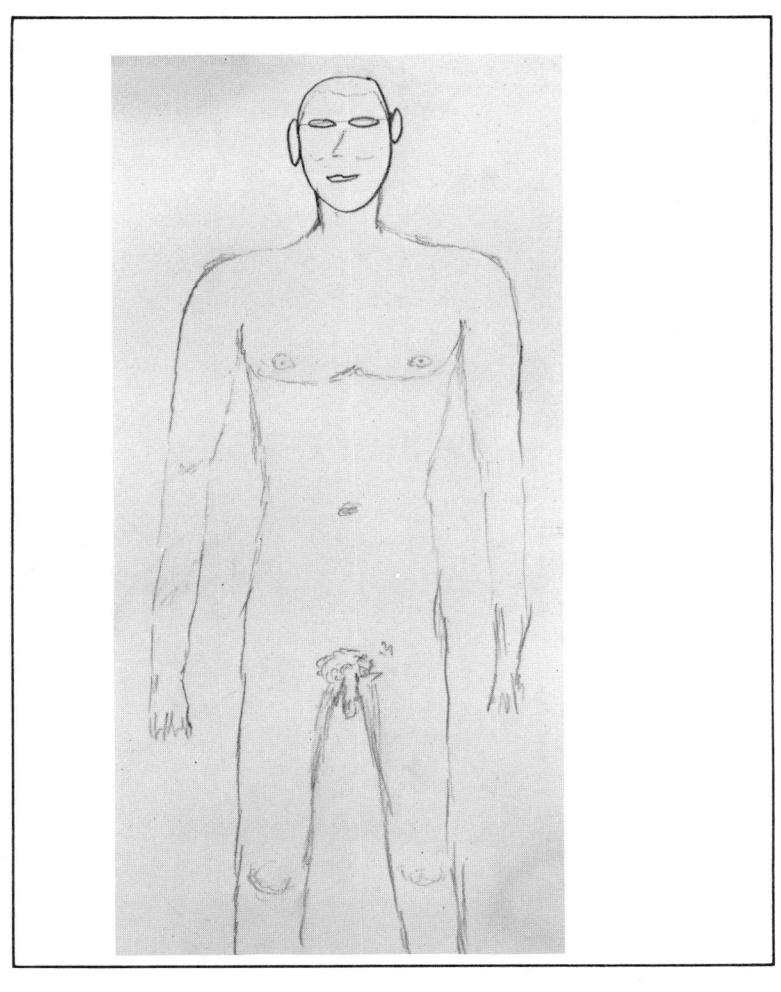
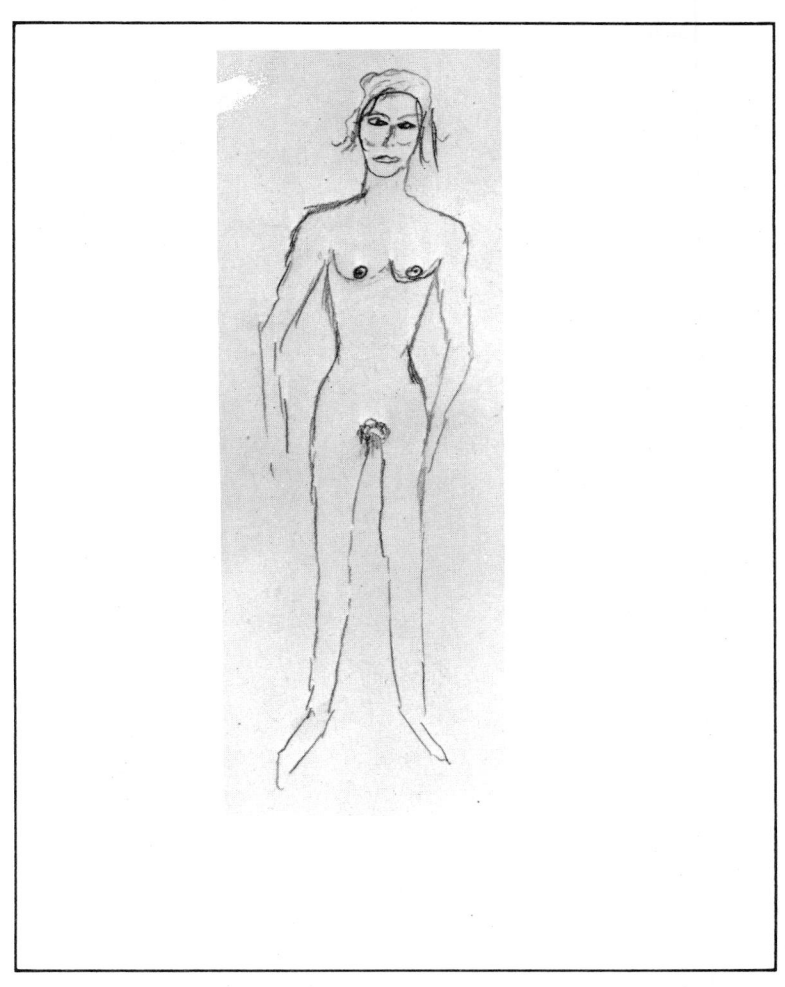

FIGURE-DRAWING CHARACTERISTICS

Structural	Male Female Both		Structural	Male	Female	Structural and Graphic	Male Female Both		Graphic, Global and Height	Male	Female	Body Proportions	Male	Female
Type		0	Omission of Appendages	3	7	Upper and Lower Halves	7	1	Hair Shading	5	3	Head	11	08
Sex Sequence		0	Position of Both Arms	0	0	Four Quarters	4	4	Nudity and Transparency	0	0	Neck	10	08
Posture	0	1	Position of Right Arm	0	5	Relative Size		0	Form	1	1	Shoulders	12	07
Perspective	0	0	Position of Left Arm	0	5	Constant Line Pressure	0	0	Detailing	1	1	Right Arm	12	
Vertical Midline	0	0	Position of Legs	6	5	Variable Line Pressure	3	1	Identity and Sex	1	1	Left Arm	12	
Bilateral Symmetry	3	3	Relation of Long Axes	1	1	Line Continuity	0	0	Sophistication	2	2	Chest	10	05
Horizontal Midline	0	0	Right and Left Halves	1	1	Body Shading	3	3	Height		07	Girth	10	05

GENERAL CHARACTERISTICS OF SUBJECT

IDENTIFICATION
No. E13
Sex M
Marital status S
Age 21 yrs. at psychological tests

PARENTAL HISTORY
Father
C H S D O
- ? - - ?
Mother
C H S D O
? - - - -

PHYSIOLOGICAL AND METABOLIC DATA

	Admission	Initial	Control	Cold pressor change	Exercise change	Smoking change
Systolic pressure	130	130	118	+22	+70	
Diastolic pressure	80	78	74	+22	-09	
Heart rate	70	72	70	+08	+18	

Age 20 yrs.	Height 70 in.	Ponderal index 12.34
	Weight 182 lbs.	Cholesterol 236 mg. per 100 ml.
	Overweight +20 %	Vital capacity 4.3 liters

HABIT SURVEY
Smoking habits: nonsmoker
Age begun yrs. Inhalation:
Habits of nervous tension: 4, 6

STRONG VOCATIONAL INTEREST TEST

Occupation	Artist	Psychologist	Architect	Physician	Osteopath	Dentist	Veterinarian	Mathematician	Physicist	Engineer	Chemist	Production Manager
Standard Score	39	25	32	50	50	38	37	10	02	05	07	16

Occupation	Farmer	Aviator	Carpenter	Printer	Math.-Sci. Teacher	Ind. Arts Teacher	Voc. Agric. Teacher	Policeman	Forest Serv. Man	Y.M.C.A. Phys. Dir.	Personnel Director	Public Administrator
Standard Score	32	14	09	21	29	10	28	27	26	49	28	28

Occupation	Y.M.C.A. Secretary	Soc. Sci. H.S. Teacher	City Sch. Sup't.	Social Worker	Minister	Musician Performer	C.P.A.	Senior C.P.A.	Accountant	Office Man	Purchasing Agent	Banker
Standard Score	41	44	36	43	64	49	20	17	13	26	14	28

Occupation	Mortician	Pharmacist	Sales Manager	Real Est. Manager	Life Ins. Salesman	Advertising Man	Lawyer	Author-Journalist	President Mfg. Co.	Interest Maturity	Occupational Level	Masculinity-Femininity
Standard Score	43	38	32	45	51	43	39	41	27	55	58	21

FIGURE-DRAWING CHARACTERISTICS

Structural	Male Female Both	Structural	Male	Female	Structural and Graphic	Male Female Both		Graphic, Global and Height	Male	Female	Body Proportions	Male	Female
Type	0	Omission of Appendages	4	5	Upper and Lower Halves	7	7	Hair Shading	3	3	Head	13	06
Sex Sequence	2	Position of Both Arms	4	6	Four Quarters	4	4	Nudity and Transparency	7	7	Neck	12	08
Posture	0 0	Position of Right Arm	7	8	Relative Size	0		Form	1	1	Shoulders		06
Perspective	2 0	Position of Left Arm	5	8	Constant Line Pressure	1	1	Detailing	3	1	Right Arm		
Vertical Midline	4 0	Position of Legs	0	2	Variable Line Pressure	0	0	Identity and Sex	1	1	Left Arm		
Bilateral Symmetry	0 3	Relation of Long Axes	1	1	Line Continuity	0	0	Sophistication	2	2	Chest	15	06
Horizontal Midline	6 4	Right and Left Halves	1	1	Body Shading	0	3	Height			Girth	16	06

GENERAL CHARACTERISTICS OF SUBJECT

IDENTIFICATION
No. 330
Sex M
Marital status M
Age 26 yrs. at
psychological tests

PARENTAL HISTORY
Father
C H S D O
(?) - - - ?
Mother
C H S D O
- - - - -

PHYSIOLOGICAL AND METABOLIC DATA

	Admission	Initial	Control	Cold pressor change	Exercise change	Smoking change
Systolic pressure	120	110	106	+06	+24	
Diastolic pressure	60	70	62	+22	+02	
Heart rate	72	66	63	+04	+08	

Age 25 yrs.	Height 68 in.	Ponderal index 12.97
	Weight 144 lbs.	Cholesterol 128 mg. per 100 ml.
	Overweight -03 %	Vital capacity 5.0 liters

HABIT SURVEY
Smoking habits: heavy cigarette smoker
Age begun 13 yrs.   Inhalation: yes
Habits of nervous tension: 2, 5, 6, 9, 14, 16

Plate 614   **MODERATELY SOPHISTICATED DRAWINGS**   661

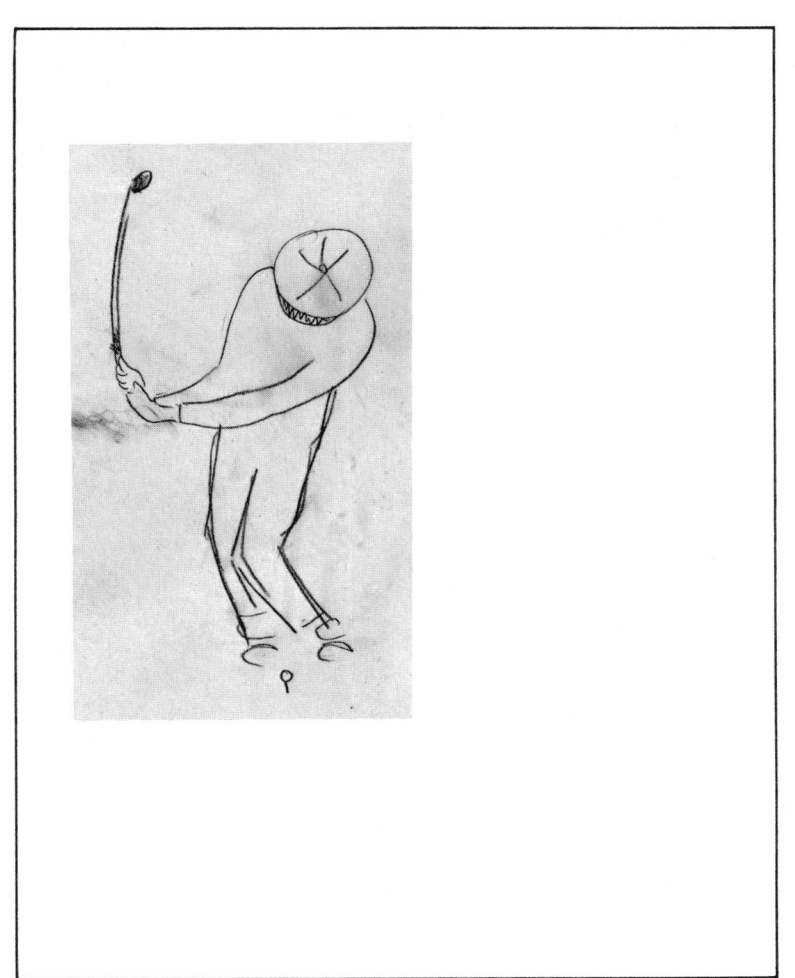

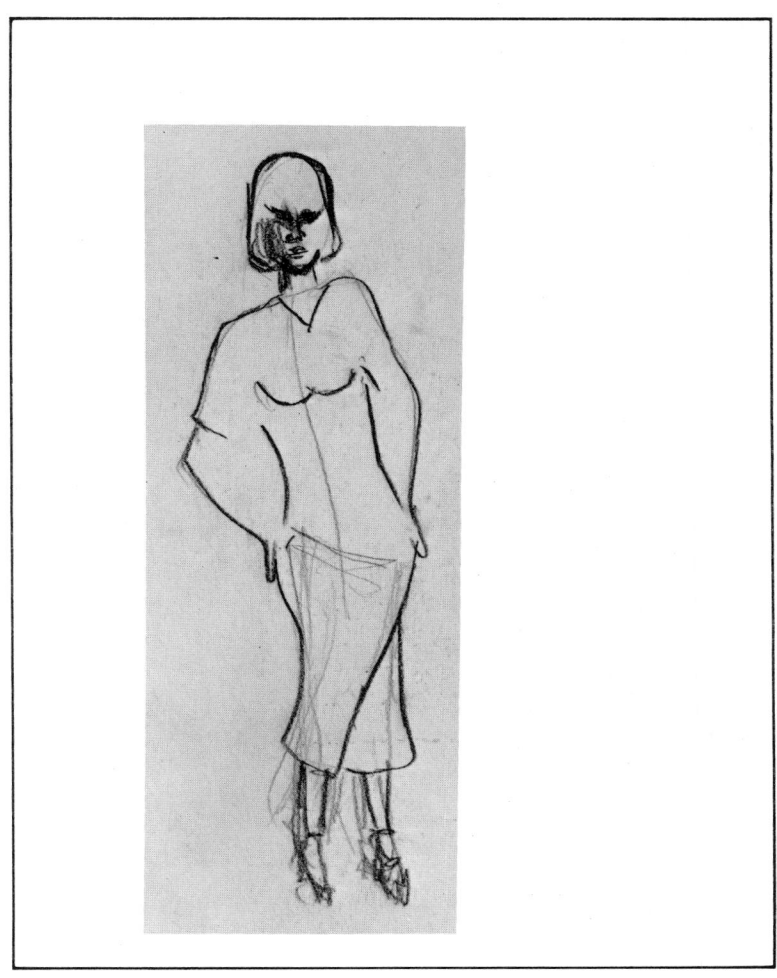

FIGURE-DRAWING CHARACTERISTICS

Structural	Male	Female	Structural	Male	Female	Structural and Graphic	Male	Female	Graphic, Global and Height	Male	Female	Body Proportions	Male	Female
	Both						Both							
Type	0		Omission of Appendages	0	0	Upper and Lower Halves	1	3	Hair Shading	0	1	Head		10
Sex Sequence	0		Position of Both Arms	0	0	Four Quarters	4	4	Nudity and Transparency	7	7	Neck		06
Posture	6	1	Position of Right Arm	6	5	Relative Size		4		Form	1	1	Shoulders		06
Perspective	9	0	Position of Left Arm	6	5	Constant Line Pressure	5	5	Detailing	1	1	Right Arm		06
Vertical Midline	0	1	Position of Legs	8	4	Variable Line Pressure	0	0	Identity and Sex	1	1	Left Arm	06	06
Bilateral Symmetry	9	1	Relation of Long Axes	0	0	Line Continuity	4	4	Sophistication	2	2	Chest		06
Horizontal Midline	0	0	Right and Left Halves	2	1	Body Shading	0	3	Height		08	Girth		06

GENERAL CHARACTERISTICS OF SUBJECT

IDENTIFICATION

No. 420

Sex M

Marital status M

Age 26 yrs. at psychological tests

PARENTAL HISTORY

Father

C	H	S	D	O
(?)	(+)	(+)	-	-

Mother

C	H	S	D	O
-	?	-	-	-

PHYSIOLOGICAL AND METABOLIC DATA

	Admission	Initial	Control	Cold pressor change	Exercise change	Smoking change
Systolic pressure	130	117	115	+18	+15	
Diastolic pressure	75	72	70	+20	-10	
Heart rate	70	70	58	+12	+21	

Age 23 yrs.

Height 71 in.
Weight 159 lbs.
Overweight 00 %

Ponderal index 13.10
Cholesterol 217 mg. per 100 ml.
Vital capacity 5.3 liters

HABIT SURVEY

Smoking habits: former smoker

Age begun   yrs.   Inhalation:

Habits of nervous tension: 5, 6, 16, 25

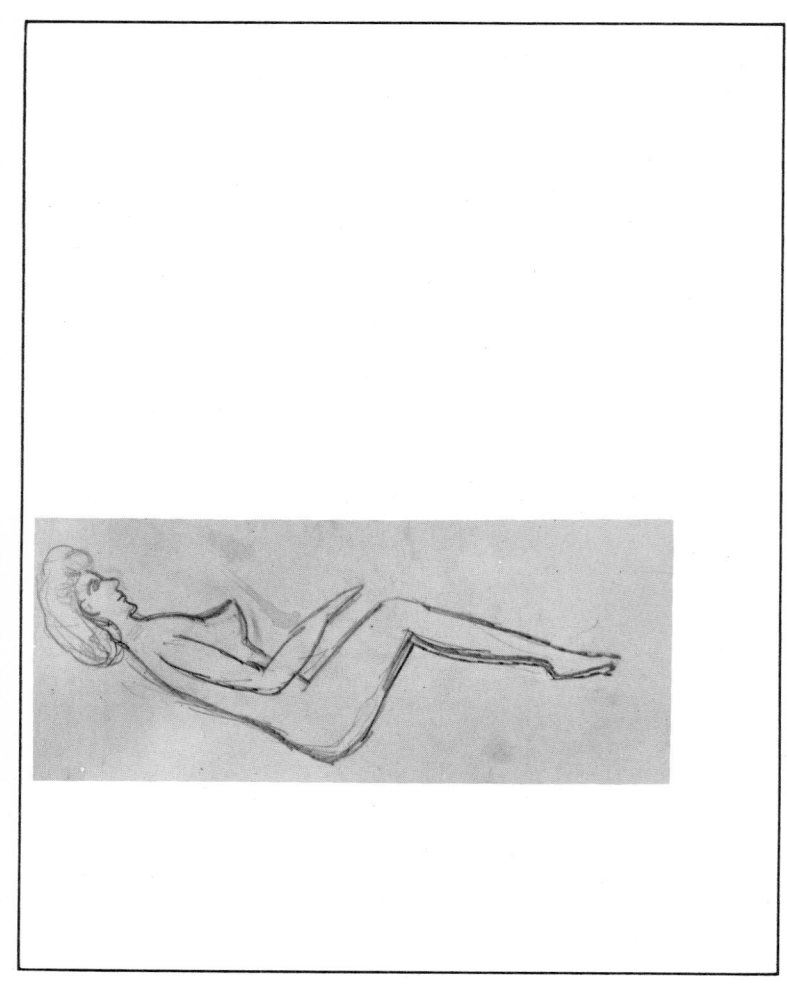

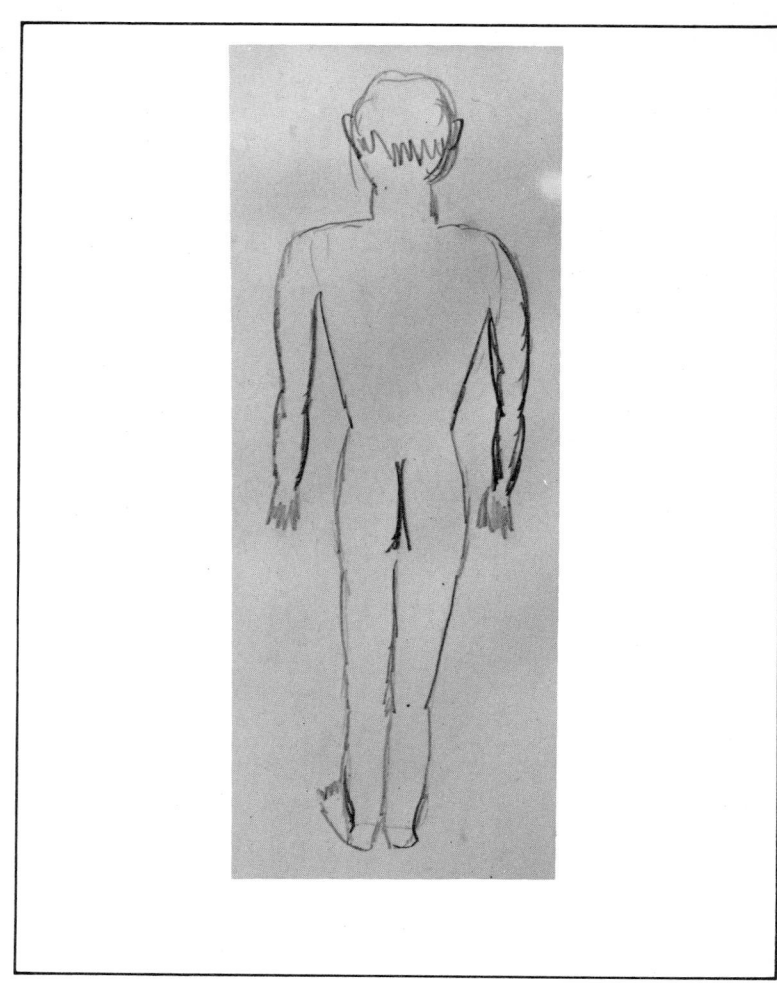

FIGURE-DRAWING CHARACTERISTICS

Structural	Male	Female	Structural	Male	Female	Structural and Graphic	Male	Female	Graphic, Global and Height	Male	Female	Body Proportions	Male	Female
	Both						Both							
Type	0		Omission of Appendages	0	0	Upper and Lower Halves	1	1	Hair Shading	5	1	Head		06
Sex Sequence	1		Position of Both Arms	0	2	Four Quarters	4	4	Nudity and Transparency	0	0	Neck		04
Posture	1	6	Position of Right Arm	0	4	Relative Size	0		Form	1	1	Shoulders	09	
Perspective	3	2	Position of Left Arm	0	7	Constant Line Pressure	0	0	Detailing	5	3	Right Arm	06	06
Vertical Midline	8	4	Position of Legs	2	1	Variable Line Pressure	5	5	Identity and Sex	1	1	Left Arm	06	
Bilateral Symmetry	4	0	Relation of Long Axes	1	0	Line Continuity	0	0	Sophistication	2	2	Chest	08	05
Horizontal Midline	0	0	Right and Left Halves	3	2	Body Shading	0	0	Height	08		Girth	06	06

GENERAL CHARACTERISTICS OF SUBJECT

IDENTIFICATION
No. 778
Sex M
Marital status S
Age 24 yrs. at psychological tests

PARENTAL HISTORY
Father
C   H   S   D   O
(?)   -   -   -   +
Mother
C   H   S   D   O
-    +   -   -   +

PHYSIOLOGICAL AND METABOLIC DATA

	Admission	Initial	Control	Cold pressor change	Exercise change	Smoking change
Systolic pressure	125	130	123	+31	+35	00
Diastolic pressure	65	58	63	+22	-07	+02
Heart rate	72	64	67	+08	+08	+02

Age 24 yrs.	Height 72 in.	Ponderal index 12.18
	Weight 206 lbs.	Cholesterol 190 mg. per 100 ml.
	Overweight +25 %	Vital capacity liters

HABIT SURVEY
Smoking habits: occasional smoker
Age begun   yrs.   Inhalation: no
Habits of nervous tension: 1, 4, 5, 6, 9, 11,
12, 14, 16, 17, 23

FIGURE-DRAWING CHARACTERISTICS

Structural	Male Female Both		Structural	Male	Female	Structural and Graphic	Male Female Both		Graphic, Global and Height	Male	Female	Body Proportions	Male	Female
Type	0		Omission of Appendages	0	2	Upper and Lower Halves	0	3	Hair Shading	3	1	Head	07	06
Sex Sequence	1		Position of Both Arms	0	4	Four Quarters	4	4	Nudity and Transparency	7	7	Neck	04	04
Posture	1	1	Position of Right Arm	0	8	Relative Size	4		Form	1	1	Shoulders	05	04
Perspective	0	0	Position of Left Arm	0	4	Constant Line Pressure	0	0	Detailing	3	3	Right Arm	04	
Vertical Midline	3	0	Position of Legs	4	4	Variable Line Pressure	2	1	Identity and Sex	1	1	Left Arm	04	04
Bilateral Symmetry	2	3	Relation of Long Axes	1	1	Line Continuity	2	2	Sophistication	2	2	Chest	04	04
Horizontal Midline	6	4	Right and Left Halves	2	1	Body Shading	6	5	Height	05	05	Girth	05	03

GENERAL CHARACTERISTICS OF SUBJECT

IDENTIFICATION
No. 731
Sex F
Marital status S
Age 23 yrs. at psychological tests

PARENTAL HISTORY				
Father				
C	H	S	D	O
–	+	+	–	–
Mother				
C	H	S	D	O
–	+	–	–	+

PHYSIOLOGICAL AND METABOLIC DATA

	Admission	Initial	Control	Cold pressor change	Exercise change	Smoking change
Systolic pressure	120	122	114	+24	+26	
Diastolic pressure	80	80	82	+22	+14	
Heart rate	80	84	73	+16	+27	

Age 23 yrs.	Height	65 in.	Ponderal index 12.82	
	Weight	130 lbs.	Cholesterol 197	mg. per 100 ml.
	Overweight 00 %		Vital capacity	liters

HABIT SURVEY

Smoking habits: nonsmoker

Age begun   yrs.   Inhalation:

Habits of nervous tension: 4, 5, 6, 9, 11, 22

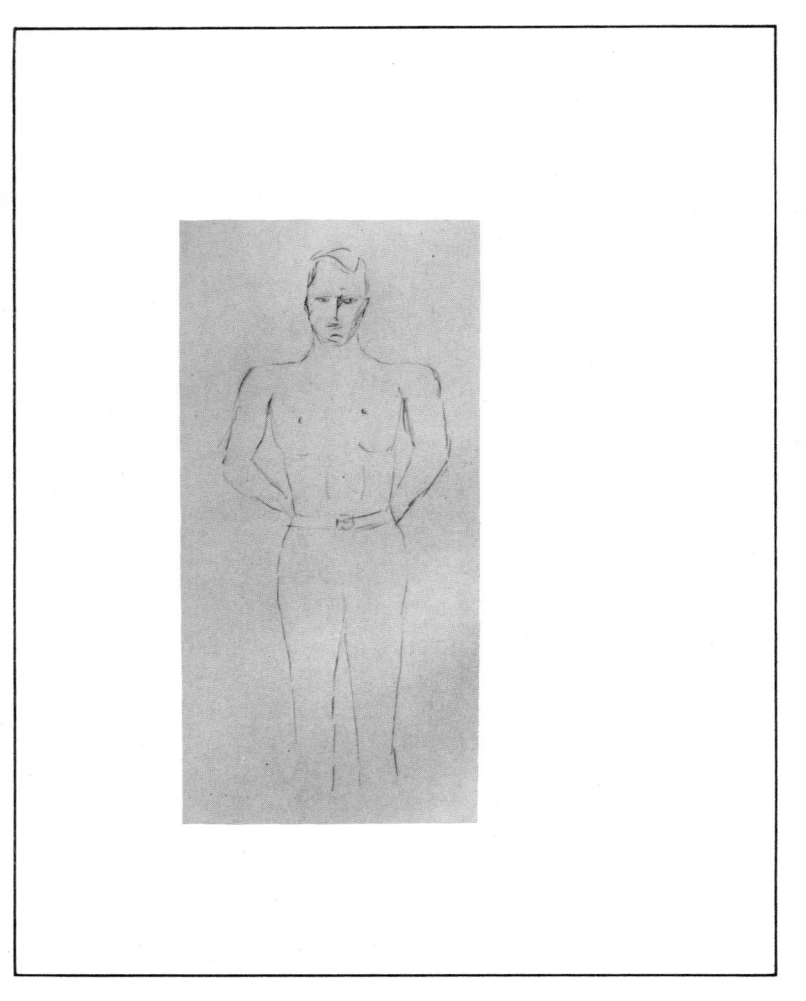

FIGURE-DRAWING CHARACTERISTICS

Structural	Male Female Both		Structural	Male	Female	Structural and Graphic	Male Female Both		Graphic, Global and Height	Male	Female	Body Proportions	Male	Female
Type	0		Omission of Appendages	4	5	Upper and Lower Halves	0	3	Hair Shading	5	5	Head	07	07
Sex Sequence	0		Position of Both Arms	0	3	Four Quarters	4	4	Nudity and Transparency	3	0	Neck	05	06
Posture	0	1	Position of Right Arm	5	5	Relative Size	5		Form	1	1	Shoulders	08	07
Perspective	0	0	Position of Left Arm	5	8	Constant Line Pressure	1	1	Detailing	3	3	Right Arm		
Vertical Midline	0	0	Position of Legs	4	6	Variable Line Pressure	0	0	Identity and Sex	1	1	Left Arm		
Bilateral Symmetry	3	3	Relation of Long Axes	1	1	Line Continuity	0	0	Sophistication	2	2	Chest	06	06
Horizontal Midline	4	0	Right and Left Halves	1	1	Body Shading	1	1	Height		06	Girth	06	06

GENERAL CHARACTERISTICS OF SUBJECT

<table>
<tr><th colspan="2">IDENTIFICATION</th></tr>
<tr><td colspan="2">No. G04</td></tr>
<tr><td colspan="2">Sex M</td></tr>
<tr><td colspan="2">Marital status S</td></tr>
<tr><td colspan="2">Age 24 yrs. at</td></tr>
<tr><td colspan="2">psychological tests</td></tr>
</table>

PARENTAL HISTORY				
Father				
C	H	S	D	O
-	+	?	-	?
Mother				
C	H	S	D	O
-	+	+	-	-

PHYSIOLOGICAL AND METABOLIC DATA

	Admission	Initial	Control	Cold pressor change	Exercise change	Smoking change
Systolic pressure	122	122	120	+10	+40	+07
Diastolic pressure	80	64	70	+22	-10	+02
Heart rate	88	68	75	+32	+02	+11

	Height 74 in.	Ponderal index 13.21	
Age 23 yrs.	Weight 176 lbs.	Cholesterol 188 mg. per 100 ml.	
	Overweight +01 %	Vital capacity liters	

HABIT SURVEY

Smoking habits: heavy cigarette smoker

Age begun 17 yrs.   Inhalation: yes

Habits of nervous tension: 1, 2, 4, 5, 8, 9, 11, 12, 14, 16, 17, 21, 22, 23

STRONG VOCATIONAL INTEREST TEST

Occupation	Artist	Psychologist	Architect	Physician	Osteopath	Dentist	Veterinarian	Mathematician	Physicist	Engineer	Chemist	Production Manager
Standard Score	49	47	49	64	61	52	30	26	31	34	43	33

Occupation	Farmer	Aviator	Carpenter	Printer	Math.-Sci. Teacher	Ind. Arts Teacher	Voc. Agric. Teacher	Policeman	Forest Serv. Man	Y.M.C.A. Phys. Dir.	Personnel Director	Public Administrator
Standard Score	36	45	27	44	36	30	30	29	35	32	31	41

Occupation	Y.M.C.A. Secretary	Soc. Sci. H.S. Teacher	City Sch. Sup't.	Social Worker	Minister	Musician Performer	C.P.A.	Senior C.P.A.	Accountant	Office Man	Purchasing Agent	Banker
Standard Score	27	27	20	44	59	67	19	31	12	21	14	13

Occupation	Mortician	Pharmacist	Sales Manager	Real Est. Manager	Life Ins. Salesman	Advertising Man	Lawyer	Author-Journalist	President Mfg. Co.	Interest Maturity	Occupational Level	Masculinity-Femininity
Standard Score	30	29	24	34	30	45	35	43	31	53	53	36

Plate 618 MODERATELY SOPHISTICATED DRAWINGS 665

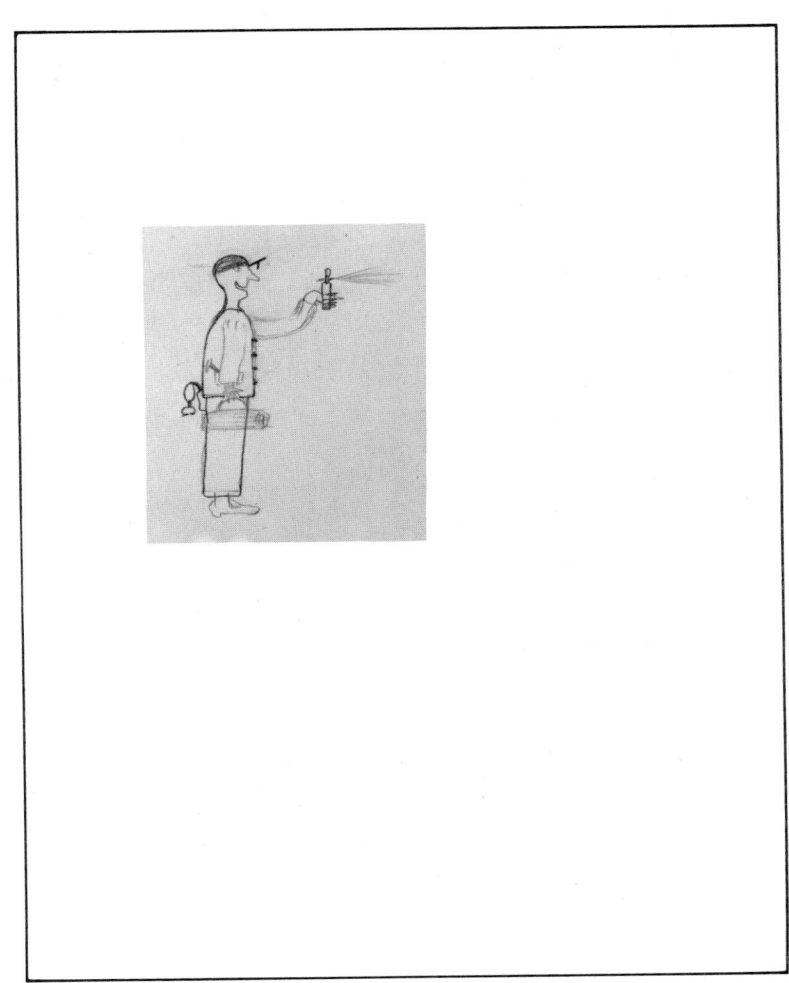

FIGURE-DRAWING CHARACTERISTICS

Structural	Male	Female	Structural	Male	Female	Structural and Graphic	Male	Female	Graphic, Global and Height	Male	Female	Body Proportions	Male	Female
	Both						Both							
Type	0		Omission of Appendages	0	0	Upper and Lower Halves	1	1	Hair Shading	0	3	Head	03	03
Sex Sequence	1		Position of Both Arms	1	2	Four Quarters	4	4	Nudity and Transparency	7	2	Neck	02	03
Posture	1	1	Position of Right Arm	0	3	Relative Size	4		Form	1	3	Shoulders		
Perspective	2	2	Position of Left Arm	2	7	Constant Line Pressure	0	0	Detailing	3	3	Right Arm	02	02
Vertical Midline	7	4	Position of Legs	1	1	Variable Line Pressure	3	1	Identity and Sex	1	1	Left Arm		
Bilateral Symmetry	0	0	Relation of Long Axes	1	1	Line Continuity	2	0	Sophistication	2	2	Chest	03	02
Horizontal Midline	6	4	Right and Left Halves	2	2	Body Shading	4	0	Height	02	03	Girth	03	02

GENERAL CHARACTERISTICS OF SUBJECT

IDENTIFICATION
No. 718
Sex M
Marital status S
Age 24 yrs. at
psychological tests

PARENTAL HISTORY
Father
C   H   S   D   O
-    +   (+)   -   -
Mother
C   H   S   D   O
-    (+)   -   (+)   +

PHYSIOLOGICAL AND METABOLIC DATA

	Admission	Initial	Control	Cold pressor change	Exercise change	Smoking change
Systolic pressure	136	120	116	+14	+24	
Diastolic pressure	70	56	54	+10	+12	
Heart rate	80	96	91	+08	+16	

Age 24 yrs.	Height 70 in.	Ponderal index 13.15
	Weight 151 lbs.	Cholesterol 375 mg. per 100 ml.
	Overweight −03 %	Vital capacity 5.6 liters

HABIT SURVEY

Smoking habits: light cigarette smoker

Age begun 22 yrs.   Inhalation: yes

Habits of nervous tension: 4, 5, 6, 9, 10, 21

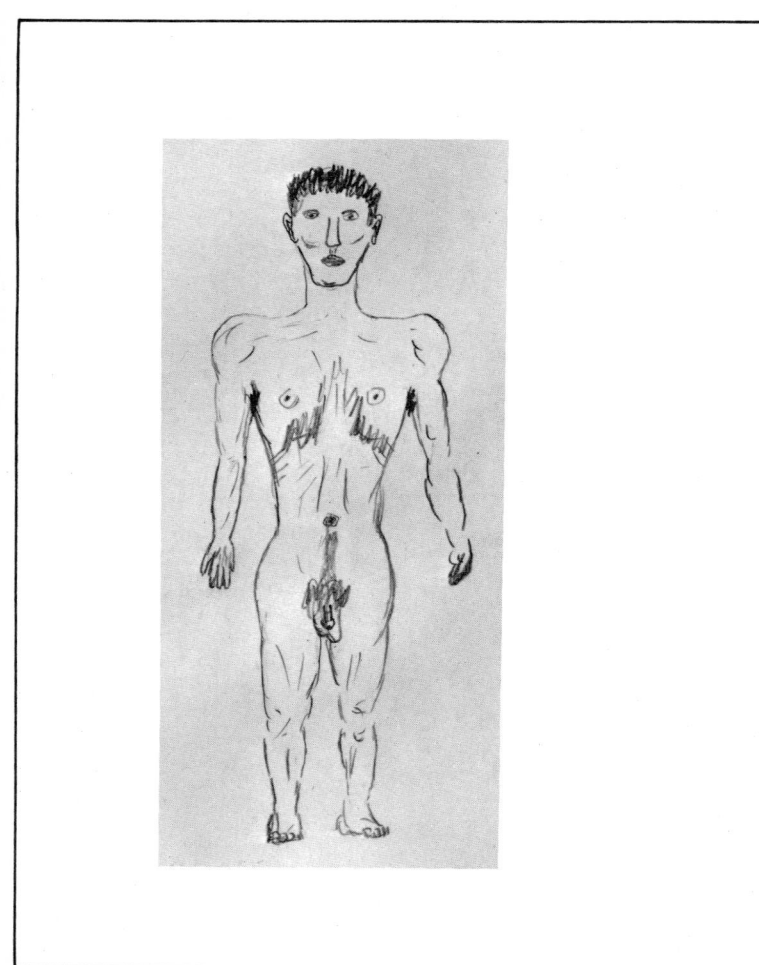

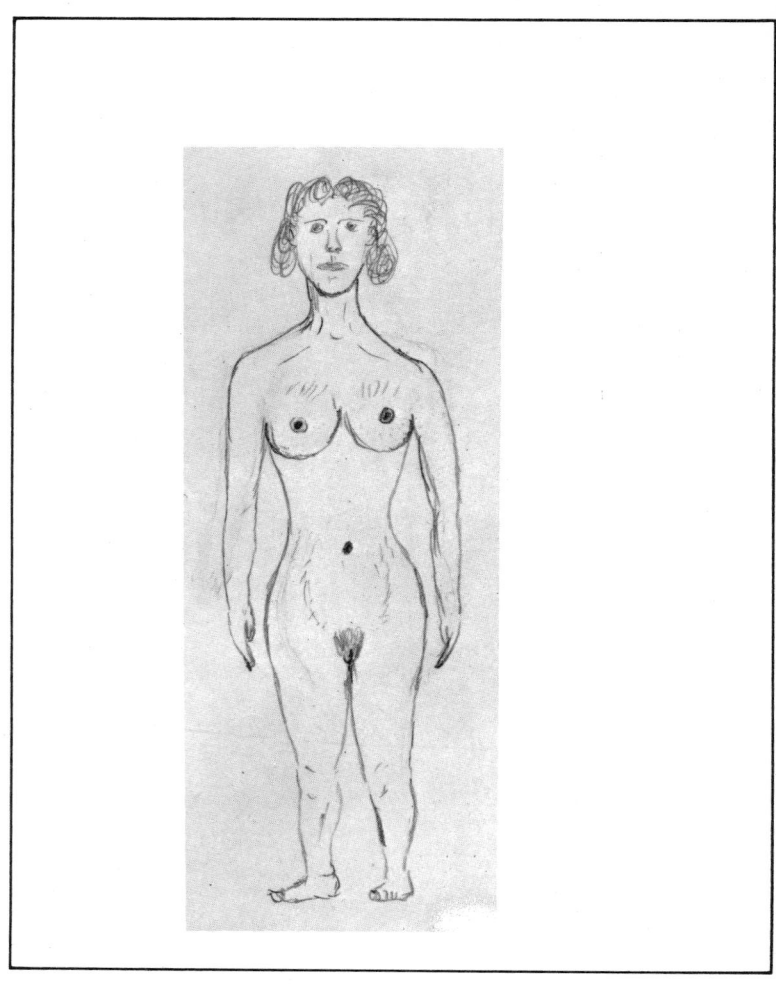

FIGURE-DRAWING CHARACTERISTICS

Structural	Male Female Both	Structural	Male	Female	Structural and Graphic	Male Female Both		Graphic, Global and Height	Male	Female	Body Proportions	Male	Female
Type	0	Omission of Appendages	0	0	Upper and Lower Halves	0	3	Hair Shading	3	3	Head	09	09
Sex Sequence	0	Position of Both Arms	1	0	Four Quarters	4	4	Nudity and Transparency	0	0	Neck	10	12
Posture	1 1	Position of Right Arm	0	0	Relative Size	4		Form	3	3	Shoulders	09	08
Perspective	0 0	Position of Left Arm	1	0	Constant Line Pressure	0	0	Detailing	1	1	Right Arm	06	08
Vertical Midline	0 0	Position of Legs	4	4	Variable Line Pressure	5	5	Identity and Sex	1	1	Left Arm	06	08
Bilateral Symmetry	5 4	Relation of Long Axes	1	1	Line Continuity	0	0	Sophistication	2	2	Chest	07	07
Horizontal Midline	0 0	Right and Left Halves	1	1	Body Shading	3	3	Height	07	07	Girth	06	07

GENERAL CHARACTERISTICS OF SUBJECT

IDENTIFICATION
No. G07
Sex M
Marital status S
Age 26 yrs. at
psychological tests

PARENTAL HISTORY
Father
C H S D O
- (+) (+) - -
Mother
C H S D O
- + + - -

PHYSIOLOGICAL AND METABOLIC DATA

	Admission	Initial	Control	Cold pressor change	Exercise change	Smoking change
Systolic pressure	140	140	120	+10	+38	+08
Diastolic pressure	100	80	70	+16	00	+08
Heart rate	86	76	77	-12	-10	-01

Age 25 yrs.	Height 75 in.	Ponderal index 13.51
	Weight 171 lbs.	Cholesterol 266 mg. per 100 ml.
	Overweight -07 %	Vital capacity liters

HABIT SURVEY
Smoking habits: nonsmoker
Age begun   yrs.   Inhalation:
Habits of nervous tension: 5, 6, 9

Plate 620   **MODERATELY SOPHISTICATED DRAWINGS**   667

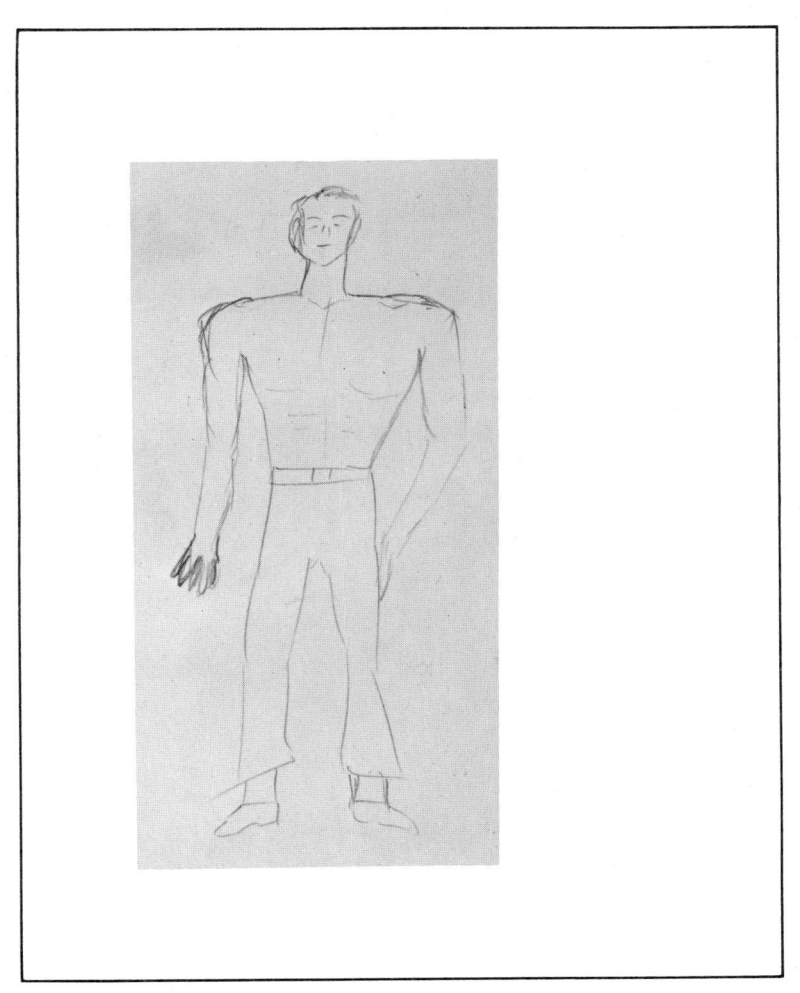

FIGURE-DRAWING CHARACTERISTICS

Structural	Male Female Both		Structural	Male	Female	Structural and Graphic	Male	Female Both		Graphic, Global and Height	Male	Female	Body Proportions	Male	Female
Type	0		Omission of Appendages	0	0	Upper and Lower Halves	3	3		Hair Shading	3	1	Head	06	06
Sex Sequence	2		Position of Both Arms	1	4	Four Quarters	4	4		Nudity and Transparency	3	7	Neck	12	08
Posture	1	1	Position of Right Arm	0	7	Relative Size	0			Form	1	1	Shoulders	11	
Perspective	0	2	Position of Left Arm	5	0	Constant Line Pressure	0	1		Detailing	3	3	Right Arm	06	
Vertical Midline	0	4	Position of Legs	6	1	Variable Line Pressure	1	0		Identity and Sex	1	1	Left Arm	08	06
Bilateral Symmetry	3	0	Relation of Long Axes	1	1	Line Continuity	0	0		Sophistication	2	2	Chest	08	06
Horizontal Midline	4	4	Right and Left Halves	1	2	Body Shading	1	0		Height	06	06	Girth	06	04

GENERAL CHARACTERISTICS OF SUBJECT

IDENTIFICATION
No. 409
Sex M
Marital status S
Age 25 yrs. at
psychological tests

PARENTAL HISTORY
Father
C   H   S   D   O
–   +   –   –   ?
Mother
C   H   S   D   O
–   ?   –   –   +

PHYSIOLOGICAL AND METABOLIC DATA

	Admission	Initial	Control	Cold pressor change	Exercise change	Smoking change
Systolic pressure	136	138	118	+10	+20	–06
Diastolic pressure	76	60	72	+10	–08	–02
Heart rate	76	78	70	00	+12	+03

Age 22 yrs.	Height	71 in.	Ponderal index 11.39
	Weight	242 lbs.	Cholesterol 265 mg. per 100 ml.
	Overweight +59 %		Vital capacity 5.1 liters

HABIT SURVEY
Smoking habits: *occasional smoker*
Age begun   yrs.   Inhalation:
Habits of nervous tension:

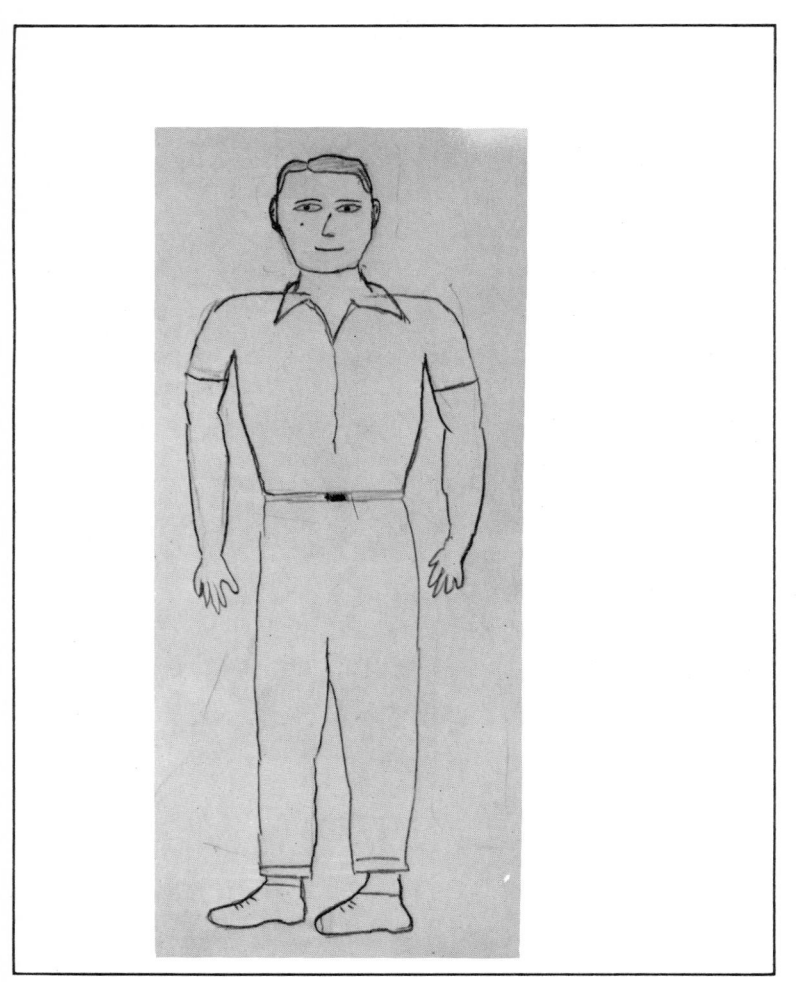

FIGURE-DRAWING CHARACTERISTICS

Structural	Male Female Both		Structural	Male	Female	Structural and Graphic	Male Female Both		Graphic, Global and Height	Male	Female	Body Proportions	Male	Female
Type	0		Omission of Appendages	0	0	Upper and Lower Halves	3	3	Hair Shading	1	1	Head	09	13
Sex Sequence	0		Position of Both Arms	0	0	Four Quarters	4	4	Nudity and Transparency	7	7	Neck	07	12
Posture	1	1	Position of Right Arm	0	5	Relative Size	4		Form	3	3	Shoulders	09	08
Perspective	0	0	Position of Left Arm	0	5	Constant Line Pressure	0	0	Detailing	1	1	Right Arm	08	06
Vertical Midline	3	0	Position of Legs	4	4	Variable Line Pressure	5	5	Identity and Sex	1	1	Left Arm	08	06
Bilateral Symmetry	4	3	Relation of Long Axes	1	1	Line Continuity	1	3	Sophistication	2	2	Chest	09	08
Horizontal Midline	4	4	Right and Left Halves	1	1	Body Shading	4	5	Height	08	09	Girth	09	08

GENERAL CHARACTERISTICS OF SUBJECT

IDENTIFICATION
No. A55
Sex M
Marital status S
Age 22 yrs. at
psychological tests

PARENTAL HISTORY
Father
C H S D O
- + - - +
Mother
C H S D O
- ? - - +

PHYSIOLOGICAL AND METABOLIC DATA

	Admission	Initial	Control	Cold pressor change	Exercise change	Smoking change
Systolic pressure	130	130	124	+22	+40	+08
Diastolic pressure	80	60	80	+26	-33	+06
Heart rate	92	69	65	+08	+10	+08

Age 21 yrs.	Height	68 in.	Ponderal index	11.47	
	Weight	209 lbs.	Cholesterol	258	mg. per 100 ml.
	Overweight +44 %		Vital capacity		liters

HABIT SURVEY

Smoking habits: heavy cigarette smoker

Age begun 18 yrs.   Inhalation: yes

Habits of nervous tension: 6, 7, 8, 10, 23

STRONG VOCATIONAL INTEREST TEST

Occupation	Artist	Psychologist	Architect	Physician	Osteopath	Dentist	Veterinarian	Mathematician	Physicist	Engineer	Chemist	Production Manager
Standard Score	6	9	8	7	4	4	1	7	7	4	6	2

Occupation	Farmer	Aviator	Carpenter	Printer	Math.-Sci. Teacher	Ind. Arts Teacher	Voc. Agric. Teacher	Policeman	Forest Serv. Man	Y.M.C.A. Phys. Dir.	Personnel Director	Public Administrator
Standard Score	3	5	2	5	6	2	2	2	2	3	5	6

Occupation	Y.M.C.A. Secretary	Soc. Sci. H.S. Teacher	City Sch. Sup't.	Social Worker	Minister	Musician Performer	C.P.A.	Senior C.P.A.	Accountant	Office Man	Purchasing Agent	Banker
Standard Score	3	5	6	6	6	8	5	5	2	4	1	1

Occupation	Mortician	Pharmacist	Sales Manager	Real Est. Manager	Life Ins. Salesman	Advertising Man	Lawyer	Author-Journalist	President Mfg. Co.	Interest Maturity	Occupational Level	Masculinity-Femininity
Standard Score	2	3	2	4	2	6	5	7	4	5	5	3

Plate 622   MODERATELY SOPHISTICATED DRAWINGS   669

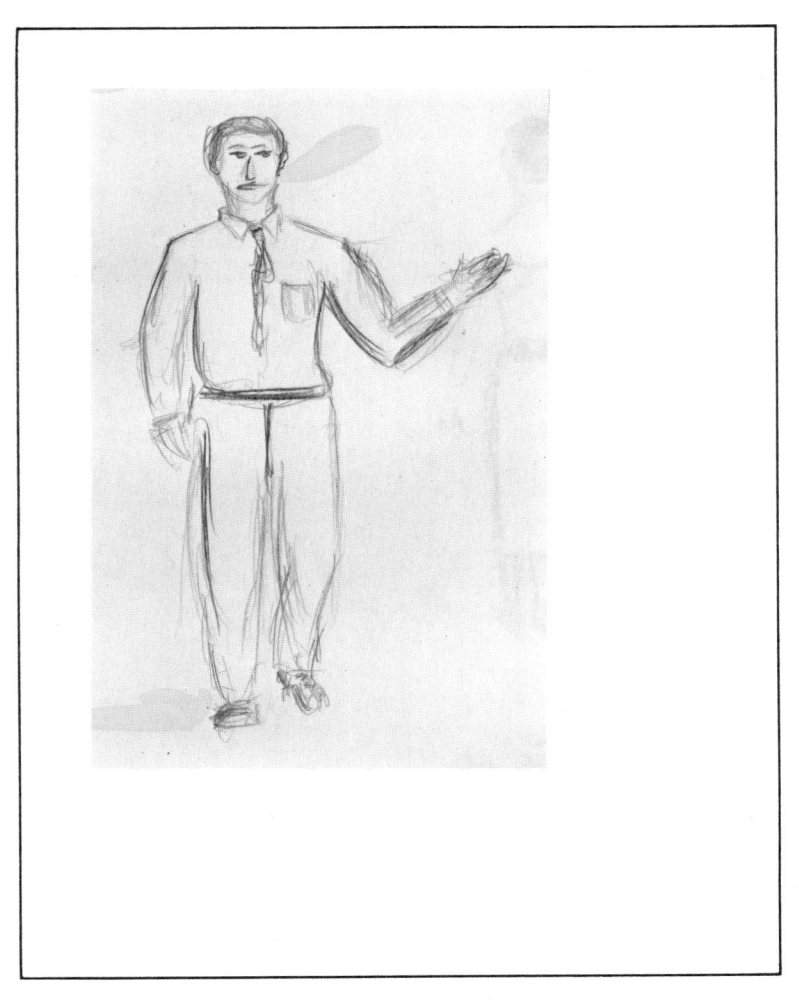

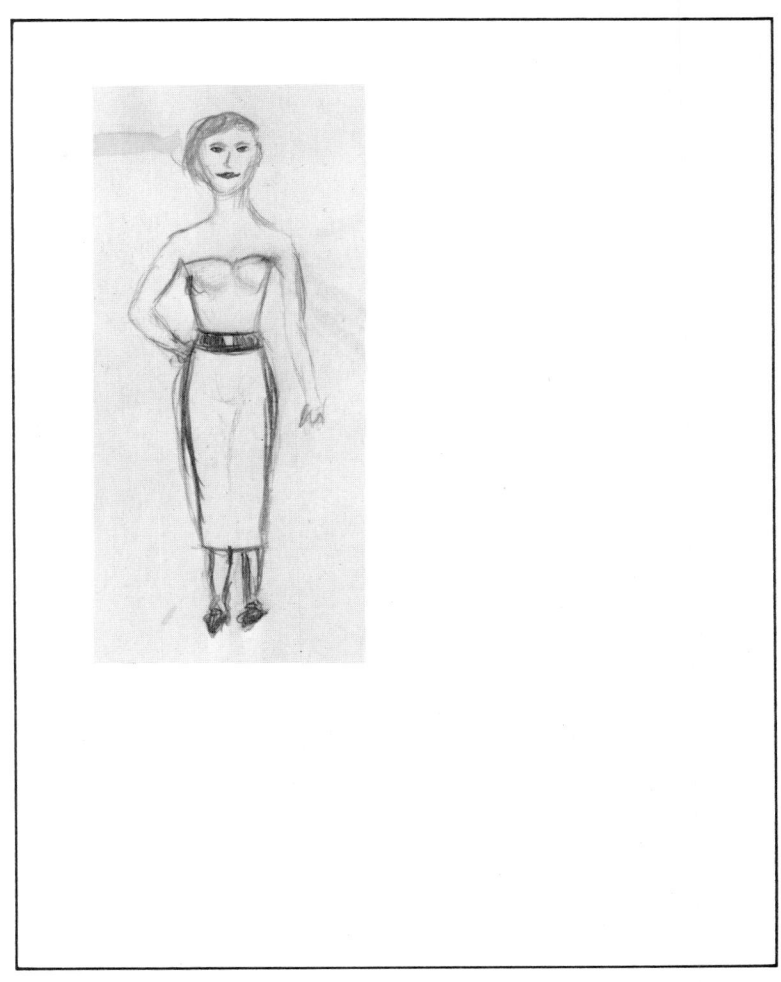

FIGURE-DRAWING CHARACTERISTICS

Structural	Male Female Both		Structural	Male	Female	Structural and Graphic	Male Female Both		Graphic, Global and Height	Male	Female	Body Proportions	Male	Female
Type	0		Omission of Appendages	0	7	Upper and Lower Halves	1	1	Hair Shading	3	3	Head	06	06
Sex Sequence	0		Position of Both Arms	1	1	Four Quarters	4	4	Nudity and Transparency	7	7	Neck	06	08
Posture	2	1	Position of Right Arm	0	5	Relative Size	0		Form	1	1	Shoulders	07	05
Perspective	0	0	Position of Left Arm	2	0	Constant Line Pressure	0	0	Detailing	3	3	Right Arm	04	04
Vertical Midline	3	0	Position of Legs	8	4	Variable Line Pressure	3	3	Identity and Sex	1	1	Left Arm	05	04
Bilateral Symmetry	3	4	Relation of Long Axes	1	1	Line Continuity	0	0	Sophistication	2	2	Chest	06	04
Horizontal Midline	4	4	Right and Left Halves	2	2	Body Shading	7	7	Height	06	05	Girth	08	04

GENERAL CHARACTERISTICS OF SUBJECT

IDENTIFICATION
No. C69
Sex M
Marital status S
Age 22 yrs. at
psychological tests

PARENTAL HISTORY					
Father					
C	H	S	D	O	
–	+	–	–	+	
Mother					
C	H	S	D	O	
–	U	–	–	U	

PHYSIOLOGICAL AND METABOLIC DATA

	Admission	Initial	Control	Cold pressor change	Exercise change	Smoking change
Systolic pressure	148	125	120	+20	+20	+11
Diastolic pressure	90	80	80	+20	-10	+13
Heart rate	78	76	71	+04	+08	+05

Age 23 yrs.	Height	72	in.	Ponderal index 11.78
	Weight	228	lbs.	Cholesterol	186	mg. per 100 ml.
	Overweight +40 %			Vital capacity	5.0	liters

HABIT SURVEY
Smoking habits: heavy cigarette smoker
Age begun 14 yrs.   Inhalation: yes
Habits of nervous tension: 4, 5, 6, 9, 10, 17,
18, 22, 23, 25

STRONG VOCATIONAL INTEREST TEST

Occupation	Artist	Psychologist	Architect	Physician	Osteopath	Dentist	Veterinarian	Mathematician	Physicist	Engineer	Chemist	Production Manager
Standard Score	32	51	37	54	50	35	18	15	14	27	29	35

Occupation	Farmer	Aviator	Carpenter	Printer	Math.-Sci. Teacher	Ind. Arts Teacher	Voc. Agric. Teacher	Policeman	Forest Serv. Man	Y.M.C.A. Phys. Dir.	Personnel Director	Public Administrator
Standard Score	21	36	18	37	38	22	23	32	23	53	65	55

Occupation	Y.M.C.A. Secretary	Soc. Sci. H.S. Teacher	City Sch. Sup't.	Social Worker	Minister	Musician Performer	C.P.A.	Senior C.P.A.	Accountant	Office Man	Purchasing Agent	Banker
Standard Score	46	44	36	62	62	55	33	39	24	33	16	13

Occupation	Mortician	Pharmacist	Sales Manager	Real Est. Manager	Life Ins. Salesman	Advertising Man	Lawyer	Author- Journalist	President Mfg. Co.	Interest Maturity	Occupational Level	Masculinity- Femininity
Standard Score	34	33	36	36	38	46	36	34	30	63	54	40

FIGURE-DRAWING CHARACTERISTICS

Structural	Male Female Both		Structural	Male	Female	Structural and Graphic	Male Female Both		Graphic, Global and Height	Male	Female	Body Proportions	Male	Female
Type	0		Omission of Appendages	3	6	Upper and Lower Halves	7	7	Hair Shading	5	3	Head	09	10
Sex Sequence	1		Position of Both Arms	4	4	Four Quarters	4	4	Nudity and Transparency	6	6	Neck	06	12
Posture	0	0	Position of Right Arm	7	7	Relative Size	5		Form	3	3	Shoulders		
Perspective	2	2	Position of Left Arm	4	4	Constant Line Pressure	0	0	Detailing	1	3	Right Arm		
Vertical Midline	4	0	Position of Legs	1	1	Variable Line Pressure	5	3	Identity and Sex	1	1	Left Arm	06	
Bilateral Symmetry	0	0	Relation of Long Axes	1	1	Line Continuity	0	0	Sophistication	2	2	Chest	09	09
Horizontal Midline	6	4	Right and Left Halves	2	1	Body Shading	3	0	Height			Girth	05	06

GENERAL CHARACTERISTICS OF SUBJECT

IDENTIFICATION
No. 263
Sex M
Marital status S
Age 24 yrs. at psychological tests

PARENTAL HISTORY				
Father				
C	H	S	D	O
−	+	−	−	+
Mother				
C	H	S	D	O
−	−	−	−	−

PHYSIOLOGICAL AND METABOLIC DATA

	Admission	Initial	Control	Cold pressor change	Exercise change	Smoking change
Systolic pressure	114	112	105	+01	+25	
Diastolic pressure	66	66	66	+06	−14	
Heart rate	80	70	64	+04	+19	

Age 24 yrs.	Height 70 in.	Ponderal index 13.42
	Weight 142 lbs.	Cholesterol 208 mg. per 100 ml.
	Overweight −09 %	Vital capacity 5.0 liters

HABIT SURVEY
Smoking habits: heavy cigarette smoker
Age begun 16 yrs.   Inhalation: yes
Habits of nervous tension: 1, 3, 4, 5, 6, 10, 15, 19, 20, 22

FIGURE-DRAWING CHARACTERISTICS

Structural	Male Female Both		Structural	Male	Female	Structural and Graphic	Male Female Both		Graphic, Global and Height	Male	Female	Body Proportions	Male	Female
Type	0		Omission of Appendages	0	0	Upper and Lower Halves	3	1	Hair Shading	1	3	Head	08	08
Sex Sequence	1		Position of Both Arms	0	1	Four Quarters	4	4	Nudity and Transparency	7	6	Neck	08	08
Posture	1	1	Position of Right Arm	5	5	Relative Size	2		Form	1	1	Shoulders	06	05
Perspective	0	0	Position of Left Arm	5	0	Constant Line Pressure	5	0	Detailing	1	3	Right Arm	04	04
Vertical Midline	3	0	Position of Legs	4	4	Variable Line Pressure	0	5	Identity and Sex	1	1	Left Arm	04	04
Bilateral Symmetry	5	3	Relation of Long Axes	1	1	Line Continuity	0	0	Sophistication	2	2	Chest	05	05
Horizontal Midline	6	4	Right and Left Halves	2	2	Body Shading	4	1	Height	05	05	Girth	06	05

GENERAL CHARACTERISTICS OF SUBJECT

IDENTIFICATION
No.   304
Sex   M
Marital status   S
Age   25 yrs. at
psychological tests

PARENTAL HISTORY				
Father				
C	H	S	D	O
-	+	-	-	+
Mother				
C	H	S	D	O
-	-	-	+	-

PHYSIOLOGICAL AND METABOLIC DATA

	Admission	Initial	Control	Cold pressor change	Exercise change	Smoking change
Systolic pressure	138	128	116	+02	+28	00
Diastolic pressure	70	76	86	+06	-04	-02
Heart rate	88	66	64	+04	+22	00

Age 23 yrs.	Height 70 in.	Ponderal index 12.09
	Weight 194 lbs.	Cholesterol 222 mg. per 100 ml.
	Overweight +25 %	Vital capacity 4.7 liters

HABIT SURVEY

Smoking habits: moderate cigarette smoker

Age begun 15 yrs.   Inhalation: yes

Habits of nervous tension: 4, 5, 6, 9, 10,

17, 18, 19, 22, 25

FIGURE-DRAWING CHARACTERISTICS

Structural	Male Female Both	Structural	Male	Female	Structural and Graphic	Male Female Both		Graphic, Global and Height	Male	Female	Body Proportions	Male	Female
Type	0	Omission of Appendages	0	0	Upper and Lower Halves	1	0	Hair Shading	3	3	Head	08	09
Sex Sequence	1	Position of Both Arms	0	0	Four Quarters	4	4	Nudity and Transparency	7	7	Neck	10	10
Posture	1 1	Position of Right Arm	2	5	Relative Size	2		Form	1	1	Shoulders	09	07
Perspective	0 0	Position of Left Arm	2	5	Constant Line Pressure	0	0	Detailing	1	1	Right Arm	06	06
Vertical Midline	3 3	Position of Legs	6	6	Variable Line Pressure	5	5	Identity and Sex	1	1	Left Arm	06	06
Bilateral Symmetry	3 3	Relation of Long Axes	1	1	Line Continuity	0	0	Sophistication	2	2	Chest	08	07
Horizontal Midline	4 4	Right and Left Halves	1	1	Body Shading	7	5	Height	07	07	Girth	09	08

GENERAL CHARACTERISTICS OF SUBJECT

IDENTIFICATION
No. 336
Sex M
Marital status S
Age 24 yrs. at
psychological tests

PARENTAL HISTORY
Father
C   H   S   D   O
-   +   +   -   -
Mother
C   H   S   D   O
-   -   -   -   -

PHYSIOLOGICAL AND METABOLIC DATA

	Admission	Initial	Control	Cold pressor change	Exercise change	Smoking change
Systolic pressure	118	126	112	+04	+20	+04
Diastolic pressure	72	60	58	+10	00	+04
Heart rate	76	88	81	00	+19	00

Age 21 yrs.

Height	70 in.	Ponderal index 13.06
Weight	154 lbs.	Cholesterol 200 mg. per 100 ml.
Overweight +01 %		Vital capacity 5.6 liters

HABIT SURVEY

Smoking habits: nonsmoker

Age begun   yrs.   Inhalation:

Habits of nervous tension: 1, 2, 4, 5, 6, 16, 17, 25

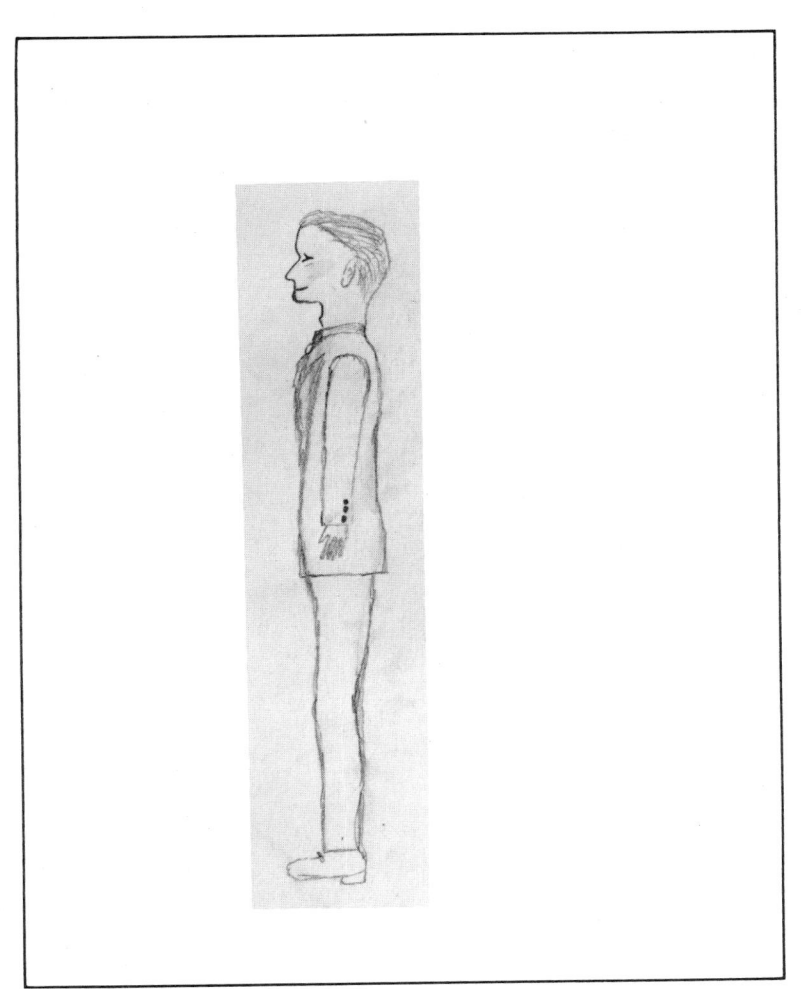

FIGURE-DRAWING CHARACTERISTICS

Structural	Male Female / Both	Structural	Male	Female	Structural and Graphic	Male Female / Both	Graphic, Global and Height	Male	Female	Body Proportions	Male	Female
Type	0	Omission of Appendages	0	0	Upper and Lower Halves	3 3	Hair Shading	3	3	Head	07	07
Sex Sequence	0	Position of Both Arms	4	4	Four Quarters	4 4	Nudity and Transparency	7	7	Neck	10	08
Posture	1 1	Position of Right Arm	7	7	Relative Size	0	Form	1	1	Shoulders		
Perspective	2 2	Position of Left Arm	0	0	Constant Line Pressure	0 0	Detailing	1	1	Right Arm		
Vertical Midline	7 4	Position of Legs	1	1	Variable Line Pressure	5 5	Identity and Sex	1	1	Left Arm	04	04
Bilateral Symmetry	0 0	Relation of Long Axes	1	1	Line Continuity	0 0	Sophistication	2	2	Chest	06	04
Horizontal Midline	6 0	Right and Left Halves	2	2	Body Shading	4 6	Height	07	07	Girth	06	05

GENERAL CHARACTERISTICS OF SUBJECT

IDENTIFICATION
No. 423
Sex M
Marital status M
Age 23 yrs. at psychological tests

PARENTAL HISTORY
Father
C   H   S   D   O
-   +   +   ?   +
Mother
C   H   S   D   O
-   -   -   -   -

PHYSIOLOGICAL AND METABOLIC DATA

	Admission	Initial	Control	Cold pressor change	Exercise change	Smoking change
Systolic pressure	120	123	110	+22	+24	
Diastolic pressure	72	68	64	+26	00	
Heart rate	92	96	88	+02	+23	

Age 21 yrs.	Height 72 in.	Ponderal index 11.98
	Weight 217 lbs.	Cholesterol 210 mg. per 100 ml.
	Overweight +34 %	Vital capacity 4.3 liters

HABIT SURVEY

Smoking habits: light cigarette smoker

Age begun 18 yrs.   Inhalation: yes

Habits of nervous tension: 5, 6, 16

FIGURE-DRAWING CHARACTERISTICS

Structural	Male Female Both	Structural	Male	Female	Structural and Graphic	Male Female Both		Graphic, Global and Height	Male	Female	Body Proportions	Male	Female
Type	0	Omission of Appendages	0	0	Upper and Lower Halves	0	1	Hair Shading	3	1	Head	07	06
Sex Sequence	1	Position of Both Arms	0	0	Four Quarters	4	4	Nudity and Transparency	7	7	Neck	08	06
Posture	2 1	Position of Right Arm	0	5	Relative Size	0		Form	3	3	Shoulders	09	06
Perspective	0 0	Position of Left Arm	0	5	Constant Line Pressure	5	5	Detailing	1	1	Right Arm	06	04
Vertical Midline	3 0	Position of Legs	8	4	Variable Line Pressure	0	0	Identity and Sex	1	1	Left Arm	06	04
Bilateral Symmetry	5 5	Relation of Long Axes	1	1	Line Continuity	4	4	Sophistication	2	2	Chest	07	04
Horizontal Midline	4 4	Right and Left Halves	1	0	Body Shading	3	7	Height	06	05	Girth	07	04

GENERAL CHARACTERISTICS OF SUBJECT

IDENTIFICATION
No. 432
Sex M
Marital status M
Age 25 yrs. at
psychological tests

PARENTAL HISTORY
Father
C H S D O
– + – – ?
Mother
C H S D O
– – – – –

PHYSIOLOGICAL AND METABOLIC DATA

	Admission	Initial	Control	Cold pressor change	Exercise change	Smoking change
Systolic pressure	134	112	90	+09	+30	–06
Diastolic pressure	80	66	60	+08	00	+04
Heart rate	70	78	63	–06	+25	+09

Age 22 yrs.	Height 72 in.	Ponderal index 12.39
	Weight 196 lbs.	Cholesterol 300 mg. per 100 ml.
	Overweight +20 %	Vital capacity 4.3 liters

HABIT SURVEY
Smoking habits: mixed smoker
Age begun 17 yrs.   Inhalation: no
Habits of nervous tension: 5, 6, 25

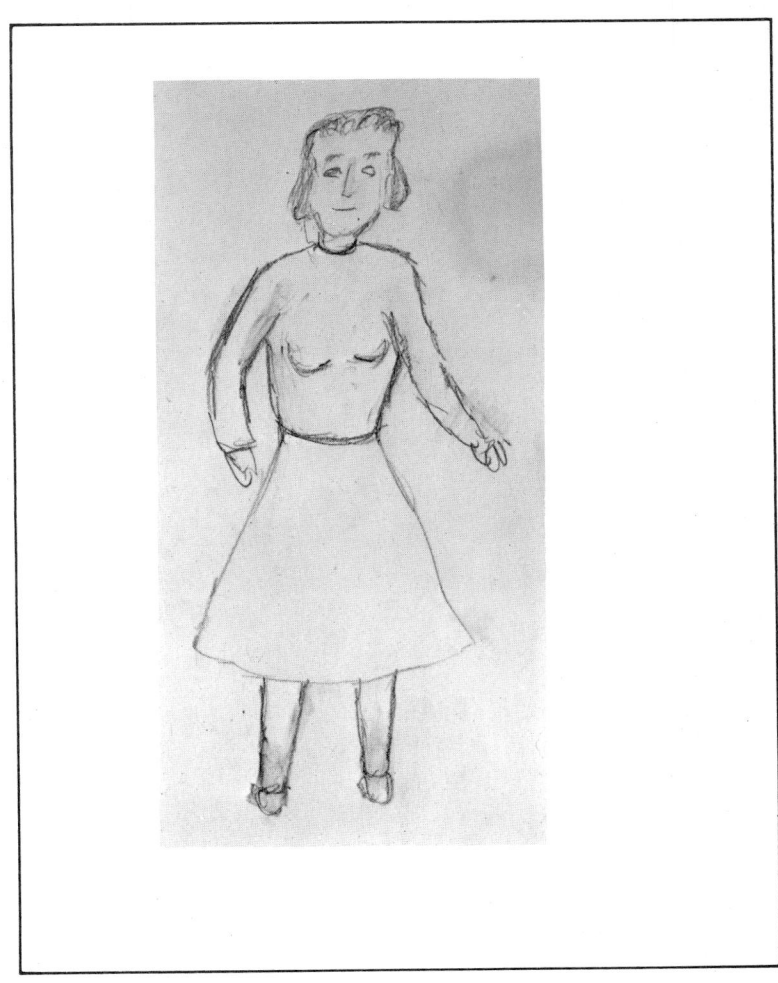

FIGURE-DRAWING CHARACTERISTICS

Structural	Male	Female	Structural	Male	Female	Structural and Graphic	Male	Female	Graphic, Global and Height	Male	Female	Body Proportions	Male	Female
	Both						Both							
Type	0		Omission of Appendages	7	0	Upper and Lower Halves	3	1	Hair Shading	3	3	Head	11	09
Sex Sequence	0		Position of Both Arms	0	1	Four Quarters	4	4	Nudity and Transparency	7	7	Neck	08	05
Posture	1	1	Position of Right Arm	5	5	Relative Size	0		Form	3	3	Shoulders	09	06
Perspective	0	0	Position of Left Arm	5	2	Constant Line Pressure	5	0	Detailing	3	3	Right Arm	06	06
Vertical Midline	3	0	Position of Legs	6	6	Variable Line Pressure	0	3	Identity and Sex	1	1	Left Arm	06	06
Bilateral Symmetry	3	3	Relation of Long Axes	1	1	Line Continuity	0	0	Sophistication	2	2	Chest	08	06
Horizontal Midline	4	4	Right and Left Halves	1	1	Body Shading	4	1	Height	09	07	Girth	07	06

GENERAL CHARACTERISTICS OF SUBJECT

IDENTIFICATION

No. 719

Sex M

Marital status S

Age 25 yrs. at

psychological tests

PARENTAL HISTORY

Father

C	H	S	D	O
-	+	-	-	?

Mother

C	H	S	D	O
-	-	-	-	-

PHYSIOLOGICAL AND METABOLIC DATA

	Admission	Initial	Control	Cold pressor change	Exercise change	Smoking change
Systolic pressure	130	110	108	+06	+30	00
Diastolic pressure	80	58	62	+12	-10	+06
Heart rate	80	68	64	-06	+36	-09

Age 25 yrs.	Height	70 in.	Ponderal index	13.21	
	Weight	149 lbs.	Cholesterol	210	mg. per 100 ml.
	Overweight	-05 %	Vital capacity	5.5	liters

HABIT SURVEY

Smoking habits: nonsmoker

Age begun   yrs.   Inhalation:

Habits of nervous tension: 3, 12, 16, 19, 22

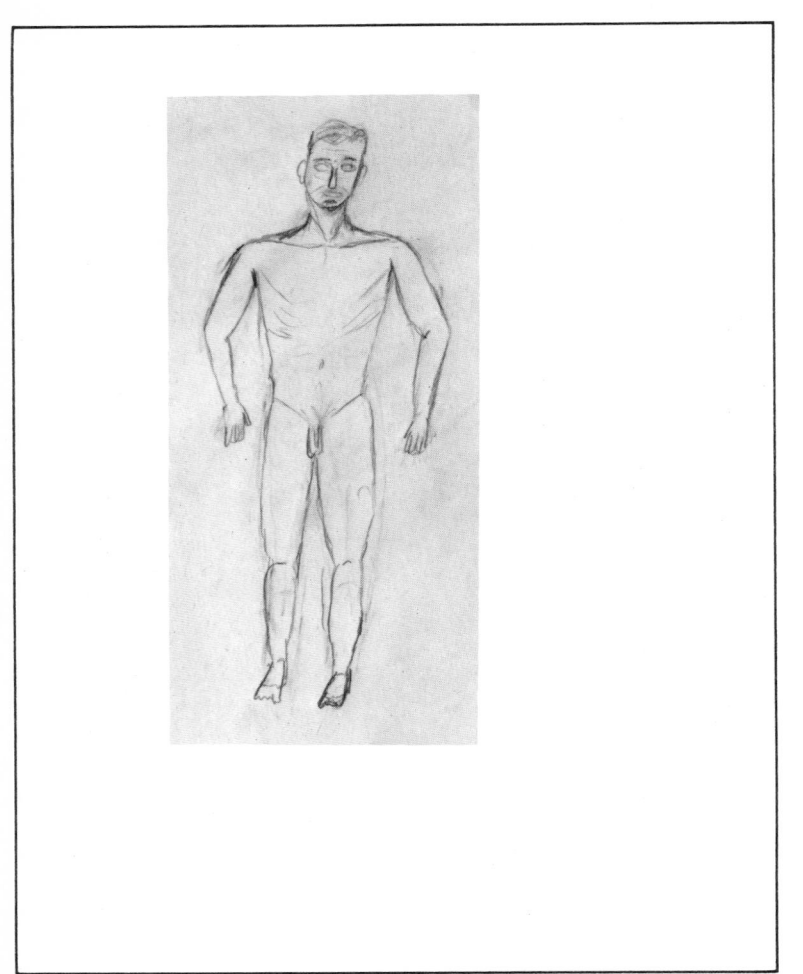

FIGURE-DRAWING CHARACTERISTICS

Structural	Male Female Both	Structural	Male	Female	Structural and Graphic	Male Female Both	Graphic, Global and Height	Male	Female	Body Proportions	Male	Female
Type	0	Omission of Appendages	0		Upper and Lower Halves	1	Hair Shading	3		Head	07	
Sex Sequence	3	Position of Both Arms	0		Four Quarters	4	Nudity and Transparency	0		Neck	07	
Posture	1	Position of Right Arm	5		Relative Size	7	Form	1		Shoulders	07	
Perspective	0	Position of Left Arm	5		Constant Line Pressure	0	Detailing	1		Right Arm	04	
Vertical Midline	0	Position of Legs	4		Variable Line Pressure	5	Identity and Sex	1		Left Arm	04	
Bilateral Symmetry	4	Relation of Long Axes	1		Line Continuity	0	Sophistication	2		Chest	06	
Horizontal Midline	0	Right and Left Halves	1		Body Shading	3	Height	06		Girth	06	

GENERAL CHARACTERISTICS OF SUBJECT

IDENTIFICATION
No. 772
Sex M
Marital status S
Age 22 yrs. at
psychological tests

PARENTAL HISTORY
Father
C   H   S   D   O
–   +   –   –   ?
Mother
C   H   S   D   O
–   –   –   –   –

PHYSIOLOGICAL AND METABOLIC DATA

	Admission	Initial	Control	Cold pressor change	Exercise change	Smoking change
Systolic pressure	110	114	104	00	+38	00
Diastolic pressure	60	50	60	+12	–08	–13
Heart rate	92	80	73	–10	+27	–03

Age 22 yrs.	Height 68 in.	Ponderal index 12.41
	Weight 165 lbs.	Cholesterol 254 mg. per 100 ml.
	Overweight +13 %	Vital capacity 5.1 liters

HABIT SURVEY
Smoking habits: former smoker
Age begun   yrs.   Inhalation:
Habits of nervous tension: 1, 3, 5, 6, 9, 18, 19, 22

FIGURE-DRAWING CHARACTERISTICS

Structural	Male	Female	Structural	Male	Female	Structural and Graphic	Male	Female	Graphic, Global and Height	Male	Female	Body Proportions	Male	Female
	Both						Both							
Type	0		Omission of Appendages	0	0	Upper and Lower Halves	0	1	Hair Shading	1	5	Head	12	07
Sex Sequence	0		Position of Both Arms	0	2	Four Quarters	4	4	Nudity and Transparency	7	7	Neck	03	08
Posture	1	1	Position of Right Arm	0	0	Relative Size	0		Form	3	3	Shoulders	09	
Perspective	0	6	Position of Left Arm	0	7	Constant Line Pressure	0	0	Detailing	1	3	Right Arm	06	04
Vertical Midline	3	4	Position of Legs	4	4	Variable Line Pressure	2	5	Identity and Sex	1	1	Left Arm	06	
Bilateral Symmetry	3	0	Relation of Long Axes	1	1	Line Continuity	0	0	Sophistication	2	2	Chest	07	
Horizontal Midline	4	2	Right and Left Halves	0	1	Body Shading	7	7	Height	07	06	Girth	08	

GENERAL CHARACTERISTICS OF SUBJECT

<table>
<tr><th colspan="2">IDENTIFICATION</th><th colspan="2">PARENTAL HISTORY</th><th colspan="8">PHYSIOLOGICAL AND METABOLIC DATA</th><th colspan="3">HABIT SURVEY</th></tr>
</table>

IDENTIFICATION	PARENTAL HISTORY
No. F67	Father
Sex M	C H S D O
Marital status S	- + - - -
Age 24 yrs. at	Mother
psychological tests	C H S D O
	- - - - -

PHYSIOLOGICAL AND METABOLIC DATA

	Admission	Initial	Control	Cold pressor change	Exercise change	Smoking change
Systolic pressure	136	120	120	+12	+20	+10
Diastolic pressure	68	78	82	+18	+10	+10
Heart rate	68	68	75	+16	+01	+12

Age 22 yrs.	Height 72 in.	Ponderal index 13.36
	Weight 157 lbs.	Cholesterol 265 mg. per 100 ml.
	Overweight -04 %	Vital capacity liters

HABIT SURVEY

Smoking habits: occasional smoker

Age begun 18 yrs.   Inhalation: yes

Habits of nervous tension: 5, 6, 9, 10, 16, 18, 23

STRONG VOCATIONAL INTEREST TEST

Occupation	Artist	Psychologist	Architect	Physician	Osteopath	Dentist	Veterinarian	Mathematician	Physicist	Engineer	Chemist	Production Manager
Standard Score	22	41	29	50	41	27	16	22	22	40	43	40

Occupation	Farmer	Aviator	Carpenter	Printer	Math.-Sci. Teacher	Ind. Arts Teacher	Voc. Agric. Teacher	Policeman	Forest Serv. Man	Y.M.C.A. Phys. Dir.	Personnel Director	Public Administrator
Standard Score	26	43	11	26	35	09	11	31	29	37	47	60

Occupation	Y.M.C.A. Secretary	Soc. Sci. H.S. Teacher	City Sch. Sup't.	Social Worker	Minister	Musician Performer	C.P.A.	Senior C.P.A.	Accountant	Office Man	Purchasing Agent	Banker
Standard Score	30	30	27	45	58	38	36	50	29	34	25	18

Occupation	Mortician	Pharmacist	Sales Manager	Real Est. Manager	Life Ins. Salesman	Advertising Man	Lawyer	Author-Journalist	President Mfg. Co.	Interest Maturity	Occupational Level	Masculinity-Femininity
Standard Score	20	22	31	29	30	31	38	29	35	62	58	55

FIGURE-DRAWING CHARACTERISTICS

Structural	Male Female Both		Structural	Male	Female	Structural and Graphic	Male	Female Both	Graphic, Global and Height	Male	Female	Body Proportions	Male	Female
Type	0		Omission of Appendages	0	0	Upper and Lower Halves	2	2	Hair Shading	3	3	Head	04	04
Sex Sequence	0		Position of Both Arms	4	0	Four Quarters	4	0	Nudity and Transparency	0	7	Neck	02	01
Posture	5	1	Position of Right Arm	7	5	Relative Size	0		Form	1	1	Shoulders		03
Perspective	2	0	Position of Left Arm	6	5	Constant Line Pressure	5	5	Detailing	3	1	Right Arm		02
Vertical Midline	4	0	Position of Legs	8	6	Variable Line Pressure	0	0	Identity and Sex	1	1	Left Arm	02	02
Bilateral Symmetry	0	3	Relation of Long Axes	3	1	Line Continuity	2	3	Sophistication	2	2	Chest	03	02
Horizontal Midline	2	0	Right and Left Halves	1	2	Body Shading	0	5	Height		02	Girth	03	03

GENERAL CHARACTERISTICS OF SUBJECT

IDENTIFICATION
No. G33
Sex M
Marital status S
Age 23 yrs. at
psychological tests

PARENTAL HISTORY					
Father					
C	H	S	D	O	
-	+	-	-	+	
Mother					
C	H	S	D	O	
-	-	-	-	-	

PHYSIOLOGICAL AND METABOLIC DATA

	Admission	Initial	Control	Cold pressor change	Exercise change	Smoking change
Systolic pressure	130	130	122	+32	+20	+09
Diastolic pressure	70	86	62	+40	00	+06
Heart rate	76	60	60	+18	+04	+09

Age 22 yrs.	Height	73 in.	Ponderal index 12.87
	Weight	182 lbs.	Cholesterol 214 mg. per 100 ml.
	Overweight +08 %		Vital capacity liters

HABIT SURVEY

Smoking habits: heavy cigarette smoker

Age begun 16 yrs.   Inhalation: yes

Habits of nervous tension: 4, 5, 6, 9, 11, 23

STRONG VOCATIONAL INTEREST TEST

Occupation	Artist	Psychologist	Architect	Physician	Osteopath	Dentist	Veterinarian	Mathematician	Physicist	Engineer	Chemist	Production Manager
Standard Score	40	37	42	60	55	48	33	28	26	35	45	26

Occupation	Farmer	Aviator	Carpenter	Printer	Math.-Sci. Teacher	Ind. Arts Teacher	Voc. Agric. Teacher	Policeman	Forest Serv. Man	Y.M.C.A. Phys. Dir.	Personnel Director	Public Administrator
Standard Score	30	44	11	29	31	08	12	23	18	32	27	33

Occupation	Y.M.C.A. Secretary	Soc. Sci. H.S. Teacher	City Sch. Sup't.	Social Worker	Minister	Musician Performer	C.P.A.	Senior C.P.A.	Accountant	Office Man	Purchasing Agent	Banker
Standard Score	11	22	22	29	59	42	32	33	17	26	24	13

Occupation	Mortician	Pharmacist	Sales Manager	Real Est. Manager	Life Ins. Salesman	Advertising Man	Lawyer	Author- Journalist	President Mfg. Co.	Interest Maturity	Occupational Level	Masculinity- Femininity
Standard Score	31	42	37	43	40	45	47	42	33	50	64	46

FIGURE-DRAWING CHARACTERISTICS

Structural	Male Female Both	Structural	Male	Female	Structural and Graphic	Male	Female Both	Graphic, Global and Height	Male	Female	Body Proportions	Male	Female
Type	0	Omission of Appendages	0	0	Upper and Lower Halves	0	3	Hair Shading	7	1	Head	08	07
Sex Sequence	1	Position of Both Arms	0	1	Four Quarters	4	4	Nudity and Transparency	7	7	Neck	05	06
Posture	1 1	Position of Right Arm	5	4	Relative Size	4		Form	1	1	Shoulders	08	06
Perspective	0 0	Position of Left Arm	5	5	Constant Line Pressure	4	4	Detailing	3	3	Right Arm	04	04
Vertical Midline	3 0	Position of Legs	4	4	Variable Line Pressure	0	0	Identity and Sex	1	1	Left Arm	04	05
Bilateral Symmetry	5 3	Relation of Long Axes	1	1	Line Continuity	4	4	Sophistication	2	2	Chest	07	06
Horizontal Midline	6 2	Right and Left Halves	1	1	Body Shading	0	0	Height	06	07	Girth	08	06

GENERAL CHARACTERISTICS OF SUBJECT

IDENTIFICATION

No. A02

Sex F

Marital status S

Age 23 yrs. at psychological tests

PARENTAL HISTORY

Father

C	H	S	D	O
-	+	-	-	-

Mother

C	H	S	D	O
-	-	-	-	-

PHYSIOLOGICAL AND METABOLIC DATA

	Admission	Initial	Control	Cold pressor change	Exercise change	Smoking change
Systolic pressure	110	110	104	+10	+29	+09
Diastolic pressure	70	55	58	+13	+04	+04
Heart rate	96	80	71	+20	+23	+14

Age 22 yrs.   Height 65 in.   Ponderal index 13.49

Weight 112 lbs.   Cholesterol 210 mg. per 100 ml.

Overweight -13 %   Vital capacity   liters

HABIT SURVEY

Smoking habits: moderate cigarette smoker

Age begun 17 yrs.   Inhalation: yes

Habits of nervous tension: 2, 5, 6, 9, 18, 23, 25

STRONG VOCATIONAL INTEREST TEST

Occupation	Artist	Psychologist	Architect	Physician	Osteopath	Dentist	Veterinarian	Mathematician	Physicist	Engineer	Chemist	Production Manager
Standard Score	7	7	7	7	4	4	2	6	7	5	6	2

Occupation	Farmer	Aviator	Carpenter	Printer	Math.-Sci. Teacher	Ind. Arts Teacher	Voc. Agric. Teacher	Policeman	Forest Serv. Man	Y.M.C.A. Phys. Dir.	Personnel Director	Public Administrator
Standard Score	6	5	3	5	4	0	2	2	7	2	5	5

Occupation	Y.M.C.A. Secretary	Soc. Sci. H.S. Teacher	City Sch. Sup't.	Social Worker	Minister	Musician Performer	C.P.A.	Senior C.P.A.	Accountant	Office Man	Purchasing Agent	Banker
Standard Score	1	2	1	3	6	7	3	4	1	5	2	2

Occupation	Mortician	Pharmacist	Sales Manager	Real Est. Manager	Life Ins. Salesman	Advertising Man	Lawyer	Author-Journalist	President Mfg. Co.	Interest Maturity	Occupational Level	Masculinity-Femininity
Standard Score	2	3	2	5	2	6	6	7	4	2	4	4

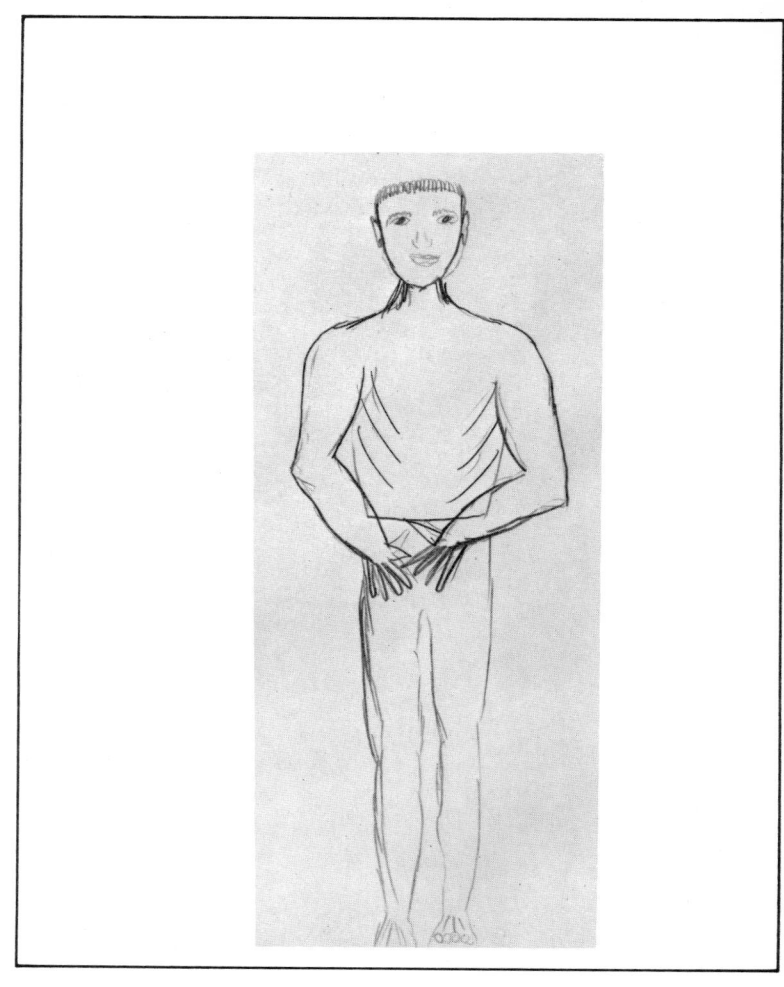

FIGURE-DRAWING CHARACTERISTICS

Structural	Male Female Both	Structural	Male	Female	Structural and Graphic	Male Female Both		Graphic, Global and Height	Male	Female	Body Proportions	Male	Female
Type	0	Omission of Appendages	0	0	Upper and Lower Halves	3	0	Hair Shading	3	5	Head	08	09
Sex Sequence	1	Position of Both Arms	0	4	Four Quarters	4	4	Nudity and Transparency	8	7	Neck	07	12
Posture	1 1	Position of Right Arm	5	7	Relative Size	2		Form	1	1	Shoulders	09	
Perspective	0 2	Position of Left Arm	5	4	Constant Line Pressure	0	0	Detailing	3	3	Right Arm	06	
Vertical Midline	0 4	Position of Legs	4	1	Variable Line Pressure	4	3	Identity and Sex	1	1	Left Arm	06	06
Bilateral Symmetry	3 0	Relation of Long Axes	1	1	Line Continuity	2	4	Sophistication	2	2	Chest	07	07
Horizontal Midline	4 2	Right and Left Halves	3	2	Body Shading	1	0	Height	08	08	Girth	07	05

GENERAL CHARACTERISTICS OF SUBJECT

IDENTIFICATION

No. A18
Sex M
Marital status M
Age 23 yrs. at
psychological tests

PARENTAL HISTORY

Father
C	H	S	D	O
-	+	-	+	?

Mother
C	H	S	D	O
-	-	-	-	-

PHYSIOLOGICAL AND METABOLIC DATA

	Admission	Initial	Control	Cold pressor change	Exercise change	Smoking change
Systolic pressure	124	115	105	+08	+23	+10
Diastolic pressure	68	54	59	+18	-04	+14
Heart rate	92	68	63	+12	+20	+17

Age 22 yrs.

Height	70 in.	Ponderal index	12.82	
Weight	163 lbs.	Cholesterol	273	mg. per 100 ml.
Overweight	+06 %	Vital capacity		liters

HABIT SURVEY

Smoking habits: heavy cigarette smoker
Age begun 15 yrs.   Inhalation: yes
Habits of nervous tension: 4, 5, 6, 9, 11, 16,
19, 23

STRONG VOCATIONAL INTEREST TEST

Occupation	Artist	Psychologist	Architect	Physician	Osteopath	Dentist	Veterinarian	Mathematician	Physicist	Engineer	Chemist	Production Manager
Standard Score	5	3	5	6	6	4	2	3	3	5	4	3

Occupation	Farmer	Aviator	Carpenter	Printer	Math.-Sci. Teacher	Ind. Arts Teacher	Voc. Agric. Teacher	Policeman	Forest Serv. Man	Y.M.C.A. Phys. Dir.	Personnel Director	Public Administrator
Standard Score	4	6	2	4	4	0	1	4	4	4	3	3

Occupation	Y.M.C.A. Secretary	Soc. Sci. H.S. Teacher	City Sch. Sup't.	Social Worker	Minister	Musician Performer	C.P.A.	Senior C.P.A.	Accountant	Office Man	Purchasing Agent	Banker
Standard Score	2	2	6	6	6	5	3	3	2	4	3	2

Occupation	Mortician	Pharmacist	Sales Manager	Real Est. Manager	Life Ins. Salesman	Advertising Man	Lawyer	Author-Journalist	President Mfg. Co.	Interest Maturity	Occupational Level	Masculinity-Femininity
Standard Score	4	4	3	4	3	4	4	6	3	4	5	3

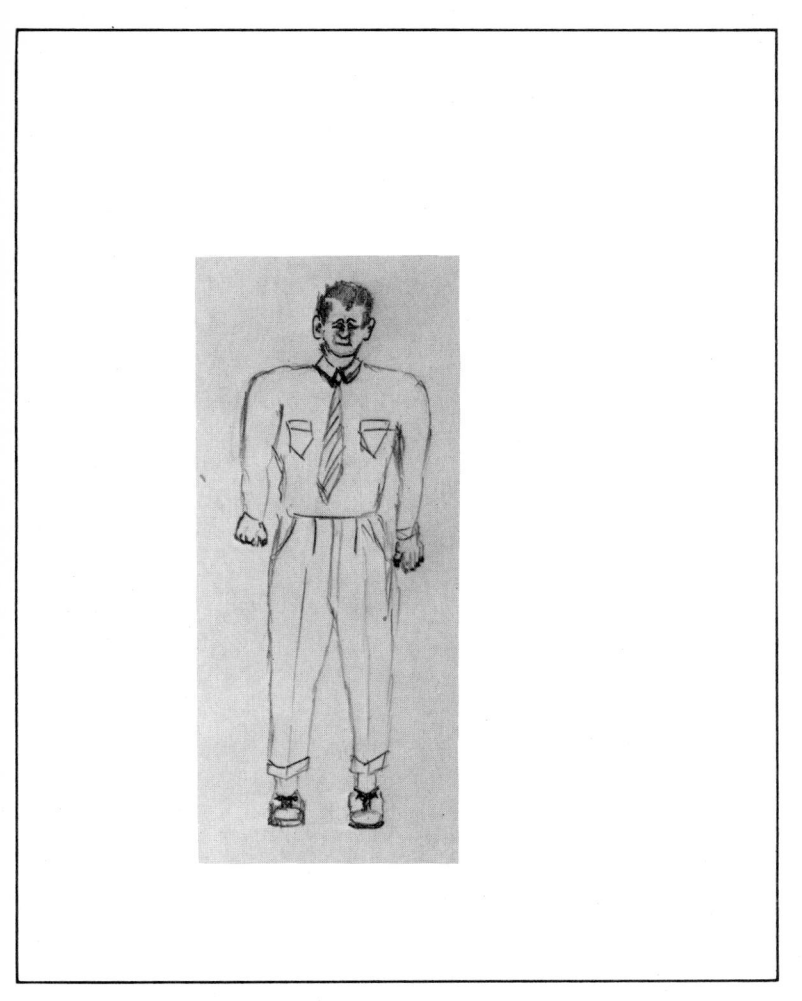
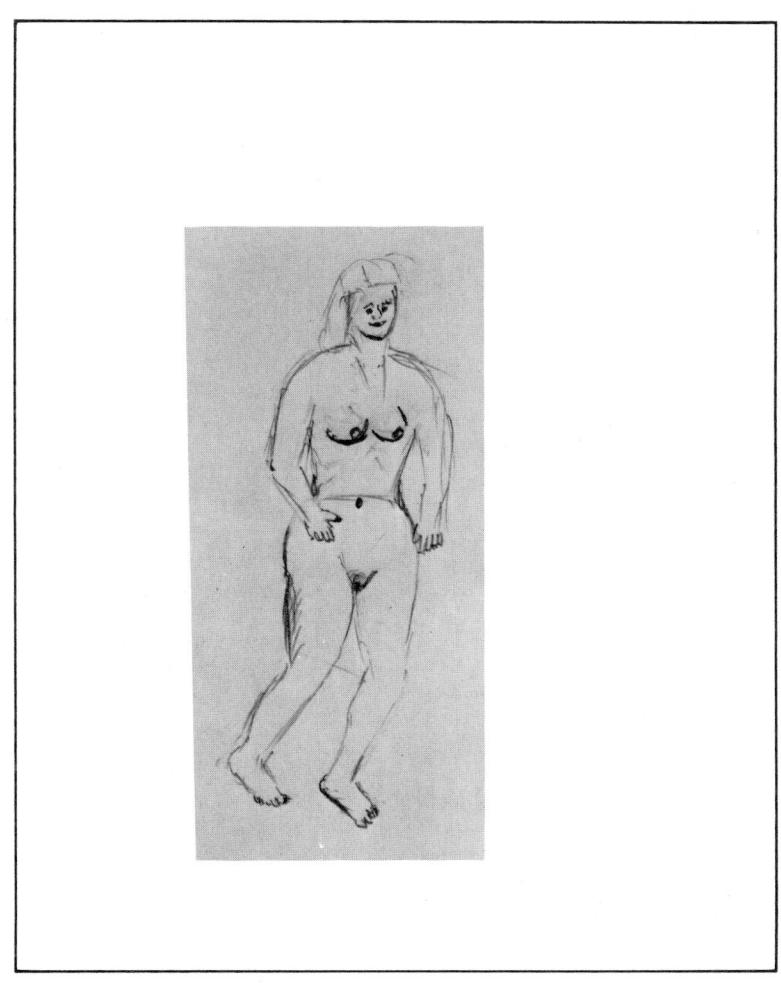

FIGURE-DRAWING CHARACTERISTICS

Structural	Male Female Both		Structural	Male	Female	Structural and Graphic	Male Female Both		Graphic, Global and Height	Male	Female	Body Proportions	Male	Female
Type	0		Omission of Appendages	0	0	Upper and Lower Halves	3	3	Hair Shading	3	5	Head	05	06
Sex Sequence	0		Position of Both Arms	0	1	Four Quarters	4	4	Nudity and Transparency	7	0	Neck	04	03
Posture	1	2	Position of Right Arm	0	5	Relative Size	4		Form	1	1	Shoulders	07	
Perspective	0	1	Position of Left Arm	0	0	Constant Line Pressure	0	0	Detailing	1	1	Right Arm	04	04
Vertical Midline	3	4	Position of Legs	5	8	Variable Line Pressure	1	3	Identity and Sex	1	1	Left Arm	04	04
Bilateral Symmetry	4	0	Relation of Long Axes	1	1	Line Continuity	0	0	Sophistication	2	2	Chest	05	
Horizontal Midline	4	2	Right and Left Halves	1	1	Body Shading	6	3	Height	05	06	Girth	06	

GENERAL CHARACTERISTICS OF SUBJECT

IDENTIFICATION
No. A78
Sex M
Marital status M
Age 23 yrs. at
psychological tests

PARENTAL HISTORY				
Father				
C	H	S	D	O
-	+	-	+	+
Mother				
C	H	S	D	O
-	-	-	-	+

PHYSIOLOGICAL AND METABOLIC DATA

	Admission	Initial	Control	Cold pressor change	Exercise change	Smoking change
Systolic pressure	130	118	116	+10	+18	00
Diastolic pressure	85	62	65	+22	-05	+05
Heart rate	74	72	53	+02	+27	+05

Age 22 yrs.
Height 68 in.
Weight 173 lbs.
Overweight +18 %
Ponderal index 12.21
Cholesterol 250 mg. per 100 ml.
Vital capacity liters

HABIT SURVEY

Smoking habits: nonsmoker
Age begun yrs. Inhalation:
Habits of nervous tension: 5, 6, 8, 11, 19

STRONG VOCATIONAL INTEREST TEST

Occupation	Artist	Psychologist	Architect	Physician	Osteopath	Dentist	Veterinarian	Mathematician	Physicist	Engineer	Chemist	Production Manager
Standard Score	25	50	28	65	58	42	32	28	25	38	45	35

Occupation	Farmer	Aviator	Carpenter	Printer	Math.-Sci. Teacher	Ind. Arts Teacher	Voc. Agric. Teacher	Policeman	Forest Serv. Man	Y.M.C.A. Phys. Dir.	Personnel Director	Public Administrator
Standard Score	31	40	16	27	47	17	30	35	31	53	51	55

Occupation	Y.M.C.A. Secretary	Soc. Sci. H.S. Teacher	City Sch. Sup't.	Social Worker	Minister	Musician Performer	C.P.A.	Senior C.P.A.	Accountant	Office Man	Purchasing Agent	Banker
Standard Score	39	43	45	52	60	53	40	46	25	31	22	17

Occupation	Mortician	Pharmacist	Sales Manager	Real Est. Manager	Life Ins. Salesman	Advertising Man	Lawyer	Author-Journalist	President Mfg. Co.	Interest Maturity	Occupational Level	Masculinity-Femininity
Standard Score	30	36	36	33	38	32	44	32	28	59	62	49

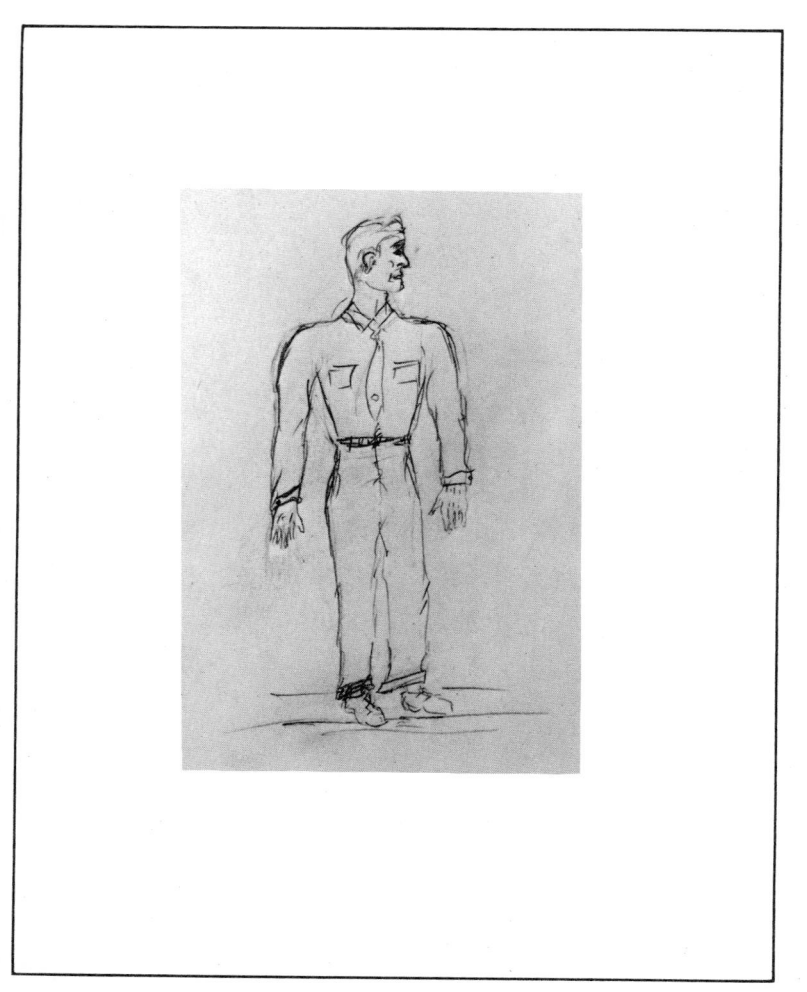

FIGURE-DRAWING CHARACTERISTICS

Structural	Male	Female	Structural	Male	Female	Structural and Graphic	Male	Female	Graphic, Global and Height	Male	Female	Body Proportions	Male	Female
	Both						Both							
Type	0		Omission of Appendages	0	0	Upper and Lower Halves	1	3	Hair Shading	3	3	Head	05	05
Sex Sequence	0		Position of Both Arms	0	0	Four Quarters	4	4	Nudity and Transparency	7	7	Neck	08	06
Posture	1	1	Position of Right Arm	0	0	Relative Size	2		Form	1	1	Shoulders	06	05
Perspective	5	0	Position of Left Arm	0	0	Constant Line Pressure	0	0	Detailing	1	1	Right Arm	04	04
Vertical Midline	3	3	Position of Legs	4	4	Variable Line Pressure	3	4	Identity and Sex	1	1	Left Arm	04	04
Bilateral Symmetry	3	3	Relation of Long Axes	1	1	Line Continuity	0	0	Sophistication	2	2	Chest	05	04
Horizontal Midline	4	4	Right and Left Halves	1	3	Body Shading	7	3	Height	05	05	Girth	04	04

GENERAL CHARACTERISTICS OF SUBJECT

IDENTIFICATION

No. B02

Sex M

Marital status M

Age 22 yrs. at psychological tests

PARENTAL HISTORY

Father

C	H	S	D	O
–	+	–	–	?

Mother

C	H	S	D	O
–	–	–	–	–

PHYSIOLOGICAL AND METABOLIC DATA

	Admission	Initial	Control	Cold pressor change	Exercise change	Smoking change
Systolic pressure	110	124	114	+10	+50	+10
Diastolic pressure	56	66	68	+18	–04	+10
Heart rate	84	96	80	+04	+35	+18

Age 22 yrs.	Height 67 in.	Ponderal index 13.54
	Weight 121 lbs.	Cholesterol 200 mg. per 100 ml.
	Overweight –15 %	Vital capacity 5.0 liters

HABIT SURVEY

Smoking habits: mixed smoker

Age begun 20 yrs.   Inhalation: sometimes

Habits of nervous tension: 1, 2, 3, 4, 5, 6, 8, 11, 21, 23

STRONG VOCATIONAL INTEREST TEST

Occupation	Artist	Psychologist	Architect	Physician	Osteopath	Dentist	Veterinarian	Mathematician	Physicist	Engineer	Chemist	Production Manager
Standard Score	45	42	48	69	63	50	31	38	45	55	58	32

Occupation	Farmer	Aviator	Carpenter	Printer	Math.-Sci. Teacher	Ind. Arts Teacher	Voc. Agric. Teacher	Policeman	Forest Serv. Man	Y.M.C.A. Phys. Dir.	Personnel Director	Public Administrator
Standard Score	30	48	25	32	36	16	08	30	28	24	15	36

Occupation	Y.M.C.A. Secretary	Soc. Sci. H.S. Teacher	City Sch. Sup't.	Social Worker	Minister	Musician Performer	C.P.A.	Senior C.P.A.	Accountant	Office Man	Purchasing Agent	Banker
Standard Score	07	12	09	26	61	44	39	31	16	19	19	14

Occupation	Mortician	Pharmacist	Sales Manager	Real Est. Manager	Life Ins. Salesman	Advertising Man	Lawyer	Author-Journalist	President Mfg. Co.	Interest Maturity	Occupational Level	Masculinity-Femininity
Standard Score	17	31	19	32	20	29	41	42	36	46	61	49

Plate 636   MODERATELY SOPHISTICATED DRAWINGS   683

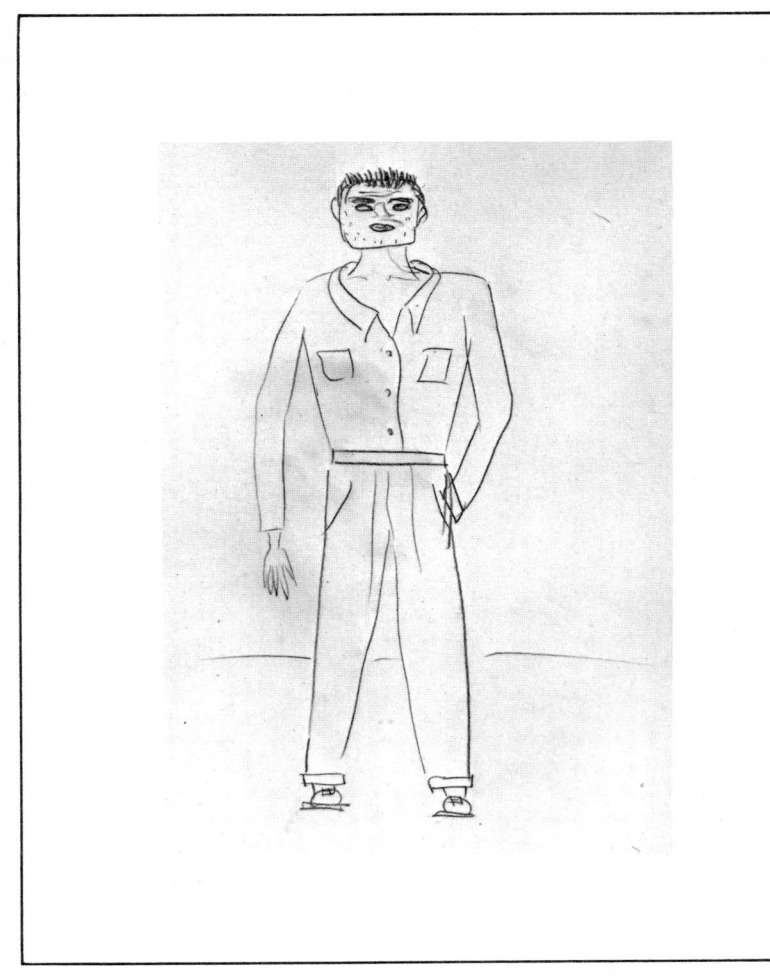

FIGURE-DRAWING CHARACTERISTICS

Structural	Male Female Both		Structural	Male	Female	Structural and Graphic	Male Female Both		Graphic, Global and Height	Male	Female	Body Proportions	Male	Female
Type	0		Omission of Appendages	7	7	Upper and Lower Halves	0	3	Hair Shading	3	3	Head	05	05
Sex Sequence	0		Position of Both Arms	1	0	Four Quarters	4	4	Nudity and Transparency	7	7	Neck	08	06
Posture	1	1	Position of Right Arm	0	5	Relative Size	0		Form	3	1	Shoulders	08	06
Perspective	0	0	Position of Left Arm	5	5	Constant Line Pressure	0	0	Detailing	3	3	Right Arm	08	
Vertical Midline	3	0	Position of Legs	6	4	Variable Line Pressure	4	1	Identity and Sex	1	1	Left Arm		06
Bilateral Symmetry	3	4	Relation of Long Axes	1	1	Line Continuity	4	2	Sophistication	2	2	Chest	07	05
Horizontal Midline	4	4	Right and Left Halves	1	3	Body Shading	3	7	Height	06	06	Girth	07	06

GENERAL CHARACTERISTICS OF SUBJECT

IDENTIFICATION
No. B29
Sex M
Marital status S
Age 22 yrs. at
psychological tests

PARENTAL HISTORY				
Father				
C	H	S	D	O
-	+	-	-	+
Mother				
C	H	S	D	O
-	-	-	-	-

PHYSIOLOGICAL AND METABOLIC DATA

	Admission	Initial	Control	Cold pressor change	Exercise change	Smoking change
Systolic pressure	90	136	134	+24	+28	
Diastolic pressure	65	74	76	+16	-12	
Heart rate	66	75	61	+10	+46	

Age 22 yrs.	Height	70 in.	Ponderal index 12.80	
	Weight	164 lbs.	Cholesterol 225 mg. per 100 ml.	
	Overweight +06 %		Vital capacity 5.7 liters	

HABIT SURVEY
Smoking habits: nonsmoker
Age begun   yrs.   Inhalation:
Habits of nervous tension: 5, 23, 25

STRONG VOCATIONAL INTEREST TEST

Occupation	Artist	Psychologist	Architect	Physician	Osteopath	Dentist	Veterinarian	Mathematician	Physicist	Engineer	Chemist	Production Manager
Standard Score	38	55	46	60	45	41	19	49	54	57	67	45

Occupation	Farmer	Aviator	Carpenter	Printer	Math.-Sci. Teacher	Ind. Arts Teacher	Voc. Agric. Teacher	Policeman	Forest Serv. Man	Y.M.C.A. Phys. Dir.	Personnel Director	Public Administrator
Standard Score	37	56	38	46	50	38	21	31	27	23	31	41

Occupation	Y.M.C.A. Secretary	Soc. Sci. H.S. Teacher	City Sch. Sup't.	Social Worker	Minister	Musician Performer	C.P.A.	Senior C.P.A.	Accountant	Office Man	Purchasing Agent	Banker
Standard Score	14	17	15	27	61	47	32	47	28	25	24	09

Occupation	Mortician	Pharmacist	Sales Manager	Real Est. Manager	Life Ins. Salesman	Advertising Man	Lawyer	Author- Journalist	President Mfg. Co.	Interest Maturity	Occupational Level	Masculinity- Femininity
Standard Score	11	29	12	22	09	27	25	35	34	50	53	60

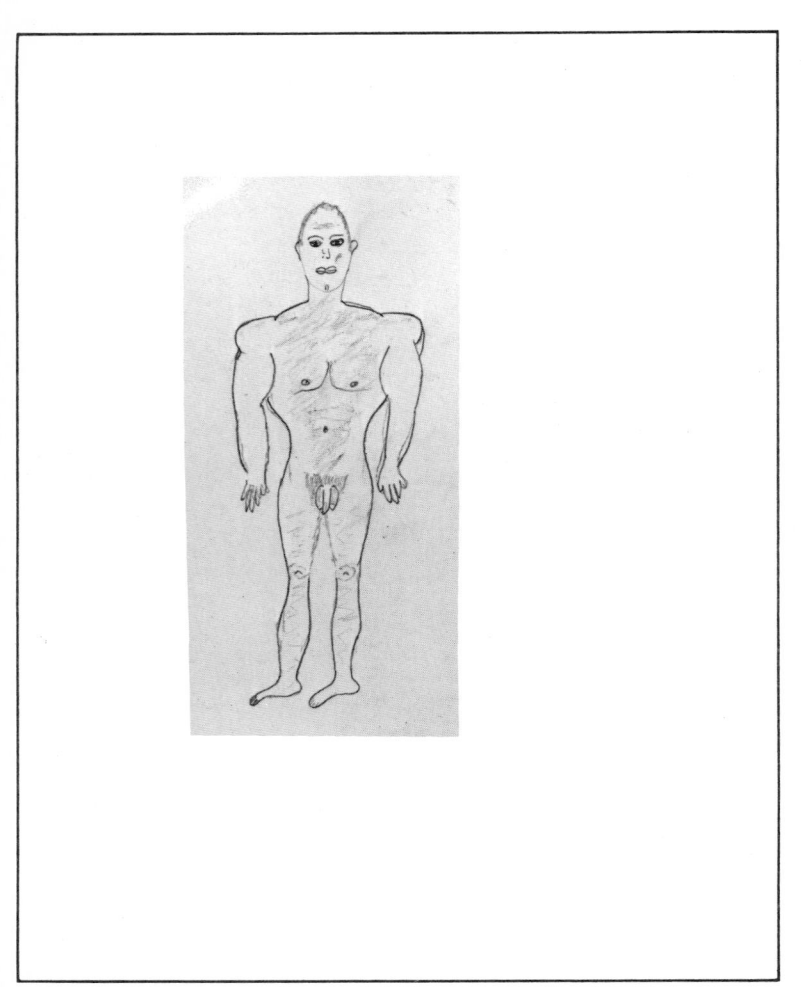

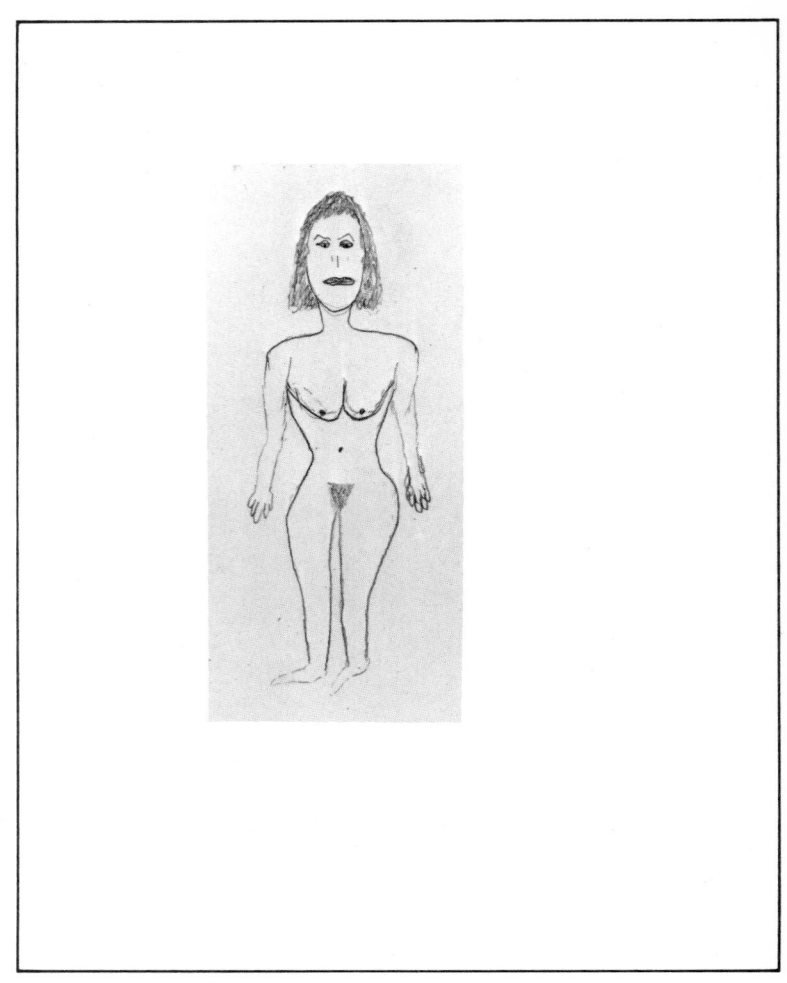

FIGURE-DRAWING CHARACTERISTICS

Structural	Male Female Both	Structural	Male	Female	Structural and Graphic	Male Female Both		Graphic, Global and Height	Male	Female	Body Proportions	Male	Female
Type	0	Omission of Appendages	0	0	Upper and Lower Halves	1	1	Hair Shading	3	3	Head	07	09
Sex Sequence	0	Position of Both Arms	0	1	Four Quarters	4	4	Nudity and Transparency	0	0	Neck	06	07
Posture	1 1	Position of Right Arm	0	1	Relative Size	0		Form	3	3	Shoulders	07	06
Perspective	0 0	Position of Left Arm	0	0	Constant Line Pressure	5	0	Detailing	1	1	Right Arm	04	04
Vertical Midline	0 0	Position of Legs	4	4	Variable Line Pressure	0	3	Identity and Sex	1	1	Left Arm	04	04
Bilateral Symmetry	5 3	Relation of Long Axes	1	1	Line Continuity	4	1	Sophistication	2	2	Chest	05	05
Horizontal Midline	0 0	Right and Left Halves	1	1	Body Shading	3	3	Height	05	05	Girth	04	04

GENERAL CHARACTERISTICS OF SUBJECT

IDENTIFICATION
No. C25
Sex M
Marital status S
Age 22 yrs. at
psychological tests

PARENTAL HISTORY				
Father				
C	H	S	D	O
-	+	+	-	+
Mother				
C	H	S	D	O
-	-	-	-	?

PHYSIOLOGICAL AND METABOLIC DATA

	Admission	Initial	Control	Cold pressor change	Exercise change	Smoking change
Systolic pressure	170	130	120	+20	+30	+06
Diastolic pressure	80	70	70	+25	00	+06
Heart rate	120	80	77	+16	+38	+08

Age 23 yrs.	Height 70 in.	Ponderal index 12.50
	Weight 176 lbs.	Cholesterol 212 mg. per 100 ml.
	Overweight +14 %	Vital capacity 4.4 liters

HABIT SURVEY

Smoking habits: pipe smoker

Age begun 19 yrs.   Inhalation: sometimes

Habits of nervous tension: 1, 3, 4, 5, 7, 8, 9, 10, 11, 12, 14, 16, 17, 18, 22

STRONG VOCATIONAL INTEREST TEST

Occupation	Artist	Psychologist	Architect	Physician	Osteopath	Dentist	Veterinarian	Mathematician	Physicist	Engineer	Chemist	Production Manager
Standard Score	48	45	41	52	38	40	01	36	34	33	41	27

Occupation	Farmer	Aviator	Carpenter	Printer	Math.-Sci. Teacher	Ind. Arts Teacher	Voc. Agric. Teacher	Policeman	Forest Serv. Man	Y.M.C.A. Phys. Dir.	Personnel Director	Public Administrator
Standard Score	09	21	-02	17	18	-10	-10	12	-09	16	21	30

Occupation	Y.M.C.A. Secretary	Soc. Sci. H.S. Teacher	City Sch. Sup't.	Social Worker	Minister	Musician Performer	C.P.A.	Senior C.P.A.	Accountant	Office Man	Purchasing Agent	Banker
Standard Score	13	11	22	29	62	48	48	17	19	15	18	14

Occupation	Mortician	Pharmacist	Sales Manager	Real Est. Manager	Life Ins. Salesman	Advertising Man	Lawyer	Author- Journalist	President Mfg. Co.	Interest Maturity	Occupational Level	Masculinity- Femininity
Standard Score	18	31	40	40	40	54	55	55	51	49	75	32

FIGURE-DRAWING CHARACTERISTICS

Structural	Male Female Both		Structural	Male	Female	Structural and Graphic Both	Male	Female	Graphic, Global and Height	Male	Female	Body Proportions	Male	Female
Type	0		Omission of Appendages	0	0	Upper and Lower Halves	3	0	Hair Shading	1	3	Head	04	05
Sex Sequence	0		Position of Both Arms	0	2	Four Quarters	4	4	Nudity and Transparency	7	7	Neck	03	03
Posture	1	1	Position of Right Arm	0	0	Relative Size	0		Form	3	1	Shoulders	04	
Perspective	0	1	Position of Left Arm	0	7	Constant Line Pressure	1	0	Detailing	1	1	Right Arm	04	04
Vertical Midline	3	4	Position of Legs	3	1	Variable Line Pressure	0	3	Identity and Sex	1	1	Left Arm	04	
Bilateral Symmetry	3	0	Relation of Long Axes	1	1	Line Continuity	1	2	Sophistication	2	2	Chest	03	
Horizontal Midline	6	4	Right and Left Halves	2	1	Body Shading	2	7	Height	05	05	Girth	03	

GENERAL CHARACTERISTICS OF SUBJECT

IDENTIFICATION
No. C55
Sex M
Marital status S
Age 22 yrs. at
psychological tests

PARENTAL HISTORY
Father
C H S D O
- + - - +
Mother
C H S D O
- - - - -

PHYSIOLOGICAL AND METABOLIC DATA

	Admission	Initial	Control	Cold pressor change	Exercise change	Smoking change
Systolic pressure	140	108	109	+14	+22	-02
Diastolic pressure	90	84	80	+07	+21	00
Heart rate	80	56	56	-04	+23	+09

Age 22 yrs.	Height	70	in.	Ponderal index 11.95	
	Weight	201	lbs.	Cholesterol	256 mg. per 100 ml.
	Overweight +31 %			Vital capacity 4.5 liters	

HABIT SURVEY
Smoking habits: nonsmoker
Age begun   yrs.   Inhalation:
Habits of nervous tension: 1, 3, 5, 6, 9, 10, 19, 24, 25

STRONG VOCATIONAL INTEREST TEST

Occupation	Artist	Psychologist	Architect	Physician	Osteopath	Dentist	Veterinarian	Mathematician	Physicist	Engineer	Chemist	Production Manager
Standard Score	14	44	16	46	52	30	21	15	12	23	31	32

Occupation	Farmer	Aviator	Carpenter	Printer	Math.-Sci. Teacher	Ind. Arts Teacher	Voc. Agric. Teacher	Policeman	Forest Serv. Man	Y.M.C.A. Phys. Dir.	Personnel Director	Public Administrator
Standard Score	18	31	16	36	49	13	18	44	24	56	52	57

Occupation	Y.M.C.A. Secretary	Soc. Sci. H.S. Teacher	City Sch. Sup't.	Social Worker	Minister	Musician Performer	C.P.A.	Senior C.P.A.	Accountant	Office Man	Purchasing Agent	Banker
Standard Score	47	55	43	55	62	37	40	47	35	45	21	24

Occupation	Mortician	Pharmacist	Sales Manager	Real Est. Manager	Life Ins. Salesman	Advertising Man	Lawyer	Author- Journalist	President Mfg. Co.	Interest Maturity	Occupational Level	Masculinity- Femininity
Standard Score	33	42	30	35	38	32	39	27	20	65	53	47

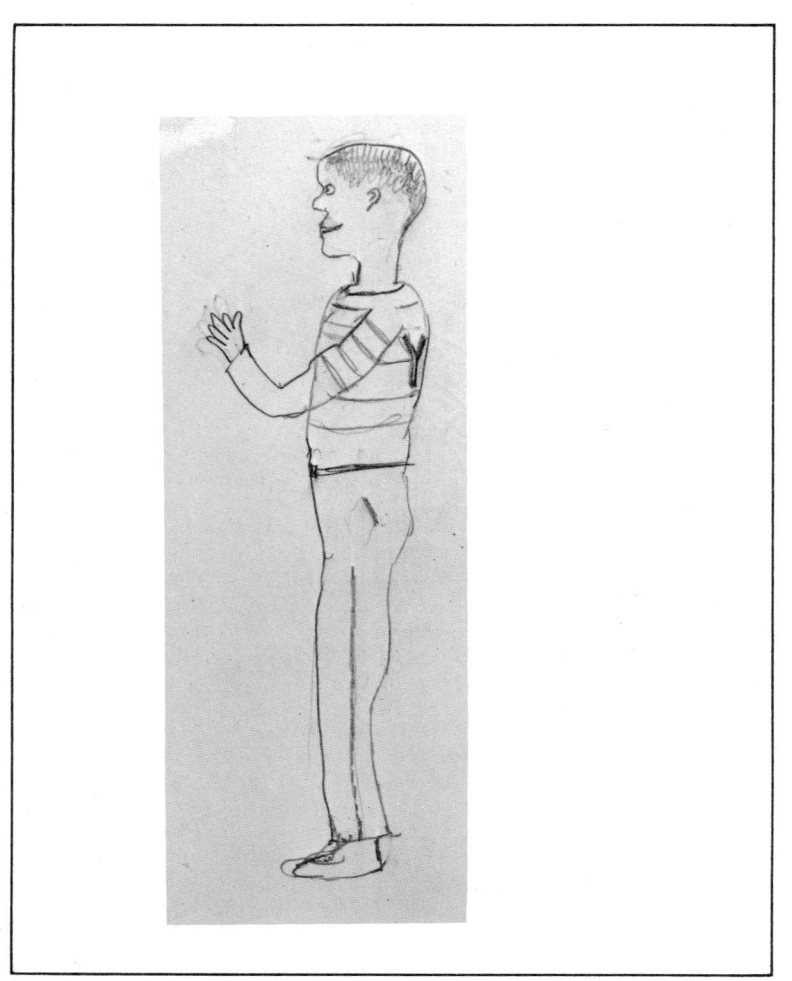

FIGURE-DRAWING CHARACTERISTICS

Structural	Male Female Both	Structural	Male	Female	Structural and Graphic	Male Female Both	Graphic, Global and Height	Male	Female	Body Proportions	Male	Female
Type	0	Omission of Appendages	0	0	Upper and Lower Halves	0 1	Hair Shading	1	1	Head	09	07
Sex Sequence	2	Position of Both Arms	4	4	Four Quarters	4 4	Nudity and Transparency	7	7	Neck	08	05
Posture	1 1	Position of Right Arm	7	7	Relative Size	0	Form	3	3	Shoulders		
Perspective	2 2	Position of Left Arm	4	4	Constant Line Pressure	0 0	Detailing	3	1	Right Arm		
Vertical Midline	4 4	Position of Legs	1	1	Variable Line Pressure	5 2	Identity and Sex	1	1	Left Arm	07	04
Bilateral Symmetry	0 0	Relation of Long Axes	1	0	Line Continuity	2 1	Sophistication	2	2	Chest	08	05
Horizontal Midline	4 4	Right and Left Halves	1	1	Body Shading	6 3	Height	07	05	Girth	07	07

GENERAL CHARACTERISTICS OF SUBJECT

IDENTIFICATION
No. D39
Sex M
Marital status S
Age 23 yrs. at
psychological tests

PARENTAL HISTORY
Father
C H S D O
- + - - -
Mother
C H S D O
- - - - -

PHYSIOLOGICAL AND METABOLIC DATA

	Admission	Initial	Control	Cold pressor change	Exercise change	Smoking change
Systolic pressure	130	120	105	+17	+45	+06
Diastolic pressure	70	62	72	+10	-13	-06
Heart rate	75	60	58	+08	+25	+11

Age 23 yrs.

Height	70 in.
Weight	158 lbs.
Overweight	+02 %

Ponderal index	12.94
Cholesterol	270 mg. per 100 ml.
Vital capacity	4.7 liters

HABIT SURVEY

Smoking habits: former smoker

Age begun 14 yrs.   Inhalation:

Habits of nervous tension: 1, 3, 4, 5, 6, 8, 18, 19, 22, 24

STRONG VOCATIONAL INTEREST TEST

Occupation	Artist	Psychologist	Architect	Physician	Osteopath	Dentist	Veterinarian	Mathematician	Physicist	Engineer	Chemist	Production Manager
Standard Score	33	44	29	41	39	29	15	27	27	33	36	29

Occupation	Farmer	Aviator	Carpenter	Printer	Math.-Sci. Teacher	Ind. Arts Teacher	Voc. Agric. Teacher	Policeman	Forest Serv. Man	Y.M.C.A. Phys. Dir.	Personnel Director	Public Administrator
Standard Score	21	27	05	23	25	04	11	18	04	20	38	38

Occupation	Y.M.C.A. Secretary	Soc. Sci. H.S. Teacher	City Sch. Sup't.	Social Worker	Minister	Musician Performer	C.P.A.	Senior C.P.A.	Accountant	Office Man	Purchasing Agent	Banker
Standard Score	20	27	28	39	63	34	32	24	19	26	22	23

Occupation	Mortician	Pharmacist	Sales Manager	Real Est. Manager	Life Ins. Salesman	Advertising Man	Lawyer	Author- Journalist	President Mfg. Co.	Interest Maturity	Occupational Level	Masculinity- Femininity
Standard Score	31	34	38	47	42	45	48	42	45	49	67	43

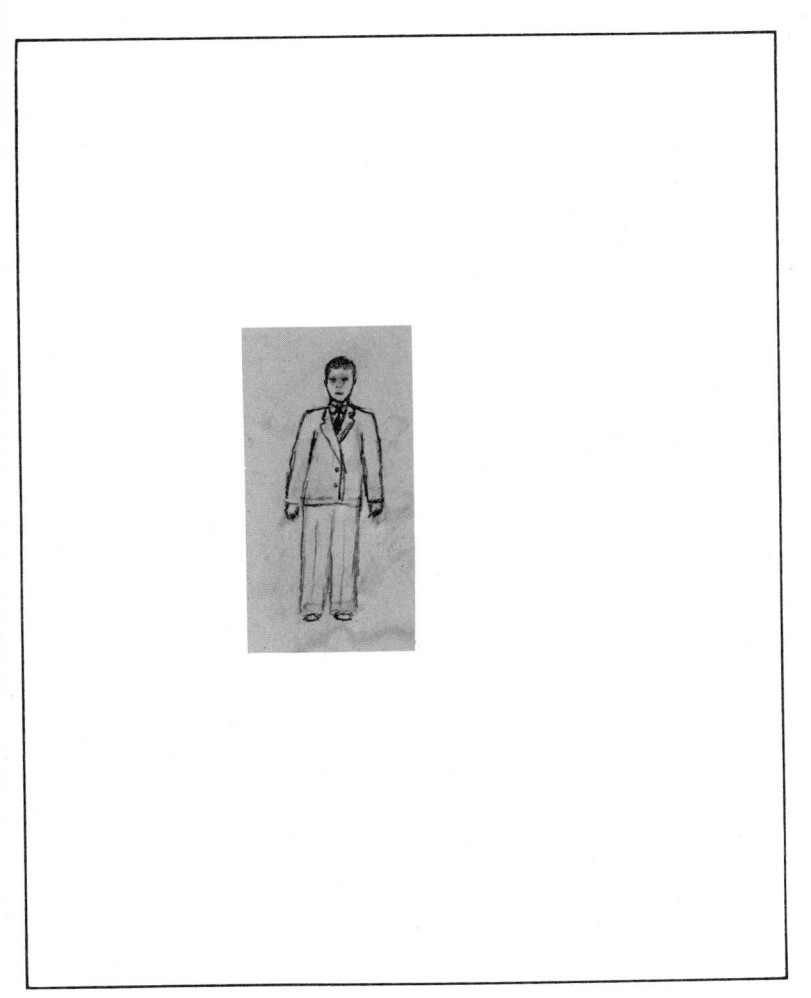

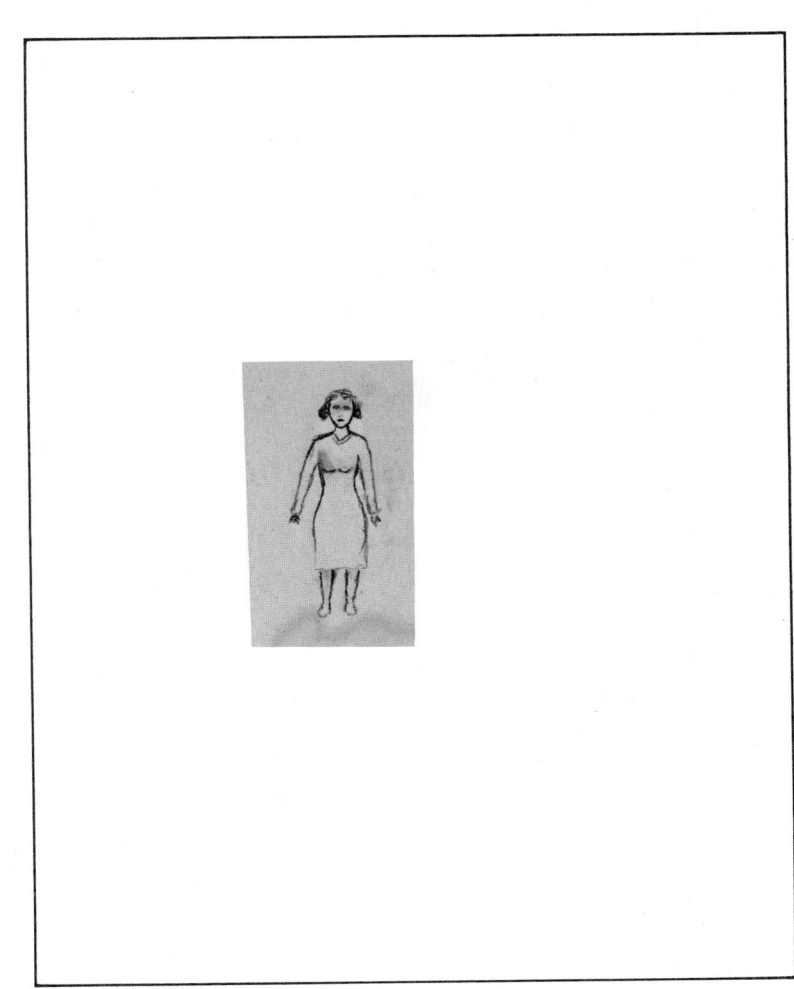

FIGURE-DRAWING CHARACTERISTICS

Structural	Male Female Both		Structural	Male	Female	Structural and Graphic	Male Female Both		Graphic, Global and Height	Male	Female	Body Proportions	Male	Female
Type	0		Omission of Appendages	0	0	Upper and Lower Halves	1	1	Hair Shading	3	3	Head	04	03
Sex Sequence	0		Position of Both Arms	0	1	Four Quarters	4	4	Nudity and Transparency	7	7	Neck	02	02
Posture	1	1	Position of Right Arm	0	2	Relative Size	0		Form	1	1	Shoulders	03	02
Perspective	0	0	Position of Left Arm	0	0	Constant Line Pressure	0	0	Detailing	1	1	Right Arm	02	02
Vertical Midline	3	0	Position of Legs	4	4	Variable Line Pressure	5	5	Identity and Sex	1	1	Left Arm	02	02
Bilateral Symmetry	5	3	Relation of Long Axes	1	1	Line Continuity	2	2	Sophistication	2	2	Chest	02	02
Horizontal Midline	6	0	Right and Left Halves	2	2	Body Shading	6	1	Height	02	02	Girth	03	02

GENERAL CHARACTERISTICS OF SUBJECT

<table>
<tr><td colspan="2">IDENTIFICATION</td></tr>
<tr><td colspan="2">No. 228</td></tr>
<tr><td colspan="2">Sex M</td></tr>
<tr><td colspan="2">Marital status S</td></tr>
<tr><td colspan="2">Age 28 yrs. at</td></tr>
<tr><td colspan="2">psychological tests</td></tr>
</table>

PARENTAL HISTORY					
Father					
C	H	S	D	O	
–	–	–	+	–	
Mother					
C	H	S	D	O	
–	+	–	–	?	

PHYSIOLOGICAL AND METABOLIC DATA

	Admission	Initial	Control	Cold pressor change	Exercise change	Smoking change
Systolic pressure	96	118	114	00	+36	
Diastolic pressure	68	68	66	+04	00	
Heart rate	64	82	79	+04	+21	

Age 26 yrs.	Height	66	in.	Ponderal index	12.96	
	Weight	132	lbs.	Cholesterol	245	mg. per 100 ml.
	Overweight	–07	%	Vital capacity	3.7	liters

HABIT SURVEY
Smoking habits: nonsmoker
Age begun   yrs.   Inhalation:
Habits of nervous tension: 5, 6, 17, 18

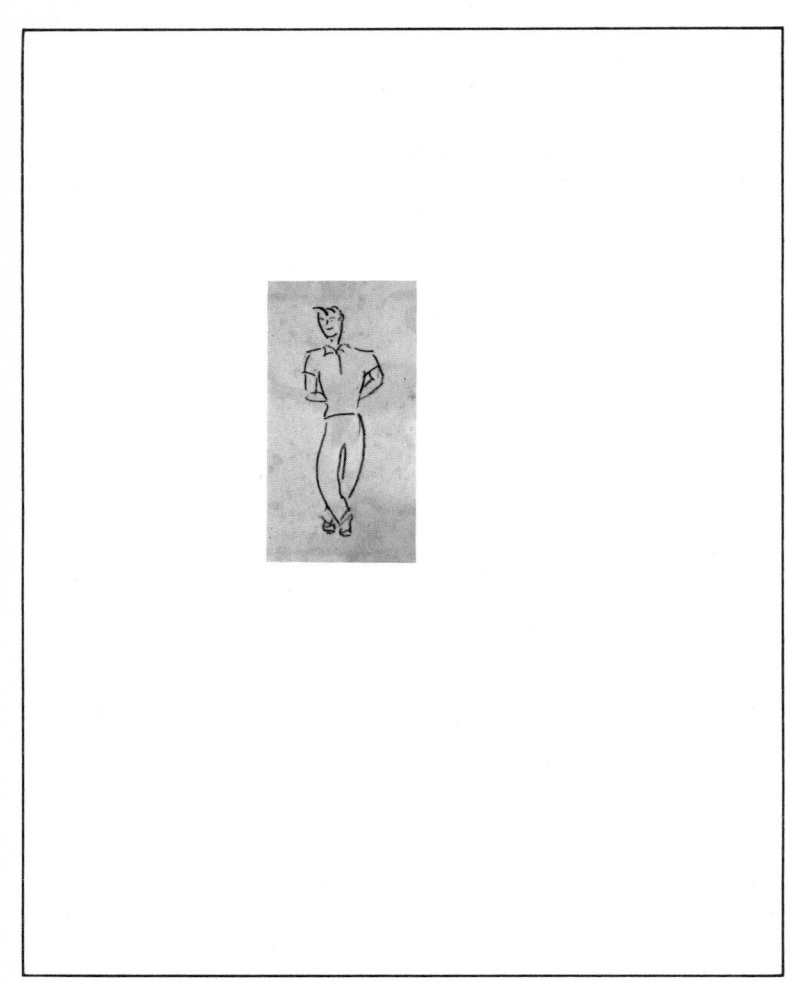

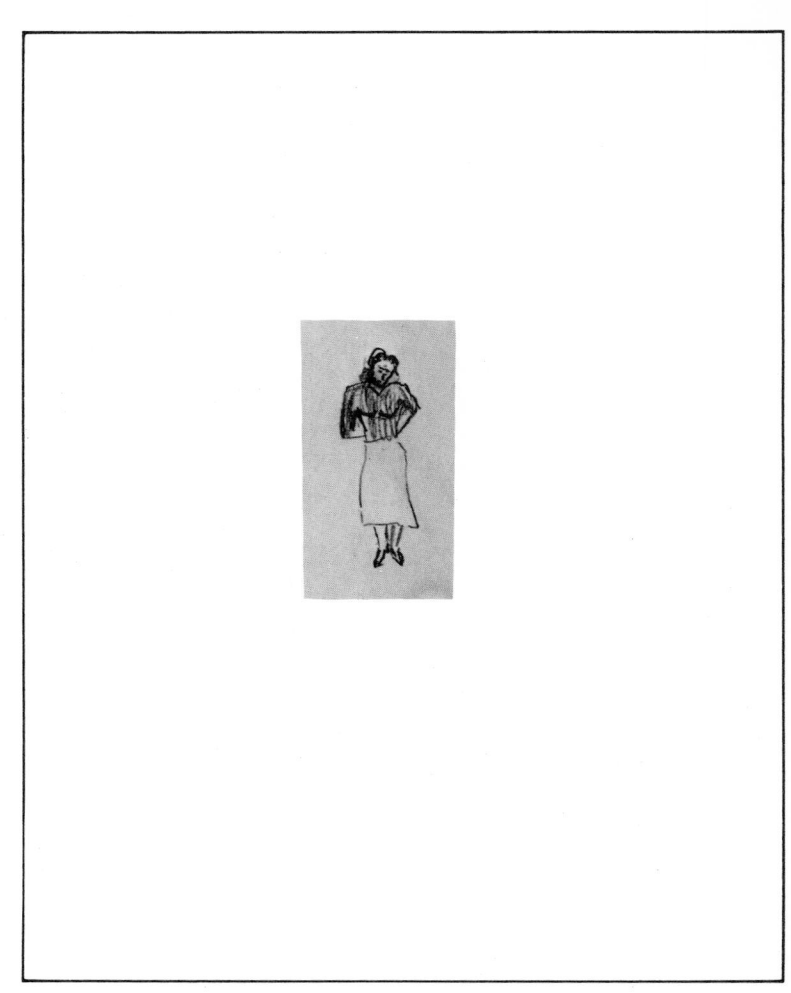

FIGURE-DRAWING CHARACTERISTICS

Structural	Male Female Both		Structural	Male	Female	Structural and Graphic	Male	Female Both		Graphic, Global and Height	Male	Female	Body Proportions	Male	Female
Type	0		Omission of Appendages	7	7	Upper and Lower Halves	2	1		Hair Shading	7	1	Head	02	02
Sex Sequence	0		Position of Both Arms	0	0	Four Quarters	0	4		Nudity and Transparency	7	7	Neck	04	00
Posture	1	1	Position of Right Arm	5	5	Relative Size	2			Form	1	1	Shoulders	02	02
Perspective	0	0	Position of Left Arm	5	5	Constant Line Pressure	0	0		Detailing	3	1	Right Arm		
Vertical Midline	3	0	Position of Legs	7	4	Variable Line Pressure	5	5		Identity and Sex	1	1	Left Arm		
Bilateral Symmetry	3	3	Relation of Long Axes	1	1	Line Continuity	2	2		Sophistication	2	2	Chest	02	02
Horizontal Midline	4	4	Right and Left Halves	2	2	Body Shading	0	1		Height	02	02	Girth	02	02

GENERAL CHARACTERISTICS OF SUBJECT

IDENTIFICATION
No. 281
Sex M
Marital status M
Age 28 yrs. at
psychological tests

PARENTAL HISTORY				
Father				
C	H	S	D	O
-	-	-	-	-
Mother				
C	H	S	D	O
-	+	+	-	+

PHYSIOLOGICAL AND METABOLIC DATA

	Admission	Initial	Control	Cold pressor change	Exercise change	Smoking change
Systolic pressure	120	118	110	+04	+22	
Diastolic pressure	76	64	68	+28	+02	
Heart rate	100	88	71	+02	+08	

Age 28 yrs.	Height	73	in.	Ponderal index 12.50
	Weight	199	lbs.	Cholesterol 197 mg. per 100 ml.
	Overweight +13 %			Vital capacity 5.4 liters

HABIT SURVEY

Smoking habits: occasional smoker

Age begun 21 yrs.   Inhalation: no

Habits of nervous tension: 4, 6, 9, 10, 16, 22

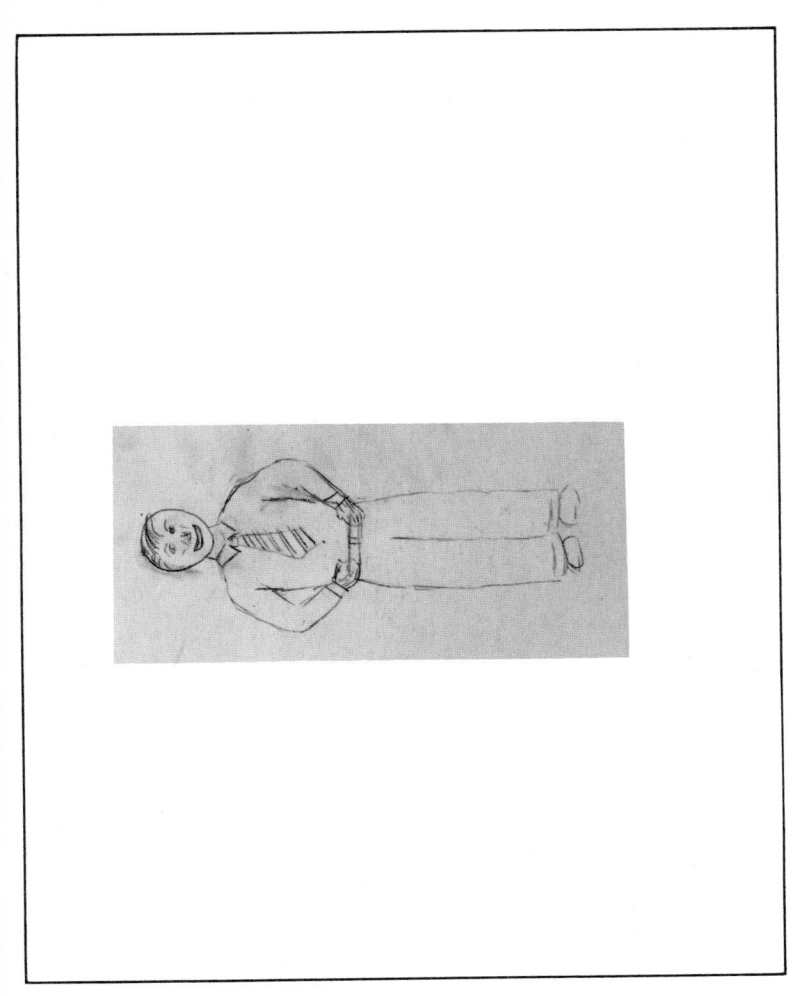

FIGURE-DRAWING CHARACTERISTICS

Structural	Male Female Both	Structural	Male	Female	Structural and Graphic	Male Female Both		Graphic, Global and Height	Male	Female	Body Proportions	Male	Female
Type	0	Omission of Appendages	0	0	Upper and Lower Halves	1	3	Hair Shading	1	1	Head	06	05
Sex Sequence	0	Position of Both Arms	0	0	Four Quarters	4	4	Nudity and Transparency	7	7	Neck	04	06
Posture	1 1	Position of Right Arm	5	5	Relative Size	0		Form	1	1	Shoulders	05	05
Perspective	0 0	Position of Left Arm	5	5	Constant Line Pressure	0	0	Detailing	3	3	Right Arm	04	02
Vertical Midline	3 0	Position of Legs	2	5	Variable Line Pressure	1	3	Identity and Sex	1	1	Left Arm	04	02
Bilateral Symmetry	4 4	Relation of Long Axes	2	2	Line Continuity	0	0	Sophistication	2	2	Chest	04	04
Horizontal Midline	4 0	Right and Left Halves	1	1	Body Shading	0	1	Height	04	03	Girth	05	05

GENERAL CHARACTERISTICS OF SUBJECT

<table>
<tr><th colspan="2">IDENTIFICATION</th><th colspan="2">PARENTAL HISTORY</th><th colspan="7">PHYSIOLOGICAL AND METABOLIC DATA</th><th colspan="2">HABIT SURVEY</th></tr>
</table>

IDENTIFICATION	PARENTAL HISTORY
No. 402	**Father**
Sex M	C H S D O
Marital status M	-- -- (+) -- --
Age 25 yrs. at	**Mother**
psychological tests	C H S D O
	-- + -- -- ?

PHYSIOLOGICAL AND METABOLIC DATA

	Admission	Initial	Control	Cold pressor change	Exercise change	Smoking change
Systolic pressure	142	134	120	+16	+44	
Diastolic pressure	80	84	72	+38	-02	
Heart rate	72	70	65	+12	+13	

Age 22 yrs.   Height 69 in.   Ponderal index 12.24
Weight 179 lbs.   Cholesterol 237 mg. per 100 ml.
Overweight +19 %   Vital capacity 5.4 liters

HABIT SURVEY

Smoking habits: occasional smoker
  Age begun 17 yrs.   Inhalation: sometimes
Habits of nervous tension: 2, 4, 5, 6, 9, 11

FIGURE-DRAWING CHARACTERISTICS

Structural	Male Female Both	Structural	Male	Female	Structural and Graphic	Male Female Both	Graphic, Global and Height	Male	Female	Body Proportions	Male	Female
Type	0	Omission of Appendages	4	3	Upper and Lower Halves	9 7	Hair Shading	3	1	Head	23	17
Sex Sequence	2	Position of Both Arms	4	0	Four Quarters	4 4	Nudity and Transparency	7	7	Neck	14	12
Posture	0 0	Position of Right Arm	0	5	Relative Size	0	Form	2	3	Shoulders	19	12
Perspective	1 1	Position of Left Arm	5	5	Constant Line Pressure	5 0	Detailing	3	3	Right Arm	12	08
Vertical Midline	7 7	Position of Legs	0	0	Variable Line Pressure	0 5	Identity and Sex	1	1	Left Arm	12	10
Bilateral Symmetry	0 0	Relation of Long Axes	1	1	Line Continuity	2 2	Sophistication	2	2	Chest	15	10
Horizontal Midline	0 0	Right and Left Halves	0	1	Body Shading	4 1	Height			Girth	21	16

GENERAL CHARACTERISTICS OF SUBJECT

IDENTIFICATION
No. 416
Sex M
Marital status S
Age 29 yrs. at
psychological tests

PARENTAL HISTORY
Father
C   H   S   D   O
−   −   −   −   +
Mother
C   H   S   D   O
−   +   −   −   +

PHYSIOLOGICAL AND METABOLIC DATA

	Admission	Initial	Control	Cold pressor change	Exercise change	Smoking change
Systolic pressure	130	108	98	+10	+62	+04
Diastolic pressure	78	68	72	+12	+06	−06
Heart rate	68	56	60	+04	+14	00

Age 27 yrs.

Height 68 in.
Weight 176 lbs.
Overweight +17 %

Ponderal index 12.13
Cholesterol 222 mg. per 100 ml.
Vital capacity 4.5 liters

HABIT SURVEY
Smoking habits: nonsmoker
Age begun   yrs.   Inhalation:
Habits of nervous tension: 5, 6, 16, 25

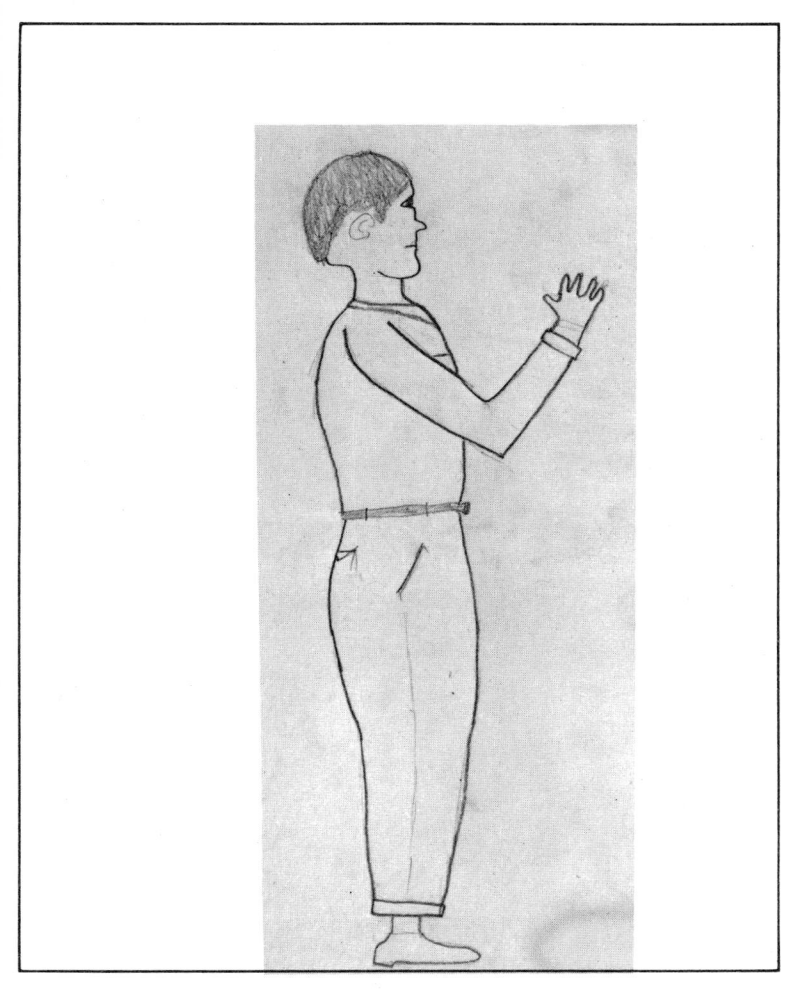
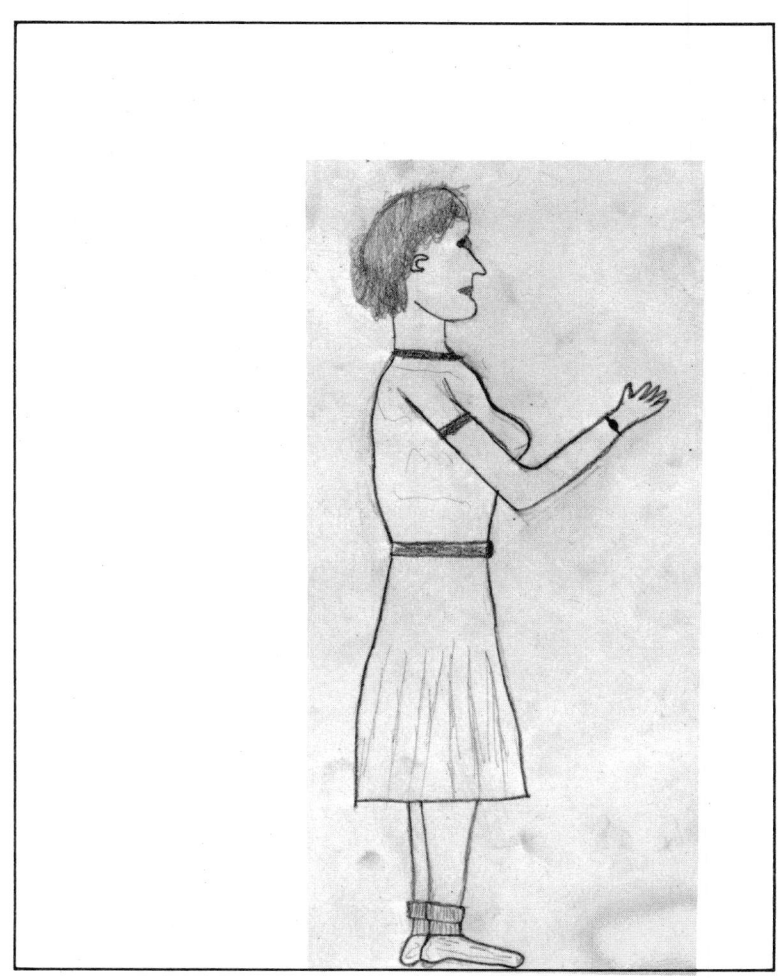

FIGURE-DRAWING CHARACTERISTICS

Structural	Male Female Both	Structural	Male	Female	Structural and Graphic	Male Female Both		Graphic, Global and Height	Male	Female	Body Proportions	Male	Female
Type	0	Omission of Appendages	0	0	Upper and Lower Halves	3	3	Hair Shading	2	3	Head	10	10
Sex Sequence	2	Position of Both Arms	2	2	Four Quarters	4	4	Nudity and Transparency	7	7	Neck	08	10
Posture	1 1	Position of Right Arm	3	3	Relative Size	1		Form	1	1	Shoulders		
Perspective	2 2	Position of Left Arm	7	7	Constant Line Pressure	5	5	Detailing	3	1	Right Arm	08	08
Vertical Midline	4 4	Position of Legs	1	1	Variable Line Pressure	0	0	Identity and Sex	1	1	Left Arm		
Bilateral Symmetry	0 0	Relation of Long Axes	1	1	Line Continuity	4	4	Sophistication	2	2	Chest	10	08
Horizontal Midline	4 4	Right and Left Halves	3	3	Body Shading	4	6	Height	08	08	Girth	09	09

GENERAL CHARACTERISTICS OF SUBJECT

IDENTIFICATION
No. 573
Sex M
Marital status S
Age 25 yrs. at
psychological tests

PARENTAL HISTORY
Father
C   H   S   D   O
-   -   -   -   -
Mother
C   H   S   D   O
-   +   -   -   -

PHYSIOLOGICAL AND METABOLIC DATA

	Admission	Initial	Control	Cold pressor change	Exercise change	Smoking change
Systolic pressure	145	136	120	+10	+10	
Diastolic pressure	85	84	70	00	00	
Heart rate	74	94	88	+18	+19	

Age 22 yrs.	Height	70	in.	Ponderal index	12.22	
	Weight	188	lbs.	Cholesterol	273	mg. per 100 ml.
	Overweight +22 %			Vital capacity	4.6	liters

HABIT SURVEY

Smoking habits: occasional smoker

  Age begun 19 yrs.   Inhalation: yes

Habits of nervous tension: 3, 4, 5, 6, 10, 21

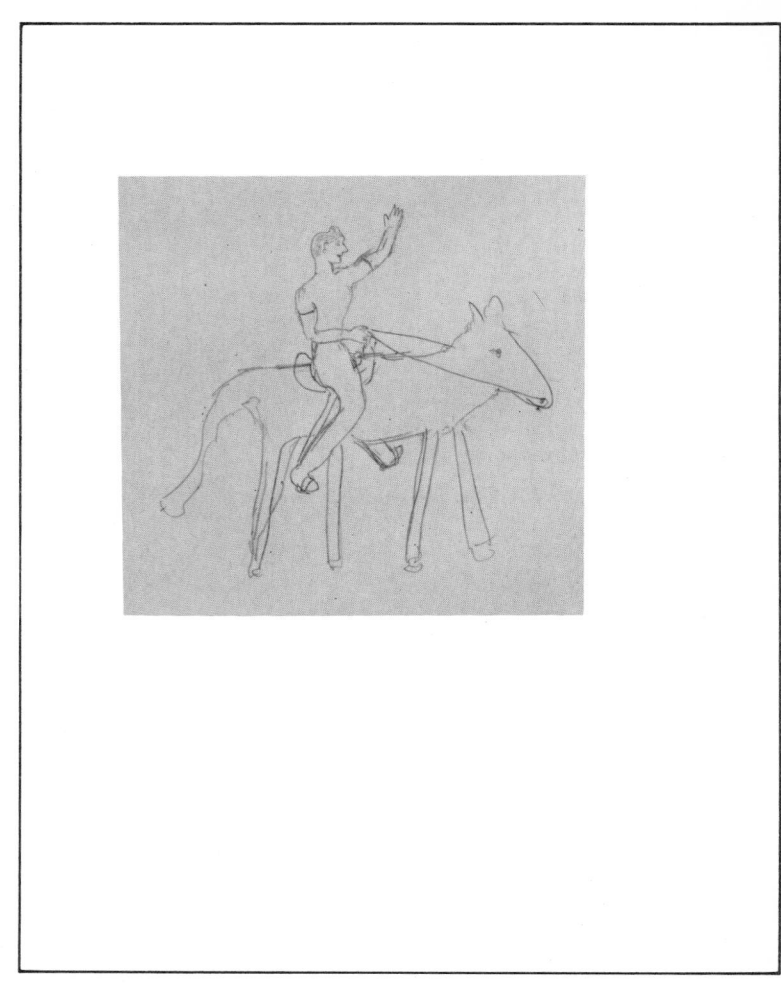

FIGURE-DRAWING CHARACTERISTICS

Structural	Male Female Both	Structural	Male	Female	Structural and Graphic	Male Female Both		Graphic, Global and Height	Male	Female	Body Proportions	Male	Female
Type	0	Omission of Appendages	0	0	Upper and Lower Halves	2	2	Hair Shading	1	3	Head	02	02
Sex Sequence	1	Position of Both Arms	1	1	Four Quarters	0	0	Nudity and Transparency	7	7	Neck	04	03
Posture	6	1	Position of Right Arm	4	0	Relative Size	0		Form	1	1	Shoulders		
Perspective	9	6	Position of Left Arm	2	2	Constant Line Pressure	0	4	Detailing	1	1	Right Arm	02	02
Vertical Midline	9	4	Position of Legs	8	4	Variable Line Pressure	2	0	Identity and Sex	1	1	Left Arm	02	02
Bilateral Symmetry	0	0	Relation of Long Axes	0	1	Line Continuity	0	1	Sophistication	2	2	Chest		
Horizontal Midline	2	4	Right and Left Halves	2	2	Body Shading	0	3	Height		02	Girth		

GENERAL CHARACTERISTICS OF SUBJECT

<table>
<tr><th>IDENTIFICATION</th><th>PARENTAL HISTORY</th><th colspan="7">PHYSIOLOGICAL AND METABOLIC DATA</th><th>HABIT SURVEY</th></tr>
<tr><td>No. 605</td><td>Father</td><td></td><td>Admission</td><td>Initial</td><td>Control</td><td>Cold pressor change</td><td>Exercise change</td><td>Smoking change</td><td>Smoking habits: moderate cigarette smoker</td></tr>
<tr><td>Sex M</td><td>C   H   S   D   O</td><td>Systolic pressure</td><td>105</td><td>118</td><td>110</td><td>+12</td><td>+30</td><td>00</td><td>Age begun 13 yrs.   Inhalation: yes</td></tr>
<tr><td>Marital status M</td><td>-   -   +   -   ?</td><td>Diastolic pressure</td><td>80</td><td>88</td><td>76</td><td>+08</td><td>+02</td><td>+06</td><td>Habits of nervous tension: 1, 3, 6, 9, 11,</td></tr>
<tr><td>Age 25 yrs. at</td><td>Mother</td><td>Heart rate</td><td>84</td><td>88</td><td>89</td><td>-04</td><td>+26</td><td>+09</td><td>18, 21, 22</td></tr>
<tr><td>psychological tests</td><td>C   H   S   D   O</td><td colspan="2">Height   72   in.</td><td colspan="2">Ponderal index 12.83</td><td></td><td></td><td></td></tr>
<tr><td></td><td>-   +   -   +   +</td><td>Age 22 yrs.</td><td colspan="2">Weight   177   lbs.</td><td colspan="2">Cholesterol   265   mg. per 100 ml.</td><td></td><td></td><td></td></tr>
<tr><td></td><td></td><td></td><td colspan="2">Overweight +09 %</td><td colspan="2">Vital capacity   4.7   liters</td><td></td><td></td><td></td></tr>
</table>

FIGURE-DRAWING CHARACTERISTICS

Structural	Male Female Both		Structural	Male	Female	Structural and Graphic	Male Female Both		Graphic, Global and Height	Male	Female	Body Proportions	Male	Female
Type	0		Omission of Appendages	0	0	Upper and Lower Halves	0	3	Hair Shading	3	3	Head		05
Sex Sequence	0		Position of Both Arms	1	1	Four Quarters	4	4	Nudity and Transparency	7	7	Neck		03
Posture	2	1	Position of Right Arm	4	0	Relative Size	5		Form	1	1	Shoulders		
Perspective	1	1	Position of Left Arm	9	5	Constant Line Pressure	1	1	Detailing	1	3	Right Arm		04
Vertical Midline	7	4	Position of Legs	8	5	Variable Line Pressure	0	0	Identity and Sex	1	1	Left Arm		04
Bilateral Symmetry	0	0	Relation of Long Axes	1	1	Line Continuity	0	0	Sophistication	2	2	Chest		
Horizontal Midline	0	4	Right and Left Halves	1	3	Body Shading	3	3	Height		05	Girth		

GENERAL CHARACTERISTICS OF SUBJECT

IDENTIFICATION
No. 737
Sex M
Marital status S
Age 22 yrs. at
psychological tests

PARENTAL HISTORY
Father
C H S D O
- - - - +
Mother
C H S D O
- + - - ?

PHYSIOLOGICAL AND METABOLIC DATA

	Admission	Initial	Control	Cold pressor change	Exercise change	Smoking change
Systolic pressure	120	106	110	+20	+24	+15
Diastolic pressure	80	60	74	+26	-26	+10
Heart rate	80	72	55	+12	+24	+03

Age 21 yrs.	Height 67 in.	Ponderal index 12.64
	Weight 149 lbs.	Cholesterol 250 mg. per 100 ml.
	Overweight +06 %	Vital capacity 5.5 liters

HABIT SURVEY
Smoking habits: nonsmoker
Age begun   yrs.   Inhalation:
Habits of nervous tension: 2, 5, 6, 11, 15, 18, 23

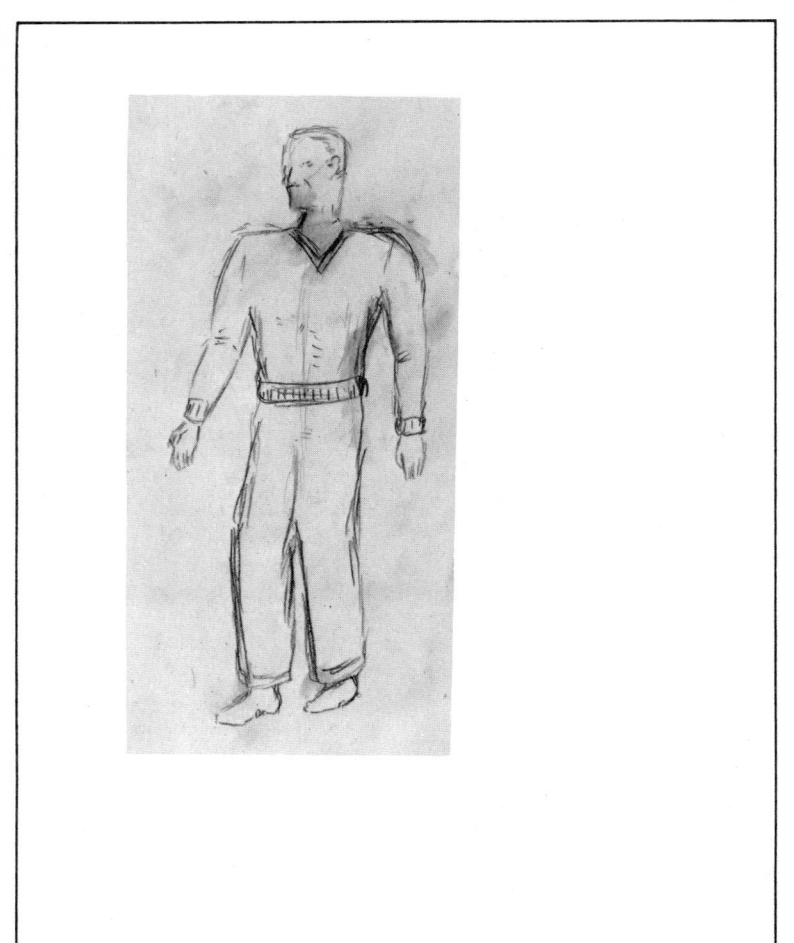

FIGURE-DRAWING CHARACTERISTICS

Structural	Male Female Both	Structural	Male	Female	Structural and Graphic	Male Female Both		Graphic, Global and Height	Male	Female	Body Proportions	Male	Female
Type	0	Omission of Appendages	0	0	Upper and Lower Halves	1	1	Hair Shading	3	1	Head	06	04
Sex Sequence	0	Position of Both Arms	1	1	Four Quarters	4	4	Nudity and Transparency	7	7	Neck	06	06
Posture	2 1	Position of Right Arm	2	5	Relative Size	0		Form	1	1	Shoulders	07	
Perspective	5 1	Position of Left Arm	0	2	Constant Line Pressure	0	0	Detailing	3	5	Right Arm	06	02
Vertical Midline	1 7	Position of Legs	8	4	Variable Line Pressure	2	3	Identity and Sex	1	1	Left Arm	06	02
Bilateral Symmetry	3 0	Relation of Long Axes	1	1	Line Continuity	0	0	Sophistication	2	2	Chest	06	
Horizontal Midline	4 4	Right and Left Halves	1	1	Body Shading	7	3	Height	06	04	Girth	07	

GENERAL CHARACTERISTICS OF SUBJECT

IDENTIFICATION
No.   743
Sex M
Marital status   S
Age 22 yrs. at
psychological tests

PARENTAL HISTORY
Father
C   H   S   D   O
-    -   -   -   -
Mother
C   H   S   D   O
-    +   -   -   -

PHYSIOLOGICAL AND METABOLIC DATA

	Admission	Initial	Control	Cold pressor change	Exercise change	Smoking change
Systolic pressure	110	112	100	+10	+48	-01
Diastolic pressure	68	68	68	+20	-14	+08
Heart rate	70	76	72	-08	+16	00

Age 22 yrs.	Height	68	in.	Ponderal index	13.15	
	Weight	138	lbs.	Cholesterol	234	mg. per 100 ml.
	Overweight	-05	%	Vital capacity	4.8	liters

HABIT SURVEY
Smoking habits: nonsmoker
Age begun   yrs.   Inhalation:
Habits of nervous tension: 3, 4, 5, 6, 9, 10,
21, 22

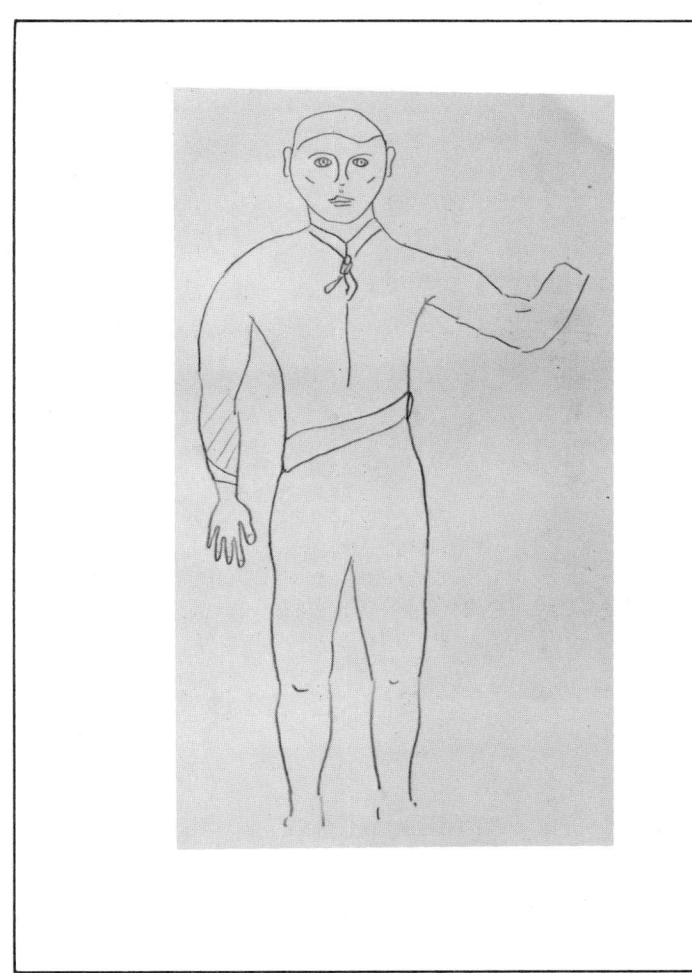
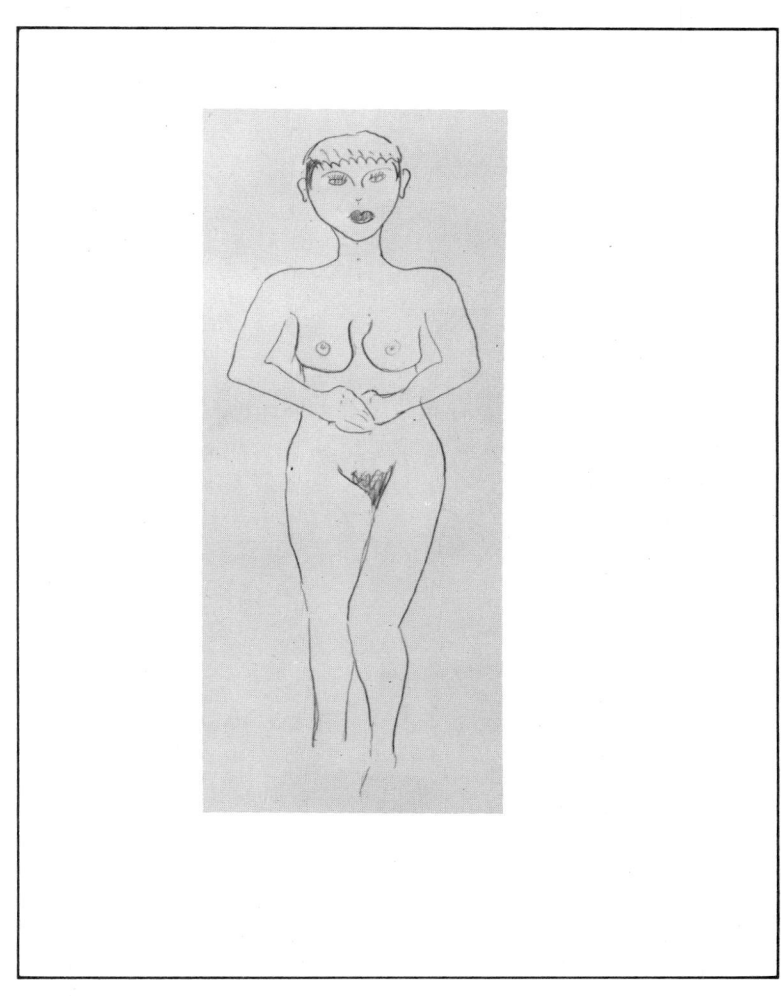

FIGURE-DRAWING CHARACTERISTICS

Structural	Male Female Both	Structural	Male	Female	Structural and Graphic	Male Female Both		Graphic, Global and Height	Male	Female	Body Proportions	Male	Female
Type	0	Omission of Appendages	6	8	Upper and Lower Halves	1	1	Hair Shading	5	1	Head	09	09
Sex Sequence	0	Position of Both Arms	1	0	Four Quarters	4	4	Nudity and Transparency	7	0	Neck	06	08
Posture	0	1	Position of Right Arm	0	5	Relative Size	5		Form	1	1	Shoulders	09	08
Perspective	0	0	Position of Left Arm	2	5	Constant Line Pressure	5	0	Detailing	3	1	Right Arm	07	06
Vertical Midline	3	0	Position of Legs	4	3	Variable Line Pressure	0	4	Identity and Sex	1	1	Left Arm		05
Bilateral Symmetry	2	3	Relation of Long Axes	1	1	Line Continuity	4	4	Sophistication	2	2	Chest	07	06
Horizontal Midline	4	2	Right and Left Halves	1	1	Body Shading	3	2	Height			Girth	08	08

GENERAL CHARACTERISTICS OF SUBJECT

IDENTIFICATION
No. G48
Sex M
Marital status M
Age 30 yrs. at psychological tests

PARENTAL HISTORY				
Father				
C	H	S	D	O
−	−	−	−	−
Mother				
C	H	S	D	O
−	+	−	−	+

PHYSIOLOGICAL AND METABOLIC DATA

	Admission	Initial	Control	Cold pressor change	Exercise change	Smoking change
Systolic pressure	120	130	118	+14	+24	+04
Diastolic pressure	80	80	76	+14	+02	+07
Heart rate	80	80	52	+08	+13	+05

Age 29 yrs.	Height 71 in.	Ponderal index 12.22
	Weight 196 lbs.	Cholesterol 244 mg. per 100 ml.
	Overweight +19 %	Vital capacity liters

HABIT SURVEY
Smoking habits: moderate cigarette smoker
Age begun 25 yrs.   Inhalation: yes
Habits of nervous tension: 2, 4, 5, 6, 10, 16

STRONG VOCATIONAL INTEREST TEST

Occupation	Artist	Psychologist	Architect	Physician	Osteopath	Dentist	Veterinarian	Mathematician	Physicist	Engineer	Chemist	Production Manager
Standard Score	46	53	42	44	33	29	05	41	29	26	35	12

Occupation	Farmer	Aviator	Carpenter	Printer	Math.-Sci. Teacher	Ind. Arts Teacher	Voc. Agric. Teacher	Policeman	Forest Serv. Man	Y.M.C.A. Phys. Dir.	Personnel Director	Public Administrator
Standard Score	19	17	01	30	28	−09	13	11	11	18	29	40

Occupation	Y.M.C.A. Secretary	Soc. Sci. H.S. Teacher	City Sch. Sup't.	Social Worker	Minister	Musician Performer	C.P.A.	Senior C.P.A.	Accountant	Office Man	Purchasing Agent	Banker
Standard Score	22	29	40	40	59	40	40	23	10	15	06	17

Occupation	Mortician	Pharmacist	Sales Manager	Real Est. Manager	Life Ins. Salesman	Advertising Man	Lawyer	Author-Journalist	President Mfg. Co.	Interest Maturity	Occupational Level	Masculinity-Femininity
Standard Score	11	17	21	35	29	43	56	54	28	51	64	28

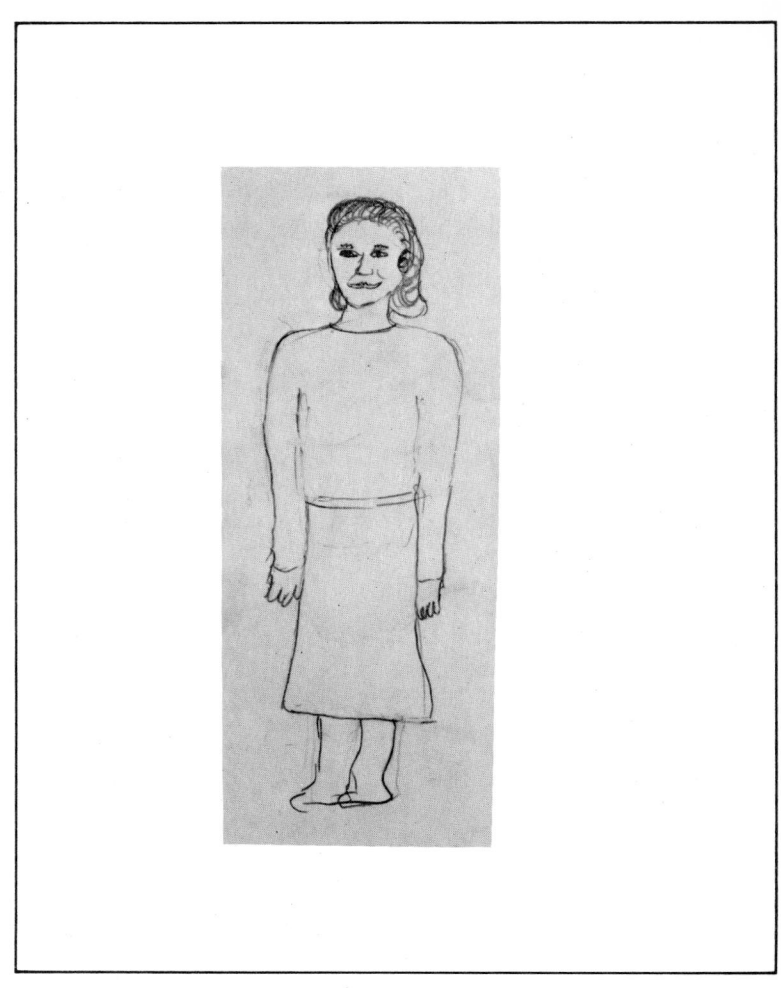

FIGURE-DRAWING CHARACTERISTICS

Structural	Male	Female	Structural	Male	Female	Structural and Graphic	Male	Female	Graphic, Global and Height	Male	Female	Body Proportions	Male	Female
	Both						Both							
Type		0	Omission of Appendages	0	0	Upper and Lower Halves	3	0	Hair Shading	3	2	Head	08	09
Sex Sequence		0	Position of Both Arms	0	0	Four Quarters	4	4	Nudity and Transparency	6	7	Neck	06	06
Posture	1	1	Position of Right Arm	0	0	Relative Size		2	Form	1	3	Shoulders	07	07
Perspective	0	0	Position of Left Arm	0	0	Constant Line Pressure	0	0	Detailing	1	3	Right Arm	06	06
Vertical Midline	3	0	Position of Legs	6	2	Variable Line Pressure	5	2	Identity and Sex	1	1	Left Arm	06	06
Bilateral Symmetry	4	3	Relation of Long Axes	1	1	Line Continuity	0	0	Sophistication	2	2	Chest	06	06
Horizontal Midline	4	4	Right and Left Halves	1	1	Body Shading	0	0	Height	06	06	Girth	06	07

GENERAL CHARACTERISTICS OF SUBJECT

IDENTIFICATION
No. A66
Sex M
Marital status S
Age 23 yrs. at
psychological tests

PARENTAL HISTORY
Father
C H S D O
- - - - ?
Mother
C H S D O
- + - - -

PHYSIOLOGICAL AND METABOLIC DATA

	Admission	Initial	Control	Cold pressor change	Exercise change	Smoking change
Systolic pressure	128	134	116	+12	+29	00
Diastolic pressure	76	82	70	+16	-03	+10
Heart rate	88	92	71	+10	+29	+06

Age 22 yrs.	Height 70 in.	Ponderal index 12.87
	Weight 161 lbs.	Cholesterol 177 mg. per 100 ml.
	Overweight +05 %	Vital capacity liters

HABIT SURVEY

Smoking habits: heavy cigarette smoker

Age begun 17 yrs.   Inhalation: yes

Habits of nervous tension: 4, 5, 16, 17

STRONG VOCATIONAL INTEREST TEST

Occupation	Artist	Psychologist	Architect	Physician	Osteopath	Dentist	Veterinarian	Mathematician	Physicist	Engineer	Chemist	Production Manager
Standard Score	49	57	48	72	56	53	21	54	55	50	66	27

Occupation	Farmer	Aviator	Carpenter	Printer	Math.-Sci. Teacher	Ind. Arts Teacher	Voc. Agric. Teacher	Policeman	Forest Serv. Man	Y.M.C.A. Phys. Dir.	Personnel Director	Public Administrator
Standard Score	37	42	15	35	39	10	19	22	29	16	23	38

Occupation	Y.M.C.A. Secretary	Soc. Sci. H.S. Teacher	City Sch. Sup't.	Social Worker	Minister	Musician Performer	C.P.A.	Senior C.P.A.	Accountant	Office Man	Purchasing Agent	Banker
Standard Score	09	17	22	31	60	54	38	36	17	21	14	13

Occupation	Mortician	Pharmacist	Sales Manager	Real Est. Manager	Life Ins. Salesman	Advertising Man	Lawyer	Author-Journalist	President Mfg. Co.	Interest Maturity	Occupational Level	Masculinity-Femininity
Standard Score	14	29	17	26	17	35	41	47	29	49	65	44

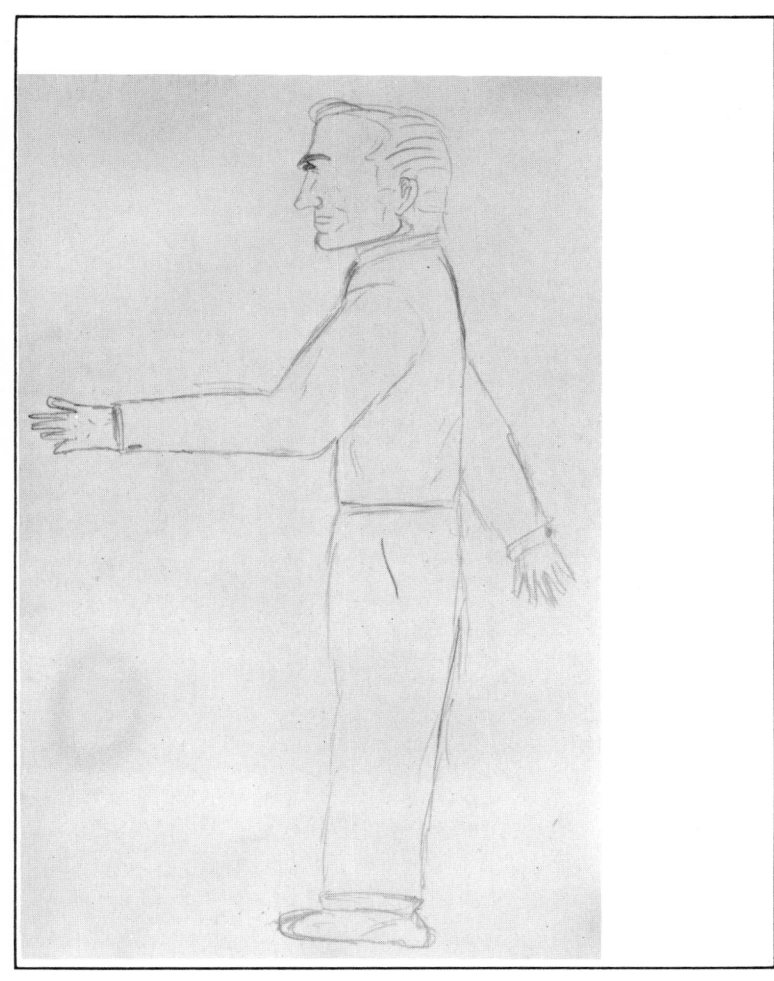

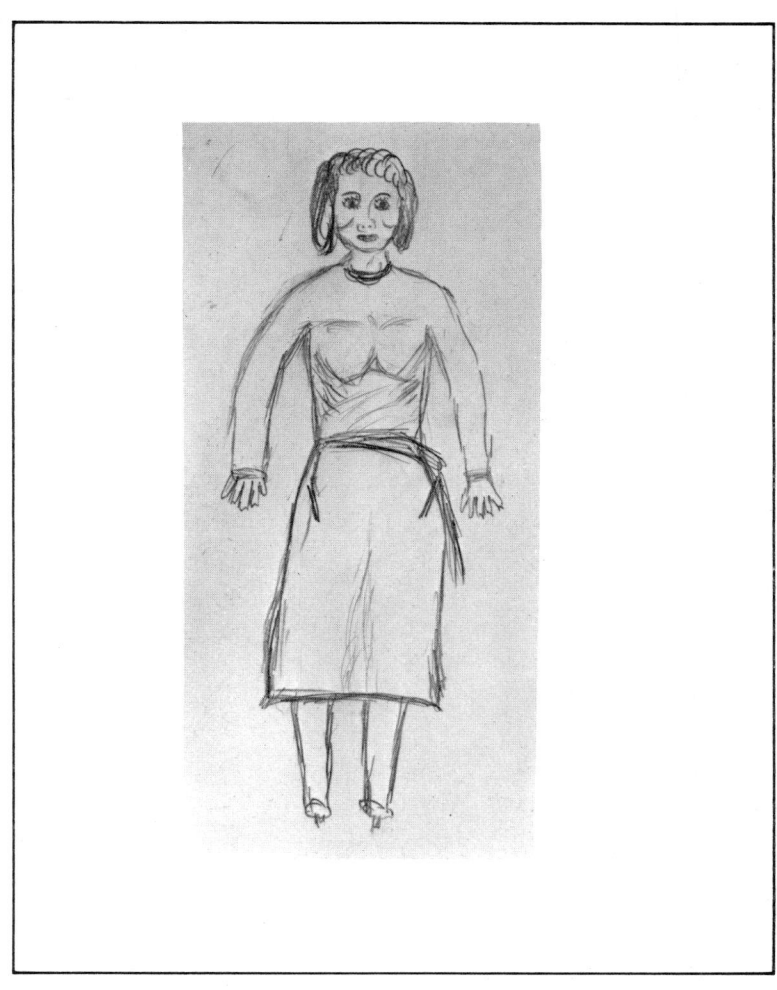

FIGURE-DRAWING CHARACTERISTICS

Structural	Male Female Both	Structural	Male	Female	Structural and Graphic	Male Female Both		Graphic, Global and Height	Male	Female	Body Proportions	Male	Female
Type	0	Omission of Appendages	0	0	Upper and Lower Halves	3	0	Hair Shading	3	3	Head	12	07
Sex Sequence	0	Position of Both Arms	4	0	Four Quarters	4	4	Nudity and Transparency	7	6	Neck	06	06
Posture	1 1	Position of Right Arm	7	2	Relative Size	0		Form	1	1	Shoulders		06
Perspective	2 0	Position of Left Arm	3	2	Constant Line Pressure	1	0	Detailing	3	1	Right Arm		05
Vertical Midline	4 0	Position of Legs	1	4	Variable Line Pressure	0	1	Identity and Sex	1	1	Left Arm	10	06
Bilateral Symmetry	0 3	Relation of Long Axes	1	1	Line Continuity	0	0	Sophistication	2	2	Chest	09	06
Horizontal Midline	4 4	Right and Left Halves	1	1	Body Shading	5	7	Height	09	07	Girth	09	07

GENERAL CHARACTERISTICS OF SUBJECT

IDENTIFICATION
No. B20
Sex M
Marital status S
Age 21 yrs. at psychological tests

PARENTAL HISTORY				
Father				
C	H	S	D	O
-	-	-	-	?
Mother				
C	H	S	D	O
-	+	-	-	?

PHYSIOLOGICAL AND METABOLIC DATA

	Admission	Initial	Control	Cold pressor change	Exercise change	Smoking change
Systolic pressure	120	110	111	+12	+21	
Diastolic pressure	65	56	60	+10	-02	
Heart rate	80	76	71	+02	+16	

Age 21 yrs.	Height 69 in.	Ponderal index 13.69
	Weight 128 lbs.	Cholesterol 248 mg. per 100 ml.
	Overweight -14 %	Vital capacity 3.8 liters

HABIT SURVEY
Smoking habits: nonsmoker
Age begun   yrs.   Inhalation:
Habits of nervous tension: 3, 5, 11, 22

STRONG VOCATIONAL INTEREST TEST

Occupation	Artist	Psychologist	Architect	Physician	Osteopath	Dentist	Veterinarian	Mathematician	Physicist	Engineer	Chemist	Production Manager
Standard Score	38	48	34	53	45	37	28	19	14	14	28	21

Occupation	Farmer	Aviator	Carpenter	Printer	Math.-Sci. Teacher	Ind. Arts Teacher	Voc. Agric. Teacher	Policeman	Forest Serv. Man	Y.M.C.A. Phys. Dir.	Personnel Director	Public Administrator
Standard Score	29	34	10	40	31	13	30	28	11	38	40	42

Occupation	Y.M.C.A. Secretary	Soc. Sci. H.S. Teacher	City Sch. Sup't.	Social Worker	Minister	Musician Performer	C.P.A.	Senior C.P.A.	Accountant	Office Man	Purchasing Agent	Banker
Standard Score	31	44	28	48	61	54	32	35	18	31	14	17

Occupation	Mortician	Pharmacist	Sales Manager	Real Est. Manager	Life Ins. Salesman	Advertising Man	Lawyer	Author-Journalist	President Mfg. Co.	Interest Maturity	Occupational Level	Masculinity-Femininity
Standard Score	34	38	32	40	39	51	44	45	29	54	53	40

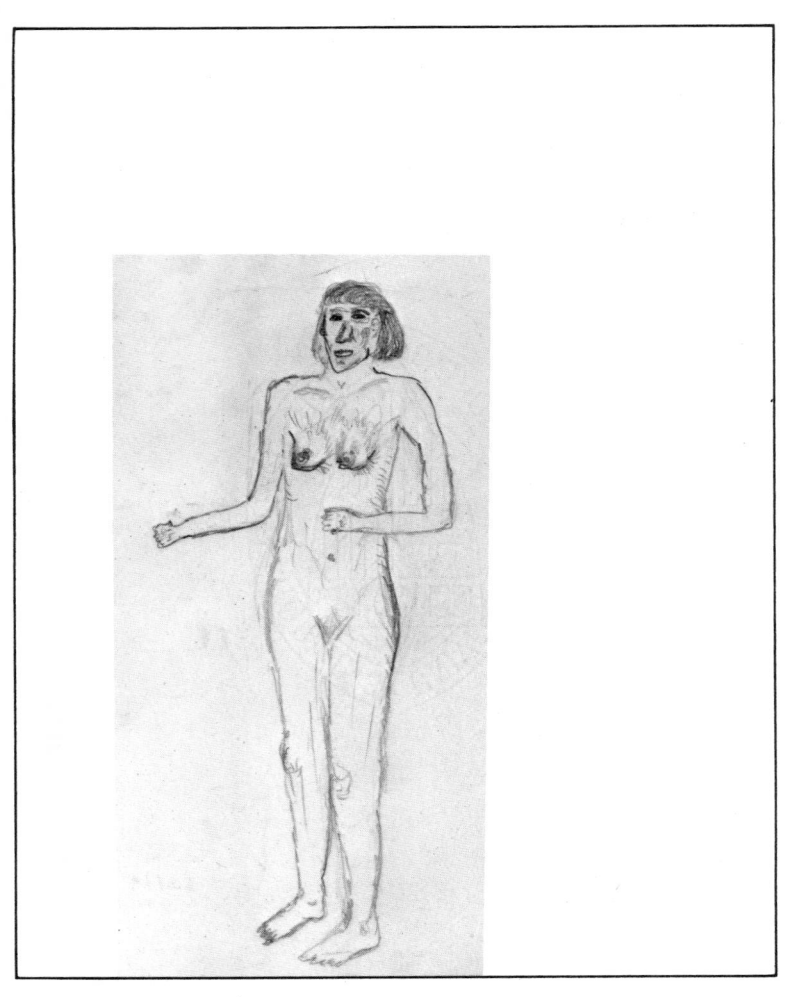

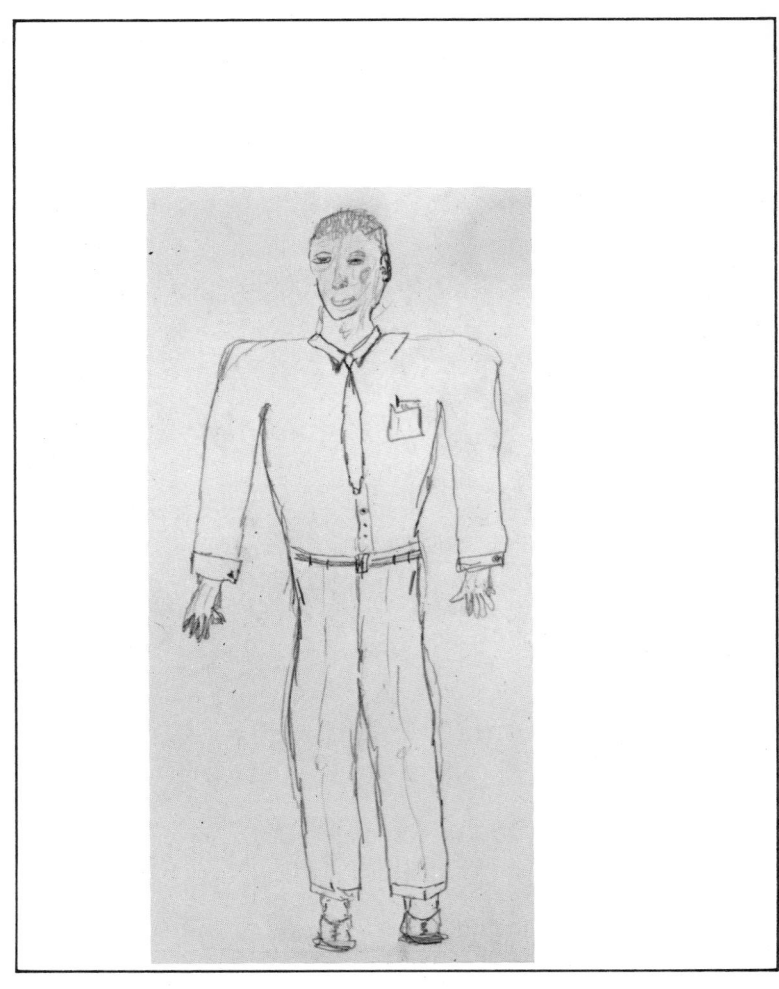

FIGURE-DRAWING CHARACTERISTICS

Structural	Male Female Both		Structural	Male	Female	Structural and Graphic	Male Female Both		Graphic, Global and Height	Male	Female	Body Proportions	Male	Female
Type	0		Omission of Appendages	0	0	Upper and Lower Halves	3	3	Hair Shading	3	2	Head	09	06
Sex Sequence	1		Position of Both Arms	0	1	Four Quarters	4	4	Nudity and Transparency	7	0	Neck	06	03
Posture	1	1	Position of Right Arm	2	4	Relative Size	0		Form	3	3	Shoulders	11	
Perspective	0	1	Position of Left Arm	2	5	Constant Line Pressure	0	0	Detailing	1	1	Right Arm	06	06
Vertical Midline	3	4	Position of Legs	4	3	Variable Line Pressure	4	4	Identity and Sex	1	1	Left Arm	06	06
Bilateral Symmetry	3	0	Relation of Long Axes	1	1	Line Continuity	0	0	Sophistication	2	2	Chest	08	
Horizontal Midline	4	0	Right and Left Halves	1	1	Body Shading	6	3	Height	07	07	Girth	08	

GENERAL CHARACTERISTICS OF SUBJECT

IDENTIFICATION
No. C19
Sex M
Marital status M
Age 22 yrs. at psychological tests

PARENTAL HISTORY				
Father				
C	H	S	D	O
–	–	–	–	+
Mother				
C	H	S	D	O
–	+	–	–	–

PHYSIOLOGICAL AND METABOLIC DATA

	Admission	Initial	Control	Cold pressor change	Exercise change	Smoking change
Systolic pressure	126	130	126	+02	+34	–04
Diastolic pressure	76	78	78	+18	+02	–02
Heart rate	86	68	68	–04	+05	+04

Age 23 yrs.	Height 72 in.	Ponderal index 13.56
	Weight 150 lbs.	Cholesterol 180 mg. per 100 ml.
	Overweight –09%	Vital capacity 5.2 liters

HABIT SURVEY

Smoking habits: mixed smoker

Age begun 21 yrs.   Inhalation: yes

Habits of nervous tension: 5, 6, 9, 11, 22, 24

STRONG VOCATIONAL INTEREST TEST

Occupation	Artist	Psychologist	Architect	Physician	Osteopath	Dentist	Veterinarian	Mathematician	Physicist	Engineer	Chemist	Production Manager
Standard Score	35	34	43	58	49	52	33	33	28	38	42	30

Occupation	Farmer	Aviator	Carpenter	Printer	Math.-Sci. Teacher	Ind. Arts Teacher	Voc. Agric. Teacher	Policeman	Forest Serv. Man	Y.M.C.A. Phys. Dir.	Personnel Director	Public Administrator
Standard Score	39	37	23	32	44	26	34	27	32	39	17	30

Occupation	Y.M.C.A. Secretary	Soc. Sci. H.S. Teacher	City Sch. Sup't.	Social Worker	Minister	Musician Performer	C.P.A.	Senior C.P.A.	Accountant	Office Man	Purchasing Agent	Banker
Standard Score	18	26	25	24	62	36	33	33	24	26	27	19

Occupation	Mortician	Pharmacist	Sales Manager	Real Est. Manager	Life Ins. Salesman	Advertising Man	Lawyer	Author-Journalist	President Mfg. Co.	Interest Maturity	Occupational Level	Masculinity-Femininity
Standard Score	26	37	30	33	31	27	31	33	32	50	61	49

Plate 652   MODERATELY SOPHISTICATED DRAWINGS   699

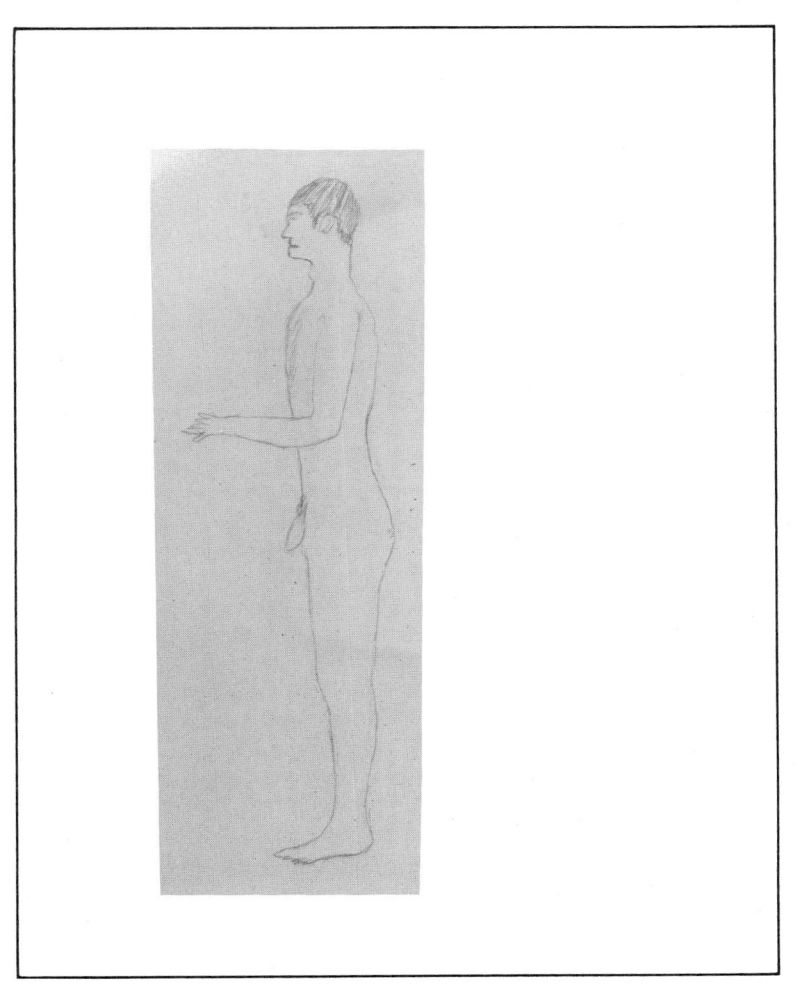
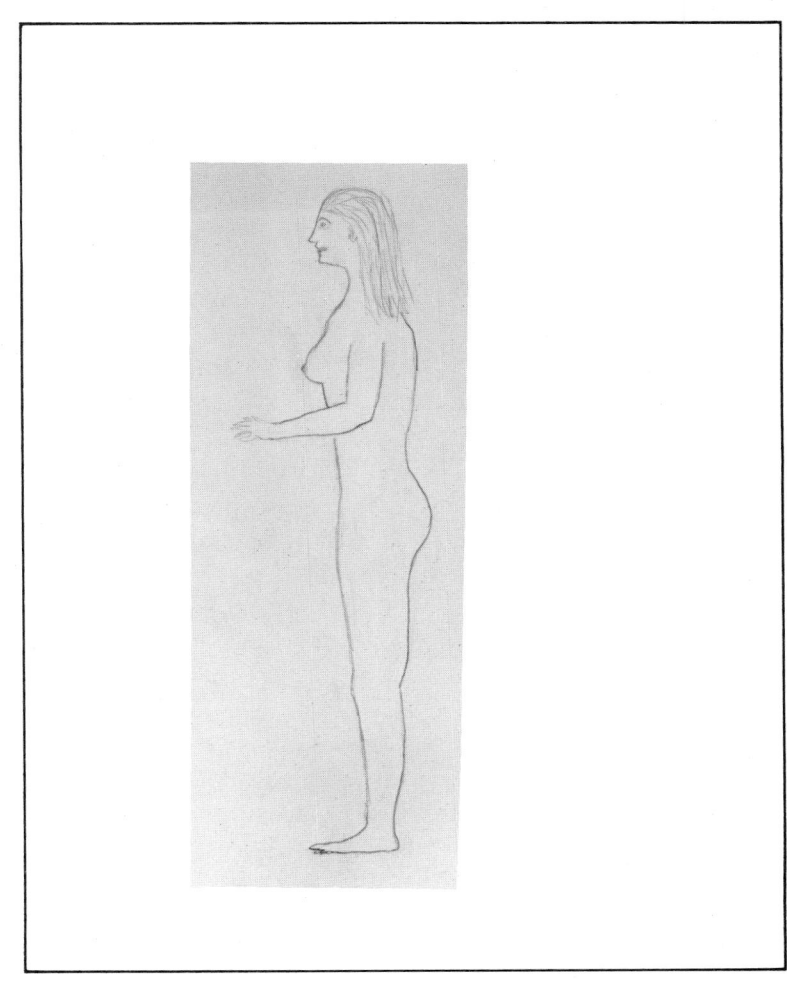

FIGURE-DRAWING CHARACTERISTICS

Structural	Male	Female	Structural	Male	Female	Structural and Graphic	Male	Female	Graphic, Global and Height	Male	Female	Body Proportions	Male	Female
	Both						Both							
Type	0		Omission of Appendages	0	0	Upper and Lower Halves	3	3	Hair Shading	1	3	Head	06	05
Sex Sequence	0		Position of Both Arms	4	4	Four Quarters	4	4	Nudity and Transparency	0	0	Neck	08	08
Posture	1	1	Position of Right Arm	7	7	Relative Size	1		Form	1	1	Shoulders		
Perspective	2	2	Position of Left Arm	4	4	Constant Line Pressure	1	3	Detailing	3	3	Right Arm		
Vertical Midline	4	4	Position of Legs	1	1	Variable Line Pressure	0	0	Identity and Sex	1	1	Left Arm	06	04
Bilateral Symmetry	0	0	Relation of Long Axes	1	1	Line Continuity	0	2	Sophistication	2	2	Chest	07	07
Horizontal Midline	0	0	Right and Left Halves	2	2	Body Shading	3	0	Height	07	07	Girth	05	06

GENERAL CHARACTERISTICS OF SUBJECT

IDENTIFICATION
No. C29
Sex M
Marital status S
Age 22 yrs. at
psychological tests

PARENTAL HISTORY

Father

C	H	S	D	O
-	-	-	-	?

Mother

C	H	S	D	O
-	+	-	-	+

PHYSIOLOGICAL AND METABOLIC DATA

	Admission	Initial	Control	Cold pressor change	Exercise change	Smoking change
Systolic pressure	130	120	116	+06	+54	
Diastolic pressure	50	70	62	+18	-12	
Heart rate	68	72	65	+08	+25	

Age 23 yrs.	Height 76 in.	Ponderal index 13.36
	Weight 184 lbs.	Cholesterol 148 mg. per 100 ml.
	Overweight -01 %	Vital capacity 4.8 liters

HABIT SURVEY

Smoking habits: nonsmoker

Age begun   yrs.   Inhalation:

Habits of nervous tension: 5, 6, 9, 11, 21

STRONG VOCATIONAL INTEREST TEST

Occupation	Artist	Psychologist	Architect	Physician	Osteopath	Dentist	Veterinarian	Mathematician	Physicist	Engineer	Chemist	Production Manager
Standard Score	28	36	31	56	49	46	41	28	21	31	44	26

Occupation	Farmer	Aviator	Carpenter	Printer	Math.-Sci. Teacher	Ind. Arts Teacher	Voc. Agric. Teacher	Policeman	Forest Serv. Man	Y.M.C.A. Phys. Dir.	Personnel Director	Public Administrator
Standard Score	48	46	35	51	50	25	33	46	46	40	25	38

Occupation	Y.M.C.A. Secretary	Soc. Sci. H.S. Teacher	City Sch. Sup't.	Social Worker	Minister	Musician Performer	C.P.A.	Senior C.P.A.	Accountant	Office Man	Purchasing Agent	Banker
Standard Score	29	39	22	37	62	48	26	50	25	40	21	27

Occupation	Mortician	Pharmacist	Sales Manager	Real Est. Manager	Life Ins. Salesman	Advertising Man	Lawyer	Author-Journalist	President Mfg. Co.	Interest Maturity	Occupational Level	Masculinity-Femininity
Standard Score	20	36	12	24	19	20	29	28	16	56	44	45

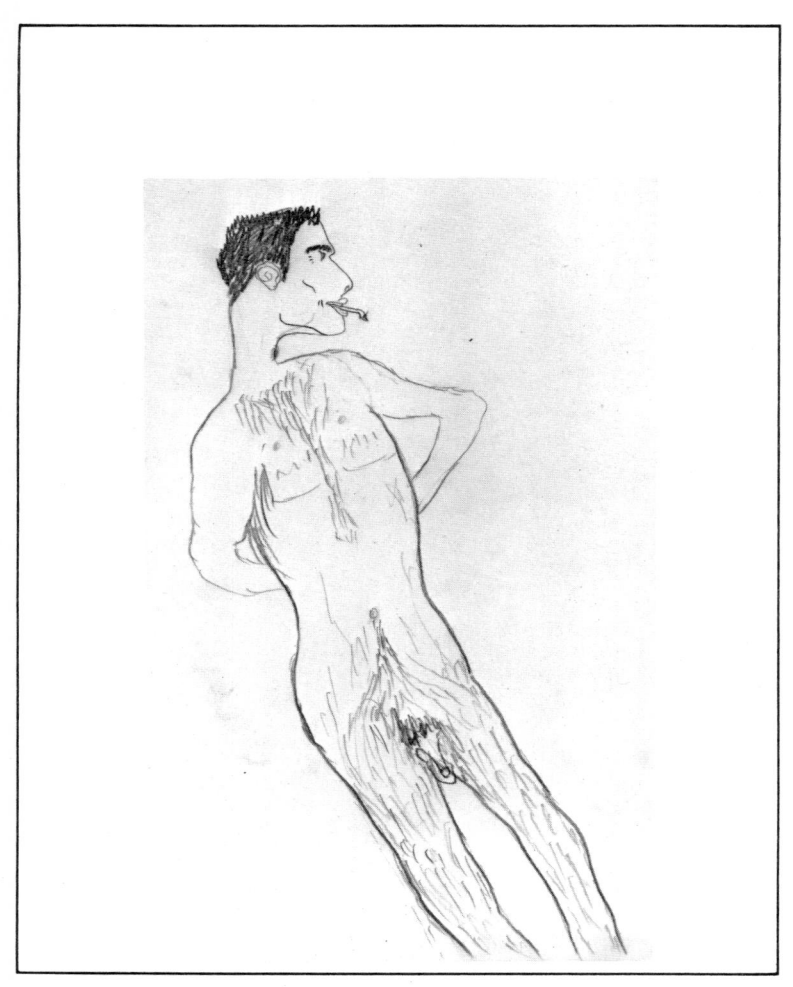

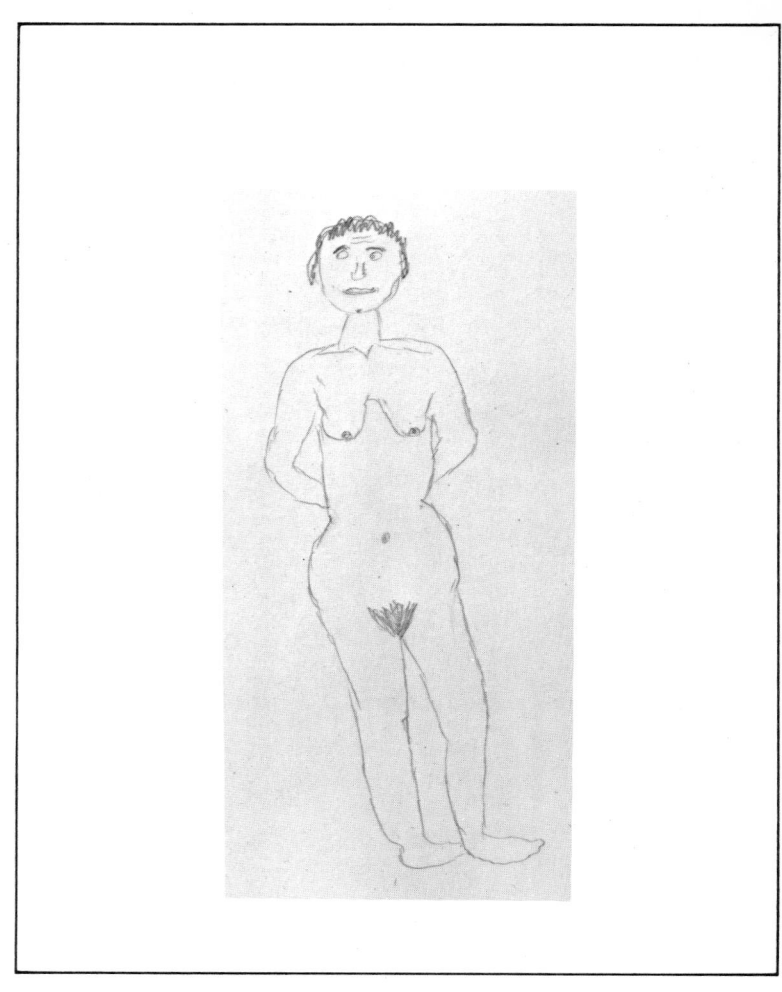

FIGURE-DRAWING CHARACTERISTICS

Structural	Male Female Both		Structural	Male	Female	Structural and Graphic	Male Female Both		Graphic, Global and Height	Male	Female	Body Proportions	Male	Female
Type	0		Omission of Appendages	1	2	Upper and Lower Halves	7	3	Hair Shading	3	3	Head	10	08
Sex Sequence	0		Position of Both Arms	0	0	Four Quarters	4	4	Nudity and Transparency	0	0	Neck	12	10
Posture	0	1	Position of Right Arm	5	5	Relative Size	0		Form	1	1	Shoulders		06
Perspective	5	0	Position of Left Arm	5	5	Constant Line Pressure	0	2	Detailing	1	1	Right Arm		
Vertical Midline	0	0	Position of Legs	5	4	Variable Line Pressure	3	0	Identity and Sex	1	1	Left Arm		
Bilateral Symmetry	3	3	Relation of Long Axes	3	1	Line Continuity	2	0	Sophistication	2	2	Chest		06
Horizontal Midline	0	0	Right and Left Halves	1	0	Body Shading	3	3	Height		07	Girth		06

GENERAL CHARACTERISTICS OF SUBJECT

IDENTIFICATION
No. D65
Sex F
Marital status S
Age 23 yrs. at
psychological tests

PARENTAL HISTORY				
Father				
C	H	S	D	O
-	-	-	-	+
Mother				
C	H	S	D	O
-	+	(+)	+	+

PHYSIOLOGICAL AND METABOLIC DATA

	Admission	Initial	Control	Cold pressor change	Exercise change	Smoking change
Systolic pressure	140	120	118	+10	+52	00
Diastolic pressure	80	62	68	+30	-03	+02
Heart rate	72	76	75	+04	+40	-02

Age 23 yrs.	Height	70	in.	Ponderal index 13.41
	Weight	142	lbs.	Cholesterol 209 mg. per 100 ml.
	Overweight -05 %			Vital capacity 4.2 liters

HABIT SURVEY

Smoking habits: former smoker

Age begun   yrs.   Inhalation:

Habits of nervous tension: 5, 6, 8, 10, 23

STRONG VOCATIONAL INTEREST TEST

Occupation	Artist	Psychologist	Architect	Physician	Osteopath	Dentist	Veterinarian	Mathematician	Physicist	Engineer	Chemist	Production Manager
Standard Score	43	44	45	54	29	33	08	42	34	34	44	23

Occupation	Farmer	Aviator	Carpenter	Printer	Math.-Sci. Teacher	Ind. Arts Teacher	Voc. Agric. Teacher	Policeman	Forest Serv. Man	Y.M.C.A. Phys. Dir.	Personnel Director	Public Administrator
Standard Score	17	27	09	23	27	-08	09	16	11	28	29	34

Occupation	Y.M.C.A. Secretary	Soc. Sci. H.S. Teacher	City Sch. Sup't.	Social Worker	Minister	Musician Performer	C.P.A.	Senior C.P.A.	Accountant	Office Man	Purchasing Agent	Banker
Standard Score	16	19	27	30	63	44	45	34	26	24	21	17

Occupation	Mortician	Pharmacist	Sales Manager	Real Est. Manager	Life Ins. Salesman	Advertising Man	Lawyer	Author-Journalist	President Mfg. Co.	Interest Maturity	Occupational Level	Masculinity-Femininity
Standard Score	18	38	33	35	32	44	41	46	37	49	66	32

FIGURE-DRAWING CHARACTERISTICS

Structural	Male Female Both		Structural	Male	Female	Structural and Graphic	Male Female Both		Graphic, Global and Height	Male	Female	Body Proportions	Male	Female
Type	0		Omission of Appendages	2	2	Upper and Lower Halves	1	1	Hair Shading	5	5	Head	05	04
Sex Sequence	0		Position of Both Arms	2	2	Four Quarters	4	4	Nudity and Transparency	7	7	Neck	04	08
Posture	1	1	Position of Right Arm	5	5	Relative Size	0		Form	1	3	Shoulders	06	05
Perspective	5	5	Position of Left Arm	8	8	Constant Line Pressure	5	5	Detailing	3	3	Right Arm	04	04
Vertical Midline	3	3	Position of Legs	6	6	Variable Line Pressure	0	0	Identity and Sex	1	3	Left Arm		
Bilateral Symmetry	4	4	Relation of Long Axes	1	1	Line Continuity	4	4	Sophistication	2	2	Chest	05	04
Horizontal Midline	4	4	Right and Left Halves	1	1	Body Shading	0	1	Height	04	04	Girth	05	05

GENERAL CHARACTERISTICS OF SUBJECT

IDENTIFICATION
No. D70
Sex M
Marital status S
Age 22 yrs. at
psychological tests

PARENTAL HISTORY				
Father				
C	H	S	D	O
-	-	-	-	-
Mother				
C	H	S	D	O
-	+	-	-	-

PHYSIOLOGICAL AND METABOLIC DATA

	Admission	Initial	Control	Cold pressor change	Exercise change	Smoking change
Systolic pressure	132					+05
Diastolic pressure	70					+06
Heart rate	88					+09

Age 22 yrs.	Height	71	in.		Ponderal index	13.12	
	Weight	158	lbs.		Cholesterol	172	mg. per 100 ml.
	Overweight	00 %			Vital capacity		liters

HABIT SURVEY
Smoking habits: occasional smoker
Age begun 20 yrs. Inhalation: no
Habits of nervous tension: 1, 3, 8, 14

STRONG VOCATIONAL INTEREST TEST

Occupation	Artist	Psychologist	Architect	Physician	Osteopath	Dentist	Veterinarian	Mathematician	Physicist	Engineer	Chemist	Production Manager
Standard Score	18	30	15	33	41	24	22	14	11	21	28	27

Occupation	Farmer	Aviator	Carpenter	Printer	Math.-Sci. Teacher	Ind. Arts Teacher	Voc. Agric. Teacher	Policeman	Forest Serv. Man	Y.M.C.A. Phys. Dir.	Personnel Director	Public Administrator
Standard Score	27	35	09	32	40	14	21	37	19	46	42	39

Occupation	Y.M.C.A. Secretary	Soc. Sci. H.S. Teacher	City Sch. Sup't.	Social Worker	Minister	Musician Performer	C.P.A.	Senior C.P.A.	Accountant	Office Man	Purchasing Agent	Banker
Standard Score	38	42	27	41	63	28	27	39	28	41	27	19

Occupation	Mortician	Pharmacist	Sales Manager	Real Est. Manager	Life Ins. Salesman	Advertising Man	Lawyer	Author-Journalist	President Mfg. Co.	Interest Maturity	Occupational Level	Masculinity-Femininity
Standard Score	27	31	34	40	42	32	32	25	32	61	54	48

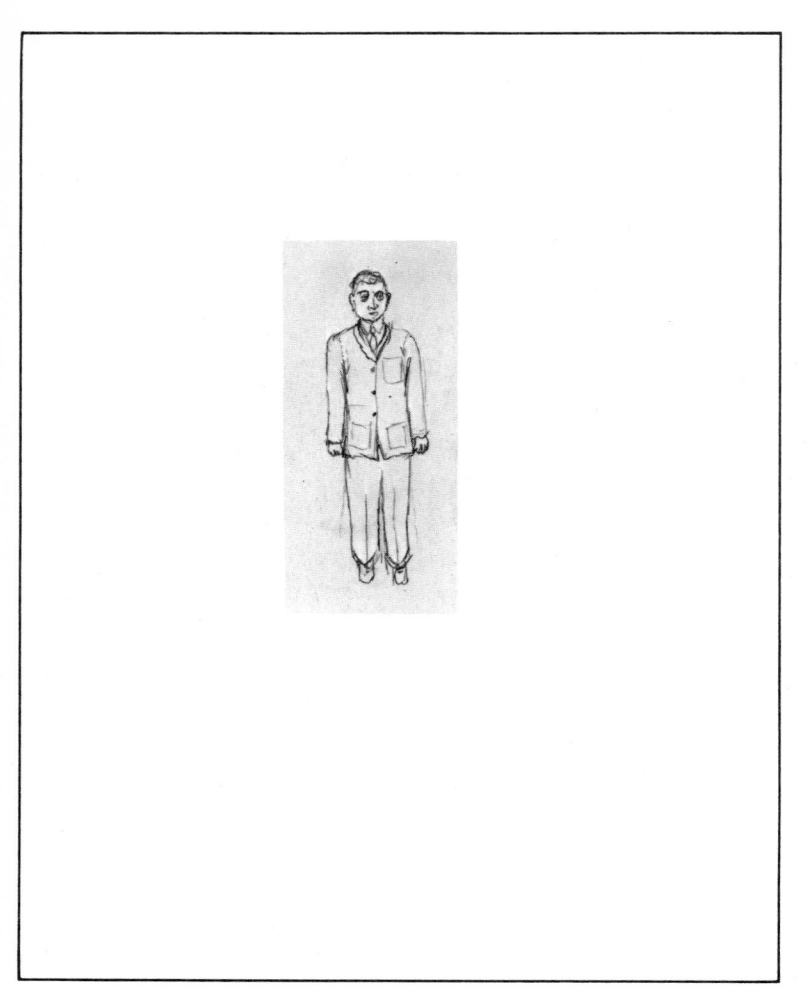

FIGURE-DRAWING CHARACTERISTICS

Structural	Male	Female	Structural	Male	Female	Structural and Graphic	Male	Female	Graphic, Global and Height	Male	Female	Body Proportions	Male	Female
	Both						Both							
Type	0		Omission of Appendages	0	0	Upper and Lower Halves	1	1	Hair Shading	3	5	Head	04	03
Sex Sequence	0		Position of Both Arms	0	1	Four Quarters	4	4	Nudity and Transparency	7	7	Neck	02	02
Posture	1	1	Position of Right Arm	0	4	Relative Size	2		Form	1	1	Shoulders	03	03
Perspective	0	0	Position of Left Arm	0	2	Constant Line Pressure	0	0	Detailing	1	3	Right Arm	02	02
Vertical Midline	3	0	Position of Legs	4	2	Variable Line Pressure	3	5	Identity and Sex	1	1	Left Arm	02	02
Bilateral Symmetry	4	4	Relation of Long Axes	1	1	Line Continuity	0	2	Sophistication	2	2	Chest	03	02
Horizontal Midline	6	6	Right and Left Halves	1	2	Body Shading	3	1	Height	03	03	Girth	03	02

GENERAL CHARACTERISTICS OF SUBJECT

IDENTIFICATION
No. F44
Sex M
Marital status M
Age 23 yrs. at
psychological tests

PARENTAL HISTORY					
Father					
C	H	S	D	O	
-	?	-	-	-	
Mother					
C	H	S	D	O	
-	-	-	-	-	

PHYSIOLOGICAL AND METABOLIC DATA

	Admission	Initial	Control	Cold pressor change	Exercise change	Smoking change
Systolic pressure	122	116	108	+04	+44	+08
Diastolic pressure	74	80	78	+12	+22	+10
Heart rate	70	60	61	+04	+33	+04

Age 21 yrs.	Height	69	in.	Ponderal index 12.75
	Weight	158	lbs.	Cholesterol 217 mg. per 100 ml.
	Overweight +06 %			Vital capacity liters

HABIT SURVEY
Smoking habits: nonsmoker
Age begun yrs. Inhalation:
Habits of nervous tension: 1, 2, 3, 4, 8, 9,
11, 18, 19, 22

STRONG VOCATIONAL INTEREST TEST

Occupation	Artist	Psychologist	Architect	Physician	Osteopath	Dentist	Veterinarian	Mathematician	Physicist	Engineer	Chemist	Production Manager
Standard Score	32	50	43	59	50	44	14	34	40	51	58	48

Occupation	Farmer	Aviator	Carpenter	Printer	Math.-Sci. Teacher	Ind. Arts Teacher	Voc. Agric. Teacher	Policeman	Forest Serv. Man	Y.M.C.A. Phys. Dir.	Personnel Director	Public Administrator
Standard Score	30	53	31	44	45	40	20	31	37	34	50	50

Occupation	Y.M.C.A. Secretary	Soc. Sci. H.S. Teacher	City Sch. Sup't.	Social Worker	Minister	Musician Performer	C.P.A.	Senior C.P.A.	Accountant	Office Man	Purchasing Agent	Banker
Standard Score	24	32	26	38	58	44	25	43	26	23	20	09

Occupation	Mortician	Pharmacist	Sales Manager	Real Est. Manager	Life Ins. Salesman	Advertising Man	Lawyer	Author-Journalist	President Mfg. Co.	Interest Maturity	Occupational Level	Masculinity-Femininity
Standard Score	23	27	20	20	12	30	24	30	28	57	53	51

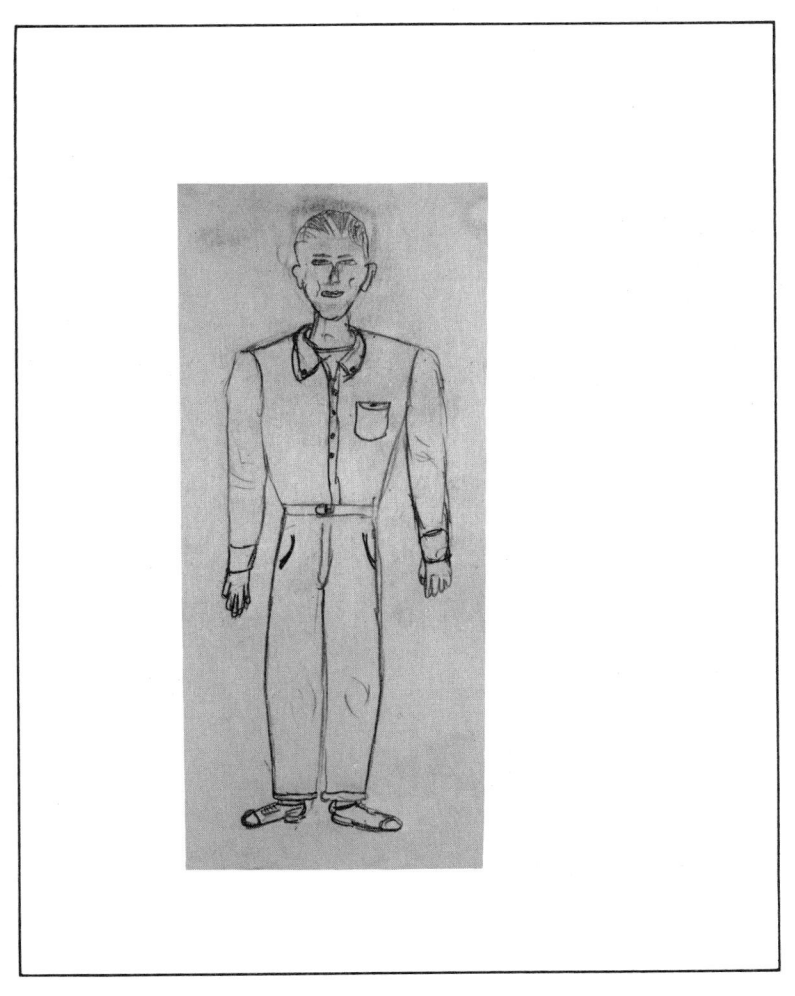

FIGURE-DRAWING CHARACTERISTICS

Structural	Male Female Both	Structural	Male	Female	Structural and Graphic	Male Female Both		Graphic, Global and Height	Male	Female	Body Proportions	Male	Female
Type	0	Omission of Appendages	0	0	Upper and Lower Halves	3	3	Hair Shading	2	3	Head	09	07
Sex Sequence	0	Position of Both Arms	0	1	Four Quarters	4	4	Nudity and Transparency	7	7	Neck	08	07
Posture	1 1	Position of Right Arm	0	5	Relative Size	4		Form	1	1	Shoulders	08	07
Perspective	0 0	Position of Left Arm	0	2	Constant Line Pressure	0	0	Detailing	1	1	Right Arm	06	06
Vertical Midline	3 3	Position of Legs	2	4	Variable Line Pressure	4	4	Identity and Sex	1	1	Left Arm	06	06
Bilateral Symmetry	4 3	Relation of Long Axes	1	1	Line Continuity	2	0	Sophistication	2	2	Chest	07	08
Horizontal Midline	4 4	Right and Left Halves	1	1	Body Shading	7	5	Height	06	08	Girth	06	07

GENERAL CHARACTERISTICS OF SUBJECT

IDENTIFICATION

No. C54

Sex M

Marital status S

Age 22 yrs. at psychological tests

PARENTAL HISTORY

Father

C   H   S   D   O
-   ?   -   -   +

Mother

C   H   S   D   O
-   -   -   -   ?

PHYSIOLOGICAL AND METABOLIC DATA

	Admission	Initial	Control	Cold pressor change	Exercise change	Smoking change
Systolic pressure	180	150	130	+15	+35	
Diastolic pressure	110	80	78	+04	-08	
Heart rate	110	72	70	+20	+27	

Age 23 yrs.

Height 74 in.
Weight 179 lbs.
Overweight +02 %

Ponderal index 13.12
Cholesterol 212 mg. per 100 ml.
Vital capacity 5.5 liters

HABIT SURVEY

Smoking habits: former smoker

Age begun 18 yrs.   Inhalation: yes

Habits of nervous tension: 5, 6, 10, 19, 21

STRONG VOCATIONAL INTEREST TEST

Occupation	Artist	Psychologist	Architect	Physician	Osteopath	Dentist	Veterinarian	Mathematician	Physicist	Engineer	Chemist	Production Manager
Standard Score	30	45	35	58	49	38	31	25	18	29	38	31

Occupation	Farmer	Aviator	Carpenter	Printer	Math.-Sci. Teacher	Ind. Arts Teacher	Voc. Agric. Teacher	Policeman	Forest Serv. Man	Y.M.C.A. Phys. Dir.	Personnel Director	Public Administrator
Standard Score	28	31	07	33	33	10	22	27	20	36	42	45

Occupation	Y.M.C.A. Secretary	Soc. Sci. H.S. Teacher	City Sch. Sup't.	Social Worker	Minister	Musician Performer	C.P.A.	Senior C.P.A.	Accountant	Office Man	Purchasing Agent	Banker
Standard Score	31	43	35	43	62	43	33	41	24	25	21	19

Occupation	Mortician	Pharmacist	Sales Manager	Real Est. Manager	Life Ins. Salesman	Advertising Man	Lawyer	Author-Journalist	President Mfg. Co.	Interest Maturity	Occupational Level	Masculinity-Femininity
Standard Score	29	34	34	32	37	40	45	37	31	57	61	47

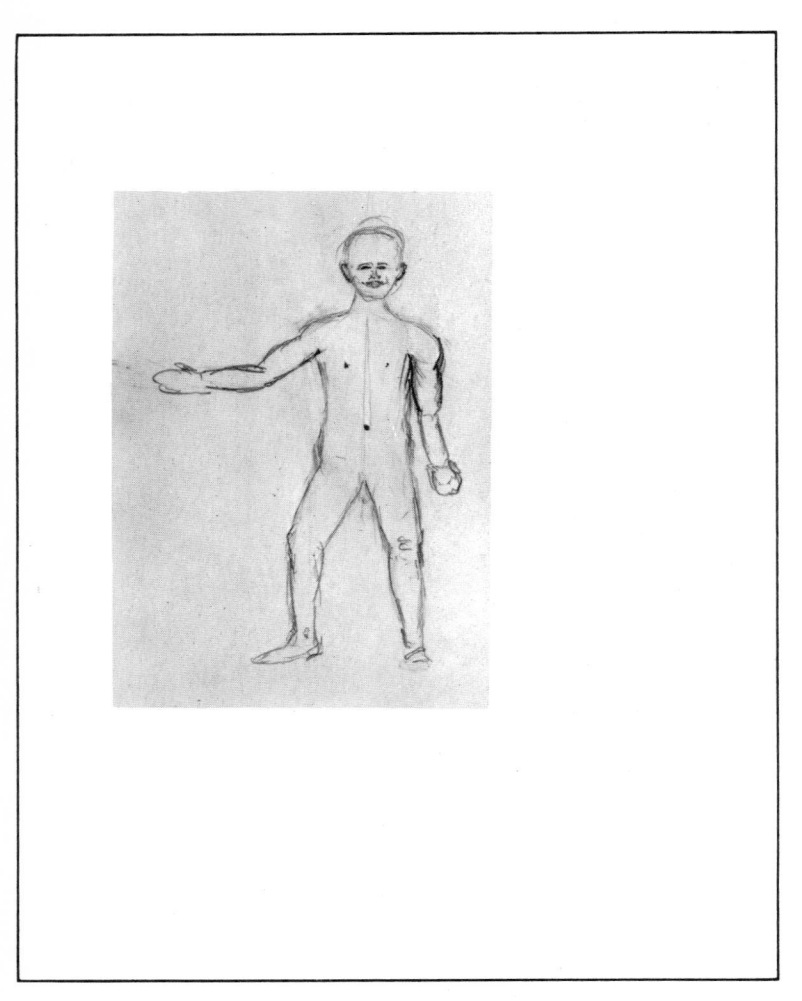

FIGURE-DRAWING CHARACTERISTICS

Structural	Male Female Both	Structural	Male	Female	Structural and Graphic	Male Female Both		Graphic, Global and Height	Male	Female	Body Proportions	Male	Female
Type	0	Omission of Appendages	0	8	Upper and Lower Halves	1	0	Hair Shading	3	3	Head	05	06
Sex Sequence	0	Position of Both Arms	1	1	Four Quarters	4	4	Nudity and Transparency	0	0	Neck	06	08
Posture	1 3	Position of Right Arm	2	5	Relative Size	5		Form	1	1	Shoulders	05	
Perspective	0 8	Position of Left Arm	0	5	Constant Line Pressure	0	3	Detailing	1	1	Right Arm	04	
Vertical Midline	1 7	Position of Legs	6	4	Variable Line Pressure	3	0	Identity and Sex	1	1	Left Arm	04	06
Bilateral Symmetry	3 0	Relation of Long Axes	1	0	Line Continuity	0	0	Sophistication	2	2	Chest	04	
Horizontal Midline	0 0	Right and Left Halves	1	0	Body Shading	2	3	Height	04		Girth	05	

GENERAL CHARACTERISTICS OF SUBJECT

IDENTIFICATION
No. D05
Sex M
Marital status S
Age 22 yrs. at
psychological tests

PARENTAL HISTORY
Father
C   H   S   D   O
-    ?   -   -   ?
Mother
C   H   S   D   O
-    -   -   -   -

PHYSIOLOGICAL AND METABOLIC DATA

	Admission	Initial	Control	Cold pressor change	Exercise change	Smoking change
Systolic pressure	120	120	120	-02	+20	+16
Diastolic pressure	80	60	60	-02	-05	+14
Heart rate	80	76	68	+16	+30	+09

Age 22 yrs.	Height	71 in.		Ponderal index	13.25	
	Weight	154 lbs.		Cholesterol	199	mg. per 100 ml.
	Overweight	-03 %		Vital capacity	5.6	liters

HABIT SURVEY

Smoking habits: nonsmoker

Age begun   yrs.   Inhalation:

Habits of nervous tension: 1, 3, 4, 8, 11, 23, 24

STRONG VOCATIONAL INTEREST TEST

Occupation	Artist	Psychologist	Architect	Physician	Osteopath	Dentist	Veterinarian	Mathematician	Physicist	Engineer	Chemist	Production Manager
Standard Score	40	43	46	57	43	41	14	36	35	37	39	22

Occupation	Farmer	Aviator	Carpenter	Printer	Math.-Sci. Teacher	Ind. Arts Teacher	Voc. Agric. Teacher	Policeman	Forest Serv. Man	Y.M.C.A. Phys. Dir.	Personnel Director	Public Administrator
Standard Score	27	26	17	22	39	20	24	18	22	31	34	39

Occupation	Y.M.C.A. Secretary	Soc. Sci. H.S. Teacher	City Sch. Sup't.	Social Worker	Minister	Musician Performer	C.P.A.	Senior C.P.A.	Accountant	Office Man	Purchasing Agent	Banker
Standard Score	32	28	37	36	63	47	38	28	20	18	08	14

Occupation	Mortician	Pharmacist	Sales Manager	Real Est. Manager	Life Ins. Salesman	Advertising Man	Lawyer	Author-Journalist	President Mfg. Co.	Interest Maturity	Occupational Level	Masculinity-Femininity
Standard Score	16	24	22	29	31	35	37	40	33	58	68	34

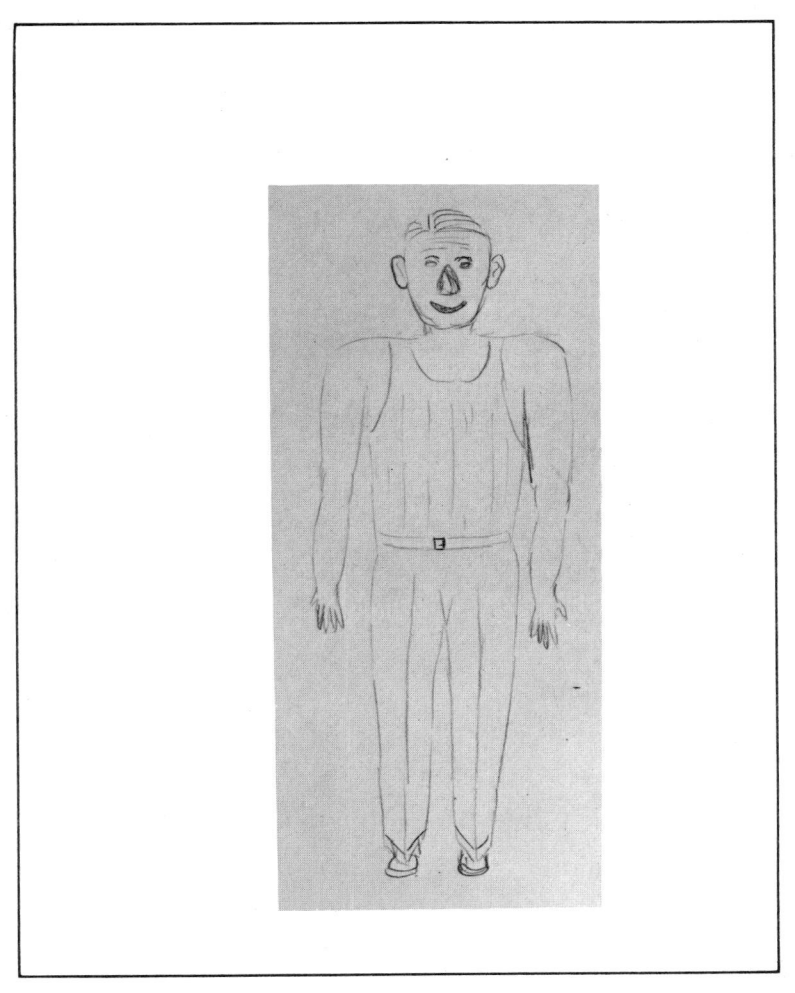

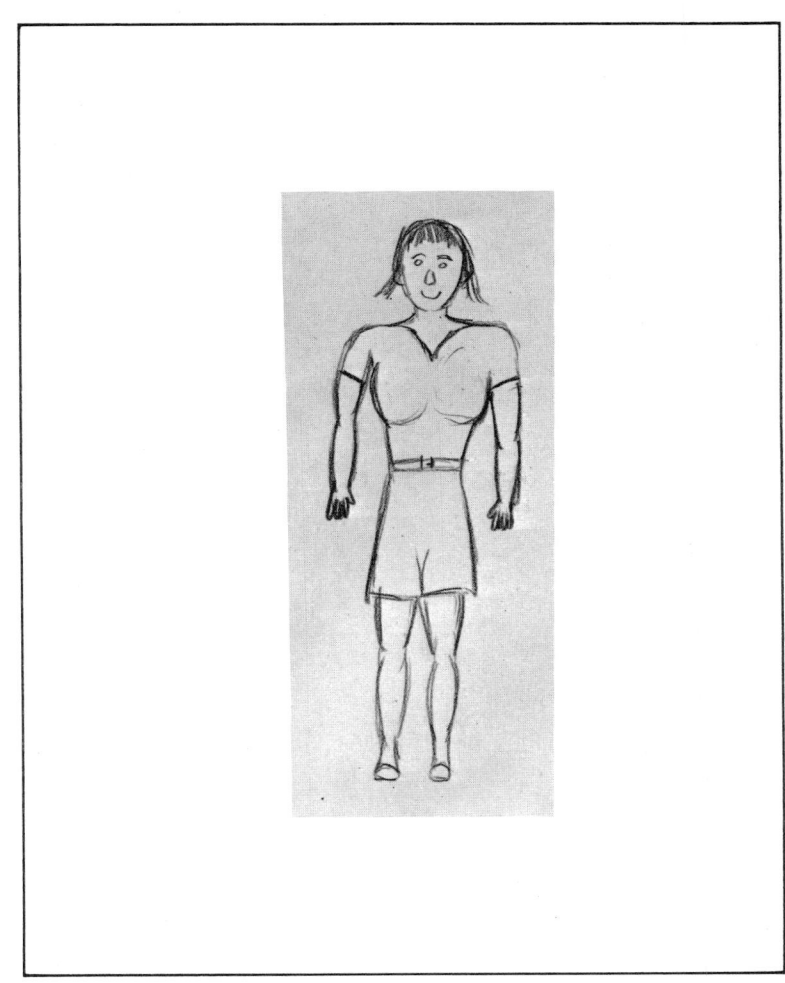

FIGURE-DRAWING CHARACTERISTICS

Structural	Male Female Both	Structural	Male	Female	Structural and Graphic	Male Female Both		Graphic, Global and Height	Male	Female	Body Proportions	Male	Female
Type	0	Omission of Appendages	0	0	Upper and Lower Halves	3	1	Hair Shading	7	3	Head	09	07
Sex Sequence	0	Position of Both Arms	0	0	Four Quarters	4	4	Nudity and Transparency	2	2	Neck	04	06
Posture	1 1	Position of Right Arm	0	0	Relative Size	0		Form	1	1	Shoulders	09	06
Perspective	0 0	Position of Left Arm	0	0	Constant Line Pressure	1	5	Detailing	3	3	Right Arm	06	04
Vertical Midline	0 0	Position of Legs	4	4	Variable Line Pressure	0	0	Identity and Sex	1	1	Left Arm	06	04
Bilateral Symmetry	5 5	Relation of Long Axes	1	1	Line Continuity	0	1	Sophistication	2	2	Chest	07	06
Horizontal Midline	4 4	Right and Left Halves	3	3	Body Shading	3	3	Height	07	05	Girth	09	05

GENERAL CHARACTERISTICS OF SUBJECT

IDENTIFICATION
No. 540
Sex M
Marital status S
Age 24 yrs. at psychological tests

PARENTAL HISTORY				
Father				
C	H	S	D	O
–	–	–	+	?
Mother				
C	H	S	D	O
–	?	–	–	+

PHYSIOLOGICAL AND METABOLIC DATA

	Admission	Initial	Control	Cold pressor change	Exercise change	Smoking change
Systolic pressure	130	134	116	+32	+42	+06
Diastolic pressure	70	68	68	+34	00	+06
Heart rate	74	84	77	+06	+11	–02

Age 22 yrs.   Height 70 in.   Weight 164 lbs.   Overweight +06 %

Ponderal index 12.79   Cholesterol 172 mg. per 100 ml.   Vital capacity 4.6 liters

HABIT SURVEY
Smoking habits: occasional smoker
Age begun 18 yrs.   Inhalation:
Habits of nervous tension: 2, 5, 6, 9, 25

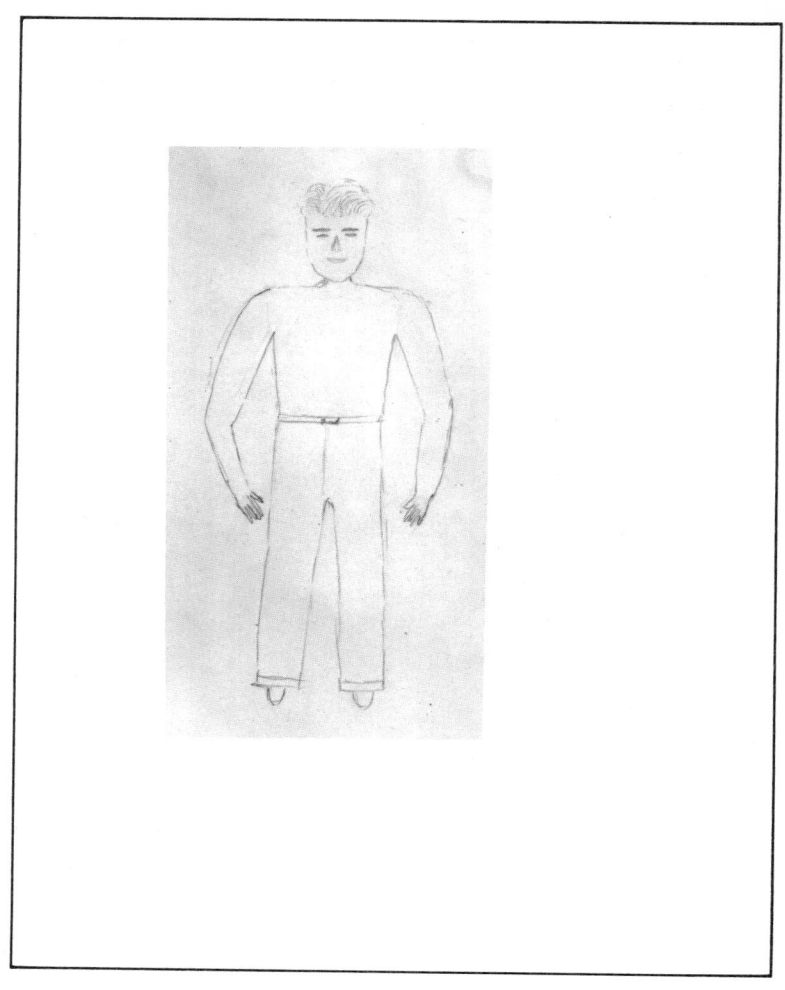

FIGURE-DRAWING CHARACTERISTICS

Structural	Male Female Both	Structural	Male	Female	Structural and Graphic	Male Female Both		Graphic, Global and Height	Male	Female	Body Proportions	Male	Female
Type	0	Omission of Appendages	0	0	Upper and Lower Halves	1	1	Hair Shading	3	3	Head	07	06
Sex Sequence	1	Position of Both Arms	0	1	Four Quarters	4	4	Nudity and Transparency	3	7	Neck	01	02
Posture	1 1	Position of Right Arm	5	0	Relative Size	2		Form	1	1	Shoulders	07	06
Perspective	0 0	Position of Left Arm	5	5	Constant Line Pressure	1	1	Detailing	3	1	Right Arm	06	04
Vertical Midline	3 0	Position of Legs	4	1	Variable Line Pressure	0	0	Identity and Sex	1	1	Left Arm	06	04
Bilateral Symmetry	4 3	Relation of Long Axes	1	1	Line Continuity	0	0	Sophistication	2	2	Chest	05	05
Horizontal Midline	4 0	Right and Left Halves	1	2	Body Shading	0	3	Height	05	05	Girth	06	05

GENERAL CHARACTERISTICS OF SUBJECT

IDENTIFICATION
No. F19
Sex M
Marital status S
Age 32 yrs. at
psychological tests

PARENTAL HISTORY				
Father				
C	H	S	D	O
-	-	-	-	-
Mother				
C	H	S	D	O
-	?	-	-	+

PHYSIOLOGICAL AND METABOLIC DATA

	Admission	Initial	Control	Cold pressor change	Exercise change	Smoking change
Systolic pressure	130	122	122	+18	+28	+16
Diastolic pressure	68	88	90	+20	+20	-06
Heart rate	94	88	97	+12	+16	+19

Age 32 yrs.	Height	66 in.	Ponderal index	12.77	
	Weight	138 lbs.	Cholesterol	244	mg. per 100 ml.
	Overweight	-05 %	Vital capacity		liters

HABIT SURVEY

Smoking habits: former smoker

   Age begun 22 yrs.   Inhalation:

Habits of nervous tension: 5, 6, 9, 11, 16

STRONG VOCATIONAL INTEREST TEST

Occupation	Artist	Psychologist	Architect	Physician	Osteopath	Dentist	Veterinarian	Mathematician	Physicist	Engineer	Chemist	Production Manager
Standard Score	32	39	39	43	35	39	17	35	31	37	39	26

Occupation	Farmer	Aviator	Carpenter	Printer	Math.-Sci. Teacher	Ind. Arts Teacher	Voc. Agric. Teacher	Policeman	Forest Serv. Man	Y.M.C.A. Phys. Dir.	Personnel Director	Public Administrator
Standard Score	38	28	16	32	33	13	26	19	31	24	28	39

Occupation	Y.M.C.A. Secretary	Soc. Sci. H.S. Teacher	City Sch. Sup't.	Social Worker	Minister	Musician Performer	C.P.A.	Senior C.P.A.	Accountant	Office Man	Purchasing Agent	Banker
Standard Score	18	29	25	28	58	34	38	39	29	28	31	23

Occupation	Mortician	Pharmacist	Sales Manager	Real Est. Manager	Life Ins. Salesman	Advertising Man	Lawyer	Author-Journalist	President Mfg. Co.	Interest Maturity	Occupational Level	Masculinity-Femininity
Standard Score	22	31	28	30	26	33	36	38	36	51	66	40

Plate 660   MODERATELY SOPHISTICATED DRAWINGS   707

FIGURE-DRAWING CHARACTERISTICS

Structural	Male	Female	Structural	Male	Female	Structural and Graphic	Male	Female	Graphic, Global and Height	Male	Female	Body Proportions	Male	Female
	Both						Both							
Type	0		Omission of Appendages	7	5	Upper and Lower Halves	1	1	Hair Shading	3	1	Head	04	04
Sex Sequence	0		Position of Both Arms	0	6	Four Quarters	4	4	Nudity and Transparency	7	7	Neck	04	06
Posture	1	0	Position of Right Arm	5	8	Relative Size	4		Form	1	1	Shoulders	05	06
Perspective	0	0	Position of Left Arm	5	8	Constant Line Pressure	2	0	Detailing	1	1	Right Arm		
Vertical Midline	3	0	Position of Legs	4	1	Variable Line Pressure	0	1	Identity and Sex	1	1	Left Arm		
Bilateral Symmetry	2	3	Relation of Long Axes	1	1	Line Continuity	0	0	Sophistication	2	2	Chest	04	05
Horizontal Midline	4	4	Right and Left Halves	2	1	Body Shading	3	3	Height	04	05	Girth	04	04

GENERAL CHARACTERISTICS OF SUBJECT

IDENTIFICATION
No. G08
Sex M
Marital status S
Age 22 yrs. at psychological tests

PARENTAL HISTORY
Father
C H S D O
- - - - -
Mother
C H S D O
- ? - - +

PHYSIOLOGICAL AND METABOLIC DATA

	Admission	Initial	Control	Cold pressor change	Exercise change	Smoking change
Systolic pressure	150	148	140	+02	+30	
Diastolic pressure	70	72	78	+28	-08	
Heart rate	90	76	85	+12	+15	
Age 21 yrs.	Height 72 in.		Ponderal index 12.74			
	Weight 180 lbs.		Cholesterol 230 mg. per 100 ml.			
	Overweight +11 %		Vital capacity liters			

HABIT SURVEY

Smoking habits: nonsmoker

Age begun   yrs.   Inhalation:

Habits of nervous tension: 1, 6, 18, 21, 24, 25

STRONG VOCATIONAL INTEREST TEST

Occupation	Artist	Psychologist	Architect	Physician	Osteopath	Dentist	Veterinarian	Mathematician	Physicist	Engineer	Chemist	Production Manager
Standard Score	31	28	26	40	42	34	21	26	21	34	32	29

Occupation	Farmer	Aviator	Carpenter	Printer	Math.-Sci. Teacher	Ind. Arts Teacher	Voc. Agric. Teacher	Policeman	Forest Serv. Man	Y.M.C.A. Phys. Dir.	Personnel Director	Public Administrator
Standard Score	21	28	-07	13	18	-10	04	27	13	28	23	38

Occupation	Y.M.C.A. Secretary	Soc. Sci. H.S. Teacher	City Sch. Sup't.	Social Worker	Minister	Musician Performer	C.P.A.	Senior C.P.A.	Accountant	Office Man	Purchasing Agent	Banker
Standard Score	15	18	22	26	59	27	46	28	26	25	28	24

Occupation	Mortician	Pharmacist	Sales Manager	Real Est. Manager	Life Ins. Salesman	Advertising Man	Lawyer	Author-Journalist	President Mfg. Co.	Interest Maturity	Occupational Level	Masculinity-Femininity
Standard Score	33	35	37	42	43	42	50	43	43	50	72	39

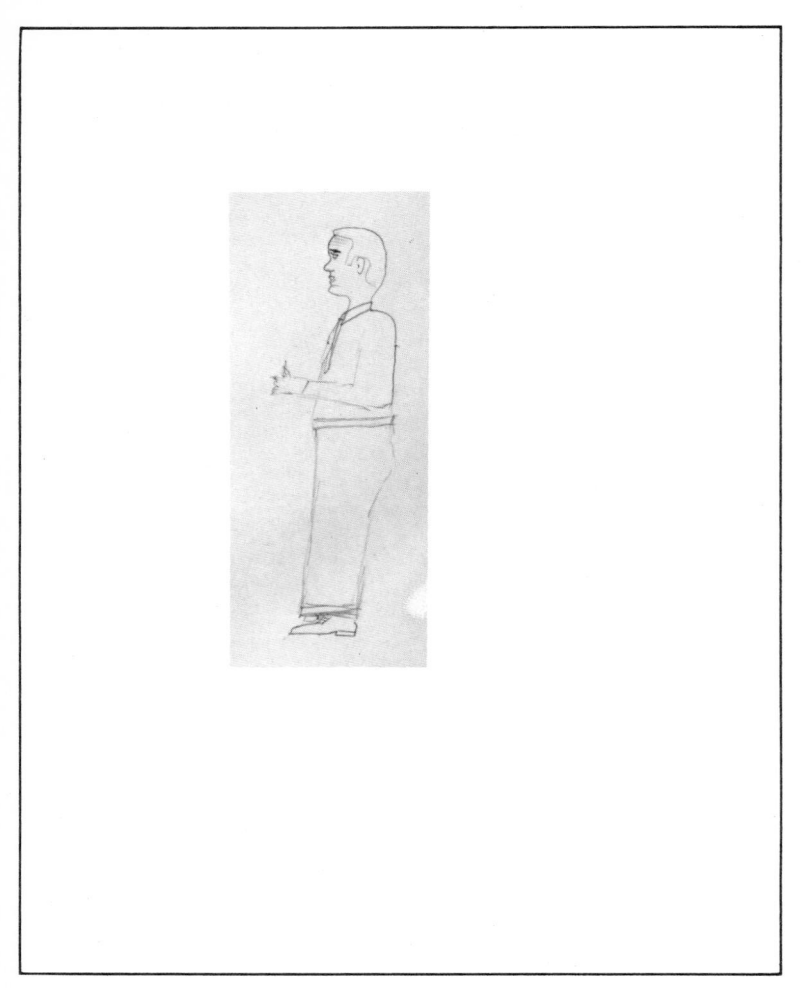

FIGURE-DRAWING CHARACTERISTICS

Structural	Male	Female	Structural	Male	Female	Structural and Graphic	Male	Female	Graphic, Global and Height	Male	Female	Body Proportions	Male	Female
	Both						Both							
Type	0		Omission of Appendages	0	0	Upper and Lower Halves	1	3	Hair Shading	5	1	Head	05	06
Sex Sequence	0		Position of Both Arms	4	4	Four Quarters	4	4	Nudity and Transparency	7	7	Neck	04	08
Posture	1	1	Position of Right Arm	7	7	Relative Size	4		Form	1	3	Shoulders		
Perspective	2	2	Position of Left Arm	4	4	Constant Line Pressure	0	0	Detailing	3	3	Right Arm		
Vertical Midline	7	4	Position of Legs	1	1	Variable Line Pressure	2	2	Identity and Sex	1	1	Left Arm	04	04
Bilateral Symmetry	0	0	Relation of Long Axes	1	1	Line Continuity	1	1	Sophistication	2	2	Chest	05	04
Horizontal Midline	4	4	Right and Left Halves	2	2	Body Shading	0	0	Height	04	05	Girth	06	04

GENERAL CHARACTERISTICS OF SUBJECT

IDENTIFICATION
No. G20
Sex M
Marital status S
Age 22 yrs. at
psychological tests

PARENTAL HISTORY
Father
C H S D O
- - - - -
Mother
C H S D O
- ? - - -

PHYSIOLOGICAL AND METABOLIC DATA

	Admission	Initial	Control	Cold pressor change	Exercise change	Smoking change
Systolic pressure	120	130	120	+18	+40	+01
Diastolic pressure	80	82	74	+26	+04	+06
Heart rate	80	72	63	+12	+35	+29

Age 21 yrs.	Height	75 in.	Ponderal index 13.04
	Weight	190 lbs.	Cholesterol 222 mg. per 100 ml.
	Overweight +07 %		Vital capacity liters

HABIT SURVEY
Smoking habits: moderate cigarette smoker
Age begun 18 yrs.   Inhalation: yes
Habits of nervous tension: 4, 5, 25

STRONG VOCATIONAL INTEREST TEST

Occupation	Artist	Psychologist	Architect	Physician	Osteopath	Dentist	Veterinarian	Mathematician	Physicist	Engineer	Chemist	Production Manager
Standard Score	20	32	26	54	52	41	30	13	17	41	41	41

Occupation	Farmer	Aviator	Carpenter	Printer	Math.-Sci. Teacher	Ind. Arts Teacher	Voc. Agric. Teacher	Policeman	Forest Serv. Man	Y.M.C.A. Phys. Dir.	Personnel Director	Public Administrator
Standard Score	39	48	27	33	45	34	35	38	37	35	49	50

Occupation	Y.M.C.A. Secretary	Soc. Sci. H.S. Teacher	City Sch. Sup't.	Social Worker	Minister	Musician Performer	C.P.A.	Senior C.P.A.	Accountant	Office Man	Purchasing Agent	Banker
Standard Score	26	29	27	38	59	33	18	47	25	36	28	11

Occupation	Mortician	Pharmacist	Sales Manager	Real Est. Manager	Life Ins. Salesman	Advertising Man	Lawyer	Author-Journalist	President Mfg. Co.	Interest Maturity	Occupational Level	Masculinity-Femininity
Standard Score	26	35	33	30	27	29	26	24	34	64	54	55

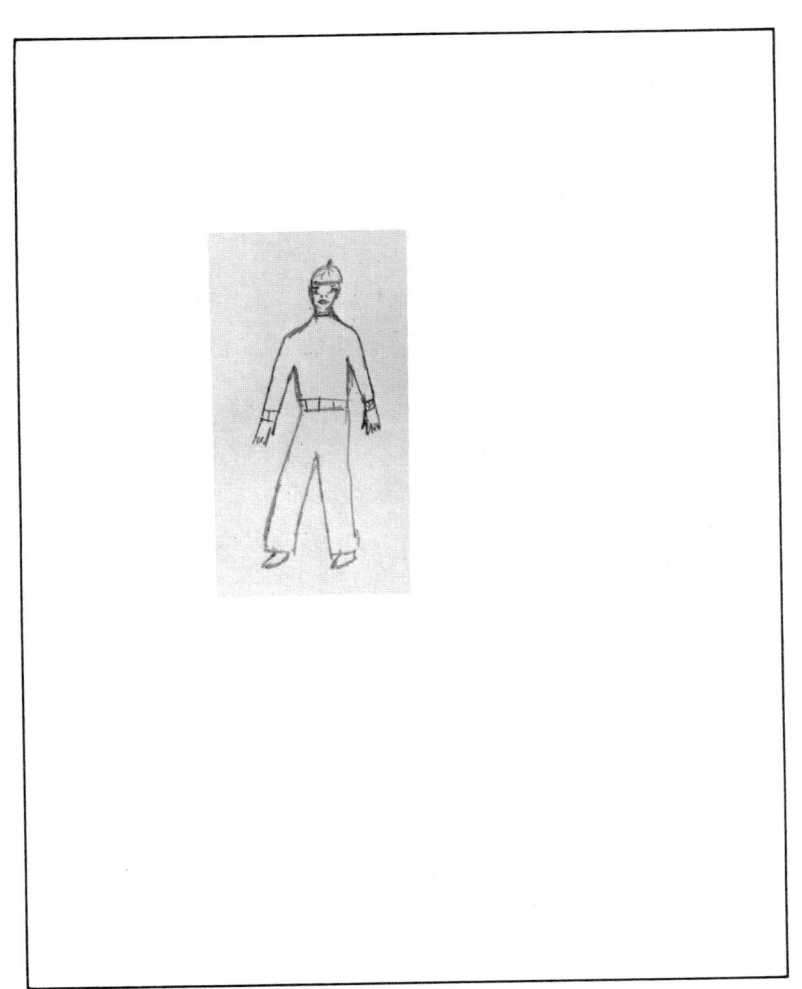

FIGURE-DRAWING CHARACTERISTICS

Structural	Male Female Both	Structural	Male	Female	Structural and Graphic	Male Female Both		Graphic, Global and Height	Male	Female	Body Proportions	Male	Female
Type	0	Omission of Appendages	0	0	Upper and Lower Halves	1	2	Hair Shading	0	1	Head	03	03
Sex Sequence	2	Position of Both Arms	0	0	Four Quarters	4	0	Nudity and Transparency	7	7	Neck	02	02
Posture	1 1	Position of Right Arm	2	2	Relative Size	0		Form	3	1	Shoulders	03	02
Perspective	0 0	Position of Left Arm	2	2	Constant Line Pressure	0	5	Detailing	3	3	Right Arm	02	02
Vertical Midline	0 0	Position of Legs	6	4	Variable Line Pressure	5	0	Identity and Sex	1	1	Left Arm	02	02
Bilateral Symmetry	3 3	Relation of Long Axes	1	1	Line Continuity	0	0	Sophistication	2	2	Chest	02	02
Horizontal Midline	4 4	Right and Left Halves	2	2	Body Shading	0	6	Height	03	02	Girth	03	02

GENERAL CHARACTERISTICS OF SUBJECT

IDENTIFICATION
No. 428
Sex M
Marital status S
Age 24 yrs. at psychological tests

PARENTAL HISTORY				
Father				
C	H	S	D	O
-	(?)	-	+	+
Mother				
C	H	S	D	O
-	-	-	-	?

PHYSIOLOGICAL AND METABOLIC DATA

	Admission	Initial	Control	Cold pressor change	Exercise change	Smoking change
Systolic pressure	144	122	120	+02	+16	+06
Diastolic pressure	86	82	72	+08	00	+12
Heart rate	72	96	86	-12	+17	+19

Age 22 yrs.	Height 70 in.	Ponderal index 12.52
	Weight 175 lbs.	Cholesterol 290 mg. per 100 ml.
	Overweight +14 %	Vital capacity 5.2 liters

HABIT SURVEY
Smoking habits: light cigarette smoker
Age begun   yrs.   Inhalation:
Habits of nervous tension:

FIGURE-DRAWING CHARACTERISTICS

Structural	Male Female — Both	Structural	Male	Female	Structural and Graphic	Male Female — Both		Graphic, Global and Height	Male	Female	Body Proportions	Male	Female
Type	0	Omission of Appendages	0	0	Upper and Lower Halves	3	1	Hair Shading	1	1	Head	10	07
Sex Sequence	0	Position of Both Arms	0	4	Four Quarters	4	4	Nudity and Transparency	7	6	Neck	08	08
Posture	1	1	Position of Right Arm	0	7	Relative Size	0		Form	3	3	Shoulders	09	
Perspective	0	2	Position of Left Arm	0	4	Constant Line Pressure	5	5	Detailing	1	1	Right Arm	06	
Vertical Midline	3	4	Position of Legs	2	1	Variable Line Pressure	0	0	Identity and Sex	1	1	Left Arm	06	04
Bilateral Symmetry	5	0	Relation of Long Axes	1	1	Line Continuity	4	2	Sophistication	2	2	Chest	07	05
Horizontal Midline	6	0	Right and Left Halves	0	3	Body Shading	7	7	Height	07	05	Girth	10	07

GENERAL CHARACTERISTICS OF SUBJECT

IDENTIFICATION
No. 306
Sex M
Marital status M
Age 25 yrs. at
psychological tests

PARENTAL HISTORY
Father
C H S D O
− − − + +
Mother
C H S D O
− − − − −

PHYSIOLOGICAL AND METABOLIC DATA

	Admission	Initial	Control	Cold pressor change	Exercise change	Smoking change
Systolic pressure	110	112	106	+06	+26	
Diastolic pressure	68	74	74	+12	−02	
Heart rate	80	84	71	00	+29	

Age 23 yrs.	Height 72 in.	Ponderal index 12.87
	Weight 175 lbs.	Cholesterol 265 mg. per 100 ml.
	Overweight +07 %	Vital capacity 4.0 liters

HABIT SURVEY
Smoking habits: nonsmoker
Age begun   yrs.   Inhalation:
Habits of nervous tension: 9, 18, 25

Plate 664   MODERATELY SOPHISTICATED DRAWINGS   711

FIGURE-DRAWING CHARACTERISTICS

Structural	Male Female Both	Structural	Male	Female	Structural and Graphic	Male Female Both		Graphic, Global and Height	Male	Female	Body Proportions	Male	Female
Type	0	Omission of Appendages	0	0	Upper and Lower Halves	1	1	Hair Shading	0	3	Head	05	05
Sex Sequence	2	Position of Both Arms	0	4	Four Quarters	4	4	Nudity and Transparency	7	7	Neck	04	04
Posture	1	1	Position of Right Arm	0	7	Relative Size	0		Form	3	3	Shoulders	05	
Perspective	0	2	Position of Left Arm	0	4	Constant Line Pressure	0	3	Detailing	3	3	Right Arm	04	
Vertical Midline	3	4	Position of Legs	6	1	Variable Line Pressure	5	0	Identity and Sex	1	1	Left Arm	04	02
Bilateral Symmetry	3	0	Relation of Long Axes	1	1	Line Continuity	0	0	Sophistication	2	2	Chest	04	03
Horizontal Midline	4	4	Right and Left Halves	1	2	Body Shading	6	0	Height	05	04	Girth	05	

GENERAL CHARACTERISTICS OF SUBJECT

IDENTIFICATION

No. 442

Sex M

Marital status S

Age 25 yrs. at psychological tests

PARENTAL HISTORY

Father

C	H	S	D	O
-	-	-	+	-

Mother

C	H	S	D	O
-	-	-	-	+

PHYSIOLOGICAL AND METABOLIC DATA

	Admission	Initial	Control	Cold pressor change	Exercise change	Smoking change
Systolic pressure	135	108	114	+23	+30	+20
Diastolic pressure	60	64	68	+06	00	+10
Heart rate	80	84	71	−06	+08	+10

Age 23 yrs.

Height   71 in.
Weight   147 lbs.
Overweight −08 %

Ponderal index 13.45
Cholesterol   290   mg. per 100 ml.
Vital capacity   4.7   liters

HABIT SURVEY

Smoking habits: moderate cigarette smoker

Age begun 14 yrs.   Inhalation: yes

Habits of nervous tension: 5

FIGURE-DRAWING CHARACTERISTICS

Structural	Male Female Both		Structural	Male	Female	Structural and Graphic	Male Female Both		Graphic, Global and Height	Male	Female	Body Proportions	Male	Female
Type	0		Omission of Appendages	0	0	Upper and Lower Halves	3	0	Hair Shading	1	2	Head	13	13
Sex Sequence	2		Position of Both Arms	3	3	Four Quarters	4	4	Nudity and Transparency	7	7	Neck	08	08
Posture	2	2	Position of Right Arm	7	7	Relative Size	4		Form	3	3	Shoulders		
Perspective	2	2	Position of Left Arm	4	4	Constant Line Pressure	0	0	Detailing	1	1	Right Arm		
Vertical Midline	7	4	Position of Legs	8	8	Variable Line Pressure	5	5	Identity and Sex	1	1	Left Arm	08	08
Bilateral Symmetry	0	0	Relation of Long Axes	1	1	Line Continuity	1	0	Sophistication	2	2	Chest	13	09
Horizontal Midline	6	4	Right and Left Halves	1	0	Body Shading	3	7	Height	08	08	Girth	12	09

GENERAL CHARACTERISTICS OF SUBJECT

IDENTIFICATION
No. F24
Sex M
Marital status
Age 24 yrs. at psychological tests

PARENTAL HISTORY

Father

C	H	S	D	O
-	-	-	+	+

Mother

C	H	S	D	O
-	-	-	-	+

PHYSIOLOGICAL AND METABOLIC DATA

	Admission	Initial	Control	Cold pressor change	Exercise change	Smoking change
Systolic pressure	128	128	112	+13	+24	-02
Diastolic pressure	74	86	80	+20	+12	+09
Heart rate	82	76	78	+20	+09	+32

Age 22 yrs.	Height 70 in.	Ponderal index 12.54
	Weight 174 lbs.	Cholesterol 234 mg. per 100 ml.
	Overweight +13 %	Vital capacity liters

HABIT SURVEY

Smoking habits: occasional smoker

Age begun 12 yrs.   Inhalation: sometimes

Habits of nervous tension: 4, 9, 11, 12, 14, 16, 22

Plate 666　　　　　MODERATELY SOPHISTICATED DRAWINGS　　　　　713

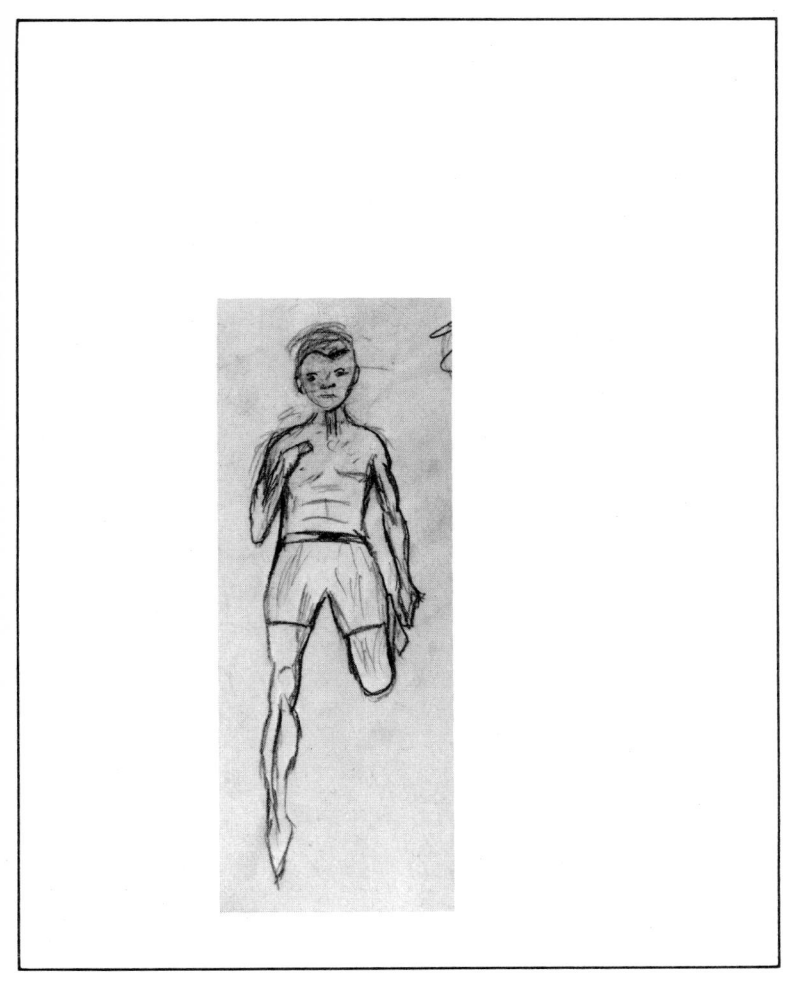

FIGURE-DRAWING CHARACTERISTICS

Structural	Male Female Both	Structural	Male	Female	Structural and Graphic	Male Female Both		Graphic, Global and Height	Male	Female	Body Proportions	Male	Female
Type	0	Omission of Appendages	0	0	Upper and Lower Halves	3	3	Hair Shading	3	3	Head	06	06
Sex Sequence	0	Position of Both Arms	0	4	Four Quarters	4	4	Nudity and Transparency	3	0	Neck	04	06
Posture	5　6	Position of Right Arm	6	7	Relative Size	4		Form	1	1	Shoulders	04	
Perspective	0　2	Position of Left Arm	6	6	Constant Line Pressure	0	0	Detailing	1	1	Right Arm		
Vertical Midline	0　4	Position of Legs	8	8	Variable Line Pressure	5	1	Identity and Sex	1	1	Left Arm	04	06
Bilateral Symmetry	3　0	Relation of Long Axes	1	3	Line Continuity	0	0	Sophistication	2	2	Chest	04	05
Horizontal Midline	4　0	Right and Left Halves	1	1	Body Shading	7	1	Height	06	07	Girth	05	05

GENERAL CHARACTERISTICS OF SUBJECT

IDENTIFICATION

No. B33
Sex M
Marital status S
Age 23 yrs. at
psychological tests

PARENTAL HISTORY

Father

C	H	S	D	O
-	-	-	+	+

Mother

C	H	S	D	O
-	-	-	-	-

PHYSIOLOGICAL AND METABOLIC DATA

	Admission	Initial	Control	Cold pressor change	Exercise change	Smoking change
Systolic pressure	115	116	108	+10	+34	+08
Diastolic pressure	65	66	72	+28	-24	00
Heart rate	68	66	64	+10	+19	00

Age 23 yrs.

Height	72	in.	Ponderal index	12.83	
Weight	177	lbs.	Cholesterol	233	mg. per 100 ml.
Overweight	+08	%	Vital capacity	5.3	liters

HABIT SURVEY

Smoking habits: nonsmoker

Age begun　yrs.　Inhalation:

Habits of nervous tension: 5, 6, 9, 11, 15

STRONG VOCATIONAL INTEREST TEST

Occupation	Artist	Psychologist	Architect	Physician	Osteopath	Dentist	Veterinarian	Mathematician	Physicist	Engineer	Chemist	Production Manager
Standard Score	52	57	56	71	49	49	19	48	51	48	61	23

Occupation	Farmer	Aviator	Carpenter	Printer	Math.-Sci. Teacher	Ind. Arts Teacher	Voc. Agric. Teacher	Policeman	Forest Serv. Man	Y.M.C.A. Phys. Dir.	Personnel Director	Public Administrator
Standard Score	41	50	30	48	36	23	21	20	31	29	23	40

Occupation	Y.M.C.A. Secretary	Soc. Sci. H.S. Teacher	City Sch. Sup't.	Social Worker	Minister	Musician Performer	C.P.A.	Senior C.P.A.	Accountant	Office Man	Purchasing Agent	Banker
Standard Score	11	17	15	34	61	64	26	34	12	18	11	10

Occupation	Mortician	Pharmacist	Sales Manager	Real Est. Manager	Life Ins. Salesman	Advertising Man	Lawyer	Author-Journalist	President Mfg. Co.	Interest Maturity	Occupational Level	Masculinity-Femininity
Standard Score	11	22	19	26	17	39	37	46	29	47	54	44

FIGURE-DRAWING CHARACTERISTICS

Structural	Male Female Both	Structural	Male	Female	Structural and Graphic	Male Female Both	Graphic, Global and Height	Male	Female	Body Proportions	Male	Female
Type	0	Omission of Appendages	7	0	Upper and Lower Halves	3 1	Hair Shading	3	3	Head	07	07
Sex Sequence	1	Position of Both Arms	0	1	Four Quarters	4 4	Nudity and Transparency	7	7	Neck	08	08
Posture	1 1	Position of Right Arm	5	5	Relative Size	0	Form	3	1	Shoulders	10	07
Perspective	0 0	Position of Left Arm	5	0	Constant Line Pressure	0 0	Detailing	3	3	Right Arm		06
Vertical Midline	3 0	Position of Legs	5	6	Variable Line Pressure	3 3	Identity and Sex	1	1	Left Arm		06
Bilateral Symmetry	2 3	Relation of Long Axes	1	1	Line Continuity	0 0	Sophistication	2	2	Chest	07	06
Horizontal Midline	6 4	Right and Left Halves	1	1	Body Shading	7 7	Height	07	07	Girth	14	06

GENERAL CHARACTERISTICS OF SUBJECT

IDENTIFICATION
No. B37
Sex M
Marital status S
Age 25 yrs. at
psychological tests

PARENTAL HISTORY				
Father				
C	H	S	D	O
-	-	-	+	+
Mother				
C	H	S	D	O
-	-	-	-	?

PHYSIOLOGICAL AND METABOLIC DATA

	Admission	Initial	Control	Cold pressor change	Exercise change	Smoking change
Systolic pressure	120	114	112	+10	+42	+08
Diastolic pressure	75	64	72	+20	-04	00
Heart rate	84	84	67	+04	+21	+09

Age 25 yrs.

Height 70 in.   Ponderal index 12.57
Weight 173 lbs.   Cholesterol 248 mg. per 100 ml.
Overweight +10 %   Vital capacity 4.5 liters

HABIT SURVEY

Smoking habits: nonsmoker

Age begun   yrs.   Inhalation:

Habits of nervous tension: 6, 19, 25

STRONG VOCATIONAL INTEREST TEST

Occupation	Artist	Psychologist	Architect	Physician	Osteopath	Dentist	Veterinarian	Mathematician	Physicist	Engineer	Chemist	Production Manager
Standard Score	37	43	40	65	53	55	41	35	36	44	51	32

Occupation	Farmer	Aviator	Carpenter	Printer	Math.-Sci. Teacher	Ind. Arts Teacher	Voc. Agric. Teacher	Policeman	Forest Serv. Man	Y.M.C.A. Phys. Dir.	Personnel Director	Public Administrator
Standard Score	47	46	32	44	44	36	39	34	36	36	21	32

Occupation	Y.M.C.A. Secretary	Soc. Sci. H.S. Teacher	City Sch. Sup't.	Social Worker	Minister	Musician Performer	C.P.A.	Senior C.P.A.	Accountant	Office Man	Purchasing Agent	Banker
Standard Score	23	24	19	30	61	49	16	33	16	21	19	14

Occupation	Mortician	Pharmacist	Sales Manager	Real Est. Manager	Life Ins. Salesman	Advertising Man	Lawyer	Author-Journalist	President Mfg. Co.	Interest Maturity	Occupational Level	Masculinity-Femininity
Standard Score	18	31	19	28	22	28	31	32	26	52	54	54

FIGURE-DRAWING CHARACTERISTICS

Structural	Male Female Both	Structural	Male	Female	Structural and Graphic	Male Female Both		Graphic, Global and Height	Male	Female	Body Proportions	Male	Female
Type	0	Omission of Appendages	7	0	Upper and Lower Halves	3	3	Hair Shading	3	5	Head	06	06
Sex Sequence	1	Position of Both Arms	4	4	Four Quarters	4	4	Nudity and Transparency	7	7	Neck	05	05
Posture	1 1	Position of Right Arm	7	7	Relative Size	2		Form	1	1	Shoulders		
Perspective	1 1	Position of Left Arm	5	5	Constant Line Pressure	5	5	Detailing	1	3	Right Arm		05
Vertical Midline	7 4	Position of Legs	1	4	Variable Line Pressure	0	0	Identity and Sex	1	1	Left Arm		04
Bilateral Symmetry	0 0	Relation of Long Axes	1	1	Line Continuity	4	4	Sophistication	2	2	Chest		
Horizontal Midline	4 4	Right and Left Halves	1	0	Body Shading	0	1	Height	05	05	Girth		

GENERAL CHARACTERISTICS OF SUBJECT

IDENTIFICATION
No. B06
Sex M
Marital status S
Age 22 yrs. at
psychological tests

PARENTAL HISTORY
Father
C H S D O
- - - - ?
Mother
C H S D O
- - - ? +

PHYSIOLOGICAL AND METABOLIC DATA

	Admission	Initial	Control	Cold pressor change	Exercise change	Smoking change
Systolic pressure	130	122	116	+10	+34	+12
Diastolic pressure	74	68	68	+16	-02	+08
Heart rate	84	98	74	+04	+29	+15

Age 22 yrs.	Height	72 in.	Ponderal index 12.83
	Weight	177 lbs.	Cholesterol 160 mg. per 100 ml.
	Overweight +09 %		Vital capacity 4.3 liters

HABIT SURVEY

Smoking habits: mixed smoker

    Age begun 18 yrs.   Inhalation: sometimes

Habits of nervous tension: 16, 19

FIGURE-DRAWING CHARACTERISTICS

Structural	Male Female Both	Structural	Male	Female	Structural and Graphic	Male Female Both		Graphic, Global and Height	Male	Female	Body Proportions	Male	Female
Type	0	Omission of Appendages	0	0	Upper and Lower Halves	3	3	Hair Shading	3	1	Head	06	05
Sex Sequence	1	Position of Both Arms	1	2	Four Quarters	4	4	Nudity and Transparency	7	7	Neck	08	08
Posture	1　　1	Position of Right Arm	0	4	Relative Size	4		Form	3	3	Shoulders	06	
Perspective	0　　6	Position of Left Arm	4	7	Constant Line Pressure	0	0	Detailing	3	3	Right Arm	04	04
Vertical Midline	3　　4	Position of Legs	6	6	Variable Line Pressure	3	1	Identity and Sex	1	1	Left Arm	04	
Bilateral Symmetry	3　　0	Relation of Long Axes	1	1	Line Continuity	0	0	Sophistication	2	2	Chest	04	
Horizontal Midline	4　　4	Right and Left Halves	1	2	Body Shading	0	3	Height	04	05	Girth	04	

GENERAL CHARACTERISTICS OF SUBJECT

IDENTIFICATION
No. 475
Sex F
Marital status S
Age 25 yrs. at
psychological tests

PARENTAL HISTORY
Father
C　H　S　D　O
-　-　-　-　+
Mother
C　H　S　D　O
-　-　-　-　+

PHYSIOLOGICAL AND METABOLIC DATA

	Admission	Initial	Control	Cold pressor change	Exercise change	Smoking change
Systolic pressure	110	106	100	+05	+36	
Diastolic pressure	70	62	64	+09	-04	
Heart rate	76	84	77	+02	+45	

Age 22 yrs.	Height	68	in.	Ponderal index 12.88	
	Weight	147	lbs.	Cholesterol	250	mg. per 100 ml.
	Overweight +04 %			Vital capacity	3.9	liters

HABIT SURVEY
Smoking habits: nonsmoker
Age begun　　yrs.　　Inhalation:
Habits of nervous tension: 2, 4, 6, 9, 11,
16, 23

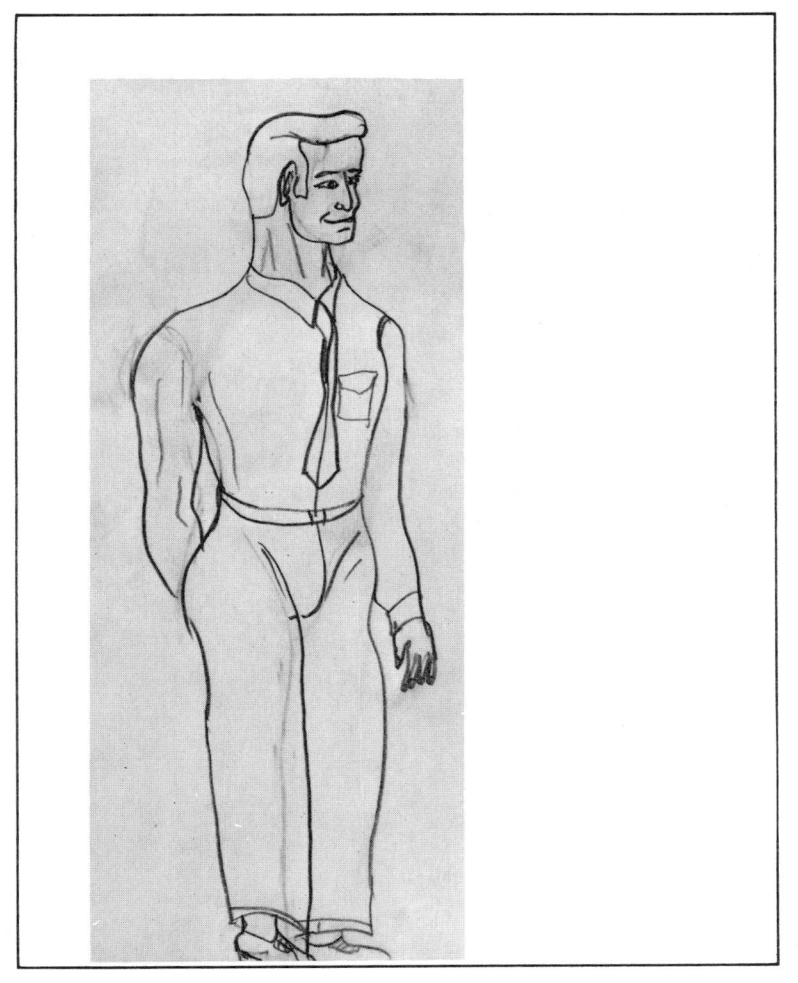

FIGURE-DRAWING CHARACTERISTICS

Structural	Male Female Both	Structural	Male	Female	Structural and Graphic	Male Female Both		Graphic, Global and Height	Male	Female	Body Proportions	Male	Female
Type	0	Omission of Appendages	2	2	Upper and Lower Halves	7	3	Hair Shading	5	5	Head	09	09
Sex Sequence	0	Position of Both Arms	4	4	Four Quarters	4	4	Nudity and Transparency	7	7	Neck	08	14
Posture	1 1	Position of Right Arm	7	8	Relative Size	0		Form	1	1	Shoulders		08
Perspective	1 5	Position of Left Arm	0	0	Constant Line Pressure	5	5	Detailing	1	1	Right Arm		
Vertical Midline	7 0	Position of Legs	2	4	Variable Line Pressure	0	0	Identity and Sex	1	1	Left Arm	08	08
Bilateral Symmetry	0 4	Relation of Long Axes	1	1	Line Continuity	3	3	Sophistication	2	2	Chest		07
Horizontal Midline	4 0	Right and Left Halves	1	1	Body Shading	3	1	Height	09	08	Girth		07

GENERAL CHARACTERISTICS OF SUBJECT

IDENTIFICATION
No. 655
Sex M
Marital status S
Age 23 yrs. at
psychological tests

PARENTAL HISTORY				
Father				
C	H	S	D	O
-	-	-	-	+
Mother				
C	H	S	D	O
-	-	-	-	?

PHYSIOLOGICAL AND METABOLIC DATA

	Admission	Initial	Control	Cold pressor change	Exercise change	Smoking change
Systolic pressure	120	120	110	+28	+38	
Diastolic pressure	86	70	70	+12	+02	
Heart rate	80	76	81	-12	+09	

Age 22 yrs.	Height 74 in.	Ponderal index 13.01
	Weight 184 lbs.	Cholesterol 167 mg. per 100 ml.
	Overweight +06 %	Vital capacity 5.9 liters

HABIT SURVEY

Smoking habits: nonsmoker

Age begun   yrs.   Inhalation:

Habits of nervous tension: 2, 4, 5, 6, 9, 11,

15, 16, 17, 18, 23

FIGURE-DRAWING CHARACTERISTICS

Structural	Male Female Both	Structural	Male	Female	Structural and Graphic	Male Female Both		Graphic, Global and Height	Male	Female	Body Proportions	Male	Female
Type	0	Omission of Appendages	8	2	Upper and Lower Halves	3	0	Hair Shading	5	5	Head	09	06
Sex Sequence	0	Position of Both Arms	1	6	Four Quarters	4	4	Nudity and Transparency	7	7	Neck	06	06
Posture	1 2	Position of Right Arm	2	8	Relative Size	0		Form	1	1	Shoulders	07	06
Perspective	0 0	Position of Left Arm	0	8	Constant Line Pressure	1	1	Detailing	5	3	Right Arm	06	
Vertical Midline	3 0	Position of Legs	4	8	Variable Line Pressure	0	0	Identity and Sex	1	1	Left Arm	06	
Bilateral Symmetry	3 3	Relation of Long Axes	1	1	Line Continuity	0	0	Sophistication	2	2	Chest	06	05
Horizontal Midline	4 4	Right and Left Halves	1	1	Body Shading	0	1	Height	06	05	Girth	07	05

GENERAL CHARACTERISTICS OF SUBJECT

IDENTIFICATION
No. A07
Sex M
Marital status S
Age 24 yrs. at
psychological tests

PARENTAL HISTORY				
Father				
C	H	S	D	O
-	-	-	-	+
Mother				
C	H	S	D	O
-	-	-	-	?

PHYSIOLOGICAL AND METABOLIC DATA

	Admission	Initial	Control	Cold pressor change	Exercise change	Smoking change
Systolic pressure	135	128	128	+05	+16	+04
Diastolic pressure	80	62	70	+10	+05	+09
Heart rate	74	60	55	+06	+20	+18

Age 23 yrs.	Height	71 in.	Ponderal index 12.35
	Weight	190 lbs.	Cholesterol 243 mg. per 100 ml.
	Overweight +19 %		Vital capacity liters

HABIT SURVEY

Smoking habits: light cigarette smoker

Age begun 20 yrs.   Inhalation: yes

Habits of nervous tension: 5, 9, 14, 16, 22

STRONG VOCATIONAL INTEREST TEST

Occupation	Artist	Psychologist	Architect	Physician	Osteopath	Dentist	Veterinarian	Mathematician	Physicist	Engineer	Chemist	Production Manager
Standard Score	3	2	1	4	5	3	2	1	0	1	1	2

Occupation	Farmer	Aviator	Carpenter	Printer	Math.-Sci. Teacher	Ind. Arts Teacher	Voc. Agric. Teacher	Policeman	Forest Serv. Man	Y.M.C.A. Phys. Dir.	Personnel Director	Public Administrator
Standard Score	3	1	1	2	4	0	1	2	2	4	3	3

Occupation	Y.M.C.A. Secretary	Soc. Sci. H.S. Teacher	City Sch. Sup't.	Social Worker	Minister	Musician Performer	C.P.A.	Senior C.P.A.	Accountant	Office Man	Purchasing Agent	Banker
Standard Score	4	6	4	4	6	5	4	2	1	3	2	2

Occupation	Mortician	Pharmacist	Sales Manager	Real Est. Manager	Life Ins. Salesman	Advertising Man	Lawyer	Author- Journalist	President Mfg. Co.	Interest Maturity	Occupational Level	Masculinity- Femininity
Standard Score	4	4	5	6	7	6	7	5	3	6	6	2

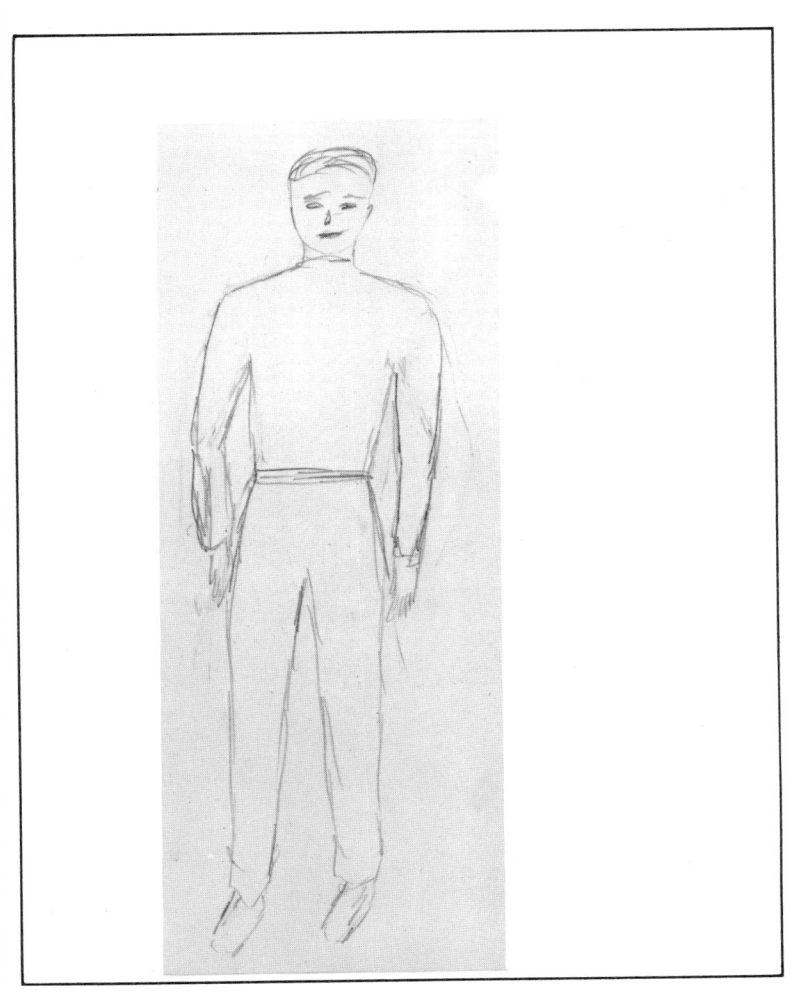

FIGURE-DRAWING CHARACTERISTICS

Structural	Male Female Both	Structural	Male	Female	Structural and Graphic	Male Female Both		Graphic, Global and Height	Male	Female	Body Proportions	Male	Female
Type	0	Omission of Appendages	0	7	Upper and Lower Halves	3	0	Hair Shading	3	3	Head	08	07
Sex Sequence	0	Position of Both Arms	1	0	Four Quarters	4	4	Nudity and Transparency	7	7	Neck	06	05
Posture	1 1	Position of Right Arm	5	5	Relative Size	0		Form	1	1	Shoulders	08	06
Perspective	0 0	Position of Left Arm	0	5	Constant Line Pressure	0	0	Detailing	3	3	Right Arm	08	
Vertical Midline	0 0	Position of Legs	5	4	Variable Line Pressure	2	2	Identity and Sex	1	1	Left Arm	08	
Bilateral Symmetry	5 5	Relation of Long Axes	1	1	Line Continuity	0	0	Sophistication	2	2	Chest	07	05
Horizontal Midline	4 0	Right and Left Halves	1	1	Body Shading	4	0	Height	08	07	Girth	07	04

GENERAL CHARACTERISTICS OF SUBJECT

IDENTIFICATION
No. D72
Sex F
Marital status S
Age 22 yrs. at
psychological tests

PARENTAL HISTORY				
Father				
C	H	S	D	0
–	–	–	–	+
Mother				
C	H	S	D	0
–	–	–	–	?

PHYSIOLOGICAL AND METABOLIC DATA

	Admission	Initial	Control	Cold pressor change	Exercise change	Smoking change
Systolic pressure	140	98	96	–04	+24	
Diastolic pressure	80	75	78	+09	–16	
Heart rate	72	56	59	+04	+29	

Age 22 yrs.	Height	69 in.	Ponderal index 13.42
	Weight	136 lbs.	Cholesterol 212 mg. per 100 ml.
	Overweight –06 %		Vital capacity 3.4 liters

HABIT SURVEY

Smoking habits: nonsmoker

    Age begun   yrs.   Inhalation:

Habits of nervous tension: 4, 8, 10, 14, 16, 17, 23

STRONG VOCATIONAL INTEREST TEST

Occupation	Artist	Psychologist	Architect	Physician	Osteopath	Dentist	Veterinarian	Mathematician	Physicist	Engineer	Chemist	Production Manager
Standard Score	41	27	41	46	37	42	18	32	25	26	35	17

Occupation	Farmer	Aviator	Carpenter	Printer	Math.-Sci. Teacher	Ind. Arts Teacher	Voc. Agric. Teacher	Policeman	Forest Serv. Man	Y.M.C.A. Phys. Dir.	Personnel Director	Public Administrator
Standard Score	36	19	14	30	31	00	14	15	19	26	22	24

Occupation	Y.M.C.A. Secretary	Soc. Sci. H.S. Teacher	City Sch. Sup't.	Social Worker	Minister	Musician Performer	C.P.A.	Senior C.P.A.	Accountant	Office Man	Purchasing Agent	Banker
Standard Score	22	26	25	21	63	45	29	30	28	31	18	23

Occupation	Mortician	Pharmacist	Sales Manager	Real Est. Manager	Life Ins. Salesman	Advertising Man	Lawyer	Author-Journalist	President Mfg. Co.	Interest Maturity	Occupational Level	Masculinity-Femininity
Standard Score	25	26	17	28	25	34	32	42	29	51	61	24

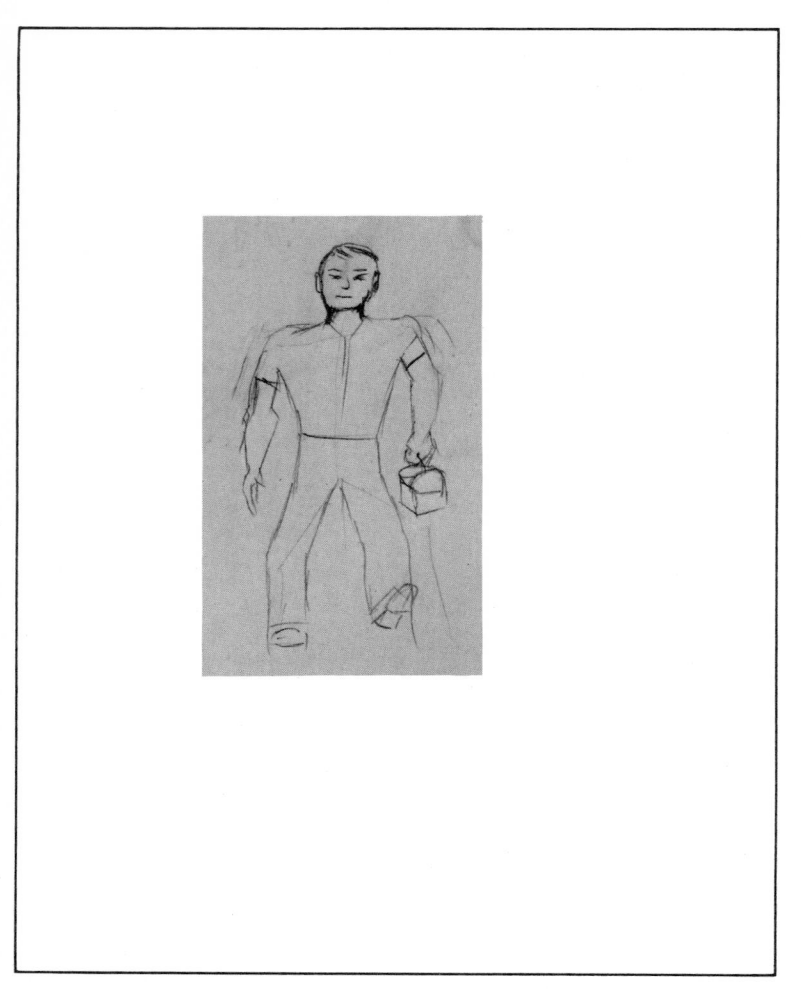

FIGURE-DRAWING CHARACTERISTICS

Structural	Male Female Both		Structural	Male	Female	Structural and Graphic	Male	Female Both		Graphic, Global and Height	Male	Female	Body Proportions	Male	Female
Type	0		Omission of Appendages	0	0	Upper and Lower Halves	1	1		Hair Shading	3	3	Head	05	06
Sex Sequence	0		Position of Both Arms	0	0	Four Quarters	4	4		Nudity and Transparency	7	7	Neck	04	04
Posture	2	1	Position of Right Arm	6	2	Relative Size	0			Form	1	1	Shoulders	06	04
Perspective	0	0	Position of Left Arm	6	2	Constant Line Pressure	0	0		Detailing	1	1	Right Arm	04	02
Vertical Midline	3	3	Position of Legs	8	5	Variable Line Pressure	1	4		Identity and Sex	1	1	Left Arm		02
Bilateral Symmetry	3	3	Relation of Long Axes	1	1	Line Continuity	0	0		Sophistication	2	2	Chest	05	04
Horizontal Midline	4	4	Right and Left Halves	1	2	Body Shading	0	3		Height	04	04	Girth	05	03

GENERAL CHARACTERISTICS OF SUBJECT

IDENTIFICATION
No. 210
Sex M
Marital status M
Age 24 yrs. at
psychological tests

PARENTAL HISTORY
Father
C H S D O
- - - - ?
Mother
C H S D O
- - - - +

PHYSIOLOGICAL AND METABOLIC DATA

	Admission	Initial	Control	Cold pressor change	Exercise change	Smoking change
Systolic pressure	112	124	112	+10	+20	
Diastolic pressure	62	78	70	+06	00	
Heart rate	64	86	48	-02	+27	

Age 21 yrs.	Height	73 in.		Ponderal index	12.59	
	Weight	195 lbs.		Cholesterol	183	mg. per 100 ml.
	Overweight	+17%		Vital capacity	5.7	liters

HABIT SURVEY
Smoking habits: occasional smoker
Age begun 19 yrs. Inhalation: no
Habits of nervous tension: 2, 3, 4, 5, 6, 7, 10, 16, 21

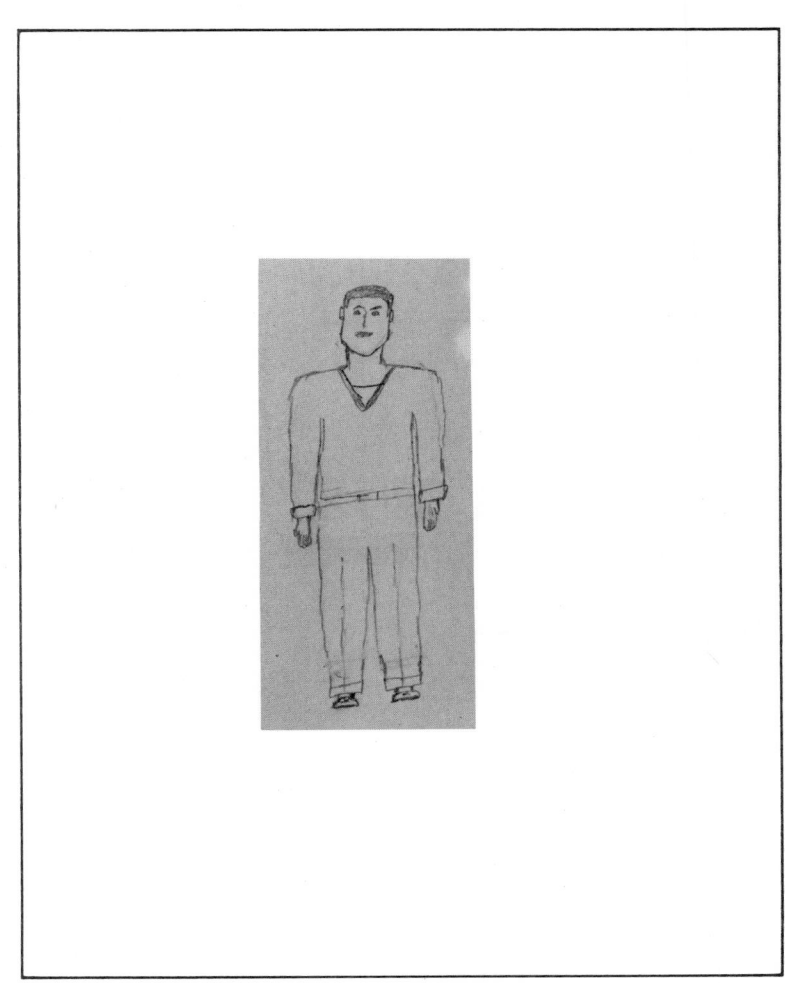

FIGURE-DRAWING CHARACTERISTICS

Structural	Male	Female	Structural	Male	Female	Structural and Graphic	Male	Female	Graphic, Global and Height	Male	Female	Body Proportions	Male	Female
	Both						Both							
Type	0		Omission of Appendages	0	3	Upper and Lower Halves	0	7	Hair Shading	1	1	Head	05	09
Sex Sequence	1		Position of Both Arms	0	0	Four Quarters	4	4	Nudity and Transparency	7	7	Neck	05	06
Posture	1	0	Position of Right Arm	0	0	Relative Size	4		Form	3	3	Shoulders	06	08
Perspective	0	0	Position of Left Arm	0	0	Constant Line Pressure	0	0	Detailing	3	1	Right Arm	04	06
Vertical Midline	0	3	Position of Legs	4	0	Variable Line Pressure	1	1	Identity and Sex	1	1	Left Arm	04	06
Bilateral Symmetry	3	3	Relation of Long Axes	1	1	Line Continuity	0	0	Sophistication	2	2	Chest	04	07
Horizontal Midline	4	4	Right and Left Halves	1	1	Body Shading	6	1	Height	04		Girth	06	08

GENERAL CHARACTERISTICS OF SUBJECT

IDENTIFICATION

No. 735

Sex M

Marital status S

Age 23 yrs. at

psychological tests

PARENTAL HISTORY

Father

C   H   S   D   O

–   –   –   –   ?

Mother

C   H   S   D   O

–   –   –   –   +

PHYSIOLOGICAL AND METABOLIC DATA

	Admission	Initial	Control	Cold pressor change	Exercise change	Smoking change
Systolic pressure	130	110	106	+10	+44	
Diastolic pressure	76	70	74	+04	–14	
Heart rate	72	80	73	–08	+13	

Age 23 yrs.

Height 70 in.

Weight 131 lbs.

Overweight –15 %

Ponderal index 13.78

Cholesterol 185 mg. per 100 ml.

Vital capacity 4.2 liters

HABIT SURVEY

Smoking habits: nonsmoker

Age begun   yrs.   Inhalation:

Habits of nervous tension: 4, 8, 11, 21, 22,

23

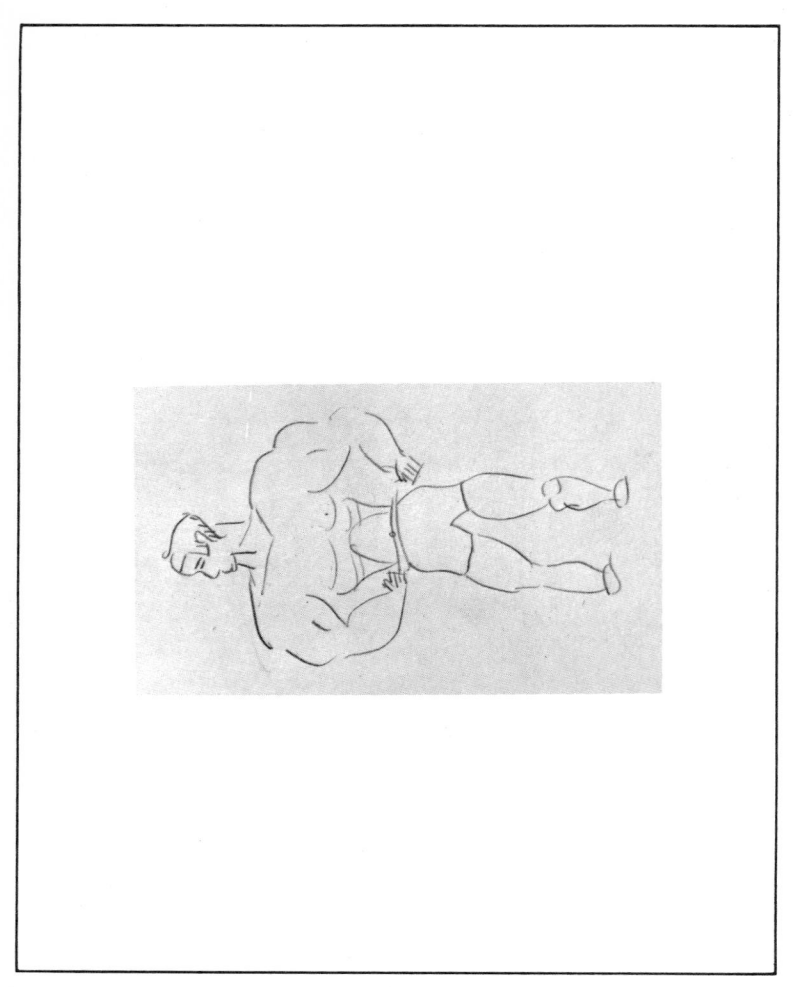

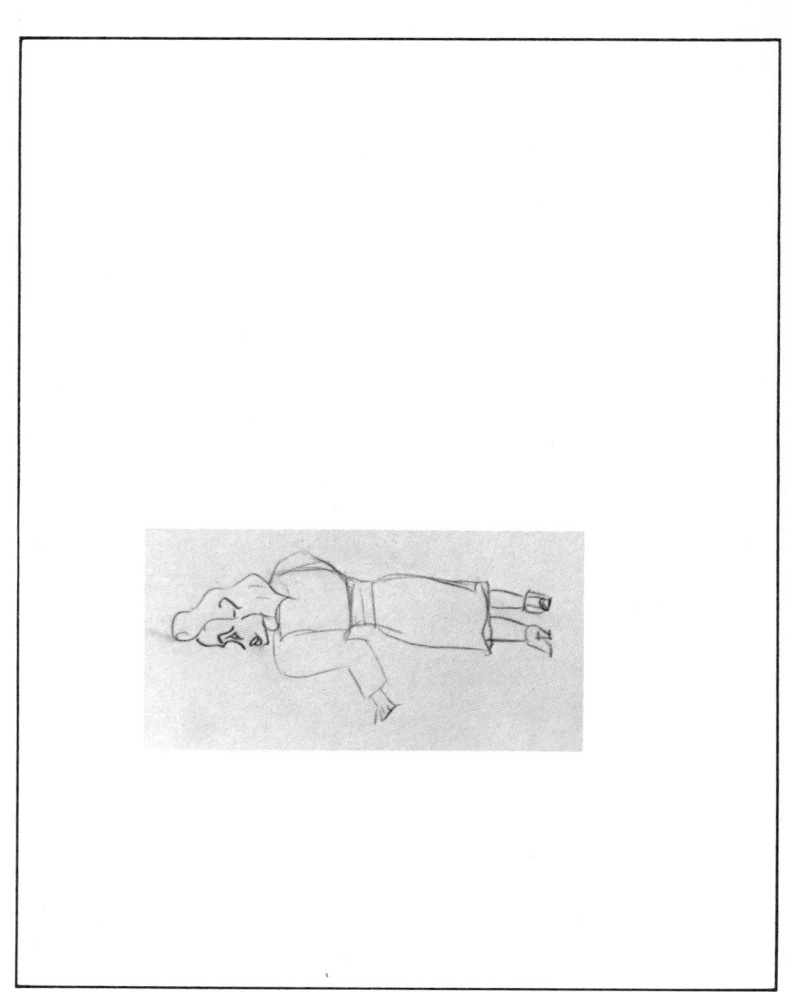

FIGURE-DRAWING CHARACTERISTICS

Structural	Male Female Both	Structural	Male	Female	Structural and Graphic	Male Female Both		Graphic, Global and Height	Male	Female	Body Proportions	Male	Female
Type	0	Omission of Appendages	0	0	Upper and Lower Halves	0	1	Hair Shading	1	1	Head	05	06
Sex Sequence	0	Position of Both Arms	0	4	Four Quarters	4	4	Nudity and Transparency	3	7	Neck	06	
Posture	1 1	Position of Right Arm	5	7	Relative Size	0		Form	3	3	Shoulders	08	
Perspective	5 8	Position of Left Arm	5	4	Constant Line Pressure	5	0	Detailing	3	3	Right Arm	04	
Vertical Midline	0 9	Position of Legs	6	4	Variable Line Pressure	0	3	Identity and Sex	1	1	Left Arm	04	02
Bilateral Symmetry	3 0	Relation of Long Axes	2	2	Line Continuity	2	2	Sophistication	2	2	Chest	05	
Horizontal Midline	4 4	Right and Left Halves	1	2	Body Shading	1	6	Height	04	03	Girth	04	

GENERAL CHARACTERISTICS OF SUBJECT

IDENTIFICATION
No. 415
Sex M
Marital status S
Age 25 yrs. at
psychological tests

PARENTAL HISTORY
Father
C H S D O
− − − − +
Mother
C H S D O
− − − − −

PHYSIOLOGICAL AND METABOLIC DATA

	Admission	Initial	Control	Cold pressor change	Exercise change	Smoking change
Systolic pressure	120	116	110	+20	+32	
Diastolic pressure	70	74	64	+10	−02	
Heart rate	72	84	79	+06	+21	

Age 23 yrs.

Height 72 in.
Weight 171 lbs.
Overweight +04 %

Ponderal index 12.97
Cholesterol 210 mg. per 100 ml.
Vital capacity 6.0 liters

HABIT SURVEY
Smoking habits: unknown
Age begun yrs. Inhalation:
Habits of nervous tension:

FIGURE-DRAWING CHARACTERISTICS

Structural	Male Female Both	Structural	Male	Female	Structural and Graphic	Male Female Both		Graphic, Global and Height	Male	Female	Body Proportions	Male	Female
Type	0	Omission of Appendages	0	0	Upper and Lower Halves	1	1	Hair Shading	3	3	Head	06	07
Sex Sequence	2	Position of Both Arms	0	1	Four Quarters	4	4	Nudity and Transparency	7	7	Neck	08	05
Posture	1　1	Position of Right Arm	0	0	Relative Size	2		Form	3	3	Shoulders	07	05
Perspective	0　0	Position of Left Arm	0	5	Constant Line Pressure	0	0	Detailing	1	1	Right Arm	04	04
Vertical Midline	3　0	Position of Legs	4	6	Variable Line Pressure	1	2	Identity and Sex	1	1	Left Arm	04	04
Bilateral Symmetry	3　3	Relation of Long Axes	1	1	Line Continuity	0	0	Sophistication	2	2	Chest	06	05
Horizontal Midline	6　4	Right and Left Halves	1	2	Body Shading	4	3	Height	05	05	Girth	08	05

GENERAL CHARACTERISTICS OF SUBJECT

IDENTIFICATION
No.　F16
Sex　M
Marital status　S
Age　24　yrs. at
psychological tests

PARENTAL HISTORY
Father
C　H　S　D　O
-　-　-　-　+
Mother
C　H　S　D　O
-　-　-　-　-

PHYSIOLOGICAL AND METABOLIC DATA

	Admission	Initial	Control	Cold pressor change	Exercise change	Smoking change
Systolic pressure	156	128	120	+20	+42	+02
Diastolic pressure	84	78	84	+38	-04	00
Heart rate	80	80	73	-12	+40	+17

Age 23 yrs.　　Height　71　in.　　Ponderal index 13.12

Weight　158　lbs.　　Cholesterol　188　mg. per 100 ml.

Overweight -01 %　　Vital capacity　　liters

HABIT SURVEY
Smoking habits: heavy cigarette smoker
Age begun　18　yrs.　　Inhalation:　yes
Habits of nervous tension: 5

FIGURE-DRAWING CHARACTERISTICS

Structural	Male Female Both	Structural	Male	Female	Structural and Graphic	Male Female Both		Graphic, Global and Height	Male	Female	Body Proportions	Male	Female
Type	0	Omission of Appendages	7	7	Upper and Lower Halves	0	0	Hair Shading	2	2	Head	07	09
Sex Sequence	1	Position of Both Arms	0	0	Four Quarters	4	4	Nudity and Transparency	7	6	Neck	03	03
Posture	1 1	Position of Right Arm	5	5	Relative Size	4		Form	3	3	Shoulders	06	08
Perspective	0 0	Position of Left Arm	5	5	Constant Line Pressure	0	0	Detailing	3	3	Right Arm		
Vertical Midline	3 0	Position of Legs	6	4	Variable Line Pressure	4	3	Identity and Sex	1	1	Left Arm		
Bilateral Symmetry	2 3	Relation of Long Axes	1	1	Line Continuity	0	0	Sophistication	2	2	Chest	06	07
Horizontal Midline	4 4	Right and Left Halves	0	3	Body Shading	7	1	Height	06	06	Girth	08	07

GENERAL CHARACTERISTICS OF SUBJECT

IDENTIFICATION
No. G31
Sex M
Marital status S
Age 23 yrs. at
psychological tests

PARENTAL HISTORY
Father
C H S D O
− − − − +
Mother
C H S D O
− − − − −

PHYSIOLOGICAL AND METABOLIC DATA

	Admission	Initial	Control	Cold pressor change	Exercise change	Smoking change
Systolic pressure	110	124	118	+14	+32	+08
Diastolic pressure	60	68	72	+18	−04	+06
Heart rate	74	56	51	−12	+21	+04

Age 22 yrs.

Height 73 in.	Ponderal index 12.90
Weight 181 lbs.	Cholesterol 197 mg. per 100 ml.
Overweight +08 %	Vital capacity liters

HABIT SURVEY

Smoking habits: *occasional smoker*

Age begun 21 yrs.   Inhalation: yes

Habits of nervous tension: 5, 6, 9, 11

STRONG VOCATIONAL INTEREST TEST

Occupation	Artist	Psychologist	Architect	Physician	Osteopath	Dentist	Veterinarian	Mathematician	Physicist	Engineer	Chemist	Production Manager
Standard Score	34	48	43	59	30	31	25	42	34	43	47	26

Occupation	Farmer	Aviator	Carpenter	Printer	Math.-Sci. Teacher	Ind. Arts Teacher	Voc. Agric. Teacher	Policeman	Forest Serv. Man	Y.M.C.A. Phys. Dir.	Personnel Director	Public Administrator
Standard Score	36	45	16	28	34	16	28	22	31	23	25	38

Occupation	Y.M.C.A. Secretary	Soc. Sci. H.S. Teacher	City Sch. Sup't.	Social Worker	Minister	Musician Performer	C.P.A.	Senior C.P.A.	Accountant	Office Man	Purchasing Agent	Banker
Standard Score	12	18	19	32	59	45	41	49	24	24	20	21

Occupation	Mortician	Pharmacist	Sales Manager	Real Est. Manager	Life Ins. Salesman	Advertising Man	Lawyer	Author-Journalist	President Mfg. Co.	Interest Maturity	Occupational Level	Masculinity-Femininity
Standard Score	08	25	28	31	19	37	38	38	32	51	57	52

Plate 678   MODERATELY SOPHISTICATED DRAWINGS   725

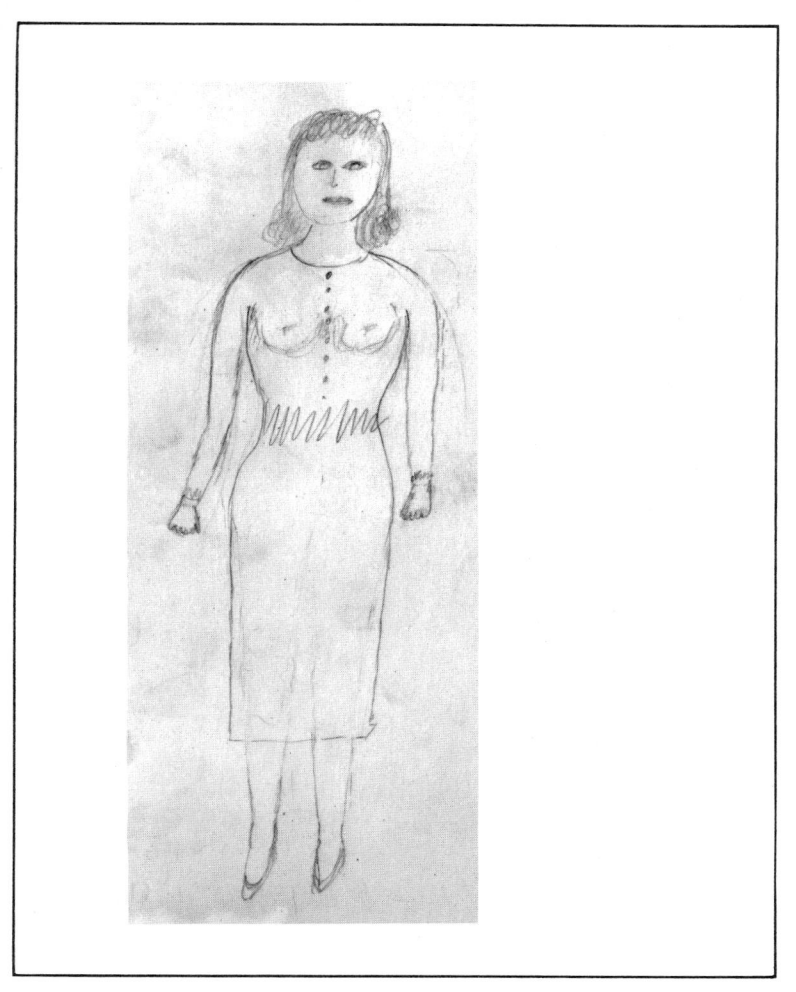

FIGURE-DRAWING CHARACTERISTICS

Structural	Male Female Both	Structural	Male	Female	Structural and Graphic	Male Female Both		Graphic, Global and Height	Male	Female	Body Proportions	Male	Female
Type	0	Omission of Appendages	7	0	Upper and Lower Halves	3	3	Hair Shading	3	3	Head	09	09
Sex Sequence	1	Position of Both Arms	1	1	Four Quarters	4	4	Nudity and Transparency	7	6	Neck	06	06
Posture	2 1	Position of Right Arm	4	4	Relative Size	2		Form	1	1	Shoulders	08	08
Perspective	0 0	Position of Left Arm	5	0	Constant Line Pressure	0	0	Detailing	3	3	Right Arm	08	06
Vertical Midline	3 3	Position of Legs	8	4	Variable Line Pressure	1	1	Identity and Sex	1	1	Left Arm		06
Bilateral Symmetry	3 3	Relation of Long Axes	1	1	Line Continuity	0	0	Sophistication	2	2	Chest	07	08
Horizontal Midline	4 4	Right and Left Halves	1	1	Body Shading	0	5	Height	08	08	Girth	08	08

GENERAL CHARACTERISTICS OF SUBJECT

IDENTIFICATION
No. B03
Sex M
Marital status S
Age 23 yrs. at
psychological tests

PARENTAL HISTORY

Father

C	H	S	D	O
-	-	-	-	+

Mother

C	H	S	D	O
-	-	-	-	-

PHYSIOLOGICAL AND METABOLIC DATA

	Admission	Initial	Control	Cold pressor change	Exercise change	Smoking change
Systolic pressure	110	102	98	+12	+30	+02
Diastolic pressure	60	50	64	+26	-24	+06
Heart rate	84	68	56	+23	+25	+04

Age 22 yrs.	Height 70 in.	Ponderal index 12.77
	Weight 165 lbs.	Cholesterol 240 mg. per 100 ml.
	Overweight +07 %	Vital capacity liters

HABIT SURVEY

Smoking habits: nonsmoker

Age begun   yrs.   Inhalation:

Habits of nervous tension: 2, 4, 5, 6

STRONG VOCATIONAL INTEREST TEST

Occupation	Artist	Psychologist	Architect	Physician	Osteopath	Dentist	Veterinarian	Mathematician	Physicist	Engineer	Chemist	Production Manager
Standard Score	40	32	40	50	41	38	11	40	46	53	53	38

Occupation	Farmer	Aviator	Carpenter	Printer	Math.-Sci. Teacher	Ind. Arts Teacher	Voc. Agric. Teacher	Policeman	Forest Serv. Man	Y.M.C.A. Phys. Dir.	Personnel Director	Public Administrator
Standard Score	29	38	25	24	22	12	03	19	02	15	18	21

Occupation	Y.M.C.A. Secretary	Soc. Sci. H.S. Teacher	City Sch. Sup't.	Social Worker	Minister	Musician Performer	C.P.A.	Senior C.P.A.	Accountant	Office Man	Purchasing Agent	Banker
Standard Score	04	00	02	15	61	34	34	27	18	22	31	15

Occupation	Mortician	Pharmacist	Sales Manager	Real Est. Manager	Life Ins. Salesman	Advertising Man	Lawyer	Author- Journalist	President Mfg. Co.	Interest Maturity	Occupational Level	Masculinity- Femininity
Standard Score	32	37	32	39	29	39	36	41	51	41	65	48

FIGURE-DRAWING CHARACTERISTICS

Structural	Male Female Both	Structural	Male	Female	Structural and Graphic	Male Female Both	Graphic, Global and Height	Male	Female	Body Proportions	Male	Female
Type	0	Omission of Appendages	0	0	Upper and Lower Halves	1 1	Hair Shading	3	3	Head	07	07
Sex Sequence	0	Position of Both Arms	0	0	Four Quarters	4 4	Nudity and Transparency	7	7	Neck	08	07
Posture	1 1	Position of Right Arm	2	2	Relative Size	0	Form	1	1	Shoulders	09	08
Perspective	0 0	Position of Left Arm	2	2	Constant Line Pressure	1 0	Detailing	3	3	Right Arm	06	06
Vertical Midline	3 0	Position of Legs	6	5	Variable Line Pressure	0 1	Identity and Sex	1	1	Left Arm	06	06
Bilateral Symmetry	4 4	Relation of Long Axes	1	1	Line Continuity	0 0	Sophistication	2	2	Chest	06	07
Horizontal Midline	4 4	Right and Left Halves	1	1	Body Shading	2 3	Height	07	07	Girth	08	07

GENERAL CHARACTERISTICS OF SUBJECT

IDENTIFICATION
No. B49
Sex M
Marital status M
Age 23 yrs. at
psychological tests

PARENTAL HISTORY				
Father				
C	H	S	D	O
–	–	–	–	+
Mother				
C	H	S	D	O
–	–	–	–	–

PHYSIOLOGICAL AND METABOLIC DATA

	Admission	Initial	Control	Cold pressor change	Exercise change	Smoking change
Systolic pressure	118	130	116	+16	+38	
Diastolic pressure	70	70	66	+20	–14	
Heart rate	96	96	77	+18	+26	

Age 22 yrs.	Height 72 in.	Ponderal index 12.44
	Weight 194 lbs.	Cholesterol 278 mg. per 100 ml.
	Overweight +19 %	Vital capacity liters

HABIT SURVEY

Smoking habits: nonsmoker

Age begun   yrs.   Inhalation:

Habits of nervous tension: 4, 5, 21

STRONG VOCATIONAL INTEREST TEST

Occupation	Artist	Psychologist	Architect	Physician	Osteopath	Dentist	Veterinarian	Mathematician	Physicist	Engineer	Chemist	Production Manager
Standard Score	33	35	38	68	55	55	44	41	48	57	58	34

Occupation	Farmer	Aviator	Carpenter	Printer	Math.-Sci. Teacher	Ind. Arts Teacher	Voc. Agric. Teacher	Policeman	Forest Serv. Man	Y.M.C.A. Phys. Dir.	Personnel Director	Public Administrator
Standard Score	50	52	33	41	46	34	29	35	44	24	14	31

Occupation	Y.M.C.A. Secretary	Soc. Sci. H.S. Teacher	City Sch. Sup't.	Social Worker	Minister	Musician Performer	C.P.A.	Senior C.P.A.	Accountant	Office Man	Purchasing Agent	Banker
Standard Score	07	11	15	17	61	28	20	38	18	19	21	14

Occupation	Mortician	Pharmacist	Sales Manager	Real Est. Manager	Life Ins. Salesman	Advertising Man	Lawyer	Author-Journalist	President Mfg. Co.	Interest Maturity	Occupational Level	Masculinity-Femininity
Standard Score	11	28	10	18	13	18	27	33	31	50	57	61

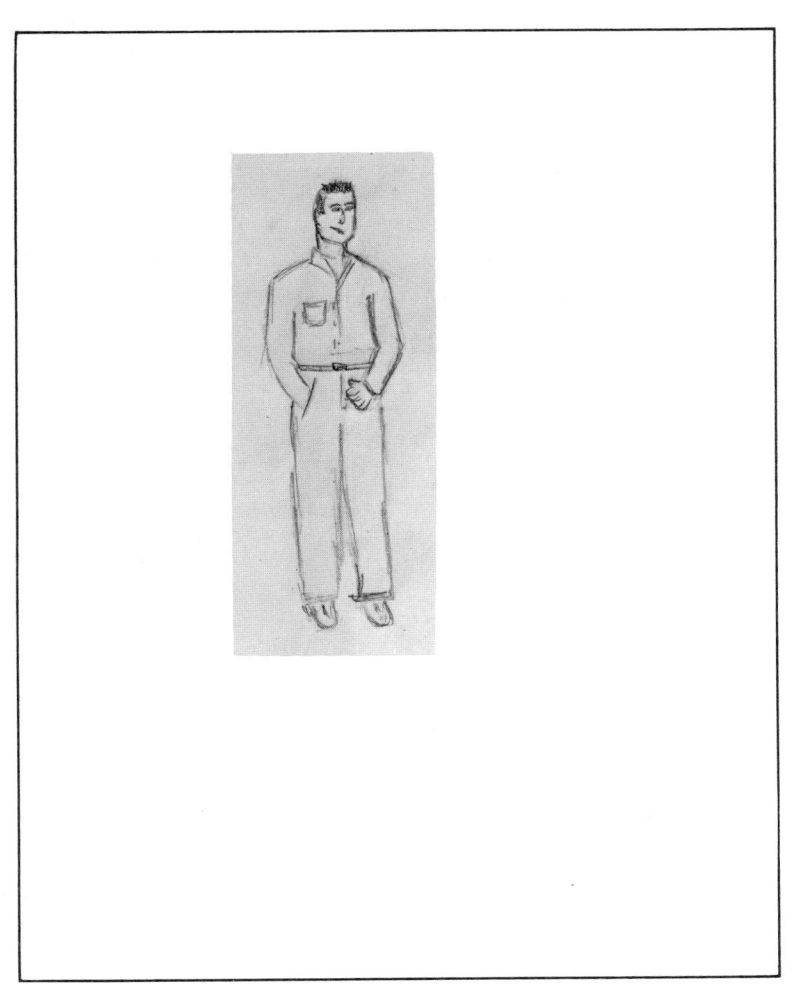

FIGURE-DRAWING CHARACTERISTICS

Structural	Male Female Both		Structural	Male	Female	Structural and Graphic	Male Female Both		Graphic, Global and Height	Male	Female	Body Proportions	Male	Female
Type	0		Omission of Appendages	7	0	Upper and Lower Halves	1	0	Hair Shading	3	3	Head	04	05
Sex Sequence	0		Position of Both Arms	0	0	Four Quarters	4	4	Nudity and Transparency	7	7	Neck	04	06
Posture	1	1	Position of Right Arm	5	5	Relative Size	4		Form	1	1	Shoulders	05	04
Perspective	0	0	Position of Left Arm	5	5	Constant Line Pressure	0	3	Detailing	3	3	Right Arm		03
Vertical Midline	3	3	Position of Legs	4	4	Variable Line Pressure	1	0	Identity and Sex	1	1	Left Arm	02	02
Bilateral Symmetry	3	4	Relation of Long Axes	1	1	Line Continuity	0	0	Sophistication	2	2	Chest	03	03
Horizontal Midline	4	4	Right and Left Halves	2	1	Body Shading	4	6	Height	04	05	Girth	04	03

GENERAL CHARACTERISTICS OF SUBJECT

IDENTIFICATION
No. B70
Sex F
Marital status S
Age 22 yrs. at
psychological tests

PARENTAL HISTORY				
Father				
C	H	S	D	0
–	–	–	–	+
Mother				
C	H	S	D	0
–	–	–	–	–

PHYSIOLOGICAL AND METABOLIC DATA

	Admission	Initial	Control	Cold pressor change	Exercise change	Smoking change
Systolic pressure	120	118	112	+12	+46	
Diastolic pressure	80	68	70	+20	+02	
Heart rate	88	88	79	+14	+38	

Age 22 yrs.	Height	66	in.	Ponderal index	12.53	
	Weight	146	lbs.	Cholesterol	355	mg. per 100 ml.
	Overweight +10 %			Vital capacity	3.7	liters

HABIT SURVEY
Smoking habits: nonsmoker
Age begun   yrs.   Inhalation:
Habits of nervous tension: 6, 9, 10

STRONG VOCATIONAL INTEREST TEST

Occupation	Artist	Psychologist	Architect	Physician	Osteopath	Dentist	Veterinarian	Mathematician	Physicist	Engineer	Chemist	Production Manager
Standard Score	48	39	45	54	36	39	12	40	36	34	44	22

Occupation	Farmer	Aviator	Carpenter	Printer	Math.-Sci. Teacher	Ind. Arts Teacher	Voc. Agric. Teacher	Policeman	Forest Serv. Man	Y.M.C.A. Phys. Dir.	Personnel Director	Public Administrator
Standard Score	13	19	10	21	24	-10	-07	17	08	29	21	30

Occupation	Y.M.C.A. Secretary	Soc. Sci. H.S. Teacher	City Sch. Sup't.	Social Worker	Minister	Musician Performer	C.P.A.	Senior C.P.A.	Accountant	Office Man	Purchasing Agent	Banker
Standard Score	21	13	21	29	61	53	31	19	13	18	14	18

Occupation	Mortician	Pharmacist	Sales Manager	Real Est. Manager	Life Ins. Salesman	Advertising Man	Lawyer	Author-Journalist	President Mfg. Co.	Interest Maturity	Occupational Level	Masculinity-Femininity
Standard Score	24	26	33	32	35	45	45	49	44	46	65	26

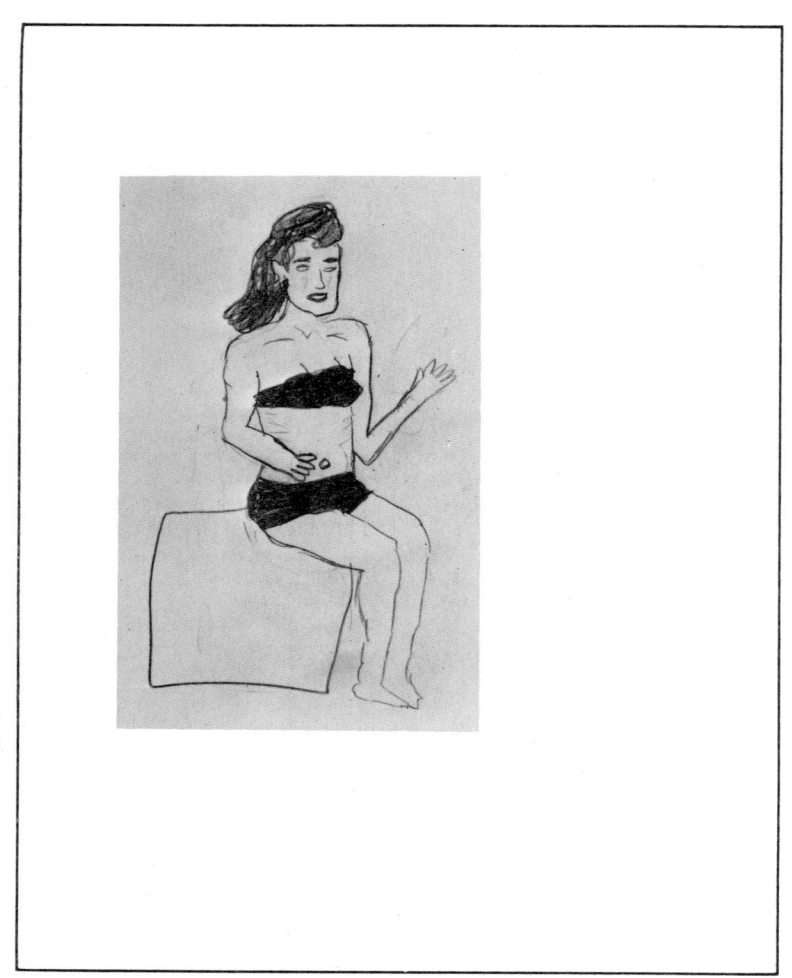

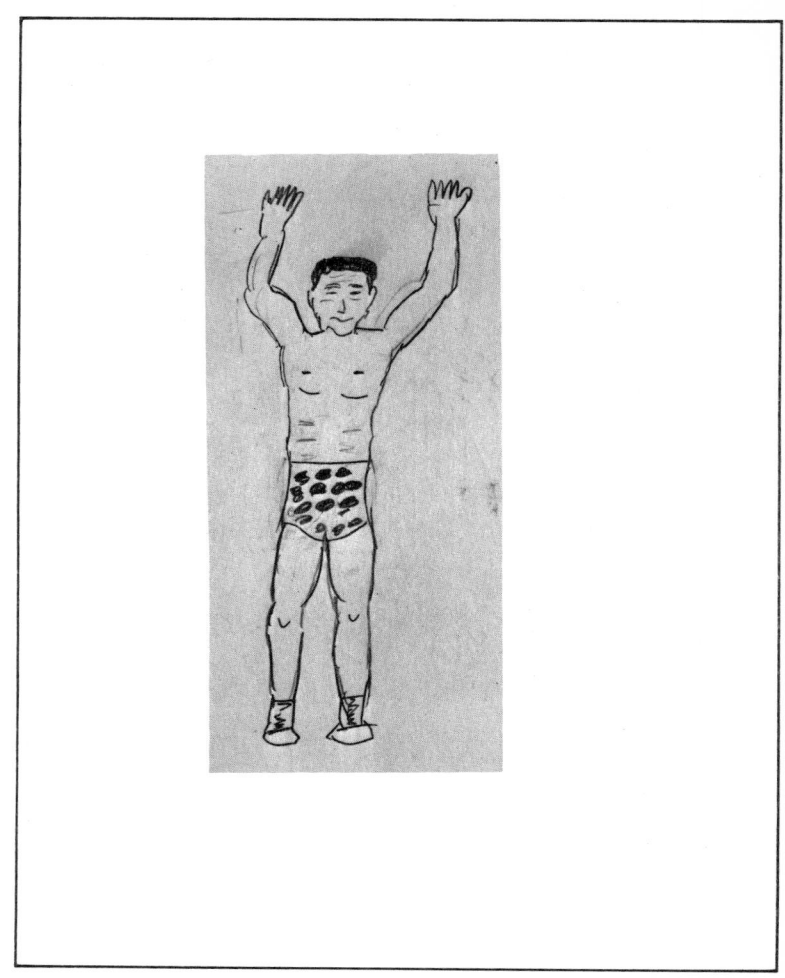

FIGURE-DRAWING CHARACTERISTICS

Structural	Male Female Both		Structural	Male	Female	Structural and Graphic	Male Female Both		Graphic, Global and Height	Male	Female	Body Proportions	Male	Female
Type	0		Omission of Appendages	0	0	Upper and Lower Halves	0	1	Hair Shading	1	3	Head	06	07
Sex Sequence	1		Position of Both Arms	0	0	Four Quarters	4	4	Nudity and Transparency	3	2	Neck	00	04
Posture	1	3	Position of Right Arm	2	4	Relative Size	4		Form	1	1	Shoulders		
Perspective	0	1	Position of Left Arm	2	4	Constant Line Pressure	5	0	Detailing	1	1	Right Arm	04	04
Vertical Midline	0	4	Position of Legs	5	1	Variable Line Pressure	0	4	Identity and Sex	1	1	Left Arm	04	06
Bilateral Symmetry	3	0	Relation of Long Axes	1	0	Line Continuity	1	0	Sophistication	2	2	Chest	05	
Horizontal Midline	4	4	Right and Left Halves	1	1	Body Shading	3	3	Height	05		Girth	05	

GENERAL CHARACTERISTICS OF SUBJECT

IDENTIFICATION

No. C67
Sex M
Marital status S
Age 22 yrs. at
psychological tests

PARENTAL HISTORY

Father
C	H	S	D	O
-	-	-	-	+

Mother
C	H	S	D	O
-	-	-	-	-

PHYSIOLOGICAL AND METABOLIC DATA

	Admission	Initial	Control	Cold pressor change	Exercise change	Smoking change
Systolic pressure	140	140	130	00	+30	
Diastolic pressure	70	60	68	+05	-13	
Heart rate	72	60	57	+12	+13	

Age 23 yrs.
Height 76 in.　Ponderal index 12.56
Weight 221 lbs.　Cholesterol 122 mg. per 100 ml.
Overweight +19 %　Vital capacity 5.2 liters

HABIT SURVEY

Smoking habits: nonsmoker
Age begun　yrs.　Inhalation:
Habits of nervous tension: 6, 9, 18

STRONG VOCATIONAL INTEREST TEST

Occupation	Artist	Psychologist	Architect	Physician	Osteopath	Dentist	Veterinarian	Mathematician	Physicist	Engineer	Chemist	Production Manager
Standard Score	17	38	21	46	48	34	25	21	18	33	36	35

Occupation	Farmer	Aviator	Carpenter	Printer	Math.-Sci. Teacher	Ind. Arts Teacher	Voc. Agric. Teacher	Policeman	Forest Serv. Man	Y.M.C.A. Phys. Dir.	Personnel Director	Public Administrator
Standard Score	27	41	13	32	39	18	21	38	31	52	48	51

Occupation	Y.M.C.A. Secretary	Soc. Sci. H.S. Teacher	City Sch. Sup't.	Social Worker	Minister	Musician Performer	C.P.A.	Senior C.P.A.	Accountant	Office Man	Purchasing Agent	Banker
Standard Score	37	37	32	42	62	33	40	56	41	41	30	21

Occupation	Mortician	Pharmacist	Sales Manager	Real Est. Manager	Life Ins. Salesman	Advertising Man	Lawyer	Author- Journalist	President Mfg. Co.	Interest Maturity	Occupational Level	Masculinity- Femininity
Standard Score	27	31	32	32	33	29	35	26	36	63	58	51

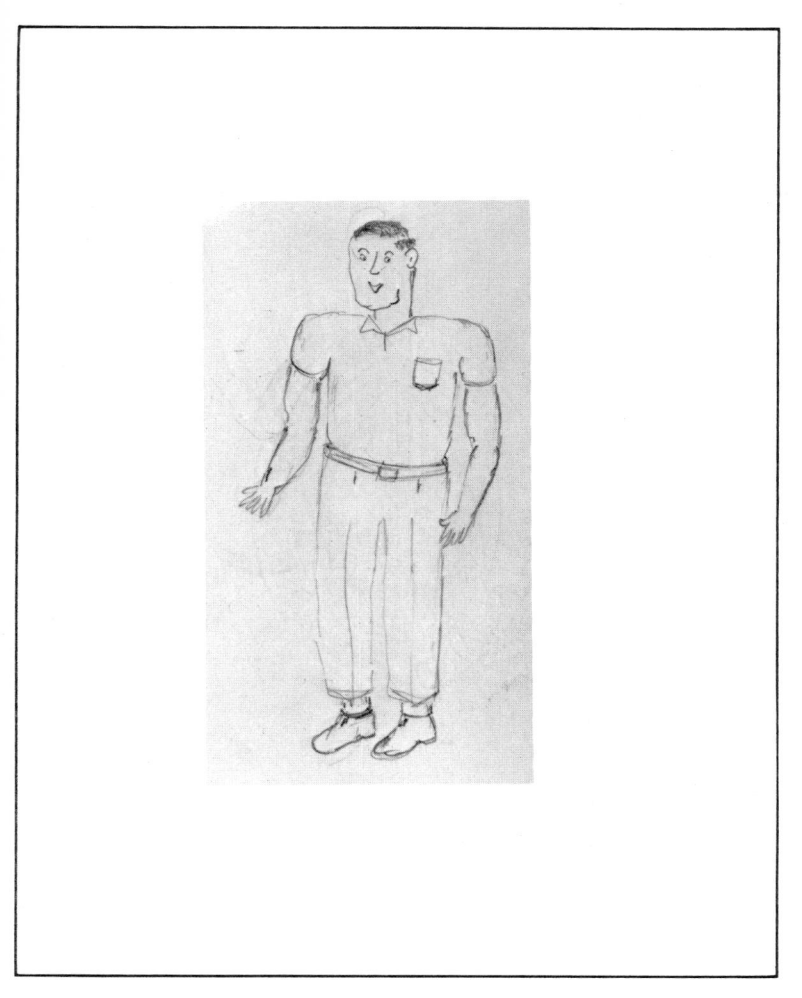

FIGURE-DRAWING CHARACTERISTICS

Structural	Male Female Both	Structural	Male	Female	Structural and Graphic	Male Female Both	Graphic, Global and Height	Male	Female	Body Proportions	Male	Female
Type	0	Omission of Appendages	0	0	Upper and Lower Halves	0 0	Hair Shading	3	3	Head	07	06
Sex Sequence	0	Position of Both Arms	1	0	Four Quarters	4 4	Nudity and Transparency	7	7	Neck	07	06
Posture	1 1	Position of Right Arm	4	0	Relative Size	0	Form	1	1	Shoulders	08	06
Perspective	0 0	Position of Left Arm	5	0	Constant Line Pressure	0 1	Detailing	1	1	Right Arm	04	04
Vertical Midline	1 0	Position of Legs	4	4	Variable Line Pressure	1 0	Identity and Sex	1	1	Left Arm	05	04
Bilateral Symmetry	3 3	Relation of Long Axes	1	1	Line Continuity	0 0	Sophistication	2	2	Chest	06	05
Horizontal Midline	4 4	Right and Left Halves	1	1	Body Shading	6 5	Height	05	05	Girth	07	06

GENERAL CHARACTERISTICS OF SUBJECT

IDENTIFICATION
No. D52
Sex M
Marital status S
Age 22 yrs. at
psychological tests

PARENTAL HISTORY
Father
C   H   S   D   O
-   -   -   -   +
Mother
C   H   S   D   O
-   -   -   -   -

PHYSIOLOGICAL AND METABOLIC DATA

	Admission	Initial	Control	Cold pressor change	Exercise change	Smoking change
Systolic pressure	115	122	112	+15	+26	00
Diastolic pressure	60	68	66	+14	-21	+02
Heart rate	100	80	72	-04	+21	-06

Age 22 yrs.
Height 74 in.   Ponderal index 12.80
Weight 193 lbs.   Cholesterol 193 mg. per 100 ml.
Overweight +12 %   Vital capacity liters

HABIT SURVEY

Smoking habits: nonsmoker

Age begun yrs.   Inhalation:

Habits of nervous tension: 1, 5, 6, 10, 15, 25

STRONG VOCATIONAL INTEREST TEST

Occupation	Artist	Psychologist	Architect	Physician	Osteopath	Dentist	Veterinarian	Mathematician	Physicist	Engineer	Chemist	Production Manager
Standard Score	35	48	27	27	12	10	-10	33	18	14	20	16

Occupation	Farmer	Aviator	Carpenter	Printer	Math.-Sci. Teacher	Ind. Arts Teacher	Voc. Agric. Teacher	Policeman	Forest Serv. Man	Y.M.C.A. Phys. Dir.	Personnel Director	Public Administrator
Standard Score	11	13	-09	24	21	-10	01	17	-07	21	44	42

Occupation	Y.M.C.A. Secretary	Soc. Sci. H.S. Teacher	City Sch. Sup't.	Social Worker	Minister	Musician Performer	C.P.A.	Senior C.P.A.	Accountant	Office Man	Purchasing Agent	Banker
Standard Score	27	39	44	49	63	50	54	30	21	23	16	22

Occupation	Mortician	Pharmacist	Sales Manager	Real Est. Manager	Life Ins. Salesman	Advertising Man	Lawyer	Author-Journalist	President Mfg. Co.	Interest Maturity	Occupational Level	Masculinity-Femininity
Standard Score	11	19	36	42	42	52	64	51	33	54	65	28

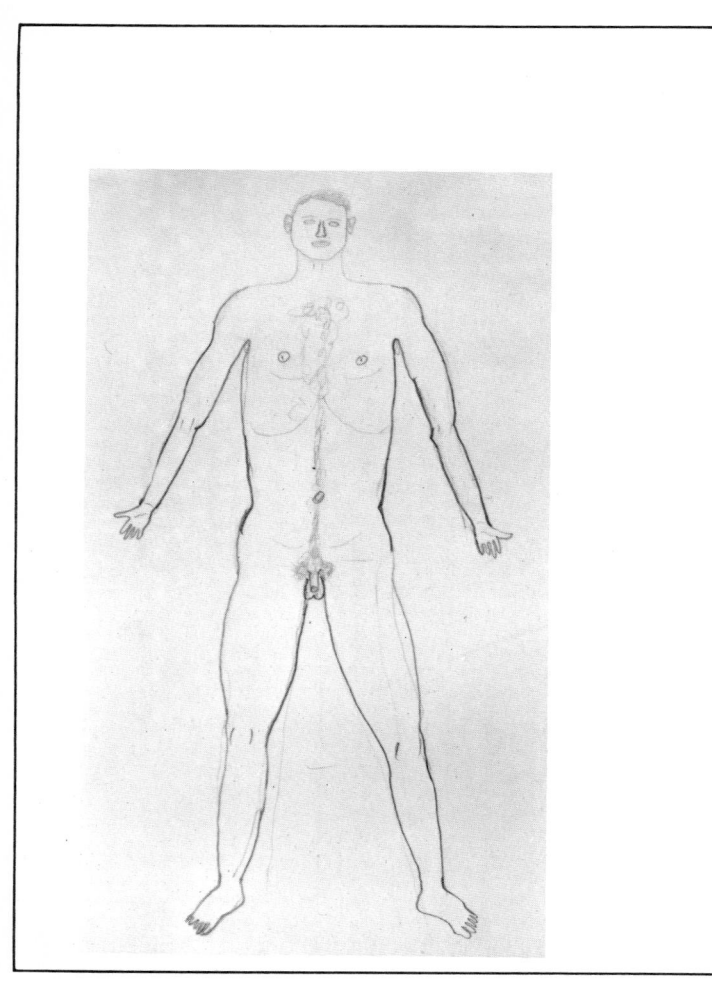

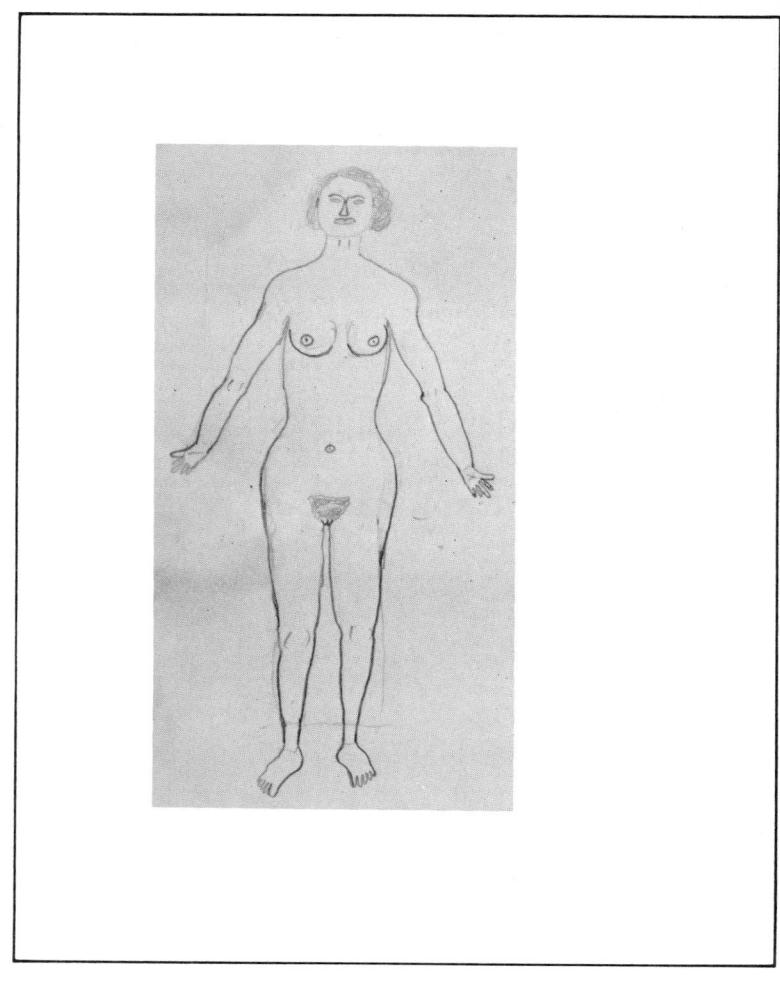

FIGURE-DRAWING CHARACTERISTICS

Structural	Male Female Both		Structural	Male	Female	Structural and Graphic	Male Female Both		Graphic, Global and Height	Male	Female	Body Proportions	Male	Female
Type	0		Omission of Appendages	0	0	Upper and Lower Halves	3	0	Hair Shading	3	3	Head	05	05
Sex Sequence	0		Position of Both Arms	0	0	Four Quarters	4	4	Nudity and Transparency	0	0	Neck	07	06
Posture	1	1	Position of Right Arm	2	2	Relative Size	0		Form	3	1	Shoulders	08	06
Perspective	0	0	Position of Left Arm	2	2	Constant Line Pressure	0	0	Detailing	1	1	Right Arm	06	04
Vertical Midline	0	0	Position of Legs	6	4	Variable Line Pressure	3	3	Identity and Sex	1	1	Left Arm	06	06
Bilateral Symmetry	5	4	Relation of Long Axes	1	1	Line Continuity	3	3	Sophistication	2	2	Chest	07	05
Horizontal Midline	0	0	Right and Left Halves	1	1	Body Shading	3	2	Height	08	06	Girth	08	06

GENERAL CHARACTERISTICS OF SUBJECT

IDENTIFICATION
No. D73
Sex M
Marital status M
Age 23 yrs. at psychological tests

PARENTAL HISTORY				
Father				
C	H	S	D	O
-	-	-	-	+
Mother				
C	H	S	D	O
-	-	-	-	-

PHYSIOLOGICAL AND METABOLIC DATA

	Admission	Initial	Control	Cold pressor change	Exercise change	Smoking change
Systolic pressure	134	122	118	+02	+62	+04
Diastolic pressure	80	70	70	+24	00	+02
Heart rate	68	100	94	+12	+21	-03

Age 22 yrs.	Height	72 in.	Ponderal index 12.50
	Weight	191 lbs.	Cholesterol 193 mg. per 100 ml.
	Overweight +17 %		Vital capacity liters

HABIT SURVEY
Smoking habits: nonsmoker
Age begun yrs. Inhalation:
Habits of nervous tension: 1, 4, 5, 9, 17, 20 21, 25

STRONG VOCATIONAL INTEREST TEST

Occupation	Artist	Psychologist	Architect	Physician	Osteopath	Dentist	Veterinarian	Mathematician	Physicist	Engineer	Chemist	Production Manager
Standard Score	37	37	36	54	45	39	26	42	34	36	43	23

Occupation	Farmer	Aviator	Carpenter	Printer	Math.-Sci. Teacher	Ind. Arts Teacher	Voc. Agric. Teacher	Policeman	Forest Serv. Man	Y.M.C.A. Phys. Dir.	Personnel Director	Public Administrator
Standard Score	30	27	11	25	34	11	19	28	19	38	21	42

Occupation	Y.M.C.A. Secretary	Soc. Sci. H.S. Teacher	City Sch. Sup't.	Social Worker	Minister	Musician Performer	C.P.A.	Senior C.P.A.	Accountant	Office Man	Purchasing Agent	Banker
Standard Score	29	29	32	33	63	45	26	33	13	25	14	21

Occupation	Mortician	Pharmacist	Sales Manager	Real Est. Manager	Life Ins. Salesman	Advertising Man	Lawyer	Author-Journalist	President Mfg. Co.	Interest Maturity	Occupational Level	Masculinity-Femininity
Standard Score	25	25	21	26	31	34	41	40	29	52	62	37

FIGURE-DRAWING CHARACTERISTICS

Structural	Male — Female (Both)	Structural	Male	Female	Structural and Graphic	Male — Female (Both)	Graphic, Global and Height	Male	Female	Body Proportions	Male	Female
Type	0	Omission of Appendages	0	0	Upper and Lower Halves	1 1	Hair Shading	3	3	Head	05	05
Sex Sequence	0	Position of Both Arms	2	2	Four Quarters	4 4	Nudity and Transparency	7	7	Neck	04	04
Posture	1 1	Position of Right Arm	0	4	Relative Size	4	Form	3	1	Shoulders		
Perspective	2 2	Position of Left Arm	7	7	Constant Line Pressure	1 0	Detailing	1	1	Right Arm	04	04
Vertical Midline	5 4	Position of Legs	1	5	Variable Line Pressure	0 1	Identity and Sex	1	1	Left Arm		
Bilateral Symmetry	0 0	Relation of Long Axes	3	1	Line Continuity	0 0	Sophistication	2	2	Chest	05	05
Horizontal Midline	6 4	Right and Left Halves	2	2	Body Shading	0 7	Height	05	05	Girth	05	05

GENERAL CHARACTERISTICS OF SUBJECT

IDENTIFICATION
No. 256
Sex M
Marital status M
Age 24 yrs. at psychological tests

PARENTAL HISTORY				
Father				
C	H	S	D	O
-	-	-	-	-
Mother				
C	H	S	D	O
-	-	-	-	+

PHYSIOLOGICAL AND METABOLIC DATA

	Admission	Initial	Control	Cold pressor change	Exercise change	Smoking change
Systolic pressure	118	110	102	+05	+25	
Diastolic pressure	72	62	60	+08	00	
Heart rate	84	78	79	+04	+24	

Age 24 yrs.   Height 68 in.   Ponderal index 12.91

Weight 146 lbs.   Cholesterol 183 mg. per 100 ml.

Overweight -01 %   Vital capacity 5.6 liters

HABIT SURVEY
Smoking habits: light cigarette smoker
Age begun 17 yrs.   Inhalation: yes
Habits of nervous tension: 2, 4, 5, 6, 10

FIGURE-DRAWING CHARACTERISTICS

Structural	Male Female Both	Structural	Male	Female	Structural and Graphic	Male Female Both		Graphic, Global and Height	Male	Female	Body Proportions	Male	Female
Type	0	Omission of Appendages	0	0	Upper and Lower Halves	1	3	Hair Shading	1	0	Head	05	07
Sex Sequence	2	Position of Both Arms	0	0	Four Quarters	4	4	Nudity and Transparency	7	7	Neck	06	08
Posture	1	1	Position of Right Arm	5	2	Relative Size	4		Form	1	1	Shoulders	07	06
Perspective	0	5	Position of Left Arm	5	2	Constant Line Pressure	0	0	Detailing	1	1	Right Arm	04	04
Vertical Midline	3	3	Position of Legs	4	5	Variable Line Pressure	5	5	Identity and Sex	1	3	Left Arm	04	04
Bilateral Symmetry	5	5	Relation of Long Axes	1	1	Line Continuity	2	2	Sophistication	2	2	Chest	06	07
Horizontal Midline	4	4	Right and Left Halves	1	1	Body Shading	4	5	Height	05	07	Girth	04	06

GENERAL CHARACTERISTICS OF SUBJECT

IDENTIFICATION
No. 445
Sex M
Marital status S
Age 26 yrs. at
psychological tests

PARENTAL HISTORY
Father
C H S D O
- - - - -
Mother
C H S D O
- - - - +

PHYSIOLOGICAL AND METABOLIC DATA

	Admission	Initial	Control	Cold pressor change	Exercise change	Smoking change
Systolic pressure	156	128	120	+14	+38	+04
Diastolic pressure	90	76	74	+02	00	00
Heart rate	84	96	83	+04	+11	-06

Age 25 yrs.	Height	76 in.	Ponderal index	12.89	
	Weight	205 lbs.	Cholesterol	273	mg. per 100 ml.
	Overweight	+08 %	Vital capacity	5.8	liters

HABIT SURVEY
Smoking habits: light cigarette smoker
Age begun 21 yrs.   Inhalation: yes
Habits of nervous tension: 1, 19, 25

FIGURE-DRAWING CHARACTERISTICS

Structural	Male Female Both		Structural	Male	Female	Structural and Graphic	Male Female Both		Graphic, Global and Height	Male	Female	Body Proportions	Male	Female
Type	0		Omission of Appendages	0	0	Upper and Lower Halves	3	0	Hair Shading	3	3	Head	07	07
Sex Sequence	0		Position of Both Arms	4	4	Four Quarters	4	4	Nudity and Transparency	7	7	Neck	08	07
Posture	2	2	Position of Right Arm	7	7	Relative Size	0		Form	3	3	Shoulders		
Perspective	2	2	Position of Left Arm	4	4	Constant Line Pressure	0	0	Detailing	1	1	Right Arm		
Vertical Midline	4	4	Position of Legs	8	8	Variable Line Pressure	5	5	Identity and Sex	1	1	Left Arm	04	04
Bilateral Symmetry	0	0	Relation of Long Axes	1	1	Line Continuity	1	0	Sophistication	2	2	Chest	08	06
Horizontal Midline	4	4	Right and Left Halves	1	2	Body Shading	0	4	Height	07	06	Girth	06	06

GENERAL CHARACTERISTICS OF SUBJECT

IDENTIFICATION

No. 744

Sex M

Marital status S

Age 23 yrs. at psychological tests

PARENTAL HISTORY

Father

C H S D O

– – – – –

Mother

C H S D O

– – – – +

PHYSIOLOGICAL AND METABOLIC DATA

	Admission	Initial	Control	Cold pressor change	Exercise change	Smoking change
Systolic pressure	120	104	96	+07	+24	+20
Diastolic pressure	70	44	60	+06	–14	00
Heart rate	88	76	70	00	+05	–09

Age 23 yrs.

Height 73 in.

Weight 185 lbs.

Overweight +09 %

Ponderal index 12.81

Cholesterol 244 mg. per 100 ml.

Vital capacity 5.4 liters

HABIT SURVEY

Smoking habits: nonsmoker

Age begun   yrs.   Inhalation:

Habits of nervous tension: 5, 6, 9, 16, 23, 24

FIGURE-DRAWING CHARACTERISTICS

Structural	Male Female Both		Structural	Male	Female	Structural and Graphic	Male Female Both		Graphic, Global and Height	Male	Female	Body Proportions	Male	Female
Type	0		Omission of Appendages	0	7	Upper and Lower Halves	1	1	Hair Shading	0	3	Head	06	05
Sex Sequence	2		Position of Both Arms	0	1	Four Quarters	4	4	Nudity and Transparency	7	7	Neck	03	05
Posture	1	1	Position of Right Arm	0	2	Relative Size	0		Form	3	3	Shoulders	06	04
Perspective	0	0	Position of Left Arm	0	5	Constant Line Pressure	0	0	Detailing	1	1	Right Arm	04	02
Vertical Midline	3	3	Position of Legs	4	4	Variable Line Pressure	1	2	Identity and Sex	1	1	Left Arm	04	
Bilateral Symmetry	2	3	Relation of Long Axes	1	1	Line Continuity	2	1	Sophistication	2	2	Chest	05	04
Horizontal Midline	6	4	Right and Left Halves	2	2	Body Shading	7	7	Height	04	04	Girth	06	03

GENERAL CHARACTERISTICS OF SUBJECT

IDENTIFICATION
No. F54
Sex M
Marital status
Age 24 yrs. at
psychological tests

PARENTAL HISTORY				
Father				
C	H	S	D	O
-	-	-	-	-
Mother				
C	H	S	D	O
-	-	-	-	+

PHYSIOLOGICAL AND METABOLIC DATA

	Admission	Initial	Control	Cold pressor change	Exercise change	Smoking change
Systolic pressure	150	130	120	+24	+40	+08
Diastolic pressure	70	70	78	+20	+22	+10
Heart rate	88	96	90	-12	+09	-03

Age 23 yrs.	Height 72 in.	Ponderal index 12.97
	Weight 171 lbs.	Cholesterol 204 mg. per 100 ml.
	Overweight +04 %	Vital capacity liters

HABIT SURVEY
Smoking habits: occasional smoker
Age begun yrs. Inhalation:
Habits of nervous tension:

Plate 688   **MODERATELY SOPHISTICATED DRAWINGS**   735

FIGURE-DRAWING CHARACTERISTICS

Structural	Male Female Both		Structural	Male	Female	Structural and Graphic	Male Female Both		Graphic, Global and Height	Male	Female	Body Proportions	Male	Female
Type	0		Omission of Appendages	0	0	Upper and Lower Halves	0	0	Hair Shading	3	3	Head	09	09
Sex Sequence	0		Position of Both Arms	0	0	Four Quarters	4	4	Nudity and Transparency	7	7	Neck	03	03
Posture	1	1	Position of Right Arm	0	0	Relative Size	0		Form	3	3	Shoulders	08	06
Perspective	0	0	Position of Left Arm	0	0	Constant Line Pressure	1	1	Detailing	3	3	Right Arm	06	04
Vertical Midline	3	1	Position of Legs	6	4	Variable Line Pressure	0	0	Identity and Sex	1	1	Left Arm	06	04
Bilateral Symmetry	2	3	Relation of Long Axes	1	1	Line Continuity	0	0	Sophistication	2	2	Chest	07	05
Horizontal Midline	4	4	Right and Left Halves	1	1	Body Shading	0	1	Height	07	06	Girth	09	04

GENERAL CHARACTERISTICS OF SUBJECT

IDENTIFICATION
No. G32
Sex M
Marital status S
Age 22 yrs. at
psychological tests

PARENTAL HISTORY
Father
C H S D O
-   -   -   -   -
Mother
C H S D O
-   -   -   -   +

PHYSIOLOGICAL AND METABOLIC DATA

	Admission	Initial	Control	Cold pressor change	Exercise change	Smoking change
Systolic pressure	140	126	120	+28	+30	00
Diastolic pressure	90	72	72	+24	-04	+07
Heart rate	80	76	70	-08	+25	+07

Age 21 yrs.	Height 68 in.	Ponderal index 11.85
	Weight 189 lbs.	Cholesterol 217 mg. per 100 ml.
	Overweight +30 %	Vital capacity liters

HABIT SURVEY
Smoking habits: occasional smoker
Age begun 19 yrs.   Inhalation: no
Habits of nervous tension: 1, 3, 4, 5, 11, 16,
23

STRONG VOCATIONAL INTEREST TEST

Occupation	Artist	Psychologist	Architect	Physician	Osteopath	Dentist	Veterinarian	Mathematician	Physicist	Engineer	Chemist	Production Manager
Standard Score	34	40	33	52	45	47	23	38	37	42	52	33

Occupation	Farmer	Aviator	Carpenter	Printer	Math.-Sci. Teacher	Ind. Arts Teacher	Voc. Agric. Teacher	Policeman	Forest Serv. Man	Y.M.C.A. Phys. Dir.	Personnel Director	Public Administrator
Standard Score	42	49	31	55	47	24	15	36	28	32	19	32

Occupation	Y.M.C.A. Secretary	Soc. Sci. H.S. Teacher	City Sch. Sup't.	Social Worker	Minister	Musician Performer	C.P.A.	Senior C.P.A.	Accountant	Office Man	Purchasing Agent	Banker
Standard Score	19	25	19	26	59	49	25	41	30	35	26	21

Occupation	Mortician	Pharmacist	Sales Manager	Real Est. Manager	Life Ins. Salesman	Advertising Man	Lawyer	Author-Journalist	President Mfg. Co.	Interest Maturity	Occupational Level	Masculinity-Femininity
Standard Score	23	29	19	26	16	26	28	36	22	51	48	45

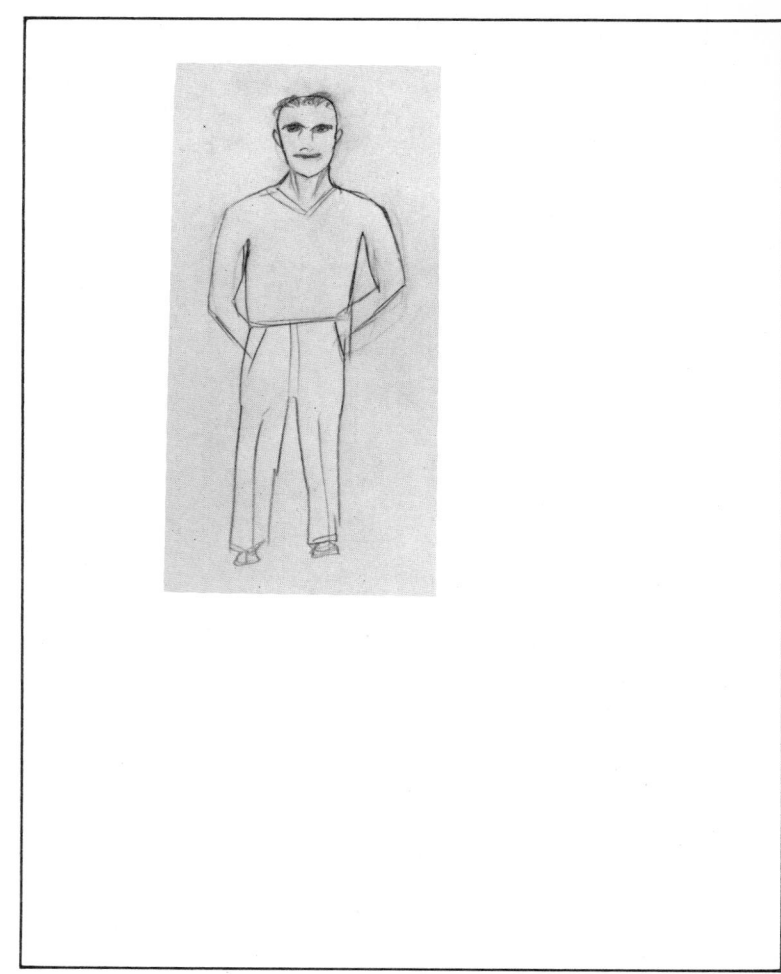

FIGURE-DRAWING CHARACTERISTICS

Structural	Male Female Both	Structural	Male	Female	Structural and Graphic	Male Female Both		Graphic, Global and Height	Male	Female	Body Proportions	Male	Female
Type	0	Omission of Appendages	7	7	Upper and Lower Halves	1	1	Hair Shading	3	3	Head	05	07
Sex Sequence	1	Position of Both Arms	0	0	Four Quarters	4	4	Nudity and Transparency	7	7	Neck	05	05
Posture	1 1	Position of Right Arm	5	5	Relative Size	4		Form	1	3	Shoulders	06	07
Perspective	0 0	Position of Left Arm	5	5	Constant Line Pressure	0	0	Detailing	1	1	Right Arm		04
Vertical Midline	3 3	Position of Legs	4	4	Variable Line Pressure	5	4	Identity and Sex	1	1	Left Arm		04
Bilateral Symmetry	3 3	Relation of Long Axes	1	1	Line Continuity	2	2	Sophistication	2	2	Chest	05	06
Horizontal Midline	4 4	Right and Left Halves	2	2	Body Shading	6	5	Height	05	06	Girth	06	07

GENERAL CHARACTERISTICS OF SUBJECT

IDENTIFICATION

No. G55

Sex M

Marital status S

Age 23 yrs. at psychological tests

PARENTAL HISTORY

Father

C	H	S	D	O
-	-	-	-	-

Mother

C	H	S	D	O
-	-	-	-	+

PHYSIOLOGICAL AND METABOLIC DATA

	Admission	Initial	Control	Cold pressor change	Exercise change	Smoking change
Systolic pressure	130	128	122	+20	+38	+03
Diastolic pressure	80	70	72	+18	-22	+10
Heart rate	120	84	82	+22	+16	+11

Age 22 yrs.	Height	71	in.	Ponderal index	12.52	
	Weight	182	lbs.	Cholesterol	258	mg. per 100 ml.
	Overweight	+15	%	Vital capacity		liters

HABIT SURVEY

Smoking habits: heavy cigarette smoker

Age begun 18 yrs.   Inhalation: yes

Habits of nervous tension: 5, 6, 9, 10, 16, 17, 21, 22

Plate 690   MODERATELY SOPHISTICATED DRAWINGS   737

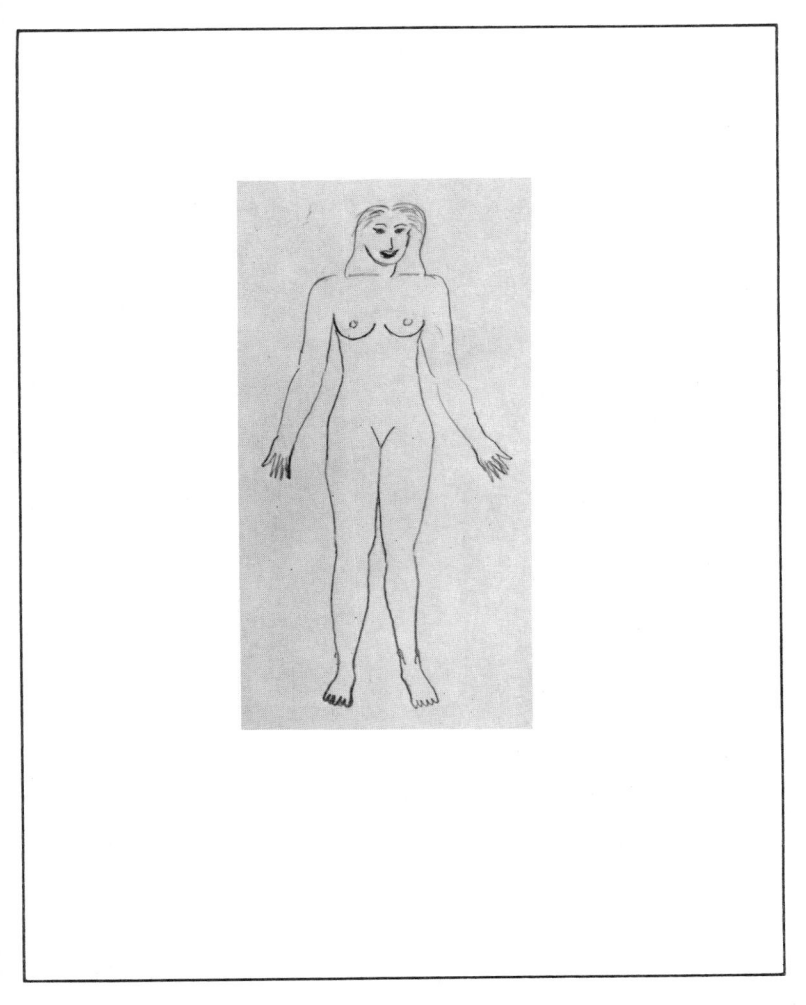
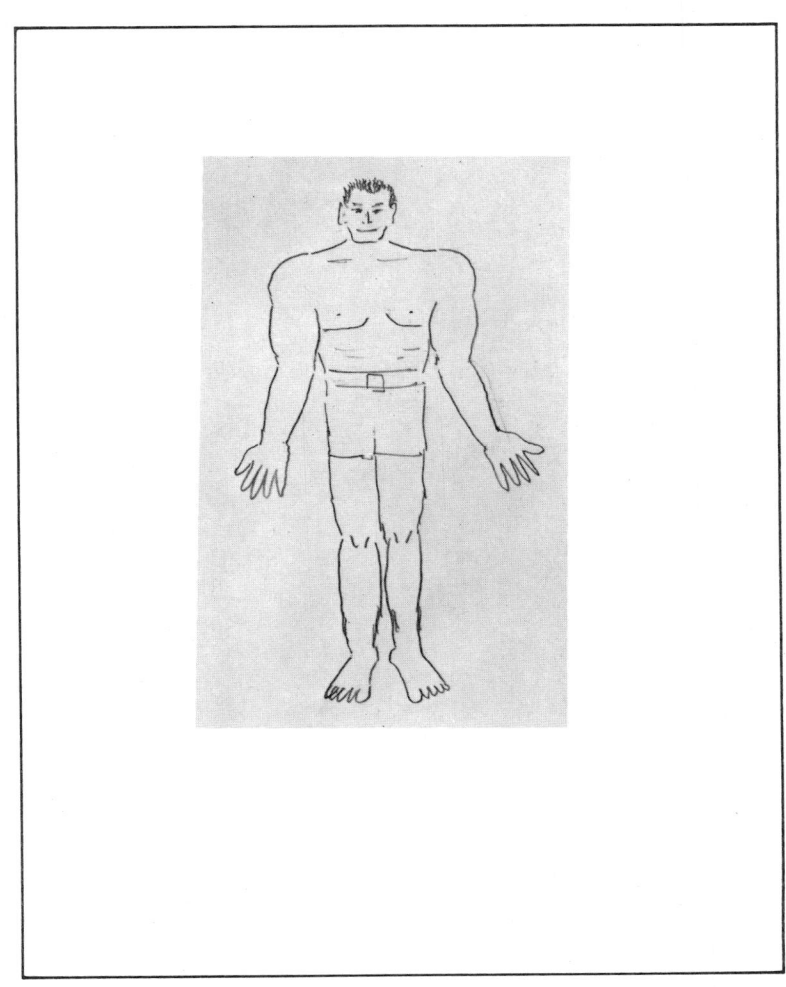

FIGURE-DRAWING CHARACTERISTICS

Structural	Male Female — Both		Structural	Male	Female	Structural and Graphic	Male Female — Both		Graphic, Global and Height	Male	Female	Body Proportions	Male	Female
Type	0		Omission of Appendages	0	0	Upper and Lower Halves	1	1	Hair Shading	3	2	Head	05	04
Sex Sequence	1		Position of Both Arms	0	0	Four Quarters	4	4	Nudity and Transparency	3	0	Neck	02	04
Posture	1	1	Position of Right Arm	3	3	Relative Size	0		Form	3	1	Shoulders	08	05
Perspective	0	0	Position of Left Arm	3	3	Constant Line Pressure	5	0	Detailing	1	3	Right Arm	06	04
Vertical Midline	0	0	Position of Legs	2	4	Variable Line Pressure	0	5	Identity and Sex	1	1	Left Arm	06	04
Bilateral Symmetry	5	5	Relation of Long Axes	1	1	Line Continuity	1	2	Sophistication	2	2	Chest	05	04
Horizontal Midline	4	0	Right and Left Halves	1	1	Body Shading	3	0	Height	05	05	Girth	06	05

GENERAL CHARACTERISTICS OF SUBJECT

IDENTIFICATION
No. A29
Sex M
Marital status M
Age 27 yrs. at
psychological tests

PARENTAL HISTORY				
Father				
C	H	S	D	O
-	-	-	-	-
Mother				
C	H	S	D	O
-	-	-	-	+

PHYSIOLOGICAL AND METABOLIC DATA

	Admission	Initial	Control	Cold pressor change	Exercise change	Smoking change
Systolic pressure	150	146	129	+08	+69	
Diastolic pressure	75	68	60	+07	-10	
Heart rate	80	96	70	+12	+29	

Age 27 yrs.	Height 74 in.	Ponderal index 13.11
	Weight 180 lbs.	Cholesterol 217 mg. per 100 ml.
	Overweight -01 %	Vital capacity liters

HABIT SURVEY

Smoking habits: light cigarette smoker

Age begun 17 yrs.   Inhalation: sometimes

Habits of nervous tension: 2, 4, 5, 6, 9, 11, 14, 16, 17, 25

STRONG VOCATIONAL INTEREST TEST

Occupation	Artist	Psychologist	Architect	Physician	Osteopath	Dentist	Veterinarian	Mathematician	Physicist	Engineer	Chemist	Production Manager
Standard Score	5	8	8	7	5	4	2	5	7	5	6	2

Occupation	Farmer	Aviator	Carpenter	Printer	Math.-Sci. Teacher	Ind. Arts Teacher	Voc. Agric. Teacher	Policeman	Forest Serv. Man	Y.M.C.A. Phys. Dir.	Personnel Director	Public Administrator
Standard Score	5	5	4	7	7	4	4	3	5	4	5	6

Occupation	Y.M.C.A. Secretary	Soc. Sci. H.S. Teacher	City Sch. Sup't.	Social Worker	Minister	Musician Performer	C.P.A.	Senior C.P.A.	Accountant	Office Man	Purchasing Agent	Banker
Standard Score	4	5	4	7	6	8	4	7	2	3	1	1

Occupation	Mortician	Pharmacist	Sales Manager	Real Est. Manager	Life Ins. Salesman	Advertising Man	Lawyer	Author-Journalist	President Mfg. Co.	Interest Maturity	Occupational Level	Masculinity-Femininity
Standard Score	1	2	1	3	2	4	3	4	2	6	4	4

FIGURE-DRAWING CHARACTERISTICS

Structural	Male Female Both	Structural	Male	Female	Structural and Graphic	Male Female Both	Graphic, Global and Height	Male	Female	Body Proportions	Male	Female
Type	0	Omission of Appendages	0	0	Upper and Lower Halves	2 2	Hair Shading	2	5	Head	05	04
Sex Sequence	1	Position of Both Arms	4	4	Four Quarters	0 0	Nudity and Transparency	7	7	Neck	04	02
Posture	2 1	Position of Right Arm	7	7	Relative Size	2	Form	1	1	Shoulders		
Perspective	2 2	Position of Left Arm	4	4	Constant Line Pressure	0 0	Detailing	3	3	Right Arm		
Vertical Midline	4 4	Position of Legs	8	1	Variable Line Pressure	3 3	Identity and Sex	1	1	Left Arm	02	02
Bilateral Symmetry	0 0	Relation of Long Axes	1	1	Line Continuity	0 0	Sophistication	2	2	Chest	03	02
Horizontal Midline	4 4	Right and Left Halves	2	2	Body Shading	0 0	Height	03	03	Girth	03	03

GENERAL CHARACTERISTICS OF SUBJECT

IDENTIFICATION

No. A40
Sex M
Marital status M
Age 23 yrs. at
psychological tests

PARENTAL HISTORY

Father
C H S D O
– – – – –

Mother
C H S D O
– – – – +

PHYSIOLOGICAL AND METABOLIC DATA

	Admission	Initial	Control	Cold pressor change	Exercise change	Smoking change
Systolic pressure	140	136	124	+14	+50	+08
Diastolic pressure	70	58	54	+17	+05	+08
Heart rate	68	79	67	+05	+05	+05

Age 22 yrs.

Height	70	in.	Ponderal index	12.41	
Weight	179	lbs.	Cholesterol	217	mg. per 100 ml.
Overweight +16 %			Vital capacity		liters

HABIT SURVEY

Smoking habits: moderate cigarette smoker
   Age begun 14 yrs.   Inhalation: yes
Habits of nervous tension: 4, 5, 6, 11, 16

STRONG VOCATIONAL INTEREST TEST

Occupation	Artist	Psychologist	Architect	Physician	Osteopath	Dentist	Veterinarian	Mathematician	Physicist	Engineer	Chemist	Production Manager
Standard Score	2	5	1	4	4	2	2	1	0	2	2	3

Occupation	Farmer	Aviator	Carpenter	Printer	Math.-Sci. Teacher	Ind. Arts Teacher	Voc. Agric. Teacher	Policeman	Forest Serv. Man	Y.M.C.A. Phys. Dir.	Personnel Director	Public Administrator
Standard Score	4	4	2	5	5	0	3	3	2	5	7	7

Occupation	Y.M.C.A. Secretary	Soc. Sci. H.S. Teacher	City Sch. Sup't.	Social Worker	Minister	Musician Performer	C.P.A.	Senior C.P.A.	Accountant	Office Man	Purchasing Agent	Banker
Standard Score	5	8	5	7	6	5	6	7	5	6	4	3

Occupation	Mortician	Pharmacist	Sales Manager	Real Est. Manager	Life Ins. Salesman	Advertising Man	Lawyer	Author-Journalist	President Mfg. Co.	Interest Maturity	Occupational Level	Masculinity-Femininity
Standard Score	5	6	5	6	6	4	6	3	3	7	4	4

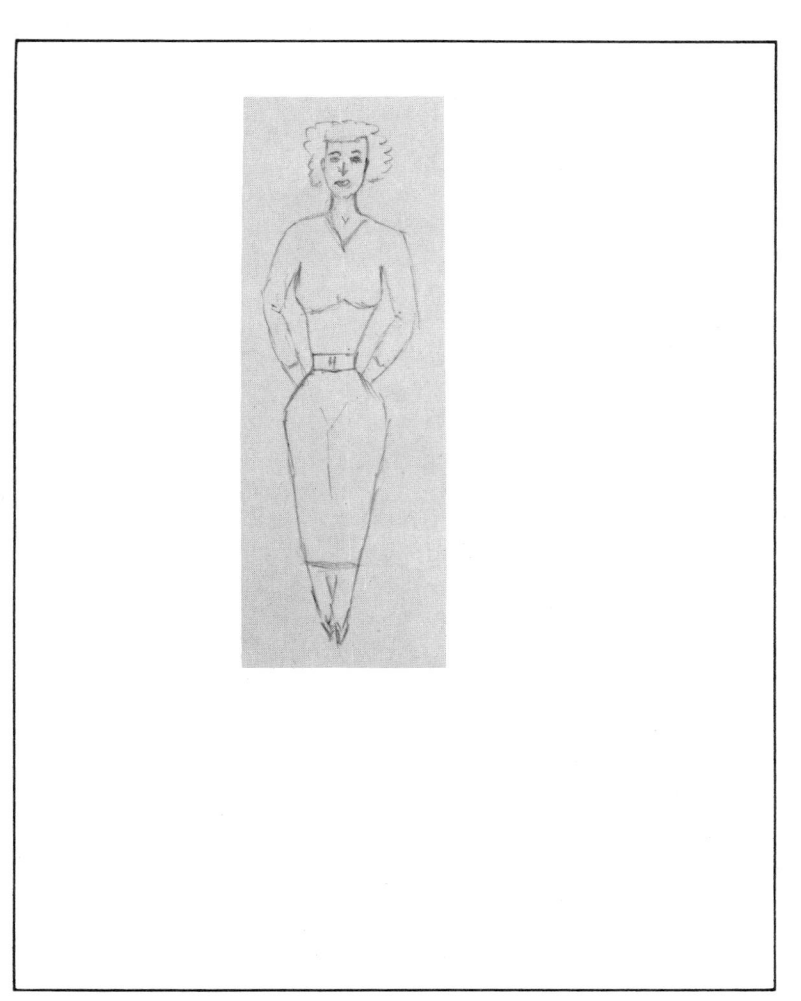

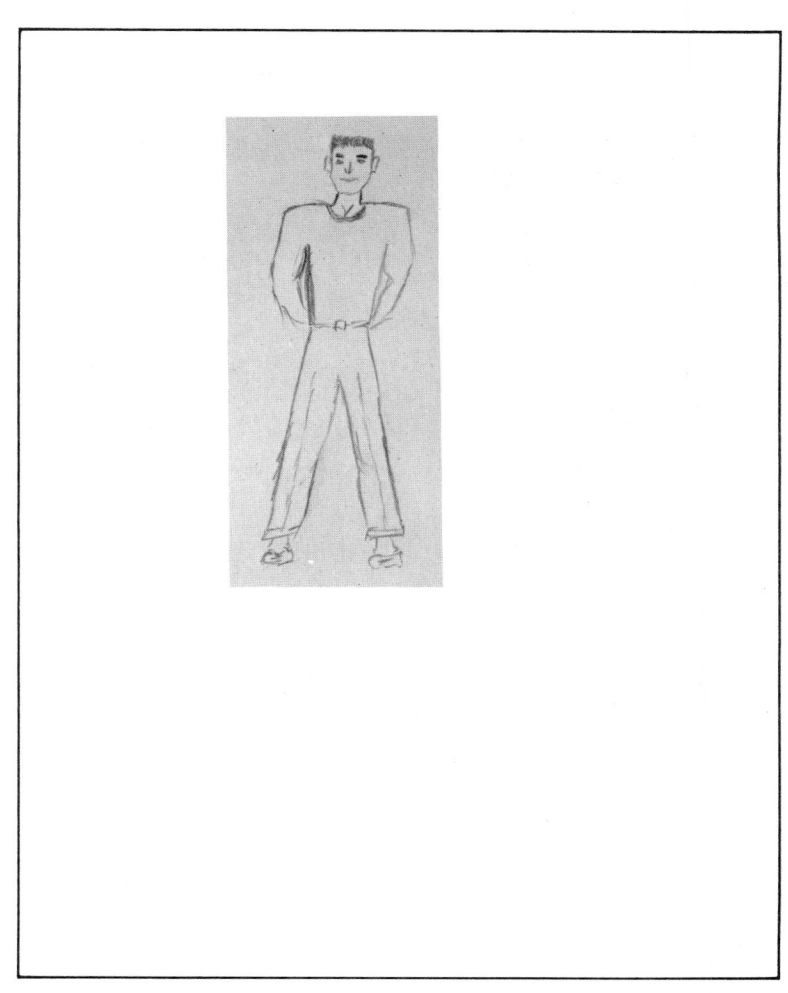

FIGURE-DRAWING CHARACTERISTICS

Structural	Male Female Both	Structural	Male	Female	Structural and Graphic	Male Female Both		Graphic, Global and Height	Male	Female	Body Proportions	Male	Female
Type	0	Omission of Appendages	7	7	Upper and Lower Halves	1	1	Hair Shading	3	5	Head	04	05
Sex Sequence	1	Position of Both Arms	0	0	Four Quarters	4	4	Nudity and Transparency	7	7	Neck	04	06
Posture	1	1	Position of Right Arm	5	5	Relative Size	4		Form	1	1	Shoulders	05	05
Perspective	0	0	Position of Left Arm	5	5	Constant Line Pressure	0	0	Detailing	3	3	Right Arm		
Vertical Midline	0	0	Position of Legs	6	2	Variable Line Pressure	1	1	Identity and Sex	1	1	Left Arm		
Bilateral Symmetry	4	4	Relation of Long Axes	1	1	Line Continuity	0	0	Sophistication	2	2	Chest	03	04
Horizontal Midline	4	4	Right and Left Halves	1	1	Body Shading	7	3	Height	04	05	Girth	03	02

GENERAL CHARACTERISTICS OF SUBJECT

IDENTIFICATION

No. A73

Sex M

Marital status M

Age 23 yrs. at
psychological tests

PARENTAL HISTORY

Father

C   H   S   D   O

–   –   –   –   –

Mother

C   H   S   D   O

–   –   –   –   +

PHYSIOLOGICAL AND METABOLIC DATA

	Admission	Initial	Control	Cold pressor change	Exercise change	Smoking change
Systolic pressure	125	118	104	+20	+38	00
Diastolic pressure	80	62	65	+33	–08	+09
Heart rate	80	68	61	+27	+20	+03

Age 22 yrs.   Height 74 in.   Weight 175 lbs.   Overweight +01 %

Ponderal index 13.24   Cholesterol 237 mg. per 100 ml.   Vital capacity liters

HABIT SURVEY

Smoking habits: former smoker

  Age begun 17 yrs.   Inhalation:

Habits of nervous tension: 5, 6, 9, 10, 14,
16, 18, 21

STRONG VOCATIONAL INTEREST TEST

Occupation	Artist	Psychologist	Architect	Physician	Osteopath	Dentist	Veterinarian	Mathematician	Physicist	Engineer	Chemist	Production Manager
Standard Score	22	39	31	52	50	44	29	34	38	56	51	44

Occupation	Farmer	Aviator	Carpenter	Printer	Math.-Sci. Teacher	Ind. Arts Teacher	Voc. Agric. Teacher	Policeman	Forest Serv. Man	Y.M.C.A. Phys. Dir.	Personnel Director	Public Administrator
Standard Score	37	51	29	33	42	31	23	34	24	19	34	47

Occupation	Y.M.C.A. Secretary	Soc. Sci. H.S. Teacher	City Sch. Sup't.	Social Worker	Minister	Musician Performer	C.P.A.	Senior C.P.A.	Accountant	Office Man	Purchasing Agent	Banker
Standard Score	09	18	19	26	60	25	48	53	46	36	39	25

Occupation	Mortician	Pharmacist	Sales Manager	Real Est. Manager	Life Ins. Salesman	Advertising Man	Lawyer	Author-Journalist	President Mfg. Co.	Interest Maturity	Occupational Level	Masculinity-Femininity
Standard Score	29	41	30	32	25	25	35	29	47	54	64	58

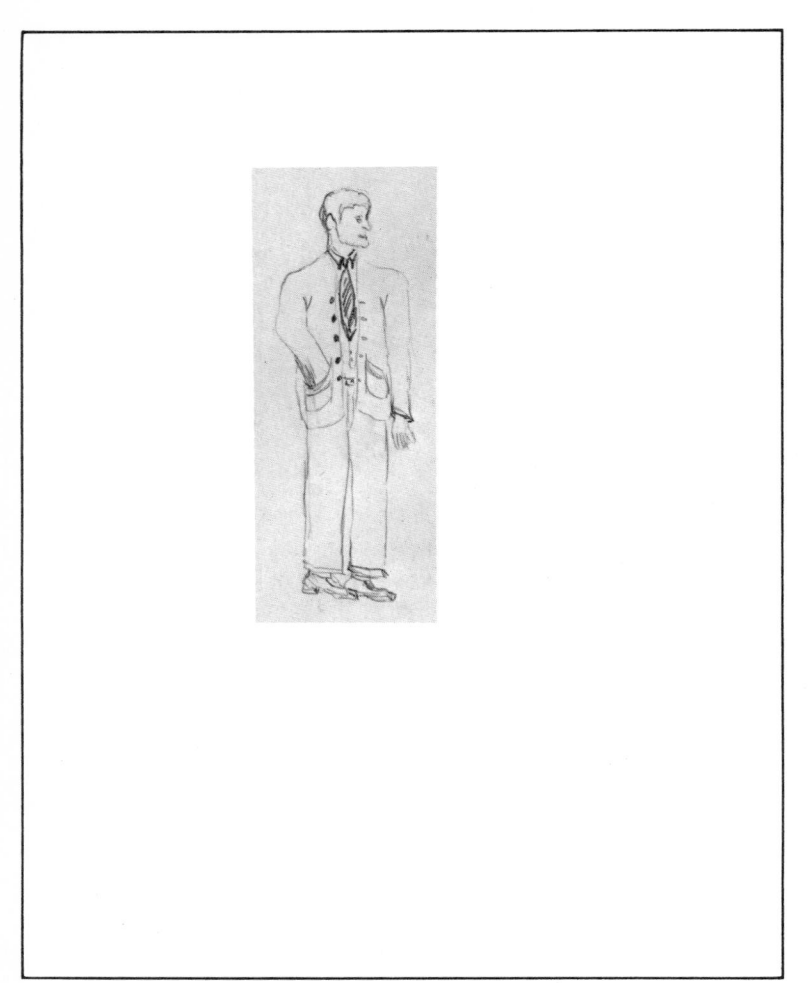

FIGURE-DRAWING CHARACTERISTICS

Structural	Male Female Both	Structural	Male	Female	Structural and Graphic	Male Female Both		Graphic, Global and Height	Male	Female	Body Proportions	Male	Female
Type	0	Omission of Appendages	7	0	Upper and Lower Halves	1	1	Hair Shading	5	3	Head	04	04
Sex Sequence	0	Position of Both Arms	1	1	Four Quarters	4	4	Nudity and Transparency	7	7	Neck	06	04
Posture	1 1	Position of Right Arm	5	0	Relative Size	0		Form	1	1	Shoulders	05	04
Perspective	5 0	Position of Left Arm	0	4	Constant Line Pressure	0	0	Detailing	1	1	Right Arm		02
Vertical Midline	3 3	Position of Legs	4	4	Variable Line Pressure	1	5	Identity and Sex	1	1	Left Arm	04	02
Bilateral Symmetry	3 3	Relation of Long Axes	1	1	Line Continuity	0	0	Sophistication	2	2	Chest	03	03
Horizontal Midline	4 4	Right and Left Halves	1	2	Body Shading	5	7	Height	04	04	Girth	05	04

GENERAL CHARACTERISTICS OF SUBJECT

IDENTIFICATION
No. 433
Sex M
Marital status M
Age 25 yrs. at
psychological tests

PARENTAL HISTORY
Father
C H S D O
- - - - ?
Mother
C H S D O
- - - - ?

PHYSIOLOGICAL AND METABOLIC DATA

	Admission	Initial	Control	Cold pressor change	Exercise change	Smoking change
Systolic pressure	125	124	110	+05	+34	
Diastolic pressure	70	72	74	+06	-08	
Heart rate	72	78	82	+08	+23	

Age 22 yrs.	Height 74 in.	Ponderal index 13.41
	Weight 168 lbs.	Cholesterol 265 mg. per 100 ml.
	Overweight -03 %	Vital capacity 5.2 liters

HABIT SURVEY
Smoking habits: nonsmoker
Age begun   yrs.   Inhalation:
Habits of nervous tension: 4, 5, 19, 22

FIGURE-DRAWING CHARACTERISTICS

Structural	Male	Female	Structural	Male	Female	Structural and Graphic	Male	Female	Graphic, Global and Height	Male	Female	Body Proportions	Male	Female
	Both						Both							
Type	0		Omission of Appendages	0	7	Upper and Lower Halves	1	1	Hair Shading	3	3	Head	05	04
Sex Sequence	0		Position of Both Arms	0	0	Four Quarters	4	4	Nudity and Transparency	7	7	Neck	03	02
Posture	1	1	Position of Right Arm	5	5	Relative Size	0		Form	3	3	Shoulders	07	03
Perspective	0	0	Position of Left Arm	5	5	Constant Line Pressure	1	0	Detailing	3	3	Right Arm	04	02
Vertical Midline	3	0	Position of Legs	4	4	Variable Line Pressure	0	2	Identity and Sex	1	1	Left Arm	04	02
Bilateral Symmetry	3	3	Relation of Long Axes	1	1	Line Continuity	1	1	Sophistication	2	2	Chest	06	03
Horizontal Midline	4	4	Right and Left Halves	1	1	Body Shading	4	1	Height	05	03	Girth	06	03

GENERAL CHARACTERISTICS OF SUBJECT

IDENTIFICATION

No. B09
Sex M
Marital status S
Age 21 yrs. at
psychological tests

PARENTAL HISTORY

Father
C H S D O
- - - - ?
Mother
C H S D O
- - - - ?

PHYSIOLOGICAL AND METABOLIC DATA

	Admission	Initial	Control	Cold pressor change	Exercise change	Smoking change
Systolic pressure	130	117	110	+28	+16	+10
Diastolic pressure	80	56	64	+24	-16	00
Heart rate	80	65	57	+10	+18	+06

Age 21 yrs.
Height 70 in.
Weight 145 lbs.
Overweight -05 %

Ponderal index 13.33
Cholesterol 175 mg. per 100 ml.
Vital capacity 5.2 liters

HABIT SURVEY

Smoking habits: nonsmoker
Age begun yrs. Inhalation:
Habits of nervous tension: 25

STRONG VOCATIONAL INTEREST TEST

Occupation	Artist	Psychologist	Architect	Physician	Osteopath	Dentist	Veterinarian	Mathematician	Physicist	Engineer	Chemist	Production Manager
Standard Score	37	45	35	55	36	35	26	47	38	36	46	23

Occupation	Farmer	Aviator	Carpenter	Printer	Math.-Sci. Teacher	Ind. Arts Teacher	Voc. Agric. Teacher	Policeman	Forest Serv. Man	Y.M.C.A. Phys. Dir.	Personnel Director	Public Administrator
Standard Score	27	25	08	24	35	02	23	19	20	28	29	39

Occupation	Y.M.C.A. Secretary	Soc. Sci. H.S. Teacher	City Sch. Sup't.	Social Worker	Minister	Musician Performer	C.P.A.	Senior C.P.A.	Accountant	Office Man	Purchasing Agent	Banker
Standard Score	17	25	32	31	61	43	39	33	22	21	18	21

Occupation	Mortician	Pharmacist	Sales Manager	Real Est. Manager	Life Ins. Salesman	Advertising Man	Lawyer	Author-Journalist	President Mfg. Co.	Interest Maturity	Occupational Level	Masculinity-Femininity
Standard Score	20	32	33	29	29	42	45	44	33	48	62	40

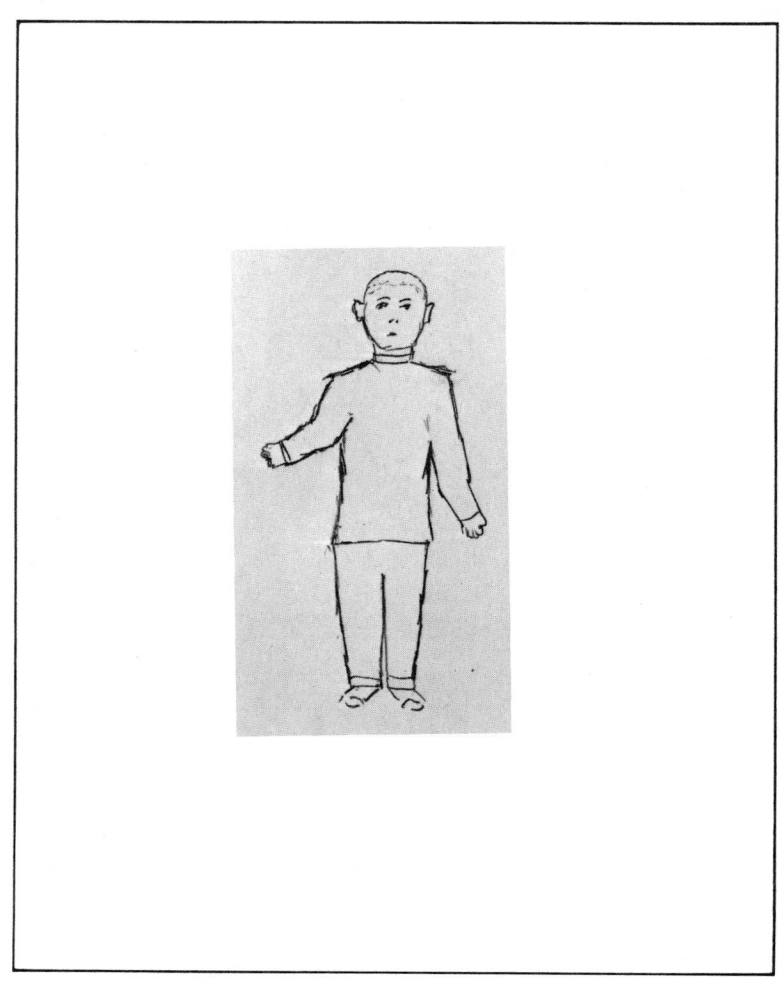

FIGURE-DRAWING CHARACTERISTICS

Structural	Male Female Both		Structural	Male	Female	Structural and Graphic	Male Female Both		Graphic, Global and Height	Male	Female	Body Proportions	Male	Female
Type	0		Omission of Appendages	0	0	Upper and Lower Halves	1	0	Hair Shading	5	2	Head	06	09
Sex Sequence	1		Position of Both Arms	1	1	Four Quarters	4	4	Nudity and Transparency	7	7	Neck	04	06
Posture	1	1	Position of Right Arm	3	2	Relative Size	4		Form	3	1	Shoulders	05	05
Perspective	0	0	Position of Left Arm	4	5	Constant Line Pressure	5	0	Detailing	3	3	Right Arm	02	04
Vertical Midline	0	0	Position of Legs	3	4	Variable Line Pressure	0	5	Identity and Sex	1	1	Left Arm	04	04
Bilateral Symmetry	3	3	Relation of Long Axes	1	1	Line Continuity	0	0	Sophistication	2	2	Chest	04	05
Horizontal Midline	6	0	Right and Left Halves	0	1	Body Shading	0	2	Height	04	05	Girth	05	05

GENERAL CHARACTERISTICS OF SUBJECT

IDENTIFICATION
No. B10
Sex M
Marital status S
Age 21 yrs. at psychological tests

PARENTAL HISTORY
Father
C   H   S   D   O
-   -   -   -   ?
Mother
C   H   S   D   O
-   -   -   -   ?

PHYSIOLOGICAL AND METABOLIC DATA

	Admission	Initial	Control	Cold pressor change	Exercise change	Smoking change
Systolic pressure	110	128	122	+22	+26	+04
Diastolic pressure	60	64	64	+34	−26	+16
Heart rate	64	68	51	+18	+13	−02

Age 21 yrs.	Height	69	in.	Ponderal index	12.68	
	Weight	161	lbs.	Cholesterol	212	mg. per 100 ml.
	Overweight	+08	%	Vital capacity	5.1	liters

HABIT SURVEY

Smoking habits: nonsmoker

Age begun   yrs.   Inhalation:

Habits of nervous tension: 4, 5

STRONG VOCATIONAL INTEREST TEST

Occupation	Artist	Psychologist	Architect	Physician	Osteopath	Dentist	Veterinarian	Mathematician	Physicist	Engineer	Chemist	Production Manager
Standard Score	47	40	47	36	21	32	00	51	41	34	42	19

Occupation	Farmer	Aviator	Carpenter	Printer	Math.-Sci. Teacher	Ind. Arts Teacher	Voc. Agric. Teacher	Policeman	Forest Serv. Man	Y.M.C.A. Phys. Dir.	Personnel Director	Public Administrator
Standard Score	28	20	20	34	27	05	12	13	03	13	12	21

Occupation	Y.M.C.A. Secretary	Soc. Sci. H.S. Teacher	City Sch. Sup't.	Social Worker	Minister	Musician Performer	C.P.A.	Senior C.P.A.	Accountant	Office Man	Purchasing Agent	Banker
Standard Score	19	21	22	24	61	50	40	24	23	18	17	23

Occupation	Mortician	Pharmacist	Sales Manager	Real Est. Manager	Life Ins. Salesman	Advertising Man	Lawyer	Author-Journalist	President Mfg. Co.	Interest Maturity	Occupational Level	Masculinity-Femininity
Standard Score	07	21	24	32	21	42	40	50	33	45	59	35

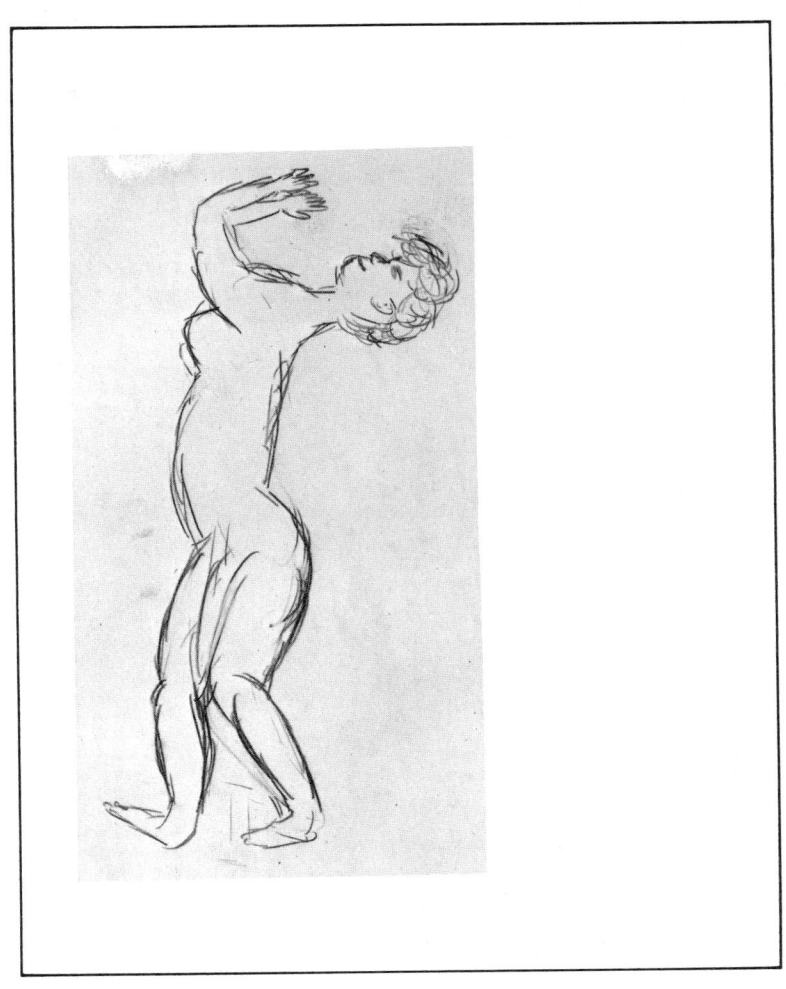

FIGURE-DRAWING CHARACTERISTICS

Structural	Male Female Both	Structural	Male	Female	Structural and Graphic	Male Female Both	Graphic, Global and Height	Male	Female	Body Proportions	Male	Female
Type	0	Omission of Appendages	0	0	Upper and Lower Halves	1 0	Hair Shading	3	3	Head	05	07
Sex Sequence	0	Position of Both Arms	1	4	Four Quarters	4 4	Nudity and Transparency	6	0	Neck	06	08
Posture	6 6	Position of Right Arm	2	7	Relative Size	4	Form	1	1	Shoulders	07	
Perspective	0 2	Position of Left Arm	0	2	Constant Line Pressure	0 0	Detailing	3	3	Right Arm	06	
Vertical Midline	3 4	Position of Legs	8	8	Variable Line Pressure	5 5	Identity and Sex	1	1	Left Arm	06	04
Bilateral Symmetry	3 0	Relation of Long Axes	1	0	Line Continuity	2 0	Sophistication	2	2	Chest	06	06
Horizontal Midline	4 0	Right and Left Halves	1	1	Body Shading	0 0	Height	06		Girth	05	09

GENERAL CHARACTERISTICS OF SUBJECT

IDENTIFICATION

No. B55
Sex M
Marital status S
Age 22 yrs. at
psychological tests

PARENTAL HISTORY

Father
C H S D O
- - - - ?

Mother
C H S D O
- - - - ?

PHYSIOLOGICAL AND METABOLIC DATA

	Admission	Initial	Control	Cold pressor change	Exercise change	Smoking change
Systolic pressure	120	128	116	+10	+28	+12
Diastolic pressure	80	68	70	+14	-12	+04
Heart rate	88	64	53	+02	+20	+16

Age 22 yrs.
Height 71 in.   Ponderal index 12.97
Weight 164 lbs.   Cholesterol 142 mg. per 100 ml.
Overweight +04 %   Vital capacity 5.1 liters

HABIT SURVEY

Smoking habits: former smoker
Age begun   yrs.   Inhalation:
Habits of nervous tension: 1, 2, 5, 6, 8, 11,
20, 25

STRONG VOCATIONAL INTEREST TEST

Occupation	Artist	Psychologist	Architect	Physician	Osteopath	Dentist	Veterinarian	Mathematician	Physicist	Engineer	Chemist	Production Manager
Standard Score	24	50	27	52	52	29	25	20	20	25	31	28

Occupation	Farmer	Aviator	Carpenter	Printer	Math.-Sci. Teacher	Ind. Arts Teacher	Voc. Agric. Teacher	Policeman	Forest Serv. Man	Y.M.C.A. Phys. Dir.	Personnel Director	Public Administrator
Standard Score	36	36	16	36	46	23	34	35	34	55	52	54

Occupation	Y.M.C.A. Secretary	Soc. Sci. H.S. Teacher	City Sch. Sup't.	Social Worker	Minister	Musician Performer	C.P.A.	Senior C.P.A.	Accountant	Office Man	Purchasing Agent	Banker
Standard Score	52	50	48	58	61	43	26	36	24	28	11	14

Occupation	Mortician	Pharmacist	Sales Manager	Real Est. Manager	Life Ins. Salesman	Advertising Man	Lawyer	Author-Journalist	President Mfg. Co.	Interest Maturity	Occupational Level	Masculinity-Femininity
Standard Score	25	31	25	27	33	31	34	31	19	64	57	48

FIGURE-DRAWING CHARACTERISTICS

Structural	Male Female Both	Structural	Male	Female	Structural and Graphic	Male Female Both		Graphic, Global and Height	Male	Female	Body Proportions	Male	Female
Type	0	Omission of Appendages	7	7	Upper and Lower Halves	1	1	Hair Shading	2	3	Head	04	04
Sex Sequence	0	Position of Both Arms	1	0	Four Quarters	4	4	Nudity and Transparency	7	7	Neck	02	02
Posture	1 1	Position of Right Arm	3	5	Relative Size	0		Form	3	3	Shoulders	04	04
Perspective	0 0	Position of Left Arm	5	5	Constant Line Pressure	1	1	Detailing	3	3	Right Arm	02	02
Vertical Midline	3 1	Position of Legs	4	4	Variable Line Pressure	0	0	Identity and Sex	1	1	Left Arm	02	02
Bilateral Symmetry	3 3	Relation of Long Axes	1	1	Line Continuity	0	0	Sophistication	2	2	Chest	04	04
Horizontal Midline	6 4	Right and Left Halves	1	1	Body Shading	3	5	Height	04	03	Girth	05	05

GENERAL CHARACTERISTICS OF SUBJECT

IDENTIFICATION
No. C06
Sex M
Marital status S
Age 23 yrs. at
psychological tests

PARENTAL HISTORY				
Father				
C	H	S	D	0
–	–	–	–	?
Mother				
C	H	S	D	0
–	–	–	–	?

PHYSIOLOGICAL AND METABOLIC DATA

	Admission	Initial	Control	Cold pressor change	Exercise change	Smoking change
Systolic pressure	102	100	100	00	+10	00
Diastolic pressure	72	70	70	+10	00	+01
Heart rate	72	70	75	–04	+13	+03

Age 24 yrs.   Height 67 in.   Weight 124 lbs.   Overweight –14 %   Ponderal index 13.43   Cholesterol 148 mg. per 100 ml.   Vital capacity 3.8 liters

HABIT SURVEY
Smoking habits: occasional smoker
Age begun 19 yrs.   Inhalation: no
Habits of nervous tension: 1, 3, 6, 9

STRONG VOCATIONAL INTEREST TEST

Occupation	Artist	Psychologist	Architect	Physician	Osteopath	Dentist	Veterinarian	Mathematician	Physicist	Engineer	Chemist	Production Manager
Standard Score	14	24	14	31	43	26	29	09	09	30	21	36

Occupation	Farmer	Aviator	Carpenter	Printer	Math.-Sci. Teacher	Ind. Arts Teacher	Voc. Agric. Teacher	Policeman	Forest Serv. Man	Y.M.C.A. Phys. Dir.	Personnel Director	Public Administrator
Standard Score	43	36	29	33	39	28	42	39	42	38	50	49

Occupation	Y.M.C.A. Secretary	Soc. Sci. H.S. Teacher	City Sch. Sup't.	Social Worker	Minister	Musician Performer	C.P.A.	Senior C.P.A.	Accountant	Office Man	Purchasing Agent	Banker
Standard Score	46	39	34	37	62	22	09	32	23	31	24	27

Occupation	Mortician	Pharmacist	Sales Manager	Real Est. Manager	Life Ins. Salesman	Advertising Man	Lawyer	Author-Journalist	President Mfg. Co.	Interest Maturity	Occupational Level	Masculinity-Femininity
Standard Score	25	21	32	36	35	23	29	24	25	63	55	53

Plate 698　　　　MODERATELY SOPHISTICATED DRAWINGS　　　　745

FIGURE-DRAWING CHARACTERISTICS

Structural	Male	Female	Structural	Male	Female	Structural and Graphic	Male	Female	Graphic, Global and Height	Male	Female	Body Proportions	Male	Female
	Both						Both							
Type	0		Omission of Appendages	0	0	Upper and Lower Halves	1	1	Hair Shading	3	3	Head	04	05
Sex Sequence	1		Position of Both Arms	0	0	Four Quarters	4	4	Nudity and Transparency	7	7	Neck	06	06
Posture	1	1	Position of Right Arm	0	0	Relative Size	1		Form	1	1	Shoulders	04	03
Perspective	0	0	Position of Left Arm	0	0	Constant Line Pressure	0	3	Detailing	1	1	Right Arm	04	02
Vertical Midline	3	3	Position of Legs	4	4	Variable Line Pressure	5	0	Identity and Sex	1	1	Left Arm	04	02
Bilateral Symmetry	5	5	Relation of Long Axes	1	1	Line Continuity	1	4	Sophistication	2	2	Chest	03	03
Horizontal Midline	4	6	Right and Left Halves	2	2	Body Shading	4	5	Height	04	04	Girth	03	02

GENERAL CHARACTERISTICS OF SUBJECT

IDENTIFICATION

No. D46

Sex F

Marital status S

Age 22 yrs. at

psychological tests

PARENTAL HISTORY

Father

C　H　S　D　O

−　−　−　−　?

Mother

C　H　S　D　O

−　−　−　−　?

PHYSIOLOGICAL AND METABOLIC DATA

	Admission	Initial	Control	Cold pressor change	Exercise change	Smoking change
Systolic pressure	118	110	98	+14	+30	+06
Diastolic pressure	76	60	64	+12	−14	+08
Heart rate	76	84	79	+12	+31	+06

Age 22 yrs.　Height 62 in.　Ponderal index 12.86

Weight 112 lbs.　Cholesterol 232 mg. per 100 ml.

Overweight −07 %　Vital capacity 3.0 liters

HABIT SURVEY

Smoking habits: light cigarette smoker

Age begun 16 yrs.　Inhalation: yes

Habits of nervous tension: 4, 6, 11, 14, 23

STRONG VOCATIONAL INTEREST TEST

Occupation	Artist	Psychologist	Architect	Physician	Osteopath	Dentist	Veterinarian	Mathematician	Physicist	Engineer	Chemist	Production Manager
Standard Score	48	66	51	61	32	30	07	46	37	31	45	22

Occupation	Farmer	Aviator	Carpenter	Printer	Math.-Sci. Teacher	Ind. Arts Teacher	Voc. Agric. Teacher	Policeman	Forest Serv. Man	Y.M.C.A. Phys. Dir.	Personnel Director	Public Administrator
Standard Score	14	17	02	28	30	−09	05	11	05	22	39	45

Occupation	Y.M.C.A. Secretary	Soc. Sci. H.S. Teacher	City Sch. Sup't.	Social Worker	Minister	Musician Performer	C.P.A.	Senior C.P.A.	Accountant	Office Man	Purchasing Agent	Banker
Standard Score	22	28	42	48	63	65	52	33	12	23	10	14

Occupation	Mortician	Pharmacist	Sales Manager	Real Est. Manager	Life Ins. Salesman	Advertising Man	Lawyer	Author-Journalist	President Mfg. Co.	Interest Maturity	Occupational Level	Masculinity-Femininity
Standard Score	14	26	24	31	30	51	54	53	34	54	66	24

FIGURE-DRAWING CHARACTERISTICS

Structural	Male	Female	Structural	Male	Female	Structural and Graphic	Male	Female	Graphic, Global and Height	Male	Female	Body Proportions	Male	Female
	Both						Both							
Type	0		Omission of Appendages	0	7	Upper and Lower Halves	1	1	Hair Shading	3	3	Head	05	06
Sex Sequence	0		Position of Both Arms	1	0	Four Quarters	4	4	Nudity and Transparency	5	7	Neck	03	05
Posture	1	1	Position of Right Arm	3	5	Relative Size	3		Form	1	1	Shoulders		04
Perspective	6	6	Position of Left Arm	5	5	Constant Line Pressure	5	3	Detailing	1	1	Right Arm	02	02
Vertical Midline	4	3	Position of Legs	6	4	Variable Line Pressure	0	0	Identity and Sex	1	1	Left Arm	02	
Bilateral Symmetry	0	0	Relation of Long Axes	1	1	Line Continuity	2	1	Sophistication	2	2	Chest		04
Horizontal Midline	4	4	Right and Left Halves	2	2	Body Shading	3	5	Height	04	04	Girth		04

GENERAL CHARACTERISTICS OF SUBJECT

IDENTIFICATION

No. D60

Sex M

Marital status M

Age 23 yrs. at

psychological tests

PARENTAL HISTORY

Father

C　H　S　D　O

–　–　–　–　?

Mother

C　H　S　D　O

–　–　–　–　?

PHYSIOLOGICAL AND METABOLIC DATA

	Admission	Initial	Control	Cold pressor change	Exercise change	Smoking change
Systolic pressure	110	128	116	+21	+59	00
Diastolic pressure	70	62	64	+36	–15	+06
Heart rate	64	72	64	+08	+11	00

Age 23 yrs.	Height	68	in.	Ponderal index	12.45	
	Weight	163	lbs.	Cholesterol	190	mg. per 100 ml.
	Overweight +11 %			Vital capacity	4.8	liters

HABIT SURVEY

Smoking habits: nonsmoker

Age begun　　yrs.　　Inhalation:

Habits of nervous tension: 4, 5, 6, 9, 19

STRONG VOCATIONAL INTEREST TEST

Occupation	Artist	Psychologist	Architect	Physician	Osteopath	Dentist	Veterinarian	Mathematician	Physicist	Engineer	Chemist	Production Manager
Standard Score	33	46	39	59	45	44	22	28	27	37	43	28

Occupation	Farmer	Aviator	Carpenter	Printer	Math.-Sci. Teacher	Ind. Arts Teacher	Voc. Agric. Teacher	Policeman	Forest Serv. Man	Y.M.C.A. Phys. Dir.	Personnel Director	Public Administrator
Standard Score	36	41	17	33	42	22	25	29	34	40	44	48

Occupation	Y.M.C.A. Secretary	Soc. Sci. H.S. Teacher	City Sch. Sup't.	Social Worker	Minister	Musician Performer	C.P.A.	Senior C.P.A.	Accountant	Office Man	Purchasing Agent	Banker
Standard Score	32	34	37	42	63	47	35	41	29	31	14	09

Occupation	Mortician	Pharmacist	Sales Manager	Real Est. Manager	Life Ins. Salesman	Advertising Man	Lawyer	Author-Journalist	President Mfg. Co.	Interest Maturity	Occupational Level	Masculinity-Femininity
Standard Score	14	22	19	30	28	34	41	36	25	58	59	45

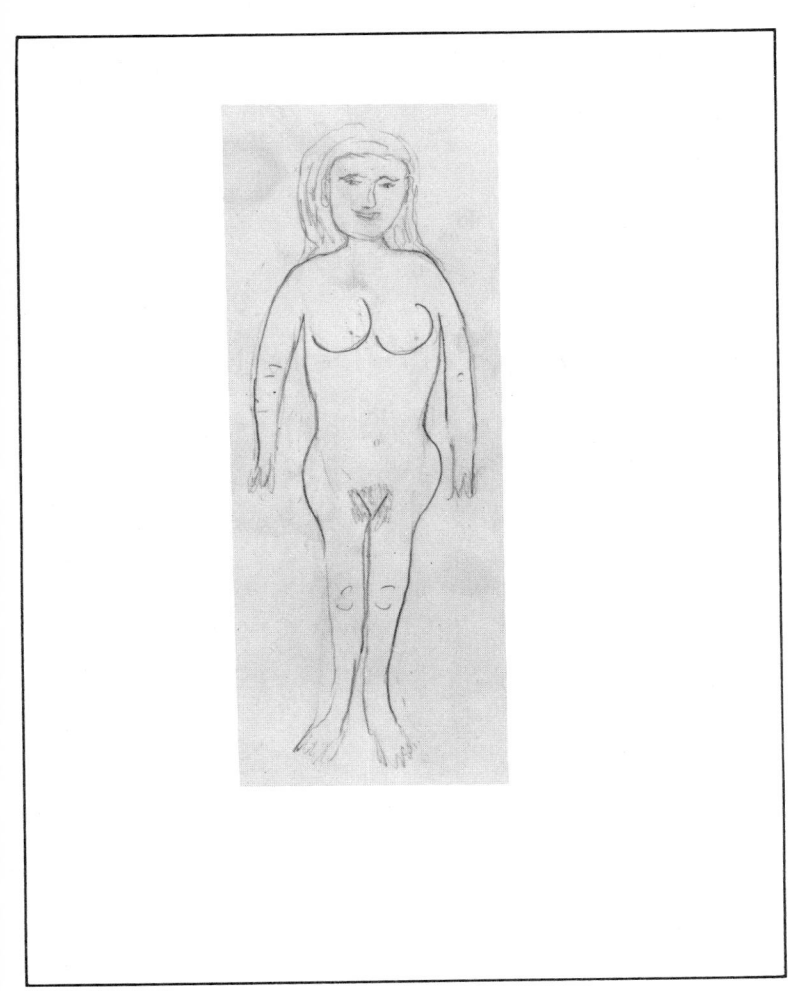

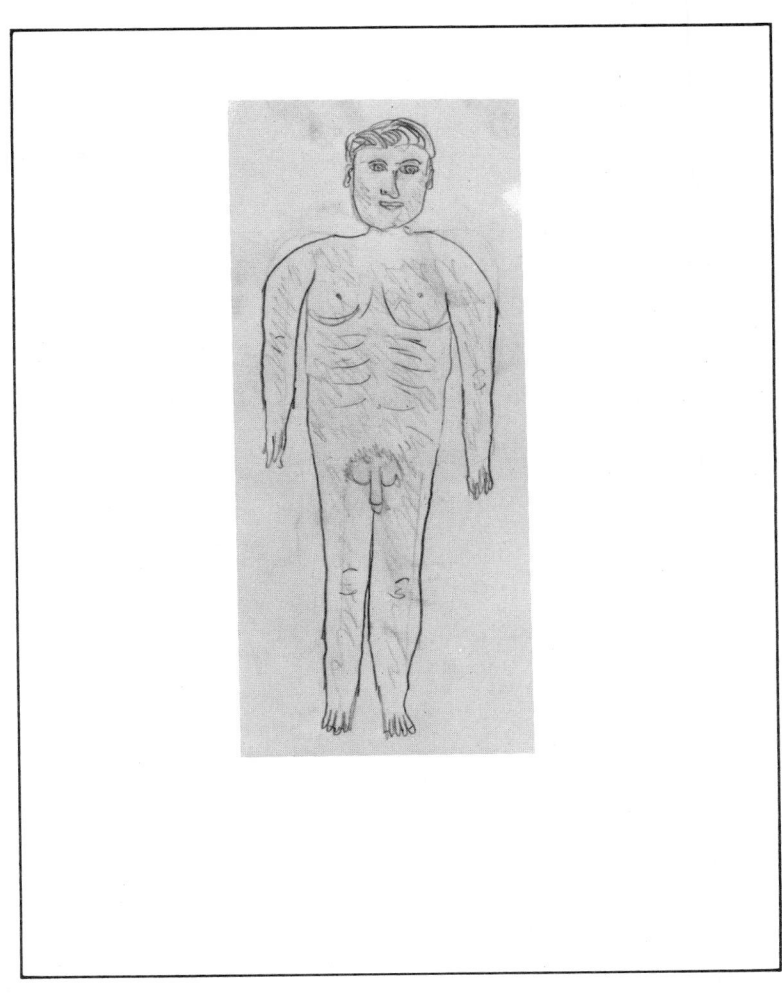

FIGURE-DRAWING CHARACTERISTICS

Structural	Male Female Both	Structural	Male	Female	Structural and Graphic	Male Female Both	Graphic, Global and Height	Male	Female	Body Proportions	Male	Female
Type	0	Omission of Appendages	0	0	Upper and Lower Halves	1 1	Hair Shading	3	3	Head	09	08
Sex Sequence	1	Position of Both Arms	0	0	Four Quarters	4 4	Nudity and Transparency	0	0	Neck	02	03
Posture	1 1	Position of Right Arm	0	0	Relative Size	3	Form	3	3	Shoulders	08	06
Perspective	0 0	Position of Left Arm	0	0	Constant Line Pressure	0 0	Detailing	1	1	Right Arm	04	04
Vertical Midline	0 0	Position of Legs	2	2	Variable Line Pressure	4 3	Identity and Sex	1	1	Left Arm	06	06
Bilateral Symmetry	3 3	Relation of Long Axes	1	1	Line Continuity	2 2	Sophistication	2	2	Chest	07	07
Horizontal Midline	0 0	Right and Left Halves	1	1	Body Shading	3 3	Height	06	06	Girth	08	07

GENERAL CHARACTERISTICS OF SUBJECT

IDENTIFICATION

No. D76
Sex M
Marital status S
Age 22 yrs. at
psychological tests

PARENTAL HISTORY

Father
C H S D O
- - - - ?

Mother
C H S D O
- - - - ?

PHYSIOLOGICAL AND METABOLIC DATA

	Admission	Initial	Control	Cold pressor change	Exercise change	Smoking change
Systolic pressure	130	120	108	+22	+32	+04
Diastolic pressure	80	70	62	+18	-04	00
Heart rate	90	72	71	+04	+23	+01

Age 22 yrs.	Height	70	in.	Ponderal index	13.21	
	Weight	149	lbs.	Cholesterol	205	mg. per 100 ml.
	Overweight	-03 %		Vital capacity	4.7	liters

HABIT SURVEY

Smoking habits: former smoker
  Age begun 17 yrs.   Inhalation:
Habits of nervous tension: 5, 6, 9, 11, 20, 21, 22

STRONG VOCATIONAL INTEREST TEST

Occupation	Artist	Psychologist	Architect	Physician	Osteopath	Dentist	Veterinarian	Mathematician	Physicist	Engineer	Chemist	Production Manager
Standard Score	46	56	44	64	56	46	32	36	36	35	47	27

Occupation	Farmer	Aviator	Carpenter	Printer	Math.-Sci. Teacher	Ind. Arts Teacher	Voc. Agric. Teacher	Policeman	Forest Serv. Man	Y.M.C.A. Phys. Dir.	Personnel Director	Public Administrator
Standard Score	27	29	22	32	38	20	32	31	39	42	40	48

Occupation	Y.M.C.A. Secretary	Soc. Sci. H.S. Teacher	City Sch. Sup't.	Social Worker	Minister	Musician Performer	C.P.A.	Senior C.P.A.	Accountant	Office Man	Purchasing Agent	Banker
Standard Score	30	38	43	53	63	58	31	25	16	18	08	16

Occupation	Mortician	Pharmacist	Sales Manager	Real Est. Manager	Life Ins. Salesman	Advertising Man	Lawyer	Author-Journalist	President Mfg. Co.	Interest Maturity	Occupational Level	Masculinity-Femininity
Standard Score	18	30	20	28	29	38	46	46	34	57	57	33

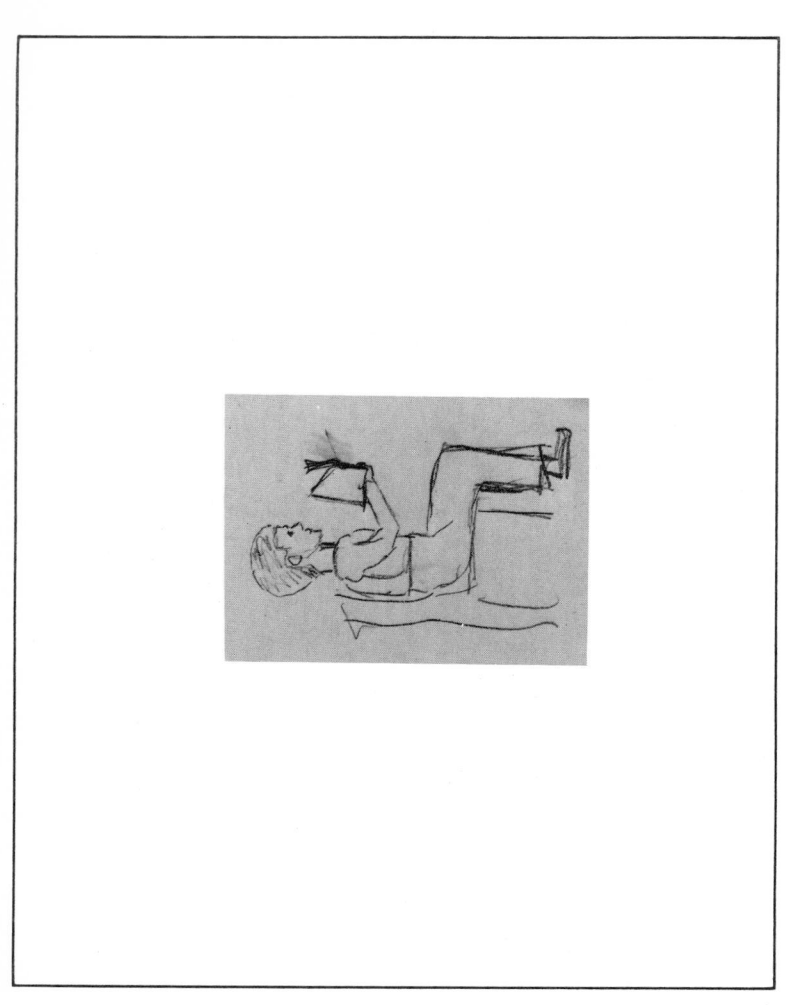

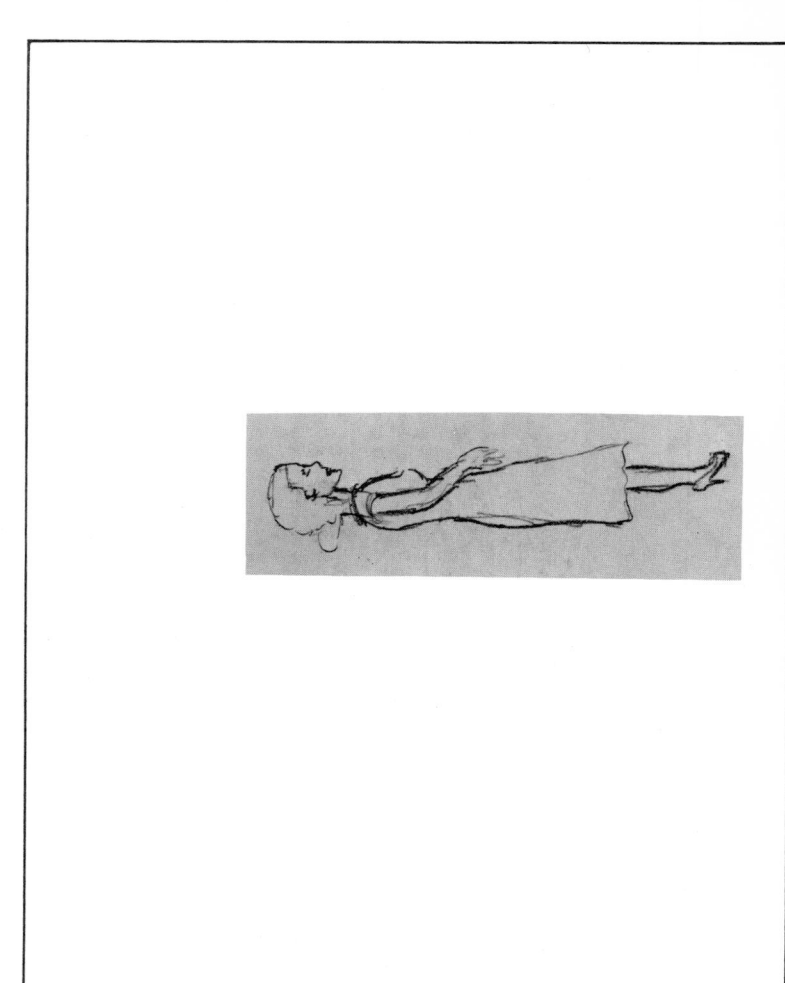

FIGURE-DRAWING CHARACTERISTICS

Structural	Male Female Both	Structural	Male	Female	Structural and Graphic	Male Female Both		Graphic, Global and Height	Male	Female	Body Proportions	Male	Female
Type	0	Omission of Appendages	0	0	Upper and Lower Halves	0	3	Hair Shading	1	5	Head	05	06
Sex Sequence	0	Position of Both Arms	2	2	Four Quarters	4	4	Nudity and Transparency	7	7	Neck	04	06
Posture	3	1	Position of Right Arm	4	5	Relative Size	5		Form	1	1	Shoulders		
Perspective	2	2	Position of Left Arm	7	7	Constant Line Pressure	0	0	Detailing	1	1	Right Arm	02	02
Vertical Midline	4	4	Position of Legs	1	1	Variable Line Pressure	5	3	Identity and Sex	1	1	Left Arm		
Bilateral Symmetry	0	0	Relation of Long Axes	0	2	Line Continuity	0	0	Sophistication	2	2	Chest	05	03
Horizontal Midline	4	0	Right and Left Halves	1	3	Body Shading	7	0	Height		04	Girth	04	04

GENERAL CHARACTERISTICS OF SUBJECT

IDENTIFICATION

No. 231

Sex M

Marital status M

Age 27 yrs. at

psychological tests

PARENTAL HISTORY

Father

C   H   S   D   O

–   –   –   –   ?

Mother

C   H   S   D   O

–   –   –   –   –

PHYSIOLOGICAL AND METABOLIC DATA

	Admission	Initial	Control	Cold pressor change	Exercise change	Smoking change
Systolic pressure	124	120	100	+20	+40	
Diastolic pressure	80	70	70	+30	+10	
Heart rate	80	96	80	-12	+34	

Age 28 yrs.

Height   70 in.

Weight   178 lbs.

Overweight +12 %

Ponderal index 12.44

Cholesterol   230   mg. per 100 ml.

Vital capacity   4.2   liters

HABIT SURVEY

Smoking habits: unknown

Age begun   yrs.   Inhalation:

Habits of nervous tension:

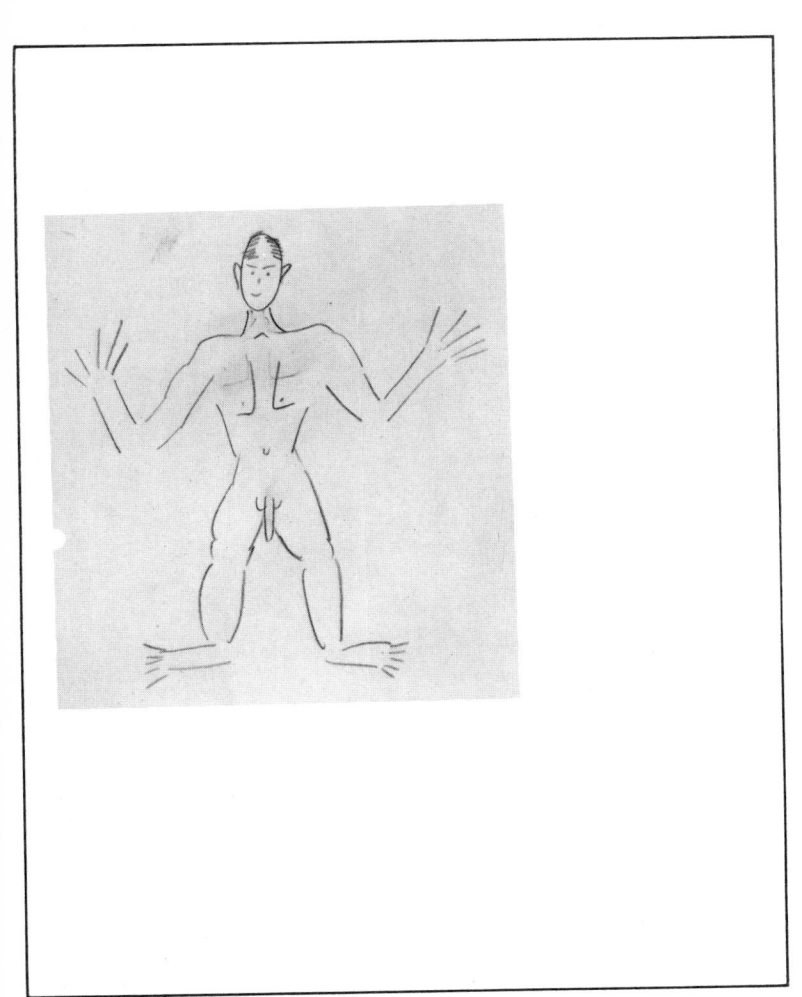

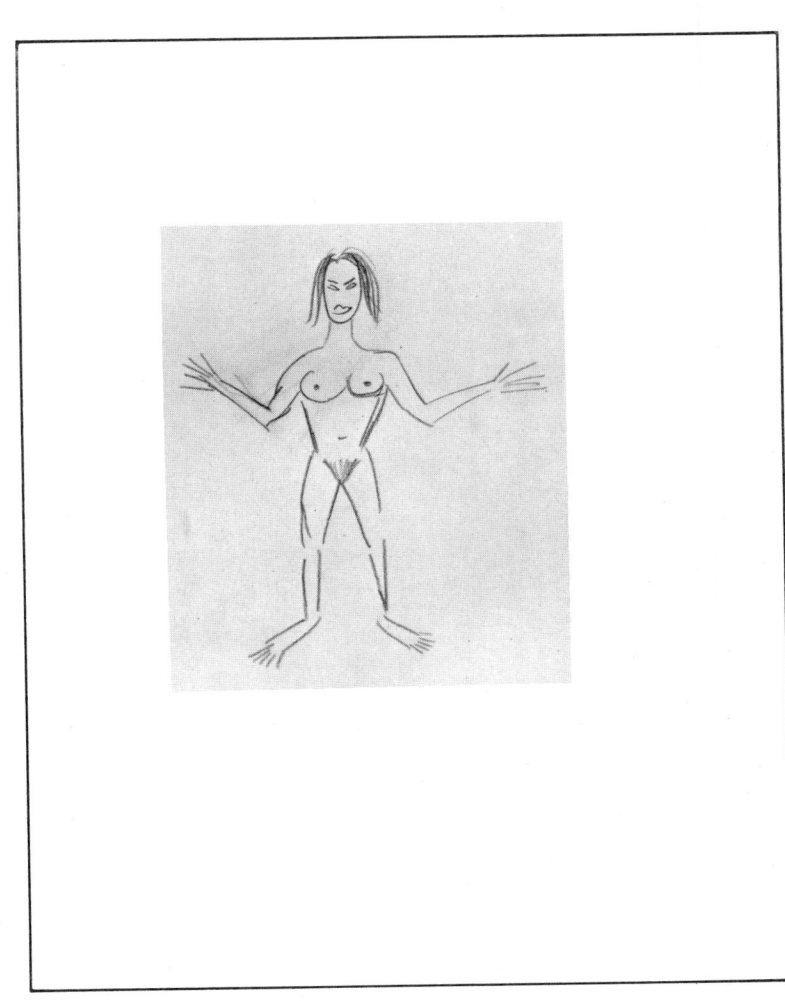

FIGURE-DRAWING CHARACTERISTICS

Structural	Male Female Both		Structural	Male	Female	Structural and Graphic	Male Female Both		Graphic, Global and Height	Male	Female	Body Proportions	Male	Female
Type	0		Omission of Appendages	0	0	Upper and Lower Halves	1	1	Hair Shading	3	3	Head	06	05
Sex Sequence	0		Position of Both Arms	0	0	Four Quarters	4	4	Nudity and Transparency	0	0	Neck	08	08
Posture	1	1	Position of Right Arm	2	2	Relative Size	0		Form	3	3	Shoulders	06	04
Perspective	0	0	Position of Left Arm	2	2	Constant Line Pressure	5	5	Detailing	3	3	Right Arm	04	02
Vertical Midline	0	0	Position of Legs	6	6	Variable Line Pressure	0	0	Identity and Sex	1	1	Left Arm	04	04
Bilateral Symmetry	5	5	Relation of Long Axes	1	1	Line Continuity	2	2	Sophistication	2	2	Chest	05	04
Horizontal Midline	0	0	Right and Left Halves	2	2	Body Shading	1	2	Height	04	04	Girth	03	03

GENERAL CHARACTERISTICS OF SUBJECT

IDENTIFICATION
No. 422
Sex M
Marital status S
Age 27 yrs. at
psychological tests

PARENTAL HISTORY
Father
C H S D O
– – – – ?
Mother
C H S D O
– – – – –

PHYSIOLOGICAL AND METABOLIC DATA

	Admission	Initial	Control	Cold pressor change	Exercise change	Smoking change
Systolic pressure	120	124	123	+08	+35	
Diastolic pressure	88	76	84	–04	–04	
Heart rate	76	80	75	+06	+14	

Age 25 yrs.	Height 70 in.	Ponderal index 12.64
	Weight 170 lbs.	Cholesterol 210 mg. per 100 ml.
	Overweight +08 %	Vital capacity 5.0 liters

HABIT SURVEY

Smoking habits: nonsmoker

   Age begun   yrs.   Inhalation:

Habits of nervous tension: 1, 3, 5, 9, 11, 14, 20, 23

FIGURE-DRAWING CHARACTERISTICS

Structural	Male Female Both	Structural	Male	Female	Structural and Graphic	Male Female Both	Graphic, Global and Height	Male	Female	Body Proportions	Male	Female
Type	0	Omission of Appendages	7	7	Upper and Lower Halves	1 1	Hair Shading	0	7	Head	06	
Sex Sequence	2	Position of Both Arms	0	0	Four Quarters	4 4	Nudity and Transparency	7	7	Neck	18	
Posture	1 1	Position of Right Arm	5	2	Relative Size	0	Form	3	3	Shoulders		
Perspective	9 2	Position of Left Arm	5	2	Constant Line Pressure	5 5	Detailing	3	3	Right Arm		04
Vertical Midline	4 4	Position of Legs	1	1	Variable Line Pressure	0 0	Identity and Sex	1	1	Left Arm		
Bilateral Symmetry	0 0	Relation of Long Axes	3	1	Line Continuity	4 4	Sophistication	2	2	Chest		05
Horizontal Midline	0 0	Right and Left Halves	2	2	Body Shading	0 2	Height	06	05	Girth	08	07

GENERAL CHARACTERISTICS OF SUBJECT

IDENTIFICATION
No. F30
Sex M
Marital status M
Age 24 yrs. at psychological tests

PARENTAL HISTORY
Father
C   H   S   D   O
-   -   -   -   ?
Mother
C   H   S   D   O
-   -   -   -   -

PHYSIOLOGICAL AND METABOLIC DATA

	Admission	Initial	Control	Cold pressor change	Exercise change	Smoking change
Systolic pressure	130	140	122	+16	+44	+02
Diastolic pressure	80	76	78	+18	+10	+01
Heart rate	80	92	90	+12	+23	+04

Age 22 yrs.	Height	69 in.	Ponderal index 13.19
	Weight	143 lbs.	Cholesterol 320 mg. per 100 ml.
	Overweight -05 %		Vital capacity liters

HABIT SURVEY
Smoking habits: former smoker
Age begun 16 yrs.   Inhalation:
Habits of nervous tension: 1, 3, 5, 6, 9, 10, 20, 22

Plate 704

MODERATELY SOPHISTICATED DRAWINGS

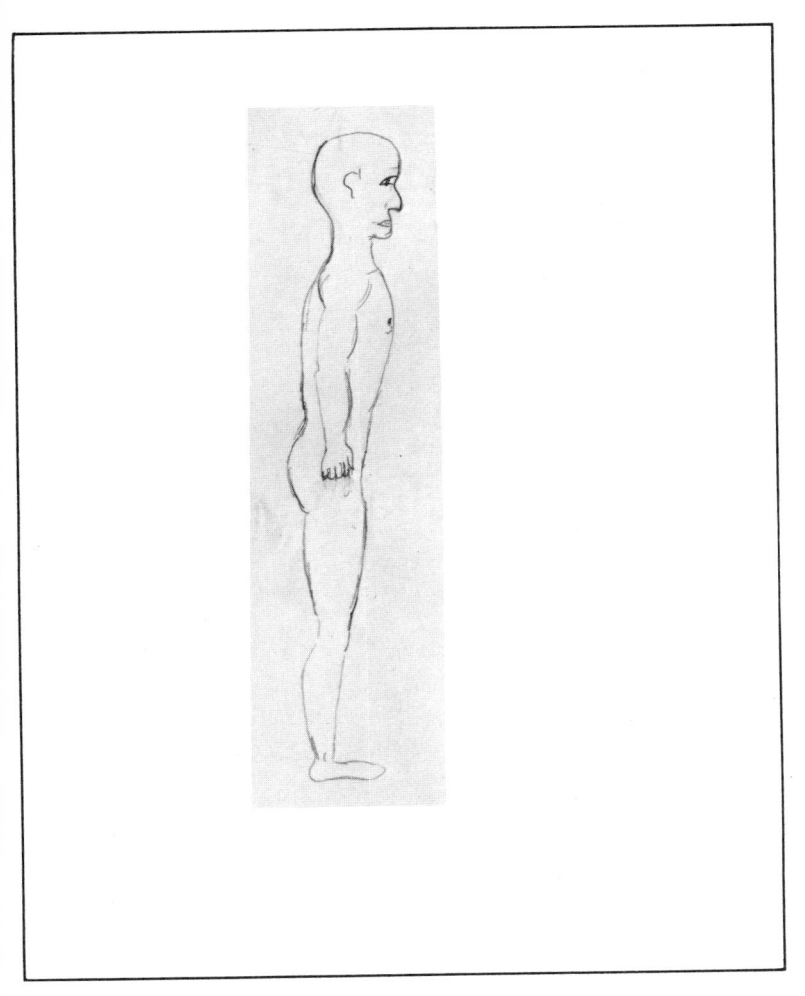
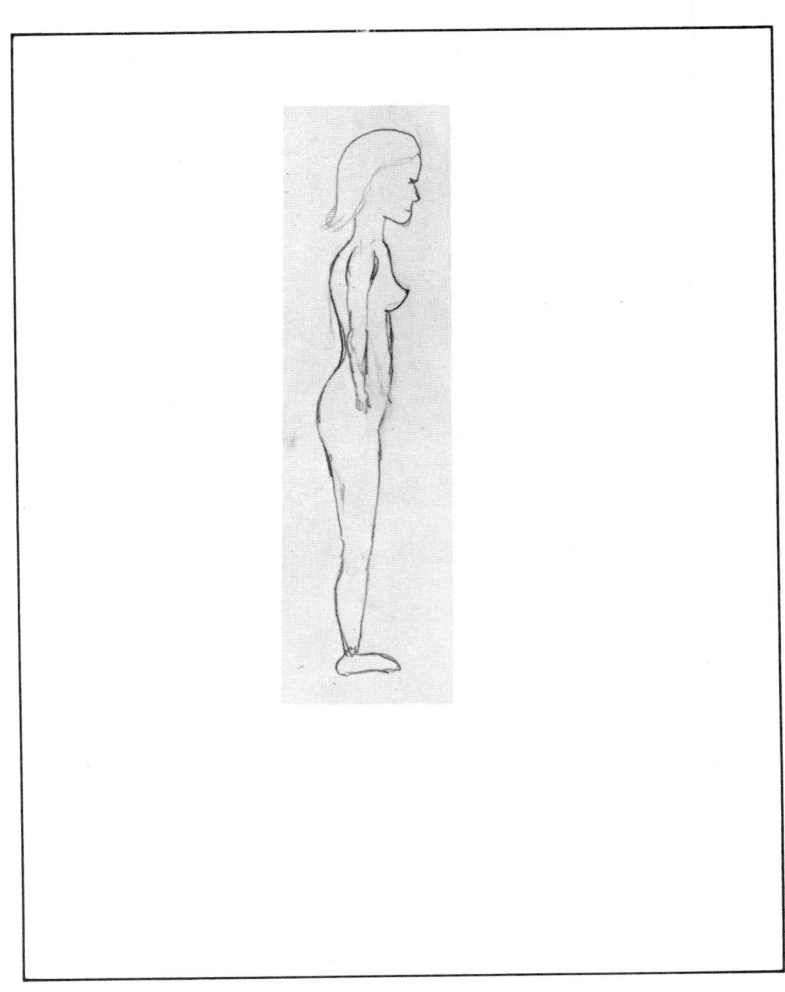

FIGURE-DRAWING CHARACTERISTICS

Structural	Male Female Both		Structural	Male	Female	Structural and Graphic	Male Female Both		Graphic, Global and Height	Male	Female	Body Proportions	Male	Female
Type	0		Omission of Appendages	0	0	Upper and Lower Halves	1	1	Hair Shading	0	5	Head	08	07
Sex Sequence	0		Position of Both Arms	2	2	Four Quarters	4	4	Nudity and Transparency	0	0	Neck	07	06
Posture	1	1	Position of Right Arm	0	0	Relative Size	0		Form	1	1	Shoulders		
Perspective	2	2	Position of Left Arm	7	7	Constant Line Pressure	0	0	Detailing	3	3	Right Arm	04	04
Vertical Midline	4	4	Position of Legs	1	1	Variable Line Pressure	2	5	Identity and Sex	1	1	Left Arm		
Bilateral Symmetry	0	0	Relation of Long Axes	1	1	Line Continuity	0	0	Sophistication	2	2	Chest	06	04
Horizontal Midline	0	0	Right and Left Halves	2	2	Body Shading	3	0	Height	06	05	Girth	05	05

GENERAL CHARACTERISTICS OF SUBJECT

IDENTIFICATION
No. G10
Sex M
Marital status S
Age 23 yrs. at
psychological tests

PARENTAL HISTORY
Father
C H S D O
– – – – ?
Mother
C H S D O
– – – – –

PHYSIOLOGICAL AND METABOLIC DATA

	Admission	Initial	Control	Cold pressor change	Exercise change	Smoking change
Systolic pressure	150	158	110	+10	+60	+02
Diastolic pressure	80	88	62	+20	00	+04
Heart rate	74	72	76	+08	+22	–05

Age 22 yrs.	Height 72 in.	Ponderal index 12.74
	Weight 180 lbs.	Cholesterol 203 mg. per 100 ml.
	Overweight +10 %	Vital capacity liters

HABIT SURVEY

Smoking habits: mixed smoker

Age begun 21 yrs.   Inhalation: no

Habits of nervous tension: 1, 4, 5, 6, 9, 10, 14, 17, 18, 19, 21, 22

STRONG VOCATIONAL INTEREST TEST

Occupation	Artist	Psychologist	Architect	Physician	Osteopath	Dentist	Veterinarian	Mathematician	Physicist	Engineer	Chemist	Production Manager
Standard Score	38	37	29	56	63	35	36	12	07	14	27	22

Occupation	Farmer	Aviator	Carpenter	Printer	Math.-Sci. Teacher	Ind. Arts Teacher	Voc. Agric. Teacher	Policeman	Forest Serv. Man	Y.M.C.A. Phys. Dir.	Personnel Director	Public Administrator
Standard Score	31	39	17	41	33	14	24	39	35	59	42	44

Occupation	Y.M.C.A. Secretary	Soc. Sci. H.S. Teacher	City Sch. Sup't.	Social Worker	Minister	Musician Performer	C.P.A.	Senior C.P.A.	Accountant	Office Man	Purchasing Agent	Banker
Standard Score	42	47	30	54	59	59	13	32	11	34	12	17

Occupation	Mortician	Pharmacist	Sales Manager	Real Est. Manager	Life Ins. Salesman	Advertising Man	Lawyer	Author-Journalist	President Mfg. Co.	Interest Maturity	Occupational Level	Masculinity-Femininity
Standard Score	34	31	29	38	43	42	36	39	17	56	49	36

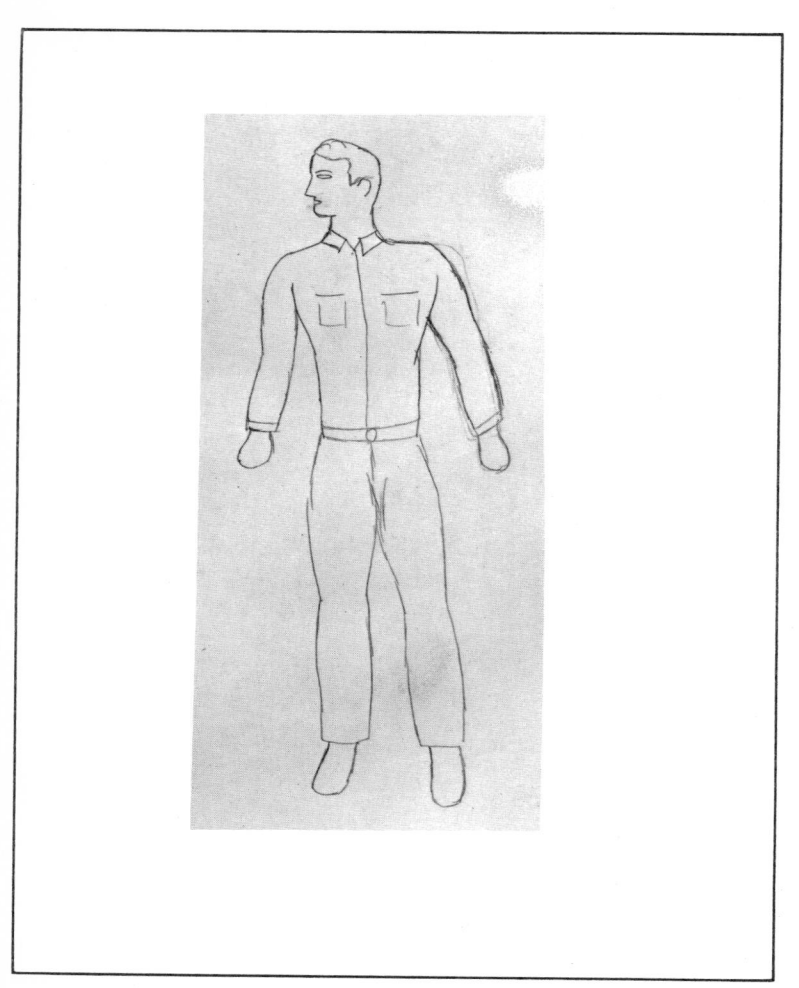
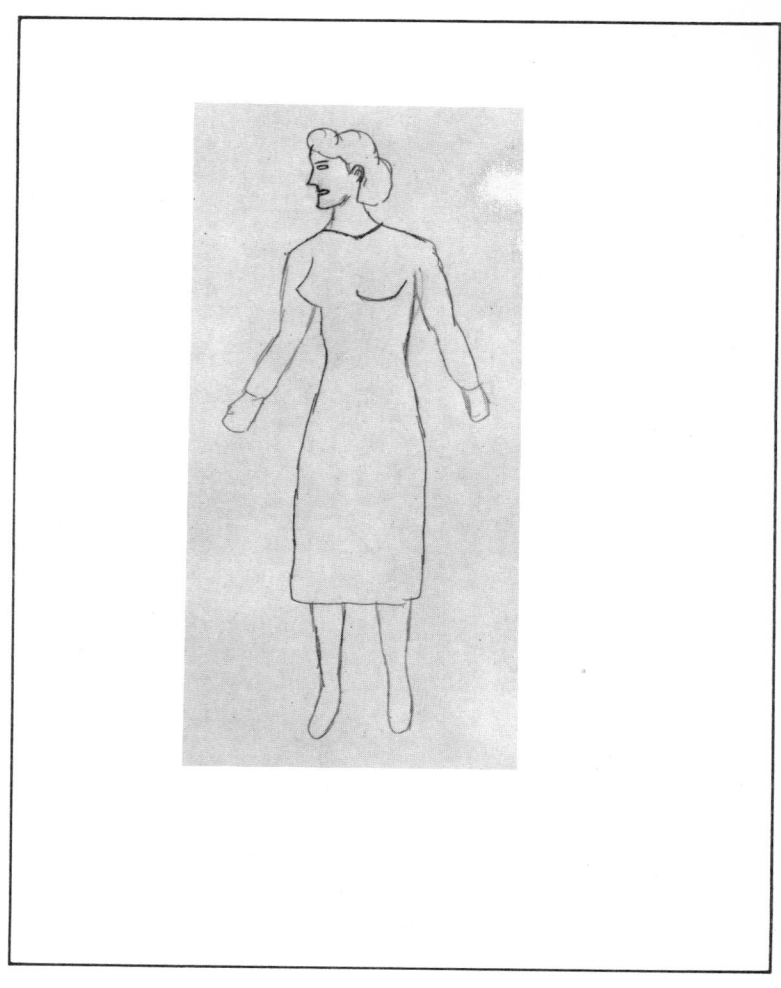

FIGURE-DRAWING CHARACTERISTICS

Structural	Male	Female	Structural	Male	Female	Structural and Graphic	Male	Female	Graphic, Global and Height	Male	Female	Body Proportions	Male	Female
	Both						Both							
Type	0		Omission of Appendages	0	0	Upper and Lower Halves	1	1	Hair Shading	5	5	Head	06	06
Sex Sequence	0		Position of Both Arms	0	0	Four Quarters	4	4	Nudity and Transparency	7	7	Neck	08	07
Posture	1	1	Position of Right Arm	2	2	Relative Size	0		Form	1	1	Shoulders	07	
Perspective	5	6	Position of Left Arm	2	2	Constant Line Pressure	0	0	Detailing	3	3	Right Arm	04	04
Vertical Midline	3	4	Position of Legs	4	4	Variable Line Pressure	5	5	Identity and Sex	1	1	Left Arm	06	04
Bilateral Symmetry	3	0	Relation of Long Axes	1	1	Line Continuity	0	0	Sophistication	2	2	Chest	06	
Horizontal Midline	4	0	Right and Left Halves	1	1	Body Shading	2	1	Height	07	06	Girth	06	

GENERAL CHARACTERISTICS OF SUBJECT

IDENTIFICATION
No. G53
Sex M
Marital status S
Age 23 yrs. at
psychological tests

PARENTAL HISTORY
Father
C   H   S   D   O
–   –   –   –   ?
Mother
C   H   S   D   O
–   –   –   –   –

PHYSIOLOGICAL AND METABOLIC DATA

	Admission	Initial	Control	Cold pressor change	Exercise change	Smoking change
Systolic pressure	120	142	126	+06	+44	+05
Diastolic pressure	60	82	80	+10	00	+04
Heart rate	72	84	70	−04	+21	−01

Age 22 yrs.	Height	74	in.	Ponderal index	12.50	
	Weight	208	lbs.	Cholesterol	222	mg. per 100 ml.
	Overweight	+14	%	Vital capacity		liters

HABIT SURVEY

Smoking habits: nonsmoker

Age begun   yrs.   Inhalation:

Habits of nervous tension: 1, 5, 6, 10, 19, 21, 25

STRONG VOCATIONAL INTEREST TEST

Occupation	Artist	Psychologist	Architect	Physician	Osteopath	Dentist	Veterinarian	Mathematician	Physicist	Engineer	Chemist	Production Manager
Standard Score	48	51	47	58	38	39	11	51	43	43	50	25

Occupation	Farmer	Aviator	Carpenter	Printer	Math.-Sci. Teacher	Ind. Arts Teacher	Voc. Agric. Teacher	Policeman	Forest Serv. Man	Y.M.C.A. Phys. Dir.	Personnel Director	Public Administrator
Standard Score	21	36	08	24	26	02	05	19	15	23	23	40

Occupation	Y.M.C.A. Secretary	Soc. Sci. H.S. Teacher	City Sch. Sup't.	Social Worker	Minister	Musician Performer	C.P.A.	Senior C.P.A.	Accountant	Office Man	Purchasing Agent	Banker
Standard Score	11	21	23	30	59	47	36	24	17	10	18	15

Occupation	Mortician	Pharmacist	Sales Manager	Real Est. Manager	Life Ins. Salesman	Advertising Man	Lawyer	Author- Journalist	President Mfg. Co.	Interest Maturity	Occupational Level	Masculinity- Femininity
Standard Score	14	29	28	30	26	44	45	50	42	43	67	39

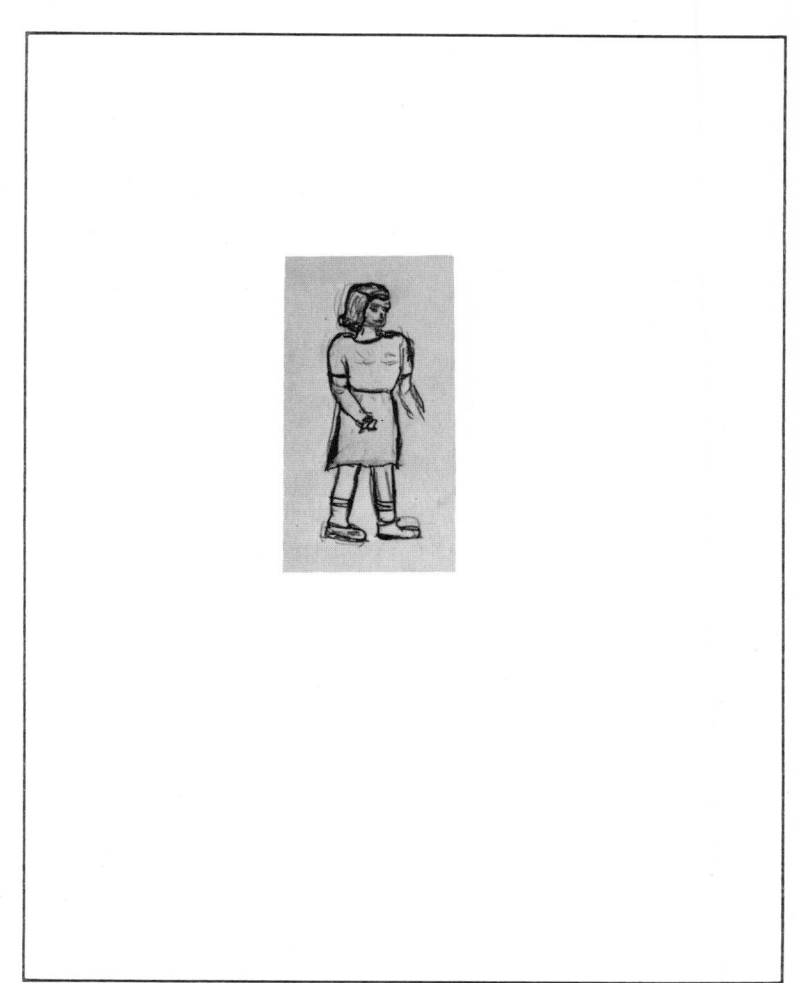

FIGURE-DRAWING CHARACTERISTICS

Structural	Male Female Both	Structural	Male	Female	Structural and Graphic	Male Female Both		Graphic, Global and Height	Male	Female	Body Proportions	Male	Female
Type	0	Omission of Appendages	0	7	Upper and Lower Halves	1	1	Hair Shading	1	1	Head	04	03
Sex Sequence	0	Position of Both Arms	1	1	Four Quarters	4	4	Nudity and Transparency	7	7	Neck	02	02
Posture	2 1	Position of Right Arm	5	5	Relative Size	0		Form	1	1	Shoulders		
Perspective	1 1	Position of Left Arm	0	4	Constant Line Pressure	5	5	Detailing	1	1	Right Arm	02	02
Vertical Midline	7 4	Position of Legs	8	6	Variable Line Pressure	0	0	Identity and Sex	1	1	Left Arm	02	
Bilateral Symmetry	0 0	Relation of Long Axes	1	1	Line Continuity	1	1	Sophistication	2	2	Chest		
Horizontal Midline	2 4	Right and Left Halves	2	2	Body Shading	7	7	Height	03	02	Girth		

GENERAL CHARACTERISTICS OF SUBJECT

IDENTIFICATION

No. A62

Sex M

Marital status S

Age 24 yrs. at

psychological tests

PARENTAL HISTORY

Father

C   H   S   D   O

–   –   –   –   ?

Mother

C   H   S   D   O

–   –   –   –   –

PHYSIOLOGICAL AND METABOLIC DATA

	Admission	Initial	Control	Cold pressor change	Exercise change	Smoking change
Systolic pressure	110	120	120	+20	+18	+10
Diastolic pressure	60	72	68	+28	–08	+04
Heart rate	88	72	67	+04	+07	–05

Age 22 yrs. Height 72 in. Weight 158 lbs. Overweight –03 %

Ponderal index 13.32 Cholesterol 237 mg. per 100 ml. Vital capacity liters

HABIT SURVEY

Smoking habits: nonsmoker

Age begun yrs. Inhalation:

Habits of nervous tension: 4, 5, 21, 25

STRONG VOCATIONAL INTEREST TEST

Occupation	Artist	Psychologist	Architect	Physician	Osteopath	Dentist	Veterinarian	Mathematician	Physicist	Engineer	Chemist	Production Manager
Standard Score	2	4	4	6	6	4	3	2	3	5	4	5

Occupation	Farmer	Aviator	Carpenter	Printer	Math.-Sci. Teacher	Ind. Arts Teacher	Voc. Agric. Teacher	Policeman	Forest Serv. Man	Y.M.C.A. Phys. Dir.	Personnel Director	Public Administrator
Standard Score	7	6	5	6	7	5	5	5	7	5	4	5

Occupation	Y.M.C.A. Secretary	Soc. Sci. H.S. Teacher	City Sch. Sup't.	Social Worker	Minister	Musician Performer	C.P.A.	Senior C.P.A.	Accountant	Office Man	Purchasing Agent	Banker
Standard Score	4	4	3	5	6	5	2	6	4	5	2	2

Occupation	Mortician	Pharmacist	Sales Manager	Real Est. Manager	Life Ins. Salesman	Advertising Man	Lawyer	Author-Journalist	President Mfg. Co.	Interest Maturity	Occupational Level	Masculinity-Femininity
Standard Score	4	3	2	4	3	2	2	2	2	6	4	5

FIGURE-DRAWING CHARACTERISTICS

Structural	Male Female Both	Structural	Male	Female	Structural and Graphic	Male Female Both	Graphic, Global and Height	Male	Female	Body Proportions	Male	Female
Type	0	Omission of Appendages	0	0	Upper and Lower Halves	1 1	Hair Shading	3	3	Head	06	06
Sex Sequence	1	Position of Both Arms	0	0	Four Quarters	4 4	Nudity and Transparency	7	7	Neck	04	06
Posture	1 1	Position of Right Arm	2	2	Relative Size	2	Form	1	1	Shoulders	05	05
Perspective	0 0	Position of Left Arm	2	2	Constant Line Pressure	4 4	Detailing	1	1	Right Arm	06	04
Vertical Midline	3 0	Position of Legs	6	4	Variable Line Pressure	0 0	Identity and Sex	1	1	Left Arm	04	04
Bilateral Symmetry	4 3	Relation of Long Axes	1	1	Line Continuity	0 0	Sophistication	2	2	Chest	05	04
Horizontal Midline	6 4	Right and Left Halves	1	1	Body Shading	7 7	Height	06	06	Girth	07	03

GENERAL CHARACTERISTICS OF SUBJECT

IDENTIFICATION

No. B43
Sex M
Marital status S
Age 22 yrs. at
psychological tests

PARENTAL HISTORY

Father

C	H	S	D	O
-	-	-	-	?

Mother

C	H	S	D	O
-	-	-	-	-

PHYSIOLOGICAL AND METABOLIC DATA

	Admission	Initial	Control	Cold pressor change	Exercise change	Smoking change
Systolic pressure	120	112	114	+24	+34	+10
Diastolic pressure	70	46	52	+28	-14	+02
Heart rate	80	76	71	+06	+19	+20

Age 22 yrs.

Height 71 in.
Weight 158 lbs.
Overweight 00 %

Ponderal index 13.12
Cholesterol 233 mg. per 100 ml.
Vital capacity 5.2 liters

HABIT SURVEY

Smoking habits: occasional smoker

Age begun 16 yrs.   Inhalation: yes

Habits of nervous tension: 2, 4, 5, 9, 11, 21, 22

STRONG VOCATIONAL INTEREST TEST

Occupation	Artist	Psychologist	Architect	Physician	Osteopath	Dentist	Veterinarian	Mathematician	Physicist	Engineer	Chemist	Production Manager
Standard Score	33	38	27	55	53	38	34	22	18	23	33	22

Occupation	Farmer	Aviator	Carpenter	Printer	Math.-Sci. Teacher	Ind. Arts Teacher	Voc. Agric. Teacher	Policeman	Forest Serv. Man	Y.M.C.A. Phys. Dir.	Personnel Director	Public Administrator
Standard Score	30	36	11	35	29	02	18	33	25	44	36	48

Occupation	Y.M.C.A. Secretary	Soc. Sci. H.S. Teacher	City Sch. Sup't.	Social Worker	Minister	Musician Performer	C.P.A.	Senior C.P.A.	Accountant	Office Man	Purchasing Agent	Banker
Standard Score	31	39	32	42	61	49	35	40	23	34	18	19

Occupation	Mortician	Pharmacist	Sales Manager	Real Est. Manager	Life Ins. Salesman	Advertising Man	Lawyer	Author-Journalist	President Mfg. Co.	Interest Maturity	Occupational Level	Masculinity-Femininity
Standard Score	38	33	29	39	39	39	45	41	22	56	56	35

Plate 708　　　　　MODERATELY SOPHISTICATED DRAWINGS　　　　　755

FIGURE-DRAWING CHARACTERISTICS

Structural	Male Female Both		Structural	Male	Female	Structural and Graphic	Male Female Both		Graphic, Global and Height	Male	Female	Body Proportions	Male	Female
Type	0		Omission of Appendages	0	0	Upper and Lower Halves	0	3	Hair Shading	5	1	Head	09	14
Sex Sequence	0		Position of Both Arms	1	1	Four Quarters	4	4	Nudity and Transparency	7	7	Neck	08	08
Posture	1	3	Position of Right Arm	4	2	Relative Size	4		Form	1	1	Shoulders	08	
Perspective	0	1	Position of Left Arm	5	4	Constant Line Pressure	0	0	Detailing	1	3	Right Arm	06	08
Vertical Midline	3	7	Position of Legs	4	3	Variable Line Pressure	5	5	Identity and Sex	1	1	Left Arm	06	10
Bilateral Symmetry	3	0	Relation of Long Axes	1	0	Line Continuity	0	0	Sophistication	2	2	Chest	07	
Horizontal Midline	6	4	Right and Left Halves	1	1	Body Shading	7	1	Height	08		Girth	09	

GENERAL CHARACTERISTICS OF SUBJECT

IDENTIFICATION
No. B56
Sex M
Marital status S
Age 23 yrs. at
psychological tests

PARENTAL HISTORY				
Father				
C	H	S	D	O
-	-	-	-	?
Mother				
C	H	S	D	O
-	-	-	-	-

PHYSIOLOGICAL AND METABOLIC DATA

	Admission	Initial	Control	Cold pressor change	Exercise change	Smoking change
Systolic pressure	140	144	116	+16	+42	+10
Diastolic pressure	40	68	64	+16	-20	+03
Heart rate	80	64	55	+04	+24	+05

Age 23 yrs.	Height 68 in.	Ponderal index 13.00
	Weight 143 lbs.	Cholesterol 287 mg. per 100 ml.
	Overweight -03 %	Vital capacity 5.3 liters

HABIT SURVEY

Smoking habits: pipe smoker

Age begun 16 yrs.　　Inhalation: no

Habits of nervous tension: 1, 4, 5, 6, 8, 11, 12, 14, 16, 22

STRONG VOCATIONAL INTEREST TEST

Occupation	Artist	Psychologist	Architect	Physician	Osteopath	Dentist	Veterinarian	Mathematician	Physicist	Engineer	Chemist	Production Manager
Standard Score	49	36	55	62	50	57	27	32	41	48	49	32

Occupation	Farmer	Aviator	Carpenter	Printer	Math.-Sci. Teacher	Ind. Arts Teacher	Voc. Agric. Teacher	Policeman	Forest Serv. Man	Y.M.C.A. Phys. Dir.	Personnel Director	Public Administrator
Standard Score	37	42	22	25	26	21	23	23	24	22	14	28

Occupation	Y.M.C.A. Secretary	Soc. Sci. H.S. Teacher	City Sch. Sup't.	Social Worker	Minister	Musician Performer	C.P.A.	Senior C.P.A.	Accountant	Office Man	Purchasing Agent	Banker
Standard Score	08	12	12	17	61	40	19	17	05	09	16	13

Occupation	Mortician	Pharmacist	Sales Manager	Real Est. Manager	Life Ins. Salesman	Advertising Man	Lawyer	Author-Journalist	President Mfg. Co.	Interest Maturity	Occupational Level	Masculinity-Femininity
Standard Score	22	34	23	36	26	36	38	46	45	41	61	47

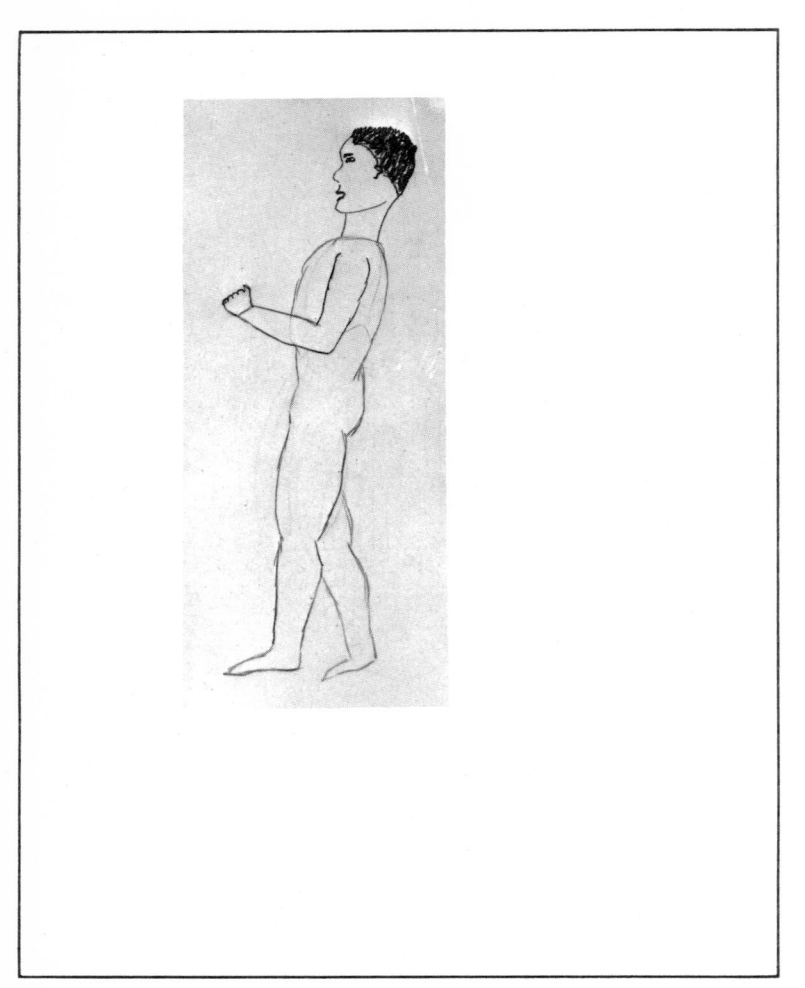

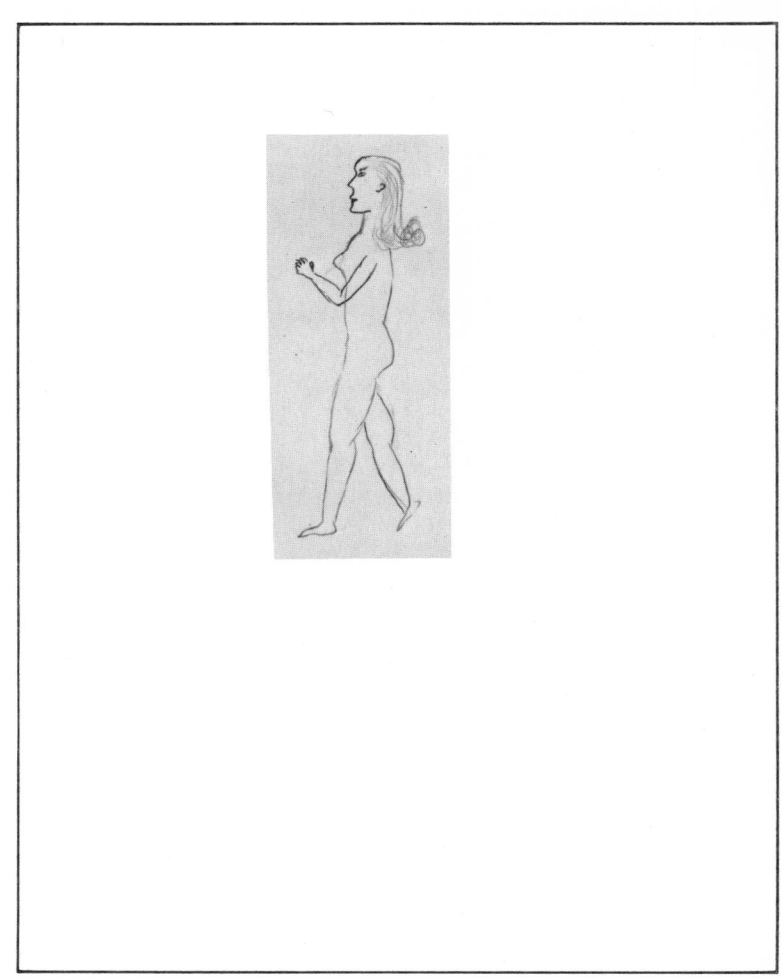

FIGURE-DRAWING CHARACTERISTICS

Structural	Male Female Both	Structural	Male	Female	Structural and Graphic	Male Female Both		Graphic, Global and Height	Male	Female	Body Proportions	Male	Female
Type	0	Omission of Appendages	0	0	Upper and Lower Halves	1	1	Hair Shading	3	2	Head	07	04
Sex Sequence	0	Position of Both Arms	4	4	Four Quarters	4	4	Nudity and Transparency	0	0	Neck	06	05
Posture	2 2	Position of Right Arm	7	7	Relative Size	0		Form	1	1	Shoulders		
Perspective	2 2	Position of Left Arm	4	4	Constant Line Pressure	0	0	Detailing	3	3	Right Arm		
Vertical Midline	4 4	Position of Legs	8	8	Variable Line Pressure	3	3	Identity and Sex	1	1	Left Arm	04	02
Bilateral Symmetry	0 0	Relation of Long Axes	1	1	Line Continuity	0	2	Sophistication	2	2	Chest	06	03
Horizontal Midline	0 0	Right and Left Halves	1	1	Body Shading	0	0	Height	05	04	Girth	05	03

GENERAL CHARACTERISTICS OF SUBJECT

IDENTIFICATION
No. C74
Sex M
Marital status M
Age 22 yrs. at
psychological tests

PARENTAL HISTORY
Father
C H S D O
– – – – ?
Mother
C H S D O
– – – –

PHYSIOLOGICAL AND METABOLIC DATA

	Admission	Initial	Control	Cold pressor change	Exercise change	Smoking change
Systolic pressure	114	120	110	+02	+28	
Diastolic pressure	74	60	60	+10	–10	
Heart rate	64	76	65	+04	+29	

Age 23 yrs.	Height 72 in.	Ponderal index 12.12
	Weight 210 lbs.	Cholesterol 208 mg. per 100 ml.
	Overweight +28 %	Vital capacity 5.0 liters

HABIT SURVEY

Smoking habits: nonsmoker

Age begun yrs. Inhalation:

Habits of nervous tension: 2, 5, 6, 21

STRONG VOCATIONAL INTEREST TEST

Occupation	Artist	Psychologist	Architect	Physician	Osteopath	Dentist	Veterinarian	Mathematician	Physicist	Engineer	Chemist	Production Manager
Standard Score	11	23	09	34	35	22	29	09	00	10	08	32

Occupation	Farmer	Aviator	Carpenter	Printer	Math.-Sci. Teacher	Ind. Arts Teacher	Voc. Agric. Teacher	Policeman	Forest Serv. Man	Y.M.C.A. Phys. Dir.	Personnel Director	Public Administrator
Standard Score	41	32	20	37	43	21	40	43	29	43	38	43

Occupation	Y.M.C.A. Secretary	Soc. Sci. H.S. Teacher	City Sch. Sup't.	Social Worker	Minister	Musician Performer	C.P.A.	Senior C.P.A.	Accountant	Office Man	Purchasing Agent	Banker
Standard Score	39	51	44	38	62	26	24	38	33	43	25	39

Occupation	Mortician	Pharmacist	Sales Manager	Real Est. Manager	Life Ins. Salesman	Advertising Man	Lawyer	Author-Journalist	President Mfg. Co.	Interest Maturity	Occupational Level	Masculinity-Femininity
Standard Score	26	29	33	33	35	27	36	25	19	60	49	53

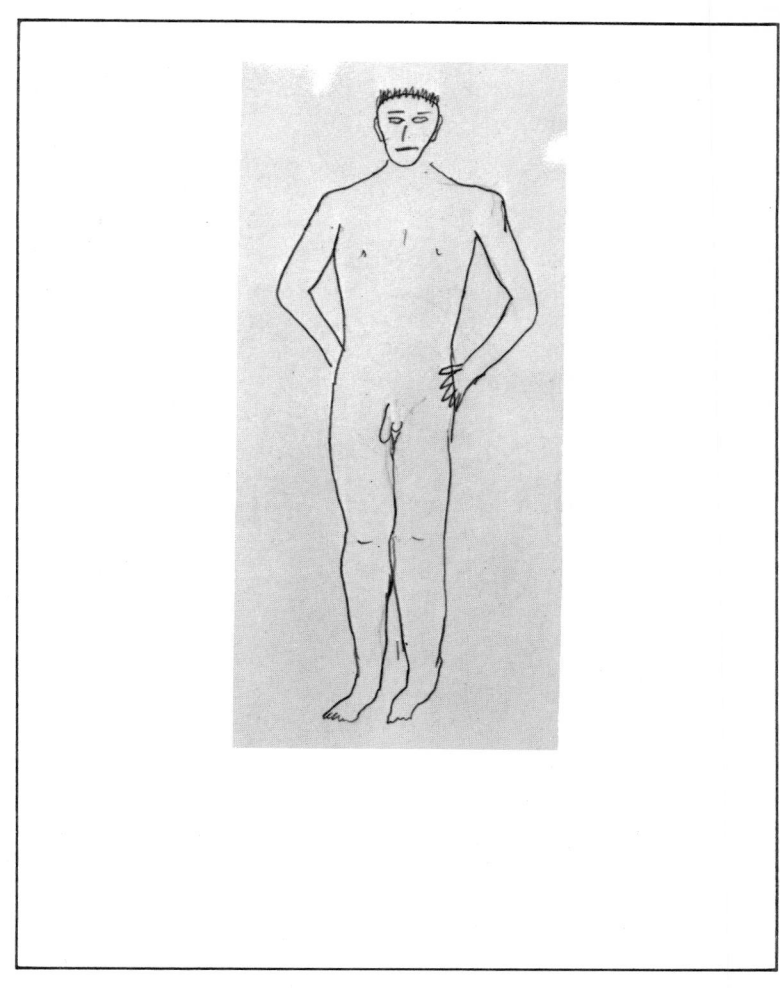

FIGURE-DRAWING CHARACTERISTICS

Structural	Male / Female (Both)	Structural	Male	Female	Structural and Graphic	Male / Female (Both)	Graphic, Global and Height	Male	Female	Body Proportions	Male	Female
Type	0	Omission of Appendages	7	7	Upper and Lower Halves	1 1	Hair Shading	3	3	Head	06	06
Sex Sequence	1	Position of Both Arms	0	0	Four Quarters	4 4	Nudity and Transparency	0	0	Neck	05	10
Posture	1 1	Position of Right Arm	5	5	Relative Size	2	Form	1	1	Shoulders	07	
Perspective	0 1	Position of Left Arm	5	5	Constant Line Pressure	5 5	Detailing	3	3	Right Arm		
Vertical Midline	0 4	Position of Legs	3	3	Variable Line Pressure	0 0	Identity and Sex	1	1	Left Arm	06	04
Bilateral Symmetry	3 0	Relation of Long Axes	1	1	Line Continuity	4 4	Sophistication	2	2	Chest	06	
Horizontal Midline	0 0	Right and Left Halves	0	1	Body Shading	3 0	Height	06	06	Girth	07	

GENERAL CHARACTERISTICS OF SUBJECT

IDENTIFICATION

No. D04

Sex M

Marital status M

Age 23 yrs. at psychological tests

PARENTAL HISTORY

Father

C   .H   S   D   O

–   –   –   –   ?

Mother

C   H   S   D   O

–   –   –   –   –

PHYSIOLOGICAL AND METABOLIC DATA

	Admission	Initial	Control	Cold pressor change	Exercise change	Smoking change
Systolic pressure	130	138	118	+12	+42	00
Diastolic pressure	80	62	72	+16	-14	00
Heart rate	80	84	73	+08	+34	+01

Age 23 yrs.	Height	72 in.	Ponderal index	12.57	
	Weight	188 lbs.	Cholesterol	296	mg. per 100 ml.
	Overweight +15 %		Vital capacity	4.4	liters

HABIT SURVEY

Smoking habits: heavy cigarette smoker

Age begun 14 yrs.   Inhalation: yes

Habits of nervous tension: 5, 6, 11, 21

STRONG VOCATIONAL INTEREST TEST

Occupation	Artist	Psychologist	Architect	Physician	Osteopath	Dentist	Veterinarian	Mathematician	Physicist	Engineer	Chemist	Production Manager
Standard Score	37	50	36	49	33	29	25	30	26	43	45	35

Occupation	Farmer	Aviator	Carpenter	Printer	Math.-Sci. Teacher	Ind. Arts Teacher	Voc. Agric. Teacher	Policeman	Forest Serv. Man	Y.M.C.A. Phys. Dir.	Personnel Director	Public Administrator
Standard Score	37	50	09	32	27	10	22	20	29	22	32	47

Occupation	Y.M.C.A. Secretary	Soc. Sci. H.S. Teacher	City Sch. Sup't.	Social Worker	Minister	Musician Performer	C.P.A.	Senior C.P.A.	Accountant	Office Man	Purchasing Agent	Banker
Standard Score	16	20	20	36	63	41	27	38	12	15	18	09

Occupation	Mortician	Pharmacist	Sales Manager	Real Est. Manager	Life Ins. Salesman	Advertising Man	Lawyer	Author-Journalist	President Mfg. Co.	Interest Maturity	Occupational Level	Masculinity-Femininity
Standard Score	17	27	36	40	28	51	40	43	40	48	61	55

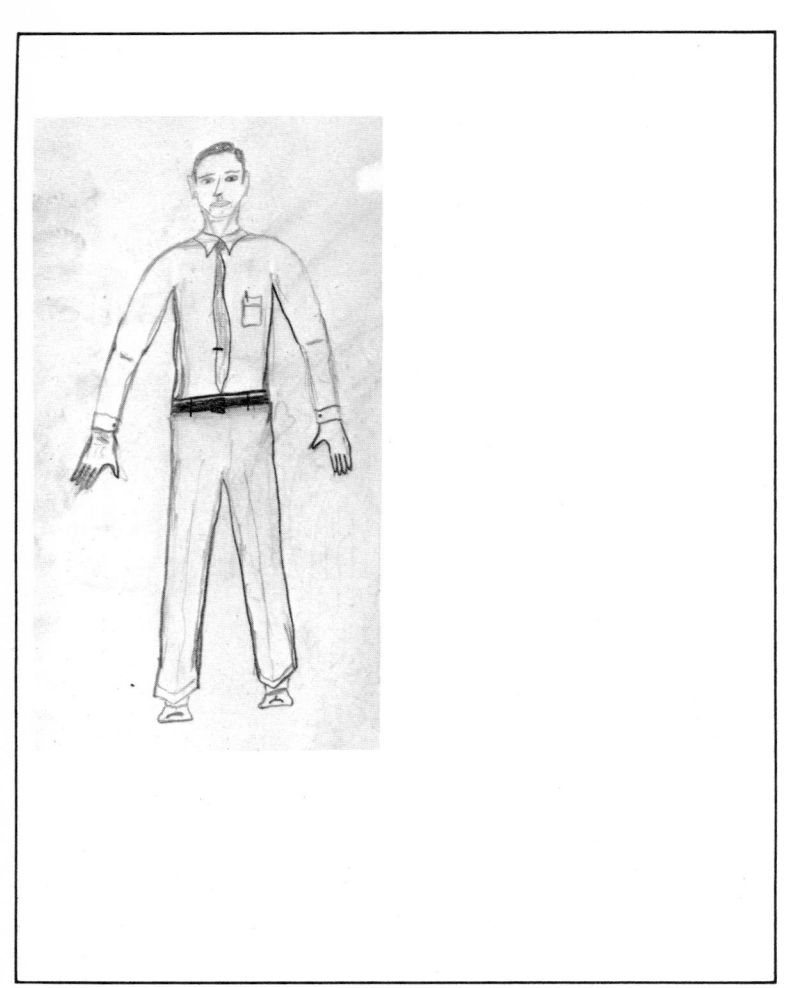

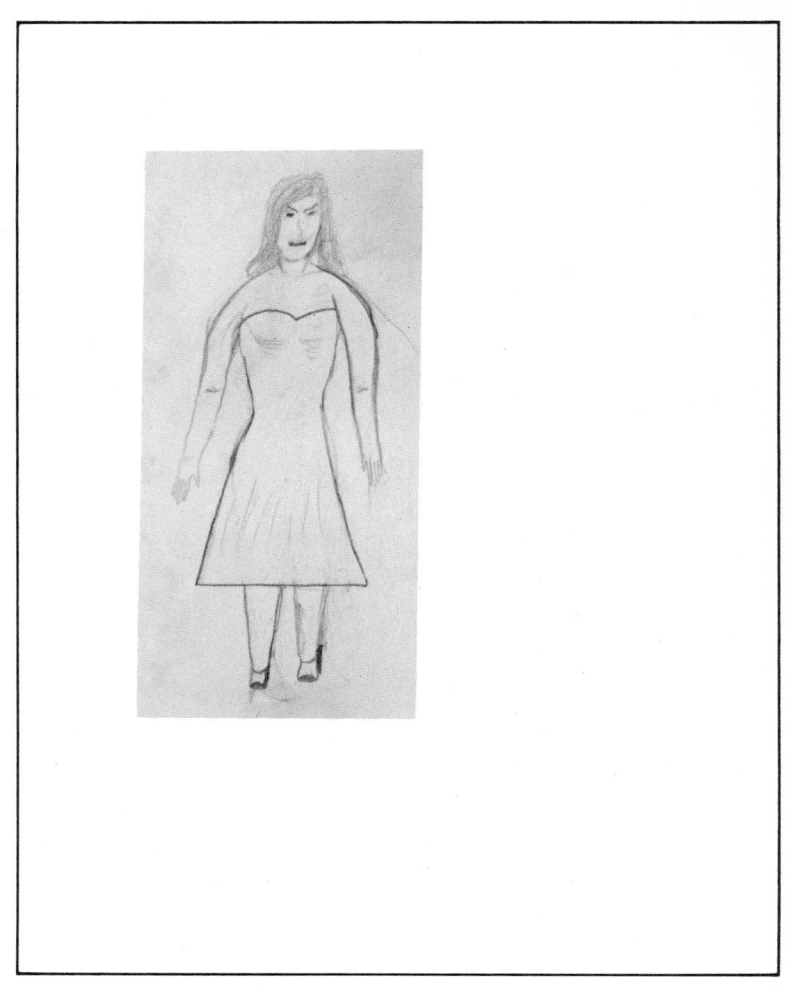

FIGURE-DRAWING CHARACTERISTICS

Structural	Male Female Both	Structural	Male	Female	Structural and Graphic	Male Female Both		Graphic, Global and Height	Male	Female	Body Proportions	Male	Female
Type	0	Omission of Appendages	0	0	Upper and Lower Halves	1	1	Hair Shading	3	3	Head	06	06
Sex Sequence	0	Position of Both Arms	0	0	Four Quarters	4	4	Nudity and Transparency	7	7	Neck	07	04
Posture	1 1	Position of Right Arm	2	2	Relative Size	0		Form	1	1	Shoulders	06	05
Perspective	0 0	Position of Left Arm	2	2	Constant Line Pressure	0	0	Detailing	1	1	Right Arm	06	04
Vertical Midline	3 0	Position of Legs	6	5	Variable Line Pressure	3	3	Identity and Sex	1	1	Left Arm	06	04
Bilateral Symmetry	3 3	Relation of Long Axes	1	1	Line Continuity	2	2	Sophistication	2	2	Chest	04	05
Horizontal Midline	4 0	Right and Left Halves	2	2	Body Shading	7	7	Height	06	05	Girth	05	04

GENERAL CHARACTERISTICS OF SUBJECT

IDENTIFICATION
No. D66
Sex M
Marital status S
Age 21 yrs. at
psychological tests

PARENTAL HISTORY
Father
C H S D O
- - - - ?
Mother
C H S D O
- - - - -

PHYSIOLOGICAL AND METABOLIC DATA

	Admission	Initial	Control	Cold pressor change	Exercise change	Smoking change
Systolic pressure	135	122	122	+07	+42	+10
Diastolic pressure	75	72	72	+22	-10	+06
Heart rate	70	60	57	+04	+31	+12

Age 20 yrs.	Height 70 in.	Ponderal index 11.86
	Weight 205 lbs.	Cholesterol 296 mg. per 100 ml.
	Overweight +35 %	Vital capacity 4.6 liters

HABIT SURVEY

Smoking habits: heavy cigarette smoker

Age begun 14 yrs.   Inhalation: yes

Habits of nervous tension: 4, 5, 6, 10, 15, 19, 22

STRONG VOCATIONAL INTEREST TEST

Occupation	Artist	Psychologist	Architect	Physician	Osteopath	Dentist	Veterinarian	Mathematician	Physicist	Engineer	Chemist	Production Manager
Standard Score	23	39	20	50	51	28	20	16	12	23	30	30

Occupation	Farmer	Aviator	Carpenter	Printer	Math.-Sci. Teacher	Ind. Arts Teacher	Voc. Agric. Teacher	Policeman	Forest Serv. Man	Y.M.C.A. Phys. Dir.	Personnel Director	Public Administrator
Standard Score	15	26	00	25	25	-06	-08	31	11	39	42	53

Occupation	Y.M.C.A. Secretary	Soc. Sci. H.S. Teacher	City Sch. Sup't.	Social Worker	Minister	Musician Performer	C.P.A.	Senior C.P.A.	Accountant	Office Man	Purchasing Agent	Banker
Standard Score	31	38	33	48	63	37	47	41	34	36	27	24

Occupation	Mortician	Pharmacist	Sales Manager	Real Est. Manager	Life Ins. Salesman	Advertising Man	Lawyer	Author- Journalist	President Mfg. Co.	Interest Maturity	Occupational Level	Masculinity- Femininity
Standard Score	40	43	36	37	44	41	52	37	39	57	64	37

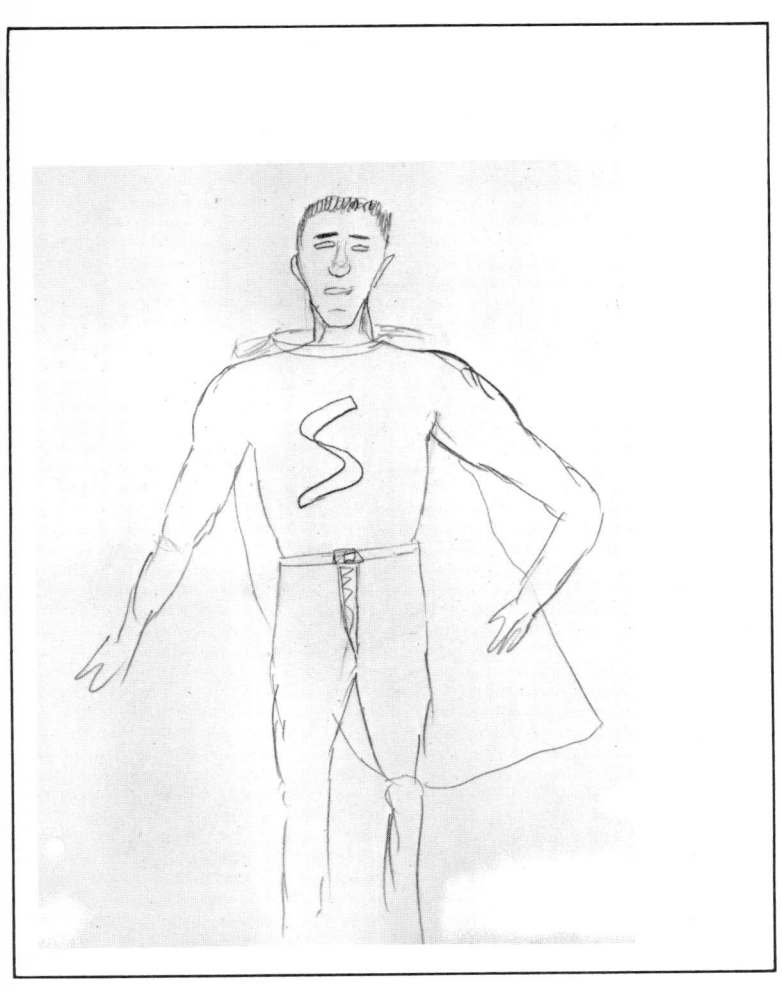

FIGURE-DRAWING CHARACTERISTICS

Structural	Male Female Both	Structural	Male	Female	Structural and Graphic	Male Female Both		Graphic, Global and Height	Male	Female	Body Proportions	Male	Female
Type	0	Omission of Appendages	3	3	Upper and Lower Halves	3	3	Hair Shading	3	3	Head	10	11
Sex Sequence	0	Position of Both Arms	1	0	Four Quarters	4	4	Nudity and Transparency	7	2	Neck	08	08
Posture	0	0	Position of Right Arm	2	2	Relative Size	0		Form	1	1	Shoulders	10	10
Perspective	0	0	Position of Left Arm	5	2	Constant Line Pressure	0	0	Detailing	1	1	Right Arm	08	06
Vertical Midline	3	0	Position of Legs	6	6	Variable Line Pressure	5	5	Identity and Sex	1	1	Left Arm	08	06
Bilateral Symmetry	3	3	Relation of Long Axes	1	1	Line Continuity	0	0	Sophistication	2	2	Chest	08	08
Horizontal Midline	4	6	Right and Left Halves	1	1	Body Shading	2	2	Height			Girth	09	06

GENERAL CHARACTERISTICS OF SUBJECT

IDENTIFICATION

No. E51

Sex M

Marital status S

Age 23 yrs. at psychological tests

PARENTAL HISTORY

Father

C   H   S   D   O

–   –   –   –   ?

Mother

C   H   S   D   O

–   –   –   –   –

PHYSIOLOGICAL AND METABOLIC DATA

	Admission	Initial	Control	Cold pressor change	Exercise change	Smoking change
Systolic pressure	130	130	120	+11	-03	
Diastolic pressure	100	80	80	+24	-10	
Heart rate	84	120	100	+12	+38	

Age 22 yrs.

Height 69 in.   Ponderal index 12.32

Weight 176 lbs.   Cholesterol 355 mg. per 100 ml.

Overweight +17%   Vital capacity 3.9 liters

HABIT SURVEY

Smoking habits: pipe smoker

Age begun 20 yrs.   Inhalation: no

Habits of nervous tension: 1, 3, 5, 6, 7, 11, 12, 16, 18, 21, 23, 24

STRONG VOCATIONAL INTEREST TEST

Occupation	Artist	Psychologist	Architect	Physician	Osteopath	Dentist	Veterinarian	Mathematician	Physicist	Engineer	Chemist	Production Manager
Standard Score	42	49	54	51	28	35	06	40	35	45	51	29

Occupation	Farmer	Aviator	Carpenter	Printer	Math.-Sci. Teacher	Ind. Arts Teacher	Voc. Agric. Teacher	Policeman	Forest Serv. Man	Y.M.C.A. Phys. Dir.	Personnel Director	Public Administrator
Standard Score	26	39	09	26	27	-06	12	14	14	13	31	39

Occupation	Y.M.C.A. Secretary	Soc. Sci. H.S. Teacher	City Sch. Sup't.	Social Worker	Minister	Musician Performer	C.P.A.	Senior C.P.A.	Accountant	Office Man	Purchasing Agent	Banker
Standard Score	07	13	16	27	64	49	41	34	17	19	25	09

Occupation	Mortician	Pharmacist	Sales Manager	Real Est. Manager	Life Ins. Salesman	Advertising Man	Lawyer	Author-Journalist	President Mfg. Co.	Interest Maturity	Occupational Level	Masculinity-Femininity
Standard Score	18	26	36	35	29	47	44	45	43	45	66	45

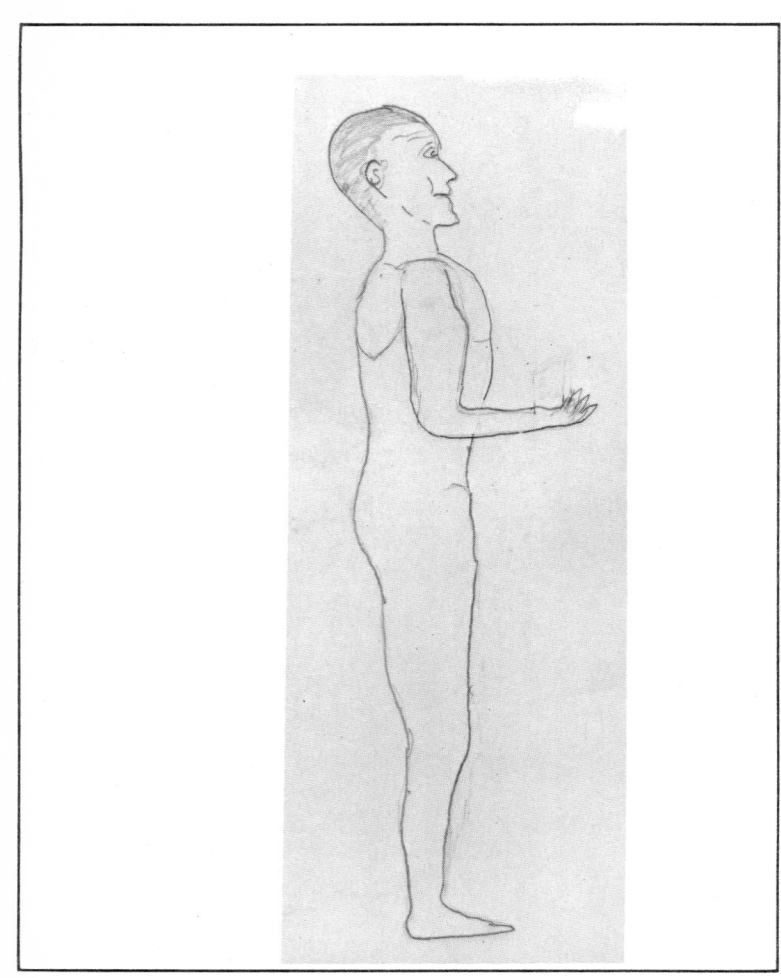

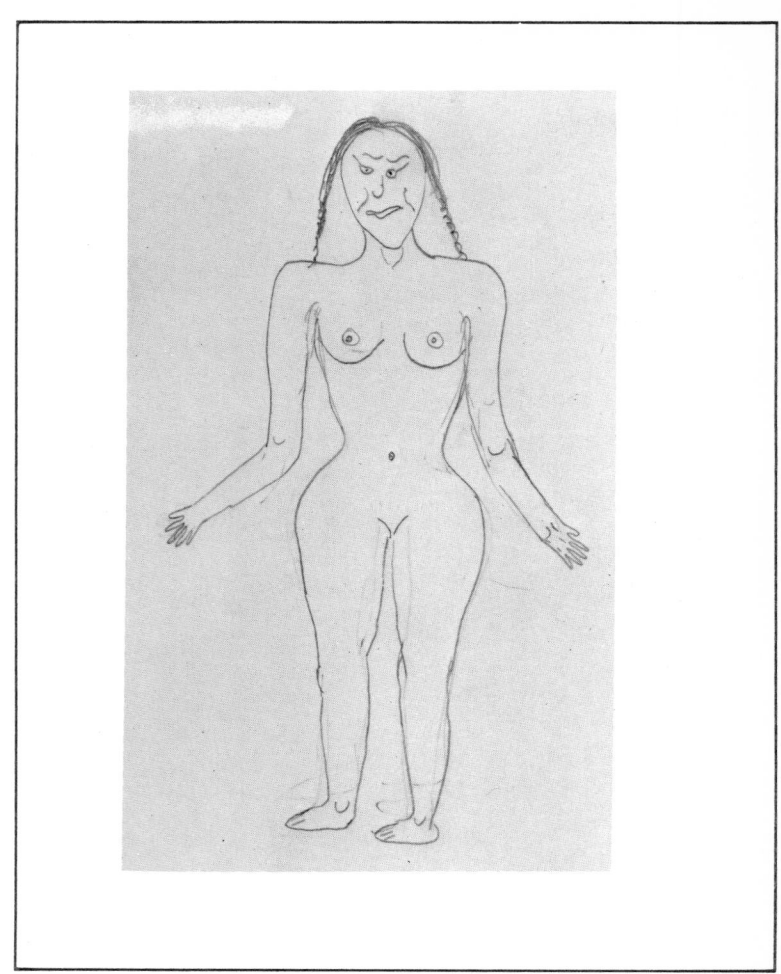

FIGURE-DRAWING CHARACTERISTICS

Structural	Male Female Both		Structural	Male	Female	Structural and Graphic	Male Female Both		Graphic, Global and Height	Male	Female	Body Proportions	Male	Female
Type	0		Omission of Appendages	0	0	Upper and Lower Halves	0	1	Hair Shading	1	3	Head	09	10
Sex Sequence	0		Position of Both Arms	2	0	Four Quarters	4	4	Nudity and Transparency	9	0	Neck	08	06
Posture	1	1	Position of Right Arm	4	4	Relative Size	0		Form	1	1	Shoulders		09
Perspective	2	0	Position of Left Arm	7	4	Constant Line Pressure	3	3	Detailing	1	1	Right Arm	07	08
Vertical Midline	4	0	Position of Legs	1	4	Variable Line Pressure	0	0	Identity and Sex	1	1	Left Arm		08
Bilateral Symmetry	0	4	Relation of Long Axes	1	1	Line Continuity	2	2	Sophistication	2	2	Chest	10	08
Horizontal Midline	0	0	Right and Left Halves	3	1	Body Shading	1	3	Height	09	07	Girth	08	07

GENERAL CHARACTERISTICS OF SUBJECT

IDENTIFICATION
No. E83
Sex M
Marital status S
Age 22 yrs. at
psychological tests

PARENTAL HISTORY
Father
C H S D O
- - - - ?
Mother
C H S D O
- - - - -

PHYSIOLOGICAL AND METABOLIC DATA

	Admission	Initial	Control	Cold pressor change	Exercise change	Smoking change
Systolic pressure	120	118	120	+22	+48	-04
Diastolic pressure	68	60	70	+40	-20	-02
Heart rate	68	60	56	00	+27	+05

Age 22 yrs.	Height 72 in.	Ponderal index 13.14
	Weight 165 lbs.	Cholesterol 225 mg. per 100 ml.
	Overweight +01 %	Vital capacity liters

HABIT SURVEY

Smoking habits: *occasional smoker*

   Age begun 18 yrs.   Inhalation: yes

Habits of nervous tension: 5, 6, 16, 25

STRONG VOCATIONAL INTEREST TEST

Occupation	Artist	Psychologist	Architect	Physician	Osteopath	Dentist	Veterinarian	Mathematician	Physicist	Engineer	Chemist	Production Manager
Standard Score	42	36	39	57	42	42	26	31	29	41	45	27

Occupation	Farmer	Aviator	Carpenter	Printer	Math.-Sci. Teacher	Ind. Arts Teacher	Voc. Agric. Teacher	Policeman	Forest Serv. Man	Y.M.C.A. Phys. Dir.	Personnel Director	Public Administrator
Standard Score	45	46	24	30	35	12	25	27	42	26	23	37

Occupation	Y.M.C.A. Secretary	Soc. Sci. H.S. Teacher	City Sch. Sup't.	Social Worker	Minister	Musician Performer	C.P.A.	Senior C.P.A.	Accountant	Office Man	Purchasing Agent	Banker
Standard Score	21	18	18	27	64	46	24	34	15	21	13	17

Occupation	Mortician	Pharmacist	Sales Manager	Real Est. Manager	Life Ins. Salesman	Advertising Man	Lawyer	Author- Journalist	President Mfg. Co.	Interest Maturity	Occupational Level	Masculinity- Femininity
Standard Score	16	24	23	30	21	35	34	40	30	51	57	45

Plate 714　　　MODERATELY SOPHISTICATED DRAWINGS　　　761

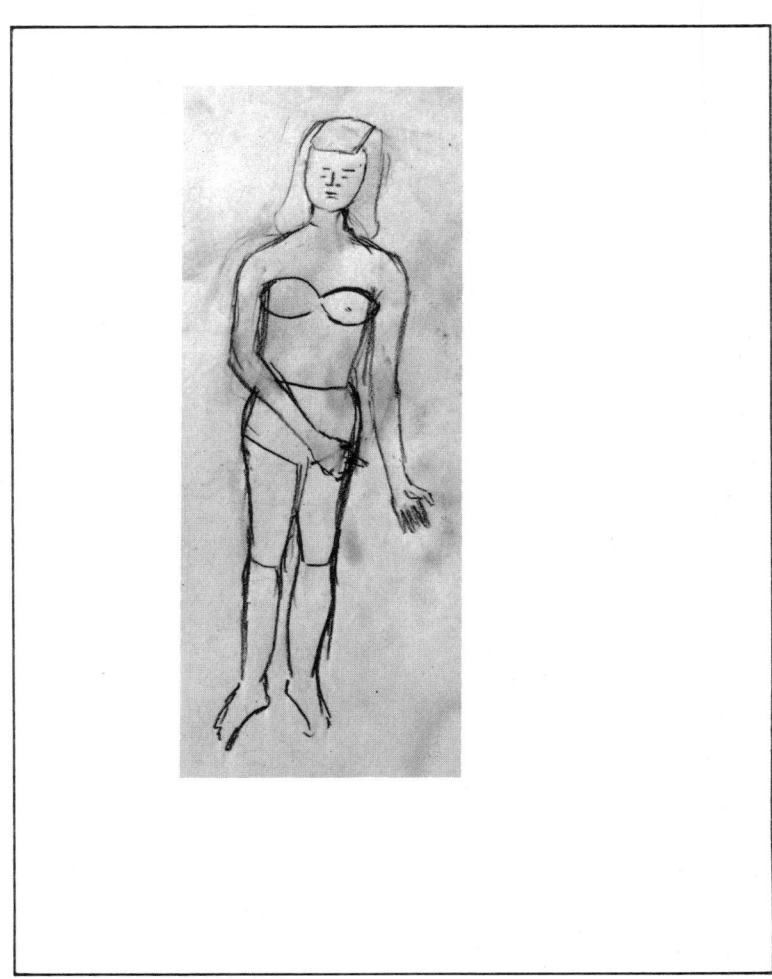

FIGURE-DRAWING CHARACTERISTICS

Structural	Male	Female	Structural	Male	Female	Structural and Graphic	Male	Female	Graphic, Global and Height	Male	Female	Body Proportions	Male	Female
	Both						Both							
Type	0		Omission of Appendages	0	0	Upper and Lower Halves	1	1	Hair Shading	5	5	Head	07	07
Sex Sequence	0		Position of Both Arms	4	1	Four Quarters	4	4	Nudity and Transparency	7	2	Neck	06	06
Posture	2	1	Position of Right Arm	7	5	Relative Size	2		Form	1	1	Shoulders		06
Perspective	2	0	Position of Left Arm	6	4	Constant Line Pressure	0	0	Detailing	3	3	Right Arm		06
Vertical Midline	5	0	Position of Legs	8	4	Variable Line Pressure	5	5	Identity and Sex	1	1	Left Arm	06	06
Bilateral Symmetry	0	3	Relation of Long Axes	1	1	Line Continuity	0	0	Sophistication	2	2	Chest	07	06
Horizontal Midline	6	4	Right and Left Halves	2	2	Body Shading	4	2	Height	06	07	Girth	07	06

GENERAL CHARACTERISTICS OF SUBJECT

<table>
<tr><th colspan="2">IDENTIFICATION</th><th colspan="2">PARENTAL HISTORY</th><th colspan="7">PHYSIOLOGICAL AND METABOLIC DATA</th><th colspan="2">HABIT SURVEY</th></tr>
</table>

IDENTIFICATION

No. 235

Sex M

Marital status M

Age 23 yrs. at psychological tests

PARENTAL HISTORY

Father

C H S D O

- - - - -

Mother

C H S D O

- - - - ?

PHYSIOLOGICAL AND METABOLIC DATA

	Admission	Initial	Control	Cold pressor change	Exercise change	Smoking change
Systolic pressure	110	106	104	+08	+20	
Diastolic pressure	70	72	74	+07	-02	
Heart rate	72	66	63	+02	+14	

Age 21 yrs.	Height	68 in.	Ponderal index 12.80
	Weight	150 lbs.	Cholesterol 170 mg. per 100 ml.
	Overweight +03 %		Vital capacity 4.1 liters

HABIT SURVEY

Smoking habits: nonsmoker

Age begun   yrs.　Inhalation:

Habits of nervous tension: 5, 10, 23

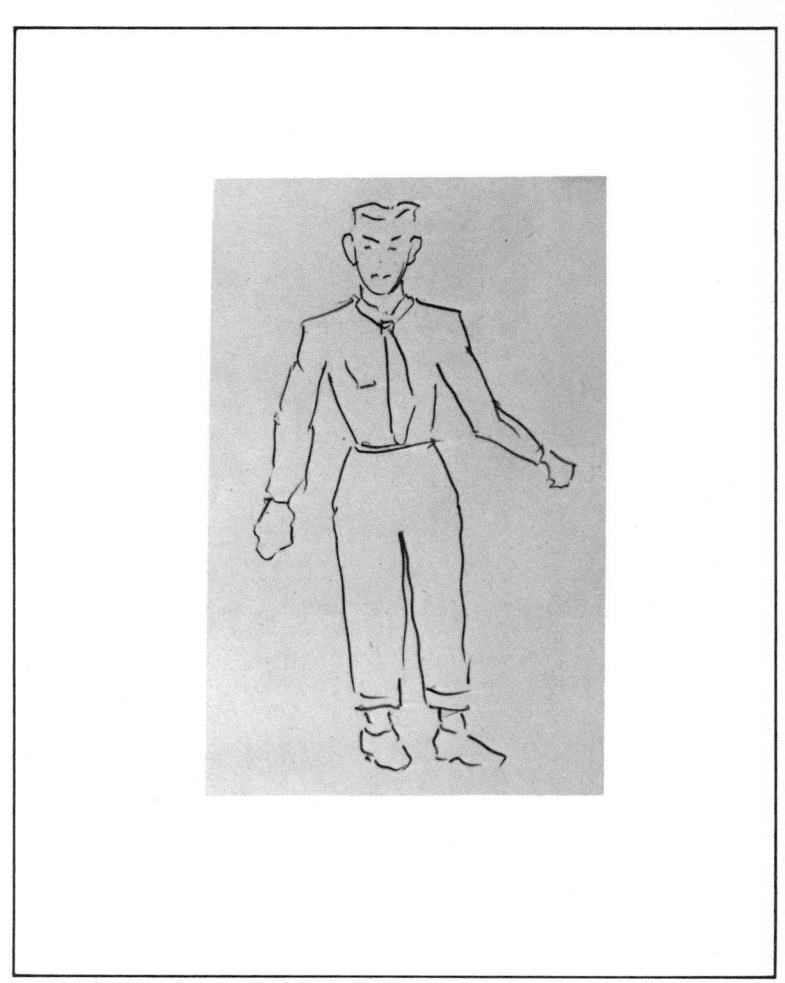

FIGURE-DRAWING CHARACTERISTICS

Structural	Male Female Both	Structural	Male	Female	Structural and Graphic	Male Female Both	Graphic, Global and Height	Male	Female	Body Proportions	Male	Female
Type	0	Omission of Appendages	0	0	Upper and Lower Halves	1 1	Hair Shading	5	5	Head	07	07
Sex Sequence	1	Position of Both Arms	0	0	Four Quarters	4 4	Nudity and Transparency	7	7	Neck	06	06
Posture	1 1	Position of Right Arm	2	2	Relative Size	0	Form	1	1	Shoulders	06	06
Perspective	0 0	Position of Left Arm	2	2	Constant Line Pressure	5 0	Detailing	3	3	Right Arm	06	04
Vertical Midline	3 0	Position of Legs	4	5	Variable Line Pressure	0 5	Identity and Sex	1	1	Left Arm	06	04
Bilateral Symmetry	3 3	Relation of Long Axes	1	1	Line Continuity	2 2	Sophistication	2	2	Chest	05	06
Horizontal Midline	4 4	Right and Left Halves	0	1	Body Shading	0 1	Height	06	05	Girth	05	05

GENERAL CHARACTERISTICS OF SUBJECT

IDENTIFICATION
No.   380
Sex M
Marital status   S
Age 27 yrs. at
psychological tests

PARENTAL HISTORY
Father
C   H   S   D   O
-    -   -   -   -
Mother
C   H   S   D   O
-    -   -   -   ?

PHYSIOLOGICAL AND METABOLIC DATA

	Admission	Initial	Control	Cold pressor change	Exercise change	Smoking change
Systolic pressure	140	124	114	+06	+36	
Diastolic pressure	80	72	72	+10	+08	
Heart rate	72	88	75	+04	+19	

Age 26 yrs.	Height 68 in.	Ponderal index 12.53	
	Weight 160 lbs.	Cholesterol 185 mg. per 100 ml.	
	Overweight +07 %	Vital capacity 5.1 liters	

HABIT SURVEY
Smoking habits: occasional smoker
Age begun 18 yrs.   Inhalation: no
Habits of nervous tension: 2, 4, 5, 16, 18, 23, 25

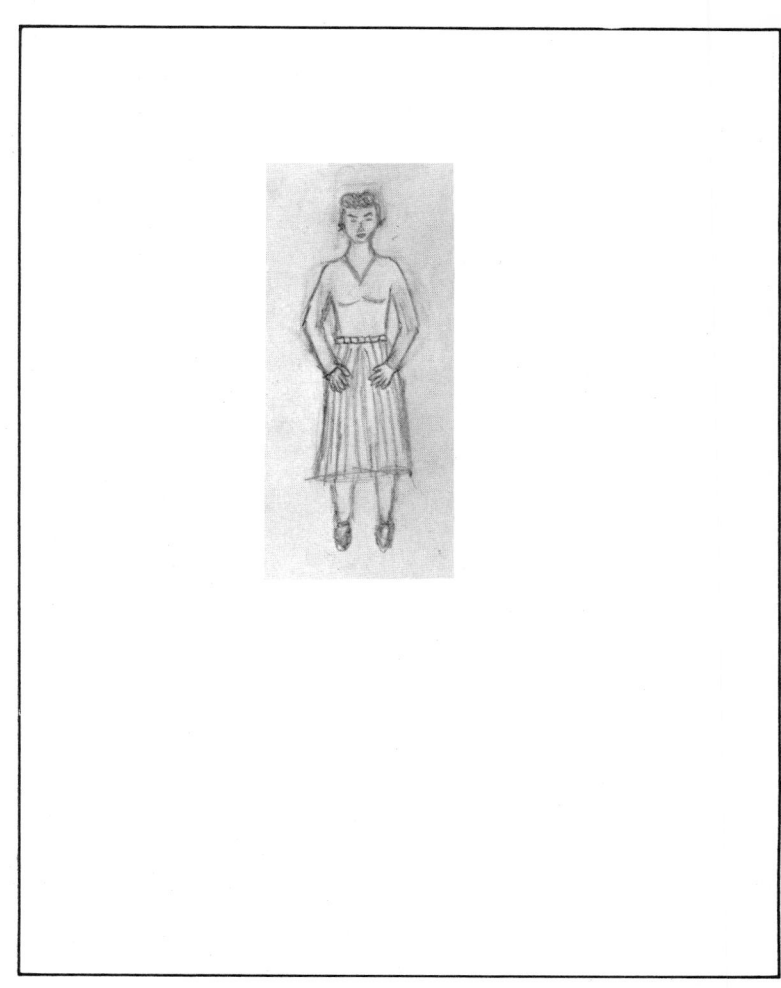

FIGURE-DRAWING CHARACTERISTICS

Structural	Male Female Both	Structural	Male	Female	Structural and Graphic	Male Female Both		Graphic, Global and Height	Male	Female	Body Proportions	Male	Female
Type	0	Omission of Appendages	0	0	Upper and Lower Halves	2	1	Hair Shading	3	3	Head	04	03
Sex Sequence	0	Position of Both Arms	0	0	Four Quarters	4	4	Nudity and Transparency	7	7	Neck	04	06
Posture	1 1	Position of Right Arm	5	5	Relative Size	4		Form	1	1	Shoulders	03	03
Perspective	0 0	Position of Left Arm	5	5	Constant Line Pressure	3	3	Detailing	1	1	Right Arm	02	02
Vertical Midline	3 0	Position of Legs	4	4	Variable Line Pressure	0	0	Identity and Sex	1	1	Left Arm	04	02
Bilateral Symmetry	5 5	Relation of Long Axes	1	1	Line Continuity	0	0	Sophistication	2	2	Chest	03	03
Horizontal Midline	4 4	Right and Left Halves	1	1	Body Shading	6	7	Height	03	03	Girth	03	03

GENERAL CHARACTERISTICS OF SUBJECT

IDENTIFICATION
No. 465
Sex M
Marital status M
Age 24 yrs. at
psychological tests

PARENTAL HISTORY
Father
C H S D O
– – – – –
Mother
C H S D O
– – – – ?

PHYSIOLOGICAL AND METABOLIC DATA

	Admission	Initial	Control	Cold pressor change	Exercise change	Smoking change
Systolic pressure	120	108	102		+08	
Diastolic pressure	80	74	76		–06	
Heart rate	88	76	71		+04	

Age 22 yrs.	Height 75 in.	Ponderal index 13.93
	Weight 156 lbs.	Cholesterol 190 mg. per 100 ml.
	Overweight –12 %	Vital capacity 5.1 liters

HABIT SURVEY

Smoking habits: nonsmoker

Age begun   yrs.   Inhalation:

Habits of nervous tension: 6, 9

FIGURE-DRAWING CHARACTERISTICS

Structural	Male Female Both	Structural	Male	Female	Structural and Graphic	Male Female Both		Graphic, Global and Height	Male	Female	Body Proportions	Male	Female
Type	0	Omission of Appendages	0	0	Upper and Lower Halves	1	0	Hair Shading	1	1	Head	05	06
Sex Sequence	0	Position of Both Arms	4	4	Four Quarters	4	4	Nudity and Transparency	7	7	Neck	05	04
Posture	1	1	Position of Right Arm	7	7	Relative Size	2		Form	1	1	Shoulders		
Perspective	2	2	Position of Left Arm	4	4	Constant Line Pressure	0	0	Detailing	3	3	Right Arm		
Vertical Midline	7	4	Position of Legs	1	1	Variable Line Pressure	5	2	Identity and Sex	1	1	Left Arm	04	03
Bilateral Symmetry	0	0	Relation of Long Axes	1	1	Line Continuity	0	0	Sophistication	2	2	Chest	04	04
Horizontal Midline	4	4	Right and Left Halves	2	2	Body Shading	3	4	Height	04	04	Girth	04	02

GENERAL CHARACTERISTICS OF SUBJECT

IDENTIFICATION
No. 623
Sex M
Marital status   M
Age 24 yrs. at
psychological tests

PARENTAL HISTORY				
Father				
C	H	S	D	O
-	-	-	-	-
Mother				
C	H	S	D	O
-	-	-	-	?

PHYSIOLOGICAL AND METABOLIC DATA

	Admission	Initial	Control	Cold pressor change	Exercise change	Smoking change
Systolic pressure	108	118	106	+10	+36	00
Diastolic pressure	70	74	70	+16	+10	+14
Heart rate	84	92	81	-20	+30	+04

Age 21 yrs.	Height 68 in.	Ponderal index 13.13
	Weight 139 lbs.	Cholesterol 237 mg. per 100 ml.
	Overweight -04 %	Vital capacity 4.1 liters

HABIT SURVEY
Smoking habits: heavy cigarette smoker

Age begun 13 yrs.   Inhalation: yes

Habits of nervous tension: 2, 4, 5, 6, 9, 11, 15, 18, 22

Plate 718   **MODERATELY SOPHISTICATED DRAWINGS**   765

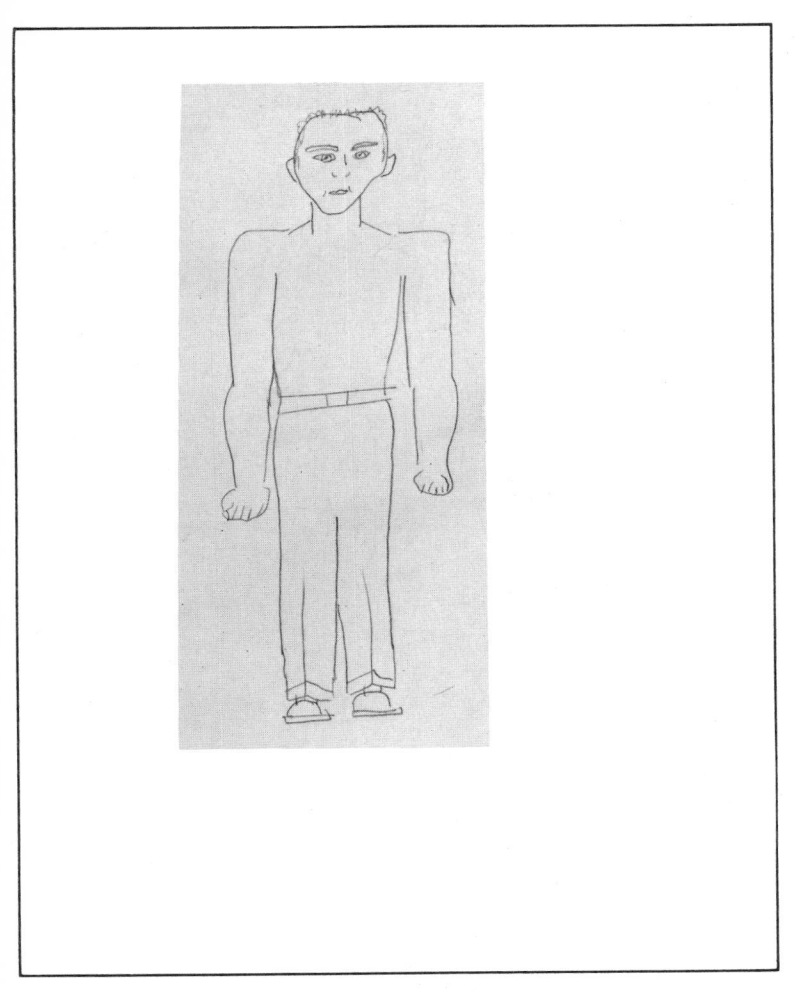

FIGURE-DRAWING CHARACTERISTICS

Structural	Male	Female	Structural	Male	Female	Structural and Graphic	Male	Female	Graphic, Global and Height	Male	Female	Body Proportions	Male	Female
	Both						Both							
Type	0		Omission of Appendages	0	7	Upper and Lower Halves	1	1	Hair Shading	7	1	Head	08	05
Sex Sequence	0		Position of Both Arms	0	0	Four Quarters	4	4	Nudity and Transparency	3	7	Neck	07	02
Posture	1	1	Position of Right Arm	0	8	Relative Size	0		Form	1	1	Shoulders	09	05
Perspective	0	0	Position of Left Arm	0	8	Constant Line Pressure	5	0	Detailing	3	3	Right Arm	06	
Vertical Midline	0	0	Position of Legs	3	4	Variable Line Pressure	0	5	Identity and Sex	1	1	Left Arm	06	
Bilateral Symmetry	3	3	Relation of Long Axes	1	1	Line Continuity	4	3	Sophistication	2	2	Chest	06	04
Horizontal Midline	4	0	Right and Left Halves	1	1	Body Shading	2	3	Height	06	05	Girth	06	05

GENERAL CHARACTERISTICS OF SUBJECT

IDENTIFICATION
No. G65
Sex M
Marital status S
Age 23 yrs. at
psychological tests

PARENTAL HISTORY
Father
C   H   S   D   O
–   –   –   –   –
Mother
C   H   S   D   O
–   –   –   –   ?

PHYSIOLOGICAL AND METABOLIC DATA

	Admission	Initial	Control	Cold pressor change	Exercise change	Smoking change
Systolic pressure	150	154	140	+26	+42	+08
Diastolic pressure	82	82	62	+14	+24	+12
Heart rate	76	60	69	+10	+15	+01

Age 22 yrs.	Height 74 in.	Ponderal index 12.16
	Weight 178 lbs.	Cholesterol 207 mg. per 100 ml.
	Overweight +03 %	Vital capacity liters

HABIT SURVEY

Smoking habits: nonsmoker

Age begun yrs. Inhalation:

Habits of nervous tension: 3, 4, 16, 23

STRONG VOCATIONAL INTEREST TEST

Occupation	Artist	Psychologist	Architect	Physician	Osteopath	Dentist	Veterinarian	Mathematician	Physicist	Engineer	Chemist	Production Manager
Standard Score	42	49	49	63	38	45	15	48	54	62	59	32

Occupation	Farmer	Aviator	Carpenter	Printer	Math.-Sci. Teacher	Ind. Arts Teacher	Voc. Agric. Teacher	Policeman	Forest Serv. Man	Y.M.C.A. Phys. Dir.	Personnel Director	Public Administrator
Standard Score	41	50	25	29	39	26	25	21	31	11	22	31

Occupation	Y.M.C.A. Secretary	Soc. Sci. H.S. Teacher	City Sch. Sup't.	Social Worker	Minister	Musician Performer	C.P.A.	Senior C.P.A.	Accountant	Office Man	Purchasing Agent	Banker
Standard Score	03	03	15	18	59	36	32	30	19	14	17	09

Occupation	Mortician	Pharmacist	Sales Manager	Real Est. Manager	Life Ins. Salesman	Advertising Man	Lawyer	Author-Journalist	President Mfg. Co.	Interest Maturity	Occupational Level	Masculinity-Femininity
Standard Score	05	22	15	26	12	28	35	39	33	48	62	58

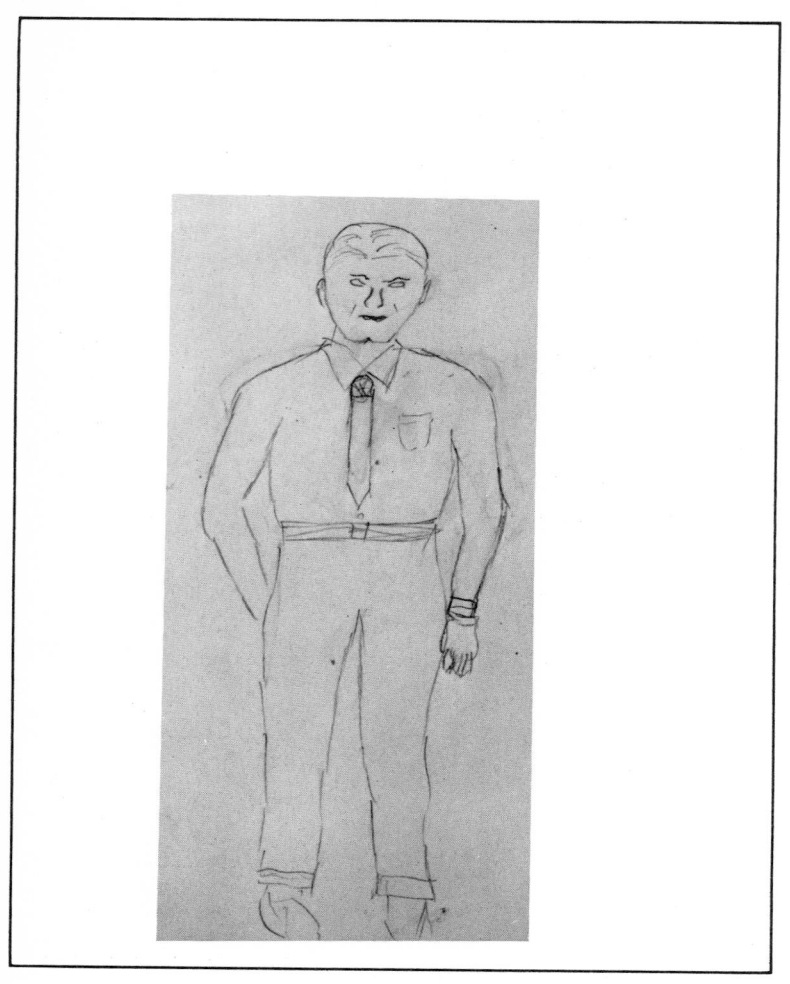

FIGURE-DRAWING CHARACTERISTICS

Structural	Male Female Both		Structural	Male	Female	Structural and Graphic	Male Female Both		Graphic, Global and Height	Male	Female	Body Proportions	Male	Female
Type	0		Omission of Appendages	7	7	Upper and Lower Halves	3	3	Hair Shading	1	5	Head	09	09
Sex Sequence	0		Position of Both Arms	0	0	Four Quarters	4	4	Nudity and Transparency	7	7	Neck	06	06
Posture	1	1	Position of Right Arm	5	5	Relative Size	4		Form	1	1	Shoulders	11	08
Perspective	0	0	Position of Left Arm	5	5	Constant Line Pressure	3	0	Detailing	3	3	Right Arm		
Vertical Midline	3	0	Position of Legs	4	4	Variable Line Pressure	0	1	Identity and Sex	1	1	Left Arm	08	
Bilateral Symmetry	3	3	Relation of Long Axes	1	1	Line Continuity	0	0	Sophistication	2	2	Chest	09	07
Horizontal Midline	4	4	Right and Left Halves	1	1	Body Shading	4	5	Height	07	08	Girth	10	08

GENERAL CHARACTERISTICS OF SUBJECT

IDENTIFICATION
No. 215
Sex M
Marital status S
Age 24 yrs. at
psychological tests

PARENTAL HISTORY
Father
C   H   S   D   O
-    -   -   -   -
Mother
C   H   S   D   O
-    -   -   -   -

PHYSIOLOGICAL AND METABOLIC DATA

	Admission	Initial	Control	Cold pressor change	Exercise change	Smoking change
Systolic pressure	112					
Diastolic pressure	72					
Heart rate	64					

Age 21 yrs.	Height 70 in.	Ponderal index 13.92
	Weight 127 lbs.	Cholesterol 177 mg. per 100 ml.
	Overweight -17 %	Vital capacity liters

HABIT SURVEY
Smoking habits: nonsmoker
Age begun   yrs.   Inhalation:
Habits of nervous tension: 3, 4, 5, 9, 15, 21

FIGURE-DRAWING CHARACTERISTICS

Structural	Male Female Both		Structural	Male	Female	Structural and Graphic	Male Female Both		Graphic, Global and Height	Male	Female	Body Proportions	Male	Female
Type	0		Omission of Appendages	0	0	Upper and Lower Halves	1	0	Hair Shading	0	3	Head	06	06
Sex Sequence	0		Position of Both Arms	0	0	Four Quarters	4	4	Nudity and Transparency	7	7	Neck	06	06
Posture	1	1	Position of Right Arm	2	2	Relative Size	0		Form	3	3	Shoulders	07	05
Perspective	0	0	Position of Left Arm	2	2	Constant Line Pressure	0	0	Detailing	1	1	Right Arm	04	04
Vertical Midline	3	0	Position of Legs	6	4	Variable Line Pressure	5	5	Identity and Sex	1	1	Left Arm	04	04
Bilateral Symmetry	3	3	Relation of Long Axes	1	1	Line Continuity	0	0	Sophistication	2	2	Chest	06	05
Horizontal Midline	4	4	Right and Left Halves	1	1	Body Shading	3	3	Height	07	05	Girth	05	05

GENERAL CHARACTERISTICS OF SUBJECT

IDENTIFICATION

No. 224

Sex M

Marital status M

Age 26 yrs. at psychological tests

PARENTAL HISTORY

Father

C   H   S   D   0

–   –   –   –   –

Mother

C   H   S   D   0

–   –   –   –   –

PHYSIOLOGICAL AND METABOLIC DATA

	Admission	Initial	Control	Cold pressor change	Exercise change	Smoking change
Systolic pressure	114	122	102	+18	+50	
Diastolic pressure	64	52	54	+30	-06	
Heart rate	66	80	73	+14	+04	

Age 23 yrs.

Height 72 in.

Weight 166 lbs.

Overweight +01 %

Ponderal index 13.10

Cholesterol 230 mg. per 100 ml.

Vital capacity 4.9 liters

HABIT SURVEY

Smoking habits: moderate cigarette smoker

Age begun 19 yrs.   Inhalation: yes

Habits of nervous tension: 5, 6, 9, 11, 15, 21

FIGURE-DRAWING CHARACTERISTICS

Structural	Male Female Both		Structural	Male	Female	Structural and Graphic	Male Both	Female	Graphic, Global and Height	Male	Female	Body Proportions	Male	Female
Type	0		Omission of Appendages	0	0	Upper and Lower Halves	2	1	Hair Shading	5	1	Head	06	06
Sex Sequence	0		Position of Both Arms	0	0	Four Quarters	0	4	Nudity and Transparency	7	2	Neck	08	06
Posture	1	1	Position of Right Arm	0	0	Relative Size	2		Form	1	1	Shoulders	05	04
Perspective	0	0	Position of Left Arm	0	0	Constant Line Pressure	5	5	Detailing	3	1	Right Arm	04	02
Vertical Midline	3	0	Position of Legs	4	4	Variable Line Pressure	0	0	Identity and Sex	1	1	Left Arm	04	02
Bilateral Symmetry	3	5	Relation of Long Axes	1	1	Line Continuity	4	4	Sophistication	2	2	Chest	03	03
Horizontal Midline	4	4	Right and Left Halves	2	2	Body Shading	2	3	Height	04	04	Girth	03	03

GENERAL CHARACTERISTICS OF SUBJECT

<table>
<tr><td>IDENTIFICATION</td><td>PARENTAL HISTORY</td><td colspan="7">PHYSIOLOGICAL AND METABOLIC DATA</td><td>HABIT SURVEY</td></tr>
</table>

IDENTIFICATION
No. 272
Sex M
Marital status M
Age 23 yrs. at
psychological tests

PARENTAL HISTORY
Father
C H S D O
- - - - -
Mother
C H S D O
- - - - -

PHYSIOLOGICAL AND METABOLIC DATA

	Admission	Initial	Control	Cold pressor change	Exercise change	Smoking change
Systolic pressure	110	112	106	+08	+28	
Diastolic pressure	72	74	68	+12	00	
Heart rate	80	90	88	+12	+24	

Age 21 yrs.

Height 72 in. Ponderal index 13.74
Weight 144 lbs. Cholesterol 180 mg. per 100 ml.
Overweight -11 % Vital capacity liters

HABIT SURVEY

Smoking habits: unknown
　Age begun　yrs.　Inhalation:
Habits of nervous tension:

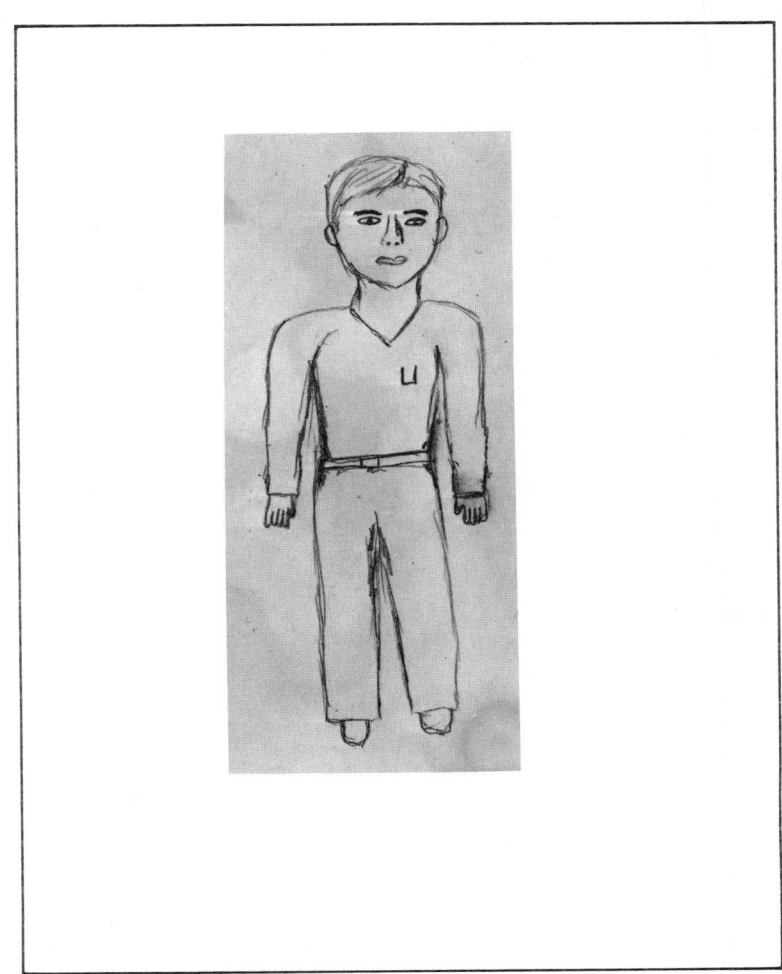

FIGURE-DRAWING CHARACTERISTICS

Structural	Male Female Both	Structural	Male	Female	Structural and Graphic	Male Female Both		Graphic, Global and Height	Male	Female	Body Proportions	Male	Female
Type	0	Omission of Appendages	0	3	Upper and Lower Halves	1	7	Hair Shading	3	3	Head	11	13
Sex Sequence	1	Position of Both Arms	0	0	Four Quarters	4	4	Nudity and Transparency	7	7	Neck	10	10
Posture	1 0	Position of Right Arm	0	0	Relative Size	5		Form	3	3	Shoulders	08	10
Perspective	0 0	Position of Left Arm	0	0	Constant Line Pressure	0	0	Detailing	3	3	Right Arm	04	04
Vertical Midline	0 0	Position of Legs	4	0	Variable Line Pressure	5	5	Identity and Sex	1	1	Left Arm	04	04
Bilateral Symmetry	5 3	Relation of Long Axes	1	1	Line Continuity	0	0	Sophistication	2	2	Chest	06	07
Horizontal Midline	4 4	Right and Left Halves	1	1	Body Shading	0	6	Height	06		Girth	07	07

GENERAL CHARACTERISTICS OF SUBJECT

<table>
<tr><td rowspan="2">

IDENTIFICATION

No. 311

Sex F

Marital status S

Age 24 yrs. at

psychological tests

</td><td rowspan="2">

PARENTAL HISTORY

Father

C   H   S   D   O

–   –   –   –   –

Mother

C   H   S   D   O

–   –   –   –   –

</td><td colspan="6">PHYSIOLOGICAL AND METABOLIC DATA</td><td rowspan="2">

HABIT SURVEY

Smoking habits: nonsmoker

   Age begun   yrs.   Inhalation:

Habits of nervous tension: 5, 6, 23

</td></tr>
<tr><td></td><td>Admission</td><td>Initial</td><td>Control</td><td>Cold pressor change</td><td>Exercise change</td><td>Smoking change</td></tr>
<tr><td colspan="2"></td><td>Systolic pressure</td><td>110</td><td>102</td><td>92</td><td>+20</td><td>+34</td><td></td><td></td></tr>
<tr><td colspan="2"></td><td>Diastolic pressure</td><td>64</td><td>52</td><td>52</td><td>+16</td><td>+18</td><td></td><td></td></tr>
<tr><td colspan="2"></td><td>Heart rate</td><td>84</td><td>94</td><td>86</td><td>+10</td><td>+21</td><td></td><td></td></tr>
<tr><td colspan="2"></td><td colspan="3">Height   62   in.</td><td colspan="3">Ponderal index 12.33</td><td></td></tr>
<tr><td colspan="2"></td><td>Age 22 yrs.</td><td colspan="2">Weight   127   lbs.</td><td colspan="3">Cholesterol   265   mg. per 100 ml.</td><td></td></tr>
<tr><td colspan="2"></td><td colspan="3">Overweight +06 %</td><td colspan="3">Vital capacity   2.5   liters</td><td></td></tr>
</table>

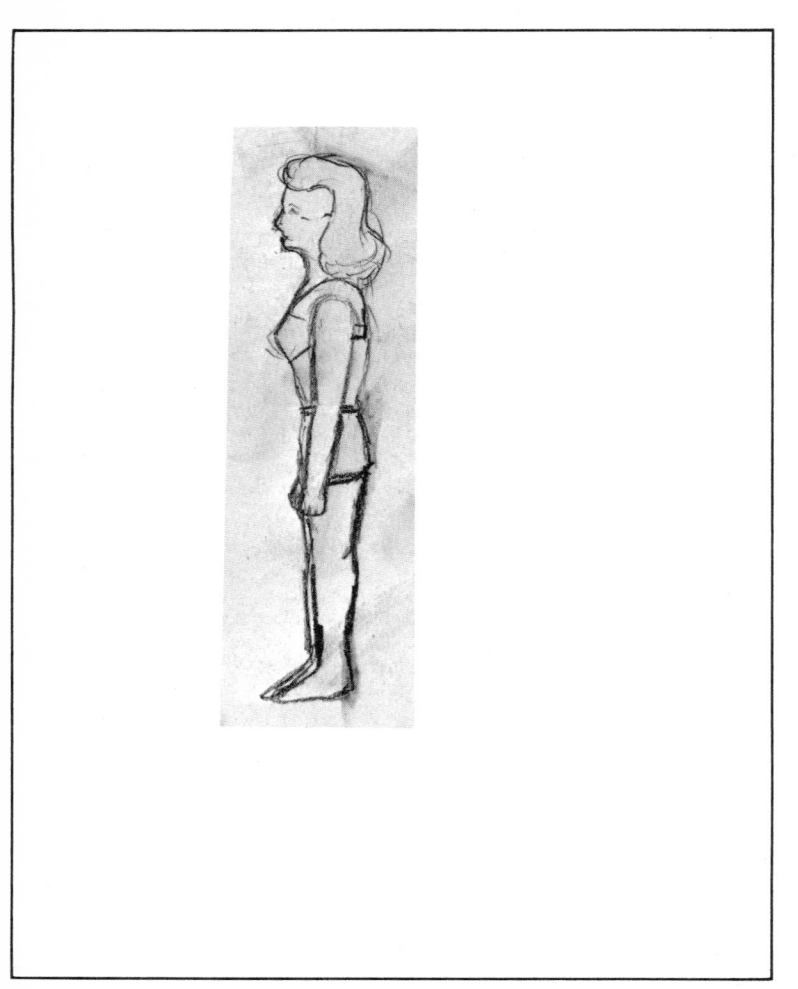

FIGURE-DRAWING CHARACTERISTICS

Structural	Male Female Both	Structural	Male	Female	Structural and Graphic	Male Female Both		Graphic, Global and Height	Male	Female	Body Proportions	Male	Female
Type	0	Omission of Appendages	0	0	Upper and Lower Halves	1	1	Hair Shading	5	3	Head	04	07
Sex Sequence	1	Position of Both Arms	4	4	Four Quarters	4	4	Nudity and Transparency	7	2	Neck	00	06
Posture	1 1	Position of Right Arm	7	7	Relative Size	4		Form	1	1	Shoulders		
Perspective	2 2	Position of Left Arm	0	0	Constant Line Pressure	0	0	Detailing	1	1	Right Arm		
Vertical Midline	4 4	Position of Legs	1	1	Variable Line Pressure	5	5	Identity and Sex	1	1	Left Arm	02	04
Bilateral Symmetry	0 0	Relation of Long Axes	3	1	Line Continuity	0	0	Sophistication	2	2	Chest	04	05
Horizontal Midline	4 4	Right and Left Halves	3	2	Body Shading	4	0	Height	02	05	Girth	03	05

GENERAL CHARACTERISTICS OF SUBJECT

IDENTIFICATION
No. 316
Sex M
Marital status M
Age 23 yrs. at
psychological tests

PARENTAL HISTORY				
Father				
C	H	S	D	O
-	-	-	-	-
Mother				
C	H	S	D	O
-	-	-	-	-

PHYSIOLOGICAL AND METABOLIC DATA

	Admission	Initial	Control	Cold pressor change	Exercise change	Smoking change
Systolic pressure	124	118	110	+10	+20	
Diastolic pressure	76	60	66	+18	+04	
Heart rate	84	94	77	+04	+10	

Age 20 yrs.	Height	72 in.	Ponderal index 13.49
	Weight	152 lbs.	Cholesterol 215 mg. per 100 ml.
	Overweight -06 %		Vital capacity 4.6 liters

HABIT SURVEY

Smoking habits: heavy cigarette smoker

Age begun 15 yrs.   Inhalation: yes

Habits of nervous tension: 1, 3, 5, 11, 23

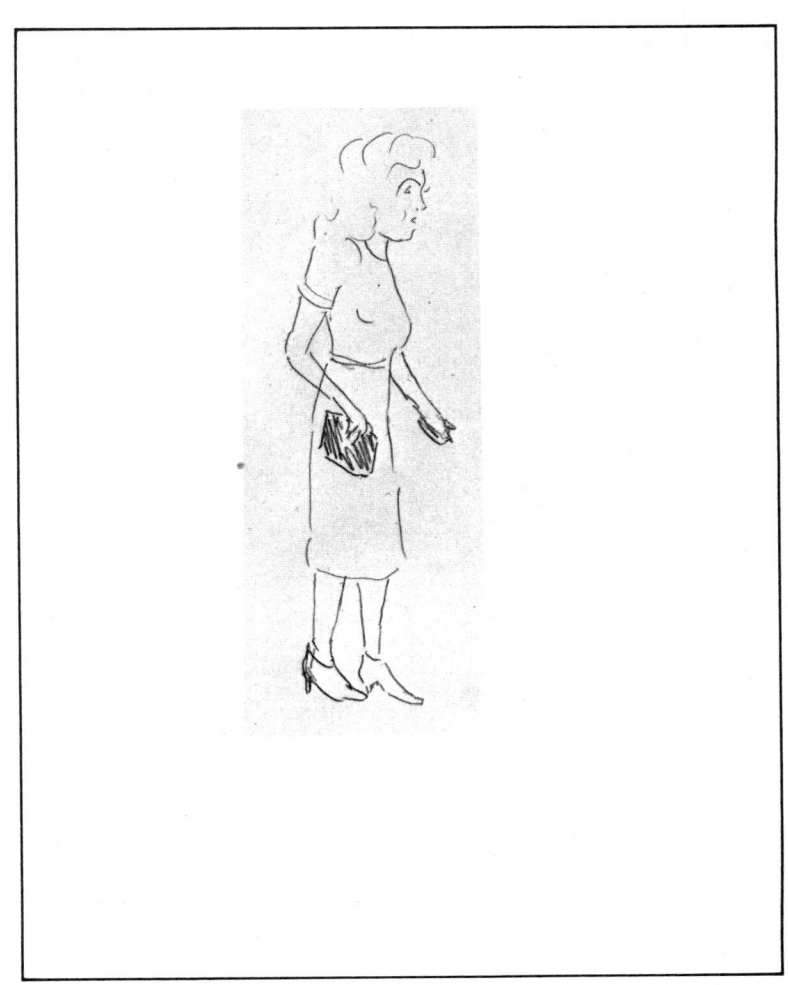

FIGURE-DRAWING CHARACTERISTICS

Structural	Male Female Both		Structural	Male	Female	Structural and Graphic	Male Female Both		Graphic, Global and Height	Male	Female	Body Proportions	Male	Female
Type	0		Omission of Appendages	7	0	Upper and Lower Halves	1	1	Hair Shading	5	7	Head	08	07
Sex Sequence	2		Position of Both Arms	0	2	Four Quarters	4	4	Nudity and Transparency	7	7	Neck	12	06
Posture	1	1	Position of Right Arm	5	5	Relative Size	0		Form	1	1	Shoulders	07	
Perspective	5	2	Position of Left Arm	5	7	Constant Line Pressure	3	0	Detailing	3	3	Right Arm		06
Vertical Midline	3	4	Position of Legs	6	4	Variable Line Pressure	0	5	Identity and Sex	1	1	Left Arm		
Bilateral Symmetry	3	0	Relation of Long Axes	1	1	Line Continuity	2	2	Sophistication	2	2	Chest	06	05
Horizontal Midline	4	4	Right and Left Halves	1	2	Body Shading	2	5	Height	06	06	Girth	06	06

GENERAL CHARACTERISTICS OF SUBJECT

IDENTIFICATION
No.   319
Sex   M
Marital status   S
Age   28   yrs. at
psychological tests

PARENTAL HISTORY
Father
C   H   S   D   O
-    -   -   -   -
Mother
C   H   S   D   O
-    -   -   -   -

PHYSIOLOGICAL AND METABOLIC DATA

	Admission	Initial	Control	Cold pressor change	Exercise change	Smoking change
Systolic pressure	112	144	130	+10	+34	-06
Diastolic pressure	60	78	70	+08	+04	00
Heart rate	72	90	88	+02	+12	+13

Age 26 yrs.	Height 69 in.	Ponderal index 12.47	
	Weight 169 lbs.	Cholesterol 135 mg. per 100 ml.	
	Overweight +10 %	Vital capacity 4.2 liters	

HABIT SURVEY
Smoking habits: heavy cigarette smoker
Age begun 18 yrs.   Inhalation: yes
Habits of nervous tension: 5, 6, 9, 11, 14

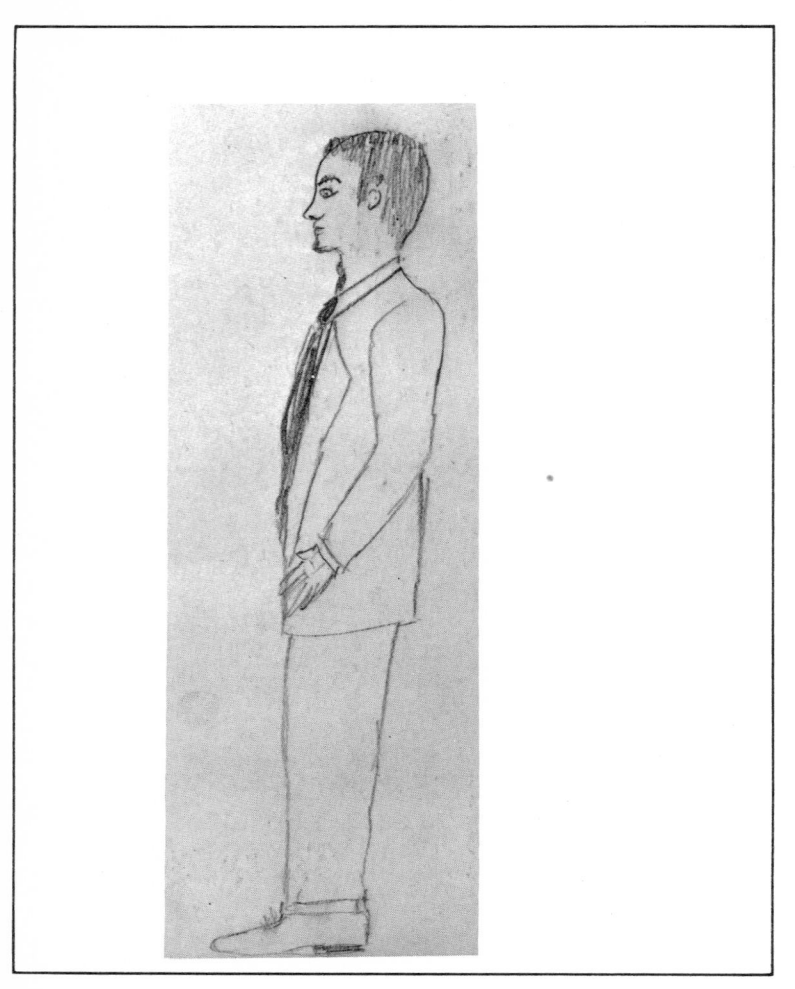

FIGURE-DRAWING CHARACTERISTICS

Structural	Male Female Both		Structural	Male	Female	Structural and Graphic	Male Female Both		Graphic, Global and Height	Male	Female	Body Proportions	Male	Female
Type	0		Omission of Appendages	0	0	Upper and Lower Halves	3	3	Hair Shading	3	3	Head	09	10
Sex Sequence	0		Position of Both Arms	4	4	Four Quarters	4	4	Nudity and Transparency	7	7	Neck	12	14
Posture	1	1	Position of Right Arm	7	7	Relative Size	2		Form	1	1	Shoulders		
Perspective	2	2	Position of Left Arm	5	4	Constant Line Pressure	0	0	Detailing	3	3	Right Arm		
Vertical Midline	7	4	Position of Legs	1	1	Variable Line Pressure	5	3	Identity and Sex	1	1	Left Arm	08	08
Bilateral Symmetry	0	0	Relation of Long Axes	1	1	Line Continuity	0	0	Sophistication	2	2	Chest	09	08
Horizontal Midline	6	4	Right and Left Halves	1	1	Body Shading	4	4	Height	08	08	Girth	11	08

GENERAL CHARACTERISTICS OF SUBJECT

IDENTIFICATION
No. 338
Sex M
Marital status S
Age 24 yrs. at
psychological tests

PARENTAL HISTORY
Father
C   H   S   D   O
-   -   -   -   -
Mother
C   H   S   D   O
-   -   -   -   -

PHYSIOLOGICAL AND METABOLIC DATA

	Admission	Initial	Control	Cold pressor change	Exercise change	Smoking change
Systolic pressure	135	130	116	+14	+28	
Diastolic pressure	85	64	70	+06	+02	
Heart rate	100	96	81	00	+22	

Age 22 yrs.	Height 72 in.	Ponderal index 12.80
	Weight 178 lbs.	Cholesterol 190 mg. per 100 ml.
	Overweight +09 %	Vital capacity 5.0 liters

HABIT SURVEY

Smoking habits: light cigarette smoker

Age begun 20 yrs.   Inhalation: yes

Habits of nervous tension: 3, 4, 5, 6, 9, 21, 22

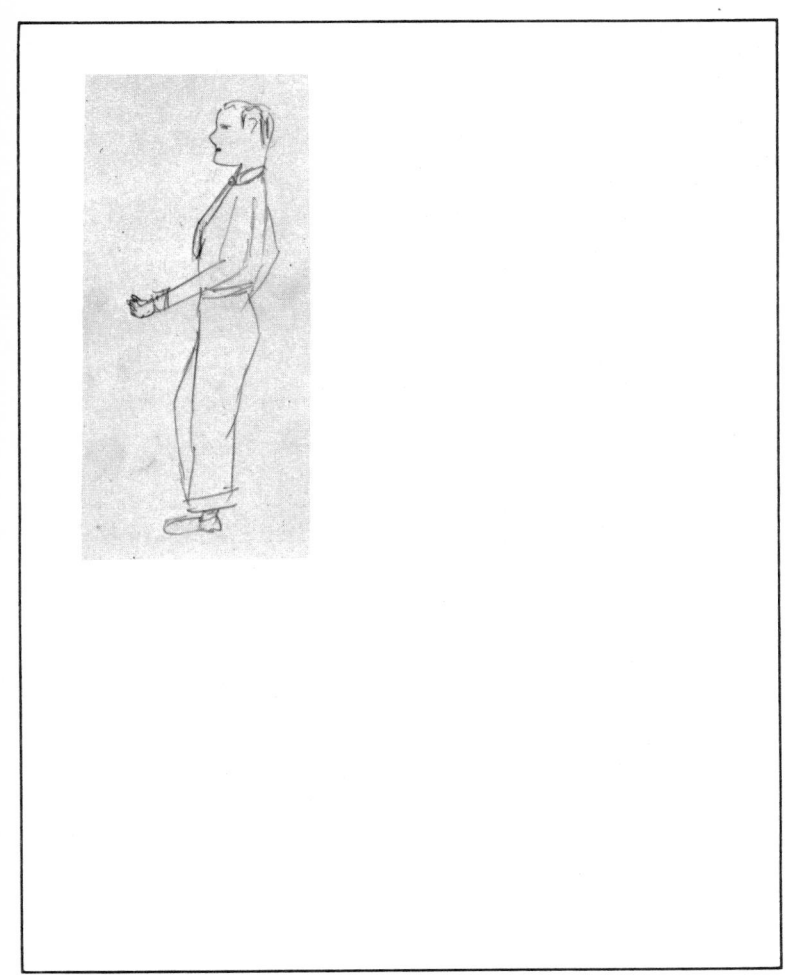

FIGURE-DRAWING CHARACTERISTICS

Structural	Male Female Both	Structural	Male	Female	Structural and Graphic	Male Female Both		Graphic, Global and Height	Male	Female	Body Proportions	Male	Female
Type	0	Omission of Appendages	0	0	Upper and Lower Halves	1	1	Hair Shading	7	3	Head	05	06
Sex Sequence	2	Position of Both Arms	4	4	Four Quarters	4	4	Nudity and Transparency	7	7	Neck	04	
Posture	1 1	Position of Right Arm	7	7	Relative Size	4		Form	1	1	Shoulders		
Perspective	2 2	Position of Left Arm	4	4	Constant Line Pressure	0	0	Detailing	3	3	Right Arm		
Vertical Midline	7 4	Position of Legs	1	1	Variable Line Pressure	1	1	Identity and Sex	1	1	Left Arm	04	04
Bilateral Symmetry	0 0	Relation of Long Axes	1	1	Line Continuity	0	0	Sophistication	2	2	Chest	05	05
Horizontal Midline	4 4	Right and Left Halves	2	2	Body Shading	0	0	Height	04	05	Girth	04	05

GENERAL CHARACTERISTICS OF SUBJECT

IDENTIFICATION
No. 370
Sex M
Marital status M
Age 24 yrs. at
psychological tests

PARENTAL HISTORY
Father
C   H   S   D   O
–   –   –   –   –
Mother
C   H   S   D   O
–   –   –   –   –

PHYSIOLOGICAL AND METABOLIC DATA

	Admission	Initial	Control	Cold pressor change	Exercise change	Smoking change
Systolic pressure	120	112	106	+29	+30	
Diastolic pressure	75	72	76	+36	–08	
Heart rate	76	60	53	+12	+18	

Age 22 yrs.	Height 70 in.	Ponderal index 12.84
	Weight 162 lbs.	Cholesterol 215 mg. per 100 ml.
	Overweight +05 %	Vital capacity 4.5 liters

HABIT SURVEY
Smoking habits: pipe smoker
Age begun 22 yrs.   Inhalation: no
Habits of nervous tension: 2, 5, 25

FIGURE-DRAWING CHARACTERISTICS

Structural	Male Female Both		Structural	Male	Female	Structural and Graphic	Male Female Both		Graphic, Global and Height	Male	Female	Body Proportions	Male	Female
Type	0		Omission of Appendages	7	0	Upper and Lower Halves	1	1	Hair Shading	5	5	Head	09	08
Sex Sequence	0		Position of Both Arms	0	1	Four Quarters	4	4	Nudity and Transparency	7	7	Neck	08	06
Posture	1	1	Position of Right Arm	5	2	Relative Size	0		Form	1	1	Shoulders	09	07
Perspective	0	0	Position of Left Arm	5	5	Constant Line Pressure	0	0	Detailing	5	3	Right Arm		06
Vertical Midline	0	3	Position of Legs	4	4	Variable Line Pressure	5	5	Identity and Sex	1	1	Left Arm		06
Bilateral Symmetry	3	3	Relation of Long Axes	1	1	Line Continuity	2	2	Sophistication	2	2	Chest	06	05
Horizontal Midline	6	6	Right and Left Halves	3	3	Body Shading	0	0	Height	07	06	Girth	08	07

GENERAL CHARACTERISTICS OF SUBJECT

IDENTIFICATION
No. 372
Sex M
Marital status S
Age 28 yrs. at psychological tests

PARENTAL HISTORY
Father
C   H   S   D   O
-   -   -   -   -
Mother
C   H   S   D   O
-   -   -   -   -

PHYSIOLOGICAL AND METABOLIC DATA

	Admission	Initial	Control	Cold pressor change	Exercise change	Smoking change
Systolic pressure	114	114	104	+08	+12	-02
Diastolic pressure	72	70	74	+02	-04	+04
Heart rate	76	96	94	+06	+03	+08

Age 26 yrs.	Height 72 in.	Ponderal index 13.43
	Weight 154 lbs.	Cholesterol 265 mg. per 100 ml.
	Overweight -08 %	Vital capacity 5.3 liters

HABIT SURVEY

Smoking habits: heavy cigarette smoker

Age begun 26 yrs.   Inhalation: yes

Habits of nervous tension: 5, 6, 11, 16, 21, 23

Plate 728   **MODERATELY SOPHISTICATED DRAWINGS**   775

FIGURE-DRAWING CHARACTERISTICS

Structural	Male Female — Both	Structural	Male	Female	Structural and Graphic	Male Female — Both		Graphic, Global and Height	Male	Female	Body Proportions	Male	Female
Type	0	Omission of Appendages	0	0	Upper and Lower Halves	3	0	Hair Shading	3	3	Head	07	05
Sex Sequence	0	Position of Both Arms	0	0	Four Quarters	4	4	Nudity and Transparency	7	7	Neck	07	07
Posture	1 1	Position of Right Arm	2	2	Relative Size	0		Form	3	3	Shoulders	07	06
Perspective	0 0	Position of Left Arm	2	2	Constant Line Pressure	0	3	Detailing	1	1	Right Arm	06	06
Vertical Midline	3 3	Position of Legs	6	6	Variable Line Pressure	1	0	Identity and Sex	1	1	Left Arm	06	06
Bilateral Symmetry	3 3	Relation of Long Axes	1	1	Line Continuity	0	0	Sophistication	2	2	Chest	06	05
Horizontal Midline	6 4	Right and Left Halves	1	1	Body Shading	7	7	Height	07	06	Girth	09	06

GENERAL CHARACTERISTICS OF SUBJECT

IDENTIFICATION
No. 613
Sex M
Marital status S
Age 24 yrs. at
psychological tests

PARENTAL HISTORY
Father
C   H   S   D   O
–   –   –   –   –
Mother
C   H   S   D   O
–   –   –   –   –

PHYSIOLOGICAL AND METABOLIC DATA

	Admission	Initial	Control	Cold pressor change	Exercise change	Smoking change
Systolic pressure	140	116	114	+20	+38	+02
Diastolic pressure	80	68	76	+30	00	+08
Heart rate	80	68	68	–08	+35	+03

Age 22 yrs.	Height 73 in.	Ponderal index 13.18
	Weight 170 lbs.	Cholesterol 222 mg. per 100 ml.
	Overweight +01 %	Vital capacity 5.3 liters

HABIT SURVEY
Smoking habits: nonsmoker
Age begun   yrs.   Inhalation:
Habits of nervous tension: 2, 5, 6, 9, 18, 21

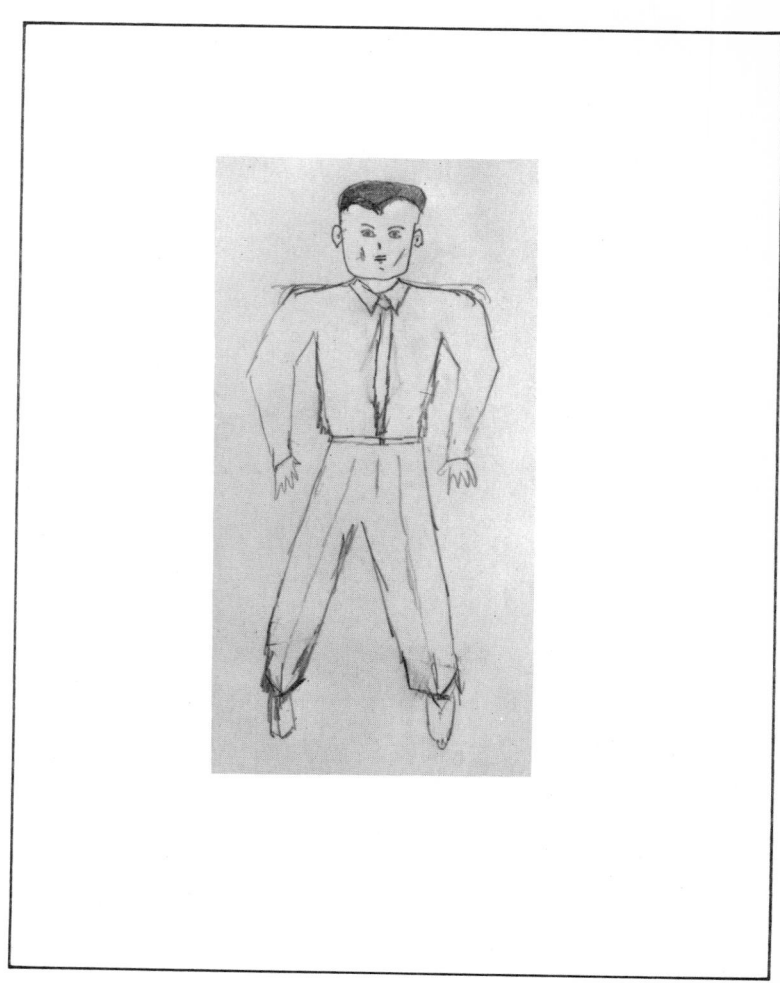

FIGURE-DRAWING CHARACTERISTICS

Structural	Male Female Both		Structural	Male	Female	Structural and Graphic	Male Female Both		Graphic, Global and Height	Male	Female	Body Proportions	Male	Female
Type	0		Omission of Appendages	0	0	Upper and Lower Halves	1	0	Hair Shading	1	3	Head	07	07
Sex Sequence	1		Position of Both Arms	0	0	Four Quarters	4	4	Nudity and Transparency	7	7	Neck	04	03
Posture	1	1	Position of Right Arm	5	2	Relative Size	2		Form	1	1	Shoulders	08	06
Perspective	0	0	Position of Left Arm	5	2	Constant Line Pressure	0	0	Detailing	1	1	Right Arm	04	04
Vertical Midline	3	3	Position of Legs	6	4	Variable Line Pressure	4	4	Identity and Sex	1	1	Left Arm	04	04
Bilateral Symmetry	3	3	Relation of Long Axes	1	1	Line Continuity	0	0	Sophistication	2	2	Chest	06	06
Horizontal Midline	4	4	Right and Left Halves	1	1	Body Shading	2	7	Height	06	06	Girth	05	05

GENERAL CHARACTERISTICS OF SUBJECT

IDENTIFICATION
No. 705
Sex M
Marital status S
Age 23 yrs. at psychological tests

PARENTAL HISTORY
Father
C   H   S   D   O
-    -   -   -   -
Mother
C   H   S   D   O
-    -   -   -   -

PHYSIOLOGICAL AND METABOLIC DATA

	Admission	Initial	Control	Cold pressor change	Exercise change	Smoking change
Systolic pressure	110	108	108	+16	+32	+07
Diastolic pressure	81	30	60	+30	-10	+15
Heart rate	78	80	75	00	+32	+16

Age 21 yrs.	Height	75 in.	Ponderal index 13.74
	Weight	163 lbs.	Cholesterol 177 mg. per 100 ml.
	Overweight -08 %		Vital capacity 5.4 liters

HABIT SURVEY
Smoking habits: former smoker
Age begun 17 yrs.   Inhalation:
Habits of nervous tension: 2, 4, 5, 6, 10, 16, 17, 22, 23

FIGURE-DRAWING CHARACTERISTICS

Structural	Male Female Both		Structural	Male	Female	Structural and Graphic	Male Female Both		Graphic, Global and Height	Male	Female	Body Proportions	Male	Female
Type	0		Omission of Appendages	0	0	Upper and Lower Halves	0	3	Hair Shading	1	2	Head	07	07
Sex Sequence	0		Position of Both Arms	0	1	Four Quarters	4	4	Nudity and Transparency	7	7	Neck	08	05
Posture	1	1	Position of Right Arm	0	4	Relative Size	2		Form	3	1	Shoulders	08	07
Perspective	0	0	Position of Left Arm	0	1	Constant Line Pressure	0	0	Detailing	1	1	Right Arm	06	06
Vertical Midline	3	0	Position of Legs	2	4	Variable Line Pressure	5	5	Identity and Sex	1	1	Left Arm	06	04
Bilateral Symmetry	4	3	Relation of Long Axes	1	1	Line Continuity	0	0	Sophistication	2	2	Chest	06	06
Horizontal Midline	4	4	Right and Left Halves	1	1	Body Shading	2	3	Height	06	07	Girth	09	07

GENERAL CHARACTERISTICS OF SUBJECT

IDENTIFICATION
No. 727
Sex M
Marital status S
Age 23 yrs. at psychological tests

PARENTAL HISTORY
Father
C H S D O
- - - - -
Mother
C H S D O
- - - - -

PHYSIOLOGICAL AND METABOLIC DATA

	Admission	Initial	Control	Cold pressor change	Exercise change	Smoking change
Systolic pressure	118	128	108	+14	+40	+15
Diastolic pressure	76	72	64	+22	-04	+15
Heart rate	72	104	102	+08	+34	+03

Age 22 yrs.	Height 70 in.	Ponderal index 13.38
	Weight 143 lbs.	Cholesterol 150 mg. per 100 ml.
	Overweight -07 %	Vital capacity 5.7 liters

HABIT SURVEY
Smoking habits: mixed smoker
Age begun 19 yrs.   Inhalation: yes
Habits of nervous tension: 2, 5, 6, 22

FIGURE-DRAWING CHARACTERISTICS

Structural	Male Female Both	Structural	Male	Female	Structural and Graphic	Male Female Both		Graphic, Global and Height	Male	Female	Body Proportions	Male	Female
Type	0	Omission of Appendages	0	0	Upper and Lower Halves	1	3	Hair Shading	3	3	Head	07	07
Sex Sequence	0	Position of Both Arms	4	0	Four Quarters	4	4	Nudity and Transparency	7	7	Neck	08	08
Posture	1 1	Position of Right Arm	7	5	Relative Size	4		Form	1	3	Shoulders		06
Perspective	2 0	Position of Left Arm	2	5	Constant Line Pressure	0	5	Detailing	1	1	Right Arm	04	04
Vertical Midline	4 0	Position of Legs	1	5	Variable Line Pressure	4	0	Identity and Sex	1	1	Left Arm	05	04
Bilateral Symmetry	0 4	Relation of Long Axes	1	1	Line Continuity	0	0	Sophistication	2	2	Chest	06	05
Horizontal Midline	4 4	Right and Left Halves	1	1	Body Shading	7	5	Height	06	06	Girth	05	07

GENERAL CHARACTERISTICS OF SUBJECT

IDENTIFICATION
No. 741
Sex M
Marital status M
Age 24 yrs. at psychological tests

PARENTAL HISTORY				
Father				
C	H	S	D	O
-	-	-	-	-
Mother				
C	H	S	D	O
-	-	-	-	-

PHYSIOLOGICAL AND METABOLIC DATA

	Admission	Initial	Control	Cold pressor change	Exercise change	Smoking change
Systolic pressure	150	124	102	+36	+52	+03
Diastolic pressure	80	64	60	+34	+10	+08
Heart rate	70	68	77	+12	+17	00

Age 22 yrs.	Height	74 in.	Ponderal index 12.85
	Weight	191 lbs.	Cholesterol 244 mg. per 100 ml.
	Overweight +10 %		Vital capacity 6.6 liters

HABIT SURVEY
Smoking habits: mixed smoker
Age begun 20 yrs.   Inhalation: no
Habits of nervous tension: 5, 9, 10, 18, 21

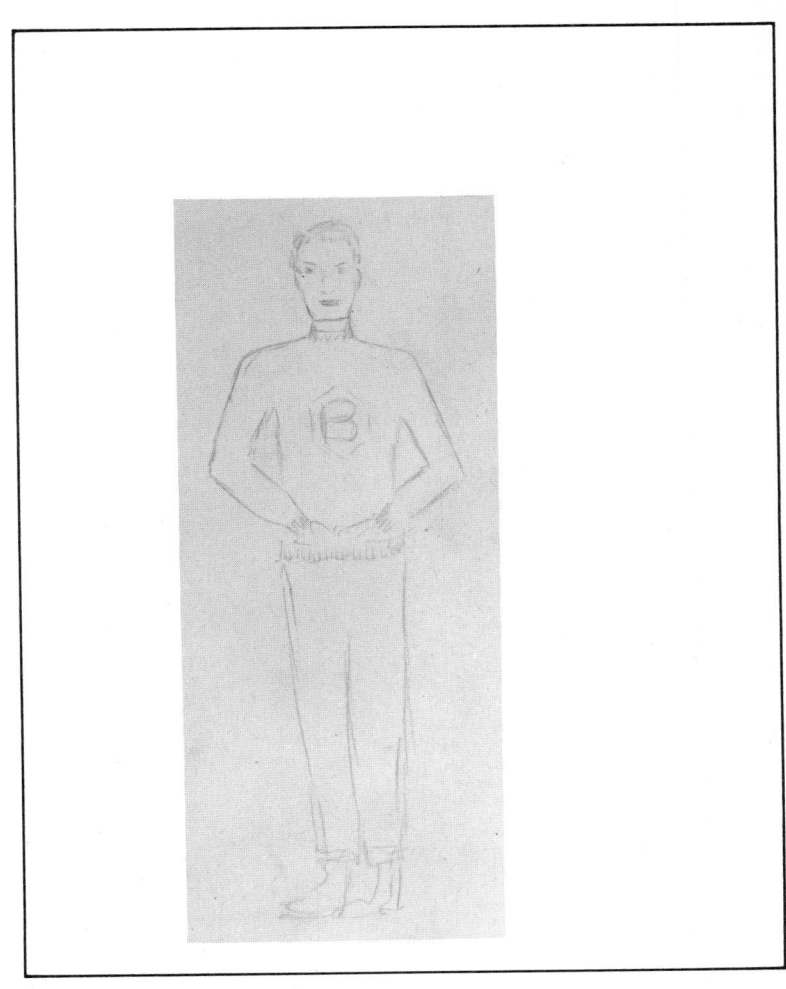

FIGURE-DRAWING CHARACTERISTICS

Structural	Male Female Both		Structural	Male	Female	Structural and Graphic	Male Female Both		Graphic, Global and Height	Male	Female	Body Proportions	Male	Female
Type	0		Omission of Appendages	7	0	Upper and Lower Halves	3	3	Hair Shading	3	3	Head	08	06
Sex Sequence	1		Position of Both Arms	0	0	Four Quarters	4	4	Nudity and Transparency	7	7	Neck	06	05
Posture	1	1	Position of Right Arm	5	5	Relative Size	0		Form	1	1	Shoulders	07	04
Perspective	0	0	Position of Left Arm	5	5	Constant Line Pressure	1	0	Detailing	3	3	Right Arm		04
Vertical Midline	0	0	Position of Legs	3	4	Variable Line Pressure	0	1	Identity and Sex	1	1	Left Arm		04
Bilateral Symmetry	4	4	Relation of Long Axes	1	1	Line Continuity	0	0	Sophistication	2	2	Chest	06	04
Horizontal Midline	4	4	Right and Left Halves	1	1	Body Shading	4	0	Height	07	06	Girth	07	04

GENERAL CHARACTERISTICS OF SUBJECT

IDENTIFICATION

No. F01

Sex F

Marital status M

Age 26 yrs. at psychological tests

PARENTAL HISTORY

Father

C H S D O

- - - - -

Mother

C H S D O

- - - - -

PHYSIOLOGICAL AND METABOLIC DATA

	Admission	Initial	Control	Cold pressor change	Exercise change	Smoking change
Systolic pressure	105	114	100	−08	+36	
Diastolic pressure	60	45	48	+20	−12	
Heart rate	80	88	95	−16	+23	

Age 23 yrs.

Height 67 in.

Weight 133 lbs.

Overweight −04 %

Ponderal index 13.14

Cholesterol 254 mg. per 100 ml.

Vital capacity liters

HABIT SURVEY

Smoking habits: nonsmoker

Age begun yrs. Inhalation:

Habits of nervous tension:

STRONG VOCATIONAL INTEREST TEST

Occupation	Artist	Psychologist	Architect	Physician	Osteopath	Dentist	Veterinarian	Mathematician	Physicist	Engineer	Chemist	Production Manager
Standard Score	42	23	39	39	38	29	26	19	12	13	13	20

Occupation	Farmer	Aviator	Carpenter	Printer	Math.-Sci. Teacher	Ind. Arts Teacher	Voc. Agric. Teacher	Policeman	Forest Serv. Man	Y.M.C.A. Phys. Dir.	Personnel Director	Public Administrator
Standard Score	18	11	10	20	15	00	11	19	10	35	32	33

Occupation	Y.M.C.A. Secretary	Soc. Sci. H.S. Teacher	City Sch. Sup't.	Social Worker	Minister	Musician Performer	C.P.A.	Senior C.P.A.	Accountant	Office Man	Purchasing Agent	Banker
Standard Score	33	24	27	38	58	44	23	18	14	29	23	27

Occupation	Mortician	Pharmacist	Sales Manager	Real Est. Manager	Life Ins. Salesman	Advertising Man	Lawyer	Author-Journalist	President Mfg. Co.	Interest Maturity	Occupational Level	Masculinity-Femininity
Standard Score	45	37	41	49	51	51	40	42	36	52	62	18

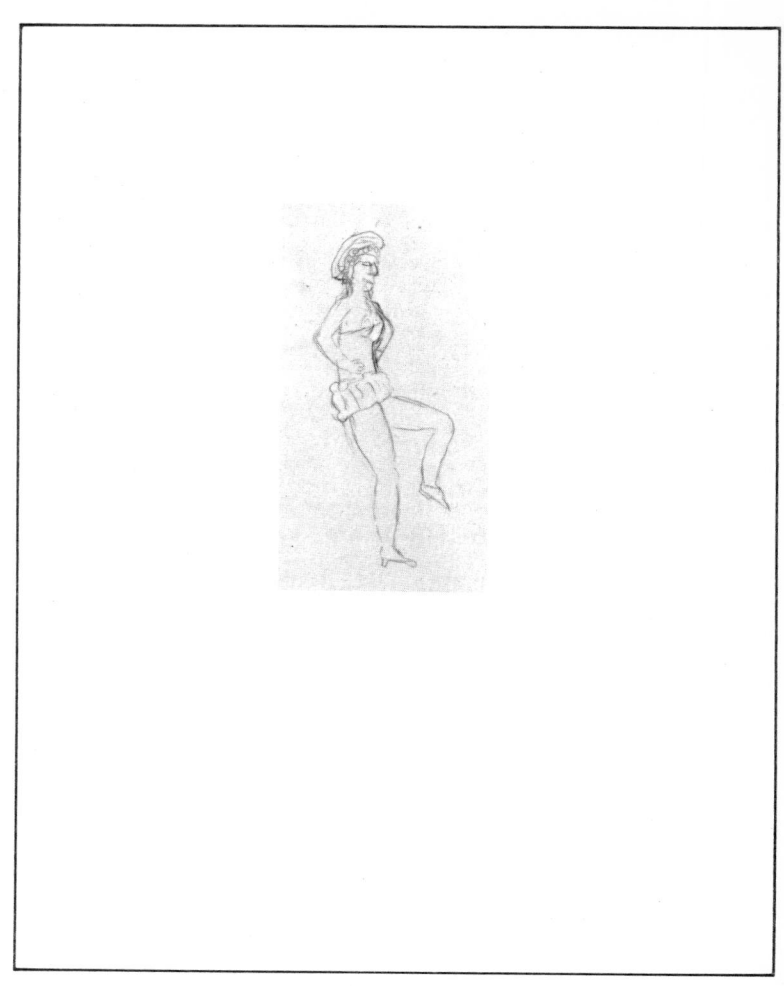

FIGURE-DRAWING CHARACTERISTICS

Structural	Male	Female	Structural	Male	Female	Structural and Graphic	Male	Female	Graphic, Global and Height	Male	Female	Body Proportions	Male	Female
	Both						Both							
Type	0		Omission of Appendages	0	0	Upper and Lower Halves	1	1	Hair Shading	5	3	Head	06	03
Sex Sequence	0		Position of Both Arms	2	2	Four Quarters	4	4	Nudity and Transparency	7	2	Neck	05	02
Posture	1	6	Position of Right Arm	4	5	Relative Size	0		Form	3	1	Shoulders		
Perspective	2	1	Position of Left Arm	7	7	Constant Line Pressure	1	0	Detailing	3	3	Right Arm	04	02
Vertical Midline	4	4	Position of Legs	1	8	Variable Line Pressure	0	1	Identity and Sex	1	1	Left Arm		
Bilateral Symmetry	0	0	Relation of Long Axes	1	1	Line Continuity	0	0	Sophistication	2	2	Chest	04	
Horizontal Midline	6	4	Right and Left Halves	2	1	Body Shading	3	3	Height	04	03	Girth	04	

GENERAL CHARACTERISTICS OF SUBJECT

IDENTIFICATION

No. F18

Sex M

Marital status S

Age 24 yrs. at psychological tests

PARENTAL HISTORY

Father

C   H   S   D   O

-   -   -   -   -

Mother

C   H   S   D   O

-   -   -   -   -

PHYSIOLOGICAL AND METABOLIC DATA

	Admission	Initial	Control	Cold pressor change	Exercise change	Smoking change
Systolic pressure	92	98	96	+08	+18	+06
Diastolic pressure	70	68	62	+28	00	+04
Heart rate	66	64	67	+16	+15	+08

Age 22 yrs.

Height 72 in.   Ponderal index 13.16

Weight 164 lbs.   Cholesterol 234 mg. per 100 ml.

Overweight +01 %   Vital capacity liters

HABIT SURVEY

Smoking habits: nonsmoker

Age begun yrs.   Inhalation:

Habits of nervous tension: 6, 21, 25

STRONG VOCATIONAL INTEREST TEST

Occupation	Artist	Psychologist	Architect	Physician	Osteopath	Dentist	Veterinarian	Mathematician	Physicist	Engineer	Chemist	Production Manager
Standard Score	17	30	22	34	32	28	09	25	22	41	36	43

Occupation	Farmer	Aviator	Carpenter	Printer	Math.-Sci. Teacher	Ind. Arts Teacher	Voc. Agric. Teacher	Policeman	Forest Serv. Man	Y.M.C.A. Phys. Dir.	Personnel Director	Public Administrator
Standard Score	32	41	20	36	38	19	14	31	28	32	50	46

Occupation	Y.M.C.A. Secretary	Soc. Sci. H.S. Teacher	City Sch. Sup't.	Social Worker	Minister	Musician Performer	C.P.A.	Senior C.P.A.	Accountant	Office Man	Purchasing Agent	Banker
Standard Score	34	34	28	36	58	29	44	58	52	44	25	24

Occupation	Mortician	Pharmacist	Sales Manager	Real Est. Manager	Life Ins. Salesman	Advertising Man	Lawyer	Author-Journalist	President Mfg. Co.	Interest Maturity	Occupational Level	Masculinity-Femininity
Standard Score	22	16	21	27	23	27	29	26	32	62	57	49

F60 - 1

FIGURE-DRAWING CHARACTERISTICS

Structural	Male Female Both	Structural	Male	Female	Structural and Graphic	Male Female Both		Graphic, Global and Height	Male	Female	Body Proportions	Male	Female
Type	0	Omission of Appendages	0	0	Upper and Lower Halves	3	1	Hair Shading	3	3	Head	08	09
Sex Sequence	1	Position of Both Arms	4	0	Four Quarters	4	4	Nudity and Transparency	7	0	Neck	00	04
Posture	1 1	Position of Right Arm	7	2	Relative Size	2		Form	1	1	Shoulders		
Perspective	2 2	Position of Left Arm	4	2	Constant Line Pressure	5	0	Detailing	3	3	Right Arm		04
Vertical Midline	4 4	Position of Legs	1	1	Variable Line Pressure	0	4	Identity and Sex	3	1	Left Arm	06	
Bilateral Symmetry	0 0	Relation of Long Axes	1	1	Line Continuity	1	1	Sophistication	2	2	Chest	07	06
Horizontal Midline	4 0	Right and Left Halves	3	3	Body Shading	5	2	Height	06	06	Girth	07	07

GENERAL CHARACTERISTICS OF SUBJECT

IDENTIFICATION

No. F60
Sex M
Marital status S
Age 23 yrs. at
psychological tests

PARENTAL HISTORY

Father

C	H	S	D	O
-	-	-	-	-

Mother

C	H	S	D	O
-	-	-	-	-

PHYSIOLOGICAL AND METABOLIC DATA

	Admission	Initial	Control	Cold pressor change	Exercise change	Smoking change
Systolic pressure	126	110	104	+23	+21	00
Diastolic pressure	68	72	70	+30	+10	00
Heart rate	68	64	60	+08	+12	+13

Age 21 yrs.   Height 72 in.   Ponderal index 13.43
Weight 154 lbs.   Cholesterol 222 mg. per 100 ml.
Overweight −05 %   Vital capacity   liters

HABIT SURVEY

Smoking habits: nonsmoker
Age begun yrs.   Inhalation:
Habits of nervous tension: 5, 6, 9, 10, 14, 18, 23

STRONG VOCATIONAL INTEREST TEST

Occupation	Artist	Psychologist	Architect	Physician	Osteopath	Dentist	Veterinarian	Mathematician	Physicist	Engineer	Chemist	Production Manager
Standard Score	23	44	27	49	41	38	21	34	36	44	47	45

Occupation	Farmer	Aviator	Carpenter	Printer	Math.-Sci. Teacher	Ind. Arts Teacher	Voc. Agric. Teacher	Policeman	Forest Serv. Man	Y.M.C.A. Phys. Dir.	Personnel Director	Public Administrator
Standard Score	40	52	31	46	42	25	21	39	30	28	34	42

Occupation	Y.M.C.A. Secretary	Soc. Sci. H.S. Teacher	City Sch. Sup't.	Social Worker	Minister	Musician Performer	C.P.A.	Senior C.P.A.	Accountant	Office Man	Purchasing Agent	Banker
Standard Score	16	28	24	32	58	30	38	49	34	32	23	21

Occupation	Mortician	Pharmacist	Sales Manager	Real Est. Manager	Life Ins. Salesman	Advertising Man	Lawyer	Author- Journalist	President Mfg. Co.	Interest Maturity	Occupational Level	Masculinity- Femininity
Standard Score	18	26	18	25	18	27	39	32	23	53	52	60

FIGURE-DRAWING CHARACTERISTICS

Structural	Male Female / Both	Structural	Male	Female	Structural and Graphic	Male Female / Both	Graphic, Global and Height	Male	Female	Body Proportions	Male	Female
Type	0	Omission of Appendages	0	0	Upper and Lower Halves	1 1	Hair Shading	2	2	Head	09	08
Sex Sequence	0	Position of Both Arms	0	0	Four Quarters	4 4	Nudity and Transparency	7	7	Neck	03	06
Posture	1 1	Position of Right Arm	0	0	Relative Size	0	Form	1	1	Shoulders	08	06
Perspective	0 0	Position of Left Arm	0	0	Constant Line Pressure	0 0	Detailing	1	1	Right Arm	04	04
Vertical Midline	3 0	Position of Legs	4	6	Variable Line Pressure	3 5	Identity and Sex	1	1	Left Arm	04	04
Bilateral Symmetry	4 4	Relation of Long Axes	1	1	Line Continuity	1 0	Sophistication	2	2	Chest	07	05
Horizontal Midline	4 4	Right and Left Halves	1	1	Body Shading	6 7	Height	06	06	Girth	10	06

GENERAL CHARACTERISTICS OF SUBJECT

IDENTIFICATION
No. G58
Sex M
Marital status M
Age 21 yrs. at
psychological tests

PARENTAL HISTORY
Father
C   H   S   D   O
–   –   –   –   –
Mother
C   H   S   D   O
–   –   –   –   –

PHYSIOLOGICAL AND METABOLIC DATA

	Admission	Initial	Control	Cold pressor change	Exercise change	Smoking change
Systolic pressure		120	116	+08	+24	+07
Diastolic pressure		58	60	+18	00	+06
Heart rate	82	68	65	+16	+17	+12

Age 20 yrs.	Height 67 in.	Ponderal index 12.76
	Weight 145 lbs.	Cholesterol 243 mg. per 100 ml.
	Overweight +04 %	Vital capacity liters

HABIT SURVEY

Smoking habits: heavy cigarette smoker

Age begun 17 yrs.   Inhalation: yes

Habits of nervous tension: 3, 5, 8, 10, 22

STRONG VOCATIONAL INTEREST TEST

Occupation	Artist	Psychologist	Architect	Physician	Osteopath	Dentist	Veterinarian	Mathematician	Physicist	Engineer	Chemist	Production Manager
Standard Score	34	53	32	52	34	30	15	41	29	32	44	27

Occupation	Farmer	Aviator	Carpenter	Printer	Math.-Sci. Teacher	Ind. Arts Teacher	Voc. Agric. Teacher	Policeman	Forest Serv. Man	Y.M.C.A. Phys. Dir.	Personnel Director	Public Administrator
Standard Score	17	30	01	24	36	-06	08	24	11	30	44	45

Occupation	Y.M.C.A. Secretary	Soc. Sci. H.S. Teacher	City Sch. Sup't.	Social Worker	Minister	Musician Performer	C.P.A.	Senior C.P.A.	Accountant	Office Man	Purchasing Agent	Banker
Standard Score	26	34	40	45	59	52	41	36	21	28	21	21

Occupation	Mortician	Pharmacist	Sales Manager	Real Est. Manager	Life Ins. Salesman	Advertising Man	Lawyer	Author-Journalist	President Mfg. Co.	Interest Maturity	Occupational Level	Masculinity-Femininity
Standard Score	25	34	37	37	34	45	51	44	35	53	65	37

FIGURE-DRAWING CHARACTERISTICS

Structural	Male / Female Both	Structural	Male	Female	Structural and Graphic Both	Male	Female	Graphic, Global and Height	Male	Female	Body Proportions	Male	Female
Type	0	Omission of Appendages	0	0	Upper and Lower Halves	1	1	Hair Shading	3	3	Head	06	05
Sex Sequence	1	Position of Both Arms	1	1	Four Quarters	4	4	Nudity and Transparency	7	7	Neck	03	05
Posture	1	1	Position of Right Arm	5	0	Relative Size	2		Form	1	1	Shoulders	06	05
Perspective	0	0	Position of Left Arm	0	5	Constant Line Pressure	0	1	Detailing	3	3	Right Arm	06	04
Vertical Midline	3	3	Position of Legs	4	4	Variable Line Pressure	1	0	Identity and Sex	1	1	Left Arm	06	06
Bilateral Symmetry	3	3	Relation of Long Axes	1	1	Line Continuity	0	0	Sophistication	2	2	Chest	05	05
Horizontal Midline	6	4	Right and Left Halves	1	1	Body Shading	0	2	Height	06	05	Girth	07	06

GENERAL CHARACTERISTICS OF SUBJECT

IDENTIFICATION

No. A04
Sex F
Marital status S
Age 21 yrs. at
psychological tests

PARENTAL HISTORY

Father
C   H   S   D   O
–   –   –   –   –

Mother
C   H   S   D   O
–   –   –   –   –

PHYSIOLOGICAL AND METABOLIC DATA

	Admission	Initial	Control	Cold pressor change	Exercise change	Smoking change
Systolic pressure	98	113	108	+20	+18	+04
Diastolic pressure	68	68	58	+33	+04	-03
Heart rate	72	68	64	+10	+16	+05

Age 20 yrs.
Height 69 in.
Weight 149 lbs.
Overweight +04 %
Ponderal index 13.02
Cholesterol 197 mg. per 100 ml.
Vital capacity liters

HABIT SURVEY

Smoking habits: nonsmoker
   Age begun yrs.   Inhalation:
Habits of nervous tension: 4, 5, 6, 10, 11, 14, 23

STRONG VOCATIONAL INTEREST TEST

Occupation	Artist	Psychologist	Architect	Physician	Osteopath	Dentist	Veterinarian	Mathematician	Physicist	Engineer	Chemist	Production Manager
Standard Score	25	41	32	64	58	45	35	30	26	31	36	32

Occupation	Farmer	Aviator	Carpenter	Printer	Math.-Sci. Teacher	Ind. Arts Teacher	Voc. Agric. Teacher	Policeman	Forest Serv. Man	Y.M.C.A. Phys. Dir.	Personnel Director	Public Administrator
Standard Score	37	35	32	45	57	36	36	39	20	49	36	36

Occupation	Y.M.C.A. Secretary	Soc. Sci. H.S. Teacher	City Sch. Sup't.	Social Worker	Minister	Musician Performer	C.P.A.	Senior C.P.A.	Accountant	Office Man	Purchasing Agent	Banker
Standard Score	42	46	36	45	60	59	24	41	29	45	21	23

Occupation	Mortician	Pharmacist	Sales Manager	Real Est. Manager	Life Ins. Salesman	Advertising Man	Lawyer	Author-Journalist	President Mfg. Co.	Interest Maturity	Occupational Level	Masculinity-Femininity
Standard Score	35	43	22	28	25	21	21	24	13	61	45	37

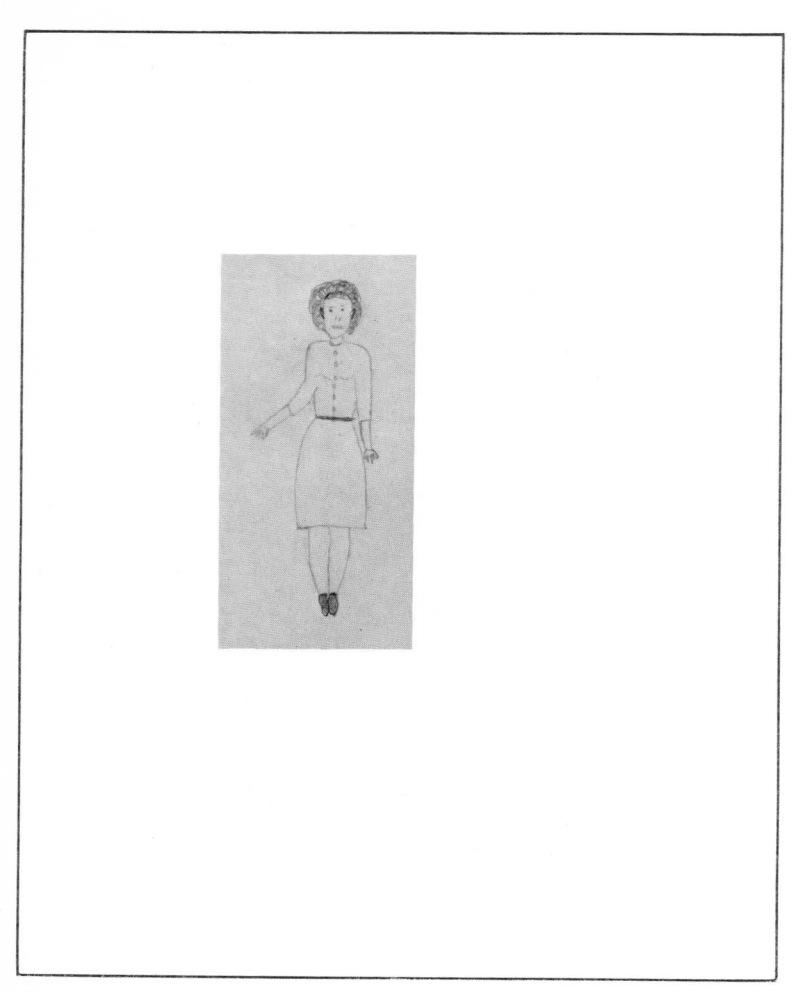
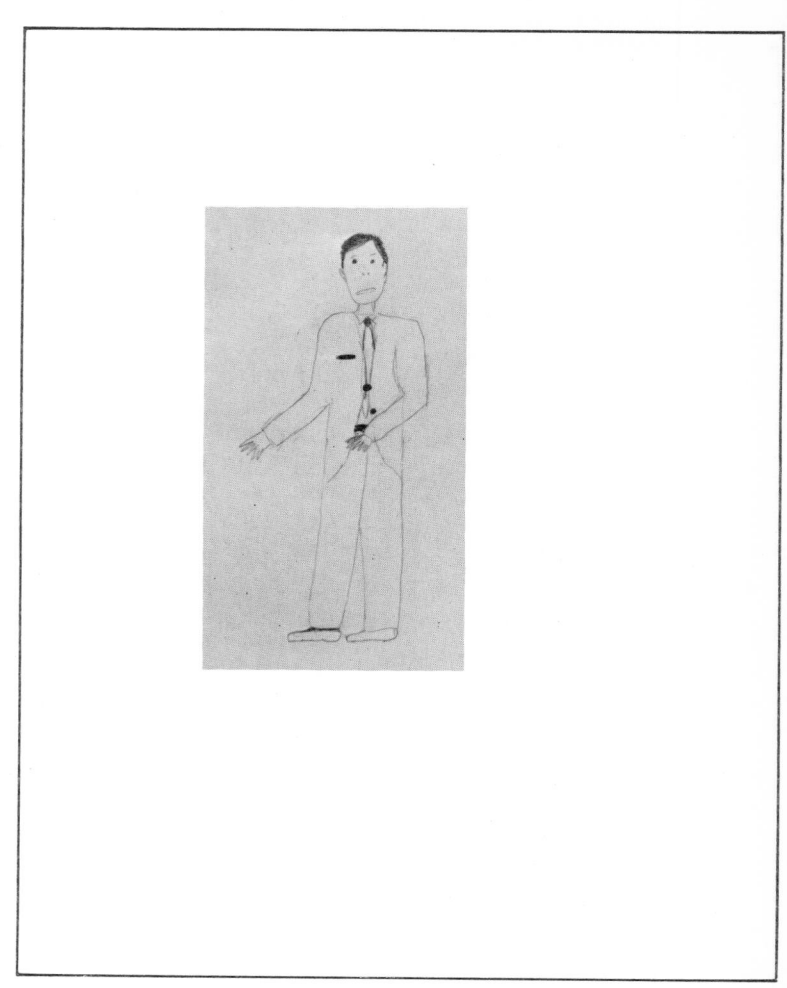

FIGURE-DRAWING CHARACTERISTICS

Structural	Male	Female	Structural	Male	Female	Structural and Graphic	Male	Female	Graphic, Global and Height	Male	Female	Body Proportions	Male	Female
		Both						Both						
Type		0	Omission of Appendages	0	0	Upper and Lower Halves	1	1	Hair Shading	2	2	Head	05	04
Sex Sequence		1	Position of Both Arms	1	1	Four Quarters	4	4	Nudity and Transparency	7	7	Neck	02	01
Posture	1	1	Position of Right Arm	4	4	Relative Size		0	Form	1	1	Shoulders	04	02
Perspective	0	0	Position of Left Arm	5	0	Constant Line Pressure	1	1	Detailing	3	1	Right Arm	04	02
Vertical Midline	3	3	Position of Legs	4	2	Variable Line Pressure	0	0	Identity and Sex	1	1	Left Arm	04	02
Bilateral Symmetry	3	3	Relation of Long Axes	1	1	Line Continuity	3	2	Sophistication	2	2	Chest	03	02
Horizontal Midline	4	4	Right and Left Halves	1	2	Body Shading	4	5	Height	04	03	Girth	04	02

GENERAL CHARACTERISTICS OF SUBJECT

IDENTIFICATION
No. A24
Sex M
Marital status S
Age 24 yrs. at
psychological tests

PARENTAL HISTORY				
Father				
C	H	S	D	O
-	-	-	-	-
Mother				
C	H	S	D	O
-	-	-	-	-

PHYSIOLOGICAL AND METABOLIC DATA

	Admission	Initial	Control	Cold pressor change	Exercise change	Smoking change
Systolic pressure	120	118	117	+09	+43	00
Diastolic pressure	70	63	67	+08	-13	+01
Heart rate	68	80	70	+10	+27	+02

Age 23 yrs.	Height 68 in.	Ponderal index 12.76	
	Weight 151 lbs.	Cholesterol 243	mg. per 100 ml.
	Overweight +03 %	Vital capacity	liters

HABIT SURVEY
Smoking habits: occasional smoker
Age begun 21 yrs.   Inhalation: no
Habits of nervous tension: 2, 6, 9

STRONG VOCATIONAL INTEREST TEST

Occupation	Artist	Psychologist	Architect	Physician	Osteopath	Dentist	Veterinarian	Mathematician	Physicist	Engineer	Chemist	Production Manager
Standard Score	4	6	4	6	6	3	2	2	1	2	3	2

Occupation	Farmer	Aviator	Carpenter	Printer	Math.-Sci. Teacher	Ind. Arts Teacher	Voc. Agric. Teacher	Policeman	Forest Serv. Man	Y.M.C.A. Phys. Dir.	Personnel Director	Public Administrator
Standard Score	4	4	2	6	6	2	2	4	2	5	6	7

Occupation	Y.M.C.A. Secretary	Soc. Sci. H.S. Teacher	City Sch. Sup't.	Social Worker	Minister	Musician Performer	C.P.A.	Senior C.P.A.	Accountant	Office Man	Purchasing Agent	Banker
Standard Score	6	8	4	7	6	7	4	6	3	6	2	2

Occupation	Mortician	Pharmacist	Sales Manager	Real Est. Manager	Life Ins. Salesman	Advertising Man	Lawyer	Author- Journalist	President Mfg. Co.	Interest Maturity	Occupational Level	Masculinity- Femininity
Standard Score	4	5	2	4	4	5	4	4	2	6	4	2

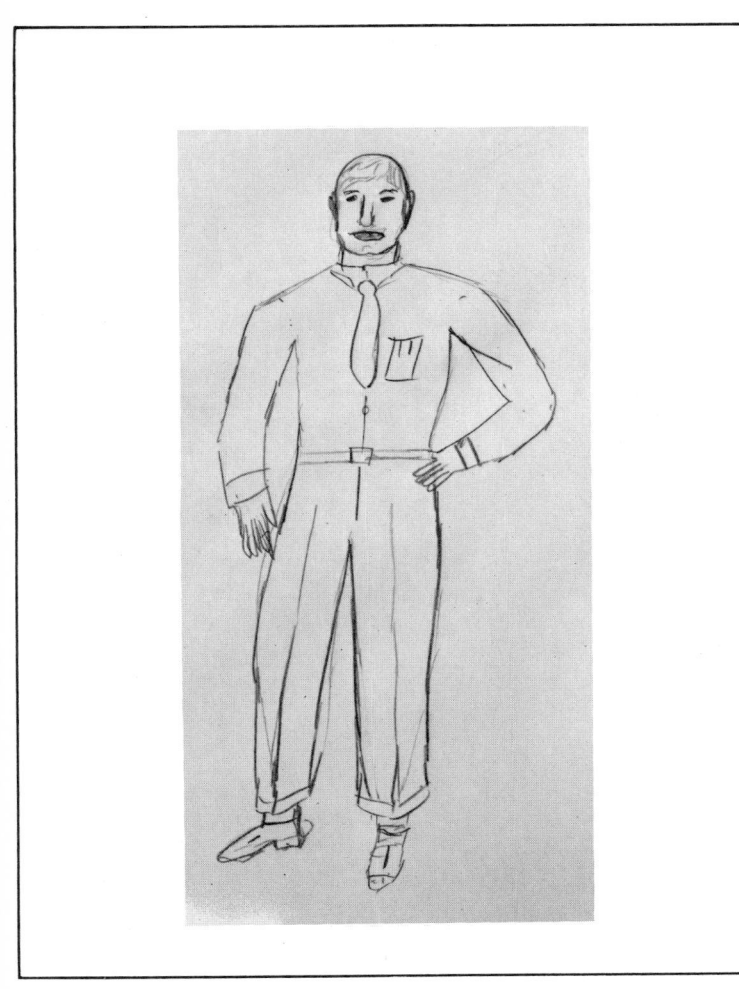

FIGURE-DRAWING CHARACTERISTICS

Structural	Male Female Both	Structural	Male	Female	Structural and Graphic	Male Female Both		Graphic, Global and Height	Male	Female	Body Proportions	Male	Female
Type	0	Omission of Appendages	0	1	Upper and Lower Halves	0	1	Hair Shading	1	3	Head	08	09
Sex Sequence	0	Position of Both Arms	0	6	Four Quarters	4	4	Nudity and Transparency	7	7	Neck	04	08
Posture	1 0	Position of Right Arm	5	8	Relative Size	5		Form	1	3	Shoulders	09	09
Perspective	0 0	Position of Left Arm	5	8	Constant Line Pressure	3	5	Detailing	1	3	Right Arm	06	
Vertical Midline	3 3	Position of Legs	5	6	Variable Line Pressure	0	0	Identity and Sex	1	1	Left Arm	06	
Bilateral Symmetry	3 3	Relation of Long Axes	1	1	Line Continuity	0	0	Sophistication	2	2	Chest	07	07
Horizontal Midline	4 4	Right and Left Halves	1	1	Body Shading	2	7	Height	07		Girth	09	06

GENERAL CHARACTERISTICS OF SUBJECT

IDENTIFICATION
No. A46
Sex M
Marital status S
Age 22 yrs. at
psychological tests

PARENTAL HISTORY
Father
C H S D O
- - - - -
Mother
C H S D O
- - - - -

PHYSIOLOGICAL AND METABOLIC DATA

	Admission	Initial	Control	Cold pressor change	Exercise change	Smoking change
Systolic pressure	112	126	126	+12	+30	+01
Diastolic pressure	70	70	78	+08	-10	-04
Heart rate	80	76	68	+06	+11	+04

Age 22 yrs.	Height 74 in.	Ponderal index 12.89
	Weight 189 lbs.	Cholesterol 222 mg. per 100 ml.
	Overweight +09 %	Vital capacity liters

HABIT SURVEY
Smoking habits: occasional smoker
Age begun yrs. Inhalation:
Habits of nervous tension: 5, 9

STRONG VOCATIONAL INTEREST TEST

Occupation	Artist	Psychologist	Architect	Physician	Osteopath	Dentist	Veterinarian	Mathematician	Physicist	Engineer	Chemist	Production Manager
Standard Score	30	53	38	59	46	41	18	38	40	48	58	39

Occupation	Farmer	Aviator	Carpenter	Printer	Math.-Sci. Teacher	Ind. Arts Teacher	Voc. Agric. Teacher	Policeman	Forest Serv. Man	Y.M.C.A. Phys. Dir.	Personnel Director	Public Administrator
Standard Score	42	59	31	45	47	28	34	33	30	26	40	45

Occupation	Y.M.C.A. Secretary	Soc. Sci. H.S. Teacher	City Sch. Sup't.	Social Worker	Minister	Musician Performer	C.P.A.	Senior C.P.A.	Accountant	Office Man	Purchasing Agent	Banker
Standard Score	17	25	18	35	60	44	45	56	40	36	33	26

Occupation	Mortician	Pharmacist	Sales Manager	Real Est. Manager	Life Ins. Salesman	Advertising Man	Lawyer	Author-Journalist	President Mfg. Co.	Interest Maturity	Occupational Level	Masculinity-Femininity
Standard Score	22	30	23	28	16	33	36	36	26	49	49	62

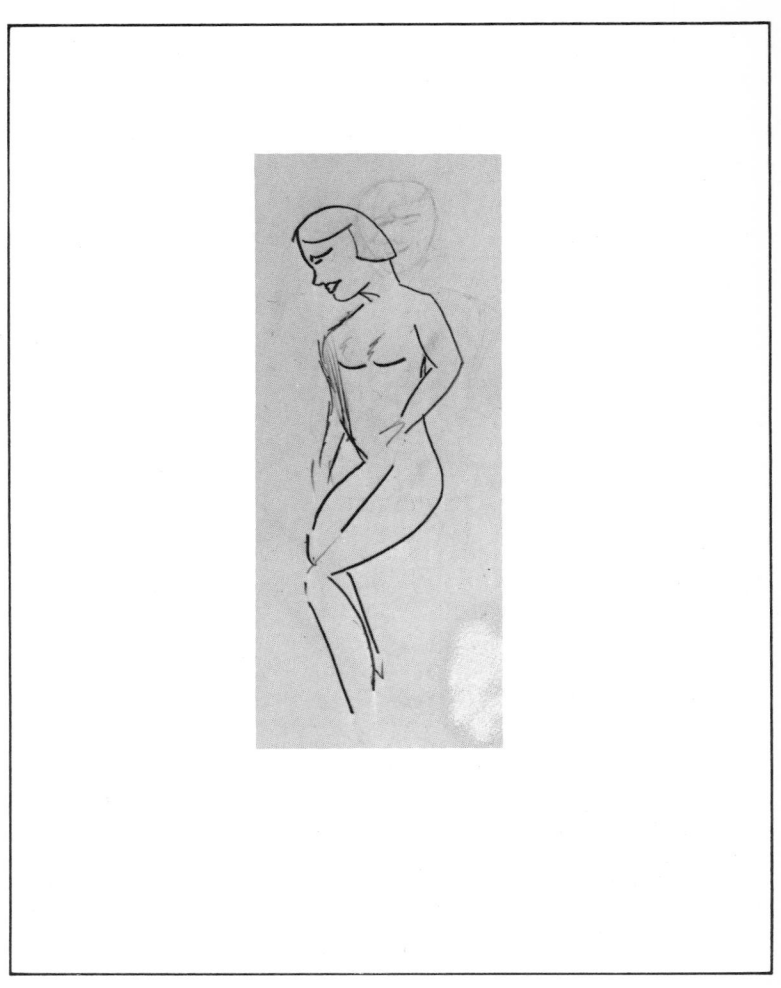

FIGURE-DRAWING CHARACTERISTICS

Structural	Male Female Both	Structural	Male	Female	Structural and Graphic	Male Female Both		Graphic, Global and Height	Male	Female	Body Proportions	Male	Female
Type	0	Omission of Appendages	9	6	Upper and Lower Halves	3	1	Hair Shading	5	5	Head	09	07
Sex Sequence	2	Position of Both Arms	0	4	Four Quarters	4	4	Nudity and Transparency	7	0	Neck	05	03
Posture	1 0	Position of Right Arm	0	7	Relative Size	0		Form	1	1	Shoulders	10	
Perspective	0 6	Position of Left Arm	0	5	Constant Line Pressure	0	5	Detailing	3	3	Right Arm	08	
Vertical Midline	3 4	Position of Legs	6	1	Variable Line Pressure	1	0	Identity and Sex	1	1	Left Arm	08	
Bilateral Symmetry	3 0	Relation of Long Axes	1	0	Line Continuity	1	3	Sophistication	2	2	Chest	08	
Horizontal Midline	6 0	Right and Left Halves	1	1	Body Shading	0	1	Height	08		Girth	09	

GENERAL CHARACTERISTICS OF SUBJECT

IDENTIFICATION		PARENTAL HISTORY				
No. B21		Father				
Sex M		C H S D O				
Marital status S		– – – – –				
Age 24 yrs. at		Mother				
psychological tests		C H S D O				
		– – – – –				

PHYSIOLOGICAL AND METABOLIC DATA

	Admission	Initial	Control	Cold pressor change	Exercise change	Smoking change
Systolic pressure	120	118	110	+06	+18	
Diastolic pressure	78	58	64	+08	–04	
Heart rate	80	70	66	–02	+13	

Age 24 yrs.	Height 73 in.	Ponderal index 12.88
	Weight 182 lbs.	Cholesterol 263 mg. per 100 ml.
	Overweight +06 %	Vital capacity liters

HABIT SURVEY

Smoking habits: heavy cigarette smoker

Age begun 20 yrs.   Inhalation: yes

Habits of nervous tension: 1, 3, 4, 5, 6, 9, 22

STRONG VOCATIONAL INTEREST TEST

Occupation	Artist	Psychologist	Architect	Physician	Osteopath	Dentist	Veterinarian	Mathematician	Physicist	Engineer	Chemist	Production Manager
Standard Score	34	56	37	55	36	32	05	37	31	34	47	28

Occupation	Farmer	Aviator	Carpenter	Printer	Math.-Sci. Teacher	Ind. Arts Teacher	Voc. Agric. Teacher	Policeman	Forest Serv. Man	Y.M.C.A. Phys. Dir.	Personnel Director	Public Administrator
Standard Score	22	34	12	44	42	03	15	31	16	30	47	44

Occupation	Y.M.C.A. Secretary	Soc. Sci. H.S. Teacher	City Sch. Sup't.	Social Worker	Minister	Musician Performer	C.P.A.	Senior C.P.A.	Accountant	Office Man	Purchasing Agent	Banker
Standard Score	25	36	40	46	61	57	43	42	29	35	21	17

Occupation	Mortician	Pharmacist	Sales Manager	Real Est. Manager	Life Ins. Salesman	Advertising Man	Lawyer	Author-Journalist	President Mfg. Co.	Interest Maturity	Occupational Level	Masculinity-Femininity
Standard Score	14	28	28	32	27	44	47	41	24	55	58	40

FIGURE-DRAWING CHARACTERISTICS

Structural	Male Female Both	Structural	Male	Female	Structural and Graphic	Male Female Both		Graphic, Global and Height	Male	Female	Body Proportions	Male	Female
Type	0	Omission of Appendages	0	0	Upper and Lower Halves	3	3	Hair Shading	2	3	Head	08	07
Sex Sequence	0	Position of Both Arms	0	4	Four Quarters	4	4	Nudity and Transparency	7	7	Neck	07	07
Posture	1 1	Position of Right Arm	2	7	Relative Size	0		Form	1	1	Shoulders	08	
Perspective	0 2	Position of Left Arm	2	4	Constant Line Pressure	1	1	Detailing	3	3	Right Arm	06	
Vertical Midline	0 4	Position of Legs	4	4	Variable Line Pressure	0	0	Identity and Sex	1	1	Left Arm	06	04
Bilateral Symmetry	3 0	Relation of Long Axes	1	1	Line Continuity	0	0	Sophistication	2	2	Chest	06	05
Horizontal Midline	4 4	Right and Left Halves	1	1	Body Shading	3	3	Height	07	06	Girth	06	05

GENERAL CHARACTERISTICS OF SUBJECT

IDENTIFICATION
No. B30
Sex M
Marital status S
Age 22 yrs. at
psychological tests

PARENTAL HISTORY
Father
C   H   S   D   O
-   -   -   -   -
Mother
C   H   S   D   O
-   -   -   -   -

PHYSIOLOGICAL AND METABOLIC DATA

	Admission	Initial	Control	Cold pressor change	Exercise change	Smoking change
Systolic pressure	132	112	108	-03	+28	+10
Diastolic pressure	80	68	72	+12	-14	+06
Heart rate	80	60	56	+13	+20	-03

Age 22 yrs.	Height	73 in.	Ponderal index	13.70	
	Weight	151 lbs.	Cholesterol	170	mg. per 100 ml.
	Overweight	+10 %	Vital capacity	4.5	liters

HABIT SURVEY

Smoking habits: nonsmoker

Age begun   yrs.   Inhalation:

Habits of nervous tension: 4, 5, 6, 9, 11, 16, 17, 18, 23, 24

STRONG VOCATIONAL INTEREST TEST

Occupation	Artist	Psychologist	Architect	Physician	Osteopath	Dentist	Veterinarian	Mathematician	Physicist	Engineer	Chemist	Production Manager
Standard Score	34	43	39	52	39	41	11	49	41	41	49	22

Occupation	Farmer	Aviator	Carpenter	Printer	Math.-Sci. Teacher	Ind. Arts Teacher	Voc. Agric. Teacher	Policeman	Forest Serv. Man	Y.M.C.A. Phys. Dir.	Personnel Director	Public Administrator
Standard Score	27	27	15	32	42	09	14	20	14	24	18	34

Occupation	Y.M.C.A. Secretary	Soc. Sci. H.S. Teacher	City Sch. Sup't.	Social Worker	Minister	Musician Performer	C.P.A.	Senior C.P.A.	Accountant	Office Man	Purchasing Agent	Banker
Standard Score	21	29	29	29	61	40	42	39	25	24	17	20

Occupation	Mortician	Pharmacist	Sales Manager	Real Est. Manager	Life Ins. Salesman	Advertising Man	Lawyer	Author-Journalist	President Mfg. Co.	Interest Maturity	Occupational Level	Masculinity-Femininity
Standard Score	15	22	12	26	20	26	47	40	27	53	62	37

FIGURE-DRAWING CHARACTERISTICS

Structural	Male Female Both	Structural	Male	Female	Structural and Graphic	Male Female Both		Graphic, Global and Height	Male	Female	Body Proportions	Male	Female
Type	0	Omission of Appendages	7	0	Upper and Lower Halves	0	1	Hair Shading	1	2	Head	05	05
Sex Sequence	2	Position of Both Arms	0	0	Four Quarters	4	4	Nudity and Transparency	7	7	Neck	06	04
Posture	1　1	Position of Right Arm	5	5	Relative Size	0		Form	1	1	Shoulders	06	04
Perspective	0　0	Position of Left Arm	5	5	Constant Line Pressure	0	0	Detailing	1	1	Right Arm	04	02
Vertical Midline	3　0	Position of Legs	2	4	Variable Line Pressure	3	1	Identity and Sex	1	1	Left Arm	04	02
Bilateral Symmetry	5　5	Relation of Long Axes	1	1	Line Continuity	2	0	Sophistication	2	2	Chest	05	03
Horizontal Midline	6　0	Right and Left Halves	0	1	Body Shading	6	4	Height	04	04	Girth	06	04

GENERAL CHARACTERISTICS OF SUBJECT

IDENTIFICATION
No. B39
Sex M
Marital status S
Age 23 yrs. at
psychological tests

PARENTAL HISTORY
Father
C　H　S　D　O
-　-　-　-　-
Mother
C　H　S　D　O
-　-　-　-　-

PHYSIOLOGICAL AND METABOLIC DATA

	Admission	Initial	Control	Cold pressor change	Exercise change	Smoking change
Systolic pressure	130	126	112	+10	+40	+04
Diastolic pressure	72	60	56	+20	-18	+12
Heart rate	72	68	66	+06	+13	+03

Age 23 yrs.	Height 74 in.	Ponderal index 13.01
	Weight 184 lbs.	Cholesterol 270 mg. per 100 ml.
	Overweight +05 %	Vital capacity 5.9 liters

HABIT SURVEY

Smoking habits: occasional smoker

Age begun 19 yrs.　　Inhalation: no

Habits of nervous tension: 5, 6

STRONG VOCATIONAL INTEREST TEST

Occupation	Artist	Psychologist	Architect	Physician	Osteopath	Dentist	Veterinarian	Mathematician	Physicist	Engineer	Chemist	Production Manager
Standard Score	32	48	40	34	22	14	02	29	18	21	30	23

Occupation	Farmer	Aviator	Carpenter	Printer	Math.-Sci. Teacher	Ind. Arts Teacher	Voc. Agric. Teacher	Policeman	Forest Serv. Man	Y.M.C.A. Phys. Dir.	Personnel Director	Public Administrator
Standard Score	18	28	00	32	28	02	17	16	24	22	48	47

Occupation	Y.M.C.A. Secretary	Soc. Sci. H.S. Teacher	City Sch. Sup't.	Social Worker	Minister	Musician Performer	C.P.A.	Senior C.P.A.	Accountant	Office Man	Purchasing Agent	Banker
Standard Score	26	39	31	49	61	49	43	45	27	34	28	22

Occupation	Mortician	Pharmacist	Sales Manager	Real Est. Manager	Life Ins. Salesman	Advertising Man	Lawyer	Author-Journalist	President Mfg. Co.	Interest Maturity	Occupational Level	Masculinity-Femininity
Standard Score	18	27	39	41	33	49	43	38	28	58	61	38

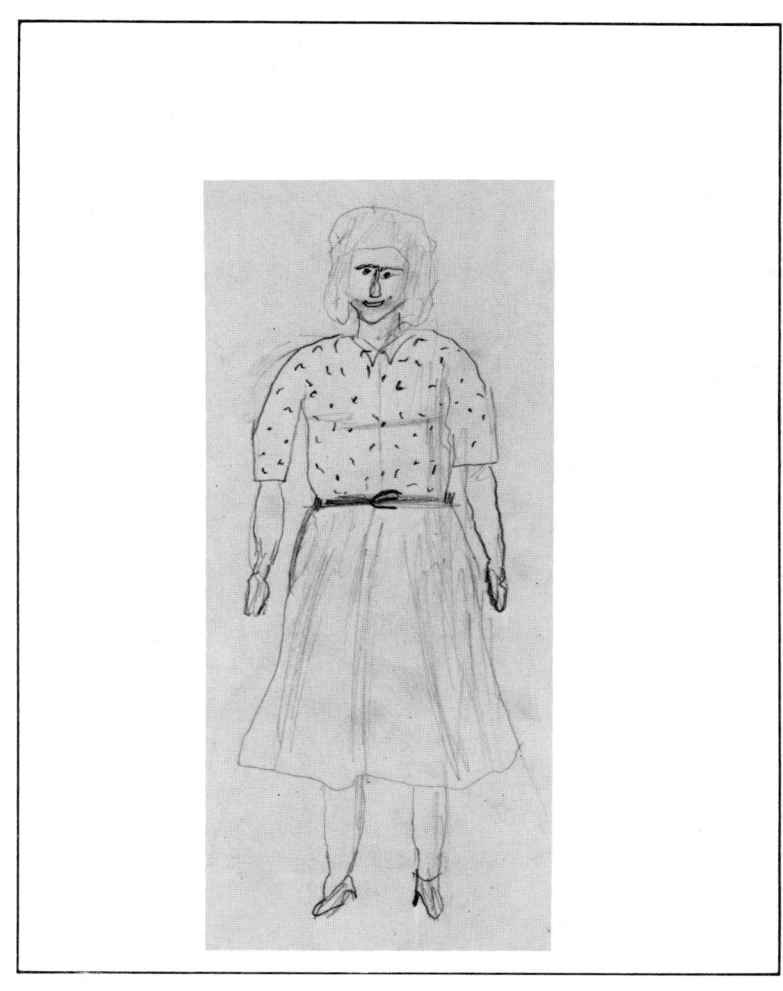

FIGURE-DRAWING CHARACTERISTICS

Structural	Male Female Both	Structural	Male	Female	Structural and Graphic	Male Female Both		Graphic, Global and Height	Male	Female	Body Proportions	Male	Female
Type	0	Omission of Appendages	0	0	Upper and Lower Halves	3	3	Hair Shading	2	2	Head	11	09
Sex Sequence	0	Position of Both Arms	1	0	Four Quarters	4	4	Nudity and Transparency	6	7	Neck	01	05
Posture	4	1	Position of Right Arm	5	0	Relative Size	2		Form	1	1	Shoulders	09	08
Perspective	0	0	Position of Left Arm	2	0	Constant Line Pressure	0	0	Detailing	3	3	Right Arm	06	06
Vertical Midline	3	3	Position of Legs	1	4	Variable Line Pressure	3	3	Identity and Sex	1	1	Left Arm	07	06
Bilateral Symmetry	3	3	Relation of Long Axes	1	1	Line Continuity	2	1	Sophistication	2	2	Chest	09	07
Horizontal Midline	6	4	Right and Left Halves	3	1	Body Shading	7	7	Height	08	07	Girth	11	09

GENERAL CHARACTERISTICS OF SUBJECT

IDENTIFICATION
No. B65
Sex M
Marital status S
Age 22 yrs. at psychological tests

PARENTAL HISTORY
Father
C H S D O
– – – – –
Mother
C H S D O
– – – – –

PHYSIOLOGICAL AND METABOLIC DATA

	Admission	Initial	Control	Cold pressor change	Exercise change	Smoking change
Systolic pressure	126	112	106	+16	+42	+16
Diastolic pressure	66	50	56	+32	-30	-02
Heart rate	88	64	60	+26	+15	+30

Age 22 yrs.	Height	73	in.	Ponderal index	13.44	
	Weight	160	lbs.	Cholesterol	270	mg. per 100 ml.
	Overweight	-05	%	Vital capacity	5.4	liters

HABIT SURVEY

Smoking habits: nonsmoker

Age begun   yrs.   Inhalation:

Habits of nervous tension: 4, 5, 8, 10, 16, 23, 25

STRONG VOCATIONAL INTEREST TEST

Occupation	Artist	Psychologist	Architect	Physician	Osteopath	Dentist	Veterinarian	Mathematician	Physicist	Engineer	Chemist	Production Manager
Standard Score	32	53	36	59	55	39	25	33	32	38	51	28

Occupation	Farmer	Aviator	Carpenter	Printer	Math.-Sci. Teacher	Ind. Arts Teacher	Voc. Agric. Teacher	Policeman	Forest Serv. Man	Y.M.C.A. Phys. Dir.	Personnel Director	Public Administrator
Standard Score	30	42	28	46	49	28	17	38	31	42	40	52

Occupation	Y.M.C.A. Secretary	Soc. Sci. H.S. Teacher	City Sch. Sup't.	Social Worker	Minister	Musician Performer	C.P.A.	Senior C.P.A.	Accountant	Office Man	Purchasing Agent	Banker
Standard Score	34	37	27	52	61	53	28	42	24	28	06	13

Occupation	Mortician	Pharmacist	Sales Manager	Real Est. Manager	Life Ins. Salesman	Advertising Man	Lawyer	Author-Journalist	President Mfg. Co.	Interest Maturity	Occupational Level	Masculinity-Femininity
Standard Score	18	21	15	26	27	27	37	36	20	62	48	36

FIGURE-DRAWING CHARACTERISTICS

Structural	Male Female Both	Structural	Male	Female	Structural and Graphic	Male Female Both		Graphic, Global and Height	Male	Female	Body Proportions	Male	Female
Type	0	Omission of Appendages	0	0	Upper and Lower Halves	1	1	Hair Shading	2	2	Head	05	07
Sex Sequence	0	Position of Both Arms	1	0	Four Quarters	4	4	Nudity and Transparency	7	7	Neck	05	03
Posture	1	1	Position of Right Arm	0	5	Relative Size	0		Form	1	1	Shoulders	06	04
Perspective	0	0	Position of Left Arm	4	5	Constant Line Pressure	3	3	Detailing	1	1	Right Arm	04	02
Vertical Midline	3	0	Position of Legs	5	4	Variable Line Pressure	0	0	Identity and Sex	1	1	Left Arm	04	02
Bilateral Symmetry	4	5	Relation of Long Axes	1	1	Line Continuity	4	2	Sophistication	2	2	Chest	06	04
Horizontal Midline	4	4	Right and Left Halves	1	2	Body Shading	7	5	Height	05	04	Girth	07	03

GENERAL CHARACTERISTICS OF SUBJECT

IDENTIFICATION
No. C14
Sex M
Marital status S
Age 22 yrs. at
psychological tests

PARENTAL HISTORY
Father
C   H   S   D   O
-   -   -   -   -
Mother
C   H   S   D   O
-   -   -   -   -

PHYSIOLOGICAL AND METABOLIC DATA

	Admission	Initial	Control	Cold pressor change	Exercise change	Smoking change
Systolic pressure	120	110	102	+10	+38	+15
Diastolic pressure	60	55	60	+22	-10	+08
Heart rate	82	80	71	+20	+12	+21

Age 22 yrs.

Height	71 in.	Ponderal index 13.81
Weight	136 lbs.	Cholesterol 202 mg. per 100 ml.
Overweight -14 %		Vital capacity 4.4 liters

HABIT SURVEY

Smoking habits: occasional smoker

  Age begun 18 yrs.   Inhalation: yes

Habits of nervous tension: 4, 5, 6, 9, 16, 21, 23

STRONG VOCATIONAL INTEREST TEST

Occupation	Artist	Psychologist	Architect	Physician	Osteopath	Dentist	Veterinarian	Mathematician	Physicist	Engineer	Chemist	Production Manager
Standard Score	39	55	44	69	49	47	18	41	40	45	51	33

Occupation	Farmer	Aviator	Carpenter	Printer	Math.-Sci. Teacher	Ind. Arts Teacher	Voc. Agric. Teacher	Policeman	Forest Serv. Man	Y.M.C.A. Phys. Dir.	Personnel Director	Public Administrator
Standard Score	28	38	25	41	46	24	29	29	32	37	44	46

Occupation	Y.M.C.A. Secretary	Soc. Sci. H.S. Teacher	City Sch. Sup't.	Social Worker	Minister	Musician Performer	C.P.A.	Senior C.P.A.	Accountant	Office Man	Purchasing Agent	Banker
Standard Score	29	28	39	43	62	55	36	39	27	24	17	16

Occupation	Mortician	Pharmacist	Sales Manager	Real Est. Manager	Life Ins. Salesman	Advertising Man	Lawyer	Author-Journalist	President Mfg. Co.	Interest Maturity	Occupational Level	Masculinity-Femininity
Standard Score	11	23	25	27	26	34	41	38	28	57	60	48

FIGURE-DRAWING CHARACTERISTICS

Structural	Male Female Both		Structural	Male	Female	Structural and Graphic	Male Female Both		Graphic, Global and Height	Male	Female	Body Proportions	Male	Female
Type	0		Omission of Appendages	3	2	Upper and Lower Halves	1	7	Hair Shading	3	3	Head		
Sex Sequence	1		Position of Both Arms	2	2	Four Quarters	1	4	Nudity and Transparency	0	0	Neck		
Posture	9	3	Position of Right Arm	2	2	Relative Size	4		Form	3	3	Shoulders		
Perspective	4	2	Position of Left Arm	2	7	Constant Line Pressure	1	0	Detailing	3	3	Right Arm		
Vertical Midline	4	4	Position of Legs	7	4	Variable Line Pressure	0	1	Identity and Sex	1	1	Left Arm		
Bilateral Symmetry	0	0	Relation of Long Axes	1	1	Line Continuity	0	1	Sophistication	2	2	Chest		06
Horizontal Midline	0	0	Right and Left Halves	0	1	Body Shading	1	1	Height			Girth		08

GENERAL CHARACTERISTICS OF SUBJECT

IDENTIFICATION

No. C48

Sex M

Marital status S

Age 22 yrs. at

psychological tests

PARENTAL HISTORY

Father

C   H   S   D   O

–   –   –   –   –

Mother

C   H   S   D   O

–   –   –   –   –

PHYSIOLOGICAL AND METABOLIC DATA

	Admission	Initial	Control	Cold pressor change	Exercise change	Smoking change
Systolic pressure	110	110	100	+10	+30	+10
Diastolic pressure	60	60	60	+25	-10	+14
Heart rate	82	68	64	+08	+07	00

Age 23 yrs.   Height 70 in.   Weight 135 lbs.   Overweight -13 %

Ponderal index 13.65   Cholesterol 157 mg. per 100 ml.   Vital capacity 5.0 liters

HABIT SURVEY

Smoking habits: occasional smoker

Age begun 18 yrs.   Inhalation: yes

Habits of nervous tension: 2, 5, 6, 9, 11

STRONG VOCATIONAL INTEREST TEST

Occupation	Artist	Psychologist	Architect	Physician	Osteopath	Dentist	Veterinarian	Mathematician	Physicist	Engineer	Chemist	Production Manager
Standard Score	43	37	43	55	43	38	25	25	20	25	30	18

Occupation	Farmer	Aviator	Carpenter	Printer	Math.-Sci. Teacher	Ind. Arts Teacher	Voc. Agric. Teacher	Policeman	Forest Serv. Man	Y.M.C.A. Phys. Dir.	Personnel Director	Public Administrator
Standard Score	42	39	17	39	35	14	30	27	35	34	30	38

Occupation	Y.M.C.A. Secretary	Soc. Sci. H.S. Teacher	City Sch. Sup't.	Social Worker	Minister	Musician Performer	C.P.A.	Senior C.P.A.	Accountant	Office Man	Purchasing Agent	Banker
Standard Score	28	34	27	34	62	54	29	34	15	27	18	17

Occupation	Mortician	Pharmacist	Sales Manager	Real Est. Manager	Life Ins. Salesman	Advertising Man	Lawyer	Author-Journalist	President Mfg. Co.	Interest Maturity	Occupational Level	Masculinity-Femininity
Standard Score	20	29	24	37	27	40	38	40	16	54	54	38

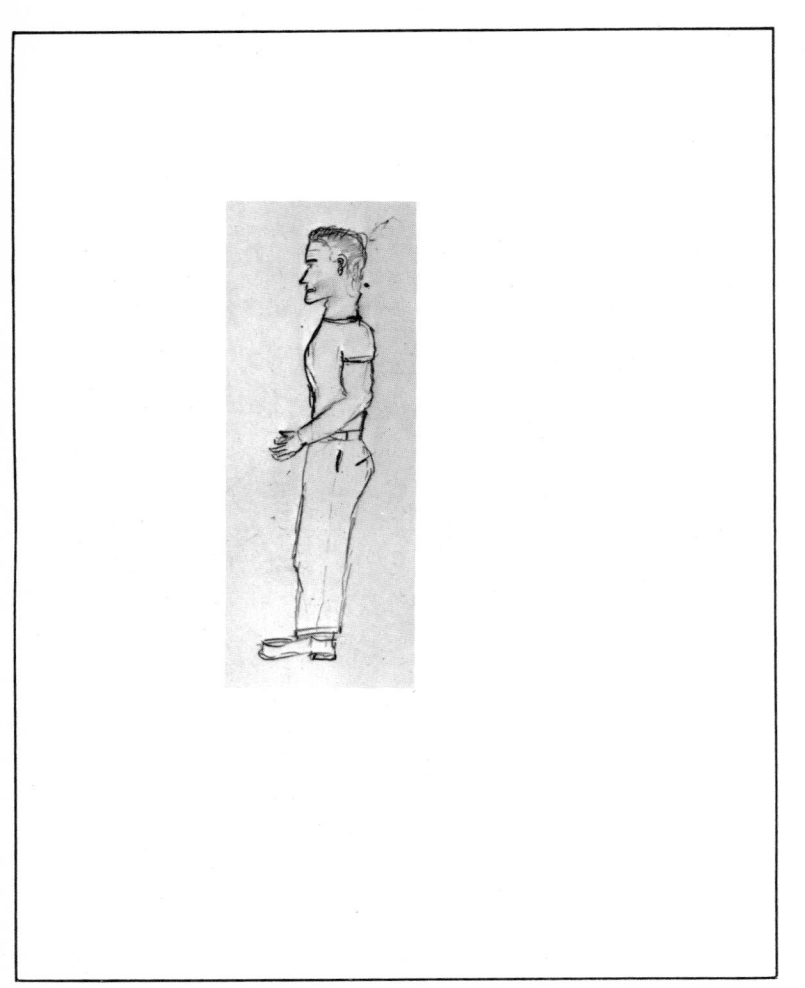

FIGURE-DRAWING CHARACTERISTICS

Structural	Male Female Both	Structural	Male	Female	Structural and Graphic	Male Female Both		Graphic, Global and Height	Male	Female	Body Proportions	Male	Female
Type	0	Omission of Appendages	0	0	Upper and Lower Halves	1	1	Hair Shading	3	7	Head	06	06
Sex Sequence	0	Position of Both Arms	4	4	Four Quarters	4	4	Nudity and Transparency	7	7	Neck	06	07
Posture	1 1	Position of Right Arm	7	7	Relative Size	0		Form	1	1	Shoulders		
Perspective	2 2	Position of Left Arm	4	0	Constant Line Pressure	0	0	Detailing	1	3	Right Arm		
Vertical Midline	4 4	Position of Legs	1	1	Variable Line Pressure	3	3	Identity and Sex	1	1	Left Arm	04	02
Bilateral Symmetry	0 0	Relation of Long Axes	1	1	Line Continuity	0	0	Sophistication	2	2	Chest	05	03
Horizontal Midline	4 4	Right and Left Halves	2	2	Body Shading	0	0	Height	04	04	Girth	04	04

GENERAL CHARACTERISTICS OF SUBJECT

IDENTIFICATION
No. C78
Sex M
Marital status S
Age 22 yrs. at
psychological tests

PARENTAL HISTORY
Father
C H S D O
− − − − −
Mother
C H S D O
− − − − −

PHYSIOLOGICAL AND METABOLIC DATA

	Admission	Initial	Control	Cold pressor change	Exercise change	Smoking change
Systolic pressure	130	124	116	+32	+32	+14
Diastolic pressure	90	62	68	+34	−16	+14
Heart rate	64	68	57	+06	+07	+08

Age 22 yrs. Height 74 in. Ponderal index 12.98

Weight 185 lbs. Cholesterol 295 mg. per 100 ml.

Overweight +13 % Vital capacity 6.1 liters

HABIT SURVEY

Smoking habits: pipe smoker

 Age begun 22 yrs. Inhalation: no

Habits of nervous tension: 2, 5, 11

STRONG VOCATIONAL INTEREST TEST

Occupation	Artist	Psychologist	Architect	Physician	Osteopath	Dentist	Veterinarian	Mathematician	Physicist	Engineer	Chemist	Production Manager
Standard Score	41	49	44	51	35	38	18	45	43	46	54	30

Occupation	Farmer	Aviator	Carpenter	Printer	Math.-Sci. Teacher	Ind. Arts Teacher	Voc. Agric. Teacher	Policeman	Forest Serv. Man	Y.M.C.A. Phys. Dir.	Personnel Director	Public Administrator
Standard Score	40	58	20	43	34	18	29	27	27	24	29	36

Occupation	Y.M.C.A. Secretary	Soc. Sci. H.S. Teacher	City Sch. Sup't.	Social Worker	Minister	Musician Performer	C.P.A.	Senior C.P.A.	Accountant	Office Man	Purchasing Agent	Banker
Standard Score	10	20	15	29	62	50	33	42	17	22	21	13

Occupation	Mortician	Pharmacist	Sales Manager	Real Est. Manager	Life Ins. Salesman	Advertising Man	Lawyer	Author-Journalist	President Mfg. Co.	Interest Maturity	Occupational Level	Masculinity-Femininity
Standard Score	10	20	28	32	23	40	41	43	31	41	53	59

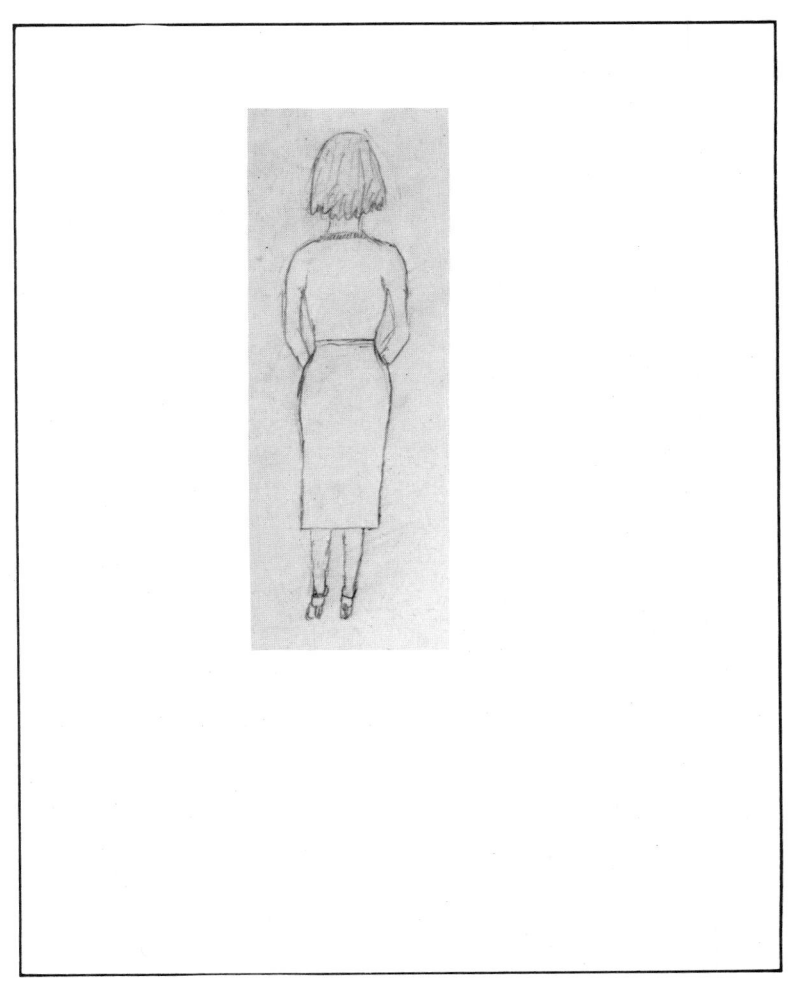

FIGURE-DRAWING CHARACTERISTICS

Structural	Male Female Both	Structural	Male	Female	Structural and Graphic	Male Female Both		Graphic, Global and Height	Male	Female	Body Proportions	Male	Female
Type	0	Omission of Appendages	3	7	Upper and Lower Halves	7	1	Hair Shading	1	1	Head	09	
Sex Sequence	0	Position of Both Arms	1	0	Four Quarters	4	4	Nudity and Transparency	7	7	Neck	07	
Posture	1 1	Position of Right Arm	5	5	Relative Size	0		Form	3	1	Shoulders	09	04
Perspective	0 3	Position of Left Arm	0	5	Constant Line Pressure	0	0	Detailing	1	1	Right Arm	08	
Vertical Midline	3 9	Position of Legs	5	5	Variable Line Pressure	1	1	Identity and Sex	1	1	Left Arm	07	
Bilateral Symmetry	4 4	Relation of Long Axes	1	1	Line Continuity	0	0	Sophistication	2	2	Chest	08	04
Horizontal Midline	6 4	Right and Left Halves	1	2	Body Shading	4	0	Height	09	05	Girth	12	04

GENERAL CHARACTERISTICS OF SUBJECT

IDENTIFICATION
No. D15
Sex M
Marital status S
Age 22 yrs. at
psychological tests

PARENTAL HISTORY
Father
C H S D O
- - - - -
Mother
C H S D O
- - - - -

PHYSIOLOGICAL AND METABOLIC DATA

	Admission	Initial	Control	Cold pressor change	Exercise change	Smoking change
Systolic pressure	120	118	112	+12	+30	+22
Diastolic pressure	80	70	70	+17	-14	+10
Heart rate	72	60	65	00	+10	+25

Age 22 yrs.	Height 78 in.	Ponderal index 14.03
	Weight 172 lbs.	Cholesterol 196 mg. per 100 ml.
	Overweight -11 %	Vital capacity 5.8 liters

HABIT SURVEY

Smoking habits: former smoker

Age begun   yrs.   Inhalation:

Habits of nervous tension: 6, 9, 16, 25

STRONG VOCATIONAL INTEREST TEST

Occupation	Artist	Psychologist	Architect	Physician	Osteopath	Dentist	Veterinarian	Mathematician	Physicist	Engineer	Chemist	Production Manager
Standard Score	43	41	43	52	35	43	22	47	40	35	49	22

Occupation	Farmer	Aviator	Carpenter	Printer	Math.-Sci. Teacher	Ind. Arts Teacher	Voc. Agric. Teacher	Policeman	Forest Serv. Man	Y.M.C.A. Phys. Dir.	Personnel Director	Public Administrator
Standard Score	36	29	19	39	35	14	18	17	12	17	19	27

Occupation	Y.M.C.A. Secretary	Soc. Sci. H.S. Teacher	City Sch. Sup't.	Social Worker	Minister	Musician Performer	C.P.A.	Senior C.P.A.	Accountant	Office Man	Purchasing Agent	Banker
Standard Score	18	28	24	24	63	50	31	30	18	23	14	21

Occupation	Mortician	Pharmacist	Sales Manager	Real Est. Manager	Life Ins. Salesman	Advertising Man	Lawyer	Author-Journalist	President Mfg. Co.	Interest Maturity	Occupational Level	Masculinity-Femininity
Standard Score	15	25	20	28	22	38	39	45	28	50	57	37

FIGURE-DRAWING CHARACTERISTICS

Structural	Male Female Both	Structural	Male	Female	Structural and Graphic	Male Female Both		Graphic, Global and Height	Male	Female	Body Proportions	Male	Female
Type	0	Omission of Appendages	0	0	Upper and Lower Halves	1	1	Hair Shading	3	3	Head	07	07
Sex Sequence	0	Position of Both Arms	1	1	Four Quarters	4	4	Nudity and Transparency	7	2	Neck	04	06
Posture	1 1	Position of Right Arm	2	2	Relative Size	0		Form	3	3	Shoulders	06	06
Perspective	5 5	Position of Left Arm	0	0	Constant Line Pressure	1	1	Detailing	3	3	Right Arm	06	04
Vertical Midline	3 3	Position of Legs	6	6	Variable Line Pressure	0	0	Identity and Sex	1	1	Left Arm	06	04
Bilateral Symmetry	3 3	Relation of Long Axes	1	3	Line Continuity	0	0	Sophistication	2	2	Chest	05	05
Horizontal Midline	6 4	Right and Left Halves	1	1	Body Shading	7	7	Height	07	06	Girth	07	07

GENERAL CHARACTERISTICS OF SUBJECT

IDENTIFICATION		PARENTAL HISTORY
No. D37		Father
Sex M		C H S D O
Marital status S		− − − − −
Age 23 yrs. at		Mother
psychological tests		C H S D O
		− − − − −

PHYSIOLOGICAL AND METABOLIC DATA

	Admission	Initial	Control	Cold pressor change	Exercise change	Smoking change
Systolic pressure	130	116	106	+10	+46	+16
Diastolic pressure	84	60	58	+22	−08	+17
Heart rate	81	64	65	−04	+26	−02

Age 22 yrs.

Height 76 in.   Ponderal index 13.31
Weight 186 lbs.   Cholesterol 229 mg. per 100 ml.
Overweight +02 %   Vital capacity 6.7 liters

HABIT SURVEY

Smoking habits: nonsmoker

Age begun yrs. Inhalation:

Habits of nervous tension: 4, 5, 9, 11, 16, 18, 22, 25

STRONG VOCATIONAL INTEREST TEST

Occupation	Artist	Psychologist	Architect	Physician	Osteopath	Dentist	Veterinarian	Mathematician	Physicist	Engineer	Chemist	Production Manager
Standard Score	40	41	42	59	50	49	26	40	48	53	54	38

Occupation	Farmer	Aviator	Carpenter	Printer	Math.-Sci. Teacher	Ind. Arts Teacher	Voc. Agric. Teacher	Policeman	Forest Serv. Man	Y.M.C.A. Phys. Dir.	Personnel Director	Public Administrator
Standard Score	45	55	26	36	42	28	24	32	32	30	25	45

Occupation	Y.M.C.A. Secretary	Soc. Sci. H.S. Teacher	City Sch. Sup't.	Social Worker	Minister	Musician Performer	C.P.A.	Senior C.P.A.	Accountant	Office Man	Purchasing Agent	Banker
Standard Score	19	24	24	29	63	48	19	33	14	17	18	15

Occupation	Mortician	Pharmacist	Sales Manager	Real Est. Manager	Life Ins. Salesman	Advertising Man	Lawyer	Author-Journalist	President Mfg. Co.	Interest Maturity	Occupational Level	Masculinity-Femininity
Standard Score	11	27	19	23	16	30	32	39	33	50	57	53

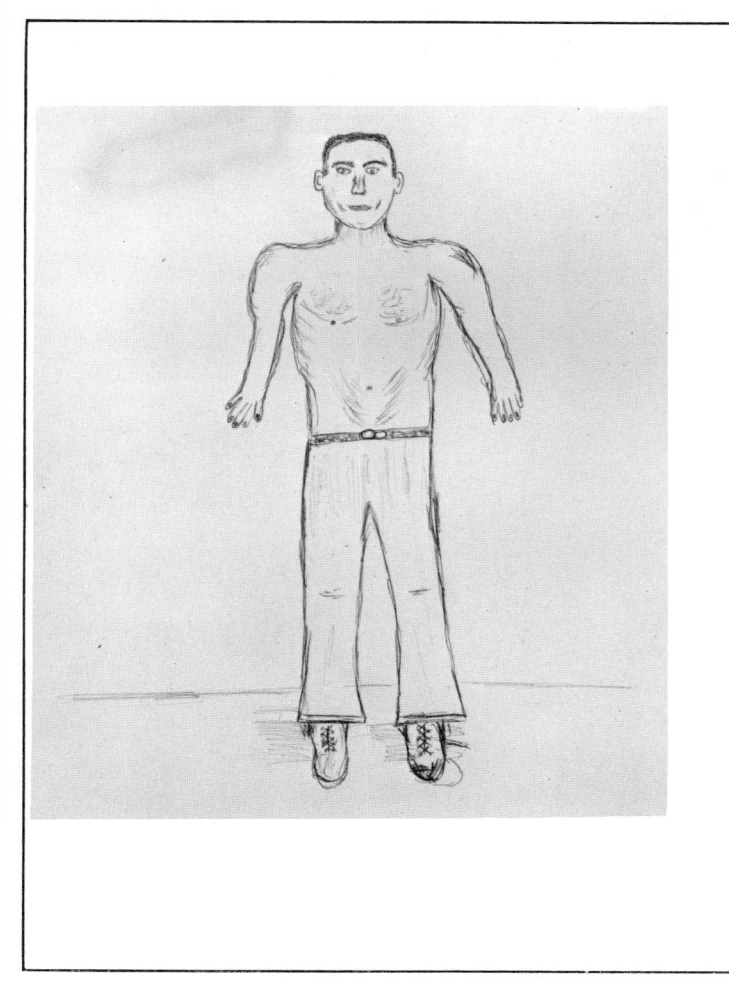

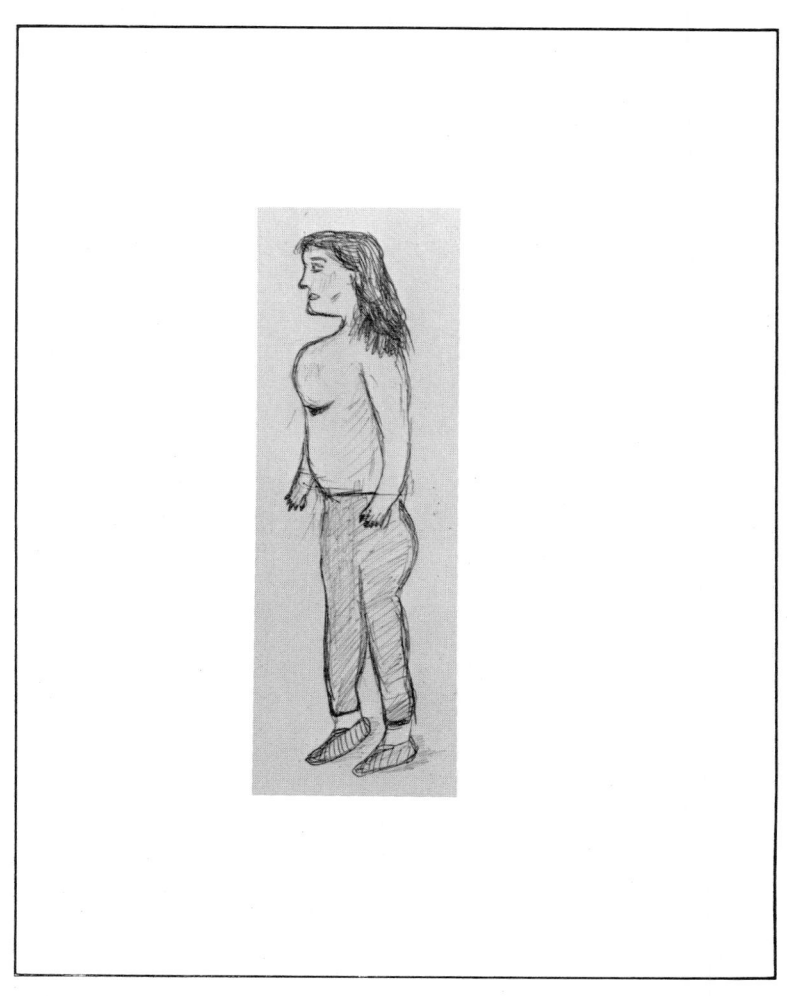

FIGURE-DRAWING CHARACTERISTICS

Structural	Male Female Both	Structural	Male	Female	Structural and Graphic	Male Female Both		Graphic, Global and Height	Male	Female	Body Proportions	Male	Female
Type	0	Omission of Appendages	0	0	Upper and Lower Halves	1	0	Hair Shading	2	3	Head	08	06
Sex Sequence	0	Position of Both Arms	0	4	Four Quarters	4	4	Nudity and Transparency	3	5	Neck	05	05
Posture	1 1	Position of Right Arm	2	7	Relative Size	0		Form	3	3	Shoulders	09	
Perspective	0 2	Position of Left Arm	2	0	Constant Line Pressure	0	0	Detailing	1	1	Right Arm	04	
Vertical Midline	0 4	Position of Legs	5	4	Variable Line Pressure	5	5	Identity and Sex	1	1	Left Arm	04	04
Bilateral Symmetry	4 0	Relation of Long Axes	1	1	Line Continuity	0	0	Sophistication	2	2	Chest	07	07
Horizontal Midline	4 4	Right and Left Halves	1	2	Body Shading	7	3	Height	07	05	Girth	08	07

GENERAL CHARACTERISTICS OF SUBJECT

IDENTIFICATION
No. D49
Sex M
Marital status S
Age 21 yrs. at
psychological tests

PARENTAL HISTORY				
Father				
C	H	S	D	O
-	-	-	-	-
Mother				
C	H	S	D	O
-	-	-	-	-

PHYSIOLOGICAL AND METABOLIC DATA

	Admission	Initial	Control	Cold pressor change	Exercise change	Smoking change
Systolic pressure	110	120	116	-10	+22	+06
Diastolic pressure	70	70	70	-04	-05	+08
Heart rate	80	72	61	00	+16	+06

Age 21 yrs.   Height 76 in.   Ponderal index 13.72
Weight 170 lbs.   Cholesterol 154 mg. per 100 ml.
Overweight -07 %   Vital capacity 6.1 liters

HABIT SURVEY
Smoking habits: heavy cigarette smoker
Age begun 17 yrs.   Inhalation: yes
Habits of nervous tension: 5, 6, 9, 16, 22

STRONG VOCATIONAL INTEREST TEST

Occupation	Artist	Psychologist	Architect	Physician	Osteopath	Dentist	Veterinarian	Mathematician	Physicist	Engineer	Chemist	Production Manager
Standard Score	29	38	25	39	32	30	19	31	22	24	31	22

Occupation	Farmer	Aviator	Carpenter	Printer	Math.-Sci. Teacher	Ind. Arts Teacher	Voc. Agric. Teacher	Policeman	Forest Serv. Man	Y.M.C.A. Phys. Dir.	Personnel Director	Public Administrator
Standard Score	32	26	18	43	41	14	28	29	15	29	35	37

Occupation	Y.M.C.A. Secretary	Soc. Sci. H.S. Teacher	City Sch. Sup't.	Social Worker	Minister	Musician Performer	C.P.A.	Senior C.P.A.	Accountant	Office Man	Purchasing Agent	Banker
Standard Score	31	40	29	36	63	41	38	45	35	45	19	36

Occupation	Mortician	Pharmacist	Sales Manager	Real Est. Manager	Life Ins. Salesman	Advertising Man	Lawyer	Author-Journalist	President Mfg. Co.	Interest Maturity	Occupational Level	Masculinity-Femininity
Standard Score	27	29	24	35	32	39	37	37	25	52	52	43

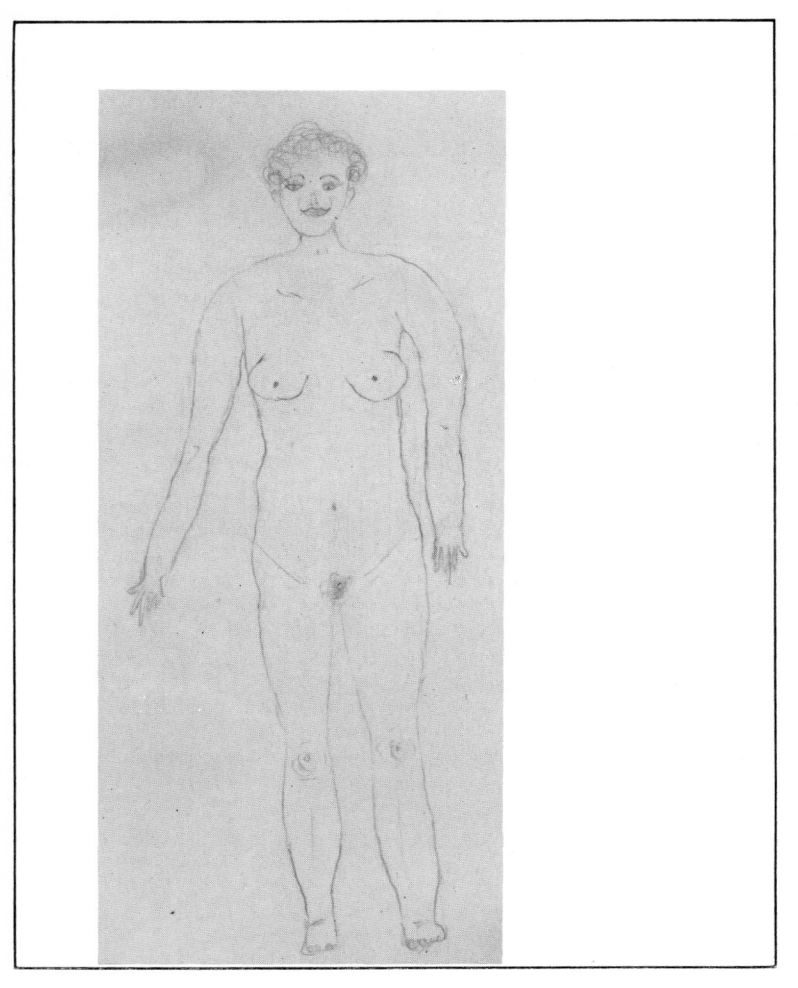

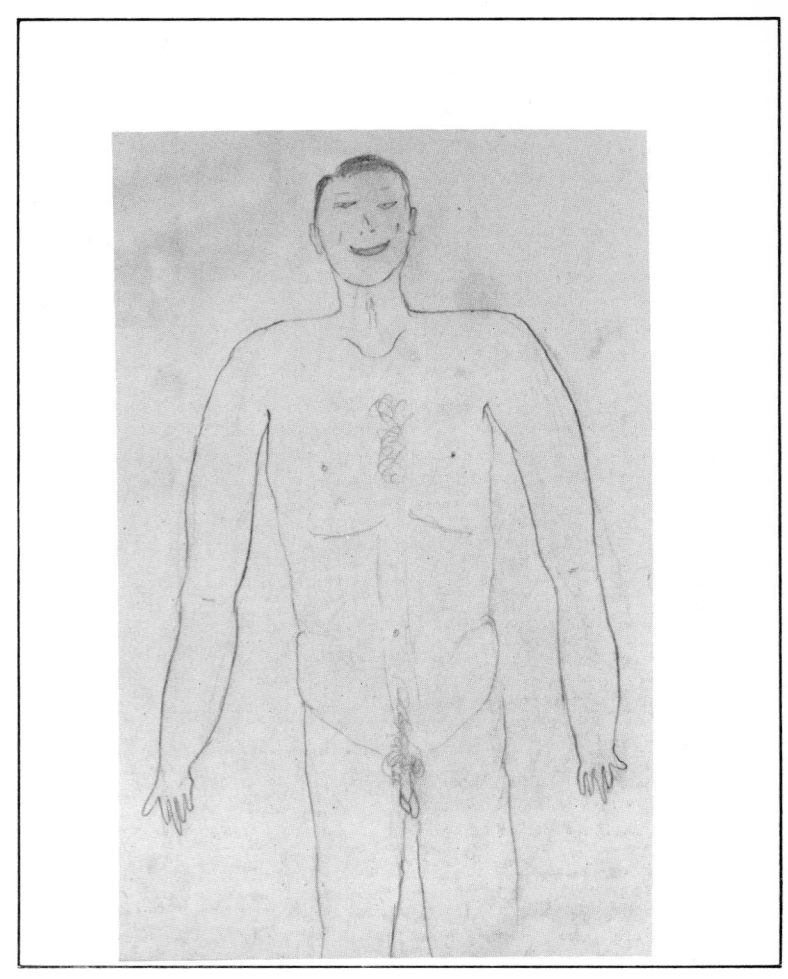

FIGURE-DRAWING CHARACTERISTICS

Structural	Male Female Both	Structural	Male	Female	Structural and Graphic	Male Female Both	Graphic, Global and Height	Male	Female	Body Proportions	Male	Female
Type	0	Omission of Appendages	3	0	Upper and Lower Halves	7 3	Hair Shading	3	3	Head	11	09
Sex Sequence	1	Position of Both Arms	0	1	Four Quarters	4 4	Nudity and Transparency	0	0	Neck	12	07
Posture	0 1	Position of Right Arm	2	2	Relative Size	0	Form	1	1	Shoulders	12	09
Perspective	0 0	Position of Left Arm	2	0	Constant Line Pressure	0 1	Detailing	1	1	Right Arm	12	08
Vertical Midline	0 0	Position of Legs	0	4	Variable Line Pressure	3 0	Identity and Sex	1	1	Left Arm	12	08
Bilateral Symmetry	4 4	Relation of Long Axes	1	1	Line Continuity	1 0	Sophistication	2	2	Chest	10	08
Horizontal Midline	0 0	Right and Left Halves	1	1	Body Shading	3 3	Height		09	Girth	12	09

GENERAL CHARACTERISTICS OF SUBJECT

IDENTIFICATION				
No. D61				
Sex M				
Marital status S				
Age 23 yrs. at				
psychological tests				

PARENTAL HISTORY				
Father				
C	H	S	D	0
-	-	-	-	-
Mother				
C	H	S	D	0
-	-	-	-	-

PHYSIOLOGICAL AND METABOLIC DATA

	Admission	Initial	Control	Cold pressor change	Exercise change	Smoking change
Systolic pressure	110	138	114	+06	+44	+06
Diastolic pressure	70	78	74	+26	+04	00
Heart rate	76	104	75	+08	+45	-02

Age 23 yrs.	Height	68 in.	Ponderal index 13.13	
	Weight	139 lbs.	Cholesterol	240 mg. per 100 ml.
	Overweight	-05%	Vital capacity	4.4 liters

HABIT SURVEY

Smoking habits: nonsmoker

  Age begun   yrs.   Inhalation:

Habits of nervous tension: 2, 3, 4, 5, 8, 12, 16, 18, 19, 21, 23, 25

STRONG VOCATIONAL INTEREST TEST

Occupation	Artist	Psychologist	Architect	Physician	Osteopath	Dentist	Veterinarian	Mathematician	Physicist	Engineer	Chemist	Production Manager
Standard Score	40	58	38	49	37	34	12	36	29	31	38	27

Occupation	Farmer	Aviator	Carpenter	Printer	Math.-Sci. Teacher	Ind. Arts Teacher	Voc. Agric. Teacher	Policeman	Forest Serv. Man	Y.M.C.A. Phys. Dir.	Personnel Director	Public Administrator
Standard Score	18	17	05	32	31	06	10	13	07	26	44	50

Occupation	Y.M.C.A. Secretary	Soc. Sci. H.S. Teacher	City Sch. Sup't.	Social Worker	Minister	Musician Performer	C.P.A.	Senior C.P.A.	Accountant	Office Man	Purchasing Agent	Banker
Standard Score	29	37	38	54	63	54	40	34	25	27	12	11

Occupation	Mortician	Pharmacist	Sales Manager	Real Est. Manager	Life Ins. Salesman	Advertising Man	Lawyer	Author-Journalist	President Mfg. Co.	Interest Maturity	Occupational Level	Masculinity-Femininity
Standard Score	18	25	25	31	33	40	43	45	37	58	61	29

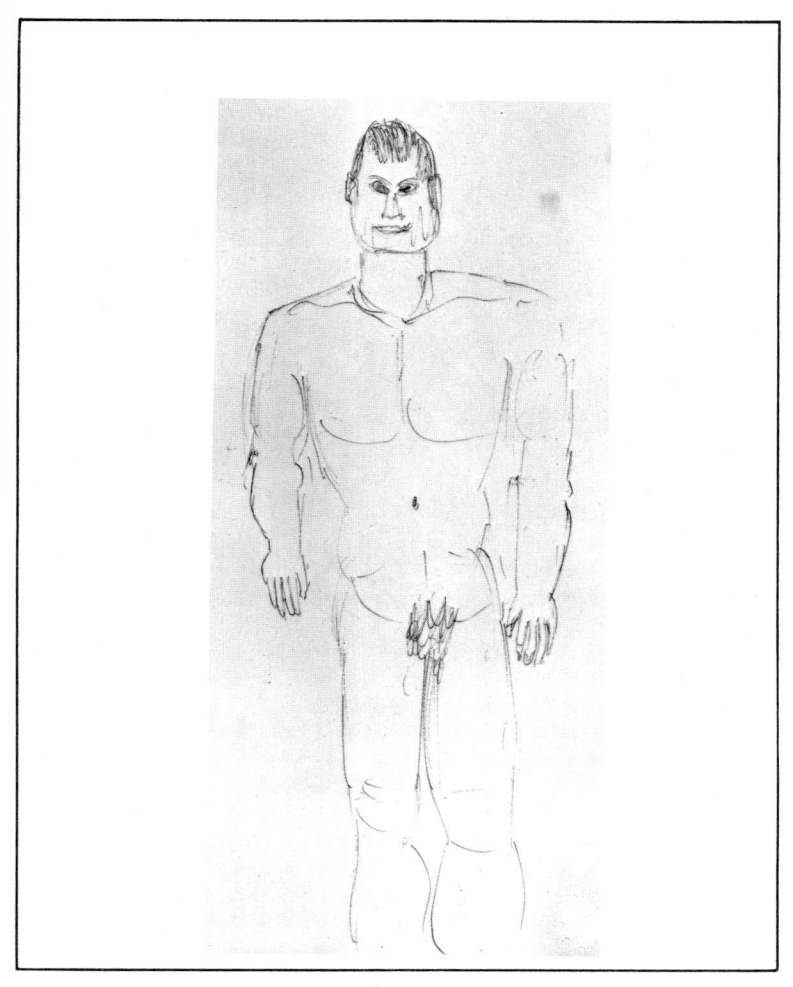

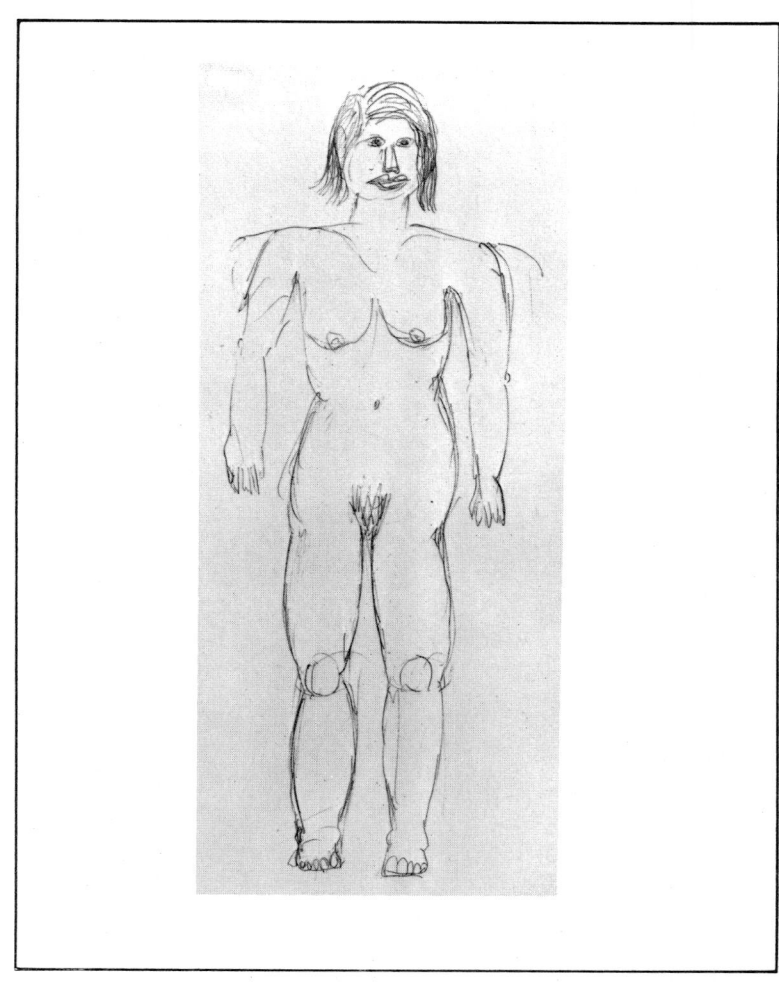

FIGURE-DRAWING CHARACTERISTICS

Structural	Male Female		Structural	Male	Female	Structural and Graphic	Male Female		Graphic, Global and Height	Male	Female	Body Proportions	Male	Female
	Both						Both							
Type	0		Omission of Appendages	3	0	Upper and Lower Halves	7	0	Hair Shading	3	3	Head	10	09
Sex Sequence	0		Position of Both Arms	0	0	Four Quarters	4	4	Nudity and Transparency	0	0	Neck	18	10
Posture	0	1	Position of Right Arm	0	0	Relative Size	0		Form	1	1	Shoulders	12	10
Perspective	0	0	Position of Left Arm	0	0	Constant Line Pressure	1	0	Detailing	1	1	Right Arm	06	06
Vertical Midline	0	0	Position of Legs	3	4	Variable Line Pressure	0	1	Identity and Sex	1	1	Left Arm	07	06
Bilateral Symmetry	3	3	Relation of Long Axes	1	1	Line Continuity	0	0	Sophistication	2	2	Chest	10	08
Horizontal Midline	0	0	Right and Left Halves	3	1	Body Shading	3	3	Height		08	Girth	08	09

GENERAL CHARACTERISTICS OF SUBJECT

IDENTIFICATION

No. E06
Sex M
Marital status S
Age 22 yrs. at
psychological tests

PARENTAL HISTORY

Father

C H S D O
- - - - -

Mother

C H S D O
- - - - -

PHYSIOLOGICAL AND METABOLIC DATA

	Admission	Initial	Control	Cold pressor change	Exercise change	Smoking change
Systolic pressure	120	120	112	+14	+48	
Diastolic pressure	80	62	70	+30	-16	
Heart rate	76	56	59	+12	+20	

Age 22 yrs.

Height 73 in.
Weight 171 lbs.
Overweight +02 %

Ponderal index 13.15
Cholesterol 200 mg. per 100 ml.
Vital capacity liters

HABIT SURVEY

Smoking habits: former smoker
Age begun yrs. Inhalation:
Habits of nervous tension: 2, 5, 6, 18, 22

STRONG VOCATIONAL INTEREST TEST

Occupation	Artist	Psychologist	Architect	Physician	Osteopath	Dentist	Veterinarian	Mathematician	Physicist	Engineer	Chemist	Production Manager
Standard Score	38	43	42	48	42	40	19	36	36	42	48	32

Occupation	Farmer	Aviator	Carpenter	Printer	Math.-Sci. Teacher	Ind. Arts Teacher	Voc. Agric. Teacher	Policeman	Forest Serv. Man	Y.M.C.A. Phys. Dir.	Personnel Director	Public Administrator
Standard Score	32	46	26	34	27	21	13	32	19	26	28	43

Occupation	Y.M.C.A. Secretary	Soc. Sci. H.S. Teacher	City Sch. Sup't.	Social Worker	Minister	Musician Performer	C.P.A.	Senior C.P.A.	Accountant	Office Man	Purchasing Agent	Banker
Standard Score	17	18	22	33	64	45	34	37	20	21	14	09

Occupation	Mortician	Pharmacist	Sales Manager	Real Est. Manager	Life Ins. Salesman	Advertising Man	Lawyer	Author-Journalist	President Mfg. Co.	Interest Maturity	Occupational Level	Masculinity-Femininity
Standard Score	19	13	19	28	23	36	38	39	33	49	54	46

FIGURE-DRAWING CHARACTERISTICS

Structural	Male Female Both	Structural	Male	Female	Structural and Graphic	Male	Female Both	Graphic, Global and Height	Male	Female	Body Proportions	Male	Female
Type	0	Omission of Appendages	0	8	Upper and Lower Halves	3	7	Hair Shading	3	2	Head	11	11
Sex Sequence	1	Position of Both Arms	0	0	Four Quarters	4	4	Nudity and Transparency	7	7	Neck	14	12
Posture	1 1	Position of Right Arm	0	0	Relative Size	0		Form	1	1	Shoulders	09	07
Perspective	0 0	Position of Left Arm	0	0	Constant Line Pressure	0	0	Detailing	1	1	Right Arm	08	06
Vertical Midline	3 0	Position of Legs	4	4	Variable Line Pressure	4	4	Identity and Sex	1	1	Left Arm	08	06
Bilateral Symmetry	5 5	Relation of Long Axes	1	1	Line Continuity	0	0	Sophistication	2	2	Chest	06	06
Horizontal Midline	4 4	Right and Left Halves	1	1	Body Shading	4	5	Height	08		Girth	07	05

GENERAL CHARACTERISTICS OF SUBJECT

IDENTIFICATION
No. E29
Sex F
Marital status S
Age 21 yrs. at
psychological tests

PARENTAL HISTORY
Father
C   H   S   D   O
-   -   -   -   -
Mother
C   H   S   D   O
-   -   -   -   -

PHYSIOLOGICAL AND METABOLIC DATA

	Admission	Initial	Control	Cold pressor change	Exercise change	Smoking change
Systolic pressure	100	98	98	+12	+32	00
Diastolic pressure	65	70	68	+24	-18	00
Heart rate	76	80	88	00	+23	00

Age 21 yrs.   Height 65 in.   Ponderal index 13.21
Weight 119 lbs.   Cholesterol 240 mg. per 100 ml.
Overweight -08 %   Vital capacity   liters

HABIT SURVEY

Smoking habits: occasional smoker
Age begun 22 yrs.   Inhalation: no
Habits of nervous tension: 3, 5, 8, 9, 11, 14, 16, 19, 22, 23

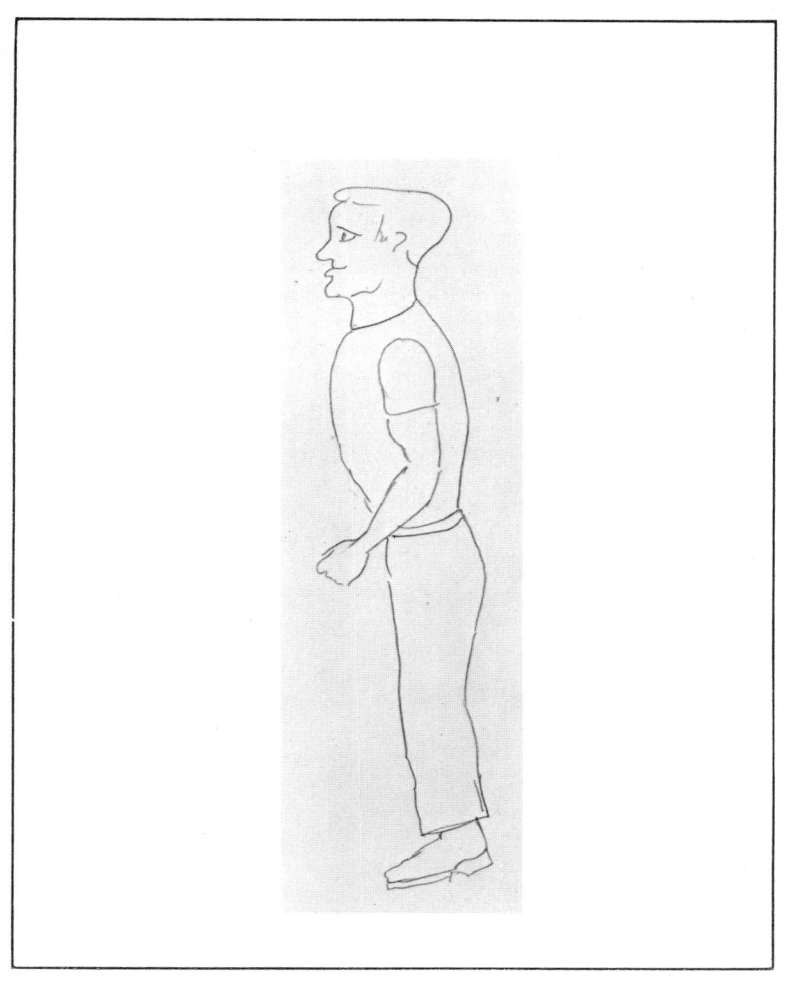

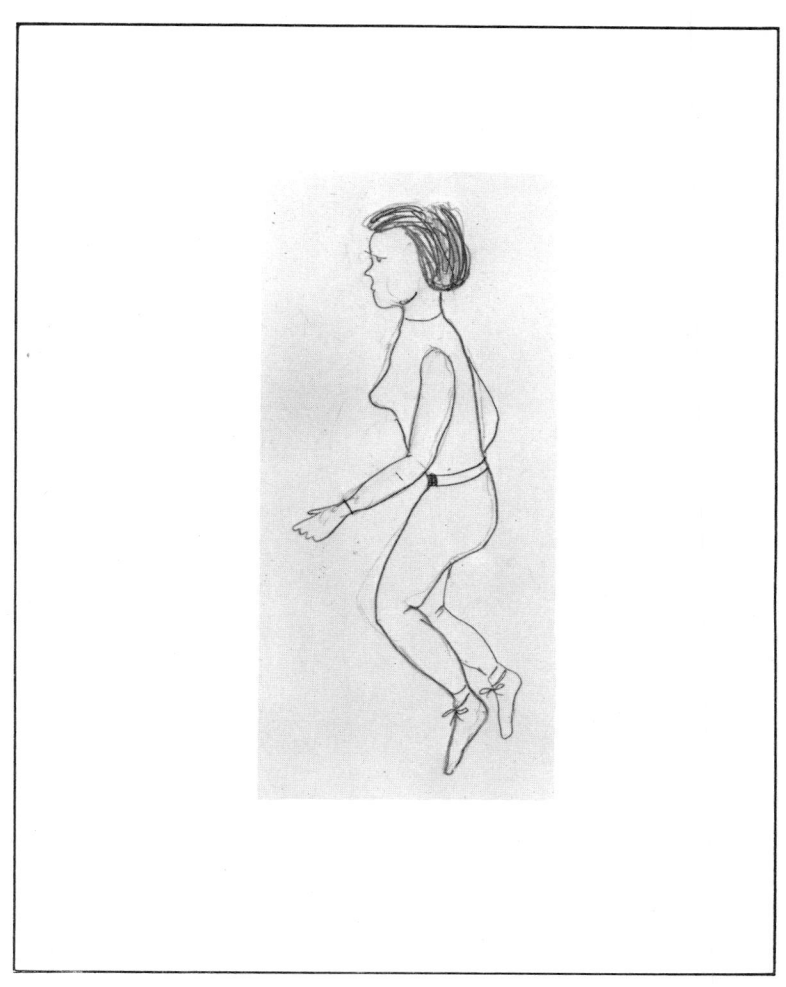

FIGURE-DRAWING CHARACTERISTICS

Structural	Male Female Both	Structural	Male	Female	Structural and Graphic	Male Female Both		Graphic, Global and Height	Male	Female	Body Proportions	Male	Female
Type	0	Omission of Appendages	0	0	Upper and Lower Halves	3	0	Hair Shading	5	3	Head	08	07
Sex Sequence	0	Position of Both Arms	4	4	Four Quarters	4	4	Nudity and Transparency	7	7	Neck	10	05
Posture	1 6	Position of Right Arm	7	7	Relative Size	0		Form	1	1	Shoulders		
Perspective	2 2	Position of Left Arm	4	4	Constant Line Pressure	4	5	Detailing	3	3	Right Arm		
Vertical Midline	4 4	Position of Legs	1	8	Variable Line Pressure	0	0	Identity and Sex	1	1	Left Arm	06	06
Bilateral Symmetry	0 0	Relation of Long Axes	1	0	Line Continuity	2	4	Sophistication	2	2	Chest	09	05
Horizontal Midline	4 4	Right and Left Halves	3	3	Body Shading	0	6	Height	07		Girth	06	06

GENERAL CHARACTERISTICS OF SUBJECT

IDENTIFICATION

No. E56
Sex M
Marital status S
Age 23 yrs. at
psychological tests

PARENTAL HISTORY

Father
C H S D O
- - - - -
Mother
C H S D O
- - - - -

PHYSIOLOGICAL AND METABOLIC DATA

	Admission	Initial	Control	Cold pressor change	Exercise change	Smoking change
Systolic pressure	130	118	122	+20	+38	00
Diastolic pressure	80	60	62	+18	00	+03
Heart rate	100	100	88	+24	+37	-01

Age 22 yrs.
Height 73 in.
Weight 156 lbs.
Overweight -07 %
Ponderal index 13.57
Cholesterol 240 mg. per 100 ml.
Vital capacity 4.7 liters

HABIT SURVEY

Smoking habits: cigar smoker
Age begun 21 yrs. Inhalation: no
Habits of nervous tension: 4, 5, 8, 9, 12, 13, 17, 20

STRONG VOCATIONAL INTEREST TEST

Occupation	Artist	Psychologist	Architect	Physician	Osteopath	Dentist	Veterinarian	Mathematician	Physicist	Engineer	Chemist	Production Manager
Standard Score	44	24	38	21	18	29	-07	26	14	14	20	21

Occupation	Farmer	Aviator	Carpenter	Printer	Math.-Sci. Teacher	Ind. Arts Teacher	Voc. Agric. Teacher	Policeman	Forest Serv. Man	Y.M.C.A. Phys. Dir.	Personnel Director	Public Administrator
Standard Score	21	05	03	25	10	-09	02	08	-08	04	13	24

Occupation	Y.M.C.A. Secretary	Soc. Sci. H.S. Teacher	City Sch. Sup't.	Social Worker	Minister	Musician Performer	C.P.A.	Senior C.P.A.	Accountant	Office Man	Purchasing Agent	Banker
Standard Score	10	23	25	22	64	34	33	12	17	21	27	30

Occupation	Mortician	Pharmacist	Sales Manager	Real Est. Manager	Life Ins. Salesman	Advertising Man	Lawyer	Author-Journalist	President Mfg. Co.	Interest Maturity	Occupational Level	Masculinity-Femininity
Standard Score	29	26	32	43	37	53	50	53	40	45	68	24

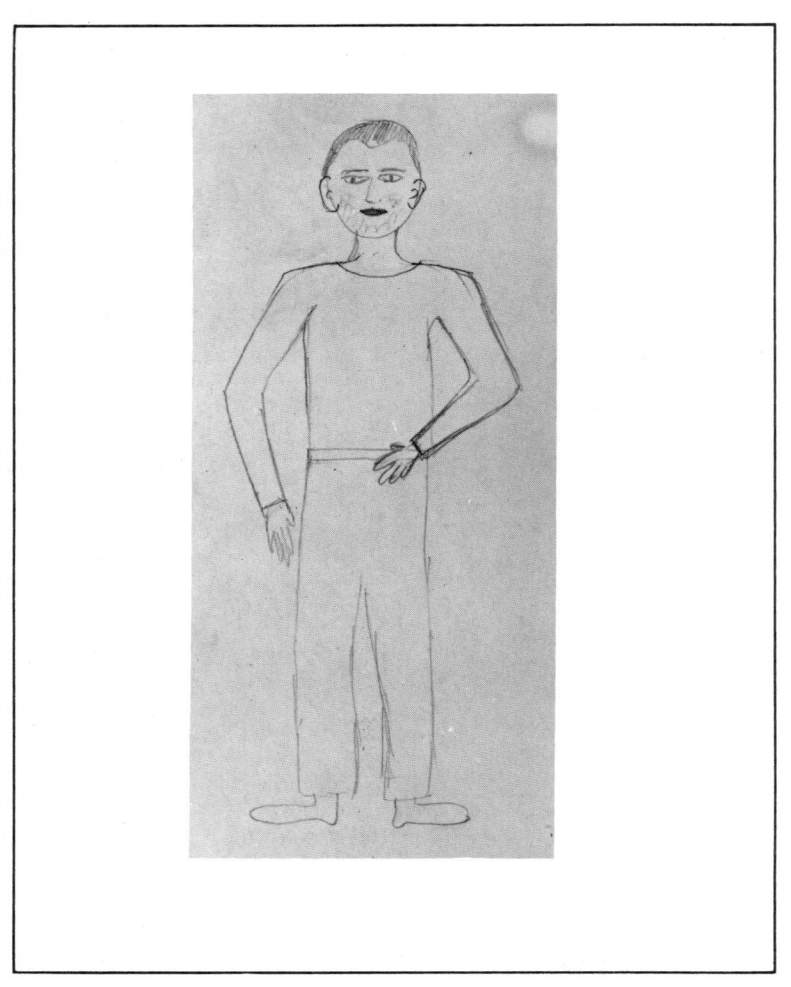

FIGURE-DRAWING CHARACTERISTICS*

Structural	Male Female Both		Structural	Male	Female	Structural and Graphic	Male Female Both		Graphic, Global and Height	Male	Female	Body Proportions	Male	Female
Type	0		Omission of Appendages	0	4	Upper and Lower Halves	1	7	Hair Shading	1	5	Head	10	15
Sex Sequence	2		Position of Both Arms	0	0	Four Quarters	4	4	Nudity and Transparency	7	7	Neck	10	10
Posture	1	0	Position of Right Arm	5	5	Relative Size	4		Form	3	3	Shoulders	08	11
Perspective	0	0	Position of Left Arm	5	5	Constant Line Pressure	0	0	Detailing	3	3	Right Arm	06	
Vertical Midline	0	0	Position of Legs	4	0	Variable Line Pressure	1	1	Identity and Sex	1	1	Left Arm	06	
Bilateral Symmetry	3	5	Relation of Long Axes	1	1	Line Continuity	0	0	Sophistication	2	2	Chest	06	11
Horizontal Midline	4	4	Right and Left Halves	1	1	Body Shading	0	5	Height	07	13	Girth	08	11

GENERAL CHARACTERISTICS OF SUBJECT

IDENTIFICATION
No. 327
Sex F
Marital status S
Age 24 yrs. at
psychological tests

PARENTAL HISTORY
Father
C H S D O
- - - - -
Mother
C H S D O
- - - - -

PHYSIOLOGICAL AND METABOLIC DATA

	Admission	Initial	Control	Cold pressor change	Exercise change	Smoking change
Systolic pressure	96	114	105	+16	+37	+06
Diastolic pressure	60	64	60	+12	+04	00
Heart rate	80	108	100	00	+15	+07

Age 23 yrs.

Height	72 in.	Ponderal index	13.87
Weight	140 lbs.	Cholesterol	245 mg. per 100 ml.
Overweight	-11 %	Vital capacity	3.8 liters

HABIT SURVEY
Smoking habits: light cigarette smoker
Age begun 18 yrs.   Inhalation: yes
Habits of nervous tension: 2, 3, 5, 6, 9, 11, 17

FIGURE-DRAWING CHARACTERISTICS

Structural	Male	Female	Structural	Male	Female	Structural and Graphic	Male	Female	Graphic, Global and Height	Male	Female	Body Proportions	Male	Female
	Both						Both							
Type	0		Omission of Appendages	0	0	Upper and Lower Halves	1	0	Hair Shading	7	1	Head	05	05
Sex Sequence	0		Position of Both Arms	0	0	Four Quarters	4	4	Nudity and Transparency	7	7	Neck	06	08
Posture	1	1	Position of Right Arm	0	0	Relative Size	4		Form	1	1	Shoulders	06	05
Perspective	0	0	Position of Left Arm	0	0	Constant Line Pressure	1	0	Detailing	3	3	Right Arm	04	04
Vertical Midline	3	0	Position of Legs	2	4	Variable Line Pressure	0	4	Identity and Sex	1	1	Left Arm	04	04
Bilateral Symmetry	3	3	Relation of Long Axes	1	1	Line Continuity	0	0	Sophistication	2	2	Chest	05	05
Horizontal Midline	6	0	Right and Left Halves	1	1	Body Shading	3	1	Height	04	05	Girth	05	03

GENERAL CHARACTERISTICS OF SUBJECT

IDENTIFICATION
No. 523
Sex M
Marital status S
Age 24 yrs. at
psychological tests

PARENTAL HISTORY				
Father				
C	H	S	D	O
U	U	U	U	U
Mother				
C	H	S	D	O
–	–	–	–	–

PHYSIOLOGICAL AND METABOLIC DATA

	Admission	Initial	Control	Cold pressor change	Exercise change	Smoking change
Systolic pressure	145	128	120	+02	+50	+06
Diastolic pressure	80	88	78	+06	+10	+08
Heart rate	80	84	78	+10	+47	00

Age 22 yrs.	Height	64 in.	Ponderal index 12.57
	Weight	132 lbs.	Cholesterol 237 mg. per 100 ml.
	Overweight +01 %		Vital capacity 3.8 liters

HABIT SURVEY

Smoking habits: nonsmoker

Age begun   yrs.   Inhalation:

Habits of nervous tension: 1, 3, 5, 8, 12, 21, 23, 25

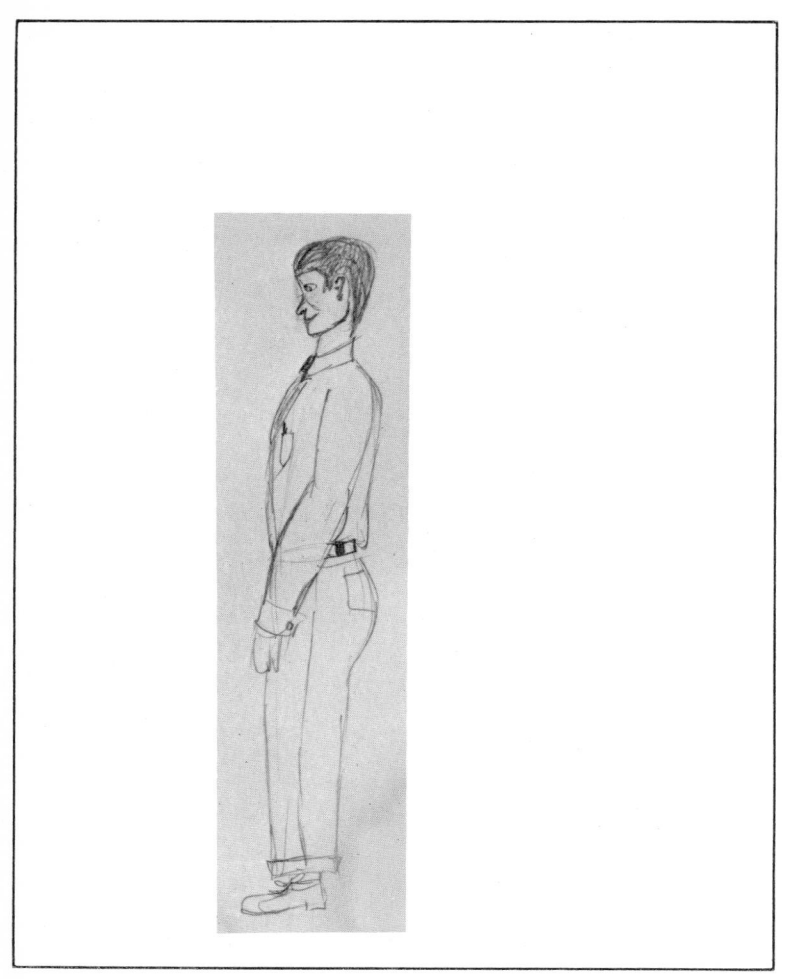

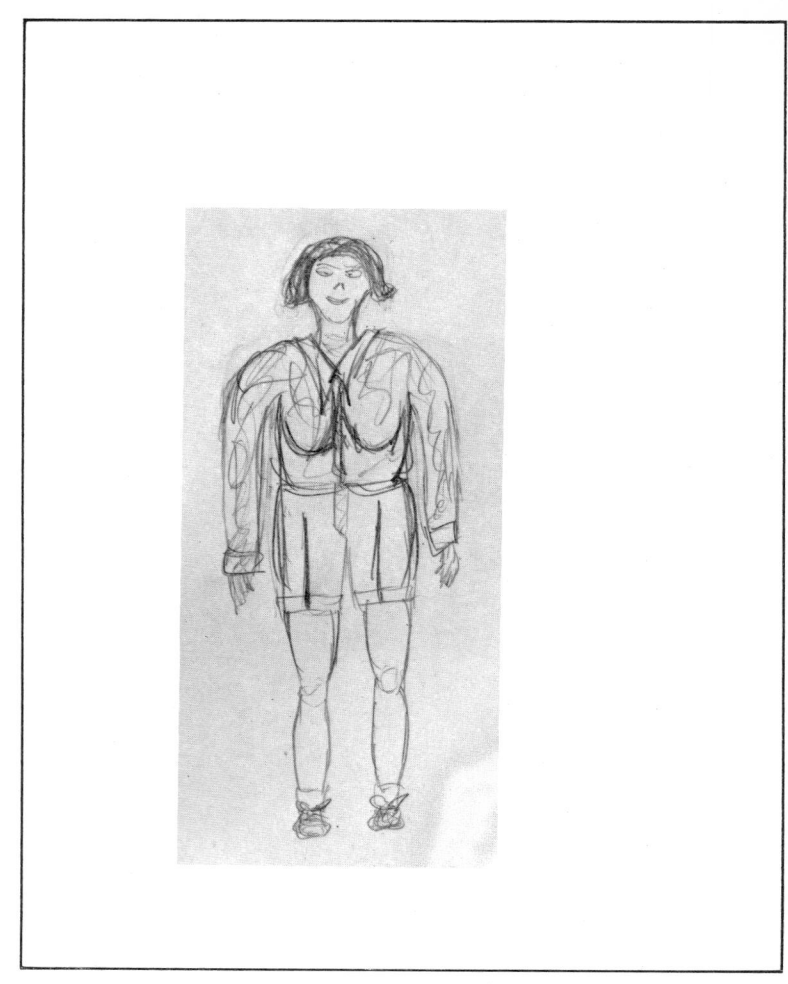

FIGURE-DRAWING CHARACTERISTICS

Structural	Male Female Both		Structural	Male	Female	Structural and Graphic	Male Female Both		Graphic, Global and Height	Male	Female	Body Proportions	Male	Female
Type	0		Omission of Appendages	0	0	Upper and Lower Halves	3	3	Hair Shading	3	3	Head	07	06
Sex Sequence	0		Position of Both Arms	4	0	Four Quarters	4	4	Nudity and Transparency	7	2	Neck	07	07
Posture	1	1	Position of Right Arm	7	0	Relative Size	0		Form	1	1	Shoulders		08
Perspective	2	0	Position of Left Arm	5	0	Constant Line Pressure	0	0	Detailing	1	1	Right Arm		06
Vertical Midline	7	3	Position of Legs	1	5	Variable Line Pressure	1	3	Identity and Sex	1	1	Left Arm	08	06
Bilateral Symmetry	0	3	Relation of Long Axes	1	1	Line Continuity	0	0	Sophistication	2	2	Chest	07	06
Horizontal Midline	4	4	Right and Left Halves	2	1	Body Shading	5	7	Height	07	06	Girth	06	08

GENERAL CHARACTERISTICS OF SUBJECT

IDENTIFICATION
No. 612
Sex M
Marital status S
Age 23 yrs. at psychological tests

PARENTAL HISTORY				
Father				
C	H	S	D	0
U	U	U	U	-
Mother				
C	H	S	D	0
-	-	-	-	-

PHYSIOLOGICAL AND METABOLIC DATA

	Admission	Initial	Control	Cold pressor change	Exercise change	Smoking change
Systolic pressure	110	110	104	+10	+34	+10
Diastolic pressure	68	62	58	+18	-02	+10
Heart rate	78	64	68	-12	+32	+02

Age 22 yrs.	Height 73 in.	Ponderal index 12.83
	Weight 184 lbs.	Cholesterol 197 mg. per 100 ml.
	Overweight +10 %	Vital capacity 5.4 liters

HABIT SURVEY
Smoking habits: occasional smoker
Age begun 18 yrs.   Inhalation: no
Habits of nervous tension: 2, 5, 6, 9, 11

FIGURE-DRAWING CHARACTERISTICS

Structural	Male Female Both		Structural	Male	Female	Structural and Graphic	Male Female Both		Graphic, Global and Height	Male	Female	Body Proportions	Male	Female
Type	0		Omission of Appendages	0	0	Upper and Lower Halves	0	1	Hair Shading	2	2	Head	09	05
Sex Sequence	0		Position of Both Arms	0	0	Four Quarters	4	4	Nudity and Transparency	7	7	Neck	08	03
Posture	1	1	Position of Right Arm	0	5	Relative Size	0		Form	3	1	Shoulders	08	05
Perspective	0	0	Position of Left Arm	0	5	Constant Line Pressure	2	2	Detailing	1	1	Right Arm	06	04
Vertical Midline	3	0	Position of Legs	4	4	Variable Line Pressure	0	0	Identity and Sex	1	1	Left Arm	06	04
Bilateral Symmetry	3	3	Relation of Long Axes	1	1	Line Continuity	0	0	Sophistication	2	2	Chest	06	04
Horizontal Midline	4	4	Right and Left Halves	1	2	Body Shading	6	7	Height	08	05	Girth	09	04

GENERAL CHARACTERISTICS OF SUBJECT

<table>
<tr><th colspan="2">IDENTIFICATION</th></tr>
<tr><td colspan="2">No. 757</td></tr>
<tr><td colspan="2">Sex M</td></tr>
<tr><td colspan="2">Marital status S</td></tr>
<tr><td colspan="2">Age 22 yrs. at</td></tr>
<tr><td colspan="2">psychological tests</td></tr>
</table>

PARENTAL HISTORY				
Father				
C	H	S	D	0
U	U	U	U	U
Mother				
C	H	S	D	0
-	-	-	-	-

PHYSIOLOGICAL AND METABOLIC DATA

	Admission	Initial	Control	Cold pressor change	Exercise change	Smoking change
Systolic pressure	140	117	92	+02	+38	+04
Diastolic pressure	70	50	52	+14	-02	+06
Heart rate	96	92	84	+08	+16	+15

Age 22 yrs.	Height 76 in.	Ponderal index 13.13
	Weight 194 lbs.	Cholesterol 190 mg. per 100 ml.
	Overweight +06 %	Vital capacity 5.8 liters

HABIT SURVEY
Smoking habits: nonsmoker
Age begun yrs.   Inhalation:
Habits of nervous tension: 2, 5, 6, 9, 11

XI. MIXED SOPHISTICATED DRAWINGS

In this section, represented by eleven subjects, one drawing of each pair is moderately sophisticated and the other is most sophisticated.

FIGURE-DRAWING CHARACTERISTICS

Structural	Male Female Both	Structural	Male	Female	Structural and Graphic	Male Female Both		Graphic, Global and Height	Male	Female	Body Proportions	Male	Female
Type	0	Omission of Appendages	0	0	Upper and Lower Halves	3	3	Hair Shading	5	5	Head	09	11
Sex Sequence	0	Position of Both Arms	0	0	Four Quarters	4	4	Nudity and Transparency	7	0	Neck	08	06
Posture	1	8	Position of Right Arm	5	2	Relative Size	4		Form	3	1	Shoulders	07	
Perspective	0	6	Position of Left Arm	5	2	Constant Line Pressure	0	0	Detailing	1	1	Right Arm	08	10
Vertical Midline	3	4	Position of Legs	5	9	Variable Line Pressure	5	3	Identity and Sex	1	1	Left Arm	08	10
Bilateral Symmetry	2	0	Relation of Long Axes	1	0	Line Continuity	2	2	Sophistication	2	1	Chest	07	
Horizontal Midline	4	0	Right and Left Halves	1	3	Body Shading	7	3	Height	08		Girth	09	

GENERAL CHARACTERISTICS OF SUBJECT

IDENTIFICATION	PARENTAL HISTORY
No. F33 Sex M Marital status M Age 25 yrs. at psychological tests	Father C H S D O + - + + + Mother C H S D O ? - - - +

PHYSIOLOGICAL AND METABOLIC DATA

	Admission	Initial	Control	Cold pressor change	Exercise change	Smoking change
Systolic pressure	122	114	108	+08	+28	+03
Diastolic pressure	60	70	76	+28	+14	+02
Heart rate	74	72	70	-12	+18	+13

Age 22 yrs.	Height	70 in.	Ponderal index 12.87
	Weight	161 lbs.	Cholesterol 190 mg. per 100 ml.
	Overweight +05 %		Vital capacity liters

HABIT SURVEY

Smoking habits: mixed smoker

Age begun 16 yrs.   Inhalation: yes

Habits of nervous tension: 2, 3, 4, 5, 6, 9,

11, 14, 16, 17, 18, 21, 23, 25

STRONG VOCATIONAL INTEREST TEST

Occupation	Artist	Psychologist	Architect	Physician	Osteopath	Dentist	Veterinarian	Mathematician	Physicist	Engineer	Chemist	Production Manager
Standard Score	34	46	42	58	41	49	30	36	38	49	56	42

Occupation	Farmer	Aviator	Carpenter	Printer	Math.-Sci. Teacher	Ind. Arts Teacher	Voc. Agric. Teacher	Policeman	Forest Serv. Man	Y.M.C.A. Phys. Dir.	Personnel Director	Public Administrator
Standard Score	46	47	34	43	41	42	41	27	29	22	36	39

Occupation	Y.M.C.A. Secretary	Soc. Sci. H.S. Teacher	City Sch. Sup't.	Social Worker	Minister	Musician Performer	C.P.A.	Senior C.P.A.	Accountant	Office Man	Purchasing Agent	Banker
Standard Score	14	20	16	31	58	41	17	37	17	25	28	13

Occupation	Mortician	Pharmacist	Sales Manager	Real Est. Manager	Life Ins. Salesman	Advertising Man	Lawyer	Author-Journalist	President Mfg. Co.	Interest Maturity	Occupational Level	Masculinity-Femininity
Standard Score	18	27	19	24	16	31	25	34	36	51	53	61

Plate 758   MIXED SOPHISTICATED DRAWINGS   807

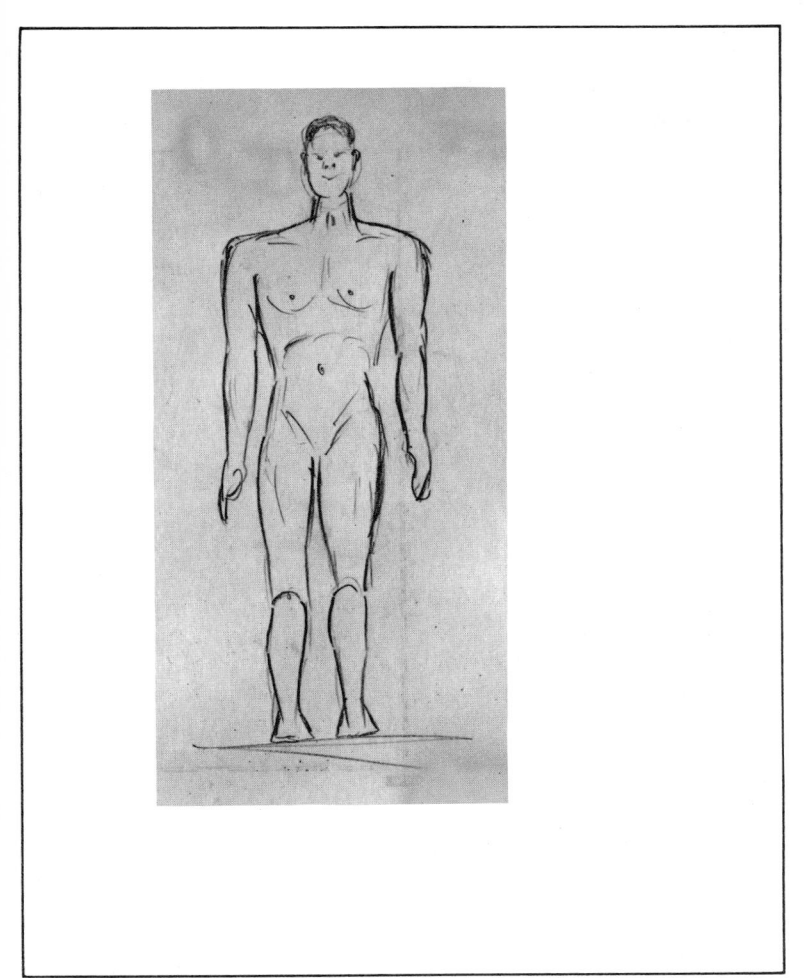

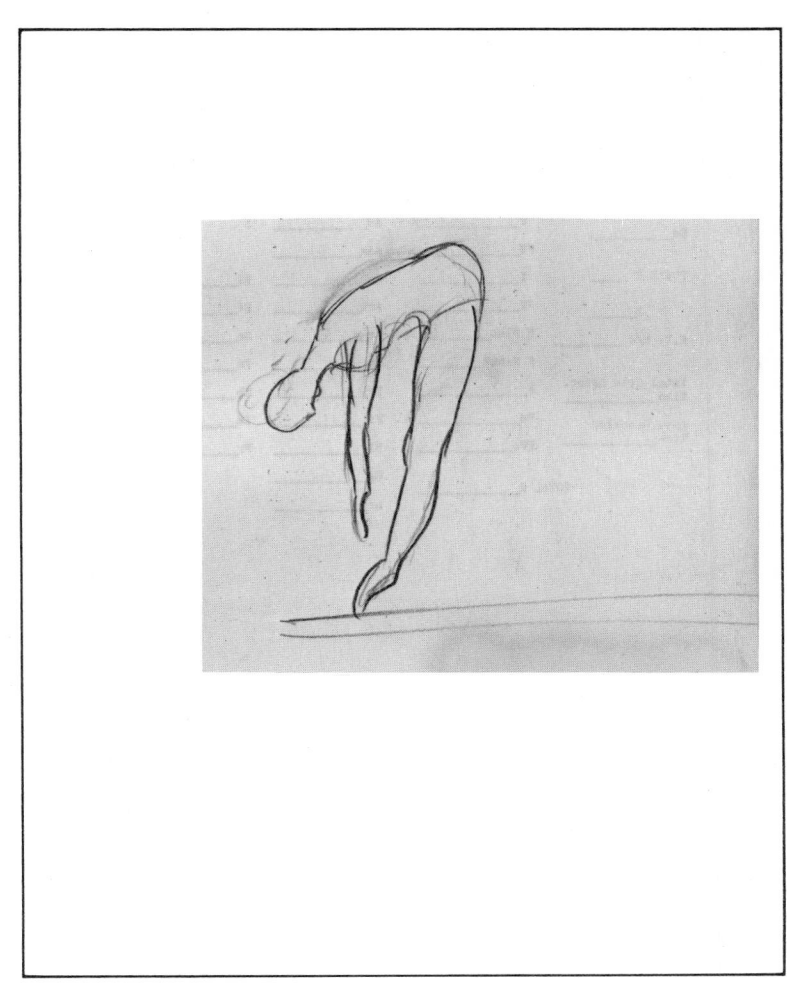

FIGURE-DRAWING CHARACTERISTICS

Structural	Male	Female	Structural	Male	Female	Structural and Graphic	Male	Female	Graphic, Global and Height	Male	Female	Body Proportions	Male	Female
	Both						Both							
Type	0		Omission of Appendages	0	0	Upper and Lower Halves	1	1	Hair Shading	3	0	Head	06	05
Sex Sequence	0		Position of Both Arms	0	4	Four Quarters	4	4	Nudity and Transparency	0	2	Neck	07	07
Posture	1	6	Position of Right Arm	0	6	Relative Size	0		Form	1	1	Shoulders	08	
Perspective	0	2	Position of Left Arm	0	6	Constant Line Pressure	5	5	Detailing	1	3	Right Arm	06	
Vertical Midline	0	4	Position of Legs	4	8	Variable Line Pressure	0	0	Identity and Sex	1	1	Left Arm	06	04
Bilateral Symmetry	5	0	Relation of Long Axes	1	0	Line Continuity	2	2	Sophistication	1	2	Chest	06	04
Horizontal Midline	0	0	Right and Left Halves	1	3	Body Shading	3	0	Height	06		Girth	06	05

GENERAL CHARACTERISTICS OF SUBJECT

IDENTIFICATION
No. 201
Sex M
Marital status M
Age 25 yrs. at
psychological tests

PARENTAL HISTORY
Father
C   H   S   D   O
+   -   -   -   -
Mother
C   H   S   D   O
-   -   -   -   -

PHYSIOLOGICAL AND METABOLIC DATA

	Admission	Initial	Control	Cold pressor change	Exercise change	Smoking change
Systolic pressure	118	130	116	+32	+31	
Diastolic pressure	70	72	80	+28	-02	
Heart rate	82	82	60	+06	+07	

Age 22 yrs.	Height	74	in.	Ponderal index 12.87
	Weight	190	lbs.	Cholesterol 190 mg. per 100 ml.
	Overweight +10 %			Vital capacity 5.5 liters

HABIT SURVEY

Smoking habits: heavy cigarette smoker

Age begun 19 yrs.   Inhalation: yes

Habits of nervous tension: 5, 18, 19, 21

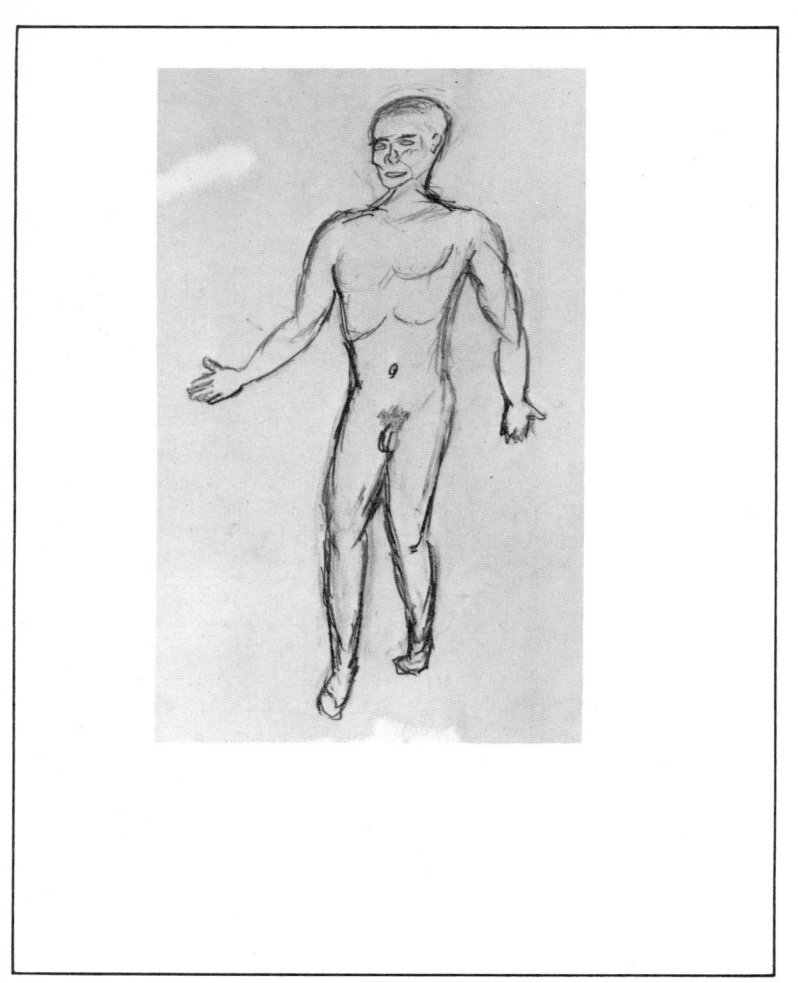

FIGURE-DRAWING CHARACTERISTICS

Structural	Male Female Both	Structural	Male	Female	Structural and Graphic	Male Female Both		Graphic, Global and Height	Male	Female	Body Proportions	Male	Female
Type	0	Omission of Appendages	0	0	Upper and Lower Halves	1	1	Hair Shading	2	3	Head	07	05
Sex Sequence	0	Position of Both Arms	0	4	Four Quarters	4	4	Nudity and Transparency	0	0	Neck	06	04
Posture	2 8	Position of Right Arm	6	7	Relative Size	0		Form	1	1	Shoulders	07	
Perspective	0 1	Position of Left Arm	6	2	Constant Line Pressure	0	0	Detailing	1	3	Right Arm	06	
Vertical Midline	0 4	Position of Legs	8	1	Variable Line Pressure	5	5	Identity and Sex	1	1	Left Arm	06	
Bilateral Symmetry	3 0	Relation of Long Axes	1	0	Line Continuity	0	0	Sophistication	1	2	Chest	06	
Horizontal Midline	0 0	Right and Left Halves	0	1	Body Shading	3	3	Height	06		Girth	06	

GENERAL CHARACTERISTICS OF SUBJECT

IDENTIFICATION

No. D36
Sex M
Marital status M
Age 24 yrs. at
psychological tests

PARENTAL HISTORY

Father
C H S D O
+ + − − ?
Mother
C H S D O
− − − − −

PHYSIOLOGICAL AND METABOLIC DATA

	Admission	Initial	Control	Cold pressor change	Exercise change	Smoking change
Systolic pressure	110	116	112	−04	+23	+08
Diastolic pressure	80	68	72	+10	−15	−04
Heart rate	75	64	65	−04	+21	+17

Age 24 yrs.   Height 72 in.   Weight 170 lbs.   Overweight +03 %
Ponderal index 13.00   Cholesterol 248 mg. per 100 ml.   Vital capacity 5.6 liters

HABIT SURVEY

Smoking habits: occasional smoker
Age begun 12 yrs.   Inhalation: sometimes
Habits of nervous tension: 1, 2, 3, 4, 5, 6,
9, 11, 14, 16, 18, 19, 24, 25

STRONG VOCATIONAL INTEREST TEST

Occupation	Artist	Psychologist	Architect	Physician	Osteopath	Dentist	Veterinarian	Mathematician	Physicist	Engineer	Chemist	Production Manager
Standard Score	45	43	43	54	47	41	23	29	18	23	34	15

Occupation	Farmer	Aviator	Carpenter	Printer	Math.-Sci. Teacher	Ind. Arts Teacher	Voc. Agric. Teacher	Policeman	Forest Serv. Man	Y.M.C.A. Phys. Dir.	Personnel Director	Public Administrator
Standard Score	30	31	17	39	33	16	22	21	22	31	36	37

Occupation	Y.M.C.A. Secretary	Soc. Sci. H.S. Teacher	City Sch. Sup't.	Social Worker	Minister	Musician Performer	C.P.A.	Senior C.P.A.	Accountant	Office Man	Purchasing Agent	Banker
Standard Score	35	42	35	46	63	64	25	29	14	26	10	18

Occupation	Mortician	Pharmacist	Sales Manager	Real Est. Manager	Life Ins. Salesman	Advertising Man	Lawyer	Author-Journalist	President Mfg. Co.	Interest Maturity	Occupational Level	Masculinity-Femininity
Standard Score	21	23	23	36	32	46	45	47	19	56	54	33

Plate 760

MIXED SOPHISTICATED DRAWINGS

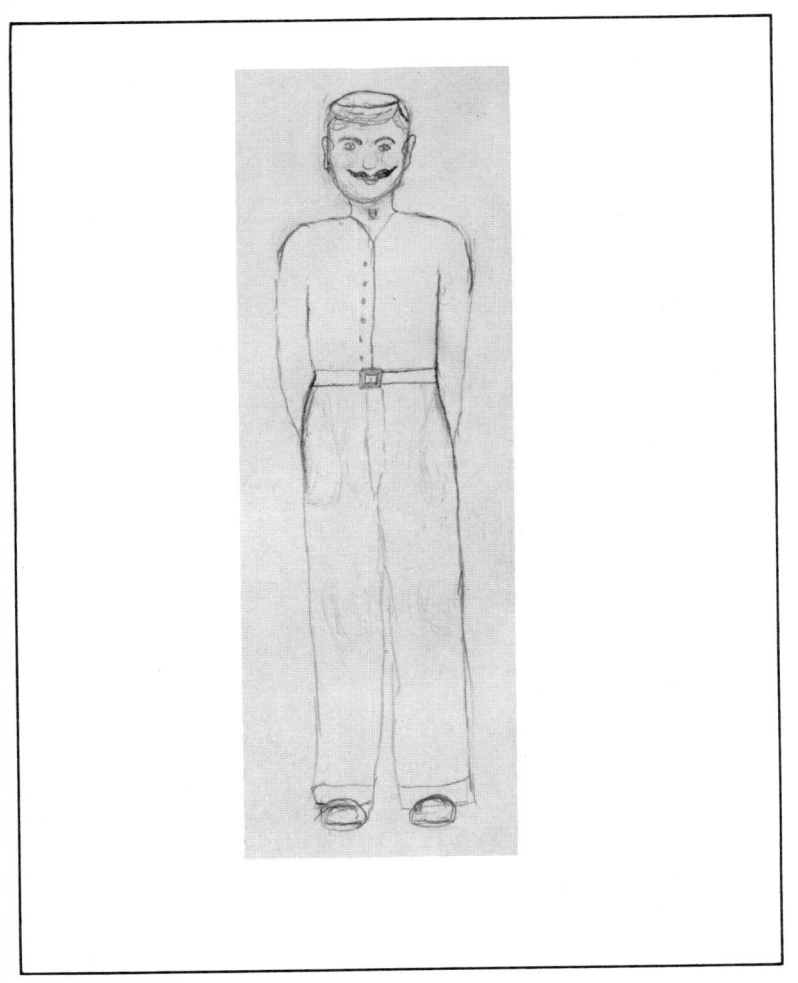

FIGURE-DRAWING CHARACTERISTICS

Structural	Male Female Both	Structural	Male	Female	Structural and Graphic	Male Female Both		Graphic, Global and Height	Male	Female	Body Proportions	Male	Female
Type	0	Omission of Appendages	2	0	Upper and Lower Halves	1	1	Hair Shading	1	1	Head	09	07
Sex Sequence	0	Position of Both Arms	6	4	Four Quarters	4	4	Nudity and Transparency	7	7	Neck	06	07
Posture	1	1	Position of Right Arm	8	7	Relative Size	0		Form	1	1	Shoulders	07	
Perspective	0	2	Position of Left Arm	8	4	Constant Line Pressure	0	0	Detailing	1	3	Right Arm		
Vertical Midline	3	4	Position of Legs	4	1	Variable Line Pressure	2	1	Identity and Sex	3	1	Left Arm		06
Bilateral Symmetry	4	0	Relation of Long Axes	1	1	Line Continuity	0	0	Sophistication	1	2	Chest	06	04
Horizontal Midline	4	4	Right and Left Halves	1	1	Body Shading	6	1	Height	07	07	Girth	08	06

GENERAL CHARACTERISTICS OF SUBJECT

IDENTIFICATION
No. 627
Sex F
Marital status S
Age 22 yrs. at
psychological tests

PARENTAL HISTORY
Father
C H S D O
? + - - -
Mother
C H S D O
- - - - -

PHYSIOLOGICAL AND METABOLIC DATA

	Admission	Initial	Control	Cold pressor change	Exercise change	Smoking change
Systolic pressure	110	112	98	+08	+32	-06
Diastolic pressure	70	64	64	+26	+04	-02
Heart rate	80	72	63		+23	-02

Age 22 yrs.	Height 68 in.	Ponderal index 12.50
	Weight 161 lbs.	Cholesterol 222 mg. per 100 ml.
	Overweight +14 %	Vital capacity 3.6 liters

HABIT SURVEY
Smoking habits: nonsmoker
Age begun   yrs.   Inhalation:
Habits of nervous tension: 1, 4, 6, 21, 25

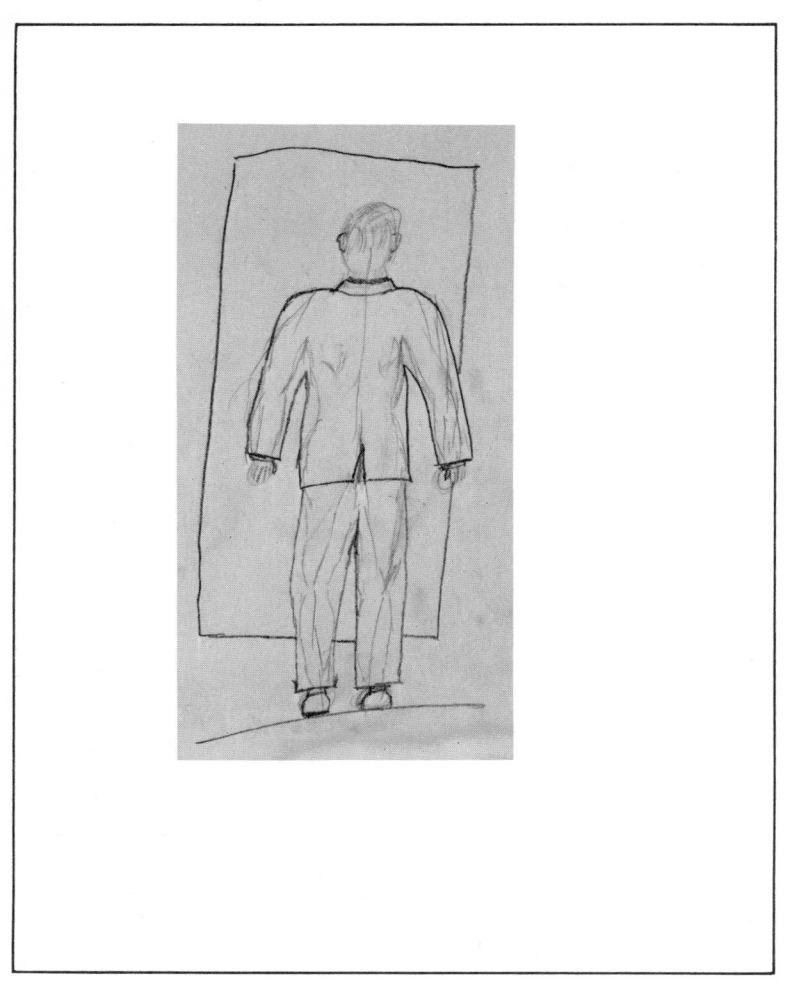

FIGURE-DRAWING CHARACTERISTICS

Structural	Male Female Both	Structural	Male	Female	Structural and Graphic	Male Female Both		Graphic, Global and Height	Male	Female	Body Proportions	Male	Female
Type	0	Omission of Appendages	0	0	Upper and Lower Halves	1	1	Hair Shading	3	3	Head		07
Sex Sequence	0	Position of Both Arms	0	4	Four Quarters	4	4	Nudity and Transparency	6	6	Neck		10
Posture	1　1	Position of Right Arm	0	7	Relative Size	4		Form	1	1	Shoulders	06	
Perspective	3　2	Position of Left Arm	0	5	Constant Line Pressure	0	0	Detailing	1	1	Right Arm	04	
Vertical Midline	9　4	Position of Legs	4	1	Variable Line Pressure	3	3	Identity and Sex	1	1	Left Arm	04	04
Bilateral Symmetry	5　0	Relation of Long Axes	1	1	Line Continuity	0	0	Sophistication	2	1	Chest	05	05
Horizontal Midline	6　4	Right and Left Halves	1	2	Body Shading	0	0	Height	05	06	Girth	04	07

GENERAL CHARACTERISTICS OF SUBJECT

IDENTIFICATION
No. 247
Sex M
Marital status M
Age 24 yrs. at
psychological tests

PARENTAL HISTORY
Father
C　H　S　D　O
-　-　-　-　-
Mother
C　H　S　D　O
?　-　-　-　?

PHYSIOLOGICAL AND METABOLIC DATA

	Admission	Initial	Control	Cold pressor change	Exercise change	Smoking change
Systolic pressure	118	128	116	+07	+30	
Diastolic pressure	66	64	66	+10	-04	
Heart rate	80	78	68	-06	+20	

Age 24 yrs.	Height 70 in.	Ponderal index 12.76
	Weight 165 lbs.	Cholesterol 284 mg. per 100 ml.
	Overweight +06 %	Vital capacity 5.4 liters

HABIT SURVEY
Smoking habits: nonsmoker
Age begun yrs. Inhalation:
Habits of nervous tension: 4, 6, 9, 14, 25

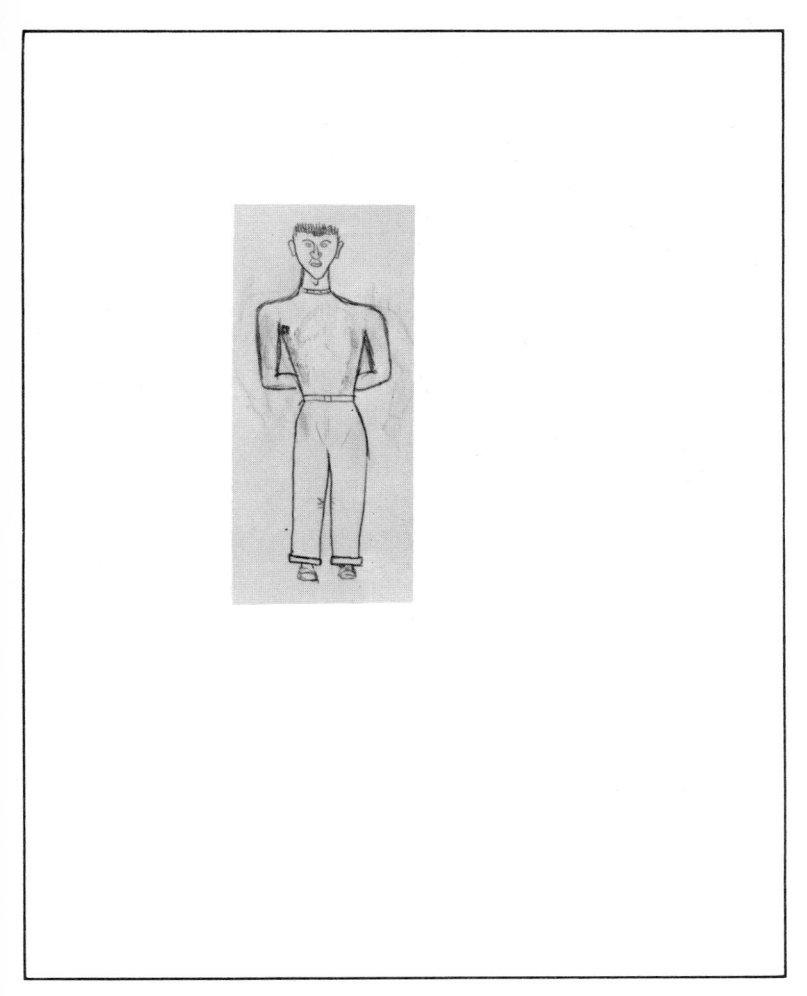

FIGURE-DRAWING CHARACTERISTICS

Structural	Male Female Both	Structural	Male	Female	Structural and Graphic	Male Female Both	Graphic, Global and Height	Male	Female	Body Proportions	Male	Female
Type	0	Omission of Appendages	7	0	Upper and Lower Halves	1	1	Hair Shading	3	3	Head	04	04
Sex Sequence	0	Position of Both Arms	0	4	Four Quarters	4	4	Nudity and Transparency	7	2	Neck	05	07
Posture	1 2	Position of Right Arm	5	7	Relative Size	4		Form	1	1	Shoulders	05	
Perspective	0 1	Position of Left Arm	5	2	Constant Line Pressure	5	5	Detailing	1	1	Right Arm		02
Vertical Midline	2 4	Position of Legs	4	8	Variable Line Pressure	0	0	Identity and Sex	1	1	Left Arm		02
Bilateral Symmetry	2 0	Relation of Long Axes	1	1	Line Continuity	2	2	Sophistication	2	1	Chest	03	
Horizontal Midline	4 0	Right and Left Halves	2	1	Body Shading	3	3	Height	03	04	Girth	03	

GENERAL CHARACTERISTICS OF SUBJECT

IDENTIFICATION

No. CO4

Sex M

Marital status S

Age 21 yrs. at

psychological tests

PARENTAL HISTORY

Father

C	H	S	D	O
-	+	-	-	?

Mother

C	H	S	D	O
-	-	-	-	?

PHYSIOLOGICAL AND METABOLIC DATA

	Admission	Initial	Control	Cold pressor change	Exercise change	Smoking change
Systolic pressure	130	130	120	+15	+30	-12
Diastolic pressure	80	75	80	+05	-10	00
Heart rate	88	88	82	00	+01	+09

Age 21 yrs.   Height 67 in.   Ponderal index 12.38

Weight 158 lbs.   Cholesterol 196 mg. per 100 ml.

Overweight +12 %   Vital capacity 4.4 liters

HABIT SURVEY

Smoking habits: light cigarette smoker

Age begun 18 yrs.   Inhalation: yes

Habits of nervous tension: 3, 5, 9, 11, 12, 18, 19, 24

STRONG VOCATIONAL INTEREST TEST

Occupation	Artist	Psychologist	Architect	Physician	Osteopath	Dentist	Veterinarian	Mathematician	Physicist	Engineer	Chemist	Production Manager
Standard Score	32	49	37	60	52	40	28	25	18	21	32	23

Occupation	Farmer	Aviator	Carpenter	Printer	Math.-Sci. Teacher	Ind. Arts Teacher	Voc. Agric. Teacher	Policeman	Forest Serv. Man	Y.M.C.A. Phys. Dir.	Personnel Director	Public Administrator
Standard Score	32	36	21	44	43	22	29	35	31	50	45	50

Occupation	Y.M.C.A. Secretary	Soc. Sci. H.S. Teacher	City Sch. Sup't.	Social Worker	Minister	Musician Performer	C.P.A.	Senior C.P.A.	Accountant	Office Man	Purchasing Agent	Banker
Standard Score	42	48	37	50	62	59	27	42	18	36	14	21

Occupation	Mortician	Pharmacist	Sales Manager	Real Est. Manager	Life Ins. Salesman	Advertising Man	Lawyer	Author-Journalist	President Mfg. Co.	Interest Maturity	Occupational Level	Masculinity-Femininity
Standard Score	26	31	25	29	32	38	34	36	14	58	51	41

FIGURE-DRAWING CHARACTERISTICS

Structural	Male Female Both	Structural	Male	Female	Structural and Graphic	Male Female Both		Graphic, Global and Height	Male	Female	Body Proportions	Male	Female
Type	0	Omission of Appendages	7	0	Upper and Lower Halves	0	3	Hair Shading	3	3	Head	06	07
Sex Sequence	0	Position of Both Arms	4	1	Four Quarters	4	4	Nudity and Transparency	7	7	Neck	07	06
Posture	2 1	Position of Right Arm	7	0	Relative Size	2		Form	1	3	Shoulders		
Perspective	2 1	Position of Left Arm	5	5	Constant Line Pressure	0	0	Detailing	1	1	Right Arm		06
Vertical Midline	7 7	Position of Legs	8	6	Variable Line Pressure	1	1	Identity and Sex	1	1	Left Arm		06
Bilateral Symmetry	0 0	Relation of Long Axes	1	1	Line Continuity	0	0	Sophistication	1	2	Chest	07	
Horizontal Midline	4 0	Right and Left Halves	1	0	Body Shading	7	3	Height	06	07	Girth	08	

GENERAL CHARACTERISTICS OF SUBJECT

IDENTIFICATION
No. 531
Sex M
Marital status S
Age 25 yrs. at psychological tests

PARENTAL HISTORY				
Father				
C	H	S	D	O
-	-	-	-	-
Mother				
C	H	S	D	O
-	+	-	-	?

PHYSIOLOGICAL AND METABOLIC DATA

	Admission	Initial	Control	Cold pressor change	Exercise change	Smoking change
Systolic pressure	140	130	124	+14	+50	
Diastolic pressure	98	74	84	+12	+08	
Heart rate	64	72	73	-12	+30	

Age 23 yrs.	Height	71 in.	Ponderal index 12.18
	Weight	198 lbs.	Cholesterol 258 mg. per 100 ml.
	Overweight +25 %		Vital capacity 5.1 liters

HABIT SURVEY
Smoking habits: heavy cigarette smoker
Age begun 21 yrs.   Inhalation: yes
Habits of nervous tension: 2, 6, 9, 10, 11, 16, 25

FIGURE-DRAWING CHARACTERISTICS

Structural	Male Female Both	Structural	Male	Female	Structural and Graphic	Male Female Both		Graphic, Global and Height	Male	Female	Body Proportions	Male	Female
Type	0	Omission of Appendages	7	7	Upper and Lower Halves	0	0	Hair Shading	2	5	Head	09	09
Sex Sequence	0	Position of Both Arms	0	1	Four Quarters	4	4	Nudity and Transparency	7	7	Neck	12	12
Posture	1 1	Position of Right Arm	5	2	Relative Size	0		Form	1	1	Shoulders	10	07
Perspective	0 5	Position of Left Arm	5	5	Constant Line Pressure	4	0	Detailing	1	3	Right Arm	08	06
Vertical Midline	3 0	Position of Legs	6	4	Variable Line Pressure	0	1	Identity and Sex	1	1	Left Arm	08	06
Bilateral Symmetry	3 3	Relation of Long Axes	1	1	Line Continuity	0	0	Sophistication	1	2	Chest	09	07
Horizontal Midline	6 4	Right and Left Halves	1	0	Body Shading	7	7	Height	09	08	Girth	11	07

GENERAL CHARACTERISTICS OF SUBJECT

IDENTIFICATION
No. F11
Sex M
Marital status S
Age 24 yrs. at
psychological tests

PARENTAL HISTORY				
Father				
C	H	S	D	O
-	-	-	-	-
Mother				
C	H	S	D	O
-	+	-	-	-

PHYSIOLOGICAL AND METABOLIC DATA

	Admission	Initial	Control	Cold pressor change	Exercise change	Smoking change
Systolic pressure	120	110	110	+24	+10	+01
Diastolic pressure	75	70	74	+34	+06	+08
Heart rate	76	68	73	+08	+04	+08

Age 22 yrs.	Height 74 in.	Ponderal index 12.98
	Weight 185 lbs.	Cholesterol 197 mg. per 100 ml.
	Overweight +07 %	Vital capacity liters

HABIT SURVEY

Smoking habits: pipe smoker

  Age begun 16 yrs.   Inhalation: no

Habits of nervous tension: 4, 5, 6, 10, 14, 16, 22

STRONG VOCATIONAL INTEREST TEST

Occupation	Artist	Psychologist	Architect	Physician	Osteopath	Dentist	Veterinarian	Mathematician	Physicist	Engineer	Chemist	Production Manager
Standard Score	28	37	32	54	38	36	34	17	05	20	22	28

Occupation	Farmer	Aviator	Carpenter	Printer	Math.-Sci. Teacher	Ind. Arts Teacher	Voc. Agric. Teacher	Policeman	Forest Serv. Man	Y.M.C.A. Phys. Dir.	Personnel Director	Public Administrator
Standard Score	31	40	10	37	36	14	23	33	27	52	38	42

Occupation	Y.M.C.A. Secretary	Soc. Sci. H.S. Teacher	City Sch. Sup't.	Social Worker	Minister	Musician Performer	C.P.A.	Senior C.P.A.	Accountant	Office Man	Purchasing Agent	Banker
Standard Score	36	41	36	47	58	48	28	45	25	31	18	20

Occupation	Mortician	Pharmacist	Sales Manager	Real Est. Manager	Life Ins. Salesman	Advertising Man	Lawyer	Author-Journalist	President Mfg. Co.	Interest Maturity	Occupational Level	Masculinity-Femininity
Standard Score	31	36	35	39	40	43	37	33	23	60	53	41

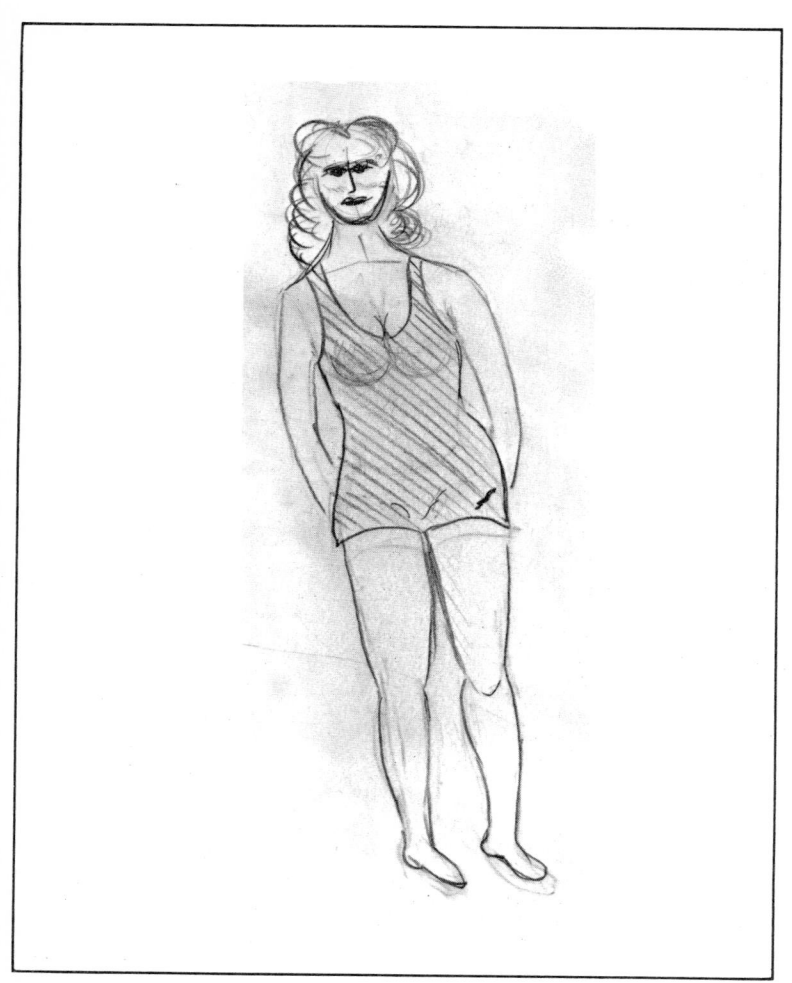

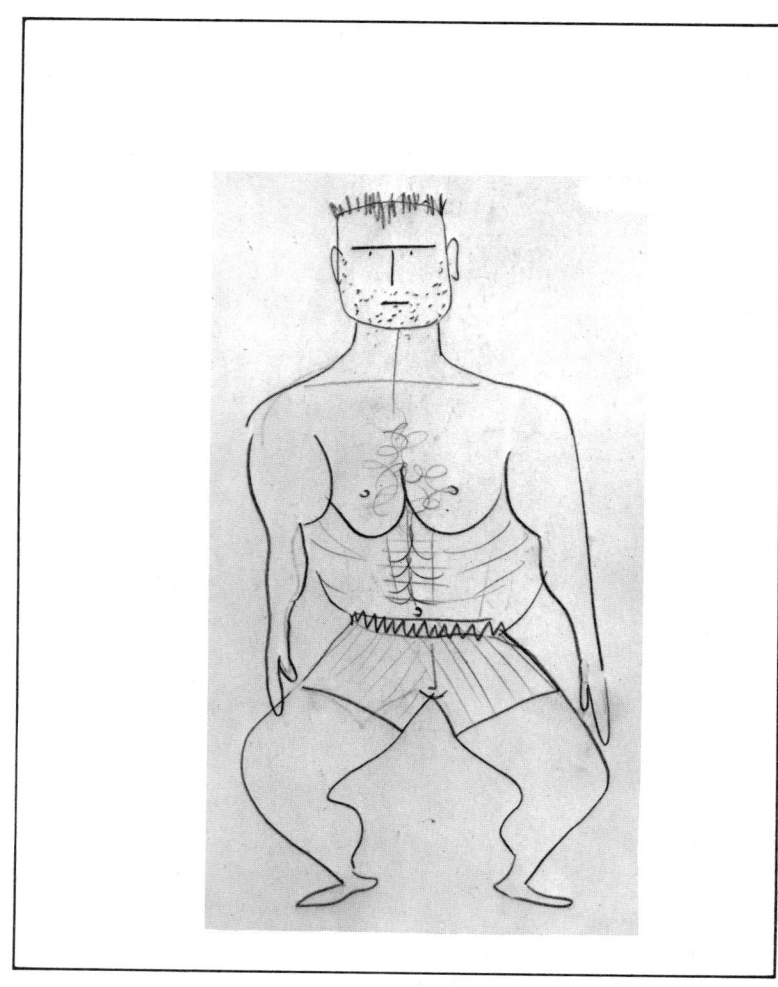

FIGURE-DRAWING CHARACTERISTICS

Structural	Male Female Both	Structural	Male	Female	Structural and Graphic	Male Female Both		Graphic, Global and Height	Male	Female	Body Proportions	Male	Female
Type	0	Omission of Appendages	0	7	Upper and Lower Halves	3	0	Hair Shading	3	3	Head	10	08
Sex Sequence	1	Position of Both Arms	0	0	Four Quarters	4	4	Nudity and Transparency	3	2	Neck	12	10
Posture	8 1	Position of Right Arm	0	5	Relative Size	5		Form	3	1	Shoulders	12	07
Perspective	0 0	Position of Left Arm	0	5	Constant Line Pressure	5	0	Detailing	3	1	Right Arm	08	
Vertical Midline	2 0	Position of Legs	6	4	Variable Line Pressure	0	5	Identity and Sex	1	1	Left Arm	08	
Bilateral Symmetry	3 3	Relation of Long Axes	1	1	Line Continuity	4	4	Sophistication	2	1	Chest	08	07
Horizontal Midline	4 0	Right and Left Halves	0	0	Body Shading	1	3	Height		08	Girth	10	08

GENERAL CHARACTERISTICS OF SUBJECT

IDENTIFICATION

No. D06

Sex M

Marital status S

Age 22 yrs. at

psychological tests

PARENTAL HISTORY

Father

C	H	S	D	O
-	-	-	-	?

Mother

C	H	S	D	O
-	-	-	-	-

PHYSIOLOGICAL AND METABOLIC DATA

	Admission	Initial	Control	Cold pressor change	Exercise change	Smoking change
Systolic pressure	120	130	120	+20	+20	+02
Diastolic pressure	75	60	70	+30	-10	00
Heart rate	75	80	71	+08	+19	+02

Age 22 yrs.	Height 72 in.	Ponderal index 12.85
	Weight 176 lbs.	Cholesterol 232 mg. per 100 ml.
	Overweight +08 %	Vital capacity 5.2 liters

HABIT SURVEY

Smoking habits: occasional smoker

    Age begun 18 yrs.   Inhalation: no

Habits of nervous tension: 1, 3, 5, 8, 10, 16, 18

STRONG VOCATIONAL INTEREST TEST

Occupation	Artist	Psychologist	Architect	Physician	Osteopath	Dentist	Veterinarian	Mathematician	Physicist	Engineer	Chemist	Production Manager
Standard Score	31	42	40	44	46	41	19	25	29	40	42	42

Occupation	Farmer	Aviator	Carpenter	Printer	Math.-Sci. Teacher	Ind. Arts Teacher	Voc. Agric. Teacher	Policeman	Forest Serv. Man	Y.M.C.A. Phys. Dir.	Personnel Director	Public Administrator
Standard Score	35	40	36	40	42	44	30	30	27	31	40	39

Occupation	Y.M.C.A. Secretary	Soc. Sci. H.S. Teacher	City Sch. Sup't.	Social Worker	Minister	Musician Performer	C.P.A.	Senior C.P.A.	Accountant	Office Man	Purchasing Agent	Banker
Standard Score	29	32	24	40	63	48	16	35	28	31	28	13

Occupation	Mortician	Pharmacist	Sales Manager	Real Est. Manager	Life Ins. Salesman	Advertising Man	Lawyer	Author-Journalist	President Mfg. Co.	Interest Maturity	Occupational Level	Masculinity-Femininity
Standard Score	33	35	28	27	25	37	21	28	38	61	53	43

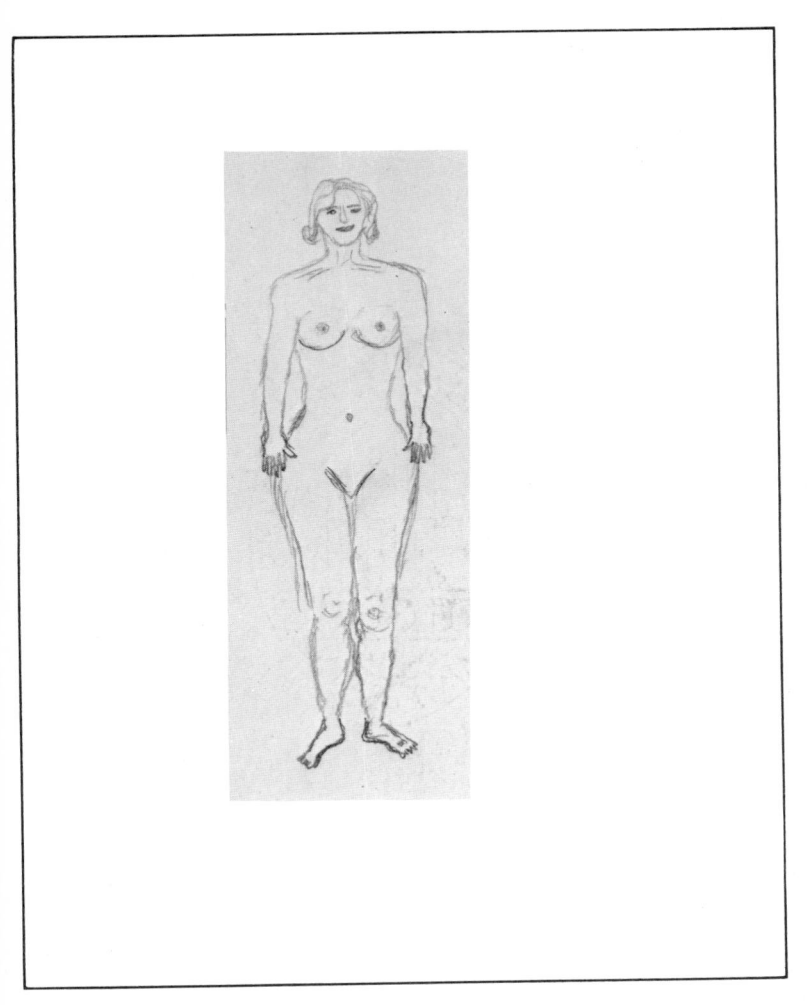

FIGURE-DRAWING CHARACTERISTICS

Structural	Male Female Both		Structural	Male	Female	Structural and Graphic	Male Female Both		Graphic, Global and Height	Male	Female	Body Proportions	Male	Female
Type	0		Omission of Appendages	0	0	Upper and Lower Halves	0	1	Hair Shading	3	2	Head	06	05
Sex Sequence	1		Position of Both Arms	0	0	Four Quarters	4	4	Nudity and Transparency	7	0	Neck	07	06
Posture	1	1	Position of Right Arm	0	0	Relative Size	0		Form	3	1	Shoulders	09	06
Perspective	0	0	Position of Left Arm	0	0	Constant Line Pressure	0	0	Detailing	1	1	Right Arm	04	04
Vertical Midline	3	0	Position of Legs	4	2	Variable Line Pressure	4	2	Identity and Sex	1	1	Left Arm	04	04
Bilateral Symmetry	5	5	Relation of Long Axes	1	1	Line Continuity	0	0	Sophistication	2	1	Chest	07	05
Horizontal Midline	6	0	Right and Left Halves	1	1	Body Shading	7	3	Height	07	06	Girth	10	05

GENERAL CHARACTERISTICS OF SUBJECT

IDENTIFICATION

No. D71
Sex M
Marital status S
Age 22 yrs. at
psychological tests

PARENTAL HISTORY

Father
C H S D O
- - - - ?

Mother
C H S D O
- - - - -

PHYSIOLOGICAL AND METABOLIC DATA

	Admission	Initial	Control	Cold pressor change	Exercise change	Smoking change
Systolic pressure	120	130	115	+35	+53	00
Diastolic pressure	80	69	70	+28	-12	-04
Heart rate	80	84	77	+03	+23	+07

Age 22 yrs.
Height 75 in.
Weight 186 lbs.
Overweight +04 %

Ponderal index 13.13
Cholesterol 193 mg. per 100 ml.
Vital capacity 5.2 liters

HABIT SURVEY

Smoking habits: pipe smoker
Age begun 10 yrs. Inhalation: yes
Habits of nervous tension: 4, 5, 6, 17, 19, 21, 22

STRONG VOCATIONAL INTEREST TEST

Occupation	Artist	Psychologist	Architect	Physician	Osteopath	Dentist	Veterinarian	Mathematician	Physicist	Engineer	Chemist	Production Manager
Standard Score	21	37	31	53	55	45	44	19	21	37	42	35

Occupation	Farmer	Aviator	Carpenter	Printer	Math.-Sci. Teacher	Ind. Arts Teacher	Voc. Agric. Teacher	Policeman	Forest Serv. Man	Y.M.C.A. Phys. Dir.	Personnel Director	Public Administrator
Standard Score	43	50	40	49	55	48	43	40	45	38	36	44

Occupation	Y.M.C.A. Secretary	Soc. Sci. H.S. Teacher	City Sch. Sup't.	Social Worker	Minister	Musician Performer	C.P.A.	Senior C.P.A.	Accountant	Office Man	Purchasing Agent	Banker
Standard Score	28	34	15	37	63	45	26	51	39	41	28	27

Occupation	Mortician	Pharmacist	Sales Manager	Real Est. Manager	Life Ins. Salesman	Advertising Man	Lawyer	Author-Journalist	President Mfg. Co.	Interest Maturity	Occupational Level	Masculinity-Femininity
Standard Score	36	45	32	37	30	24	14	18	33	64	46	53

FIGURE-DRAWING CHARACTERISTICS

Structural	Male Female Both	Structural	Male	Female	Structural and Graphic	Male Female Both	Graphic, Global and Height	Male	Female	Body Proportions	Male	Female
Type	0	Omission of Appendages	7	7	Upper and Lower Halves	1 1	Hair Shading	3	3	Head	05	07
Sex Sequence	0	Position of Both Arms	0	0	Four Quarters	4 4	Nudity and Transparency	3	0	Neck	06	08
Posture	1 1	Position of Right Arm	5	2	Relative Size	4	Form	1	1	Shoulders	06	06
Perspective	0 0	Position of Left Arm	5	2	Constant Line Pressure	0 0	Detailing	1	3	Right Arm	04	
Vertical Midline	0 0	Position of Legs	6	2	Variable Line Pressure	5 5	Identity and Sex	1	1	Left Arm	04	
Bilateral Symmetry	5 3	Relation of Long Axes	1	1	Line Continuity	0 0	Sophistication	1	2	Chest	05	06
Horizontal Midline	4 0	Right and Left Halves	3	1	Body Shading	3 3	Height	05	06	Girth	05	06

GENERAL CHARACTERISTICS OF SUBJECT

IDENTIFICATION
No. E76
Sex M
Marital status S
Age 21 yrs. at
psychological tests

PARENTAL HISTORY
Father
C   H   S   D   O
-   -   -   -   ?
Mother
C   H   S   D   O
-   -   -   -   -

PHYSIOLOGICAL AND METABOLIC DATA

	Admission	Initial	Control	Cold pressor change	Exercise change	Smoking change
Systolic pressure	126	120	112	+26	+33	
Diastolic pressure	80	68	68	+21	-26	
Heart rate	70	68	60	+04	+26	

Age 20 yrs.	Height	72 in.		Ponderal index	12.97	
	Weight	171 lbs.		Cholesterol	154	mg. per 100 ml.
	Overweight	+06 %		Vital capacity	5.5	liters

HABIT SURVEY
Smoking habits: nonsmoker
Age begun   yrs.   Inhalation:
Habits of nervous tension: 7, 25

STRONG VOCATIONAL INTEREST TEST

Occupation	Artist	Psychologist	Architect	Physician	Osteopath	Dentist	Veterinarian	Mathematician	Physicist	Engineer	Chemist	Production Manager
Standard Score	18	24	24	30	26	18	18	13	08	24	20	31

Occupation	Farmer	Aviator	Carpenter	Printer	Math.-Sci. Teacher	Ind. Arts Teacher	Voc. Agric. Teacher	Policeman	Forest Serv. Man	Y.M.C.A. Phys. Dir.	Personnel Director	Public Administrator
Standard Score	29	37	18	31	34	14	20	35	33	39	44	45

Occupation	Y.M.C.A. Secretary	Soc. Sci. H.S. Teacher	City Sch. Sup't.	Social Worker	Minister	Musician Performer	C.P.A.	Senior C.P.A.	Accountant	Office Man	Purchasing Agent	Banker
Standard Score	32	44	34	39	64	33	39	45	36	39	35	31

Occupation	Mortician	Pharmacist	Sales Manager	Real Est. Manager	Life Ins. Salesman	Advertising Man	Lawyer	Author-Journalist	President Mfg. Co.	Interest Maturity	Occupational Level	Masculinity-Femininity
Standard Score	25	28	36	38	34	33	41	27	24	57	55	52

XII. MOST SOPHISTICATED DRAWINGS

These drawings, by seventy-eight subjects, show the highest degree of sophistication-of-body-concept. They manifest high form level. The appendages and details are represented in proper relation to body outline, with some expressiveness or individuality in mode of presentation and appropriate, even imaginative detailing. In general, great emphasis is given to detail of head, facial expression, clothing, body features and shape, and/or sex attributes. There is rational integration of body parts and of clothing accessories, all decisively and purposefully drawn.

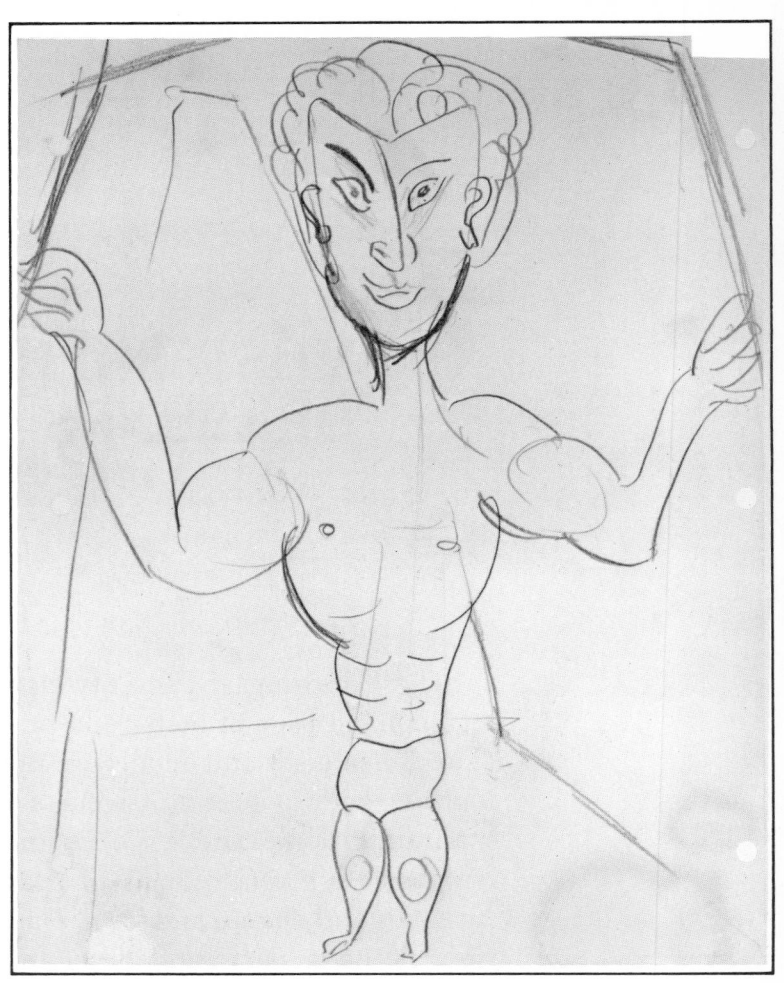

FIGURE-DRAWING CHARACTERISTICS

Structural	Male Female Both		Structural	Male	Female	Structural and Graphic	Male Female Both		Graphic, Global and Height	Male	Female	Body Proportions	Male	Female
Type	0		Omission of Appendages	0	0	Upper and Lower Halves	0	0	Hair Shading	3	3	Head	22	16
Sex Sequence	1		Position of Both Arms	0	1	Four Quarters	4	4	Nudity and Transparency	3	7	Neck	14	08
Posture	1	1	Position of Right Arm	2	0	Relative Size	0		Form	3	3	Shoulders	12	08
Perspective	0	0	Position of Left Arm	2	2	Constant Line Pressure	0	0	Detailing	1	1	Right Arm	10	08
Vertical Midline	0	3	Position of Legs	5	4	Variable Line Pressure	5	5	Identity and Sex	1	1	Left Arm	10	08
Bilateral Symmetry	3	3	Relation of Long Axes	1	1	Line Continuity	2	1	Sophistication	1	1	Chest	10	07
Horizontal Midline	4	4	Right and Left Halves	0	3	Body Shading	3	3	Height	09	09	Girth	05	08

GENERAL CHARACTERISTICS OF SUBJECT

IDENTIFICATION
No. B46
Sex M
Marital status S
Age 22 yrs. at
psychological tests

PARENTAL HISTORY				
Father				
C	H	S	D	O
+	-	-	-	?
Mother				
C	H	S	D	O
+	+	-	-	-

PHYSIOLOGICAL AND METABOLIC DATA

	Admission	Initial	Control	Cold pressor change	Exercise change	Smoking change
Systolic pressure	115	136	124	+20	+24	
Diastolic pressure	70	52	54	+16	-12	
Heart rate	80	74	68	+08	+31	

Age 22 yrs.	Height	72	in.	Ponderal index 13.21
	Weight	162	lbs.	Cholesterol 248 mg. per 100 ml.
	Overweight -01 %			Vital capacity 5.5 liters

HABIT SURVEY

Smoking habits: nonsmoker

Age begun   yrs.   Inhalation:

Habits of nervous tension: 4, 5, 6, 9, 23

FIGURE-DRAWING CHARACTERISTICS

Structural	Male	Female	Structural	Male	Female	Structural and Graphic	Male	Female	Graphic, Global and Height	Male	Female	Body Proportions	Male	Female
	Both						Both							
Type	0		Omission of Appendages	7	2	Upper and Lower Halves	0	7	Hair Shading	7	3	Head	15	12
Sex Sequence	1		Position of Both Arms	4	6	Four Quarters	4	4	Nudity and Transparency	7	7	Neck		14
Posture	2	2	Position of Right Arm	7	7	Relative Size	0		Form	1	1	Shoulders		
Perspective	2	4	Position of Left Arm	0	7	Constant Line Pressure	0	5	Detailing	3	3	Right Arm		
Vertical Midline	5	4	Position of Legs	8	4	Variable Line Pressure	5	0	Identity and Sex	1	1	Left Arm		
Bilateral Symmetry	0	0	Relation of Long Axes	1	3	Line Continuity	2	2	Sophistication	1	1	Chest	14	
Horizontal Midline	6	0	Right and Left Halves	3	3	Body Shading	0	3	Height	09	09	Girth	10	

GENERAL CHARACTERISTICS OF SUBJECT

IDENTIFICATION

No. F22

Sex M

Marital status M

Age 29 yrs. at

psychological tests

PARENTAL HISTORY

Father

C	H	S	D	O
+	-	(+)	+	-

Mother

C	H	S	D	O
?	-	-	-	-

PHYSIOLOGICAL AND METABOLIC DATA

	Admission	Initial	Control	Cold pressor change	Exercise change	Smoking change
Systolic pressure	110	110	108	+14	+36	+07
Diastolic pressure	70	74	72	+12	+16	00
Heart rate	68	64	73	-04	+09	+25

Age 27 yrs.   Height 69 in.   Weight 144 lbs.   Overweight -06 %

Ponderal index 13.17   Cholesterol 150 mg. per 100 ml.   Vital capacity liters

HABIT SURVEY

Smoking habits: moderate cigarette smoker

Age begun 18 yrs.   Inhalation: yes

Habits of nervous tension: 4, 5, 6, 10, 18, 25

STRONG VOCATIONAL INTEREST TEST

Occupation	Artist	Psychologist	Architect	Physician	Osteopath	Dentist	Veterinarian	Mathematician	Physicist	Engineer	Chemist	Production Manager
Standard Score	42	46	42	49	32	37	12	35	33	43	43	32

Occupation	Farmer	Aviator	Carpenter	Printer	Math.-Sci. Teacher	Ind. Arts Teacher	Voc. Agric. Teacher	Policeman	Forest Serv. Man	Y.M.C.A. Phys. Dir.	Personnel Director	Public Administrator
Standard Score	22	23	02	17	21	02	08	19	20	21	28	42

Occupation	Y.M.C.A. Secretary	Soc. Sci. H.S. Teacher	City Sch. Sup't.	Social Worker	Minister	Musician Performer	C.P.A.	Senior C.P.A.	Accountant	Office Man	Purchasing Agent	Banker
Standard Score	14	18	31	30	58	33	40	21	19	14	21	19

Occupation	Mortician	Pharmacist	Sales Manager	Real Est. Manager	Life Ins. Salesman	Advertising Man	Lawyer	Author-Journalist	President Mfg. Co.	Interest Maturity	Occupational Level	Masculinity-Femininity
Standard Score	17	26	32	32	27	45	49	48	49	47	71	44

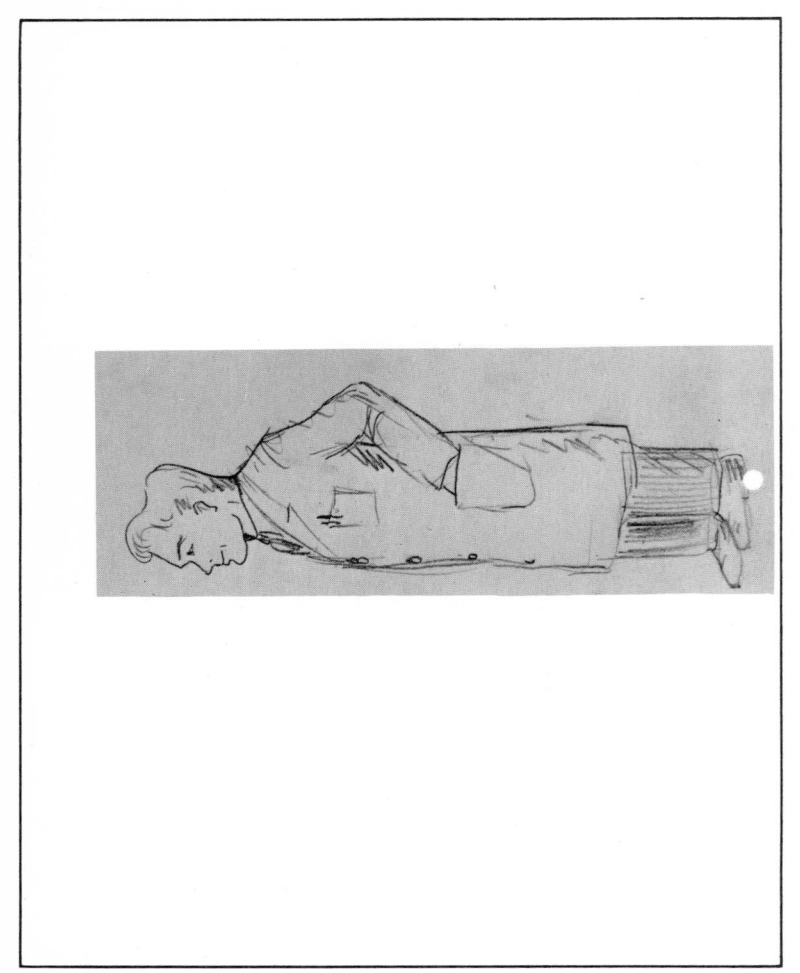

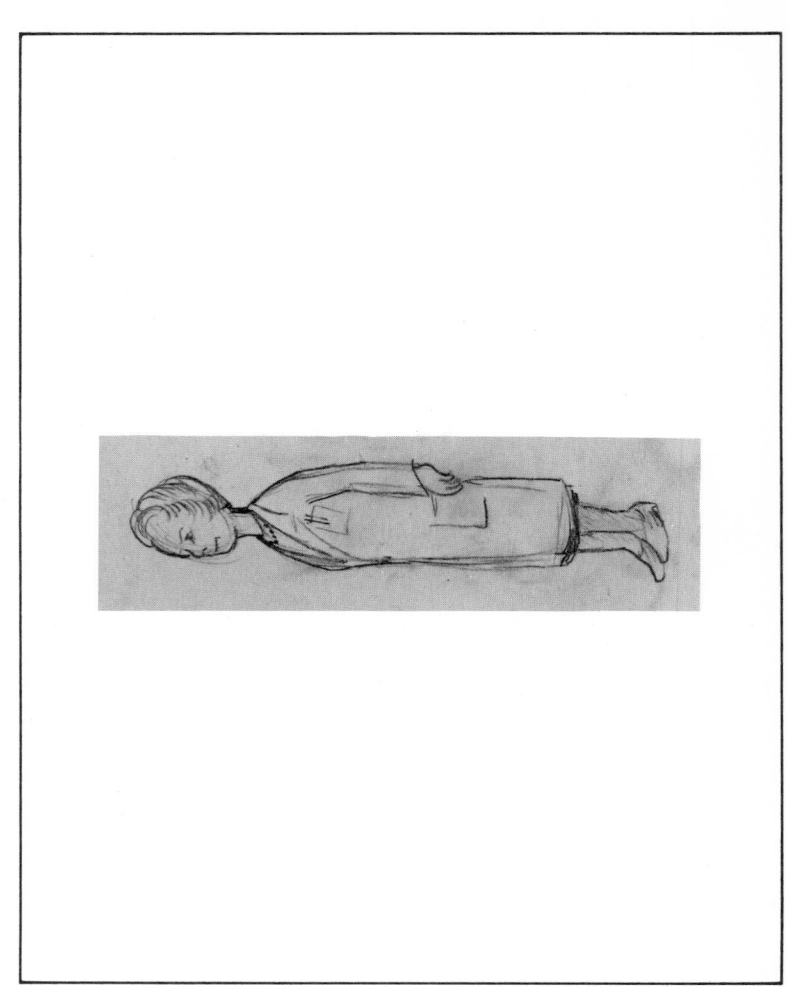

FIGURE-DRAWING CHARACTERISTICS

Structural	Male Female Both	Structural	Male	Female	Structural and Graphic	Male Female Both		Graphic, Global and Height	Male	Female	Body Proportions	Male	Female
Type	0	Omission of Appendages	7	0	Upper and Lower Halves	3	0	Hair Shading	1	3	Head	08	07
Sex Sequence	2	Position of Both Arms	4	4	Four Quarters	4	4	Nudity and Transparency	7	7	Neck	06	08
Posture	1 1	Position of Right Arm	7	7	Relative Size	0		Form	1	1	Shoulders		
Perspective	2 1	Position of Left Arm	5	0	Constant Line Pressure	0	0	Detailing	1	1	Right Arm		
Vertical Midline	7 7	Position of Legs	2	2	Variable Line Pressure	5	5	Identity and Sex	1	1	Left Arm		04
Bilateral Symmetry	0 0	Relation of Long Axes	2	2	Line Continuity	0	0	Sophistication	1	1	Chest	09	
Horizontal Midline	0 0	Right and Left Halves	1	1	Body Shading	7	7	Height	06	05	Girth	10	

GENERAL CHARACTERISTICS OF SUBJECT

IDENTIFICATION
No. 230
Sex F
Marital status S
Age 24 yrs. at
psychological tests

PARENTAL HISTORY				
Father				
C	H	S	D	O
+	+	–	–	?
Mother				
C	H	S	D	O
–	+	–	–	?

PHYSIOLOGICAL AND METABOLIC DATA

	Admission	Initial	Control	Cold pressor change	Exercise change	Smoking change
Systolic pressure	116	108	108	+16	+26	+04
Diastolic pressure	68	62	60	+24	–06	+08
Heart rate	80	100	81	+16	+55	+07

Age 27 yrs.	Height 68 in.	Ponderal index 12.83
	Weight 149 lbs.	Cholesterol 190 mg. per 100 ml.
	Overweight +03 %	Vital capacity liters

HABIT SURVEY

Smoking habits: heavy cigarette smoker

Age begun 18 yrs.   Inhalation: yes

Habits of nervous tension: 5, 6, 9, 11, 19, 23

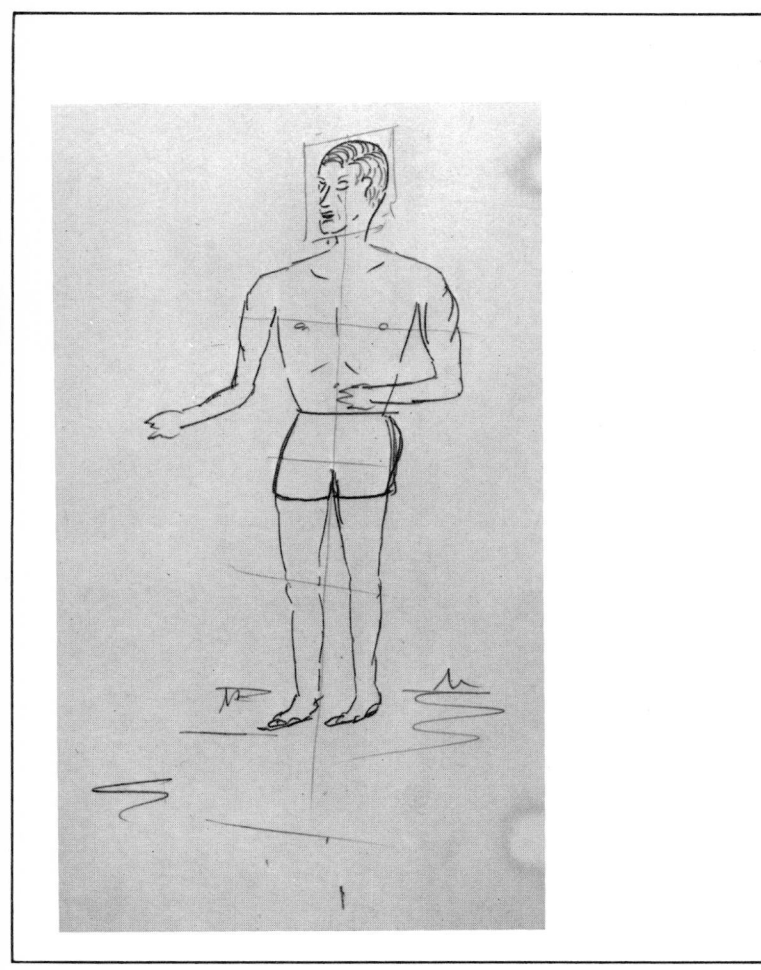

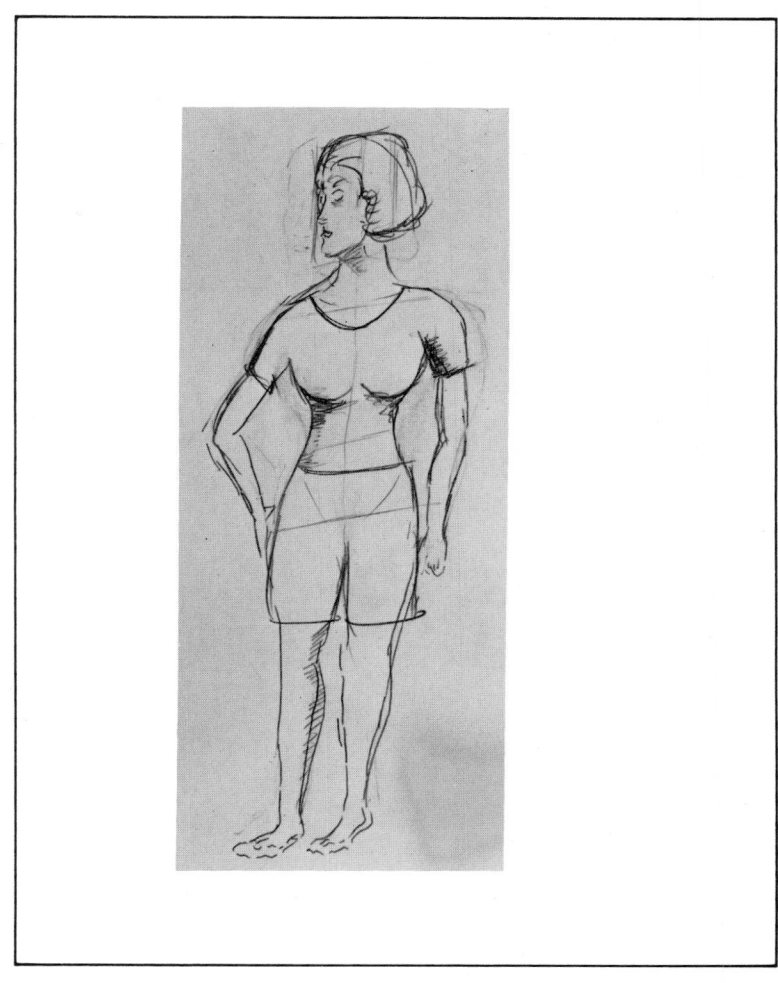

FIGURE-DRAWING CHARACTERISTICS

Structural	Male Female Both	Structural	Male	Female	Structural and Graphic	Male Female Both		Graphic, Global and Height	Male	Female	Body Proportions	Male	Female
Type	0	Omission of Appendages	0	0	Upper and Lower Halves	1	0	Hair Shading	1	3	Head	07	10
Sex Sequence	2	Position of Both Arms	1	1	Four Quarters	4	4	Nudity and Transparency	3	2	Neck	06	14
Posture	1 1	Position of Right Arm	4	5	Relative Size	4		Form	1	1	Shoulders		07
Perspective	1 5	Position of Left Arm	5	0	Constant Line Pressure	0	5	Detailing	3	1	Right Arm	04	06
Vertical Midline	0 0	Position of Legs	4	4	Variable Line Pressure	5	0	Identity and Sex	1	1	Left Arm	04	06
Bilateral Symmetry	3 3	Relation of Long Axes	1	1	Line Continuity	0	0	Sophistication	1	1	Chest		07
Horizontal Midline	4 4	Right and Left Halves	1	1	Body Shading	1	3	Height	06	07	Girth		06

GENERAL CHARACTERISTICS OF SUBJECT

IDENTIFICATION
No. 276
Sex M
Marital status S
Age 25 yrs. at
psychological tests

PARENTAL HISTORY
Father
C   H   S   D   O
+   -   -   -   ?
Mother
C   H   S   D   O
-   ?   -   -   -

PHYSIOLOGICAL AND METABOLIC DATA

	Admission	Initial	Control	Cold pressor change	Exercise change	Smoking change
Systolic pressure	120	120	100	+10	+38	
Diastolic pressure	72	70	70	+10	-06	
Heart rate		90	83	00	+20	

Age 23 yrs.	Height 72 in.	Ponderal index 12.95
	Weight 172 lbs.	Cholesterol 290 mg. per 100 ml.
	Overweight +05 %	Vital capacity 5.5 liters

HABIT SURVEY

Smoking habits: heavy cigarette smoker

Age begun 18 yrs.   Inhalation: yes

Habits of nervous tension: 1, 2, 3, 4, 5, 6, 8, 9, 15, 16, 17, 18, 19, 20, 22, 23, 24, 25

FIGURE-DRAWING CHARACTERISTICS

Structural	Male Female Both		Structural	Male	Female	Structural and Graphic	Male Female Both		Graphic, Global and Height	Male	Female	Body Proportions	Male	Female
Type	0		Omission of Appendages	7	6	Upper and Lower Halves	1	1	Hair Shading	1	1	Head	08	09
Sex Sequence	1		Position of Both Arms	0	0	Four Quarters	4	4	Nudity and Transparency	7	7	Neck	06	08
Posture	1	1	Position of Right Arm	5	5	Relative Size	0		Form	1	1	Shoulders	10	07
Perspective	0	0	Position of Left Arm	5	5	Constant Line Pressure	0	1	Detailing	1	1	Right Arm		
Vertical Midline	3	0	Position of Legs	4	1	Variable Line Pressure	1	0	Identity and Sex	1	1	Left Arm		
Bilateral Symmetry	3	3	Relation of Long Axes	1	1	Line Continuity	0	0	Sophistication	1	1	Chest	08	07
Horizontal Midline	6	0	Right and Left Halves	1	1	Body Shading	2	3	Height	08	07	Girth	11	05

GENERAL CHARACTERISTICS OF SUBJECT

IDENTIFICATION
No. 321
Sex M
Marital status S
Age 26 yrs. at
psychological tests

PARENTAL HISTORY
Father
C H S D O
+ + - - -
Mother
C H S D O
- + - - -

PHYSIOLOGICAL AND METABOLIC DATA

	Admission	Initial	Control	Cold pressor change	Exercise change	Smoking change
Systolic pressure	130	120	108	+04	+28	00
Diastolic pressure	84	68	64	+14	+04	+08
Heart rate	72	66	68	+02	+22	+06

Age 24 yrs.	Height 71 in.	Ponderal index 12.48
	Weight 184 lbs.	Cholesterol 314 mg. per 100 ml.
	Overweight +15 %	Vital capacity 4.8 liters

HABIT SURVEY
Smoking habits: occasional smoker
Age begun 20 yrs.   Inhalation: no
Habits of nervous tension: 5

FIGURE-DRAWING CHARACTERISTICS

Structural	Male	Female	Structural	Male	Female	Structural and Graphic	Male	Female	Graphic, Global and Height	Male	Female	Body Proportions	Male	Female
	Both						Both							
Type	0		Omission of Appendages	7	0	Upper and Lower Halves	0	1	Hair Shading	5	5	Head	07	06
Sex Sequence	2		Position of Both Arms	2	2	Four Quarters	4	4	Nudity and Transparency	7	6	Neck	03	05
Posture	1	1	Position of Right Arm	5	5	Relative Size	0		Form	1	1	Shoulders		
Perspective	1	6	Position of Left Arm	7	7	Constant Line Pressure	3	1	Detailing	1	1	Right Arm	06	04
Vertical Midline	7	4	Position of Legs	1	1	Variable Line Pressure	1	0	Identity and Sex	1	1	Left Arm		
Bilateral Symmetry	0	0	Relation of Long Axes	1	1	Line Continuity	0	0	Sophistication	1	1	Chest		
Horizontal Midline	4	4	Right and Left Halves	1	2	Body Shading	7	7	Height	06	05	Girth		

GENERAL CHARACTERISTICS OF SUBJECT

IDENTIFICATION

No. F68

Sex M

Marital status S

Age 24 yrs. at

psychological tests

PARENTAL HISTORY

Father

C	H	S	D	O
+	+	-	-	+

Mother

C	H	S	D	O
-	-	-	-	-

PHYSIOLOGICAL AND METABOLIC DATA

	Admission	Initial	Control	Cold pressor change	Exercise change	Smoking change
Systolic pressure	116	102	100	+20	+26	+06
Diastolic pressure	86	70	70	+32	+20	+12
Heart rate	74	76	73	+08	+20	+08

Age 22 yrs.

Height 68 in.

Weight 121 lbs.

Overweight -17 %

Ponderal index 13.74

Cholesterol 217 mg. per 100 ml.

Vital capacity liters

HABIT SURVEY

Smoking habits: nonsmoker

Age begun yrs. Inhalation:

Habits of nervous tension: 4, 8, 11, 12, 21

FIGURE-DRAWING CHARACTERISTICS

Structural	Male	Female	Structural	Male	Female	Structural and Graphic	Male	Female	Graphic, Global and Height	Male	Female	Body Proportions	Male	Female
	Both						Both							
Type	0		Omission of Appendages	3	2	Upper and Lower Halves	7	1	Hair Shading	0	1	Head	09	08
Sex Sequence	1		Position of Both Arms	4	6	Four Quarters	4	4	Nudity and Transparency	7	7	Neck	14	05
Posture	0	1	Position of Right Arm	7	8	Relative Size	0		Form	1	1	Shoulders		08
Perspective	2	0	Position of Left Arm	4	8	Constant Line Pressure	0	0	Detailing	1	3	Right Arm		
Vertical Midline	4	0	Position of Legs	1	4	Variable Line Pressure	1	1	Identity and Sex	1	1	Left Arm	10	
Bilateral Symmetry	0	3	Relation of Long Axes	1	1	Line Continuity	0	0	Sophistication	1	1	Chest		07
Horizontal Midline	4	4	Right and Left Halves	4	4	Body Shading	5	2	Height		07	Girth	09	08

GENERAL CHARACTERISTICS OF SUBJECT

IDENTIFICATION
No. G66
Sex F
Marital status S
Age 24 yrs. at
psychological tests

PARENTAL HISTORY				
Father				
C	H	S	D	O
+	+	-	-	+
Mother				
C	H	S	D	O
-	-	-	-	+

PHYSIOLOGICAL AND METABOLIC DATA

	Admission	Initial	Control	Cold pressor change	Exercise change	Smoking change
Systolic pressure	120	106	104	+16	+46	+11
Diastolic pressure	80	82	70	+10	+08	+08
Heart rate	86	88	86	-08	+02	+15

Age 23 yrs.	Height 66 in.	Ponderal index 12.69
	Weight 141 lbs.	Cholesterol 190 mg. per 100 ml.
	Overweight +05 %	Vital capacity liters

HABIT SURVEY

Smoking habits: moderate cigarette smoker

Age begun 21 yrs.   Inhalation: yes

Habits of nervous tension: 2, 4, 5, 6, 10, 14, 16, 22

STRONG VOCATIONAL INTEREST TEST

Occupation	Artist	Psychologist	Architect	Physician	Osteopath	Dentist	Veterinarian	Mathematician	Physicist	Engineer	Chemist	Production Manager
Standard Score	48	51	52	62	62	54	19	37	37	35	46	22

Occupation	Farmer	Aviator	Carpenter	Printer	Math.-Sci. Teacher	Ind. Arts Teacher	Voc. Agric. Teacher	Policeman	Forest Serv. Man	Y.M.C.A. Phys. Dir.	Personnel Director	Public Administrator
Standard Score	26	19	14	32	36	09	11	20	23	38	31	45

Occupation	Y.M.C.A. Secretary	Soc. Sci. H.S. Teacher	City Sch. Sup't.	Social Worker	Minister	Musician Performer	C.P.A.	Senior C.P.A.	Accountant	Office Man	Purchasing Agent	Banker
Standard Score	34	34	43	47	59	57	33	28	11	21	09	17

Occupation	Mortician	Pharmacist	Sales Manager	Real Est. Manager	Life Ins. Salesman	Advertising Man	Lawyer	Author-Journalist	President Mfg. Co.	Interest Maturity	Occupational Level	Masculinity-Femininity
Standard Score	25	26	19	26	34	36	44	46	24	60	67	20

FIGURE-DRAWING CHARACTERISTICS

Structural	Male Female Both	Structural	Male	Female	Structural and Graphic	Male Female Both		Graphic, Global and Height	Male	Female	Body Proportions	Male	Female
Type	0	Omission of Appendages	0	0	Upper and Lower Halves	1	1	Hair Shading	2	3	Head	04	04
Sex Sequence	0	Position of Both Arms	0	0	Four Quarters	4	4	Nudity and Transparency	7	7	Neck	03	03
Posture	1 1	Position of Right Arm	0	0	Relative Size	1		Form	1	1	Shoulders	05	04
Perspective	0 0	Position of Left Arm	0	0	Constant Line Pressure	0	2	Detailing	1	1	Right Arm	04	04
Vertical Midline	3 3	Position of Legs	4	4	Variable Line Pressure	1	0	Identity and Sex	1	1	Left Arm	04	04
Bilateral Symmetry	5 5	Relation of Long Axes	1	1	Line Continuity	0	0	Sophistication	1	1	Chest	04	04
Horizontal Midline	6 4	Right and Left Halves	1	1	Body Shading	7	7	Height	05	05	Girth	05	03

GENERAL CHARACTERISTICS OF SUBJECT

IDENTIFICATION
No. C09
Sex M
Marital status S
Age 23 yrs. at
psychological tests

PARENTAL HISTORY				
Father				
C	H	S	D	O
+	+	-	-	+
Mother				
C	H	S	D	O
-	-	-	-	+

PHYSIOLOGICAL AND METABOLIC DATA

	Admission	Initial	Control	Cold pressor change	Exercise change	Smoking change
Systolic pressure	150	150	128	+10	+47	+04
Diastolic pressure	100	75	76	+12	-06	+05
Heart rate	90	80	70	00	+30	00

Age 23 yrs.
Height 72 in.   Ponderal index 12.86
Weight 176 lbs.   Cholesterol 202 mg. per 100 ml.
Overweight +07 %   Vital capacity 4.9 liters

HABIT SURVEY

Smoking habits: nonsmoker

Age begun   yrs.   Inhalation:

Habits of nervous tension: 5, 6, 9, 10, 16, 18, 22, 23, 24

STRONG VOCATIONAL INTEREST TEST

Occupation	Artist	Psychologist	Architect	Physician	Osteopath	Dentist	Veterinarian	Mathematician	Physicist	Engineer	Chemist	Production Manager
Standard Score	32	42	41	57	41	45	22	29	22	27	37	22

Occupation	Farmer	Aviator	Carpenter	Printer	Math.-Sci. Teacher	Ind. Arts Teacher	Voc. Agric. Teacher	Policeman	Forest Serv. Man	Y.M.C.A. Phys. Dir.	Personnel Director	Public Administrator
Standard Score	35	29	22	44	49	27	36	26	28	39	34	37

Occupation	Y.M.C.A. Secretary	Soc. Sci. H.S. Teacher	City Sch. Sup't.	Social Worker	Minister	Musician Performer	C.P.A.	Senior C.P.A.	Accountant	Office Man	Purchasing Agent	Banker
Standard Score	37	41	32	41	62	58	25	40	21	33	17	18

Occupation	Mortician	Pharmacist	Sales Manager	Real Est. Manager	Life Ins. Salesman	Advertising Man	Lawyer	Author-Journalist	President Mfg. Co.	Interest Maturity	Occupational Level	Masculinity-Femininity
Standard Score	17	33	12	23	19	26	28	29	16	61	52	42

FIGURE-DRAWING CHARACTERISTICS

Structural	Male	Female	Structural	Male	Female	Structural and Graphic	Male	Female	Graphic, Global and Height	Male	Female	Body Proportions	Male	Female
	Both						Both							
Type	0		Omission of Appendages	0	0	Upper and Lower Halves	2	2	Hair Shading	3	1	Head	04	03
Sex Sequence	2		Position of Both Arms	0	4	Four Quarters	9	9	Nudity and Transparency	2	2	Neck	03	04
Posture	1	3	Position of Right Arm	5	7	Relative Size	5		Form	1	1	Shoulders	04	
Perspective	0	2	Position of Left Arm	5	2	Constant Line Pressure	0	1	Detailing	1	1	Right Arm	02	
Vertical Midline	3	4	Position of Legs	4	1	Variable Line Pressure	1	0	Identity and Sex	1	1	Left Arm	02	02
Bilateral Symmetry	3	0	Relation of Long Axes	1	0	Line Continuity	0	0	Sophistication	1	1	Chest	03	03
Horizontal Midline	4	0	Right and Left Halves	9	9	Body Shading	7	3	Height	03		Girth	03	04

GENERAL CHARACTERISTICS OF SUBJECT

IDENTIFICATION

No. C31

Sex M

Marital status S

Age 22 yrs. at
psychological tests

PARENTAL HISTORY

Father

C	H	S	D	O
+	−	−	−	+

Mother

C	H	S	D	O
−	−	−	−	−

PHYSIOLOGICAL AND METABOLIC DATA

	Admission	Initial	Control	Cold pressor change	Exercise change	Smoking change
Systolic pressure	105	115	118	+22	+32	
Diastolic pressure	70	70	70	+40	00	
Heart rate	84	80	65	+12	+29	

Age 23 yrs.

Height	74 in.	Ponderal index	13.01
Weight	184 lbs.	Cholesterol	270 mg. per 100 ml.
Overweight	+05 %	Vital capacity	5.9 liters

HABIT SURVEY

Smoking habits: pipe and cigar smoker

Age begun 20 yrs.   Inhalation:

Habits of nervous tension:

STRONG VOCATIONAL INTEREST TEST

Occupation	Artist	Psychologist	Architect	Physician	Osteopath	Dentist	Veterinarian	Mathematician	Physicist	Engineer	Chemist	Production Manager
Standard Score	30	30	32	43	44	38	22	23	17	30	30	25

Occupation	Farmer	Aviator	Carpenter	Printer	Math.-Sci. Teacher	Ind. Arts Teacher	Voc. Agric. Teacher	Policeman	Forest Serv. Man	Y.M.C.A. Phys. Dir.	Personnel Director	Public Administrator
Standard Score	30	37	09	24	37	09	14	31	24	42	32	30

Occupation	Y.M.C.A. Secretary	Soc. Sci. H.S. Teacher	City Sch. Sup't.	Social Worker	Minister	Musician Performer	C.P.A.	Senior C.P.A.	Accountant	Office Man	Purchasing Agent	Banker
Standard Score	27	33	31	29	62	37	27	33	20	30	18	17

Occupation	Mortician	Pharmacist	Sales Manager	Real Est. Manager	Life Ins. Salesman	Advertising Man	Lawyer	Author-Journalist	President Mfg. Co.	Interest Maturity	Occupational Level	Masculinity-Femininity
Standard Score	18	25	26	39	36	35	42	34	20	55	60	49

Plate 777   MOST SOPHISTICATED DRAWINGS   827

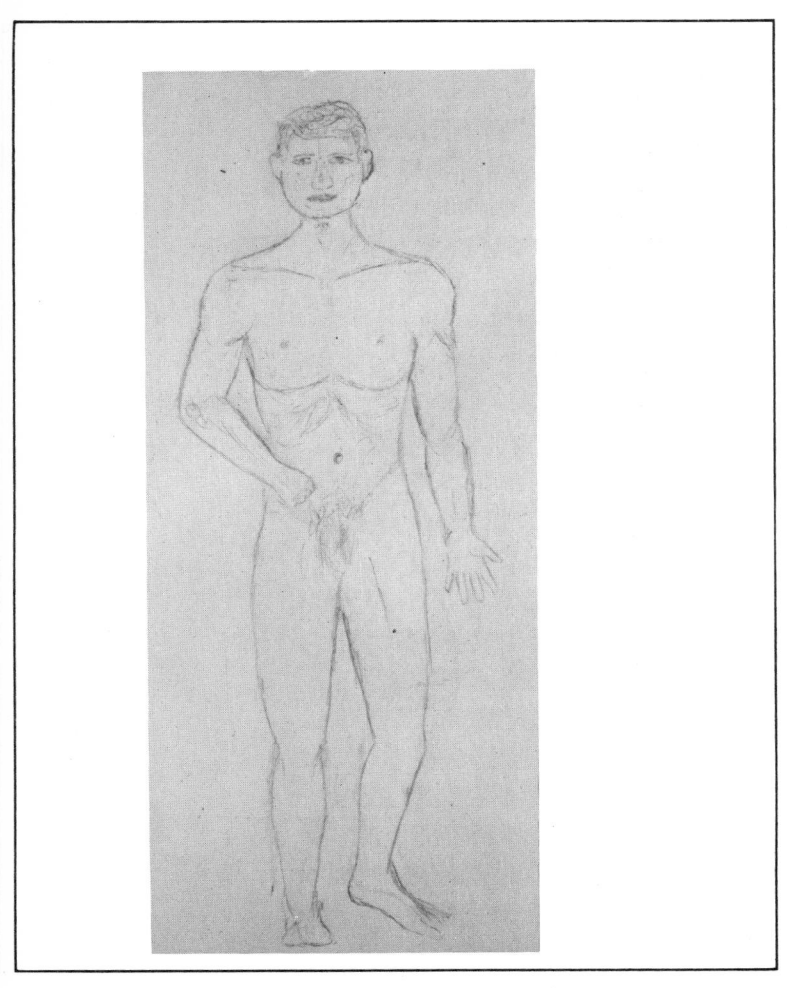

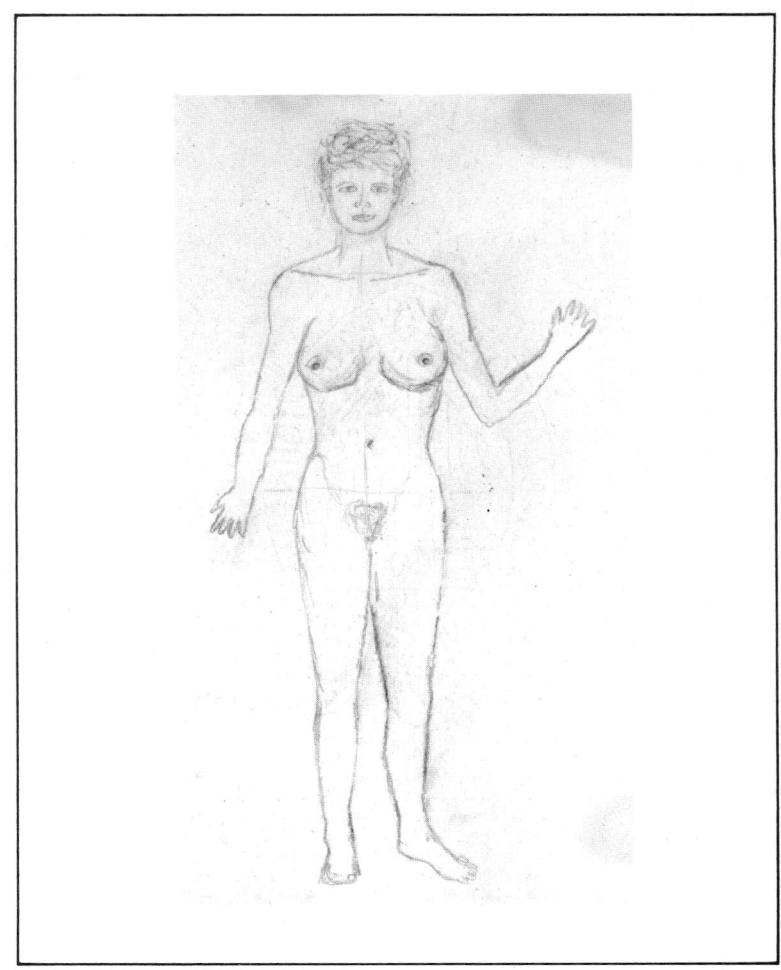

FIGURE-DRAWING CHARACTERISTICS

Structural	Male Female Both	Structural	Male	Female	Structural and Graphic	Male Female Both		Graphic, Global and Height	Male	Female	Body Proportions	Male	Female
Type	0	Omission of Appendages	0	0	Upper and Lower Halves	3	0	Hair Shading	3	3	Head	09	09
Sex Sequence	0	Position of Both Arms	1	1	Four Quarters	4	4	Nudity and Transparency	0	0	Neck	08	05
Posture	2 1	Position of Right Arm	5	2	Relative Size	0		Form	1	1	Shoulders	10	07
Perspective	0 0	Position of Left Arm	0	4	Constant Line Pressure	1	0	Detailing	1	1	Right Arm	07	06
Vertical Midline	0 0	Position of Legs	8	4	Variable Line Pressure	0	2	Identity and Sex	1	1	Left Arm	08	06
Bilateral Symmetry	3 3	Relation of Long Axes	1	1	Line Continuity	0	0	Sophistication	1	1	Chest	08	07
Horizontal Midline	0 0	Right and Left Halves	1	1	Body Shading	3	3	Height	09	08	Girth	08	07

GENERAL CHARACTERISTICS OF SUBJECT

IDENTIFICATION
No. C47
Sex M
Marital status S
Age 23 yrs. at
psychological tests

PARENTAL HISTORY				
Father				
C	H	S	D	O
+	+	−	−	−
Mother				
C	H	S	D	O
−	−	−	−	−

PHYSIOLOGICAL AND METABOLIC DATA

	Admission	Initial	Control	Cold pressor change	Exercise change	Smoking change
Systolic pressure	126	100	100	+50	+50	+06
Diastolic pressure	74	75	76	+23	−07	+06
Heart rate	72	60	58	+08	+12	+01

Age 24 yrs.

Height	77 in.
Weight	196 lbs.
Overweight	+02 %

Ponderal index	13.25
Cholesterol	202 mg. per 100 ml.
Vital capacity	6.7 liters

HABIT SURVEY

Smoking habits: nonsmoker

Age begun   yrs.   Inhalation:

Habits of nervous tension:

STRONG VOCATIONAL INTEREST TEST

Occupation	Artist	Psychologist	Architect	Physician	Osteopath	Dentist	Veterinarian	Mathematician	Physicist	Engineer	Chemist	Production Manager
Standard Score	35	32	33	49	41	29	25	25	19	28	29	23

Occupation	Farmer	Aviator	Carpenter	Printer	Math.-Sci. Teacher	Ind. Arts Teacher	Voc. Agric. Teacher	Policeman	Forest Serv. Man	Y.M.C.A. Phys. Dir.	Personnel Director	Public Administrator
Standard Score	36	40	11	23	39	12	30	27	35	43	39	41

Occupation	Y.M.C.A. Secretary	Soc. Sci. H.S. Teacher	City Sch. Sup't.	Social Worker	Minister	Musician Performer	C.P.A.	Senior C.P.A.	Accountant	Office Man	Purchasing Agent	Banker
Standard Score	37	41	35	36	62	46	25	39	18	26	14	21

Occupation	Mortician	Pharmacist	Sales Manager	Real Est. Manager	Life Ins. Salesman	Advertising Man	Lawyer	Author-Journalist	President Mfg. Co.	Interest Maturity	Occupational Level	Masculinity-Femininity
Standard Score	22	30	28	32	31	37	36	35	23	56	58	44

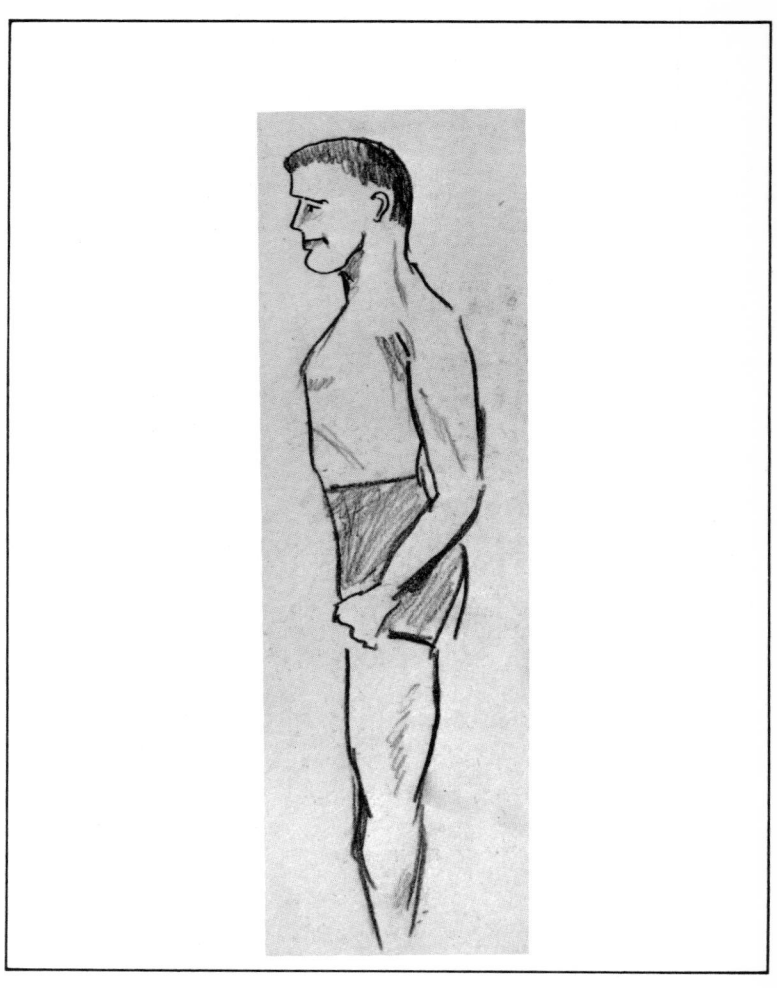

FIGURE-DRAWING CHARACTERISTICS

Structural	Male Female Both	Structural	Male	Female	Structural and Graphic	Male Female Both		Graphic, Global and Height	Male	Female	Body Proportions	Male	Female
Type	0	Omission of Appendages	8	0	Upper and Lower Halves	7	1	Hair Shading	1	3	Head	11	04
Sex Sequence	1	Position of Both Arms	4	2	Four Quarters	4	4	Nudity and Transparency	3	2	Neck	12	04
Posture	0 3	Position of Right Arm	7	2	Relative Size	0		Form	1	1	Shoulders		
Perspective	2 9	Position of Left Arm	5	7	Constant Line Pressure	5	0	Detailing	1	1	Right Arm		04
Vertical Midline	4 4	Position of Legs	1	1	Variable Line Pressure	0	3	Identity and Sex	1	1	Left Arm	10	
Bilateral Symmetry	0 0	Relation of Long Axes	1	0	Line Continuity	3	0	Sophistication	1	1	Chest	10	
Horizontal Midline	4 4	Right and Left Halves	1	1	Body Shading	3	3	Height			Girth	07	

GENERAL CHARACTERISTICS OF SUBJECT

IDENTIFICATION
No. 441
Sex M
Marital status S
Age 28 yrs. at
psychological tests

PARENTAL HISTORY
Father
C H S D O
- - - - +
Mother
C H S D O
+ + - - -

PHYSIOLOGICAL AND METABOLIC DATA

	Admission	Initial	Control	Cold pressor change	Exercise change	Smoking change
Systolic pressure	146	116	100	+06	+64	-02
Diastolic pressure	84	64	74	+06	-08	-04
Heart rate	88	84	68	+02	+57	-06

Age 26 yrs.	Height	72 in.	Ponderal index	13.10	
	Weight	166 lbs.	Cholesterol	280	mg. per 100 ml.
	Overweight	-01 %	Vital capacity	4.4	liters

HABIT SURVEY

Smoking habits: moderate cigarette smoker

Age begun 19 yrs.   Inhalation: yes

Habits of nervous tension: 2, 5, 6, 16, 18

Plate 779   **MOST SOPHISTICATED DRAWINGS**   829

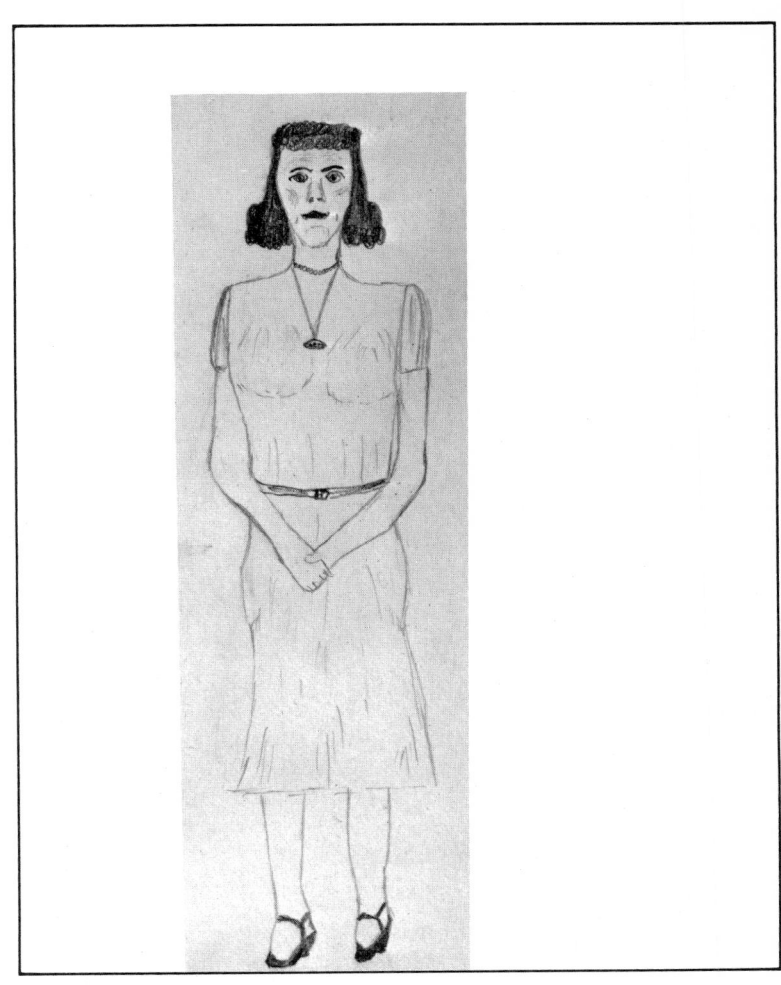

FIGURE-DRAWING CHARACTERISTICS

Structural	Male Female Both	Structural	Male	Female	Structural and Graphic	Male Female Both		Graphic, Global and Height	Male	Female	Body Proportions	Male	Female
Type	0	Omission of Appendages	0	7	Upper and Lower Halves	3	3	Hair Shading	2	2	Head	12	09
Sex Sequence	2	Position of Both Arms	1	0	Four Quarters	4	4	Nudity and Transparency	7	7	Neck	12	10
Posture	1 1	Position of Right Arm	5	5	Relative Size	0		Form	1	1	Shoulders	12	08
Perspective	0 0	Position of Left Arm	0	5	Constant Line Pressure	1	1	Detailing	1	1	Right Arm	10	08
Vertical Midline	3 0	Position of Legs	4	4	Variable Line Pressure	0	0	Identity and Sex	1	1	Left Arm	10	08
Bilateral Symmetry	3 3	Relation of Long Axes	1	1	Line Continuity	0	0	Sophistication	1	1	Chest	12	08
Horizontal Midline	4 4	Right and Left Halves	1	1	Body Shading	7	7	Height	09	09	Girth	15	09

GENERAL CHARACTERISTICS OF SUBJECT

IDENTIFICATION
No. 517
Sex M
Marital status M
Age 23 yrs. at
psychological tests

PARENTAL HISTORY
Father
C   H   S   D   0
-    -   -   -   ?
Mother
C   H   S   D   0
+   +   +   -   -

PHYSIOLOGICAL AND METABOLIC DATA

	Admission	Initial	Control	Cold pressor change	Exercise change	Smoking change
Systolic pressure	118	110	106	+10	+24	
Diastolic pressure	68	66	64	+16	-06	
Heart rate	68	72	71	+06	+12	

Age 21 yrs.	Height 74 in.	Ponderal index 13.33
	Weight 171 lbs.	Cholesterol 222 mg. per 100 ml.
	Overweight -01 %	Vital capacity 5.8 liters

HABIT SURVEY

Smoking habits: former smoker

Age begun   yrs.   Inhalation:

Habits of nervous tension: 2, 4, 5, 8, 9, 21, 22, 23

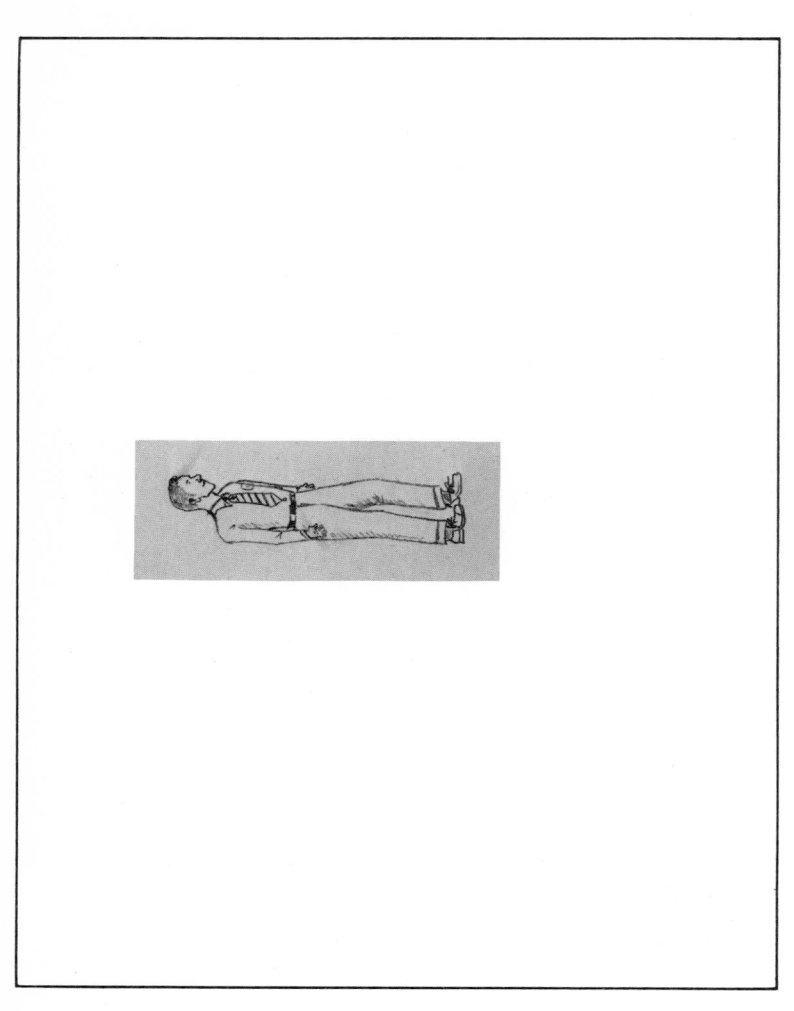

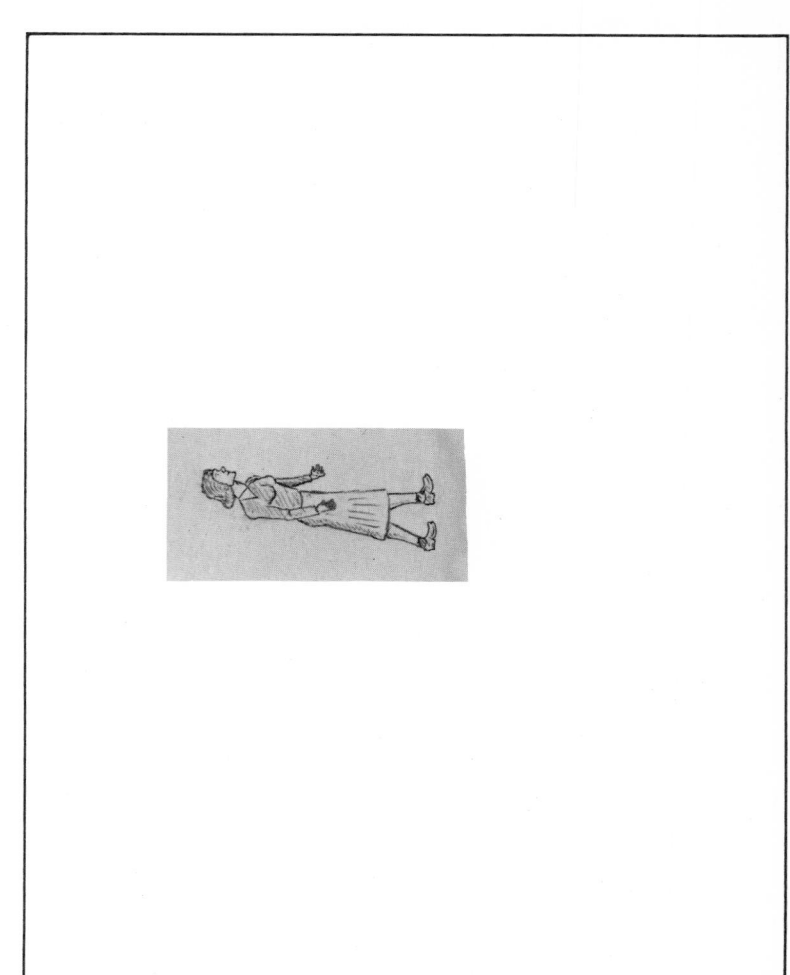

FIGURE-DRAWING CHARACTERISTICS

Structural	Male Female Both	Structural	Male	Female	Structural and Graphic	Male Female Both		Graphic, Global and Height	Male	Female	Body Proportions	Male	Female
Type	0	Omission of Appendages	0	0	Upper and Lower Halves	1	1	Hair Shading	1	1	Head	03	02
Sex Sequence	2	Position of Both Arms	2	2	Four Quarters	4	4	Nudity and Transparency	7	7	Neck	04	04
Posture	2 2	Position of Right Arm	0	6	Relative Size	0		Form	1	1	Shoulders		
Perspective	6 6	Position of Left Arm	7	7	Constant Line Pressure	3	3	Detailing	1	1	Right Arm	02	02
Vertical Midline	7 4	Position of Legs	8	8	Variable Line Pressure	0	0	Identity and Sex	1	1	Left Arm		
Bilateral Symmetry	0 0	Relation of Long Axes	2	2	Line Continuity	4	4	Sophistication	1	1	Chest		
Horizontal Midline	4 4	Right and Left Halves	0	3	Body Shading	7	7	Height	03	02	Girth		

GENERAL CHARACTERISTICS OF SUBJECT

<table>
<tr><td colspan="2">IDENTIFICATION</td></tr>
<tr><td colspan="2">No. 232</td></tr>
<tr><td colspan="2">Sex M</td></tr>
<tr><td colspan="2">Marital status S</td></tr>
<tr><td colspan="2">Age 27 yrs. at</td></tr>
<tr><td colspan="2">psychological tests</td></tr>
</table>

PARENTAL HISTORY				
Father				
C	H	S	D	O
(+)	–	–	–	–
Mother				
C	H	S	D	O
–	+	–	+	?

PHYSIOLOGICAL AND METABOLIC DATA

	Admission	Initial	Control	Cold pressor change	Exercise change	Smoking change
Systolic pressure	110	118	108	+02	+28	
Diastolic pressure	70	76	68	+12	00	
Heart rate	72	60	52	+02	+07	

Age 25 yrs.   Height   70 in.   Ponderal index 12.87
               Weight   161 lbs. Cholesterol   252   mg. per 100 ml.
               Overweight +03 %   Vital capacity 5.2   liters

HABIT SURVEY

Smoking habits: unknown

Age begun   yrs.   Inhalation:

Habits of nervous tension:

FIGURE-DRAWING CHARACTERISTICS

Structural	Male Female Both		Structural	Male	Female	Structural and Graphic	Male Female Both		Graphic, Global and Height	Male	Female	Body Proportions	Male	Female
Type	0		Omission of Appendages	0	4	Upper and Lower Halves	0	3	Hair Shading	3	3	Head	09	06
Sex Sequence	0		Position of Both Arms	4	1	Four Quarters	4	4	Nudity and Transparency	7	7	Neck	08	08
Posture	3	0	Position of Right Arm	7	2	Relative Size	5		Form	1	1	Shoulders		08
Perspective	2	0	Position of Left Arm	5	5	Constant Line Pressure	0	0	Detailing	1	3	Right Arm		04
Vertical Midline	7	3	Position of Legs	1	4	Variable Line Pressure	3	1	Identity and Sex	1	1	Left Arm	08	06
Bilateral Symmetry	0	2	Relation of Long Axes	0	1	Line Continuity	0	0	Sophistication	1	1	Chest	10	07
Horizontal Midline	6	4	Right and Left Halves	1	1	Body Shading	7	3	Height			Girth		07

GENERAL CHARACTERISTICS OF SUBJECT

IDENTIFICATION

No. 527

Sex M

Marital status S

Age 31 yrs. at

psychological tests

PARENTAL HISTORY

Father

C	H	S	D	O
-	(+)	(?)	-	?

Mother

C	H	S	D	O
(+)	(?)	-	-	+

PHYSIOLOGICAL AND METABOLIC DATA

	Admission	Initial	Control	Cold pressor change	Exercise change	Smoking change
Systolic pressure	140	122	122	+06	+23	
Diastolic pressure	80	68	70	+16	-10	
Heart rate	78	84	71	+12	+23	

Age 28 yrs.

Height 71 in.

Weight 150 lbs.

Overweight -09 %

Ponderal index 13.36

Cholesterol 250 mg. per 100 ml.

Vital capacity 5.0 liters

HABIT SURVEY

Smoking habits: mixed smoker

   Age begun 18 yrs.   Inhalation: no

Habits of nervous tension: 2, 4, 11, 14,

16, 18

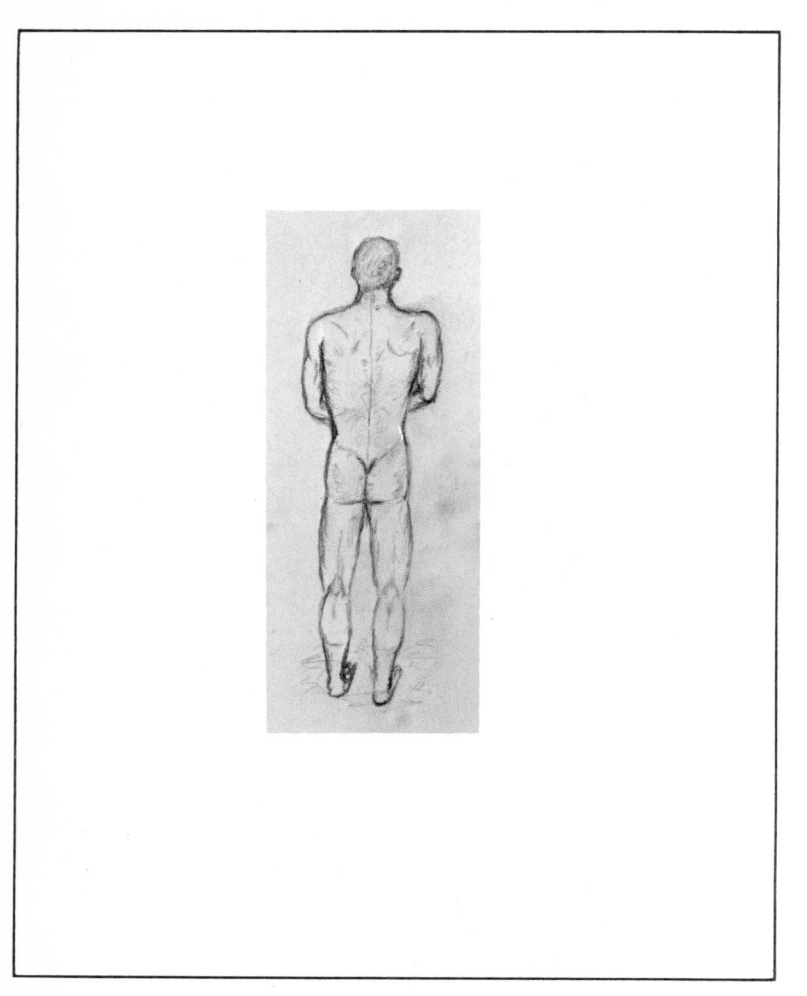

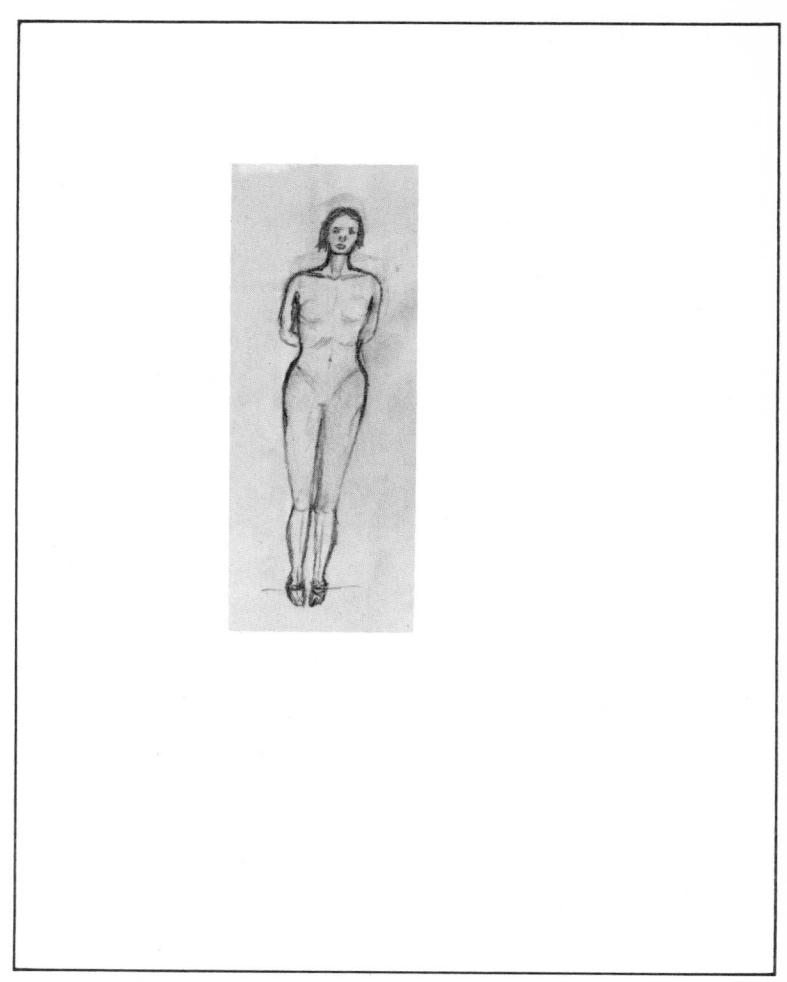

FIGURE-DRAWING CHARACTERISTICS

Structural	Male Female Both		Structural	Male	Female	Structural and Graphic	Male Female Both		Graphic, Global and Height	Male	Female	Body Proportions	Male	Female
Type	0		Omission of Appendages	2	2	Upper and Lower Halves	1	1	Hair Shading	2	3	Head		04
Sex Sequence	2		Position of Both Arms	0	0	Four Quarters	4	4	Nudity and Transparency	0	0	Neck		06
Posture	1	1	Position of Right Arm	5	5	Relative Size	0		Form	1	1	Shoulders	05	03
Perspective	3	0	Position of Left Arm	5	5	Constant Line Pressure	0	0	Detailing	1	1	Right Arm		
Vertical Midline	8	0	Position of Legs	4	4	Variable Line Pressure	3	3	Identity and Sex	1	1	Left Arm		
Bilateral Symmetry	4	5	Relation of Long Axes	1	1	Line Continuity	0	0	Sophistication	1	1	Chest	04	03
Horizontal Midline	0	0	Right and Left Halves	1	2	Body Shading	3	3	Height	05	04	Girth	04	03

GENERAL CHARACTERISTICS OF SUBJECT

IDENTIFICATION
No. D43
Sex M
Marital status S
Age 23 yrs. at
psychological tests

PARENTAL HISTORY
Father
C H S D O
? - - - -
Mother
C H S D O
? + - - -

PHYSIOLOGICAL AND METABOLIC DATA

	Admission	Initial	Control	Cold pressor change	Exercise change	Smoking change
Systolic pressure	140	110	106	+16	+39	+16
Diastolic pressure	80	60	60	+20	-10	+04
Heart rate	80	68	71	+04	+19	+13

Age 22 yrs.	Height 74 in.	Ponderal index 13.63
	Weight 160 lbs.	Cholesterol 170 mg. per 100 ml.
	Overweight -08 %	Vital capacity 4.4 liters

HABIT SURVEY

Smoking habits: moderate cigarette smoker

Age begun 20 yrs.   Inhalation: yes

Habits of nervous tension: 2, 3, 5, 6, 9

STRONG VOCATIONAL INTEREST TEST

Occupation	Artist	Psychologist	Architect	Physician	Osteopath	Dentist	Veterinarian	Mathematician	Physicist	Engineer	Chemist	Production Manager
Standard Score	40	58	41	64	61	42	26	35	31	31	44	35

Occupation	Farmer	Aviator	Carpenter	Printer	Math.-Sci. Teacher	Ind. Arts Teacher	Voc. Agric. Teacher	Policeman	Forest Serv. Man	Y.M.C.A. Phys. Dir.	Personnel Director	Public Administrator
Standard Score	30	32	20	42	46	22	27	35	35	57	49	60

Occupation	Y.M.C.A. Secretary	Soc. Sci. H.S. Teacher	City Sch. Sup't.	Social Worker	Minister	Musician Performer	C.P.A.	Senior C.P.A.	Accountant	Office Man	Purchasing Agent	Banker
Standard Score	52	52	47	61	63	60	34	38	21	29	10	22

Occupation	Mortician	Pharmacist	Sales Manager	Real Est. Manager	Life Ins. Salesman	Advertising Man	Lawyer	Author-Journalist	President Mfg. Co.	Interest Maturity	Occupational Level	Masculinity-Femininity
Standard Score	29	24	17	23	31	33	46	39	20	61	50	36

Plate 783   MOST SOPHISTICATED DRAWINGS   833

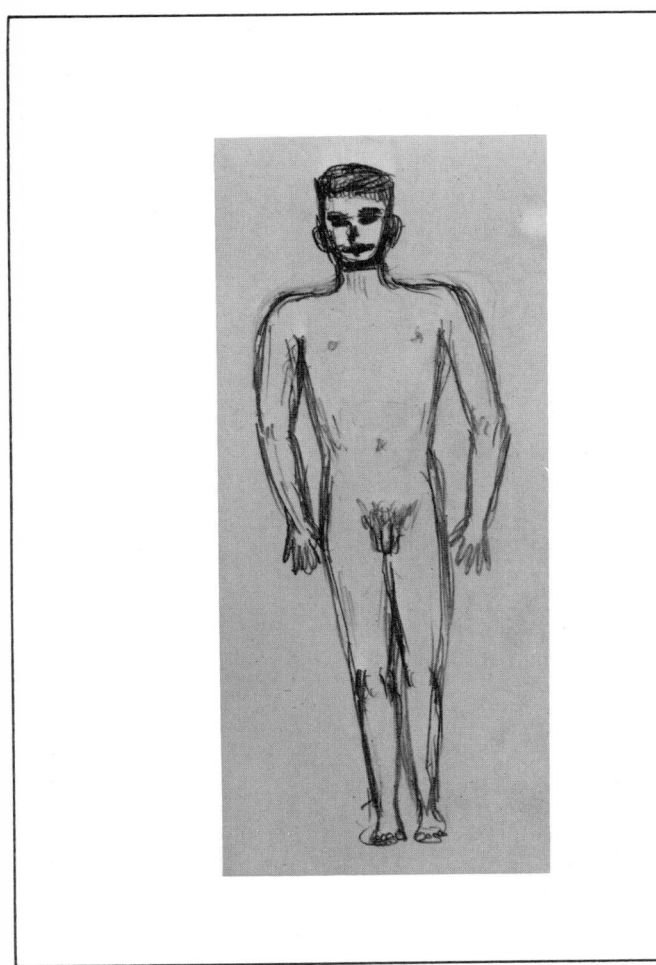

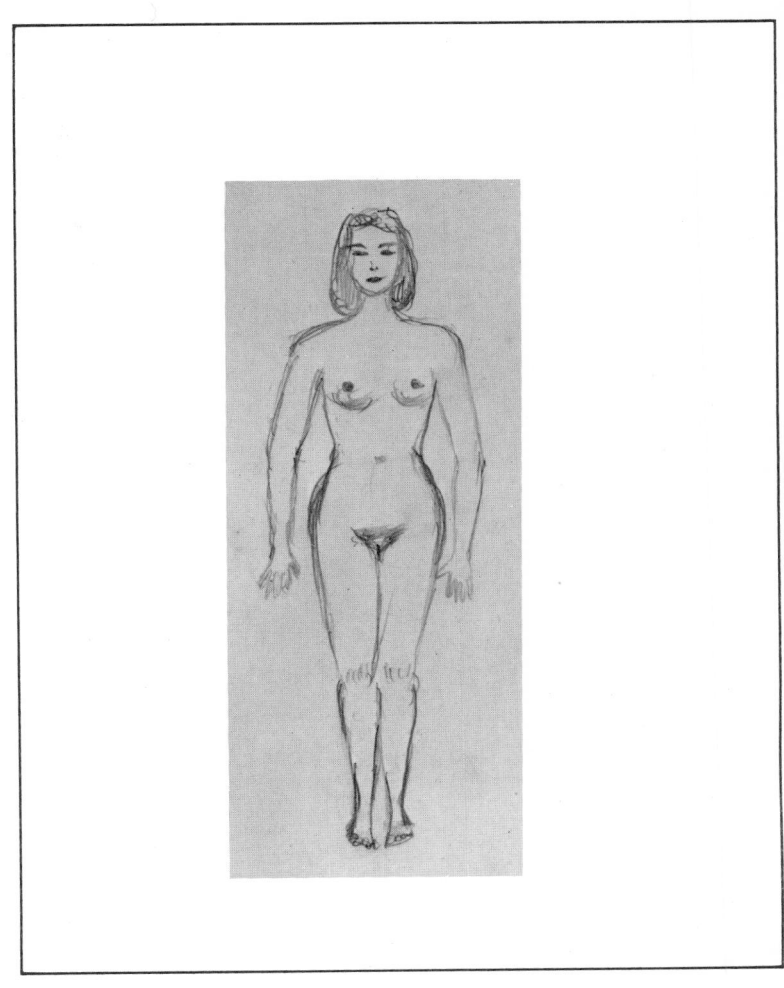

FIGURE-DRAWING CHARACTERISTICS

Structural	Male Female Both	Structural	Male	Female	Structural and Graphic	Male Female Both	Graphic, Global and Height	Male	Female	Body Proportions	Male	Female
Type	0	Omission of Appendages	0	0	Upper and Lower Halves	0 3	Hair Shading	3	3	Head	07	06
Sex Sequence	0	Position of Both Arms	0	0	Four Quarters	4 4	Nudity and Transparency	0	0	Neck	08	08
Posture	1 1	Position of Right Arm	0	0	Relative Size	0	Form	1	1	Shoulders	08	06
Perspective	0 0	Position of Left Arm	0	0	Constant Line Pressure	5 0	Detailing	1	1	Right Arm	06	06
Vertical Midline	0 0	Position of Legs	2	2	Variable Line Pressure	0 3	Identity and Sex	1	1	Left Arm	06	06
Bilateral Symmetry	5 5	Relation of Long Axes	1	1	Line Continuity	0 0	Sophistication	1	1	Chest	06	05
Horizontal Midline	0 0	Right and Left Halves	1	1	Body Shading	3 3	Height	07	06	Girth	07	06

GENERAL CHARACTERISTICS OF SUBJECT

IDENTIFICATION
No. 760
Sex M
Marital status S
Age 26 yrs. at psychological tests

PARENTAL HISTORY
Father
C   H   S   D   O
?   -   -   -   +
Mother
C   H   S   D   O
-   -   -   -   +

PHYSIOLOGICAL AND METABOLIC DATA

	Admission	Initial	Control	Cold pressor change	Exercise change	Smoking change
Systolic pressure	110	128	114	+18	+32	+10
Diastolic pressure	84	76	68	+30	-08	+05
Heart rate	64	72	71	+20	+17	+03

Age 23 yrs.	Height	72 in.	Ponderal index 13.09
	Weight	166 lbs.	Cholesterol 250 mg. per 100 ml.
	Overweight +01 %		Vital capacity 6.6 liters

HABIT SURVEY

Smoking habits: nonsmoker

Age begun   yrs.   Inhalation:

Habits of nervous tension: 4, 5, 18, 21

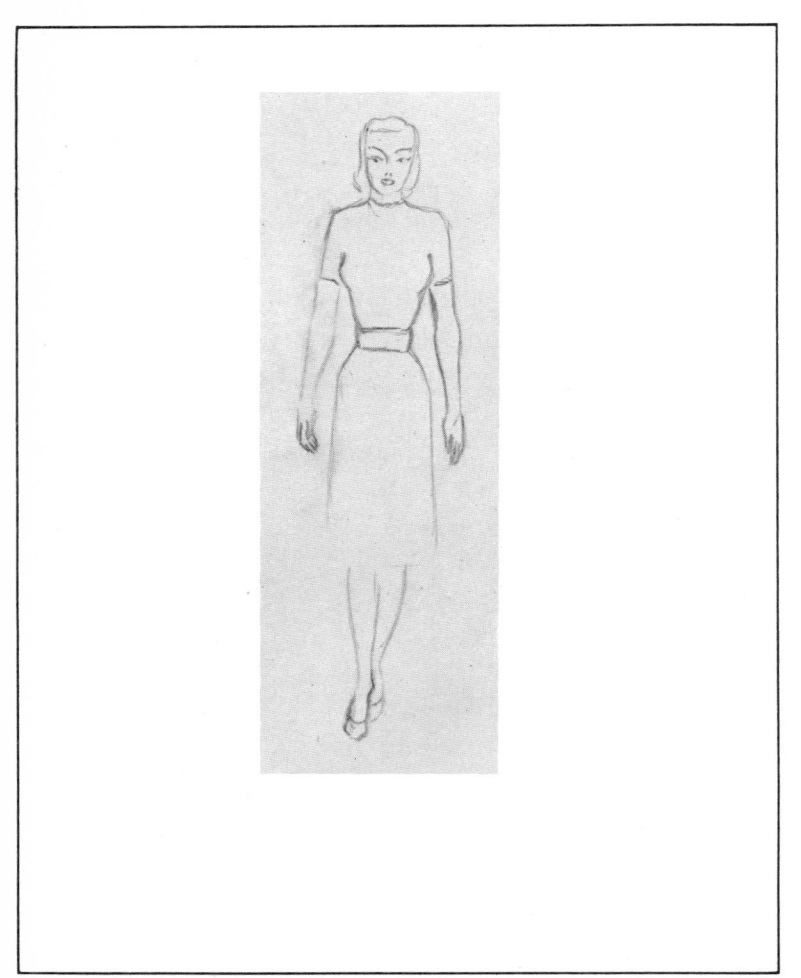

FIGURE-DRAWING CHARACTERISTICS

Structural	Male Female Both	Structural	Male	Female	Structural and Graphic	Male Female Both	Graphic, Global and Height	Male	Female	Body Proportions	Male	Female
Type	0	Omission of Appendages	0	0	Upper and Lower Halves	1　1	Hair Shading	1	5	Head	06	06
Sex Sequence	1	Position of Both Arms	0	0	Four Quarters	4　4	Nudity and Transparency	7	7	Neck	01	03
Posture	1　2	Position of Right Arm	0	0	Relative Size	0	Form	1	1	Shoulders	07	04
Perspective	0　0	Position of Left Arm	0	0	Constant Line Pressure	0　0	Detailing	3	3	Right Arm	06	06
Vertical Midline	3　0	Position of Legs	4	8	Variable Line Pressure	1　1	Identity and Sex	1	1	Left Arm	06	06
Bilateral Symmetry	3　5	Relation of Long Axes	1	1	Line Continuity	1　1	Sophistication	1	1	Chest	06	04
Horizontal Midline	6　4	Right and Left Halves	3	0	Body Shading	4　0	Height	06	06	Girth	06	03

GENERAL CHARACTERISTICS OF SUBJECT

IDENTIFICATION
No. G61
Sex F
Marital status S
Age 27 yrs. at
psychological tests

PARENTAL HISTORY					
Father					
	C	H	S	D	O
	?	+	+	-	+
Mother					
	C	H	S	D	O
	-	-	-	-	+

PHYSIOLOGICAL AND METABOLIC DATA

	Admission	Initial	Control	Cold pressor change	Exercise change	Smoking change
Systolic pressure	105	108	102	+16	+30	+06
Diastolic pressure	60	80	80	+20	+20	+08
Heart rate	84	76	75	+12	+47	+10

Age 26 yrs.　　Height　66 in.　　Ponderal index 13.23
Weight　124 lbs.　　Cholesterol　237　mg. per 100 ml.
Overweight −08 %　　Vital capacity　　liters

HABIT SURVEY
Smoking habits: former smoker
Age begun 16 yrs.　　Inhalation:
Habits of nervous tension: 4, 6, 16, 21, 22

STRONG VOCATIONAL INTEREST TEST

Occupation	Artist	Psychologist	Architect	Physician	Osteopath	Dentist	Veterinarian	Mathematician	Physicist	Engineer	Chemist	Production Manager
Standard Score	41	44	44	49	35	37	12	26	17	24	34	27

Occupation	Farmer	Aviator	Carpenter	Printer	Math.-Sci. Teacher	Ind. Arts Teacher	Voc. Agric. Teacher	Policeman	Forest Serv. Man	Y.M.C.A. Phys. Dir.	Personnel Director	Public Administrator
Standard Score	17	21	00	28	24	−07	07	17	11	30	37	41

Occupation	Y.M.C.A. Secretary	Soc. Sci. H.S. Teacher	City Sch. Sup't.	Social Worker	Minister	Musician Performer	C.P.A.	Senior C.P.A.	Accountant	Office Man	Purchasing Agent	Banker
Standard Score	27	29	32	38	59	51	31	24	15	25	23	14

Occupation	Mortician	Pharmacist	Sales Manager	Real Est. Manager	Life Ins. Salesman	Advertising Man	Lawyer	Author-Journalist	President Mfg. Co.	Interest Maturity	Occupational Level	Masculinity-Femininity
Standard Score	33	31	38	40	38	55	45	47	33	54	65	24

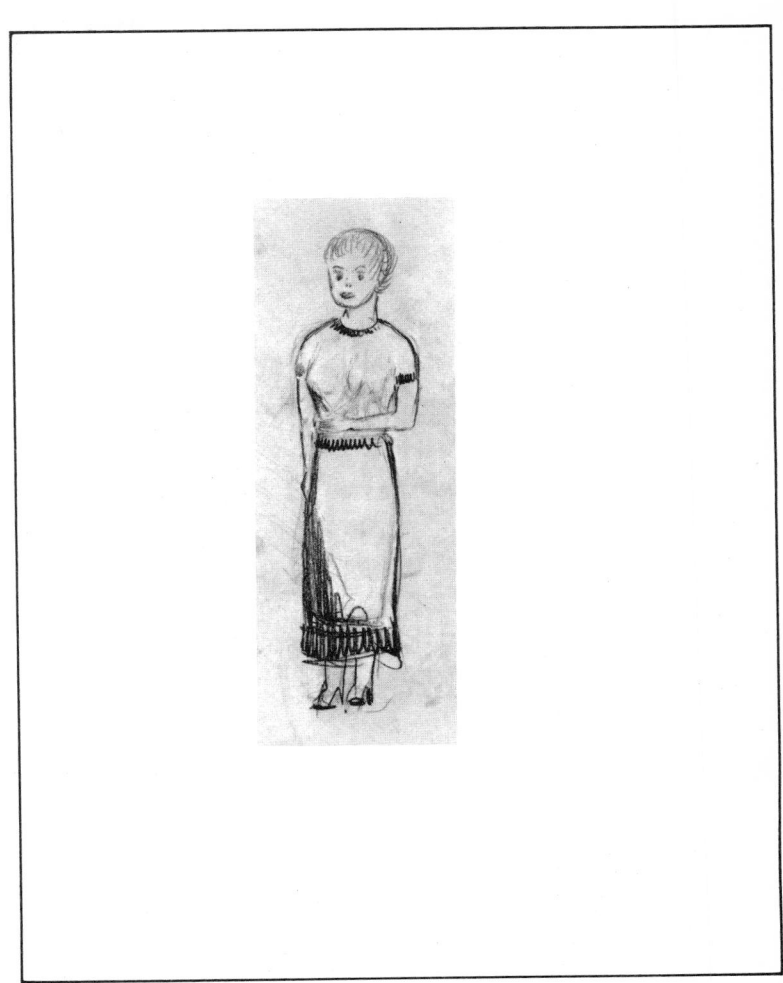

FIGURE-DRAWING CHARACTERISTICS

Structural	Male	Female	Structural	Male	Female	Structural and Graphic	Male	Female	Graphic, Global and Height	Male	Female	Body Proportions	Male	Female
	Both						Both							
Type	0		Omission of Appendages	7	0	Upper and Lower Halves	1	1	Hair Shading	1	3	Head	05	06
Sex Sequence	0		Position of Both Arms	4	1	Four Quarters	4	4	Nudity and Transparency	7	7	Neck	04	05
Posture	1	1	Position of Right Arm	7	0	Relative Size	4		Form	1	1	Shoulders		04
Perspective	2	1	Position of Left Arm	0	5	Constant Line Pressure	0	0	Detailing	1	1	Right Arm		04
Vertical Midline	7	4	Position of Legs	1	4	Variable Line Pressure	4	3	Identity and Sex	1	1	Left Arm	04	04
Bilateral Symmetry	0	0	Relation of Long Axes	1	1	Line Continuity	0	1	Sophistication	1	1	Chest	06	
Horizontal Midline	0	4	Right and Left Halves	1	1	Body Shading	3	7	Height	04	05	Girth	06	

GENERAL CHARACTERISTICS OF SUBJECT

IDENTIFICATION
No. B07
Sex M
Marital status M
Age 22 yrs. at
psychological tests

PARENTAL HISTORY				
Father				
C	H	S	D	O
?	-	-	-	?
Mother				
C	H	S	D	O
-	-	-	-	?

PHYSIOLOGICAL AND METABOLIC DATA

	Admission	Initial	Control	Cold pressor change	Exercise change	Smoking change
Systolic pressure	112	120	114	+18	+50	+08
Diastolic pressure	80	64	64	+16	-02	+06
Heart rate	96	88	64	+26	+24	+09

Age 21 yrs.	Height 68 in.	Ponderal index 12.69	
	Weight 154 lbs.	Cholesterol 233 mg. per 100 ml.	
	Overweight +06 %	Vital capacity 5.2 liters	

HABIT SURVEY

Smoking habits: nonsmoker

Age begun   yrs.   Inhalation:

Habits of nervous tension: 1, 2, 5, 9, 11, 16

FIGURE-DRAWING CHARACTERISTICS

Structural	Male	Female	Structural	Male	Female	Structural and Graphic	Male	Female	Graphic, Global and Height	Male	Female	Body Proportions	Male	Female
	Both						Both							
Type	0		Omission of Appendages	0	3	Upper and Lower Halves	1	7	Hair Shading	3	3	Head	07	10
Sex Sequence	0		Position of Both Arms	4	4	Four Quarters	4	4	Nudity and Transparency	7	2	Neck	06	12
Posture	1	0	Position of Right Arm	7	7	Relative Size	4		Form	1	1	Shoulders		
Perspective	2	2	Position of Left Arm	4	4	Constant Line Pressure	3	0	Detailing	1	1	Right Arm		
Vertical Midline	7	4	Position of Legs	1	1	Variable Line Pressure	0	4	Identity and Sex	1	1	Left Arm	06	08
Bilateral Symmetry	0	0	Relation of Long Axes	1	1	Line Continuity	0	0	Sophistication	1	1	Chest	06	06
Horizontal Midline	6	0	Right and Left Halves	2	1	Body Shading	5	1	Height	06		Girth	07	07

GENERAL CHARACTERISTICS OF SUBJECT

IDENTIFICATION
No. D09
Sex M
Marital status S
Age 22 yrs. at
psychological tests

PARENTAL HISTORY
Father
C　H　S　D　O
?　+　-　-　?
Mother
C　H　S　D　O
-　-　-　-　-

PHYSIOLOGICAL AND METABOLIC DATA

	Admission	Initial	Control	Cold pressor change	Exercise change	Smoking change
Systolic pressure	106	120	120	-02	+10	+10
Diastolic pressure	68	72	70	+10	-20	+12
Heart rate	64	60	63	+04	+37	+23

Age 22 yrs.	Height 72 in.	Ponderal index 12.97
	Weight 171 lbs.	Cholesterol 200 mg. per 100 ml.
	Overweight +05 %	Vital capacity 6.3 liters

HABIT SURVEY

Smoking habits: moderate cigarette smoker

Age begun 18 yrs.　Inhalation: yes

Habits of nervous tension: 4, 5, 6, 9, 11, 18, 24

STRONG VOCATIONAL INTEREST TEST

Occupation	Artist	Psychologist	Architect	Physician	Osteopath	Dentist	Veterinarian	Mathematician	Physicist	Engineer	Chemist	Production Manager
Standard Score	52	54	53	71	63	61	22	36	39	45	52	25

Occupation	Farmer	Aviator	Carpenter	Printer	Math.-Sci. Teacher	Ind. Arts Teacher	Voc. Agric. Teacher	Policeman	Forest Serv. Man	Y.M.C.A. Phys. Dir.	Personnel Director	Public Administrator
Standard Score	37	48	22	36	37	19	18	30	26	36	31	39

Occupation	Y.M.C.A. Secretary	Soc. Sci. H.S. Teacher	City Sch. Sup't.	Social Worker	Minister	Musician Performer	C.P.A.	Senior C.P.A.	Accountant	Office Man	Purchasing Agent	Banker
Standard Score	16	23	18	38	63	60	32	34	12	15	14	01

Occupation	Mortician	Pharmacist	Sales Manager	Real Est. Manager	Life Ins. Salesman	Advertising Man	Lawyer	Author-Journalist	President Mfg. Co.	Interest Maturity	Occupational Level	Masculinity-Femininity
Standard Score	20	28	23	31	29	41	43	47	28	50	56	41

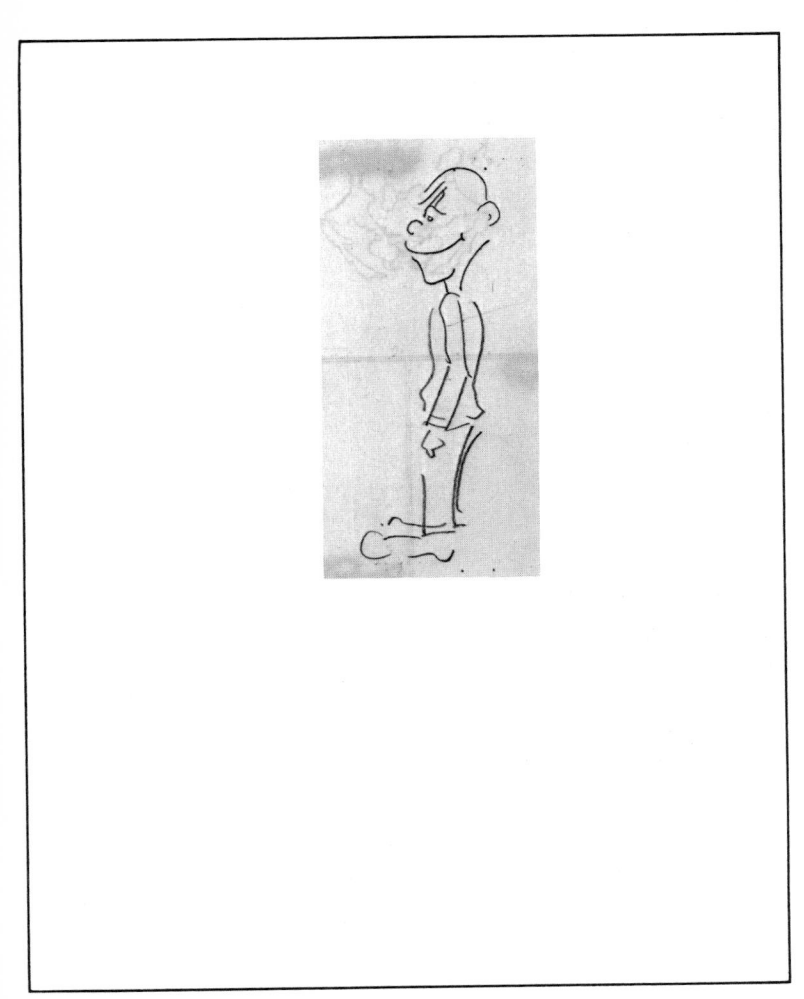

FIGURE-DRAWING CHARACTERISTICS

Structural	Male	Female	Structural	Male	Female	Structural and Graphic	Male	Female	Graphic, Global and Height	Male	Female	Body Proportions	Male	Female
	Both						Both							
Type	0		Omission of Appendages	0	0	Upper and Lower Halves	1	1	Hair Shading	7	1	Head	10	07
Sex Sequence	2		Position of Both Arms	4	4	Four Quarters	4	4	Nudity and Transparency	7	7	Neck	04	04
Posture	1	1	Position of Right Arm	7	7	Relative Size	2		Form	1	1	Shoulders		
Perspective	2	2	Position of Left Arm	0	0	Constant Line Pressure	5	3	Detailing	3	3	Right Arm		
Vertical Midline	4	4	Position of Legs	1	1	Variable Line Pressure	0	0	Identity and Sex	1	1	Left Arm	04	04
Bilateral Symmetry	0	0	Relation of Long Axes	1	1	Line Continuity	3	3	Sophistication	1	1	Chest	04	04
Horizontal Midline	6	4	Right and Left Halves	4	0	Body Shading	0	0	Height	04	04	Girth	04	03

GENERAL CHARACTERISTICS OF SUBJECT

IDENTIFICATION
No. 259
Sex M
Marital status M
Age 25 yrs. at
psychological tests

PARENTAL HISTORY
Father
C H S D O
- - - - +
Mother
C H S D O
? - - - -

PHYSIOLOGICAL AND METABOLIC DATA

	Admission	Initial	Control	Cold pressor change	Exercise change	Smoking change
Systolic pressure	130	142	124	+14	+14	
Diastolic pressure	68	74	72	+04	+02	
Heart rate	76	102	94	+06	+13	

Age 23 yrs.	Height	72 in.	Ponderal index 13.15
	Weight	164 lbs.	Cholesterol 230 mg. per 100 ml.
	Overweight 00 %		Vital capacity 5.1 liters

HABIT SURVEY
Smoking habits: heavy cigarette smoker
Age begun 15 yrs.   Inhalation: yes
Habits of nervous tension: 4, 5, 6, 9, 12, 17, 18

FIGURE-DRAWING CHARACTERISTICS

Structural	Male Female Both		Structural	Male	Female	Structural and Graphic	Male Female Both		Graphic, Global and Height	Male	Female	Body Proportions	Male	Female
Type	0		Omission of Appendages	0	0	Upper and Lower Halves	0	1	Hair Shading	1	1	Head	07	07
Sex Sequence	1		Position of Both Arms	1	1	Four Quarters	4	4	Nudity and Transparency	7	7	Neck	06	06
Posture	1	1	Position of Right Arm	4	4	Relative Size	0		Form	1	1	Shoulders		
Perspective	1	1	Position of Left Arm	0	0	Constant Line Pressure	0	0	Detailing	1	1	Right Arm		
Vertical Midline	7	4	Position of Legs	2	2	Variable Line Pressure	5	5	Identity and Sex	1	1	Left Arm	06	04
Bilateral Symmetry	0	0	Relation of Long Axes	1	1	Line Continuity	0	0	Sophistication	1	1	Chest		
Horizontal Midline	6	0	Right and Left Halves	2	2	Body Shading	7	3	Height	07	07	Girth		

GENERAL CHARACTERISTICS OF SUBJECT

IDENTIFICATION
No. 466
Sex M
Marital status S
Age 24 yrs. at
psychological tests

PARENTAL HISTORY
Father
C H S D O
- - - - -
Mother
C H S D O
? - - - +

PHYSIOLOGICAL AND METABOLIC DATA

	Admission	Initial	Control	Cold pressor change	Exercise change	Smoking change
Systolic pressure	144	124	114	+04	+44	
Diastolic pressure	80	70	64	+14	00	
Heart rate	96	102	81	00	+14	

Age 21 yrs.

Height 69 in.   Ponderal index 13.02
Weight 149 lbs.   Cholesterol 317 mg. per 100 ml.
Overweight 00 %   Vital capacity 3.4 liters

HABIT SURVEY
Smoking habits: heavy cigarette smoker
Age begun 16 yrs.   Inhalation: yes
Habits of nervous tension: 2, 4, 5, 6, 9, 11, 17, 19, 25

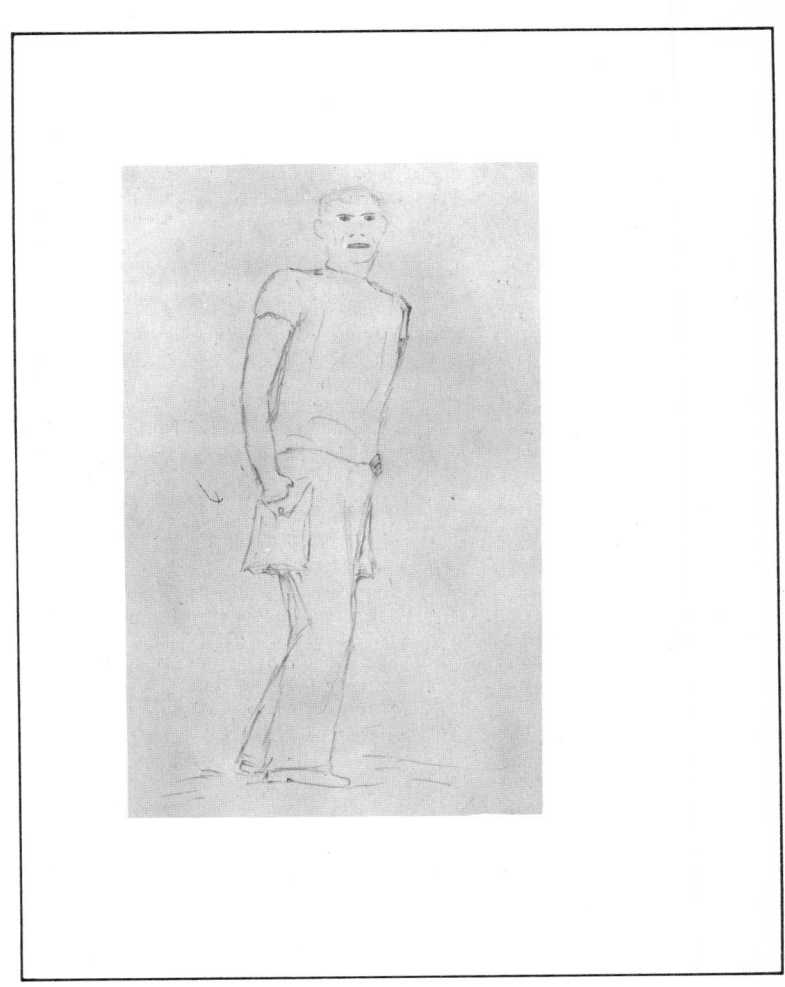

FIGURE-DRAWING CHARACTERISTICS

Structural	Male Female Both		Structural	Male	Female	Structural and Graphic	Male Female Both		Graphic, Global and Height	Male	Female	Body Proportions	Male	Female
Type	0		Omission of Appendages	0	0	Upper and Lower Halves	1	3	Hair Shading	3	3	Head	06	07
Sex Sequence	1		Position of Both Arms	2	2	Four Quarters	4	4	Nudity and Transparency	7	7	Neck	06	07
Posture	2	2	Position of Right Arm	5	5	Relative Size	4		Form	1	1	Shoulders		
Perspective	1	1	Position of Left Arm	7	7	Constant Line Pressure	1	1	Detailing	1	1	Right Arm	06	06
Vertical Midline	4	7	Position of Legs	8	8	Variable Line Pressure	0	0	Identity and Sex	1	1	Left Arm		
Bilateral Symmetry	0	0	Relation of Long Axes	1	1	Line Continuity	0	0	Sophistication	1	1	Chest		
Horizontal Midline	4	4	Right and Left Halves	2	2	Body Shading	3	1	Height	06	08	Girth		

GENERAL CHARACTERISTICS OF SUBJECT

IDENTIFICATION
No. 723
Sex M
Marital status S
Age 26 yrs. at
psychological tests

PARENTAL HISTORY
Father
C   H   S   D   O
-   -   -   -   -
Mother
C   H   S   D   O
?   -   -   -   -

PHYSIOLOGICAL AND METABOLIC DATA

	Admission	Initial	Control	Cold pressor change	Exercise change	Smoking change
Systolic pressure	100	100	92	+12	+38	+04
Diastolic pressure	62	52	58	+22	00	+04
Heart rate	72	60	64	00	+07	+03

Age 24 yrs.

Height	67 in.	Ponderal index 12.43
Weight	157 lbs.	Cholesterol 280 mg. per 100 ml.
Overweight +09 %		Vital capacity 5.6 liters

HABIT SURVEY

Smoking habits: nonsmoker

Age begun   yrs.   Inhalation:

Habits of nervous tension: 1, 4, 5, 6, 9, 11, 16, 17, 18, 21, 22, 23, 24

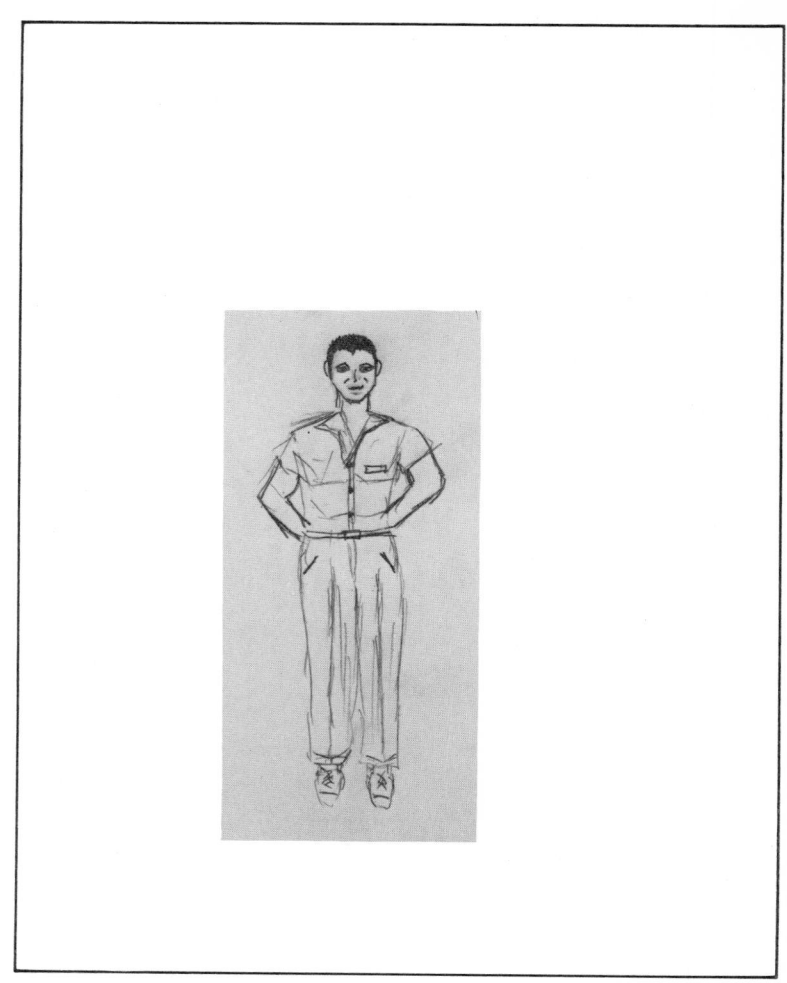

FIGURE-DRAWING CHARACTERISTICS

Structural	Male Female Both	Structural	Male	Female	Structural and Graphic	Male Female Both		Graphic, Global and Height	Male	Female	Body Proportions	Male	Female
Type	0	Omission of Appendages	7	7	Upper and Lower Halves	3	0	Hair Shading	3	3	Head	05	05
Sex Sequence	1	Position of Both Arms	0	0	Four Quarters	4	4	Nudity and Transparency	7	7	Neck	05	04
Posture	1 1	Position of Right Arm	5	5	Relative Size	0		Form	1	1	Shoulders	05	04
Perspective	0 0	Position of Left Arm	5	5	Constant Line Pressure	0	0	Detailing	1	1	Right Arm		
Vertical Midline	3 0	Position of Legs	4	4	Variable Line Pressure	5	3	Identity and Sex	1	1	Left Arm		
Bilateral Symmetry	5 5	Relation of Long Axes	1	1	Line Continuity	0	0	Sophistication	1	1	Chest	04	03
Horizontal Midline	4 4	Right and Left Halves	1	2	Body Shading	7	5	Height	05	04	Girth	05	03

GENERAL CHARACTERISTICS OF SUBJECT

IDENTIFICATION
No. B50
Sex M
Marital status M
Age 22 yrs. at
psychological tests

PARENTAL HISTORY
Father
C   H   S   D   O
–   –   –   –   –
Mother
C   H   S   D   O
?   –   –   –   +

PHYSIOLOGICAL AND METABOLIC DATA

	Admission	Initial	Control	Cold pressor change	Exercise change	Smoking change
Systolic pressure	120	116	114	+08	+56	+06
Diastolic pressure	76	52	58	+16	-14	+08
Heart rate	88	64	55	+20	+28	+09

Age 22 yrs.

Height	72 in.	Ponderal index 13.21
Weight	162 lbs.	Cholesterol 170 mg. per 100 ml.
Overweight -01 %		Vital capacity 5.1 liters

HABIT SURVEY
Smoking habits: heavy cigarette smoker
Age begun 16 yrs.   Inhalation: yes
Habits of nervous tension: 1, 3, 4, 5, 8, 9, 10

STRONG VOCATIONAL INTEREST TEST

Occupation	Artist	Psychologist	Architect	Physician	Osteopath	Dentist	Veterinarian	Mathematician	Physicist	Engineer	Chemist	Production Manager
Standard Score	33	52	30	63	50	42	43	33	28	33	43	30

Occupation	Farmer	Aviator	Carpenter	Printer	Math.-Sci. Teacher	Ind. Arts Teacher	Voc. Agric. Teacher	Policeman	Forest Serv. Man	Y.M.C.A. Phys. Dir.	Personnel Director	Public Administrator
Standard Score	33	35	13	28	43	16	41	28	32	42	33	45

Occupation	Y.M.C.A. Secretary	Soc. Sci. H.S. Teacher	City Sch. Sup't.	Social Worker	Minister	Musician Performer	C.P.A.	Senior C.P.A.	Accountant	Office Man	Purchasing Agent	Banker
Standard Score	24	37	36	41	61	48	35	38	16	20	23	21

Occupation	Mortician	Pharmacist	Sales Manager	Real Est. Manager	Life Ins. Salesman	Advertising Man	Lawyer	Author-Journalist	President Mfg. Co.	Interest Maturity	Occupational Level	Masculinity-Femininity
Standard Score	22	37	25	29	26	32	44	40	26	51	58	49

Plate 791   **MOST SOPHISTICATED DRAWINGS**   841

FIGURE-DRAWING CHARACTERISTICS

Structural	Male Female Both		Structural	Male	Female	Structural and Graphic	Male Female Both		Graphic, Global and Height	Male	Female	Body Proportions	Male	Female
Type	0		Omission of Appendages	0	0	Upper and Lower Halves	0	3	Hair Shading	1	1	Head	07	08
Sex Sequence	0		Position of Both Arms	1	1	Four Quarters	4	4	Nudity and Transparency	7	7	Neck	05	08
Posture	1	1	Position of Right Arm	4	4	Relative Size	4		Form	1	1	Shoulders	07	
Perspective	1	1	Position of Left Arm	5	5	Constant Line Pressure	0	0	Detailing	1	1	Right Arm	06	06
Vertical Midline	7	7	Position of Legs	4	4	Variable Line Pressure	2	2	Identity and Sex	1	1	Left Arm	06	06
Bilateral Symmetry	0	0	Relation of Long Axes	1	1	Line Continuity	0	0	Sophistication	1	1	Chest	05	
Horizontal Midline	6	4	Right and Left Halves	1	1	Body Shading	6	3	Height	06	07	Girth	08	

GENERAL CHARACTERISTICS OF SUBJECT

IDENTIFICATION
No. D58
Sex M
Marital status S
Age 24 yrs. at psychological tests

PARENTAL HISTORY				
Father				
C	H	S	D	O
–	–	–	–	?
Mother				
C	H	S	D	O
?	–	–	–	?

PHYSIOLOGICAL AND METABOLIC DATA

	Admission	Initial	Control	Cold pressor change	Exercise change	Smoking change
Systolic pressure	120	120	122	+20	+38	
Diastolic pressure	80	68	70	+30	–12	
Heart rate	82	60	57	+08	+13	

Age 24 yrs.	Height 73 in.	Ponderal index 12.78
	Weight 186 lbs.	Cholesterol 222 mg. per 100 ml.
	Overweight +09 %	Vital capacity 5.5 liters

HABIT SURVEY

Smoking habits: nonsmoker

Age begun   yrs.   Inhalation:

Habits of nervous tension: 5, 6

STRONG VOCATIONAL INTEREST TEST

Occupation	Artist	Psychologist	Architect	Physician	Osteopath	Dentist	Veterinarian	Mathematician	Physicist	Engineer	Chemist	Production Manager
Standard Score	20	46	24	64	55	41	31	28	21	30	38	34

Occupation	Farmer	Aviator	Carpenter	Printer	Math.-Sci. Teacher	Ind. Arts Teacher	Voc. Agric. Teacher	Policeman	Forest Serv. Man	Y.M.C.A. Phys. Dir.	Personnel Director	Public Administrator
Standard Score	36	46	29	43	57	30	33	46	42	66	53	58

Occupation	Y.M.C.A. Secretary	Soc. Sci. H.S. Teacher	City Sch. Sup't.	Social Worker	Minister	Musician Performer	C.P.A.	Senior C.P.A.	Accountant	Office Man	Purchasing Agent	Banker
Standard Score	50	47	45	54	63	48	24	52	29	41	14	18

Occupation	Mortician	Pharmacist	Sales Manager	Real Est. Manager	Life Ins. Salesman	Advertising Man	Lawyer	Author-Journalist	President Mfg. Co.	Interest Maturity	Occupational Level	Masculinity-Femininity
Standard Score	27	28	26	28	30	26	33	24	16	64	48	53

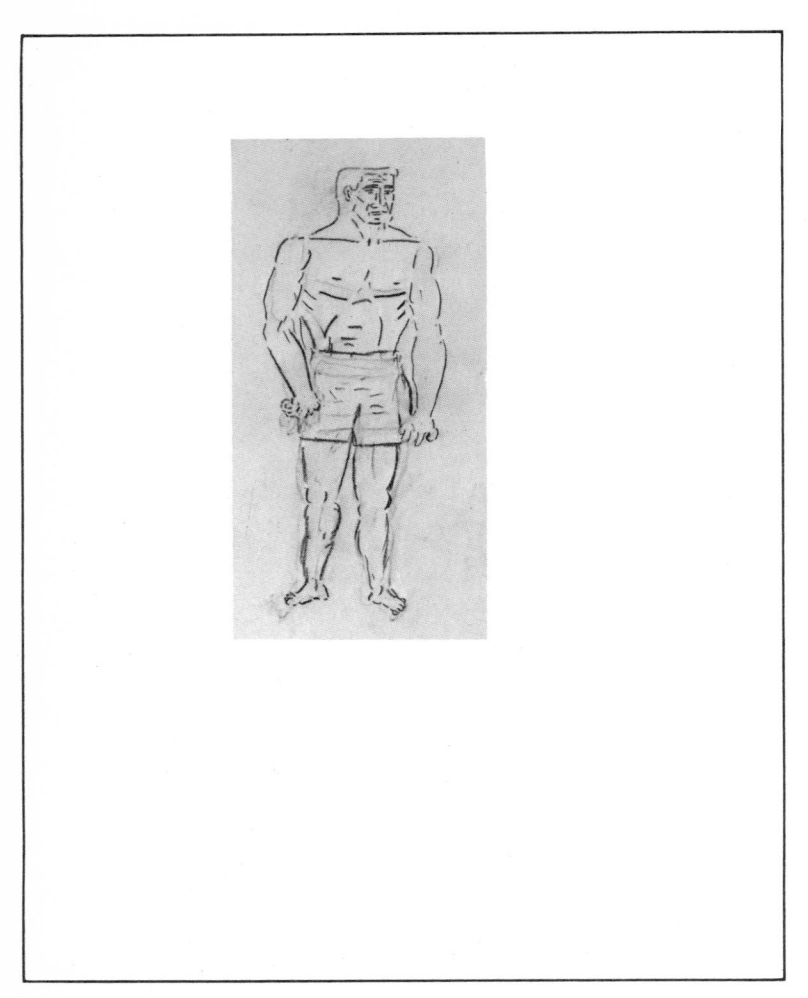

FIGURE-DRAWING CHARACTERISTICS

Structural	Male Female / Both		Structural	Male	Female	Structural and Graphic	Male Female / Both		Graphic, Global and Height	Male	Female	Body Proportions	Male	Female
Type	0		Omission of Appendages	0	0	Upper and Lower Halves	1	1	Hair Shading	5	5	Head	04	03
Sex Sequence	0		Position of Both Arms	1	0	Four Quarters	4	4	Nudity and Transparency	3	0	Neck	03	02
Posture	1	2	Position of Right Arm	5	5	Relative Size	0		Form	1	1	Shoulders	06	04
Perspective	9	1	Position of Left Arm	0	5	Constant Line Pressure	3	0	Detailing	1	1	Right Arm	04	02
Vertical Midline	0	0	Position of Legs	6	8	Variable Line Pressure	0	1	Identity and Sex	1	1	Left Arm	04	02
Bilateral Symmetry	4	0	Relation of Long Axes	1	0	Line Continuity	1	1	Sophistication	1	1	Chest	05	03
Horizontal Midline	4	0	Right and Left Halves	1	1	Body Shading	3	3	Height	04	03	Girth	05	03

GENERAL CHARACTERISTICS OF SUBJECT

IDENTIFICATION
No. B19
Sex M
Marital status M
Age 23 yrs. at
psychological tests

PARENTAL HISTORY				
Father				
C	H	S	D	O
(?)	-	(+)	-	-
Mother				
C	H	S	D	O
-	-	-	-	-

PHYSIOLOGICAL AND METABOLIC DATA

	Admission	Initial	Control	Cold pressor change	Exercise change	Smoking change
Systolic pressure	120	110	103	+12	+45	+11
Diastolic pressure	80	64	64	+12	-12	+11
Heart rate	75	60	64	+09	+14	+10

Age 22 yrs.	Height	72	in.	Ponderal index	13.38	
	Weight	156	lbs.	Cholesterol	186	mg. per 100 ml.
	Overweight	-04	%	Vital capacity	5.3	liters

HABIT SURVEY
Smoking habits: nonsmoker
Age begun   yrs.   Inhalation:
Habits of nervous tension: 1, 3, 4, 5, 7, 8, 10, 18, 22

STRONG VOCATIONAL INTEREST TEST

Occupation	Artist	Psychologist	Architect	Physician	Osteopath	Dentist	Veterinarian	Mathematician	Physicist	Engineer	Chemist	Production Manager
Standard Score	39	49	39	62	53	43	30	29	25	34	41	28

Occupation	Farmer	Aviator	Carpenter	Printer	Math.-Sci. Teacher	Ind. Arts Teacher	Voc. Agric. Teacher	Policeman	Forest Serv. Man	Y.M.C.A. Phys. Dir.	Personnel Director	Public Administrator
Standard Score	27	31	18	40	37	16	26	30	32	48	38	48

Occupation	Y.M.C.A. Secretary	Soc. Sci. H.S. Teacher	City Sch. Sup't.	Social Worker	Minister	Musician Performer	C.P.A.	Senior C.P.A.	Accountant	Office Man	Purchasing Agent	Banker
Standard Score	38	39	36	52	61	53	30	36	18	26	14	18

Occupation	Mortician	Pharmacist	Sales Manager	Real Est. Manager	Life Ins. Salesman	Advertising Man	Lawyer	Author-Journalist	President Mfg. Co.	Interest Maturity	Occupational Level	Masculinity-Femininity
Standard Score	27	35	32	31	38	42	39	41	40	58	57	37

Plate 793   **MOST SOPHISTICATED DRAWINGS**   843

FIGURE-DRAWING CHARACTERISTICS

Structural	Male Female Both	Structural	Male	Female	Structural and Graphic	Male Female Both		Graphic, Global and Height	Male	Female	Body Proportions	Male	Female
Type	0	Omission of Appendages	8	0	Upper and Lower Halves	0	3	Hair Shading	3	2	Head	06	07
Sex Sequence	2	Position of Both Arms	0	0	Four Quarters	4	4	Nudity and Transparency	3	7	Neck	06	08
Posture	3 1	Position of Right Arm	2	0	Relative Size	4		Form	1	1	Shoulders	05	07
Perspective	0 0	Position of Left Arm	2	0	Constant Line Pressure	0	0	Detailing	1	1	Right Arm	05	05
Vertical Midline	0 3	Position of Legs	6	4	Variable Line Pressure	5	5	Identity and Sex	1	1	Left Arm	04	04
Bilateral Symmetry	3 3	Relation of Long Axes	0	1	Line Continuity	0	0	Sophistication	1	1	Chest	04	06
Horizontal Midline	4 0	Right and Left Halves	1	1	Body Shading	3	7	Height		06	Girth	04	07

GENERAL CHARACTERISTICS OF SUBJECT

IDENTIFICATION
No. 538
Sex M
Marital status S
Age 24 yrs. at
psychological tests

PARENTAL HISTORY
Father
C   H   S   D   O
-   +   -   -   -
Mother
C   H   S   D   O
-   -   -   -   -

PHYSIOLOGICAL AND METABOLIC DATA

	Admission	Initial	Control	Cold pressor change	Exercise change	Smoking change
Systolic pressure	130	132	118	+08	+26	+10
Diastolic pressure	80	80	80	+06	-10	+02
Heart rate	80	76	64	+10	+13	+09

Age 22 yrs.

Height   70 in.   Ponderal index 12.84
Weight   162 lbs.   Cholesterol   243   mg. per 100 ml.
Overweight +05 %   Vital capacity 5.0   liters

HABIT SURVEY
Smoking habits: nonsmoker
Age begun   yrs.   Inhalation:
Habits of nervous tension: 4, 6, 9, 11, 22

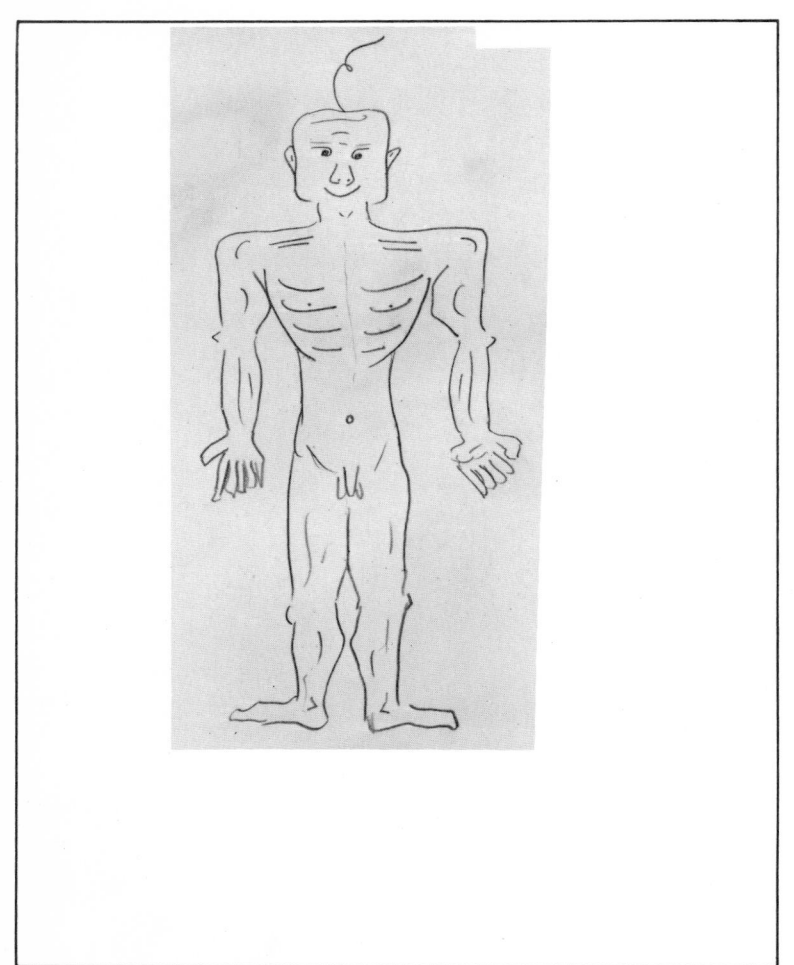
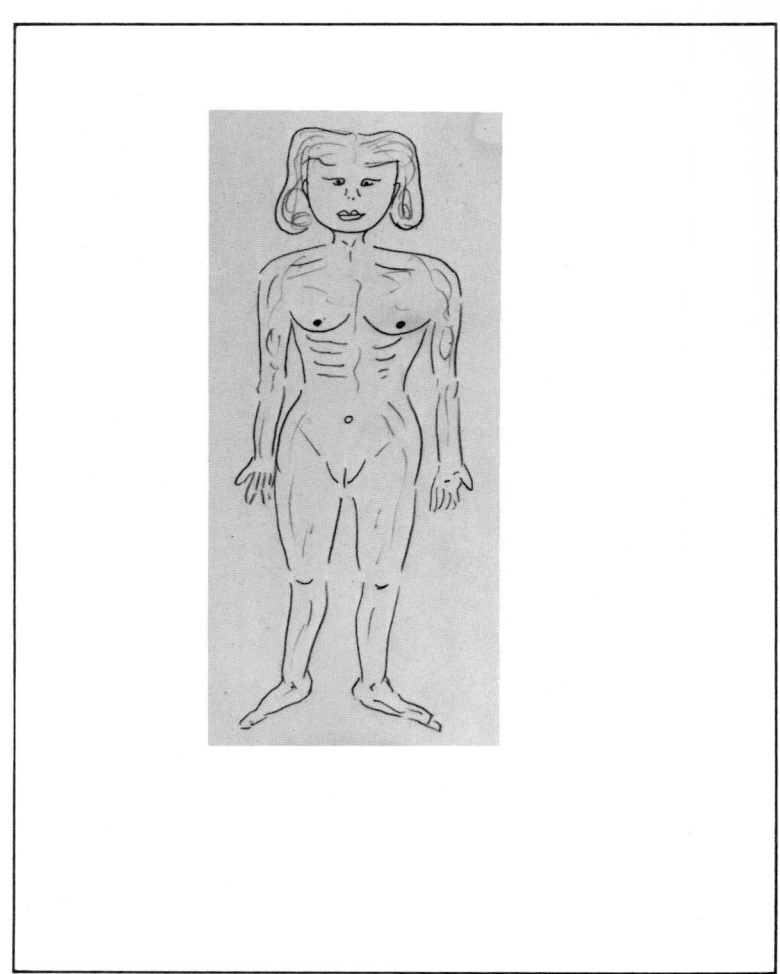

FIGURE-DRAWING CHARACTERISTICS

Structural	Male Female Both	Structural	Male	Female	Structural and Graphic	Male Female Both	Graphic, Global and Height	Male	Female	Body Proportions	Male	Female
Type	0	Omission of Appendages	0	0	Upper and Lower Halves	1　　1	Hair Shading	7	1	Head		08
Sex Sequence	2	Position of Both Arms	0	0	Four Quarters	4　　4	Nudity and Transparency	0	0	Neck		04
Posture	1　　1	Position of Right Arm	0	0	Relative Size	0	Form	3	1	Shoulders	11	08
Perspective	0　　0	Position of Left Arm	0	0	Constant Line Pressure	5　　5	Detailing	1	1	Right Arm	06	05
Vertical Midline	0　　0	Position of Legs	3	4	Variable Line Pressure	0　　0	Identity and Sex	1	1	Left Arm	06	06
Bilateral Symmetry	5　　5	Relation of Long Axes	1	1	Line Continuity	4　　4	Sophistication	1	1	Chest	07	06
Horizontal Midline	0　　0	Right and Left Halves	1	1	Body Shading	3　　3	Height	06	06	Girth	05	07

GENERAL CHARACTERISTICS OF SUBJECT

IDENTIFICATION
No.　F34
Sex　M
Marital status　S
Age　24　yrs. at
psychological tests

PARENTAL HISTORY
Father
C　H　S　D　O
-　+　-　-　-
Mother
C　H　S　D　O
-　-　-　-　-

PHYSIOLOGICAL AND METABOLIC DATA

	Admission	Initial	Control	Cold pressor change	Exercise change	Smoking change
Systolic pressure	138	112	110	+12	+30	+06
Diastolic pressure	78	80	80	+18	+20	+06
Heart rate	94	80	85	+04	+17	+12

Age 22 yrs.	Height	73	in.	Ponderal index	13.70	
	Weight	151	lbs.	Cholesterol	386	mg. per 100 ml.
	Overweight	-10	%	Vital capacity		liters

HABIT SURVEY
Smoking habits: light cigarette smoker
Age begun 16 yrs.　Inhalation: yes
Habits of nervous tension: 1, 5, 8, 9, 10,
16, 17

Plate 795   **MOST SOPHISTICATED DRAWINGS**   845

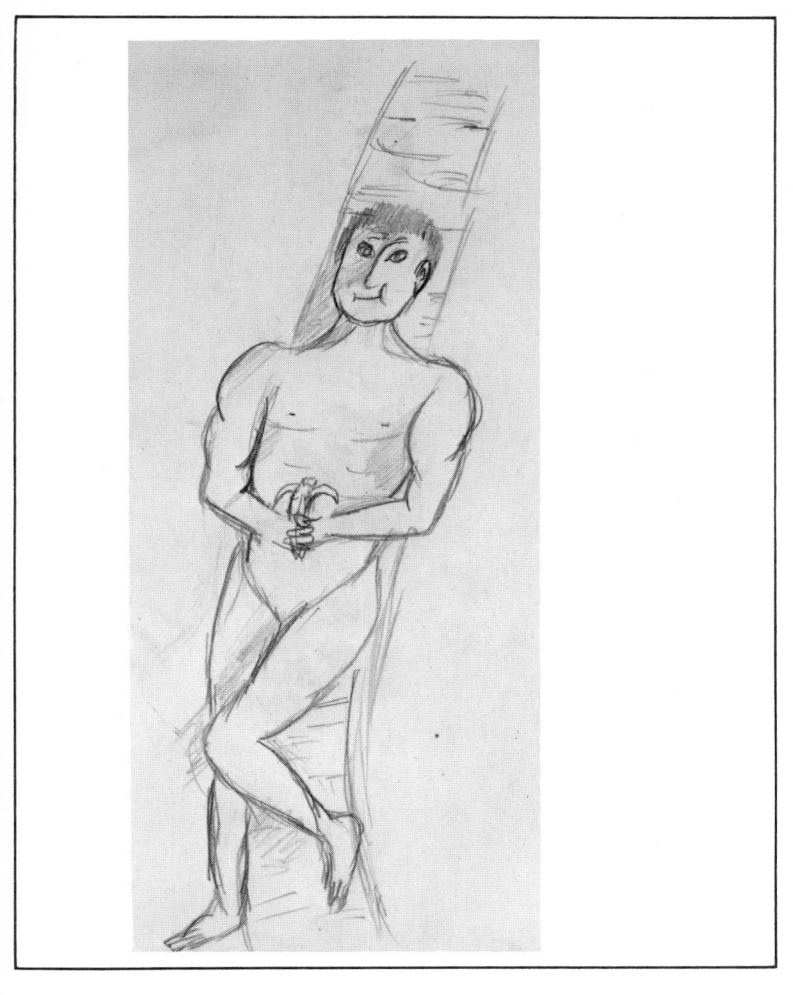

FIGURE-DRAWING CHARACTERISTICS

Structural	Male Female Both	Structural	Male	Female	Structural and Graphic	Male Female Both	Graphic, Global and Height	Male	Female	Body Proportions	Male	Female
Type	0	Omission of Appendages	7	7	Upper and Lower Halves	3 1	Hair Shading	3	3	Head	09	07
Sex Sequence	0	Position of Both Arms	0	0	Four Quarters	4 4	Nudity and Transparency	0	0	Neck	08	08
Posture	4 8	Position of Right Arm	5	5	Relative Size	5	Form	1	1	Shoulders	10	05
Perspective	0 9	Position of Left Arm	5	5	Constant Line Pressure	5 0	Detailing	1	1	Right Arm	06	
Vertical Midline	0 0	Position of Legs	1	2	Variable Line Pressure	0 5	Identity and Sex	1	1	Left Arm	06	
Bilateral Symmetry	3 3	Relation of Long Axes	3	0	Line Continuity	0 2	Sophistication	1	1	Chest	07	06
Horizontal Midline	0 0	Right and Left Halves	1	1	Body Shading	3 3	Height	08		Girth	08	

GENERAL CHARACTERISTICS OF SUBJECT

IDENTIFICATION

No. D29
Sex M
Marital status S
Age 22 yrs. at
psychological tests

PARENTAL HISTORY

Father

C	H	S	D	O
–	+	–	–	+

Mother

C	H	S	D	O
–	–	–	–	

PHYSIOLOGICAL AND METABOLIC DATA

	Admission	Initial	Control	Cold pressor change	Exercise change	Smoking change
Systolic pressure	90	120	120	00	+32	00
Diastolic pressure	60	65	70	+20	-12	+02
Heart rate	68	76	67	+12	+33	-01

Age 22 yrs.
Height 76 in.
Weight 195 lbs.
Overweight +07 %

Ponderal index 13.10
Cholesterol 252 mg. per 100 ml.
Vital capacity 6.2 liters

HABIT SURVEY

Smoking habits: heavy cigarette smoker
Age begun 16 yrs.   Inhalation: yes
Habits of nervous tension: 4, 5, 6, 9, 11, 15, 16, 18, 19, 22, 25

STRONG VOCATIONAL INTEREST TEST

Occupation	Artist	Psychologist	Architect	Physician	Osteopath	Dentist	Veterinarian	Mathematician	Physicist	Engineer	Chemist	Production Manager
Standard Score	41	29	45	46	42	36	08	25	24	35	34	28

Occupation	Farmer	Aviator	Carpenter	Printer	Math.-Sci. Teacher	Ind. Arts Teacher	Voc. Agric. Teacher	Policeman	Forest Serv. Man	Y.M.C.A. Phys. Dir.	Personnel Director	Public Administrator
Standard Score	22	36	11	33	24	13	12	26	12	24	32	31

Occupation	Y.M.C.A. Secretary	Soc. Sci. H.S. Teacher	City Sch. Sup't.	Social Worker	Minister	Musician Performer	C.P.A.	Senior C.P.A.	Accountant	Office Man	Purchasing Agent	Banker
Standard Score	17	19	15	26	63	46	22	22	22	28	32	23

Occupation	Mortician	Pharmacist	Sales Manager	Real Est. Manager	Life Ins. Salesman	Advertising Man	Lawyer	Author-Journalist	President Mfg. Co.	Interest Maturity	Occupational Level	Masculinity-Femininity
Standard Score	33	31	34	36	29	46	38	42	35	50	62	39

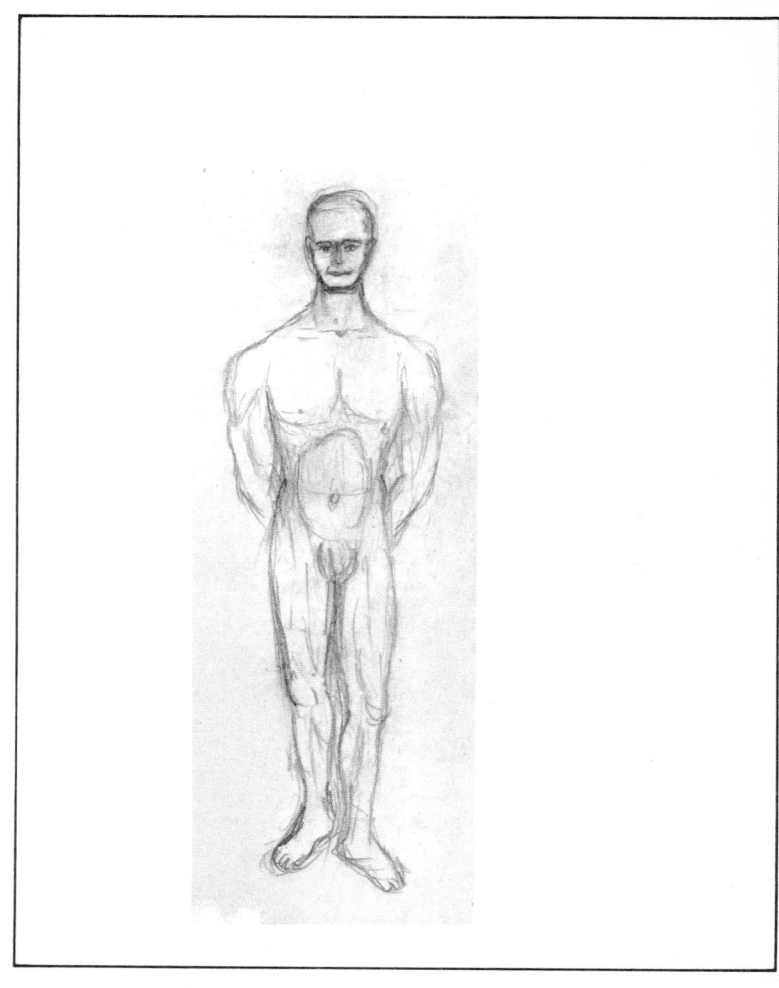

FIGURE-DRAWING CHARACTERISTICS

Structural	Male Female Both		Structural	Male	Female	Structural and Graphic	Male Female Both		Graphic, Global and Height	Male	Female	Body Proportions	Male	Female
Type	0		Omission of Appendages	2	2	Upper and Lower Halves	3	0	Hair Shading	3	3	Head	08	06
Sex Sequence	1		Position of Both Arms	0	1	Four Quarters	4	4	Nudity and Transparency	0	0	Neck	10	07
Posture	1	1	Position of Right Arm	5	3	Relative Size	0		Form	1	1	Shoulders	08	04
Perspective	0	0	Position of Left Arm	5	5	Constant Line Pressure	1	1	Detailing	1	1	Right Arm		06
Vertical Midline	0	0	Position of Legs	2	4	Variable Line Pressure	0	0	Identity and Sex	1	1	Left Arm		
Bilateral Symmetry	5	4	Relation of Long Axes	1	1	Line Continuity	0	0	Sophistication	1	1	Chest	06	04
Horizontal Midline	0	0	Right and Left Halves	1	2	Body Shading	3	3	Height	07	05	Girth	06	03

GENERAL CHARACTERISTICS OF SUBJECT

IDENTIFICATION

No. D67
Sex M
Marital status S
Age 22 yrs. at
psychological tests

PARENTAL HISTORY

Father

C	H	S	D	O
-	+	-	-	-

Mother

C	H	S	D	O
-	-	-	-	?

PHYSIOLOGICAL AND METABOLIC DATA

	Admission	Initial	Control	Cold pressor change	Exercise change	Smoking change
Systolic pressure	130	128	120	+10	+08	+08
Diastolic pressure	80	70	72	+08	-16	+12
Heart rate	85	56	55	00	+26	+32

Age 22 yrs.

Height 73 in. Ponderal index 12.97
Weight 178 lbs. Cholesterol 274 mg. per 100 ml.
Overweight +06 % Vital capacity 5.7 liters

HABIT SURVEY

Smoking habits: light cigarette smoker
Age begun 21 yrs.　Inhalation: yes
Habits of nervous tension: 1, 2, 4, 5, 6, 8,
9, 10, 12, 16, 21, 22, 25

STRONG VOCATIONAL INTEREST TEST

Occupation	Artist	Psychologist	Architect	Physician	Osteopath	Dentist	Veterinarian	Mathematician	Physicist	Engineer	Chemist	Production Manager
Standard Score	34	58	40	63	60	48	20	28	31	44	48	33

Occupation	Farmer	Aviator	Carpenter	Printer	Math.-Sci. Teacher	Ind. Arts Teacher	Voc. Agric. Teacher	Policeman	Forest Serv. Man	Y.M.C.A. Phys. Dir.	Personnel Director	Public Administrator
Standard Score	28	43	18	39	42	23	21	32	32	45	51	54

Occupation	Y.M.C.A. Secretary	Soc. Sci. H.S. Teacher	City Sch. Sup't.	Social Worker	Minister	Musician Performer	C.P.A.	Senior C.P.A.	Accountant	Office Man	Purchasing Agent	Banker
Standard Score	37	36	40	55	63	56	30	35	17	22	14	10

Occupation	Mortician	Pharmacist	Sales Manager	Real Est. Manager	Life Ins. Salesman	Advertising Man	Lawyer	Author- Journalist	President Mfg. Co.	Interest Maturity	Occupational Level	Masculinity- Femininity
Standard Score	22	29	25	28	31	38	45	38	26	61	58	44

FIGURE-DRAWING CHARACTERISTICS

Structural	Male Female Both	Structural	Male	Female	Structural and Graphic	Male Female Both		Graphic, Global and Height	Male	Female	Body Proportions	Male	Female
Type	0	Omission of Appendages	7	0	Upper and Lower Halves	1	0	Hair Shading	1	5	Head	07	06
Sex Sequence	0	Position of Both Arms	1	1	Four Quarters	4	4	Nudity and Transparency	7	7	Neck	06	06
Posture	4	3	Position of Right Arm	0	2	Relative Size	0		Form	1	1	Shoulders	07	
Perspective	0	1	Position of Left Arm	5	9	Constant Line Pressure	5	0	Detailing	1	1	Right Arm	06	06
Vertical Midline	3	4	Position of Legs	2	7	Variable Line Pressure	0	5	Identity and Sex	1	1	Left Arm		06
Bilateral Symmetry	3	0	Relation of Long Axes	1	0	Line Continuity	0	0	Sophistication	1	1	Chest	07	
Horizontal Midline	6	4	Right and Left Halves	1	1	Body Shading	7	7	Height	06		Girth	07	

GENERAL CHARACTERISTICS OF SUBJECT

IDENTIFICATION

No. 234

Sex M

Marital status M

Age 24 yrs. at psychological tests

PARENTAL HISTORY

Father

C   H   S   D   O

\-   \-   \-   \-   \-

Mother

C   H   S   D   O

\-   +   \-   \-   \-

PHYSIOLOGICAL AND METABOLIC DATA

	Admission	Initial	Control	Cold pressor change	Exercise change	Smoking change
Systolic pressure	136	134	114	+12	+32	
Diastolic pressure	68	62	64	+04	-02	
Heart rate	88	84	79	00	+39	

Age 22 yrs.

Height 68 in.   Ponderal index 12.94

Weight 145 lbs.   Cholesterol 245 mg. per 100 ml.

Overweight -01 %   Vital capacity 4.3 liters

HABIT SURVEY

Smoking habits: light cigarette smoker

Age begun 15 yrs.   Inhalation: yes

Habits of nervous tension: 4, 5, 6, 10, 18, 20, 22

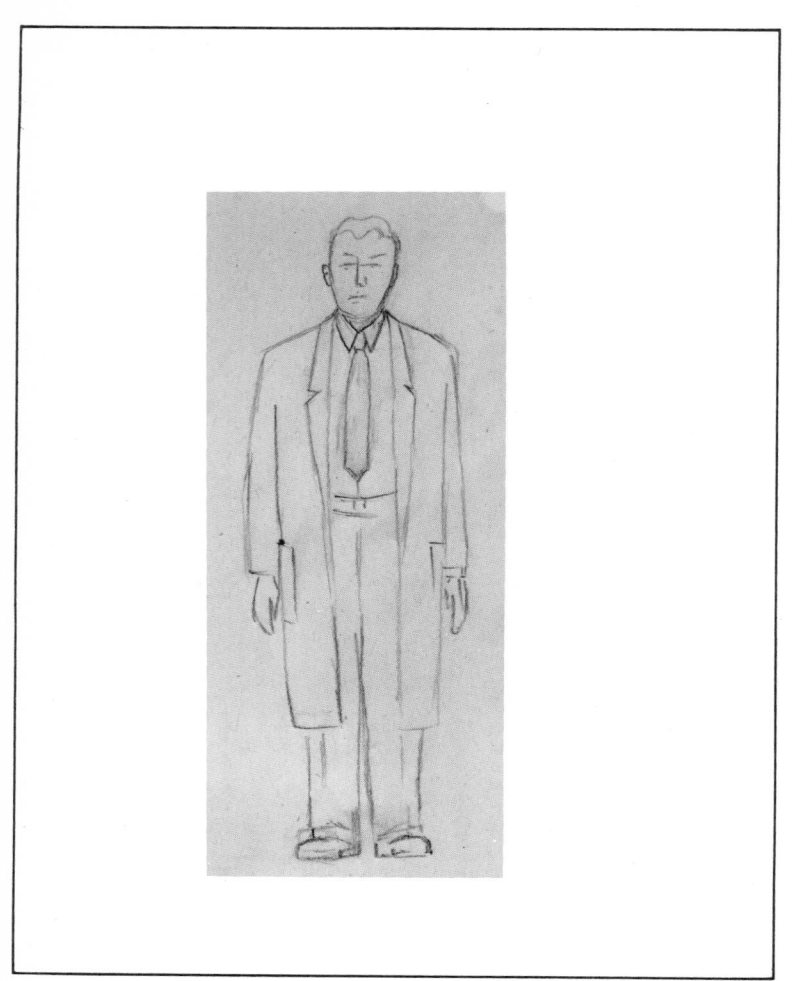

FIGURE-DRAWING CHARACTERISTICS

Structural	Male Female Both	Structural	Male	Female	Structural and Graphic	Male Female Both		Graphic, Global and Height	Male	Female	Body Proportions	Male	Female
Type	0	Omission of Appendages	0	0	Upper and Lower Halves	3	0	Hair Shading	5	1	Head	07	08
Sex Sequence	0	Position of Both Arms	0	0	Four Quarters	4	4	Nudity and Transparency	7	7	Neck	04	08
Posture	1 3	Position of Right Arm	0	5	Relative Size	0		Form	1	1	Shoulders	07	
Perspective	0 1	Position of Left Arm	0	5	Constant Line Pressure	0	0	Detailing	1	1	Right Arm	06	06
Vertical Midline	3 4	Position of Legs	4	7	Variable Line Pressure	1	5	Identity and Sex	1	1	Left Arm	06	06
Bilateral Symmetry	4 0	Relation of Long Axes	1	0	Line Continuity	1	4	Sophistication	1	1	Chest	08	
Horizontal Midline	4 0	Right and Left Halves	1	3	Body Shading	2	3	Height	06		Girth	11	

GENERAL CHARACTERISTICS OF SUBJECT

IDENTIFICATION
No. 722
Sex M
Marital status M
Age 23 yrs. at
psychological tests

PARENTAL HISTORY				
Father				
C	H	S	D	O
-	-	?	-	?
Mother				
C	H	S	D	O
-	+	-	-	-

PHYSIOLOGICAL AND METABOLIC DATA

	Admission	Initial	Control	Cold pressor change	Exercise change	Smoking change
Systolic pressure	132	105	96	+02	+14	+04
Diastolic pressure	76	48	56	+28	+04	+01
Heart rate	80	60	56	+12	+19	+08

Age 23 yrs.	Height	71 in.	Ponderal index	12.72	
	Weight	174 lbs.	Cholesterol	217	mg. per 100 ml.
	Overweight	+09 %	Vital capacity	4.6	liters

FIGURE-DRAWING CHARACTERISTICS

Structural	Male Female Both	Structural	Male	Female	Structural and Graphic	Male Female Both		Graphic, Global and Height	Male	Female	Body Proportions	Male	Female
Type	0	Omission of Appendages	0	0	Upper and Lower Halves	2	1	Hair Shading	1	1	Head	04	06
Sex Sequence	0	Position of Both Arms	4	4	Four Quarters	4	4	Nudity and Transparency	6	7	Neck	03	04
Posture	2 1	Position of Right Arm	7	7	Relative Size	4		Form	1	1	Shoulders		
Perspective	2 2	Position of Left Arm	4	4	Constant Line Pressure	0	5	Detailing	1	1	Right Arm		
Vertical Midline	7 4	Position of Legs	8	1	Variable Line Pressure	3	0	Identity and Sex	1	5	Left Arm	04	04
Bilateral Symmetry	0 0	Relation of Long Axes	1	1	Line Continuity	2	4	Sophistication	1	1	Chest	03	03
Horizontal Midline	4 0	Right and Left Halves	3	1	Body Shading	7	7	Height	03	04	Girth	04	05

GENERAL CHARACTERISTICS OF SUBJECT

IDENTIFICATION
No. F47
Sex M
Marital status S
Age 23 yrs. at psychological tests

PARENTAL HISTORY				
Father				
C	H	S	D	O
–	–	–	–	+
Mother				
C	H	S	D	O
–	+	–	–	–

PHYSIOLOGICAL AND METABOLIC DATA

	Admission	Initial	Control	Cold pressor change	Exercise change	Smoking change
Systolic pressure	120	138	112	+22	+44	+14
Diastolic pressure	70	92	80	+18	+12	+16
Heart rate	84	84	76	+16	+24	+05

Age 21 yrs.	Height 75 in.	Ponderal index 13.71
	Weight 164 lbs.	Cholesterol 188 mg. per 100 ml.
	Overweight –07 %	Vital capacity liters

HABIT SURVEY

Smoking habits: nonsmoker

Age begun   yrs.   Inhalation:

Habits of nervous tension: 5, 11, 12, 16, 25

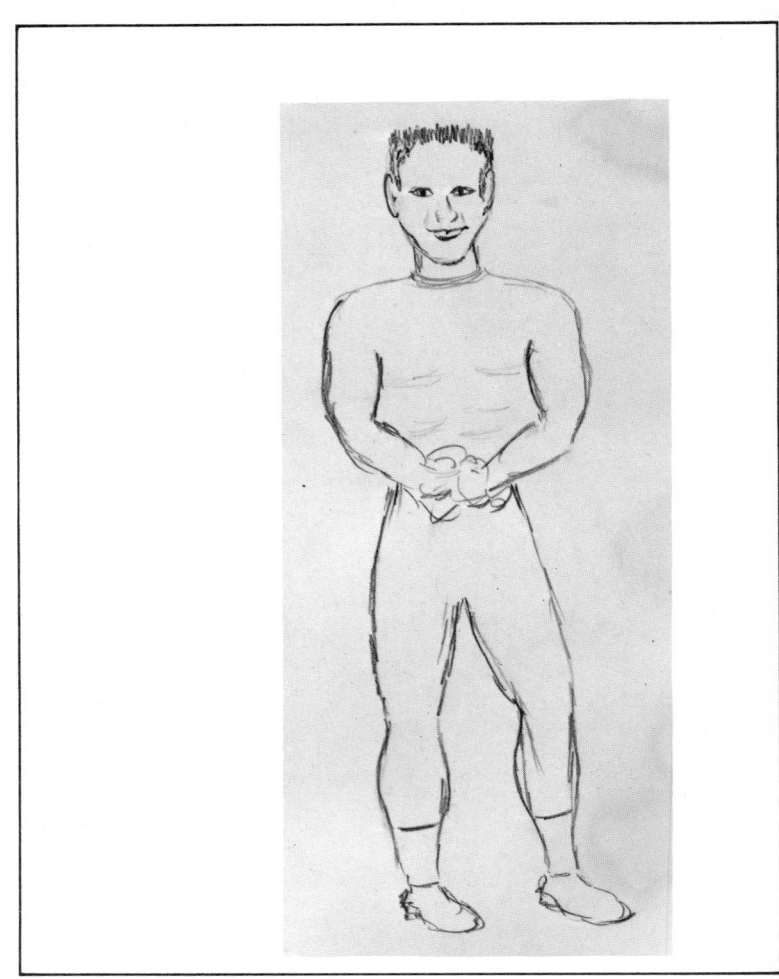

FIGURE-DRAWING CHARACTERISTICS

Structural	Male Female Both		Structural	Male	Female	Structural and Graphic	Male Female Both		Graphic, Global and Height	Male	Female	Body Proportions	Male	Female
Type	0		Omission of Appendages	7	7	Upper and Lower Halves	3	3	Hair Shading	3	3	Head	11	11
Sex Sequence	1		Position of Both Arms	0	0	Four Quarters	4	4	Nudity and Transparency	2	7	Neck	06	05
Posture	1	1	Position of Right Arm	5	5	Relative Size	3		Form	1	1	Shoulders	10	
Perspective	0	1	Position of Left Arm	5	5	Constant Line Pressure	0	0	Detailing	1	1	Right Arm	07	04
Vertical Midline	0	4	Position of Legs	6	3	Variable Line Pressure	4	4	Identity and Sex	1	1	Left Arm	07	05
Bilateral Symmetry	4	0	Relation of Long Axes	1	1	Line Continuity	0	0	Sophistication	1	1	Chest	07	
Horizontal Midline	0	0	Right and Left Halves	3	1	Body Shading	5	1	Height	08	08	Girth	07	

GENERAL CHARACTERISTICS OF SUBJECT

IDENTIFICATION
No. C13
Sex M
Marital status S
Age 22 yrs. at
psychological tests

PARENTAL HISTORY
Father
C H S D O
– – – – –
Mother
C H S D O
– + – – ?

PHYSIOLOGICAL AND METABOLIC DATA

	Admission	Initial	Control	Cold pressor change	Exercise change	Smoking change
Systolic pressure	120	124	106	+12	+36	+07
Diastolic pressure	72	64	66	+08	+02	+02
Heart rate	68	60	79	+20	+04	+12

Age 22 yrs.	Height 75 in.	Ponderal index 13.23
	Weight 182 lbs.	Cholesterol 193 mg. per 100 ml.
	Overweight +02 %	Vital capacity 5.6 liters

HABIT SURVEY

Smoking habits: nonsmoker

  Age begun   yrs.   Inhalation:

Habits of nervous tension: 9, 16

STRONG VOCATIONAL INTEREST TEST

Occupation	Artist	Psychologist	Architect	Physician	Osteopath	Dentist	Veterinarian	Mathematician	Physicist	Engineer	Chemist	Production Manager
Standard Score	22	38	34	58	52	41	39	28	29	45	43	42

Occupation	Farmer	Aviator	Carpenter	Printer	Math.-Sci. Teacher	Ind. Arts Teacher	Voc. Agric. Teacher	Policeman	Forest Serv. Man	Y.M.C.A. Phys. Dir.	Personnel Director	Public Administrator
Standard Score	49	55	45	40	59	53	55	46	48	51	43	45

Occupation	Y.M.C.A. Secretary	Soc. Sci. H.S. Teacher	City Sch. Sup't.	Social Worker	Minister	Musician Performer	C.P.A.	Senior C.P.A.	Accountant	Office Man	Purchasing Agent	Banker
Standard Score	34	35	32	35	62	41	22	48	29	35	20	14

Occupation	Mortician	Pharmacist	Sales Manager	Real Est. Manager	Life Ins. Salesman	Advertising Man	Lawyer	Author-Journalist	President Mfg. Co.	Interest Maturity	Occupational Level	Masculinity-Femininity
Standard Score	25	31	17	24	19	18	18	21	17	59	48	57

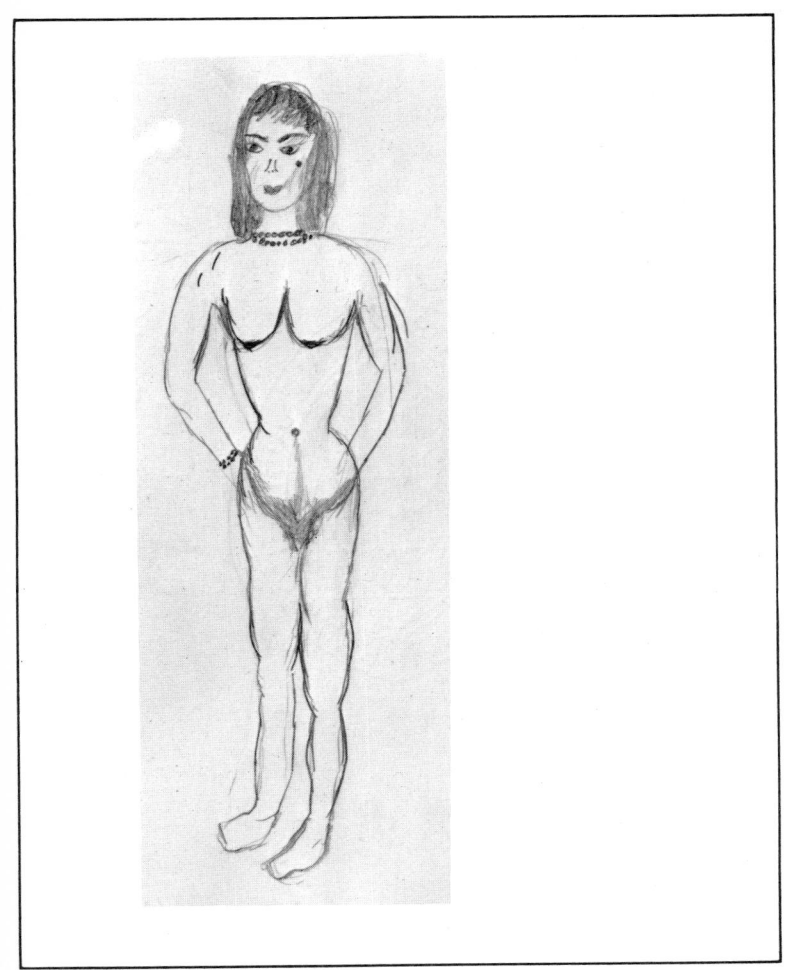
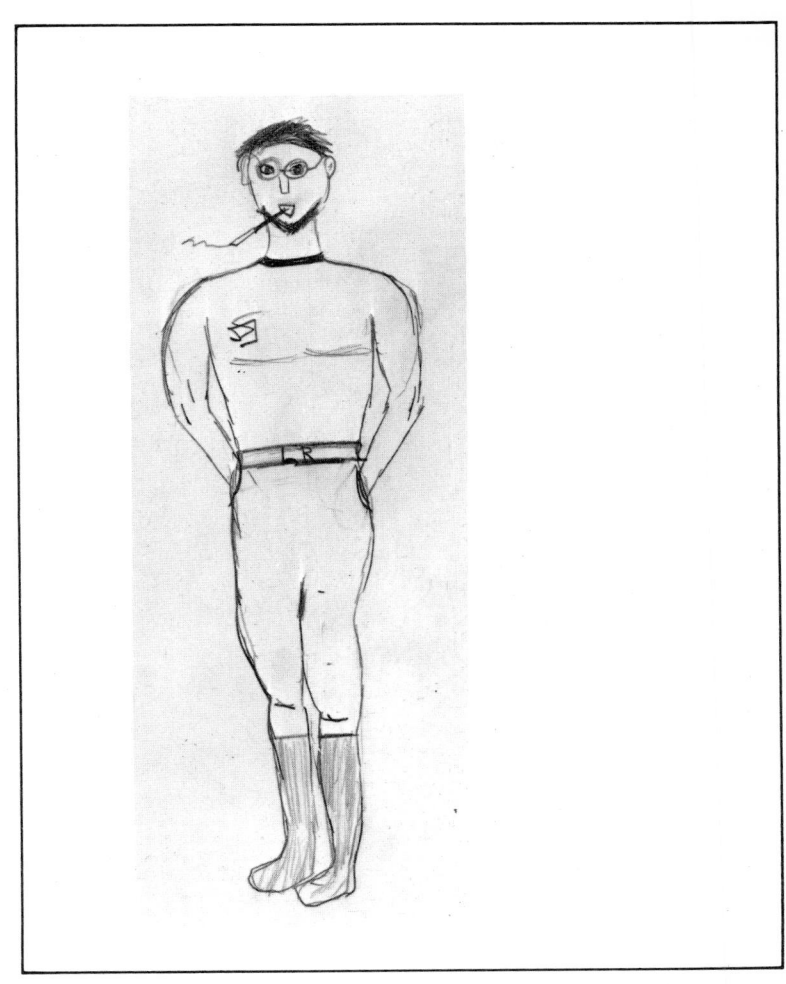

FIGURE-DRAWING CHARACTERISTICS

Structural	Male Female Both	Structural	Male	Female	Structural and Graphic	Male Female Both		Graphic, Global and Height	Male	Female	Body Proportions	Male	Female
Type	0	Omission of Appendages	7	7	Upper and Lower Halves	3	0	Hair Shading	3	3	Head	09	09
Sex Sequence	1	Position of Both Arms	0	0	Four Quarters	4	4	Nudity and Transparency	2	0	Neck	12	08
Posture	1 1	Position of Right Arm	5	5	Relative Size	2		Form	1	1	Shoulders	09	07
Perspective	0 0	Position of Left Arm	5	5	Constant Line Pressure	0	0	Detailing	1	1	Right Arm	06	06
Vertical Midline	0 0	Position of Legs	4	4	Variable Line Pressure	5	4	Identity and Sex	1	1	Left Arm		07
Bilateral Symmetry	3 3	Relation of Long Axes	1	1	Line Continuity	0	0	Sophistication	1	1	Chest	07	06
Horizontal Midline	4 0	Right and Left Halves	1	2	Body Shading	7	7	Height	08	08	Girth	07	04

GENERAL CHARACTERISTICS OF SUBJECT

IDENTIFICATION

No. C20

Sex M

Marital status S

Age 20 yrs. at psychological tests

PARENTAL HISTORY

Father

C H S D O

– – + – ?

Mother

C H S D O

– + – + +

PHYSIOLOGICAL AND METABOLIC DATA

	Admission	Initial	Control	Cold pressor change	Exercise change	Smoking change
Systolic pressure	125	105	105	+23	+33	–04
Diastolic pressure	75	70	70	+28	–12	–07
Heart rate	76	72	68	+12	+29	–01

Age 21 yrs.

Height 68 in.   Ponderal index 12.83

Weight 149 lbs.   Cholesterol 244 mg. per 100 ml.

Overweight +03 %   Vital capacity 3.6 liters

HABIT SURVEY

Smoking habits: nonsmoker

Age begun   yrs.   Inhalation:

Habits of nervous tension: 1, 2, 3, 4, 5, 6, 7, 8, 9, 10, 11, 16, 20, 22, 23

STRONG VOCATIONAL INTEREST TEST

Occupation	Artist	Psychologist	Architect	Physician	Osteopath	Dentist	Veterinarian	Mathematician	Physicist	Engineer	Chemist	Production Manager
Standard Score	48	62	38	56	46	32	06	40	32	26	40	17

Occupation	Farmer	Aviator	Carpenter	Printer	Math.-Sci. Teacher	Ind. Arts Teacher	Voc. Agric. Teacher	Policeman	Forest Serv. Man	Y.M.C.A. Phys. Dir.	Personnel Director	Public Administrator
Standard Score	07	12	–09	20	21	–10	–05	12	–07	30	36	48

Occupation	Y.M.C.A. Secretary	Soc. Sci. H.S. Teacher	City Sch. Sup't.	Social Worker	Minister	Musician Performer	C.P.A.	Senior C.P.A.	Accountant	Office Man	Purchasing Agent	Banker
Standard Score	27	32	37	55	62	56	55	24	15	14	08	14

Occupation	Mortician	Pharmacist	Sales Manager	Real Est. Manager	Life Ins. Salesman	Advertising Man	Lawyer	Author-Journalist	President Mfg. Co.	Interest Maturity	Occupational Level	Masculinity-Femininity
Standard Score	18	31	28	36	42	48	63	59	36	54	67	20

FIGURE-DRAWING CHARACTERISTICS

Structural	Male Female Both		Structural	Male	Female	Structural and Graphic Both	Male	Female	Graphic, Global and Height	Male	Female	Body Proportions	Male	Female
Type	0		Omission of Appendages	7	7	Upper and Lower Halves	0	3	Hair Shading	1	1	Head	06	06
Sex Sequence	0		Position of Both Arms	1	0	Four Quarters	4	4	Nudity and Transparency	7	7	Neck	03	06
Posture	1	1	Position of Right Arm	0	5	Relative Size	4		Form	1	1	Shoulders	06	05
Perspective	0	0	Position of Left Arm	5	5	Constant Line Pressure	1	1	Detailing	1	1	Right Arm	04	04
Vertical Midline	3	3	Position of Legs	3	4	Variable Line Pressure	0	0	Identity and Sex	1	1	Left Arm	04	
Bilateral Symmetry	3	3	Relation of Long Axes	1	1	Line Continuity	0	0	Sophistication	1	1	Chest	05	04
Horizontal Midline	6	4	Right and Left Halves	1	2	Body Shading	5	7	Height	05	05	Girth	07	04

GENERAL CHARACTERISTICS OF SUBJECT

IDENTIFICATION
No. C51
Sex F
Marital status S
Age 22 yrs. at
psychological tests

PARENTAL HISTORY
Father
C H S D O
- - - - +
Mother
C H S D O
- + - - +

PHYSIOLOGICAL AND METABOLIC DATA

	Admission	Initial	Control	Cold pressor change	Exercise change	Smoking change
Systolic pressure	130	122	108	+14	+40	+01
Diastolic pressure	80	64	60	+20	+10	+02
Heart rate	80	88	94	+16	+21	+11

Age 22 yrs.	Height 67 in.	Ponderal index 13.32
	Weight 127 lbs.	Cholesterol 209 mg. per 100 ml.
	Overweight -07 %	Vital capacity 3.5 liters

HABIT SURVEY

Smoking habits: nonsmoker

Age begun   yrs.   Inhalation:

Habits of nervous tension: 5, 6, 9, 10, 16, 22

STRONG VOCATIONAL INTEREST TEST

Occupation	Artist	Psychologist	Architect	Physician	Osteopath	Dentist	Veterinarian	Mathematician	Physicist	Engineer	Chemist	Production Manager
Standard Score	38	49	40	62	50	40	25	33	26	29	36	22

Occupation	Farmer	Aviator	Carpenter	Printer	Math.-Sci. Teacher	Ind. Arts Teacher	Voc. Agric. Teacher	Policeman	Forest Serv. Man	Y.M.C.A. Phys. Dir.	Personnel Director	Public Administrator
Standard Score	22	21	11	31	37	08	18	27	26	43	41	43

Occupation	Y.M.C.A. Secretary	Soc. Sci. H.S. Teacher	City Sch. Sup't.	Social Worker	Minister	Musician Performer	C.P.A.	Senior C.P.A.	Accountant	Office Man	Purchasing Agent	Banker
Standard Score	34	35	44	48	62	54	41	34	22	29	10	17

Occupation	Mortician	Pharmacist	Sales Manager	Real Est. Manager	Life Ins. Salesman	Advertising Man	Lawyer	Author-Journalist	President Mfg. Co.	Interest Maturity	Occupational Level	Masculinity-Femininity
Standard Score	30	42	26	30	40	36	41	39	31	58	62	25

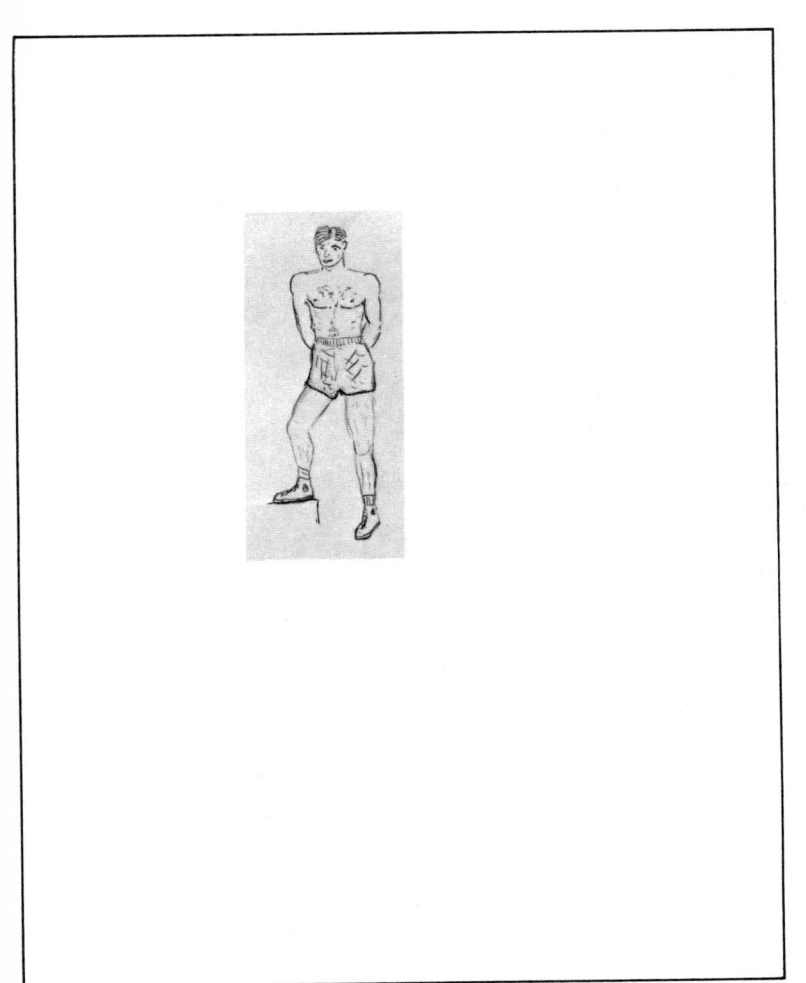

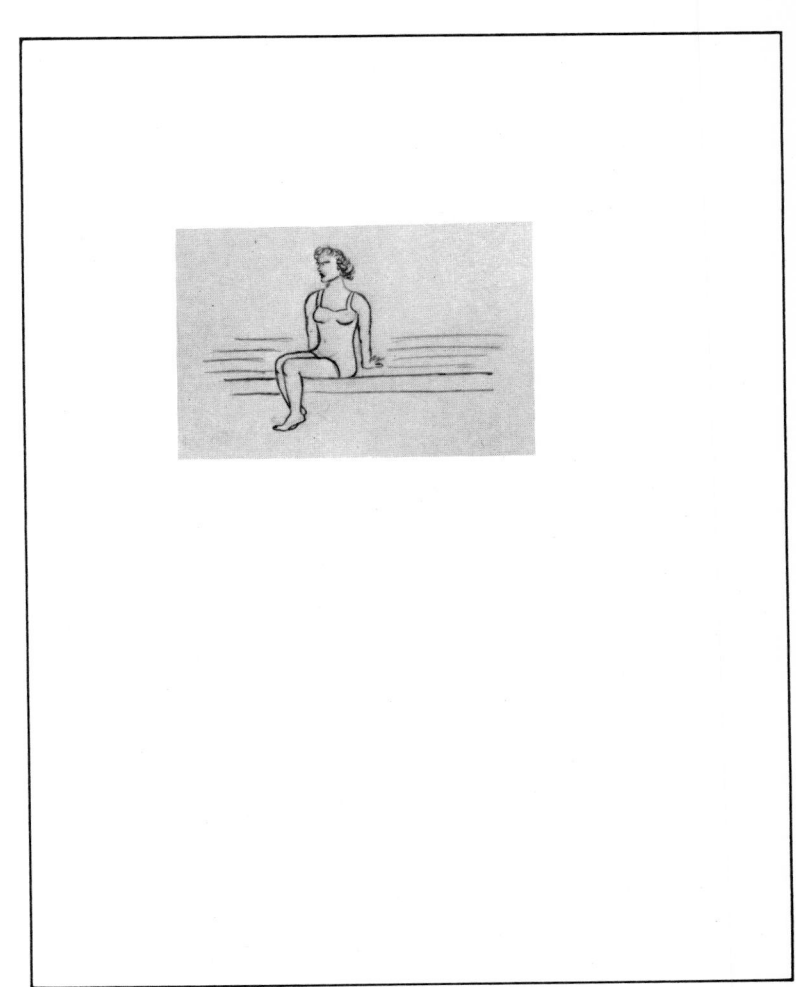

FIGURE-DRAWING CHARACTERISTICS

Structural	Male Female Both	Structural	Male	Female	Structural and Graphic	Male Female Both		Graphic, Global and Height	Male	Female	Body Proportions	Male	Female
Type	0	Omission of Appendages	2	0	Upper and Lower Halves	1	2	Hair Shading	2	3	Head	03	02
Sex Sequence	0	Position of Both Arms	6	4	Four Quarters	4	0	Nudity and Transparency	3	2	Neck	01	02
Posture	1 3	Position of Right Arm	8	7	Relative Size	0		Form	1	1	Shoulders	03	
Perspective	0 1	Position of Left Arm	8	0	Constant Line Pressure	0	5	Detailing	1	1	Right Arm		
Vertical Midline	1 4	Position of Legs	6	2	Variable Line Pressure	3	0	Identity and Sex	1	1	Left Arm		02
Bilateral Symmetry	3 0	Relation of Long Axes	1	0	Line Continuity	0	1	Sophistication	1	1	Chest	02	
Horizontal Midline	4 0	Right and Left Halves	2	2	Body Shading	7	1	Height	03		Girth	03	

GENERAL CHARACTERISTICS OF SUBJECT

IDENTIFICATION
No. 650
Sex M
Marital status M
Age 24 yrs. at
psychological tests

PARENTAL HISTORY
Father
C H S D 0
– – – – +
Mother
C H S D 0
– + – – +

PHYSIOLOGICAL AND METABOLIC DATA

	Admission	Initial	Control	Cold pressor change	Exercise change	Smoking change
Systolic pressure	110	122	106	+28	+24	+06
Diastolic pressure	70	64	64	+16	-06	+04
Heart rate	68	52	48		+13	+10

Age 21 yrs.	Height 80 in.	Ponderal index 13.14
	Weight 226 lbs.	Cholesterol 167 mg. per 100 ml.
	Overweight +12 %	Vital capacity 6.4 liters

HABIT SURVEY
Smoking habits: pipe smoker
Age begun 21 yrs.   Inhalation: no
Habits of nervous tension: 4, 5, 9

FIGURE-DRAWING CHARACTERISTICS

Structural	Male Female Both		Structural	Male	Female	Structural and Graphic	Male Female Both		Graphic, Global and Height	Male	Female	Body Proportions	Male	Female
Type	0		Omission of Appendages	0	7	Upper and Lower Halves	3	1	Hair Shading	0	1	Head	07	
Sex Sequence	1		Position of Both Arms	4	0	Four Quarters	4	4	Nudity and Transparency	7	7	Neck	06	
Posture	1	1	Position of Right Arm	7	5	Relative Size	0		Form	1	1	Shoulders		07
Perspective	2	3	Position of Left Arm	5	5	Constant Line Pressure	5	4	Detailing	1	1	Right Arm		
Vertical Midline	4	8	Position of Legs	5	2	Variable Line Pressure	0	0	Identity and Sex	1	1	Left Arm	06	
Bilateral Symmetry	0	5	Relation of Long Axes	1	1	Line Continuity	4	0	Sophistication	1	1	Chest		06
Horizontal Midline	4	4	Right and Left Halves	2	2	Body Shading	1	4	Height	08	06	Girth		03

GENERAL CHARACTERISTICS OF SUBJECT

IDENTIFICATION
No. 248
Sex M
Marital status S
Age 23 yrs. at
psychological tests

PARENTAL HISTORY				
Father				
C	H	S	D	O
-	?	-	-	+
Mother				
C	H	S	D	O
-	-	-	-	-

PHYSIOLOGICAL AND METABOLIC DATA

	Admission	Initial	Control	Cold pressor change	Exercise change	Smoking change
Systolic pressure	106					
Diastolic pressure	62					
Heart rate	64					

Age 20 yrs.

Height 76 in.   Ponderal index 13.61
Weight 174 lbs.   Cholesterol 183 mg. per 100 ml.
Overweight −04 %   Vital capacity liters

HABIT SURVEY
Smoking habits: unknown
Age begun yrs. Inhalation:
Habits of nervous tension:

Plate 805　　　　　　　　　　MOST SOPHISTICATED DRAWINGS　　　　　　　　　　855

FIGURE-DRAWING CHARACTERISTICS

Structural	Male Female Both	Structural	Male	Female	Structural and Graphic	Male Female Both		Graphic, Global and Height	Male	Female	Body Proportions	Male	Female
Type	0	Omission of Appendages	6	7	Upper and Lower Halves	7	3	Hair Shading	3	3	Head	11	09
Sex Sequence	0	Position of Both Arms	0	0	Four Quarters	4	4	Nudity and Transparency	3	0	Neck	12	08
Posture	1　1	Position of Right Arm	5	5	Relative Size	2		Form	1	1	Shoulders		
Perspective	1　1	Position of Left Arm	5	5	Constant Line Pressure	3	3	Detailing	1	1	Right Arm		06
Vertical Midline	4　4	Position of Legs	6	1	Variable Line Pressure	0	0	Identity and Sex	1	1	Left Arm	07	
Bilateral Symmetry	0　0	Relation of Long Axes	1	1	Line Continuity	0	0	Sophistication	1	1	Chest		
Horizontal Midline	4　0	Right and Left Halves	1	2	Body Shading	3	3	Height		08	Girth		

GENERAL CHARACTERISTICS OF SUBJECT

IDENTIFICATION
No. D17
Sex M
Marital status S
Age 22 yrs. at
psychological tests

PARENTAL HISTORY				
Father				
C	H	S	D	O
-	-	-	?	-
Mother				
C	H	S	D	O
-	?	-	-	+

PHYSIOLOGICAL AND METABOLIC DATA

	Admission	Initial	Control	Cold pressor change	Exercise change	Smoking change
Systolic pressure	134	140	132	+05	+28	+06
Diastolic pressure	80	80	80	+10	-10	+02
Heart rate	74	88	68	+08	+32	+08

Age 22 yrs.	Height	75 in.	Ponderal index 13.49
	Weight	172 lbs.	Cholesterol 248 mg. per 100 ml.
	Overweight -03 %		Vital capacity 5.1 liters

HABIT SURVEY

Smoking habits: former smoker

Age begun 7 yrs.　　Inhalation: no

Habits of nervous tension: 4, 5, 9, 14

STRONG VOCATIONAL INTEREST TEST

Occupation	Artist	Psychologist	Architect	Physician	Osteopath	Dentist	Veterinarian	Mathematician	Physicist	Engineer	Chemist	Production Manager
Standard Score	49	54	45	60	39	40	27	47	38	33	50	18

Occupation	Farmer	Aviator	Carpenter	Printer	Math.-Sci. Teacher	Ind. Arts Teacher	Voc. Agric. Teacher	Policeman	Forest Serv. Man	Y.M.C.A. Phys. Dir.	Personnel Director	Public Administrator
Standard Score	35	39	23	51	39	22	30	26	23	26	24	39

Occupation	Y.M.C.A. Secretary	Soc. Sci. H.S. Teacher	City Sch. Sup't.	Social Worker	Minister	Musician Performer	C.P.A.	Senior C.P.A.	Accountant	Office Man	Purchasing Agent	Banker
Standard Score	14	32	24	37	63	59	33	36	16	24	18	22

Occupation	Mortician	Pharmacist	Sales Manager	Real Est. Manager	Life Ins. Salesman	Advertising Man	Lawyer	Author-Journalist	President Mfg. Co.	Interest Maturity	Occupational Level	Masculinity-Femininity
Standard Score	25	42	23	30	19	42	38	47	26	44	50	40

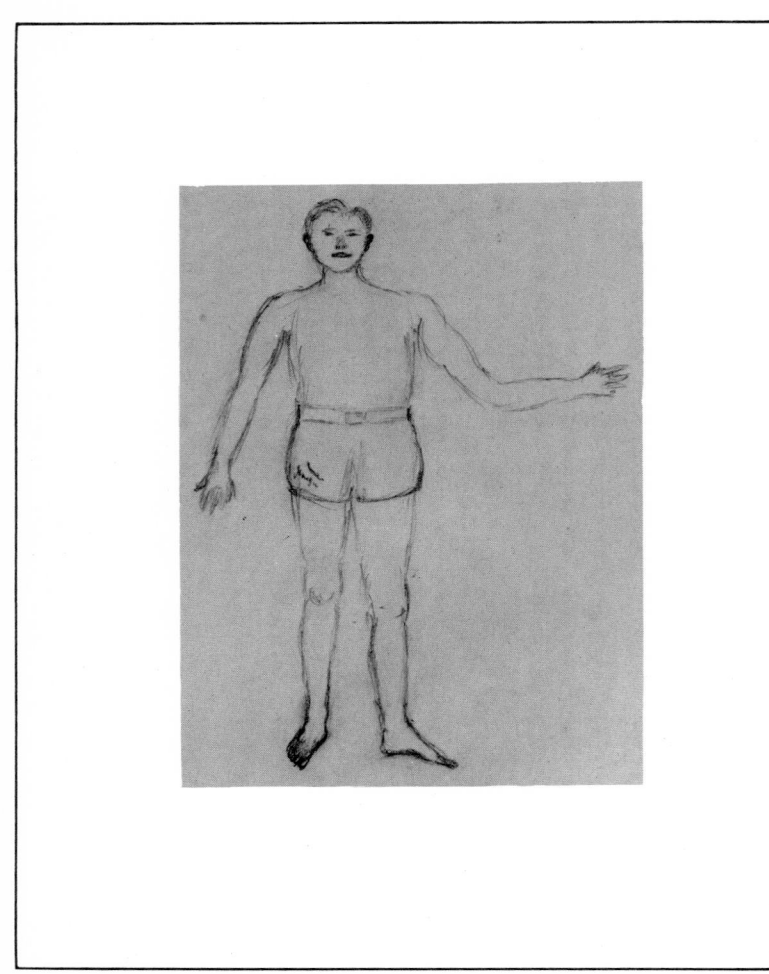

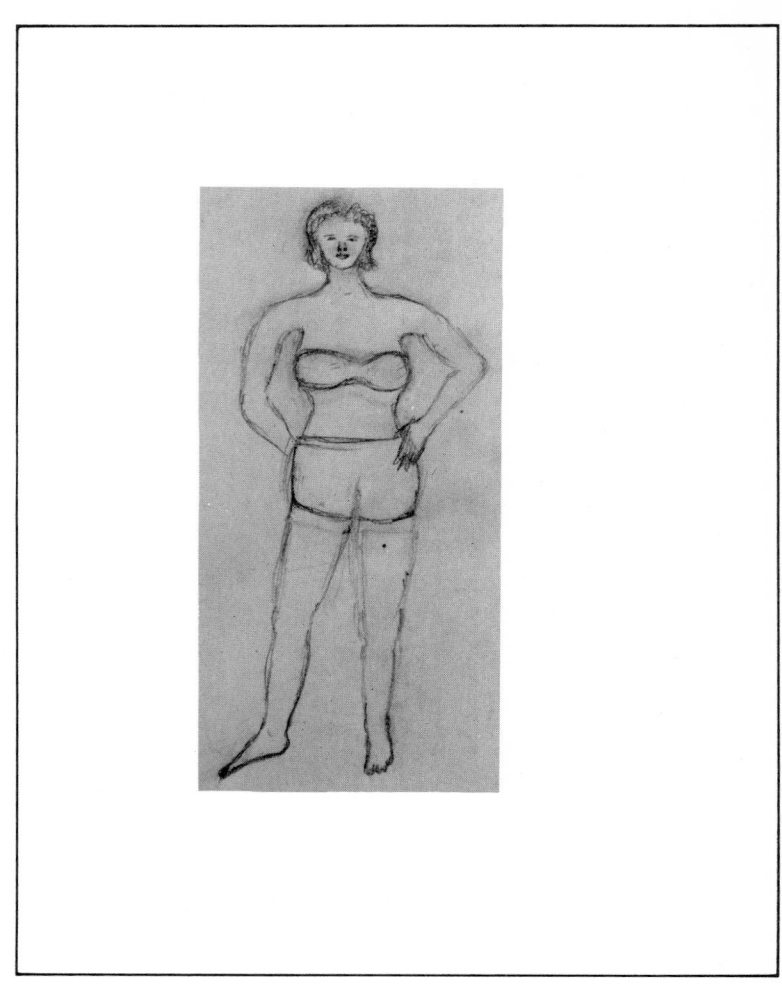

FIGURE-DRAWING CHARACTERISTICS

Structural	Male / Female Both	Structural	Male	Female	Structural and Graphic	Male / Female Both		Graphic, Global and Height	Male	Female	Body Proportions	Male	Female
Type	0	Omission of Appendages	0	7	Upper and Lower Halves	0	0	Hair Shading	3	3	Head	05	05
Sex Sequence	0	Position of Both Arms	0	0	Four Quarters	4	4	Nudity and Transparency	3	2	Neck	04	08
Posture	1 1	Position of Right Arm	2	5	Relative Size	2		Form	1	1	Shoulders	07	07
Perspective	0 0	Position of Left Arm	2	5	Constant Line Pressure	0	0	Detailing	1	1	Right Arm	04	
Vertical Midline	0 0	Position of Legs	4	4	Variable Line Pressure	3	3	Identity and Sex	1	1	Left Arm	06	06
Bilateral Symmetry	3 3	Relation of Long Axes	1	1	Line Continuity	0	0	Sophistication	1	1	Chest	06	05
Horizontal Midline	4 4	Right and Left Halves	1	1	Body Shading	3	3	Height	06	06	Girth	07	06

GENERAL CHARACTERISTICS OF SUBJECT

IDENTIFICATION
No. 229
Sex M
Marital status M
Age 29 yrs. at
psychological tests

PARENTAL HISTORY
Father
C   H   S   D   O
-   (?)   -   -   -
Mother
C   H   S   D   O
-   -   -   -

PHYSIOLOGICAL AND METABOLIC DATA

	Admission	Initial	Control	Cold pressor change	Exercise change	Smoking change
Systolic pressure	120	118	114	+04	+14	
Diastolic pressure	72	74	76	+04	-12	
Heart rate	52	62	52	00	+10	

Age 27 yrs.

Height 71 in.   Ponderal index 13.42
Weight 148 lbs.   Cholesterol 208 mg. per 100 ml.
Overweight -09 %   Vital capacity 5.0 liters

HABIT SURVEY
Smoking habits: nonsmoker
Age begun   yrs.   Inhalation:
Habits of nervous tension: 5, 6, 10, 19

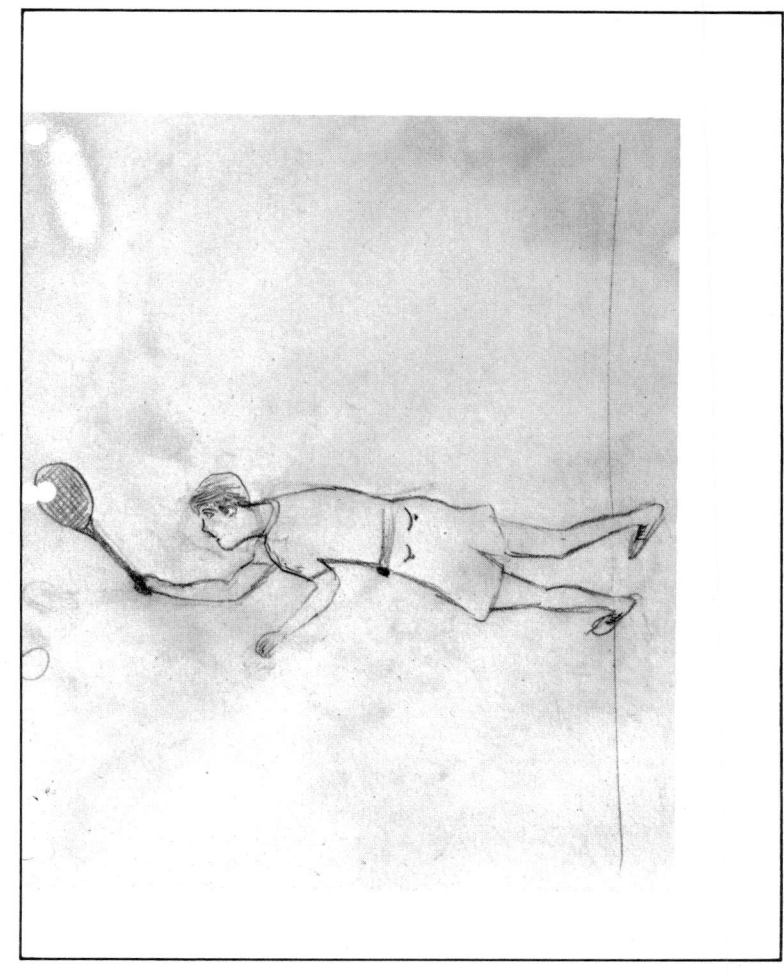

FIGURE-DRAWING CHARACTERISTICS

Structural	Male	Female	Structural	Male	Female	Structural and Graphic	Male	Female	Graphic, Global and Height	Male	Female	Body Proportions	Male	Female
	Both						Both							
Type	0		Omission of Appendages	0	0	Upper and Lower Halves	0	1	Hair Shading	2	2	Head	06	05
Sex Sequence	1		Position of Both Arms	0	4	Four Quarters	4	4	Nudity and Transparency	2	7	Neck	04	02
Posture	6	2	Position of Right Arm	6	7	Relative Size	0		Form	1	1	Shoulders		
Perspective	8	2	Position of Left Arm	6	0	Constant Line Pressure	0	0	Detailing	1	1	Right Arm		
Vertical Midline	4	7	Position of Legs	8	8	Variable Line Pressure	1	3	Identity and Sex	1	1	Left Arm	03	02
Bilateral Symmetry	0	0	Relation of Long Axes	2	2	Line Continuity	0	1	Sophistication	1	1	Chest		04
Horizontal Midline	4	4	Right and Left Halves	2	2	Body Shading	4	4	Height	04	04	Girth		04

GENERAL CHARACTERISTICS OF SUBJECT

IDENTIFICATION
No. 530
Sex M
Marital status S
Age 26 yrs. at
psychological tests

PARENTAL HISTORY				
Father				
C	H	S	D	O
-	-	-	-	+
Mother				
C	H	S	D	O
-	(?)	-	-	-

PHYSIOLOGICAL AND METABOLIC DATA

	Admission	Initial	Control	Cold pressor change	Exercise change	Smoking change
Systolic pressure	120	120	104	+04	+16	-04
Diastolic pressure	70	64	66	+06	-10	+04
Heart rate	72	64	55	00	+13	+09

Age 25 yrs.	Height	74 in.	Ponderal index 12.74
	Weight	196 lbs.	Cholesterol 243 mg. per 100 ml.
	Overweight +09 %		Vital capacity 5.9 liters

HABIT SURVEY
Smoking habits: heavy cigarette smoker
Age begun 17 yrs.   Inhalation: yes
Habits of nervous tension: 4, 5, 6, 8, 11,
16, 25

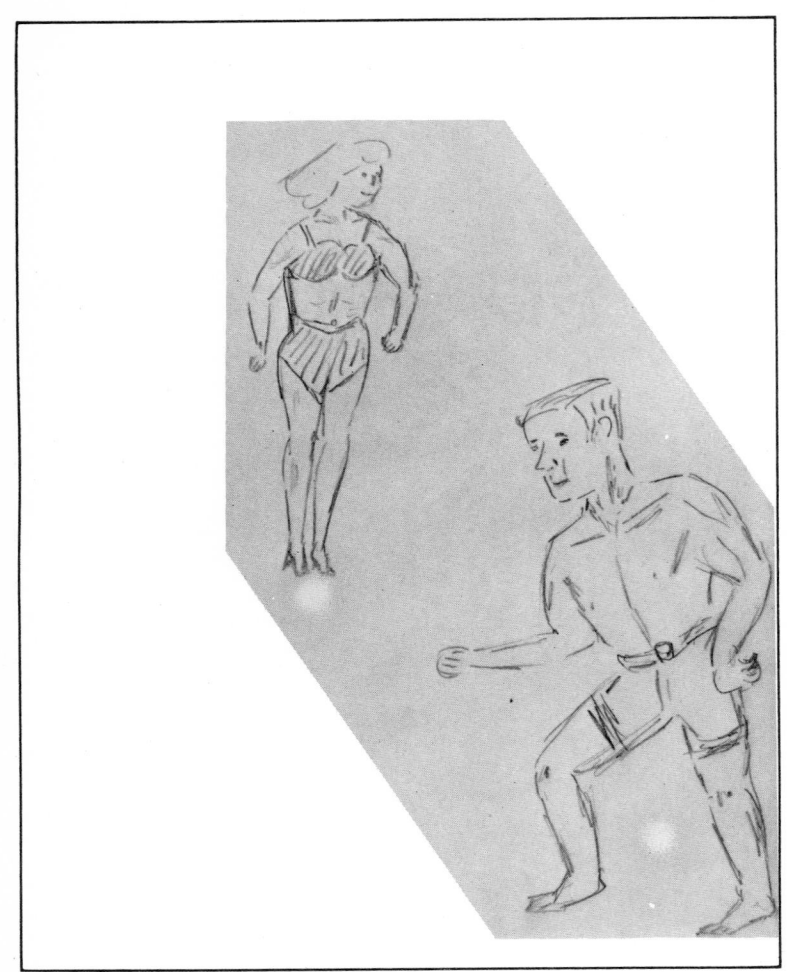

FIGURE-DRAWING CHARACTERISTICS

Structural	Male / Female Both	Structural	Male	Female	Structural and Graphic	Male	Female (Both)	Graphic, Global and Height	Male	Female	Body Proportions	Male	Female
Type	0	Omission of Appendages	0	0	Upper and Lower Halves	9	9	Hair Shading	1	5	Head	09	04
Sex Sequence	2	Position of Both Arms	1	0	Four Quarters	4	4	Nudity and Transparency	3	2	Neck	06	03
Posture	6 / 1	Position of Right Arm	4	5	Relative Size	0		Form	1	1	Shoulders		05
Perspective	1 / 9	Position of Left Arm	5	5	Constant Line Pressure	3	3	Detailing	1	1	Right Arm	06	04
Vertical Midline	7 / 0	Position of Legs	8	4	Variable Line Pressure	0	0	Identity and Sex	1	1	Left Arm	06	02
Bilateral Symmetry	0 / 3	Relation of Long Axes	0	1	Line Continuity	0	0	Sophistication	1	1	Chest		05
Horizontal Midline	4 / 4	Right and Left Halves	9	9	Body Shading	7	3	Height	06	04	Girth		05

GENERAL CHARACTERISTICS OF SUBJECT

IDENTIFICATION
No. 643
Sex M
Marital status S
Age 25 yrs. at
psychological tests

PARENTAL HISTORY
Father
C H S D O
- - - + -
Mother
C H S D O
- - - - -

PHYSIOLOGICAL AND METABOLIC DATA

	Admission	Initial	Control	Cold pressor change	Exercise change	Smoking change
Systolic pressure	110	114	110	+18	+24	
Diastolic pressure	80	62	68	+10	-04	
Heart rate	80	70	70	+18	+21	

Age 22 yrs.	Height	73 in.	Ponderal index 13.93	
	Weight	144 lbs.	Cholesterol 217	mg. per 100 ml.
	Overweight -14 %		Vital capacity	liters

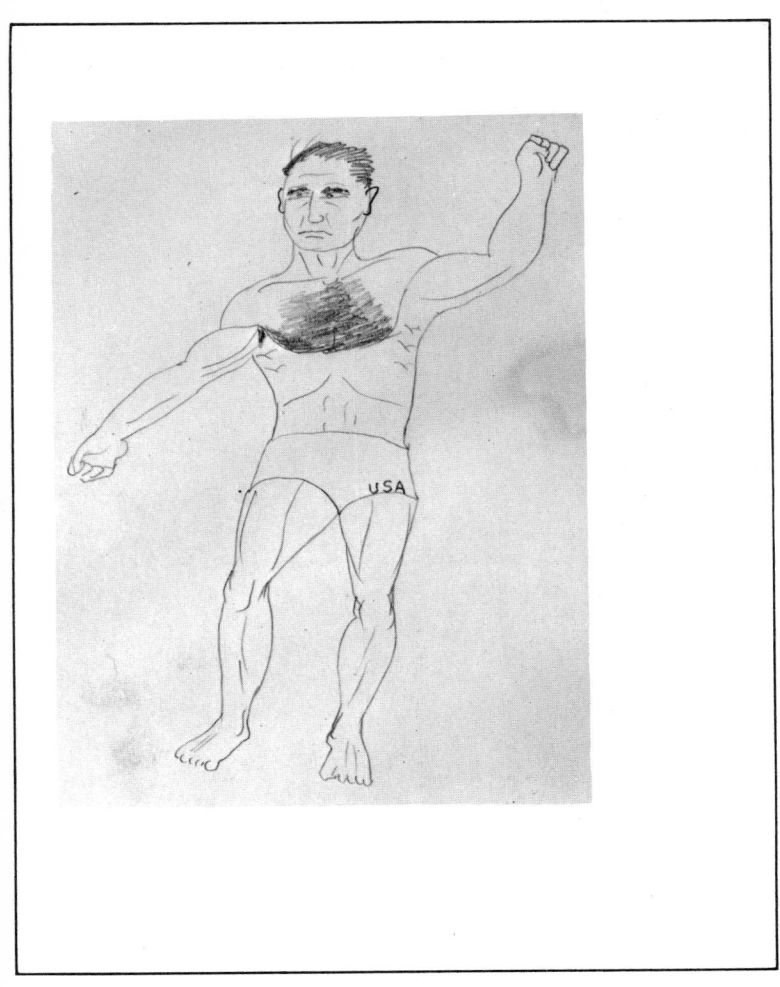

FIGURE-DRAWING CHARACTERISTICS

Structural	Male Female Both	Structural	Male	Female	Structural and Graphic	Male Female Both		Graphic, Global and Height	Male	Female	Body Proportions	Male	Female
Type	0	Omission of Appendages	0	7	Upper and Lower Halves	1	1	Hair Shading	3	5	Head	09	08
Sex Sequence	0	Position of Both Arms	0	1	Four Quarters	4	4	Nudity and Transparency	3	0	Neck	07	05
Posture	1	8	Position of Right Arm	6	2	Relative Size	5		Form	1	1	Shoulders	08	
Perspective	0	1	Position of Left Arm	6	7	Constant Line Pressure	3	3	Detailing	1	1	Right Arm	06	06
Vertical Midline	0	4	Position of Legs	6	1	Variable Line Pressure	0	0	Identity and Sex	1	1	Left Arm		
Bilateral Symmetry	3	0	Relation of Long Axes	1	0	Line Continuity	2	2	Sophistication	1	1	Chest	07	
Horizontal Midline	4	0	Right and Left Halves	1	1	Body Shading	3	3	Height	06		Girth	09	

GENERAL CHARACTERISTICS OF SUBJECT

IDENTIFICATION

No. G56

Sex M

Marital status S

Age 29 yrs. at

psychological tests

PARENTAL HISTORY

Father

C H S D O

– – – – –

Mother

C H S D O

– – – + –

PHYSIOLOGICAL AND METABOLIC DATA

	Admission	Initial	Control	Cold pressor change	Exercise change	Smoking change
Systolic pressure	110	130	130	+02	+44	+16
Diastolic pressure	80	82	84	+08	+04	+06
Heart rate	80	112	83	–16	+47	+06

Age 28 yrs.

Height 70 in.

Weight 133 lbs.

Overweight –16 %

Ponderal index 13.73

Cholesterol 190 mg. per 100 ml.

Vital capacity liters

HABIT SURVEY

Smoking habits: pipe smoker

Age begun 23 yrs.   Inhalation: no

Habits of nervous tension: 3, 4, 5, 18, 23, 24

STRONG VOCATIONAL INTEREST TEST

Occupation	Artist	Psychologist	Architect	Physician	Osteopath	Dentist	Veterinarian	Mathematician	Physicist	Engineer	Chemist	Production Manager
Standard Score	45	38	38	40	18	34	08	56	45	33	36	10

Occupation	Farmer	Aviator	Carpenter	Printer	Math.-Sci. Teacher	Ind. Arts Teacher	Voc. Agric. Teacher	Policeman	Forest Serv. Man	Y.M.C.A. Phys. Dir.	Personnel Director	Public Administrator
Standard Score	31	17	09	23	27	03	20	09	09	02	06	24

Occupation	Y.M.C.A. Secretary	Soc. Sci. H.S. Teacher	City Sch. Sup't.	Social Worker	Minister	Musician Performer	C.P.A.	Senior C.P.A.	Accountant	Office Man	Purchasing Agent	Banker
Standard Score	10	20	26	15	59	32	45	28	21	16	19	33

Occupation	Mortician	Pharmacist	Sales Manager	Real Est. Manager	Life Ins. Salesman	Advertising Man	Lawyer	Author-Journalist	President Mfg. Co.	Interest Maturity	Occupational Level	Masculinity-Femininity
Standard Score	09	19	16	25	18	31	44	47	34	42	66	40

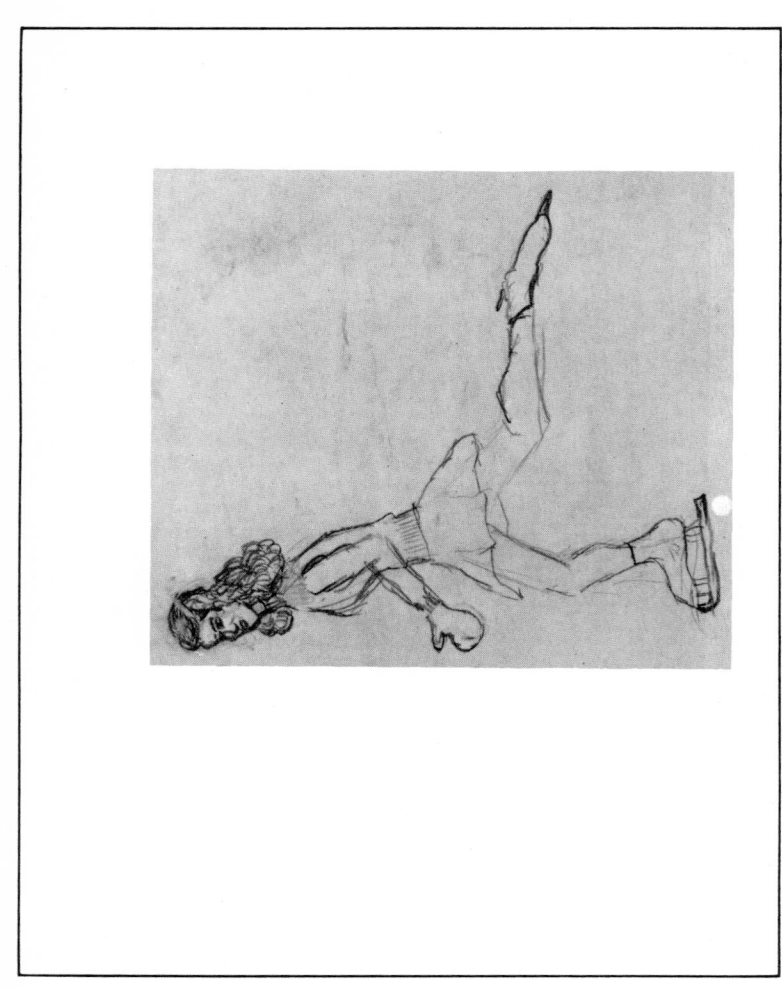

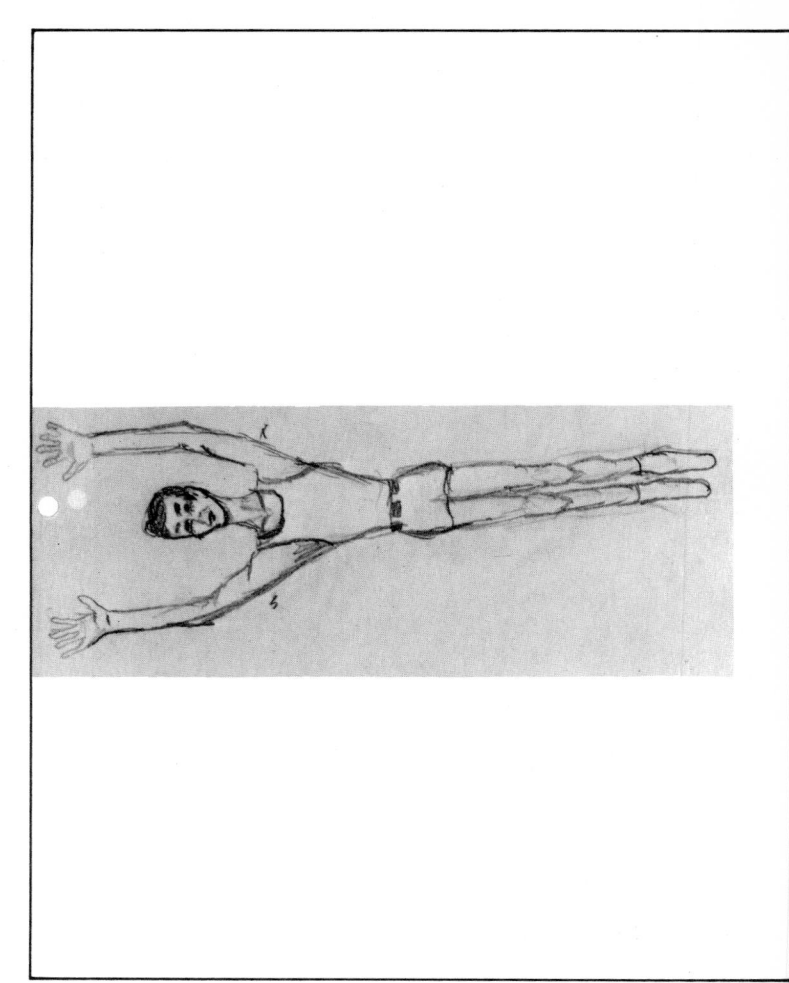

FIGURE-DRAWING CHARACTERISTICS

Structural	Male Female Both	Structural	Male	Female	Structural and Graphic	Male Female Both		Graphic, Global and Height	Male	Female	Body Proportions	Male	Female
Type	0	Omission of Appendages	0	0	Upper and Lower Halves	0	3	Hair Shading	2	2	Head	06	06
Sex Sequence	1	Position of Both Arms	0	4	Four Quarters	4	4	Nudity and Transparency	2	5	Neck	10	08
Posture	6 6	Position of Right Arm	6	7	Relative Size	5		Form	1	1	Shoulders	04	
Perspective	0 9	Position of Left Arm	6	4	Constant Line Pressure	0	0	Detailing	1	1	Right Arm	06	
Vertical Midline	0 4	Position of Legs	8	8	Variable Line Pressure	4	2	Identity and Sex	1	1	Left Arm	05	04
Bilateral Symmetry	3 0	Relation of Long Axes	2	2	Line Continuity	0	0	Sophistication	1	1	Chest	03	05
Horizontal Midline	4 4	Right and Left Halves	0	1	Body Shading	7	7	Height	05		Girth	03	05

GENERAL CHARACTERISTICS OF SUBJECT

IDENTIFICATION
No. A75
Sex F
Marital status S
Age 21 yrs. at
psychological tests

PARENTAL HISTORY				
Father				
C	H	S	D	O
-	-	-	?	?
Mother				
C	H	S	D	O
-	-	-	-	-

PHYSIOLOGICAL AND METABOLIC DATA

	Admission	Initial	Control	Cold pressor change	Exercise change	Smoking change
Systolic pressure	95	93	104	+20	+16	
Diastolic pressure	60	43	49	+24	-29	
Heart rate	82	64	59	+14	+29	

Age 20 yrs.	Height	68 in.	Ponderal index 12.64		
	Weight	156 lbs.	Cholesterol	237	mg. per 100 ml.
	Overweight +11 %		Vital capacity		liters

HABIT SURVEY

Smoking habits: nonsmoker

Age begun   yrs.   Inhalation:

Habits of nervous tension: 2, 5, 8, 9, 10, 18, 20, 22, 23, 24

STRONG VOCATIONAL INTEREST TEST

Occupation	Artist	Psychologist	Architect	Physician	Osteopath	Dentist	Veterinarian	Mathematician	Physicist	Engineer	Chemist	Production Manager
Standard Score	7	7	7	6	5	4	2	5	7	4	5	2

Occupation	Farmer	Aviator	Carpenter	Printer	Math.-Sci. Teacher	Ind. Arts Teacher	Voc. Agric. Teacher	Policeman	Forest Serv. Man	Y.M.C.A. Phys. Dir.	Personnel Director	Public Administrator
Standard Score	4	4	2	6	5	1	2	2	1	3	2	3

Occupation	Y.M.C.A. Secretary	Soc. Sci. H.S. Teacher	City Sch. Sup't.	Social Worker	Minister	Musician Performer	C.P.A.	Senior C.P.A.	Accountant	Office Man	Purchasing Agent	Banker
Standard Score	2	2	3	6	3	7	4	4	2	3	1	1

Occupation	Mortician	Pharmacist	Sales Manager	Real Est. Manager	Life Ins. Salesman	Advertising Man	Lawyer	Author-Journalist	President Mfg. Co.	Interest Maturity	Occupational Level	Masculinity-Femininity
Standard Score	2	3	2	4	4	6	5	7	4	3	5	2

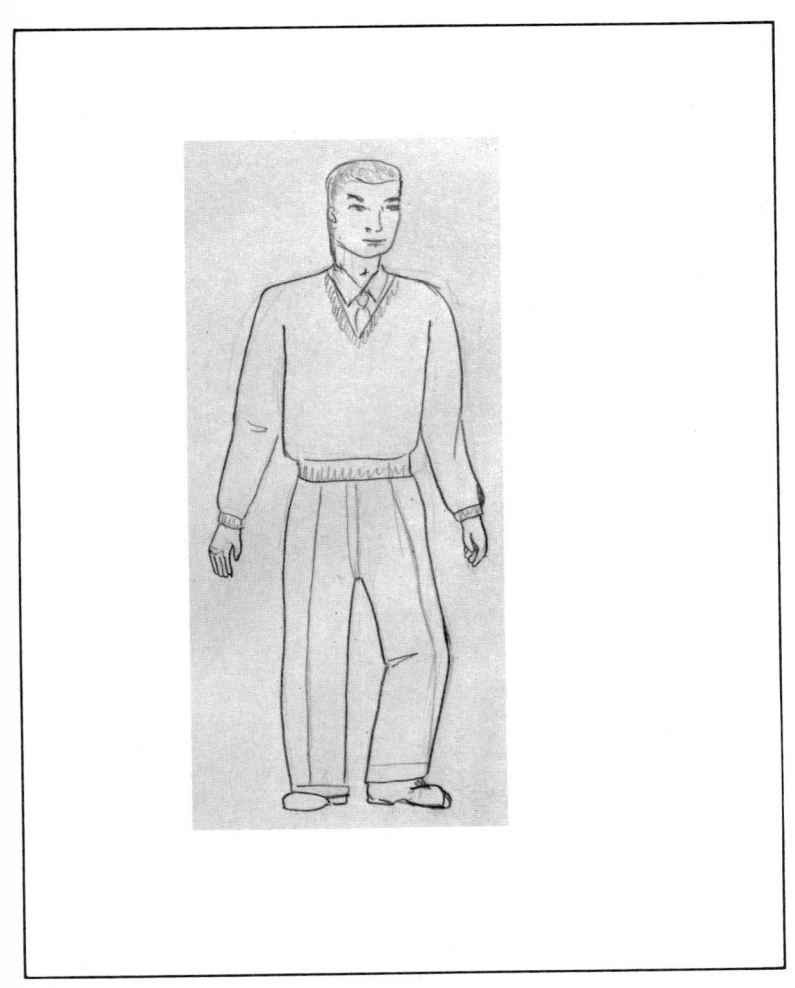

FIGURE-DRAWING CHARACTERISTICS

Structural	Male Female Both		Structural	Male	Female	Structural and Graphic	Male Female Both		Graphic, Global and Height	Male	Female	Body Proportions	Male	Female
Type	0		Omission of Appendages	0	0	Upper and Lower Halves	1	0	Hair Shading	1	1	Head	07	07
Sex Sequence	0		Position of Both Arms	0	0	Four Quarters	4	4	Nudity and Transparency	7	7	Neck	10	10
Posture	1	1	Position of Right Arm	4	0	Relative Size	2		Form	1	1	Shoulders	07	06
Perspective	0	0	Position of Left Arm	4	0	Constant Line Pressure	5	5	Detailing	1	1	Right Arm	06	06
Vertical Midline	3	3	Position of Legs	4	4	Variable Line Pressure	0	0	Identity and Sex	1	1	Left Arm	06	06
Bilateral Symmetry	3	3	Relation of Long Axes	1	1	Line Continuity	4	4	Sophistication	1	1	Chest	07	06
Horizontal Midline	4	4	Right and Left Halves	1	1	Body Shading	7	7	Height	07	07	Girth	07	05

GENERAL CHARACTERISTICS OF SUBJECT

IDENTIFICATION

No. 648

Sex F

Marital status S

Age 24 yrs. at psychological tests

PARENTAL HISTORY

Father

C H S D O

— — — — —

Mother

C H S D O

— — ? —

PHYSIOLOGICAL AND METABOLIC DATA

	Admission	Initial	Control	Cold pressor change	Exercise change	Smoking change
Systolic pressure	110	114	98	+20	+52	
Diastolic pressure	58	62	54	+26	-02	
Heart rate	80	80	70	+04	+30	

Age 22 yrs.

Height 66 in.

Weight 135 lbs.

Overweight +02 %

Ponderal index 12.87

Cholesterol 197 mg. per 100 ml.

Vital capacity 4.1 liters

HABIT SURVEY

Smoking habits: heavy cigarette smoker

Age begun 15 yrs.   Inhalation: yes

Habits of nervous tension: 1, 3, 4, 5, 7, 9, 10, 11, 14, 22, 23

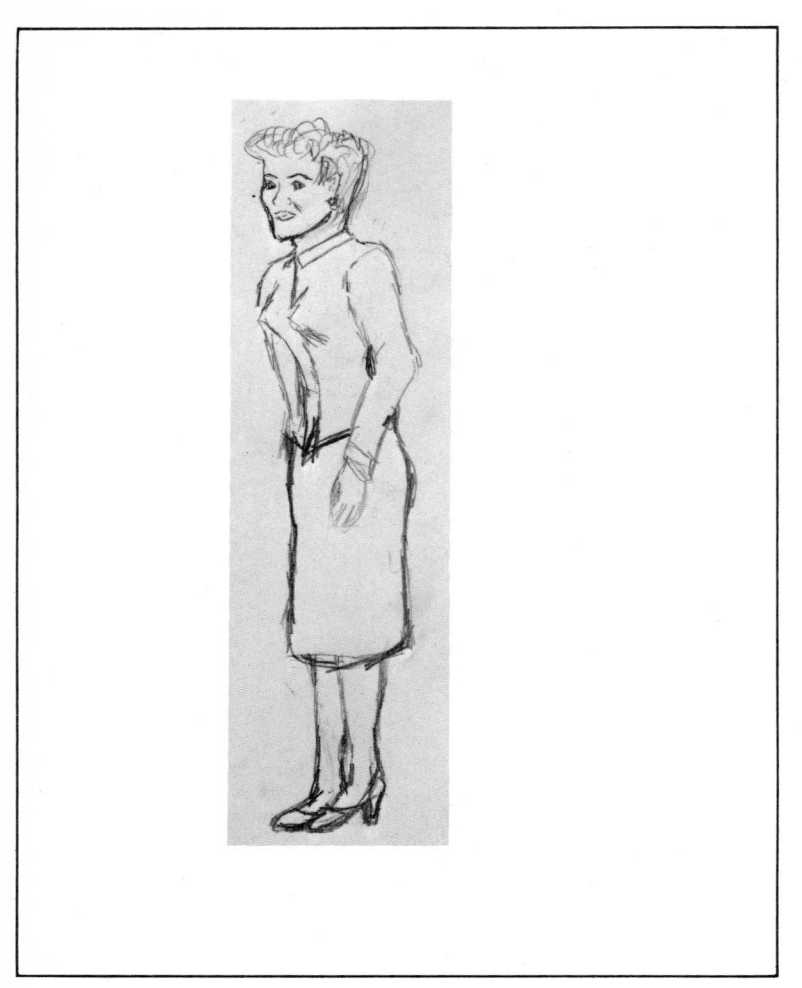

FIGURE-DRAWING CHARACTERISTICS

Structural	Male Female Both	Structural	Male	Female	Structural and Graphic	Male Female Both	Graphic, Global and Height	Male	Female	Body Proportions	Male	Female
Type	0	Omission of Appendages	0	0	Upper and Lower Halves	3 0	Hair Shading	3	3	Head	09	07
Sex Sequence	1	Position of Both Arms	4	4	Four Quarters	4 4	Nudity and Transparency	7	7	Neck	06	05
Posture	1 1	Position of Right Arm	7	7	Relative Size	0	Form	1	1	Shoulders		
Perspective	1 1	Position of Left Arm	5	5	Constant Line Pressure	0 0	Detailing	1	1	Right Arm		
Vertical Midline	7 7	Position of Legs	1	1	Variable Line Pressure	4 4	Identity and Sex	1	1	Left Arm	10	06
Bilateral Symmetry	0 0	Relation of Long Axes	1	1	Line Continuity	0 0	Sophistication	1	1	Chest		
Horizontal Midline	6 6	Right and Left Halves	1	1	Body Shading	7 5	Height	09	07	Girth		

GENERAL CHARACTERISTICS OF SUBJECT

IDENTIFICATION
No. B61
Sex M
Marital status M
Age 24 yrs. at
psychological tests

PARENTAL HISTORY				
Father				
C	H	S	D	O
-	-	-	-	+
Mother				
C	H	S	D	O
-	-	-	-	+

PHYSIOLOGICAL AND METABOLIC DATA

	Admission	Initial	Control	Cold pressor change	Exercise change	Smoking change
Systolic pressure	130	124	114	+22	+20	+02
Diastolic pressure	80	80	78	+28	-08	+02
Heart rate	96	88	69	+04	+17	+06

Age 23 yrs.	Height	70	in.	Ponderal index 12.11
	Weight	193	lbs.	Cholesterol 278 mg. per 100 ml.
	Overweight +25 %			Vital capacity 4.8 liters

HABIT SURVEY
Smoking habits: occasional smoker
Age begun 20 yrs.   Inhalation: no
Habits of nervous tension: 5, 9, 10

STRONG VOCATIONAL INTEREST TEST

Occupation	Artist	Psychologist	Architect	Physician	Osteopath	Dentist	Veterinarian	Mathematician	Physicist	Engineer	Chemist	Production Manager
Standard Score	33	33	36	59	52	41	37	32	23	31	34	26

Occupation	Farmer	Aviator	Carpenter	Printer	Math.-Sci. Teacher	Ind. Arts Teacher	Voc. Agric. Teacher	Policeman	Forest Serv. Man	Y.M.C.A. Phys. Dir.	Personnel Director	Public Administrator
Standard Score	31	23	18	25	35	11	26	32	25	47	25	34

Occupation	Y.M.C.A. Secretary	Soc. Sci. H.S. Teacher	City Sch. Sup't.	Social Worker	Minister	Musician Performer	C.P.A.	Senior C.P.A.	Accountant	Office Man	Purchasing Agent	Banker
Standard Score	31	32	32	33	61	43	38	30	22	26	24	26

Occupation	Mortician	Pharmacist	Sales Manager	Real Est. Manager	Life Ins. Salesman	Advertising Man	Lawyer	Author-Journalist	President Mfg. Co.	Interest Maturity	Occupational Level	Masculinity-Femininity
Standard Score	33	38	31	36	38	26	40	35	33	52	60	35

FIGURE-DRAWING CHARACTERISTICS

Structural	Male Female Both	Structural	Male	Female	Structural and Graphic	Male Female Both		Graphic, Global and Height	Male	Female	Body Proportions	Male	Female
Type	0	Omission of Appendages	0	0	Upper and Lower Halves	3	3	Hair Shading	0	3	Head	07	07
Sex Sequence	0	Position of Both Arms	2	2	Four Quarters	4	4	Nudity and Transparency	7	6	Neck	03	07
Posture	1 1	Position of Right Arm	5	5	Relative Size	2		Form	1	1	Shoulders		
Perspective	1 1	Position of Left Arm	7	7	Constant Line Pressure	0	0	Detailing	1	1	Right Arm	08	06
Vertical Midline	7 4	Position of Legs	5	1	Variable Line Pressure	5	5	Identity and Sex	1	1	Left Arm	08	06
Bilateral Symmetry	0 0	Relation of Long Axes	1	1	Line Continuity	2	1	Sophistication	1	1	Chest		
Horizontal Midline	6 6	Right and Left Halves	3	3	Body Shading	6	1	Height	08	08	Girth		

GENERAL CHARACTERISTICS OF SUBJECT

IDENTIFICATION
No. A10
Sex M
Marital status M
Age 29 yrs. at
psychological tests

PARENTAL HISTORY				
Father				
C	H	S	D	O
–	–	–	–	+
Mother				
C	H	S	D	O
–	–	–	–	?

PHYSIOLOGICAL AND METABOLIC DATA

	Admission	Initial	Control	Cold pressor change	Exercise change	Smoking change
Systolic pressure	120	138	136	+14	+44	00
Diastolic pressure	80	66	70	+02	–06	+07
Heart rate	82	76	66	+04	+17	–02

Age 29 yrs.	Height 70 in.	Ponderal index 12.59
	Weight 172 lbs.	Cholesterol 237 mg. per 100 ml.
	Overweight +08 %	Vital capacity liters

HABIT SURVEY
Smoking habits: heavy cigarette smoker
Age begun 15 yrs.   Inhalation: yes
Habits of nervous tension: 5, 6, 18

STRONG VOCATIONAL INTEREST TEST

Occupation	Artist	Psychologist	Architect	Physician	Osteopath	Dentist	Veterinarian	Mathematician	Physicist	Engineer	Chemist	Production Manager
Standard Score	38	25	35	43	30	38	25	26	17	28	27	17

Occupation	Farmer	Aviator	Carpenter	Printer	Math.-Sci. Teacher	Ind. Arts Teacher	Voc. Agric. Teacher	Policeman	Forest Serv. Man	Y.M.C.A. Phys. Dir.	Personnel Director	Public Administrator
Standard Score	33	34	16	39	26	08	20	28	25	26	21	29

Occupation	Y.M.C.A. Secretary	Soc. Sci. H.S. Teacher	City Sch. Sup't.	Social Worker	Minister	Musician Performer	C.P.A.	Senior C.P.A.	Accountant	Office Man	Purchasing Agent	Banker
Standard Score	15	21	16	24	60	37	20	27	20	30	27	24

Occupation	Mortician	Pharmacist	Sales Manager	Real Est. Manager	Life Ins. Salesman	Advertising Man	Lawyer	Author-Journalist	President Mfg. Co.	Interest Maturity	Occupational Level	Masculinity-Femininity
Standard Score	22	27	31	39	32	44	36	44	29	50	56	45

FIGURE-DRAWING CHARACTERISTICS

Structural	Male Female Both		Structural	Male	Female	Structural and Graphic	Male Female Both		Graphic, Global and Height	Male	Female	Body Proportions	Male	Female
Type	0		Omission of Appendages	7	0	Upper and Lower Halves	3	0	Hair Shading	3	3	Head	07	07
Sex Sequence	1		Position of Both Arms	0	1	Four Quarters	4	4	Nudity and Transparency	7	7	Neck	07	06
Posture	1	1	Position of Right Arm	5	4	Relative Size	0		Form	1	1	Shoulders	07	
Perspective	0	1	Position of Left Arm	5	5	Constant Line Pressure	4	0	Detailing	1	1	Right Arm	06	05
Vertical Midline	3	4	Position of Legs	4	4	Variable Line Pressure	0	5	Identity and Sex	1	1	Left Arm		05
Bilateral Symmetry	3	0	Relation of Long Axes	1	1	Line Continuity	3	2	Sophistication	1	1	Chest	06	
Horizontal Midline	6	4	Right and Left Halves	1	1	Body Shading	2	1	Height	07	06	Girth	09	

GENERAL CHARACTERISTICS OF SUBJECT

IDENTIFICATION
No. E19
Sex F
Marital status S
Age 25 yrs. at
psychological tests

PARENTAL HISTORY				
Father				
C	H	S	D	O
-	-	-	-	?
Mother				
C	H	S	D	O
-	-	-	-	+

PHYSIOLOGICAL AND METABOLIC DATA

	Admission	Initial	Control	Cold pressor change	Exercise change	Smoking change
Systolic pressure	120	110	100	+18	+62	00
Diastolic pressure	70	70	70	+14	-10	+04
Heart rate	70	84	84	00	+31	-02

Age 25 yrs.	Height	64	in.	Ponderal index	13.09	
	Weight	117	lbs.	Cholesterol	260	mg. per 100 ml.
	Overweight -09 %			Vital capacity	3.3	liters

HABIT SURVEY

Smoking habits: heavy cigarette smoker

Age begun 18 yrs.   Inhalation: yes

Habits of nervous tension: 1, 2, 3, 5, 8, 9, 10, 11, 16, 17, 18, 23

STRONG VOCATIONAL INTEREST TEST

Occupation	Artist	Psychologist	Architect	Physician	Osteopath	Dentist	Veterinarian	Mathematician	Physicist	Engineer	Chemist	Production Manager
Standard Score	45	43	42	55	57	45	14	38	31	28	40	19

Occupation	Farmer	Aviator	Carpenter	Printer	Math.-Sci. Teacher	Ind. Arts Teacher	Voc. Agric. Teacher	Policeman	Forest Serv. Man	Y.M.C.A. Phys. Dir.	Personnel Director	Public Administrator
Standard Score	13	18	06	25	24	02	-10	19	-10	15	25	30

Occupation	Y.M.C.A. Secretary	Soc. Sci. H.S. Teacher	City Sch. Sup't.	Social Worker	Minister	Musician Performer	C.P.A.	Senior C.P.A.	Accountant	Office Man	Purchasing Agent	Banker
Standard Score	17	25	24	33	64	47	40	19	20	27	14	21

Occupation	Mortician	Pharmacist	Sales Manager	Real Est. Manager	Life Ins. Salesman	Advertising Man	Lawyer	Author-Journalist	President Mfg. Co.	Interest Maturity	Occupational Level	Masculinity-Femininity
Standard Score	32	38	21	35	35	44	50	50	41	51	66	20

Plate 815   MOST SOPHISTICATED DRAWINGS   865

FIGURE-DRAWING CHARACTERISTICS *

Structural	Male Female Both	Structural	Male	Female	Structural and Graphic	Male Female Both		Graphic, Global and Height	Male	Female	Body Proportions	Male	Female
Type	0	Omission of Appendages	3		Upper and Lower Halves	7		Hair Shading	2		Head	11	
Sex Sequence	9	Position of Both Arms	1		Four Quarters	4		Nudity and Transparency	7		Neck	05	
Posture	0	Position of Right Arm	2		Relative Size		7	Form	3		Shoulders		
Perspective	1	Position of Left Arm	5		Constant Line Pressure	1		Detailing	1		Right Arm		
Vertical Midline	4	Position of Legs	0		Variable Line Pressure	0		Identity and Sex	1		Left Arm	07	
Bilateral Symmetry	0	Relation of Long Axes	2		Line Continuity	0		Sophistication	1		Chest		
Horizontal Midline	0	Right and Left Halves	9		Body Shading	3		Height			Girth		

GENERAL CHARACTERISTICS OF SUBJECT

IDENTIFICATION
No. 577
Sex M
Marital status M
Age 25 yrs. at
psychological tests

PARENTAL HISTORY
Father
C   H   S   D   O
–   –   –   –   +
Mother
C   H   S   D   O
–   –   –   –   –

PHYSIOLOGICAL AND METABOLIC DATA

	Admission	Initial	Control	Cold pressor change	Exercise change	Smoking change
Systolic pressure	120	120	110	+08	+32	+05
Diastolic pressure	70	78	70	+10	+02	+05
Heart rate	80	84	88	+20	+15	+05

Age 25 yrs.	Height	70	in.	Ponderal index 12.54	
	Weight	174	lbs.	Cholesterol	230	mg. per 100 ml.
	Overweight +11 %			Vital capacity	5.0	liters

HABIT SURVEY

Smoking habits: occasional smoker

Age begun   yrs.   Inhalation: no

Habits of nervous tension: 1, 2, 3, 4, 5, 6, 7,
8, 9, 10, 11, 12, 16, 17, 18, 19, 20,
21, 22, 23, 24

*These two male figures were evidently copied from a photograph of Sargent's portrait, "The Four Doctors", which hung in the room where the test was taken. Only the right-hand figure (Dr. William Osler) has been coded.

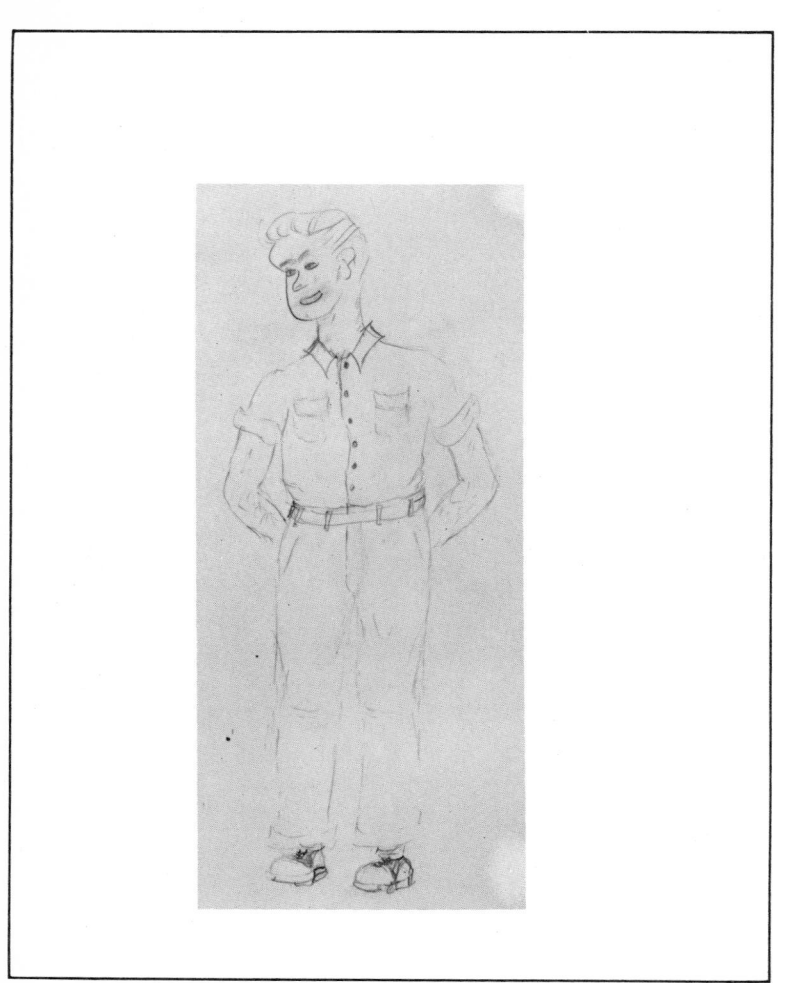

FIGURE-DRAWING CHARACTERISTICS

Structural	Male Female Both	Structural	Male	Female	Structural and Graphic	Male Female Both	Graphic, Global and Height	Male	Female	Body Proportions	Male	Female
Type	0	Omission of Appendages	7	7	Upper and Lower Halves	3 0	Hair Shading	1	3	Head	08	08
Sex Sequence	0	Position of Both Arms	0	0	Four Quarters	4 4	Nudity and Transparency	6	6	Neck	14	12
Posture	1 1	Position of Right Arm	5	5	Relative Size	4	Form	1	1	Shoulders	07	09
Perspective	0 0	Position of Left Arm	5	5	Constant Line Pressure	0 0	Detailing	1	1	Right Arm		
Vertical Midline	3 0	Position of Legs	4	5	Variable Line Pressure	3 2	Identity and Sex	1	1	Left Arm		
Bilateral Symmetry	3 3	Relation of Long Axes	1	1	Line Continuity	0 0	Sophistication	1	1	Chest	07	08
Horizontal Midline	4 0	Right and Left Halves	1	1	Body Shading	7 7	Height	07	07	Girth	09	07

GENERAL CHARACTERISTICS OF SUBJECT

IDENTIFICATION
No. 755
Sex M
Marital status S
Age 23 yrs. at
psychological tests

PARENTAL HISTORY
Father
C   H   S   D   O
−   −   −   −   +
Mother
C   H   S   D   O
−   −   −   −   −

PHYSIOLOGICAL AND METABOLIC DATA

	Admission	Initial	Control	Cold pressor change	Exercise change	Smoking change
Systolic pressure	135	124	118	+14	+32	+06
Diastolic pressure	80	78	72	+20	−06	+04
Heart rate	80	76	66	+16	+31	−03

Age 22 yrs.	Height	73 in.	Ponderal index	12.97	
	Weight	178 lbs.	Cholesterol	203	mg. per 100 ml.
	Overweight +06 %		Vital capacity	5.2	liters

HABIT SURVEY

Smoking habits: occasional smoker

Age begun   yrs.   Inhalation:

Habits of nervous tension: 1, 4, 5, 6, 8, 23

Plate 817　　　　　　　　MOST SOPHISTICATED DRAWINGS　　　　　　　　867

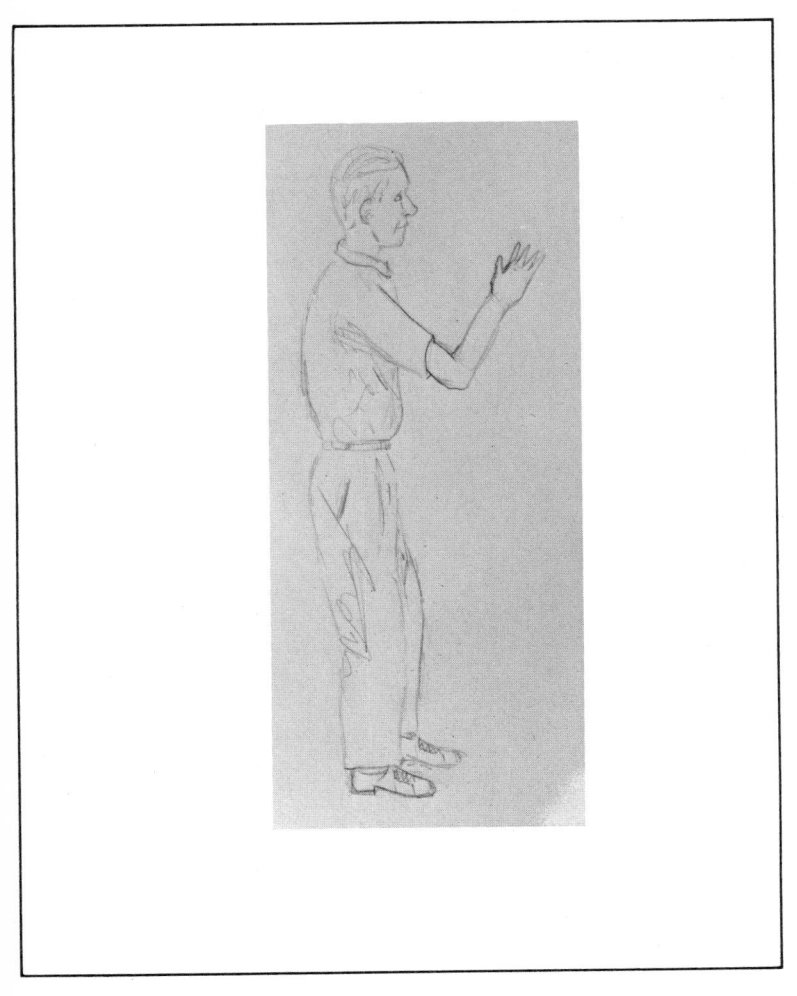

FIGURE-DRAWING CHARACTERISTICS

Structural	Male	Female	Structural	Male	Female	Structural and Graphic	Male	Female	Graphic, Global and Height	Male	Female	Body Proportions	Male	Female
	Both						Both							
Type	0		Omission of Appendages	0	0	Upper and Lower Halves	1	1	Hair Shading	1	1	Head	07	09
Sex Sequence	0		Position of Both Arms	2	0	Four Quarters	4	4	Nudity and Transparency	7	7	Neck	05	04
Posture	1	1	Position of Right Arm	2	2	Relative Size		2	Form	1	1	Shoulders		06
Perspective	2	0	Position of Left Arm	7	2	Constant Line Pressure	1	0	Detailing	1	1	Right Arm	06	04
Vertical Midline	4	3	Position of Legs	1	4	Variable Line Pressure	0	1	Identity and Sex	1	1	Left Arm		04
Bilateral Symmetry	0	3	Relation of Long Axes	1	1	Line Continuity	0	0	Sophistication	1	1	Chest	07	06
Horizontal Midline	4	4	Right and Left Halves	1	3	Body Shading	7	7	Height	07	06	Girth	05	05

GENERAL CHARACTERISTICS OF SUBJECT

IDENTIFICATION
No. B22
Sex M
Marital status M
Age 24 yrs. at
psychological tests

PARENTAL HISTORY
Father
C　H　S　D　O
-　-　-　-　+
Mother
C　H　S　D　O
-　-　-　-　-

PHYSIOLOGICAL AND METABOLIC DATA

	Admission	Initial	Control	Cold pressor change	Exercise change	Smoking change
Systolic pressure	130	120	112	+16	+14	+11
Diastolic pressure	75	54	60	+24	-16	+16
Heart rate	54	80	71	+19	+11	+10

Age 24 yrs.	Height	72	in.	Ponderal index	13.41	
	Weight	155	lbs.	Cholesterol	170	mg. per 100 ml.
	Overweight	-06	%	Vital capacity		liters

HABIT SURVEY

Smoking habits: heavy cigarette smoker

Age begun　16 yrs.　　　Inhalation:　yes

Habits of nervous tension: 4, 5, 6, 17

STRONG VOCATIONAL INTEREST TEST

Occupation	Artist	Psychologist	Architect	Physician	Osteopath	Dentist	Veterinarian	Mathematician	Physicist	Engineer	Chemist	Production Manager
Standard Score	29	33	34	47	52	39	22	31	25	33	40	29

Occupation	Farmer	Aviator	Carpenter	Printer	Math.-Sci. Teacher	Ind. Arts Teacher	Voc. Agric. Teacher	Policeman	Forest Serv. Man	Y.M.C.A. Phys. Dir.	Personnel Director	Public Administrator
Standard Score	30	35	31	48	44	25	22	38	20	30	25	36

Occupation	Y.M.C.A. Secretary	Soc. Sci. H.S. Teacher	City Sch. Sup't.	Social Worker	Minister	Musician Performer	C.P.A.	Senior C.P.A.	Accountant	Office Man	Purchasing Agent	Banker
Standard Score	16	35	22	32	61	43	41	45	38	41	28	26

Occupation	Mortician	Pharmacist	Sales Manager	Real Est. Manager	Life Ins. Salesman	Advertising Man	Lawyer	Author-Journalist	President Mfg. Co.	Interest Maturity	Occupational Level	Masculinity-Femininity
Standard Score	30	38	21	30	24	29	35	33	23	52	49	45

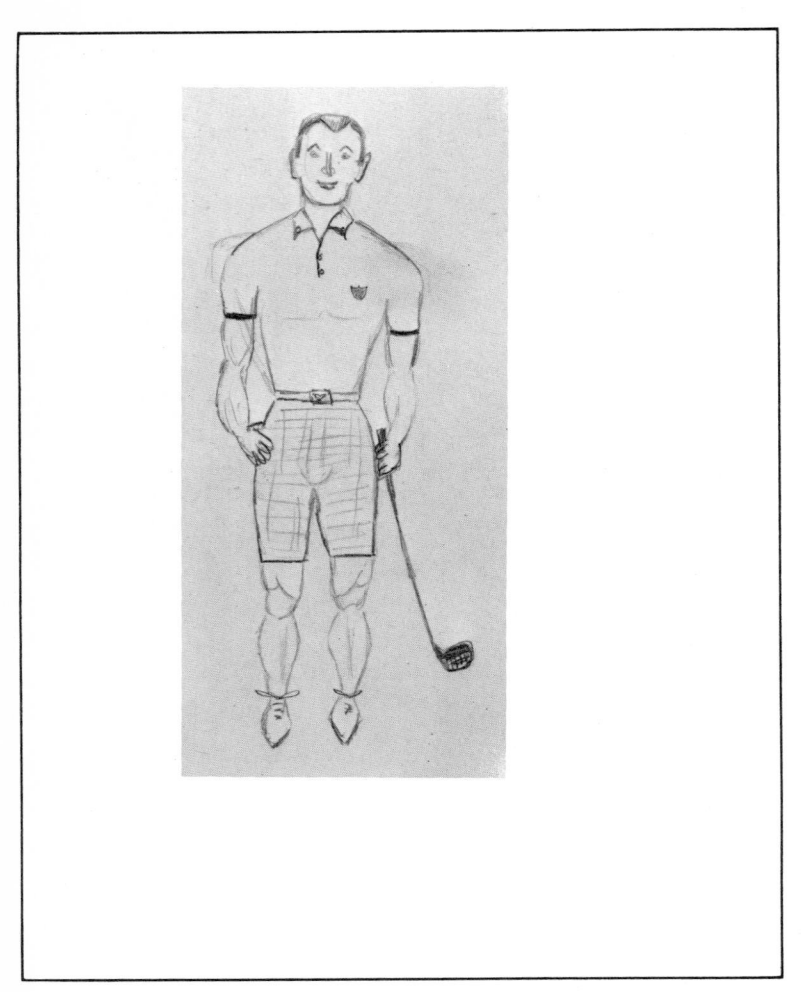

FIGURE-DRAWING CHARACTERISTICS

Structural	Male Female Both		Structural	Male	Female	Structural and Graphic	Male Female Both		Graphic, Global and Height	Male	Female	Body Proportions	Male	Female
Type	0		Omission of Appendages	0	0	Upper and Lower Halves	1	1	Hair Shading	1	1	Head	07	06
Sex Sequence	0		Position of Both Arms	0	0	Four Quarters	4	4	Nudity and Transparency	2	7	Neck	05	08
Posture	1	1	Position of Right Arm	0	5	Relative Size	0		Form	1	1	Shoulders	07	05
Perspective	0	0	Position of Left Arm	0	5	Constant Line Pressure	0	0	Detailing	1	1	Right Arm	06	04
Vertical Midline	3	0	Position of Legs	4	4	Variable Line Pressure	4	3	Identity and Sex	1	1	Left Arm	06	04
Bilateral Symmetry	3	5	Relation of Long Axes	1	1	Line Continuity	0	0	Sophistication	1	1	Chest	06	04
Horizontal Midline	4	0	Right and Left Halves	1	1	Body Shading	7	5	Height	06	05	Girth	05	04

GENERAL CHARACTERISTICS OF SUBJECT

IDENTIFICATION

No. C32

Sex M

Marital status S

Age 22 yrs. at

psychological tests

PARENTAL HISTORY

Father

C H S D O

– – – – +

Mother

C H S D O

– – – – –

PHYSIOLOGICAL AND METABOLIC DATA

	Admission	Initial	Control	Cold pressor change	Exercise change	Smoking change
Systolic pressure	130					-04
Diastolic pressure	80					+02
Heart rate	90					+12

Age 21 yrs.

Height   68 in.   Ponderal index 12.98

Weight 144 lbs.   Cholesterol 226 mg. per 100 ml.

Overweight -01 %   Vital capacity 4.6 liters

HABIT SURVEY

Smoking habits: heavy cigarette smoker

Age begun 18 yrs.   Inhalation: yes

Habits of nervous tension: 5, 6, 9, 11, 16, 19

STRONG VOCATIONAL INTEREST TEST

Occupation	Artist	Psychologist	Architect	Physician	Osteopath	Dentist	Veterinarian	Mathematician	Physicist	Engineer	Chemist	Production Manager
Standard Score	28	41	17	43	46	23	26	06	-09	01	12	21

Occupation	Farmer	Aviator	Carpenter	Printer	Math.-Sci. Teacher	Ind. Arts Teacher	Voc. Agric. Teacher	Policeman	Forest Serv. Man	Y.M.C.A. Phys. Dir.	Personnel Director	Public Administrator
Standard Score	18	28	07	38	30	05	24	34	20	51	44	49

Occupation	Y.M.C.A. Secretary	Soc. Sci. H.S. Teacher	City Sch. Sup't.	Social Worker	Minister	Musician Performer	C.P.A.	Senior C.P.A.	Accountant	Office Man	Purchasing Agent	Banker
Standard Score	46	57	38	62	62	54	26	35	17	36	17	22

Occupation	Mortician	Pharmacist	Sales Manager	Real Est. Manager	Life Ins. Salesman	Advertising Man	Lawyer	Author-Journalist	President Mfg. Co.	Interest Maturity	Occupational Level	Masculinity-Femininity
Standard Score	43	43	46	44	56	51	45	37	27	61	50	34

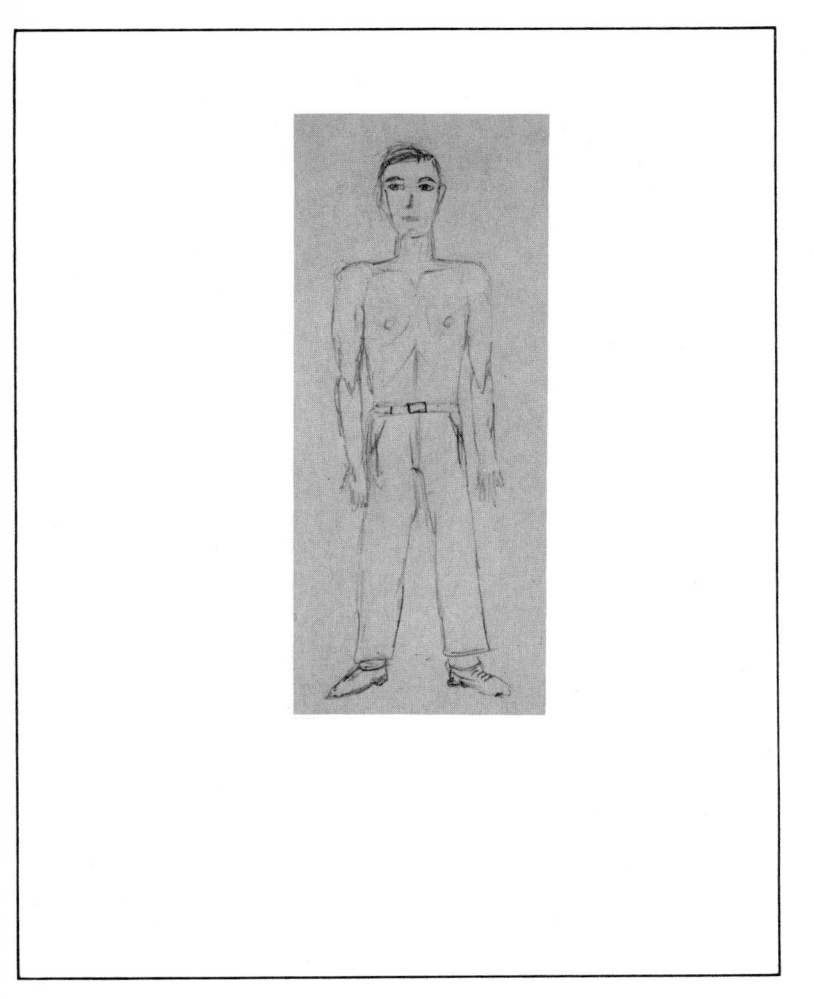

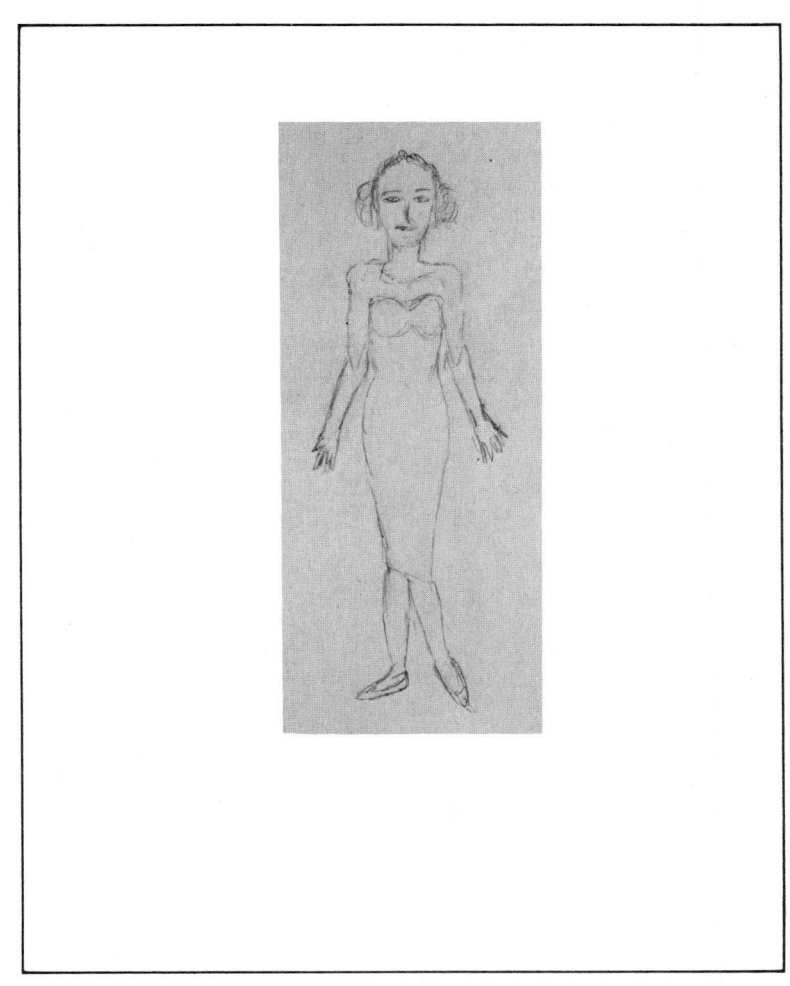

FIGURE-DRAWING CHARACTERISTICS

Structural	Male Female Both		Structural	Male	Female	Structural and Graphic	Male Female Both		Graphic, Global and Height	Male	Female	Body Proportions	Male	Female
Type	0		Omission of Appendages	0	0	Upper and Lower Halves	1	1	Hair Shading	3	3	Head	07	07
Sex Sequence	0		Position of Both Arms	0	0	Four Quarters	4	4	Nudity and Transparency	3	7	Neck	06	05
Posture	1	1	Position of Right Arm	0	4	Relative Size	1		Form	1	1	Shoulders	06	04
Perspective	0	0	Position of Left Arm	0	4	Constant Line Pressure	1	0	Detailing	1	1	Right Arm	06	04
Vertical Midline	3	0	Position of Legs	6	3	Variable Line Pressure	0	1	Identity and Sex	1	1	Left Arm	06	04
Bilateral Symmetry	5	3	Relation of Long Axes	1	1	Line Continuity	0	0	Sophistication	1	1	Chest	05	03
Horizontal Midline	4	0	Right and Left Halves	3	0	Body Shading	3	1	Height	05	05	Girth	05	04

GENERAL CHARACTERISTICS OF SUBJECT

IDENTIFICATION
No. C61
Sex M
Marital status S
Age 23 yrs. at
psychological tests

PARENTAL HISTORY				
Father				
C	H	S	D	O
−	−	−	−	+
Mother				
C	H	S	D	O
−	−	−	−	−

PHYSIOLOGICAL AND METABOLIC DATA

	Admission	Initial	Control	Cold pressor change	Exercise change	Smoking change
Systolic pressure	120	112	118	+04	+10	+06
Diastolic pressure	70	86	88	+02	+02	+02
Heart rate	84	62	63	+04	+02	−06

Age 23 yrs.	Height 75 in.	Ponderal index 13.76
	Weight 162 lbs.	Cholesterol 168 mg. per 100 ml.
	Overweight −10 %	Vital capacity 4.4 liters

HABIT SURVEY
Smoking habits: nonsmoker
Age begun yrs. Inhalation:
Habits of nervous tension: 4, 5, 6, 9, 11, 16, 21

STRONG VOCATIONAL INTEREST TEST

Occupation	Artist	Psychologist	Architect	Physician	Osteopath	Dentist	Veterinarian	Mathematician	Physicist	Engineer	Chemist	Production Manager
Standard Score	32	46	33	59	46	42	33	46	45	47	56	28

Occupation	Farmer	Aviator	Carpenter	Printer	Math.-Sci. Teacher	Ind. Arts Teacher	Voc. Agric. Teacher	Policeman	Forest Serv. Man	Y.M.C.A. Phys. Dir.	Personnel Director	Public Administrator
Standard Score	40	34	28	39	47	22	32	32	26	37	25	40

Occupation	Y.M.C.A. Secretary	Soc. Sci. H.S. Teacher	City Sch. Sup't.	Social Worker	Minister	Musician Performer	C.P.A.	Senior C.P.A.	Accountant	Office Man	Purchasing Agent	Banker
Standard Score	27	24	26	28	62	42	33	41	30	33	18	21

Occupation	Mortician	Pharmacist	Sales Manager	Real Est. Manager	Life Ins. Salesman	Advertising Man	Lawyer	Author-Journalist	President Mfg. Co.	Interest Maturity	Occupational Level	Masculinity-Femininity
Standard Score	17	32	21	23	21	24	30	34	20	52	57	49

FIGURE-DRAWING CHARACTERISTICS

Structural	Male Female Both	Structural	Male	Female	Structural and Graphic	Male Female Both		Graphic, Global and Height	Male	Female	Body Proportions	Male	Female
Type	0	Omission of Appendages	0	0	Upper and Lower Halves	0	0	Hair Shading	0	3	Head	06	06
Sex Sequence	0	Position of Both Arms	4	4	Four Quarters	4	4	Nudity and Transparency	7	6	Neck		06
Posture	1 2	Position of Right Arm	7	7	Relative Size	1		Form	1	1	Shoulders		
Perspective	1 1	Position of Left Arm	5	5	Constant Line Pressure	0	0	Detailing	1	1	Right Arm		
Vertical Midline	7 4	Position of Legs	2	8	Variable Line Pressure	1	4	Identity and Sex	1	1	Left Arm	06	04
Bilateral Symmetry	0 0	Relation of Long Axes	1	1	Line Continuity	0	0	Sophistication	1	1	Chest		
Horizontal Midline	6 0	Right and Left Halves	0	1	Body Shading	7	3	Height	05	05	Girth		

GENERAL CHARACTERISTICS OF SUBJECT

IDENTIFICATION
No. D11
Sex M
Marital status S
Age 23 yrs. at psychological tests

PARENTAL HISTORY
Father
C   H   S   D   O
−   −   −   −   +
Mother
C   H   S   D   O
−   −   −   −   −

PHYSIOLOGICAL AND METABOLIC DATA

	Admission	Initial	Control	Cold pressor change	Exercise change	Smoking change
Systolic pressure	140	128	120	+02	+30	+02
Diastolic pressure	70	70	70	+28	−10	−02
Heart rate	70	92	81	00	+13	+07
Age 22 yrs.	Height 71 in.	Weight 171 lbs.	Overweight +08 %	Ponderal index 12.79	Cholesterol 291 mg. per 100 ml.	Vital capacity 5.3 liters

HABIT SURVEY

Smoking habits: nonsmoker

Age begun   yrs.   Inhalation:

Habits of nervous tension: 2, 4, 6, 11, 25

STRONG VOCATIONAL INTEREST TEST

Occupation	Artist	Psychologist	Architect	Physician	Osteopath	Dentist	Veterinarian	Mathematician	Physicist	Engineer	Chemist	Production Manager
Standard Score	35	37	37	48	38	36	18	29	23	31	39	32

Occupation	Farmer	Aviator	Carpenter	Printer	Math.-Sci. Teacher	Ind. Arts Teacher	Voc. Agric. Teacher	Policeman	Forest Serv. Man	Y.M.C.A. Phys. Dir.	Personnel Director	Public Administrator
Standard Score	36	38	22	47	41	23	24	34	19	33	28	34

Occupation	Y.M.C.A. Secretary	Soc. Sci. H.S. Teacher	City Sch. Sup't.	Social Worker	Minister	Musician Performer	C.P.A.	Senior C.P.A.	Accountant	Office Man	Purchasing Agent	Banker
Standard Score	29	38	29	37	63	49	24	40	24	37	17	19

Occupation	Mortician	Pharmacist	Sales Manager	Real Est. Manager	Life Ins. Salesman	Advertising Man	Lawyer	Author-Journalist	President Mfg. Co.	Interest Maturity	Occupational Level	Masculinity-Femininity
Standard Score	23	24	18	26	20	36	31	37	18	56	52	46

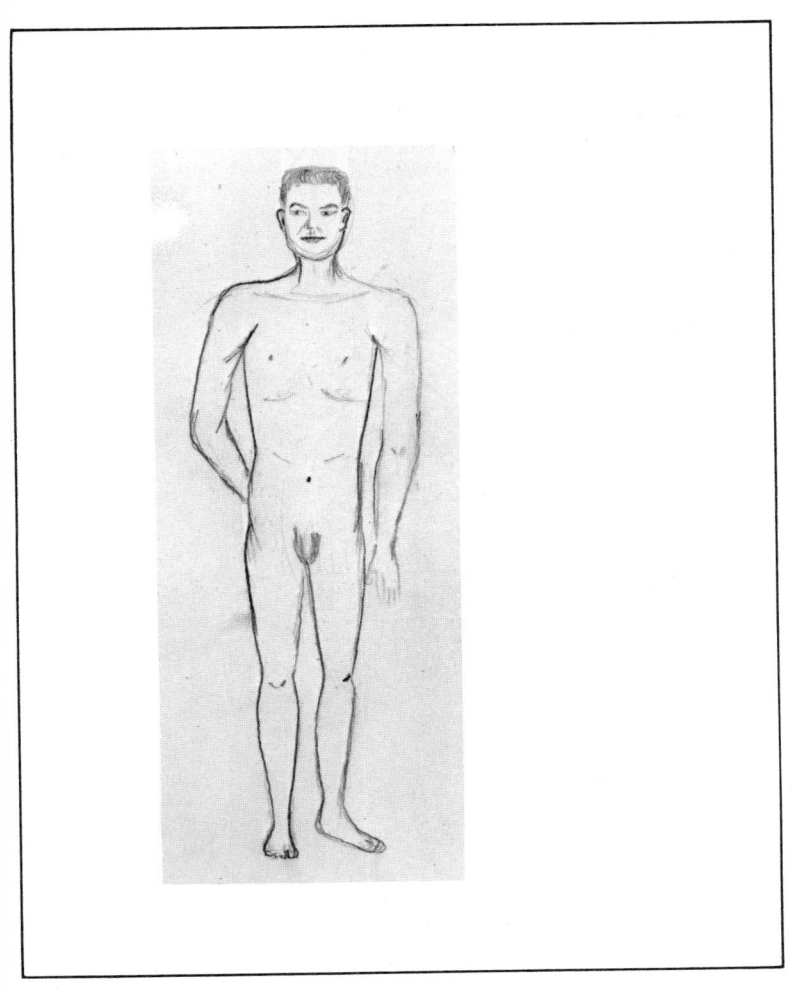
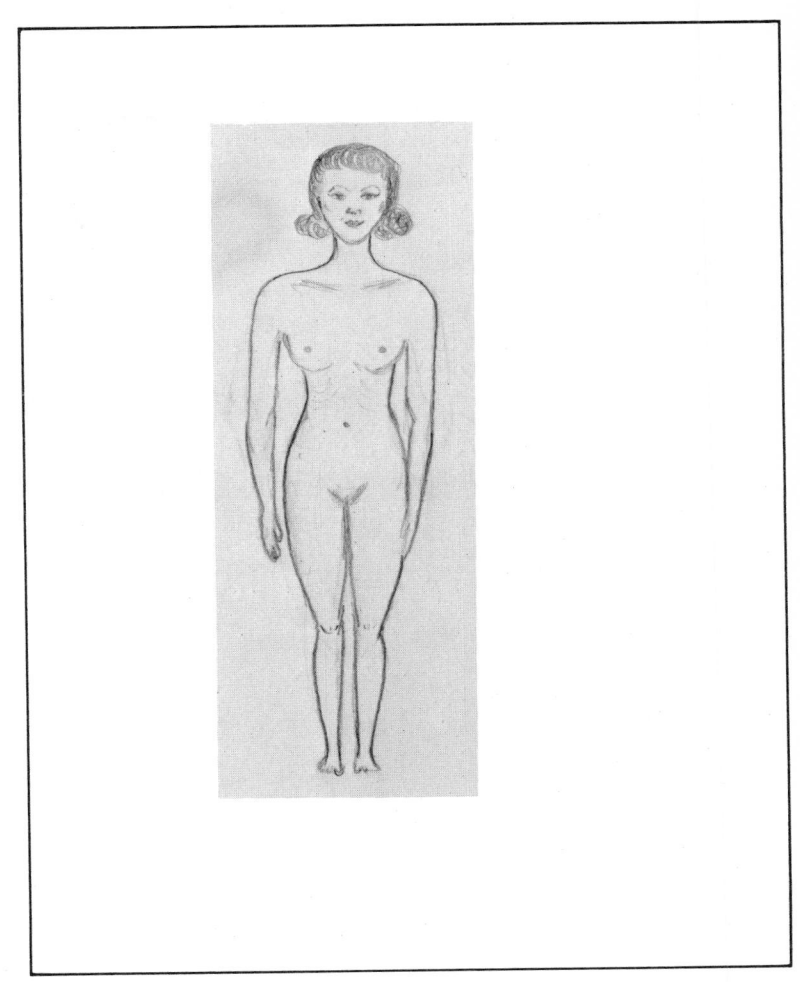

FIGURE-DRAWING CHARACTERISTICS

Structural	Male Female Both	Structural	Male	Female	Structural and Graphic	Male Female Both		Graphic, Global and Height	Male	Female	Body Proportions	Male	Female
Type	0	Omission of Appendages	7	0	Upper and Lower Halves	0	1	Hair Shading	3	3	Head	07	08
Sex Sequence	2	Position of Both Arms	1	0	Four Quarters	4	4	Nudity and Transparency	0	0	Neck	07	08
Posture	1 1	Position of Right Arm	5	0	Relative Size	0		Form	1	1	Shoulders	08	07
Perspective	0 0	Position of Left Arm	0	0	Constant Line Pressure	0	0	Detailing	1	1	Right Arm		06
Vertical Midline	0 0	Position of Legs	4	4	Variable Line Pressure	3	4	Identity and Sex	1	1	Left Arm	08	06
Bilateral Symmetry	4 5	Relation of Long Axes	1	1	Line Continuity	2	3	Sophistication	1	1	Chest	06	06
Horizontal Midline	0 0	Right and Left Halves	1	1	Body Shading	3	3	Height	07	06	Girth	06	05

GENERAL CHARACTERISTICS OF SUBJECT

IDENTIFICATION

No. D59
Sex F
Marital status S
Age 29 yrs. at psychological tests

PARENTAL HISTORY

Father
C H S D O
- - - - -

Mother
C H S D O
- - - - +

PHYSIOLOGICAL AND METABOLIC DATA

	Admission	Initial	Control	Cold pressor change	Exercise change	Smoking change
Systolic pressure	120	98	94	−05	+44	00
Diastolic pressure	66	68	64	−01	−06	+08
Heart rate	76	84	79	−04	+46	+06

Age 29 yrs.
Height 66 in.
Weight 124 lbs.
Overweight −09 %

Ponderal index 13.23
Cholesterol 252 mg. per 100 ml.
Vital capacity liters

HABIT SURVEY

Smoking habits: heavy cigarette smoker
Age begun yrs. Inhalation:
Habits of nervous tension:

STRONG VOCATIONAL INTEREST TEST

Occupation	Artist	Psychologist	Architect	Physician	Osteopath	Dentist	Veterinarian	Mathematician	Physicist	Engineer	Chemist	Production Manager
Standard Score	24	44	30	54	45	32	30	20	13	18	28	28

Occupation	Farmer	Aviator	Carpenter	Printer	Math.-Sci. Teacher	Ind. Arts Teacher	Voc. Agric. Teacher	Policeman	Forest Serv. Man	Y.M.C.A. Phys. Dir.	Personnel Director	Public Administrator
Standard Score	29	27	17	41	43	14	31	33	25	48	52	54

Occupation	Y.M.C.A. Secretary	Soc. Sci. H.S. Teacher	City Sch. Sup't.	Social Worker	Minister	Musician Performer	C.P.A.	Senior C.P.A.	Accountant	Office Man	Purchasing Agent	Banker
Standard Score	45	48	42	54	63	54	27	41	29	34	14	25

Occupation	Mortician	Pharmacist	Sales Manager	Real Est. Manager	Life Ins. Salesman	Advertising Man	Lawyer	Author-Journalist	President Mfg. Co.	Interest Maturity	Occupational Level	Masculinity-Femininity
Standard Score	36	31	27	27	33	30	33	29	20	62	52	32

FIGURE-DRAWING CHARACTERISTICS

Structural	Male Female Both		Structural	Male	Female	Structural and Graphic	Male Female Both		Graphic, Global and Height	Male	Female	Body Proportions	Male	Female
Type	0		Omission of Appendages	2	2	Upper and Lower Halves	1	1	Hair Shading	7	1	Head	06	06
Sex Sequence	1		Position of Both Arms	6	2	Four Quarters	4	4	Nudity and Transparency	7	7	Neck	06	04
Posture	1	1	Position of Right Arm	8	0	Relative Size	0		Form	1	1	Shoulders	05	04
Perspective	0	0	Position of Left Arm	8	8	Constant Line Pressure	1	0	Detailing	1	1	Right Arm		04
Vertical Midline	3	0	Position of Legs	6	4	Variable Line Pressure	0	1	Identity and Sex	1	1	Left Arm		04
Bilateral Symmetry	3	3	Relation of Long Axes	1	1	Line Continuity	0	0	Sophistication	1	1	Chest	04	03
Horizontal Midline	4	4	Right and Left Halves	1	1	Body Shading	3	2	Height	05	05	Girth	04	04

GENERAL CHARACTERISTICS OF SUBJECT

IDENTIFICATION
No. E59
Sex F
Marital status S
Age 22 yrs. at
psychological tests

PARENTAL HISTORY
Father
C   H   S   D   O
-   -   -   -   -
Mother
C   H   S   D   O
-   -   -   -   +

PHYSIOLOGICAL AND METABOLIC DATA

	Admission	Initial	Control	Cold pressor change	Exercise change	Smoking change
Systolic pressure	120	108	99	+24	+27	+04
Diastolic pressure	76	71	64	+27	+08	+03
Heart rate	88	84	71	+26	+40	+11

Age 24 yrs.	Height	65	in.	Ponderal index	13.57	
	Weight	110	lbs.	Cholesterol	212	mg. per 100 ml.
	Overweight	-15	%	Vital capacity	2.9	liters

HABIT SURVEY
Smoking habits: light cigarette smoker
Age begun 19 yrs.   Inhalation: yes
Habits of nervous tension: 1, 3, 4, 5, 6, 8,
9, 11, 17, 18, 19, 23, 24

STRONG VOCATIONAL INTEREST TEST

Occupation	Artist	Psychologist	Architect	Physician	Osteopath	Dentist	Veterinarian	Mathematician	Physicist	Engineer	Chemist	Production Manager
Standard Score	49	58	47	58	38	38	05	43	38	25	40	22

Occupation	Farmer	Aviator	Carpenter	Printer	Math.-Sci. Teacher	Ind. Arts Teacher	Voc. Agric. Teacher	Policeman	Forest Serv. Man	Y.M.C.A. Phys. Dir.	Personnel Director	Public Administrator
Standard Score	22	21	19	39	37	11	11	21	06	27	32	34

Occupation	Y.M.C.A. Secretary	Soc. Sci. H.S. Teacher	City Sch. Sup't.	Social Worker	Minister	Musician Performer	C.P.A.	Senior C.P.A.	Accountant	Office Man	Purchasing Agent	Banker
Standard Score	27	36	36	46	64	64	41	28	20	25	11	19

Occupation	Mortician	Pharmacist	Sales Manager	Real Est. Manager	Life Ins. Salesman	Advertising Man	Lawyer	Author-Journalist	President Mfg. Co.	Interest Maturity	Occupational Level	Masculinity-Femininity
Standard Score	14	28	17	29	21	45	47	49	30	53	54	24

Plate 823   MOST SOPHISTICATED DRAWINGS   873

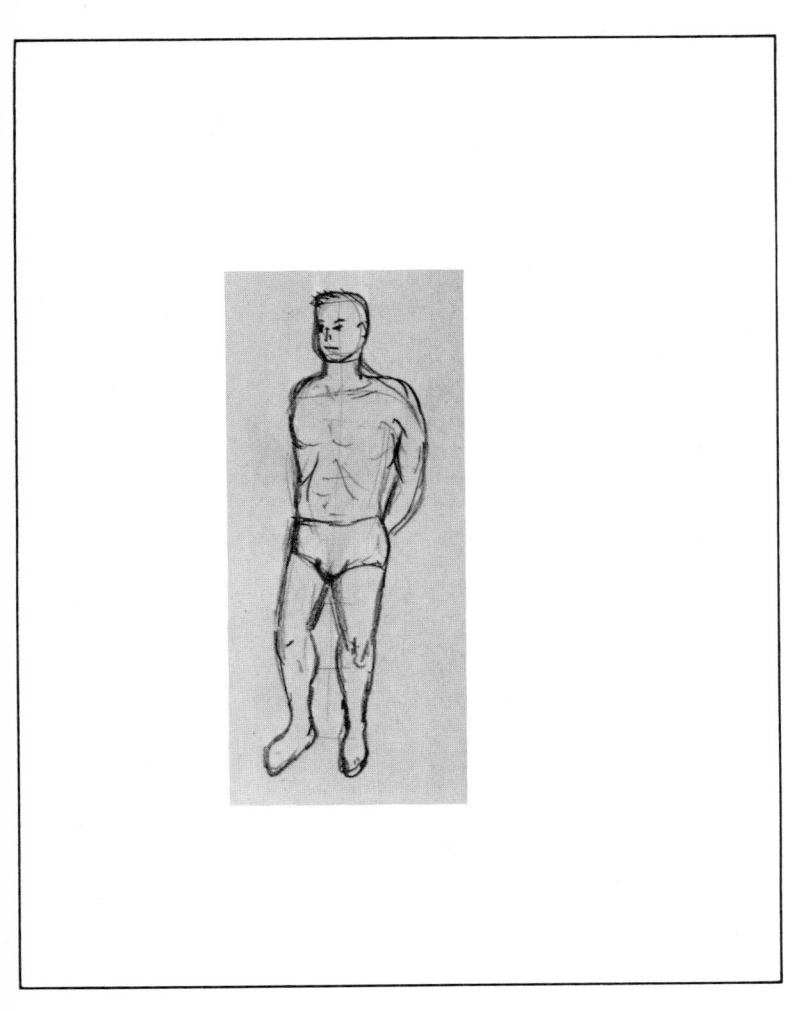

FIGURE-DRAWING CHARACTERISTICS

Structural	Male Female Both	Structural	Male	Female	Structural and Graphic	Male Female Both	Graphic, Global and Height	Male	Female	Body Proportions	Male	Female
Type	0	Omission of Appendages	7	0	Upper and Lower Halves	0 3	Hair Shading	3	2	Head	06	07
Sex Sequence	0	Position of Both Arms	4	1	Four Quarters	4 4	Nudity and Transparency	3	0	Neck	05	08
Posture	1 1	Position of Right Arm	7	2	Relative Size	4	Form	1	1	Shoulders		06
Perspective	1 0	Position of Left Arm	5	5	Constant Line Pressure	5 0	Detailing	1	1	Right Arm		05
Vertical Midline	4 0	Position of Legs	4	2	Variable Line Pressure	0 1	Identity and Sex	1	1	Left Arm		04
Bilateral Symmetry	0 4	Relation of Long Axes	1	1	Line Continuity	0 0	Sophistication	1	1	Chest		06
Horizontal Midline	4 0	Right and Left Halves	1	1	Body Shading	3 3	Height	05	06	Girth		05

GENERAL CHARACTERISTICS OF SUBJECT

IDENTIFICATION

No. D77

Sex M

Marital status S

Age 22 yrs. at

psychological tests

PARENTAL HISTORY

Father

C H S D O

–   –   –   –   ?

Mother

C H S D O

–   –   –   –   ?

PHYSIOLOGICAL AND METABOLIC DATA

	Admission	Initial	Control	Cold pressor change	Exercise change	Smoking change
Systolic pressure	110	108	99	+33	+41	00
Diastolic pressure	70	70	70	+20	-31	+04
Heart rate	70	64	59	+16	+41	+15

Age 22 yrs.

Height 70 in.   Ponderal index 13.86

Weight 129 lbs.   Cholesterol 215 mg. per 100 ml.

Overweight -16 %   Vital capacity 4.4 liters

HABIT SURVEY

Smoking habits: heavy cigarette smoker

Age begun 18 yrs.   Inhalation: yes

Habits of nervous tension: 3, 5, 9, 11, 14, 15,

16, 22, 25

STRONG VOCATIONAL INTEREST TEST

Occupation	Artist	Psychologist	Architect	Physician	Osteopath	Dentist	Veterinarian	Mathematician	Physicist	Engineer	Chemist	Production Manager
Standard Score	40	47	37	54	46	38	22	23	12	10	27	17

Occupation	Farmer	Aviator	Carpenter	Printer	Math.-Sci. Teacher	Ind. Arts Teacher	Voc. Agric. Teacher	Policeman	Forest Serv. Man	Y.M.C.A. Phys. Dir.	Personnel Director	Public Administrator
Standard Score	21	16	07	41	38	12	25	21	15	47	36	43

Occupation	Y.M.C.A. Secretary	Soc. Sci. H.S. Teacher	City Sch. Sup't.	Social Worker	Minister	Musician Performer	C.P.A.	Senior C.P.A.	Accountant	Office Man	Purchasing Agent	Banker
Standard Score	44	50	47	52	63	59	31	31	17	32	15	22

Occupation	Mortician	Pharmacist	Sales Manager	Real Est. Manager	Life Ins. Salesman	Advertising Man	Lawyer	Author-Journalist	President Mfg. Co.	Interest Maturity	Occupational Level	Masculinity-Femininity
Standard Score	33	34	32	39	41	54	46	44	24	60	63	24

FIGURE-DRAWING CHARACTERISTICS

Structural	Male Female Both	Structural	Male	Female	Structural and Graphic	Male Female Both	Graphic, Global and Height	Male	Female	Body Proportions	Male	Female
Type	0	Omission of Appendages	0	0	Upper and Lower Halves	0 3	Hair Shading	1	3	Head	09	08
Sex Sequence	1	Position of Both Arms	0	4	Four Quarters	4 4	Nudity and Transparency	7	7	Neck	10	06
Posture	1 2	Position of Right Arm	0	7	Relative Size	2	Form	1	1	Shoulders	08	
Perspective	0 1	Position of Left Arm	0	5	Constant Line Pressure	0 0	Detailing	1	1	Right Arm	08	
Vertical Midline	0 4	Position of Legs	6	8	Variable Line Pressure	5 4	Identity and Sex	1	1	Left Arm	08	08
Bilateral Symmetry	3 0	Relation of Long Axes	1	1	Line Continuity	0 0	Sophistication	1	1	Chest	07	
Horizontal Midline	4 4	Right and Left Halves	1	1	Body Shading	5 7	Height	07	07	Girth	08	

GENERAL CHARACTERISTICS OF SUBJECT

IDENTIFICATION
No. E67
Sex F
Marital status S
Age 22 yrs. at
psychological tests

PARENTAL HISTORY				
Father				
C	H	S	D	O
–	–	–	–	?
Mother				
C	H	S	D	O
–	–	–	–	?

PHYSIOLOGICAL AND METABOLIC DATA

	Admission	Initial	Control	Cold pressor change	Exercise change	Smoking change
Systolic pressure	120	105	102	+02	+30	
Diastolic pressure	70	69	66	+07	–04	
Heart rate	80	68	62	+11	+34	

Age 23 yrs.	Height	64	in.	Ponderal index	12.73	
	Weight	127	lbs.	Cholesterol	284	mg. per 100 ml.
	Overweight	00	%	Vital capacity	3.4	liters

HABIT SURVEY

Smoking habits: nonsmoker

Age begun   yrs.   Inhalation:

Habits of nervous tension: 1, 4, 6, 8, 10, 11,
14, 17, 22, 25

STRONG VOCATIONAL INTEREST TEST

Occupation	Artist	Psychologist	Architect	Physician	Osteopath	Dentist	Veterinarian	Mathematician	Physicist	Engineer	Chemist	Production Manager
Standard Score	37	46	37	58	50	38	27	26	18	21	35	22

Occupation	Farmer	Aviator	Carpenter	Printer	Math.-Sci. Teacher	Ind. Arts Teacher	Voc. Agric. Teacher	Policeman	Forest Serv. Man	Y.M.C.A. Phys. Dir.	Personnel Director	Public Administrator
Standard Score	27	26	11	35	39	11	25	27	31	45	40	46

Occupation	Y.M.C.A. Secretary	Soc. Sci. H.S. Teacher	City Sch. Sup't.	Social Worker	Minister	Musician Performer	C.P.A.	Senior C.P.A.	Accountant	Office Man	Purchasing Agent	Banker
Standard Score	37	41	37	52	64	57	34	38	25	34	13	17

Occupation	Mortician	Pharmacist	Sales Manager	Real Est. Manager	Life Ins. Salesman	Advertising Man	Lawyer	Author-Journalist	President Mfg. Co.	Interest Maturity	Occupational Level	Masculinity-Femininity
Standard Score	31	35	28	32	39	40	37	39	25	59	58	22

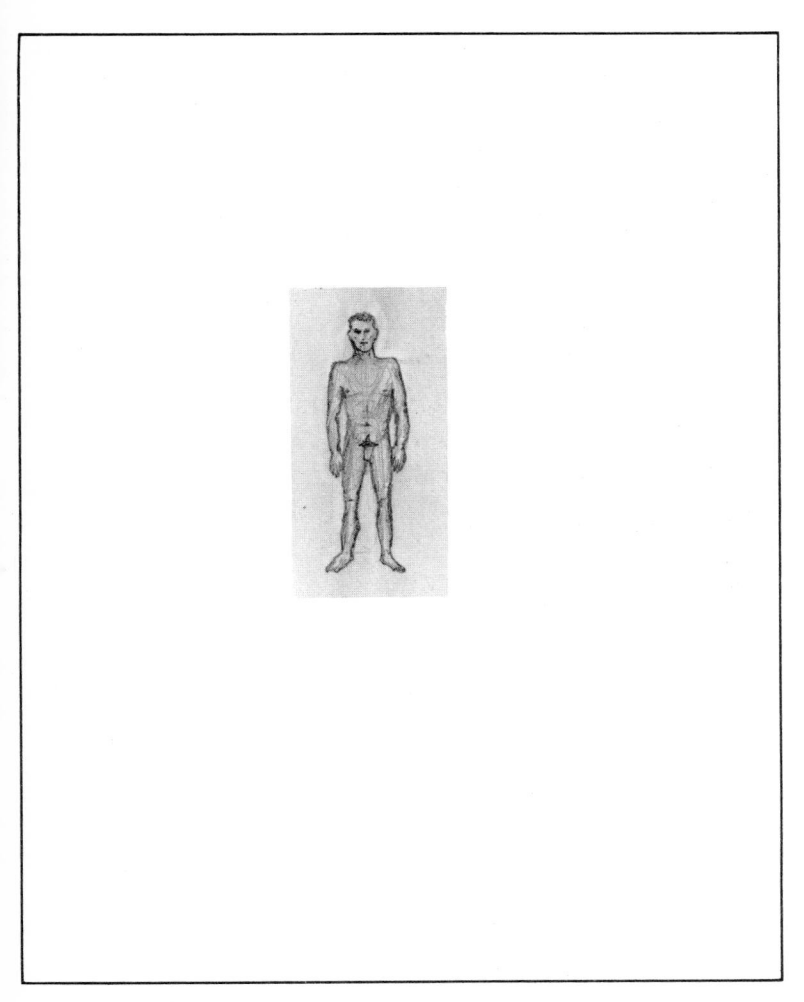

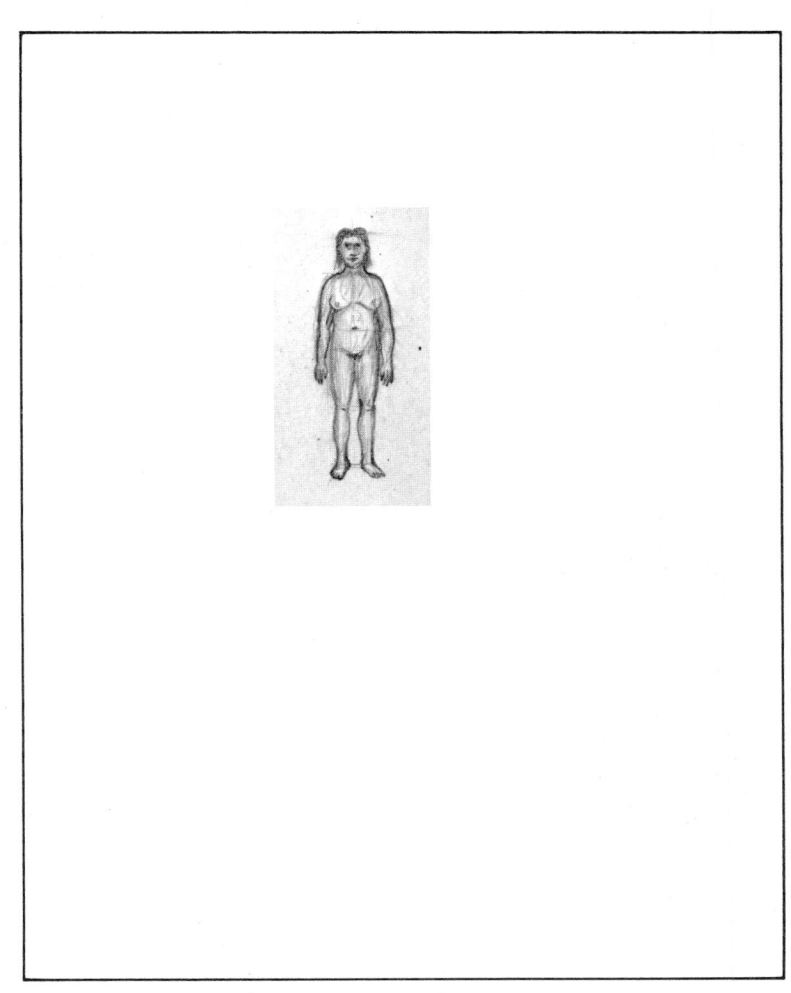

FIGURE-DRAWING CHARACTERISTICS

Structural	Male Female Both	Structural	Male	Female	Structural and Graphic	Male Female Both		Graphic, Global and Height	Male	Female	Body Proportions	Male	Female
Type	0	Omission of Appendages	0	0	Upper and Lower Halves	1	2	Hair Shading	2	2	Head	03	03
Sex Sequence	2	Position of Both Arms	0	0	Four Quarters	4	0	Nudity and Transparency	0	0	Neck	02	02
Posture	1 1	Position of Right Arm	0	0	Relative Size	2		Form	1	1	Shoulders	02	02
Perspective	0 0	Position of Left Arm	0	0	Constant Line Pressure	0	0	Detailing	1	1	Right Arm	02	02
Vertical Midline	0 0	Position of Legs	6	4	Variable Line Pressure	5	5	Identity and Sex	1	1	Left Arm	02	02
Bilateral Symmetry	5 5	Relation of Long Axes	1	1	Line Continuity	3	3	Sophistication	1	1	Chest	02	02
Horizontal Midline	0 0	Right and Left Halves	1	2	Body Shading	3	3	Height	02	02	Girth	02	02

GENERAL CHARACTERISTICS OF SUBJECT

IDENTIFICATION
No. F61
Sex M
Marital status S
Age 29 yrs. at
psychological tests

PARENTAL HISTORY
Father
C   H   S   D   0
–   –   –   –   ?
Mother
C   H   S   D   0
–   –   –   –   –

PHYSIOLOGICAL AND METABOLIC DATA

	Admission	Initial	Control	Cold pressor change	Exercise change	Smoking change
Systolic pressure	120	122	108	+18	+28	+01
Diastolic pressure	80	64	62	+30	00	+02
Heart rate	80	76	72	+14	+11	-03

Height	74 in.	Ponderal index	13.55
Weight	163 lbs.	Cholesterol	203 mg. per 100 ml.
Age 26 yrs. Overweight	-09 %	Vital capacity	5.5 liters

HABIT SURVEY

Smoking habits: pipe and cigar smoker

Age begun 21 yrs.   Inhalation: no

Habits of nervous tension: 5, 9, 18, 25

STRONG VOCATIONAL INTEREST TEST

Occupation	Artist	Psychologist	Architect	Physician	Osteopath	Dentist	Veterinarian	Mathematician	Physicist	Engineer	Chemist	Production Manager
Standard Score	50	33	51	30	15	34	-10	54	44	39	43	20

Occupation	Farmer	Aviator	Carpenter	Printer	Math.-Sci. Teacher	Ind. Arts Teacher	Voc. Agric. Teacher	Policeman	Forest Serv. Man	Y.M.C.A. Phys. Dir.	Personnel Director	Public Administrator
Standard Score	21	08	17	33	21	06	-08	10	-10	-03	06	14

Occupation	Y.M.C.A. Secretary	Soc. Sci. H.S. Teacher	City Sch. Sup't.	Social Worker	Minister	Musician Performer	C.P.A.	Senior C.P.A.	Accountant	Office Man	Purchasing Agent	Banker
Standard Score	05	13	16	09	58	33	46	16	21	17	14	29

Occupation	Mortician	Pharmacist	Sales Manager	Real Est. Manager	Life Ins. Salesman	Advertising Man	Lawyer	Author-Journalist	President Mfg. Co.	Interest Maturity	Occupational Level	Masculinity-Femininity
Standard Score	06	12	06	21	16	40	46	54	37	38	64	31

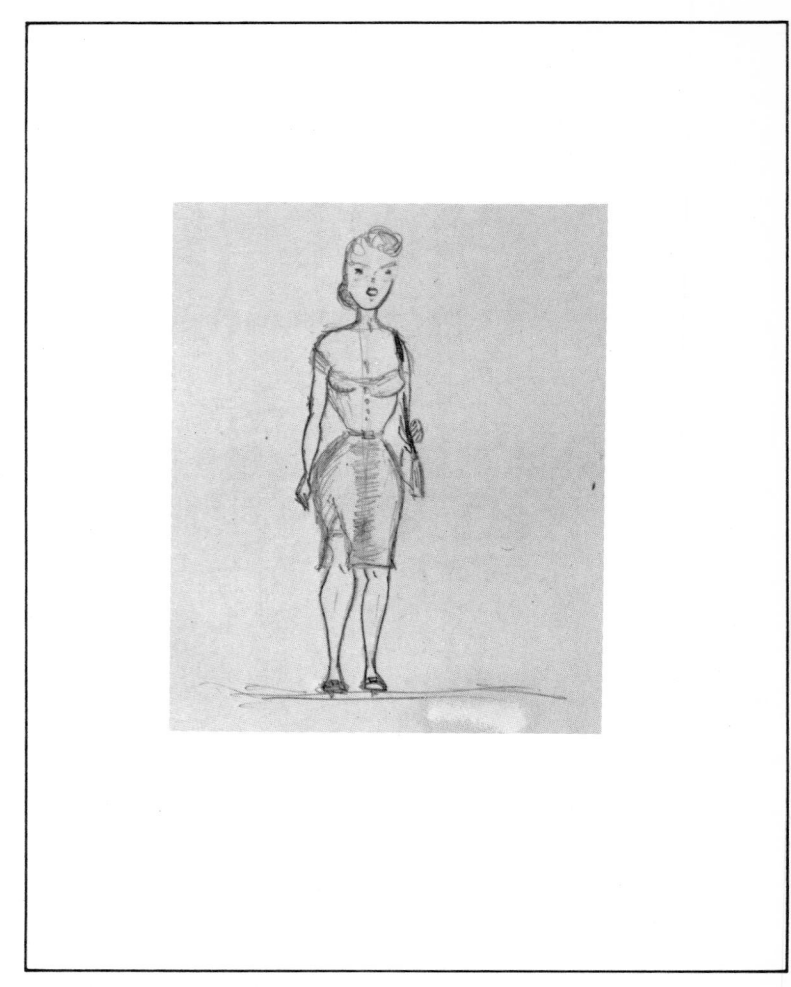

FIGURE-DRAWING CHARACTERISTICS

Structural	Male Female Both	Structural	Male	Female	Structural and Graphic	Male Female Both		Graphic, Global and Height	Male	Female	Body Proportions	Male	Female
Type	0	Omission of Appendages	0	0	Upper and Lower Halves	1	1	Hair Shading	3	3	Head	05	06
Sex Sequence	0	Position of Both Arms	0	1	Four Quarters	4	4	Nudity and Transparency	7	7	Neck	06	05
Posture	1 1	Position of Right Arm	0	0	Relative Size	2		Form	1	1	Shoulders	04	03
Perspective	0 0	Position of Left Arm	0	4	Constant Line Pressure	0	0	Detailing	1	1	Right Arm	04	04
Vertical Midline	3 3	Position of Legs	2	4	Variable Line Pressure	2	5	Identity and Sex	1	1	Left Arm	04	
Bilateral Symmetry	3 3	Relation of Long Axes	1	1	Line Continuity	0	1	Sophistication	1	1	Chest	04	03
Horizontal Midline	4 4	Right and Left Halves	1	1	Body Shading	7	7	Height	04	04	Girth	04	02

GENERAL CHARACTERISTICS OF SUBJECT

IDENTIFICATION

No. G12
Sex M
Marital status S
Age 21 yrs. at
psychological tests

PARENTAL HISTORY

Father

C	H	S	D	O
-	-	-	-	?

Mother

C	H	S	D	O
-	-	-	-	

PHYSIOLOGICAL AND METABOLIC DATA

	Admission	Initial	Control	Cold pressor change	Exercise change	Smoking change
Systolic pressure	124	132	112	+20	+08	
Diastolic pressure	80	70	68	+10	-08	
Heart rate	76	80	75	-08	+13	

Age 20 yrs.　Height 72 in.　Ponderal index 13.19
Weight 163 lbs.　Cholesterol 230 mg. per 100 ml.
Overweight +01 %　Vital capacity liters

HABIT SURVEY

Smoking habits: nonsmoker
Age begun yrs. Inhalation:
Habits of nervous tension: 1, 5, 6, 16, 18, 21, 25

STRONG VOCATIONAL INTEREST TEST

Occupation	Artist	Psychologist	Architect	Physician	Osteopath	Dentist	Veterinarian	Mathematician	Physicist	Engineer	Chemist	Production Manager
Standard Score	39	32	47	49	49	41	23	20	19	36	29	33

Occupation	Farmer	Aviator	Carpenter	Printer	Math.-Sci. Teacher	Ind. Arts Teacher	Voc. Agric. Teacher	Policeman	Forest Serv. Man	Y.M.C.A. Phys. Dir.	Personnel Director	Public Administrator
Standard Score	32	47	34	43	35	36	28	41	32	42	36	30

Occupation	Y.M.C.A. Secretary	Soc. Sci. H.S. Teacher	City Sch. Sup't.	Social Worker	Minister	Musician Performer	C.P.A.	Senior C.P.A.	Accountant	Office Man	Purchasing Agent	Banker
Standard Score	25	26	19	35	59	53	23	36	22	36	23	17

Occupation	Mortician	Pharmacist	Sales Manager	Real Est. Manager	Life Ins. Salesman	Advertising Man	Lawyer	Author-Journalist	President Mfg. Co.	Interest Maturity	Occupational Level	Masculinity-Femininity
Standard Score	36	32	30	35	30	42	28	37	30	56	53	37

Plate 827   MOST SOPHISTICATED DRAWINGS   877

white Rock   Back view

FIGURE-DRAWING CHARACTERISTICS

Structural	Male	Female	Structural	Male	Female	Structural and Graphic	Male	Female	Graphic, Global and Height	Male	Female	Body Proportions	Male	Female
	Both						Both							
Type	0		Omission of Appendages	0	0	Upper and Lower Halves	1	2	Hair Shading	0	3	Head	05	04
Sex Sequence	0		Position of Both Arms	1	1	Four Quarters	4	4	Nudity and Transparency	0	0	Neck	08	06
Posture	1	8	Position of Right Arm	2	5	Relative Size	5		Form	1	1	Shoulders	06	
Perspective	0	1	Position of Left Arm	5	2	Constant Line Pressure	0	3	Detailing	1	1	Right Arm	04	02
Vertical Midline	0	4	Position of Legs	5	1	Variable Line Pressure	5	0	Identity and Sex	1	1	Left Arm	04	02
Bilateral Symmetry	3	0	Relation of Long Axes	1	0	Line Continuity	0	0	Sophistication	1	1	Chest	05	
Horizontal Midline	0	0	Right and Left Halves	1	9	Body Shading	3	1	Height	05		Girth	04	

GENERAL CHARACTERISTICS OF SUBJECT

IDENTIFICATION
No. D18
Sex M
Marital status S
Age 22 yrs. at
psychological tests

PARENTAL HISTORY
Father
C H S D O
- - - - ?
Mother
C H S D O
- - - - -

PHYSIOLOGICAL AND METABOLIC DATA

	Admission	Initial	Control	Cold pressor change	Exercise change	Smoking change
Systolic pressure	130	130	116	+14	+58	
Diastolic pressure	82	80	78	+16	-20	
Heart rate	76	92	79	+20	+04	

Age 22 yrs.	Height 72 in.	Ponderal index 13.56
	Weight 150 lbs.	Cholesterol 282 mg. per 100 ml.
	Overweight -08 %	Vital capacity 4.2 liters

HABIT SURVEY

Smoking habits: nonsmoker

Age begun   yrs.   Inhalation:

Habits of nervous tension: 2, 6, 10, 11, 16, 21, 22

STRONG VOCATIONAL INTEREST TEST

Occupation	Artist	Psychologist	Architect	Physician	Osteopath	Dentist	Veterinarian	Mathematician	Physicist	Engineer	Chemist	Production Manager
Standard Score	41	41	41	61	52	49	30	33	37	44	48	31

Occupation	Farmer	Aviator	Carpenter	Printer	Math.-Sci. Teacher	Ind. Arts Teacher	Voc. Agric. Teacher	Policeman	Forest Serv. Man	Y.M.C.A. Phys. Dir.	Personnel Director	Public Administrator
Standard Score	40	46	29	40	37	28	28	32	28	31	19	26

Occupation	Y.M.C.A. Secretary	Soc. Sci. H.S. Teacher	City Sch. Sup't.	Social Worker	Minister	Musician Performer	C.P.A.	Senior C.P.A.	Accountant	Office Man	Purchasing Agent	Banker
Standard Score	17	21	13	27	63	50	17	33	22	24	17	14

Occupation	Mortician	Pharmacist	Sales Manager	Real Est. Manager	Life Ins. Salesman	Advertising Man	Lawyer	Author-Journalist	President Mfg. Co.	Interest Maturity	Occupational Level	Masculinity-Femininity
Standard Score	22	37	23	29	23	33	28	37	32	50	56	45

FIGURE-DRAWING CHARACTERISTICS

Structural	Male Female Both	Structural	Male	Female	Structural and Graphic	Male Female Both	Graphic, Global and Height	Male	Female	Body Proportions	Male	Female
Type	0	Omission of Appendages	7	0	Upper and Lower Halves	0 3	Hair Shading	1	3	Head	09	07
Sex Sequence	0	Position of Both Arms	0	0	Four Quarters	4 4	Nudity and Transparency	0	0	Neck	07	07
Posture	6 5	Position of Right Arm	6	6	Relative Size	5	Form	1	1	Shoulders		
Perspective	1 1	Position of Left Arm	6	6	Constant Line Pressure	5 0	Detailing	1	1	Right Arm		06
Vertical Midline	4 4	Position of Legs	8	8	Variable Line Pressure	0 5	Identity and Sex	1	1	Left Arm	10	05
Bilateral Symmetry	0 0	Relation of Long Axes	1	0	Line Continuity	0 0	Sophistication	1	1	Chest		
Horizontal Midline	0 0	Right and Left Halves	1	3	Body Shading	3 3	Height	08		Girth		

GENERAL CHARACTERISTICS OF SUBJECT

IDENTIFICATION
No. C40
Sex M
Marital status S
Age 22 yrs. at
psychological tests

PARENTAL HISTORY
Father
C   H   S   D   O
-    -   -   -   -
Mother
C   H   S   D   O
-    -   -   -   ?

PHYSIOLOGICAL AND METABOLIC DATA

	Admission	Initial	Control	Cold pressor change	Exercise change	Smoking change
Systolic pressure	130	120	115	-03	+50	+10
Diastolic pressure	80	65	65	+15	00	+04
Heart rate	80	72	70	-04	+30	+01

Age 23 yrs.	Height 73 in.	Ponderal index 13.39
	Weight 162 lbs.	Cholesterol 180 mg. per 100 ml.
	Overweight -04 %	Vital capacity 4.7 liters

HABIT SURVEY

Smoking habits: nonsmoker

Age begun   yrs.   Inhalation:

Habits of nervous tension: 6, 10, 16

STRONG VOCATIONAL INTEREST TEST

Occupation	Artist	Psychologist	Architect	Physician	Osteopath	Dentist	Veterinarian	Mathematician	Physicist	Engineer	Chemist	Production Manager
Standard Score	45	38	45	58	54	55	46	34	34	36	44	26

Occupation	Farmer	Aviator	Carpenter	Printer	Math.-Sci. Teacher	Ind. Arts Teacher	Voc. Agric. Teacher	Policeman	Forest Serv. Man	Y.M.C.A. Phys. Dir.	Personnel Director	Public Administrator
Standard Score	45	37	40	39	43	43	51	32	32	32	15	30

Occupation	Y.M.C.A. Secretary	Soc. Sci. H.S. Teacher	City Sch. Sup't.	Social Worker	Minister	Musician Performer	C.P.A.	Senior C.P.A.	Accountant	Office Man	Purchasing Agent	Banker
Standard Score	20	28	18	30	62	54	14	35	14	26	15	21

Occupation	Mortician	Pharmacist	Sales Manager	Real Est. Manager	Life Ins. Salesman	Advertising Man	Lawyer	Author-Journalist	President Mfg. Co.	Interest Maturity	Occupational Level	Masculinity-Femininity
Standard Score	33	46	17	27	20	31	24	37	23	48	50	40

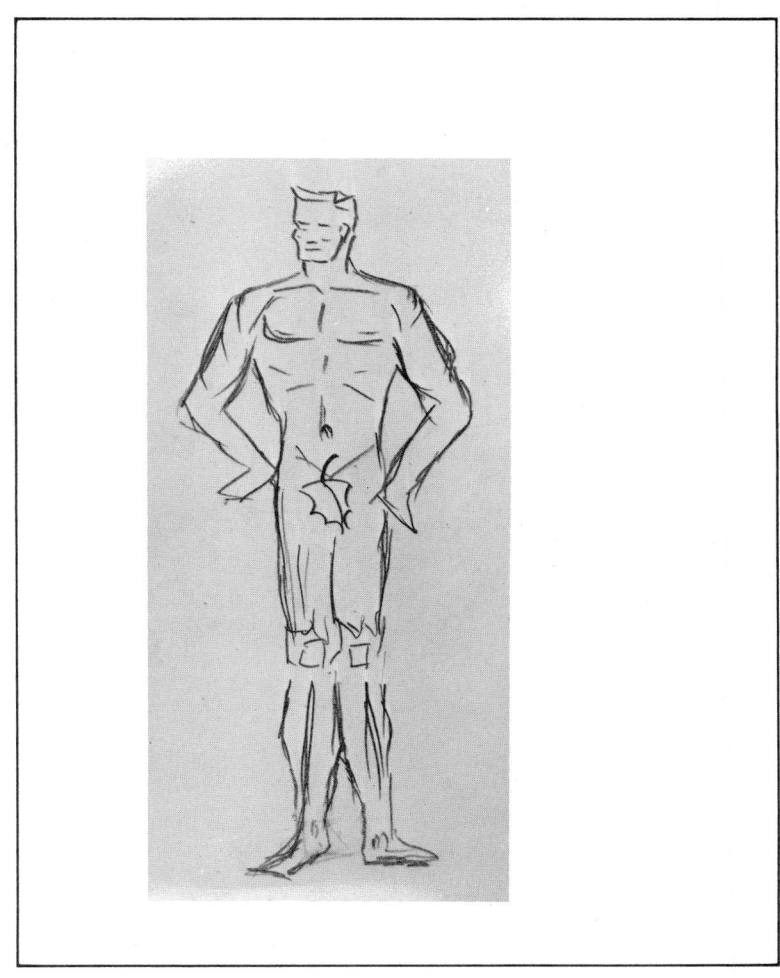

FIGURE-DRAWING CHARACTERISTICS

Structural	Male / Female (Both)		Structural	Male	Female	Structural and Graphic	Male / Female (Both)		Graphic, Global and Height	Male	Female	Body Proportions	Male	Female
Type	0		Omission of Appendages	0	0	Upper and Lower Halves	3	0	Hair Shading	5	1	Head	05	05
Sex Sequence	1		Position of Both Arms	0	0	Four Quarters	4	4	Nudity and Transparency	0	0	Neck	05	05
Posture	1	2	Position of Right Arm	5	6	Relative Size	0		Form	1	1	Shoulders	07	
Perspective	0	1	Position of Left Arm	5	6	Constant Line Pressure	5	0	Detailing	1	1	Right Arm	06	06
Vertical Midline	0	4	Position of Legs	2	8	Variable Line Pressure	0	5	Identity and Sex	1	1	Left Arm	06	06
Bilateral Symmetry	4	0	Relation of Long Axes	1	1	Line Continuity	0	0	Sophistication	1	1	Chest	06	
Horizontal Midline	0	0	Right and Left Halves	1	1	Body Shading	3	1	Height	07	06	Girth	06	

GENERAL CHARACTERISTICS OF SUBJECT

IDENTIFICATION

No. D25
Sex M
Marital status S
Age 22 yrs. at psychological tests

PARENTAL HISTORY

Father
C H S D O
- - - - -

Mother
C H S D O
- - - - ?

PHYSIOLOGICAL AND METABOLIC DATA

	Admission	Initial	Control	Cold pressor change	Exercise change	Smoking change
Systolic pressure	145	130	120	+10	+20	+04
Diastolic pressure	70	60	60	+10	-05	+04
Heart rate		64	71	+16	+32	-01

Age 21 yrs.   Height 70 in.   Weight 168 lbs.   Overweight +10 %

Ponderal index 12.60   Cholesterol 248 mg. per 100 ml.   Vital capacity 5.2 liters

HABIT SURVEY

Smoking habits: nonsmoker
Age begun   yrs.   Inhalation:
Habits of nervous tension: 2, 4, 6, 9, 18, 25

STRONG VOCATIONAL INTEREST TEST

Occupation	Artist	Psychologist	Architect	Physician	Osteopath	Dentist	Veterinarian	Mathematician	Physicist	Engineer	Chemist	Production Manager
Standard Score	54	51	51	61	46	43	31	40	31	27	36	24

Occupation	Farmer	Aviator	Carpenter	Printer	Math.-Sci. Teacher	Ind. Arts Teacher	Voc. Agric. Teacher	Policeman	Forest Serv. Man	Y.M.C.A. Phys. Dir.	Personnel Director	Public Administrator
Standard Score	33	18	19	25	30	13	26	20	27	43	26	40

Occupation	Y.M.C.A. Secretary	Soc. Sci. H.S. Teacher	City Sch. Sup't.	Social Worker	Minister	Musician Performer	C.P.A.	Senior C.P.A.	Accountant	Office Man	Purchasing Agent	Banker
Standard Score	34	33	39	48	63	62	25	16	08	17	03	20

Occupation	Mortician	Pharmacist	Sales Manager	Real Est. Manager	Life Ins. Salesman	Advertising Man	Lawyer	Author-Journalist	President Mfg. Co.	Interest Maturity	Occupational Level	Masculinity-Femininity
Standard Score	22	32	23	32	33	44	40	50	33	52	60	24

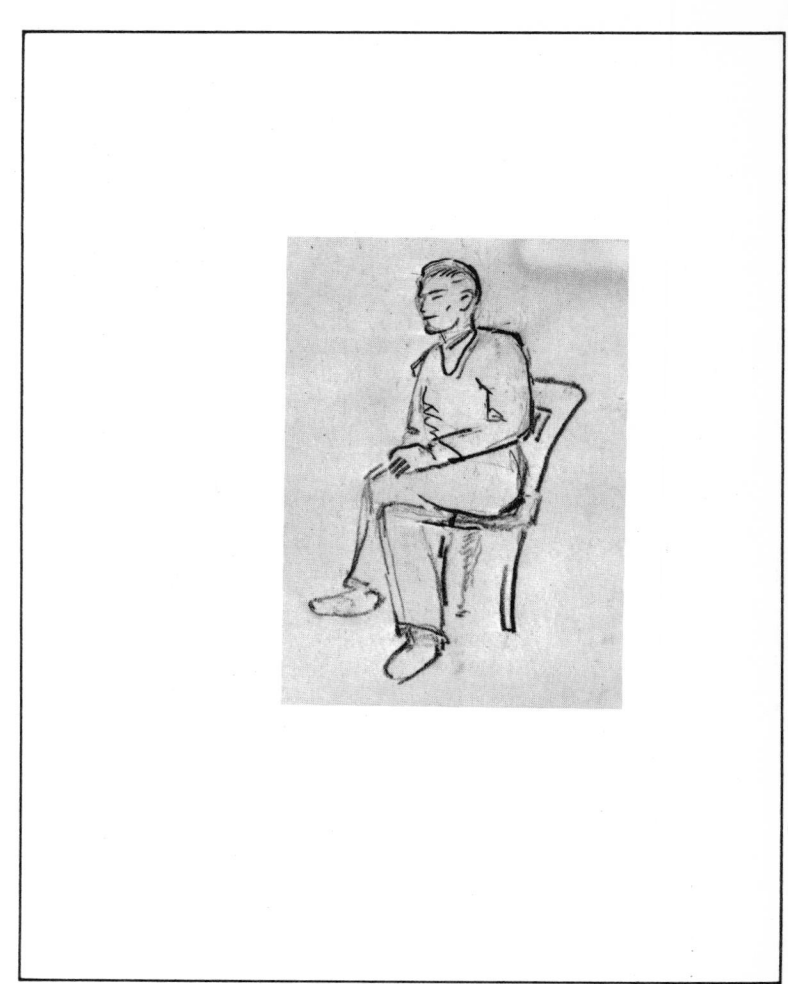

FIGURE-DRAWING CHARACTERISTICS

Structural	Male Female Both	Structural	Male	Female	Structural and Graphic	Male Female Both		Graphic, Global and Height	Male	Female	Body Proportions	Male	Female
Type	0	Omission of Appendages	0	0	Upper and Lower Halves	1	1	Hair Shading	1	1	Head	06	05
Sex Sequence	1	Position of Both Arms	4	1	Four Quarters	4	4	Nudity and Transparency	7	7	Neck	04	04
Posture	3 2	Position of Right Arm	7	0	Relative Size	5		Form	1	1	Shoulders		04
Perspective	6 0	Position of Left Arm	5	2	Constant Line Pressure	0	5	Detailing	1	1	Right Arm		04
Vertical Midline	4 0	Position of Legs	7	8	Variable Line Pressure	3	0	Identity and Sex	1	1	Left Arm	04	04
Bilateral Symmetry	0 3	Relation of Long Axes	0	1	Line Continuity	2	2	Sophistication	1	1	Chest		05
Horizontal Midline	0 4	Right and Left Halves	3	1	Body Shading	3	3	Height		05	Girth		04

GENERAL CHARACTERISTICS OF SUBJECT

<table>
<tr><th>IDENTIFICATION</th><th colspan="2">PARENTAL HISTORY</th><th colspan="7">PHYSIOLOGICAL AND METABOLIC DATA</th><th colspan="2">HABIT SURVEY</th></tr>
<tr><td>No. 335</td><td colspan="2">Father</td><td></td><td>Admission</td><td>Initial</td><td>Control</td><td>Cold pressor change</td><td>Exercise change</td><td>Smoking change</td><td colspan="2">Smoking habits: unknown</td></tr>
<tr><td>Sex M</td><td colspan="2">C H S D O</td><td>Systolic pressure</td><td>120</td><td>124</td><td>106</td><td>+06</td><td>+28</td><td></td><td colspan="2">Age begun   yrs.   Inhalation:</td></tr>
<tr><td>Marital status S</td><td colspan="2">- - - - -</td><td>Diastolic pressure</td><td>80</td><td>64</td><td>66</td><td>+08</td><td>+08</td><td></td><td colspan="2">Habits of nervous tension:</td></tr>
<tr><td>Age 23 yrs. at</td><td colspan="2">Mother</td><td>Heart rate</td><td>70</td><td>78</td><td>77</td><td>00</td><td>+20</td><td></td><td colspan="2"></td></tr>
<tr><td>psychological tests</td><td colspan="2">C H S D O</td><td rowspan="3"></td><td colspan="2">Height   71 in.</td><td colspan="4">Ponderal index 13.64</td><td colspan="2"></td></tr>
<tr><td></td><td colspan="2">- - - - -</td><td colspan="2">Weight 141 lbs.</td><td colspan="4">Cholesterol   210 mg. per 100 ml.</td><td colspan="2"></td></tr>
<tr><td></td><td colspan="2">Age 22 yrs.</td><td colspan="2">Overweight -11 %</td><td colspan="4">Vital capacity 5.6 liters</td><td colspan="2"></td></tr>
</table>

Plate 831   MOST SOPHISTICATED DRAWINGS   881

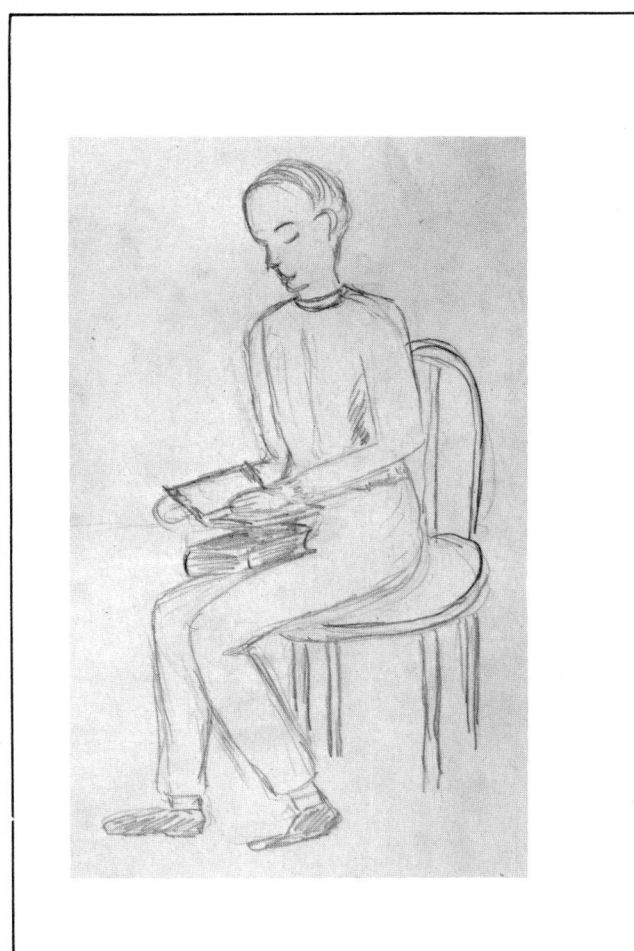

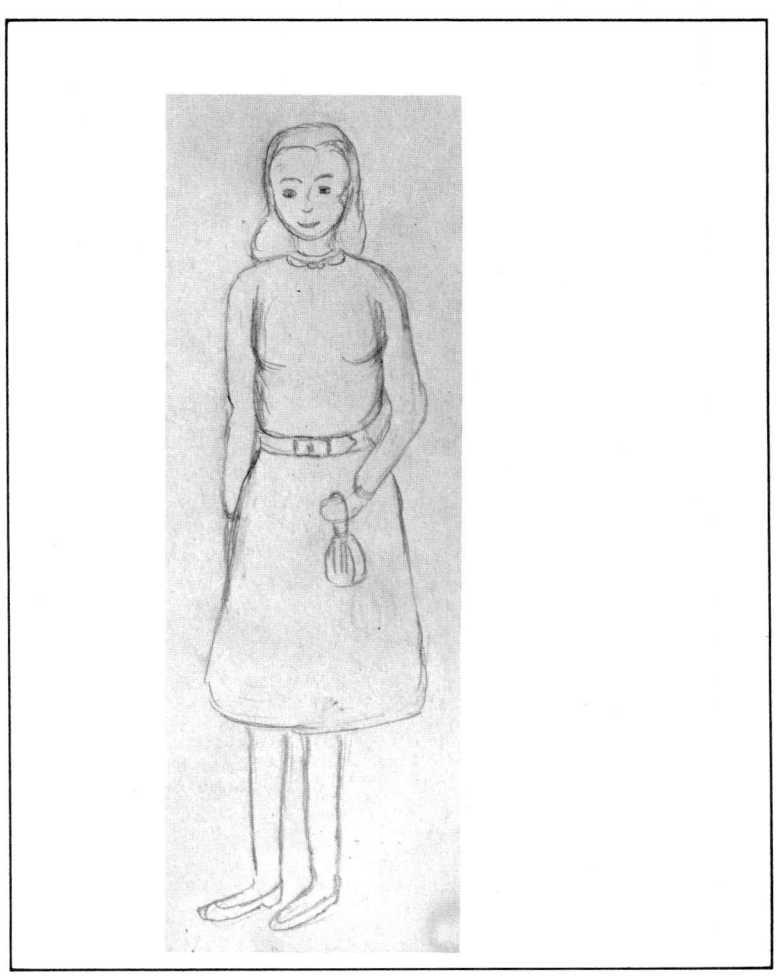

FIGURE-DRAWING CHARACTERISTICS

Structural	Male Female Both		Structural	Male	Female	Structural and Graphic	Male Female Both		Graphic, Global and Height	Male	Female	Body Proportions	Male	Female
Type	0		Omission of Appendages	0	0	Upper and Lower Halves	0	3	Hair Shading	3	1	Head	11	10
Sex Sequence	0		Position of Both Arms	0	1	Four Quarters	4	4	Nudity and Transparency	7	7	Neck	04	06
Posture	3	1	Position of Right Arm	4	0	Relative Size	5		Form	1	1	Shoulders		07
Perspective	6	0	Position of Left Arm	4	5	Constant Line Pressure	0	0	Detailing	1	1	Right Arm		06
Vertical Midline	5	0	Position of Legs	9	4	Variable Line Pressure	1	1	Identity and Sex	3	1	Left Arm	08	06
Bilateral Symmetry	0	3	Relation of Long Axes	0	1	Line Continuity	0	0	Sophistication	1	1	Chest		06
Horizontal Midline	4	4	Right and Left Halves	1	1	Body Shading	7	5	Height		08	Girth		07

GENERAL CHARACTERISTICS OF SUBJECT

IDENTIFICATION
No. 438
Sex F
Marital status M
Age 24 yrs. at
psychological tests

PARENTAL HISTORY
Father
C   H   S   D   0
-   -   -   -   -
Mother
C   H   S   D   0
-   -   -   -   -

PHYSIOLOGICAL AND METABOLIC DATA

	Admission	Initial	Control	Cold pressor change	Exercise change	Smoking change
Systolic pressure	110	102	106	+14	+14	
Diastolic pressure	70	70	74	+22	-02	
Heart rate	72	70	94	+06	+13	

Age 22 yrs.	Height	60	in.	Ponderal index 12.52		
	Weight	110	lbs.	Cholesterol	273	mg. per 100 ml.
	Overweight -04 %			Vital capacity		liters

HABIT SURVEY
Smoking habits: nonsmoker
Age begun   yrs.   Inhalation:
Habits of nervous tension: 3, 5, 6, 18

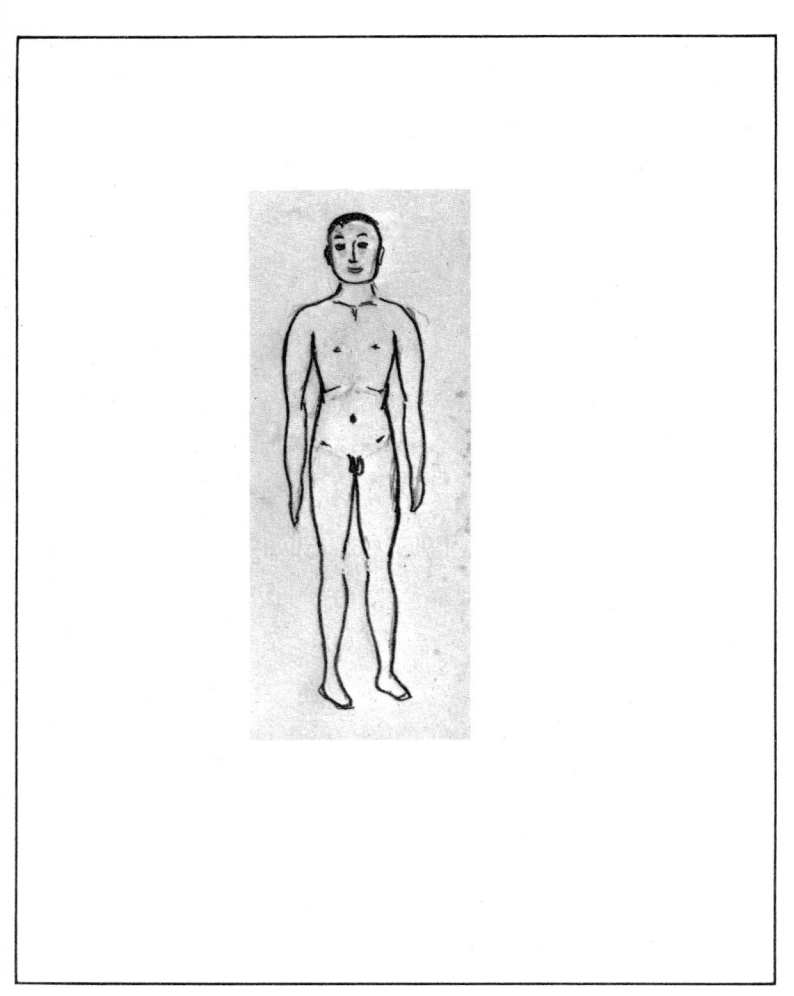

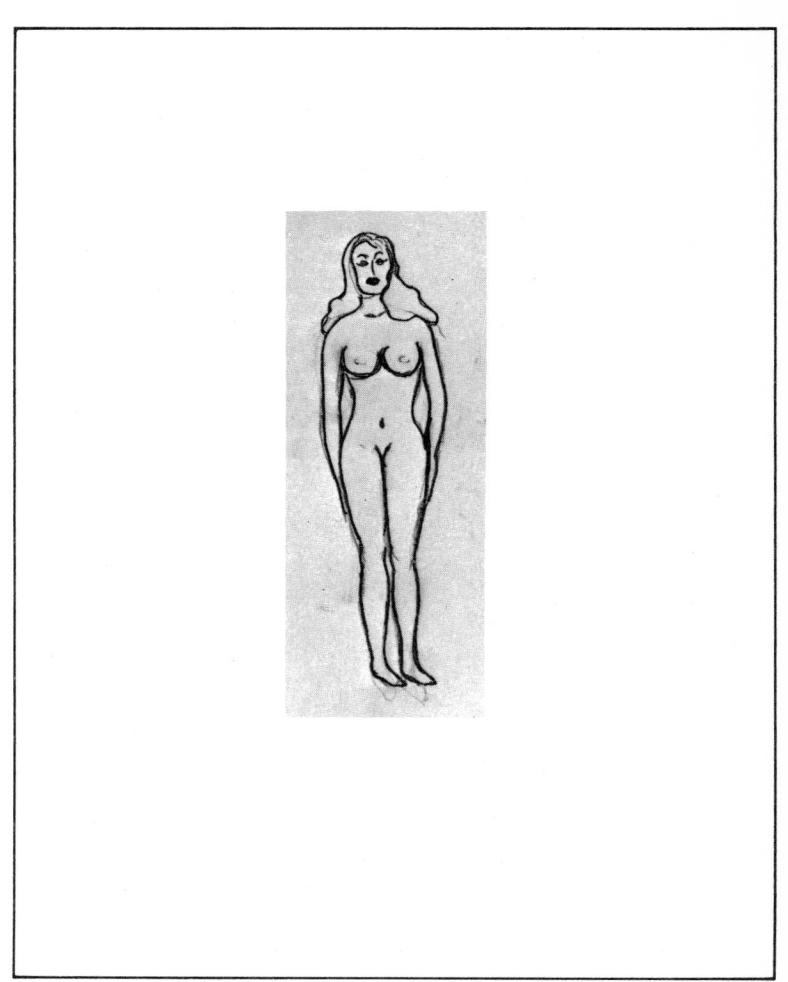

FIGURE-DRAWING CHARACTERISTICS

Structural	Male Female Both	Structural	Male	Female	Structural and Graphic	Male Female Both	Graphic, Global and Height	Male	Female	Body Proportions	Male	Female
Type	0	Omission of Appendages	0	0	Upper and Lower Halves	1 1	Hair Shading	1	2	Head	05	04
Sex Sequence	0	Position of Both Arms	0	0	Four Quarters	4 4	Nudity and Transparency	0	0	Neck	06	06
Posture	1 1	Position of Right Arm	0	0	Relative Size	0	Form	1	1	Shoulders	04	04
Perspective	0 0	Position of Left Arm	0	0	Constant Line Pressure	5 5	Detailing	1	1	Right Arm	04	04
Vertical Midline	0 0	Position of Legs	4	3	Variable Line Pressure	0 0	Identity and Sex	1	1	Left Arm	04	04
Bilateral Symmetry	5 5	Relation of Long Axes	1	1	Line Continuity	4 4	Sophistication	1	1	Chest	04	04
Horizontal Midline	0 0	Right and Left Halves	1	1	Body Shading	3 1	Height	05	04	Girth	04	04

GENERAL CHARACTERISTICS OF SUBJECT

IDENTIFICATION
No. 570
Sex M
Marital status S
Age 25 yrs. at psychological tests

PARENTAL HISTORY
Father
C H S D 0
- - - - -
Mother
C H S D 0
- - - - -

PHYSIOLOGICAL AND METABOLIC DATA

	Admission	Initial	Control	Cold pressor change	Exercise change	Smoking change
Systolic pressure	110	118	108	+04	+38	
Diastolic pressure	70	68	66	+09	+04	
Heart rate	96	84	90	00	+04	

Age 23 yrs.	Height 70 in.	Ponderal index 13.23
	Weight 148 lbs.	Cholesterol 265 mg. per 100 ml.
	Overweight −05 %	Vital capacity 4.8 liters

HABIT SURVEY

Smoking habits: heavy cigarette smoker

Age begun 13 yrs.   Inhalation: yes

Habits of nervous tension: 6, 23, 25

Plate 833   MOST SOPHISTICATED DRAWINGS   883

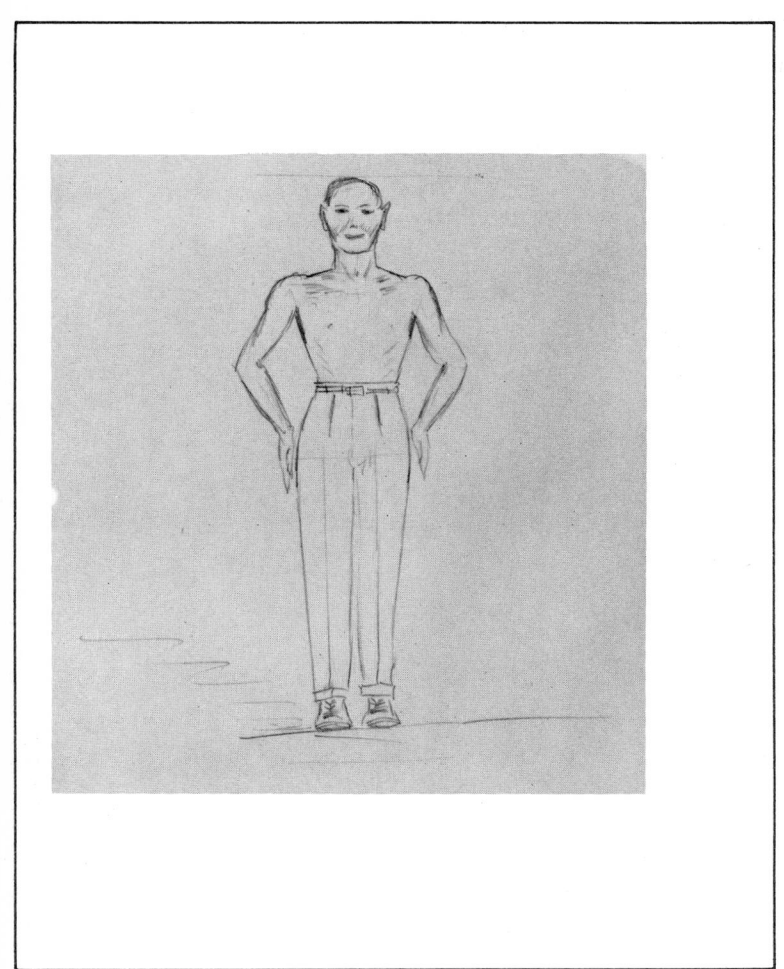

FIGURE-DRAWING CHARACTERISTICS

Structural	Male Female Both	Structural	Male	Female	Structural and Graphic	Male Female Both		Graphic, Global and Height	Male	Female	Body Proportions	Male	Female
Type	0	Omission of Appendages	0	0	Upper and Lower Halves	1	1	Hair Shading	3	1	Head	06	05
Sex Sequence	0	Position of Both Arms	0	0	Four Quarters	4	4	Nudity and Transparency	3	7	Neck	06	06
Posture	1 1	Position of Right Arm	5	5	Relative Size	0		Form	1	1	Shoulders	06	05
Perspective	0 0	Position of Left Arm	5	5	Constant Line Pressure	0	4	Detailing	1	1	Right Arm	05	04
Vertical Midline	3 0	Position of Legs	4	2	Variable Line Pressure	5	0	Identity and Sex	1	1	Left Arm	04	04
Bilateral Symmetry	4 3	Relation of Long Axes	1	1	Line Continuity	0	0	Sophistication	1	1	Chest	05	04
Horizontal Midline	4 4	Right and Left Halves	1	0	Body Shading	3	3	Height	05	05	Girth	05	05

GENERAL CHARACTERISTICS OF SUBJECT

IDENTIFICATION
No. 602
Sex M
Marital status M
Age 29 yrs. at
psychological tests

PARENTAL HISTORY
Father
C   H   S   D   O
–   –   –   –   –
Mother
C   H   S   D   O
–   –   –   –   –

PHYSIOLOGICAL AND METABOLIC DATA

	Admission	Initial	Control	Cold pressor change	Exercise change	Smoking change
Systolic pressure	110	124	116	+14	+36	+08
Diastolic pressure	70	74	70	+20	00	+04
Heart rate	80	68	68	00	+27	+08

Age 26 yrs.	Height 72 in.	Ponderal index 12.80
	Weight 178 lbs.	Cholesterol 217 mg. per 100 ml.
	Overweight +06 %	Vital capacity 5.3 liters

HABIT SURVEY

Smoking habits: heavy cigarette smoker

Age begun 21 yrs.   Inhalation: yes

Habits of nervous tension: 5, 6, 10, 17, 21

FIGURE-DRAWING CHARACTERISTICS

Structural	Male Female Both		Structural	Male	Female	Structural and Graphic	Male Female Both		Graphic, Global and Height	Male	Female	Body Proportions	Male	Female
Type	0		Omission of Appendages	0	6	Upper and Lower Halves	0	1	Hair Shading	0	3	Head	04	03
Sex Sequence	0		Position of Both Arms	0	0	Four Quarters	4	4	Nudity and Transparency	7	7	Neck	02	02
Posture	1	3	Position of Right Arm	6	5	Relative Size	5		Form	1	1	Shoulders	03	03
Perspective	0	0	Position of Left Arm	6	5	Constant Line Pressure	2	3	Detailing	1	1	Right Arm	02	02
Vertical Midline	1	3	Position of Legs	6	0	Variable Line Pressure	0	0	Identity and Sex	1	1	Left Arm	02	02
Bilateral Symmetry	3	5	Relation of Long Axes	1	1	Line Continuity	0	0	Sophistication	1	1	Chest	02	
Horizontal Midline	0	0	Right and Left Halves	1	1	Body Shading	7	1	Height	03		Girth	02	

GENERAL CHARACTERISTICS OF SUBJECT

IDENTIFICATION
No. 614
Sex F
Marital status S
Age 27 yrs. at
psychological tests

PARENTAL HISTORY
Father
C   H   S   D   O
-   -   -   -   -
Mother
C   H   S   D   O
-   -   -   -   -

PHYSIOLOGICAL AND METABOLIC DATA

	Admission	Initial	Control	Cold pressor change	Exercise change	Smoking change
Systolic pressure	124	114	114	+16	+40	+05
Diastolic pressure	78	70	70	+22	-04	-02
Heart rate	80	80	71	00	+44	+02

Age 24 yrs.	Height	72 in.	Ponderal index 12.68
	Weight	183 lbs.	Cholesterol 217 mg. per 100 ml.
	Overweight +16 %		Vital capacity 5.0 liters

HABIT SURVEY
Smoking habits: heavy cigarette smoker
Age begun 21 yrs.   Inhalation: yes
Habits of nervous tension: 4, 5, 6, 10, 15,
16, 25

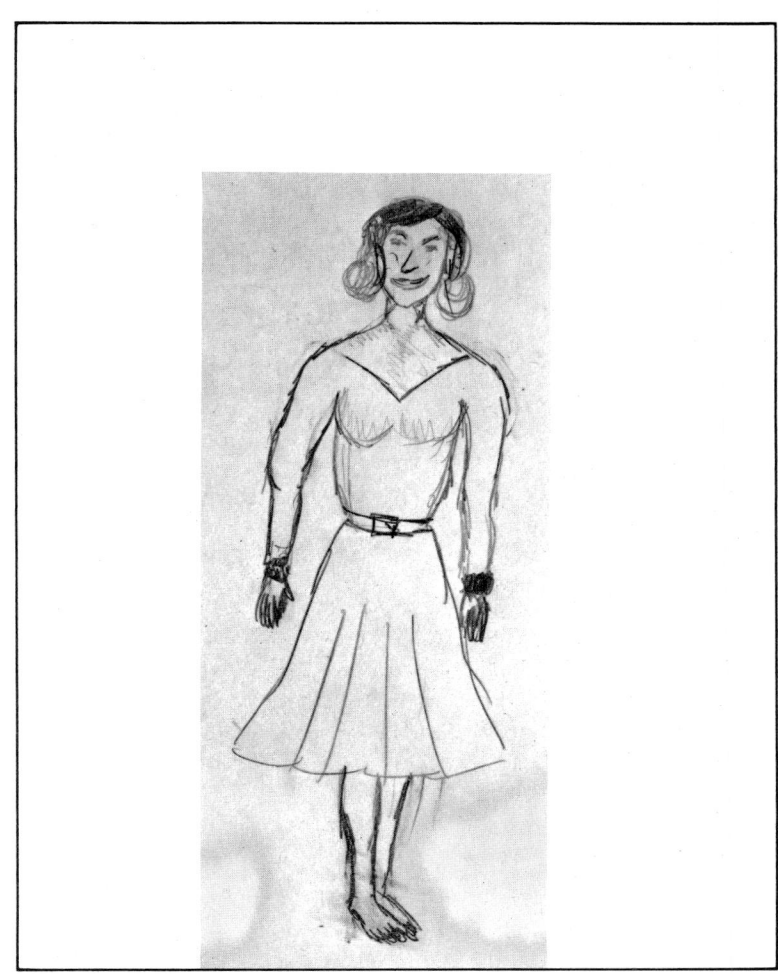

FIGURE-DRAWING CHARACTERISTICS

Structural	Male Female Both	Structural	Male	Female	Structural and Graphic	Male Female Both		Graphic, Global and Height	Male	Female	Body Proportions	Male	Female
Type	0	Omission of Appendages	0	0	Upper and Lower Halves	1	3	Hair Shading	3	3	Head	07	09
Sex Sequence	0	Position of Both Arms	4	0	Four Quarters	4	4	Nudity and Transparency	7	7	Neck	07	07
Posture	1 1	Position of Right Arm	7	0	Relative Size	4		Form	1	1	Shoulders		08
Perspective	2 0	Position of Left Arm	4	0	Constant Line Pressure	0	0	Detailing	1	1	Right Arm		06
Vertical Midline	7 0	Position of Legs	1	2	Variable Line Pressure	5	5	Identity and Sex	1	1	Left Arm	06	06
Bilateral Symmetry	0 3	Relation of Long Axes	1	1	Line Continuity	0	0	Sophistication	1	1	Chest	09	06
Horizontal Midline	4 4	Right and Left Halves	0	1	Body Shading	7	7	Height	06	08	Girth	08	05

GENERAL CHARACTERISTICS OF SUBJECT

IDENTIFICATION
No. 626
Sex M
Marital status S
Age 24 yrs. at
psychological tests

PARENTAL HISTORY
Father
C   H   S   D   O
–   –   –   –   –
Mother
C   H   S   D   O
–   –   –   –   –

PHYSIOLOGICAL AND METABOLIC DATA

	Admission	Initial	Control	Cold pressor change	Exercise change	Smoking change
Systolic pressure	120	134	116	+06	+16	00
Diastolic pressure	80	70	62	+04	–08	+10
Heart rate	80	72	74	+10	+20	+05

Age 22 yrs.   Height 78 in.   Ponderal index 13.43

Weight 196 lbs.   Cholesterol 167 mg. per 100 ml.

Overweight +02 %   Vital capacity liters

HABIT SURVEY
Smoking habits: nonsmoker
Age begun   yrs.   Inhalation:
Habits of nervous tension: 5, 21, 22

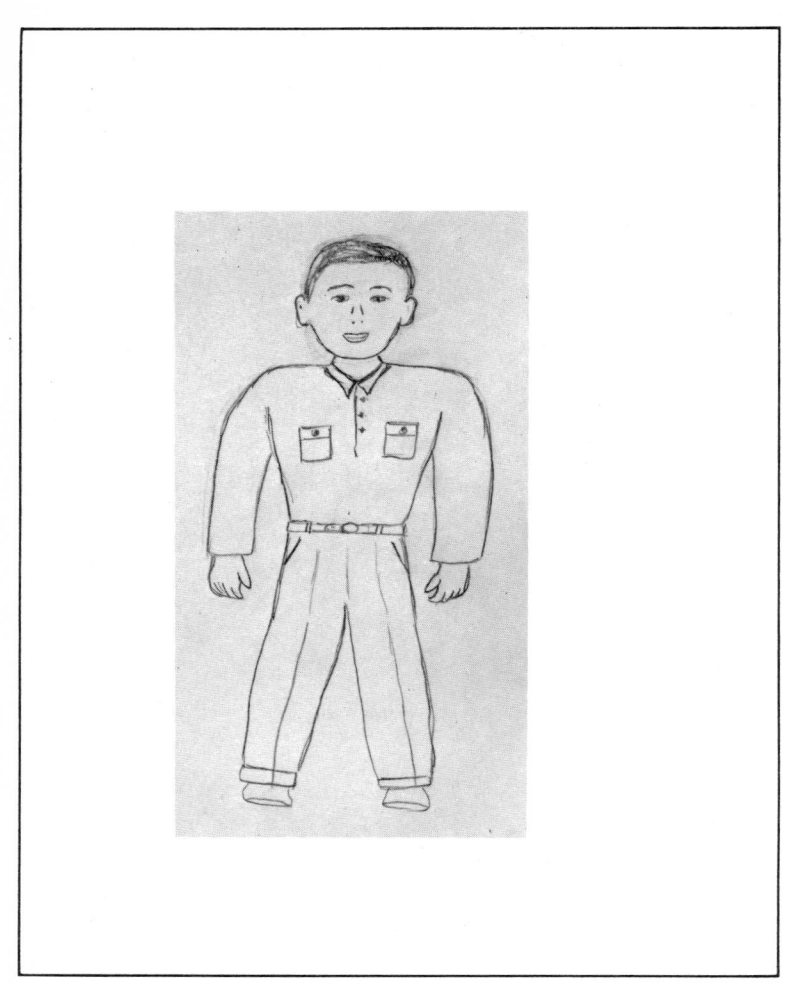

FIGURE-DRAWING CHARACTERISTICS

Structural	Male Female Both	Structural	Male	Female	Structural and Graphic	Male Female Both		Graphic, Global and Height	Male	Female	Body Proportions	Male	Female
Type	0	Omission of Appendages	0	0	Upper and Lower Halves	3	0	Hair Shading	2	2	Head	09	06
Sex Sequence	0	Position of Both Arms	0	0	Four Quarters	4	4	Nudity and Transparency	7	7	Neck	05	03
Posture	1 1	Position of Right Arm	0	2	Relative Size	0		Form	1	1	Shoulders	09	05
Perspective	0 0	Position of Left Arm	0	2	Constant Line Pressure	5	0	Detailing	1	1	Right Arm	06	04
Vertical Midline	3 0	Position of Legs	6	6	Variable Line Pressure	0	5	Identity and Sex	1	1	Left Arm	06	04
Bilateral Symmetry	5 3	Relation of Long Axes	1	1	Line Continuity	1	1	Sophistication	1	1	Chest	07	05
Horizontal Midline	4 4	Right and Left Halves	1	1	Body Shading	2	3	Height	06	05	Girth	07	05

GENERAL CHARACTERISTICS OF SUBJECT

IDENTIFICATION
No. 641
Sex M
Marital status S
Age 29 yrs. at
psychological tests

PARENTAL HISTORY
Father
C   H   S   D   O
-   -   -   -   -
Mother
C   H   S   D   O
-   -   -   -   -

PHYSIOLOGICAL AND METABOLIC DATA

	Admission	Initial	Control	Cold pressor change	Exercise change	Smoking change
Systolic pressure	132	130	114	+18	+44	+10
Diastolic pressure	80	76	72	+26	+06	+02
Heart rate	80	80	72	+12	+48	-03

Age 26 yrs.	Height	68	in.	Ponderal index	12.62	
	Weight	157	lbs.	Cholesterol	265	mg. per 100 ml.
	Overweight +05 %			Vital capacity	4.4	liters

HABIT SURVEY
Smoking habits: occasional smoker
Age begun 17 yrs.   Inhalation: no
Habits of nervous tension: 16, 17, 25

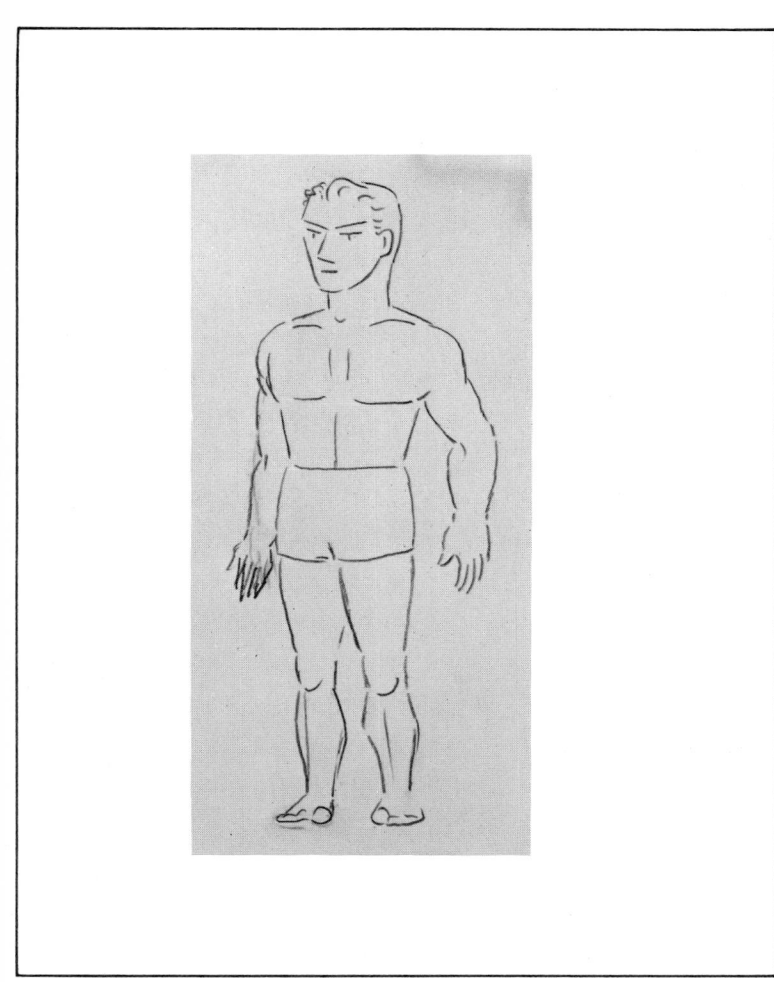

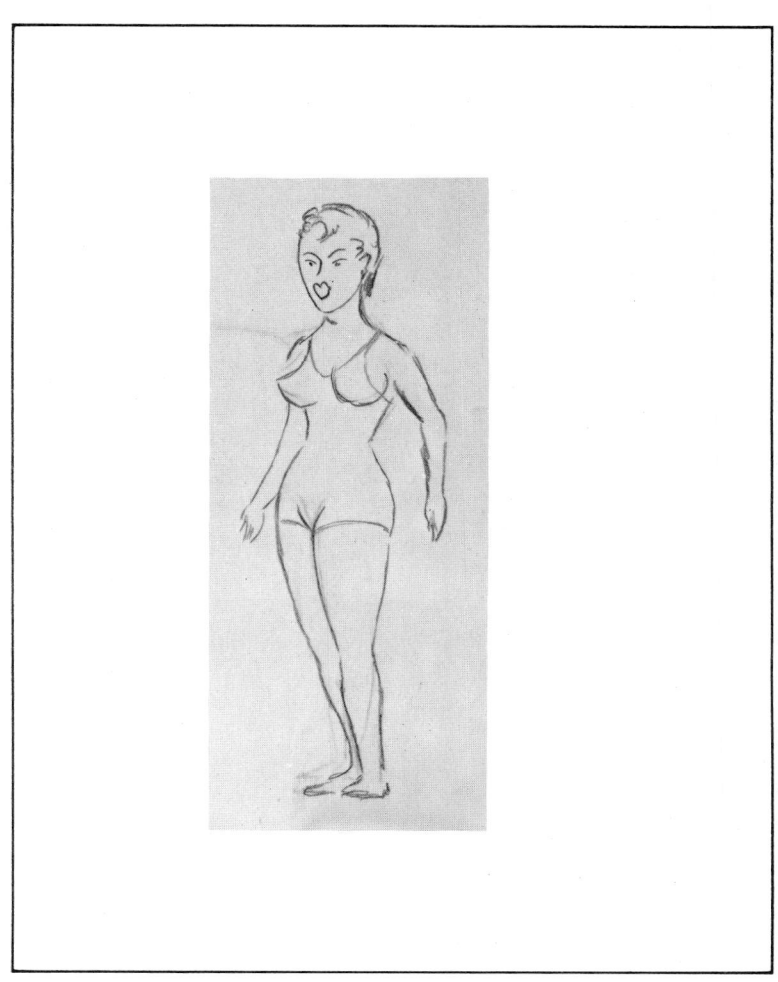

FIGURE-DRAWING CHARACTERISTICS

Structural	Male Female Both	Structural	Male	Female	Structural and Graphic	Male Female Both		Graphic, Global and Height	Male	Female	Body Proportions	Male	Female
Type	0	Omission of Appendages	0	0	Upper and Lower Halves	0	0	Hair Shading	7	1	Head	09	09
Sex Sequence	0	Position of Both Arms	1	4	Four Quarters	4	4	Nudity and Transparency	3	2	Neck	08	06
Posture	1	1	Position of Right Arm	0	7	Relative Size	0		Form	1	1	Shoulders		
Perspective	1	1	Position of Left Arm	2	2	Constant Line Pressure	5	3	Detailing	1	1	Right Arm	06	04
Vertical Midline	4	4	Position of Legs	4	2	Variable Line Pressure	0	0	Identity and Sex	1	1	Left Arm	06	04
Bilateral Symmetry	0	0	Relation of Long Axes	1	1	Line Continuity	1	0	Sophistication	1	1	Chest		
Horizontal Midline	4	0	Right and Left Halves	1	1	Body Shading	3	3	Height	07	06	Girth		

GENERAL CHARACTERISTICS OF SUBJECT

IDENTIFICATION
No. 734
Sex M
Marital status S
Age 26 yrs. at psychological tests

PARENTAL HISTORY				
Father				
C	H	S	D	0
-	-	-	-	-
Mother				
C	H	S	D	0
-	-	-	-	-

PHYSIOLOGICAL AND METABOLIC DATA

	Admission	Initial	Control	Cold pressor change	Exercise change	Smoking change
Systolic pressure	140	120	104	+18	+30	+13
Diastolic pressure	70	52	60	+12	+06	00
Heart rate	80	100	88	+12	+37	+45

Age 23 yrs.	Height 73 in.	Ponderal index 13.13
	Weight 172 lbs.	Cholesterol 250 mg. per 100 ml.
	Overweight +02 %	Vital capacity 6.0 liters

HABIT SURVEY

Smoking habits: former smoker

  Age begun 18 yrs.   Inhalation:

Habits of nervous tension: 5, 6, 21

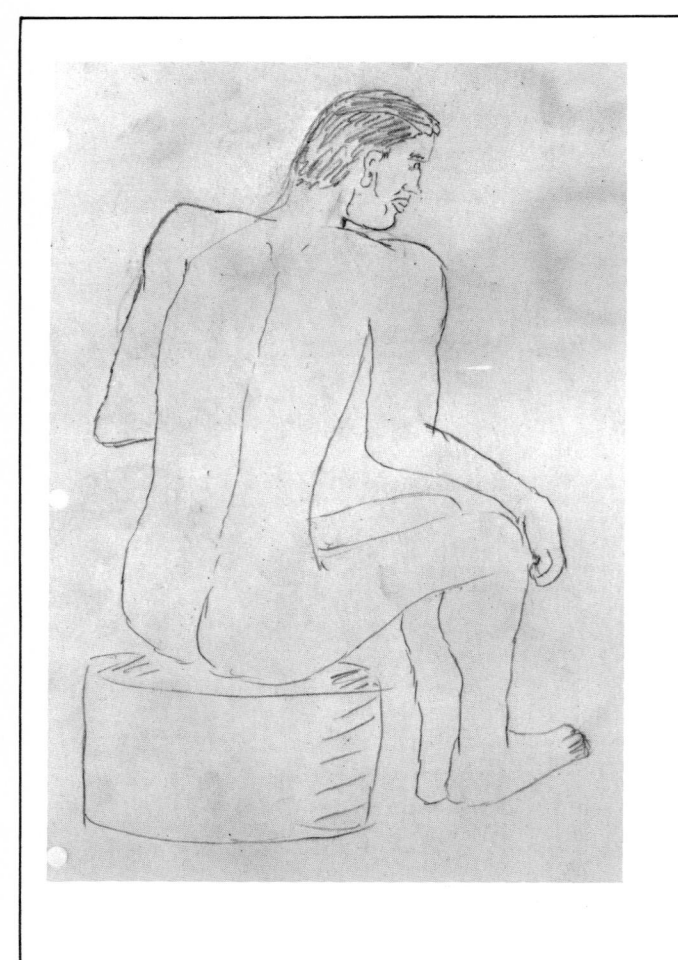

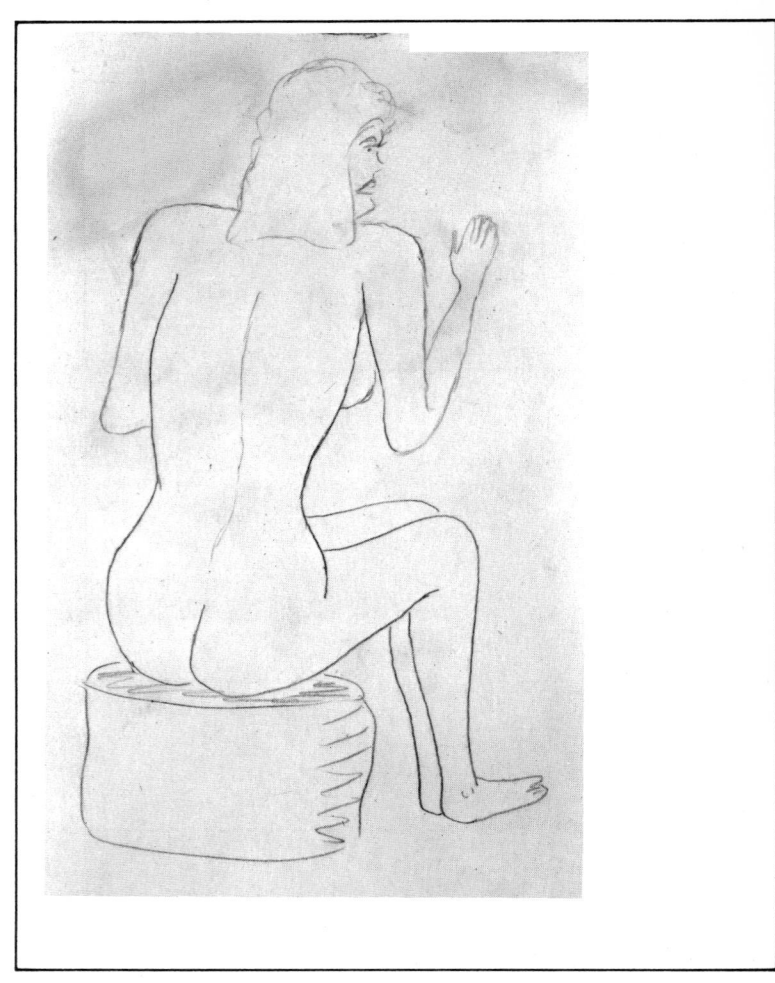

FIGURE-DRAWING CHARACTERISTICS

Structural	Male Female Both	Structural	Male	Female	Structural and Graphic	Male Female Both		Graphic, Global and Height	Male	Female	Body Proportions	Male	Female
Type	0	Omission of Appendages	0	0	Upper and Lower Halves	1	1	Hair Shading	3	5	Head	11	09
Sex Sequence	2	Position of Both Arms	2	2	Four Quarters	4	4	Nudity and Transparency	0	0	Neck	04	
Posture	3 3	Position of Right Arm	5	3	Relative Size	2		Form	1	1	Shoulders		
Perspective	8 8	Position of Left Arm	7	7	Constant Line Pressure	0	0	Detailing	3	3	Right Arm	10	10
Vertical Midline	8 8	Position of Legs	1	1	Variable Line Pressure	2	4	Identity and Sex	1	1	Left Arm		
Bilateral Symmetry	0 0	Relation of Long Axes	0	0	Line Continuity	0	2	Sophistication	1	1	Chest		
Horizontal Midline	0 0	Right and Left Halves	1	1	Body Shading	0	2	Height			Girth		

GENERAL CHARACTERISTICS OF SUBJECT

IDENTIFICATION
No. F55
Sex M
Marital status M
Age 24 yrs. at
psychological tests

PARENTAL HISTORY				
Father				
C	H	S	D	O
-	-	-	-	-
Mother				
C	H	S	D	O
-	-	-	-	-

PHYSIOLOGICAL AND METABOLIC DATA

	Admission	Initial	Control	Cold pressor change	Exercise change	Smoking change
Systolic pressure	134	130	110	+24	+40	+01
Diastolic pressure	72	80	80	+20	+10	+02
Heart rate	72	84	79	-12	+24	+13

Age 22 yrs.	Height	73	in.	Ponderal index 13.83	
	Weight	147	lbs.	Cholesterol	170 mg. per 100 ml.
	Overweight -12 %			Vital capacity	liters

HABIT SURVEY

Smoking habits: mixed smoker

Age begun 19 yrs.   Inhalation: yes

Habits of nervous tension: 1, 2, 3, 4, 5, 7, 8, 9, 18, 19, 20, 22, 23, 25

STRONG VOCATIONAL INTEREST TEST

Occupation	Artist	Psychologist	Architect	Physician	Osteopath	Dentist	Veterinarian	Mathematician	Physicist	Engineer	Chemist	Production Manager
Standard Score	37	47	49	63	54	46	25	40	44	48	56	39

Occupation	Farmer	Aviator	Carpenter	Printer	Math.-Sci. Teacher	Ind. Arts Teacher	Voc. Agric. Teacher	Policeman	Forest Serv. Man	Y.M.C.A. Phys. Dir.	Personnel Director	Public Administrator
Standard Score	41	53	39	49	51	40	37	38	40	36	33	49

Occupation	Y.M.C.A. Secretary	Soc. Sci. H.S. Teacher	City Sch. Sup't.	Social Worker	Minister	Musician Performer	C.P.A.	Senior C.P.A.	Accountant	Office Man	Purchasing Agent	Banker
Standard Score	15	24	22	35	58	47	27	44	30	28	20	16

Occupation	Mortician	Pharmacist	Sales Manager	Real Est. Manager	Life Ins. Salesman	Advertising Man	Lawyer	Author-Journalist	President Mfg. Co.	Interest Maturity	Occupational Level	Masculinity-Femininity
Standard Score	21	29	10	22	09	29	24	32	19	54	50	44

FIGURE-DRAWING CHARACTERISTICS

Structural	Male Female Both	Structural	Male	Female	Structural and Graphic	Male Female Both		Graphic, Global and Height	Male	Female	Body Proportions	Male	Female
Type	0	Omission of Appendages	0	0	Upper and Lower Halves	1	1	Hair Shading	3	3	Head	08	07
Sex Sequence	1	Position of Both Arms	0	0	Four Quarters	4	4	Nudity and Transparency	7	7	Neck	06	03
Posture	1 1	Position of Right Arm	0	0	Relative Size	0		Form	1	1	Shoulders	07	05
Perspective	0 0	Position of Left Arm	0	0	Constant Line Pressure	0	0	Detailing	1	1	Right Arm	07	06
Vertical Midline	3 0	Position of Legs	4	4	Variable Line Pressure	5	5	Identity and Sex	1	1	Left Arm	06	04
Bilateral Symmetry	3 3	Relation of Long Axes	1	1	Line Continuity	0	0	Sophistication	1	1	Chest	06	05
Horizontal Midline	4 4	Right and Left Halves	1	2	Body Shading	7	7	Height	07	06	Girth	07	06

GENERAL CHARACTERISTICS OF SUBJECT

IDENTIFICATION

No. G36

Sex F

Marital status S

Age 24 yrs. at

psychological tests

PARENTAL HISTORY

Father

C   H   S   D   O

–   –   –   –   –

Mother

C   H   S   D   O

–   –   –   –   –

PHYSIOLOGICAL AND METABOLIC DATA

	Admission	Initial	Control	Cold pressor change	Exercise change	Smoking change
Systolic pressure	125	122	112	+06	+54	+06
Diastolic pressure	60	58	58	+06	+02	-02
Heart rate	80	76	78	+18	+23	+06

Age 23 yrs.

Height 64 in.

Weight 136 lbs.

Overweight +07 %

Ponderal index 12.45

Cholesterol 144 mg. per 100 ml.

Vital capacity   liters

HABIT SURVEY

Smoking habits: occasional smoker

Age begun 13 yrs.   Inhalation: no

Habits of nervous tension: 4, 5, 6, 8, 11, 14, 16, 22, 23, 25

STRONG VOCATIONAL INTEREST TEST

Occupation	Artist	Psychologist	Architect	Physician	Osteopath	Dentist	Veterinarian	Mathematician	Physicist	Engineer	Chemist	Production Manager
Standard Score	56	44	45	49	38	31	22	36	25	16	24	04

Occupation	Farmer	Aviator	Carpenter	Printer	Math.-Sci. Teacher	Ind. Arts Teacher	Voc. Agric. Teacher	Policeman	Forest Serv. Man	Y.M.C.A. Phys. Dir.	Personnel Director	Public Administrator
Standard Score	22	05	03	20	17	-09	20	08	06	20	18	30

Occupation	Y.M.C.A. Secretary	Soc. Sci. H.S. Teacher	City Sch. Sup't.	Social Worker	Minister	Musician Performer	C.P.A.	Senior C.P.A.	Accountant	Office Man	Purchasing Agent	Banker
Standard Score	21	27	35	39	59	53	27	10	-07	13	07	24

Occupation	Mortician	Pharmacist	Sales Manager	Real Est. Manager	Life Ins. Salesman	Advertising Man	Lawyer	Author-Journalist	President Mfg. Co.	Interest Maturity	Occupational Level	Masculinity-Femininity
Standard Score	33	33	28	40	41	51	48	58	40	45	66	14

FIGURE-DRAWING CHARACTERISTICS

Structural	Male Female Both		Structural	Male	Female	Structural and Graphic	Male Female Both		Graphic, Global and Height	Male	Female	Body Proportions	Male	Female
Type	0		Omission of Appendages	0	2	Upper and Lower Halves	3	1	Hair Shading	1	1	Head	08	
Sex Sequence	0		Position of Both Arms	4	6	Four Quarters	4	4	Nudity and Transparency	7	0	Neck	08	
Posture	1	3	Position of Right Arm	7	8	Relative Size	5		Form	1	1	Shoulders		06
Perspective	2	3	Position of Left Arm	0	8	Constant Line Pressure	0	1	Detailing	1	1	Right Arm		
Vertical Midline	7	9	Position of Legs	1	0	Variable Line Pressure	1	0	Identity and Sex	1	1	Left Arm	07	
Bilateral Symmetry	0	3	Relation of Long Axes	1	0	Line Continuity	0	0	Sophistication	1	1	Chest	06	05
Horizontal Midline	4	0	Right and Left Halves	1	1	Body Shading	7	0	Height	07		Girth	06	05

GENERAL CHARACTERISTICS OF SUBJECT

IDENTIFICATION
No. D53
Sex M
Marital status S
Age 22 yrs. at psychological tests

PARENTAL HISTORY
Father
C H S D O
– – – – –
Mother
C H S D O
– – – – –

PHYSIOLOGICAL AND METABOLIC DATA

	Admission	Initial	Control	Cold pressor change	Exercise change	Smoking change
Systolic pressure	120	118	116	-02	+22	-04
Diastolic pressure	70	70	72	+08	-04	+02
Heart rate	70	80	86	-04	+11	-03

Age 22 yrs.	Height	73 in.	Ponderal index 12.70
	Weight	190 lbs.	Cholesterol 176 mg. per 100 ml.
	Overweight +13 %		Vital capacity 5.3 liters

HABIT SURVEY

Smoking habits: occasional smoker

Age begun 22 yrs.   Inhalation: no

Habits of nervous tension: 2, 5, 6, 9, 11, 16, 18

STRONG VOCATIONAL INTEREST TEST

Occupation	Artist	Psychologist	Architect	Physician	Osteopath	Dentist	Veterinarian	Mathematician	Physicist	Engineer	Chemist	Production Manager
Standard Score	23	53	24	62	57	32	29	18	14	19	33	29

Occupation	Farmer	Aviator	Carpenter	Printer	Math.-Sci. Teacher	Ind. Arts Teacher	Voc. Agric. Teacher	Policeman	Forest Serv. Man	Y.M.C.A. Phys. Dir.	Personnel Director	Public Administrator
Standard Score	31	44	25	47	56	36	42	43	41	55	54	60

Occupation	Y.M.C.A. Secretary	Soc. Sci. H.S. Teacher	City Sch. Sup't.	Social Worker	Minister	Musician Performer	C.P.A.	Senior C.P.A.	Accountant	Office Man	Purchasing Agent	Banker
Standard Score	44	57	48	60	63	57	20	48	24	34	13	18

Occupation	Mortician	Pharmacist	Sales Manager	Real Est. Manager	Life Ins. Salesman	Advertising Man	Lawyer	Author-Journalist	President Mfg. Co.	Interest Maturity	Occupational Level	Masculinity-Femininity
Standard Score	29	41	23	27	29	31	33	27	15	65	46	45

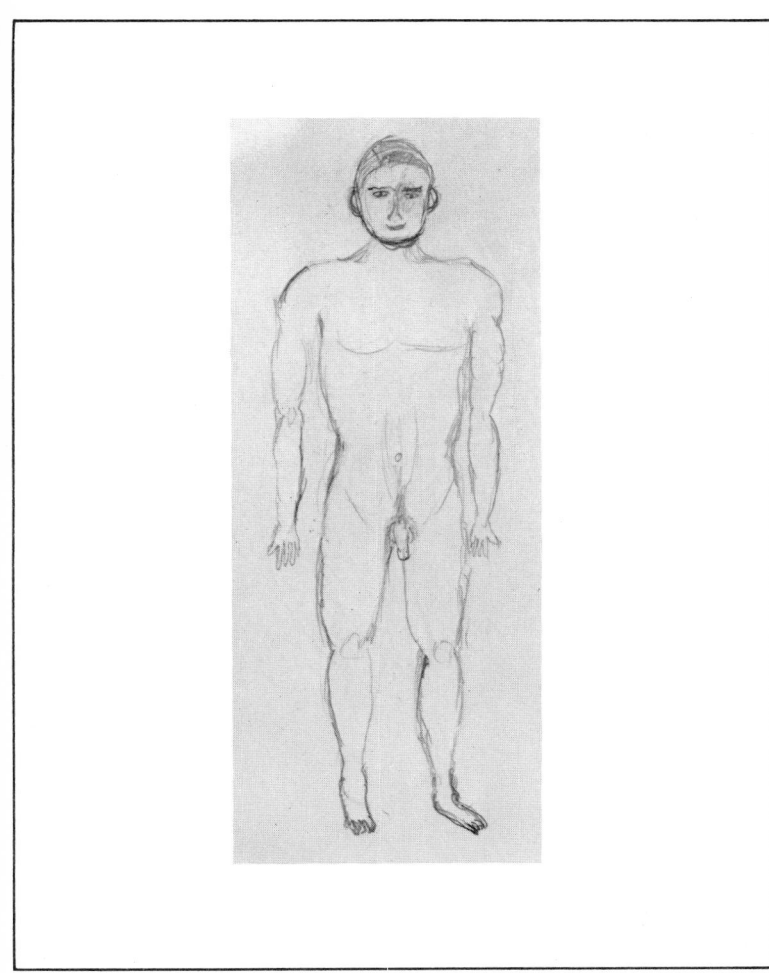

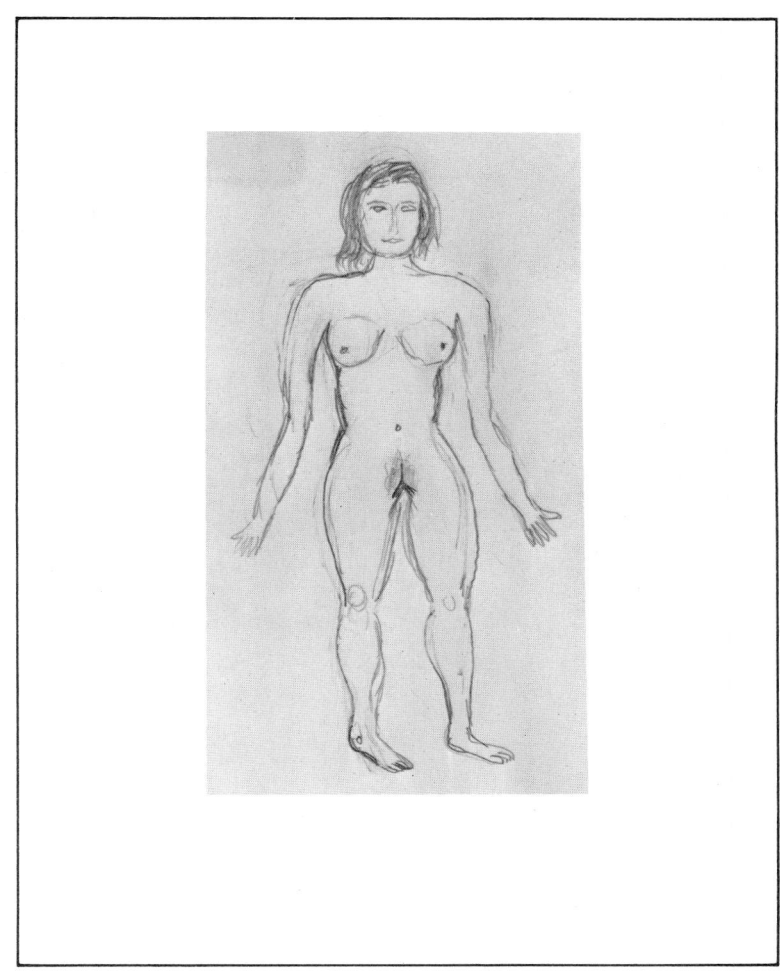

FIGURE-DRAWING CHARACTERISTICS

Structural	Male	Female	Structural	Male	Female	Structural and Graphic	Male	Female	Graphic, Global and Height	Male	Female	Body Proportions	Male	Female
	Both						Both							
Type	0		Omission of Appendages	0	0	Upper and Lower Halves	0	1	Hair Shading	3	3	Head	08	07
Sex Sequence	0		Position of Both Arms	0	0	Four Quarters	4	4	Nudity and Transparency	0	0	Neck	07	06
Posture	1	1	Position of Right Arm	0	3	Relative Size	0		Form	1	1	Shoulders	09	07
Perspective	0	0	Position of Left Arm	0	3	Constant Line Pressure	0	0	Detailing	1	1	Right Arm	06	06
Vertical Midline	0	0	Position of Legs	5	6	Variable Line Pressure	2	3	Identity and Sex	1	1	Left Arm	06	06
Bilateral Symmetry	3	3	Relation of Long Axes	1	1	Line Continuity	0	0	Sophistication	1	1	Chest	07	06
Horizontal Midline	0	0	Right and Left Halves	1	0	Body Shading	3	3	Height	07	06	Girth	07	06

GENERAL CHARACTERISTICS OF SUBJECT

IDENTIFICATION

No. D74

Sex M

Marital status S

Age 22 yrs. at

psychological tests

PARENTAL HISTORY

Father

C   H   S   D   0

–   –   –   –   –

Mother

C   H   S   D   0

–   –   –   –   –

PHYSIOLOGICAL AND METABOLIC DATA

	Admission	Initial	Control	Cold pressor change	Exercise change	Smoking change
Systolic pressure	130	122	108	+16	+32	+02
Diastolic pressure	60	60	66	+30	–08	00
Heart rate	64	80	67	+12	+48	+01

Age 22 yrs.   Height 71 in.   Ponderal index 13.10

Weight 159 lbs.   Cholesterol 202 mg. per 100 ml.

Overweight +01 %   Vital capacity 5.0 liters

HABIT SURVEY

Smoking habits: occasional smoker

Age begun 20 yrs.   Inhalation: no

Habits of nervous tension: 1, 4, 6, 8, 10, 14, 16

STRONG VOCATIONAL INTEREST TEST

Occupation	Artist	Psychologist	Architect	Physician	Osteopath	Dentist	Veterinarian	Mathematician	Physicist	Engineer	Chemist	Production Manager
Standard Score	45	62	43	65	44	41	13	45	47	42	58	28

Occupation	Farmer	Aviator	Carpenter	Printer	Math.-Sci. Teacher	Ind. Arts Teacher	Voc. Agric. Teacher	Policeman	Forest Serv. Man	Y.M.C.A. Phys. Dir.	Personnel Director	Public Administrator
Standard Score	36	40	27	47	49	27	25	23	27	42	35	50

Occupation	Y.M.C.A. Secretary	Soc. Sci. H.S. Teacher	City Sch. Sup't.	Social Worker	Minister	Musician Performer	C.P.A.	Senior C.P.A.	Accountant	Office Man	Purchasing Agent	Banker
Standard Score	38	38	36	51	63	64	26	35	18	21	09	10

Occupation	Mortician	Pharmacist	Sales Manager	Real Est. Manager	Life Ins. Salesman	Advertising Man	Lawyer	Author-Journalist	President Mfg. Co.	Interest Maturity	Occupational Level	Masculinity-Femininity
Standard Score	17	22	14	19	17	35	34	42	24	54	53	37

FIGURE-DRAWING CHARACTERISTICS

Structural	Male Female Both		Structural	Male	Female	Structural and Graphic	Male Female Both		Graphic, Global and Height	Male	Female	Body Proportions	Male	Female
Type	0		Omission of Appendages	9	1	Upper and Lower Halves	3	7	Hair Shading	1	2	Head	14	
Sex Sequence	1		Position of Both Arms	4	6	Four Quarters	4	4	Nudity and Transparency	7	0	Neck		
Posture	3	0	Position of Right Arm	7	7	Relative Size	0		Form	3	1	Shoulders		08
Perspective	8	3	Position of Left Arm	4	8	Constant Line Pressure	0	0	Detailing	1	1	Right Arm		
Vertical Midline	4	9	Position of Legs	1	3	Variable Line Pressure	1	1	Identity and Sex	1	1	Left Arm	14	
Bilateral Symmetry	0	3	Relation of Long Axes	0	1	Line Continuity	1	2	Sophistication	1	1	Chest		09
Horizontal Midline	4	0	Right and Left Halves	3	1	Body Shading	7	3	Height			Girth		06

GENERAL CHARACTERISTICS OF SUBJECT

IDENTIFICATION

No. E36

Sex M

Marital status S

Age 23 yrs. at psychological tests

PARENTAL HISTORY

Father

C H S D O

- - - - -

Mother

C H S D O

- - - - -

PHYSIOLOGICAL AND METABOLIC DATA

	Admission	Initial	Control	Cold pressor change	Exercise change	Smoking change
Systolic pressure		112	106	+25	+44	
Diastolic pressure		64	66	+28	-06	
Heart rate		78	72	+08	+11	

Age 22 yrs.

Height 72 in.

Weight 162 lbs.

Overweight -01 %

Ponderal index 13.21

Cholesterol 210 mg. per 100 ml.

Vital capacity 4.0 liters

HABIT SURVEY

Smoking habits: nonsmoker

Age begun yrs. Inhalation:

Habits of nervous tension: 3, 4, 5, 9, 11

STRONG VOCATIONAL INTEREST TEST

Occupation	Artist	Psychologist	Architect	Physician	Osteopath	Dentist	Veterinarian	Mathematician	Physicist	Engineer	Chemist	Production Manager
Standard Score	28	41	34	54	41	44	23	39	35	45	51	32

Occupation	Farmer	Aviator	Carpenter	Printer	Math.-Sci. Teacher	Ind. Arts Teacher	Voc. Agric. Teacher	Policeman	Forest Serv. Man	Y.M.C.A. Phys. Dir.	Personnel Director	Public Administrator
Standard Score	41	41	26	39	51	26	25	34	25	37	26	33

Occupation	Y.M.C.A. Secretary	Soc. Sci. H.S. Teacher	City Sch. Sup't.	Social Worker	Minister	Musician Performer	C.P.A.	Senior C.P.A.	Accountant	Office Man	Purchasing Agent	Banker
Standard Score	32	33	26	32	64	40	28	43	24	27	13	13

Occupation	Mortician	Pharmacist	Sales Manager	Real Est. Manager	Life Ins. Salesman	Advertising Man	Lawyer	Author-Journalist	President Mfg. Co.	Interest Maturity	Occupational Level	Masculinity-Femininity
Standard Score	06	22	14	21	15	19	25	28	22	57	53	55

FIGURE-DRAWING CHARACTERISTICS

Structural	Male Female Both	Structural	Male	Female	Structural and Graphic	Male Female Both		Graphic, Global and Height	Male	Female	Body Proportions	Male	Female
Type	0	Omission of Appendages	0	7	Upper and Lower Halves	3	1	Hair Shading	7	5	Head	10	06
Sex Sequence	0	Position of Both Arms	0	0	Four Quarters	4	4	Nudity and Transparency	7	7	Neck	10	02
Posture	1 3	Position of Right Arm	5	2	Relative Size	5		Form	1	1	Shoulders	08	
Perspective	0 2	Position of Left Arm	5	2	Constant Line Pressure	0	0	Detailing	1	1	Right Arm	06	
Vertical Midline	3 4	Position of Legs	6	1	Variable Line Pressure	5	5	Identity and Sex	1	1	Left Arm	06	06
Bilateral Symmetry	3 0	Relation of Long Axes	1	0	Line Continuity	0	0	Sophistication	1	1	Chest	07	07
Horizontal Midline	4 0	Right and Left Halves	1	1	Body Shading	3	5	Height	07		Girth	07	07

GENERAL CHARACTERISTICS OF SUBJECT

IDENTIFICATION
No. E48
Sex M
Marital status S
Age 22 yrs. at psychological tests

PARENTAL HISTORY
Father
C H S D O
– – – – –
Mother
C H S D O
– – – – –

PHYSIOLOGICAL AND METABOLIC DATA

	Admission	Initial	Control	Cold pressor change	Exercise change	Smoking change
Systolic pressure	110	108	112	+10	+38	+02
Diastolic pressure	80	62	70	+28	–20	+06
Heart rate	64	56	60	+04	+04	–08

Age 22 yrs.	Height 70 in.	Ponderal index 12.34
	Weight 182 lbs.	Cholesterol 230 mg. per 100 ml.
	Overweight +18 %	Vital capacity 5.1 liters

HABIT SURVEY

Smoking habits: heavy cigarette smoker

Age begun 19 yrs.   Inhalation: yes

Habits of nervous tension: 3. 4, 5, 6, 9, 10, 25

STRONG VOCATIONAL INTEREST TEST

Occupation	Artist	Psychologist	Architect	Physician	Osteopath	Dentist	Veterinarian	Mathematician	Physicist	Engineer	Chemist	Production Manager
Standard Score	44	56	48	74	65	48	34	29	37	43	51	32

Occupation	Farmer	Aviator	Carpenter	Printer	Math.-Sci. Teacher	Ind. Arts Teacher	Voc. Agric. Teacher	Policeman	Forest Serv. Man	Y.M.C.A. Phys. Dir.	Personnel Director	Public Administrator
Standard Score	33	49	29	35	39	29	26	36	36	40	39	49

Occupation	Y.M.C.A. Secretary	Soc. Sci. H.S. Teacher	City Sch. Sup't.	Social Worker	Minister	Musician Performer	C.P.A.	Senior C.P.A.	Accountant	Office Man	Purchasing Agent	Banker
Standard Score	25	22	23	45	64	57	26	33	09	19	09	06

Occupation	Mortician	Pharmacist	Sales Manager	Real Est. Manager	Life Ins. Salesman	Advertising Man	Lawyer	Author-Journalist	President Mfg. Co.	Interest Maturity	Occupational Level	Masculinity-Femininity
Standard Score	22	28	23	32	34	35	37	39	33	53	53	49

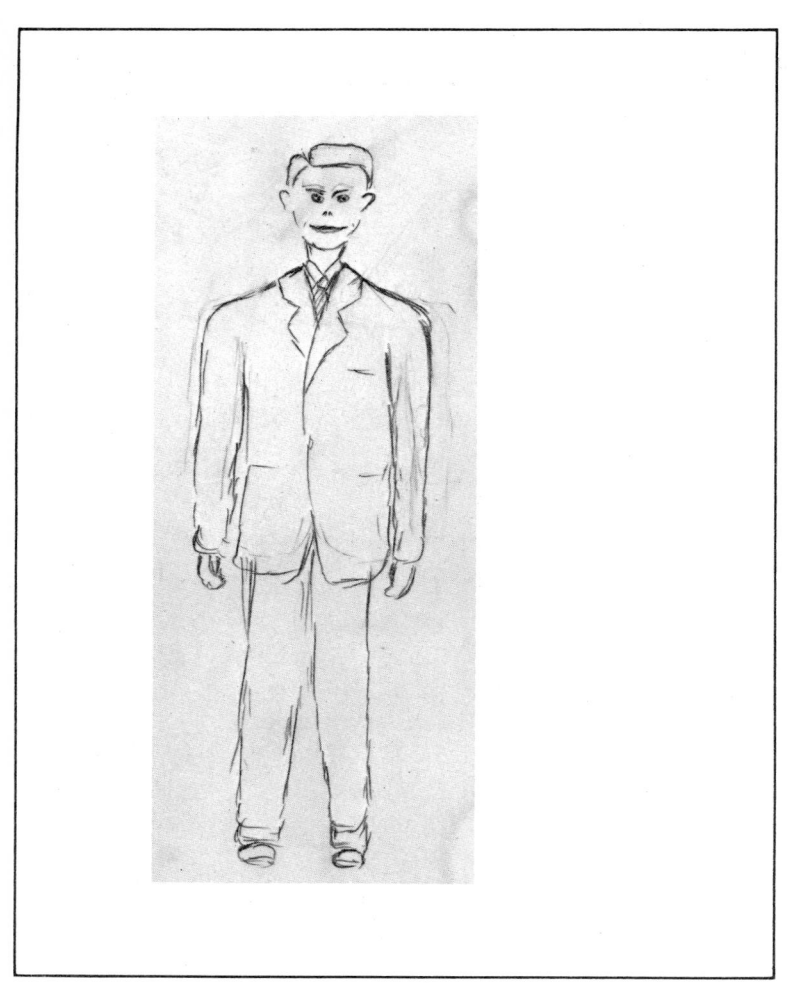

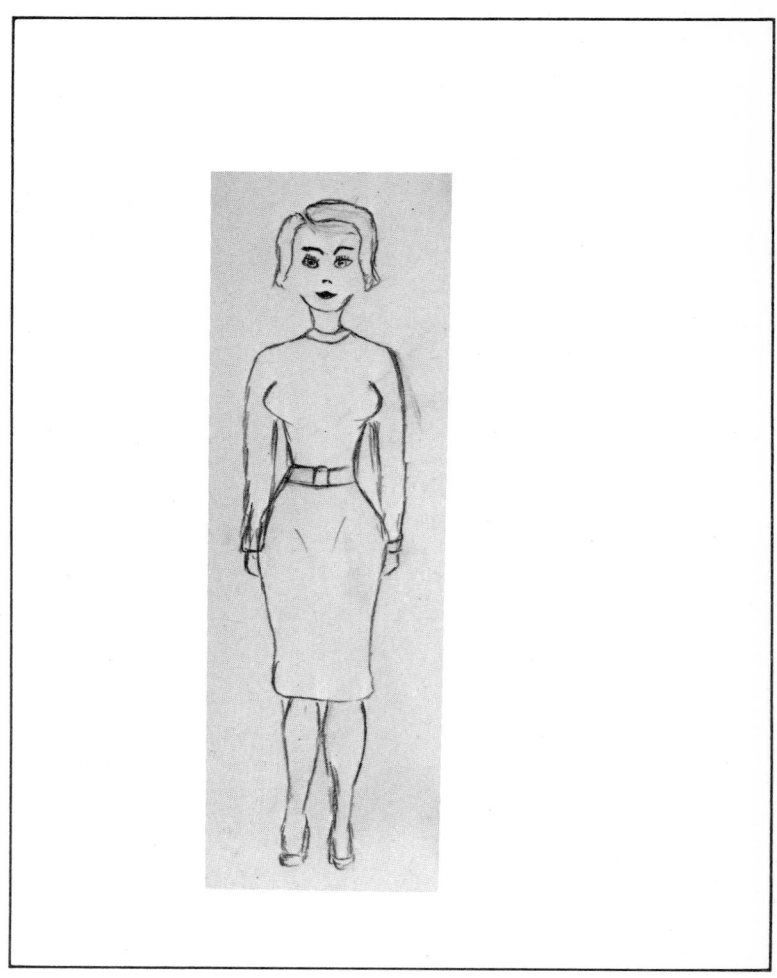

FIGURE-DRAWING CHARACTERISTICS

Structural	Male Female Both	Structural	Male	Female	Structural and Graphic	Male Female Both		Graphic, Global and Height	Male	Female	Body Proportions	Male	Female
Type	0	Omission of Appendages	0	0	Upper and Lower Halves	0	3	Hair Shading	5	5	Head	09	09
Sex Sequence	0	Position of Both Arms	0	0	Four Quarters	4	4	Nudity and Transparency	7	7	Neck	07	07
Posture	1 1	Position of Right Arm	0	0	Relative Size	0		Form	1	1	Shoulders	09	06
Perspective	0 0	Position of Left Arm	0	0	Constant Line Pressure	0	0	Detailing	1	1	Right Arm	06	06
Vertical Midline	3 0	Position of Legs	4	3	Variable Line Pressure	5	5	Identity and Sex	1	1	Left Arm	06	06
Bilateral Symmetry	4 5	Relation of Long Axes	1	1	Line Continuity	0	0	Sophistication	1	1	Chest	07	05
Horizontal Midline	6 4	Right and Left Halves	1	2	Body Shading	4	3	Height	07	07	Girth	09	04

GENERAL CHARACTERISTICS OF SUBJECT

IDENTIFICATION
No. F75
Sex M
Marital status S
Age 24 yrs. at
psychological tests

PARENTAL HISTORY
Father
C H S D O
U U U U U
Mother
C H S D O
U U U U

PHYSIOLOGICAL AND METABOLIC DATA

	Admission	Initial	Control	Cold pressor change	Exercise change	Smoking change
Systolic pressure	100	114	112	+08	+28	+08
Diastolic pressure	60	76	78	+14	+12	00
Heart rate	56	64	64	+16	+09	−01

Age 22 yrs.	Height 74 in.	Ponderal index 12.65
	Weight 200 lbs.	Cholesterol 222 mg. per 100 ml.
	Overweight +16 %	Vital capacity liters

HABIT SURVEY
Smoking habits: occasional smoker
Age begun yrs. Inhalation: no
Habits of nervous tension: 2, 3, 4, 5, 6, 9,
11, 14, 18

STRONG VOCATIONAL INTEREST TEST

Occupation	Artist	Psychologist	Architect	Physician	Osteopath	Dentist	Veterinarian	Mathematician	Physicist	Engineer	Chemist	Production Manager
Standard Score	27	38	31	51	52	45	36	17	15	24	32	25

Occupation	Farmer	Aviator	Carpenter	Printer	Math.-Sci. Teacher	Ind. Arts Teacher	Voc. Agric. Teacher	Policeman	Forest Serv. Man	Y.M.C.A. Phys. Dir.	Personnel Director	Public Administrator
Standard Score	44	45	22	46	45	25	40	36	36	38	36	41

Occupation	Y.M.C.A. Secretary	Soc. Sci. H.S. Teacher	City Sch. Sup't.	Social Worker	Minister	Musician Performer	C.P.A.	Senior C.P.A.	Accountant	Office Man	Purchasing Agent	Banker
Standard Score	31	42	20	41	58	45	21	49	26	36	18	26

Occupation	Mortician	Pharmacist	Sales Manager	Real Est. Manager	Life Ins. Salesman	Advertising Man	Lawyer	Author-Journalist	President Mfg. Co.	Interest Maturity	Occupational Level	Masculinity-Femininity
Standard Score	26	30	20	33	27	31	29	27	21	58	47	52

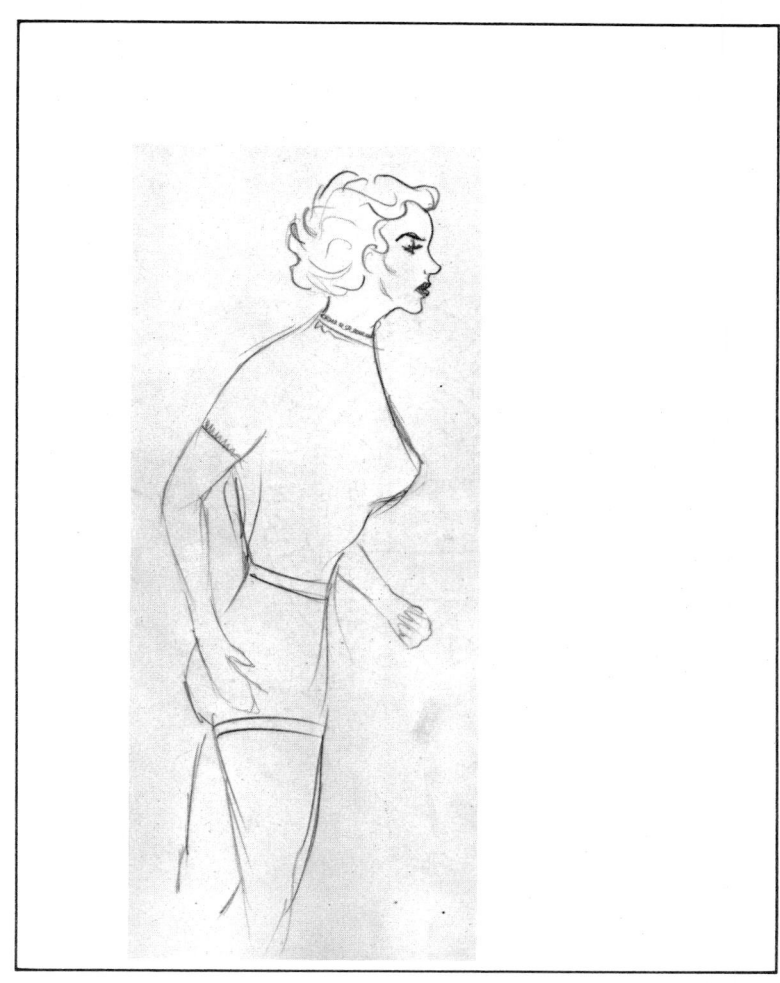

FIGURE-DRAWING CHARACTERISTICS

Structural	Male Female Both		Structural	Male	Female	Structural and Graphic	Male Female Both		Graphic, Global and Height	Male	Female	Body Proportions	Male	Female
Type	0		Omission of Appendages	0	3	Upper and Lower Halves	0	7	Hair Shading	5	2	Head	07	09
Sex Sequence	0		Position of Both Arms	2	2	Four Quarters	4	4	Nudity and Transparency	7	2	Neck	05	12
Posture	1	0	Position of Right Arm	0	5	Relative Size	4		Form	1	1	Shoulders		
Perspective	2	2	Position of Left Arm	7	7	Constant Line Pressure	0	0	Detailing	1	1	Right Arm	06	08
Vertical Midline	7	4	Position of Legs	1	1	Variable Line Pressure	2	3	Identity and Sex	1	1	Left Arm		
Bilateral Symmetry	0	0	Relation of Long Axes	1	1	Line Continuity	3	1	Sophistication	1	1	Chest	09	11
Horizontal Midline	4	4	Right and Left Halves	1	2	Body Shading	4	0	Height	06		Girth	07	08

GENERAL CHARACTERISTICS OF SUBJECT

IDENTIFICATION

No. DO7
Sex M
Marital status S
Age 22 yrs. at
psychological tests

PARENTAL HISTORY

Father
C   H   S   D   O
U   U   U   U   U
Mother
C   H   S   D   O
–   –   –   –   –

PHYSIOLOGICAL AND METABOLIC DATA

	Admission	Initial	Control	Cold pressor change	Exercise change	Smoking change
Systolic pressure	120	125	115	+15	+25	+01
Diastolic pressure	70	70	68	+24	–08	+10
Heart rate	65	64	64	+04	+24	+08

Age 22 yrs.
Height 74 in.   Ponderal index 13.14
Weight 178 lbs.   Cholesterol 236 mg. per 100 ml.
Overweight +03 %   Vital capacity 6.4 liters

HABIT SURVEY

Smoking habits: nonsmoker
Age begun yrs.   Inhalation:
Habits of nervous tension: 4, 8, 23

STRONG VOCATIONAL INTEREST TEST

Occupation	Artist	Psychologist	Architect	Physician	Osteopath	Dentist	Veterinarian	Mathematician	Physicist	Engineer	Chemist	Production Manager
Standard Score	56	43	45	59	49	41	34	29	22	14	28	12

Occupation	Farmer	Aviator	Carpenter	Printer	Math.-Sci. Teacher	Ind. Arts Teacher	Voc. Agric. Teacher	Policeman	Forest Serv. Man	Y.M.C.A. Phys. Dir.	Personnel Director	Public Administrator
Standard Score	36	34	10	34	23	05	29	23	25	28	13	31

Occupation	Y.M.C.A. Secretary	Soc. Sci. H.S. Teacher	City Sch. Sup't.	Social Worker	Minister	Musician Performer	C.P.A.	Senior C.P.A.	Accountant	Office Man	Purchasing Agent	Banker
Standard Score	15	32	22	37	63	60	25	19	05	15	02	19

Occupation	Mortician	Pharmacist	Sales Manager	Real Est. Manager	Life Ins. Salesman	Advertising Man	Lawyer	Author-Journalist	President Mfg. Co.	Interest Maturity	Occupational Level	Masculinity-Femininity
Standard Score	16	31	23	40	31	54	49	57	24	46	54	32

XIII. DRAWINGS BY SUBJECTS OF NON-EUROPEAN ANCESTRY

For the sake of homogeneity, the foregoing sections contain only figure drawings by male and female subjects of European ancestry. In addition, twenty-five subjects of non-European origin took the Figure-drawing Test, and their drawings appear in the following section. They are arranged in the same fashion as the main body of drawings, but because of the small numbers involved the sophistication-of-body-concept subdivisions are not indicated. For purposes of confidentiality, the ancestral country of each subject is not given, but the countries represented include Turkey, Lebanon, Iran, Iraq, China, Japan, Malaya, and Korea.

FIGURE-DRAWING CHARACTERISTICS

Structural	Male Female Both	Structural	Male	Female	Structural and Graphic	Male Female Both		Graphic, Global and Height	Male	Female	Body Proportions	Male	Female
Type	0	Omission of Appendages	2	2	Upper and Lower Halves	0	1	Hair Shading	7	0	Head	17	24
Sex Sequence	1	Position of Both Arms	6	6	Four Quarters	4	4	Nudity and Transparency	9	9	Neck	10	24
Posture	1 1	Position of Right Arm	8	8	Relative Size	5		Form	5	5	Shoulders	12	
Perspective	5 0	Position of Left Arm	8	8	Constant Line Pressure	0	0	Detailing	5	5	Right Arm		
Vertical Midline	0 3	Position of Legs	6	6	Variable Line Pressure	1	3	Identity and Sex	5	5	Left Arm		
Bilateral Symmetry	1 1	Relation of Long Axes	1	1	Line Continuity	0	4	Sophistication	5	5	Chest		
Horizontal Midline	0 0	Right and Left Halves	1	0	Body Shading	0	0	Height	08	06	Girth		

GENERAL CHARACTERISTICS OF SUBJECT

IDENTIFICATION
No. 463
Sex M
Marital status S
Age 28 yrs. at
psychological tests

PARENTAL HISTORY
Father
C   H   S   D   O
?   -   -   -   -
Mother
C   H   S   D   O
-   -   -   +   +

PHYSIOLOGICAL AND METABOLIC DATA

	Admission	Initial	Control	Cold pressor change	Exercise change	Smoking change
Systolic pressure	118	104	102	+20	+28	00
Diastolic pressure	68	68	72	+20	-04	00
Heart rate	64	60	65	+06	+08	-04

Age 26 yrs.	Height 68 in.	Ponderal index 12.74
	Weight 152 lbs.	Cholesterol 185 mg. per 100 ml.
	Overweight +01 %	Vital capacity 4.8 liters

HABIT SURVEY
Smoking habits: nonsmoker
Age begun   yrs.   Inhalation:
Habits of nervous tension:

FIGURE-DRAWING CHARACTERISTICS

Structural	Male Female Both	Structural	Male	Female	Structural and Graphic	Male Female Both		Graphic, Global and Height	Male	Female	Body Proportions	Male	Female
Type	0	Omission of Appendages	0	0	Upper and Lower Halves	0	0	Hair Shading	3	3	Head	14	17
Sex Sequence	0	Position of Both Arms	0	4	Four Quarters	4	4	Nudity and Transparency	9	9	Neck	16	16
Posture	1 2	Position of Right Arm	2	7	Relative Size	4		Form	5	5	Shoulders	09	
Perspective	0 2	Position of Left Arm	2	3	Constant Line Pressure	0	0	Detailing	5	5	Right Arm	04	
Vertical Midline	3 4	Position of Legs	6	8	Variable Line Pressure	5	5	Identity and Sex	3	1	Left Arm	02	06
Bilateral Symmetry	3 0	Relation of Long Axes	1	1	Line Continuity	0	0	Sophistication	4	4	Chest	09	10
Horizontal Midline	0 0	Right and Left Halves	1	3	Body Shading	0	0	Height	07	08	Girth	06	10

GENERAL CHARACTERISTICS OF SUBJECT

IDENTIFICATION
No. 661
Sex M
Marital status S
Age 29 yrs. at
psychological tests

PARENTAL HISTORY
Father
C H S D O
– ? – – +
Mother
C H S D O
– – – – +

PHYSIOLOGICAL AND METABOLIC DATA

	Admission	Initial	Control	Cold pressor change	Exercise change	Smoking change
Systolic pressure	124	126	112	+08	+24	+08
Diastolic pressure	80	74	74	+18	–08	+02
Heart rate	60	84	74	–14	+41	+12

Age 27 yrs.	Height 68 in.	Ponderal index 13.10
	Weight 140 lbs.	Cholesterol 243 mg. per 100 ml.
	Overweight –07 %	Vital capacity 3.6 liters

HABIT SURVEY
Smoking habits: moderate cigarette smoker
Age begun 21 yrs.   Inhalation: yes
Habits of nervous tension: 5, 6

FIGURE-DRAWING CHARACTERISTICS

Structural	Male	Female	Structural	Male	Female	Structural and Graphic	Male	Female	Graphic, Global and Height	Male	Female	Body Proportions	Male	Female
	Both						Both							
Type	0		Omission of Appendages	1	1	Upper and Lower Halves	1	9	Hair Shading	3	3	Head	26	21
Sex Sequence	2		Position of Both Arms	6	6	Four Quarters	9	9	Nudity and Transparency	9	9	Neck		
Posture	0	0	Position of Right Arm	8	8	Relative Size	9		Form	5	5	Shoulders	14	13
Perspective	0	0	Position of Left Arm	8	8	Constant Line Pressure	0	5	Detailing	5	5	Right Arm		
Vertical Midline	0	0	Position of Legs	0	0	Variable Line Pressure	5	0	Identity and Sex	3	3	Left Arm		
Bilateral Symmetry	9	9	Relation of Long Axes	9	9	Line Continuity	2	0	Sophistication	4	4	Chest	16	13
Horizontal Midline	9	9	Right and Left Halves	1	9	Body Shading	9	9	Height			Girth		

GENERAL CHARACTERISTICS OF SUBJECT

IDENTIFICATION
No. F20
Sex M
Marital status M
Age 25 yrs. at
psychological tests

PARENTAL HISTORY				
Father				
C	H	S	D	O
-	-	-	-	-
Mother				
C	H	S	D	O
-	U	+	-	-

PHYSIOLOGICAL AND METABOLIC DATA

	Admission	Initial	Control	Cold pressor change	Exercise change	Smoking change
Systolic pressure	120	120	110	+06	+10	
Diastolic pressure	70	90	90	+08	+02	
Heart rate	72	68	64	+08	+17	

Age 22 yrs.	Height 67 in.	Ponderal index 13.37
	Weight 126 lbs.	Cholesterol 250 mg. per 100 ml.
	Overweight −11 %	Vital capacity liters

HABIT SURVEY

Smoking habits: nonsmoker

  Age begun   yrs.   Inhalation:

Habits of nervous tension: 1, 3, 4, 7, 11, 14, 19, 20, 21

Plate 849   DRAWINGS BY SUBJECTS OF NON-EUROPEAN ANCESTRY   901

FIGURE-DRAWING CHARACTERISTICS

Structural	Male Female Both	Structural	Male	Female	Structural and Graphic	Male Female Both		Graphic, Global and Height	Male	Female	Body Proportions	Male	Female
Type	0	Omission of Appendages	0	8	Upper and Lower Halves	3	3	Hair Shading	7	7	Head	08	
Sex Sequence	1	Position of Both Arms	0	0	Four Quarters	4	4	Nudity and Transparency	7	7	Neck		
Posture	1 1	Position of Right Arm	2	2	Relative Size	4		Form	3	3	Shoulders	06	
Perspective	0 3	Position of Left Arm	2	2	Constant Line Pressure	0	2	Detailing	3	3	Right Arm	06	04
Vertical Midline	3 9	Position of Legs	4	6	Variable Line Pressure	1	0	Identity and Sex	1	1	Left Arm	06	04
Bilateral Symmetry	2 3	Relation of Long Axes	1	1	Line Continuity	1	0	Sophistication	3	3	Chest	06	07
Horizontal Midline	6 4	Right and Left Halves	1	1	Body Shading	0	2	Height	07	08	Girth	07	09

GENERAL CHARACTERISTICS OF SUBJECT

IDENTIFICATION
No. 728
Sex F
Marital status S
Age 23 yrs. at
psychological tests

PARENTAL HISTORY					
Father					
C	H	S	D	O	
-	+	-	-	-	
Mother					
C	H	S	D	O	
-	-	-	-	-	

PHYSIOLOGICAL AND METABOLIC DATA

	Admission	Initial	Control	Cold pressor change	Exercise change	Smoking change
Systolic pressure	98	100	90	+20	+20	+02
Diastolic pressure	60	72	68	+18	+10	+12
Heart rate	72	100	97	00	+20	+33

Age 23 yrs.	Height 64 in.	Ponderal index 13.28
	Weight 112 lbs.	Cholesterol 243 mg. per 100 ml.
	Overweight -12 %	Vital capacity liters

HABIT SURVEY
Smoking habits: occasional smoker
Age begun 20 yrs.   Inhalation: yes
Habits of nervous tension: 3, 4, 5, 9, 11

FIGURE-DRAWING CHARACTERISTICS

Structural	Male Female Both		Structural	Male	Female	Structural and Graphic	Male Female Both		Graphic, Global and Height	Male	Female	Body Proportions	Male	Female
Type	0		Omission of Appendages	0	0	Upper and Lower Halves	1	1	Hair Shading	1	3	Head	07	06
Sex Sequence	0		Position of Both Arms	0	0	Four Quarters	4	4	Nudity and Transparency	7	7	Neck	04	04
Posture	1	1	Position of Right Arm	0	0	Relative Size	1		Form	3	3	Shoulders	10	06
Perspective	0	0	Position of Left Arm	0	0	Constant Line Pressure	5	0	Detailing	3	3	Right Arm	04	03
Vertical Midline	3	3	Position of Legs	2	4	Variable Line Pressure	0	5	Identity and Sex	1	1	Left Arm	04	02
Bilateral Symmetry	4	2	Relation of Long Axes	1	1	Line Continuity	4	2	Sophistication	3	3	Chest	06	05
Horizontal Midline	6	4	Right and Left Halves	1	1	Body Shading	6	5	Height	05	05	Girth	07	06

GENERAL CHARACTERISTICS OF SUBJECT

IDENTIFICATION
No. C63
Sex M
Marital status S
Age 23 yrs. at
psychological tests

PARENTAL HISTORY				
Father				
C	H	S	D	O
-	+	-	-	+
Mother				
C	H	S	D	O
-	-	-	-	-

PHYSIOLOGICAL AND METABOLIC DATA

	Admission	Initial	Control	Cold pressor change	Exercise change	Smoking change
Systolic pressure	100	112	110	+20	+35	+07
Diastolic pressure	60	70	68	+24	-18	+10
Heart rate	72	72	65	+04	+35	+14

Age 23 yrs.	Height	67 in.	Ponderal index 13.81
	Weight	114 lbs.	Cholesterol 287 mg. per 100 ml.
	Overweight -20 %		Vital capacity 3.2 liters

HABIT SURVEY

Smoking habits: nonsmoker

Age begun   yrs.   Inhalation:

Habits of nervous tension: 8

STRONG VOCATIONAL INTEREST TEST

Occupation	Artist	Psychologist	Architect	Physician	Osteopath	Dentist	Veterinarian	Mathematician	Physicist	Engineer	Chemist	Production Manager
Standard Score	17	35	13	38	49	29	24	17	12	25	30	33

Occupation	Farmer	Aviator	Carpenter	Printer	Math.-Sci. Teacher	Ind. Arts Teacher	Voc. Agric. Teacher	Policeman	Forest Serv. Man	Y.M.C.A. Phys. Dir.	Personnel Director	Public Administrator
Standard Score	26	31	23	42	47	21	20	46	29	52	59	57

Occupation	Y.M.C.A. Secretary	Soc. Sci. H.S. Teacher	City Sch. Sup't.	Social Worker	Minister	Musician Performer	C.P.A.	Senior C.P.A.	Accountant	Office Man	Purchasing Agent	Banker
Standard Score	50	55	43	56	62	39	24	45	40	50	23	26

Occupation	Mortician	Pharmacist	Sales Manager	Real Est. Manager	Life Ins. Salesman	Advertising Man	Lawyer	Author-Journalist	President Mfg. Co.	Interest Maturity	Occupational Level	Masculinity-Femininity
Standard Score	34	28	30	28	37	30	28	25	26	69	46	40

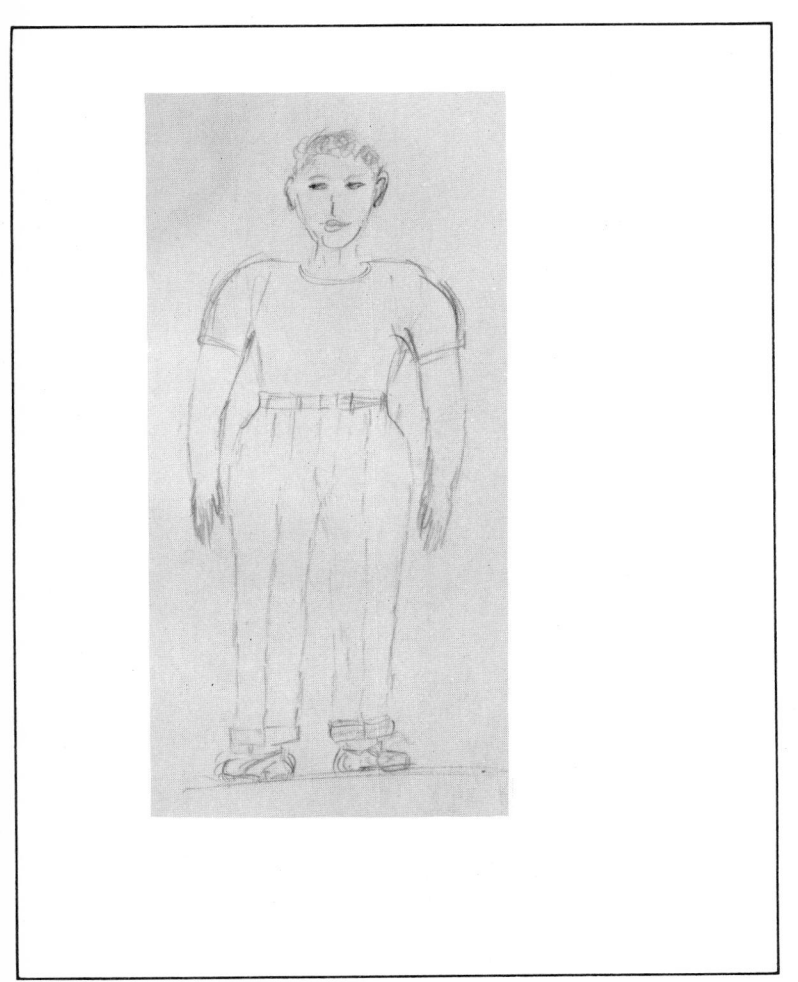

FIGURE-DRAWING CHARACTERISTICS

Structural	Male Female Both	Structural	Male	Female	Structural and Graphic	Male Female Both		Graphic, Global and Height	Male	Female	Body Proportions	Male	Female
Type	0	Omission of Appendages	0	0	Upper and Lower Halves	1	3	Hair Shading	3	3	Head	09	09
Sex Sequence	0	Position of Both Arms	0	4	Four Quarters	4	4	Nudity and Transparency	7	7	Neck	05	07
Posture	1 1	Position of Right Arm	0	7	Relative Size	4		Form	3	3	Shoulders	10	
Perspective	0 2	Position of Left Arm	0	0	Constant Line Pressure	0	0	Detailing	1	3	Right Arm	06	
Vertical Midline	3 4	Position of Legs	4	1	Variable Line Pressure	1	1	Identity and Sex	1	1	Left Arm	06	08
Bilateral Symmetry	4 0	Relation of Long Axes	1	1	Line Continuity	0	0	Sophistication	3	3	Chest	07	09
Horizontal Midline	4 0	Right and Left Halves	1	1	Body Shading	6	0	Height	06	08	Girth	08	08

GENERAL CHARACTERISTICS OF SUBJECT

IDENTIFICATION

No. F39
Sex M
Marital status M
Age 28 yrs. at
psychological tests

PARENTAL HISTORY

Father

C	H	S	D	O
-	-	-	-	-

Mother

C	H	S	D	O
-	+	+	+	+

PHYSIOLOGICAL AND METABOLIC DATA

	Admission	Initial	Control	Cold pressor change	Exercise change	Smoking change
Systolic pressure	122	110	102	+14	+32	00
Diastolic pressure	58	74	70	+16	+14	+01
Heart rate	72	64	64	+12	+24	+16

Age 26 yrs.

Height	66 in.	Ponderal index 12.43
Weight	150 lbs.	Cholesterol 320 mg. per 100 ml.
Overweight +06 %		Vital capacity liters

HABIT SURVEY

Smoking habits: light cigarette smoker
  Age begun 23 yrs.   Inhalation: yes
Habits of nervous tension: 5, 9, 11, 18, 23, 25

STRONG VOCATIONAL INTEREST TEST

Occupation	Artist	Psychologist	Architect	Physician	Osteopath	Dentist	Veterinarian	Mathematician	Physicist	Engineer	Chemist	Production Manager
Standard Score	23	43	34	53	46	41	34	32	36	44	48	42

Occupation	Farmer	Aviator	Carpenter	Printer	Math.-Sci. Teacher	Ind. Arts Teacher	Voc. Agric. Teacher	Policeman	Forest Serv. Man	Y.M.C.A. Phys. Dir.	Personnel Director	Public Administrator
Standard Score	45	49	47	52	58	57	55	43	38	39	43	48

Occupation	Y.M.C.A. Secretary	Soc. Sci. H.S. Teacher	City Sch. Sup't.	Social Worker	Minister	Musician Performer	C.P.A.	Senior C.P.A.	Accountant	Office Man	Purchasing Agent	Banker
Standard Score	24	37	29	35	58	45	26	51	34	38	28	26

Occupation	Mortician	Pharmacist	Sales Manager	Real Est. Manager	Life Ins. Salesman	Advertising Man	Lawyer	Author- Journalist	President Mfg. Co.	Interest Maturity	Occupational Level	Masculinity- Femininity
Standard Score	28	33	20	26	14	23	20	23	31	55	44	56

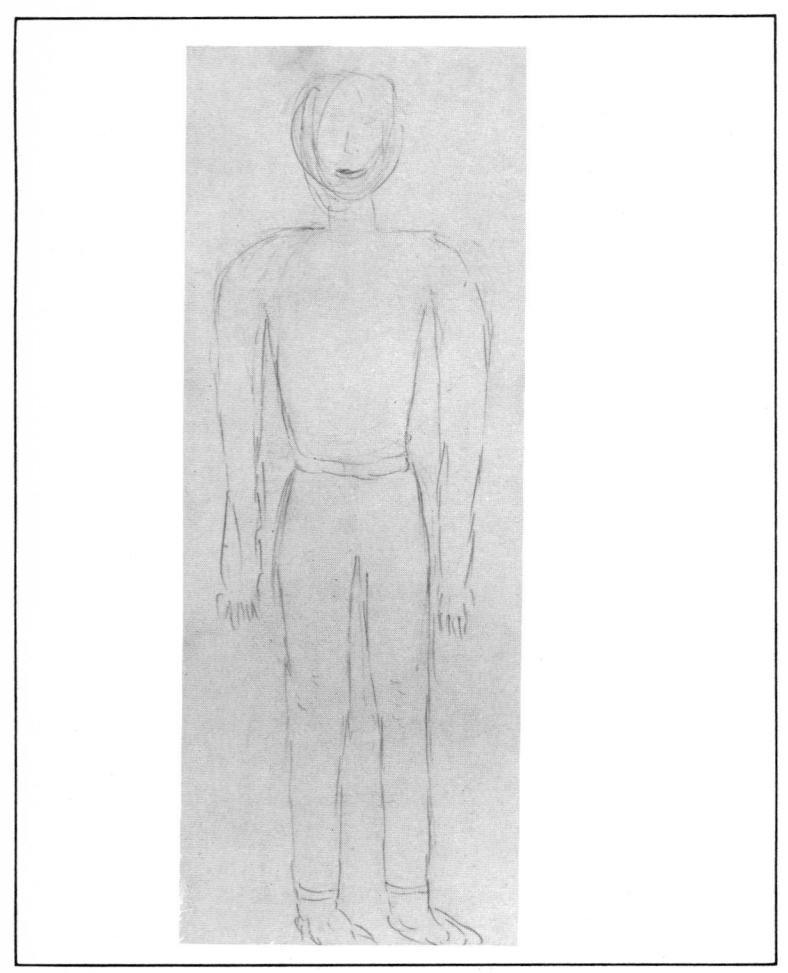

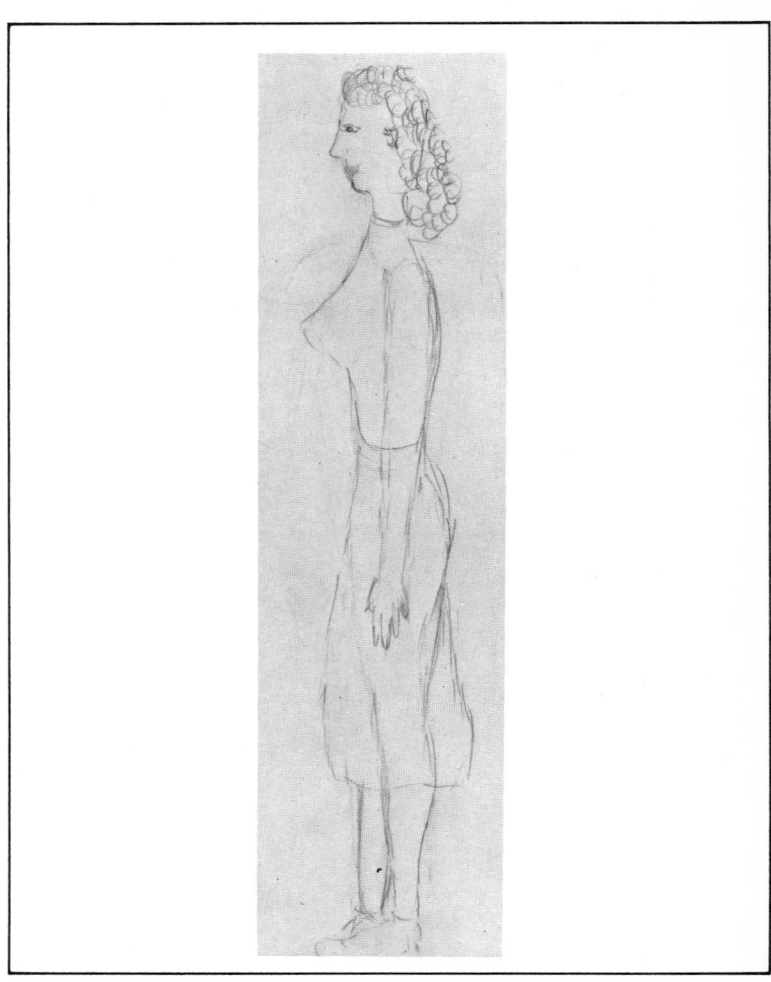

FIGURE-DRAWING CHARACTERISTICS

Structural	Male Female Both	Structural	Male	Female	Structural and Graphic	Male Female Both		Graphic, Global and Height	Male	Female	Body Proportions	Male	Female
Type	0	Omission of Appendages	0	0	Upper and Lower Halves	3	0	Hair Shading	0	3	Head		
Sex Sequence	0	Position of Both Arms	0	4	Four Quarters	4	4	Nudity and Transparency	3	6	Neck		
Posture	1	1	Position of Right Arm	0	7	Relative Size	2		Form	1	1	Shoulders		
Perspective	0	2	Position of Left Arm	0	0	Constant Line Pressure	1	1	Detailing	5	3	Right Arm		
Vertical Midline	0	4	Position of Legs	4	1	Variable Line Pressure	0	0	Identity and Sex	1	1	Left Arm		
Bilateral Symmetry	4	0	Relation of Long Axes	1	1	Line Continuity	0	0	Sophistication	3	3	Chest	07	07
Horizontal Midline	4	4	Right and Left Halves	1	1	Body Shading	2	0	Height	09		Girth	07	07

GENERAL CHARACTERISTICS OF SUBJECT

IDENTIFICATION
No. G64
Sex M
Marital status S
Age 24 yrs. at
psychological tests

PARENTAL HISTORY				
Father				
C	H	S	D	O
-	-	-	-	-
Mother				
C	H	S	D	O
-	+	-	-	?

PHYSIOLOGICAL AND METABOLIC DATA

	Admission	Initial	Control	Cold pressor change	Exercise change	Smoking change
Systolic pressure	154	134	120	+04	+18	
Diastolic pressure	86	90	84	+18	+04	
Heart rate	84	76	74	+04	+15	

Age 22 yrs.	Height	70	in.	Ponderal index	11.69	
	Weight	215	lbs.	Cholesterol	288	mg. per 100 ml.
	Overweight +40 %			Vital capacity		liters

HABIT SURVEY

Smoking habits: nonsmoker

Age begun   yrs.   Inhalation:

Habits of nervous tension: 7, 9, 19, 21, 22

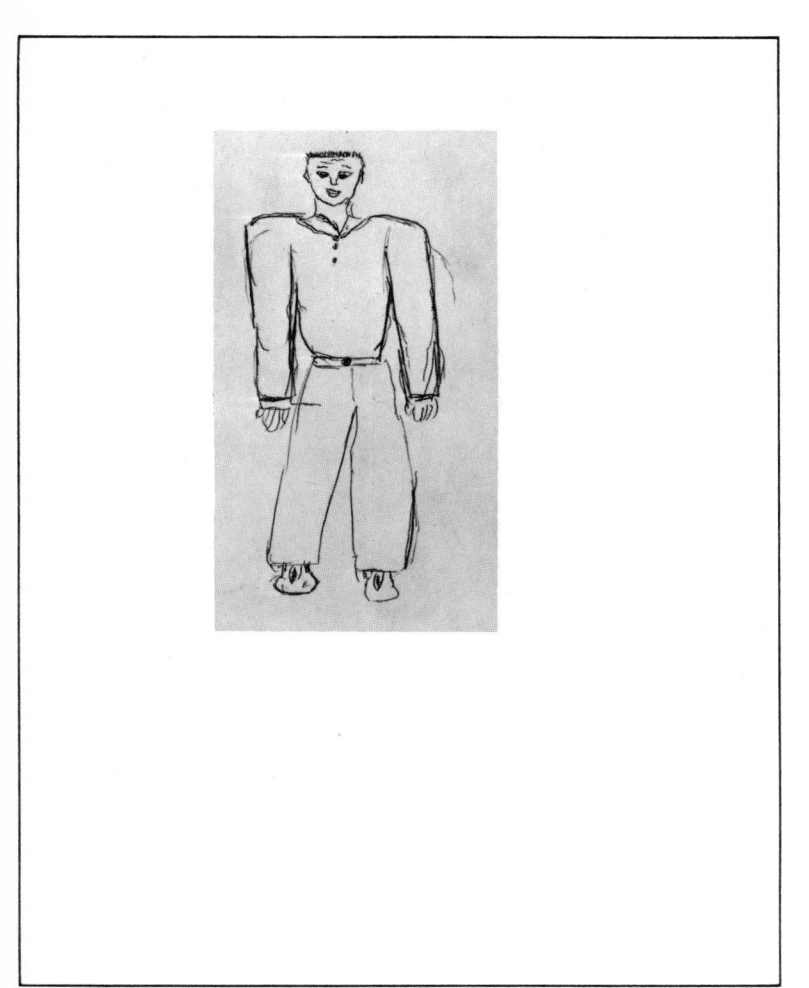

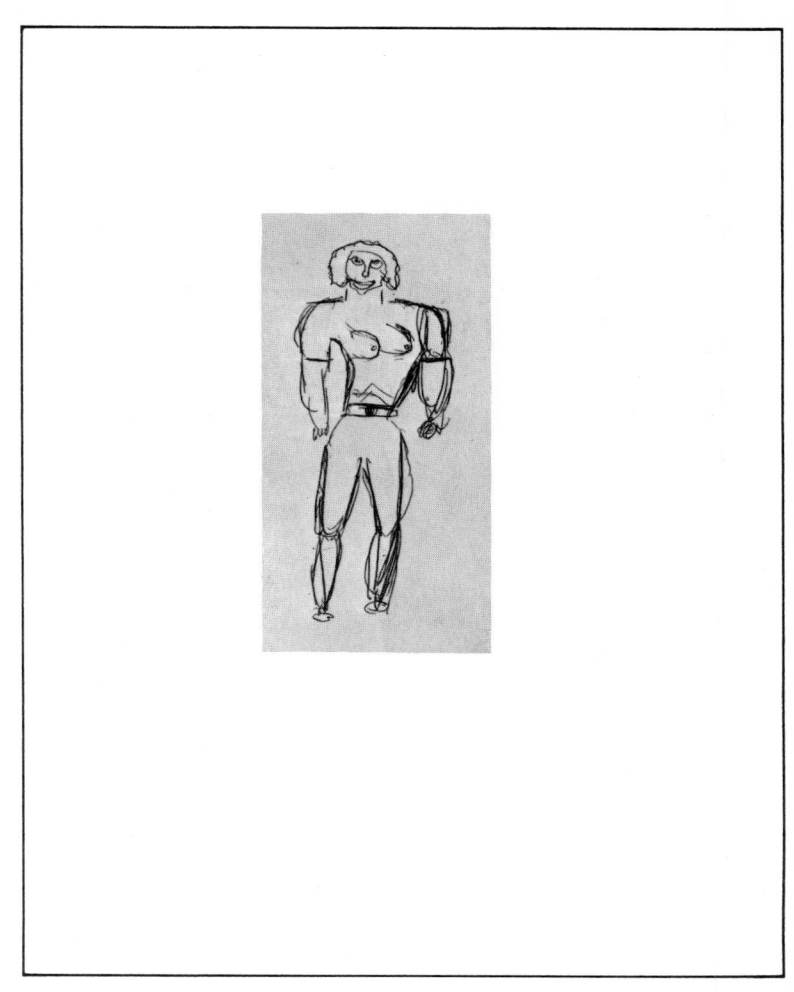

FIGURE-DRAWING CHARACTERISTICS

Structural	Male Female Both	Structural	Male	Female	Structural and Graphic	Male Female Both		Graphic, Global and Height	Male	Female	Body Proportions	Male	Female
Type	0	Omission of Appendages	0	0	Upper and Lower Halves	1	1	Hair Shading	3	5	Head	04	04
Sex Sequence	0	Position of Both Arms	0	0	Four Quarters	4	4	Nudity and Transparency	7	5	Neck	04	03
Posture	1 1	Position of Right Arm	0	0	Relative Size	0		Form	3	5	Shoulders	07	05
Perspective	0 0	Position of Left Arm	0	5	Constant Line Pressure	0	0	Detailing	3	3	Right Arm	04	02
Vertical Midline	3 0	Position of Legs	6	1	Variable Line Pressure	4	5	Identity and Sex	1	1	Left Arm	04	02
Bilateral Symmetry	3 1	Relation of Long Axes	1	1	Line Continuity	0	0	Sophistication	3	3	Chest	04	04
Horizontal Midline	4 4	Right and Left Halves	1	1	Body Shading	4	7	Height	04	04	Girth	04	03

GENERAL CHARACTERISTICS OF SUBJECT

IDENTIFICATION
No. A48
Sex M
Marital status S
Age 22 yrs. at
psychological tests

PARENTAL HISTORY
Father
C   H   S   D   0
–   –   –   –   +
Mother
C   H   S   D   0
–   –   –   –

PHYSIOLOGICAL AND METABOLIC DATA

	Admission	Initial	Control	Cold pressor change	Exercise change	Smoking change
Systolic pressure	120	122	115	+16	+29	+04
Diastolic pressure	70	58	65	+18	-17	+10
Heart rate	80	72	70	+06	+26	+05

Age 22 yrs.	Height 72 in.	Ponderal index 12.86
	Weight 176 lbs.	Cholesterol 155 mg. per 100 ml.
	Overweight +08 %	Vital capacity liters

HABIT SURVEY

Smoking habits: occasional smoker

Age begun 18 yrs.   Inhalation: yes

Habits of nervous tension: 4, 5, 6, 9, 11, 17, 21, 23

STRONG VOCATIONAL INTEREST TEST

Occupation	Artist	Psychologist	Architect	Physician	Osteopath	Dentist	Veterinarian	Mathematician	Physicist	Engineer	Chemist	Production Manager
Standard Score	29	32	18	48	52	35	27	09	-06	08	20	26

Occupation	Farmer	Aviator	Carpenter	Printer	Math.-Sci. Teacher	Ind. Arts Teacher	Voc. Agric. Teacher	Policeman	Forest Serv. Man	Y.M.C.A. Phys. Dir.	Personnel Director	Public Administrator
Standard Score	10	17	-07	24	27	-04	08	27	01	42	31	35

Occupation	Y.M.C.A. Secretary	Soc. Sci. H.S. Teacher	City Sch. Sup't.	Social Worker	Minister	Musician Performer	C.P.A.	Senior C.P.A.	Accountant	Office Man	Purchasing Agent	Banker
Standard Score	41	48	37	51	60	48	34	26	18	33	17	23

Occupation	Mortician	Pharmacist	Sales Manager	Real Est. Manager	Life Ins. Salesman	Advertising Man	Lawyer	Author-Journalist	President Mfg. Co.	Interest Maturity	Occupational Level	Masculinity-Femininity
Standard Score	44	48	47	46	59	50	48	40	36	61	62	28

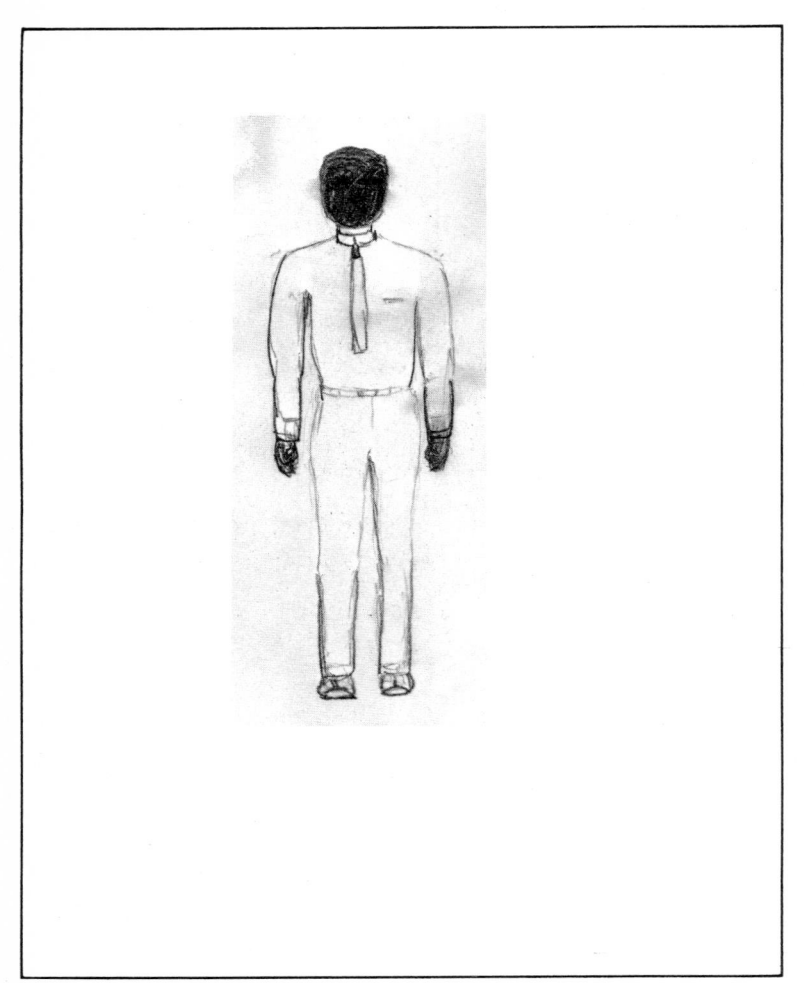

FIGURE-DRAWING CHARACTERISTICS

Structural	Male Female Both		Structural	Male	Female	Structural and Graphic	Male Female Both		Graphic, Global and Height	Male	Female	Body Proportions	Male	Female
Type	0		Omission of Appendages	0	0	Upper and Lower Halves	1	1	Hair Shading	1	3	Head	06	04
Sex Sequence	0		Position of Both Arms	0	0	Four Quarters	4	4	Nudity and Transparency	6	7	Neck	03	01
Posture	1	1	Position of Right Arm	0	0	Relative Size	0		Form	1	3	Shoulders	06	04
Perspective	0	0	Position of Left Arm	0	0	Constant Line Pressure	0	0	Detailing	3	3	Right Arm	05	04
Vertical Midline	3	3	Position of Legs	4	4	Variable Line Pressure	3	4	Identity and Sex	1	1	Left Arm	04	04
Bilateral Symmetry	3	3	Relation of Long Axes	1	1	Line Continuity	0	1	Sophistication	3	3	Chest	05	03
Horizontal Midline	4	4	Right and Left Halves	1	1	Body Shading	4	7	Height	05	04	Girth	05	04

GENERAL CHARACTERISTICS OF SUBJECT

IDENTIFICATION
No. F48
Sex M
Marital status S
Age 24 yrs. at
psychological tests

PARENTAL HISTORY
Father
C H S D O
- - - - -
Mother
C H S D O
- - - - -

PHYSIOLOGICAL AND METABOLIC DATA

	Admission	Initial	Control	Cold pressor change	Exercise change	Smoking change
Systolic pressure	130	120	110	+08	+16	+04
Diastolic pressure	60	74	74	+16	+06	+16
Heart rate	78	76	81	+08	+26	+04

	Height	66 in.	Ponderal index 12.34
Age 22 yrs.	Weight	153 lbs.	Cholesterol 310 mg. per 100 ml.
	Overweight +10 %		Vital capacity liters

HABIT SURVEY

Smoking habits: nonsmoker

Age begun   yrs.   Inhalation:

Habits of nervous tension: 1, 5, 6, 10, 19,

21, 22, 25

STRONG VOCATIONAL INTEREST TEST

Occupation	Artist	Psychologist	Architect	Physician	Osteopath	Dentist	Veterinarian	Mathematician	Physicist	Engineer	Chemist	Production Manager
Standard Score	23	38	24	46	58	35	30	12	14	27	36	41

Occupation	Farmer	Aviator	Carpenter	Printer	Math.-Sci. Teacher	Ind. Arts Teacher	Voc. Agric. Teacher	Policeman	Forest Serv. Man	Y.M.C.A. Phys. Dir.	Personnel Director	Public Administrator
Standard Score	27	38	31	43	45	33	21	49	32	57	57	54

Occupation	Y.M.C.A. Secretary	Soc. Sci. H.S. Teacher	City Sch. Sup't.	Social Worker	Minister	Musician Performer	C.P.A.	Senior C.P.A.	Accountant	Office Man	Purchasing Agent	Banker
Standard Score	47	45	36	53	58	42	20	40	36	46	26	21

Occupation	Mortician	Pharmacist	Sales Manager	Real Est. Manager	Life Ins. Salesman	Advertising Man	Lawyer	Author- Journalist	President Mfg. Co.	Interest Maturity	Occupational Level	Masculinity- Femininity
Standard Score	40	36	34	35	43	32	26	27	33	67	49	41

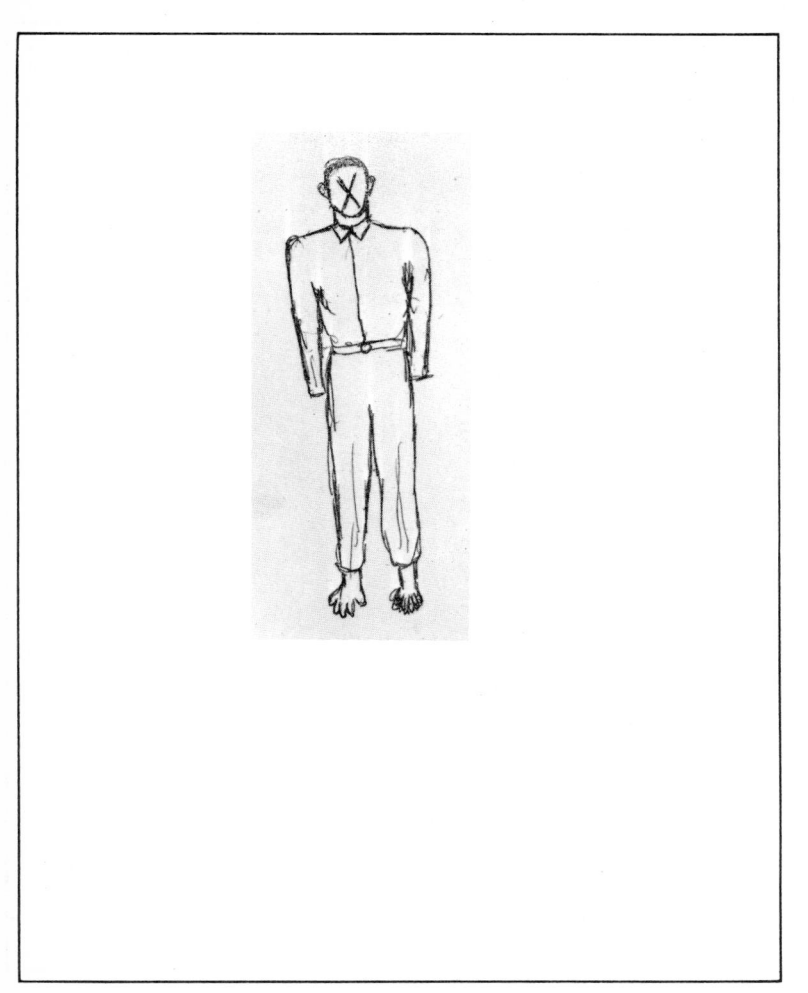

FIGURE-DRAWING CHARACTERISTICS

Structural	Male Female Both		Structural	Male	Female	Structural and Graphic	Male Female Both		Graphic, Global and Height	Male	Female	Body Proportions	Male	Female
Type	0		Omission of Appendages	7	1	Upper and Lower Halves	1	1	Hair Shading	3	3	Head	05	05
Sex Sequence	0		Position of Both Arms	0	6	Four Quarters	4	4	Nudity and Transparency	7	7	Neck	04	07
Posture	1	0	Position of Right Arm	0	8	Relative Size	4		Form	1	1	Shoulders	05	05
Perspective	0	0	Position of Left Arm	0	8	Constant Line Pressure	3	3	Detailing	3	3	Right Arm		
Vertical Midline	3	0	Position of Legs	4	4	Variable Line Pressure	0	0	Identity and Sex	1	1	Left Arm		
Bilateral Symmetry	3	3	Relation of Long Axes	1	1	Line Continuity	0	0	Sophistication	3	3	Chest	04	04
Horizontal Midline	4	4	Right and Left Halves	1	1	Body Shading	3	4	Height	04		Girth	04	04

GENERAL CHARACTERISTICS OF SUBJECT

IDENTIFICATION
No. E58
Sex M
Marital status S
Age 23 yrs. at
psychological tests

PARENTAL HISTORY					
Father					
C	H	S	D	O	
-	-	-	-	-	
Mother					
C	H	S	D	O	
-	-	-	-	-	

PHYSIOLOGICAL AND METABOLIC DATA

	Admission	Initial	Control	Cold pressor change	Exercise change	Smoking change
Systolic pressure	154	120	108	-02	+28	-02
Diastolic pressure	90	72	72	+08	-02	+01
Heart rate	80	68	69	-04	+25	-10

Age 22 yrs.	Height 67 in.	Ponderal index 12.98
	Weight 137 lbs.	Cholesterol 263 mg. per 100 ml.
	Overweight -04 %	Vital capacity liters

HABIT SURVEY

Smoking habits: pipe smoker

  Age begun 21 yrs.   Inhalation: no

Habits of nervous tension: 5, 9, 11

STRONG VOCATIONAL INTEREST TEST

Occupation	Artist	Psychologist	Architect	Physician	Osteopath	Dentist	Veterinarian	Mathematician	Physicist	Engineer	Chemist	Production Manager
Standard Score	50	46	49	65	36	47	33	52	48	43	57	20

Occupation	Farmer	Aviator	Carpenter	Printer	Math.-Sci. Teacher	Ind. Arts Teacher	Voc. Agric. Teacher	Policeman	Forest Serv. Man	Y.M.C.A. Phys. Dir.	Personnel Director	Public Administrator
Standard Score	43	40	25	34	41	15	24	18	31	16	08	27

Occupation	Y.M.C.A. Secretary	Soc. Sci. H.S. Teacher	City Sch. Sup't.	Social Worker	Minister	Musician Performer	C.P.A.	Senior C.P.A.	Accountant	Office Man	Purchasing Agent	Banker
Standard Score	01	19	19	22	64	46	32	30	07	15	14	16

Occupation	Mortician	Pharmacist	Sales Manager	Real Est. Manager	Life Ins. Salesman	Advertising Man	Lawyer	Author-Journalist	President Mfg. Co.	Interest Maturity	Occupational Level	Masculinity-Femininity
Standard Score	06	32	18	28	17	35	38	48	35	41	57	45

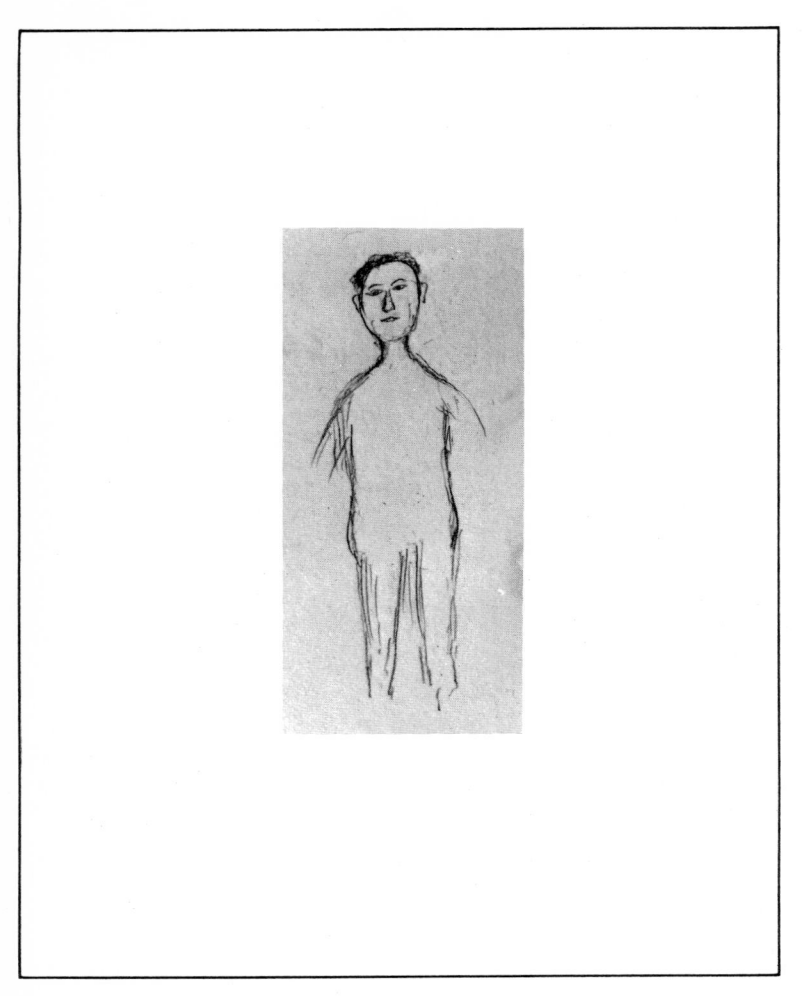

FIGURE-DRAWING CHARACTERISTICS

Structural	Male Female Both	Structural	Male	Female	Structural and Graphic	Male Female Both		Graphic, Global and Height	Male	Female	Body Proportions	Male	Female
Type	0	Omission of Appendages	1	1	Upper and Lower Halves	1	1	Hair Shading	3	3	Head	07	07
Sex Sequence	0	Position of Both Arms	6	6	Four Quarters	4	4	Nudity and Transparency	0	7	Neck	06	08
Posture	0 0	Position of Right Arm	8	8	Relative Size	5		Form	3	3	Shoulders	04	04
Perspective	0 0	Position of Left Arm	8	8	Constant Line Pressure	0	0	Detailing	3	3	Right Arm		
Vertical Midline	0 0	Position of Legs	0	0	Variable Line Pressure	5	1	Identity and Sex	3	3	Left Arm		
Bilateral Symmetry	9 9	Relation of Long Axes	1	1	Line Continuity	0	0	Sophistication	3	3	Chest	04	05
Horizontal Midline	0 0	Right and Left Halves	3	0	Body Shading	0	0	Height			Girth	06	04

GENERAL CHARACTERISTICS OF SUBJECT

IDENTIFICATION
No. 314
Sex M
Marital status S
Age 31 yrs. at
psychological tests

PARENTAL HISTORY				
Father				
C	H	S	D	O
U	U	U	U	U
Mother				
C	H	S	D	O
U	U	U	U	U

PHYSIOLOGICAL AND METABOLIC DATA

	Admission	Initial	Control	Cold pressor change	Exercise change	Smoking change
Systolic pressure	110	98	100	+02	+15	
Diastolic pressure	80	74	74	+02	-10	
Heart rate	82	66	75	00	+28	

Age 29 yrs.	Height 68 in.	Ponderal index 13.79
	Weight 120 lbs.	Cholesterol 265 mg. per 100 ml.
	Overweight -21 %	Vital capacity 4.2 liters

HABIT SURVEY

Smoking habits: nonsmoker

Age begun   yrs.   Inhalation:

Habits of nervous tension: 1, 3, 11, 19, 25

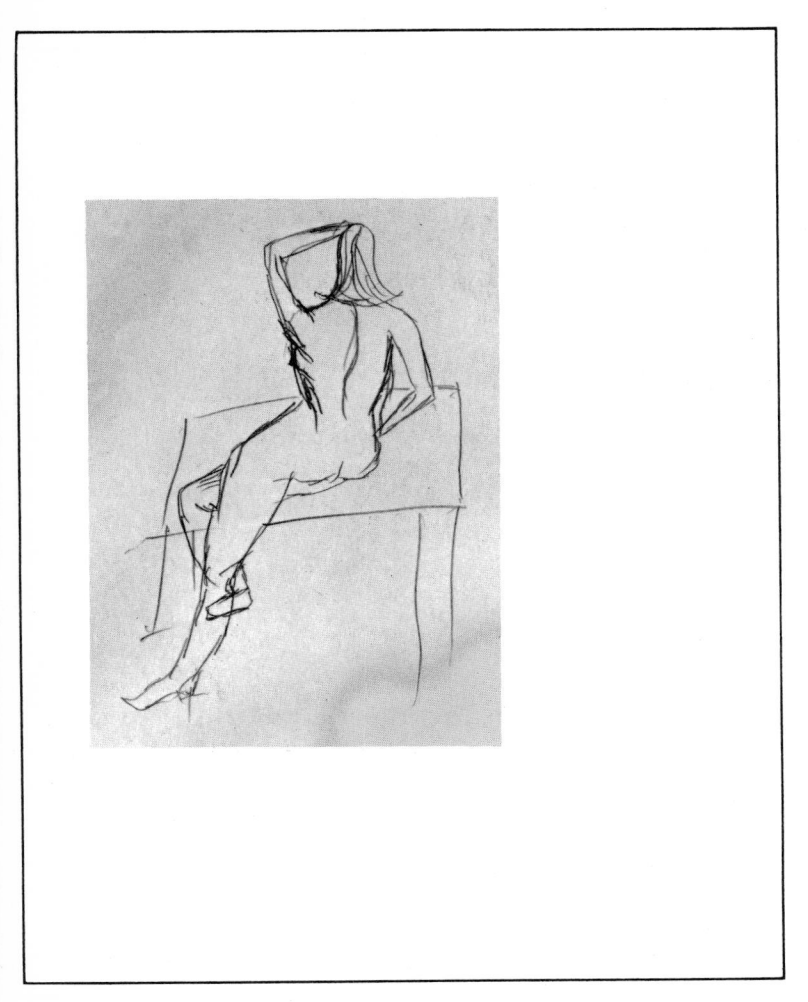

FIGURE-DRAWING CHARACTERISTICS

Structural	Male / Female (Both)		Structural	Male	Female	Structural and Graphic	Male / Female (Both)		Graphic, Global and Height	Male	Female	Body Proportions	Male	Female
Type	0		Omission of Appendages	0	7	Upper and Lower Halves	1	1	Hair Shading	3	1	Head	07	
Sex Sequence	1		Position of Both Arms	0	0	Four Quarters	4	4	Nudity and Transparency	7	0	Neck	06	
Posture	1	3	Position of Right Arm	4	5	Relative Size	5		Form	3	1	Shoulders		
Perspective	6	4	Position of Left Arm	4	5	Constant Line Pressure	0	0	Detailing	3	3	Right Arm	03	
Vertical Midline	7	7	Position of Legs	4	7	Variable Line Pressure	5	5	Identity and Sex	1	1	Left Arm	04	
Bilateral Symmetry	0	0	Relation of Long Axes	3	0	Line Continuity	0	0	Sophistication	3	2	Chest		
Horizontal Midline	6	0	Right and Left Halves	0	1	Body Shading	0	1	Height	04		Girth		

GENERAL CHARACTERISTICS OF SUBJECT

IDENTIFICATION
No. 670
Sex M
Marital status S
Age 26 yrs. at
psychological tests

PARENTAL HISTORY					
Father					
C	H	S	D	0	
?	-	-	-	+	
Mother					
C	H	S	D	0	
?	+	-	-	+	

PHYSIOLOGICAL AND METABOLIC DATA

	Admission	Initial	Control	Cold pressor change	Exercise change	Smoking change
Systolic pressure	120	132	136	+08	+36	+02
Diastolic pressure	80	84	80	+12	-06	+12
Heart rate	80	84	81	+12	+30	+01

Age 24 yrs.	Height	70 in.	Ponderal index 13.23
	Weight	148 lbs.	Cholesterol 167 mg. per 100 ml.
	Overweight -05 %		Vital capacity 4.0 liters

HABIT SURVEY

Smoking habits: occasional smoker

   Age begun 21 yrs.   Inhalation: no

Habits of nervous tension: 6, 11, 16, 25

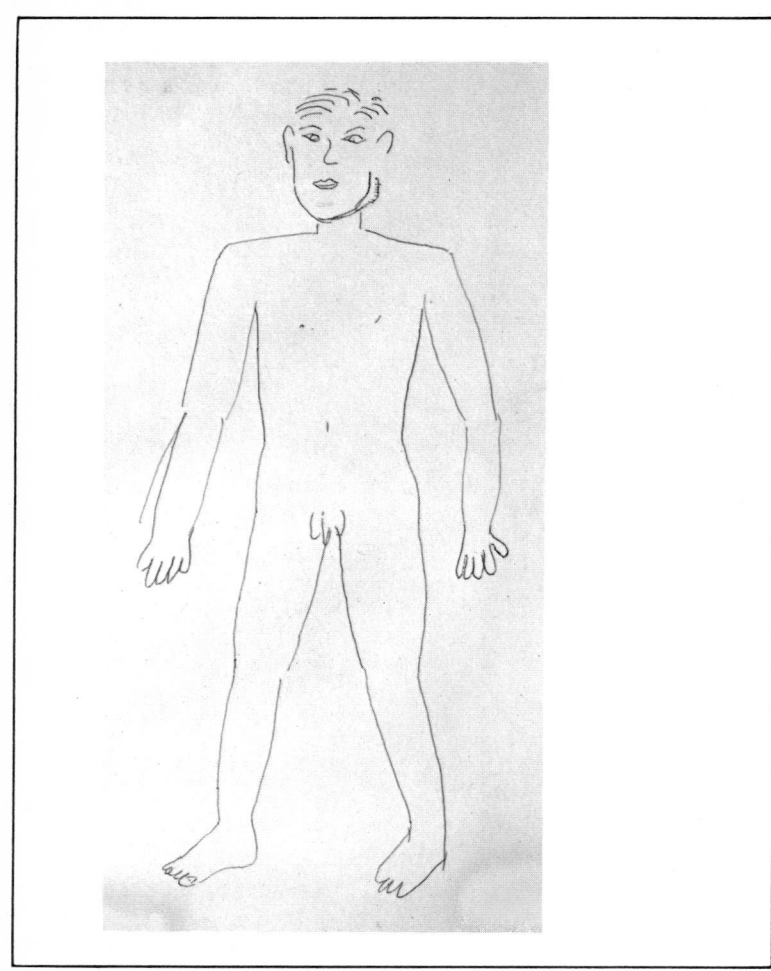

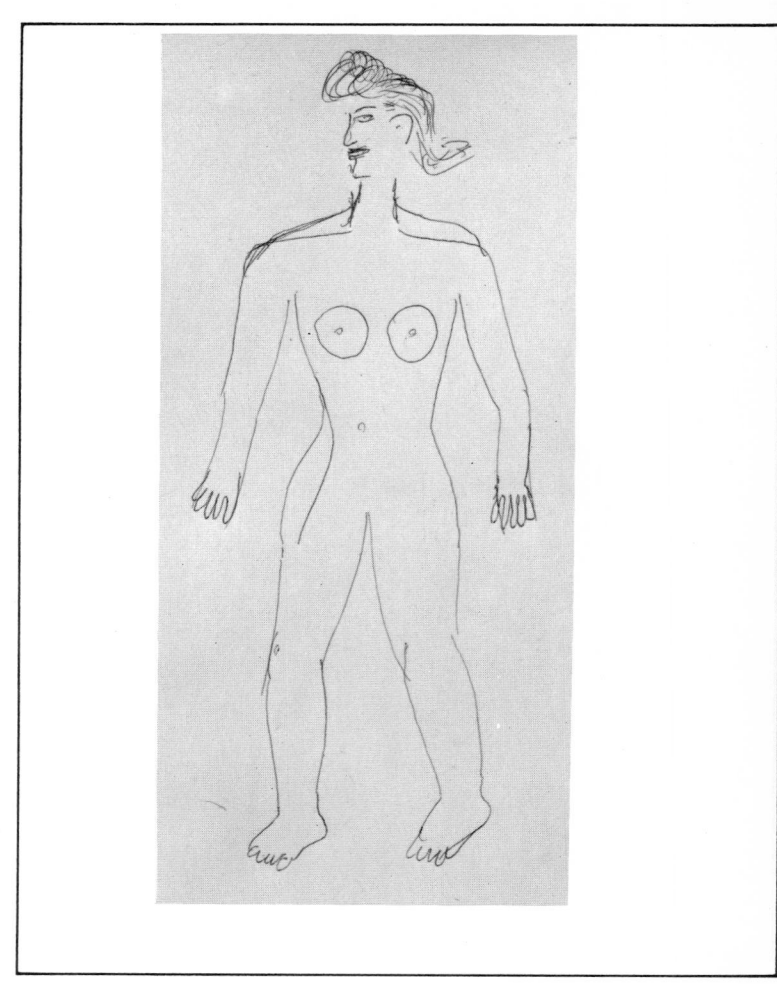

FIGURE-DRAWING CHARACTERISTICS

Structural	Male Female Both	Structural	Male	Female	Structural and Graphic	Male Female Both		Graphic, Global and Height	Male	Female	Body Proportions	Male	Female
Type	0	Omission of Appendages	0	0	Upper and Lower Halves	0	1	Hair Shading	7	3	Head		
Sex Sequence	0	Position of Both Arms	0	0	Four Quarters	4	4	Nudity and Transparency	0	0	Neck	04	12
Posture	1 2	Position of Right Arm	2	2	Relative Size	2		Form	1	3	Shoulders	09	10
Perspective	0 5	Position of Left Arm	2	2	Constant Line Pressure	4	4	Detailing	3	3	Right Arm	08	06
Vertical Midline	0 0	Position of Legs	6	8	Variable Line Pressure	0	0	Identity and Sex	1	1	Left Arm	08	06
Bilateral Symmetry	3 2	Relation of Long Axes	1	1	Line Continuity	3	2	Sophistication	2	3	Chest	08	08
Horizontal Midline	0 0	Right and Left Halves	1	1	Body Shading	0	0	Height	08		Girth	09	07

GENERAL CHARACTERISTICS OF SUBJECT

IDENTIFICATION
No. A38
Sex M
Marital status S
Age 27 yrs. at psychological tests

PARENTAL HISTORY
Father
C   H   S   D   O
?   -   -   -   -
Mother
C   H   S   D   O
-   -   -   -   -

PHYSIOLOGICAL AND METABOLIC DATA

	Admission	Initial	Control	Cold pressor change	Exercise change	Smoking change
Systolic pressure	96	132		+10		+04
Diastolic pressure	68	74		+06		+10
Heart rate	84	64		+03		+06

Age 27 yrs.	Height	66 in.	Ponderal index 12.60
	Weight	144 lbs.	Cholesterol 265 mg. per 100 ml.
	Overweight +01%		Vital capacity liters

HABIT SURVEY

Smoking habits: nonsmoker

Age begun yrs.   Inhalation:

Habits of nervous tension: 4, 5, 6, 10, 19, 21, 25

STRONG VOCATIONAL INTEREST TEST

Occupation	Artist	Psychologist	Architect	Physician	Osteopath	Dentist	Veterinarian	Mathematician	Physicist	Engineer	Chemist	Production Manager
Standard Score	4	7	5	6	2	3	1	5	7	6	6	6

Occupation	Farmer	Aviator	Carpenter	Printer	Math.-Sci. Teacher	Ind. Arts Teacher	Voc. Agric. Teacher	Policeman	Forest Serv. Man	Y.M.C.A. Phys. Dir.	Personnel Director	Public Administrator
Standard Score	5	5	3	5	5	2	2	3	4	1	4	5

Occupation	Y.M.C.A. Secretary	Soc. Sci. H.S. Teacher	City Sch. Sup't.	Social Worker	Minister	Musician Performer	C.P.A.	Senior C.P.A.	Accountant	Office Man	Purchasing Agent	Banker
Standard Score	2	2	3	3	6	5	7	7	4	3	2	2

Occupation	Mortician	Pharmacist	Sales Manager	Real Est. Manager	Life Ins. Salesman	Advertising Man	Lawyer	Author- Journalist	President Mfg. Co.	Interest Maturity	Occupational Level	Masculinity- Femininity
Standard Score	1	4	2	4	2	4	5	5	5	4	5	6

FIGURE-DRAWING CHARACTERISTICS

Structural	Male Female Both	Structural	Male	Female	Structural and Graphic	Male Female Both		Graphic, Global and Height	Male	Female	Body Proportions	Male	Female
Type	0	Omission of Appendages	7	2	Upper and Lower Halves	1	0	Hair Shading	1	1	Head	08	06
Sex Sequence	0	Position of Both Arms	4	6	Four Quarters	4	4	Nudity and Transparency	7	7	Neck	04	02
Posture	1 1	Position of Right Arm	8	8	Relative Size	0		Form	1	1	Shoulders	06	05
Perspective	5 5	Position of Left Arm	0	8	Constant Line Pressure	1	1	Detailing	1	1	Right Arm		
Vertical Midline	3 0	Position of Legs	2	2	Variable Line Pressure	0	0	Identity and Sex	1	1	Left Arm		
Bilateral Symmetry	3 3	Relation of Long Axes	1	1	Line Continuity	2	2	Sophistication	2	2	Chest	05	03
Horizontal Midline	4 4	Right and Left Halves	2	2	Body Shading	4	4	Height	07	06	Girth	06	04

GENERAL CHARACTERISTICS OF SUBJECT

IDENTIFICATION
No. 629
Sex F
Marital status S
Age 25 yrs. at
psychological tests

PARENTAL HISTORY
Father
C H S D O
? ? - - -
Mother
C H S D O
- - - - -

PHYSIOLOGICAL AND METABOLIC DATA

	Admission	Initial	Control	Cold pressor change	Exercise change	Smoking change
Systolic pressure	100	96	90	+20	+30	+18
Diastolic pressure	70	60	58	+14	+04	+16
Heart rate	80	72	62	-14	+63	+09

Age 22 yrs.	Height	62	in.	Ponderal index	12.97	
	Weight	109	lbs.	Cholesterol	273	mg. per 100 ml.
	Overweight	-09	%	Vital capacity	2.7	liters

HABIT SURVEY
Smoking habits: occasional smoker
Age begun 19 yrs.   Inhalation: yes
Habits of nervous tension: 6

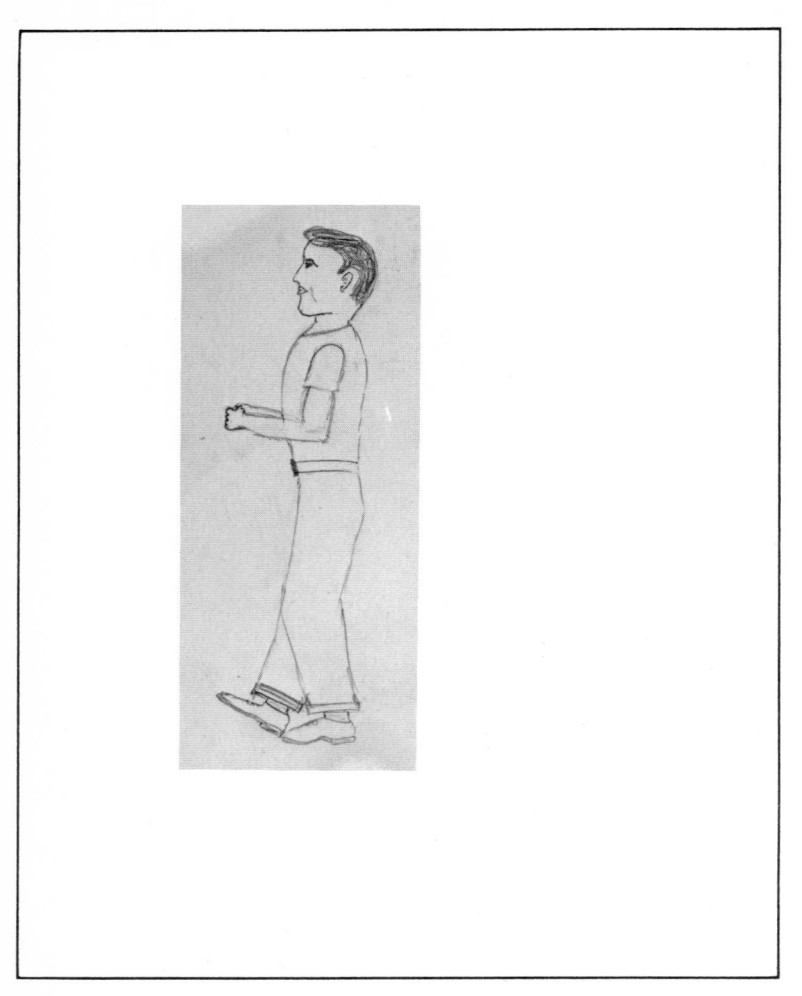

FIGURE-DRAWING CHARACTERISTICS

Structural	Male Female Both	Structural	Male	Female	Structural and Graphic	Male Female Both		Graphic, Global and Height	Male	Female	Body Proportions	Male	Female
Type	0	Omission of Appendages	0	0	Upper and Lower Halves	0	3	Hair Shading	2	2	Head	06	08
Sex Sequence	0	Position of Both Arms	4	4	Four Quarters	4	4	Nudity and Transparency	7	7	Neck	04	06
Posture	2 2	Position of Right Arm	7	7	Relative Size	4		Form	1	1	Shoulders		
Perspective	2 2	Position of Left Arm	4	3	Constant Line Pressure	0	0	Detailing	3	3	Right Arm		
Vertical Midline	4 4	Position of Legs	8	8	Variable Line Pressure	2	4	Identity and Sex	1	1	Left Arm	04	06
Bilateral Symmetry	0 0	Relation of Long Axes	1	1	Line Continuity	0	0	Sophistication	2	2	Chest	06	06
Horizontal Midline	4 4	Right and Left Halves	2	2	Body Shading	4	4	Height	05	07	Girth	05	07

GENERAL CHARACTERISTICS OF SUBJECT

IDENTIFICATION
No. F25
Sex M
Marital status S
Age 23 yrs. at
psychological tests

PARENTAL HISTORY
Father
C H S D O
- - - - +
Mother
C H S D O
- + - - -

PHYSIOLOGICAL AND METABOLIC DATA

	Admission	Initial	Control	Cold pressor change	Exercise change	Smoking change
Systolic pressure	120	110	108	+20	+14	+04
Diastolic pressure	80	72	76	+26	+06	00
Heart rate	78	80	71	+28	+06	+23

Age 21 yrs.	Height 74 in.	Ponderal index 13.14
	Weight 178 lbs.	Cholesterol 280 mg. per 100 ml.
	Overweight +03 %	Vital capacity liters

HABIT SURVEY
Smoking habits: heavy cigarette smoker
Age begun 18 yrs.   Inhalation: yes
Habits of nervous tension: 5, 6, 16

STRONG VOCATIONAL INTEREST TEST

Occupation	Artist	Psychologist	Architect	Physician	Osteopath	Dentist	Veterinarian	Mathematician	Physicist	Engineer	Chemist	Production Manager
Standard Score	48	49	58	71	50	45	29	40	43	49	53	33

Occupation	Farmer	Aviator	Carpenter	Printer	Math.-Sci. Teacher	Ind. Arts Teacher	Voc. Agric. Teacher	Policeman	Forest Serv. Man	Y.M.C.A. Phys. Dir.	Personnel Director	Public Administrator
Standard Score	32	46	25	28	34	23	22	20	32	27	27	45

Occupation	Y.M.C.A. Secretary	Soc. Sci. H.S. Teacher	City Sch. Sup't.	Social Worker	Minister	Musician Performer	C.P.A.	Senior C.P.A.	Accountant	Office Man	Purchasing Agent	Banker
Standard Score	12	15	19	30	58	51	32	34	15	15	21	12

Occupation	Mortician	Pharmacist	Sales Manager	Real Est. Manager	Life Ins. Salesman	Advertising Man	Lawyer	Author- Journalist	President Mfg. Co.	Interest Maturity	Occupational Level	Masculinity- Femininity
Standard Score	25	34	33	38	32	42	40	43	45	49	65	47

FIGURE-DRAWING CHARACTERISTICS

Structural	Male	Female	Structural	Male	Female	Structural and Graphic	Male	Female	Graphic, Global and Height	Male	Female	Body Proportions	Male	Female
		Both						Both						
Type		0	Omission of Appendages	0	0	Upper and Lower Halves	1	2	Hair Shading	3	3	Head	06	03
Sex Sequence		0	Position of Both Arms	0	2	Four Quarters	4	4	Nudity and Transparency	7	7	Neck	04	02
Posture	1	3	Position of Right Arm	0	4	Relative Size	5		Form	1	1	Shoulders	06	
Perspective	0	2	Position of Left Arm	0	7	Constant Line Pressure	0	0	Detailing	1	1	Right Arm	04	02
Vertical Midline	3	4	Position of Legs	6	1	Variable Line Pressure	5	3	Identity and Sex	1	1	Left Arm	04	
Bilateral Symmetry	2	0	Relation of Long Axes	1	0	Line Continuity	0	0	Sophistication	2	2	Chest	06	03
Horizontal Midline	6	4	Right and Left Halves	1	1	Body Shading	4	5	Height	05		Girth	07	03

GENERAL CHARACTERISTICS OF SUBJECT

IDENTIFICATION
No. 707
Sex M
Marital status S
Age 20 yrs. at
psychological tests

PARENTAL HISTORY
Father
C H S D O
– – – – –
Mother
C H S D O
– ? – – –

PHYSIOLOGICAL AND METABOLIC DATA

	Admission	Initial	Control	Cold pressor change	Exercise change	Smoking change
Systolic pressure	120	120	114	+08	+42	+06
Diastolic pressure	80	60	60	+16	–12	+06
Heart rate	80	80	83	+24	+37	–06

	Height 68 in.	Ponderal index 12.62
Age 20 yrs.	Weight 157 lbs.	Cholesterol 172 mg. per 100 ml.
	Overweight +09 %	Vital capacity 4.5 liters

HABIT SURVEY
Smoking habits: nonsmoker
Age begun yrs. Inhalation:
Habits of nervous tension: 4, 5

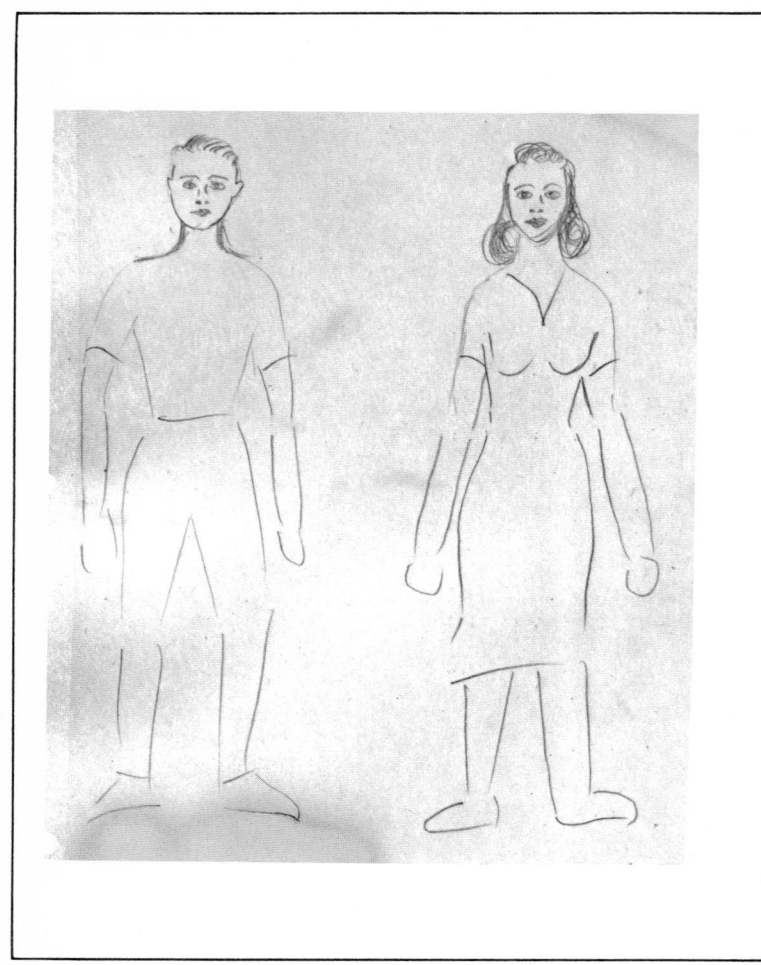

FIGURE-DRAWING CHARACTERISTICS

Structural	Male Female Both		Structural	Male	Female	Structural and Graphic	Male Female Both		Graphic, Global and Height	Male	Female	Body Proportions	Male	Female
Type	0		Omission of Appendages	0	0	Upper and Lower Halves	0	0	Hair Shading	3	3	Head	07	07
Sex Sequence	2		Position of Both Arms	0	0	Four Quarters	4	4	Nudity and Transparency	7	7	Neck	07	08
Posture	1	1	Position of Right Arm	0	0	Relative Size	2		Form	1	1	Shoulders	06	05
Perspective	0	0	Position of Left Arm	0	0	Constant Line Pressure	0	0	Detailing	1	1	Right Arm	08	08
Vertical Midline	0	0	Position of Legs	6	6	Variable Line Pressure	1	1	Identity and Sex	1	1	Left Arm	08	08
Bilateral Symmetry	3	3	Relation of Long Axes	1	1	Line Continuity	2	2	Sophistication	2	2	Chest	05	05
Horizontal Midline	4	0	Right and Left Halves	9	9	Body Shading	0	1	Height	07	07	Girth	05	05

GENERAL CHARACTERISTICS OF SUBJECT

<table>
<tr><th colspan="2">IDENTIFICATION</th></tr>
<tr><td colspan="2">No. 628</td></tr>
<tr><td colspan="2">Sex M</td></tr>
<tr><td colspan="2">Marital status   S</td></tr>
<tr><td colspan="2">Age 26 yrs. at</td></tr>
<tr><td colspan="2">psychological tests</td></tr>
</table>

PARENTAL HISTORY

Father

C	H	S	D	O
-	-	-	-	?

Mother

C	H	S	D	O
-	-	-	-	-

PHYSIOLOGICAL AND METABOLIC DATA

	Admission	Initial	Control	Cold pressor change	Exercise change	Smoking change
Systolic pressure	120	118	110	+10	+30	
Diastolic pressure	80	68	70	+14	+02	
Heart rate	76	92	84	-10	+31	

Age 23 yrs.	Height	67	in.	Ponderal index	12.62	
	Weight	150	lbs.	Cholesterol	190	mg. per 100 ml.
	Overweight +05 %			Vital capacity	3.5	liters

HABIT SURVEY

Smoking habits: nonsmoker

   Age begun   yrs.   Inhalation:

Habits of nervous tension: 4, 5, 6

FIGURE-DRAWING CHARACTERISTICS

Structural	Male Female Both		Structural	Male	Female	Structural and Graphic	Male Female Both		Graphic, Global and Height	Male	Female	Body Proportions	Male	Female
Type	0		Omission of Appendages	7	7	Upper and Lower Halves	3	0	Hair Shading	5	5	Head	06	07
Sex Sequence	0		Position of Both Arms	1	4	Four Quarters	4	4	Nudity and Transparency	7	7	Neck	05	05
Posture	1	1	Position of Right Arm	0	7	Relative Size	0		Form	1	1	Shoulders		
Perspective	1	1	Position of Left Arm	5	5	Constant Line Pressure	0	5	Detailing	3	3	Right Arm	06	
Vertical Midline	7	7	Position of Legs	5	4	Variable Line Pressure	4	0	Identity and Sex	1	3	Left Arm		
Bilateral Symmetry	0	0	Relation of Long Axes	1	1	Line Continuity	1	1	Sophistication	2	2	Chest		
Horizontal Midline	6	0	Right and Left Halves	2	1	Body Shading	4	0	Height	06	06	Girth		

GENERAL CHARACTERISTICS OF SUBJECT

IDENTIFICATION
No. C70
Sex M
Marital status S
Age 20 yrs. at psychological tests

PARENTAL HISTORY
Father
C H S D O
– – – – ?
Mother
C H S D O
– – – –

PHYSIOLOGICAL AND METABOLIC DATA

	Admission	Initial	Control	Cold pressor change	Exercise change	Smoking change
Systolic pressure	150	110	110	+04	+30	
Diastolic pressure	80	70	70	+08	–10	
Heart rate	80	80	71	+08	+49	

Age 21 yrs.	Height 66 in.	Ponderal index 12.89
	Weight 134 lbs.	Cholesterol 229 mg. per 100 ml.
	Overweight –03 %	Vital capacity liters

HABIT SURVEY

Smoking habits: nonsmoker

Age begun yrs. Inhalation:

Habits of nervous tension: 2, 3, 5, 11, 21

STRONG VOCATIONAL INTEREST TEST

Occupation	Artist	Psychologist	Architect	Physician	Osteopath	Dentist	Veterinarian	Mathematician	Physicist	Engineer	Chemist	Production Manager
Standard Score	23	44	31	53	40	38	26	38	36	45	51	32

Occupation	Farmer	Aviator	Carpenter	Printer	Math.-Sci. Teacher	Ind. Arts Teacher	Voc. Agric. Teacher	Policeman	Forest Serv. Man	Y.M.C.A. Phys. Dir.	Personnel Director	Public Administrator
Standard Score	44	50	31	44	57	37	37	37	43	45	38	46

Occupation	Y.M.C.A. Secretary	Soc. Sci. H.S. Teacher	City Sch. Sup't.	Social Worker	Minister	Musician Performer	C.P.A.	Senior C.P.A.	Accountant	Office Man	Purchasing Agent	Banker
Standard Score	37	42	34	34	62	37	17	51	30	33	11	15

Occupation	Mortician	Pharmacist	Sales Manager	Real Est. Manager	Life Ins. Salesman	Advertising Man	Lawyer	Author-Journalist	President Mfg. Co.	Interest Maturity	Occupational Level	Masculinity-Femininity
Standard Score	03	16	13	15	13	20	24	25	14	60	49	60

FIGURE-DRAWING CHARACTERISTICS

Structural	Male	Female	Structural	Male	Female	Structural and Graphic	Male	Female	Graphic, Global and Height	Male	Female	Body Proportions	Male	Female
	Both						Both							
Type	0		Omission of Appendages	0	0	Upper and Lower Halves	3	0	Hair Shading	3	3	Head	08	08
Sex Sequence	0		Position of Both Arms	1	0	Four Quarters	4	4	Nudity and Transparency	7	2	Neck	10	03
Posture	1	1	Position of Right Arm	4	5	Relative Size	0		Form	1	1	Shoulders		06
Perspective	0	0	Position of Left Arm	5	5	Constant Line Pressure	0	0	Detailing	1	3	Right Arm	06	06
Vertical Midline	3	0	Position of Legs	6	6	Variable Line Pressure	5	4	Identity and Sex	1	1	Left Arm	06	06
Bilateral Symmetry	2	3	Relation of Long Axes	1	1	Line Continuity	0	0	Sophistication	2	2	Chest	06	
Horizontal Midline	4	0	Right and Left Halves	0	0	Body Shading	7	3	Height	08	07	Girth	07	10

GENERAL CHARACTERISTICS OF SUBJECT

IDENTIFICATION
No. D16
Sex M
Marital status S
Age 22 yrs. at
psychological tests

PARENTAL HISTORY
Father
C H S D O
– – – – ?
Mother
C H S D O
– – – – –

PHYSIOLOGICAL AND METABOLIC DATA

	Admission	Initial	Control	Cold pressor change	Exercise change	Smoking change
Systolic pressure	130	120	120	-08	+25	+02
Diastolic pressure	85	70	70	+30	-15	+02
Heart rate	75	92	79	+04	+36	+07

Age 22 yrs.	Height 68 in.	Ponderal index 12.90
	Weight 146 lbs.	Cholesterol 252 mg. per 100 ml.
	Overweight 00 %	Vital capacity 3.9 liters

HABIT SURVEY

Smoking habits: light cigarette smoker

Age begun 17 yrs.   Inhalation:

Habits of nervous tension: 4, 5, 9, 10, 11, 20, 23

STRONG VOCATIONAL INTEREST TEST

Occupation	Artist	Psychologist	Architect	Physician	Osteopath	Dentist	Veterinarian	Mathematician	Physicist	Engineer	Chemist	Production Manager
Standard Score	34	50	40	58	53	41	32	32	31	39	52	27

Occupation	Farmer	Aviator	Carpenter	Printer	Math.-Sci. Teacher	Ind. Arts Teacher	Voc. Agric. Teacher	Policeman	Forest Serv. Man	Y.M.C.A. Phys. Dir.	Personnel Director	Public Administrator
Standard Score	50	53	43	57	53	47	42	36	43	34	34	47

Occupation	Y.M.C.A. Secretary	Soc. Sci. H.S. Teacher	City Sch. Sup't.	Social Worker	Minister	Musician Performer	C.P.A.	Senior C.P.A.	Accountant	Office Man	Purchasing Agent	Banker
Standard Score	31	39	20	45	63	56	14	44	20	31	19	11

Occupation	Mortician	Pharmacist	Sales Manager	Real Est. Manager	Life Ins. Salesman	Advertising Man	Lawyer	Author-Journalist	President Mfg. Co.	Interest Maturity	Occupational Level	Masculinity-Femininity
Standard Score	21	34	11	25	16	32	23	33	20	57	44	46

Plate 865   **DRAWINGS BY SUBJECTS OF NON-EUROPEAN ANCESTRY**   917

FIGURE-DRAWING CHARACTERISTICS

Structural	Male Female Both	Structural	Male	Female	Structural and Graphic	Male Female Both		Graphic, Global and Height	Male	Female	Body Proportions	Male	Female
Type	0	Omission of Appendages	0		Upper and Lower Halves	3		Hair Shading	1		Head	13	
Sex Sequence	3	Position of Both Arms	4		Four Quarters	4		Nudity and Transparency	3		Neck	12	
Posture	1	Position of Right Arm	7		Relative Size	7		Form	1		Shoulders		
Perspective	2	Position of Left Arm	6		Constant Line Pressure	5		Detailing	1		Right Arm		
Vertical Midline	4	Position of Legs	1		Variable Line Pressure	0		Identity and Sex	1		Left Arm	10	
Bilateral Symmetry	0	Relation of Long Axes	1		Line Continuity	4		Sophistication	2		Chest	10	
Horizontal Midline	4	Right and Left Halves	1		Body Shading	0		Height	09		Girth	10	

GENERAL CHARACTERISTICS OF SUBJECT

IDENTIFICATION
No. 346
Sex M
Marital status S
Age 25 yrs. at
psychological tests

PARENTAL HISTORY
Father
C H S D O
- - - - -
Mother
C H S D O
- - - - -

PHYSIOLOGICAL AND METABOLIC DATA

	Admission	Initial	Control	Cold pressor change	Exercise change	Smoking change
Systolic pressure	110	114	108	+10	+28	+02
Diastolic pressure	76	78	74	+16	+02	+04
Heart rate	72	90	77	+06	+12	00

Age 23 yrs.	Height 71 in.	Ponderal index 13.22
	Weight 155 lbs.	Cholesterol 217 mg. per 100 ml.
	Overweight -03 %	Vital capacity 4.7 liters

HABIT SURVEY

Smoking habits: nonsmoker

Age begun   yrs.   Inhalation:

Habits of nervous tension: 1, 2, 3, 5, 6, 7, 11, 25

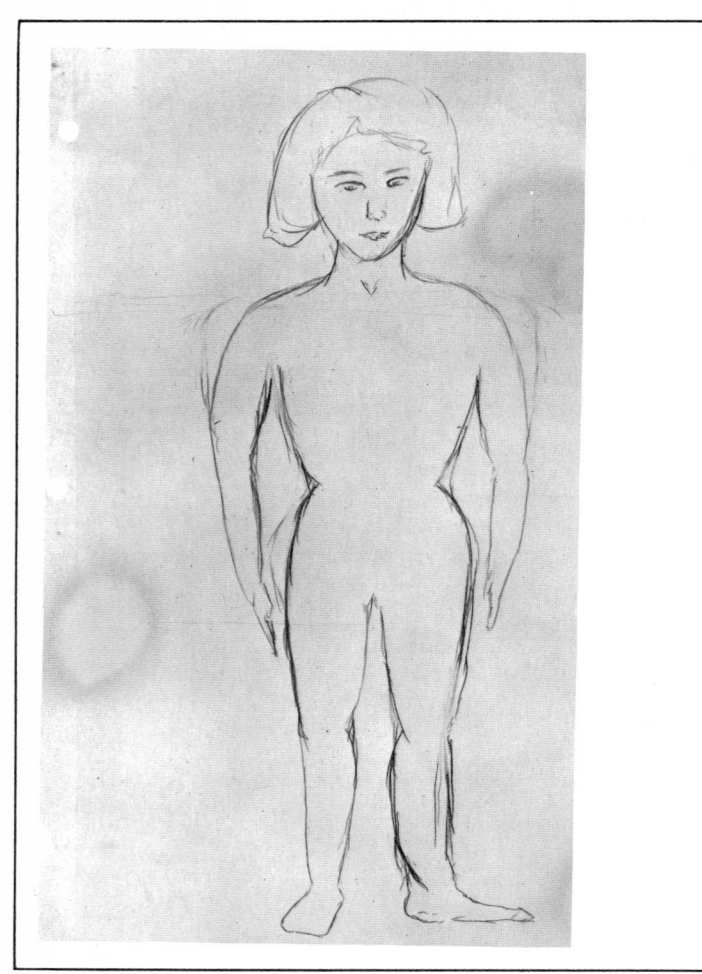

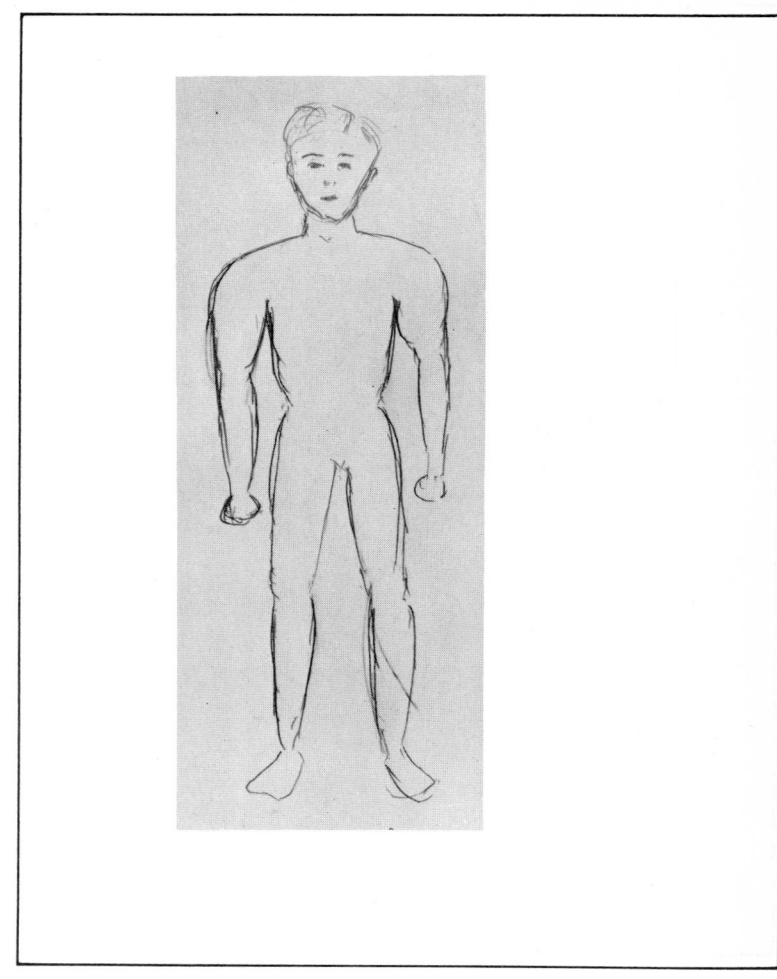

FIGURE-DRAWING CHARACTERISTICS

Structural	Male Female Both		Structural	Male	Female	Structural and Graphic	Male Female Both		Graphic, Global and Height	Male	Female	Body Proportions	Male	Female
Type	0		Omission of Appendages	0	0	Upper and Lower Halves	1	0	Hair Shading	3	5	Head	08	12
Sex Sequence	1		Position of Both Arms	0	0	Four Quarters	4	4	Nudity and Transparency	0	0	Neck	06	10
Posture	1	1	Position of Right Arm	0	0	Relative Size	4		Form	1	1	Shoulders		
Perspective	0	0	Position of Left Arm	0	0	Constant Line Pressure	0	0	Detailing	3	3	Right Arm	06	08
Vertical Midline	0	0	Position of Legs	6	4	Variable Line Pressure	4	4	Identity and Sex	1	1	Left Arm	06	08
Bilateral Symmetry	3	3	Relation of Long Axes	1	1	Line Continuity	0	0	Sophistication	2	2	Chest	06	10
Horizontal Midline	0	0	Right and Left Halves	1	1	Body Shading	1	1	Height	07	08	Girth	06	08

GENERAL CHARACTERISTICS OF SUBJECT

IDENTIFICATION		PARENTAL HISTORY	
No. G73		Father	
Sex M		C H S D O	
Marital status S		– – – – –	
Age 23 yrs. at		Mother	
psychological tests		C H S D O	
		– – – – –	

PHYSIOLOGICAL AND METABOLIC DATA

	Admission	Initial	Control	Cold pressor change	Exercise change	Smoking change
Systolic pressure	128	116	114	+22	+28	+01
Diastolic pressure	77	76	68	+30	–10	+04
Heart rate	80	64	66	+08	+27	+02

Age 22 yrs.	Height	65 in.	Ponderal index	12.82	
	Weight	130 lbs.	Cholesterol	265	mg. per 100 ml.
	Overweight	–04 %	Vital capacity		liters

HABIT SURVEY

Smoking habits: moderate cigarette smoker

Age begun 20 yrs.   Inhalation: yes

Habits of nervous tension: 5, 7, 9, 11, 16, 21, 22

STRONG VOCATIONAL INTEREST TEST

Occupation	Artist	Psychologist	Architect	Physician	Osteopath	Dentist	Veterinarian	Mathematician	Physicist	Engineer	Chemist	Production Manager
Standard Score	17	26	21	42	45	40	35	18	22	33	35	43

Occupation	Farmer	Aviator	Carpenter	Printer	Math.-Sci. Teacher	Ind. Arts Teacher	Voc. Agric. Teacher	Policeman	Forest Serv. Man	Y.M.C.A. Phys. Dir.	Personnel Director	Public Administrator
Standard Score	38	40	37	40	46	33	31	46	30	36	29	36

Occupation	Y.M.C.A. Secretary	Soc. Sci. H.S. Teacher	City Sch. Sup't.	Social Worker	Minister	Musician Performer	C.P.A.	Senior C.P.A.	Accountant	Office Man	Purchasing Agent	Banker
Standard Score	27	30	14	35	59	38	27	42	39	41	32	30

Occupation	Mortician	Pharmacist	Sales Manager	Real Est. Manager	Life Ins. Salesman	Advertising Man	Lawyer	Author-Journalist	President Mfg. Co.	Interest Maturity	Occupational Level	Masculinity-Femininity
Standard Score	34	45	32	32	28	22	12	20	37	58	49	45

Plate 867　　　**DRAWINGS BY SUBJECTS OF NON-EUROPEAN ANCESTRY**　　　919

FIGURE-DRAWING CHARACTERISTICS

Structural	Male Female Both		Structural	Male	Female	Structural and Graphic	Male Female Both		Graphic, Global and Height	Male	Female	Body Proportions	Male	Female
Type	0		Omission of Appendages	0	7	Upper and Lower Halves	1	1	Hair Shading	3	3	Head	06	07
Sex Sequence	0		Position of Both Arms	0	1	Four Quarters	4	4	Nudity and Transparency	7	7	Neck	04	04
Posture	1	1	Position of Right Arm	0	5	Relative Size	4		Form	3	3	Shoulders	06	06
Perspective	0	0	Position of Left Arm	0	0	Constant Line Pressure	0	0	Detailing	3	3	Right Arm	04	
Vertical Midline	3	0	Position of Legs	4	4	Variable Line Pressure	1	3	Identity and Sex	1	1	Left Arm	04	04
Bilateral Symmetry	3	2	Relation of Long Axes	1	1	Line Continuity	0	0	Sophistication	2	2	Chest	05	06
Horizontal Midline	6	4	Right and Left Halves	3	3	Body Shading	0	1	Height	05	06	Girth	07	06

GENERAL CHARACTERISTICS OF SUBJECT

IDENTIFICATION
No. 663
Sex M
Marital status S
Age 33 yrs. at psychological tests

PARENTAL HISTORY

Father

C	H	S	D	O
U	U	-	-	-

Mother

C	H	S	D	O
U	U	U	U	U

PHYSIOLOGICAL AND METABOLIC DATA

	Admission	Initial	Control	Cold pressor change	Exercise change	Smoking change
Systolic pressure	120	112	102	+14	+22	+02
Diastolic pressure	80	70	70	+08	-04	+08
Heart rate	92	76	79	-12	+16	+02

Age 32 yrs.

Height 70 in.
Weight 149 lbs.
Overweight -09 %

Ponderal index 13.21
Cholesterol 172 mg. per 100 ml.
Vital capacity liters

HABIT SURVEY

Smoking habits: occasional smoker
　Age begun 28 yrs.　　Inhalation: no
Habits of nervous tension: 2, 6, 11, 16

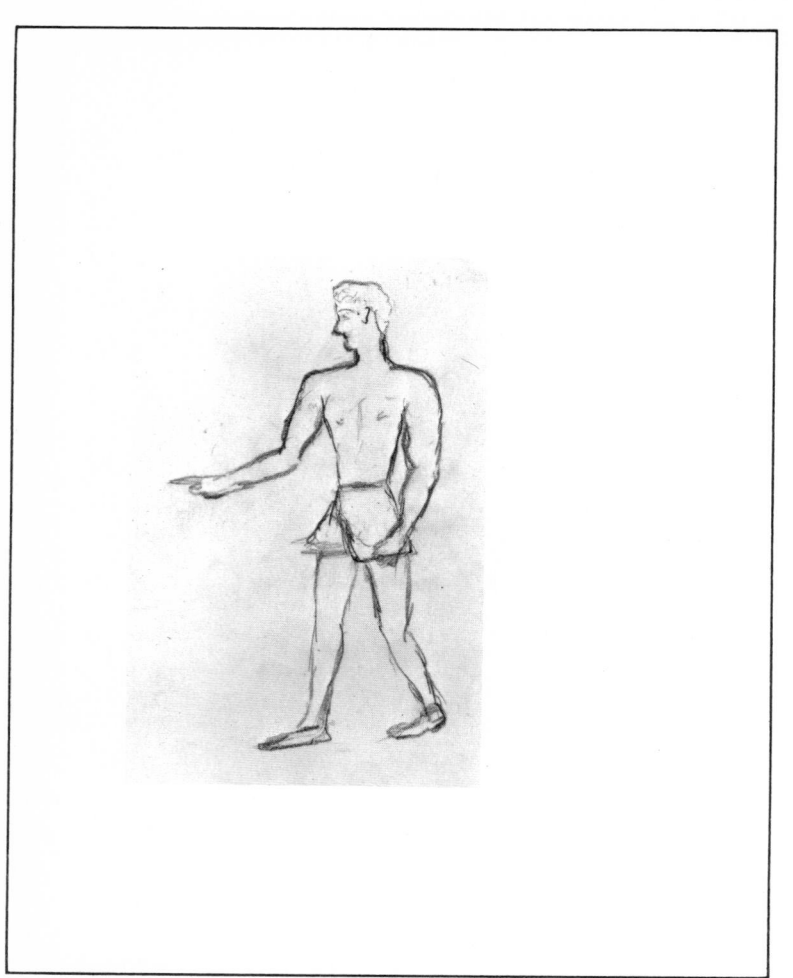

FIGURE-DRAWING CHARACTERISTICS

Structural	Male Female Both	Structural	Male	Female	Structural and Graphic	Male Female Both		Graphic, Global and Height	Male	Female	Body Proportions	Male	Female
Type	0	Omission of Appendages	0	0	Upper and Lower Halves	0	1	Hair Shading	1	1	Head	05	
Sex Sequence	2	Position of Both Arms	1	1	Four Quarters	4	4	Nudity and Transparency	3	0	Neck	04	
Posture	2 3	Position of Right Arm	2	2	Relative Size	4		Form	1	1	Shoulders	05	
Perspective	9 4	Position of Left Arm	5	5	Constant Line Pressure	0	0	Detailing	1	3	Right Arm	04	05
Vertical Midline	0 8	Position of Legs	8	1	Variable Line Pressure	5	5	Identity and Sex	1	1	Left Arm	04	04
Bilateral Symmetry	3 0	Relation of Long Axes	1	0	Line Continuity	0	2	Sophistication	2	1	Chest	03	
Horizontal Midline	4 0	Right and Left Halves	1	1	Body Shading	3	0	Height	05		Girth	03	

GENERAL CHARACTERISTICS OF SUBJECT

IDENTIFICATION
No. F80
Sex M
Marital status
Age 24 yrs. at
psychological tests

PARENTAL HISTORY					
Father					
C	H	S	D	O	
?	-	-	-	+	
Mother					
C	H	S	D	O	
?	+	-	-	+	

PHYSIOLOGICAL AND METABOLIC DATA

	Admission	Initial	Control	Cold pressor change	Exercise change	Smoking change
Systolic pressure	116	108	98	+28	+28	
Diastolic pressure	70	68	70	+16	+20	
Heart rate	70	80	79	+12	+41	

Age 22 yrs.	Height	68	in.	Ponderal index 12.63	
	Weight	156	lbs.	Cholesterol	210	mg. per 100 ml.
	Overweight +07 %			Vital capacity	liters

HABIT SURVEY
Smoking habits: unknown
Age begun   yrs.   Inhalation:
Habits of nervous tension:

Plate 869   DRAWINGS BY SUBJECTS OF NON-EUROPEAN ANCESTRY   921

FIGURE-DRAWING CHARACTERISTICS

Structural	Male Female Both		Structural	Male	Female	Structural and Graphic	Male Female Both		Graphic, Global and Height	Male	Female	Body Proportions	Male	Female
Type	0		Omission of Appendages	0	7	Upper and Lower Halves	1	1	Hair Shading	3	3	Head	18	06
Sex Sequence	1		Position of Both Arms	2	0	Four Quarters	4	4	Nudity and Transparency	7	0	Neck	14	06
Posture	1	3	Position of Right Arm	0	5	Relative Size	5		Form	3	1	Shoulders		05
Perspective	2	4	Position of Left Arm	7	5	Constant Line Pressure	5	5	Detailing	1	3	Right Arm	04	
Vertical Midline	4	8	Position of Legs	1	1	Variable Line Pressure	0	0	Identity and Sex	1	1	Left Arm		
Bilateral Symmetry	0	0	Relation of Long Axes	1	0	Line Continuity	4	2	Sophistication	1	1	Chest	12	05
Horizontal Midline	0	0	Right and Left Halves	1	1	Body Shading	2	3	Height	08		Girth	15	05

GENERAL CHARACTERISTICS OF SUBJECT

IDENTIFICATION

No. B26
Sex M
Marital status S
Age 23 yrs. at
psychological tests

PARENTAL HISTORY

Father
C H S D O
- + - - +

Mother
C H S D O
- - - - ?

PHYSIOLOGICAL AND METABOLIC DATA

	Admission	Initial	Control	Cold pressor change	Exercise change	Smoking change
Systolic pressure	110	110	110	+06	+14	+03
Diastolic pressure	70	64	64	+06	-12	+04
Heart rate	75	72	65	+04	+06	+11

Age 23 yrs.	Height 69 in.	Ponderal index 12.41
	Weight 172 lbs.	Cholesterol 212 mg. per 100 ml.
	Overweight +14 %	Vital capacity 5.4 liters

HABIT SURVEY

Smoking habits: moderate cigarette smoker
Age begun 18 yrs.   Inhalation: yes
Habits of nervous tension: 4, 5, 6, 9, 11, 16

STRONG VOCATIONAL INTEREST TEST

Occupation	Artist	Psychologist	Architect	Physician	Osteopath	Dentist	Veterinarian	Mathematician	Physicist	Engineer	Chemist	Production Manager
Standard Score	34	39	36	49	42	26	18	22	12	21	21	25

Occupation	Farmer	Aviator	Carpenter	Printer	Math.-Sci. Teacher	Ind. Arts Teacher	Voc. Agric. Teacher	Policeman	Forest Serv. Man	Y.M.C.A. Phys. Dir.	Personnel Director	Public Administrator
Standard Score	21	29	00	22	18	-04	11	22	16	38	40	47

Occupation	Y.M.C.A. Secretary	Soc. Sci. H.S. Teacher	City Sch. Sup't.	Social Worker	Minister	Musician Performer	C.P.A.	Senior C.P.A.	Accountant	Office Man	Purchasing Agent	Banker
Standard Score	27	32	34	43	61	48	34	28	13	22	20	21

Occupation	Mortician	Pharmacist	Sales Manager	Real Est. Manager	Life Ins. Salesman	Advertising Man	Lawyer	Author-Journalist	President Mfg. Co.	Interest Maturity	Occupational Level	Masculinity-Femininity
Standard Score	34	32	41	42	49	51	57	46	36	53	66	33

FIGURE-DRAWING CHARACTERISTICS

Structural	Male Female Both		Structural	Male	Female	Structural and Graphic	Male Female Both		Graphic, Global and Height	Male	Female	Body Proportions	Male	Female
Type	0		Omission of Appendages	0	2	Upper and Lower Halves	1	1	Hair Shading	5	2	Head	05	05
Sex Sequence	0		Position of Both Arms	2	6	Four Quarters	4	4	Nudity and Transparency	7	7	Neck	04	06
Posture	3	1	Position of Right Arm	4	7	Relative Size	5		Form	1	1	Shoulders		
Perspective	2	1	Position of Left Arm	7	7	Constant Line Pressure	5	0	Detailing	1	1	Right Arm	04	
Vertical Midline	7	4	Position of Legs	1	1	Variable Line Pressure	0	4	Identity and Sex	1	1	Left Arm		
Bilateral Symmetry	0	0	Relation of Long Axes	0	1	Line Continuity	1	2	Sophistication	1	1	Chest	06	
Horizontal Midline	0	0	Right and Left Halves	1	1	Body Shading	4	2	Height		06	Girth		

GENERAL CHARACTERISTICS OF SUBJECT

IDENTIFICATION

No. B34
Sex F
Marital status S
Age 22 yrs. at
psychological tests

PARENTAL HISTORY

Father
C　H　S　D　O
–　–　–　–　–
Mother
C　H　S　D　O
–　–　–　–　–

PHYSIOLOGICAL AND METABOLIC DATA

	Admission	Initial	Control	Cold pressor change	Exercise change	Smoking change
Systolic pressure	130	118	106	+14	+16	+06
Diastolic pressure	84	78	76	+18	–22	–04
Heart rate	110	84	67	+12	+50	+04

Age 21 yrs.
Height 64 in.
Weight 113 lbs.
Overweight –10 %
Ponderal index 13.25
Cholesterol 270 mg. per 100 ml.
Vital capacity 3.3 liters

HABIT SURVEY

Smoking habits: nonsmoker
Age begun　yrs.　Inhalation:
Habits of nervous tension: 4, 5, 25

STRONG VOCATIONAL INTEREST TEST

Occupation	Artist	Psychologist	Architect	Physician	Osteopath	Dentist	Veterinarian	Mathematician	Physicist	Engineer	Chemist	Production Manager
Standard Score	54	47	55	58	35	42	11	48	42	41	52	27

Occupation	Farmer	Aviator	Carpenter	Printer	Math.-Sci. Teacher	Ind. Arts Teacher	Voc. Agric. Teacher	Policeman	Forest Serv. Man	Y.M.C.A. Phys. Dir.	Personnel Director	Public Administrator
Standard Score	27	32	17	38	31	00	03	17	22	22	28	39

Occupation	Y.M.C.A. Secretary	Soc. Sci. H.S. Teacher	City Sch. Sup't.	Social Worker	Minister	Musician Performer	C.P.A.	Senior C.P.A.	Accountant	Office Man	Purchasing Agent	Banker
Standard Score	15	19	21	33	61	59	39	34	20	24	16	14

Occupation	Mortician	Pharmacist	Sales Manager	Real Est. Manager	Life Ins. Salesman	Advertising Man	Lawyer	Author- Journalist	President Mfg. Co.	Interest Maturity	Occupational Level	Masculinity- Femininity
Standard Score	17	29	28	30	28	46	45	52	33	49	61	34